THE MODERN
TEXTILE AND APPAREL DICTIONARY

By George E. Linton

APPLIED TEXTILES
(six editions)

CALLAWAY TEXTILE DICTIONARY
in collaboration with W. L. Carmichael and I. M. Price
(fourteen reprints)

DAN RIVER DICTIONARY OF TEXTILE TERMS
in collaboration with John Hoye and Richard S. Cox
(11 editions)

TEXTILES AND CHEMISTRY FOR THE LAUNDRY INDUSTRY
in collaboration with Harry Cohen

APPLIED BASIC TEXTILES
(two editions)

NATURAL AND MANMADE TEXTILE FIBERS
(two editions)

THE MODERN TEXTILE AND APPAREL DICTIONARY
(original title — THE MODERN TEXTILE DICTIONARY)

THE MODERN TEXTILE AND APPAREL DICTIONARY
FOURTH REVISED ENLARGED EDITION

GEORGE E. *dward* LINTON, PhD, Tex ScD

PROFESSOR EMERITUS, TEXTILE DEPARTMENT, FASHION INSTITUTE;
TEXTILE EDITOR FOR *AMERICAN FABRICS MAGAZINE*, NEW YORK CITY
TRUSTEE, TEXTILE MUSEUM, WASHINGTON, D.C. 20008

A DIVISION OF
BONN
INDUSTRIES, INC.

TEXTILE
BOOK The book company for the textile world
SERVICE

TEXTILE BOOK SERVICE, a division of BONN INDUSTRIES, INCORPORATED
1447 East Second Street, Plainfield, New Jersey 07060, U.S.A.

LIBRARY OF CONGRESS CATALOGUE CARD NUMBER 72-96456
ISBN: 0-87245-500-9

PRINTED AND BOUND IN THE UNITED STATES OF AMERICA
BRAUN-BRUMFIELD, INC. • ANN ARBOR, MICH.

TO

William C. Segal and the late Cora Carlyle

FOR THEIR FORESIGHT, EXPERIMENTATION, AND AR-
TISTIC, CREATIVE IDEAS WITHIN THE TEXTILE, AP-
PAREL, AND ALLIED FIELDS FROM FIBER TO FABRIC
TO FASHION

AND

American Fabrics Magazine

WHICH HAS PROMOTED GREATER INTEGRATION, IN-
CREASED COORDINATION, AND BETTER UNDERSTAND-
ING BETWEEN THE TEXTILE AND THE APPAREL
INDUSTRIES

Every man who rises above the common level has received two educations; the first from his teachers; the second, more personal and more important, from himself.

—Edward Gibbon (1737–1794)

Preface

With new fibers, fabrics, finishes, and fashions constantly before us in this day of amazing textile technological advance, textile products, and materials more and more must be able to meet all kinds of requirements and performances. The end-use of the product, whether it be for apparel, for home or decorative use, or for use in industry, is the ultimate goal of the manufacturer, who desires to produce the best article possible for the consumer.

Because of the rapid strides made by the great textile industry, with its new terms, new uses, and new significances, I am of the opinion that there is a definite need for a dictionary of this type. This fourth printing of *The Modern Textile and Apparel Dictionary* answers this need. To that end I have dedicated much of my effort and energy for the last eighteen years to produce a comprehensive and informative Dictionary, with the last six years spent in fully revising and improving the volume. In this span of time 896 new terms have been added, 104 terms have been revised, and 98 terms have been replaced with better text; 12 terms have been removed altogether. Thus, there are 1098 changes which gives this book a total of slightly more than 16,000 definitions and entries.

The textile horizon has expanded greatly within the last few years, and its influence on our present-day methods of living, both urban and rural, has been enormous. Greater knowledge and more familiarity with all things textile, in their far-reaching branches, have become more or less a prime requisite among many persons, both in and out of the industry.

The scope of the dictionary ranges from apparel to asbestos, from fabrics and finishes to fashion and style, from the history of costume to management and labor, from lace to laundry practice, from manufacturing to textile testing, and from plastics to spot and stain removal and the care of clothing.

Significant terms, old and new, domestic and foreign, commonplace or of interest to some particular world area, have been included when deemed advisable or necessary. Technical terms and phrases which are of established importance are included to cover the rapidly expanding areas of the vast textile and apparel industries.

Excerpts from the rulings and decrees of The Federal Trade Commission pertinent to the Textile Fiber Products Identification Act (effective March 3, 1960) are included in the book. With the rise of the manmade fibers, the new generic terms and their meanings, as set forth in these rulings and decrees, obviously warrant inclusion. Introduction to the Tex System for Designation of Yarn Number, sponsored by the American Society for Testing and Materials (Committee D-13 on Textiles), Philadelphia, Pennsylvania, is covered in entirety. These two items seem to be the most important to have come over the horizon in the last few years, along with certain FTC Rulings on Flammability, Care Labeling, etc., and all have had much impact in the textile and apparel industries.

Trade names, many of which are household words today, have been given their share of importance in this edition. Thus, I have made what I believe is an honest effort to include all vital terms and definitions for the enlightenment of the reader, whether he be a textile technologist, textile technician, teacher, student, trainee, manufacturer, converter, executive or secretary, stylist or designer, home economist, fashion coordinator, or novice in the textile and apparel field.

There has never been a perfect yard of fabric ever taken from a loom. By the same token, there has never been a perfect book in all details. Realizing this, I still have made every attempt to cover correctly and in readable fashion, all the highpoints of the industries. I realize, as well, that a task of this sort cannot be well-nigh perfect. To that end, I shall appreciate any constructive criticism from any reader who might take exception to some meaning or interpretation of any term or terms in the book.

I am indebted to many persons who gave of their time and effort for advice, criticisms, and suggestions to help make the book concrete and constructive in all details. I wish to thank the many textile and apparel companies who granted permission to use pictures, cuts, halftones, flow charts, etc., and for their aid in checking and rechecking some of the terms which appear here.

G.E.L.

George E. Linton

was born in the well-known textile center of the New England woolen and worsted industries, Woonsocket, Rhode Island. He is a graduate of Philadelphia College of Textiles and Science and holds a Doctor of Textile Science degree from that institution. His B.S. degree is from Teachers College, Columbia University; his M.A. and Ph.D. from Fordham University. Special graduate work was done in the University of Pennsylvania and St. John's University.

As a teacher of textiles, his experience covered a span of twenty-five years in the secondary schools of New York City and a period of twelve years as extension professor at New York University. From 1944 till 1965 Dr. Linton was Dean of the Textile Department at Fashion Insititute of Technology and Design, New York City. In 1965 retired from his teaching career and concentrated on revising his many textbooks.

Activities include: ex-president of The American Association for Textile Technology, Inc., New York City; member of The American Association of Textile Chemists and Colorists, Inc.; member of various textile committees throughout the nation, and an honorary membership in the Phi Psi Textile Fraternity.

Trustee of the Textile Museum, Washington, D.C., and writer of TV and radio texts for Freedoms Foundation, Valley Forge, Pennsylvania; articles on textiles for *Encyclopedia Americana, Encyclopedia Britannica,* and The Grolier Society. He was Textile Editor for *Random House Dictionary of the English Language* and Textile Editor for *American Fabrics Magazine* since its founding in 1946 to the present time.

Recipient of The Bronze Medal Award of The American Association for Textile Technology, Inc., New York City, 1965, and a Tex Sc D from Philadelphia College of Textiles and Science, 1967.

Dr. Linton's experience in teaching all levels of students has given him a wealth of first hand information about a student's learning process and mental development, while his research studies in the textile and apparel industries have given him a keen insight into the specific needs and requirements in these fields. With this experience behind him, the author has written several textbooks including *Applied Basic Textiles* and its companion book, *Natural and Manmade Textile Fibers.*

ACKNOWLEDGEMENTS

ADVICE AND SPECIAL AID:

Cameron A. Baker, Director of Research and Development, Better Fabrics Testing Bureau, Inc., 101 West 31 Street, New York, New York 10001.

Dr. Junius B. Bird, Curator in American Museum of Natural History, Central Park West at 79 Street, New York, New York 10024.

Grace Rogers Cooper, Curator of Division of Textiles, Smithsonian Intitution, United States National Museum, Washington, D.C. 20560.

Joseph J. Crowley, Vice-President, United States Testing Company, Inc., 1415 Park Avenue, Hoboken, New Jersey 07030.

Terrence A. Giffen, Manager, Apparel Merchandising Division, Courtaulds North America, Inc., 101 West 40 Street, New York, New York 10018.

Martin Gurley, Jr., Consultant, Textile and Paper Industries, RFD Number Four, Lexington, Virginia 24550.

Colonel John Haywood, ARTY, British Army, London, England. MBE.

Anthony N. Landreau, Executive Director, Textile Museum, 2320 S Street Northwest, Washington, D.C. 20008.

George D. Maynard, President, Chem-Mark, Inc., Roselle Park, New Jersey.

Alfred H. McCollough, Publisher, *Modern Textiles Magazine,* and *Modern Knitting Management,* W.A.B. Davidson, Assistant to the Publisher, and Kenneth A. Howry, Editor, *Modern Textiles Magazine,* Rayon Publishing Company, Inc., 303 Fifth Avenue, New York, New York 10016.

Dr. Graham M. Richardson and Technical Staff, Fiber Information Division, E.I. duPont de Nemours & Company, Inc., Wilmington, Delaware 19898.

William C. Segal, Publisher, and Cecil Lubell, Executive Editor, *American Fabrics Magazine,* Doric Publications, Inc., 24 East 38 Street, New York, New York 10016.

W. Frank Uhlig, President, Winston Print Works, Inc., Lebanon, Pennsylvania.

Robert H. Wallace, Manager of Market Research and Product Planning, Leesona Corporation, Warwick, Rhode Island.

Special acknowledgement to Mr. Sidney S. Korzenik, Executor and Counsel, and Mr. Charles Reichman, Editor, National Knitted Outerwear Association, 51 Madison Avenue, New York, New York 10010, for their aid on Knitting Terms which appear throughout this book and their permission to use terms from Mr. Reichman's *Knitting Dictionary,* copyright 1966, published by the National Knitted Outerwear Association. Their personal interest has been of inestimable value to the author; this book would not have been possible wthout their attention and interest in the compilation of the terms pertinent to Knitting.

TECHNICAL ADVISORS:

H. D. Baker, Ph.D., Division of Cotton and Other Fiber Crops, U.S.D.A., Washington, D.C.

Eastman Chemical Products, Inc., Technical Staff, 1133 Sixth Avenue, New York, New York.

FMC Corporation, American Viscose Division, Technical Staff, 350 Fifth Avenue, New York, New York 10001.

Raymond C. Gagnon, Educational Department, International Textbook Company, Inc., Scranton, Pennsylvania.

Joseph A. Garofolo, Textile Technologist, Fashion Institute of Technology, 227 West 27 Street, New York, New York 10001.

Stanley B. Hunt, Editor of Textile Organon, Textile Economics Bureau, Inc., 10 East 40 Street, New York, New York 10016.

Albert E. Johnson, Director Trade Relations, National Institute of Drycleaning, 350 Fifth Avenue, New York, New York 10001.

F.J. Kovac, Manager of Tire Reinforcing System, The Goodyear Tire and Rubber Company, Inc., Akron, Ohio 44316.

Edward Kuhnel, Assistant to the President, Clupak, Inc., 530 Fifth Avenue, New York, New York 10036.

William H. Lehmberg, President of American Felt Company, Inc., Glenville, Connecticut.

Monsanto Company, Inc., Technical Staff, Monsanto Textiles Division, 1114 Sixth Avenue, New York, New York 10036.

Chris Moroney, Sanforized Division, Cluett Peabody Company, Inc., 530 Fifth Avenue, New York, New York 10036.

Arthur Price, Chairman Textile Division, Fashion Institute of Technology, 227 West 27 Street, New York, New York 10001.

Herman Reichl, Textile Technologist, Fashion Institute of Technology, 227 West 27 Street, New York, New York 10001.

Fred Simmons, Manchester Mills, Inc., 1290 Sixth Avenue, New York, New York.

Jack Solinger, Consultant Industrial Engineer for the Textile and Apparel Industries, 601 West 115 Street, New York, New York.

Herbert W. Starky, President and Joseph C. Hirsch, Stylist, Brunswick Associates, Inc., 1290 Sixth Avenue, New York, New York.

Chester A. Strodl, Union Carbide Corporation, Fabrics and Fibers Division, 270 Park Avenue, New York, New York 10017.

Bardee Underwood, Fashion Coordiantor, Cotton Inc., Dallas, Texas.

Ann T. West, Regional Manager for Floor Covering Weekly, Atlanta, Georgia 30309.

ACKNOWLEDGEMENTS TO COMPANIES AND AGENCIES:

ASBESTOS:

Asbestos Textile Institute, Pompton Lakes, New Jersey 07442.

Raybestos-Manhattan Co., Inc., Mannheim, Pennsylvania.

COTTON:

Bibb Manufacturing Company, Inc., Macon, Georgia.

Bradford Dyeing Association (U.S.A.), Westerly, Rhode Island and New York.

Cluett, Peabody & Company, Inc., 530 Fifth Avenue, New York, New York 10036.

Cotton, Inc., 1370 Sixth Ave., New York, N.Y. 10019.

Dan River Inc., 110 West 40 Street, New York, New York 10018.

National Cotton Council, Memphis, Tennessee.

West Point-Pepperell, Inc., West Point Georgia, and 110 West 40 Steeet, New York, New York 10018.

Whitin Machine Works, Division of White Consolidated Industries, Inc., Charlotte, North Carolina.

EDUCATIONAL INSTITUTIONS:

A French Textile School, Georgia Institute of Technology, Atlanta, Georgia.

Institute of Textile Technology, Charlottesville, Virginia. (Graduate students only for advanced degrees. Ph. D. may be obtained in conjunction with University of Virginia in Charlottesville).

Lowell Technological Institute, Lowell, Massachusetts.

Philadelphia College of Textiles and Science, Philadelphia, Pennsylvania.

School of Engineering and Engineering Experiment Station, Auburn University, Auburn, Alabama.

School of Industrial Management and Textile Science, ClemsonUniversity, Clemson, South Carolina.

School of Textiles, North Carolina State College of the University of North Carolina, Raleigh, North Carolina.

Southeastern Massachusetts University (Textile Division), North Darmouth, Massachusetts.

Textile Research Institute, Princeton, New Jersey. (Graduate students only for advanced degrees. Ph. D. may be obtained in conjunction with Princeton University in Princeton.)

DYEING, PRINTING, FINISHING:

Bradford Dyeing Assoiciation (U.S.A.), Westerly, Rhode Island.

Dexter Chemical Corporation, Bronx, New York City, New York 10474.

Globe Dyeworks, Inc., Frankford, Philadeophia, Pennsylvania 19124.

Scholler Brothers, Inc., Philadelphia, Pennsylvania 19134.

Winston Print Works, Inc., Lebanon, Pennsylvania 17042.

FELT:

American Felt Company, Inc., Glenville, Connecticut.

FLAX-LINEN:

The Irish Linen Guild, New York, New York.

FLOORCOVERINGS:

The Carpet and Rug Institute, Dalton, Georgia 30720.

Floor Covering Weekly, Inc., Atlanta, Georgia 30309.

GOVERNMENT AGENCIES:

Bureau of Census, U.S. Department of Labor, Washington, D.C.

Farm Security Administration, Washington, D.C.

U.S. Department of Agriculture, Washington, D.C.

U.S. Department of Commerce, Washington, D.C.

KNITTING:

National Knitted Outerwear Association, 51 Madison Avenue, New York, New York 10001.

LACE:

Metropolitan Museum of Art, New York, New York.

LAUNDRY SCIENCE:

Cowles Detergent Company, Cleveland, Ohio.

Lever Brothers Company, New York, New York.

National Institute of Drycleaning, 350 Fifth Avenue, New York, New York 10001.

LEATHER:

Tanners' Council, New York, New York.

MANMADE FIBER PRODUCERS IN THE UNITED STATES:

This listing, in categories, provides the names and addresses of most of the major manmade fiber producers in this country. In practically all instances Fiber Trademarks are provided.

MANMADE FIBERS AND FILAMENTS, CELLULOSIC TYPES (Viscose Rayon, Bemberg Rayon, Acetate, and Triacetate):

American Enka Co., Inc., 530 Fifth Avenue, New York, New York 10036, and Enka, North Carolina 28728. *Rayon* - Englo, Enkrome, Jetspun, Kolorbon, Skybloom, Skyloft, Softglo, Suprenka, Zantrel, Zantrel 700.

Beaunit Corporation, 261 Madison Avenue, New York, New York 10016. *Rayon* - Beau-grip, Comiso, Hi-Narco, Narco, Naron, Super Narco, Xena.

Bemberg Industries, Inc., 37 West 37 Street, New York, New York 10018. *Cuprammonium Rayon* - Bembella, Bemberg, Cuprel, Flaikona, Multi-Cupioni, Nub-lite, Parfe, Strata, Stratella, Tusson.

Celanese Corporation, 1211 Sixth Avenue, New York, New York 10036. *Acetate* - Celacloud, Celacrimp, Celafil, Celaloft, Celanese, Celaperm, Celatow, Celatress, Celaweb. *Triacetate* - Arnel.

Courtaulds North America, Inc., 104 West 40 Street, New York, New York 10018. *Rayon* - Coloray, Fibro.

E. I. duPont de Nemours & Co., Inc., Wilmington, Delaware 19898. *Acetate* - Acele.

Eastman Chemical Products, Inc., Kingsport, Tennessee 37662. *Acetate* - **Ariloft, Chromspun, Estron, Estron SLR, Loftura.**

Fair Haven Mills, Inc., Fair Haven, Vermont 05743. *Rayon* - Fair Haven.

FMC, American Visco Division, 1617 John F. Kennedy Boulevard, Philadelphia, Pennsylvania 19103. *Acetate* - Avicolor, Avisco. *Rayon* - Avicolor, Aviloc, Avril, Avicron; Dynabelt and Dynacor, Fibers 40, 43, 410, and XL III; Rayflex, Super Rayflex.

IRC Division, American Cyanamid Co., Inc., Painesville, Ohio and Wayne, New Jersey 07470. *Rayon* - Cy-Lok, Strawn, Tyron. Tyweld, Villwyte, Dynabelt, and Dynacor.

MANMADE FIBERS AND FILAMENTS - NON-CELLULOSIC TYPES:

ACRYLIC:

American Cyanamid Company, Inc., Wayne, New Jersey 07470. Creslan.
Courtaulds North America, Inc., 104 West 40 Street, New York, New York 10018. Courtelle.
Dow Badische Co., Inc., Williamsburg, Virginia and 350 Fifth Avenue, New York, New York 10001. Zefkrome, Zefran II.
E. I. duPont de Nemours & Co., Inc., Wilmington, Delaware 19898. "Orlon.".
Monsanto Textiles Co., Inc., 1114 Sixth Avenue, New York City 10036. Acrilan.

ANIDEX:

See text.

GLASS FIBERS:

Ferro Corporation, Fiber Glass Road, Nashville, Tennessee 37211.
Fiber Glass Industries, Inc., Amsterdam, New York 12010.
Gustin-Bacon Mfg. Co., Inc., Box 15097, Kansas City, Kansas 66115.
Johns-Manville Fiber Glass Co., Inc., Waterville, Ohio 43566.
Modiglass Fibers, Division of Reichold Chemicals, Inc., Bremen, Ohio.
Owens-Corning-Fiberglas Co., Inc., Fiberglas Tower, Toledo, Ohio 43601.
PPG Industries, Inc., One Gateway Center, Pittsburgh, Pennsylvania 15222.
Uniglass Industries, Division of United Merchants & Manufacturers, Inc., 1407 Broadway, New York 10018.

LASTRILLE:

See text.

METALLIC FIBERS:

Brunswick Corporation, Chicago, Illinois 60602 (Metal Fibers).
Dow Badische, 350 Fifth Avenue, New York, New York 10001 (Metallic Fibers).
Malina Company, Inc., 1071 Sixth Avenue, New York, New York 10018 (Metallic Fibers).
Metlon Corporation, 1117 Douglas Avenue, Providence, Rhode Island 02904 (Metallic Fibers).
Metal Film Company, Inc., 405 Lexington Avenue, New York, New York 10017 (Metallic Fibers).
Monsanto Textiles Co., Inc., New Enterprise Division, St. Louis, Missouri 63166 (Metal Fibers).
Multi-Tex Products Corporation, Kearny, New Jersey 07032 (Metallic Fibers).
Rexham Corporation, Box 368, Matthews, North Carolina 28105 (Metallic Fibers).

MODACRYLIC:

Eastman Chemical Products, Inc., Kingsport, Tennessee 07470. Verel.
Monsanto Textiles Company, Inc., 1114 Sixth Avenue, New York City 10036. SEF®.
Union Carbide Corporation, 270 Park Avenue, New York City 10017. Dynel.

NYLON:

Allied Chemical Corporation, One Times Square, New York, New York 10036. Nylon 6. Caprolan, Anso, Touch.
American Enka Co., a part of Akzona Corporation, Enka, North Carolina 28728. Nylon 6. Blanc de Blancs, Crepeset, Enkaloft, Enkalure, Enkasheer, Spectrodye, Varilene (patented process).
Amtech, Inc., Odenton, Maryland 21113. Nylon 6 monofilament; Nylon 6,6 industrial thread.
Beaunit Corporation, 261 Madison Avenue, New York, New York, New York 10016. Nylon 6. Qulon. Nylon 6,6. Filament and BCF Carpet Yarn.
Dow Badische Company, Inc., Williamsburg, Virginia and 350 Fifth Avenue, New York, New York 10001. Nylon 6. Vivana.
E. I. duPont de Nemours & Co., Inc., Wilmington, Delaware 19898. Nylon 6,6. Antron, BCF, Cordura Industrial Yarn, Dylor, Dymetrol, duPont, Nomex, Qiana.
Fiber Industries, Inc., affiliate of Celanese Corporation, marketed by Celanese Fibers Marketing Co., Inc., Charlotte, North Carolina 28201. Cedilla, Celanese.
Firestone Synthetic Fibers Company, Inc., Division of the Firestone Tire & Rubber Co., Inc., Hopewell, Virgina 23860. Nylon 6.
Hanover Mills, Inc., Yanceyville, North Carolina 27379. Nylon 6. Hanover.
Monsanto Textiles Co., Inc., 1114 Sixth Avenue, New York, New York 10036. Nylon 6,6. Cadon, Blue-C, Cumuloft, Astro Turf, BCF Nylon , all registered trademarks.
Phillips Fibers Corporation, Subsidiary of Phillips Petroleum Co., Inc., Greenville, South Carolina 29602. Nylon 6,6. Phillips 66 Nylon.
Rohm and Haas Company, Inc., Independence Mall - West, Philadelphia, Pennsylvania 19105. Nylon 6,6.
Sauguoit Fibers Division of Rohm and Haas Company, Inc., Scranton, Pennsylvania 18503. Nylon 6.
Soo Valley Company, Inc., Subsidiary of Shakespeare Company, Inc., Columbia, South Carolina 29602. Nylons 6 and 6,6.
UniRoyal, Inc., Winnsboro, South Carolina 29180. Nylon 6 for tires.
Wall Industries, Inc., Beverly, New Jersey 08010. Nylon 6,6.
Wellman, Inc., 75 Federal Street, Boston, Massachusetts 02110. Nylon 6,6. Wellon.

NYTRIL:

See text.

OLEFIN:

This name is given to fiber popularly known as polypropylene and polyethylene. This listing includes producers of polypropylene and polyethylene monofilament, slit or split film in one form or another.

American Manufacturing Co., Inc., Brooklyn, New York, New York 11222. Amco.

Amtech, Inc., Odenton, Maryland 21113. Polypropylene filaments.

Bemis Company, Inc., Minneapolis, Minnesota 55402.

Cavalier Industries, Inc., Lumberton, North Carolina 28358.

Crowe Rope Company, Inc., Division of Andrew Crowe & Sons, Inc., Warren, Maine.

Fibers Division of Thiokol Corporation, Waynesboro, Virginia 22980. Polypropylene - Isostatic, in monofilament, DLP Group, Tufton.

Fibron, Inc., Chattanooga, Tennessee 37416. Lo-Pic, Lustreloft.

Firestone Synthetic Fibers Company, Inc., Division of The Firestone Tire & Rubber Company, Inc., Hopewell, Virginia 23860.

Hercules Inc., 910 Market Steeet, Wilmington, Delaware 19899. Herculon.

Indian Head Yarn and Thread Division of Indian Head, Inc., Blue Mountain, Alabama 36201. Olefin.

Industrial Wire and Plastics Co., Inc., Spirit Lake, Iowa 51360.

IRC Fibers Co., Inc., Division of American Cyanamid Co., Painesville, Ohio, and Wayne, New Jersey 07470.

Metlon Corporation, Providence, Rhode Island 02904. Diamond.

Monsanto Textiles Co., Inc., 1114 Sixth Avenue, New York City 10036. Chemgrass, C-Chemgrass.

Moultrie Textiles, Inc., Moultrie, Georgia 31756.

Phillips Fibers Corporation, Subsidiary of Phillips Petroleum Company, Inc., Box 66, Greenville, South Carolina 29602. Marvess.

Poly Fibers, Inc., Westminster, California 92683.

Polymer Fibers Corporation, Tampa, Florida 33611. Color-spun.

Poncar Plastic Corporation, Miami, Florida 33144. Poncar.

Tennessee Fibers, Inc., Decatur, Tennessee 37322.

The Schlegel Manufacturing Company, Inc., Chester, South Carolina 29706.

Thiokol Chemical Corporation, Textile Fibers Division, Box 460, Waynesboro, Virginia 22980.

UniRoyal Fibers and Textile Division of UniRoyal, Inc., Winnsboro, South Carolina 29180. Royalene.

Vectra Company, Inc., a Division of Chevron Chemical Corporation, Odenton, Maryland 21113. Polypropylene.

Vogt Manufacturing Company, Inc., Rochester, New York 14621. Voplex.

Wall Industries, Inc., Beverly, New Jersey 08010.

Waltrich Plastics Corporation, Tennent, New Jersey 07763. Olefin.

Wellington Synthetic Fibers, Inc., Subsidiary of Wellington Technical Industries, Inc., Pilot Mountain, North Carolina 27041. Jutelac.

POLYESTER:

American Viscose Division/FMC, 350 Fifth Avenue, New York, New York 10001. Avlin.

American Enka Co., Inc., a part of Akzona Corporation, 530 Fifth Avenue, New York, New York 10036. Encron.

Beaunit Corporation, 261 Fifth Avenue, New York, New York 10016. Vycron.

Dow Badische Company, Inc., Williamsburg, Virginia and 350 Fifth Avenue, New York, New York 10001. Anavor.

E. I. duPont de Nemours & Co., Inc., Wilmington, Delaware 19898. "Dacron."

Eastman Chemical Products, Inc., Kingsport, Tennessee 37662. Kodel.

Fiber Industries, Inc., Division of Celanese Corporation, Box 10038, Charlotte, North Carolina 28201. Fortrel, Fortrel 7.

Firestone Synthetic Fibers, Division of Firestone Tire and Rubber Co., Inc., Hopewell, Virginia 23680.

Goodyear Chemical Division of The Goodyear Tire & Rubber Co., Inc., Akron, Ohio 44306. Goodyear Polyester.

Hoechst Fibers, Inc., 1515 Broadway, New York, N.Y. Trevira.

Monsanto Textiles Company, Inc., 1114 Sixth Avenue, New York, New York 10036. Blue C-polyester, Monsanto, Spectran.

Newton Filaments, Inc., Subsidiary of Newton Line Company, Inc., Homer, New York 13070.

Phillips Fibers Corporation, Subsidiary of Phillips Petroleum Company, Inc., Box 66, Greenville, South Carolina 29602. Qunitess.

Soo Valley Company, Inc., Columbia, South Carolina 29206.

Wellman, Inc., 75 Federal Street, Boston, Massachusetts 02110. Wellene.

SARAN:

Amtech, Inc., Box 339, Odenton, Maryland 21113.

S. E. Polymers, Inc., Box 95, Clare, Michigan 48617.

SPANDEX:

Ameliotex Inc., Rocky Hill, New Jersey 18553. Numa.

E. I. duPont de Nemours & Co., Inc., Wilmington, Delaware 19898. Lycra.

Globe Manufacturing Co., Inc., Fall River, Massachusetts 02722. Glospan, Cleerspan.

Union Carbide Corporation, 270 Park Avenue, New York, New York 10017. Unel.

TEFLON:

E. I. duPont de Nemours and Company, Inc., Wilmington, Delaware 19898.

VINAL:

See text. Not manufactured in the United States at present.

VINYON:

FMC, American Viscose Division, 1617 John F. Kennedy Boulevard, Philadelphia, Pennsylvania 19103.

NONWOVEN FABRICS:

Albany Felt Co., Inc., Albany, N. Y.

American Felt Co., Inc., Glenville, Conn.

The Carborundum Co., Inc., Niagara Falls, N. Y.

Chatham Manufacturing Co., Elkin, N. C.

Chicopee Mfg. Co., Milltown, N. J.

Curlator Corporation, Textile Division, East Rochester, N. Y.

E. I. duPont de Nemours & Co., Inc., Wilmington, Del.

The B. F. Goodrich Co., Inc., Akron, Ohio, and Thomaston, Ga.

Huyck Corporation, Rensselaer, N. Y.

International Paper Co., Inc., New York, N. Y.

Johnson & Johnson, New Brunswick, N. J.

The Kendall Company, Inc., Boston, Mass.

Kimberly-Clark Corporation, Balfour, N. C.

Lowndes Products, Inc., Easley, S. C.

Ludlow Corporation, Ludlow, Mass.

Minnesota Mining & Manufacturing Co., Inc., St. Paul, Minn.

National Felt Co., Inc., Easthampton, Mass.

Ozite Corporation, Chicago, Ill.

Pellon Corporation, Lowell, Mass.

Phillips Fibers Corporation, Cartersville, Ga.

Riegel Paper Co., Inc., New York, N. Y.

Scott Paper Co., Inc., Chester, Pa.

Standard Cotton Products Co., Inc., Flint, Mich.

Stearns & Foster Co., Inc., Lockland, Ohio.

J. P. Stevens & Co., Inc., New York, N. Y. and New Milford, Conn.

Troy Mills, Inc., Troy, N. H.

Union Carbide Corporation, New York, N. Y.

Union Wadding Co., Inc., Pawtucket, R. I.

West Point-Pepperell, Inc., Fairfax, Ala.

PILE FABRICS:

Baxter, Kelly & Faust Company, Inc., Philadelphia, Pennsylvania.

PUBLICATIONS:

American Dyestuff Reporter, Howes Publishing Company, Inc., 44 East 23 Street, New York, New York.

American Fabrics Magazine Quarterly and *AF Encyclopedia of Textiles,* Doric Publications, 24 East 38 Street, New York, New York.

America's Textile Reporter/Bulletin, 106 East Stone Avenue, Box 88, Greenville, South Carolina 29602 (Successor to *America's Textile Reporter,* published since 1887, first issue made for October, 1971).

Davison's Knit Goods Trade, Davison's Textile Blue Book, Textile Catalog and Buyers Guide, and *Textile Directory for Executives and Salesmen,* Davison Publishing Company, Inc.

Fairchild Publications, Inc., 7 East 12 Street, New York, New York.

Felt Facts, The Felt Association, 74 Trinity Place, New York, New York.

Handbook of Industrial Fabrics, Wellington Sears & Co., Inc., 111 West 40 Street, New York, New York.

Modern Textiles Magazine, 303 Fifth Avenue, New York, New York.

The Story of Asbestos Textiles, Asbestos Institute, Philadelphia College of Textiles and Science, 3242 Schoolhouse Lane, Philadelphia 44, Pennsylvania.

Textile Industries Magazine, 806 Peachtree Street, Atlanta, Georgia.

Textile Mercury and Argus, Mercury House, Acton Square, Manchester, England. *The "Mercury" Dictionary of Textile Terms,* published in 1950 by the Staff of *Textile Mercury and Argus.*

Textile Organon, Textile Economic Bureau, Inc., 10 East 40 Street, New York, New York.

Textile World, McGraw-Hill Publishing Company, Inc., 330 West 42 Street, New York, New York 10036.

TEXTILE AND APPAREL ASSOCIATIONS:

1. American Apparel Manufacturer's Association, Inc., Arlington, Virginia 22209.
2. American Association for Textile Technology, Inc., 295 Fifth Avenue, New York, New York 10016.
3. American Association of Textile Chemists and Colorists, Inc., P.O. Box 12215, Research Triangle Park, North Carolina 27709.
4. American Institute of Men's and Boys' Wear, Inc., 1290 Sixth Avenue, New York, New York 10010.
5. American Textile Machinery Association, Inc., 1730 M. Street, Northwest, Washington, D. C.
6. American Textile Manufacturers Institute, Inc., 1501 Johnson Building, Charlotte, North Carolina 28202; 1457 Broadway, New York 10036; 1120 Connecticut Avenue, Northwest, Washington, D. C. 20006.
7. Boys' and Young Men's Apparel Manufacturers Association, Inc., 10 West 33rd Street, New York, New York 10001. (BAMA).
8. The Carpet and Rug Institute, Inc., P. O. Box 8, Dalton, Georgia 30720.
9. The Disposables Association, 10 East 4th Street, New York, New York 10010.
10. International Silk Association, Inc., 185 Madison Avenue, New York, New York.
11. **The Manmade Fiber Producers Association, Inc.,** 1150 Seventeenth St., Northwest, Washington, D.C. 20006.
12. National Association of Hosiery Manufacturers, Inc., 469 Park Avenue South, New York, New York 10016; 901 Johnson Building, Charlotte 2, North Carolina.
13. The National Cotton Council, Inc., Memphis, Tennessee.
14. National Knitted Outerwear Association, Inc., 51 Madison Avenue, New York, New York.
15. Silk and Rayon Printers and Dyers of America, Inc., 7 Church Street, Paterson, New Jersey 07501.
16. Textile Distributors Association, Inc., 1040 Sixth Avenue, New York, New York 10018.
17. Textile Organon, Textile Economics Bureau, Inc., 10 East 40th Street, New York, New York 10016.
18. Tricot Institute of America., Inc., 39 West 55th Street, New York, New York 10019.
19. The Underwear Institute, Inc., 350 Fifth Avenue, New York, New York 10001.
20. The Wool Bureau, Inc., 360 Lexington Avenue, New York, New York.

TEXTILE TESTING:

1. Better Fabrics Testing Bureau, Inc., 101 West 31st Street, New York, New York.
2. Hatch Textile Research, Inc., 23 East 26th Street, New York, New York.
3. Bureau of Standards, R. H. Macy Company, Inc., Herald Square, New York, New York.
4. Alfred Suter Company, Inc., Orangeburg, N.Y. 10962.
5. United States Testing Company, Inc., 1415 Park Avenue, Hoboken, New Jersey.

WEAVING:

Crompton & Knowles Corporation, 345 Park Avenue, New.York, New York.
Draper Corporation, Division of North American Rockwell Corporation, Hopedale, Massachusetts.
Philadelphia College of Textiles & Science, Germantown, Philadelphia, Pennsylvania 19144.

WOOLENS, WORSTEDS, AND FLOORCOVERINGS:

The Carpet and Rug Institute, Inc., Box 8, Dalton, Georgia 30720 and 909 Third Avenue, New York, New York.
Deering Milliken Company, Inc., 1045 Sixth Avenue, New York, New York.
Deering Milliken Research Corporation, Spartanburg, South Carolina.
Mohasco Industries, Inc., Amsterdam, New York and 295 Fifth Avenue, New York, New York.
The Wool Bureau, Inc., 360 Lexington Avenue, New York, New York.

ZEALOUS AID IN PREPARATION OF THE MANUSCRIPT:

Art Work: Professor Rosa Balenzano, Fashion Institute of Technology, 227 West 27th Street, New York, New York 10001.
Proofreading: Louise L. Dowling, Marion L. O'Brien.
Typing: Margaret M. Linton, Debra Linton, Kathleen O'Brien.

High Points in This Dictionary

Explanations and terms will be found for:

APPAREL

ASBESTOS

BLENDED FABRICS

BONDED FABRICS

COLOR

COSTUME, HISTORY OF

DOMESTICS

DRYCLEANING

DURABLE PRESS

DYEING

FABRICS

FACTORING

FASHION AND STYLE

FIBERS AND YARNS

FIBER WOVEN FABRICS

FINISHES AND FINISHING PROCESSES

FLOCKING

FLOOR COVERINGS

JACQUARDS

KNITTING

LABOR

LACE

LAMINATED AND MOLDED FABRICS

LEATHERS

MANMADE FIBERS — CELLULOSIC AND NON-CELLULOSIC

MANUFACTURING PROCESSES OF MANY TEXTILE FIBERS —
ACETATE, COTTON, NYLON, WOOL, ETC.

NONWOVEN FABRICS

PLASTICS

PRINTING

SCIENCES USED IN TRADE (TECHNOLOGY)

SPOT AND STAIN REMOVAL AND CARE OF CLOTHING

SPUNBONDED FABRICS

STRETCH FABRICS

SURE CARE SYMBOLS FOR WASHING AND IRONING —
National Retail Merchants Association

TEX SYSTEM FOR DESIGNATION OF YARN NUMBERS; A.S.T.M.

TEXTILE FIBER PRODUCTS IDENTIFICATION ACT: Federal
Trade Commission

TUFTED FABRICS

WASH AND WEAR

With illustrations, charts, flow sheets, and tables throughout.

ILLUSTRATIONS

In the text

THE MODERN
TEXTILE AND APPAREL DICTIONARY

AAL, ACH, AICH. A plant raised in India which produces a red dyestuff obtained from the roots. Suranji is the name of the resultant dye.

AATCC. American Association of Textile Chemists and Colorists, a national scientific body with active sections in various parts of the country, whose members are chemists and others active in the dyeing, finishing, and other chemical phases of the textile industry.

The objectives of AATCC are to increase knowledge of the application of dyes and chemicals in the textile industry; to encourage research on chemical processes and materials; to develop standards for fastness of dyes and finishes; to develop and improve test methods and instruments.

AATT. American Association for Textile Technology, Inc., a national society, incorporated in New York State, whose members are qualified textile technologists engaged in development work, research, operations and testing in the fields of yarns, fabrics, and finishes.

The objects of this association are to promote and increase technical knowledge of textile raw materials, processing, and finished fabrics; to encourage research and testing among members of the association and throughout the textile and affiliated industries; to promote interchange of professional knowledge among members of this association and between this association and other technical societies, associations, and organizations; to promote fraternal intercourse among technologists; to set up and promote textile standards.

ABA. A wool, hair fiber or combination-stock material used by the peasants in southern Europe and Asia. The fabric is coarse, thick, and has considerable felting applied in the finishing.

ABACA AND HEMP. The term abaca is the name given the fiber that is raised in the Philippine Islands. It has superseded hemp to a considerable degree in the making of rope. It is commonly called Manila hemp and through contraction of this term abaca and hemp are considered more or less synonymous.

The term hemp is correctly applied to the product of several fibers of the same or similar appearance. Common hemp comes from the plant *Cannabis sativa*. It will withstand water better than any other natural textile fiber.

Hemp has a very interesting history. "Hemp, twine, and rope" can be traced as far back as 2700 B.C. Shen Nung, a Chinese Emperor, developed hemp to the point where ropemaking became a great industry called "ma." India

found use for hemp in an eighth-century drug. While cotton was known to the Egyptians, Hebrews, Phoenicians and Persians, there is nothing on record to show that they knew of hemp. In Medieval times hemp found its way into Europe and Northern Africa, when the Saracens arrived. It was not until the Era of Discovery, however, that it began to take on any importance in European life. The Italian city-states of the Renaissance developed it for use in maritime circles, and it was in great demand. Spanish explorers spread the cultivation and use of the fiber in several world centers with much success. Italy, however, still produces the best hemp raised anywhere in the world, a carry-over from the days of the Renaissance.

By 1850, England had a good hemp industry. Cordage makers in this country turned to the Philippines for the abaca fiber, and soon were making the best rope in the world in the days of the old whaling ships and schooners so well known in the past history of this country.

Hemp and abaca are still important items in the commercial world. Leading centers for these fibers include Italy, India, Iran, Russia, China and Japan. Russia is the largest producer today. Kentucky is the leading hemp state in this country.

The plant attains a height of fifteen feet and the fiber is obtained from the plant by retting, the most frequently used method. One hundred parts of raw hemp stalk will give about 25 parts of raw hemp or filasse. One hundred parts of filasse will yield about 65 parts of combed fiber and about 35 parts of tow. One hundred parts of hemp seed will produce about 27 parts of oil.

The seed is about the color of a dried pea, but is not so large. (This is used for birdseed.) The fiber is tan in color, long, coarse, durable and little affected by moisture and water. The oil is yellowish-green in color and it finds favor in making varnish and artists' colors.

Uses of hemp include all kinds of twine, rope, and cordage; it is used in calking, webbing and stuffer warps, and with other yarns in the manufacture of carpets and rugs. Large, heavy cables used in maritime circles are also made of hemp. Tailors use hemp in better-quality suitings for webbing.

ABACAXI FIBER. See PINEAPPLE FIBER.

ABASSI COTTON. A fine, almost white, silklike cotton from Egypt. The staple averages 1¼ inches to 1½ inches. It spins to 100s and upwards,

will bleach, dye and mercerize very well. Fabrics made from this cotton are strong, capable of taking high finishes on sheer material, and give excellent service.

ABAT-CHAUVEE. French for low-quality wool.

ABB. 1. Low-grade wool taken from the rump and the tail of sheep. It is suitable only for low-grade yarns and is used chiefly for warp. 2. A filling pick (English term).

ABBA MANTLE CLOTH. A plain or striped Arab costume cloth, made of silk or camel's hair, used as a covering for other clothing.

ABBATRE. Showing a raised or depressed effect—quilted fabrics or articles are abbatré.

ABBOT'S CLOTH. Cotton, linen or mixture fabric, used for draperies and hangings. Basket weaves, plain or fancy, are used in the construction; the 4-4 basket is the most popular weave used. Often known as monk's cloth.

ABBOTSFORD. A light twilled-woolen cloth with a subdued check pattern.

ABC SILK. A lightweight plain-weave material made with cotton warp and spun silk filling. The cloth comes in white and in plain colors, and is used for linings and underwear.

ABDIG, ABUDIG. Medium-fine wool from Morocco.

ABDULLAH-KANI. Plain-woven, striped dress-silk material made in France for its African trade.

ABEE. Cotton warp and wool filling feature this plain-weave dress goods popular in Asia Minor.

ABELMOSCHUS FIBER. A tough Indian fiber from a plant which resembles jute; does not rot in water and is therefore extensively used for cord and rope. Local Indian name is Rei Bhenda.

ABERCROMBIE. Scottish tartan made with a blue-and-black ground, featured by an overcheck of green and white.

ABERDEEN. 1. Men's half-hose made in Scotland of coarse wool. Come in solid colors and heather mixes and is used for sports wear. 2. Back-filled sheeting or muslin that has been dyed black. 3. Sometimes used in Great Britain, it is a system of heavy yarn counts for wool, jute, and so on. The unit is based on the weight in pounds of one spindle of 14,400 yards; a 4s means that one spindle weighs four pounds.

ABERDEEN FINISH. A slightly starched finish applied to sheeting that has been dyed black; used as lining material.

ABESTON. An incombustible Egyptian flax first mentioned by Pliny.

ABESTRINE CLOTH. Name that may be applied to cloth made from asbestos.

ABITO. General Italian term for apparel, dress, garment, clothing, and so on.

ABLAQUE. A high-quality silk raised in Iran is known by this French term. Also called adassin, ardassin, ardassine, pearl silk.

ABNAKEE RUG. An American hooked' rug typified by its bold motifs and a coarse, open jute ground construction. Unbleached flannel or comparable woolen fabric is cut into narrow strips after dyeing and hooked through the low-textured burlap backing to form the pile effect.

ABRADED FILAMENT YARNS. Continuous filament yarns which have been processed by being passed over a rough surface, thereby breaking some of the filaments. The appearance is between regular continuous filament and spun-type yarns.

These yarns have a higher covering power than the original continuous filament yarns, and are considerably stronger than the equivalent size of staple spun yarns. The most prominent is Celafil, made by The Celanese Corporation. Typical sizes in denier are the 100, 120, 150, 200, 300, 450, and 600. The yarn gives materials a worsted-like appearance and hand; the fabrics can be piece-dyed in the darker shades without destroying the matté effect, since the abrasion breaks up the high sheen apparent in continuous filament yarns. Abraded yarns are usually twisted together and used with other yarns, although they have also been used singly in the coarser sizes with the proper twist.

ABRASION RESISTANCE. The degree to which a fabric is able to withstand surface wear and rubbing.

ABRASION WEAR TEST MACHINE. A testing machine which has two abrading units for testing two specimens at the same time for comparative purposes. Sample size is 4½ inches wide and 6½ inches long. One specimen is cut with the long direction parallel to the warp, while the second sample is cut with the long direction parallel to the filling. Clamps hold the samples in place, one of which is stationary, while the other applies and maintains a tension of eight pounds in the direction of the length of the specimen, distributed evenly across its width. Minimum pressure between the abradant (a #320 flexible aloxite cloth four inches wide or a piece of cloth of the same type as that being tested) and the testing specimen is 33 ounces. Heavier

fabrics may use as much as 88 ounces maximum. Pressures may be increased by weights which come with the machine.

ABRASIVE FABRIC. Cotton fabric coated on one side with emery, sandpaper, or some other abrasive. Used for polishing hard surfaces such as metals.

ABRAWAN. A high-grade Dacca, Pakistan muslin which obtains its name from the Hindu word for "running water," which is indicative of its fineness.

ABROME. A fine, silklike fiber obtained from the white bark of the plant of this name. Raised in the East Indies, the fiber has many uses similar to jute. Known for its whiteness, cleanliness, and particular properties, it has been used as a substitute for silk. Also called Abroma or devil's cotton.

ABSOLUTE HUMIDITY. The concentration or density of water vapor in the atmosphere expressed as weight per unit volume or weight per unit weight of dry air, or of water vapor and air. It is stated usually in terms of grains per cubic foot, grains per pound, or in pounds per pound.

ABSORBENCY. The ease, speed, and amount of liquids a material will absorb.

ABSORBENT. A substance noted for its ability to absorb other substances upon its own surface. It is used chiefly in stain removal, since it will absorb staining material when spread over it. Brushing follows the action. An absorbent is effective mainly on light or freshly made stains. It is harmless on all fibers. Examples include corn meal, chalk, fuller's earth.

ABSORBENT COTTON. Stock, yarn, or cloth from which the natural waxy, fatty matter has been removed in order to make it absorbent. Much used in medical and surgical fields.

ABSORPTION. 1. Taking in and holding, as a sponge taking in water or a blotter taking in ink or some other liquid. 2. Attraction and holding of gases or liquids within the pores of a fiber, filament, yarn, or material.

ABSORPTION FABRIC. Cotton, jute, or other suitable fabric treated or impregnated with chemicals to absorb gases and vapors.

ABSORPTION GAUGE. An instrument by which the rate of absorbency of a textile fabric in both the warp and filling directions may be determined. After partial submersion in water of the specimens to be tested, which are colored with potassium bichromate, the speed of migration of the solution is recorded at specific intervals.

ABSORPTION OF MOISTURE. Wool is able to absorb a large amount

of moisture without feeling damp or wet to the skin. Thus, body perspiration from the inside and moisture from the air on the outside are taken up by the yarns and evaporated.

ABSORPTION TEST. A test which measures the resistance of the fibers or filaments of a fabric to absorption of water.

ABSTERGENT. Cleansing substance; a detergent.

ABSTRACT DESIGNS. Those which possess separated parts of an original motif, or pattern or design, from which the designer takes his thoughts and ideas for completion of the design.

ABUTILON, CHINESE JUTE. A plant raised in tropical areas. Following retting, it gives a white, lustrous, rather strong bast fiber on the order of jute. See CHINGMA.

ACACIA. A genus of shrubs and trees found in the warmer areas all over the world, including the babul. It belongs to the pea family. It exudes gummy substances, one of which, gum arabic, comes from India.

ACALA. Cotton native to Mexico; now raised in Arkansas, Oklahoma, and Texas. Staple about 1¹⁄₁₆ inches. See also HOPI ACALA.

ACALA 1517. Native to Mexico, this cotton has a 1⅛-inch staple, is fairly fine, has good tensile strength, but is high in immature fiber and neppiness. Also raised in California, New Mexico, and Arizona.

ACALA 4-42. Grown by irrigation in California, this staple cotton is a development from Acala 1517 cotton. Staple length is 1¹⁄₁₆ inches, and this fiber may replace the old-time popular staple of Shafter Acala in California.

ACALA P18 C COTTON. A cotton fiber of average to good length uniformity, with fineness running from fine to average. Strength of fiber is weak to average. Used in yarns of 22s to 36s.

ACCA. A cloth used in the British Isles for formal, regal, and conventional purposes. Vestment cloth is made from Acca. It is a richly brocaded material, interspersed with silk to enhance the beauty of the fabric. Animal or pastoral designs are often worked into the construction to enrich its appearance.

ACCELERATOR. Any chemical or substance used to increase or hasten a normal or usual rate or time to consummate an action. Acids and salts are common accelerators used to hasten an action to finality.

ACCELOROTOR. A textile testing

device for quick evaluation of abrasion resistance on fabrics. Developed in the laboratories of the American Association of Textile Chemists and Colorists.

ACCOLE. Entwined around or encircling the neck; collared. Accole also means joined, overlapping, or touching at the neck. Has been used mainly on coats-of-arms, shields, etc.

ACCORDION PLEATS. An even series of folds formed close together to resemble the folds in an accordion. The folds range in size from ⅛ inch to ½ inch. To make the folds permanent the steaming process is applied before finishing the garment. They are much used in dresses and skirts.

ACCORDION STITCH. A combination of the tuck and float in knitting, this stitch affords great elasticity in the article.

ACENAPHTHENE. An aromatic hydrocarbon much used in the manufacture of vat dyes.

ACETA. Spun acetate which contains fibroin or casein; the fibers are altered in physical properties to give increased strength, rough surfaces, crimp, and other qualities.

ACETATE. Fiber, yarn, or material made by the acetate process of manufacture. It is not a regenerated cellulose like viscose or cuprammonium, but is an ester of cellulose—namely, cellulose acetate. Acetate differs from rayon in that its physical and chemical properties are different, especially in its reaction to dyes; and an entire new set of dyes have been developed for acetate dyeing. The principal developmental work for acetate was done by the two brothers Camille and Henri Dreyfus of Basel, Switzerland. See Illustrated Section.

ACETATE, HOLLOW FILAMENT. This yarn has a hollow or doughnut-shaped cross-section. Easier to process than regular acetate filament, it has a higher, more uniform luster, is crisper, has a firmer hand and smoother feel.

ACETATE, POSSIBLE ADVANTAGES OF.

1. Suppleness gives the fabric excellent draping qualities.
2. Has no natural tendency to stretch or shrink.
3. May be used for drapery and portiere purposes; hangs very well.
4. Takes the dyestuff well.
5. When wet, acetates have less loss of strength than rayons.
6. Is resistant to moisture.
7. Normal amount of moisture content varies from 3.5 per cent to 6.5 per cent.
8. Dries rapidly.

9. Does not deteriorate from salt air, mold, mildew, nor does it rot.
10. Fruit, tea, coffee, and beverage stains readily removed with soap and water.
11. Is not a substitute for, nor imitation of silk or any other fiber.
12. Acetone will readily dissolve acetate yarn or fabric.
13. Reaction to chemicals is different from that of other fibers.
14. Is not a weighted or adulterated fiber.
15. Has good hygienic qualities.
16. May be given special finishes. Retains a permanent white.
17. Acetates may be dry-cleaned and laundered, provided proper care is given in the treatments.
18. The fiber works well, in conjunction with other textile fibers, and is ideal for cross-dyeing to obtain two-tone effects. It is often worked with other fibers in woven and knitted fabrics. In this respect, it is a much desired fiber because of its versatility.
19. Because of its insulating property, acetate may be thought of as a fabric for all-season wear.
20. Acetate fabrics should be ironed on the wrong side or back of the material. The material should be slightly damp. Use a warm iron, not hot, for the best results.
21. Acetates redye well to darker shades when done with care by professional dyers.
22. Acetate fabrics will take permanent pleats well.
23. Acetate comes in continuous filaments or short fibers of specified length and diameter. May be bright or dull.

ACETATE, PRINCIPLES OF MANUFACTURE. See table.

ACETATE: PRINCIPLES INVOLVED IN MANUFACTURE

Wood Pulp or Linters		Chemical
Cellulose	plus	Glacial Acetic Acid, Acetic Anhydride, Acetone

		The Textile Filament
plus	Machinery	yields
	Spinneret	Cellulose Acetate

ACETATE, SAPONIFICATION OF. Fiber is saponified or converted on the surface to regenerated cellulose by the action of a hydrolytic agent, such as sodium hydroxite solution, in dilute form. The bath is heated to about 180° Fahrenheit and immersion lasts 30 to 45 minutes. The loss in weight of an

all-acetate material will approximate 8 per cent for partial or surface saponification up to about 40 per cent. The treatment is usually given to the goods prior to discharge printing in order to allow the use of substantive dyes, which are direct dyes for cotton and regenerated cellulose rayon fabrics.

ACETATE, SIMPLE TESTS FOR. Acetone, CH_3COCH_3, or glacial acetic acid, CH_3COOH, will destroy acetate filament. There are, however, some acetates not wholly dissolved by acetone; glacial acetic acid, nevertheless, will dissolve any acetate filament. Dyed acetate with white acetate and white, bleached cotton cloth are wrapped around a core of bleached cotton. The ends of the cotton core are dipped into a solution of 30 grams of sodium chloride, per liter, with 10 grams of acetic acid, 100 per cent strength. The bath is kept at 40° Centigrade, in a closed tube for six hours. The fabric is then rinsed and dried. Loss of depth and bleeding into white fabric are noted, and appraisals made.

ACETATE, STRONG. Acetate yarns that have a high tensile strength may be obtained by a special stretch spinning process. The yarn may be spun as fine as 10 denier, and if so desired, can be saponified to give the dyeing properties of viscose rayon yarn. It is also possible to produce it in the form of staple fiber, either straight or kinked.

ACETATE, TYPE C. Made by the Du Pont Company, it differs from regular acetate in that it has the property of taking on a wool-like crimp when immersed in boiling water.

ACETATE, TYPE F. A modified filament yarn used for draperies produced by The Celanese Corporation of America.

ACETATE AND RAYON RULES. The following trade-practice rules on the use and the identification of acetate and rayon were announced on December 11, 1951, and became effective on February 11, 1952:

The Federal Trade Commission has decreed that RAYON is to be used for man-made textile fibers and filaments composed of regenerated cellulose; and yarn, thread, or textile fabric made of such fibers and filaments. The term ACETATE is to be used for man-made textile fibers and filaments composed of cellulose acetate; and yarn, thread, and textile fabric made of such fibers.

Practices to be considered unfair are general misrepresentation, improper identification, incomplete description, juggled weight-value listings, improper fiber emphasis by the size of the printing on the label, incomplete provision of fiber description along with the trade-mark, concealed adulterants, and incomplete fabric handling information on consumer labels.

ACETATE CREPE. Finished from 45 inches up to 49 inches, the warp yarn is of the flat type acetate while the filling is viscose crepe yarn with S-twist and Z-twist. 150, 120, and 100 denier may be the choice for warp; filling is chosen from 200, 150, or 100 denier. Textures range from 96 x 46 up to 114 x 64.

Cross-dyeing, also known sometimes as "union dyeing" or "two-tone dyeing," gives beautiful coloring in the goods. The fabric is also singular in that the acetate warp provides luxury of feel, while the viscose yarn, with its ability to crepe, together with the shrinkage and resulting build-up caused by the action of the crepe filling, provides a genuine public appeal.

Variations in the fabric may be had by multi-pick arrangements, such as four S-twist and four Z-twist, or eight S-twist and eight Z-twist. A hammered effect results from this construction. Incidentally, the larger the group of one-way twist picks together, the more sensitive will be the fabric.

Terminal uses include dress coats, lining in sportswear, suiting. A texture of 96 x 48 is ideal for clothes of this type. A texture of 135 x 64 is popular for the so-called higher class trade in blouses, dress goods, and negligees.

ACETATE CREPE-BACK SATIN. Finished at 43.5 inches, the warp is flat acetate while the filling is viscose crepe yarn. Denier of the warp is 100 or 75; the filling is 150 or 100 denier. Textures range from 200 x 72 to 320 x 88. The warp is high in sley with comparatively high pickage to produce a dull, slightly creped back. The warp weight acts as a foundation for drapiness to the goods, which have a decided richness and suppleness. Used for dress goods and fur-coat linings.

ACETATE DYES. See DISPERSED DYES.

ACETATE GAMZA. This 48-inch finished fabric is made with flat acetate warp and viscose crepe filling made of S-twist and Z-twist. Denier in the warp is 150 or 120; in the filling it is 200 or 150. Texture ranges from 96 x 56 to 110 x 52.

Fancy weaves bring out the surface appeal in gamza. The crepe filling also enhances the goods in appeal. Warp sley is quite low, comparatively speaking. It should be noted that the warp side is the back of the cloth. Used in the outerwear trade, gamza is not as popular as formerly.

ACETATE NINON. Made in voile-twist yarn each way, 75 denier is used in textures of 64 x 64 or 80 x 80. This sheer, glasslike fabric is simple in construction, has appeal, and is highly suitable for curtaining. The washability of the goods is of interest to the housewife. Accessories, curtains, and evening wear are the uses for ninon.

ACETATE of IRON. An impure form of pyrolignite of iron, and known as "Iron Liquor" or "Black Liquor," it is used as a mordant for certain blacks on silk and cotton. Same as ferrous acetate.

ACETATE PANNE SATIN. Finished from 39 inches to 41.5 inches, this flat yarn fabric is made with 100 denier or 75 denier in the warp, and with 150-, 100-, or 75-denier yarn. Pick counts range from 100 x 60 to 320 x 96. Comparable with viscose rayon satin, the acetate satin seems to possess greater suppleness. The texture, 200 x 72, is popular for lining in ladies' sports coats and dress coats. Other uses include blankets, candy-box linings, dress goods, labels, trimmings, underwear.

ACETATE SHARKSKIN. Finished around 41 inches and made with flat yarn, the warp is made from 150 or 300 denier; filling is of 300, 450, or 600 denier. Pick count is from 52 x 52 to 176 x 36. This popular sportswear cloth is firm, rather stiff, and solid. The cloth is usually made from the plain, taffeta or tabby weave; occasionally fancy weaves which show short floats are used. Viscose sharkskin is too stiff for acceptance in the trade at present.

End uses of sharkskin include nurses' uniform fabric, sportswear of many types, and resort clothes for warm climates.

ACETATE STAPLE. Three firms in this country produce the yarn which is available in denier of 1½, 2, 3, 5, 5½, 8, 12, 16, and 20.

ACETATE TAFFETA. Finished from 39 inches to about 41 inches, this flat yarn cloth is made from the following denier—150, 120, 100, 75; filling denier is 300, 150, 120, or 75. Textures range from 84 x 60 to 200 x 64. There is a wide range in taffeta fabrics. While acetate "rayon" was not approved by consumers as early as viscose rayon, it has, nevertheless, made rapid strides since it has a distinctive and very appealing hand. Variations with viscose yarn in the warp are ideal for cross or two-tone dyeing. The 180 x 60 and the 200 x 64 numbers are extremely popular in the trade. Terminal uses include bedspreads, blouses, hangings, ribbon, and trimmings.

ACETATE TEST ON WOOL AND SILK. Place two separate samples in a 10 per cent caustic soda bath. Add lead acetate to each bath. The wool takes on a brownish precipitate; silk, a white precipitate.

ACETATE TWILL LINING. Made with flat yarn and finished from 37 inches to 41 inches, the warp and the filling are made from 150-denier or 75-denier yarn. Pick count ranges from 84 x 72 to 150 x 88. This fabric has a better hand than its counterpart, viscose twill lining; however, the cloth is less rugged but seems to be more luxurious. In abrasion testing viscose rayon is superior to acetate twill lining. The chief use of the lining is for garments which require a rich-looking cloth with a luxurious feel; durability is secondary.

ACETIC ACID. In concentrated form known as "glacial acetic acid." It is used in many dyeing and printing operations, in the manufacture of acetate, etc. Formula is CH_3COOH.

ACETIC ANHYDRIDE. Used in the acetylation process in the manufacture of acetate; anhydrous acetic acid.

ACETONE. A volatile, colorless liquid with an etherlike odor; obtained commercially by distilling the product of corn-mash fermentation. It is used chiefly as an industrial solvent, and has an important part in the manufacture of artificial leather, paint, explosives. It is dimethyl ketone, written chemically as CH_3COCH_3 or $2(CH_3)CO$.

Acetone will readily dissolve acetate, but will not affect rayon made on the viscose, cuprammonium or nitro-cellulose methods.

Closely allied with acetone are the following chemicals, which destroy acetate only: amyl acetate, $C_5H_{11}\cdot C_2H_3O_2$, and ethyl acetate, $C_2H_5\cdot C_2H_3O_2$.

ACETYL. The basic element in acetic acid.

ACETYLATION. The introduction of an acetyl radical into an organic molecule, an important step in the manufacture of acetate. The prepared cellulose, which is dissolved wood pulp or cotton, is acted upon by a mixture of glacial acetic acid and acetic anhydride.

ACETYLATOR. A closed mixing tank equipped with agitators for stirring the liquor in the acetylation of acetate. There is also cooling equipment in this tank to govern the heat conditions.

ACHLOROPSIA. The inability of a person to perceive the color green.

ACHROMATIC. Applied to colorants, it refers to the hueless neutral blacks, grays, and whites. See CHROMA, CHROMATIC.

ACHROMATIC CONDENSER. A compound lens used for concentrating the light on the object under the microscope.

ACID. A chemical compound which contains hydrogen replaceable by a metal. Litmus, a dyestuff made from lichens, will become red in the presence of an acid; litmus turns blue in presence of an alkali. Acids have a sour taste, a pungent or penetrating odor, and will evolve hydrogen and dissolve a metal. Vinegar is a form of acetic acid; it is sharp to the taste and has a characteristic odor noted in acids.

ACID AGEING. That which occurs when a volatile acid is present in the vapor around yarn or fabric.

ACID DOPE. A pyroxylin, nitrocellulose base used in combination with color as a coating for fabric to make it impervious or repellent to air, to water or both. The term is used in many industries for any of several liquids applied to materials.

ACID DYES. This important group of dyes are salts of color acids chiefly derived from azo compounds of benzene and toluene. There is a wide range of these dyes, which are noted for their brightness. They are used chiefly on wool because of the relatively low cost, ease of application, and good results. Also used on silk; acid dyes can also be applied to cotton and rayon to a limited degree in combination with a mordant.

ACID FADING. See FUME FADING.

ACIDIMETER. Any apparatus of alkaline solution which will determine the amount or the strength of acids.

ACIDITY. An expression of the concentration of hydrogen ions present in a solution.

ACID MILLING DYES. A group of acid dyes applied to wool which assure fastness of color to soaping, fulling, milling and scouring operations in the finishing of the goods.

ACID MORDANT DYE. A dye applied to wool in an acid bath after the wool has been treated with chrome to improve the results desired with regard to proper color shade.

ACID RESISTANCE. A cloth that will resist any acid within reason; the acid used to test should be listed as organic or inorganic.

ACIDS, SOME PROPERTIES OF. They have a sour taste such as that of vinegar, lemon juice, dilute oxalic acid, sour milk. Acids may be in liquid form, such as nitric acid, which is used to give a rich yellow color to silk and woolen fabrics or yarns. They may be in solid form, such as salicylic acid; gases, such as fuming nitric acid; strong solvents, such as aqua regia. Acids turn litmus paper red.

ACONCHADA. Originally a Spanish sheep known for its coarse wool and now raised rather extensively in South America.

ACORES. A varying quality unbleached linen fabric made in France and used for export.

ACREAGE ALLOTMENTS. It is within the power of the Secretary of Agriculture of the United States to require producers, as in the case of raising cotton, to limit their planting in order to qualify for price support loans.

ACRIDINE DYES: Basic dyestuffs that are acridine derivatives of triphenylmethane.

ACRILAN. The registered trademark of Monsanto Company, Inc., for its Acrylic fiber made from a long chain synthetic polymer composed of at least 85 percent by weight of Acrylonitrile units. Acrilan and Acrilan 16, which may be combined for a wide variety of cross-dye effects, are available in staple fiber form and as continuous filament tow.

Acrilan is characterized by its wool-like hand, its warmth, lightness in relation to bulk, wrinkle resistance, and resistance to chemical and bacteria attack. It has found acceptance in a wide variety of apparel uses, both in blends with wool and with other man-made fibers, and as a 100 per cent component. Acrilan is used extensively in floor coverings, blankets, and upholstery, and may be processed on the woolen, worsted, American, and cotton systems, or converted to yarn on the Turbo Stapler and Pacific Converter machines.

ACRILAN 16. Comparable with Acrilan but has improved whiteness and different dyeing properties veered to end uses where white or extremely bright pastel shades are desired, as in sweaters and jersey knit fabrics both in solid and cross-dyed effects. It is engineered for disperse and improved basic dyeability; has no affinity for acid, chrome, neutral premetallized, or other wool-type dyes. Both Acrilan and Acrilan 16 are often used in effective combinations in many fabrics and are products of Monsanto Company, Textiles Division, New York City.

ACRILAN 77 STAPLE. Acrilan 16 polymer serves as the base for this bright staple used for liners. Staple length is from 1-9/16 to 2-1/2 inches. Product of Monsanto Company, Textiles Division, New York City.

ACRILAN 86. Staple stock spun on the woolen system of spinning yarn. Made from Acrilan 16 polymer, it is used in blankets. Staple length ranges from 1-9/16 to 3 inches. Product of Monsanto Textiles, New York City.

ACRILAN 87. Semi-dull staple which is spun on woolen systems and used in blanketings. Acrilan 16 polymer serves as its base. Staple ranges from 1-9/16 to 3 inches. Product of Monsanto.

ACRILAN® PLUS. Registered trademark for probably the best known acrylic fiber used at present in carpeting. Unveiled early in 1972, a product of Monsanto Textiles, Inc., New York City, this fiber provides greater fiber springiness, improved brightness in color, greater resistance in wear, better colorfastness, and seems to prove that "all acrylic fibers are not alike."

ACRILAN TRADEMARK. Monsanto Chemical Company, Textiles Division, New York City, owns the trademark for Acrilan fiber and tow. The trademark for this acrylic fiber is A-Acrilan (Capital "A" with "Acrilan" overprinted on the bar of the "A"). Monsanto has a licensing program for this registered trade-mark and under it assumes the status of an ingredient trade-mark. Formerly, the trade-mark was an identifying signature for the fiber.

ACRYLIC. Designating an acid—$C_3 H_4 O_2$—which has a sharp acrid odor; prepared from acrolein or from certain derivatives of propionic acid. Used in organic synthesis in the manufacture of plastics. Another name for the acid used is propenoic. Examples of true acrylics include Acrilan, Creslan, "Orlon," and Zefran. Dynel and Verel are examples of modified acrylic fibers and classed as Modacrylic Fibers.

ACRYLIC FIBER, TYPE 61. Staple fiber of American Cyanamid Company, Inc., New York City. Formed chiefly from acrylonitrile, the polymer is dissolved, then wet spun, washed, and stretched. This round cross-section fiber is dyeable with basic and disperse dyes, and is non-receptive to acid dyes. It is resistant to both mildew and moths. Specific gravity is 1.18. Used in pile fabrics, blankets, headgear, draperies, sweatshirts, socks, sweaters, underwear, etc.

ACRYLIC FIBER, TYPE 61B. Very similar to Type 61 of American Cyanamid Company, this staple is used in stock or skein dyed forms for use in floorcoverings. The fiber has a durable crimp and comes in semi-dull, bright lusters, and in blends of these lusters.

ACRYLIC RESINS. Resins thermoplastic in nature, of the synthetic type polymerized from acrylic acid and methacrylic acid. The major resins are polymers of the methyl and ethyl esters of these acids, or copolymers of mixtures of these monomers. Properties include water-white color, transparency, and resistance to discolorization; many are resistant to acids, alcohol, alkalies, mineral oils, water.

These resins are soluble in aromatic hydrocarbons, chlorinated hydrocarbons, esters, and ketones. They are compatible with nitrocellulose and plasticizers, but not with drying oils, many types of alkyd resins, and most hard resins.

ACTINOLITE. One of the amphibole group of mineral fibers, it is an iron calcium magnesium silicate found in greenish masses of fibrous crystals.

ACTIVE CHLORINE. See CHLORINE, AVAILABLE.

ACTUAL DRAFT: See DRAFT, ACTUAL.

ADA, AIDA CANVAS. A stiff, coarse, brown or tan fabric made with a basket weave with accurately spaced meshes; generally used for art needlework.

ADAM'S NEEDLE. See YUCCA, COMMON.

ADANSONIA FIBER. A fiber used for cordage, obtained from the bark of the "monkey bread" tree in Africa.

ADAPANGIA. A type of raw silk raised in India.

ADARSA. High-quality muslin made in India.

ADATAIS, ADDATIS. A fine, high-count cotton muslin made in Bombay, India.

ADELAIDE WOOL. Obtained in and around this city in Australia, the wool is a high merino quality only slightly lower in quality than Port Philip and Sydney wools. It can spin to 60s worsted counts and finds use in high-quality worsteds made from very fine, choice fibers.

ADENOS. The best cotton of the Levant. Also means staple cotton fabric made in Syria and neighboring countries.

ADHERE. To stick to anything, as a postage stamp on an envelope.

ADHESIVE SIZE INGREDIENT. A mix which causes fibers in yarn or thread to adhere to each other, and thereby to better withstand, at all times, friction, chafing, fraying and abrasion.

Some major sizes are cornstarch, dextrine, potato starch, maize flour, rice flour, sago, soluble starch, gum tragacanth, gum arabic, wheat starch.

ADHESIVE TAPE. Strips or splits of ordinary cotton fabric covered with an adhesive coating on one side. A universal household and industrial article.

ADHI, ADDHI. Plain-weave cotton muslin made on hand looms in India. Used for shirting and may be embroidered since its construction serves as a good base for this type of work.

AD HOCK. 1. Hand-blocking of a pattern over a Jacquard motif in a fabric. 2. Overprinting on textile goods.

ADIA. A good quality cotton cloth which finds use in Africa and the Near East.

ADJECTIVE DYES. Dyes which have to be applied by the use of a mordant, which means that, without the aid of a mordant, the fibers have no affinity for dyestuff. The mordant actually fixes the dye in the fibers. Examples of adjective dyes are basic dyes and mordant dyes.

ADMIRALTY CLOTH. 1. Slang expression for melton cloth used for officers' uniforms and coats in the British navy. 2. General term for heavyweight pea jackets and officers' coats used in the American naval service.

ADRIANOPLE TWILL. The 2-up and 1-down, right-hand twill weave.

ADSORBENT. A material which has the ability to hold water or other vapors on its external surfaces, without itself being permanently changed either chemically or physically. Liquid water, hygroscopic water, and water of crystallization or water of hydration are included.

ADSORPTION. Adhesion of gases or liquids to the surface of a substance by capillary condensation. One form is really a case of very loose chemical combination, as dirt sticking to soap.

ADULTERATION. Addition of foreign substances having less value than the main substance. Starches, dextrins, gums may be adulterated. Another case of adulteration is found in the adding of some substance (such as a substitute fiber, chemical or other material) to give a fabric the appearance of better quality than it actually possesses. Also, in the addition of excess tin chloride in silk weighting; of too much flocks to overcoatings; of fibers to core and cable yarns; of salts and other ingredients to dyestuffs.

ADVANCE SAMPLES. Short lengths or blanket ranges which usually run from six to ten yards in length. They are made up for the coming season, and very often from these samples designs are chosen by the trade. Small swatches of cloth are pasted on cards and distributed to prospective buyers, who thus make their selections.

AEGAGRUS. The wild goat of Asia Minor.

AEOLIAN. Lightweight dress goods made of fine cotton warp and silk or rayon filling; not popular at present.

AERATED YARN. Special rayon yarn with a hollow center, containing air or inert gas.

AERESS. Modacrylic fiber of Union Carbide Chemicals Company used mainly for outerwear fabrics, woven and knitted. A multifilament yarn with a higher acrylonitrile and lower vinyl chloride content when compared with the company's other modacrylic fiber, Dynel.

AEROPHANE. Thin silk gauze used as trimming on dresses and headgear; made on doup weave.

AERTEX. Trade name for some leno or doup cloths dyed in solid colors and identified by the leno-effect stripes. See CELLULAR CLOTH.

AESTHETICS, TEXTILE. The characteristics or properties of a material or finished garment as observed by sight and touch. Can be categorized as: color (harmonious or contrasting); light (medium, dark, neutral), luster, loftiness, resiliency, or stiffness.

AETZ. The manufacture of lace on a Schiffli embroidery frame. Lace is embroidered on a base fabric which is later removed from the motif by chemical means. Aetz is the same as a "burnt-out pattern" effected on some fabric. For example, one made of acetate and rayon could be aetz or burnt-out by treating the fabric with acetone which will burn or dissolve the acetate, thus leaving the rayon part of the goods unscathed.

AETZSTICKEREI. German name for burned-out embroidery. See BURN-OUT LACE, BURNT-OUT, BURNT-OUT PRINTING.

AFFINITY. Attraction between two bodies or substances such as mechanical attraction, or chemical attraction. If a dye takes readily, it is said to have good affinity for the fiber. Some dyes do not take very well on certain fibers and they are classed as having no affinity for these particular fibers.

AFGHAN. A knitted or crocheted wool blanket or robe made with a series of stripes, zigzag effects, or squares, varying in size and vivid colorings; gives great warmth.

AFGHANISTAN CARPET. A knotted pile floorcovering made in Afghanistan and those countries adjacent to it. Usually made in a small dimension, about the size of the ordianry art square, the motif is either geometric or floral. The pile effect may be classed as rather long or high and is of low density in construction. Usually made of wool it can also be made of goat hair or in yarns which are a combination of the two.

AFGHAN STITCH. A type of crochet stitch used in making the crocheted squares that form an afghan when sewed together.

AFICOT. French name for the instrument used to polish the raised portions in lace motifs.

AFIUME. A low, coarse type of flax raised in Egypt.

AFRICAN COTTON. Cotton of African origin that is not Egyptian. Inferior in all respects to Egyptian cotton.

AFRICAN FIBER. Fiber from the Algerian palmetto tree, used for mattress stuffing.

AFRICAN HAIR. Used to make a cloth that simulates haircloth, this bast fiber comes from the European dwarf fan palm tree.

AFRICAN HEMP. Another name for bowstring hemp. See BOWSTRING HEMP.

AFRICAN SAFFRON. South African shrub providing an orange dye, obtained from its leaves.

AFRICAN WOOLS. Wools thus referred to come from the Union of South Africa—Orange Free State, Natal, Transvaal—and from Rhodesia. These very soft, fine, white merino wools are much sought by woolen and worsted mills all over the world. Other breeds native to Africa also furnish much of the annual yield of African wools; and it should be borne in mind that these sheep are different from the Merino breed. Low yield and inferior quality, along with careless handling, mark the wool from such native sheep. See Illustrated Section.

AFRIDI. Cotton batik cloth made by the "wax-resist" method.

AFTER-CHROMING. Mordant processing applied after stock, yarn or material has been dyed. When applied on selected direct dyes fastness to washing is improved. Vat colors are oxidized by after-chroming.

AFTER-TREATMENT. The passing of dyed material through a chemical solution in order to improve fastness of the color or to help in obtaining the shade desired. Direct dyes, for example, are after-treated to improve color-fastness.

AFTERWELT. The area at the top of a woman's stocking between the welt and the top portion of the leg; made from regulation leg yarn, which is knitted from the same yarn as the welt.

AGA, AGAMID. Used for rope and coarse fabric, it is the inner bark of the Ficus tree found in the Philippines. The fiber is obtained by maceration or crushing of the bark.

AGABANCE. A silk-embroidered cotton fabric made in Aleppo, Syria.

AGAR-AGAR. Also known as Iceland moss, this vegetable fiber has undergone much experimentation in England for use in gauzelike fabrics. The fibers become quite flexible by incorporating glycerol borax or gluten into the viscous mass before extrusion. They are said to be sufficiently resistant to atmospheric moisture and to be non-hygroscopic. Colored fabrics are made by the incorporation of ground, colored pigments or by spraying on dyes.

AGARIC. A dress fabric on the order of Turkish toweling or terry cloth. It has fine loops formed by the warp; cloth comes in all colors.

AGAVE. Bast-fiber obtained from aloe and century plants; used for cordage and rope.

AGEING, AGING. Accelerated tests of various types which use light, heat, oxygen, corrosive elements, or moisture to determine the expected life of textiles, rubber goods, hard floor coverings, leather, paints and other materials. The term is also used in reference to a steaming bath, with or without the aid of a chemical, of short duration—resorted to in the development of color onto yarn or cloth.

Ageing also implies the development, through a span of time, of ingredients that are in the partial or finished state but are to be combined with new chemicals or materials on completion of the process. This is very important in the manufacture of acetate, rayon, and other man-made textile fibers and filaments.

AGENCY SHOP. That union status agreed to by a company in which all employees in the bargaining unit must belong and pay dues to the bargaining agency, or must pay a service charge to the union, but they need not join.

AGER. A chamber to which dyed or printed cloth is sent for treatment with moist steam in the absence of air so as to develop and then fix the dyestuff onto the fibers. Steam of ammonia fumes is often used in ageing.

AGE, SILKWORM. The interval between any two moltings.

AGFA. Viscose or acetate fibers altered in physical properties to increase strength, to cause the surfaces to become rough, and to produce crimp.

AGGLOMERATE. Coagulating or bunching of fine particles into larger pieces.

AGGONED BUNDER. Raw silk produced in the East Indies and Japan; now the best grade raised in these areas.

AGILON. Trade-mark for a non-torque stretch nylon filament yarn made by Deering Milliken, Inc., New York City. This continuous mono- or multi-filament yarn, with elasticity and varying degrees of hand, ranging from softness to firmness or crispness, receives its properties by patented techniques. The basic properties of the continuous filament are always retained. It may be woven or knitted as singles yarn or as a ply yarn, with plies even or odd in number.

AGILON D. Modified form of Agilon having almost equal bulkiness but less stretch. It is designed primarily for knitted outerwear since it gives good stitch clarity because of the small amount of filament movement during fabric finishing. Product of Deering Milliken, Inc.

AGITATE. To stir or to mix, as in the case of a dye bath or solution.

AGLET. A round white staylace.

AGNELINE. A coarse, long-napped heavy woolen fabric heavily fulled to shed water. This black material is used for clothing among the poorer peoples of Europe.

AGPUI, BATIA, CATIPU. Names for a rugged bast fiber raised in Indonesia. Used to make cloth, cordage, twine, etc.

AGRA CARPET. Made in India, it is a large, thick, knotted cotton or wool carpeting which comes mainly in colors of blue, brown, and green.

AGRA GAUZE, GAZE D'AGRA. A strong, transparent gauzelike silk cloth, given a stiff finish.

AGUJA, PUNTO De AGUJA. Spanish for needle point.

AHRAMI. Plain-woven cotton fabric that has been block-printed to feature stripes embellished by flowered effects. Originated in what is now Iran.

AIGRETTE. Obtained from the egret or heron during mating season, these upright feathers or plumes are used on headgear or as a headdress. Use of genuine egret feathers is outlawed in this country. The term also refers to costume jewelry of the cluster types.

AIGUILLE, POINT A L'AIGUILLE. French for needle point.

AIGUILLETTE. The cord or braid trimming, usually of gold material, seen on military uniforms.

AILANTHUS SILK. Tussah or wild silk from the moth *Attacus atlas*.

AILANTHUS SILKWORM. A hybrid between the *Philosamia cynthia* and the *Attacus ricini*, producing a popular wild silk.

AIR BLAST GIN. A gin with a special type of nozzle which removes cotton lint from the gin saws by a powerful air blast.

AIR BRUSHING. Producing shaded effects on fabrics by employing a mechanized airbrush to blow the color onto the cloth. The hand guides the brush in its work. The method is used on silk or rayon Jacquard or dobby design fabrics.

AIR CONDITIONED. Trade-mark name for a finish of William Simpson Sons & Co., Inc., that eliminates fuzziness, lint, and straggly fibers on the surface of cotton fabrics. This action creates minute interstices throughout the goods allowing air to pass through so that the skin of the person may "breathe," despite the opaqueness of the cloth.

AIR-CONDITIONING OF FABRICS. Making fabrics cooler by increasing porosity and permeability in the construction. Fuzzy, protruding fibers are removed without impairing the tensile strength of the cloth. Perspiration evaporates quicker than usual and the humidity of the body is therefore lowered.

AIR-COOLED FINISH. A finishing technique applied to fabrics in order to keep interstices or openings among the threads, and to maintain an open or porous effect. This type of finish provides comfort in summer fabrics, often referred to as "capability of breathing." Generally speaking, no ironing or washing instructions are provided for fabrics of this sort.

AIR CURRENT. Air flow generated by fans, or vacuums, in cotton opening and picking machines and the like.

AIR JET. A device used to bulk filament yarn by means of a pressure jet which throws the filaments together devoid of any order so as to give a looped formation. It is linked with the Taslan Process of E. I. duPont de Nemours & Co., Inc., Wilmington, Delaware.

AIR LAY. Nonwoven fabric term which implies a method or technique of casting "staple fibers" from an air stream onto a backing material. This results in the random formation of a fiber web.

"Agbada" Nigerian Shirt Design

from:
Creative West African Fashion

AIR PERMEABILITY. A comparative test in the testing of textiles which shows the amount of air which will pass through materials. The test will show the openness or porosity of fabrics by measuring the air flowing through under standard test measurement on especially made machines.

AIRPLANE CLOTH. A strong ply yarn cloth, usually mercerized, of long-staple Arizona or Egyptian cotton. Used as airplane fabric, shirting, and boys' wash suits; the construction is usually square—80 x 80 to 92 x 92. It is made of 2/60s warp and filling and is finished at 36 inches wide. The cloth may be treated with a dope to make it waterproof, or water- and moisture-repellent. The goods have a breaking strength of about 75 pounds to the inch and weigh about four ounces per yard.

AIRPLANE LUGGAGE CLOTH. Lightweight pyroxylin-coated cloth used in many types of luggage.

AIRVEL. A method which imparts bulk and elasticity to spun yarns of man-made fibers, especially for those used in knitting. Du Pont owns the world rights for the process invented originally by Newhill & Earnshaw, Ltd., Bingley, Yorkshire, England, in 1961.

AIR WASHER. An enclosure in which air is drawn or forced through a spray of water so as to cleanse, humidify with warm water, and dehumidify with cooled water.

AIT MOHAD-BERBER. Moroccan sheep, which give a coarse, straight-fibered wool from a fleece of about four-pound weight.

AJIJI. Fine cotton muslin featured by colored rayon or silk stripes; made in India.

A JOUR. Openwork in embroidery. From "à jour," French implying exposed to the day.

AKASCE FIBER. See DEMARARA.

AK-HISSAR RUG. Made for centuries in Asia Minor, the basic structure is made of wool with a pile effect of mohair or some other specialty fiber. The pile is structured by means of the Ghiodes knot application.

AKIA. Rugged bast fiber raised in Hawaii and used in making rope.

AKUND FLOSS. Seed hair of the *Calotropis procera*, obtained in India. Often mixed with kapok.

AKWET-LONGYI. A plain-weave, check-motif cloth made on hand looms in India.

AKZONA CORPORATION. Formerly known as American Enka Company, Inc., Enka, North Carolina, and New York City, the new name became effective in October, 1970, and includes, as well, the International Salt Company, Inc., and Organon, Inc., a former subsidiary of the old American Enka Company and based in Willimantic, Connecticut. Enka began operations in 1928 as a single-line producer of rayon filament fiber and yarn near Asheville, Carolina. At present it has seven fiber and yarn plants, and a nylon/carpet plant in Murphy, North Carolina.

Enka showed much progress in the last decade. In 1961 Enkalur nylon, inspired by silk, was unveiled. Hi-Mod (High Modulus) rayon yarns for better dimensional stability in V-belts and hose were introduced, along with its S-6000 improved rayon tire yarn. High tenacity nylon yarn with improved abrasion resistance in auto safety belts also made their appearance in the market.

The Harford Fibers Division of Bigelow-Sanford, Inc., Rocky Hill, Connecticut, was acquired thereby adding the rights of Zantrel polynosic high wet modulus staple and of Kolorbon solution-dyed staple.

In 1962, Enkaloft continuous filament carpet nylon yarn gained market acceptance and the company is now the second largest producer of this product. In 1964, Crepeset nylon yarn was developed to supply permanently textured tricot for lingerie to match the crepe look in outerwear. Dye-resist nylon yarn for carpets was developed to increase color styling for tone-on-tone effects. Zantrel 700 made its debut and provided an improved high modulus rayon staple primarily for blends with polyester fibers. Enkakrome was brought out and was the first acid-dyeable rayon staple fiber enabling finishers to obtain a multi-colored effect in a single dyeing operation. In 1965, a deep-dye nylon yarn was made to increase styling possibilities in floorcoverings. 1966 saw the introduction of flat filament, piece-dyeable, textured rayon yarns for draperies and upholstery. Variline nylon yarn, used for upholstery, and to add beauty of an antique velvet came into being. Encron polyester also came on the market during the year.

In 1967, a torque yarn for stretch hosiery, Enkasheer, was introduced. The company's Staple Fiber Division was formed to combine both rayon and polyester staples. In 1968, Enka had developed a full line of Encron polyester staple fiber for apparel, home furnishings, fiberfill, carpet manufacturers and for industrial fabrics. Enkasheer nylon kept pace in the stretch hosiery market with its swing to pantyhose and stretch stockings made necessary by the success of the miniskirt.

1969 witnessed the introduction of Enkalite filament polyester for use in carpets, the first lustrous multi-lobal textured polyester continuous filament to appear on the market. The Chattanooga, Tennessee office was opened in order to be near the great tufted carpet area in and around Dalton, Georgia. Deep-dyeing polyester staple was brought out for the carpet trade, and modified high-luster polyester yarn was first offered for use in woven goods.

AL. The morindin dye obtained from the roots of the Indian mulberry tree.

ALADJA. Heavy Indian taffeta made with striped-effect or floral motif.

ALAGOAS COTTON. A type of Brazilian raw cotton. "Alagoas" is the Portuguese word for cotton.

ALAMBA. Alabama cotton.

ALAMODE, ALLAMOD. Used for head coverings and scarves, this plain-weave silk fabric is usually dyed black and given a lustrous finish.

ALAPINE, ALLAPEEN, ALEPINE. An old-time dress goods of wool and silk in the better grade, with cotton and mohair in the lower quality, often used for articles of mourning.

ALASKA. Dress and coat fabric of Great Britain, usually made of union fabric or mixture material. Cotton and wool are used frequently in this plain or twill woven fabric, which is given a napped finish.

ALASKA YARN. Mixture yarn of about two-thirds cotton and one-third combined wool stocks; popular in knitting and hand-weaving circles.

ALATCHA, ALATCHU. A twill-woven cotton cloth set off in blue and white stripes; a Central Asian fabric.

ALB. A long white linen garment worn by the religious, over the cassock from the neck to the ankles. It may be ornamented with embroidery or lace but must retain appearance of a long white linen garment. It is symbolic of purity of heart.

ALBANIAN EMBROIDERY. Cross and Gobelin stitches are used on a canvas-ground fabric to produce geometrical or flower motifs made of the primary or secondary colors.

ALBARAZINE. Medium-quality wool from Aragon, Spain.

ALBATROSS. 1. Rayon gabardine with a definite worsted appearance and feel ("hand"), used in men's all-purpose rainwear. Certain finishes are applied to the fabric for the worsted effect and to impart durable water repellency. The finish on the goods also gives resistance to water-soluble stains such as beverages, ink, and milk. Repeated dry cleanings have little effect on the finish, which will last for the life of the garment. 2. Plain-woven cotton cloth with a soft nap. Worsted albatross is fine, lightweight, and soft in hand. It is made of high-count worsted yarn in plain or open fancy weave repeats, in order to enhance the crepe feel and pebble surface effect.

ALBA VELVET. Jacquard velvet sometimes is known by this name.

ALBERT CLOTH. Formal fabric named in honor of Prince Albert of England; made on the principle of double-cloth construction. Added weight, texture, and warmth result from the manner in which the cloth is made. Used for Prince Albert coats and other dressy attire. Often used with velvet as collar.

ALBERT CREPE. This dress-goods cloth on plain weave is made of silk, silk and rayon, cotton and rayon, and many other yarns.

ALBERTS. A 1-up and 3-down or a 1-up and 4-down twill weave is used to make these cloths which are dyed dark colors and given high luster finish. Used in lining and pocketing, they are made of cotton warp and alpaca filling.

ALBERT TIE. A type of bow necktie.

ALBERT TWILL. 1. The 1-up and 3-down twill weave. 2. A lining material is made of this weave. It has cotton warp and alpaca filling.

ALBESINE. A popular Spanish wool.

ALBINISM. Deficiency of ordinary pigment causing lack of color in eyes, hair, skin, textile fibers.

ALBUMEN, ALBUMIN. Substance found in the white of eggs and in animals' blood, milk, and muscle; one of a group of complex organic substances which largely make up the non-fatty portions of flesh. Albumen is found in all body excretions, such as perspiration. It is set or coagulated at about 160° F. and therefore made insoluble in hot water.

ALCANTARA. A low-grade Spanish wool.

ALCATQUEN. Persian knotted rugs interwoven with gold threads, used on divans.

ALCOHOLS. Solvents in dry-cleaning, liquid fuels; burn with a clear flame which is very hot. "Canned heat" consists of colloidal jelly of alcohol and stearic acid. Main general information on different kinds follows:

1. ETHYL ALCOHOL, ETHANOL, GRAIN ALCOHOL: C_2H_5OH or CH_3CH_2OH. Stimulant in small amounts, narcotic in large amounts. Excellent solvent which dissolves resins, gums, oils, paints. Used in varnishes, fermented liquors, rectified spirits.

2. METHYL ALCOHOL, METHANOL: CH_3OH. Poisonous; vapors attack optic nerves and may cause partial or total blindness. Good fuel-hot flame, no smoke. Good solvent of oils, shellac, resins. Light, volatile, inflammable liquid with a "fuel odor." Usually made from distillate of wood. Also known as wood alcohol.

3. PROPYL ALCOHOL, PROPANOL: C_3H_7OH. Used for fuel and as a solvent.

4. DENATURED ALCOHOL: Ethyl alcohol and methyl alcohol are combined and may be used as anti-freeze. Pyridene may be mixed with ethyl alcohol in lieu of methyl alcohol.

5. RUBBING ALCOHOL. Could be a mixture of ethyl alcohol and methyl alcohol plus other suitable chemicals.

ALDEHYDES. Chemical compounds formed from alcohol by partial oxidation, and having a CHO group. The most important aldehyde is formaldehyde, obtained from wood alcohol.

ALENÇON, POINT D'ALENÇON.
1. Fine needle-point lace first made in the French town of Alençon, famous as a world lace center in the seventeenth century. Alençon differs from the other needle-point lace in the manner in which the outline of the cordonnet is made to the edge of the motif. The groundwork is made of double-twisted threads, held in place by tiny stitches, to give a semi-net effect. Hexagonal meshwork is seen in the background of the product; it is filled in with buttonhole stitch. The edges are supported by horsehair to sustain the cordonnet. The patterns are of birds, foliage, and other

"pot effects." Machine-made simulations that have a hand-run cording cannot properly be called Alençon unless the lace was actually made in that town.

Jean Baptiste Colbert, great prime minister for Louis XIV, and the son of a draper, may be considered the "Father of the Lace Industry" in France. He stated that "Fashion is to France what the Mines of Peru are to Spain." He brought to his country a great many expert lacemakers from the Italian States—and some of this group, under the direction of Colbert, founded the first school for lacemaking in Alençon. 2. Alençon, as a woven fabric, is a sheer lightweight cloth made of cotton and silk; ideal for summer dress goods.

ALENÇONNES. Norman-French linen fabric used in the half-bleached state for many domestic or household purposes.

ALEXANDER TWILL. Alpaca lining fabric made with cotton warp and alpaca filling; small, fancy twill used.

ALEXANDRETTE. Raw cotton of Syria.

ALEXANDRIA. Dress fabric made of cotton warp and wool filling, identified by small motifs—for instance, in printed or dobby designs or embroidered.

ALEXANDRINE. 1. Popular European cotton fabric noted for its fancy dobby-effect patterns and high counts of yarn. 2. Fine linen fabric on the order of the cotton material but characterized by a higher luster finish; used for dress goods.

ALFA. *Stipa tenacissima*. See ESPARTO.

ALFORGAS. A heavy type of English duck.

ALGA, ALGAE. Any plant of the subdivision (Algae) of the Thallophyta, consisting of primitive chlorophyll-bearing plants widely distributed in fresh and salt water and in moist land habitats. It includes kelps, diatoms, seaweeds, pond scums, and stoneworts. Adjective form is algal. Serves as basis for alginate fibers.

ALGERIAN FIBER. Small palm leaf obtained by a shredding process; this palm is grown extensively in North Africa.

ALGERIAN SILK. A coarse, crude, irregular "silk" fabric made with a cotton warp. It is called a "silk" cloth because the filling is silk frison, which covers up the cotton warp to a marked degree.

ALGERIAN STRIPES. 1. Material formerly made with alternate stripes of coarse cotton and fine silk, with possibly a golden thread running through the fabric. 2. Cloth of contrasting color schemes on the order of Roman and regimental stripes. Cloth of this type is used in lightweight fabrics made of silk, rayon, cotton, where the stripe effect is a high point in the material; stripings are generally vivid and varied. Used in dress goods and neckwear.

ALGERIENNE. Cloth used for awnings, curtains, and tent fabric—identified by its wide stripes in warp or filling direction. Fast dyes are used, since the fabric is expected to withstand the elements.

ALGIL. A polystyrene fiber made into batting form from a fine diameter filament which does not absorb moisture. Algil is acid- and alkali-vapor resistant, is thermoplastic, and will burn under flame. Used as a substitute for kapok and as a filtering medium. Product of Polymers, Inc.

ALGIN. A product obtained from certain marine algae. It may be extracted from kelp or seaweed and has been spun into filaments on a commercial basis. Also used in printing pastes and as a dressing material.

ALGINATE FIBERS. Made with a calcium alginate base, the fibers are produced by extruding alginate solution through spinnerets into solutions of beryllium sulphate or other chemicals. Made in a white, continuous filament that is sensitive to bacteria and sunlight, acids, and weak alkalis. It does not burn; resists moths as well as organic solvents. Cotton dyestuffs are best for application on alginates. Specific gravity is 1.78. Alginates differ in their respective properties and have resistance to mildew. The fibers are used in yarns that are subsequently dissolved out of the goods to provide imitation and fancy effects in the fabric; also used in garnishing camouflage netting and used as scaffolding thread in the manufacture of some stockings.

ALGINATE YARNS. Made from one of the main ingredients of seaweed, alginic acid. The yarns may be twisted with fine worsted and then these are removed from the fabric by a scouring treatment which allows the worsted yarn to remain intact.

Calcium alginate yarns are used as separating courses between half-hose where it is used as a "disappearing fiber or yarn."

ALGOA CORD. Fancy corduroy is sometimes known by this name in Great Britain.

ALGONDON. A Spanish term for cotton.

ALHAMBRA. English cotton quilting, elaborate in pattern.

ALHAMBRA QUILTING. Elabo-

rately figured fabrics woven on Jacquard looms in varicolored yarn. Texture ranges from 80 to 100 ends by 28 to 36 picks per inch. Warp yarns used could be two ends of 2/40s and one end of a 24s, all reeded in one dent; filling yarn is about 5s or 6s.

ALIPHATIC. Refers to a group of carbon compounds which are in open-chain formation and fatty in nature, such as paraffin. Taken from the Greek, the term means fat, oil. See ATOM, CARBON.

ALIZARIN, ALIZARINE. The chief coloring matter in madder. Also, in an extensive series of chemical colors produced from anthracene, one of the coal tar hydrocarbons, discovered in 1868.

ALIZARIN, ALIZARINE DYES. Originally obtained from madder root, made now from synthetic bases. Ideal for dyeing of wool, and can be used on cotton. Brilliance, sun-resistance, and easy washability are provided by fabrics colored with these dyes. Most of the dyes are derivatives of anthracene.

ALIZARINE OIL. Same as sulphonated oil.

ALKALI. A chemical substance belonging to a certain classification designated by chemists. There are a number of different alkalies and they are the chemical opposites of acids, and produce an alkaline reaction in water. Alkali turns litmus paper blue, acid turns it red.

ALKALI, ACTIVE. Alkali that is available for detergent use. Both active and inactive alkalies may be present in the same solution. See AVAILABILITY, CHEMICAL.

ALKALI CELLULOSE. In viscose rayon manufacture, the cellulose which has been treated with caustic soda. After disintegrating, known as alkali cellulose crumbs.

ALKALIMETRY. The determination of the percentage of alkali in a mixture or solution, usually volumetrically, by means of a standard acid solution.

ALKALINE DETERGENT. A water-soluble product, having an alkaline reaction and detergent qualities, but containing no soap.

ALKALINITY. An expression of the total basic anions, hydroxyl groups, present in a solution. It also represents, chiefly in water analysis, the bicarbonate, the carbonate, and sometimes the borate, phosphate, and silicate salts which will react with water to produce the hydroxyl groups.

ALKALINITY, LATENT. Alkalinity present in the water supply, either as bicarbonate from zeolite softener operation or as alkaline water-hardness salts.

ALKALOID. An organic substance of alkaline character obtained from vegetable sources, may have marked physiological action with several medicinal uses; for example, morphine from the poppy seed.

ALKANET. Dyestuff which gives a purplish red color; produced from alkanna. See ALKANNA.

ALKANNA. Red coloring matter, produced by Russian red cabbage.

ALKYL ARYL SODIUM SULPHONATE. A detergent whose molecule consists of an aromatic nucleus, a large aliphatic chain, and a sulphonate group which confers water-soluble properties on one end of the molecule. See SULPHATED FATTY ALCOHOL.

ALLAHABAD. Name of city in India, formerly used to identify high-grade cotton fabrics exported from there. Since World War II, the city has become one of the outstanding centers for cotton manufacture in the Eastern world.

ALLEANTHUS FIBER. Tough bast fiber produced by tree *Alleanthus zeylanica* in Ceylon.

ALLEMANDE. A twill-woven, silk dress cloth made in France, and identified by the cord effect in it because of the compactness in weaving the goods. Also used for vestings.

ALLERGY. State of being sensitive to some protein such as the pollen of ragweed or some textile fiber.

ALLEY. The space between the breaker card and the finisher card in which the so-called "alley-tender" works.

ALLIGATOR CALF LEATHER. Simulates genuine alligator and made from genuine cowhide leather neatly embossed with the alligator "look." Cost is around half that of the true alligator product.

ALLIGATOR CLOTH. Plain-weave, cotton or bast fiber cloth coated with a veneer or varnish and given a finish to resemble alligator skin. The material can be given an embossed or raised finish to enhance the appearance. Used for seat coverings, suitcases, briefcases, handbags, shoes, covers.

ALLOA. Scottish method for numbering woolen yarns, based on a standard of the number of "spyndles" of 11,520 yards each which weigh 24 pounds.

ALLOVER DESIGN. Term sometimes applied to a design covering almost the entire surface of the material, so that the basic construction is decidedly in the background. It is seen on certain print cloths, lace, and on Jacquard fabrics.

ALLOVER NET. Lace devoid of top or scallop, but made with motif of set width and set length, repeated to the full width of the lace frame. Net, however, has no specified length. Widths range from 18 inches to 72 inches depending upon the end-use. Result is a popular lace for blouses, flouncings, and yokes where wide lines may be used.

ALLOY. A mixture of a base metal and one or more other metals.

ALL-WOOL. Material of any description whose yarns are all wool, understood to be the wool of sheep. The term has to be weighed carefully, since "all-wool" includes, in addition to the pure, new fibers, other stocks, such as shoddy, mungo, extract wool, reused wool, remanufactured wool. All-wool is often misunderstood in the trade, when purchasing fabrics or garments, and the consumer may be the loser. Cotton, for example, may cost more per pound than some fibers that go into an all-wool fabric. Distributive and consumer education can do much to avoid possible misunderstandings which, at times, may confuse the purchaser.

ALL-WOOL OR 100 OR ONE HUNDRED PER CENT WOOL. Where the product or the fabric to which the stamp, tag, label, or mark of identification applies is composed wholly of one kind of fiber, either the word "All" or the term "100 per cent" may be used with the correct fiber name; as for example, "100 per cent Wool," "All Wool," "100 per cent Reprocessed Wool," "All Reprocessed Wool," "100 per cent Reused Wool," "All Reused Wool." If any such product is composed wholly of one fiber with the exception of the fiber ornamentation not exceeding 5 per cent, such term "All" or "100 per cent" as qualifying the name of fiber may also be used, provided it is immediately followed by the phrase "exclusive of ornamentation," or by a phrase of like meaning; such as, for example: "All Wool—Exclusive of Ornamentation," or "100 per cent Wool—Exclusive of Ornamentation."

ALMA CLOTH. Cloth double-twilled from left to right in a diagonal order. The original fabric was a mourning cloth. The name is derived from the Egyptian, and implies a mourner or funeral chanter. The left-hand twill wales are quite pronounced.

ALMUCE. An ecclesiastical garment formerly used to cover the head and worn in choir by chanters. Since the biretta came into use, the almuce today is more of a hood, hanging down at the back of the head; the hood of a mozetta.

See Biretta, Mozzetta.

ALNAGE. Also called ell, or aune; an old-time measurement of 45 inches.

ALNAGER. An officer in England in the days of monastery wool, who inspected and attested to the quality of the fabrics made from these wools.

ALNEESTLONI. A twill-woven blanket made by the Navajo Indians in the American Southwest. The pattern on the face is different from the one on the back.

ALNEIN. Golden-yellow coloring matter, furnished by the alder tree.

ALOE, BOWSTRING HEMP, PITEIRA. A minor bast fiber of the agave group, used to make lace and net in Italy, Paraguay, the Philippines, and Spain.

ALOE HEMP. General broad term for bast fibers obtained from the many species of agave plants and trees. Sansevieria is included in this class.

ALOE LACE. Bobbin lace made by tatting of fine aloe yarns; produced in the southern European countries.

ALON. Acetylated high-tenacity viscose staple fiber of Toho Rayon Company, Ltd., Osaka, Japan. Known by this name only in local markets of Japan. When exported the product is called Tohalon. See TOHALON.

ALOST. Belgian bobbin lace comparable with Valenciennes; threads of the ground mesh are twisted four or five times.

ALPACA. 1. Raised in the Andes Mountains, these fleeces are usually obtained after a two-year growth. The fiber diameter is about $\frac{1}{800}$ inches. The fiber is lustrous, soft to touch, strong, rather wavy; the fleece will weigh about ten pounds. Fine alpaca is from 4½ inches to 8 inches in length; medium alpaca is 5½ inches to 9 inches long; coarse alpaca is from 7 inches to 11 inches in staple length. In color, fibers range from white to brown or black. The two types obtained from the 180-pound animal are soft wool-like hair; stiff beard hair. Alpaca is coarser than either camel or vicuna.

2. Alpaca fabric is a fine, silklike, soft, lightweight material. Obtained from the animal of this name, the resultant yarn is often used as filling in some cotton warp cloths. Alpaca resembles mohair and is imitated in cheaper cloths or those in combination with the genuine. The cloth has much luster and is boardy in some instances. Much "alpaca" is now made from wool-and-rayon blends. It is used for women's spring or fall coats, suits, sportswear.

3. Smooth, glossy material made of

mohair and cotton or rayon. Has strong wearing qualities and is used for linings and men's summer suits.

ALPACA CREPE. Fabric simulating woolen cloth of that name. It is made of two-ply yarn.

ALPACA LINING. Lining fabric made chiefly in England, having cotton warp and alpaca filling.

ALPACA RAYON, RAYON ALPACA. Soft, nonlustrous, plain-woven fabric made in rather low construction from two-ply or four-ply yarns. One popular alpaca has a texture of 36 x 34 with a denier filament of 75/100 and yarn size of four-ply, all one twist. Another texture is 44 x 38 with a 150/150-denier filament, and the two-ply yarn used is all one twist. One of the most popular dress goods in women's wear at present. Incidentally, there is no true alpaca fiber or yarn in this fabric.

ALPACA YARN. Does not refer to yarn in which alpaca fiber is used. It is a misnomer since it is incorrectly applied to yarn in some rayon fabrics called rayon alpaca, and cloth made solely from a combination of acetate and rayon staple stocks but sold with the word "alpaca" used in the fabric name.

ALPARGATA. A sandal made of jute, hemp, or similar fibers.

ALPHA CELLULOSE. A form of cellulose insoluble in 17.5 per cent cold sodium hydroxide solution. Rayon pulp has an alpha content of 91 to 96 per cent, which is based on the type of rayon to be manufactured.

ALPRONA LL. A fiber made with actually 67 percent PVA/Casein in the contents. It is stronger than its earlier version, Alprona which was 70 percent casein in content. The LL type has better resistance to chemical, water, and high temperatures. Product of Lodz Manmade Fiber Works, Lodz, Poland.

ALSATIAN BOW. A large, flat bow with even loops and loosely tied, used in headdress and headgear.

ALTERATION. The process of changing a garment to fit the individual or dress form more precisely, commonly resorted to in retail establishments and dress shops.

ALTER-EASE. Durable press garments may be altered by the use of this chemical spray available in aerosol cans. The technique is based on spraying and then pressing the portion of the garment to be altered. Existing creases can be removed and new ones introduced when desired. No change is needed in existing durable press technology to accomodate this development of the J.P. Stevens &

Co., Inc., New York City.

ALUM. Also known as potash alum —$Al_2(SO_4)3 \cdot K_2SO_4 \cdot 24H_2O$; colorless crystals readily soluble in water, used extensively as a mordant for alizarine dyes, as an agent with alizarin in printing woolens, and also used in leather tanning and paper making.

ALUMINA. Aluminum oxide.

ALUMINUM ACETATE, FORMATE, SULPHATE. Compounds used with soap to make fabrics water repellent. Aluminum acetate and soap (usually tallow) will give aluminum stearate.

ALUMINUM CHLORATE. $Al_2(ClO_3)3$, a very unstable compound used as a strong oxidizing agent in discharge printing, and to print cottons with aniline black.

ALUMINUM SULPHATE. A white, odorless, crystalline powder—$Al_2(SO_4)3$. Soluble in water. It is also a yellowish-white to a bluish-white crystalline salt of aluminum sulphate used as a mordant in dyeing textiles.

ALUM LEATHER. Refers to a tanning process produced by alum used in combination with egg yolk, salt, and other substances. Prior to chrome-tanning, this was the principal method of tanning with mineral agents. The process is now used chiefly for glove leather.

AMADAURE, AMADOWRY. A minor variety of Egyptian cotton.

AMAMEE. An Indian cotton cloth made in plain weave with fine, smooth yarns of about 35s to 40s yarn count. It comes in white or may be dyed or printed. The finest quality is known as Bissuti, while the term Tissuti is used to identify the coarsest grades. Used in counterpanes, coverings, shirtings, skirtings, etc.

AMANA. Any of the products, textiles included, made by the Amana Society located in Iowa. This community-owned enterprise produces, to suit their needs, cotton and woolen woven cloth and knitgoods.

AMAZON. A woolen-worsted dress goods in which the fabric finish completely covers the weave construction. Made on a five-end satin, worsted warp and wool filling, the fabric presents a solid worsted effect on the face and the woolen yarn used gives the soft, full hand to the goods. A 2-up and 2-down warp-faced twill weave may be used in the construction.

AMAZONES. General term for woolen fabrics in many South American markets.

AMBARI HEMP. See KENAF.

AMBURGOS. Heavily filled white shirting fabric made in England for the North African export trade.

AMENS. Worsted fabrics formerly used for church vestments, with a cord-effect warp stripe; small fancy patterns are also featured in the material. Used for dress goods.

AMERICAINE. Popular Continental dress goods made of all silk or silk and rayon in fancy cord effect; comparable with various popular cords used as dress goods here, such as Russian cord, Ottoman, rib-weave effects, corded fabrics.

AMERICAN ALOE. Another name for the yucca plant.

AMERICAN CLOTH. English name for an enameled oilcloth used for upholstery in the home.

AMERICAN COTTON. Term used in world cotton markets to signify cotton raised in the United States as apart from that raised elsewhere. The word Upland is more or less synonymous with the term American Cotton, since the former, from the standpoint of production, is the leading staple raised in this country.

AMERICAN COTTONS. See Cottons, American.

AMERICAN CYANAMID COMPANY TRADEMARK. A registered trademark reserved for use only on fabrics and consumer products that have been tested and approved by the American Cyanamid Company, Inc. All fiber is sold as Cyanamid acrylic fiber.

AMERICAN-EGYPTIAN COTTON. About 140 years ago there was an exchange of cotton seed made between American and Egyptian cotton growers. Both countries benefited by the transaction. Today the strains are raised in the irrigated areas of Arizona and California, states coming to the fore in the raising of cotton.

One of the outstanding staples is Pima, raised in the Pima Valley of Arizona; another is the well-known SxP (cross between Sakellaridis, Egyptian and Pima, American) used in high-quality broadcloth, shirting, dress goods, etc. Staple is 1½ inches or better. See ACALA; HOPI ACALA.

AMERICAN-EGYPTIAN COTTON STANDARDS. Effective August 1, 1952, the grade designations were revised. The new table no longer designates cotton in "half" grades. The old and the new designations follow:

OLD:	NEW:
1	1
1½	2

2	3
2½	4
3	5
3½	6
4	7
4½	8
5	9

AMERICAN FASHION AND STYLE, THE DEBUT AND PROGRESS OF. American Fashion and Style made its debut about ten years after the end of World War One. For the next thirty years, to about 1947, its progress was phenomenal. The year 1947 may be said to be the time that it reached maturity, for at that time the New Look, the Sad Sack dress, and the beginning of the so-called revolution in all types and kinds of fashions for men, women, and children were an actuality. The following is a chronological story of its rise to the year, 1938, when the American designers were acclaimed as major contributors to the Fashion World.

1927: The Lord & Taylor Company, Inc., New York City, under the aegis of Miss Dorothy Shaver, president, launched their campaign to make the American woman conscious of Fashion and Style pointing to individualism in the matter of dress. Clothes and accessories made Milady of America the most talked-about and the most looked-up to individual in the manner and matter of apparel and accessories. Contributors in these pioneer days included Ralph Barton, Rene Clark, C.B. Falls, Neysa McMein, and Katharine Sturges.

1932: In April, the movement to recognize American designers in the Apparel Industry witnessed the rise of Elizabeth Hawes (Fashion is Spinach), Muriel King, Edith Marie Reuss, and Annette Simpson.

1933: In April, sportswear designers made their debut and resulting impact with luminaries such as Emma L. Brown, Clarepotter, Donald Deskey, Marie Leeds, Tom Lamb, Ruth Payne, Constance Ripley, Alice Smith, and Salley Victor. October saw contributions to the American designers for the younger generation included Marie Leeds and Constance Ripley.

1934: In March, original American designing was considered to be "over-the-top" because of the outstanding effort of the following in creativity, originality, and in furthering the cause of individuality in clothes—Helen Cookman and Emmy Wylie; Natalie Bixby, Katharine Burton, Margot Kops, Joan Lanham, Mary Mabie, and Melisse.

1936: In May, recognition of American Fashions and Styles, with local American color was presented in clothes created by Dorothy Cox, Margaret Montague, Renee Montague; Alice Evans, and Marguerite Mergentime.

The personal contribution of Lord & Taylor Company to fashion and style, and to American Decoration, came in October with the launching of the famous Pahlman Salon created and sustained under the aegis of William Pahlman.

1937: The famous Nan Westley dress designed by Lord & Taylor emerged an American classic and creation. Nan Westley and Bond Morgan were names constantly before the public at this time.

In December, the movement was further fostered to recognize American designers for the Children's Apparel Industry by promoting the Young Creed Fashions under the guidance of Kay Martin and Ruth MacFarlane.

1938: In February, Conde Nast Publications unveiled its famous *Americana Issue* which contained the best to date in American Design. The past in design was brought up to the present, organized, coordinated and given to the eager American woman. Full recognition was given Lord & Taylor for the outstanding work that had been done to date in fashion and style—the well-dressed American woman was now here to stay and to march on to new heights in world leadership with regard to dress in all respects. This issue of VOGUE is still in the mind and memory of old-timers in the field; it has been a collector's item for many years and up to this time, 1938, was the greatest single item that promoted American Fashion and Style. This 176 page issue carried a splendid article by Mrs. Hortense Odlum, president of Bonwit Teller on the rise of fashion and style, and feature advertisers included Best & Company, Bonwit Teller, Lord & Taylor, and Henri Bendel & Company, as well as Saks Fifth Avenue Store.

Top names at this time included John Stein Bugler, Roger Conant, Perry Fisher, and Vera Maxwell.

1939: Vogue's Americana Issue, the previous year, aroused great and fantastic interest in fashion and style. A host of new names in the Fashion World came over the horizon. The following tabulations are interesting:
NEW YORK DEPARTMENT STORE DESIGNERS:
ALTMAN STORE—Foxbrownie (Miss Brownie).
BEST & COMPANY—Fira Benenson, Kalmour.
BERGDOFF GOODMAN STORE—John Dean, Ethel Frankau, Mary Gleason, Philip Hulitor, Alice Kelly, Mark Mooring, Leslie Morris, Peggy Morris.
BONWIT TELLER STORE - Clarepotter, Louise Barnes Gallagher, Philip Mangone, Germaine Monteil, Nettie Rosenstein, B. H. Wragge.
HATTIE CARNEGIE - Hattie Carnegie, Jean Berthault, Bruno, Madame Lyolene, Claire McCardell, Norman Norell.
JAY THORPE - Wilson Folmar.
HOUSE OF JONAI-Joseph Whitehead.
NEIMAN-MARCUS (DALLAS) - Anthony Blotta.
PATTULLO-DENVER - Jo Copeland.
RUSSEK'S - Charles Armour, Leonard Kagel, Ralph Marano.
SAK'S FIFTH AVENUE STORE - Mrs. Adam Gimbel (Sophie), Emmett Joyce, Florence Gayner.
STERN'S DEPARTMENT STORE- Eisenberg.
LORD & TAYLOR STORE - Thomas Brigance, Helen Cookman, Vera Maxwell, McMullen.

NEW YORK DESIGNERS:
Abrade, Dorine
Arcuri
Barker, Shirley
Bennett, Eve
Carol
Copeland, Jo
Falkenstein
Fields, Pauline
Kiam, Omar
Krausz, Lisbeth
Kops, Margot
Mainbocher
Montague, Renee
Norman, Bernard
Smithline, Adele
Parker, Gladys
Renke, Natalie
Smith, Alice
Stein and Blaine

NEW YORK DESIGNING RETAILERS:
Clyne, Frances
Fiffi
Hawes, Elizabeth
Frances, Polly
Franklin, Mrs. W.B.
Hoyt, Peggy
Jaeckel, Tracy
Kramer, Alan
King, Muriel
Louisesanders
Manning, Maybelle

MILLINERY DESIGNERS IN NEW YORK:

Dache, Lilly
Florell
Florence Reichman
John-Frederics
Madam Pauline
Sally Victor

HOLLYWOOD DESIGNERS:

Adrian
Anderson, Milo
Banton, Travis
Greer, Howard
Head, Edith
Irene
Kalloch
King, Muriel
Orry-Kelly
Parker, Gladys
Plunkett, Walter
Renee
Royer
Shoup, Howard
Stevenson, Edward
Tree, Dolly
Wakeling, Gwen
West, Vera

HOLLYWOOD MILLINER - Galor.
HOLLYWOOD DRESSES AND
ACCESSORIES - Voris.
HOLLYWOOD HOSIERY - Willys.
HOLLYWOOD SHOES - Aprile.
HOLLYWOOD GLOVES - Dalbouz,
Madame of Paris (Also in New York).

NOTED FRENCH DESIGNERS:

Alix
Ardense
Augustabernard
Balenciaga
Bernard et Compagnie
Borea, Vera
Boulanger, Louise
Bruyere, Marie
Callot Soeurs
Chanel, Gabrielle
Carette, Yvonne
Creed, Henry
Cheruit
Dikusha
Francvrament
Goupy
Jenny
Lanvin
Rouff, Maggy
Schieparelli, Elsa
Vionnet
House of Worth
Redfern
Rochas

FRENCH FABRIC MANUFACTURERS:

Bianchini
Boussac
Colcombat
Coudurier
Doucet
Rodier.

PARISIAN MILLINERS:

Descat, Rose
Regny, Jane
Reboux
Suzy
Talbot, Suzanne
Valois, Rose

NOTED LONDON DESIGNERS:

Barry, Nargaret
Busvine, Richard
De Wolkoff, Anna
Glenny, Dennis
Hartnell, Norman
Isobel
Lachasse
Luytens, Eva
House of Motley
Morton, Digby
House of Rahvis
Russell, Peter
Stiebel, Victor
Strassner

The year 1938 is taken as the year that American Fashion and Style was established in the United States. Hence, the debut and progress of American Designers which began in a very small way at the turn of the century had come over the horizon in 1938 and in 1947 reached the age of maturity. From this year on designers in this country have progressed to almost limitless attainment whether in conservative, conventional design or in that which is bizarre, offbeat and, at times, outlandish.

AMERICAN HEMP. Another name for the century plant.

AMERICAN INSTITUTE OF LAUNDERING. A trade association of commercial laundries interested in assisting laundries to improve their methods and to increase consumer satisfaction.

AMERICAN JUTE. Indian mallow or velvetleaf, *Abutilon Avicennae*, which is considered more or less as a weedlike fiber and has never been developed to any marked degree.

AMERICAN MERINO, VERMONT MERINO. The type of Merino bred in this country in the early 1800's. The foundation flocks were imported from Spain, and they laid the basis for the Merino sheep industry in this country. Around the time of the War of 1812, and thereafter for many years, Vermont was the leading state for Merino sheep and for crossbreeding many of the types still extant today. Londonderry, Vermont, was the great Merino center. Vermont Merino is now practically extinct.

AMERICAN SET. A set of pillowcases and bolster with open ends. Each article is embroidered.

AMERICAN-SPUN YARN. Really a short-cut method to make worsted yarn, which begins with previously prepared worsted top stock. Originally brought out in 1920; following a rather slow acceptance, the method now has had outstanding acceptance in the trade.

When first used the system could process fibers of about 2½-inch staple; today it can manipulate fibers up to 7 inches long.

No specific carding or combing of the fibers has to be done to prepare the top, which does not have an inserted twist, for action. Nonstatic oil can be added in the top to insure static free processing. The tops average 3 ounces per 5 yards in size. Unlike the Bradford (English) System or the French System, where the fibers after combing pass through six or more machine treatments, in the American System the top is processed in five steps on three basic machines—gills or pin drafters, roving and spinning frames. Spinning is done only on the ring spinning frame, which is now indistinguishable from the other methods of spinning worsted yarn— mule, cap, and flyer. Appearance and smoothness are features of American-spun worsted yarn.

AMERICAN UPLANDS COTTON. There are several varieties included in this category, such as Deltapine 16, Stoneville 7A, Acala 1517, Lankart 57, etc. Acala 1517 is raised in the El Paso, Texas area; Deltapine 16 is found in the delta area of the Mississippi River Valley; Lankart in the Texas cotton belt. Stoneville is raised around the city of this name in Mississippi. Leading American-Egyptian cottons include Pima 5-3 and 5-4, raised in Arizona, New Mexico, and Southern California. See American Cotton, See Cotton, Arizona; Cottons, Data on General World; Cottons, American; Uplands Cotton.

AMERICAN VISCOSE DIVISION OF FMC CORPORATION, TRADEMARKS OF. These follow:

Avceram: Cellulosic fibers sinterable ceramic material; also, after burning, sintered ceramic fibers. See Sinter, Sinterable.

Avicel: Microcrystalline cellulose for food, pharmaceutical, or cosmetic use. A pure non-fibrous form of natural cellulose, non-caloric, absorbent, for thixotropic gel applications, tableting, etc.

Avicolor: Solution-dyed fiber and/or yarn made of Avisco acetate or rayon. The fiber has excellent colorfastness to laundering, perspiration, drycleaning, sunlight, and gas fumes. Formerly known as Colorspun.

Avicron: A rayon which contains a latent crimp which is activated in normal bleaching and dyeing operations. This makes possible unique textures for area rugs, upholstery and other home furnishings.

Aviloc: High tenacity yarns which are cord treated to provide improved adhesion to natural and synthetic rubbers.

Aviloc II: A family of adhesive treated cord and yarn that improves adhesion from 25 to 150 percent in mechanical rubber goods. *Rayon Type 57* is used for horizontal and vertical braiders and as filling for circular looms. Fraying and shedding of yarn is at a maximum, *Rayon Tye 46 Aviloc II* treated yarns do not have yarn-to-yarn tack and are used for production on Wardwell braiders and other low tension machines, as well as for use on twisters and winders.

Avirin: Microcrystalline cellulose for industrial use. A purified form of non-fibrous cellulose; for thixotropic gel applications preparation of cellulose derivatives, drying agent, structural products, etc.

Avisco: Trademark used for all products of the American Viscose Company Division of FMC Corporation, 1617 John F. Kennedy Boulevard, Philadelphia, Pennsylvania, 19103. Includes acetate, rayon, and its polyester yarns, staples, tow, and Vinyon resin yarn and staples.

Avisco Acetate, Type 25: A cellulose acetate filament yarn modified to give significantly greater bulkiness in yarn and fabric than regular acetate.

Avisco V-22: An intermediate tenacity rayon staple which produces yarns of greater strength than regular rayon. Used for apparel, in the home and in industry.

Avisco XL-I: A high tenacity, high elongations rayon staple fiber for use in industry.

Avistrap: Industrial strapping materials made of either rayon cord or polyprolene in a variety of thicknesses and widths. Benefits include economy, ease of handling, safety, toughness, lightweight, and impact resistance. The trademark also applies to a complete range of tools, machines and accessory items for many different applications.

Avlin Polyester Fiber: Formerly known as Fiber 200, it is a melt spun fiber of the polyester type. Elongation and strength are practically unaffected by water; excellent heat resistance, little discoloration, and good resistance to sunlight under glass are other strong points of the product, as well as retention, wrinkle resistance, strength, and abrasion qualities.

Filament stock is used for apparel, especially dressgoods, and knit tricot fabrics. In blends the fiber is heavily used in many types of apparel, durable press fabrics, marquisette, and for filled products such as comforters, pillows and furniture stuffing. The name can be used only to identify fabrics which meet the standards set-up by American Viscose Company.

Avril: Formerly known as Fiber 40, it is a unique modified rayon combined with cotton in respect to elongation and elastic properties and equals best grades of cotton in fabric strength. The name can be used only to identify fabrics, or the Fiber 40 content of such fabrics, which meet the standards of American Viscose Company.

Avron: Formerly known as Avisco XL, the term is used to identify fabrics which are blends of cotton and Avron, a high strength rayon staple that is 70 per cent strong when wet, and 40 per cent stronger when dry, in the conditioned state, than conventional rayons. The fiber is compatable with acrylic, modacrylic, and polyester fibers for blends and is ideal in the lighter-weight, minimum care fabrics. Cotron, also an American Viscose Company fabric, is a trade name for fabrics made from blends of cotton and regular rayon staple stock.

Avron XL: A high standard Avisco rayon staple fiber of excellent tensile strength, high elongation, improved abrasion resistance, Avron assures lighter weight, greater depth of color, softer hand, exceptional performance in wash-and-wear applications, and better fabric evenness than previously available.

Purilon: A special type of rayon staple fiber designed for use in the medical-surgical fields. Resists discolorization during sterilization.

Rayflex: A high-strength continuous filament rayon yarn.

RD 101: This Type Designation is a self-bonding rayon fiber specially designed for the preparation of papers and other wet-formed nonwoven materials.

Super L: A specially engineered rayon carpet fiber which features excellent wear and soil resistant characteristics.

Super Rayflex: A high-strength continuous filament rayon yarn that is approximately 40 percent stronger than regular Rayflex yarn.

Super Rayflex MR: High tenacity yarn with low wet contraction and contractilling force. Designed for mechanical rubber goods applications.

AMERICAN WOOL CLIP. The annual clip of wool in this country is about 300 million pounds, about one third that of Australian wool. America is surpassed only by Australia and Argentina in annual wool clippage. This country has about 7 per cent of the world sheep population of 720 million sheep. Wool is raised in every state in the Union; Texas leads with about 25 per cent of the annual clip and the number of sheep. Wyoming, Montana, and California, in that order, follow Texas, with percentages of about 8, 8, and 6.

AMIANTHUS. Asbestos fiber of high quality.

AMICE. A white linen worn by the religious, about 32 inches by 24 inches, with cross embroidered on the center; covers neck and shoulders. It is symbolic of the "helmet of salvation" and the "discipline of the tongue."

AMIDATED COTTON. A British cotton yarn modified from immunized cotton fiber whose properties differ from the latter as well as from untreated cotton. The yarn has good affinity for cotton colors and acid dyes.

AMIDE. Name for derivatives of ammonia (NH_3) in which one atom of hydrogen (H) was exchanged for a metal or organic radical, acid or basic, being viewed as compounds of the metal or organic radical with amidogen (NH_2). Also, generic term for the compound ammonias in which one or more atoms of hydrogen are released by an acid radical. It is also the resultant product of heating and combining a dibasic acid and a diamine. See AMMONIA, DIAMINE, RADICAL.

AMIENS. A hard twisted worsted cloth which originated in the city of Amiens, France. Twill weave in solid colors or patterns.

AMILAN. Trade name for a caprolactam; "Nylon 6," made in Japan.

AMINE. Generic term for one of a large group of compound ammonias in which one or more atoms of hydrogen are replaced by alcohol or other base-radicals, organic in nature. The word is also a suffix from the Greek, meaning an amine, such as methylamine. See ALKYL, ORGANIC.

AMINO. A prefix which pertains to and showing that the compound contains the NH_2 group combined with a non-acid radical, such as amino-acetone, aminoformic, et al.

AMINO ACID. Any of a group of organic compounds which have the formula $NH_2 \cdot R \cdot COOH$ and form an essential part of the protein molecule. The $\cdot R \cdot$ in the formula may be an acid group, a basic group, or hydroxyl group. See ACID, BASE, HYDROXYL.

AMISH COSTUME. See Costume, Amish.

AMMONIA. An alkaline really a gas and, though marketed as a liquefied gas for certain purposes, usually known in its water solution. "Strong ammonia" contains 29 per cent of the gas "ammonia." It is a weak alkali chemically and has a pungent, stifling odor. Formula is NH_4OH.

AMMONIA OXIDATION UNIT. An apparatus for combining ammonia with oxygen in proper proportions.

AMMONIUM ACID FLUORIDE, AMMONIUM BIFLUORIDE. A readily soluble salt of ammonium and hydrofluoric acid. Sometimes used in laundry sours, it possesses high neutralizing power and iron-removing properties.

AMMONIUM FLUOSILICATE. A crystalline, soluble, acid-reacting salt of high neutralizing power used as a laundry sour. It reacts with neutral sodium salts such as sodium chloride to form the sparingly soluble sodium

fluosilicate.

AMMONIUM SILICO FLUORIDE. A crystalline, soluble, acid-reacting salt of high neutralizing power sometimes used as a laundry sour. It reacts with neutral sodium salts such as sodium chloride to form the sparingly soluble sodium silico fluoride.

AMORGIS. Ancient Greek term for a fine linen, often dyed purple.

AMORPHOUS. Soft, noncrystalline, shapeless.

AMORPHOUS AREAS. This term relates to loosely packed molecular chains in fibers. In cotton (cellulose), for example, about sixty percent of the fiber is packed loosely in the amorphous or changeable areas.

AMOSITE. This African fiber occurs as a silicate of iron, gray to brown in color. It is used as a filler for asbestos.

AMOUR. Oval or round motifs feature this table linen which originated in Caen, France. Also known as lace d'amour.

AMPERE. The unit in which the rate of transmission of electric energy is expressed.

AMPHIBOLE. An Italian asbestos found in Italy. It has about 5 per cent water of crystallization and is not suited for use in textiles.

AMRAD GUM. A product of the babul tree of Africa, this gum is used as a substitute for gum arabic.

AMRITSAR. A coarse Indian wool used chiefly in home consumption.

AMSTERDAM. Famous for the reproduction of French Alençon, Argentan, and Brussels laces. Dentelle à la Reine was a generic term applied to these Amsterdam needle-point laces.

AMUNO. A special treatment given to animal fibers, down, and feathers, to prevent damage by moths and carpet beetles. It is nontoxic, odorless, and does not impair the warmth, strength, handle, moisture, luster, texture or color of treated fabrics. A chemical compound impregnates the fiber; the control of application is necessary for success.

AMYL ACETATE. A colorless liquid with the odor of a banana; hence, the use of the term, "banana oil." Used as nitrocellulose solvent in the manufacture of pyroxylin lacquers. Formula is $CH_3 CO_2 C_5 H_{11}$.

ANACOSTA. High texture and quality worsted dress goods, made in Great Britain. Filling texture is higher than warp. Piece-dyed.

ANACOTE. Central European worsted serge with smooth sheen and finish.

Small twill weave used in making the material. Cloth has demand among the religious orders, and also finds a market in regular trade.

ANALAO. A cordage fiber raised in the Philippines. Also called Analas.

ANAL HORN. The horn upon the posterior end of the body of a silkworm.

ANALYSIS, CHEMICAL. Determination of chemical composition.

ANALYSIS, STAPLE. The determination of the staple length of a group of lint cotton fibers, done by a fiber sorting device. A prescribed method is followed to obtain the results.

ANANAS HEMP. Bast fibers from Ananas, a kin of the Bromelia genus, in the West Indies and South America.

ANANONG. A Philippine bast fiber used for cordage.

ANAPHE SILKWORM. A genus of silkworm found in Uganda and other parts of Africa. Feeds on the leaves of a species of fig tree. The nest and cocoons, which are formed in considerable numbers, are used for waste silk. In Nigeria, Anaphe is blended with cotton to make their so-called "Soyan cloths."

ANATOLIAN. 1. A small, all-wool rug made in Asia Minor and used for pillows; the soft, long pile is tied in Ghiordes knot. There is much color and design in these rugs, which are finished with an all-around selvage and a fringe or binding at the ends. Large-size Anatolians have a long, compact pile. 2. Long, medium-grade wool from Caraman sheep, native to the homeland of the Turks, Anatolia. These flat-tailed sheep supply much of the carpet wool for the Turkish rug industry.

ANATOLIAN SILK. A medium-quality silk raised in Anatolia.

ANAVOR. Polyester fiber manufactured in a plant opened in mid-1969 in Anderson, South Carolina, by Dow Badische Company, Inc. Dow also produces Zefkrome®, a producer-dyed second generation acrylic; Zefran®, a dyeable acrylic fiber; Weatherbright, a trademark for acrylic blend for indoor-outdoor floorcovering, and Lurex®, the well-known and popular metallic yarn.

ANCON SHEEP. Former breed used in this country, easily recognized by long body and short, crooked legs. Also known as Otter sheep.

ANCUBE. Type of wool rug made in Belgium.

ANDALUSIANS. Fine worsted dress goods made from Spanish merino wool and comparable grades. Made in England; in a variety of twill constructions and fabric weights.

ANDALUSIAN WOOL. 1. Medium-fine Spanish wool. 2. Very fine, four-ply worsted yarn much used for knitting in the British Isles.

ANDALUSIAN YARN. A four-ply very fine worsted knitting yarn, much used in Great Britain. Ideal in outer garments for winter wear.

ANDERSON GINGHAM. A staple Scotch gingham of many years standing that has been very popular in the United States as well as in Britain and on the Continent. Shirting of the material, known by the same name, is high in yarn count, texture, and is always given a splendid, distinctive finish embellished by clean, clear, color effects. A name brand fabric for several decades.

ANDES COTTON. See PERUVIAN COTTON.

ANGEL'S HAIR. 1. Fine tinsel yarn. 2. Fine spun glass. 3. A peruke.

ANGEL SKIN. See PEAU D'ANGE.

ANGEL SLEEVE. A kind of very wide sleeve, usually hanging loose from the shoulder.

ANGLED DRAFT. Warp ends drawn in from the first to the last harness, and then back to the first harness in regular sequence. This plan can be used for broken twill and pointed twill effects, if desired.

ANGLESEY WOOL. A type of wool obtained from a Welsh breed of sheep.

ANGLE STRIPPER. The small stripper roll cylinder that sets between the main cylinder and the doffer roller on woolen cards. Its function is to serve both rollers as the stock is being carded from roller to roller.

ANGLETERRE, POINT D'ANGLE-TERRE. Originally a Brussels lace smuggled into England and called Angleterre to avoid duty; subsequently made in England. The lace is sometimes classified as needle-point lace, although the net is bobbinet, only the designs being made with a needle.

ANGLICANUM, OPUS ANGLICA-NUM. Broad term including English cutwork, needlework, and embroidery work.

ANGLO-CONTINENTAL DRAW-ING. A combination of the Bradford or English system and the French or Franco-Belgian system, in drafting and drawing worsted fibers. In this method, it is possible to draft shorter wools, as oiled top on the "porcupine" or French system.

ANGLO-SWISS MUSLIN. Simulation of Clipspot Swiss muslin.

ANGOLA CLOTH. 1. Cloth made of a twill weave. The woven material is usually dyed some shade of red. 2. A cotton- and wool-mix yarn. 3. An overcoating material made of a low texture twill weave; the cloth is heavily napped, rather thick and substantial.

ANGOLA MENDINGS. English yarn of cotton and wool mixture, used for darning stockings.

ANGOLA YARN. A yarn made of about 80 per cent wool and 20 per cent cotton; low-quality wool is used in 'his yarn, spun on the woolen system.

ANGORA. 1. Goat hair; the white fleece of long, fine fibers. When manufactured is called MOHAIR. Because of its smoothness and softness, it must be combined with other fibers in weaving. 2. Rabbit hair; Angora rabbits possess light in weight and furnishes much warmth to the wearer of garments thus made. This fiber is often blended and mixed with wool to lower the price of the finished article and to obtain fancy or novelty effects in weaving. Must be designated as ANGORA RABBIT HAIR. 3. A highly finished, plain-woven fabric made of cotton warp and mohair filling. 4. A twill woven overcoating with a shaggy, fuzzy surface effect. 5. A soft yarn used for knitting purposes. See ANGORA YARN. 6. The well-known, highly cherished Angora shawl. This luxury heirloom article gives excellent wear for many years.

ANGORA GOAT. A species of goat originally bred in Anatolia, the homeland of the Turks, and later introduced in South Africa, South America, and Texas. The genuine long silky mohair fiber is obtained from the animal.

ANGORA RABBIT. Raised chiefly in Great Britain and the Low Countries on the Continent and noted for its fine fur. Clipped annually, the breed will give 10 to 16 ounces of hair fiber which ranges from 3 to 5 inches in length. Very soft, fluffy, appealing in feel, the hair is usually pure white. Often blended in small but varying amounts with wool or rayon in the manufacture of woven or knitted dress goods.

ANGORA SWEATER YARN. See ANGORA; ANGORA RABBIT; ANGORA YARN.

ANGORA, UNION. Plain-weave dress goods made of cotton warp and mohair or worsted filling. There is also a twill-woven Angora fabric which shows a shaggy, fuzzy face. The name of the animal that gives the mohair fiber used as filling yarn is the Angora goat.

ANGORA WOOL. Sometimes applied to mohair.

ANGORA YARN. Considered the same as mohair yarn, this imitation of genuine Angora is made with varying amounts of rabbit hair blended with it. It is a very popular yarn in the United States. Genuine Angora, rare here, comes chiefly from France; will sell from fifteen to twenty-five dollars a pound.

ANGUILLA COTTON. Seeds from the island of Anguilla were planted on the Sea Islands off the coast of Georgia in the 1780's by James Spaulding of Charleston, S. C. It is from these early plantings that Sea Island cotton, the best in the world, is obtained.

ANHYDRIDE. An organic radical or element capable of forming an acid by uniting with the elements of water, or formed from an acid by the abstraction of water. Acetic acid goes to acetic anhydride by the extraction of water.

ANHYDROUS SOAP. Pure soap, free from water and its concomitants.

ANIDEX. In accordance with the rules of the Textile Fiber Products Identification Act of 1960, the Federal Trade Commission amended Rule 7 to provide a new generic term, Anidex, a manufactured fiber in which the fiber-forming substance is any long chain synthetic polymer composed of a least 50% by weight of one or more esters of a monohydric alcohol and acrylic acid. Effective on October 31st, 1969. This is the eighteenth term in the list of Manmade Fibers as decreed by the Federal Trade Commission, Washington, D.C. Modacrylic was redefined to exclude those fibers which qualify under the Anidex group. See Anim/8™.

ANIL. This West Indian shrub, Indigofera Anil, is a source for indigo.

ANILINE. A coal tar derivative used to produce aniline black and other dyestuffs, and extensively used in printing and dyeing. This base is an oily, poisonous, basic liquid, which is colorless when pure, and is now made chiefly by the reduction of nitrobenzene. Aniline was originally distilled from indigo in 1826 by Unverdorben, and made commercially valuable in 1856 when Sir William H. Perkin discovered mauve as a product of indigo. Since the War between the States, aniline has been highly desirable in dyeing animal and vegetable fibers, and is much used in dyeing fur. Soluble in alcohol and ether, the formula is $C_6H_5NH_2$.

ANILINE BLACK. A fast black on cotton made possible by the oxidation of aniline on the fiber. Care has to be exercised in using this color since tendering may result from the oxidizing agent as well as from the acid in the bath. Very fast to light, washing, and chlorine, it is much used in resist printing.

ANILINE DYE. A dye or coloring matter prepared as a derivative from coal tar products of which aniline, a chemical substance, is a prominent member and often the starting point in the dye production.

ANILINE-DYED LEATHER. This term is used to distinguish leather which has been colored with aniline dyes from that which has been colored with pigment or other opaque materials.

ANILINE SALT. Aniline hydrochloride, which is made by mixing aniline and hydrochloric acid. Easily soluble in water, it is used in printing with aniline black.

ANILINISM. A poisonous disease caused by inhaling the fumes in the manufacture of aniline.

ANILO. Philippine bast fiber, the inner bark of which is used for cordage.

ANIM/8 TM. This generic fiber in the category of *Anidex,* decreed by the Federal Trade Commission effective October 31, 1960, is the property of Rohm and Haas Company, Inc., Philadelphia, Pennsylvania, and Fayetteville, North Carolina. Claimed as the first truly new fiber in the last ten years this acrylate polymer is the first of its kind in a projected family of *Anidex Fibers.*

This product can be incorporated into any fiber and imparts additional stretch and recovery to fibers such as cotton and wool without either losing their identity. Features of this fiber include chemical resistance, appealing hand, ease of care. This practical elastomeric fiber can be chlorine bleached and cleaned, two characteristics not usually found in rubber and spandex. It can be used with any fabric or finish extant. Research span covered fifteen years while development cost around $20 million. See Anidex.

ANIMAL FIBERS, ACTION OF CAUSTIC SODA ON. If a sample containing wool or silk, and cotton, is boiled about 15 or 20 minutes in a 5 per cent solution of caustic soda, the wool or silk will dissolve; the cotton is unaffected. In this test, rayon is not materially injured but it is weakened.

ANIMAL FIBERS AND FILAMENTS. Obtained from an animal for purposes of weaving, knitting, or felting into fabric; examples are alpaca, angora goat hair, camel hair, cashmere, cow hair, extract wool, fur, horsehair, llama, mohair, mungo, noil, shoddy, silk, spun silk, tussah or wild silk, vicuna, wool, worsted, worsted top.

ANIMALIZED COTTON. Cotton treated with solutions of silk or other animal fiber matter such as albumen, casein or gelatine. Cotton is thus made capable of being dyed in a more uniform manner in mixture fabrics containing silk, wool, or other animal fibers. Also used to obtain cross-dyed effects with nontreated cotton.

ANIMALIZED VISCOSE RAYON. Also known as Modified Cellulose Fiber, Modified Rayon, Modified Staple Fiber. See BASIFIED VISCOSE.

ANIMALIZING. Chemical treatment which provides fibers other than wool with an affinity such as dyestuffs used on wool possess.

ANION. A negatively charged ion that moves toward the anode under the influence of an electric field. Anionic materials are used in the leather, paper, and textile trades for emulsifying, scouring, wetting, and as dispersing agents for dyes. Alkyl sulphates and sulphates of long chain alcohols fall into this sphere.

Anions are opposed to cations, and therefore it is essential that materials which are strongly anionic in nature must not be used in a bath in which strongly cationic materials are being used. If these two types of material are used in the one bath, there is danger that a precipitation or breaking of the bath will occur.

ANKLETS. Short socks that are usually made with fancy "turnover" tops.

ANNABERG. Famous for its early bobbin laces, this town is the resting place of Barbara Uttmann, who introduced bobbin lace-making in Germany.

ANNATTA. A dye also known as Annotto, Arnotto, Roucou, obtained from the pulp which surrounds the seeds of the *Bixa Orellana;* used chiefly in dyeing silk an orange color which is fugitive in nature.

ANNUALS. Those races of silkworms which produce one brood in a year.

ANODENDRON. A tough but fine bast fiber obtained from the climbing plant *Anodendron paniculatum,* in Ceylon and India.

ANSO NYLON. This product of Allied Chemical Corporation, New York City, is an anti-soil Nylon Type 6 (Caprolan) and its opaqueness reduces the visual double effect observed when comparing it with, for example, regular nylon. This product has excellent color retention and high resistance to fading. It is a very fine soil absorber, is non-allergic, mothproof, resistant to insects and mildew and does not support combustion. It is an ideal fiber for use in floorcoverings of many types.

ANTELOPE FINISH SUEDE. Lambskin, goatskin, or calfskin that has been sueded and finished to resemble antelope.

ANTELOPE LEATHER. Fine, soft leather made from antelope skin, silklike or velvety in sheen and texture. It is sueded on the flesh side.

ANTENNAE. The feathery feelers on the head of a moth; used in sericulture or raising of silkworms.

ANTHEREA, ANTHAEREA. The general, collective, and scientific name for various wild silks of China, India, and Japan. The leading varieties include Maxankoorie, Muga or Assamo, Mylitta, Paphia or Tussah, Pernyi, Roylei, and Yama-Mai. See also ANTHEREA MYLITTA; ANTHEREA PERNYI; ANTHEREA YAMA-MAI.

ANTHEREA MYLITTA. One of the outstanding Tussah silkworms, raised in India and feeding on leaves of the castor oil plant. Cocoon length is 3 to 5 centimeters. This silk will give a yardage that even surpasses that of mulberry-fed true silkworms (*Bombyx mori*). Anywhere from 600 yards to 2000 yards have been obtained from this cocoon. Its color ranges from gray to tannish brown.

ANTHEREA PERNYI. Classed as a wild silkworm, attempts have been made to domesticate it within recent years. It feeds on large oak leaves and is yellowish in color. The cocoon is large and averages four centimeters in length.

ANTHEREA YAMA-MAI. Cocoon native to Japan, from a grayish-green caterpillar that feeds on oak leaves. It is large, greenish in cast; silk resembles true silk. Much trouble is usually encountered in dyeing and bleaching Yama-Mai.

ANTHRACAEMIA, ANTHRACEMIA. Same as ANTHRAX, which see.

ANTHRACENE. Used in the making of dyes, it is a hydrocarbon made from the fractional distillation of coal tar. Insoluble in water, and to some degree in alcohol and ether, it dissolves readily in benzene. It will crystallize in colorless tablet formation.

ANTHRACNOSE. Fungus disease, also known as pink boll rot. It wreaks havoc on cotton plants, particularly those in humid areas. Rainy seasons also permit the rot to do its damage. Plants in any stage of development are affected. Control measures are applied whenever possible.

ANTHRAQUINONE VAT DYES. Dyes with amino-anthraquinone as base. Ideal for vat-dying.

ANTHRAX. General term for several varieties of a malignant infectious disease often contracted from handling or inhaling dust from animal fibers, especially wool. Both animal and man can pick up this disease. While not always fatal, it is painful. If confined to the skin alone a cure can often be effected. The pulmonary variety often is called woolsorter's disease.

ANTI-BACTERIAL FINISH. Treatment applied to fabrics to make them resistant to microorganism attack.

ANTICHLOR. A chemical substance which will decompose or destroy chlorine bleach. Sours will do this, but a reducing agent, such as bisulphite or oxalic acid, imparts a directly opposite chemical or neutralizing action.

ANTI-CREASE FINISH. Result of treating fabrics with a synthetic resin that helps them resist and recover from wrinkling. Used on cotton, rayon, linen, and combination fabrics. Silk and wool have a natural resistance to wrinkling.

ANTIFEIT PROCESS FOR MILITARY USE, APPROVED.
1. Chatham Continuous Chlorination Method
2. Dylanize SW
3. Dylanize X
4. Harriset
5. Kelpie
6. Kroy
7. Melafix II
8. QM Controlled Chlorination
9. Schollerize
10. WB-7
11. Whitaker Process WH-2
Resin Treatments:
1. Kymene 557
2. Lanaset
3. Resloom M-75
4. Wurlan

ANTI-FUME FINISH. Applied particularly to acetate fabrics, the finish raises their resistance to or prevents discoloration by atmospheric fumes, chiefly those caused by combustion or those which are acidic in character.

ANTIMACASSAR. A loose cover over back or arms of furniture to protect from soiling; originally, Macassar oil hairdressing was the reason for its popularity in earlier days. Usually small, of doily-like, detachable white linen or lace. Also called a tidy.

ANTIPERSPIRANT AND DEODORANT STAIN REMOVAL. Sponge or wash well with soap or detergent in warm water. If the stain is not removed, use a chlorine or peroxide bleach. Both products con-

tain aluminum chloride, stearic acid, and they may alter the color which may be restored by sponging with ammonia in dilute form and on natural fibers. Use a ratio of equal parts of each, ammonia and water. Final rinsing should be done.

ANTIQUE. 1. Several types of textiles, furniture, glassware, painting, sculpture etc., made more than 100 years ago. Dating from an early period, these are not modern in any sense of the word. On February 1, 1967, the United States Customs Service decreed 1830 as the latest date which would entitle an item to be called an antique. 2. The term applied to certain textile fabrics which simulate silk fabrics of prior centuries, such as satin antique, moire antique, along with a few other decorative fabrics.

ANTIQUE GRAIN. A surface of striations or markings, often irregular, in which the depressed areas or valleys have been given a contrasting color or shade to provide a two-tone or two-color effect.

ANTIQUE LACE. Handmade pillow lace constructed with heavy linen thread in large, open, rectangular knotted mesh formation.

ANTI-RUN BACK COURSE. A course designed to prevent garter tears running below the knee of a stocking. This consists usually of a course of tuck stitches a few inches below the welt.

ANTI-SAG. A broad term which implies that fabric, under the usual conditions, will not sag or lose its shape.

ANTISEPTIC. A substance which retards or prevents decay or putrefaction. Antiseptic chemicals are used on cottons to prevent mildew. Examples of antiseptics include carbolic acid, boric acid, salicylic acid, formaldehyde, and salts of copper and zinc.

ANTI-STATIC AGENT. An auxiliary agent applied to textile materials to control static generation of the material.

ANTI-TWIST. General term applied to material that, under ordinary conditions, will not twist or recede from original shape.

"ANTRON." The Du Pont trademark for a type of nylon fiber which has a trilobal cross-section, the first nylon fiber the company has given a trade-mark since nylon came into the textile market in 1939. Dress fabrics of "Antron" have a pleasing hand, rich, three-dimensional highlights, and clear print definition. Fabrics for foundation garments benefit from the influence of the fiber on hand and wicking action.

Women's wear fabrics used for uniforms show increased opacity or cover. "Antron" has excellent dyeability, drape, and wash-and-wear properties comparable with those of regular nylon.

ANTRON III. A nylon yarn of duPont, Wilmington, Delaware, which has built-in anti-static properties and used chiefly in lingerie. The anti-static property is permanent and not affected in laundering.

ANTWERP. City in Flanders, in the seventeenth century noted for its laces; Mechlin, Lille, Brussels, and others. Many of these laces are also called Antwerp laces. Still a lace center.

AOUDAD SHEEP. See ARGALI.

APISHAMORE, APISHAMEAN. American frontier term for a saddle blanket.

APOU. A ramie fabric made in China; noted for its high luster.

APPARATINE. The result of treating starch with caustic soda, a sizing ingredient.

APPAREL. 1. The clothing or attire worn by the human race. 2. Ready-to-wear clothing-industry products.

APPAREL; also known as PARATURA. A piece of colored brocade or other rich-looking fabric, usually the same color as the vestments used in religious circles, which is attached to the neckband edge of the amice and could be removed when washing the amice. It served to form a collar on the vested cleric. Though still in use in some cities such as Florence and Milan, and in Spain and Portugal, it is not now recognized for liturgical usage.

APPAREL COMPANIES-STORES, SOME MAJOR. These follow:

Bobbie Brooks, Inc.
Botany Industries, Inc.
B.V.D. Corporation
Cluett, Peabody Co., Inc.
Eagle Clothes, Inc.
Farsh Mfg. Co., Inc.
Genesco, Inc.
Hart, Schaffner & Marx.
Hat Corporation of America
Interstate Department Stores
Koret of California (Koracorporation)
Jonathon Logan Co., Inc.
Londontown Mfg. Co.
Manhattan Industries.
McGregor-Doniger
Munsingwear, Inc.
National Bellas Hess
Palm Beach Co., Inc.
Phillips Van Heusen
Richman Brothers, Inc.
Russ Togs, Inc.

Siegel (Henry I).
Spartan Industries
Levi Straus & Co., Inc.
V.F. Corporation
Villager Industries, Inc.
Warnaco, Inc.
Wayne Gossard, Inc.

APPAREL CONSTRUCTION, OUTLINE FOR REGULATION. The following presents a general overview in apparel construction:

1. *Good Apparel Design: Parameters-*Style for emotional appeal. Utility in the ability to function properly; durability for physical performance and wear testing. *Evaluation-*Emotional appeal to include hand and optical appeal including the silhouette, color, drape surface interest, overall effect, etc. *Performance-*Utility, and ability to function in specific usage. *Permanence-*Attained by physical testing to include wear testing.

2. *Patterns, Drafting:* The *Sloper-*the fundamental pattern, made of linen or muslin, used for size only. *Grading-*the drafting process of diminishing or enlarging a style pattern into patterns for other sizes. *Function-*to give proper fit without changing the style sense of the original. *Procedure-*interpreting the design; determining the grading measurements, anthropometric data, etc. Also, sizing designations of the particular manufacturer.

3. *Cutting Production: Marker-Making-*developing the jig-saw like diagram as a guide for cutting the plies of fabric into the required component parts. *Spreading-*superimposing plies of material to permit simultaneous cutting into components; the ply alignment, ply tension; grain alignment, splicing; damage replacement, surface direction, and checking well the static electricity. *Chopping-*cutting the fabric into the exact shape for final assembly; the difference between pattern chopping and block chopping to be considered. *Position Marking-*refers to the Guide Marks on the surface or the perimeters of the cut components to make precise alignment in the assemblies. *Shading-*marking the cut components for shade matching precision and sequence with respect to cut components sequence in the spread. *Sloping-*respreading a stack of cut components for pattern chopping. *Bundling-*sorting and stacking cut components for further processing.

4. *Sewing Production: Stitch-Loop-*stitching which covers a series of stitches, a series of stitches whose function is only to ornament or encompass an edge of ply; *Seam-*two or more plies of material joined by a series of stitches; *Sewing-*the process of making the stitching or the seam.

*Federal Standard Number 751-*establishes, defines, and illustrates the requirements for the types of stitches, seams, and the stitching formation specified in U. S. Government Specifications for sewn items. Published August, 1959.

*Stitching Quality Measurements-*includes stitch size, stitch tension, stitch sequence, elongation, elasticity, resilience, yarn severance, fabric distortion, strength in breaking or rupture of fabric, and effects from abrasion testing. *Seam Quality-*includes seam depth, seam length, and seam width.

5. *Fabric Sewability:* The ability with which the fabric can be sewed qualitatively and quantitatively. Apparel manufacturing varies widely with respect to cut, make, and trim; style effect values, durability standards, sewing machines, production methods, abilities of operatives, and the efforts of a cooperative enterprise pertinent to all personnel.

6. *Production Sequence:* This depends on the local conditions in all respects in the particular manufacturing house; no two firms operate in the same manner.

7. *Components and Construction:* These include bar-tacks, belt loops, buttonholes, closures, collars, innerlinings and linings, pockets, sleeves, and cuffs, stitching, thread, trim, insignias, vents, pleats, and yokes. See all listings under Apparel. See Sloper, Grading, Grading Men's Wear Garments, Grading Women's Wear Garments.

APPAREL DESIGNER. One who supervises and coordinates designing and manufacturing; creates original designs; assumes responsibilities for the development and manufacture of the models he produces. The designer must be a master in the design of patterns; should know human anatomy and proportions; must be familiar with the working properties of textiles; must know fashion and style and all the techniques of garment manufacture and be able to organize and supervise designing and manufacturing; must know production costs and efficient methods of manufacture. See also AP-PAREL DESIGNER, ASSISTANT.

APPAREL DESIGNER, ASSISTANT. One who works out minute details of pattern-making and manufacture; grades patterns and, in most plants, cuts the hard paper patterns. He assists in the selection of fabric, lining and trimmings; should master the same knowledge which makes the apparel designer important in the apparel trade.

APPAREL DRAPER. One who possesses a feeling for color, line, form, and silhouette in addition to a working knowledge of the workability of fabrics. The draper must first drape muslin for a pattern, and then cut cloth to the figure or the model. It should be borne in mind that at this juncture a fabric may be easily derailed through lack of conveying adequate information to all persons involved.

APPAREL, FIGURE TYPES AND SIZE RANGES OF:

Infants (Babetto)
Small (Six Months) Medium (Twelve Months) Large (Eighteen Months) and Extra Large (XL) for the cubby baby. Infants and baby wear up to the age of walking.

Toddler
1T, 2T, 3T, and 4T (The T stands for Toddler) for children who walk but are not over 3 years old. Short waistlines, big tummy, baby fat. Dresses are short, they should cover diaper pants.

Children's
3, 4, 5, 6x (6x transition is a tall size 6). This size range is for children from 3 to about 6 years old. Nursery school and kindergarten age. The child is somewhat taller and thinner than the toddler. The waistline is still not clearly defined.

Girl's
7, 8, 10, 12, 14 (Many firms are discontinuing size 14 because these girls are wearing subteen sizes unless they are very heavy). This size range is for girls of elementary school age 7 to 11. Waistlines develop slowly. Some manufacturers cater to slim girls while others cater to chubbier types. There is no bust development taken into consideration even in larger sizes.

Sub-teen
8, 10, 12, 14, also 16. These are the clothes for the girl of Junior High School age 12 to 14. There is slight bust development. Waistlines are more defined although still not as clearly as in the true teen age figure. Bodices are longer waisted than girls sizes but shorter than Young Juniors. There is slight hip development.

Young Junior (Teen)
3, 5, 7, 9, 11, 13. Since the introduction of the Sub-teen size range, teen age clothes are very similar to Junior. The age group is about 13 to 16 years. Waistlines are clearly defined, bust is high and rounded and hips are developed. Teens do not like

the label TEEN. Therefore Junior Deb, Miss Junior, Young Junior are preferred.

Junior

7, 9, 11, 13 (some manufacturers add 3-5 and 15). This size range is for an adult figure with higher bustline and shorter waistline than the standard Misses figure.

Junior Petite

3, 5, 7, 9, 13. For the small woman. The bust and hips slightly smaller than Junior. Waistline shorter. Proportions of garment detail are in line with smaller figure.

Miss

6, 8, 10, 12, 14, 16, 18. Well proportioned figure, taller, longer waistline than Juniors. Sizes also continue to 22 and 24. Mail order houses and some firms buy these sizes.

Women

34 to 46. Fuller and lower bust - larger diaphragm - abdomen fuller-hips may be smaller in proportion to rest of body. A young woman who wears Misses sizes, often matures into the Women's size range.

Women's Stout

48 to 52. Same as Women's sizes only heavier.

Half Sizes

12½, 14½, 16½, 18½, 20½, 22½, 24½, 26½. Same for Women's and Stouts but with shorter waistlines.

APPAREL INDUSTRY, OUTLINE OF THE.

I. Relationships of the Major Divisions and other Lesser Functions:

A. General Garment Categories
Dresses - Casual, classics, shirtwaist, cocktail, dinner, evening
2. Sportswear - Bathing suits, slacks, shorts, skirts, blouses, jumpers, jackets, specialty items.
3. Coats and Suits
4. Intimate Apparel-Loungewear, lingerie, foundation garments, housecoats, sleepwear.
5. Rainwear
6. Knitwear and Sweaters
7. Aprons, Smocks, housedresses
8. Men's Clothing
9. Children's Clothing
10. Theatrical

B. Specialized Size Categories (for details refer to sheet on figure types)

1. Children's Wear (Infants and Toddler)
2. Teens
3. Juniors
4. Half Size
5. Misses
6. Women's
7. Petites (5' 5" and under)
8. Junior Petite
9. Tall
10. Maternity

C. Analysis of the "Creation and Production of a Garment"

I. Basic Divisions in the Wholesale Manufacturing Process

a) Design
1) Designer (Stylist)
2) Assistant Designer
3) Sketcher
4) Samplehands
5) Finisher
6) Model

b) Production
1) Piece Goods Buyer & Assistant
2) Production Manager
3) Patternmaker
4) Draper
5) Duplicate Maker
6) Grader
7) Marker
8) Cutter
9) Factory
    Foreman
    Assorter
    Operators & special machine operations
    Drapers
    Presser
    Finisher
    Examiner
    Cleaner
    Floor Girl

c) Sales and Distribution
1) Sales
    HeadSalesman
    Showroom Salesman
    Road Salesman
2) Shipping Department
    Clerks
    Order Picker
    Checker
    Packers

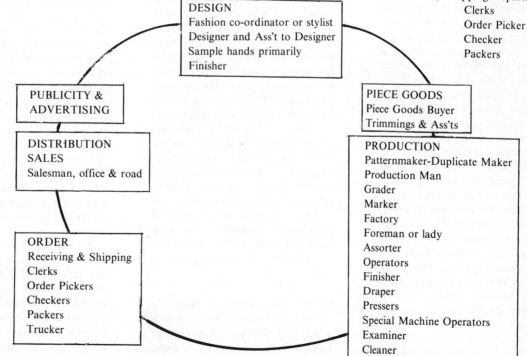

DESIGN
Fashion co-ordinator or stylist
Designer and Ass't to Designer
Sample hands primarily
Finisher

PUBLICITY & ADVERTISING

DISTRIBUTION SALES
Salesman, office & road

ORDER
Receiving & Shipping
Clerks
Order Pickers
Checkers
Packers
Trucker

PIECE GOODS
Piece Goods Buyer
Trimmings & Ass'ts

PRODUCTION
Patternmaker-Duplicate Maker
Production Man
Grader
Marker
Factory
Foreman or lady
Assorter
Operators
Finisher
Draper
Pressers
Special Machine Operators
Examiner
Cleaner

(Courtesy of Apparel Department, Fashion Institute of Technology, New York, N.Y.)

II. Allied Fields
   1. Retail Organization
      Resident offices, department stores
      specialty shops
   2. Advertising and Public Relations
   firms
   3. Fashion Publications
   4. Textile
   5. Mail Order House
III. Related Fields
   1. Commercial Pattern Co.
   2. Interior Decorating and
   Home Furnishing
   3. Trimming Firms - Laces, Button,
   braids, pleater, etc.
   4. Notions threads, zippers, yard-
   sticks, scissors
   5. Millinery
   6. Bags
   7. Gloves
   8. Shoes
   9. Belts
   10. Scarves and Neckwear
   11. Jewelry
   12. Doll's Clothes
   13. Furs

APPAREL MANUFACTURING PLANT, MAJOR UNITS IN THE.

1. *Fabric or Piece Goods Buyer:* Fabric is made from fiber, the raw material; it is then constructed into goods, colored, and made ready for processing by the apparel manufacturer. In other words, fabric is the raw material which the cut-make-trim industry makes into the finished article.

The buyer and his assistants work with the textile mills closely and in detail. Three things must be considered when buying material - its use for the particular season, the occasions for wearing the garment, and the weight of the goods. Other points to keep in mind include the weave, color, and finish. Many fabrics are bought because of the particular construction, the color of the goods and/ or the texture or hand of the material. The buyer also works closely with the textile technologists of the company with regard to the construction and specifications entailed - ends and picks per inch in woven fabric, wale and course construction, guage used in knitgoods, etc. Fibers, yarns and chemical and physical testing are all of utmost importance. Sample room, as well as factory fabrics, have to meet the specifications decreed by the buyer.

2. *The Trimming and Findings Room:* The person in charge of this work is responsible for all accessories such as hooks and eyes, zippers, flowers, fur, jewelry, lace, etc. It is also his duty to buy for the designing department and the factory. He or she is the liaison officer for appointments with the designer and must also make choices relative to the complete, finished garment.

3. *Production Man:* He is in charge of all production and scheduling. He attends to all costing items, considers all problems that may arise with the unions, and must keep abreast of all phases from beginning to end. He always works very closely with the designer as to detail, queries, grading, and sequence in manufacture.

4. *The Manufacturer:* He may be the owner, partner, or person in charge of all production for the company. The Production Man is responsible to him. In many instances the manufacturer is the head of the sales division. He is the one responsible for everything including possible risks as to whether his products will be winners or clinkers. The designer can make or break a concern and the manufacturer should always work closely with him to obtain the best possible results as to sales. Briefly, the manufacturer has to be aware "of all things at all times," whether in a large or a small company.

5. *The Purchasing Agent and the Designer:* They may or may not work closely together but to produce good results they should have confidence in each other at all times. Buying for spring is done in early fall while fall purchasing is done in May and June. The Fashion Coordinator is also an important asset to a company since she keeps abreast of the times, the market, knows "what's new" in the Rome and Paris showings, advertising, fashion journals, television, radio, etc. She must be able to differentiate between the good and the not so good - all these come as result of her constant vigilance in daily work and travels in the market, department stores, fashion shows, newspaper reports.

6. *The Department Store Buyer:* He has to know about his inventory constantly, the allotment of money for his department, amount of floor space, and expenses for advertising, etc. He is responsible to the comptroller of the store. Often the buyer works on a commission basis as an incentive to obtain the best possible results. The Resident Buyer is with the resident buying office and buys for a number of stores throughout the nation. January and June are "the flood months" along Seventh Avenue in New York City where all major buying offices have their headquarters.

7. *Labor:* This includes operating, whether machine or handstitching, and finishing, which embodies hemming, sewing and all other handwork. Finally, there is the pressing department which actually finishes-off the garment for the purchaser. Labor, which includes piece operators, finishers, pressers, etc., comes to around 65 percent of the cost of making an item. These allowances are figured with the so-called standard-of-living levels and variables and may be escalated periodically.

8. *The Floor:* This term is used to include the following: draping, examining, and the finished article. For example, on dresses that range in the $30-$50 bracket, seventy cents or seventy-five cents is added on to the cut-make-trim price. Dresses in the $5.00-$7.50 range have around fifteen cents added to the wholesale price. Dresses above the $50.00 range have one dollar or more added to the wholesale costs, depending on the listed selling price of the dress at hand.

As a general rule, unless the dress or gown is a creation, a classic, or a haute couture, the actual fabric cost ranges from one-ninth to one-eleventh of the selling price. There is some tendency at present not to use these fractions since the idea now seems to be to set a price on a dress in "what the customer can carry or afford." This has lead to varying and wide price ranges and it depends greatly on the prestige of store in which the garment was purchased; the greater the prestige of the store, the higher will be the price paid by the customer.

Another important facet in manufacturing is the cutting phase. Cutting can be done either by a contractor or in the factory itself. It is not unusual for a concern to employ several sub-contractors, even up to twenty or more, especially on low-cost products. The contractor works for around 40 percent of the total cost, down to about thirty percent for lower-priced lines.

9. *Apparel Statistics:*

Production in the apparel fields is now about $40 billion annually, with three quarters of this business being done in Seventh Avenue, New York City.

The apparel industry has been and still is beset with many problems. These include demands for higher wages, the question of imports, which is of major proportions, the suddenly and constantly changing fashions and styles, which often make or break a company of its planning is awry, insufficient diversification, and labor shortages caused by retirements, transfers to other industries, deaths, etc. Not enough competent new blood is available to fill the jobs that are open. Efforts to train new employees have not produced good results in the semiskilled and skilled operations. Training facilities are not adequate. Some trained personnel is produced in the Fashion Industries High School and The Fashion Institute of Technology and Design, from operators to designers, but these two New York City institutions do not graduate nearly the number that could be placed easily and well in the industry.

Prices now rise annually and less fabric is currently used than five or so years ago because of the prevailing styles - narrower brims on hats, much shorter skirts and dresses; rather tight-fitting clothes, and shorter coats of all types for men, women, and children. Production has also been cut somewhat because of the predominate feeling for informality.

The industry is constantly looking for new technologists, time and motion experts, better workmanship, and improved tools to work with, and management is always on the alert for possible mergers that may aid their company.

Generally, mergers are a sign of healthy business, and a good merger should benefit all parties concerned. For example, Genesco, Inc., is the giant in this particular field, and its well-known apparel units include Majestic Specialties, Inc., Berkshire Apparel Corporation, Susan Thomas, Inc., etc. Based in Nashville, Tennessee, Genesco is the world's largest allover apparel company. Kayser-Roth Corporation is the largest in the

field of women's wear trade and does a business close to $500 million annually.

Union troubles have been rampant in the industry for many years. Unions have been faced with non-union manufacturers and their number seems to increase annually. There are three mamoth unions in this country and data on these follows: Latest available figures reveal that the I.L.G.W.U. (International Ladies Garment Workers Union) has 545,000 members. The Amalgamated Workers of America, Inc., has 376,000 members while the United Garment Workers Union, Inc., which works chiefly on workclothes, has 35,000 members. Another large one is The United Hatters, Cap and Millinery Workers International Union.

The most recent figures available for textiles show that there are 958,200 employees with 852,800 of these listed as production workers. Payrolls, in millions of dollars come to $4,845.3 with production workers receiving $3,944.1 of this total.

Apparel and other textile products show 1,359,600 employed with 1,197,600 of these listed as production workers. Payrolls, in million dollars, total $6,045.0 with $4,705.5 of this total being paid to production workers.

Combining these two categories, the totals follow:
Employed (in thousands) 2,317.8
Production workers (in thousands)
2,050.4
Payrolls (in million dollars) $10,890.3
Wages (in million dollars, to
production workers) from the
above payroll total $8,649.6

As previously noted, the rise in imports of apparel and textiles has wreaked havoc, distress, and some dispair, and both industries have been more or less stymied to a rather marked degree, especially since the early 1960's.

APPAREL PIECE GOODS BUYER. Supervises the actual purchases and inventories of fabrics and materials. He works with the apparel designer in figuring costs, planning the line, and judging one fabric against another. The buyer should have technical knowledge of textile fabrics and must be aware of the trend of the times with regard to new developments in fibers, filaments, weave construction, color, and finish.

APPAREL PLANT MANAGER. The person who takes over from the

minute a fashion is approved, and ends his responsibility when he delivers finished merchandise to either the shipping clerk or the stock clerk. Supervises every manufacturing operation, from cutting to pressing. It is part of his job to keep manufacturing costs down; thus it is advisable that he be kept informed of the most efficient methods for working each type of material.

APPAREL SAMPLE HAND. One who runs up the sample garment; selected because of ability, as a machine operator, to work the material into the effect desired by the designer. In the case of a new fabric, it is desirable that the sample maker should be shown the best way to handle the material lest he find it too difficult to work.

APPAREL SKETCHER. One who makes copies of all designs created in the designing room; must know how, through the medium of crayon, pencil, and water color, to render all material and fur effects on paper. The effectiveness with which the sketcher works should convey the feeling or color of a fabric to the paper, so that a decision can be made as to whether or not the fabric should be included in the line.

APPAREL STYLIST. One who keeps the firm's designers posted on new and important fashion trends. The stylist often assists in the actual creation of new designs; sometimes sketches original styles for approval to the designer.

APPAREL TRADE TERMS, BASIC. For women's wear:
Accessories: Bags, belts, bows, buttons, collars and cuffs, cover-ups, gilets, gloves, halters, dickeys, hats, hoods, jerkins, jewelry, kerchiefs, neckwear, scarfs, shoes, vestees.
Blouses: Overblouse, peplum, tunic, tuck-in.
Coats: Belted tunic, bloused, box, cape, Chesterfield, coolie, dressmaker, fitted, mandarin, princess, redingote, reefer, reversible, swagger, tailored, topper, trench, tuxedo.
Collars: Asymmetric, Bertha or cape, convertible, draped, fichu, flared standing or rippled, Johnny, lapel and collar in one, mandarin, notched, Peter Pan, plastron, reverse rolled, sailor, shawl, tuxedo, yoke and collar in one.
Cuffs: French, hanging either flare or ruffle, shaped band, straight band, turn-back, including flared, shaped, straight.
Dresses: Basque, coat, chemise, jumper, long torso, pinafore, princessline, redingote, tunic.
Foundation Garments: Bra, combination, corset, garter belt, girdle,

pantie girdle.

HISTORIC COSTUMES: Directoire, Egyptian, Grecian, Modern, Victorian.

JACKETS: Blazer, bolero, dressmaker, kiltie, lumber jacket, mandarin, semitailored, shirtwaist, swagger, tailored, tuxedo, waistcoat.

NECKLINES: Asymmetric, bateau or boat, camisole, cowl, crew, draped, harlequin, heart-shaped, off-shoulder, plunging "V," portrait, round, slashed, square, surplice, turtle.

NEGLIGEES: Bed jackets, ensembles, including nightgowns, pajamas, robes, lounging garments, including pajamas and robes; sleeping garments, long or short.

PLAYCLOTHES: Active dress, including riding habit, skating dress, ski suit, swim suit, tennis dress; bras, culottes, halters, shorts, slacks.

SKIRTS: Asymmetric, bias, bouffant, built-up, circular, dirndl, draped, including bustle, center-front, center-back, pannier, peg-top, polonaise, and side; flounces, godets, gored, kiltie, panel and yoke, pencil slim, peplum, pleated, including box, group, inverted, kick, side, sunburst (flat accordion) and unpressed. Also, pleated gore, sectional, shirred, straight or full, swing, tiered, tunic, wraparound, and yoke.

SLEEVES: Asymmetric, bell, bishop, bloomer, cap, cape, circular, dolman, draped, drop-shoulder, epaulet, kimono, lantern, leg-of-mutton, mosquetaire, one-piece or two-piece, peasant, puffed, raglan, sectional, shirred, shirtwaist, yoke and sleeve in one.

SUITS: Dressmaker, semitailored, tailored.

THEATRICAL COSTUME: Fantastic, Historic, Modern.

TRIMMINGS: Air-tucking, appliqué beading, embroideries including Bonnaz and Schiffli, passementerie, quilting, rococo, smocking.

UNDERGARMENTS: Bloomers, bra, briefs, chemise, panties, slips (bias, princess-line, tailored).

WAISTS: Asymmetric, basque, draped or with darts, shirring, tucks, twists; fitted, fullness-yokes sometimes with darts, shirring, tucks; kimono, shirtwaist, surplice.

APPAREL WOOL. Broad term used chiefly for tariff purposes, which embraces all wools except carpet and pulled wools. Apparel wool finds much use also in blankets, felt, upholstery and similar materials.

APPENZELL EMBROIDERY. Intricate handwork in fine stitching done on muslin fabric for the ground. The industry is supposed to have originated in Appenzell, Switzerland, and is done in the home rather than in factories.

APPERLY FEED. A device that reduces the web of woolen fibers into a sliver form, and lays them, diagonally, onto a feed apron. Located between the breaker and intermediate cards, this feed builds up the stock in a lap formation which is delivered to the feeding-in end of the intermediate.

APPLICATION PRINTING. The printing onto white goods irrespective of the type of material involved; a term rather popular in printing of rayons and silks. There is no discharge or resist printing procedure involved in application printing. Sometimes known as direct printing.

APPLIED PRINTING. Printing color onto fabric, natural in color or bleached. It is done on roller or direct printing, block printing, and in screen or stencil printing.

APPLIQUÉ (APPLIED): 1. Term for lace in which the motif or design detail is made separately from the background and applied (appliqué) thereon. Appliqué lace should not be confused with tambour, which is made by working upon machine-made net a design that is perfected by a chain stitch. It should not be confused with runwork, which is made by running a thread in and out of the net in order to produce a design or pattern. 2. Any adornment applied to a solid background by means of stitches. The pieces to be used are cut out for size and effect and are then embroidered, pasted, or sewed onto the base material. Fabric lace or leather is often appliquéd. 3. Bobbin sprigs or needle point applied to a machine-made groundwork, as observed in the well-known modern Brussels lace. Point Appliqué is an application of needle-point details upon a net, and it is usually machine-made. The history of old laces practically ends with the beginning of nineteenth-century machine-made net or bobbinet. Cotton thread was used in this lace as early as 1833.

APPLIQUÉ EMBROIDERY. Design of some fabric applied to a material by means of fancy stitching.

APPLIQUÉ STITCH. Any stitch used to apply pieces to a background material.

APPRENTICESHIP. The type of training used to prepare workers to acquire a skill or craft, requiring a number of years of preparation.

APPRET. The sizing or dressing finish applied to fabrics.

APRICOT. Red-yellow color with medium saturation and high brilliance.

APRON. 1. An endless, traveling lattice belt which feeds raw material or stock to a machine such as the opener picker in cotton manufacturing, or the Bramwell Feed in wool processing. 2. Folds of wool which hang from the neck of some sheep. 3. Material extending from the waistline or shoulders and tied by strings over clothing, for protection or adornment. Cloth, lace, leather, or imitation leather are used. 4. Part of the shoe covering the instep.

APRON CHECK. Another name for an even-sided or square gingham check, generally made of a yarn coarser than that used in dress gingham. A warp and filling arrangement of an apron check might be 8 brown, 8 white, 8 blue, 8 white. A popular British export fabric.

APRON CLOTH. Colored cotton goods woven chiefly in blue and white checks. Some of the cloth is woven with a border down one side which may or may not be figured. A British export fabric.

APRON DISTRIBUTOR. See AUTOMATIC DISTRIBUTOR.

APRON DRESS. Cotton or rayon dress which has an apronlike skirt, tied at the waist and open in back.

APRON FABRICS. Fabrics used to conduct materials through machines in laundry, printing, and other trades. Webs of cotton duck ranging in width from a few inches to several feet.

APRON LEATHER. Several types of leather used on textile machinery. Comber and gill box leather is soft, mellow, and tough, tanned from steer hides, heavily stuffed and usually hand-boarded or otherwise softened.

APRONS, RUBBING. Narrow endless belts, made of leather or rubber, set around two revolving rollers on a worsted drawing frame. Placed one above the other, horizontally, they have both a lateral and an oscillating motion. The wool sliver, as it passes between the two rollers, is condensed or rubbed into a cylindrical sliver devoid of twist.

AQUA REGIA. A mixture of three parts of hydrochloric acid and one of nitric acid. Said to be the strongest acid known.

ARA. A handwoven striped cotton material used in India for skirting.

ARABESQUE. 1. A type of Arabian ornamentation consisting of fantastic patterns of plants, fruits, foliage, and so on, applied to materials. With the exception of Arabic and Moorish art, figures of men and animals also are noted. The designs are usually in combination and are geometrically balanced to give a typical effect. 2. A style of scroll design, of sixteenth-century fame. Patterns are Arabic.

ARABIAN LACET. A "Renaissance" tape curtain lace corded in imitation of Arabian or Point Arabian effect and color.

ARABIAN, POINT ARABIAN. A curtain lace usually of a drab color; tapelike figures heavily corded and connected by bridges.

ARAB WOOL. Wool from sheep raised in the Mesopotamian plains.

ARAIN. See ARMOISIN.

ARALAC. A casein fiber that had some popularity around the time of World War II. The word is broken down as follows - ARA stands for American Research Associates while the LAC stands for the Latin for milk. The home of this fiber was Taftville, Connecticut. The impact of the manmade fibers coming in after the War caused the death knell of Aralac; the price position of Aralac spelled its demise when this was compared with other competitive fibers. See Vicara.

ARAMINA. Brazilian name for the fiber of the Caesar weed, or cadillo.

ARANEUM, OPUS ARANEUM. A coarse, open form of darned work. At an early period in Italy, regular netting darned in a way to show a design was known as Lacis or Opus Filatorium.

In France, the modern survival is called Filet Compté (countable net) or Filet Brodé (embroidered or darned net).

Opus Araneum, the open and the irregular form of darning, was sometimes called Ouvrages Masches, Guipure d'Art, and later when reproduced in France, Cluny Guipure. Today the same thing is known as "Antique" and spiderwork.

ARBACCIO. Name for a native wool raised in Sardinia. See MIORO.

ARBITRATION. A means of settling a dispute between a company and a union or employees, by a third party's issuing a decision, after hearing both parties' versions and considering the merits of their viewpoints; such decision to be final and binding.

ARBITRATOR. See IMPARTIAL CHAIRMAN.

ARBOR. Inner portion of drafting roll, set over the boss.

ARCH. 1. Upper or arched framework noted on some looms. 2. Side framework on carding machines.

ARCHIL, ORCHIL, ORSEILLE. A natural dyestuff from lichens. It will dye animal fibers in shades ranging from crimson to purple, with great depth and body. As a liquid it is called archil liquor; in powder form cudbear; in paste form Persis.

ARCT PROCESS. A detailed procedure used in filament yarns which have been texturized into bulk and stretch yarns. ARCT equipment can be adjusted to process a wide range of yarns in the manmade fiber range. The process is marketed in the United States under license of Ateliers Ronnais de Constructions Textiles, Roanne, France.

ARDAMU. An Iranian raw silk.

ARDASSE. A low-quality Iranian raw silk used to make embroidery yarn.

ARDIL. A protein fiber produced from peanuts. Made in England.

AREA-WIDE BARGAINING. Collective bargaining by representatives of companies in a geographic area and of their employees with the view of arriving at one mutually acceptable agreement to cover all the companies.

AREOLOMETER. See COTTONS, OUTSTANDING AMERICAN.

AREQUIPA FLEECE. Alpaca fleece from Peru named for this export city.

ARGALI. 1. Sheep yielding long, dark gray fiber; the so-called "A" sheep of Siberia, whose fiber is ideal for carpet yarn. 2. Bearded Argali, also known as Barbary sheep. 3. A wild sheep from the Pacific Coast best known as Big Horn or Rocky Mountain.

ARGENTAN, POINT D'ARGENTAN. Around 1650, Alençon and Argentan laces were generally known as Point de France laces. The workers in Argentan were often the same people who worked in Alençon. Argentan net is firmer and larger than other needle-point nets; the pattern is bolder and flatter, and it does not employ the fine cordonnet of Alençon. Argentan excels in brides or bards, chiefly in the six-pointed star motifs to which are added three or four pearls on each side. This effect is known as bride épingle.

ARGENTELLA POINT. Early Italian needle-point net lace which resembles Argentan and Alençon laces and followed the efforts of the Italians to compete with the French markets in light net lacework. There is no raised outline in the work and the designs are conspicuous in small circles, ovals, and small spray effects. Often called Burano point, the motifs are very delicate, the thread used is exceptionally white in cast, there is no raised work effect and the entire piece is flat.

ARGENTINE CLOTH. Plain-weave, low-count cotton on the order of tarlatan. Used for curtains and dress-protecting fabric, it is given a glaze on the one side to give stiffness and body. Finish disappears on washing.

ARGENTINE MERINO. A Merino breed popular in South America. Rambouillet and Southdown sheep laid the foundation for this breed. While high in quality, the wool is not quite so fine as Australian merino, a favorite in the United States.

ARGENTINE WOOL. The chief wool nation in South America. Merino, cross-bred and carpet wools are raised in Argentina. Lower grades are often infested with burrs and other vegetable matters to the detriment of the fleece. Chief shipping center is Buenos Aires, hence this wool is sometimes called B.A. wool. Argentine wool is much used in America. New Orleans is the port of entry.

ARGOL. Tartar deposited from wines which have been completely fermented, or that deposit which adheres to the sides of casks in a hard crust formation. When purified it is known as cream of tartar.

ARGUDAN. A coarse, short-staple Chinese cotton.

ARGYLE DESIGN. Knitted-in design or motif in the form of diamond shapes of different colors. Three colors are usually used, but two-color combinations are also seen in the trade.

ARGYLE SWEATER. Sweater with Argyle designs knitted into fabric in various color schemes. Three colors are usually employed but some two-color effects are also pleasing to the eye.

ARIDEX. Trade name for a water repellent of the wax-emulsion type applied to several major textile fibers.

ARIDYE. High-volume printing method in which insoluble pigments of the pthalocyanine group are used. The paste used contains the dyestuff, soluble gum, starch, and water. The use of resins, which combine directly with the cellulose material, affords excellent penetration of color into the goods. No engraved roller is needed in this method, since the entire material is printed a solid shade. Permanent finishes, other than color, may be applied to the cloth in this way. Phthalocyanines are very fast to chemicals, heat, light, and water, which may affect blue or green but not red or yellow.

ARIGAL ® C. A rot-proof finish which prevents rot of cellulosic fibers without affecting tensile strength. Ideal for weather protection of yarns or piece goods. Up to the present time most finishes of this type have affected the tensile strength of cellulosic fibers on application, or after a period of time. The product is applied by wet fixation on continuous treatment which requires no after-wash. It is non-leaching and odorless. This product of CIBA Company, Inc., Chemical Specialties Division, Fair Lawn, New Jersey, is ideal for bags such as leno, mail, and pick; belting, automobile tops, fish nets and lines, fire hose, hammocks, insect nets, outdoor furniture and awnings, seed-bed covers, shoe uppers and laces, tarpaulins, tents, thread, tire-chafer cloths, tobacco-shade cloth, twine and cordage, umbrellas, and work gloves.

ARIGEN. Interchemical Corporation trade-mark for its several classes of synthetic dyes used in textile dyeing and printing.

ARILOFT. Registered trademark of Eastman Chemical Products, Inc., New York City, for its yarn which is a modified cross-section type with coarse denier size per filament. Developed and introduced in 1968, it is used mainly in knitgoods such as circular and tricot applications. Fabrics made of this fiber have a crispness or dryness, along with fullness, not usually associated with non-textured filament yarns. While the fabrics do give a hand similar to textured acetate it is not intended to replace it, but merely to extend the range in garments that can be made from this yarn.

ARIMINA. A Brazilian bast fiber used to make rope.

ARISTO CARPET. Term meaning the highest, finest and best carpeting, old-time Royal Axminster. Comparable to Aristo; now differs from it only in the pitch or number of points to the square inch. It is much like moquette carpeting used in this country, which is made of wool and has a thick, velvetlike nap or pile. Years ago, Aristo was one of the best carpets on the market, but in late years its popularity and quality has waned somewhat.

ARIZONA COTTON. That raised in Arizona and immediate vicinity. Refers chiefly to the American-Egyptian or Arizona-Egyptian strains. Pima and SxP are examples. Staple is 35 mm. to 45 mm.

ARIZONA-EGYPTIAN COTTON. Cotton obtained from modified forms of Gossypium barbadense, and raised in Arizona, New Mexico, and Southern California. Staple ranges from 35 mm. to 45 mm., and includes Pima cotton raised in the area. Other cottons in this group include SxP, Amsak, Pima 32, Pima S-1, and SuPima, the latter a trademark name.

ARKWRIGHT, SIR RICHARD. The Father of the Factory System in industry. He revolutionized the art of spinning in 1768, by his invention of the spinning frame that would draw the stock into a finished, spun yarn. It was the successful application of automatic spinning. He did not receive his title for his work in textile machinery inventions, as is generally believed.

His spinning machine was originally called the lantern frame, because of the fact that the sliver can used had an opening in the side, closed by a door, through which the sliver was removed, and resembled a lantern in looks. Drawing was accomplished by passing the sliver or strands of stock in rope form between two pairs of rollers that nip and momentarily hold the strands or fibers. The second pair of rollers, revolving more rapidly than the first pair, did the drawing of the fibers. The first pair was called the feeding-in set of rollers; the second pair, the delivery rollers.

The distance between the two pairs of rollers was only a little more than the length of the fibers, so that the drawing caused the fibers to slide upon one another, without actually stretching or breaking them. His frame was the first type of upright spinning machinery.

ARMENIAN. A narrow, needlework type of cotton lace made with independent beams on a Leavers machine. Used chiefly for handkerchief trimming.

ARMOISINE. Taffeta-type fabric made of silk for eighteenth-century men's and women's wear, striped or checked.

ARMORED FABRICS. Asbestos, glass, cotton, and some other textiles that are coated or impregnated with cellulose nitrate, rubber, synthetic rubbers, resins, melamines, and other substances, to protect them against the cold elements.

ARMURE. Fabric made with a small pattern in a pebble or embossed effect. Drapery fabric of this name is made with the small woven designs on a twill or rep background. The term is French.

Armure is used as a dress fabric and comes plain, striped, ribbed, or woven with a small novelty two-color motif. Any of the major fibers or fiber blends serve to make this appealing dress goods fabric.

ARMURE-LAINE. A heavy ribbed or corded silk fabric in which wool yarn is used for the filling.

ARMURE SATINE. A silk cloth which shows a fine twill armure surface and a satin back (satiné) construction.

ARMURE WEAVES. Pronounced crepe or rib weaves which give a rough, pebbled, or granular surface effect on the face of the goods.

ARMY BLUE. 1. Blue uniform fabric formerly used by the U. S. Army. Originated at the time of the War between the States. 2. Blue fabric used in making U. S. Army fabric, such as Marine blue for Marine dress uniforms.

ARMY CLOTH. Broad term for the fabrics used in uniforms of soldiers in the American Army; cavalry twill, serge, elastique, overcoating, flannel, and so on.

ARMY DUCK. A compactly woven cotton fabric of ply yarn in plain-weave formation; the weights range from 7 to 12 ounces per yard, based on a width of 28.5 inches. The Army has a very large number of constructions.

ARNEL. The trade-mark for the cellulose triacetate fiber made by The Celanese Corporation of America. When properly constructed fabrics of Arnel are suitably heat treated, such important performance characteristics as the following are obtained: exceptionally high wrinkle resistance at high as well as low humidity; unusual glazing resistance, quick drying, low shrinkage, no color loss or staining in a wide range of colors, even after repeated washings and high settings of automatic washers.

Arnel fabrics are noted for ease of care; i.e., little or no ironing, durable pleats and textures. Arnel has exceptionally good dimensional stability.

Made in filament or staple fiber form, Arnel is used in many types of wearing apparel, including men's, women's, and childrens' wear. Arnel tricot is very wrinkle-resistant, easy to care for, and has the feel, hand, comfort, opaqueness, durability, and beauty of acetate. The fiber may be blended with all other major textile fibers. Arnel melts at approximately 300° Centigrade or 572° Fahrenheit. Heat-treated Arnel will not stick when ironed at temperatures up to 250° Centigrade or 482° Fahrenheit.

ARNEL PLUS NYLON. Registered trademark of Celanese Corporation of America for its combined yarn which provides aesthetic qualities of Celanese Arnel® plus the processing strength of Celanese Nylon. It is used in untextured tricot outerwear, tricot shirtings, blouses, and shells. Textured types find use in flat bed and circular knits for men's shirtings, woven dresses, and blouses. Bright and semi-dull types are used in warp knits, yarn dyed textured double-knits, and full-fashion knits for women's dresses, sweaters, shells, as well as in men's shirtings.

ARRAIGNEE LACE. One which is featured by spider or cobweb motifs.

ARRAS. 1. Name of city in France which for centuries has been noted for its tapestry work. Arras is so well established today that people no longer use the capital "A" when speaking of an arras or tapestry wall covering; the terms are considered synonymous. 2. Certain French worsteds made in this locality. 3. A white French bobbin lace which resembles Lille lace. Arras lace is compact, strong, and has a straight edge with the mignonette used as the basic pattern.

ARRASENE. A cord of silk, acetate, nylon, rayon, or wool chenille, used for embroidery.

ARREE. Cordage fiber from the bark of the climbing plant mountain ebony, found in the East Indies.

ARRIVALS. Raw-cotton market term which implies that the cotton has yet to arrive. It may be en route, loading in this country, or still on the plantation. Arrivals may be purchased on "description" or "sealed samples."

ARROWHEAD STITCH. A triangle stitch used at the beginning of a pleat. It may be done by stitching or embroidery. It is sometimes used as a feature at ends of slash, slit, or bound pockets.

ARROWHEAD TWILL. English term for herringbone twills.

ARROW-TIE. Old-time term for the hoop-iron tie used to bale cotton.

ARSCOT. A fine Belgian serge made with high-grade woolen yarn; has woven, compact texture.

ARTIFICIAL FIBERS. See FIBER KINGDOMS.

ARTIFICIAL HORSEHAIR. A viscose rayon product made in imitation of the natural product. It consists of a single filament of very heavy denier (300 to 450) and may be round or flat and of any desired length.

ARTIFICIAL LACE. Commercial term for noncombustible lace. Asbestos is woven into the lace but merely as a curiosity, since it has little commercial value.

ARTIFICIAL LEATHER. Drill cloth, sateen, sheeting, and similar cloths treated with nitro-cellulose compounds to imitate real leather. The fabric is often embossed and is extensively used for handbags, luggage covering, upholstery, millinery accessories,

and wherever leather can be used.

ARTIFICIAL SILK. The original name of rayon. It was an imitation of natural silk, obtained chemically by treating cellulose obtained from any source, but usually from wood pulp or cotton linters by various processes: the chief objective was to impregnate the cellulose with nitrogen. See RAYON.

ARTIFICIAL STRAW. A viscose rayon specialty product made by forcing the spinning solution through a rectangular-shaped orifice in the spinneret into a suitable coagulating bath. It consists of a continuous, ribbonlike filament folded during spinning and resembling straw.

ARTIFICIAL WOOL. Broad term for any fibrous material made to simulate natural wool.

ARTILANA. A Swedish modified cellulosic fiber made by Svenska Rayon Company. Characterized by properties closely resembling those of wool, this fiber is greatly used in the wool industry. May be used alone or in blends, has good crease resistance, short drying time, and does not pill. Used chiefly in curtains, furnishing fabrics, and tufted carpets. A German viscose fiber, chemically modified to increase dye affinity is also known by this term.

ARTILLERY TWILL. A name given whipcord and made in a steep twill construction in 63, 70 or 75 degree twill, right hand or left hand. Various twill weaves are used in the weaving from a 3-up and 1-down, and 4-up and 1 or 2 down up to regulation whipcord weaves such as a $\frac{5}{1}\frac{1}{2}\frac{1}{1}$ steep twill weave. The fabric has a pronounced twill line or cord. Has some use in uniform fabric, livery, and in winter coatings for men and women.

ARTISTS' DESIGNS. Skilled artists make printed designs for all types and textures of woven goods. A knowledge of color harmony is very essential since the blending and contrasting of color is an art and a science. The motif may be a simple geometrical figure such as a square or a circle, or it may be very elaborate in that it portrays some historical event, prominent buildings, skylines, animals, birds, pastoral scenes, and a host of other possibilities. All designs must be made to proper size, conformity, and desired color or colors.

ART LINEN. Plain-weave, cylindrical yarn, soft finish. Unbleached or bleached sheeting material may be used. Widely used in needlework, as it is easy to "draw" the yarns.

ART MUSLIN. Dyed or printed fabrics used in the upholstery trade; a

loose term.

ART NEEDLEWORK. A term covering many sorts of decoration made by hand and sundry articles used in the work, such as material, stamped or plain, special yarn or thread, hoops, needles, and so on.

ART SERGE. A 2-up and 2-down woven worsted which is fine in texture, piece-dyed in many suitable colors, and used for draperies, table covers, and general decorative purposes.

ART SQUARE. A small throw-rug of practically any type.

ART TICKING. Covering material, made of cotton, linen, or a mixture of both. The cotton fabric is embellished with pattern designs to enhance appearance of the finished material. Used on medium and better mattresses and pillows.

ASALITUS. The soft under-fleece of Tibetan goats and sheep, used in making the famous shawls of Tibet.

ASAN OR AUSAN. Small, thick, felted prayer rug of India, square or circular, made of white wool often ornamented with appliqué cloth flowers.

ASBESTON. A lightweight, fire-resistant asbestos fabric used to cover ironing boards. Made of lightweight asbestos yarn, the material gives good resistance to wear. Asbeston may be washed by hand and bleached if necessary to remove stains.

ASBESTOS. The most important mineral fiber, without which it would hardly be possible to have the conveniences enjoyed today. It is found in veins of the solid rock formation of the earth's crust. Asbestos is found chiefly in the Province of Quebec; other sources are Ontario, New York, Vermont, Arizona, South Africa, and the Savoy district in Italy. Thetford, Quebec, is the greatest asbestos center in the world. Asbestos is a poor conductor of heat and electricity. It can be used where no other material will serve, and provides greater safety and longer-lived and better products in countless fields of industry. Outstanding properties of the fiber are its ability to withstand high temperatures with little physical alteration, and its noncombustibility and great electrical insulating value, so important to industrial engineering.

ASBESTOS, AMPHIBOLE. Fine fibrous, greenish crystals found in asbestos mining areas throughout the world. Also called Horneblende Asbestos.

ASBESTOS, CARDED FIBERS OF. Fibers received at the plant in a semi-opened condition and there opened, cleaned, and blended with varying percentages of cotton, rayon, or both fibers in consideration of textile end-uses. The fiber blend is then carded into roving and spun into yarn in much the same manner as cotton and wool. Processed materials from the card alone represent products wherein many fibers have been aligned and formed into a more or less compacted mass, but which have not been twisted or formed to entwine the fibers as in a yarn. These products are known and used as carded fibers for chemical filtration purposes, for thermal pack-ings, and for heat-resistant fillers. They are also used as lap for electrical insulation purposes, padding, stuffing, or wipes where thermal endurance is vital. In the roving condition, asbestos is used for electrical insulation on wires and cables.

ASBESTOS CLOTH. Cloth of asbes-tos comes in a wide variance of style, texture, grade, weight, and thickness. The standard width of fabric is 40 inches, although any width can be made for some desired purpose. Asbestos is woven in plain, twill, or herringbone effects and in either metallic or non-metallic construction. The fabric ranges in weight from a few ounces to several pounds per square yard. Thickness varies from .015 inch to .100 inch for single-ply.

Uses of asbestos fabric include the following: conveyor belting; draperies; automobile, airplane, and locomotive equipment; passenger, sleeping, express, mail, and freight car equipment; elec-trical insulation for toasters, broilers, coffee makers, sweepers, fans, refriger-ators, washing machines, etc. It is also used for friction materials, fire blankets, ironing-board covers, jackets for pipe insulation, laminated plastics, packings, safety clothing, welding, and theater curtains.

ASBESTOS CORD. A multi-ply yarn of very uniform diameter and superior tensile strength. It is used extensively as sewing thread, mantle yarn, tying cord, core for wire-wound electrical elements, gaskets and packings, and as a braided wall in the manufacture of steam hose.

ASBESTOS LACE. Name given to lace which has been treated chemically to make it nonflammable.

ASBESTOS PAPER. Fireproof paper made by adding the mineral amianthus to the wood pulp. A very poor con-ductor of heat, it is used to cover heat pipes.

ASBESTOS ROOFING. Roof ma-terial combining the crysolite type of asbestos and cotton or some other organic fiber.

ASBESTOS ROVING. Composition of a mixture of chrysotile asbestos and cotton or other organic fibers. Rein-forced roving is composed of a core of yarn consisting of organic fiber, covered with a mixture of chrysotile asbestos and organic fiber.

ASBESTOS TAPE. Also called list-ing, it comes in the plain or nonmetallic type and in the asbestos-metallic prod-uct which is the wire-inserted variety. Plain tape ranges from .010 inch to .030 inch in thickness, and its great use is in electrical insulating for motor windings. Its low heat conductivity and thermal resistance are important since its property of absorbing a high per-centage of heat is an important asset.

Heavier plain tapes are used in thermal insulation, flameproofing of sheathed cable, and as a component part of gaskets and packings.

Asbestos metallic tape is used where service conditions require a high ten-sile strength or a high coefficient of friction. Where excessively high tem-peratures are encountered, woven tape is reinforced with special alloy wire. Much of this finds use in the fabrica-tion of woven brake lining and clutch facing. Oil burner wicking and conveyor belting are two other major uses of this tape.

ASBETOS TUBING. It is woven or braided, and is used chiefly as a flex-ible sleeving for insulating electrical conductors, and as a jacket for high temperature packing. Woven asbestos tubing is used as flexible heat ducts and as the filtration medium in dust collectors.

ASBESTOS YARN. It is used as a basic component in the manufacture of cord, tubing, tape, and fabrics for innumerable applications. Asbestos yarn, which is made by spinning the roving, is used principally in weaving and braiding where thermal resistance, electrical insulating properties, fire protection, and durability are necessary engineering requirements of the textile product.

ASCLEPIAS COTTON. The soft, lus-trous fibers of the milkweed pod used mainly as stuffing. This American plant varies from ¼ inch to 1 inch in length, and is yellowish-white in color. The plant yields a bast fiber which is fine, glossy, and long, comparable with hemp in durability.

ASCOT. A cravat tied in the form of a four-in-hand from a long scarf. There are two types: 1. A scarf doubled and then tied whereby the ends appear horizontally on the sides of the knot and then cross diagonally. Held together by a scarf pin. This form is popular

formal wear for bridegrooms and other males at weddings. 2. A double scarf looped loosely and informally around the neck. Much used in sports wear and with informal jackets. The term originated at the Ascot race track, Berkshire, England, one of the world's most renowned courses.

ASH. 1. Total residue after ignition of the nonmineral constituents. 2. The noncellulose material that remains after the chemical treatment of dissolving wood pulp.

ASHMARA JUTE. A rather weak jute fiber found in India.

ASHMOUNI COTTON. See EGYP-TIAN COTTON.

ASIATIC SILKS. Broad term for the silk from China, Japan, India, and ad-jacent areas in the Far East.

ASKANYA RAMBOUILLET. A Russian breed which possesses the best qualities of American and Russian Rambouillet sheep. Fleece weight is about 15 pounds while the staple runs from 3 to 7 inches.

ASONKOBI. Wild silk, a product of empty cocoons obtained from many species in West Africa.

ASPERO. Native Peruvian cotton popular in British mills, and known as full rough Peruvian.

ASSAM. A harsh, white short-staple East Indian cotton used in English and Indian mills.

ASSAMA SILK. Indian silk taken from the large cocoons of the *Anthe-rea Assama* types.

ASSEMBLE. A plied spun silk yarn made in France.

ASSILI COTTON. A strong Egyptian staple given this name since it means thoroughbred. Tensile strength of yarn made from the cotton is very high.

ASSISTANT. Any substance added to a dye bath to help fix the dyestuff or mordant, or to aid in leveling shades and in exhausting a dye bath.

ASSORTER. In the garment indus-try, one who assorts garments and trimmings, after cutting. Garment sec-tions to make up a complete unit are assembled together and tied in a bundle. Each size is separate and the variation in color and shades of color must be matched perfectly, and separated if not matching well; keenness of eye-sight is important in this work.

ASSOUPLISSAGE. French for proc-ess by which souple silk is produced; removal of gum to give the silk mellow-ness or suppleness.

ASTARTE. Good quality twill-woven dressgoods fabric made in

France, printed with bold patterns in brilliant colors. Usually made of silk.

ASTICOTINE. French cloth of lightweight type but heavily fulled; has elasticity and stretch in both directions. Piece-dyed and used in women's wear dressgoods.

A.S.T.M. (AMERICAN SOCIETY FOR TESTING AND MATERIALS). This organization, national in scope, sets up standards for textiles and other merchandise. The A.S.T.M. Committee D-13 on textile materials covers specifications, tolerances, methods of testing, definitions and terms. A.S.T.M., 1916 Race St., Philadelphia 3, Pa., issues an annual publication each October.

ASTRAKHAN. 1. Luxuriant fur used in coatings, cloaks, and for a trimming for collar and cuff sets. Curly, wavy, and often having a tufted surface, the most popular shade of astrakhan is brown. It is secured from young lambs in the Astrakhan section of Russia and is much imitated in the trade. 2. Astrakhan fabric is woven cloth made of wool on a pile weave construction to assure curliness after the threads are cut; durable and gives warmth. Knitted astrakhan is a cheap imitation of the cloth and fur, thereby making it possible for a greater number of people to own "an Astrakhan coat."

Mohair warp adds luster and curl to the surface of the material, improvements which are brought about by steaming the mohair under tension while it is on the spindles. Astrakhan is rather becoming to the stout and can be worn by young or old. The name is spelled in a variety of ways.

ASTRAKHAN CLOTH. A term misused to describe a heavy deep-pile fabric with curled loops that resemble caracul fur. True astrakhan is a grade of caracul lambskin.

ASTRALENE-C. British false-twist textured stretch polyester yarn used in woven and knitted fabrics. Product of Cheslene & Crepes, Ltd., Macclesfield, England.

ASTRALON-C. British false-twist textured stretch nylon yarn used in woven and knitted materials. Product of Cheslene & Crepes, Ltd., Macclesfield, England.

ASTROCARB. The line of carbon fabrics produced by J.P. Stevens & Co., Inc., New York City. Made from heavy denier rayon yarn, the fabric is used for airplane nose cones, space shields, filters and comparable products. The carbonization is applied to either the yarn or the fabric and consists of a heat process varied according to specifications for heat resistance and tensile strength.

ASTROQUARTZ FABRIC. A quartz fiber product made from high purity quartz crystals. Because of its high temperature resistance (up to $2,000°F$) and its electrical properties, this product makes an outstanding reinforcement for high temperature and ablative space and missile applications. A laminate of this fabric was used in the nozzle of the descent engine of the Lunar Module of Apollo 11 and Apollo12; Apollo 11 (Aldrin-Armstrong-Collins) on July 20, 1969, and Apollo 12(Bean-Conrad-Gordon) November 19, 1969.

"ASTROSPHERE". To date, the largest dual-walled air inflatable structure ever built, it is made of "Dacron" polyester coated with neoprene and "Hypalon" synthetic rubber. Designing, engineering and construction was done under the aegis of Air Inflatable Products Company, Inc., East Haven, Connecticut. The name "Astrosphere" was coined by the sponsor of the product, American Airlines. This structure is large enough to house the entire passenger compartment of an Astrojet. The structure is 100 feet in diameter and 45 feet high and is divided into sections of 900 pounds each with a total weight of 7,200 pounds. Space between the double walls ranges from 46 to 52 inches and is filled with approximately 7,200 cubic feet. A water ballast which weighs 68,000 pounds serves as the "anchor."

ASTRO-TURF. A dense green turf which consists of ⅜ inch-long blades of nylon which stands on a ¼ inch elastomeric base. This portable turf is assembled from strips fourteen feet wide held together by concealed heavy duty zippers.

The first major league baseball team to use Astro-Turf was the Houston Astros of the National League who play in the famous Astrodome which irrespective of weather conditions outside, can accomodate a sporting event any day in the year.

The outfield and the trim areas of the field in Houston contain 2½ acres of grass. There is one continuous zipper which measures 227 feet in length, believed to be the longest in the world. Spring devices for the infield, outline, and foul line grass areas stretch taut the 12,000 square yards of turf over its soil underlayer.

The turf is resistant to abrasion, even by the spiked shoes of the athletes, fire, sunlight, and water. Even if damaged, the damaged portion can be removed and replaced with a permanent, undetectable patch or plug in minutes. Dust and litter can be swept away, hosed-off, or vacuumed. Most stains wash off with water and detergent; drycleaning solutions will remove any residue. Astro-Turf is a registered trademark of Monsanto Textiles Division, Monsanto Company, Inc., New York City. See Tartan All-weather Surface.

ATELIERS. Workshops of French designers where their ideas are translated into fashion.

ATHENS. Stiff silk goods known in Greece since the sixth century; materials are comparable with present-day taffeta.

ATLANTIC STATES COTTON. A variety of American cotton which changes color more rapidly when left in the field than does Western cotton. The staple takes on a bluish cast and may be spotted or tinged if raised in red-clay soil—conditions caused, no doubt, by greater rainfall in the Seaboard States than in the Western and Southwestern cotton belts.

ATLAS, ATLAS TRICOT. Usually a cotton fabric used extensively in the manufacture of gloves. It has a distinctive crosswise-striped appearance on the back, the stripes varying from ¾ inch to 1 inch in width. The bands are produced by the direction of the path of the yarn, not by any variation of construction or texture. There are two sets of warp ends that move in opposite directions, and after a specific number of courses have been knitted, the sets reverse. It is this change that occasions the crosswise stripes.

ATLAS ELECTRIC DEVICES COMPANY. One of the foremost manufacturers of textile testing equipment, this company produces the following:

AATCC Accelerotor: Instrument for quick determination of abrasion and wear characteristics of textiles and other flexible materials.

AATCC Crockmeter: Manual and motorized versions provide standard motion and pressure to determine colorfastness to crocking plus various other rubbing tests.

AATCC Launder-ometer: Controlled temperature and motion provide for washfastness, dyeing, drycleaning, detergency plus various other testing programs.

AATCC Perspiration Tester: Used to test dyestuff colorfastness of perspiration and water as well as dye migration in packaging materials. A multiple sample rack maintains constant pressure at all times.

Dynamic Absorption Tester: A motorized tumble jar, 12 inches deep and 6 inches in diameter, for use in AATCC, ASTM, and Federal Specifications. The built-in timer in the tester provides an automatic shutdown.

Fabric Streak Analyzer: Used to delineate between fabric imperfections in construction and streaking caused in dyeing and finishing.

Laundry Wringer and Padder: A motorized unit for extraction of liquids from test samples at constant speed and under variable controlled pressure.

Outdoor Exposure Cabinet Model DE-1: An exposure cabinet where samples are protected from external moisture. Dimensions are 32½″ x 30″ x 7″, height of 62″ with glass 24′ by 28″ with exposure area one inch or three inches from the glass pane construction.

Random Tumble Pilling Tester: 2, 4, or 6 chamber units to determine pilling and fuzzing characteristics of all types of textile fabrics.

Scorch Tester: Controlled conditions of temperature and pressure meet requirements for sublimation, retained chlorine plus dry or wet hot pressing tests.

ATLAS SILK. Wild silk from the very large moth *Attacus Atlas.* Found in India. Also called Ailanthus silk.

ATMOSPHERE, STANDARD. Air kept at relative humidity of 65 per cent and a temperature of 70° F.

ATMOSPHERIC FADING. Also known as Gas Fading or Fume Fading, it is the change of shade shown by some dyes when exposed to certain gases, especially oxides of nitrogen, given off during the burning of fuels. Inhibitors are used to counteract the action, and resistant dyes are also used.

ATOM. The smallest part of an element that can enter into the composition of a molecule. It is not a part of a chemical compound. A compound must have at least two atoms.

ATOMIC WEIGHT. A number which indicates the relative weight of any element when compared with oxygen which is 16.

ATTACUS ATLAS, ATTACUS RICINI. Tussah silks produced in Asia. There are some good grades of these stocks which are white in color and known as Eria silk.

Atlas moths are the largest known and produce Tagore or Ailanthus silk. Their silkworms feed on leaves of the castor-oil plant.

It is worthy of note, in speaking of wild silk, that the term Tussah silk has been, and still is, applied in some circles to the meaning above. The term is easier to say than some of the longer names given to some wild silks, hence, its use in a general way.

All wild silks are more difficult to unwind than true silks. The filament is much coarser but has greater strength. Wild silk has the lowest boil-off percentage of sericin or silk gum and consequently will give a larger yield when compared with Bombyx Mori.

Wild silks give trouble in dyeing, for solid shades, and bleaching must be done with the utmost care. Wild silk materials, when washed, show a creamy white color, a good test to use for comparison with true silk cloths. Because these Tussah silks are so coarse, the yarn made from them is used as filling rather than for warp.

ATTALIA. Twilled cotton fabric used in India.

ATTENUATION. To diminish the diameter, as in the case of a group of fibers when they are drafted and drawn among themselves to make a smaller size roping form. In machine manipulation of fibers the stock is made into sliver form and then attenuated into slubbing, roving, and yarn.

A-TYPE MERINO. A domestic classification for a variety of the Merino breed of sheep; characterized by the great number and size of the folds of wool on the neck and the body of the animal.

Fiber staple is 1½ to 2 inches; because of the great skin surface the yield has a high percentage of unscoured wool in its body weight. The fleece is not too uniform, however, and shrinkage runs from 65 to 70 per cent, which is very high. See Illustrated Section.

AUBURN. Low in saturation and brilliance, it is a reddish brown color, red-yellow in hue.

AUBUSSON. A fine pile carpet made to imitate the tapestries of that name made at the Royal French factory at Aubusson, France. Aubusson is now made in several world carpet centers. It is made in one piece and the designs show traces of the technique of famous East Indian needleworkers and weavers. This carpet commands a high price. Aubusson was popular in the eighteenth-century life of the French salon.

AUCTIONS, WOOL. Process for selling wool to highest bidder; practically all wool sold outside the United States is sold by auction.

AUDEMARS, GEORGE. Man who

in 1855 at Lausanne, Switzerland, used the extract obtained from alcohol and ether to bring about a combination of collodion and rubber. The mixing of mulberry bast with this extract made the fact known that a filament was possible through a process of coagulation. His efforts left food for thought for future scientists, who, in time, used his findings for further experimentation and discovery.

AUDREY PETERKIN COTTON. A black-seed American cotton which produces medium-sized bolls which are not of the cluster variety and not early-maturing. Staple ranges from 15/16 inch to 1 inch; lint is about 35 per cent. Considered as one of the best of the Rio Grande cottons, it is also known as Brazier Peterkin, Crossland, Peterkin, Texas Wood, and Wise.

AUGSBURG CHECKS. Fine-check ginghams made in Germany and this country; used in the export trade.

AUNE. Old-time measuring unit for silk; measured 45 inches or 1¼ yards.

AURANG-SHAKI. Means throne and implies a rich, East Indian silk fabric used as a silk covering for the throne of a Hindu king.

AUREOLE. The line or ring which appears round a cleaned spot on a fabric.

AURILLAC. Old plaited and coarse bobbin laces of sixteenth-century production in the French town of this name.

AUSTRALIAN BALE MARKINGS, NEW. These were adopted in February, 1958, and provide for 28 classifications in medium or large clips, and 20 for smaller clips. Classifications include "AAA M" for the best and finest of merino clips, with "AA M" and "A M" being the second and third, respectively. A comeback or crossbred clip will drop the "M" for merino and will be marked "AAA" or "AAA CBK" for identification.

AUSTRALIAN MERINO. A very high grade, distinctive breed developed from several various strains. Australia, since the days of the famous Captain MacArthur who was the "Father of the Sheep Industry" in Australia 170 years ago, has constantly improved the quality of its wool.

Sheep in this class are large in stature, thrive well in large flocks, and have the stamina to withstand drought and dry vegetation better than other breeds. The fleece is very dense and averages 8 to 10 pounds in weight. Staple length is 2½ to 4 inches. This high-quality stock can spin from 60s to 90s counts.

AUSTRALIAN WOOL, STATISTICS AND DATA ON. Annual Australian wool clippage is valued at more than 200 million dollars. This leading wool country of the world has one sixth of the sheep of the universe and produces one fourth of the world's wool. The industry is valued at about 4 billion dollars, with an annual production of about 800 million pounds. An Australian bale weighs approximately 300 pounds. About 85 per cent of this wool is merino, the highest, finest, and best in quality, which amounts to about 60 per cent of world clippage for this grade. Approximately 75 per cent of this amount is for the export trade. The balance of the Australian clip is from carpet grade to half-blood.

Originally, Negretti Merino of Germany and Rambouillet Merino of France were used with Border Leicester, English Leicester, Corriedale, Polwarth and Downs to build up the crossbred trade.

To this gigantic industry the largest Merino stud in the world is attached. It is located in New South Wales, covers 500,000 acres, and has a maximum grazing capacity for 120,000 sheep. To this blooded flock are related 80 per cent of Australia's 700 registered Merino studs. Every year about 12,000 Merino bucks are sold to stud masters and wool growers.

In 1926 the famous Merino buck, David, was sold for $21,000.

There are 11 auction selling centers and 33 selling brokers, representing 55 selling units and serving over 100,000 wool growers. The wool auctions are held at specified times. Catalogues are issued to buyer and grower. After the values have been assessed independently by buyer and broker, the sale begins in the Wool Exchange at a fixed time, usually at 3 P.M. Ten lots a minute are sold by the auctioneer and in three hours no less than 12,000 bales may change hands. Buyers settle in cash within 14 days, when the growers immediately receive an account of the sales effected and the payment therefor. In this way, wool valued at 170 million dollars and divided into 848 varying types to meet the demands is sold through the regulated auction system.

Buyers come to the auctions from all over the world and 90 per cent of the shorn wool is sold at auction. The rest is shipped to London for sale. The 11 selling centers are: Adelaide, Albany, Ballarat, Brisbane, Geelong, Hobart, Launceton, Melbourne, Newcastle, Perth, and Sydney.

The leading Australian wools come from the Botany Bay and Port Philip areas; these two types are the best wools in the world. Wool from New Zealand and Tasmania is classed with Australian. Australian fleeces are divided into the following units:

GREASE WOOL:
Merino fleece
Merino broken
Merino pieces
Merino bellies
Merino locks
Merino lambs
Comeback or 1/2-blood fleece
Comeback or 1/2-blood lambs
Crossbred fleece
Crossbred lambs

SCOURED WOOL:
Merino fleeces
Merino pieces
Merino lambs

AUSTRALIAN WOOL BALE. A "woolpack" which measures 4 feet, 6 inches by 2 feet, 3 inches when filled with wool over the minimum weight of 250 pounds for merino wool. Other minimum weights include 225 pounds for other sheep breeds, 200 pounds for lambs, 150 pounds for scoured and super lambs.

AUSTRIA. 1. Lacemakers of Austria, skilled in bobbin lace, Brussels, and crochet lacework. 2. Loose term applied to silk weavers about one hundred and fifty years ago. At that time about a thousand looms in Vienna were on silk woven goods, many of the looms being manned by Austrians and Italians who came to Vienna and taught the Austrians the art and science of silk weaving.

AUSTRIAN SHADE CLOTH. A crinkled material that has wider stripes than those seen in ordinary seersucker. Varying in color scheme, the fabric is used in bedspreads, counterpanes, and curtains. It has considerable use for shades in hotels and stores.

AUTOGENOUS BONDING. There are two methods used in the manufacture of nonwoven fabrics: 1. Bonding by means of chemically activating the surface of the fibers to an adhesive state. 2. Activating the surface of thermoplastic fibers through the application of heat.

A means of compressing the fibers so activated is necessary in both methods. In the chemical application, one method would be to pass the fiber bats through a sulphuric acid bath of proper concentration and temperature, followed by compressing with a calender, washing, and drying. In heat bonding, it is possible to use various thermoplastic fibers produced at present. The unification is accomplished with heat and pressure.

AUTOCLAVE. A large sealed chamber which, under pressure, has been filled with steam; both pressure and steam are controlled electrically. Purpose is to stabilize false twist in textured yarn. Used in manufacture of manmade yarns.

AUTOMATIC CLEANER. Machine for blowing off the lint and other particles that gather around frames, particularly spinning frames. The blower travels on an overhead track near the creel tops.

AUTOMATIC DISTRIBUTOR. Any mechanical device or mechanism used to convey cotton from one point to another in manipulation. Conveyor belts, latticed aprons, or rakes are used to move the stock from place to place.

AUTOMATIC FEEDER. A machine, device or mechanism used to keep pace automatically with the required amount of cotton necessary to supply the ensuing machine. Called also cotton feeder.

AUTOMATIC LACING MACHINE. A machine that automatically laces sets of Jacquard cards into an endless chain ready for placing in the loom.

AUTOMATIC SPOOLER. A high-speed machine used to wind yarn into a cheese. The end of the yarn on a full cheese is knotted with the yarn from a fresh bobbin so that the winding may be continuous.

AUTOMATIC SLIP-COVER FABRIC. A strong, tough, medium-weight cotton, either stock- or yarn-dyed. Saran, Velon, and kindred textile or plastic materials are also used.

AUTOMOBILE TIRE CLOTH. A rugged, heavy, durable fabric made from 9/23s, 10/23s, or 11/23s yarn. Square textures of about 24 x 24 are used. The tensile strength is generally the same in both directions. Made of cable warp yarn of long staple cotton, it has a single filling yarn of ordinary grade stock. Classed as a cord fabric which, incidentally, is always made from cabled yarn.

AUXILIARY LOOM MOTIONS. The let-off, take-up, and filling-fork or stop motion, all of which synchronize with the three major loom actions of shedding, picking, and beating-up.

AUXILIARY SHAFT. This can be attached to a loom to carry shedding cams when more are needed than would be the case in weaving only plain-weave materials.

AVA COTTON. Indian cotton of fair staple and working properties; much of it is used in British mills.

AVAILABILITY, CHEMICAL. Obtainable, in a chemical sense. Available chlorine or available alkali means these materials as found in uncombined form, not linked or tied, so that they will perform the chemical work at hand. It is possible to have both chlorine and alkali present in a solution in such form that they will do no work chemically.

AVCOSET. Trade-mark of the American Viscose Corporation for a chemical stabilization process applied to rayon fabrics by which progressive shrinkage is controlled for the duration of the life of the fabric. The process is licensed to finishers, and to qualify for identification fabrics must pass standard tests for less than 2 per cent residual shrinkage in apparel fabrics and less than 3 per cent in other fabrics.

AVERAGE ENDS, AVERAGE SLEY. 1. The number of ends per inch in a woven fabric, often called sley. 2. The average ends and picks in dimity and other corded-check effects.

AVERAGE PRICE. The price of some specified size of children's stockings, usually size 7. This price is used as a base to which is added, or from which is subtracted, a certain amount to give the price for any other size desired. This is spoken of as "the rise and fall." For example, "On 7 rise 7, fall 5" means that for each half-size above a 7, seven cents is added to the price of Size 7, while for each half-size below a 7, five cents is deducted from Size 7's price.

AVERAGE STIFFNESS. The ability of a fiber to carry a load without deformation, the property of which is based on the modulus of elasticity.

AVERAGE SHIRTING. An expensive cotton shirting made solely from Sea Island cotton; a zigzag fancy stripe running in the warp direction is a feature of the fabric.

AVIATOR STYLE. A waist-length jacket with slanting closure running from center front upward to the right shoulder. The notched collar is convertible, forming lapels when open.

AVICOLOR. Trade-mark of the American Viscose Corporation for its spun-dyed rayon and acetate yarns and fibers, as well as fabrics made thereof. Formerly called Colorspun.

AVICRON. Crimp filament rayon produced by the American Viscose Corporation.

AVIGNON. Lightweight lining fabric made of silk taffeta.

AVILA. Spanish wool from the province of this name.

AVISCO. Trade-mark for the products of the American Viscose Corporation including rayon and acetate yarns, staples, tow, and Vinyon resin yarn and staples.

AVISCO ACETATE, TYPE 25. A cellulose acetate filament yarn modified to give significantly greater bulk in yarn and fabric than regular acetate. Trade-mark of the American Viscose Corporation, New York City.

AVISCO V-22. An intermediate tenacity rayon staple which produces yarns of greater strength than regular rayon. Used for apparel, in the home, and in industry, it is a product of the American Viscose Corporation.

AVISCO XL-1. Trade-mark name of the American Viscose Corporation's high tenacity, high elongation rayon staple fiber for industrial uses.

AVISTRAP. Made from super strength Avisco rayon, it has many applications where steel strapping is required. Many times stronger than reinforced tapes, it actually outperforms steel in extensibility and impact resistance. This economical cord reduces damage, makes for fast, easy handling, has no sharp edges and does not lash out with jagged ends. There is no disposal hazard with this product of the American Viscose Corporation.

AVIVAGE. The after-treatment of desulphurized and rinsed rayon yarns in order to give a soft hand to the stock.

AVLIN. Trade-mark of the American Viscose Corporation for its cellulosic fiber that owes its properties to a special type of spinning technique wherein the yarns are flattened, giving them a triangular rather than a round cross-section. The fiber has a linenlike appearance and is used in men's, women's, and childrens' wear fabrics.

AVONET. Persian rug wool from sheep that are about three years old.

AVRIL. Formerly known as Fiber 40, this product of the American Viscose Corporation is a rayon filament yarn that is used in wash-and-wear fabrics alone or in blends. It is a modified cellulosic staple fiber with high wet modulus and low extensibility.

AVRON. Formerly called Avisco XL, made by the American Viscose Corporation, the term is used to identify fabrics which are blends of cotton and Avron, a high strength rayon staple that is 70 per cent strong when wet, and 40 per cent stronger when dry, in the conditioned state, than conventional rayons. The fiber is compatible with acrylic, modacrylic, and polyester fibers

for blends and is ideal in the lighter-weight, minimum care fabrics. Cotron, also an American Viscose Corporation fabric, is the trade name for fabrics made from blends of cotton and regular rayon staple stock.

AWASAI. An ideal carpet wool from Mesopotamia, very popular among carpet manufacturers in America.

AWASSI KARADI. Popular wool raised in Persia (Iran), ideal for use in the manufacture of carpets and rugs. Great amounts of the wool are shipped to the United States. The staple is short, strong, resilient, and its great use is filler stock in carpeting.

AWNING CLOTH. Durable, stout duck or canvas which comes in all commercial widths for awnings, shelter tents, and large umbrellas. About one half of the output is made with bright, colorfast, wide stripes; the remainder comes in printed stripe effects.

AXLINE TESTER. An apparatus used to test elastic fabrics. It is designed to stretch repeatedly an elastic fabric to its extreme elongation, and at that point allow a weight to act on the specimen to give it additional stretching force, the amount of which can be varied to suit the material under test. The action closely simulates the conditions to which a foundation garment is subjected in ordinary wear.

AXMINSTER. Carpet which takes its name from the original seat of its manufacture, Axminster, Devonshire, England. In 1775, it was made with a series of finger-tufted loops to simulate the rugs and carpets of India and Persia. Handmade eighteenth-century Axminster somewhat rivaled the work done on the oriental looms in beauty, durability, and color. Because of the cost of manufacture, however, and with the introduction of the cheaper Brussels carpet which caused the demand for Axminster to dwindle what was left of the original Axminster industry had moved to Wilton, England, by 1835. Axminster is a very low-price carpet in today's market.

AYLESHAM FABRIC. Fine linens made in and around this town in Norfolk County, England.

AZLON. A manufactured fiber in which the fiber-foming substance is composed of any regenerated naturally occurring proteins. Not manufactured in the United States at present. Formerly known as "semi-synthetic" fiber. This fiber is not, at present, manufactured in the United States. Aralac and Vicara, now defunct and obsolete, were made in this country but production ceased in 1948 and 1958 respectively. Azlon fibers are made in the following countries: Alginate, from seaweed, England. Casein fiber, from casein, Holland. Lanital, from casein, Belgium. Merinova, from skim milk, Italy.

AZO COLORS. Artificial dyestuffs, insoluble in water and developed directly on the fiber. Much used in dyeing cottons.

AZOIC DYES. Colors which are placed on fibers by an insoluble pigment by diazotizing and coupling. Diazotizing is the treatment of dyed material by a solution of nitrous acid obtained by adding sulphuric acid to sodium nitrate. Frequently called Naphthol AS Dyes, taken from the name of the first products used to make these dyes. Second only to vat dyes in importance, they have excellent fastness to chlorine, light, peroxide bleaching, and washing.

AZOTON. "Azote," the French for nitrogen, and "cotton" have been combined and modified to make this word, coined for cyanoethylated cotton products, a development of the Institute of Textile Technology, Charlottesville, Virginia. In fiber, yarn, or fabric forms, Azoton is made by the reaction of ordinary cotton with acrylonitrile, a chemical compound. The procedure brings about a new fiber material which resembles cotton but possesses many improved characteristics.

B

° Bé. Abbreviation for degrees on the Baumé Hydrometer.

BABCI. A white sisal fiber from Yucatan.

BABUL. See ACACIA.

BABY CALF. A calf skin leather obtained from small, lightweight skins with a smooth or finely boarded grain surface devoid of any semblance of an artificial motif.

BABY COMBING WOOL. Fine, choice wool fiber which ranges from 1½ inches to 2½ inches in staple length. The French method of combing is used to make high-grade worsted yarn from the stock.

BABY DELAINE. See DELAINE WOOL.

BABY FLANNEL. A plain-weave, bleached, lightweight, soft woolen cloth used in children's underwear and garments. The nap on the cloth is variable as to length, thickness, and wear, dependent on the texture and the quality of the stock used. The predominant colors are pink and blue.

BABY IRISH. A fine, flat, narrow Irish crochet lace.

BABY LACE. An all-inclusive term for any dainty, narrow lace used on infants' and children's clothes.

BABY SHARKSKIN. A shirting fabric which is cool, smooth, and soft to the touch; made in miniature cross-weave with combed cotton yarn.

BACK. The underside of cloth as it is being woven in the loom; in silk weaving, however, the fabric is usually woven face-down.

BACKBONE LINE. The line noted along the backbone of some animals, distinct in color and texture from the rest of the pelt. Observed in chipmunk, mink, skunk, etc. Simulated effect noted in fake fur fabrics.

BACK CENTER. Term used in weaving to imply the farthest point reached in the backward motion of the lay of the loom.

BACK CHROMING. An after-treatment given to cloth by the use of a chrome mordant following dyeing. Often used on logwood blacks.

BACK CLOTH. See BACK GRAY CLOTH.

BACK DRAFT. Increased air pressure set up in a dust chimney or chute to force more air through the passage.

BACKED FABRICS. Cloths made with three sets of threads—one warp and two fillings, or two warps and one filling. The former is known as a filling backed fabric; the latter, a warp backed fabric. The extra warp or filling adds weight to the cloth, gives greater warmth, and helps to cover up the spaces between the interlacings of the warp and filling threads. Cloths of this type have a wide range of design and variety. Backed fabrics are used for coating, suitings, vestings, trouserings, novelties, fancies, blankets, decorative cloths, and Frenchbacks. Much of the material is relatively low in price.

BACKED FILLING. Any fabric whose filling has been heavily sized. Examples are bookbinder fabric, shade cloth, certain muslins, and buckram.

BACK-FILLED. Heavily sized, as cotton with clay, starch, or other agents, to fill up the interstices among the interlacings of warp and filling yarns. It is much used for artists' canvas, bookbinder, shade, and sign painters' cloth.

BACK FILLING. An extra filling woven into a cloth to add weight, strength, warmth, or to define a pattern such as in pique, Marseilles quilting, Frenchback, overcoating.

BACK-FILLING FINISH. Usually applied to low-quality fabrics to give an improved effect or finish. Only one side of the material is given the treatment which may be applied from any of several fillers used in the trade—China clay, cornstarch, starch, talc, tallow, etc.

The mixture, heavy and thick, is applied by a mangle. In the filling of dyed goods, the compound is colored so that it will match the shade of the cloth. Care must be taken not to allow the filler to come to the face of the material. It is advantageous to calender the fabric prior to starching, since this will press the threads closer together, and at the same time flatten them enough to help prevent the filler from coming to the face of the material.

BACK FRAME. That side of the fly frame on which the bobbins, from which roving is drawn into the machine, are held.

BACK GRAY CLOTH. A plain cotton fabric which lies between the rubber blanket and the cloth to be printed on a printing machine. The function of this cloth is to absorb excess dyestuff that penetrates through the material as it is being printed.

BACKING. General term for any system of yarn which interlaces on the back of a textile material. Found on Frenchbacks, some manipulated fabrics, mackinac, ski cloth, and others.

BACKING CLOTH. Broad term for fabric used as base or back fabric in making textile materials. Cotton or jute is used as backing in the manufacture of linoleum and oilcloth, rugs, carpets. The term also signifies gray goods fabric, usually a print cloth, used to absorb surplus dyes and to reinforce fabric on the printing machine.

BACKING-OFF. Spinning term for the uncoiling of slack yarn from the spindle on the mule, between the spinning and winding-on periods. The yarn, which extends from the spindle by the reversal of the spindle, is unwound and carried by the winding faller into correct position for winding on the cop.

BACKING YARN. 1. In a pile fabric it means that the base yarn holds the pile yarn in place; formed by the stuffer yarn and the warp and filling yarn in the fabric. 2. Used on the face of fabric in the plating of hosiery, usually of the lower quality.

BACK LEATHER. Leather from hide first cut longitudinally along the backbone, head and the belly then cut off.

BACK LINING, HALF. One that begins at the shoulders and ends half-way down the back of a jacket or coat. The bottom of the lining is not tacked to the garment. The purpose of this lining is to keep the garment from stretching and also to guard against perspiration.

BACK PLATE. The curved metal plate which sets over the area occupied by the cylinder and licker-in rollers of the cotton card where they are close to each other. The function of the plate is to stifle possible air currents caused by fast action of the cylinder.

BACK RAIL. British term for the back rest of a loom.

BACK REST. Also called the slip roll or whip roll, it is set above the warp beam on a loom. The warp ends pass over the back rest and then proceed to the lease rods, to harnesses and heddles, on to the reed.

BACK SEAMS. A carpeting term which means that all carpet seams are found on the back of the carpet when the carpet is turned over or face-down. Those seams made when the carpet is face-up are known as face seams.

BACKSTITCH. One of the basic stitches, second in importance in the art of sewing. The stitch is made by inserting the needle about ⅛ inch in back of the end of the previous stitch and bringing it out about ⅛ inch beyond the end. This makes the under-stitch twice as long as the top stitch. It is used for firmness in plain sewing and is also applied in embroidery.

BACKSTITCH EMBROIDERY. A simple form of embroidery in which the motif is traced on the material and the lines are then followed with back-stitch.

BACK TWISTING. Twisting a single or ply yarn in the reverse direction to the one previously set.

BACK WARP. The warp which in double, triple, or quadruple fabrics actually form the back of the goods along with the back filling.

BACKWASHING. Removing oil which has been put into worsted stock in the blending, oiling-and-mixing operations when the mix was made up. The fibers are washed in an emulsion and then treated with a weak acetic acid bath and warm water to complete the scouring. This is done as the oil put in during the auxiliary processes is no longer needed for the smooth running of the stock through the machines, which follows backwashing. Final rinsing completes the scouring of the fibers, and they are then dried.

BACKWIND. Unraveling knitted fabric and then winding the yarn for future use.

BACKWINDING. 1. Rewinding yarn from a package of some sort. 2. Winding yarn as it comes raveled from knitted fabric.

BACTRIAN CAMEL. A kind of camel with two humps. See CAMEL.

BACTRIAN WOOL. Long, irregular hairy fibers obtained from camels. Mixed with cotton and wool, it is made into lining fabric for outerwear garments.

BAD. Ancient Egyptian linen fabric used by high priests; mentioned in the Bible.

BAD CASTS. A raw silk term to signify a thread with thick, irregular places in it caused by the cocoon filament not being properly attached to the thread. Bad casts are also caused by two or more filaments that are combined or joined in the thread.

BAD COVER. A defect caused by setting the warp too wide in the loom for the thickness of the yarn or by faulty weaving.

BADEN. Well-known European linen material, made in Baden, Germany, of plain weave.

BAD HAND, POOR HAND. The opposite of good, pleasing, attractive hand or feel when the fabric is handled for this effect or sensation.

BADLY BRED. Term describing wool which is thin, straggly, kempy, and generally irregular in quality.

BAD START-UP, SET-MARK. Blemishes caused by older types of looms on which, when filling became exhausted, the weaver had "to find the pick" before weaving could continue. Modern looms with battery and feeler motions are immune to these blemishes; however, in weaving filament yarn, and sometimes spun rayon, set-marks are made by the sudden and rather violent stoppage of the loom because of a severe breaking action. The shock of violent stoppage will often stretch rayon, which when once in that condition will remain so. This will rarely happen when weaving cotton, woolen, or worsted fabrics. Bad start-up may be caused by faulty beginning when the loom is put in motion. Other causes included incorrect drawing-in or reeding-in, ends out, rolling selvage, too much moisture in the weave shed, faulty picker sticks, etc.

BAER STAPLER. The mechanism which contains a single bank of combs used in close measuring in cotton staple determination.

BAFF. A plain-woven, English cotton fabric used for shrouds and loincloths; shipped to Africa and China.

BAFT RIBBON. Flat tape sometimes made from a series of threads which have been glued together to form the tape.

BAFTS, BAFTA, BAFTAH, BAFFETA. Iranian term meaning woven. Narrow gray goods about 27 inches wide and 27 yards long. Texture is about 64 x 60; cotton yarn counts range from 18s to 24s. The cloth is heavily sized and is now shipped in gray or finished state to Indian and African markets.

BAG. Small lot or sack of wool with a tare of about three pounds.

BAGASSÉ. The residue following extraction of the fiber from abaca, istle, sisal, and other fiber plants. The term also implies the crushed, juiceless sugar cane as it comes from the mill.

BAGDAD WOOL. Dark carpet wool from Mesopotamia; much used in this country.

BAGGING. 1. Loosely woven jute fabric used for covering cotton bales. 2. Cotton fabric, varying in texture and weight, used for bags and containers. 3. Broad term for any type of bag for industrial use. 4. The loading of fully assembled sweaters or sweater-strips into net bags prior to dyeing in overhead paddle machines.

BAGGY FABRIC. A loose place in a cloth which gives the appearance of a bag or pocket. Some double plain cloths show this effect because of the manner of construction; where the face and back of the cloth do not interchange there is the tendency for this pocket to appear.

BAGHEERA. One of the finest types of velvet. It is uncut and dyed in the piece, and has a roughish texture which makes it particularly crush-resistant. Used for gowns and evening wraps.

BAG LEATHER. Refers to leather used for traveling bags, suitcases, and straps. Called also case leather.

BAGS. 1. English term for tubular fabric made on the double plain-weave. 2. Loose-fitting trousers.

BAG SHEETING, COTTON. Cotton cloths made from a wide variety of fabrics. Coarse yarns, 12s to 18s, are used. Textures range from 40 square to 60 square with a weight of 2.50 to 4.00 yards to the pound. These single-ply yarn cloths are used to make bag containers for feed, food, foodstuffs, fruit, grain, salt, sugar, and other food products.

BAHAMA SISAL. This low-luster fiber is retted in sea water, cleaned by hand, and is finer and softer when compared with other sisal fibers which have been treated differently when being prepared for market. The strength of Bahama sisal, however, does not compare with similar sisal and other bast fibers. See SISAL.

BAHIA COTTON. Named for city of this name in Brazil noted as a cotton shipping port. See BRAZILIAN COTTON.

BAHMIA COTTON. A type of Sea Island cotton raised in Egypt; has been superseded by more popular staples in recent years.

BAILEY COTTON. A high-quality, long-staple Upland cotton of North Carolina from 28 mm. to 32 mm. in length with less than 30 per cent lint content.

BAIRAITI. A cotton peculiar to the East Indies.

BAIZE. 1. Coarse, long-napped, woolen fabric made in Britain for several centuries. Such materials were dyed "bay," or a brownish-red color; hence the name, which is a corruption of the plural form. At one time, the fabric was made thinner and finer in quality than the modern fabric of this name, and was used in apparel. 2. A very high-quality woolen fabric dyed green and used to cover pool and billiard tables. Also known as billiard cloth. Merino yarn of high grade must be used in this material. 3. A lower quality fabric in green or other colors, used for table covers. In other colors than green mostly used for linings or silence covers.

BAKELITE. A plastic used for buckles, buttons, household accessories, and adornments.

BAKRABADI. A medium- to high-quality Indian jute fiber.

BAKU. A very fine, dull-finished lightweight straw.

BALACLAVA, BALAKLAVA HELMET. Named for the well-known seaport city of Crimea in southwestern Russia, on the Black Sea, it is a compactly knitted woolen helmet with a lined covering to provide warmth to the wearer. It covers the head and neck, leaving the face exposed. First made to provide added warmth and comfort to British soldiers in the winter months during the Crimean War, 1858-1856, this helmet was used at the time of the charge of the Light Brigade of the British Army against the Russians in 1854.

Since 1854, the balaclava has been part of equipment issued for British soldiers who serve in cold areas throughout the world. Much used in both world wars, its use has greatly increased within recent years by skiers, mountain climbers, armed personnel, school children, students, truck drivers, etc. See Cardigan, Raglan.

BALANAC. Very strong fibers of this Philippine Islands tree, used for cordage and twine.

BALANCE. 1. Any of a number of devices or machines used to weigh swatches of fabric, chemicals, and so on. 2. The property possessed by the optimum or most efficient blend or reacted combination. Used to describe detergents.

BALANCED. Term describing cloth with the same size yarn and same number of ends and picks per inch. A truly balanced fabric is difficult to find. An example could be one of 2/40s warp and filling with a pick count or texture of 60-square, 68 threads each way in the goods, etc.

BALANCED CREPE. One in which the warp and the filling use alternate yarns of S-twist and Z-twist.

BALANCED CRIMP. When the warp and filling yarns in a fabric have an equal amount of flexibility, take-up, crimp, and so on.

BALANCED TWILL. Any even-sided twill weave or twill fabric.

BALANCED TWIST. A yarn or cord made up of single and ply twists which, after being completed, will not recede upon itself.

BALANCED YARN. That which will not kink, curl, or recede upon itself.

BALATA BELT DUCK. A compactly woven material made with hard-twisted, ply yarn. Made in broad widths, the weight of the goods is figured on the square yard basis.

BALAYEUSE. The old-time ruffle or frill sewed on the inside cuff tip or edge of a shirt.

BALBRIGGAN. A flat, knit cotton underwear fabric made on a circular machine which has one set of needles with the chains in parallel order. The cloth is generally made from Egyptian or Pima cotton and has a slight tan shade. Imitation balbriggan is made from any of the prominent types of American cottons, and is afterward tinted to simulate genuine balbriggan.

BAL COLLAR. High military collar observed on a Balmacaan coat; may be worn turned up and buttoned or allowed to lay flat.

BALDACHIN, BALDAQUIN, BAUDEKIN, BODKIN, BALDAKIN, BALDOQUIN. Costly brocades of silk interspersed throughout with gold or silver threads and further embellished by the use of precious stones. These gorgeous fabrics, many of which are still extant, reached their greatest popularity during the Crusades, the Renaissance, and other days of chivalry. Baldachin has been or is used today for canopies, ceremonial robes, pageants, trappings, armor, harness.

BALE. 1. A compressed pack of wool of a convenient form for transit, varying in weight from 150 pounds to 1000 pounds, in the countries of production. Australian bales weigh about 300 pounds; Argentine bales, 1000 pounds. Burlap is used as the covering.

2. Cotton bales vary much in size and weight. The American bale measures 54 x 27 x 27 inches, and weighs about 500 pounds. Other bale weights are: Sea Island, 380 pounds; Egyptian, 750 pounds; Indian, 400 pounds. See table.

3. The average European silk bale weighs 100 kilos or 220 American pounds. Japanese and Shanghai bales average 133.33 pounds; Canton, 106.67 pounds.

BALE

Bale Type (Rectangular)	Length in Inches	Width in Inches	Thickness in Inches	Weight in Pounds	Density in Pounds Cu. Ft.
Gin, low-density	56	28	45	500	12
Compressed standard-density	56	31	22	500	23
Compressed high-density	57	22	21	500	32
Gin, standard-density	56	22	31	500	23
(Round)	35	*22		250	32

* Diameter.

BALE BREAKER. Its function is to remove compression caused by the baling and shipping of the cotton. Its action is revolving and tumbling as it takes the raw staple for action and delivers the stock in a loose condition at the delivery end of the machine.

The main parts of the breaker include hopper, feed apron, lifting apron, pin cylinder, rollers, and a doffer beater roller which strips the cotton so that it may be presented to the next machine. In addition to opening up the cotton the machine, by its action, does some cleaning.

BALE DYEING. A very cheap method of dyeing cotton cloth. The material, without any scouring or singeing, is sent through a cold-water dye bath where the sized warp yarn will readily take on the dye. The filling will not dye since the wax in it has not been removed to admit dye absorption. Imitation chambray is sometimes bale-dyed.

BALE TARE. The weight of the covering and cooperage around a cotton bale; averages about 22 pounds per bale. The copper or steel ties are called bale ties. See BALE.

BALE TIES. The bands, steel, copper, and so forth used to wrap around the burlap on cotton bales.

BALICNONG. A Phillippine fiber used for cordage.

BALINE. 1. Garment interlining made of cotton warp and horsehair filling in plain-weave order. 2. Coarse fabric of hemp, jute, etc., used for bags and upholstery lining.

BALING. Actually packing cotton into bale form; the press box is lined with the bale covering and the ginned cotton is placed inside. When the box is about full, the cotton is subjected to pressure, made to conform to proper bale size; then the bale ties are fastened around it to make a secure bale ready for shipping.

BALING PRESS. A machine for compressing bolts or cuts of cloth, or waste, into a compact bale for shipment.

BALK. A striped or plaid fabric in which there is an incomplete color design or pattern. Often caused by carelessness on part of the designer.

BALKY, STRONG SELVAGE. One that is difficult to handle, and caused by heavy yarn, loose weave construction, or too much crowding or cramming in the reed.

BALL. The form of knitting yarn ready for use. It may be made of yarn from any of the major fibers, alone or in combination. The yarn is sold in "so many ounce balls" to the consumer.

BALL AND SECTIONAL WARPING. Ball warping is resorted to when yarn is to be shipped to some other mill. The total number of ends gathered is wound into ball form. This is covered with burlap and shipped in bale form to the consignee.

Sectional warping is used for colored stripe warps from yarn that has been previously dyed and wound on warper's bobbins. It consists of preparing the warp in sections, each of which contains one or more complete repeats of the warp pattern. The sections are wound upon a mandrel, side by side, until the required number of sections has been made up. The mandrel is a snug-fitting cylindrical or conical piece of metal upon which a piece of work may be held and by which it may be driven. After the sections have been cared for on the dressing frame, the ends are looped under some of the warp in order to offset gnarling and to keep the sections in order. The warp is then wound off the warp beam—the last portions of yarn to go on to the dressing frame, or mandrel, are the first to come off when the machine is started. It is this portion of the warp that is attached to the hub bar of the warp beam. There is a measuring device on the frame which indicates the point when the correct number of yards have been wound onto each section. This prevents waste of yarn and insures uniformity. All sections must have the same total yardage.

BALLERINA. A short, very full skirt. The fullness is currently achieved by the use of crinoline.

BALL FALL. Viscosity of a liquid is measured and then expressed in time by recording the number of seconds required for a standard sphere to descend in a column of standard length under standard conditions. In the ball fall used for viscose rayon at the stage in manufacture when it is in viscous solution, a drop of 20 centimeters and a steel ball of one-eighth of one inch in diameter are used to determine the measure. A drop of 10 centimeters and a quarter-inch steel ball are used in the case of viscosity for cellulose acetate.

BALLING. 1. Coiling or winding long chain warps into ball formation. 2. Winding wool, rayon, or other tops into ball form to facilitate handling. 3. Winding yarn, single or plied, into a small ball-like formation.

BALLING HEAD. A delivery device used on worsted cards, gill boxes, and so on, in worsted yarn manufacture. The web of fibers as they come from the doffer roller of the worsted card are converged and condensed into a sliver formation for passage through a trumpet device to be wound onto a headless wooden spool about 18 inches long. The balling head attachment may be at the center or side of the delivery end of the machine. A balling head resembles a cheese in appearance.

BALLOON FABRIC, TYPEWRITER FABRIC. Has the highest construction count of any plain-weave cotton cloth— 120 to 180 in warp, 150 to 170 in filling. Finished 38 to 45 inches wide. One great use is for typewriter ribbon, and it is de-sized so that the dye will be evenly absorbed. Balloon cloth is used for airplane coverings, gas bags, ribbons, shirting, and underwear. The cloth may be coated or treated with cellulose acetate, latex, paraffin, or rubber for use in the raincoat trade. Also used for artificial flowers, cambric, chintz, shorts.

BALLOON SPINNING. The curved path observed on yarn, caused by centrifugal force, as it is being spun between the thread guide and the ring traveler on a ring spinning frame.

BALL SIZING. Sizing warp yarn in rope or ball formation.

BALL WARPER. A machine that draws yarns from spools or cheeses into a loose rope of untwisted strands. It is the oldest method of warping and is sometimes used when the yarn is to be dyed before weaving.

BALL WARPING. 1. Process used when yarn is to be shipped to another mill. All the ends in the warp are gathered together and wound into ball form;

covered with burlap or some other suitable covering, the warp is shipped in bale form to the new mill. 2. Winding of slivers in worsted top form into convenient balls to facilitate their use in the ensuing machine or for top-dyeing. See BALLING.

BALL WINDING MACHINE. This machine winds yarn into small ball packages. Yarns for knitting, crocheting, tatting, etc., are wound this way.

BALMACAAN. Named after a Scottish moor, this loose-fitting topcoat is made of homespun or tweed, and is characterized by the natty raglan sleeve, which permits free arm and shoulder action.

BALMORAL. 1. A heavy, strong woolen fabric made in red, blue, and black stripped block-effects. 2. One of the bonnets worn with the Highland costume.

The Balmoral tartan is reserved solely for Great Britain's royal family. When George IV visited Edinburgh in 1822 the wide use of Highland dress created a general interest in tartans, but it was Queen Victoria's love of all things Highland that led to the creation of the Balmoral tartan. It was, in fact, designed for her by the Prince Consort, Albert, and was worn by the royal household on all the Queen's subsequent visits to the Highlands.

BALS. Contraction of Balmoral, it refers to a laced shoe with a closed throat. See Balmoral.

BALSO FIBER. A silklike vegetable fiber obtained from the corkwood tree.

BAMBERG. The Lyons Museum in Bamberg possesses extraordinary examples of tenth- to twelfth-century silk fabrics.

BAN. Fabric from the fibers of the banana leaf stalk; it resembles muslin. Used in the East Indies.

BANANA FIBER. Obtained from the banana plant and somewhat resembling abaca, it does not have enough strength to be of value in textiles.

BANANA YUCCA. *Yucca bacata,* a tree raised in Arizona, New Mexico, and California, only at high altitudes. It gives a coarse, stiff fiber that ranges from one foot to one yard in length. Has little value in the textile field.

BANBURY PLUSH. Made of cotton warp, woolen filling, and wool pile effect, this plush is popular in England.

BANCARE. A finish produced by Joseph Bancroft & Sons Company, Wilmington, Delaware, Division of Indian Head, Inc. The term should be written Ban-Care, with no hyphen as in the case of their well-known Ban-Lon. BanCare is tested for:

1. "Everglaze" minimum-care properties.

2. Wrinkle recovery (fabrics iron themselves smooth as they wash and dry).

3. Wrinkle resistance and strength when dry.

4. Resistance to chlorine damage. Ban-Care and Ban-Lon are both registered trade-marks.

BANCROFT, JOSEPH & SONS, COMPANY, INC., TRADEMARKS OF. This division of Indian Head, Inc., Wilmington, Delaware, owns the following group of trademarks:

"BANCARE": A trademark identifying high-performance permanent press fabrics which meet Bancroft's quality control specifications.

"BANDURA": A trademark for high-performance articles of apparel which are made primarily from microcreped fabrics and which meet Bancroft's specifications for quality and performance.

"BAN-LON": A trademark for garments and articles which are made primarily from "Textralized" yarn and which meet rigid specifications and standards of quality prescribed by Joseph Bancroft & Sons Co.

"EVERGLAZE": A trademark identifying high-performance easy-care decorative fabrics which meet Bancroft's quality control specifications.

"MINICARE": A trademark identifying high-performance minimum-care apparel fabrics which meet Bancroft's quality control specifications.

"TEXTRALIZED": A trademark identifying yarn produced by an exclusive bulking process owned and controlled by Joseph Bancroft & Sons Co. The mark may be used only on yarns which have met standards controlled and prescribed by Bancroft.

BANCROFT COTTON. Georgia-Alabama cotton, also known as Bancroft, Herlong, and Jones Herlong. This late-maturing cotton measures 20 mm. to 25 mm., grows medium large bolls, and yields about 32 per cent lint.

BAND. 1. A strip of fabric used to hold, ornament, or complete part of a garment or accessory.

2. Two front flaps on the collar worn by ministers; also known as Genoa bands.

3. Sixteenth- or seventeenth-century wide ornamental collar or ruff, usually of linen, lace, or cambric. Later it was turned down over the shoulders and became known as a "falling band."

4. Name for the Tussah or wild silk

crop of some particular month in the Bengal district of India.

5. A cotton belt or band used to drive the spindles on textile machinery.

6. A bias or straight piece of material, either single or double, used as a decorative feature on a garment. When used as part of the construction in a garment, the bands are joined to other sectional parts to complete the style effect.

7. A group or succession of picks contrasting with adjacent sections.

BANDAGE. Narrow cotton or linen cloth of plain weave and low texture. Woven in widths up to 40 inches, the gauze is split into a variety of widths for hospital purposes.

BANDALA. This strong cordage fiber, found in the Philippines, comes from the outer portion of the *Musa textilis* plant.

BANDANA, BANDANNA. Comes from the Hindustani and means to bind or knot prior to dyeing. The cloth is usually a large cotton or linen square, treated in certain places by a mordant to resist the dyestuff when the cloth is put in the dye bath. The mordanted or treated places on the cloth are afterwards removed by means of acids. The cloth then appears as an all-over color, except for the white places which were protected. Used for scarfs, furniture covering, and bunting.

BANDEAU. 1. A wide or narrow banding worn above the forehead to keep the hair in place. It is usually worn by children or by women, particularly in sports. 2. A narrow brassière. 3. A narrow strip which forms part of a hat so that proper adjustment for size is possible.

BANDELET. A wide hem used to finish the wrist of gloves, and sometimes called the bord.

BANDING. A woven or knitted narrow fabric, used for banding or tying cigars, caps, hats, bundles. A better type of banding is used for decoration on dress goods, neck banding, and to revolve cylinders on textile machinery.

BANDING MACHINE. The machine used to make spinning bands to drive the spindles on various cotton machines. The machine is equipped to produce the desired length of banding which is then given the required turns of twist to enable it to withstand the tension and friction when functioning on a machine.

BANDOLEER CLOTH. An olive-drab, high-texture, square-woven sheeting used for cartridge belts and hand grenade belts.

BAND, SPINNING. The small

twisted cotton rope or cable that drives spindles on various textile machines, chiefly the ring spinner.

BANGAR FIBER. Bast fiber used for ropes, and obtained from a species of the Sterculia, a large tree found in the Philippines.

BANGING-OFF. When the loom stops quickly for some reason; often caused by the shuttle not reaching its shuttle box. Sometimes results in broken ends toward the selvages by the shuttle flying out of the shed altogether, thereby ripping some of the warp threads.

BANI COTTON. Best cotton indigenous to India raised there. Raised chiefly in Hyderabad. Staple is 1 inch to 1⅛ inches with a lint percentage of about 25 per cent. Also known as Barsi or Hyderabad Gaorani.

BANIG. A Philippine bast fiber obtained from leaves of the buri palm and used for matting.

BANK. A creel or rack for holding sliver or yarn packages to facilitate unwinding.

BANK CREEL. The tiered rack or creel upon which the balls of wool sliver are placed to be fed into the second-breaker carding frame.

BANKUKRI COTTON. A long, silk-like cotton raised in Rajputana, India.

BAN-LON®. A trademark of Joseph Bancroft & Sons Company, a division of Indian Head, Inc., New York City. It is used to identify quality products that are made primarily of Textralized® yarn. Before the trademark Ban-Lon® may be used by Bancroft licensees to identify any product, the item must first meet or exceed rigid standards and specifications prescribed and controlled by Bancroft. Thus, Textralized® is the trademark for a unique quality-controlled yarn, while Ban-Lon® is the trademark for quality-controlled fabrics, garments, and articles made primarily from this type of yarn.

Characteristics and properties of Ban-Lon® fabrics and garments include a minimum of fuzzing or pilling, a soft, luxurious, lively hand; excellent moisture absorption, ease of washing and quick drying, controlled stretch, and a neat contour fit with a subtle cling. Also, these fabrics and garments are shrink- and stretch-resistant, never clammy or cold, soft yet sutrdy, remarkably resilient, resistant to mildew, moths, and perspiration; cool in summer, warm in winter because of the built-in air conditioning afforded the fabric.

BANNER. 1. A fabric which bears a device, insignia or symbol, suspended from a pole by a crossbar. 2. Any flag, pennant or standard. 3. An ornamental cloth supported on a crossbeam above a single upright which during a sermon is placed before the exposed Blessed Sacrament in the Roman Catholic Church. 4. Any such banner, or mounted cloth which is carried in procession as an emblem of society or an order of knighthood in the Curch. 5. A small banner is called a bannerette.

BANNER CLOTH. Another name for cotton bunting.

BANNISTER HARNESS. Arrangement used to weave wide patterns in fine reeds from a small Jacquard motif.

BANNOCKBURN. Name for a tweed, derived from village of that name where a battle was fought in 1314. Bannockburn is about twenty-five miles from Glasgow, Scotland, and a tweed center. Cloth should be made with alternating single and two-ply yarn, the latter being of contrasting colors. Used for suitings and topcoatings, and always in demand. One of the best tweeds on the market and a typical British fabric.

BANTA. An eighteenth-century lace tie worn by Italians.

BANTINE. A raw silk variety peculiar to Italy.

BANT OR BONY COTTON. Term for twist cottons, implying strength and all-round ability and utility.

BANYAN. The term comes from the banian body garment worn by the caste of Hindu merchants. It is, in the Western world, nothing more than a brightly colored wrapper such as worn in the home by the housewife while working. The banyan may or may not be colored on both sides; if colored on both sides the printed fabric is known as a duplex or register print. This East Indian dressing gown is also called banjan.

BAR. The joining thread that is thrown across the open area in needlepoint lace. Also called bride, coxcomb, leg, pearl or tie.

BARACAN, BERKAN, BOURACAN, PERKAN. Thin muslins made in seventeenth-century France by the Walloons, who had been induced to come to France because of their skill in making these materials, which were far superior to similar French fabrics. Much of the cloth was dyed or printed in delicate shades which enhanced the demand and popularity of the goods.

BARAS. A type of bagging material made in Germany.

BARATHEA. A plain twill or fancyweave fabric of English origin used as mourning fabric, cravat cloth, and dress goods. The fine texture of this silk or rayon warp, wool filling fabric is of broken character, to give the granulated or pebbled effect. Barathea is usually dyed black. One of the popular types today is made with rayon warp and cotton filling.

BARB. 1. The starched fabric which covers the throat and extends from the chin to the upper chest, a part of the headdress worn by nuns of religious communities. This linen, cotton, or combination material was formerly worn by mourners in many sections of the world. 2. The small protruding scales found on animal fibers; used in the hat industry, these barbs make it possible for the fur fibers to be felted.

BARBADOES COTTON. The original name for American cottons since seeds from the island of Anguilla in the West Indies were brought to the United States for planting about 1800. Served as the basis for cotton raising in Georgia and its Sea Islands, the Carolinas, etc. Barbadoes is still raised extensively in the West Indies.

BARCELONA. 1. A novelty twilledsilk square worn around the head or neck by women of southern Europe, northern Africa, and South America. Plaid or subdued, fancy or vivid designs are a feature of the material. 2. A cotton from Colombia.

BARDOT, BRIGETTE. Around 1960, this "French kitten" introduced the short skirt, the forerunner of the miniskirt of a few years later. The first woman to appear in really daring and revealing clothes, her effect on young women throughout the Continent, the British Isles, and the United States was phenomenal. She actually changed the thinking and the designing of the Parisian couturiers and revolutionized fashion and style among all young women. When in 1961-1962, she summered at St. Tropez, France, she gave this small, rather unknown resort a true place on the fashion map comparable with Biarritz, Mentone, Deauville, St. Moritz, and the Riviera.

BAREFACE. Broad term for any cloth devoid of a nap.

BAREGE. Sheer gauzelike fabric of wool combined with silk, cotton, or other fiber. Used for veils, dresses, etc. Fiber content must be declared. Named for Barèges, in the Pyrenees (formerly Baréges), where it was originally made. Also called Barèges.

BAR FAGOTING. An open seam stitch used to join together bands, folds, and ribbons. It forms a decorative effect much used on ladies' and children's garments. The stitch resembles small squares or a ladderlike construction.

BAR FIBER. A devitalized cellulose that becomes a highly compatible bonding agent when added to the fibers of nonwoven fabrics made by the paper and textile industries. The name comes from Bondable Avixco Rayon which is ideal for use in nonwovens since it has a high rate of absorption, affinity for a variety of bonding agents, less cost and multiple aesthetic properties.

This rayon fiber can be made into irreversible bonds so as to be truly disposable, and short fiber webs which can be made by the wet-laid or dry process. Used in health-care and consumer product fields, and industrial and medical circles. A product of American Viscose Division of FMC Corporation.

BARGAINING AGENCY FOR MEMBERS ONLY. That union status agreed to by a company in which the union is the bargaining agent for its members only.

BARGAINING UNIT. A group of employees eligible to select a bargaining agent to represent them. Also, the group over which a union has jurisdiction for the purpose of collective bargaining.

BARHAK. An East Indian camelhair fabric noted for its toughness and long service.

BARI COTTON. Local name for cotton raised in the Punjab, India.

BARIUM SULPHATE. A white, crystalline, water-insoluble powder, $Ba\,SO_4$, used mainly in the synthesis of lakes, as a pigment in paints and printing inks, as well as a delusterant, partially or wholly, on manmade fibers such as acetate and rayon, for example. See Titanium Dioxide.

BARK CLOTH. See BARK FIBERS.

BARK CREPE. Fabric which simulates the bark of a tree. Made from wool, acetate, or rayon, the surface effect provokes interest. When made of wool, the cloth is popular for women's wear fall and winter coating; acetate and rayon bark crepe is ideal for summer and spring wear.

BARK EXTRACT. Liquid secured from quercitron bark.

BARK FIBERS. Shredded bark of the redwood and other large trees of the West Coast can be used in blends for mackinac, ski cloth, etc. Heavy fabrics with 20 to 30 per cent bark fiber in content meet the testing requirements for the trade.

BARK TANNAGE. Leather tanned by the use of tannic acids that are found in barks, as apart from tanning done by mineral treatments.

BARLEYCORN WEAVES. Figured basket weaves made on a small repeat to produce geometrical motifs.

BARLOW, ALFRED. Invented the double-Jacquard weaving loom, a great boon in this method of weaving fabric, in 1849.

BAR MARKS. See BARRY, BARRE MARKS.

BARNES COTTON. A late-maturing, medium long-staple American cotton; similar to Herlong cotton.

BARNETT COTTON. A rather late-maturing Alabama cotton which runs from ⅞ inch to 1 inch in staple. The medium size bolls yield about 30 per cent lint.

BARNSLEY LINEN. High quality gray or bleached linen material used in embroidery.

BARONET SATIN. A high-luster, summer-wear material made from silk, rayon, or cotton, or from combinations of these yarns. Baronet made in this country has rayon warp and cotton filling, or vice versa. The fabric has to be handled with utmost care since it has the tendency to pull and catch if rubbed against any surface; washing of the goods requires close attention in order to preserve the luster and to prevent shabbiness.

One construction which uses cotton could be 2/50s cotton warp and 150-denier rayon with 50 picks per inch. The warp is reeded three ends per split in a 32 reed. Warp textures will vary considerably. This white or dyed fabric is used for blouses, dresses, linings, neckwear.

BAROQUE. Extravagantly ornate even to the point of being in bad taste or grotesque. Flourished in 17th Century and the first half of 18th Century. Applied to textile fabrics, the design, motif or pattern was of the "gingerbread" type and the medley of colors used was atrocious and presented a most unappealing effect. See Antique, Rococo.

BAROTOR. This is a piece-dyeing pressure machine that uses a new principle in the handling of the goods. In addition to the usual good features of jig-dyeing, there are other outstanding points of the Barotor. The cloth is strung out and over and under a cage-like structure of bars mounted on a rotor. As the rotor turns, the bars move under action of gravity in odd-shaped grooves in order to give the goods a constant motion through the dye liquor. The entire rotor assembly is inserted into an autoclave that serves as a dye kettle.

The fabric to be dyed is at open width at all times, is tensionless and wrinkle-free, and in uniform, frequent bath contact.

The machine is operable for all fabric constructions, both filament and spun. It is adaptable for runs of 100 yards to more than 1000 yards and there is a rapid bath agitation or circulation, and no attention by the operative has to be given during the dyeing. There is a wide range of bath ratios and the machine affords reproducible conditions between laboratory and the dyehouse.

The samples are representative of the entire fabric and they are removable at any time without loss of time, pressure, or heat.

The cylindrical construction of the machine is ideal for utilization of space and there is a low cost of operation and maintenance. The Barotor is a product of E. I. du Pont de Nemours & Co., Inc.

BARRACAN. A weatherproof cloaking made of wool and popular present-day blends and mixtures.

BARRAGON. Moleskin cloth of highly twisted yarn used for work clothes.

BARRAGONES. Twilled cotton trousering.

BARRATEE. A silk cloth of the barathea type. See BARATHEA.

BARRE. A French term that signifies cloth made of one-color warp and two or more colors in the filling. The picks cover up the warp yarn entirely, producing stripes or bands across the goods. This high-texture, compact material is extensively used in striped neckwear. Weaves used may include plain, basket, rib. See BAYARDERE.

BARRED TWIST. A fancy doubled yarn made of two two-fold yarns doubled together; either or both yarns may be printed in color.

BARRED WITCH STITCH. Another name for the herringbone stitch.

BARREGE. Veiling fabric of silk warp and woolen filing, very sheer. See BAREGE.

BARREL. 1. A large headless wooden tube that is used with a balling head. 2. The core of a beam, bobbin, spool, or other object upon which yarn may be wound.

BARREL CUFF. A regular type, single cuff with a one-button closure used on men's shirts; opposed to the fold-back French cuff.

BARREL PLEATING. Decorative tubular pleats, also called cartridge pleats, evenly set across a drapery heading in the home.

BARRIGUDA. This bast fiber native to Brazil is used as stuffing.

BARRY, BARRÉ MARKS. Barré is the French term. Fabrics which have bars or stripes that would be detrimental to the finished cloth are given this name. The defects are usually seen in the filling direction and may be caused by uneven weaving, mixed filling yarn, poor or irregular yarn, etc. Warpwise defects of this nature are usually due to reeding faults and errors.

BAR TACKS. A series of stitches forming a bar, and used to reinforce the edges of seams, tucks, pleats, buttonholes, pockets, etc. Bar tacks are commonly used on tailored garments.

BARTREES. The wooden frames and the pegs that are set in them, arranged so that a warp may be made by hand. Often called wall frame.

BARWOOD. See REDWOOD.

BARYTA. A heavy grayish-white, caustic, alkaline compound formed by calcining certain barium compounds. It forms barium hydrozide with water, and is used in color-making, plate glass manufacture, and as a chemical reagent. It is taken in its chemically pure form as the textile standard of whiteness—that is, 100 per cent white.

BASCO®. A trademark of Joseph Bancroft & Sons Company, a division of Indian Head, Inc., New York City. The trademark is used to identify a special starchless finish applied to cottons to simulate linen fabrics with a durable luster and lintless surface. A chemical compound is used which impregnates the fibers. Basco® fabrics can be washed without the use of starch.

BASE. A chemical alkaline compound used to remove color from a fabric with one or more hydroxyl radicals, whose water solution turns red litmus blue; for example. NaOH. Bases neutralize acids to form salts and water. Base solutions have a soapy, slippery feel and a bitter taste.

BASE, CHEMICAL. A chemical substance (hydroxide) capable of combining with an acid to form a product which is part acid and part base or alkali and known as a salt.

BASEBALL LEATHER. Usually made from the fronts of horsehides. Inexpensive baseballs are made from the skin of sheep.

BASE OR COUNTER. The key that is used in the distribution of the interlacings when plotting a satin weave on design paper. By means of the counter the correct warp end and filling pick interlacing is determined.

The counter cannot divide evenly into the number of ends in the repeat of the weave; a 9-end satin weave, for example, can be made with a base of 2 or 4, but not with a base of 3.

The weave below is a 8-shaft satin, filling-effect weave with a base or counter of three. The weave is begun in the lower left-hand corner where warp end #1 interlaces with filling pick #1. Since this is a painted block it means that the #1 warp end is over filling pick #1 at the point of interlacing. For the completion of the repeat of the weave, count three blocks

WARP ENDS

to the right of the raiser to determine the number of the warp end that is to weave with the second pick. This action continues until the repeat is completed. In counting, if the numbers go beyond the limits of the original weave, they are placed on corresponding blocks within the confines or limits of this original weave. In plain satins there is only one interlacing between the individual warp end and the individual pick; the length, therefore, of the float would be one number less than the total number of threads in the one repeat. In this case, the float would be for seven threads in repeat.

BASES, INFORMATION ON. They are bitter, slippery in feel, turn litmus paper blue, and always contain oxygen and hydrogen. Bases will dissolve greases and are used in the manufacture of soaps, and form the base for mercerization of cotton yarn or fabric when, for example, a treatment with sodium hydroxide causes the cotton to take on a permanent silklike luster that lasts for the life of the fabric. Lye, incidentally, is a base of commercial quality sodium or potassium hydroxide.

BASIC DYES. They are formed by the combination of a chloride or a sulphate with an organic color base. These coal-tar dyes can be used in alcohol, candles, fats, lacquers, and oil to produce light or dark shades of color. They will color silk and wool directly in a slightly acid bath. On vegetable fibers the basic dyes require a tannic acid mordant to provide chemical affinity to produce an insoluble color base.

BASIFIED VISCOSE. Certain synthetic resins of basic nature may be added to rayon to impart properties

of wool when it is dyed.

BASIL. Bark-tanned sheep- or lambskins that are uncolored.

BASIN CLOTH. A French fabric simulating dimity and used for the same purposes; it may or may not have the barred or corded effect.

BASIS BUYER. One who purchases raw cotton strictly on the actual prevailing figure, taking into consideration the grade and staple of the cotton in question. These two factors are taken into account when figuring the final price for the futures market quotation.

BASKET CLOTH. Any of the basket-weave fabrics—monk's cloth, hopsacking, druid cloth, etc.

BASKET STITCH. 1. A kind of stitch in which the threads running one way alternately pass above and below the cross-threads. 2. In embroidery, a couching stitch worked over a cord to give the appearance of basketwork.

BASKET WEAVE. Two or more warp ends over and two or more warp ends under, in parallel arrangement, interlacing with the filling yarn. Rather loose in construction and does not provide high tensile strength. The fabrics are usually difficult to sew on and not suitable for general wear. Attractive surface effects derive from this weave construction; a variation of the plain weave in that a simple basket weave can be made on two harnesses in the loom. A group of ends weave alike and on the order of a plain weave. The weaves will present various size squares or rectangles in accordance with the weave data. Even-series basket weaves will repeat on the number of ends stated in the data; uneven series basket weaves will be twice the size ordinarily expected when adding the total number of ends in the pattern repeat. Thus, a 4-1-4 basket weave (series of three groups of threads) would require 18 blocks in each direction to obtain a full repeat.

Hopsacking, matt, and monk's cloth are made from small-repeat basket weaves. See Illustrated Section (Fabrics 48).

BASQUE. A closely fitted bodice often featured with side-front and side-back seams. The term is derived from the Basques of the western Pyrenees. Very popular at times in women's apparel.

BASQUE SHIRT. See KNITTED SHIRTS.

BASSE-LISSÉ. French term to signify that the warp yarns in tapestry

weaving are in horizontal position (flat-leased, low-leased); in contradistinction to haute-lissé (upright-leased, vertical-leased).

BASS FIBERS. Smooth, stiff coarse, strong fibers from palm trees, used to manufacture stiff brushes.

BASSINE. Indian bast fiber used in manufacture of brushes.

BASSINETTO SILK. The waste silk from the residue of a cocoon after reeling.

BASTARD. A broad term used to imply inferior or substitute fiber, yarn or fabric; a product that does not have the necessary properties of what it is supposed to possess.

BASTARD TEAK. A yellow dye, popular in India, is obtained from the flowers of the tree *Butea frondosa*.

BAST, BAST FIBERS. Between the inner and outer core of plants there is a long, strong fiber that has many commercial uses. Examples of important bast fibers include flax, ramie, jute, hemp, pineapple fiber, sisal, istle.

Cotton is an example of a seed bast fiber; flax is a stalk bast fiber; while the pineapple fiber is a leaf bast fiber.

BASTE. To sew temporarily by hand with long, loose stitches prior to permanently stitching by hand or machine.

BASTER. One who bastes inner canvas to the forepart of the garment by hand with a loose, temporary stitch. He must be able to manipulate the fabric in order to obtain proper fullness and correct effect where necessary. The lining baster bastes the body lining to the forepart, at the side seam, at the bottom, or at the vent, by hand.

BASTERS, FIRST AND SECOND. The first or under baster bastes the facing to the forepart, by hand, running the loose basting stitches down the front edge of a garment and across the lapel. The second baster does the hand basting of the facing where it adjoins the lining.

BAST FIBERS USED IN TEXTILES.

1. Abaca	20. Mescal maguey
2. Bahama sisal	21. New Zealand
3. Canala	flax
4. China grass or	22. Palma
Rhea	23. Palmetto
5. Chingma	24. Phormium
6. Daisee jute	25. Piteira
7. Coir	26. Pineapple fiber
8. Cotton	27. Queensland
9. Flax	hemp
10. Hemp	28. Raffia
11. Henequen	29. Ramie
(henequin)	30. Rattan
12. Istle (ixtle)	31. Risten
13. Italian hemp	32. Russian hemp

14. Kapok
15. Kenaf
16. Japan mulberry fiber
17. Jute
18. Manila hemp
19. Mauritius hemp

33. Sisal
34. Straw
35. Sunn fiber
36. Tampico fiber
37. Tossa jute
38. Wisconsin hemp

BASTING. Long loose stitching used to hold two pieces of fabric in place until final sewing. *Even Basting* is used for machine-stitching or fitting. Even stitches are about one-half inch in length. *Uneven Basting* implies stitches of uneven size used where there is no strain, such as on the side of a skirt below the hipline. *Diagonal or Slanted Basting* is used for fabrics that have the tendency to slip or slide, and to attach facing to a collar.

BASTING COTTON. Low-quality cotton sewing thread, used to baste or to hold materials together before they are finally stitched.

BASTING THREAD. Cotton thread used only for basting purposes.

BAST SOAP. Boiled-off liquor.

BASUTO. South African mohair which centers around Basutoland.

BATARDE WOOL. Black wool that is shipped from the port of Aleppo, northern Syria.

BATAVIA. Lightweight fabric used for summer hats; a combination of wood fiber and cotton is used as the basis. Originated in Java.

BATAVIA TWILL. The 2-up and 2-down twill weave.

BAT, BATTING. The lap of cotton ready for the carding machine; it is about 45 inches wide and weighs about 45 pounds.

BATCH. 1. The softening treatment given to jute and comparable fibers in processing. 2. The rolling up of cloth after it has been received from some dyeing, printing, finishing, or comparable treatment. 3. The treating or processing of fiber, yarn, or fabric in a single unit method.

BATCHING. Jute fibers are softened and improved by a hand or machine treatment with a mixture of oil, soap, and water which serves as a lubricant. The treatment improves the spinning qualities.

BATES' BIG BOLL COTTON. A South Carolina cotton developed from Rio Grande cotton. The late-maturing, large bolls produce a fiber running from ⅞-inch to 1⅛ inches; there is about 35 per cent lint yield.

BATH. Any solution used for dyeing, bleaching, scouring, or other purposes.

BATH COATING. Originating in Bath, England, it is a lightweight, long-napped, soft-feeling woolen or cotton and woolen cloth. Used for coverings,

dresses, infants' blankets.

BATH MAT. A reversible rug in the "rag-rug" construction, terry cloth or chenille effect. Jacquard motifs often appear in this washable, fast-dyed home necessity.

BATH RATIO. The ratio that exists between the weight of the material and the weight of the dye bath.

BATHROBE. A full-length coatlike garment made from any of the major fibers and used at bathing time or as a dressing gown. It comes in plain colors or fancy patterns.

BATHROBE BLANKETING. A double-face cotton blanketing known for its thickness and warmth. A high-twist warp and a two-filling arrangement of loosely twisted yarn permit easy napping of the goods in order to give a rather solid effect on both sides of the material. Used for bathrobing, blankets, covers.

BATHROBE CLOTH. A soft, thick, warm, lightweight cotton fabric, napped on both sides. Colored figures and the background are usually reversible on the face and back of the cloth. Made in widths of 36 inches or 72 inches, the cloth is used for bathrobes and infants' blankets. Much bathrobe cloth is not all cotton at the present time.

BATHROBING, COTTON. This cloth is usually made from short staple cotton, preferably Chinese cotton. Two fillings are used in the construction in order to increase the possibilities of napping. The material may be plain or figured; it is piece- or yarn-dyed and comes in varying qualities.

BATIA. A bast fiber used to make rope and cordage.

BATIK. This method of hand-coloring fabrics originated in Netherlands Indies. Portions of the fabric are covered with wax, and it is only the uncovered areas that will take the color when the material is dipped into the dye liquor. The waxed area repels the color. The wax is then dissolved in boiling water. The process is usually repeated several times to obtain multicolored motifs.

BATIK DYEING, STEPS IN:

1. Drawing of the design on paper.
2. Tracing design onto the cloth.
3. Waxing of the design according to plan or motif.
4. Dyeing of the material to occur where the wax has not been applied to the cloth.
5. Removal of wax by benzene or other solvent.
6. Repetition of operation for each color to be used.
7. Proper rinsing and handling of the product.

BATISTE. Material named for Jean Baptiste, a French linen weaver. 1. In cotton a sheer fabric resembling nainsook, only finer, with a lengthwise streak. Woven of combed yarns, given a mercerized finish. Used for handkerchiefs, lingerie, infants' wear. 2. A heavier type used for linings, corsets. Similar to cotton broadcloth, plain weave. Also made of rayon and decorated with dobby woven stripes and Jacquard florals. 3. Also made of wool in a smooth, fine fabric that is lighter than challis, very similar to fine nun's veiling. Used for dresses, negligees. 4. Also a sheer silk fabric, either plain or figured, very similar to silk mull. Often called batiste de soie. Used for summer dresses. 5. Also made of spun rayon.

BATISTE, WOOL. A high grade woolen fabric, rather sheer and well finished, that is more or less synonymous with nun's veiling, drap d'eté, woolen chiffon, etc.

BATRA. A cordage fiber.

BATTEN, BEATER. That part of a loom which swings to and fro, in order to beat the filling pick into place after it has been placed loosely in the shed of the loom by the shuttle. Also called loom batten.

BATTENBERG LACE, RENAISSANCE LACE. Moern lace that is made of narrow tape or braid formed into motifs which are held together by brides to form a minor design in the effect.

BATTENING. The process of beating filling or weft threads into place in woven goods.

BATTERY. 1. A magazine on a loom that holds a full quota of bobbins, cops, or quills of filling yarn, and from which they are inserted into the shuttle by an automatic bobbin-changing device. 2. When applied to microscopy, it signifies a full range of eye-pieces and object glasses, giving a variety of magnifying power.

BATTERY HAND. The person who keeps the loom cells filled with filling bobbins.

BATTING. Name for loose fibrous material, usually cotton, used in the furniture, upholstery, quilting, and similar trades, generally as a filler or a padding. It is produced by a series of layers of webs combined to form a sheet or layer which has been lightly matted by pressure from being passed through compression rolls, also known as condenser rolls.

The webs may be obtained from a carding machine or a garnett frame, or similar web producing machine which has a main cylinder, and a doffer and comb arrangement to take off and remove the web at the delivery end of the machine. Placing the fiber in a sheet or layer form permits ease of handling and control of the weight and the thickness, allowing greater efficiency in the use of the material by industry. Loose fibers in bulk form would not have these advantages in handling and control. Batting made from bleached and sterilized cotton or cotton waste is used for hospital and medical purposes. Wool batting and batting of mixtures of wool and cotton or cotton waste are sometimes used for the higher quality and higher priced purposes.

BAUHINIA FIBER. Used for nets, ropes, and coarse fabrics, this bast fiber comes from the inner bark of a number of climbing plants that grow in tropical areas.

BAUMÉ. Hydrometer scale named after inventor, Baumé. It is used chiefly to indicate the specific gravity of sulphuric acid and some heavy oils.

BAUMÉ TESTER. A hydrometer fitted with a Baumé scale.

BAVARIAN LACE. Inexpensive torchon laces made in Bavaria.

BAVE. The two filaments of silk joined together by the silk gum or sericin make what is known as a cocoon thread or bave.

BAVELOT. Making its debut in the 1830's, this was a short curtain attached to a woman's bonnet which hung over the neck of the wearer. It served as a protection from the hot rays of the sun. See Havelock.

B.A. WOOL. Buenos Aires wool. See ARGENTINE WOOL.

BAYADERE. A fabric made with stripes in the filling direction across the fabric contrary to the usual warp-striped cloths. The color effects are usually startling or bizarre. The name is derived from Bajadere, Bayadere, or Bayadeer, a dancing girl in India, dedicated from birth to this sort of life. The bayadere costume includes the striped garment, a flimsy scarf or shawl, jeweled trousers, spangles, sequins, anklets.

BAYADERE MOIRE. Watermarked bayadere is called bayadere moiré.

BAYETA. Around 1850 European colonists who went to the Southwestern United States, brought a flannel, vegetable dyed, warmth providing fabric that was of much interest to the Navajo Indians. With skill and patience, the experienced Navajo craftsmen were able to re-weave the raveled threads into yarn in order to make a sort of standard type of bayeta or blanket as well as to dye the yarn into pleasing shades of color. It was from this beginning that the present day Navajo

Indian rug or blanket was born as we know it today. See Baize, Navajo Rug, Navajo Sheep, Improved; Navajo Wool.

BAYETAS. Plain-weave cloth of woolen yarn, piece-dyed and given a long, hairy, napped finish.

BAYEUX LACE. Alençon lace for many years has been made in this city in France. Blonde silk lace and black silk lace are made here, as well.

BAYEUX TAPESTRY. Textile heirloom discovered in Bayeux, France, in 1728. Evidently embroidered by Matilda, the wife of William the Conqueror, this linen fabric has 72 group representations in colored wool of the Norman Invasion of England. The material is 214 feet long and 20 inches wide. It is considered one of the most intricate textile materials ever made. The tapestry portrays the life in the Court of King William and the preparations and events which led to the Conquest of England in A.D. 1066 by William.

BAZAN. A five-end satin-weave cotton cloth, with alternate stripes of warp and filling used. It is British, gray-woven stripe cloth. Texture approximates 66 square; warp counts are about 26s; filling counts, about 16s. Bazan is usually dyed black for the export trade.

BCF NYLON. A bulked trilobal continuous filament carpet yarn made by E.I. duPont de Nemours & Company, Inc., Wilmington, Delaware. This nylon yarn is used in floorcoverings. The yarn is changed in manufacturing procedure before the final molecular structure is actually set. It is a soil-resistant type of fiber.

BEAD. Flaws, such as swells or slubs found in linen yarn.

BEAD, BEADED EDGE. A series of looped threads which form an edging for a ribbon or picot edge.

BEADED OR CUT VELVET. Velvet with a cut-out pattern or velvet pile effect. Often done on chiffon velvet. Brilliant designs and effects noted. Made on Jacquard loom. Principal use is for evening wear. Other uses are for hangings, decorative material, salon furnishings. Most difficult to handle and manipulate. Drapes well, will dry-clean, crushes. Wear depends on quality and type of design.

BEAD FABRIC. See CHAFER FABRIC.

BEADING. A lacelike edging made up of a succession of loops. When done as openwork trimming, a ribbon may be run through to give a decorative effect.

BEAD, IRISH. Flaws made in flax yarn because it is sometimes difficult to draw tough flax fibers from rugged flax.

BEAD LENO. Doup or leno fabric

made by the use of beads instead of a doup arrangement.

BEAD LOOM. A framelike device, used in making bead mesh, on which equidistant lateral strings are knotted to equidistant longitudinal strings before and after each bead is strung on the lateral strings.

BEAD YARN. Yarn which contains hard lumps of stock interspersed throughout the base yarn.

BEAM. 1. Large, horizontal cylinders or spools upon which the warp yarn is wound; set at the back of the loom so that the yarn may be fed into the loom evenly by the let-off motion. 2. A large spool-like device which feeds yarns to guides and needles in a warp knitting frame. The beam rests on a beam shaft at the top of the frame.

BEAM-DYEING. Method of dyeing cotton warps, particularly when they are to be woven with worsted filling. The yarn is wound on a perforated beam and then placed in a cylindrical chamber which can be made airtight. Dye liquor is forced into the chamber and penetrates from both inside and outside the yarn.

BEAMER. A machine that will wind yarn from a creel onto a beam.

BEAMING. 1. The process whereby the yarn, after being taken from the spinning frame and then spooled, is placed in a warper creel and warped onto the warper. The result is a series of section beams approximating about 450 ends each. These section beams are placed in back of the slasher. The number of ends required for the loom beam will determine the number of section beams used. The ends necessary are run through a size box containing boiling size; they are passed over heated cylinders to dry the yarn which is then led into the loom beam located in front of the slasher. The purpose of slashing or dressing is to control the warp ends during weaving.

2. A term used frequently in the silk and rayon industries where Swiss warpers and Horizontal warpers are used in warping of silk and rayon. From the creel, the threads are put on the reels of the warpers in bands of anywhere from 100–800 ends per band. These bands are repeated as many times as needed to make the complete warp. If, for instance, there is a 6000-end warp, ten bands of 600 ends or fifteen bands of 400 ends, depending on the size of the creel, are put on the reel. After this is finished, all bands which lie side by side on the reel are taken off at one time and put on a warp beam in full width. This is what is called beaming; it is a part of

a warping operation.

BEAM-WARPER. A V-shaped creel sets at the back of the warping frame capable of holding several hundred packages of yarn. The end from each package is allotted its proper place by the dresser tender to set up the warping plan. When completed the collective ends are wound in parallel order onto the warp beam. The machine is fully automatic and high rates of speed may be attained when the frame is in action.

BEAM-WARPING. The operation by which cones or spools are warped at one time in full width on a beam (section beam). Naturally the number of ends on these beams depends on the size of the creels in the back of the warper. However, it is not possible to put the total number of ends of a warp at one time on one beam. Therefore, section beams are used. The advantage of section beams is that there are very long warps because of the number of ends. These warps go up to 50,000 yards. Several of these beams are put up behind the slasher and come out as one warp. From these section beams, several warps are made by cutting them off when the warp beam is full.

BEAR CLOTH. This term may imply "bearskin." The *Oxford English Dictionary* gives the following:

1. A skin of a bear used as a wrap or a garment; also in figurative use.

2. The tall cap worn by the Guards in the British Army about the time of the War between the States here.

3. A shaggy woolen fabric used for overcoating.

4. "Bearskin" (Dreadnought and Fearnought): An American term for an overcoating cloth characterized by a shaggy surface effect. It is not applied to any particular cloth but is made of all-wool yarns with the resultant fabric very thick and heavy in weight.

BEARDED MOTES. Broken seeds contained in the longer-staple cotton fibers that were not removed during the ginning.

BEARD HAIRS. The long, smooth, slightly wavy or straight hairs which give some animals their value for fur fibers.

BEARD NEEDLE, BEARDED NEEDLE. The spring beard knitting needle in contradistinction to the other type of needle, the latch needle.

BEAR GRASS. Strong fiber obtained from the *Yucca filamentosa;* used for cordage and twine.

BEARING CLOTH. A richly embroidered fabric in which a child is wrapped at the time of baptism. Damask is the cloth used most frequently, while taffeta, crepe, or faille serve as the lining fabric. The material is often trimmed with lace.

BEARS. Raw cotton speculators who are "short" because they have sold the actual cotton or futures which they do not hold in anticipation of a falling market in order to buy cotton to cover their sales at a reduced price.

BEATER. It does most of the opening and cleaning work on cotton pickers and openers. Revolving at high speed, it beats against the fringe of cotton as the latter is fed into the machine. Types of beaters vary but the three most important are the knife blade, carding beater, and porcupine.

BEATER GUARD. Found on a woolen card, it beats out burrs, shives, motes, and other foreign matter from the wool.

BEATER LOCK. A device which prevents the lid which covers the beater sections of a cotton picker from opening while the machine is in operation.

BEATER SECTION. The feed rolls, beater, and grid bars on a cotton-picker machine which function in sequence to open and clean the stock.

BEATING. 1. The British term for extra warp ends that unwind loosely from the beam during weaving. They are used to piece-up missing, loose, tangled, broken, or defective threads in the warp. 2. Also known as brushing, it is the actual brushing of the cocoons in a hot water basin. The action loosens the sericin which cements the filaments, thereby facilitating reeling.

BEATING FLAX. Breaking up of the woody matter with the aid of wooden mallets or stamping mills. The fibers will then be easier to manipulate.

BEATING-UP. The third and last motion in the action of a loom. It is the beating of the loose pick in the shed of the loom into its proper place or component part in the cloth. Beating-up is done by the action of the reed, which is a comblike device through which the warp ends are drawn. The reed has a to-and-fro motion in its action.

BEATLES, THE. These four young men with their Teddyboy suits and long hair have done more to introduce and popularize the mod style of clothes than any other person or group. Their impact on entertainment, dress, style, manners, and morals has been unbelievable. They were the ones who began the style of longer hair on men, and it can be seen today that this effect was profound. Their clothes were so original and different from those worn at that time that they brought on a revolution in fashion and style among adolescents, and men and women as well.

In 1957, these Liverpool lads made their debut as entertainers in The Cavern, a cellar pub nightclub located in an unused warehouse under Matthew Street in Liverpool. They called themselves The Quarrymen. In 1959 they changed their name to The Beatles and their drummer, Peter Best, left the group. The other three, John Lennon, Paul McCartney, and George Harrison, added Richard Starkey (Ringo Starr) to their act.

In 1963 The Beatles made their appearance at the Palladium in London. Their efforts there placed them in the eye of the entertainment public and they were widely acclaimed on the British Isles and abroad. In recognition of The Beatles' world-wide fame and great monetary contributions to Great Britain, in June, 1965, they were on The Queen's List for Empire Awards. They were tapped for The Order of the British Empire and gave a command performance in Buckingham Palace. On their 1964 trip to America, The Beatles appeared for the first time on the Ed Sullivan Television Show and the entire American adolescent population caught "Beatlemania."

The group broke up in April 1970, after being together thirteen years. Their troubles included marriages that had tough sledding, turning to seances and religious rites in India, and professional conflicts within the group, all of which received newspaper coverage continually.

BEAT-UP. The number of tufts per inch of length in a warp row of pile in carpet weaving. The term is used in connection with Axminster, chenille, and other materials not woven over wires and is synonymous with what is called wire, used in weaving Brussels and Wiltons.

BEATRICE TWILL. The five-end, 4-up and 1-down, or 1-up and 4-down, twill weave used in making an English lining fabric which comes in varying grades and widths. Much of the cloth is sold in China.

BEAU BRUMMELL. George Bryan Brummell (1778-1840) during the height of his fabulous career, set fashions for men in Great Britain. This renowned dandy really went to extremes in fashion and style for the affluent males in the British Isles and on the Continent. For example, he always appeared with the soles of his shoes highly polished. Brummell was a friend and companion of the

British King, George IV when he was the Prince Regent. This friendship was of great value to Brummell in his meteoric rise as a fashion plate and leader in styles for men. See Pea Jacket.

BEAUFORT. The ordinary English cutaway coat which buttons only at the top.

BEAUJEU. A type of French canvas used in the manufacture of slip covers; known for its ruggedness and wear.

BEAUNIT CORPORATION REGISTERED TRADEMARKS. At the present time, the registered trademarks listed below are the property of Beaunit Corporation, a subsidiary of El Paso Natural Gas Company, Inc., and must be so identified when they are used in advertising or on hangtags and labels. All trade names must be accompanied by the generic fiber classification; for example, Vycron polyester fiber, etc.

TRADEMARK NAMES:

Polyester Fiber:

VYCRON® Staple

VYCRON® Tow for Pacific Converters

VYCRON® Tow for Direct Spinners

VYCRON® Fiberfill

VYCRON® High Tenacity Filament Yarn

VYCRON® Turbo Staplers

Viscose Rayon Yarn:

NARCO® Yarn

NARCO® Tow for Direct Spinning

HI-NARCO® Medium Tenacity Filament Yarn

SUPERNARCO® High Strength Filament Yarn

BEAUTE SATIN. A five-shaft satin weave is used to make this French material, which has a warp satin face and a plain crepe back. Crepe twist yarn used in the filling is two picks of S-twist and then two picks of Z-twist.

BEAUVAIS TAPESTRY. Tapestry woven in Beauvais, France. The French government has underwritten this enterprise for several centuries, and tapestry of this name is among the best known throughout the world. Beauvais is characterized by appealing flower patterns made with wool yarn.

BEAVER. The largest amphibious member of the rodent family, found in Europe and America. Beaver fur, like muskrat, is considered the best for felt hat manufacture. Coming from an animal which weighs about forty pounds, the fur has an average micron count of 15.8 It is soft and silky and lends itself to textile use. The hair is used by this industry only when certain shiny effects are desired in blends. Considerable de-

mand exists for beaver pelts in the fur industry. They are plucked and sheared, and because of the light belly portion they appear to be striped. Canadian beaver has a blue-brown fur fiber while other animals vary in shading from light brown to pale tawny. Early nineteenth century was when it was used most for manufacture of beaver hats, and the shiny, coarse guard hair was left on the skin for ultimate use as stoles for priests and royal officials. Today finds the pelt used in fur coats and in trimming fur and fabric garments. The wholesale price of an average good beaver pelt for furriers is about forty-five to fifty dollars. The price of beaver fibers prepared for the textile trade is twenty dollars per pound. This is because for the latter industry only the beaver pieces are used. They are pasted on paper and then cut as skins and blown.

BEAVER, ENGLISH. Originally made in England, the fabric is supposed to simulate the fur of the beaver. It is a thick woolen fabric with a napped finish; the length of the nap varies with the cloth and its use. Twill-weave construction is used in the cloth, which finishes around 50 inches. Other cloths have superseded English beaver to considerable degree.

Cotton beaver simulates the woolen fabric of this name. It is double-faced cloth, napped on both sides, and is used for caps, shoe linings, and where work is required, as in sports clothes and work clothes, and in maritime circles.

BEAVER, SHEARED. Beaver which has had some of the thick underfur sheared away, removing the tendency to curl in moist and damp weather, thereby making the garment lighter in weight and less bulky in appearance. Also known as sheared beaver, the coating is classed as one of the dressier types.

BEAVER CLOTH. 1. A heavily napped, face-finished overcoating which has the softest feel and the longest nap when compared with the other cloths in its group—melton, kersey, and broadcloth. The grade of wool used accounts for the high quality of the goods—a 64s or better of half-blood wool. Weaves used to make this double cloth material include a 2-up and 1-down twill arranged in a one-and-one order, one face end followed by one back end; or the order may be two face ends and one back end; a 3-and-1 crowfoot weave on the face may be used while the back weave would be a 1-and-3 crowfoot, thereby improving the stitching or interlocking of the two cloths into the fabric. Stitching is usually done with a 3-harness twill or a small satin construction. Other combinations may be used.

In the finishing of a beaver great care

must be exercised in all operations. After running through the soaper, the cloth is fulled from 6 to 10 hours. It is scoured in the same manner as melton, de-tacked, rolled, and then run through a bath at 180° Fahrenheit, for about 12 hours. Operations, in order, that follow include napping, wet shearing, dry gigging, wet shearing, and then dry gigging. Pressure steam is applied and the cloth is allowed to cool off before removal. If the fabric is to be carbonized the same methods as applied to meltons will suffice. The final operations, in order, then include wet gigging, blowing, finisher shear, wet brushing, and drying. Decating is optional. Pressing, steam brushing, and examining complete the gamut of finishing operations. The finished fabric resembles the fur of the animal of this name. Beaver is a formal and natty material when made into a garment, and gives excellent wear and warmth.

2. A slang expression for tall hats made of felt or silk; originally, the term implied any hat made of beaver fur.

3. A flat, rather heavy silk plush used to make hats.

4. The short, thick, velvetlike fur from the animal of that name which has a rich brown coloring. The fur is used in fur garments, hats, and muffs. See BEAVER.

BEAVER FUSTIAN. A heavyweight early nineteenth-century material made in this country, chiefly in the Philadelphia areas. This coarse, rough overcoating fabric similar to kersey is made in dark blue and is used in overcoating.

BEAVER SHAWL. Made of a reversible or broken twill, this woolen shawl fabric is heavy in weight.

BEAVERTEEN. A stout, solid color, cotton twill cloth similar to fustian. Napped on the back and sheared after dyeing, it is used for hunting clothes, chiefly in the British Isles.

BECK. A large kier, vessel, or tub used in dyeing yarns or fabrics.

BED. 1. The area on a shearing machine over which the cloth passes when being sheared. Usually implies the area under the ledger blade and the cylinder of the machine. 2. The flat, slotted piece of metal in which the needles on a flat knitting machine move up and down.

BEDFORD CORD. The practice of adopting the name of an English town for a cloth not necessarily of local make is again resorted to in naming this material. Bedford cloth has longitudinal cords that run in the warp direction. Used for coatings, suitings, riding-habit cloth and uniform material. The color of the cloth resembles that of covert cloth. Bedford cord is the sister cloth of piqué, which should have its cords in the filling direction. The corded effect is secured by having two successive ends weave in plain-weave order, thereby actually holding the fabric in place and showing the cord plainly. Cotton, silk, and rayon Bedford cord are also made today for the trade. Incidentally, New Bedford, Mass., is also claimed as the home of Bedford cord. See Illustrated Section (Fabrics 56).

BED LINEN. General term for the sheets, pillowcases, bolster shams, and so on, used on a bed. Most bed "linen" today is made of cotton fabric.

BED SHEETING. Made of muslin or percale, its basic use is for bed sheets and pillowcases. Beginning at a 45-inch width, it comes in intervals of 9 inches up to and including a 90-inch width. Formerly made of linen (see BED LINEN), now made almost entirely of cotton.

BEDSPREAD FABRICS. A wide range of fabrics. They range from very light to rather heavy dependent on use to be made of the goods. Fabrics used include acetate or rayon faille, bengaline, chintz, cotton crash, cotton crinkle, cretonne, damask, denim, dimity, dobby-woven goods, flannel gingham, Jacquard, lace, Marseilles, matelasse, Mitcheline, mohair, organdy, plissé crepe, percale, pongee, poplin, warp printed fabric, sailcloth, satin, seersucker, bark-effect cloth, monk's cloth. The spreads come in a range of effects such as quilted or stitched, crochet, tufted styles such as candlewick, chenille, sculptured, deep pile, double wedding ring chenille, hobnail, honeycomb and others.

BEDSTOUT. Also called Inlet, it is a strong cotton fabric made on a 4-end twill weave. Used as bedding in Central Europe.

BEDTICK. An oblong bag of rugged cotton ticking which extends the width of the bed. Used to hold the materials which form the mattress or padding for a bed.

BEDTICKING. Striped cotton goods made in twill or satin weaves. Ticking is a rugged, compact material used for mattresses and pillows. A typical layout for the fabric might be 90 x 60 in texture with warp yarns of 18s and filling yarns of 20s. Widths are 28½, 56, 72, and 84 inches. See Illustrated Section (Fabrics 47).

BEEGE. An unfinished, twill-woven woolen cloth, heavy in weight, that is very low in texture. Used by the poorer classes in cold countries. Beege means "drab," and this term aptly may be applied to the fabric.

BEER. An English term to signify a group of 40 threads: for example a warp made of 60 beer would have 2400 ends (60 x 40 = 2400). In the Leeds, England, district a beer is 36 threads. Reed or cotton-twine harnesses, because of the sley of the reed, must conform to the sley of the harnesses so that there will be no side pull. The term is seldom used in this country.

BEET. A bundle or sheaf of tied flax or crop straw.

BEETLES. The scourge pest which readily attacks wool, silk, and other protein fibers. Especially damaging to carpets and rugs, some of the species of beetles are black carpet, common, furrier's, wooly-bear, Japanese carpet, furniture, etc.

BEETLED FINISH. A flattened appearance gven to fabric by means of beetlers, or fallers. The spaces between warp and filling in the fabric are covered up, and tend to produce a high sheen or glasslike finish. As the cloth is wound slowly on a roller, the fallers or hammers strike the top layer of the goods with great force, and give the material its characteristic thready finish. There is also a sort of moiré effect observed on the goods by the beating of the material in layer form. Linens will show this effect rather well.

Beetled effects are often simulated by chasing finish applied to lower-priced staples. Cotton "taffetas" are given this effect, which is not permanent. The beetled finish causes the threads in the goods to be of varying heights. The effect is such that the lines of bright-and-dim effects are observed when the rays of light strike the cloth at various angles.

BEGGAR'S LACE. A coarse bobbin lace originally made in the sixteenth century in France. Also known as peasant lace, and in France as gueuse. See TORCHON.

BEGGAR'S VELVET. A strong linen or cotton warp and a fine cotton filling yarn is used to make this fabric, the latter forming the pile effect. Also known as Velours de Gueux in France.

BEIGE. 1. Cloth in the natural or undyed state. French for natural.

2. A lightweight dress material made of cotton, worsted, rayon or union yarns. This low-texture, piece-dyed or printed cloth is made on a 2-up and 2-down, right-hand twill.

3. As a color the term implies any material which has a light tan or ecru shade; an ever-popular color for women's wear.

4. A domestic dress-goods fabric made of grandrelle or print yarns. Plain or small twills are used in construction and yarns are black and white, or gray, if grandrelle; sliver printing may be resorted to, as well.

5. A twill-woven fabric consisting of fibers dyed prior to yarn spinning. Various colored fibers and stock are often used to give a mottled effect to this all-worsted fabric, which uses a 36s yarn in warp and filling and has a texture of about 76 x 72. (Sometimes spelled biege.)

BEIMEN. Japanese trade term for American raw cotton.

BELCHER. Popular in England, this blue neckerchief has large white areas or spots, with dark blue spots in the centers.

"BELFAST." In 1958, the scientists of Deering Milliken Research Corporation successfully modified the chemical structure of the cotton fiber on a commercial basis. "Belfast"-treated fabrics produce a new fabric as the result of a permanent modification of the cotton fiber itself. The fabrics or garments can be washed by hand, by automatic washing machines, including spin-dry, or by commercial laundries without loss of their self-ironing properties. The fabrics are non-chlorine retentive, have a built-in resistance to degradation by chlorine; bleaching properties superior to those of untreated cottons. "Belfast" fabrics are dimensionally stable, odor free and rust resistant, as well as being impervious to mildew and bacterial degradation; wash practically lint free, and dry about 30 per cent faster than ordinary cotton fabrics. The treatment is produced by a nonresinous process which, however, is compatible with other finishes when special features are desired.

BELGIAN LACE. Any Belgian lace except Brussels point gauze lace. The ground is machine-made while the twig motifs are made on the pillow plan of manipulation.

BELGIAN LINEN, BELGIAN TICKING. A stout, rugged lined or a linen and cotton material, made on a satin weave. Used as ticking for chairs, upholstery, and bedding; comes in striped and Jacquard effects. Some fair quality linen material of this name is used for handkerchief fabric.

BELGRADE BRAID. An openwork, flat millinery cotton braid, sized and glazed to simulate straw braid.

BELINGE. A rugged French suiting fabric made on a twill weave, linen warp, and woolen or worsted filling.

BELL, THOMAS. A mysterious Scotsman who profoundly affected the art of printing. Before Bell's time, all printing was done by means of wooden blocks or flat plates. In 1775, he perfected a method of wrapping engraved copper plates around wooden rollers so as to make a continous design on cloth. The importance of Bell's invention hinged on quick bleaching which was possible by the use of chlorine. This technique gave printing real impetus. By 1870 both Great Britian and the United States were making machines that could handle up to twenty rollers.

BELLMANIZED FINISH. Registered trademark of Bellman Brook Bleachery Company, Inc., Fairview, New Jersey, for a durable, crisp, starchless finish expecially designed for curtain and dress fabrics. It is used chiefly on cotton muslin and organdy; fabrics with this finish retain crispness through many washings.

BELLOWS PLEAT. A pocketing with fold on three sides to allow for expansion. The effect is also noted on some jacketings.

BELLOWS POCKET. A patch pocket which may be made by means of an open boxpleat in the center to give more pocket space.

BELLWARP. English worsteds which simulate American chain-break worsteds.

BELLWETHER. A wether sheep is one that has already been shorn, and in this way differs from hogget or unshorn sheep. Also means a castrated ram. When flocks go to pasture in the summer, one wether in a flock of every hundred ewes and lambs carries or wears a bell and is known as the bellwether. A black sheep is also sent along with every one hundred sheep. If either is missing at checking-time by the shepherd, chances are that other sheep are also missing. This necessitates a thorough check-up by the herder. See SHEPHERD.

BELLY. That portion of the hide from the underside of an animal; usually of inferior quality and lower in price than the upper areas of the hide.

BELLY WOOL, BELLIES. Wool from the belly, forelegs, and hind legs of a sheep. It is short, dirty, tender, and irregular, and contains much foreign matter. This stock is sorted apart from the fleece and has little value.

BELT, BELTING DUCK. See DUCK BELTING.

BELTING. A stiff knitted or woven material used at the waist of skirts to keep the garment firmly in place. Belting varies in width from one-half inch to about two inches. Some belting materials are buckram, canvas, grosgrain, and tarlatan.

BELTING DUCK, STITCHED.

Used for industrial purposes; two or more widths of regular duck are stitched together at varying specified intervals to provide extra strength.

BELT LEATHERS. This refers to the types of leathers used for men's belts as apart from leather belting used for transmission of power in machinery. Belt leather is a subclass of the so-called fancy leather. It is made of various materials; cattle hide is the commonest type. Women's belts generally use sheep- and goatskins. These leathers are often specially treated on the flesh side to obviate a lining.

BELT SHIPPER. The device, usually a fork operated by a lever, that will shift a belt from one pulley to another.

BEMBERGIZING. Worsted yarn is given a high luster and some elongation by this process, which originated in Germany. The stock is treated in shrinking. The yarn is then boiled in a weak mineral acid for about an hour, under relaxing tension. Rinsing follows to complete the treatment.

BEMBERG RAYON. The yarns and fabrics composed of products of the American Bemberg Corporation, noted for its cuprammonium stretch system of spinning. By 1924 the system was perfected to the point where it had genuine commercial value. This method of making manmade fibers is called the Stretch System because there is an actual stretching of the filaments in the spinning.

In December, 1970, The American Bemberg Division of Beaunit Corporation, New York City, a subsidiary of El Paso Natural Gas Company, Inc., was sold to Bemberg Industries, Inc., New York City.

BEMBERG RAYON NUBBI-YARNS. Owned by Bemberg Industries, Inc., New York City; these are:

1. SHORT NUBBI. A high-low, nonmechanical, short entangled slub, irregular in size and spacing, and in special type running part slub and part smooth.

2. TYPE "B" CUPIONI. A long entangled slub yarn, irregular in size and spacing, but controlled mechanically to give the appearance of Douppioni silk.

3. LONG TYPE "A" SLUB. A long, parallel, nonentangled slub for the true thick and thin appearance.

4. TYPE "C" LONG SLUB WARP YARN. A long thick and thin yarn in which the filaments are set together closely, making it suitable for warp or filling.

5. MEASLE YARN. A part tight, part loose filament yarn with different shrinkage, thereby forming a loop or boucle effect. In weaving the loops break through the surface of the fabric for decorative dot effect.

6. STRATA SLUB, MULTI-STRATA SLUB,

DREAM SLUB. A group in which torpedo-shaped slub are spaced. In the Strata the slubs are nine inches apart, six inches apart in the Multi-Strata, and eighteen inches apart in the Dream Slub.

7. FLAKE SLUB. A short, entangled slub similar to the flake slubs made with staple yarn.

BEMBERG RAYON YARNS. Produced by Bemberg Industries, Inc., New York City:

Bemberg or Cuprammonium Rayons:
BEMBERG© Reel spun and HH Continuous Spinning Filament Yarn.
BEMBELLA© Two Ends of Parfe' Filament Special Textured Yarn.
CUPIONI ® Douppioni-Type Entangled Slub Filament Yarn.

CUPRACOLOR ® Solution Dyed Bemberg Filament Yarn.

CUPREL ® Special Textured Yarns.

CUPRUSSAH ® Thick and Thin Filament Yarn.

MULTI-CUPIONI ® Douppioni-Type Multi-Entangled Slub Filament Yarn.

PARFÉ ® Intermittently Colored Filament Yarn.

DREAM SLUB ® Torpedo Slubbed Filament Yarn.

FLAIKONA ® Filament Flake Yarn.

STRATA ® Thick and Thin Filament Yarn.

MULTI-STRATA ® Heavily Slubbed Thick and Thin Filament Yarn.

TUSSON ® Shantung-Type Dull Luster Slubbed Filament Yarn.

NUB-LITE ® Short Entangled Filament Slub Yarn.

STRATELLA ® Multi-Slubbed Thick and Thin Filament Yarn.

BEMBERG SHEER. Trade name for a reversible crepe made of cuprammonium or Bemberg rayon yarn. Warp yarns are twisted in opposite directions. Ideal for summer wear in plain colors, prints, and splash prints. Product of Bemberg Industries, Inc., New York City. See Bemberg Rayon.

BENARES. 1. Another name for Sunn hemp. 2. A lightweight Indian cloth embellished with silver threads throughout the goods.

BENCHMADE. Handmade shoes made by a single craftsman.

BEND. A sole leather backbone area with the shoulder trimmed off.

BENDERS COTTON. Not a varietal name. Many years ago it was used to apply to cotton of $1\frac{1}{8}$ to $1\frac{3}{16}$ inches in staple length, which was raised along the bends of the Mississippi River in Arkansas, Louisiana, and Mississippi. Constantly being improved, Benders Cotton now implies any "extra-length" cotton staple, whether or not it was raised along the Mississippi River.

BENGAL. 1. Raw silk from the Bengal area in India. 2. Silk and hair fiber material used in women's wear in India. 3. A printed-stripe muslin.

BENGAL HEMP. Another name for Sunn hemp.

BENGALINE. A popular material made from the more important textile fibers. This heavy poplin or rib-effect fabric was first made of silk in Bengal, India. The texture is high and the use of coarse filling gives the pronounced corded effect. Bengaline appeals to the public, particularly when made of silk warp. This cycle cloth gives good wear, is very durable and finds much use as mourning material, coating, ensembles, suiting, and for women's headgear. Piece-dyed or yarn-dyed, the fabric is finished at about 40 inches. Grosgrain, incidentally, is classed as bengaline "cut to ribbon width."

BENGALINE DE SOIE. An all-silk, plain-weave fabric with distinctive cord effect in the filling. Cotton yarn may be used for the cord yarn which does not show on the face or the back of the goods.

BENGAL STRIPES. Named for Bengal, India, where the first cloth was dyed with fast Bengal indigo dyes. Today these cloths have a white background with striped effects. Bengals are made in cotton, rayon, or silk and are used in skirtings, blouses, beachwear. The term is often applied to gingham, and is popular in advertising certain gingham-effect fabrics.

BENI-AHSEN. Raised in northern Morocco, this breed of sheep is known for its neck folds of wool and all-over dense fleece, which may even reach to the hoofs of the animal. Staple is about 4 inches.

BENI-GUIL. A medium-sized Moroccan sheep known for its white fleece and colored legs.

BENI-MESKINE. A mutton sheep of Morocco.

BEN SMITH COTTON. A Louisiana cotton which has a staple of ⅞ inch to 1 inch; the medium-size bolls give about 33 per cent lint. Also known as Ben Smith Choice, Bush, Smith Standard.

BENVOISE, ANTHONY. This Italian inventor brought out the distaff in the first quarter of the 16th century. Within the next few years it was used universally on the Continent and in the British Isles. See Distaff.

BENZENE, BENZOL. A colorless, volatile, inflammable liquid hydrocarbon obtained chiefly from coal tar by fractional distillation. As a solvent it dissolves fats, resins, iodine, and other matter. It is the source for commercial aniline. A great many compounds are derived from benzene, particularly dyestuffs. This term should not be confused with benzine.

BENZENE, BENZOL TEST. Wool fibers, when immersed in benzol, will take on the color of the solution; other hair fibers will take on a different color and rise to the surface of the liquor.

BENZENE RING. It is believed that a ring of six atoms exist in the aromatic compounds. These atoms are united in some manner to give distinctive properties to compounds containing the ring.

BENZIDINE. A crystalline hydrocarbon obtained from hydrobenzene by reduction; an important item in the dye industry, chiefly for azo colors.

BERAR COTTON. An Indian cotton with a staple of ½ inch to ¾ inch; lint percentage is from 35 per cent to 40 per cent. Suitable for 12s to 14s filling yarn.

BERBER. Lightweight satin-faced fabric popular at the turn of the century. Named for the famous battle in which the English General Gordon defeated the Berbers in his campaign against the Mahdi in North Africa, 1898.

BERET. A cap, originally worn by the Basque peasants of Spain; round, rather tight-fitting, without a visor or tip.

BERGAMO, BERGAMOT, BERGAMEE. All-wool rugs from Asia Minor in which warp and filling are fully dyed. Ghiordian knots are used in making the long pile. Floral or geometrical patterns are seen in these red-to-orange rugs, which are made with a red selvage and are bound with a short fringe. Hemp, linen, and cotton may be used in making the cheap grades of this rug.

BERGERIE. French term for tapestry and embroidery in which pastoral scenes serve as the motif.

BERLIN CANVAS, BERLIN WORK. Worsted embroidery, usually cross-stitch, done on Berlin canvas.

BERLIN WOOL. Single or ply worsted yarn of good quality used for embroidering and knitting.

BERLIN YARN. Also called German wool yarn, this high-quality knitting yarn is either wool or worsted; finds much use in high-grade winterwear knit goods.

BERMUDA SHORTS. Knee-length shorts originating in the resorts in Bermuda and Nassau areas and now popular in many parts of the world, especially where comfort is desired. The shorts were introduced in an attempt by the governor-general of Bermuda to control the length of shorts worn by women. If the shorts were found to be more than two inches above the knee, the wearer would be subject to a fine for "indecent exposure."

BERRY WOOL. A splendid wool of France that is white in cast, of good fiber fineness, choice staple, and possesses some curliness. Fleece weight is about 5½ pounds.

BERTHA. Used originally to imply the short shoulder cape. Now signifies a deep capelike collar which descends from the neckline of a dress over the shoulders.

BESLON. An acrylic fiber manufactured from acrylonitrile in organic solvents by a continuous polymerization and spinning process. The fiber has a wool-like texture and appearance, good durability especially in knot strength, good elasticity (high Young's Modulus), and high heat resistance. In fabrics Beslon shows bulkiness with lightness, and has very good crease resistance. It is used in ease-of-care fabrics and may be dyed brilliant shades. Used in both woven and knit goods for apparel, it is a product of Toyo Rayon Co., Ltd., Tokyo, Japan.

BESSONETTE. A method of rolling cotton into a continuous lap or sheet form to facilitate handling and shipping. Bale diameter is from 22 inches to 24 inches and the width is from 34 inches to about 48 inches. Bale weight may run from 275 pounds to 425 pounds. Cooperage is not needed for this burlap-wrapped bale.

"BETA" FIBERGLAS FIBER. This filament is around .00010 inch in diameter, about one half the diameter of other glass fibers in use at present. Properties include improved flexibility, greater resistance to mechanical abuse to afford increased wearability, added softness and suppleness, and less irritation. "Beta" is used in apparel, home furnishings, and industrial fields. Product of Owens-Corning Fiberglas Corporation, New York City.

BETA-NAPHTHOL. One of the chief developing agents used in dyeing cotton with developed colors.

BETEELA. Outmoded at present, this East Indian muslin was used for cravats, veils, and head coverings.

BEUTANOL. Plastic-coated fabrics on the order of lawns and 80-squares, which have been given five coats of vinyl plastic to enhance pliability, hand, and finish. Fabrics thus treated may be washed and ironed, but this is usually not necessary since the fabrics are waterproof, dustproof, and stainproof, as well as fire-resistant. Vat dyes are used instead of pigments in the coloring, which precedes the coating treatment.

BHANDU. Indian term for cotton printed in spots, to imitate tie-dyeing.

BHANG. Name for the hemp plant.

BHARAL. The wild sheep of the Himalayas, *Ovis natura*.

BHARUA SILK. The mulberry silkworm of Bengal, India produces this filament used for tram filling. Tana is the name of the filament used for warp.

BHATIAL. Coarse Indian jute used for rope.

BHOGA COTTON. Coarse Indian cotton used in making very coarse fabrics and cordage.

BHOWNUGGAR COTTON. An East Indian cotton of fair, white staple but usually dirty in appearance. Used for 30s warp yarn.

BHURRA, BHURRA SCARVES. British-made cloth for the African trade. This colored cotton dress goods has a narrow stripe down the center.

BIANCAVILLE COTTON. An Italian cotton developed from American seed.

BIAS. 1. A slanting line across the warp and the filling of the goods.

2. Any edge which is off the straight grain. Most seams in garments are bias. For binding or piping, a true bias is used. True bias is the diagonal of a square and it is usually cut about 1¼ inches wide.

3. A line used in the folding and the cutting of cloth which runs diagonally across the goods. This line may run at any angle.

A true bias exists when the line is forty-five degrees in angle from the lower left-hand corner of the goods to the upper right-hand corner of the material. Undergarments are cut on the true bias to forestall sagging, rolling and twisting, and to afford better wear to the consumer. Binding cut on the true bias can be easily applied, particularly on edges which are curved.

BIAS CUTTER. A machine that cuts cloth into strips for use in making tires; the cutter guide of the machine is adjusted to cut the fabric diagonally with respect to the weave so that the material will be uniformly strong and flexible.

BIAS WEAVES. Woven fabrics in which one or more warp sets move diagonally across the fabric from selvage to selvage. Tire cord fabrics and chair canings are familiar examples. See Triaxial Fabrics.

BIAZ. A plain-weave, cotton dress goods fabric made in Central Asia to resemble linen cloth of that name.

BIB OVERALL. This is an overall made with a cloth portion above the waistband in front designed to protect the upper clothing. The bib is held in place by suspenders over the shoulders; it contains pockets to hold various and sundry articles.

BICARBONATE. A chemical substance in which an alkali is overneutralized or saturated with carbonic acid. Decomposed by heat to form a normal carbonate. See SODA, MODIFIED; TEMPORARY HARDNESS.

BICEPS. The fullest part of the arm between the shoulder and the elbow. It is often called the "muscle." The term is much used in the garment industry and must be given consideration when designing sleeves.

BI-COMPONENT. Manmade filament fiber wherein two chemical components have been combined or joined; usually, each component has a different shrinkage ratio. Since one filament shrinks more than the other, the yarn takes on a crimp-formation. These yarns are usually textured by the fiber producer but the crimp can be held latent until the fabric has been made and then finished.

BIEGE. A lightweight dress material made of cotton, worsted, rayon or union yarns. This low-texture, piece-dyed or printed fabric is made on a 2-up and 2-down right-hand twill weave. The term is often confused with beige, a popular light tan or ecru color. Biege, as a term for use in the textile and apparel trades, is used rather broadly.

BIETLE. The deerskin jacket worn by North American Indian women. This type of jacket is still popular in many areas throughout the world today. The term has also been applied to any type of Indian jacket embellished by the use of fringes at the bottom, from the elbow to the end of the sleeve, and on the usually square-shaped back collar.

BI-FIBRE. British term for carpet yarn made of cotton and wool.

BIGARRE. Multicolored fabrics are known by this name in France. Bigarré is featured by definite color contrasts in the effect.

BIG BOFFE COTTON. Raised in Minas, Brazil, this coarse, strong cotton staple is from ¾ inch to 1⅛ inches. Lint yield is about 30 per cent.

BIG BOLL COTTON. A California cotton with a staple of about ⅞ inch; lint content is about 35 per cent.

BIG HORN, ROCKY MOUNTAIN SHEEP. Wild sheep of California of the same species as Argali.

BILLIARD CLOTH. The highest grade of material made from the best of stock—Saxony, Silesia, or Australia merino wool. Two-up and one-down twill weave is used. Cloth must have body, substance, evenness, and smoothness. Set in the reed at 144 inches and finished at about 72 inches. Dyed green, its use is obvious.

BILLY. British term for a woolen roving frame.

BI-LOFT. This knitting yarn is a registered trademark of Monsanto Textiles Division, Monsanto Company, Inc., New York City. It is made on the Turbo Worsted System. The stretch-breaking tows of Type 16 Acrilan acrylic fiber and Type 57 Acrilan bicomponent acrylic fiber are delivered in random length sliver form. This sliver contains in Type 16 a shrinkage of 20%-25% while Type 57 has a shrinkage of 28%-35. Following this, either Type 16 or Type 57, depending on the type of yarn desired, is steam relaxed in an autoclave. Following relaxation, Types 16 and 57 are then blended in suitable proportions in rebreaking. Then comes pin drafting, roving formation, spinning into yarn, plying of the yarn, and winding. In the piece or yarn dyeing which follows, the unrelaxed fibers in the blend-mix shrink thereby causing the relaxed, non-shrinking fibers to buckle or crimp so as to increase bulkiness and loftiness.

Bi-Loft possesses excellent bulk, loftiness, and surface cover, all ideal for mid-bulky and bulky sweaters. In addition, sweaters made from the yarn have appealing hand, resiliency, warmth, and are dimensionally stable; affort comfort to the wearer and provide good performance. Bi-Loft yarns meet the requirements of the Monsanto Wear-Dated Program which guarantees a full year of normal wear to the owner of the article.

BIMLIPATAM JUTE, BOMBAY HEMP. A strong Indian hemp fiber used as a substitute for jute.

BINCHE LACE. This Belgian lace, on the order of Valenciennes, is made of mesh patterns over spider and rosette ground. Modern Binche is made of flat bobbin sprigs applied to machine net foundations.

BINDER. 1. An attachment on a sewing machine which applies bias binding to the edge of the cloth. 2. A band, cord, fillet, or braiding which actually holds or binds.

BINDER, BINDING WARP. Ends

or threads used in cloth construction to bind or hold two or more textures in place. These special threads weave over and under the face and the back threads in the weave according to some plan or motif that will work well with the basic weaves in the construction. Binder ends are used in Bedford cord, beaver, chinchilla, face-finished cloths, kersey, melton, pique, plaid-back overcoating, and many other cloths.

BINDER FABRIC. Rugged, strong cotton webbing which comes in several widths and thicknesses. Used for trunk straps and industrial mechanisms.

BINDER PICKS. Those used in cloth construction which hold rather long floats or pile effects in place. These picks have to stitch properly with the face and back filling arrangements in the cloth.

BINDERS, WOOL. Fibers that grow from one staple to another thereby causing a wool fleece to more or less hang together. Usually found at the tips on hogget wool; gradually work down as the sheep becomes older.

BINDER TWINE. Twine made from the harsher types of bast fibers such as abaca, henequen, sisal, and phormium. Used to tie bundles and sheaves in harvesting and threshing.

BINDING. 1. A double or single fold of tape cut on the bias, used to bind edges. Ready-made bias binding is available in white in sizes 3 to 13, and in colors in several widths. Number 3 is the narrowest type; Number 13 is the widest. Number 5 is the size which fits the sewing-machine binder and is therefore made in a wide range of colors, as well as black and white.
2. The edging around the top of a shoe, usually made of grosgrain.
3. A narrow fabric or tape, woven or cut-edge, used for piping on blankets and garments as well as on upholstery and carpets.

BINDING, GLACÉ. One-half inch wide and usually made from a 3-up and 1-down twill, this narrow fabric has highly polished cotton warp and filling in the construction. Given a subsequent stiff finish, the binding is used in the men's tailoring trade.

BINDING MUSLIN. A sized and filled, dyed and stamped cloth for bookbinding purposes.

BIN MIXING. The system of running cotton from several bales into a large bin where it is then packed carefully so as to insure uniformity.

BINPILER. An eyelet on a traverse ring to guide cloth from the bleaching range to storage pits or bins in the bleach house of a mill.

BIRD'S-EYE. 1. When applied to a worsted fabric it implies a clear-finish, staple material, the face of which is marked by small indentations produced by the weaves used to suggest the eye of a bird.
2. In cotton cloth, bird's-eye and diaper material are considered the same. The goods are soft, light, absorbent and may be a union fabric. 30s warp and 16s filling are average size yarns; the texture is about 66 x 46. Novelty twills and small diamond-effect weaves are used in the construction. No starch is applied to the cloth because the absorption properties must be of the best. Foreign matter is also missing in bird's-eye, the filling of which is loosely twisted.
3. Linen fabric of this name is used for toweling, particularly for babies. The cloth is soft, lustrous, absorbent in order not to produce friction or chafing when in contact with the skin. Frequent washing of the material causes it to lose its excessive absorbing power that rougher surfaces might have.

BIRD'S-EYE LENO. A fine cotton, doup-woven cloth made with choice Egyptian cotton yarn. Featured by small diamond motifs, this British fabric is exported to many parts of the world.

BIRD'S-EYE LINEN. Cloth made of novelty twill and small diamond weaves that resemble the eyes of birds. Also known as diaper material. Texture is about 66 x 46. Used for reversible toweling, has good absorptive properties, is durable and launders well. Loosely twisted filling aids properties of absorption. Material must be free from foreign matter. See Illustrated Section (Fabrics 50).

BIRD'S-EYE OR TWILL BACK. A salt and pepper effect on the back of knit fabric obtained by knitting every other needle on the dial while knitting all the needles on the cylinder. Actually achieved by scrambling of the colors used on the face design of the cloth.

BIRD'S-EYE PIQUE. Diamond-effect cloth which shows a raised effect on goods; made from a face and a back warp and a face and a stuffer filling. Made from carded or combed yarns, this piqué is usually of good quality.

BIRD'S-EYE WEAVE. A small spot or diamond weave with a dot in the center of the figure which resembles the eye of a bird. A broad term to cover many weaves of this type. See Illustrated Section (Fabrics 37).

BIREFRINGENCE. An optical determination of the degree of molecular orientation of nylon filaments.

BIRETTA. The ordinary headgear of priests of the Roman Catholic Church. It is made by covering heavy cardboard with black, white, or brown silk, velvet or woolen fabric. The biretta gives good wear because of the compact texture of the material and the technique used in making it. It is not advisable to wash the biretta. Priests wear black; bishops, purple; cardinals, red.

BIRETZ. A double-faced reversible fabric of silk or rayon and wool; one side has a corded effect while the reverse is made on a twill construction. Sometimes known as electoral cloth.

BIRRUS. A rough, thick, and heavy woolen used by the poorer classes during the Middle Ages. Was used chiefly as a greatcoat or cloak.

BISAGÉ. French term for cloth that has been dyed twice.

BIS, BISSO. A fine, sheer, round-thread linen fabric often referred to as church-linen since it is much used for altar cloth. Bis may be embroidered for linens of the better grade.

BISCUIT DUCK. Heavy naught duck used in bakeries for placing dough before actual baking.

BISETTE. 1. An embroidered French braid. 2. A seventeenth-century narrow, coarse linen pillow lace made in France.

BISHOP'S LAWN. A cloth formerly much in demand, slightly heavier than Swiss mulle, and lighter than India linen. It is given a Swiss finish, and is used for vestments and dress goods.

BISHOP SLEEVE. A wide sleeve similar to that of a bishop's robe.

BISSEL. Inventor of the roller cotton gin, 1788.

BISSO LINEN. Fabric, also known as altar cloth, is made of wiry yarns to give it a stiff, crisp feel. This fine, sheer linen is much used in cloth for altars. Also called Altar Lace.

BISSONATA. A coarse French woolen cloth dyed in black and brown and used for clerical vestments.

BISSUTI. See AMAMEE.

BI-SWING. A sports jacket in which the back is made with a gusset or inverted pleat from the outside tip of the shoulder to the waist.

BITE, NIP. The point of contact where two rollers meet.

BITRE. A staple linen fabric made in Brabant, Belgium.

BIVOLTINS. Those races of silkworms which produce two broods in one year.

BLAAMS LINEN. Sometimes known as Brabant linen. Made by the peasants in the Ghent area in Belgium.

BLACK. The darkest color of all, which is the result of total absence of light, or resulting from total absorption of all light rays. It has no saturation property and is of very low brilliance.

BLACK-FACE WOOL. A medium, long, kempy, lustrous wool obtained from the black-faced sheep of Scotland. This fiber, excellent for carpet yarn, is often used in mixes and is usually stock-dyed.

BLACK FIBER. This smooth, dark, glossy fiber, taken from the Caryota palm in Ceylon, is used as a substitute for horsehair.

BLACKHEAD PERSIAN. An original breed of North African sheep, now raised throughout Africa and elsewhere. The fleece is much sought for, since it is strong and smooth. Much used in making "fur" coats. The Union of South Africa, Afghanistan, and Iran are three chief centers which supply the American trade.

BLACKJACK. Leafy cotton staple.

BLACK LIQUOR. See ACETATE OF IRON.

BLACK LIST. A method used by anti-union companies to prevent the employment of individuals who were, or were suspected to be, union members or union agitators.

BLACK-NOSED SWISS SHEEP. Its fleece of long, white wool has little curl and is uneven in working properties. Fleece weight is less than five pounds.

BLACK POINTS. The dark discoloration at the points of collars, originating through the building-up of inert colored matter at the point within the plies of the collar.

BLACK RUST. See RUST.

BLACK SATEEN. Also known as cotton-back or rayon or silk-face satin. The fabric is dyed black, has a sheer luster, smooth feel, and good body. The cotton-back sateen is used for linings and pillow backs. The adroit use of satin constructions makes possible the solid-silk or rayon-face surface-effect on the material.

BLACK SEED. Cotton that has a smooth, black seed.

BLACK SUPERFINE. Name for the splendid woolens of the West of England. Fulling, napping, shearing, and final finishing make the goods ideal for dress suits.

BLACK THREAD. Linen yarn discolored by oil stains.

BLACK-TOPPED WOOL. Much dirt and grime is found in merino fleeces because they have the highest

percentage of yolk in them. This condition gives the wool a dark, muddy appearance bordering on black.

BLACK WATCH. In 1725 six companies of Highlanders were raised to preserve the peace in the Highlands. The colors chosen for them were black, blue, and green, the familiar ground of the Campbell (Chief). The somber hues, as compared with the scarlet of the English troops, gave the name of the Black Watch to these companies —which were eventually absorbed into the British Army, with both the name and the tartan retained.

BLACK WOOL. Any wool that is not white, but not necessarily black. Stock that is gray or brown in color is classed as black wool.

BLACK WORK. Embroidery done with black stitches on white fabrics. See Embroidery.

BLADE BEATER. A long steel blade or bar about 2 inches wide and ½ inch thick with a beveled edge. The blade is attached to a horizontal shaft, and as it revolves the beveled edges do their beating of the stock along the full width of the blade.

BLAMIRE LAPPER. Device used after the stock has been carded, doffed in wide web form, and doubled back and forth upon itself for the correct layer thickness. The lap is then wound into roll form at the side of the machine by this lapper.

BLANC. Any bleached French dry goods, irrespective of the material.

BLANCARD. A good texture, durable, semibleached linen yarn or cloth made in France; used for dress goods.

BLANCHET. Originally made in France, this woolen cloth was used as a nightdress. Today, the term refers to bathrobing and the garments made from the material.

BLANKET. Cloth named in honor of the man who first used it as a covering for warmth and sleeping purposes, Thomas Blanket (Blanquette). He was a Flemish weaver who lived in Bristol, England, in the fourteenth century. The cloth is made of wool, worsted, or cotton, or by combining these fibers in varying percentages in the construction. Material is heavily napped and fulled. Used for bed coverings, robes, steamer rugs. A cloth essential to people in the Temperate Zone.

BLANKET CLOTH. A cotton fabric made of plain or twill weave, 60 by 80 inches or over in size. Coarse soft filled yarns, filling heavily napped both sides. Generally bleached, yarn-dyed in plaids or stripes, or with colored filling edge. A broad term with several

implications and uses.

BLANKET, DOUBLE. Really a pair of blankets; two full length blankets woven in continuous length, finished, cut to size, and then given final finishing for market.

BLANKET FELT, CHARACTERISTICS OF.

1. Nonfraying.
2. Retains its elasticity longer than does rubber.
3. Has insulating powers and is noise-absorbing.
4. Has warmth.
5. From $\frac{1}{32}$ inch to 4 inches thick.
6. Weighs from 3 ounces per square yard to 65 pounds per square yard.
7. May be fireproofed and waterproofed.

BLANKET RANGE. A sample range or warp which runs from 6 to 20 yards in length, and is used for experimental purposes to bring out new color arrangements and patterns. The width of the sample warp is divided into a convenient number of sections, say six sections, each of which may be 9 inches wide. Each section has its own warp color arrangement, and the yarns are often the same size or count. All sections are wound onto the same beam.

When the loom is started the filling for the first section of the warp is used and about 12 inches of cloth is woven. This will be the only section where the warp and filling yarn match and give a solid effect. Then 12 inches of the second-choice filling is woven into the goods, making a solid block in the area covered by the second section of the warp and the second filling. Thus, it continues until all six sections have been woven; there will be a solid block of single-color patterns running from the lower left-hand corner of the blanket to the upper right-hand corner of the goods in the diagonal direction.

From the above plan it will be observed that for each filling used there will be one planned area of cloth and five accidental areas, all running across the goods in each 12-inch space. This particular blanket would have six planned blocks and thirty accidental blocks, a total of thirty-six new patterns in the range. Often the accidental blocks prove to be more popular in the trade than the planned areas.

BLANKETS, DATA ON. The majority of blankets today contain varying percentages of cotton, which necessitates the following information seen on the labels:

1. "All-wool" means that the wool content is from 98 to 100 per cent.
2. "Percentage of wool content in blanket" varies from 25 to 98 per cent.

3. "Part-wool, not less than 5 per cent," implies that the article contains 5 per cent up to 25 per cent wool fiber.

4. Blankets that cannot be marked with the word "wool" have from zero to 5 per cent wool content.

Wool is a nonconductor of heat, cotton does conduct heat; therefore, at least 25 per cent of a blanket should be composed of wool fibers to supply warmth to the sleeping person.

Bed blankets come in the following sizes:

Singles: 60 x 80, 60 x 84, 60 x 90 inches.

Three-quarter: 66 x 80, 70 x 80, 72 x 84, 72 x 90 inches.

Double: 72 x 84, 72 x 90, 80 x 90 inches.

Blankets should be made so that they will readily tuck in or drape well over the edge of the bed.

BLANKETS, DOUBLE WOVEN In double cloth weaving two fabrics are woven at the same time, one above the other in the loom, and they are held together by stitching threads. These threads may be of warp, of filling, or of warp and filling yarns in a combination. Satin weaves are often used as the stitching or binder warp or filling. At least five sets of yarn must be used in weaving double fabric—face warp and face filling, back warp and back filling, and the set of stitching or binder threads.

BLANKET STITCHING. Used as a trimming on blouses and dresses, and also to protect the edges of heavy woolen materials and to prevent them from fraying or "loosening."

BLANKET TWILL. Another name for the 2-up and 2-down twill weave.

BLAQUET. A rugged, heavily felted woolen fabric used on the cylinders of printing machines.

BLARNEY. 1. A staple Irish tweed suiting fabric; made with plain weave (homespun) but sold as regulation twill-tweed fabric. 2. One of the heavier, bulkier types of knitting yarns made in Ireland.

BLASHED FLAX. Also known as Waterslain Flax, the term implies flax which has been over-retted or exposed too long in the elements; this flax has lost too much of its natural gum.

BLATT STITCH. The large embroidery stitch, often known as a satin stitch, used in embroidery construction.

BLAZE. The first silk produced by a silkworm. It is the least lustrous fiber and is heavily charged with sericin or silk gum.

BLAZER. Lightweight sports jacket, with or without sleeves, semitailored, and usually in bright colors. It is so called because it was originally made with brilliant, vertical stripes. It is worn as a distinguishing garment of a school, team, college, and for general sportswear.

BLEACH. A substance which whitens. Common bleaches are chlorine bleach, peroxide, and reducing agents such as sulphites and oxalic acid.

BLEACH, DRY CHLORINE. The substance used comes in bead, crystalline, or powdered form of active chlorine. Has the same general uses as the liquid type with the same limitations.

BLEACH, DRY OXYGEN. The active oxygen used comes in crystalline, bead, or powdered form. The bleaching agent which supplies the active oxygen is usually sodium perborate. A mild bleach safe for use on all fabrics and colors.

BLEACH, LIQUID CHLORINE. A solution of sodium hypochlorite; cannot be used on animal fibers, nonbleach stable colors, and fabrics which have chlorine retentive resin finishes applied to them.

BLEACH, REDUCING. A substance is used to remove certain dyes prior to redyeing, difficult stains on white materials, and the yellow discoloration of chlorine retentive resin finishes. May be bought in a packaged color remover form, sodium hydrosulphite, and as photographer's "hypo," which is actually sodium thiosulphate.

BLEACH, SODIUM PERBORATE. This oxygen bleach is of the mild powdered type which may be used on all types of fabrics without degradation. Sodium perborate is the active ingredient used.

BLEACHERS. General name for gray goods woven for bleaching purposes.

BLEACHING. Necessary process to remove the natural and artificial impurities in fabrics to obtain clear whites for even dyeing and printing. This process increases the fabric's affinity for dyestuffs. Different chemicals are used for different fabrics, but after washing or cleaning, the natural yellowish color of the fiber may slowly return. Some linens are "grass-bleached," that is to say whitened by exposure to the sun, air, and moisture. This process is slow. Bleaching is also used on white fur to remove yellowish tinge, and on furs before they are dyed.

BLEACHING, DOUBLE. Goods that are first given an overnight bleaching in a peroxide bath and then a sequential bleach in a stoving room where the material is subjected to sulphur dioxide fumes. This treatment is in contradistinction to the peroxide bleach, an oxidation treatment and stoving which is reductive in its function.

Applied to woolen yarns or fabrics in the process, the sulphur dioxide which escapes from the burning sulphur diminishes the creamy or yellowish cast in the wool, thereby turning it a shade of white.

It should be borne in mind that a sulphur-stoving bleach is not as durable or permanent as a peroxide bleach. Thus, stoved white yarn or cloth must be stored away from colored from the latter onto the former if stored too closely to each other. It is also possible to use sodium hydrosulphite treatment in lieu of the sulphur-stoving bleach.

BLEACHING, HYPOCHLORITE. This is done by bleaching with sodium hypochlorite, usually on cottons of knitted structure.

BLEACHING, PEROXIDE. Done by the use of hydrogen peroxide, a colorless, unstable, oily liquid (H_2O_2). This aqueous solution can bleach raw stock, yarn, fabric, and is rather popular in the bleaching of knitgoods either for piece goods or for strips such as sweater-units used to make a full, completed sweater. When skeins of yarn are bleached, an overnight treatment is given in a diluted bath of the bleaching agent.

BLEACHING, SODIUM CHLORITE. Ideal for bleaching manmade textile stocks; its functions and properties are different from those used in the sodium hypochlorite bleach. The rate of liberation by the chlorine dioxide controls the bleaching action. Care must be used at all times in effecting this bleach since fumes of chlorine dioxide may prove harmful to the operatives. See Bleaching, Peroxide.

BLEACHING BATH. A chemical solution used to bleach or strip colors from a garment prior to dyeing it.

BLEACHING IN CLEAR. A rinse operation, usually the first rinse in a washing formula, where bleach is applied.

BLEACHING INTENSITY. The degree of oxidation brought about through bleach.

BLEACHING POWDER. Formula is $CaOCl_2$. A white or grayish white powder which has a slight odor of hypochlorous acid, made by treating slaked lime with chlorine. Also called chloride of lime, chemic.

BLEACH SUDS. A suds operation, usually the last suds in a washing formula, where bleach is applied. Bleaching in the last suds is commonly practiced to save time.

BLEED. Spreading of loosened or free color into another area or part of a fabric.

BLEEDING. 1. The running of color from wet dyed material onto a white material next to it. 2. When colors run together during certain finishing operations such as washing, scouring, fulling, milling. 3. The dissolving of color during washing.

BLEND. A term used to describe a yarn obtained when two or more fibers are combined in the spinning process.

BLENDED FABRIC. One which contains blended yarns in either the warp or the filling.

BLENDED YARN. Made by mixing two or more fibers before spinning.

BLENDING. 1. The combining of fibers of different colors, such as heather-mixture, or of different types of fibers such as cotton and wool before spinning. 2. Term is used for the dyeing of pale furs to make them more attractive. 3. The mixing of small amounts of same fiber type from many lots, to produce a uniform result.

BLENDING, COTTON. Proper distribution of the stock must be made in the storage bins. The bales, when the ties, bands, covering, and bagging have been removed, must be allowed to open up naturally prior to manipulation. Cotton from one bale should be spread out on the floor of the mixing bin in a thin layer. Then cotton from another bale should be placed on top of the first layer. This procedure continues until the amount desired has been built up. No two bales of cotton that have the same characteristics and properties should be run together, unless absolutely necessary.

BLENDING MACHINE. A group of devices or attachments that are synchronized to proportion definite amounts of various grades or qualities of stocks which are to be blended together. May be used for grades of the same type of fiber, or for a series of different fibers that are to be manipulated.

BLENDING RESERVE. A hopper which provides a uniform flow of cotton to the finisher beater of a single-unit cotton picker machine. This high rectangular box extends the full picker width, and is equipped with elevating aprons to carry the sheet of cotton from the second screen section upward to the cleaning section, where it is dropped into the reserve box.

BLENDS OR COMBINATIONS OF NATURAL, MAN-MADE, AND "SYNTHETIC" FIBERS. These are taking on increasing importance in fabrics of today and tomorrow. Through the use of such combinations, not only is there effective replacement of some of the scarcer natural fibers, but fabrics made from combinations seem to have novel effects and qualities not heretofore possible. The blending of staple fiber with wool, for example, has made possible the production not only of fabrics ideally suited for men's and women's outerwear but also such items for the home as blankets, rugs, decorative fabrics, upholstery.

In these so-called blends, the fibers combined may be any of the natural ones or any of the man-made types in spun or filament forms. These mixtures should not be considered as substitutes but as members of the textile family along with well-established fabrics seen in the market, some for many years.

The actual process of blending may be varied according to the effects which are desired. It is possible to ply the yarns by combining two or more ends which have been previously twisted together. Sometimes the blending is done in connection with the carding process, or a core yarn of one type may be used around which another yarn may be spun. Then, of course, there are many variations which can be obtained through interchanging the content and the kind of warp or filling yarns.

Individual manufacturers may employ one or all of these methods of blending fibers. The results are interesting and seem to be appreciated by the consumer public. They will doubtless play an important part in the future textile world, since some blends in fabrics are of the conservative type, others seem to be rather wild, conspicuous or "shot-about" in surface effect.

While it is generally possible to blend any or all fibers more or less, utmost attention should be given to the experimental work, fabric construction, fabric control, and marketing possibilities.

BLEY. Irish term for unbleached, beetled finish linen.

BLIND CHINTZ. Calendered or glazed chintz used for curtains and coverings.

BLINDING. The change in appearance of a fiber or yarn during dyeing, or some other wet treatment in finishing.

BLIND STITCH. This is used to fasten on trimming or bias bands where the stitch must not show on the right side of the goods. When finishing hems, it is applied by machine.

BLIND TICKING. Broad term for a rugged union fabric of cotton and linen made on a twill weave. Patterns are of single colors or may be striped. Textures vary considerably in this sized cloth resembling bed ticking. Bed ticking, however, is not as a general rule a union in construction.

BLIND TWILL. British term for twill woven cloths in which the twill lines are not easily discernible.

BLISS TWEED. A good quality British woolen on the order of whipcord, used especially for livery and uniform garb.

BLISS TWILL. British term for the 4-up, 2-down twill weave used to make one type of whipcord fabric; the weave is angled at either 63 degrees or 70 degrees.

BLISTERED, PUCKERED. The effect produced when six or more threads form a fancy effect in material because of a light, loose, or uneven warp tension arrangement. The effect simulates seersucker and plissé, crepe, and serpentine.

BLISTER FABRICS. 1. Cotton fabrics which have this effect are:

Two-beam-warp bedspread fabrics, which are made on a Jacquard loom to give the quilted effect; one warp is used for the tension and background effect; the other, known as the slack warp, is used for the quilted effect.

Woven seersucker, made on a tension warp and a slack warp. The effect produced will give a permanent crinkled stripe.

Plissé stripe, a lightweight fabric formed by a shrinking treatment of caustic soda. The effect will flatten out if ironed much. The effect is used on lawn, print cloth and other basic cloths used to simulate woven striped seersucker. Not durable.

Woven matelassé, a cloth which is all cotton or a cotton and rayon material made of regular and crepe-twist yarns woven in dobby designs. The crepe yarns used in the cloth will pucker up in the shrinking process and form the quilted or blister effects.

Caustic-soda printed organdy. May have large or small blister-crepe effects.

2. Silk blister material, made on a Jacquard loom because of the opportunity afforded for rather elaborate effects which are popular in some silks.

3. Some "crepe-effect" fabrics developed by careful shrinkage and used in women's wear and in children's garments.

BLOBBY WOOL. Spongy, resilient, full-handle wool.

BLOCK PRINTING. A method of printing by blocks as apart from roller printing. The material may show a groundwork that has been printed and, therefore, does not remain white. Printing blocks are made of wood, copper, linoleum, and other materials.

BLONDE. Unbleached silk lace made with varying sizes of yarns. Floral designs are used in this lustrous article, which appears in colors, black, and white. The original name for blonde was Nanking, the city in China where the natural, unbleached silk was raised.

BLONDE D'APPLICATION. Bobbin or needle sprigs are appliquéed over a machine-made groundwork.

BLONDE DE FANTAISIE. Machine-made silk lace with a net ground upon which the design has been sewed.

BLONDE EN PERSIL. Type of lace showing parsley leaves interspersed throughout the pattern.

BLONDE FAUSSE. Silk tulle embellished with floss silk in varying types of lace stitches. Caen, France, is the home of the best blonde lace.

BLOOD. A term used in connection with various fractions (½-blood, ¾-blood) to denote the percentage of Merino blood in a certain sheep. In common practice today the term denotes any wool that is of the same fineness as the wool grown on such a sheep. "Full-blood merino" implies that the wool comes from the offspring of a Merino ram and ewe.

BLOOD, EDMUND. Inventor of methods of carding and spinning silk wastes into yarn. This British inventor received his patents in London in 1671.

BLOOM. 1. A greenish-gray appearance imparted to silk and pile fabrics either by nature of the weave or by the finish. 2. The creamy-white color observed on certain cottons. These staples are of good quality, desirable color, and have luster.

BLOOMER, AMELIA JENKS (1818-1894). Born in Homer, Oneida County, New Yor, this woman was the first female known to wear trousers. Her early early career was in teaching and in time she became the wife of Dexter C. Bloomer, a lawyer in Seneca Falls, New York. In 1851, she became a great crusader against the evils of liquor and an advocate for women's rights, and she obtained much backing and publicity from Horace Greeley, founder of the now defunct "New York Tribune." She founded a periodical called "The Lily" which was devoted to temperance and women's rights. In February, 1851, "The Lily" featured an attire designed and worn by Mrs. Elizabeth Miller, cousin of Mrs. Elizabeth Cady Stanton, a noted suffra-

gette. Amelia called the attire "sanitary clothing for the female" and after giving Mrs. Miller due credit, she seemed to take over this style as her own and made her niche in history by doing so. See Bloomers.

BLOOMERS. 1. Loose trousers gathered about the knees, originally designed by Elizabeth Smith Miller around 1851 and publicized by Amelia Jenks Bloomer for women engaged in athletics. 2. A woman's undergarment of similar design.

BLOTCH GROUND ON BLOTCH PRINTING. Printed fabrics which have the ground area in black or some color. Also implies indistinct printed motifs on fabrics.

BLOTCH PRINTING. This is printing material in order to give it a dyed ground effect. Blotch-printed cloth gives the impression that the cloth may have been colored in some particular manner, but close examination will readily show that the blotch method has been used. A material is printed, and as a result of this, the groundwork will be white, if the blotch method has not been used. The large colored basic areas take the print because of the manner in which the dye paste is made to adhere to the goods. Very fine lines, from 20 to 200 per inch, will hold the dyestuff for printing so that when the machine operation is given, the entire white surface is printed. Thus, a printed groundwork will appear on the cloth, with one or more small or spot designs in their proper places on the face of the goods.

Blotch printing differs from duplex printing in that in an examination of the former, the back of the fabric will not show the same as the face. There will be some absorption on the back but not nearly enough to give a duplex effect. Some blotch prints have white in their motif as a background, as well as some other basic color, depending upon the pattern. Little duplex cloth is seen today since the process is slow, the cost is high, and other methods of printing are more popular.

BLOUSE. A loose waist or bodice of varying type and design which extends from the neckline to the waistline or below. It may be worn inside or outside of the skirt, may be loose or tight-fitting, and a belt may be worn with it. Peasant smocks are on the order of blouses since they have the fullness or bulge noted in the majority of blouses.

BLOWFLY. Larvae of the fly, *Lucilia sericata,* which attacks sheep, usually around lambing time; can wreak havoc in a flock.

BLOWING. A type of crabbing wherein steam is blown through the material while it is wound on a perforated roller.

BLOW-OF-COTTON. Southern expression used when the cotton plant pods burst forth; from the English, "blowth," meaning a blossoming.

BLUCHE, BOUCHE. Shirting cloth used by the clergy of southern Europe. This plain-weave material is made with good quality wool or cotton and is left in the undyed state, called bluché or bouché.

BLUCHER. A laced shoe with an open throat. Named for Field Marshal Gebhard von Blucher, Prussian field marshal and famous adversary of Napoleon 1.

BLUE. 1. Any color in that area of the color spectrum that comes between green and violet. 3. A color the hue of which resembles that of the zenith of a clear sky; cerulean means sky blue, ceruleus means dark blue. Cerulean blue is a light-blue pigment made by combining oxides of cobalt and tin. 3. A color blend of selected dyestuffs used to neutralize or mask the natural, undesirable yellow tint on cotton goods. See also BLUING MATERIALS.

BLUE BENDER COTTON. Inferior, blue-tinged cotton grown along the Mississippi and its branches. Difficult to use for bleaching purposes. Soil and weather conditions cause the bluish cast.

BLUEBONNET. Broad, flat, Scottish cap of blue fabric, usually wool, and of the tam-o-shanter type.

BLUE COTTON. An uncommonly white cotton.

BLUE FLAX. Dark-colored flax from Belgium. Steeped in still water.

BLUE FLEECE. Term applied to the best portions of a luster-sheep fleece of the English or crossbred types. Blue will spin to a 30s worsted count, a popular size in the trade.

BLUE GOODS. Broad term to imply cotton cloths in blue colors—certain chambrays, checked fabrics, denims, gingham stripes, institution cloths.

BLUE JEAN. Sometimes called jean, it is finer than drill, which it resembles. It is stout and durable, made on a twill weave, and comes in white, solid colors, and stripes. Used for work garments and children's clothing, and to a considerable degree for army and navy clothing.

BLUE-SKY BARGAINING. The attitude of negotiators demanding provisions or benefits in the labor agreement that are unobtainable because of their unreasonableness.

BLUE-STAINED COTTON. See GRAY COTTON.

BLUESTONE, BLUE VITRIOL. Copper sulphate, $CuSO_4$ plus $5H_2O$.

BLUE-WHITE FINISH. It is obtained by the addition of a small amount of bluing to the bleached cloth. The bluing will neutralize the yellowish effect that is often seen when cloth is run through the various finishing operations in the wet-finishing department of the plant. Storage of cloth, on its way through the plant, may cause this yellowish cast to appear. The method is comparable with that used by the housewife when bluing clothes.

BLUE WOOL. 1. The best quality combing wool in the old English wool-sorting system. 2. The choice stock from an ordinary luster fleece from crossbred or English wools.

BLUING AND BLUING MATERIALS. Methylene blue, Prussian blue, smalt blue, and ultramarine are the most common dyes used to bleach goods whiter in order for them to be more presentable. These ingredients cover up the yellowish discoloration noted especially on cottons. Detergents containing optical brighteners serve this purpose for the housewife in laundering clothes.

BLUSH. The creamy white color of certain cottons. These are of good, desirable color and luster.

BLUTEAU. 1. A finely woven silk cloth used for sifting of flour in flour mills. The fabric has a very high sley and pickage and has been largely produced on hand looms in Switzerland. It can be used as bolting cloth in screen or stencil printing. 2. A shirting fabric which is largely characterized by a mesh effect in the goods; made from silk, cotton, hair fibers, etc. There are many grades of the cloth on the market, all possessing evenness in every respect.

BNS NYLON. Produced by the British Nylon Spinners, Ltd., United Kingdom, with a registered trademark of *Bri-Nylon* to identify apparel and household articles made from the nylon yarns. This name may be used only by licensees. It has many uses in many types of apparel and clothing, as well as for belting, filter fabrics, fishnets, fire hose, tire cord, felts, parachutes, safety harness, et al.

BOARDED LEATHERS. Hides or skins that are finished by folding with the grain side in and rubbing the surface under the pressure of an instrument called a hand-board. The work can also be done by machinery. Also goes under the name of box finish or willow finish.

BOARDING. The operation by which garments are dried and left in some predetermined shape. Stocking boarding is the most common boarding operation. This involves drawing the stocking over a wooden or metal form of the proper shape and size. When boarded on wooden forms, the stockings are dried in a hot box of some type. When boarded on metal forms the stockings are dried by the form, which is heated internally with steam or electricity. Similar methods are used for boarding underwear in some places.

BOARDY. Fabrics which are hard, stiff, or tough in handling.

BOATER. Stiff headgear of sennit straw with flat brim and flat crown.

BOAT-SIDE SELVAGE. A selvage found often on cotton cloth to give added edge-strength in order to prevent curling in cloth finishing. It is made by weaving two picks and then one pick alternately in a shed.

BOBBIN. 1. A spool-like device upon which filling yarn is wound for use in a shuttle in weaving. The bobbin sets in the shuttle. Yarn should come off the nose of the bobbin in an easy, uniform manner. 2. In spinning, yarn is wound on bobbins; when full they are doffed or removed from the frame and replaced by empty bobbins to be filled. 3. Even winding on bobbins is necessary to insure good results. When full, a bobbin is said to be made up of "nose, body, and heel." 4. A metal receptacle that holds the under-thread in a sewing machine. It fits into the bobbin case underneath the metal plate below the needle.

BOBBIN BARREL. The core of the bobbin upon which yarn or thread is wound.

BOBBIN CLEANER. A machine which removes any remaining roving or yarn from bobbins or quills after they have been used in spinning frames, winders, looms, and the like.

BOBBIN DISC. An identification marker, made of thin cardboard, placed in the head of a bobbin for identifying yarn.

BOBBINET. A netted, cotton, silk, nylon, rayon or acetate fabric of either fine or coarse hexagonal mesh. The heavier weights are used for curtaining, the lighter weights for lining, trimming, and millinery material. It comes in white and colors, and is finished as 36, 45, 54, and 72 inches.

BOBBIN FINE. Name for machine-made lace on the order of shadow lace in which heavy thread outlines feature the motif.

BOBBIN LACE. Made with any number of bobbins and threads. There are two types:

1. UNCUT THREAD LACE. The outstanding types of this single-piece lace include Binche, Cluny, Malines, Old Flanders, Point de Lille, Point de Paris, common Torchon, and Valenciennes. The meshes are hexagonal, round, or square; from these types the motif is developed. Heavy outline threads are employed to set off the design.

2. UNITED LACE. Individual details are combined to give the finished fabric. Black and white Chantilly, Blonde, Bruges Duchesse, and Brussels Duchesse are the more popular types. Relief motifs are a feature in these laces.

Coarse Flanders and Point d'Angleterre are made from a combination of needle point and bobbin point. Other names for bobbin lace are bone and pillow.

BOBBIN LEAD. When the bobbin has excess speed over the flyer on the fly frames used in cotton-yarn manufacture.

BOBBIN RAIL, BOLSTER RAIL. This extends all the way across the front of the roving frame some little distance above the step rail. There are grooves on the front and the back thereby making it possible to fasten the bolsters. The arrangement permits an up-and-down reciprocating action.

BOBBIN SPINNING, FILAMENT. Filaments emerging from a bath are wound without twist onto bobbins with revolving perforated barrels. The bobbins are then placed in a pressure-type machine where purification and bleaching take place. The yarn is then dried, oiled, and twisted to a standard take-up package prior to skeining or coning. Rayon can be spun by this method. See POT SPINNING.

BOBBIN SPOOL. A spool with a head on both ends. It holds the yarn or thread for spinning, weaving, or sewing.

BOBBIN TAPE. A cotton or linen tape, round or flat, which comes in several sizes.

BOBBIN WINDER. Machine used to wind weft yarn onto the bobbin.

BOCASIN, BOCASINE. Name for the best quality buckram used in Spanish-speaking nations as far back as the fourteenth century. Conjecture is that the fabric was first made from goatskin instead of linen.

BOCASSINI. A fine bleached cotton on the order of muslin made in the Balkan countries; comes in several grades, but all of good quality.

BOCCADILLOS. Bleached, lightweight, and carefully sized linen shirting which is popular in South America, Spain, and Portugal.

BOCKING. Floor covering made of low-grade, coarse wool.

BOD. This term is found in the Old Testament of the Bible and refers to fine or bleached linen fabrics.

BODGING. Knitting term used in Great Britain to mean unsatisfactory work in mending.

BODICE. The portion of the form from the waistline to the neck. The beauty of line in dress depends a great deal upon the balance the garment shows when fitted to this part of the figure.

BODKIN. 1. A device for drawing tape through a hem. 2. A pointed instrument for piercing holes in cloth, made of steel, ivory, or other material.

BODY. 1. The area between the selvages on woven goods. 2. The sensation from handling fabric, such as bulkiness, thinness, stiffness, sleaziness.

BODY CLOTH. A blanket or covering used on horses; coarse, heavy material usually made of low-quality wool.

BODY FLEX. The degree of bending in the different parts of the human body. The term is used when determining the amount of degree of stretch needed for fabrics to give the proper amount of movement and flex.

BODYFREE. Registered trademark of Allied Chemical Corporation, New York City, for its anti-static nylon yarn. Having overcome the problems associated with comparable yarns, it will reduce possible yellowing and can withstand more than 100 washings and still retain its performance requirements. The clinging that occurs in nylon slips has been eliminated as satisfactorily in this yarn as in some of the so-called newer knit constructions. The properties of Bodyfree are imparted by chemical additives during the process of yarn manufacturing and thereby form an integral part of the product.

It is highly resistant to said redeposition which dislodges soil during washing and redeposits it in other garments thereby resulting in dull washing, especially on white goods.

BOHEMIAN. A cotton, nylon, or silk lace in which the motifs are noted for their tapelike shapes. It is made on a Leavers machine.

BOHEMIAN TICKING. A high-textured, plain-weave ticking that is feather-proof. Lighter than regular ticking, it is patterned with narrow colored stripes on white background, or may have a chambrav effect by

using unbleached white warp and blue or red filling, or an unbleached warp and filling with a red-line selvage.

BOI, BOY. A union fabric made with cotton warp and wool filling which has some noil in its content. This low-textured, rather heavy flannel is made in loose construction with plain weave.

BOILED LINEN. Linens that are degummed by boiling-out in soda lye.

BOILED LINEN YARN. Flax yarns which have undergone a 5 per cent to 10 per cent loss in weight in the soda-lye boil. Thread yarns are boiled to secure softness and flexibility or to make them lighter in color; linen yarn, for fine and lightweight fabrics, is boiled to reduce the bulk in order to obtain higher counts of yarn.

BOILED-OFF LIQUOR. The solution left after silk degumming.

BOILED-OFF SILK. Silk which has had the sericin or natural gum removed by boiling in a soap solution.

BOILED ROVE. A British term for boiling flax or soft hemp in roving form to increase spinning qualities of the stock.

BOILFAST COLOR. Applied to yarn or thread which is guaranteed fast to washing.

BOILING OFF. Removing size and impurities from cloth prior to dyeing, by circulating boiling caustic solution through the cloth in a kier or by running the cloth through a boil-off machine.

BOILING-OUT. Process in which an alkaline solution, usually made of caustic soda, removes gums and waxes from cotton, since they would tend to resist water absorption. This pressure-boil is done in large kiers.

BOIL-OFF. The percentage of water-soluble material found in nylon, rayon, and silk yarn in terms of a percentage loss in the boiling-off when the yarn is treated in accordance with certain standardized tests. See also SCOURING.

BOIL, PRESSURE. In the manufacture of cellulose textiles, it is the scouring of the cellulose with alkaline liquors in closed vats, kiers, or vessels under excess pressure. Pressure, normally, is from 20 pounds to 30 pounds per square inch.

BOISJAUNE. Fustic or yellow wood.

BOKHARA COTTON. A coarse cotton used locally in Central Asia.

BOLA. A long, rugged fiber obtained from the bark of the hibiscus plant in Bengal, India; used for cordage.

BOLBEES. 1. A French linen given a light blue color in dyeing. 2. A

coarse, stout, bleached linen made in Normandy, France.

BOLCHÉ. Shirting material, bolché is used by the clergy of southern Europe. Plain-weave cloth made of good stock and left in the undyed condition. Usually a woolen.

BOLERO. A short jacket that may be tight or loose-fitting which sets slightly above the waistline. It is made with sleeves or is sleeveless and is usually designed in harmony with the rest of the costume. This popular apparel originated in Spain.

BOLIVAR. Fabric on the order of woolen flannel, of light weight, and low texture. Dyed in solid shades, the cloth finds use in dressing gowns, housecoats, and robes.

BOLIVAR COUNTY COTTON. An early-maturing Louisiana cotton which has a yield of about 30 per cent lint.

BOLIVIA. Light-, medium-, or rather heavyweight cloth. Has napped face and is usually piece-dyed. A 3-up and 3-down twill or similar weaves used in making the cloth. This cloth "is made in the finishing." There are several types of finish available. Weight ranges from 9 to 16 or more ounces per yard.

Cloth is a cut pile, with lines or ribs cut in the warp or in the diagonal direction. The height of the pile varies much. Bolivia is used for cloakings, coatings, and has appeared in suiting cloth. Weave, color, and finish are salient selling features.

BOLL. The seed pod of the cotton plant which forms the bed of support for cotton seeds that are surrounded by fibers.

BOLLIES. Cotton taken from half-open or small bolls.

BOLL ROT. Bolls are often affected by various fungi which, in time, will actually rot the cotton so that it is of no value. Bollworm, the larvae of a moth, also destroys bolls.

BOLL STAGE, COTTON. The red seed pod of cotton plant is known as the boll. For a few days, the boll grows rapidly, but it takes about three weeks for it to grow to full size. Three more weeks are required for the bulb to mature and ripen. At this time, it resembles a green nut, and has a fairly hard shell. Each boll contains many seeds. Each seed is covered with a white, hairy group of fibers that gradually fill out and expand the cavity in the boll. Finally, when the boll is ripe, and weather conditions are favorable, the boll opens because of the collapse of the walls, and the white, fleecy cotton comes forth. See Illustrated Section.

BOLL WEEVIL. Parasite native to Mexico, attacking cotton wherever it is grown. Millions of dollars are spent annually in fighting the pest. Our government appropriates many thousands of dollars a year for this purpose and uses airplanes to spray the plants in the fields with arsenic and other poisonous chemicals.

The weevil tunnels through the pod and causes the boll to become blasted, thereby opening the pod and boll, which on inspection, prove to be infested with the pest.

However, this scourge has caused a more diversified type of agriculture in the South, and has tended to make the law of supply and demand in cotton more or less equalize itself. It has also compelled the planters in this country to fight it in order to save their crops, and place a premium on cotton free from weevil. Incidentally, there is a monument to the boll weevil in the public square of Hattiesburg, Mississippi, placed there because the planters had to combat this scourge to assure themselves of a livelihood. This monument expresses their gratitude for victory.

BOLO-BOLO. A very strong and long West African bast fiber which has about the same properties as jute. See JUTE.

BOLOGNA CREPE. Also called Valle Cypre, it is a silk mourning crepe used in the Mediterranean countries.

BOLOGNA CREPE. A fine, silk gauze mourning crepe used for veiling.

BOLOGNE HEMP. A type of European hemp also known as Great Hemp and Piedmontese Hemp. The plant attains a height of 12 to 16 feet.

BOLSTER. 1. The outside casing which forms the lower part of the ring spindle on spinning frames. The bolster passes through the spindle rail and is attached to it by a nut and bolt. The hollow inside part of the bolster is used as an oil reservoir. 2. Long, rounded, usually lozenge-shaped pillow.

BOLT, CUT, LENGTH OF CLOTH. Terms used to designate the length of the woven cloth as it comes from the loom in the gray goods state or in the finished length in the trade. Men's wear and women's wear cloth in the woolen and worsted trade will range anywhere from a 50-yard piece to a 100-yard length. The most popular cut lengths seem to be 55, 60, 72, 75, 80, 90, and 100 yards. These lengths are the most desirable for the cut-fit-and-trim trade. Cotton lengths usually run from 40 to 50 yards. Rayon and silk cloths usually range from 38 to 40

yards; however, lengths other than these are used when warranted. Ribbon comes in 10-yard lengths.

BOLTING CLOTH. A very stiff, fine, and highly textured silk or nylon material made with the gum still in the yarn. Doup weave may be used to make this strong fabric which finds much use in stencil printing, sign cloth, and as foundation fabric for toupees and wigs. Prices range from about three dollars a yard up to twelve dollars or more.

BOLTON SHEETING. A 72-inch English sheeting, unbleached or dyed cream-color, used for aprons, dresses, crewel embroidery, and hangings.

BOLTON THUMB. The main feature of this thumb is that a thumb quirk is cut in one piece with the back and the palm of a glove. The quirk is the small piece of glove fabric, diamond in shape, usually inserted in the glove at the crotch of the thumb to give more freedom of movement. The Bolton style provides excellent fit and wear. Because it is cut in the one piece, it will not rip as when the quirk is inserted as a separate piece. The Bolton thumb is found in better quality gloves.

BOMBANAS. See JIJIPAPA.

BOMBAST. Cotton or linen material of soft, loose texture used for wadding and padding garments.

BOMBAX COTTON. That fiber which grows on tropical trees and plants. Peruvian cotton, an example, is soft and lustrous but lacks strength and elasticity; hence, its great use in "woolen-mixture" fabrics. Most Bombax is used for stuffing and wadding.

BOMBAY ALOE. Raised in the northwest area of India, this bast fiber is shipped from Bombay and used for cordage and rope. Comes from the *Agave Vivipara* plant. See CANTALA, PITEIRA.

BOMBAY HAIR. An Indian fiber that simulates cashmere, but inferior to the latter in all respects. Used chiefly for knit-goods manufacture in England.

BOMBAY HEMP. Another name for Sunn hemp.

BOMBAZET, BOMBAZETTE. 1. A French dress goods fabric which has a smooth, rather glazed effect enhanced by the weave construction used— plain or small twill. This thin fabric comes in white or colors and can be produced in stripe effects. 2. A cloth similar to the above but made with Bradford or English spun-worsted yarn. Singles yarn is used and the cloth is devoid of luster or glaze.

BOMBAZINE. Name comes from the Latin "Bombycinum." It means

cloth made of silken texture. One of the oldest textile materials known, bombazine has gone through many changes through the ages. Originally it was an all-silk fabric. From time to time other fibers have been used in making the cloth. Today this cloth is made of silk or rayon warp and worsted filling. Imitations in cotton are seen on the market. When dyed black it is used in the mourning-cloth trade.

BOMBE. The French term for dressmaking and embroidery work which shows puffed or rounded (bombé) areas.

BOMBYCIDAE. The family of moths, commonly called spinners, to which the silkworm moth belongs.

BOMBYCINE. 1. Pertaining to silkworms or silk. 2. A lightweight silk fabric made in China and Japan. It comes in colors, as well as in natural shades and white.

BOMBYX MORI. 1. "Dead caterpillar or dead silkworm." The interpreted trade meaning is that it is a filament obtained from the cocoon of the silkworm; used in the sense that it means "true silk." 2. Domesticated silkworm. See Illustrated Section.

BONDED CHEMICALS. Casein, glue, gum arabic, cellulose acetate, melamines, resins, and such, used to bond or join textile fibers or fabrics.

BONDED FABRICS. Introduced in 1962, these fabrics were made possible by new developments in chemistry and textile technology. Research and development in the field of these fabrics brought forth a new group of adhesives found to be ideal for the work. These are made from acrylic or urethane bases. A permanent bonding was developed so that two fabrics could be bonded to each other to perfection. A laminated fabric is a face cloth which has a backing of polyurethane foam. Unveiled in 1958, these fabrics are known as "foambacks" in Great Britian. They provide insulation and bulkiness without adding weight to the fabric, a good buying factor for the consuming public. A bonded fabric is a development from a laminated fabric. In the bonded fabric a foam is used, not necessarily as an insulator but as an adhesive that disappears in the processing. This is called "flame bonding." Another technique which is very popular is to eliminate the foam entirely and to substitute a wet adhesive. Bonded fabrics seem to have a drape and the flexibility not possessed by the foam sandwich laminates.

BONDED FABRICS, PROPERTIES OF. These include appealing and excellent hand, crease-resistance or crease-retentiveness, resiliency, nonraveling edges, excellent stability, ideal stretch and recovery; they may be used to provide insulation and are found in sheer and light weight fabrics and garments as well as in the heavyweight categroy; they are ideal for permanent press garments, etc. With regard to uses, these fabrics, it may be said "run the gamut" and are used in practically all types of apparel — blouses, coating of varying weights, all types of dressgoods, lingerie to rainwear apparel, shirts, shorts, skirts, trousers, etc. At present, these fabrics are extremely popular with home sewers.

BONDED MAT. Definition from the American Society for Testing Materials, Committee D-13: "A bonded mat is a sheet of fibers held together with a bonding agent." See NONWOVEN FABRIC.

BONDED THREAD. Thread may be bonded or welded to provide a finished thread which has some twist but does not compare with the properties noted in single cord thread. Belding Heminway Company, Inc., New York City, has the following bonded threads on the market:

1. NYMO: Monocord type thread.
2. NYMO-TEE: A bonded multicord thread with twist.
3. NYMO-UVR: A monocord thread which is resistant to ultraviolet.
4. NYMO-CLR: A monocord thread that is chlorine-resistant.

BONDING. A method of pressing fibers into thin sheets or webs which are held together by adhesive chemicals; nonwoven fabrics are an example of bonding.

BONDING VOCABULARY. This follows:

Adhesive: A chemical "glue" used to bond two fabrics together. Adhesives are usually of the water based acrylic type or the solvent urethane type.

Backing Fabric: The fabric, usually acetate tricot, that is bonded or laminated to the reverse side of the goods.

Burn-Off: The difference between starting and finishing the thickness of foam after flame lamination.

Curing: High temperature treatment that is used to "set" the adhesive used in bonding. Curing is necessary for permanent bonding of fabrics.

Delamination: The undesirable separation of the components of bonded or laminated fabrics.

Face Fabric: The outer component or a bonded or laminated fabric.

Flame Lamination: The process used in laminating which is based on melting the surfaces of a thin sheet of polyurethane with an open flame. The face and backing fabrics are applied to the foam while the surfaces are still molten, and subsequent cooling causes them to adhere together.

Foamback: British term for a fabric laminated to urethane foam backing.

Laminated Fabric: A fabric structure formed by combining an outer, face fabric, a thin layer of foam, and a backing fabric. The flame lamination process is most frequently used.

Peel-Bond Strength: The force usually expressed in ounces, required to separate the components of a bonded or laminated fabric. Peel-bond strengths may be determined on dry fabric or on fabric wet with water or drycleaning solvents.

Polyester Foam: Urethane foam produced from polyester resin, primarily used in apparel bonding.

Polyester Foam: Urethane foam produced from polyester resins, chiefly used in automotive fabrics bedding, furniture and other non-apparel fields.

BONDYNE. Dynel-bonded fabrics in blends with various man-made or natural textile fibers; product of Reeves Brothers, Inc., New York City.

BONE DRY. Term meaning that all moisture has been removed from the sample by heating to a constant weight in an oven set at 220-230° F.

BONE LACE. A term formerly used to imply Honiton lace of the bobbin variety.

BONES. The bobbins used to manufacture pillow lace.

BONNAZ EMBROIDERY. Embroidery done on a universal feed machine; that is, the machine works or feeds in all directions and is controlled by a handle which the operator guides which allows him to follow any type of design that he desires to embroider. All embroidery does not require buckram as a base during the operation; if the texture of the material warrants it, buckram is not necessary. Some of the many uses of this novel embroidery are: on dresses, sweaters, ladies' handbags, ladies' hats, gloves, and for fancy spreads and pillowcases.

BONNET. The cap or headdress worn with the Highland costume. This may be the Balmoral or the Glengarry style. It is generally blue in color and may bear the crest of the wearer or the crest of the chief of the clan. The evergreen plant badge of the clan should

also be worn on the bonnet.

BONNET WOOL. Scottish term for fine short wool taken from the head and neck area of the sheep when sorting skin wools.

BONS COCOONS, BONS COCONS. Means "good cocoons" in French, and implies that they are at maturity, devoid of spots, compact, and in good condition for manipulation.

BONSOR'S BLACK. Used to obtain logwood black on wool in a single bath, it is a paste which contains, among other ingredients, logwood extract and ferrous sulphate.

BONY COTTON. Cotton with plenty of natural twist and strength to make it suitable for warp yarn.

BOOK. Asiatic raw silk is packed in small bundles called books. Japanese books weigh about four pounds and contain from fifty to sixty skeins. Chinese and Cantonese books are larger and heavier.

BOOKBINDER'S CLOTH. Cloth made from several of the staple cotton cloths that is given a starching, glazing, and calendering. Used in binding books of the cheaper quality. Much filler material is used to cover up the spaces between the warp and filling in this low-textured cloth, which is dyed any color. Cotton or linen fabric thus treated is also used for belts, collar stiffening, and hat crowns.

BOOKBINDING LEATHER. Made of skivers, cattlehide buffings and splits, cowhide, goatskin, sheepskin, calfskin, and sealskin.

BOOK CLOTH. A coarse, plain woven print cloth or sheeting. Dyed, heavily sized, often pyroxylin-coated or embossed. From two to six treatments are given the material to insure proper sizing and coating. Care has to be exercised in making the filling substances match the piece-dyed goods.

BOOK FOLD. A folding of cloth that allows it to be opened like the pages of a book.

BOOK LINEN. A heavily sized cotton or linen material used in stiffening collars, belts, millinery crowns, and book bindings.

BOOK MUSLIN. Coarse, low-textured heavy cotton which has been sized considerably. Usually given a glazed finish, it is used for underlining, millinery, book coverings.

BOON. See SHIVE.

BOONNEE. Hand-woven, plain-weave cotton cloth made in India. Not as fine as muslin, the fabric has a red border when worn by Hindu women and a black border when used by Mohammedan women. Comes from the root "boonna," the Hindu term meaning "to weave."

BOOT. The portion of a stocking from the heel to the knee. This term is used especially with reference to the length of the silk or nylon in a stocking leg when the top of the article is made of cotton. For example, stockings are commonly made with 18-inch, 20-inch, and 22-inch boots. This means that the lower portion, measured with the bottom of the heel from the 18-, 20-, or 22-inch mark, is silk or nylon.

BOOT, BOOTLEG DUCK. See DUCKS, BOOT.

BOOT SOCK. A long, heavy, and warm ribbed sock to be worn with rubber or leather boots.

BORANDJIK. A fine, white muslin usually given a crinkled or seersucker-type finish. Used as dress goods in the Balkan countries.

BORAX. A chemical known as sodium tetraborate, a weak alkali that is not very soluble.

BORDADILLO. Spanish term for figured silk taffeta fabric used as dress goods. Usually floral motifs accentuate the cloth.

BORDE. 1. French for bound, bordered (bordé) or edged. 2. A narrow metallic thread galloon used in upholstery.

BORDEAUX. See CLARET.

BORDER. A band or trimming along the edges of a fabric. In hand-weaving it may be either part of the selvage, which runs in the warp direction, or a part of the weft or filling.

BORDER LACE. Merely an edging.

BORDER LEICESTER. A long wool developed in the area between England and Scotland, combining English Leicester and Cheviot characteristics. The shrinkage is about 25 per cent.

BORDER TIE. A type of harness-tie set-up on a loom, so that one section controls the body of the goods while the other one controls the weaving of the border. Much used in napery fabrics.

BORIC ACID. A textile antiseptic used to prevent possible mildew on cottons. Antiseptics should be used on yarn or fabric when chloride of magnesium or other deliquescents are used. Boric acid, a very fine white powder that is soluble in water, is used as a pure sizing agent. Other popular antiseptics include zinc chloride, glycerine, salicylic acid, Shirlan (a powerful antiseptic developed in England by Shirley Institute).

BORON NITRIDE FIBER. Long staple fibers much used in mats, without a binder being used in construction. The mats are needled to afford body and resiliency. They can be cut to patterns, shaped and formed, or stiffened with appropriate binders. Porosity is 95 percent, thickness, 1/4 inch; width 10 inches and lengths come in five, ten, twenty, and thirty inches. Other thicknesses and widths are also available.

These fiber mats withstand continuous use at temperatures up to 4,500° F., in inert atmospheres and to 1,500° F., under oxidizing conditions. The high temperature capability can be utilized in special ablative composite thermal insulation; heat dissipating composites; mechanical seals, or electrical insulation. Product of The Carborundum Company, Inc., Niagara Falls, New York.

BORSALINO. This classical, distinctive, high quality, densely-textured hat for men has been made since 1850 in Alessandria, a town 60 miles southeast of Turin, Italy. Its counterpart, the Homburg, was not unveiled until the turn of the present century and these two hats are the ultra in headgear for the well-dressed man. Brought out by Borsalino & Brother, the hat has rolled brim, a dented lengthwise crown and despite its firm structure has a soft appealing hand to the wearer. Its dense texture of fur felt adds to the quality and appearance. It, like the Hombur, does without any fear of revolution in headgear. Fifty percent of the production is sold outside Italy and its a cherished article of garb among well-dressed American and British men. See Homberg.

BOSKY. British expression for hand-woven cotton-rayon shirting cloth produced in Pakistan; fancy stripes usually are woven in the design.

BOSOM SHIRT. A shirt with starched, plaited, or tucked bosom often of different fabric from that of the shirt, as a gilet, vestee, etc. See Shirt, Shirting, etc.

BOSS. 1. A knob or stud, or the enlargement of a shaft to couple with a wheel or another shaft. 2. That part of a fluted drawing roll whose largest diameter tips will grip textile fibers being manipulated. The boss is an actual part of a steel roll; in some cases, however, it is covered with cork, leather, or plastic. There are no flutes in the roll unless it is of the steel-roll type.

BOSSELE. French term for an applied motif or embossing on cloth by machine in the finishing of the goods. Bosselé finish may or may not be permanent.

BOSTON LENO. A rare but extremely attractive weave in which two doup ends cross a central ground end.

BOSTON NET. Marquisette made with individual groups of three-warp yarns crossed by leno construction with three filling yarns grouped the same as the warp.

BOTANY. The name for very fine, best type of merino wool raised in the Botany Bay area in Australia.

BOTANY BAY WOOL. Formerly classed as the best wool in the world, Class 1 merino in quality, it spins to the highest of worsted yarn counts—70s and 80s. The term today implies merino wools of high, fine quality with superior working properties. The real Botany wool is grown in an area about 100 miles from the wool center of Sydney, Australia. It is used in the most expensive suits and dress goods, billiard cloth, dress-suit fabrics.

BOTANY NOIL. Combing waste of high quality obtained when combing wool for the worsted system of yarn.

BOTANY TRADE-MARK. The trade-mark of Botany Mills, Inc., for fine quality woolen and worsted fabrics. Licensed to Chatham Manufacturing Company for woven woolens for women's and children's wear; also licensed to various men's wear garment manufacturers.

BOTANY TWILLS. Broad term applied to weaves often used in clear-finished dress fabrics and cassimeres. Weaves such as the 2-up and 2-down, 3-up and 2-down, 2-up and 3-down, 3-up and 3-down, are referred to as Botany Twills.

BOTANY WOOL. Linked with the other outstanding Australian wool, Port Philip, it is a fine merino wool in Class 1 wool classification. Botany is used in the highest-priced worsted fabrics obtainable, suiting materials which sell for two hundred dollars and over in the finished garment.

BOTANY YARNS. Fine wool, rated at 60s or better in classification, is used in these high-quality worsted yarns.

BOTRYTIS BASSIANA. Applied to sericulture, it is the fungus which causes muscardine. See MUSCARDINE.

BOTT-HAMMER. A heavy, fluted hammer used to break flax.

BOTTLE BOBBIN. A wooden frame with a large base upon which yarn is wound. The neck of the bobbin is long and uniform in size and shape. The base is cone-shaped and increases in size evenly from the neck of the bobbin to the base. This type of bobbin is popular in knitting mills.

BOTTOM. The application of a color to goods to serve as a base before they are actually dyed for final shade.

BOTTOM BOARD. The board that

sets at the bottom of a Jacquard loom. Drilled with a great many holes, it serves as the guide for neck cords of the attachment.

BOTTOM CENTER. Found on the loom, it is the point in the throw of the lay of the loom midway between the front and the back center with the crankshaft pointing downward.

BOTTOM FORMER. Found on the builder motion of textile machines, particularly on spinning frames of various types, it spaces the yarn coils at the bottom of the bobbin so that yardage may be uniformly increased, along with setting up a firm base so that a well-formed bobbin will result.

BOTTOMING. 1. Application of a mordant to goods prior to dyeing. 2. A thorough scouring or washing given to goods before bleaching. 3. Dyeing a substrate for ultimate topping. See TOPPING.

BOTTOM SHED. See LOOM, CHIEF MOTIONS OF.

BOUCHE. A plain-weave, fine French woolen fabric, bouché, is left in the undyed state. Used as a shirting material, this cloth is much used by the clergy of southern France. Sometimes called Bluché.

BOUCHONS. Also known as Foul, this French term refers to slubs and similar defects which result from poor or improper cocoon reeling or when the silk filament comes from the cocoon in an irregular manner, usually in a jerky or recessive way, or in a layer formation.

BOUCLE. From "bouclé" (French for "buckled" or "ringed"). Staple suiting fabric on the order of a worsted cheviot with drawn out, looped yarn construction. These yarns give a "ring appearance" to the face of the cloth. Also made in cottons. Bouclé yarn is very popular in the knitting trade. There are many types of this yarn to be found in this end of the textile business.

BOUCLE, LOCK-YARN. A popular novelty yarn which has curled, looped, bunched or crimped effects interspersed throughout in order to give an irregularly twisted effect. Examples include flake, frisé, frotté, ondé, ondulé.

BOUCLE YARN. Comparable with ratine yarn, but in bouclé yarn the rough surface is softer, shows less twist and a more pronounced novelty effect.

BOUFFANT. Puffed out; full; flaring; as the puffed sleeve, or the wide crinoline-supported skirt.

BOUGE. This fine, lightweight, white worsted fabric is made into shirting for those Carthusian monks who do not wear linen shirting.

BOUILLONNE. Any weave effect is bouillonné if it gives a crinkled or blister look. Also means a shirred or gathered effect on a blouse or a dress.

BOUND BUTTONHOLE. A slit in the material large enough to receive various-sized buttons. It is bound with one piece of material and forms a clean finish on the right side.

BOUND CURVES. Curved edges or scallops which are bound with bias strips to finish the edges or to add beauty to the article. The bias strip is applied to the face of the material, then turned under and stitched, leaving about ⅛ inch of bias showing.

BOUND EDGE. To cover or bind the raw edges of cloth—flat-bound, half-and-half bound, narrow-bound, and so on.

BOUND POCKET. So called because the pocket opening is bound on the principle of a bound buttonhole. The pocket section is a separate piece, either of lining or of the same material as the garment, and is arranged and finished on the inside of the garment between the outside and the lining.

BOUND SLIT OR SLASH OPENING. A slash opening which when used at the center, back, or front neck is bound with a continuous bias strip to finish the edges. Slit pocket openings are also bound at times. Slit openings are used at the center front, center back, at the lower edge of sleeves, and so forth.

BOURAT. A strong, unbleached linen tow canvas used in France.

BOURDON. Machine lace made with cotton, silk, or other fibers. This cable-edged, regular-mesh material has scroll patterns in the design. The product is bleached and is often dyed black. When dyed, a very lustrous finish is noted. Much used in dress trimming and in the millinery trade.

BOURETTE. Showing rough threads appearing in lines, straight or broken; produced by lumpy or noil yarns.

BOURETTE SILK. A material made from silk manufacturing waste. The yarn is coarse, lumpy, and irregular, with little elasticity. The fabric has good felting properties when made with the better yarn. Bourette fibers are short, and, because of this fact, along with the possible felting properties, find much use in novelty fabrics, suitings, curtainings, dress goods, and decorative materials. The yarn is made from tufts of hair, nubs, noils, silk wastes of many sorts. These tufts are interspersed throughout to give fancy novel effects with brilliant spots of color. The poorer waste from true silk is also used to make Bourette yarn.

BOURETTE YARNS. Those made from a combination of bourette silk and mohair or worsted.

BOURN, DANIEL. Brought out a carding frame in Leominster, England in 1737. John Wyatt and Louis Paul, a close friend of Bourn's, used Bourn's ideas and introduced the principle of drawing rollers in England in 1738 and brought out their own revolving cylinder carding machine. See Wyatt, John and Paul, Louis.

BOURRE. Term bourré is given to motifs which have a padded or studded effect.

* BOURRELET. Fabric which has a corded or ripple effect due to false loops across the surface of the goods. This type of material can be made by knitting and tucking or knitting and welting. In the former method of manufacture, the tucking action is performed over a successive number of feeds, usually four, while in knitting all needles are on the cylinder.

BOUT. 1. A group of warp threads tied to one tape or section of the warp beam. Usually consists of the number of warp ends necessary to thread two inches of pattern. 2. A complete round in knitting.

BOUTIQUE. A term which actually means a shop, goods, fabrics, shopkeeper. Today the word implies a garment "made from goods in a shop."

BOUTONNE. A French cotton dress goods usually made with slub or other novelty yarn in a Jacquard motif. Other constructions may also be used.

BOUTONNIERE. A blossom or bouquet worn in the buttonhole.

BOUTONNIERE, POINT DE. A buttonhole stitch used in handmade point laces.

B.O.V. Abbreviation for brown oil of vitriol, a commercial sulphuric acid about three-fourths of the strength of concentrated sulphuric acid. Organic matter in the compound gives a brownish color to the vitriol; hence, the name.

BOW, BOWED. Filling yarn in woven goods which does not keep to the right angle with the warp yarn; an off-angle, distortion, bow or bowed effect is observed in the crosswise filling in the fabric between selvage edges.

BOW, BOWS. Two or more loops of ribbon, cord, braid or other narrow fabric, etc., held together by tacking or tying or by means of some sort of clipping. Used by females from eight to eighty.

*Adopted from the *Knitting Dictionary* by Charles Reichman, Copyright 1966, published by the N.K.O.A.

BOW, TAILORED. A flat, stiff bow as seen on pumps and tailored headgear. Most of these are made from grosgrain ribbon. Periodically they are used on apparel items.

BOW TIE. A tie knotted in a bow with two straight ends or angled ends and tips.

BOW DYE. A scarlet dye named for Bow, Essex County, England.

BOWEDS COTTON. A species raised in Alabama, Georgia, and Virginia; used chiefly for filling yarn in counts ranging from 30s to 40s.

BOWKING, BOCKING. A bleaching term implying that impurities have been removed from cotton goods by boiling in lime-water solution for several hours.

BOWLER. In 1810 Locks Hats of London made the first bowler on the order of T. William Coke, who desired a sort of crash helmet for his hunt servants at Holkam Hall in Norfolk. The hats became known as Cokes (pronounced Cooks) or billycocks, so named for The Earl of Leicester who was involved in the introduction of this type of headgear and whose name was Billy Coke before he achieved peerage. British hat manufacturers still contend that the bowler is not a derby hat, although the derby is attributed to William Bowler who made a hat of this name for the 12th Earl of Derby. The original designer of this type of headgear was a French hatter by the name of Beaulieu. Now generally known as a derby hat. See Derby.

BOWSTRING HEMP. A strong, rugged bast fiber comparable with abaca, and obtained from leaves of the several types of Sansevieria plant, native to Africa. Also raised and used in America and Asia.

BOW WATER. May have some connection with "rainbow water." The so-called "rainbow" effect noted in certain warps may be caused by the soft misty effect given to warp stripes against the dark body warp and light-colored filling. The "wave" may be achieved rather well in herringbone.

BOX. See LOOMS, CHIEF MOTIONS OF.

BOX BALE. Cotton as it leaves the ginhouse is packed in bales, which measure about 5 feet by 3 feet, and are tide with iron bands. When box-baled for export, the bale is compressed to less than half its original size.

BOX CALF OR SIDES. See BOARDED LEATHERS.

BOX CHAIN. See LOOMS, CHIEF MOTIONS OF; LOOM AND WEAVING.

BOX CLOTH. A heavy, coarse, buff or tan-colored melton used for overcoating and habit cloth. Whipcord, covert, and heavy tricotine or elastique are sometimes substituted for the melton. All of these cloths may be used in formal types of clothing, and for this reason are usually made water-repellent.

BOX COAT. 1. A plain loose-fitting coat which is rather short and fitted only at the shoulder to give a squared, boxlike effect. Homespun, tweed, meleton, kersey, and comparable cloths are used to make these coats. 2. A heavy, cumbersome overcoat fitted with a heavy cape.

BOX COTTON. Cotton which is comparable with the government standards or the U. S. Department of Agriculture "Cotton Government Box of Standard Samples."

BOX DYEING. Piece dyeing of cloth in a single piece, usually in rope form, in a box, kier, jig, or vessel. See PIECE DYEING.

BOX FRONT. A plain, unfitted front of a garment.

BOX LOOM. 1. A loom with shuttle boxes on each side of the raceplate or raceway. The number of boxes may vary. In the weaving of checks, ginghams, overplaids, plaids, and similar patterns there will be one shuttle box on the one side of the lay and as many as seven boxes on the opposite side of the raceplate. This permits the use of seven colors in the filling motif used in the cloth. This arrangement makes it possible to obtain balanced and symmetrical designs of multicolored type.

Men's and women's wear looms, which take care of fabric up to 60 inches in width, have four boxes on each side of the raceplate. By this arrangement seven shuttles may be manipulated in the eight boxes without any trouble. The boxes are raised and lowered according to the plan worked in the box chain in the loom. Each shuttle can be brought into play at the proper time. Care has to be exercised in the building of the box chains and pattern chains since mistakes, blemishes, or shuttle smashes impair weaving production. Advantages of the four-box type of loom are that the designs may have a single pick of colored filling placed in the goods; a 7-and-1 arrangement requires two picks of filling. In the pattern construction the shuttle must go to the other side of the loom and then back into its original box before another shuttle can swing into action. The pattern chain regulates the raising and the lowering of the harnesses so that the correct harness will be raised at the proper time in order to make raisers in the cloth according to the design.

2. Fabric made with right-hand and left-hand twist in the filling, notably box-loom crepes. Such cloths include certain checks, ginghams, and plaids. A common name given to materials of this type made from any of the major textile fibers or fiber blends.

BOX-LOOM EFFECTS. Produced on a loom by which different colors of filling may be woven into the fabric by raising or lowering the required shuttle into the picking plane. Different colored cross-stripes are therefore possible in the filling direction, and are possible in fabrics such as plaids, tartans, blankets, dress goods, ginghams, and so on. The loom is often referred to as a multiple-box loom.

BOX MOTION. See LOOM MOTIONS, MECHANICAL; LOOM AND WEAVING.

BOX MOTION, STILL. Used on box looms, it is a device which will stop the action of the box chain the instant the filling yarn runs out from the bobbin.

BOX PLEAT. A pleat showing a rightwise and leftwise fold used mainly on skirts and the lower parts of dresses. Box pleats are made in various widths and are stitched partly down the edges to keep them in place.

BOXTRUCK. A box or container mounted on wheels and used for hauling bobbins, cones, spools, from one room to another in the mill.

BOYAUX. Ply cotton yarn of high twist, cabled for use as warp in tapestry weaving.

BOYCOTT. Concerted action by employees, and their union, to refrain from handling, purchasing, or working with the products of a particular company.

BOYD PROLIFIC. One of the Uplands type cotton with a staple of about 1 inch and a lint yield of about 32 per cent.

BRAB. The leaves of the Palmyra palm, from which sennit for straw hats is made.

BRABANCON LACE. Brussels lace.

BRABANT. Half-bleached or gray canvas made of flax waste in Belgium.

BRABANT LINEN. Linen fabrics made by the peasants in and around Ghent, Belgium.

BRABANT, LOOP. A cotton lace, made on a Leavers machine, in which the groundwork and filled-in motifs, outlined with coarse threads, are made by the warp.

BRABATINE. Italian term for bleached linen imported from the Low Countries of Europe.

BRACES. Suspenders in Great Britain with the idea in mind that bracers do "brace you" or cause you "to brace up."

BRACE WEB. An elastic or a tightly woven narrow fabric such as used in the manufacture of webbing for braces, suspenders, and comparable products.

BRADFORD LUSTER FABRICS. English term used chiefly for dress and lining fabrics. May imply the following: alpaca, brilliantine, Florentine, glacé, grenada, Lorraine-luster, luster linings, melange luster, Pekin stripes, and Sicilians. See also BRADFORD SPINNING.

BRADFORD REED COUNT. The number of beers of 20 dents in a 36-inch reed width. See BEER.

BRADFORD SPINNING. English method of spinning wool into worsted yarn. The wool is thoroughly oiled before it is combed, which produces a smooth lustrous yarn used for worsted suitings. This is distinct from the French system, which is dry spun.

BRADFORD STUFF. General term for fine Bradford worsted dress goods.

BRADYE. A dyeing method used on all-man-made yarn fabrics; may be applied to cottons as well. This durable finish is colorfast and not subject to gas-fading. Much used on draperies, blanket binding, and home furnishings. A trade name of Bradford Dyeing Association (U. S. A.).

BRAGG LONG STAPLE. A long but rather irregular staple obtained from late-maturing bolls; fiber length varies from 1¼ inches to 2½ inches. Lint yield is about 30 per cent.

BRAID. Any material made from textile fibers used for binding or trimming in widths up to three or four inches. Braid may be woven, round or tubular, or plaited flat. Some braids are: church lace, cordon braid, crochet braid, Grecian braid, fancy, French, Hercules, glacé, Russian, skirt, star.

BRAIDED RUG. A rag rug made of strips which are first twisted into wide, flat braids; they are then wound spirally around a center to form the mat.

BRAIDED TWILL WEAVES. On the order of entwining twills which are usually square in repeat; braided twills, however, will have twice as many ends as picks in the pattern, twice as wide as high in painted blocks on design paper, and in the fabrics made from these weaves.

BRAIDER. Device in which the yarns come off the respective bobbins as the latter move in and out on the frame, to permit intertwining of the yarns to make the braid.

BRAIDING. Ornamental needlework done by sewing braid over cloth, or forming braid into lace and similar work. Braiding means to entwine, interlace or weave together three or more yarns or threads.

BRAIDING MACHINE CARRIER. That part of a braider which holds the package of yarn, thread, or cord, and carries the yarn when the machine is in motion.

BRAID, WAVE. A braid on the order of rickrack braid with rounded waves rather than a serration-effect.

BRAID WOOL. Wool grading term more or less synonymous with luster wool. Compared with merino stock, it is low in quality and is used in medium- and low-quality clothing, carpets, robes, blankets, and low-priced uniform fabric.

BRAKE. The brake that stops a loom just as soon as the shipper handle is thrown out of notch.

BRAKE ARM. The long rod which reaches from the brake band to the front of the loom. It regulates the tautness of the brake band.

BRAKE BAND. The band of metal around the warp beam which governs the tension of the warp. Also known as brake drum.

BRAMWELL FEED. The automatic hopperlike feed set before the first card. The wool is carried to the top of the hopper by a series of spiked lattices, where it is weighed, evened-off, and then dropped through the weighing pan onto the feed table, which presents the stock to the feed rollers.

BRAN. See KLEANKA.

BRANCH, BRANCHING FIBER. Implies the main veins of leave motifs in bobbin lace sprigs as in Honiton and Pillow laces.

BRANCHT. Originated in the early sixteenth century, it is a colored fustian embellished with woven figured motifs.

BRANDENBURG. 1. A braided, ornamental loop or frog used to fasten the parts of a garment; used on robes, jackets, and naval officer's capes and coats. 2. A staple, popular greatcoat unveiled in the last quarter of the seventeenth century which was in favor for many years. The coat or a modified version of it is fastened by the use of frogs or loops which are still popular today in various types of winter coatings, long, medium or short; mackinac coats or jackets, and certain sportswear jackets. Strickly a coat for comfort and hard wear.

BRASS-BOBBIN YARN. Yarn which has been wound on a thin brass-bobbin for use as "filling" in the manufacture of lace curtains. This cotton yarn, in size, ranges from 2/60s to 2/300s.

BRASSIÈRE. A close-fitting foundation undergarment, a brassière gives shape to and supports the bust. Made of cotton, rayon, silk, or nylon, it is also known as bra, bandeau, or uplift.

BRASSIÈRE FABRIC. Light to heavyweight frabrics used for brassieres. Made usually in delicate shades, of cotton, silk, rayon, acetate, nylon, net. High-quality yarn must be used since the texture must be strong and firm. Some of the fabric is made with small dobby floral effects or Jacquard patterns. See COUTIL.

BRAT. General term for coarse clothing in general.

BRAT CHECK, CHECKERS. Any small check made from a warp and filling arrangement of two colored yarns followed by two white yarns.

BRATTACH. Old Celtic expression for standards or banners; actually a fabric.

BRATTICE CLOTH. A one-warp or two-warp and single-filling jute material, made in plain or twill weave, which is made rot-proof and used in mines as a wind screen and for ventilation purposes.

BRAYING. British term for the scouring of woolen gray goods from the loom to remove dirt, dressing, oil, stains, and so on.

BRAZIL, BRAZILWOOD. The red wood of a Brazilian tree, *Caesalpinia echinata,* or of several related species, used as a dyestuff; also, the dye obtained from the wood. Other types include sapanwood, limawood, and peachwood.

BRAZILIAN BAIZE. Orange-colored baize fabric which has been dyed by the extract obtained from brazilwood.

BRAZILIAN COTTON. Since 1780, Brazil has sent most of its cotton to England. This time, it will be noted, was the American Revolution period. England needed raw material for the looms of Lancashire, and since that time Brazil has carried on a lucrative business with British interests.

Since 1932, Brazil has made rapid strides in growing cotton for domestic and foreign use. At present, it raises about 500,000 tons, consumes about 150,000 tons, and exports the remainder. From the manufacturing standpoint, the 600 mills in Brazil are supplied by about 2,900 cotton gins while the by-product phases are cared for by about 2,100 presses. Planting is done in the northern area in December and January; from September to December in the southern district. Picking occurs in the north from August to December; in the south from March to May.

Pernambuco, named for the city, is the best cotton raised; it has a staple of about 1¼ inches, is golden in color, but is a trifle harsh and irregular when compared to some of the standard types. Pernambuco includes cotton raised not only there but in the districts of Ceara, Rio Grande de Norte, and Paraiba, as well. Ceara is dull white in cast and has an inconsistent staple.

In the perennial cotton group, Maco or Serido, a long-staple fiber, is the best produced. This tree cotton is silky, strong, and creamy in cast. The seed is black, bare, and has two spikes at the extremities. The flower is lemon-yellow in color, like that of most cotton plants. There are from 10 to 15 seeds in a single branch with about 150 to the tree. The trees are rooted-out every seven or eight years, but may endure as long as twenty years.

The outstanding annual cotton is the Texas staple; K.105 is another good staple from the Pernambuco district. Santos follows Ceara in quality and is dull white in color. Maranham resembles Pernambuco, has the golden tinge but is not as high in quality.

The state of Baia (Bahia) produces hybrid cottons known as Verdao and Rim de boi. Matta, an annual variety, is also raised there.

Espirito Santo, Rio de Janeiro, and São Paulo grow Texas, Piratininga, and Delfos 6102.

Maco is the best perennial tree cotton, Matta is the standard short staple, Sertao de Pernambuco is the medium standard, and Serido is the long standard.

Brazilian cotton is classified in the following manner:

First or Short is from 22 to 28 millimeters in length.
Second or Medium is from 28 to 34 millimeters in length.
Third or Long is 34 millimeters or more in length.

The five standard qualities are Good Middling, Middling, Low Middling, Strict Good Ordinary, Strict Ordinary. These qualities also have intermediate types to serve particular purposes.

Cotton bales of Brazil weigh about 250 pounds.

BREACAN. Original Gaelic term for clan tartan.

BREAD-AND-BUTTER COTTON. Those grades and staples of cotton that are medium in quality and always in demand for quick sale.

BREAK. A crack, dale, or separation sometimes observed in the surface effect of pile fabrics or true fur exposing the base or back texture in the item. If found in true fur it is considered to be a blemish or defect.

BREAK, BREAKDOWN. The preliminary or starting bath of a formula, designed to wet-down and to loosen and remove as much of the top or surface soiling as possible. Now replaced often by the first suds in modern formulae.

BREAK, BROKEN WOOL. Wool fibers, otherwise sound, which have weak, kempy places in them. Drought, disease, lack of forage, poor dipping methods, and poor care are the causes.

BREAK COMPOUND. Any detergent used in the initial operation in power laundering.

BREAKER. A machine which has a number of small rollers, finely fluted to various pitches, and used to break up the woody, pithy matter in fibers such as hemp and flax.

BREAKER CARD. The first card in either a three-set or a four-set carding arrangement for wool fibers. Made up of feed rollers, burr breast, main cylinder; a set of worker and stripper rollers (usually seven or eight of each type), fancy and doffer. The sliver from the card is automatically fed into the second card.

BREAKER FABRIC. Used in the manufacture of rubber tires, it is an open-mesh cotton fabric made with low-count yarn and leno or mock-leno weave. Nylon and rayon also used.

BREAKER LAP. A roll of loosely matted cotton fibers formed on the breaker picker machine from tufts of opened cotton.

BREAKERS, COTTON. Machines used after the bale bands are cut by shears; the bands and burlap are removed, the stock opened up. It is then thrown directly from the bale into the cotton breaker machine, the machine which starts the cotton on its way through the many necessary processes in manipulation.

The cotton is usually blown through large pipes from the bale room or storehouse to where the openers are located. The functions of the opener are to free the cotton from as much dirt as possible, get rid of the chaff, leaf, pod, and other matter, which may have clung to the fibers, even in its passage through the gin in first-time ginning.

Openers roll the cotton into a manageable lap form so that it may be readily handled. The delivered sheet form of cotton weighs about 14 ounces per yard, in lap form about 40 pounds when ready for the carding operation.

BREAKER TIRE CLOTH. An open-weave fabric of any of the following constructions: warp and filling of ply yarn, hawser cords in both directions, hawser cords in warp with single filling yarn.

BREAKING. The crushing and first separation of the woody portion from flax and similar fibers, following the retting process.

BREAKING ELONGATION. The increase in length, measured in centimeters or inches, of a material at the breaking load. See BREAKING LOAD, BREAKING TENSION.

BREAKING EXTENSION. The measure of the extension at the breaking load. See BREAKING LOAD, BREAKING TENSION.

BREAKING EXTENSION PER CENT. The extension per cent at the breaking load. See BREAKING LOAD, BREAKING TENSION.

BREAKING LENGTH. The length of a specimen whose weight is equal to the breaking load. Each breaking length should be multiplied by the local value of gravity and then divided by the set standard value which is 981 cm/sec^2 or 32.2 feet/sec^2.

BREAKING LOAD. The maximum load developed in a tension-type test brought up to rupture of the sample being tested. The number of pounds at which the fabric became ruptured can be read from the instrument scale. See Illustrated Section.

BREAKING OR OPENING MACHINES. A line or set of machines that work as a unit to tear or break apart and partially clean the matted, compressed, baled cotton.

BREAKING STRENGTH. The ability of fibers, yarns, and fabrics to resist rupture by means of tension. See Illustrated Section.

BREAKING STRESS. The breaking load divided by the area of the sample under test. Measured in grams/centimeters^2 or in pounds/inches^2.

BREAKING TENSION. The maximum tension developed in a sample or specimen stretched to the point of rupture. Expressed in terms of dynes or poundals; usually measured in gram weight or in pound weight, and if so, either weight should be multiplied by the local value of the gravity and expressed in dynes and poundals.

A dyne is a force which, when applied to a mass of one gram for one second, would give a velocity of one centimeter a second. The dyne is considered as the fundamental unit of force in the "cgs system." The "c" represents centimeters, the "g" stands for grams while the "s" means seconds in time.

A poundal is the unit of force in the foot-pound-second system which, acting on the mass of one pound for one second, imparts to it an acceleration of one foot per second, per second.

BREAST. The small cylinder on woolen and worsted cards which partially opens up the fibers before they reach the main cylinders of the machine.

BREAST BEAM. That part of the loom where the cloth comes over the beam after being woven and leaving the temples. It is located where the weaver stands or sits, at the front of the loom. This beam runs parallel to the whip roll located at the back of the loom, and is in the same plane with it; it is perpendicular to the warp and selvage edges of the warp, which complete the flat plane which makes weaving possible.

The woven material, after leaving the breast beam, passes downward and under it where it comes in contact with the sand roller; from there the cloth is wound onto the cloth roller, which may hold many yards of the newly made goods. The breast beam is a vital support for the loom.

BRED-STITCH. A type of embroidery stitch which gives the same motif on both sides of the fabric.

BREECH. See BRITCH WOOL.

BREECHCLOTH. Another name for loincloth.

BREECHES. At times called "breeks," the word comes from the Latin "brachae," which meant a leg covering. The Anglo Saxon version is "brec" which implied the lower part of the body including the buttocks. More or less interchangeable with pants, trousers, and slacks but at present not very popular term unless it implies the knickerbocker type of article used by men.

BREECHING. Clumpy, dungy, matted wool from the buttocks of the sheep.

BREEDS OF SHEEP, AMERICAN. See Illustrated Section. Their relative importance in this country at present is shown in table below.

BREEDS: RELATIVE IMPORTANCE

BREED	PER CENT	BREED	PER CENT
Rambouillet	26.80	Cheviot	104
Hampshire	22.66	Romney	0.57
Shropshire	19.93	Suffolk	0.48
Merino	12.37	Karakul	0.45
Oxford	2.90	Tunis	0.14
Southdown	2.84	Blackfaced	
Lincoln	1.59	Highland	0.12
Cotswold	1.43	Leicester	0.05
Corriedale	1.22	Ryeland	0.04
Dorset	1.08	Unspecified	4.26

BREEDS OF SHEEP BY TYPE, AMERICAN. The classification is shown in the following table.

BREEDS BY TYPE

TYPE	BREED	RAM	EWE
Fine-Wool	Rambouillet	66232-B	66233-B
	Merino	59981-B	65002-B
Medium-Fine-Wool	Targhee	77829-B	77822-B
Medium-Wool	Hampshire	65076-B	65084-B
	Shropshire	65022-B	65030-B
	Oxford	65017-B	65052-B
	Southdown	55468-B	55463-B
	Columbia	50420-B	50423-B
	Corriedale	66250-B	67744-B
	Dorset	65006-B	65038-B
	Cheviot	65088-B	59985-B
	Suffolk	71203-B	71201-B
	Tunis	65029-B	65037-B
	Ryeland	7374-B	7824-B
Coarse-Wool	Lincoln	7390-B	18578-B
	Cotswold	65049-B	66247-B
	Romney	6731-B	6771-B
	Leicester	3346-A	3174-A
	Blackfaced Highland	5675-B	37133-B
Fur	Karakul	37139-B	37845-B

BREEDS OF SHEEP, NEW AMERICAN. New breeds of sheep that have been meeting with favor in this country within the last few years include Columbia, Panama, Romeldale, and Targhee. The first three of these new breeds are of the medium-wool type, while Targhee is of the medium-fine-wool type. See Illustrated Section.

BRETANAS. Originally made in Ireland, it is an all-linen or cotton and linen plain-woven fabric made in Great Britain for export to Latin America.

BRETELLE. Decorative suspender-like shoulder-strap extending from waist-belt in front over the shoulders to waist-belt at back. Embroidered bretelles are very popular today among European peasantry. This work is such that various areas and peoples may be recognized by the effects seen on the garment.

BRETON EDGING. A popular narrow edging that is very low in price.

BRETON LACE. A net in which the design is embroidered with heavy thread, often colored. It is used for lace ground, and the fine net simulates Brussels but has a larger mesh.

BRETONNE. This is an inexpensive narrow edging that is used for lace ground. It is a fine net which simulates Brussels lace but it has a larger mesh when compared with this lace.

BRIBE. British term for damaged fabric cut from a bolt of goods.

BRICK STITCH. A flat couching stitch which is comparable with a regular course of bricks.

BRIDE. A small strip or connection which links the details of the ornamentation in lace. It may consist of threads overcast with buttonhole stitches or twisted or plaited threads. The English equivalent of this French term is pearltie.

BRIDE EPINGLE. A needle-made (epinglé) mesh ground for real lace, each side of which is covered with buttonhole stitches.

BRIDE LACE. Bone-point lace that is very popular with brides for wedding apparel. The motifs are of characteristic distinctiveness since they come in a wide range of patterns and are in keeping with the occasion.

BRIDLE LEATHER. A harness-finished strap leather.

BRIDE ORNEE. Brides in lacework embellished with loops, pearls, picots, scallops, etc. See BRIDE.

BRIEF. Knitted short pantie similar to a regular-length garment but shorter, shaped by means of a crotch, the leg slanting upward from the crotch toward the thighs, and usually fitting the leg snugly. Sometimes called "Jockey shorts," when referring to men's and boys' knit garments made in this manner. "Jockey" is the trade-mark name for briefs made exclusively by Coopers, Inc.

BRIEFS. Women's tight-fitting pants.

BRIER STITCH. A type of feather stitch.

BRIGHT AND DIM EFFECT. A warp-effect and a filling-effect satin weave, for example, could be set out in a checkerboard or some comparable arrangement to provide bright or light and dim or dark effects in a fabric as the rays of light strike the material. The effect is used to advantage in some dress goods and curtainings. The satin weaves would use a luster or bright warp and a dim or dulled filling would provide the attractive contrast in the goods.

BRIGHTENER. A compound or substance, usually a dye, which adheres to fabrics the same as dyes in order to provide better brightness or whiteness on cloths by converting the invisible ultraviolet light to visible light. Many washing products contain a brightener, but it may be purchased separately. An example of brightener would be the boiling of printed cotton fabrics in a solution of soda whereby clarity and brightness would be added to the color. Sometimes called Optical Bleach or Whitening Agent.

BRIGHTON WEAVE. Popular construction used in cotton summer dress goods. On the order of the honeycomb or waffle effect or weave, it is somewhat more complex in nature and is not reversible like the honeycomb weave. The weave produces the "hill and dale" or diamond effect and repeats on eight threads, each way. Repeats may run as high as 16 x 16 threads.

BRIGHT PICK. A bright line in cloth made by uneven tension in winding or weaving.

BRIGHT SILK. Silk which has all of the sericin or silk gum removed; may run from 10 per cent in the poorer qualities to about 30 per cent in the superior types, before degumming.

BRIGHT WOOL. A common term applied to wool raised this side of the Mississippi River, where the farm system of sheep raising is popular. Contrasted with semi-bright and Territory wools, bright wool is light in cast, contains less dirt and other foreign matter, and is a clean type of fiber.

BRIGHT YARN. General name in the rayon industry for lustrous rayon yarns as contrasted with dull, semi-dull, or extra dull.

BRILLANTE. A millinery trade fabric of the light, sheer variety. Made of raw silk warp and filling, it is piece-dyed. May have tendency to curl or "lip."

BRILLIANCE. Also called value, it is a measure of light reflected by a color. Light color has high brilliance since it reflects more light than dark color which has low brilliance.

BRILLIANT. Indicating a finish of great luster; may be applied to any fabric.

BRILLIANTE. A nainsook cotton cloth embellished with small woven lappet, clipspot, or swivel figures; includes the so-called warp-float motif.

BRILLIANTINE. Cloth in which a bird's-eye pattern is woven into the material on the Jacquard loom. Calender finish is given the goods. There is another fabric of the same name, made of cotton warp and luster worsted filling. Lincoln wool is often used for the worsted filling. The cloth may be woven on a plain loom or Jacquard to give figures. Some of this dress-goods fabric is made with mohair or some other hair fiber filling.

Printed Brilliantine is an imitation of the woven fabric.

BRIM-CURLING MACHINE. A machine that rolls or curls the brims of hats. The hat is placed on the machine with the brim between power-driven rollers that rotate the hat as they turn and feed the brim through a heated, metal guide that curls it.

BRIM FLANGE. A wooden form with which hat brims are pressed to shape them.

BRIM-IRONING MACHINE. A machine for smoothing and flattening hat brims. The machine contains a heated table, a spindle that projects above the table, and an iron suspended from an arm above the table. A hat, stretched over a hat block, is fastened to the spindle; the machine is started, and the arm is moved into contact with the hat brim to press it.

BRIM-PRESSING MACHINE. A steam press for smoothing and flattening hat brims. The machine consists of a heated, padded table with a hole made in it to receive the crown of the hat, and a heated cover or lid which is hinged to the table in such a manner that it can be closed against the table to press hat brims, and raised away from the table to remove hats from the press.

BRIM-STRETCHING MACHINE. A machine for stretching the bottoms of hat first-bodies to enlarge the part which will later become the brim. The hat body is placed on a block, with its bottom edge between two sets of metal fingers. One set of fingers vibrates, stretching the hat bottom to produce a bell-shaped flange.

BRIN. A singe filament or strand of silk from the cocoon thread. Also a rugged cotton, linen, or cotton-linen fabric used for dress goods.

BRINE. Water highly saturated or impregnated with salts.

BRINS. The two filaments cemented together by the sericin or silk gum as they are emitted by the silkworm in spinning its cocoon. See BRIN.

BRIOCHE. A foot cushion, usually knitted or braided.

BRIONNE. French term for a range of bleached linen curtain fabrics.

BRISTLE. 1. Coarse, stiff hair from the hog, boar, and so forth. 2. Any rugged, short, stiff fiber.

BRITCH WOOL, BREECH WOOL. Wool from the lower thighs or hind quarters of the sheep, usually the coarsest type found in the fleece. It has considerable length but is very irregular and of little value. This wool is used in cheap suitings and coatings, windbreakers, ski cloth, mackinac material, and carpets.

BRITISH CELANESE, LTD; TRADE-MARKS OF:

1. CELANESE: Describes fibers, yarns, fabrics and other products of the company.
2. COURLENE: Polyethylene monofil and yarn.
3. DICEL: Acetate yarn.
4. TRICEL: Triacetate fiber and yarn made from purified cotton linters or specially pure grades of wood pulp. Used alone or in blends to make blouses, dresses, lingerie, shirts, skirts, suitings, and other garments. Easy to wash, rapid-drying, little or no ironing, and the fabrics will not shrink nor stretch; it is soil and stain resistant, and can be permanently pleated and embossed.
5. CELAFIBRE: Acetate staple which provides stability in blends.
6. SERACOUR: Bulked filament acetate yarn.
7. SERATELLE: Acetate strip yarn.
8. SERACETA KN: Latent crimped acetate yarn.
9. OPACETA: Acetate yarn of special whiteness.

BRITISH GUM. One of the names under which dextrin is marketed, a thickener used in finishing.

BRITISH SHEETING AND SHIRTING. Made in Great Britain, they are given more sizing than similar cloths made in this country.

BRITISH SILK INDUSTRY. By 1600, England had a flourishing silk industry; by 1750 several thousand looms were weaving silk in Cheshire, Derbyshire, Essex, Lancashire, Norfolk, and Yorkshire. The industry improved constantly until about 1860, the time of the War between the States in this country; from that time forward the industry has declined since other nations became more silk-minded. Labor conditions and costs had much to do with this decline.

BRITISH THERMAL UNIT. The BTU or Btu is defined classically as the amount of heat necessary to raise the temperature of one gram of water one degree Fahrenheit. See B.T.U.

BRITISH WARM. A heavy, warm, greatcoat worn in cold weather by British army officers. The cloth used may be chinchilla, melton, kersey, beaver or similar face-finish fabrics, all dyed the regulation army shade.

BRITISH WOOLS. Great Britain lays claim to more breeds of sheep than any other nation. About 45 distinct breeds are raised there, practically every known distinct type. British wools are now classified into five groups: Long-fiber, Demi-luster, Down, Half-breeds, and Mountain. These sheep are chiefly of the mutton type with the fleece of secondary consideration, hence the heavy fleeces found there. Some fleeces will weigh around 30 pounds. Britain exports about half of its wool output, much of it to the United States.

BRITTANY CLOTH. Cotton, linen, or cotton-linen fabric made in Brittany, France. This white shirting and dress-goods fabric is given a high, lustrous finish. It is made on hand or power looms.

BROACH COTTON. Indian cotton of good whiteness, soft feel, and staple slightly under one inch; one of the better Indian staples.

BROAD. A straight-fibered, nonelastic wool.

BROADCLOTH. Originally the opposite of so-called narrow cloth. Considered as an inferior material. Modern broadcloth is a term used today with no particular significance, and it covers a host of materials. Unless made of silk, rayon, or cotton, the cloth in the woolen and worsted trade, with regard to quality and classification, is a splendid fabric made in staple colors, has a compact weave, and receives a high, lustrous, appealing finish.

In men's wear, black broadcloth has a limited use since it has been superseded by dress worsteds for evening and full dress purposes. The fabric is still popular in legislators', diplomats', and other formal circles.

In the same group of face-finished fabrics as beaver, kersey, and melton, popular broadcloth runs from ten to sixteen ounces per yard. An ideal weave to use is a 2-up and 1-down twill, with the goods woven face down. Some of the material may be made with a plain weave. The material is set very wide in the reed of the loom to allow for the great shrinkage in order to obtain the proper width. Higher qualities of the goods are form-fitting and ideal for women's wear tailored suitings, where drapiness and clinginess are essential.

In women's wear, the cloth is popular since it comes in a variety of popular colors and is conventional. The crowfoot weaves are ideal for use in the women's wear cloth.

The following procedure may be used in finishing broadcloth; the stock and the finish given are comparable with beaver; fulling, however, is for about three hours while all "raising" of the fibers must be done with utmost care since it is the lightest of the four cloths in this category—beaver, kersey, and melton. Only about one-half the raising as that used in a beaver will suffice in finishing broadcloth. Decating is a feature operation applied to the material. All four cloths and their finishes depend to a great degree on the original layout of the goods and the desired result. Costs have much to do with the final finish obtained.

Silk, cotton, and rayon broadcloths are rather soft, closely woven, of good texture and receive smooth, satinlike finish. These fabrics find much use in shirting, dress goods, coats, pajamas, waists, etc.

The term "broadcloth" is very broad and may, at times, be more or less of a misnomer. It is a popular term in the advertising of textiles and may be used indiscriminately when some fabrics to which the name is applied are analyzed. Incidentally, broadcloth may

be said to belong to the family of terms which have several meanings, such as all-wool, camel-hair, cashmere, crepe, Cheviot, gabardine, Shetland, serge, tweed, velour, and others.

BROAD GOODS. Woven goods of silk and/or rayon that are 12 inches or more in width; includes cloths to be used in the manufacture of neckwear. English practice is to classify any over 18 inches as broad goods.

BROADLOOM. Carpet woven wider than the 3/4 (27 inches) and 4/4 (36 inches); widths usually 6, 9, 12, 15, and 18 feet.

BROADTAIL. 1. The fur of the unborn or prematurely born lamb of the black Persian sheep of Russia, Afghanistan, and Central Asia. It differs from true Persian lamb in the degree of mottling effect of the rich, black surface. As a garment, the coat gives fair wear, and it is judged by the sleek, flat surface and pattern. Worn chiefly for dress. 2. Another name for a baby lamb.

BROADTAIL FABRIC. Pile fabric, women's wear coating material which simulates genuine broadtail fur; often called Karakul.

BROAD-TAIL SHEEP. Another name for fat-tailed sheep.

BROAD WOOL. Term for a non-elastic, straight-fibered wool that is low in serrations per inch.

BROCADE. Material generally reputed to have been developed from the original silk type to a high state of perfection in sixteenth- and seventeenth-century France, Italy and Spain. The name, very likely, comes from the Spanish "brocado" which is derived from the Latin "brocare" which means to figure. The French for brocade is "brocart." The fabric is characterized by a compact warp-effect background with one or more fillings used in the construction to make the motif or figure. The filling threads, often of gold or silver in the original fabrics of this name, float in embossed or embroidered effects in the figures.

Brocade and damask differ in that the figures in brocade are rather loose, while in damask the figure threads are actually bound into the material by the use of a tight construction or weave formation. In both cases, the background of the fabrics is usually a warp-effect satin weave.

Motifs may be of flowers, foilage, scrollwork, pastoral scenes, or other design. Many types of Jacquard patterns and designs appear in the field of brocades, the prices of which have a wide range. Some of the material,

because of the yarn and the design, will show some embossed surfaces which greatly reflect the rays of light, thereby enhancing the scintillating beauty of the fabric.

Uses include curtaining, hangings, pillows, portieres, interior decoration; it is also used in stage presentations, evening wraps, church vestments, and at state and regal occasions. See Illustrated Section (Fabrics 72).

BROCADE, COTTON. A simulation of silk brocade but more on the order of damask than true brocade. Fine yarns and high pick count feature this cloth in which raised motifs are made. Mercerized cotton yarn is used in the warp while the filling is acetate or rayon. This multicolored material uses the floats in the satin weave construction to form the pattern. The small, rather simple motifs in this fabric permit its being made on a dobby loom; larger formations are woven on a Jacquard loom.

BROCADE, FOUR-PLY. British term for napery fabric made with two warps and one set of filling in which four colors are used. The fillings form the motif and the plan of weaving is on the double plain method and could be the system known as "four colors in double plain weaving." It may be used as a decorative fabric in addition to napery—tablecloths, napkins, runners, etc.

BROCADED SATIN. Cloth made with basic satin weaves, with the design made of some contrasting weave and color to bring out the effect. Pile weaves are often resorted to, in the more expensive types of the cloth, to bring out brilliant spots of design and color.

BROCADING. Jacquard fabrics such as damask, brocade, and brocatelle enhanced by the use of gold or silver threads interspersed in the motif.

BROCADING FILLING, BROCADING WEFT. The filling used to weave hand-woven or power-woven brocade. French, trame brochée; Italian, trama di spolinato.

BROCADING SHUTTLE. Any of the types of shuttles which carry filling yarn used to weave brocade, hand-woven or power-loom woven. French, espolin; Italian, spolino.

BROCAT, BROCART. French for brocade.

BROCATELLE. Fabric, thirteenth- or fourteenth-century in origin, supposed to be an imitation of Italian tooled leather. Brocatelle is recognized by a smooth raised figure of warp-effect, usually in satin-weave construction, on a filling-effect background.

True brocatelle is a double cloth fabric made of silk and linen warp and silk and linen filling. Rayon may replace the silk in the present-day material. The silk or rayon warp weaves with the silk or rayon filling, to make the face of the fabric; a fine linen or fine cotton warp weaves with the linen filling, to make the ground. Present-day materials are somewhat changed in effect from the original fabrics, but they all have preserved the embossed figure in the tight, compact woven warp-effect.

The various warps and filling interlace with one another, but the face warp is never woven in the back of the cloth, nor does the back filling, generally speaking, show on the face of the goods. The face filling yarn does weave on the back and the back warp weaves on the face.

When not on the face of the material making the figure effect, the warp lies in between the face and the back fillings. The warp arrangement in brocatelle is either a 2-face and 1-back or a 4-face and 1-back arrangement. The filling construction is either a 1-face and 1-back or a 2-face and 1-back arrangement. Brocatelle, while classed as a flat fabric, shows patterns which stand out in "high" relief, a sort of blistered effect.

Used chiefly for drapery, furniture covering, and general decorative purposes.

BROCATELLE DE PASSEMENTERIE. A cotton warp and wool filling curtain or drapery fabric that has body and substance.

BROCATINE. Material woven to imitate couched embroidery; made with raised patterns.

BROCHÉ. 1. Broché is French for figured. Applies particularly to figures swiveled in the weave design; a loom-embroidered effect. Used in novelty and fancy dress goods. 2. A thin pinstripe or line which runs in the warp direction in dress goods, shirtings, and suitings.

BROCHÉ CARPET. Wool carpet made with a figure which is formed by the cut pile over a Brussels ground weave.

BROCHÉ COUTIL. Broché, from the French verb brocher—to figure, to emboss, to stitch, or to sew. Thus, a Jacquard design foundation fabric in which floral motifs are featured, used in the manufacture of bras and corsets. This sturdy material has a texture of around 160 x 90, and 2/50s or 2/60s mercerized yarn is used.

BROCHÉ QUILT. A bed covering made with a warp-effect weave, made

in two colors at least and arranged end-and-end to form the ground and the figure. The filling yarn is hardly discernible.

BRODÉ. Brodé is French for embroidered.

BRODERIE. French term for the embroidery of motifs.

BRODERIE DE MALINES. Broad term for simulations of Malines or Mechlin laces made by embroidering. Originated in Malines, Belgium.

BRODERIE EN LACET. Braid stitched to a satin foundation; the patterns are filled in with stitches to simulate lace.

BROKEN CHECKS. Woven check patterns in which, by weave effect, the checks are a trifle irregular as distinguished from the regular cubic form of the check.

BROKEN CROW WEAVE. A 1-up and 3-down, or a 3-up and 1-down, broken twill with 2 ends to the right and 2 ends to the left. Sometimes known as the "four-shaft satin weave." Also called crowfoot weave.

BROKEN DRAW. A manner of drawing-in warp threads from the drawing-in plan. For example, eight ends could be drawn in from 1 to 8, consecutively, while the second set of 8 threads could be broken and drawn in as follows: 4,3,2,1,8,7,6,5.

BROKEN-END, BROKEN-PICK. A warp end or filling pick that has become broken at some point in the weaving on the loom. Broken threads are fixed by the weaver's knot, by twisting the two broken ends together, or by an ordinary knot. Broken yarn should be fixed at once, otherwise the fabric may have to be classed as a "second." Broken threads or small holes in fabric may be mended with a needle after the goods have come from the loom. Fastening a bright-colored yarn to the end will facilitate finding it when mending or sewing.

BROKEN FACE EFFECT. British term for "broken effects" in sateens. Usually done by the "double satin method," which means adding an extra raiser to the top, the right, the left, or below the basic interlacing. Some quarter turns in satin weave constructions are also used.

BROKEN PATTERN. When the pattern or design has become broken because of some irregularity or error on the part of the designer or some operative. The woven pattern must be in strict accord with the original sample to produce required results and effects. Much broken pattern work occurs in weaving where the work of rectifying

mistakes is not always done correctly.

BROKEN TWILL OR TWILLS. Weaves made from a regular twill weave by running the twill in one direction for a desired number of threads and then reversing the direction of the twill from running to the right by causing it to run to the left, and by making as clear a break as possible at the "break" or "break-line."

A clear break in a weave is made by the placing of the raisers on the one thread opposite the sinkers of the adjoining thread; this is possible only in the case of certain even-sided twills.

An example of this would be to have the sinkers of the first thread of the left-hand twill come opposite the raisers of the last thread of the right-hand twill at the break-line.

2-up and 2-down twill,
eight ends to the right, and
eight ends to the left.
2 repeats high x 1 repeat wide.

2-up and 2-down twill,
four ends to the right, and
four ends to the left.
2 repeats high x 2 repeats wide.

Incidentally, all herringbones are broken twills, but all broken twills are not necessarily herringbone weaves.

See also Illustrated Section (Fabrics 34 and 36).

BROKEN TWILL SATEEN. A 5-harness satin weave, counter of 2 or 3, is used to give the effect of discernible twill lines in the goods. The "breaks" in the twill line give smooth surface-effect to the cloth.

BROKEN WOOL. Parts of a fleece that are irregular and weak. This is caused by the sheep being diseased or sick. There are some portions of the fleece that are unaffected. The term also refers to wool torn from a fleece.

BROKER. The agent or factor commissioned to contract for raw materials, unfinished cloth, gray goods, finished cloth, and so on. Brokers are sometimes commissioned to sell finished articles by textile houses.

BROKES. Wool of little use or value, taken from the neck and belly when the fleece is being sorted.

BROMELIA FIBERS. Found chiefly in tropical American countries, and named for the Swedish botanist, Olaf Bromel, 1639–1705. Spanish moss and the pineapple fiber are in this group. The fibers are fine, long, and strong in most cases.

BRONZED FABRIC. The metallic or bronzed surface effect given to some decorative fabrics; much used in theatrical circles.

BROOMROOT, BUNCHGRASS, MEXICAN WHISK, RICEROOT. A wild grass found in Texas and Central America. The long roots extend several inches into the ground and are a matted mass. Cleaned roots are yellowish in cast, over a foot long, resilient, and stiff. Used for many types of brushes.

BROUSSA. Name given to the elaborate sixteenth-century silks made in Asia Minor.

BROWN. 1. Any of a group of composite colors which vary from reddish-yellow to yellowish-red in hue. Orange, red, and yellow, mixed with black will produce shades of brown. 2. The coarse wool from the flanks and shanks of English crossbred sheep fleeces.

BROWNELL TWISTER. A machine used to give round smooth threads such as shoe laces, waxed cord, loom cord, harness cord, etc. Reverse twist is done by the main flyer of the frame which winds the thread onto a suitable bobbin.

BROWN-HEADED MUTTON SWISS. Raised chiefly for mutton purposes, this sheep gives a good 2-inch staple and fleece of about 6 pounds.

BROWN HEMP. Another name for Sunn hemp.

BROWN HOLLAND. Linen cloth in the unbleached or partially bleached condition.

BROWN MATCHING. Wool from the flanks and shanks of British crossbred fleeces; can spin to about a 28s worsted yarn.

BROWN OSNABURG. 1. Coarse British fabric made from off-color cotton, hemp, or unbleached flax, used chiefly in this country. 2. A coarse fabric woven in the Southern states. It is made from off-color cotton, or from mixtures of card strippings and other wastes, blended in the pickers and manipulated into yarn.

BROWN, ROBERT. Man who in 1802 brought out a device to make nets of all sizes. This was the first twist-net

type of frame and served as the incentive to lace mechanics and inventors of the future, who were, within the next few years, to develop lace-making machines.

BROWN SHEETING. Covers all weights of cotton goods in the gray or unfinished state. Prior to finishing, most cottons are brownish in cast; bleaching makes them white.

BROWN SHIRTING. All weights of cotton gray goods less than 40 inches wide.

BROWN SOURING. This treatment is given to cottons by placing the material in a bath of hydrochloric acid, or mild sulphuric acid, to neutralize the lime soaps and free lime used in the kier bath to complete the dissolution of the motes and sizing, and to emulsify any oil or grease which may be in the goods. This souring also removes residual portions of pectins and fats from the material. A second kier bath may be given after this treatment; bleaching then follows.

BROWN WOOL, BROWN MATCHING. Wool-sorting term for stock taken from the flanks of English crossbred fleeces; spins to about 28s.

BROWNIAN MOVEMENT. A ceaseless movement of ultramicroscopic particles of colloidal nature. Really a result of bombardment by molecules. First observed in 1827 by the botanist Robert Brown. This so-called movement is important in detergent processes.

BRUGES. The eighteenth-century Netherlands were noted for their Bruges silks, especially satins; Bruges, now in northwest Belgium, is still a textile center.

BRUNEL. Inventor of the circular knitting machine, in 1816.

BRUSH BINDING. A stiff-fringed braid used in binding the bottom of skirts.

BRUSHED GOODS. Knitted fabric which has been given a brushing or raising of fibers to produce a nap. It is done by brushes clothed with fine, pressed steel-card clothing about one inch in length.

BRUSHED MOHAIR FABRIC. This fabric made from the hair of the goat, is given a vigorous brushing to raise the natural fuzziness of the fibers. The result is a softening and muting of the motif or pattern and a deep, luxurious silk-like hand.

BRUSHED RAYON. Woven or knitted rayon fabric which has been given considerable brushing or napping by the teasel treatment or by rollers covered with card clothing used for napping purposes. Used in shirts, sleeping

garments, sportswear, and sweaters.

BRUSHED WOOL. 1. Knit or woven fabric which has been brushed, napped, or teaseled. Used in some garments, scarves, sweaters, trimmings. 2. Term in the pulled wool trade which implies fibers taken from scrubbing or brushing that is given to the stock in order to remove burrs, shives, grit, dirt, and other foreign matter. This treatment is given to the wool when it is on the pelt.

BRUSH FIBERS. Stiff coarse fibers of the vegetable family used in the manufacture of brushes.

BRUSH, FLAT BRUSH. A long cylindrical mechanism fitted with four spiral rows of bristles; purpose is to brush out and clean the revolving flats on the cotton card.

BRUSH GIN. See AIR BLAST GIN.

BRUSHING. 1. Done by various types of brushes, dependent on the material to be treated, it is the actual removal of loose fibers or yarns from the face of the goods.

2. Providing a nap for woven or knitted fabrics for pleasing surface effect. May be done by teasels or by card clothing rollers clothed with fine, pressed steel wire similar to that found on the fancy roller on the cord.

BRUSHING MACHINE. A machine set with a roller or rollers which are clothed with card clothing of fine pressed steel wire, or teasels, to brush, to nap, or to raise the more or less protruding, loose fibers on fabrics. Brushing is resorted to after shearing or a full napping treatment.

BRUSSELETTE. A pile fabric made of jute in which solid-colored yarn or printed yarn is used to reveal the pattern. It is used for cheap squares, rugs, carpets, and stair covering.

BRUSSELS CARPET. Named after this important city in Belgium, the carpet was developed after 1700, when Belgium became the rival of England in making carpets. Brussels is a staple which is made in body, border, and stair carpet sizes. There are 6 to 10 piles to the inch in texture. Tapestry and Body Brussels are in the Brussels group of fabrics.

Brussels is made with three-ply or four-ply woolen yarn. Tapestry is a printed carpet made with woolen or worsted yarn.

Within recent years carpeting called Brussels, made with a cut-pile structure, has found favor here. There is a wide range of carpeting under the name, and the variety and color patterns vary considerably.

BRUSSELS GROUND. Formerly made by hand, this machine-made lace of cotton or linen has a hexagonal mesh ground in which four threads are used in the manipulation.

BRUSSELS LACE. This is a bobbin or needle-point lace. The bobbin lace, hexagonal ground, has four sides made with four threads, plaited four times, and four sides of two threads twisted together twice. The embossed effect is achieved by cordonnet. The ground is worked around the motif in very elaborate brides and toile.

In point lace, the hexagonal ground is made in strips one inch wide and joined by rococo stitching which pieces together the individual segments to make the larger pattern. The cordonnet is not buttonholed.

Modern Brussels is made of sprigs appliquéd to machine-made groundwork. Brussels needle point has no cordonnet. The buttonhole cordonnet of Alençon is replaced by a single thread or strand. See CORDONNET.

BRUSSELS NET, BOBBINET. A machine-made net used as a basis for hand-embroidered, machine-embroidered, and appliqué laces. The machine for making it was invented by John Heathcoat, in 1808.

BRUSSELS PILLOW LACE. Fine pillow lace which has patterns joined by small loops on the edges. The pattern is completed first, and the groundwork is then built around the former.

BRUSSELS POINT LACE. An opened-closed stitch arrangement in a pattern that is used to give bright-and-dim effects in the material.

BRUSSELS, SAXONY. A curtaining made with a net ground and with the pattern obtained by laying another thickness of mesh, with the outline tamboured by hand, and then cutting away the loose, straggly outer parts and threads. See TAMBOUR.

B.T.U. Also written as BTU or Btu, it is the abbreviation for British Thermal Unit and is the quantity of heat necessary to raise the temperature of one pound of water one degree, Fahrenheit, at or near its point of maximum density—39.1 degrees, F. It is equivalent to 0.252 kilogram-calorie.

B-TYPE MERINO. Higher than A-Type and lower in classification when compared with C-Type merino, the wool is fine, strong, less wrinkled when compared with the A-Type but of longer staple.

BUCALENI. A crimped polyester yarn for use in the knitting trade. It is the first trademarked yarn of Glen Raven Mills, Inc., New York City, since its well-known Bucaroni yarn was perfected in 1963.

BUCK. 1. A male goat used for breeding purposes. 2. In the Boston and Philadelphia markets the term

means wool obtained from rams.

BUCK FLEECE. Fleeces shorn from rams.

BUCKLE. A device made of various elements used on the ends of belts for the purpose of securing and fastening the belt into position. They are sometimes made of metal or leather and are used as a decorative feature on shoes, handbags, and other accessories.

BUCKLEY BEATER. Popular type of beater found on cotton openers and pickers. It consists of several circular plates which are tautly mounted on a horizontal shaft. A series of rugged steel fingers, bent with different offsets, are fastened to each plate.

BUCKLEY OPENER. Applied to several types of cotton openers which employ the Buckley beater as an active device. The function of this opener is to continuously open the stock and to remove heavy foreign matter.

BUCKRAM. Cheap, low-textured, cotton cloth, heavily sized. Used for linings in skirtings, in the millinery and suiting trades, and in bookbinding. Sturdy in feel, stiff and boardy.

BUCKS. Used in the Boston and Philadelphia wool markets to mean wool taken from ram sheep.

BUCK SIDES. Cattle side-upper shoe leathers given a suede finish to imitate true buckskin. Often sold under proprietary trade names.

BUCKSKIN. 1. A cotton cloth with a clear surface and napped back. Better grades are made with an eight-end, filling-effect satin weave, a base of three or five being used. An extra raiser is added at the top or at the right of the basic raisers in the repeat; this affords a tighter interlacing of the warp and the filling when compared with the ordinary eight-shaft satin construction. Cheaper grades of buckskin are usually made with a five-shaft satin weave.
2. A rugged, durable, woolen fabric made on an eight-shaft, warp-effect satin weave. The cloth is heavily fulled and napped, and is then cropped so that a smooth finish results. It is used for overcoating and riding breeches.
3. A leather whose source is the skin of the elk or the deer. It is used for gloves and shoes, and to some degree in clothing.

BUCKSKIN WEAVE. An eight-end satin weave made with a base of three or five; an extra raiser is added at the top or at the right of each of the basic raisers in the repeat. This affords a tighter interlacing of the warp and the filling when compared with an ordinary eight-shaft satin weave.

BUENOS AIRES WOOL. This wool constitutes about 50 per cent of the Argentine clip. The stock, mostly of the crossbred variety, possesses good hand and ranges from 32s to 46s in quality. The term is often rather loosely used to imply the entire Argentine annual wool clip.

BUFFALO CLOTH. Once popular material. Now mackinac cloth has replaced it. Buffalo cloth was heavy in weight, made from twill weave; the finished cloth had considerable nap. Found usage in the cold sections in winter. Fabric weight ranged from 20 to 30 ounces per yard.

BUFFER. In the chemical sense, it is a substance which tends to maintain a constant pH value in the face of concentration changes brought about by dilution or neutralization.

BUFFERING. The use of certain soft, dry absorbent fabrics to provide a "cushion" for wet clothes in a dryer. Buffering may be resorted to to balance small wash loads and to lighten the washing action on very delicate or sheer fabrics or garments.

BUFFING. A very light cut of grain portion (about one half) taken from the surface of cattlehide. It is produced usually in the manufacture of upholstery leather. Used for bookbinding and fancy leather articles.

BUFFING FABRICS. A wide range of cloths used for buffing and polishing purposes.

BUGGY WHIP COTTON. Staple that is difficult to sell because of some specific reason.

BUGIS. English colored goods woven with a border down one side only. This native cotton dress goods is popular in the Straits Settlements.

BUILDER. An ingredient, usually mildly alkaline, added to an all-purpose soap or synthetic detergent to improve cleaning effectiveness and to soften water.

BUILDER FABRIC. Now largely replaced by tire cord fabric, the material is a square-woven, heavy duck made with thick, heavy-ply yarns: ten to fifteen ply is used in the yarn, and the material runs from 17 to 23 ounces.

BUILDER MOTION. Device found on several of the machines used in cotton yarn manufacture. Its purpose is to wind roving or yarn onto the bobbin in a uniform manner. The motion has an even up-and-down action.

BUILDERS, ALKALIES, ALKALINE SALTS. Chemicals used to soften water, to neutralize acidic salts, and to improve the detergent action of soap.

BUILDING. The use of an alkali to raise the detergent efficiency of a soap solution. An ordinary soap solution does not have all the necessary properties of an ideal cleanser, and is not "hardy" enough to withstand temperatures and the mechanical action in washing. It is destroyed quickly by water hardness.

To reinforce soap, alkali in one form or another, and in varying proportion, is used with the soap. Consideration must be given to the effect of the alkali selected upon the fiber, color and rinsability, as well as detergent efficiency. It has been shown scientifically and in practice that the combination of soap with efficient yet safe detergents represents the closest approach to ideal conditions.

BUILT SOAP. A mixture of soap and one or more alkaline detergents; containing not less than 50 per cent of anhydrous soap.

BULGARIAN COSTUME. See Costume, Bulgarian.

BULK CLASSING. Classing or grading small mixed lots of wool from several owners into larger lots in the wool broker's establishment or warehouse. A re-sorting of leftover wool according to breed, color, condition, length, and quality, to obtain larger lines.

BULK GRADE. The greatest percentage of the grade of wool fiber in a lot of original-bagged wool.

BULKING. Comes as a result of texturizing yarn in which the individual filaments of the yarn are taken out of parallel alignment and are fluffed-up thereby causing creation of air spaces among the filaments. This increased the loftiness of the goods and also aids in receptivity of dyestuffs applied for color.

BULKING PROCESS. Any of the several methods or procedures used to crimp, curl, or loop textile yarns so that these yarns take on a bulked appearance. Bulked yarn occupies a greater area than non-bulked yarn. High-bulk yarns are spun yarns made by blending high-shrinkage staple fibers with staple fibers of low shrinkage. Strictly speaking, bulked process yarns are not textured yarns since they are made from staple stock and not from continuous filament. Bulked yarns provide a soft, flufflike-effect or opaque effect on certain woven and knit fabrics.

BULK OR BULKED YARN. A comparatively new term for modified continuous filament yarn which simulates a spun yarn in textured effect with high loftiness and good coverage. The changed cross-section of the yarn makes it possible to obtain this bulki-ness. While the yarn does have some elasticity, it does not seem to be able to cope with the elongation and the recovery of stretch yarn. This term does not include high-bulk yarn. See TEXTURED FILAMENT YARN, HIGH-BULKED YARN.

BULKY RIB. Produced on a flat, circular rib, or links knitting machine, this coarse rib fabric is obtained by all-over tucking on a half-cardigan or full-cardigan basis. The machine cut ranges from 2½ to 5 needles per inch, and when finer cuts are used half the needles are used on an alternate basis to obtain the coarse cut loop formation.

BULLION. 1. A fringe made of gold or silver threads for use on uniforms. 2. A lace enhanced by the use of metallic threads such as gold or silver in which these threads are stitched to the ground fabric.

BULLION CORD. Certain yarns twisted around a cotton core yarn to produce a cord; the outer yarns are usually nylon, acetate, or rayon. Used chiefly in bullion fringe in which the filling in is made up of one highly twisted cord that is looped at the bottom, the two sides of the loop being then twisted together to prevent fraying. Very fine bullion fringe is known as twine fringe.

BULLION FRINGE. A fringe in which the filling consists of one end of highly twisted cord that is looped at the bottom; the two sides of the loops are then twisted together, thereby preventing fraying. When used on flags and banners it is known as banner fringe. Very fine fringe of this type is known as Twine Fringe. Bullion comes from the French "bouillion," a term that signifies the fringe used on military epaulettes originally made from gold and silver threads.

BULL MUCK. English term for tops of poor and irregular quality.

BULL'S WOOL. Colloquial term for very low-grade, coarse woolens,

BULL'S-WOOL-AND-OAKUM. Colloquialism for clothing fabrics of very low and inferior quality.

BUMBLEBEE COTTON. The very short-staple cotton always found in the market.

BUMP COTTON. Hard, flat chunks of cotton found in bales when excessive moisture, grit, and sand were present during the process of compressing the bale into form.

BUMPING. Process by which an employee, whose job is discontinued, may take over the job of another employee with less seniority than his own. The displaced employee may, in turn, take over the job of some other employee with lower seniority, or is laid off.

BUMP TOP, BUMPED TOP. The press-packing of layers of horizontally coiled sliver, slubbing, or top stock to make a package. The top is built up in a cylindrical form round a vertical spindle which is centrally located in the removable false bottom of the sliver can.

BUMP YARN. Made from low-quality cotton waste, this coarse-spun yarn with little twist comes in a yarn count of 1 or below. Used as wadding in coarse toweling, honeycombs, and quiltings.

BUNCH. 1. A linen measure for measuring yarn. Depending on the size of the yarn there may be from 1½ to 12 bundles in the bunch. 2. A length of 180,000 yards of linen yarn.

BUNDLE. 1. An Irish linen term which means that there are 60,000 yards of yarn in 10 pounds. 2. Hanks or skeins of yarn set up in 5- or 10-pound packages.

BUNDLE GOODS. Skating and ski socks, work socks, and other heavy types which weigh not less than one pound per dozen pairs, and are packed in bundles and sold in that way.

BUNDLE PRESS. A machine that makes up hanks or skeins of yarn into a bundle.

BUNDLE YARN. Hank-wound linen yarn compactly pressed into a 10-pound package ready for shipment.

BUNTAL. It is made from stalks of the unopened leaves of the buri palm of the Philippine Islands. This light fiber is used to make hat braiding.

BUNTINE. Same as bunting.

BUNTING. The name derived from the German "bunt," meaning bright. Cotton or worsted yarn is used to make this soft flimsy, plain-woven cloth. Some of the cloth is made from cotton warp and worsted filling. Cotton bunting is made from heavy cheesecloth and comes in the white or is piece-dyed. Ply yarn may be used in this plain-woven, fairly loose-textured cloth which has a texture ranging from 24 to 36 by 24 x 32. All-worsted bunting is used in making flags.

BURANO LACE. Needle point, similar to Alençon lace, made on the island of Burano, Venice. It has a square mesh, cloudy effect, and cordonnet.

BURATES. A fine, plain-weave worsted veiling used in South America.

BURATINE. Persian (Iranian) raw silk.

BURATTE. A plain-woven, well-sized linen fabric, buratté is used for drawnwork in Italy.

BURBERRY. 1. A lightweight cotton fabric which has been mercerized and waterproofed; high quality material. 2. The classic, staple cheviot for suiting, topcoats or overcoats, in a twill weave and made to be sturdy, yet elegant, casual, and correct in all details. Located in the Haymarket in London, Burberry attire made a great name for itself at the time of World War I with its officer's trenchcoat and mufti coats. Following the War, Burberry suitings and coatings made their debut in this country and have been in demand ever since.

BUR, BURR. See BURR.

BUR COTTON. An empty boll or hull after the seed cotton has been removed.

BURDER. English term for woman operative in a woolen or worsted mill who does burling, mending, and speckling in the dry-finishing department of the mill.

BURE, BUREAU. Buré, the more common name, and by which the fabric is generally known, is a French men's and women's wear fabric identified by its densely napped face effect. It is a union cloth, since cotton is used for the warp while the filling is wool in which waste wool fibers often comprise a goodly percentage of the content. This coarse, low-textured material made with a low-twist, bulky filling is used to considerable degree by the poorer economic classes in France.

BURI FIBER. Fiber furnished by the buri palm in the Philippines, and used to make bags and bagging.

BURITI FIBER. A leaf fiber from the Brazilian palm used to make straw hats.

BURL. A knot, nub, lump, or slub in yarn or fabric.

BURL, SPECK DYEING. In reality not actual dyeing but the "inking-on" over specks and particles of vegetable matter that are best treated by the use of ink. Many woolens and worsteds, because of their nature, show vegetable matter specks in piece-dyed fabrics. Special inks are used; they come in all colors.

BURLAP. A coarse fabric of plain weave, usually made of jute or allied yarns. Much of the material is woven forty inches wide and is from six to fourteen ounces in weight per yard. Comes natural or may be dyed; when printed, finds use in curtains and hangings.

BURLING. A process linked with specking, mending, and sewing in the dry-finishing department of the woolen or worsted mill. It is the removal of as much objectionable matter as pos-

sible from the goods. The burler, with the aid of a burling iron or tweezer, removes loops, nubs, faulty knots, vegetable matter, etc.

BURLINGHAM. Trade name for a coarse domestic silk cloth of Oriental character.

BURLING IRONS. Tweezers used in the dry-finishing department of the mill, for burling fabric. Made of steel, they usually have a needle attachment which enables the worker to pick out tough nubs, loops, or knots from the cloth so that they may be cut off.

BURMA. Lower in quality when compared with Indian types, this coarse wool finds use in the manufacture of carpets and rugs.

BURNETIZING. The impregnating of canvas or cordage with a solution of chloride or zinc to prevent rotting. Therefore used extensively on maritime fabrics and cordage.

BURNETTE. A brown colored dress fabric that was popular during the Middle Ages. The name is a contraction of brunette, meaning brownish in cast or color.

BURNISHING ROLLER. A roller, comparable with the striper roller on the carding machine, used to straighten and taper-off the pressed steel-wire card clothing of the various rollers of the card when they are being ground so that they can again perform their work on the card.

BURNLEY PRINTERS. Plain-woven cotton gray goods made in city of this name in England for several centuries. This popular fabric is sold all over the world for converting purposes. Texture is 64-square, yarns are 32s warp and 34s filling and cut length range to about 116 yards. Also known as Burnley Lumps.

BURN-OFF. Used in the field of laminated fabrics, it shows the variance between the beginning thickness and the finished thickness of urethane foam after it has been subjected to flame lamination.

BURNOOSE. Woolen cloak with cowl attachment worn by Arabs, Moors, and other tribes in Africa.

BURN-OUT LACE. This term is applied to lace made by embroidery methods, in which the embroidery is made of one material while the background is made of another type. The background can be destroyed by an acid treatment in order to leave a lace effect in which the embroidery motif is unaffected.

BURN-OUT OR BURNT-OUT PRINTING. A chemical method is used in this type of printing to obtain the motif. For example, a cloth may be

made of acetate and rayon; treatment in an acetone bath destroys the acetate content and leaves the rayon yarns unscathed, thereby producing the pattern. Eyelet embroidery, filigree, lace, and other burnt-out effects may be achieved in this way, including thick-and-thin effects. Fabric examples include scarves, perforations in some dressgoods, and shawls.

BURNT-OUT, ETCHED-OUT FABRIC. A material which contains two different yarns whereby the pattern effects have been produced by acid. The acid is used to treat one of the yarns in order to remove certain portions of it, to create a patterned effect or motif. Basic weaves are used in the construction. Used for dress fabric and curtains.

BURNT-OUT PRINT. Print, also known as Jacqueline or soda print, in which the burnt-out area of the pattern has been "cut" by the use of an acid.

BURNT-OUT PRINTING. Process of printing whereby the motif is printed with chemical onto woven goods of paired threads of different fibers (acetate and rayon, for example), and one of these is burnt out from the areas printed. Often used on rayon velvets and scarf fabrics.

BURNT-OUT PROCESS. A method of making some laces and embroideries.

BURR. (Textile usage, this spelling.) 1. Vegetable matter, chiefly burrs, infesting Texas and California wools. It tends to cause matting of the wool. Burrs make it necessary to sell the fleece somewhat below the price of comparable wools raised elsewhere in this country. 2. A small lump, nub, or slub found in cloth while it is being finished in the dry-finishing department of the mill, before the cloth is ready for wet-finishing operations. 3. The waste portions found in preparing raw silk for market.

BURRAH. A striped, plain-woven cotton cloth worn by African natives.

BURR BREAST. The first mechanical device, other than the Bramwell Feed, for the first breaker card, which consists of the feeding rollers, the breast cylinder with its two workers, and strippers and burr guard. In sequence, there is a brush and burr cylinder plus another burr guard; the tumbler then presents the wool to the main cylinder. The function of the entire setup, since it is clothed with garnett and similar clothing, is to open up the wool and thus admit of the taking out of considerable portions of burr, chaff and other vegetable or foreign matters.

BURR CRUSHER. The burr picker is equipped with one or more sets of crusher rollers which break open much vegetable matter found in wool as it is about to be given the burring treatment or after it has been carbonized.

BURREAU. See BIRRUS.

BURRHEL. Wild sheep in the Himalaya Mountains area.

BURRING, CARBONIZING. This is an optional operation and follows the drying which comes after the scouring process. Sometimes, too much foreign matter, particularly of a vegetable nature, is found in the wool. Dusting is not a perfect operation. This vegetable matter often causes trouble, if allowed to remain in the stock as it is being run through the several machine operations, hence a necessity of removing it from the wool. Two methods are used: 1. Merely redusting the stock. 2. Carbonizing the wool. This is a "burring-out" or a reducing to carbon of the vegetable matter contained in the wool.

The stock is put into a solution of hydrochloric or sulphuric acid, at a strength of about 3 per cent. This strength depends on the quality of the wool being treated. The wool, which is in the bath for several hours, is stirred every now and then. Cement cisterns or lead-lined vats are generally used. Care has to be given to guarding against an increase of the strength of the bath because of the lining of the container in which the wool has been placed. If the bath becomes too strong, the wool is attacked, thereby causing it to disintegrate and become inferior when worked. The wool, on being taken from the scouring bath, is put through the dryer at a temperature of about 75° Centigrade. This causes the vegetable matter to dry up and to be reduced to an ash form. In this condition, the reduced vegetable matter is, after drying, readily shaken out from the wool in the form of dust. Carbonizing is not resorted to unless absolutely necessary.

BURR PICKER. A very rugged machine that aids mechanically in removing burrs, shives and other foreign matter from wool prior to blending, oiling and mixing. One large roller, and a series of smaller rollers, all with iron spur teeth, treat the raw stock in a rigid manner as it passes between the cylinder and the rollers that make up the set that comes in contact with the main roller. Foreign matter is beaten out. Burrs and shives in wool would seriously hamper the stock in its course through the many operations from raw material to yarn.

BURRY. Burr-infested wool found to some extent in Texas and California wools. Burry wool brings a lower price in the trade.

BURRY BLANKET. A plain-woven, coarse woolen blanket which has a nap.

BUR SHALE. Minute granules of cotton bur which have been chipped from the burs in the extracting and ginning operations. Also spelled burr.

BURSON KNIT. Stockings knit on two-faced knitting frames, shaped to the contour of the leg and tubular without a seam.

BURSTING STRENGTH. 1. In general the ability of a material to resist rupture by pressure. 2. In the specific meaning, the force needed to rupture a fabric by distending it with a force applied at right angles to the plane of the cloth, under specific conditions. 3. Also covers a test, usually made on knitted fabrics, to determine the resistance of the material to an applied bursting pressure. The pressure is applied in one type of tester by a rubber diaphragm, and in another by a metal ball.

BURSTING TESTER. A machine set up to subject a fabric to great pressure; usually of the hydraulic type, it will cause the yarns to break so that strengths may be recorded. This type of machine measures the resistance of a fabric to fluid or pneumatic pressure.

BUSBY. A tall fur hat with a baglike ornament hanging from the top over the right side; worn by certain guardsmen of Great Britian. Has been used for several centuries there. See Shako.

BUSHEL. 1. To alter, mend, repair, remedy or finish-off outerwear garments. Operators who do this work are known as bushelmen or bushelwomen. 2. A tailor's thimble is sometimes called a bushel.

BUSHIREH, BUSSORAH. Low-grade carpet wool from Mesopotamia; the fleece is very irregular.

BUSH JACKET. A shirt-like jacket usually made with four pockets; a single-breasted, belted jacket.

BUSINESS AGENT. The representative of a union responsible usually for conducting affairs of a local or groups of locals.

BUSKIN. 1. A boot that extends halfway to the knee; laced with cord or ribbon; a laced half-boot. 2. A woman's modern low-cut shoe with elastic goring at the instep. 3. The ceremonial stockings worn by a bishop over the ordinary purple stockings at Pontifical Mass in the Roman Catholic Church. Made of silk or nylon, they are embroidered with gold thread and are of the same color as the outer vestments. 4. The high shoes, laced at the ankle and reaching halfway to the knee, much used in Roman Catholic ceremonial services. They are made of silk or nylon shoe fabric in compact texture, and are adorned with gems and a buckle.

BUSSU. The fiber comes from a palm tree in Brizil. Fabric of this name is used for containers, work-clothes, etc.

BUSTLE. A type of pad that is worn on the back below the waist by women, to give fullness to the skirt; popular in cycles of fashion.

BUTACITE. A plastic used in making safety glass. This transparent poly-vinyl acetate resin possesses tremendous stretch and elasticity, adheres firmly to the two sheets of glass between which it is sealed, absorbs impacts against the glass, and prevents flying fragments of broken glass.

BUTADIENE. (Vinylethylene—CH_2: $CHCH$: CH_2) . . . (gas). It polymerizes readily, especially if oxygen is present. It is used as a base for synthetic rubber filaments.

BUTANOL, BUTYL ALCOHOL. A solvent for dyes and other chemicals.

BUTCHER-BOY. A term applied to a loose, short, box-type jacket gathered into a shoulder yoke and made with a button front.

BUTCHER'S LINEN. Plain-weave, strong, stiff, substantial fabric. Term often used incorrectly in many types of cloths, and unless this material is marked Pure Linen, one may be sure that it does not contain any linen. Genuine fabric is bleached to the white, calendered and laundered. Sheds the dirt, launders well, is durable, and gives splendid wear. When buying fabrics of this type be sure to read the label. Linen-textured rayon, a popular dress goods fabric, does not contain linen fibers.

BUTS: Biblical term for fine linens.

BUTT: 1. An irregular bag or sack of wool found in the Australian wool markets which contains 196 pounds of grease wool, or 112 pounds of scoured wool, with a tare of not less than eleven pounds. 2. That part of the hide or skin which covers the rump or hind-part of the animal; for example, horse butt. Belting butt is a whole cattlehide tanned for leather belting after the head, belly, and tail have been trimmed off. The butt-end is what remains after trimming off a double shoulder.

BUTTER CLOTH. Another name for cheesecloth.

BUTTERFLY TIE. A bow tie made with a narrow knot and flared ends.

BUTTER MUSLIN. Same as cheesecloth.

BUTTERNUT. Woolen homespun cloth which was dyed brown with extracts from the butternut tree; popular at the time of the War between the States.

BUTTERY COTTON. Desirable cotton which has a creamy or light-brown cast.

BUTTON. A device for fastening or ornamenting articles of apparel; it is usually round and is designated in the trade according to the composition, purpose, shape, or style. Examples of buttons are bone, cloth, coat, cup, flat, four-hole, gilt, half-round, hard-rim, horn, ivory, leather, mother-of-pearl, overcoat, pants, quarter-round, shank, two-hole, uniform, vest, wood.

BUTTONDOWN COLLAR. Popular shirt collar with the points fastened to front of shirt with button closures.

BUTTONHOLE MAKER. Buttonholes may be made by hand or by machine. In the former case, the operator makes and sews the buttonholes in the garment by hand. He is responsible for buttonhole location, folding the edge of the garment and the cutting of folded cloth at the marked points with scissors. The operative must also sew around the hole edges to finish off the work.

There are two types of buttonhole machines—"cut-first" and "cut-last." The machine worker operates the machine which automatically cuts and stitches buttonholes in garments or in garment parts. He is responsible for positioning the garment or part with the locating mark for the buttonhole under the needle; lowering the presser foot and pressing pedal to start the machine. In addition, the operator releases the presser foot and removes the garment when the work is completed. He should also be able to cut various sizes of the buttonholes.

BUTTONHOLES, HANDMADE. These are found in men's suits and coats of the more expensive types, and in women's dresses of the better grade. Handwork may be recognized on examination of the reverse side of the buttonhole. The stitches will be more or less uneven and spaced irregularly in comparison with machinemade buttonholes which have regular and even length stitches on the reverse.

BUTTONHOLE STITCH. A stitch with a double purl used to finish the edges of tailored bottonholes. This protects the material from raveling when it comes in contact with the button.

Also used in laces and openwork embroidery.

BUTTONHOLE TWIST. 1. Cotton, silk, rayon or nylon thread given particularly hard-twist for stitching buttonholes since rigid resistance is encouraged through wear. 2. A thick, plied cotton thread of 24 strands used to support the edges of buttonholes.

BUTTONING. Bunches or lumps of fibers peculiar to warp yarn during weaving; must be eliminated prior to final inspection of the goods.

BUTTONS, CUT STEEL. They were brought out at the end of the eighteenth century by Matthew Bolton in Birmingham, England. In 1824, Leavenworth, Hayden, and Scovill, Waterbury, Connecticut, made gold buttons with a head of Marquis de Lafayette on them since this was the time of the Marquis' visit to the United States. Remade in 1876 for the Centennial Exposition in Philadelphia, Pennsylvania, they gave rise to the use of campaign buttons which are still popular today. In fact, campaign buttons have become so well liked that they are used for various events, political and otherwise.

BUTTONS, HAND-SEWED. A knotted thread end and rather uneven sewing on the underside of a garment indicates a hand-sewed button. It is often a practice, especially in heavier fabrics such as those used for suiting, topcoating, and overcoating, to leave a length of thread between fabric and button, and to wrap additional thread around this extension to further strengthen the attachment and to allow for thickness of the fabric when the garment is buttoned. This so-called "neck" allows for "give" in lighter-weight garments.

BUTTONS, MACHINE-SEWED. Those sewed on by repeated machine stitching without knotting of the thread end. The thread is clipped at the button eye and often this loose thread protrudes, indicating machine sewing. If the thread is pulled, the entire stitching will ravel out. In other machine processes, the buttons may be chain-sewed with the thread floating on the underside of the garment from button to button.

BUTTON SEWER. There are two types: 1. The hand operator who sews buttons on garments by hand, after matching the buttons and marking locations on the garment. 2. The machine operator works on a button-sewing machine which automatically sews buttons to garment parts or to the garment, itself. The work involves laying the garment with location marks for the buttons under presser foot, opening of button clamp on presser foot, placing the button in the clamp and the clos-

ing of this clamp, lowering the presser foot, and then pressing the pedal to start the machine.

BUTTON-THROUGH POCKET. A convenient buttoning used on men's work shirts. The regular pocket, without the flap, is provided with a buttonhole for buttoning to the body of the shirt, thereby giving better protection for pocketed items during working hours. See POCKET FLAP.

BUTTS. Britch or low-quality wool or matted, dungy locks that are of little or no value. Another name for tags.

BUTYL ALCOHOL. An alcohol prepared commercially by bacterial fermentation of corn and used extensively in preparation of butyric acid and solvents.

BUTYRATE. A salt or ester of butyric acid. See Butyric Acid.

BUTYRIC ACID. Either of two isomeric acids which have a formula of C_2H_2COOH. See Butyl Alcohol, Butyrate.

BUYING OFFICES, SOME MAJOR. Allied Stores Marketing Corporation, Arkwright, Inc.; Associated Dry Goods Corporation, Associated Merchandising Corporation, Federick Atkins, Inc.; Independent Retailers Syndicate, Inc.; Kirby, Block Co., Inc.; Felix Lilienthal & Co., Inc.; Mercantile Stores, Inc.; May Department Stores, Inc.; McGreevey, Werring & Howell Co., Inc.; Mutual Buying Syndicate, Inc.; O'Shaughnessy, Drewes & Klein, Inc.; Wm. M. Van Buren, Inc.; Youth Fashion Guild, Inc.

BUZZ-FUZZ COTTON. Exceedingly short-staple cotton; some of this stock is so short that the fibers seem to have only two ends and little else.

BYRD CLOTH. Registered trademark of Reeves Brothers, Inc., for their light or medium-weight fabric made from combed cotton yarns. The 2-up and 2-down twill construction shows on both sides of the material which is very high in pick count, about 300 threads per square inch-warp and filling added together. The fabric is very strong but light and supple. Used for rainwear, shirting, and sportswear, it is made wind-resistant and is also water-repellent. Named for Admiral Richard E. Byrd.

BYRO-STRETCH. A stretch quilt fabric known for its good shape retention, a product of the West Coast Quilting Company, Inc., Los Angeles, California. Of sandwich-type construction, the outer shell is nylon taffeta to affort wind resistance; the backing is a layer of "Dacron" polyester fiberfill and a thin sheet of Scott apparel foam for warmth; base fabric is a scrim of cotton cheesecloth. In combining these four materials, the foam is held under tension during stitching. When released, the foam tends to relax. The resultant fabric has a very soft, puffy texture plus a virtually permanent stretch factor in one direction and on the bias. Outstanding for visual appeal, the product retains appearance and stretch qualities indefinitely without sagging, despite long wear and repeated launderings. Gyro-Stretch has excellent drape and exceptional "hanger appeal." It comes in plain and patterned shell fabrics with a choice of design in the stitching. It is used in many types of apparel.

BYSSUS. Ecru-colored flax used by the ancient Egyptians and Hebrews. Cloth of this name was used to wrap mummies. The term from the Greek meaning "hairy" or "beard." Was also known as linum byssinum.

BYSSUS SILK, PINNA SILK. Thread made by filaments which are secreted by a gland of certain marine mollusks. Known also as sea-silk, sea-wool, and pinna.

BYZANTINE CARPET. By the addition of metallic threads at intervals in the pattern, a Brussels carpet is "converted" into a Byzantine carpet.

C

°C. Abbreviation for degrees Centigrade.

CAADAHAR. Modern reproductions of ancient carpets known for appealing motif, color richness, and deep pile.

CAAPOROPY FIBER. A bast fiber obtained chiefly in Paraguay and used for matting, ropes, twine, etc. It has a flaxlike appearance.

CABALLEROS. A Spanish merino wood much used in French woolen and worsted mills.

CABANA CLOTH. Sportswear fabrics used at the beach or resort, usually made in bright, vivid colors. Name derived from the "cabana," which may be a beach tent, beach house, or some other shelter.

CABBAGE PALM. Australian plant. Leaves are used for plaiting hats, belts, novelties, and in making rope.

CABBAGE PALMETTO. Any of the various fan palms, chiefly the cabbage palm, found in the southern United States. The leaf stems are from eight to about sixteen inches long, straight and cylindrical. This resilient reddish-brown fiber is resistant to deterioration from water and is much used to make brushes. Also known as Palmetto.

CAB, CABBAGE. English term for tailors' clippings.

CABECA. Wool from the Estremadura area in Spain.

CABIN. A place or compartment where bobbins of filling yarn are stored for future use.

CABLE. The heaviest rope manufactured, it measures over ten inches in circumference.

CABLE CORD. A very heavy cotton cloth somewhat on the order of corduroy but made with wider cords or wales. A ground weave of 2-up and 2-down twill is used, and the fabric is heavily packed by having from 250 up to 400 picks per inch in the texture. See CONSTITUTION CORD.

CABLED YARN. The twisting together of two or more ply yarns into a single arrangement. Hawser or cabled twist may be used to make this very strong yarn.

CABLE-LAID ROPE. Made of three plain-laid ropes twisted together with each consisting of three strands for a finished rope of nine strands.

CABLE NET. Net made of strong, heavy cotton yarn in which large meshes appear. Usually made in a doup construction for curtains and hangings.

CABLE SILK. A thrown silk yarn, doubled and twisted on the order of cordonnet silk. This rather bulky yarn finds use for trimming, millinery, etc.

CABLE STITCH. A raised effect in knitting stitch. Appearance on the face of knit goods simulates twisted rope.

CABLET. Rope less than ten inches in circumference.

CABLE THREAD. Sewing thread made of three-ply threads twisted together against the original twist.

CABLE TWIST. A cord, rope, or twine construction in which each successive twist is in the opposite direction to the preceding twist. This type of twist is S-Z-S or Z-S-Z.

CABLE WEBBING. A strong, heavy, round yarn or thread is used to make this twill-woven webbing.

CABLE YARN. Name given to yarn of two or more ply that has been twisted together. More than two yarns are often plied together to increase the diameter of the cable effect. Cables have good twist and high tensile strength and are used for fancy yarns in suitings, coatings, and women's dress goods of novelty or fancy design. High-twisted and specially treated yarn is used for sewing thread.

CABO NEGRO. A Philippine fiber taken from the leaves of the palm tree and used for strong cordage.

CABOTS. "American sheeting" shipped to the Far Eastern countries. Cabots are made of plain weave, may or may not be shipped in the gray, come in widths of about 30 inches, and are shipped in 40-yard lengths. Yarns used are 20s or higher and textures are about 48 x 40. Warp yarn is fairly well sized.

CABRETTA LEATHER. In this country the word is used with reference to Brazilian sheepskins and can be applied to all hair sheep. The glove and shoe leather trades use much of this leather.

CABULLA FIBER. Sisal hemp in Central America.

CABUYA. Fibers obtained from the plant of this name in Costa Rica and adjacent areas; they are from 5 to 7 feet long. Coarser than henequin, Cabuya is used for cordage and twine.

CACERES. Medium-quality Spanish wool.

CACHEMIRE. French for cashmere.

CACHEMIRE DE SOIE. A high grade taffeta, usually made of fine silk yarn which is given a finish to resemble cashmere fabric.

CADDIS. A lace, ribbon, or garter fabric formerly popular in the British Isles.

CADDOW. Hand-woven counterpane fabric made in England.

CADET CLOTH. The standard blue, gray, or indigo and white mixture, made of woolen yarn, as decreed by the United States Military Academy at West Point, New York. Other public and private institutions use this or similar cloth. Heavy in weight, durable, rather boardy in feel, it is an excellent outdoor cloth. The material is a double-cloth construction. The texture is very compact, and the fabric is heavily fulled and carefully finished.

CADILLO. Fiber from the inner stalks of the cadillo plant. It is found in tropical and subtropical areas throughout the world. The stalks are retted by scraping and cleaning, and fiber length ranges from 3 to 8 feet. It is creamy white in color, ribbon-like in formation, and somewhat resembles jute in strength and texture. Also known as blanca, aramina, guaxima, and malva.

CADIS, CADDIS. 1. Lace, ribbon, or tape made of worsted yarn. 2. Twill-woven woolen or worsted fabrics used by Scotch Highlanders.

CADIZ STITCH. In needle-point lace, this stitch consists of successive rows of buttonhole stitches to enhance the effect.

CADON. A multi-lobal nylon filament yarn whose cross-section, contrasted with traditional, round filament nylon, reflects the light, thereby imparting greater luster to yarns and fabrics. It is used in woven and knit goods for apparel, home furnishings, and upholstery. Its covering power is greater than that of conventional nylon with a round cross section. Greater opacity permits lighter weight fabrics to be used and its wicking performance is greater than ordinary nylon filament. Registered trademark of Monsanto, Inc., New York City.

CAEN. A French woolen serge.

CAFA. Spanish term for low or inferior grades of plain woven cottons.

CAFTAN, KAFTAN. An Arab and Turkish undercoat which has long sleeves and girdles with a sash. The coating appears at present in a side-slit effect. Little or considerable embellishment appears on the garment to suit the whims of fashion and style.

CAGE SECTION. See SCREEN SECTION.

CAGEWORK. The openwork in embroidery or lace.

CAIANA COTTON. A type of Brazilian cotton.

CAJUN FIBER. A strong leaf fiber, similar to sisal, obtained in Central America.

CAKE. After extrusion from the spinnerets, one way of gathering rayon and some other filaments is in a "cake" formation. They are given a slight twist and run into a fast-spinning hollow cylinder or pot where they are then collected by centrifugal force in a round shape with an open center called the "cake," and made up of thousands of yards of the continuous filament.

CAKED. Hard cakes, granules or lumps of size or starch, sometimes found when weaving or finishing cotton fabric.

CAKE DYEING. A method of dyeing rayon yarns already collected in "cakes." After washing and treating, the "cakes" are then subjected directly to the dye bath without removal for winding until after the dye processing is completed. See CAKE.

CALAMATTA. An Italian raw silk in the un-degummed state.

CALCINED. To expel volatile matter, such as water or carbon dioxide, from a compound by heat. Glauber salts, for example, can be calcined by having the water of crystallization removed by heating.

CALCINO. A silkworm disease caused by the parasites, *Botrytis bassiana* and *Botrytis tenella*. Paralysis and death soon occur after attack.

CALCIUM. An alkaline earth metal. Used as an alkali base for calcium bleach, commonly called a lime bleach. Calcium or lime salts is one of the commonest forms of water hardness.

CALCUTTA HEMP. Another name for ordinary jute.

CALCUTTA SHEEP. A mongrel breed of sheep found chiefly in the Malay Peninsula; low quality; sorts to the lower grades.

CALEDONIA. The Roman name for ancient Scotland, lying to the north of the Forth and the Clyde. The country in the south was occupied by Britons and Romans. In the fifth century the Scots came over from Ireland and 300 years later the Saxons and Scandinavians gained a foothold. The name Scotland was adopted in the eleventh century.

A Caledonian tartan may be worn by anyone who has no other clan affiliation.

CALENDER FINISH. One of the most important common finishes used on cottons, it gives the material a clean, smooth, even, regular, appealing-to-the-eye appearance. There are times, however, when a superficial glaze is observed in calender-finished cloth.

Calendering, in the mill, is merely the factory method taken from the idea of ironing in the home. Cloth to be calendered is passed between the rollers of the calender frame; the number of rollers may vary from two to seven, depending on the circumstances surrounding the cloth. The goods may be passed over the rollers three or four times, depending on the particular finish sought. The finish may be dull, flat, glazed, watered or moiré, smooth.

The frame flattens and imparts luster to the goods, as it passes between the roller sets, because of the great pressure exerted on the cloth. The heat of the rollers is also an important factor in obtaining the desired finish.

By passing the folds of the cloth through the machine, the threads of the one fold will make an impression on the threads of the other fold. This will tend to give a wiry or marked appearance to the material. Calender rollers are heavy, but hollow in order that the infusion of steam and heat may be applied to the interior of the rollers. Heat does much in developing the final appearance of the cloth.

Rollers used in calendering may be copper, nickel-chromated, iron, or crushed parchment.

CALENDERING. A mechanical method done by rollers to provide glaze, glossiness, hardness, luster, sheen, and even embossed designs to textile materials. Calendering is usually done to afford a special finish to fabrics; usually not permanent to washing.

CALENDER ROLLS. 1. The main cylinders used on the calendering machine. The number may vary from two to seven rollers. 2. Smooth or fluted rollers found on the several machines used in cotton manufacture. The function of these rollers is to compress the lap, sliver, or slubbing as it passes through the various sets of rollers on the particular machine.

CALENDER SECTION. The sets of smooth and fluted calender rolls and the winding mechanism located at the delivery end of a cotton-picker frame. The function is to condense the cotton into lap form and to wind it into a roll about 40 inches or so in width.

CALF. In the broad sense, leather made from skin of an immature bovine animal. In a stricter meaning, the term implies leather made from the skin of a bovine animal that has not been weaned or has been fed only on milk.

CALFSKIN. Leather made from skins of calves.

CALIATOUR WOOD. An East Indian insoluble redwood dye.

CALIBRATION. The determination of the diameter of a particular yarn.

CALICO. Originated in Calcutta, India, and is one of the oldest cotton staples on the market. This plain and closely woven, inexpensive cloth is made in solid colors on a white or contrasting background. Very often, one, two, or three colors are seen on the face of the goods, which are discharge- or resist-printed. Calico is not always fast in color. Medium yarn is used in the cloth, and the designs are often geometric in shape. The yarn used is 30s, and the texture is about 66 x 54. Uses are for aprons, dresses, crazy quilts.

CALICO SHIRTING. Fabric dyed or printed with colors which "shed the dirt," and popular in the British Isles; withstands hard wear.

CALICO, WHITE. South African term for bleached cotton shirting.

CALICUT. British name for many types of plain-weave, cotton cloths in the gray state. Compare CALICO.

CALIMALA WOOL GUILD. Legend has it that this guild was functioning as a unit in 1190. Centered in Florence, Italy, the wool industry had a 400 year span of prosperity especially in the 15th and 16th centuries. The guild was made up of dyers and finishers in the Italian Renaissance Period, and the amount of business done, even in those days, was very great.

The Humble Fathers of Saint Michael of Alexandria, Egypt, came to Italy around 1240. They laid the foundation for the technology and procedure to be followed and from this time forward, many Italian cities, especially Florence, began to prosper. Italy had the business of Europe when it came to the dyeing of woolen fabrics, and the Florentines built up a great business with Great Britain, as well. By the end of the 16th century, however, because of indolence, laxity, and failure to tend to business, the guild passed into oblivion.

CALIMANCO. An old-time plain or striped woolen or worsted fabric made with plain weave. Given a luster-napped finish, the material was made to simulate camel's hair cloth. Now displaced by other, more practical, fabrics.

CALL COTTON. Really a short-time system of futures in buying cotton; the short time fixed between the buying and completion of the contract.

CALL-IN PAY. Payment made to employees who report to work at the company's request, at times other than their regular working hours.

CALMUC, KALMUCK: 1. Central Asiatic wool obtained from sheep of the wandering tribes in the Khirghiz area. 2. A loosely woven, twilled woolen made from loosely spun yarn. The fabric is heavily fulled and is given a long nap which makes it suitable for winter wear in cold climates.

CALORIE, GRAM. The calorie is defined in the classical sense as the amount of heat necessary to raise the temperature of one gram of water one degree centigrade.

CALORIE, LARGE. The amount of heat necessary to raise the temperature of one kilogram of water one degree centigrade. It is, therefore, one thousand times as large as the small calorie.

CALORIE, SMALL. The amount of heat necessary to raise the temperature of one gram of water one degree centigrade.

CAM. An elementary mechanism in the form of an irregularly shaped plate that is keyed, or otherwise secured, to a shaft. The rotary motion of the shaft is converted into reciprocating motion by means of a cam follower, a roller that rides the edge of the plate, which is pinned to a rod or crank connected to other mechanisms in the machine. The cam is used chiefly as a controlling or timing element in machines rather than as a part of a power-transmission mechanism. Cams are important parts on looms and knitting machines.

CAMACAS. A Cyprian brocade that was popular in the fourteenth and fifteenth centuries. It was used by church dignitaries and persons of affluence. The name probably comes from cammaca, cammaka and/or camoca, a material that was used to drape state beds during the Middle Ages. Composition of the cloth is unknown.

CAMAK. A very old, heavy, rich fabric made of silk and camel's hair fiber, silk and cotton, or all-silk, etc. Used for curtaining, vestments, and women's garments, it is also known by names such as Camaca, Cammaka, Camoca, Camacoa.

CAMAURO. The headpiece worn by the Pope instaed of the biretta, and which is a loose, full cap of red velvet trimmed with white fur. It has no brim. Permitted only on extra-liturgical occasions, it is seldom used today but is often seen in paintings of the Popes.

CAMAYEUX. Describes the effect when the motif and ground in fabric are different shades of the same color, a two-tone effect. Silk cloth of this name is made with colored warp and black filling, with the picks in weaving the goods working alternately single and double to produce a slightly discernible cross-rib or cord effect.

CAMB. British term for a heddle eye.

CAMBAYE. Lightweight, Indian cotton cloth made in the province of Bengal. It is used in domestic and foreign trade, particularly the latter since the cost of production is low.

CAMBIUM LAYER. Mucilaginous cells between the bark and the young wood in plants.

CAMBODIA. A strong, cream-colored, uniform staple cotton raised in India. Similar to American upland cotton, it has a staple of about one inch; considered one of the best of Indian cottons.

CAMBRAYON. Cotton gray goods in Spanish. Also a plain-weave cotton of about 64 x 56 made with yarn between 44s and 50s.

CAMBRE. Italian name for a very lightweight linen fabric. Cambré is of open veil-like structure.

CAMBRESINE. French term for good quality cotton and linen cloths which resemble cambric.

CAMBRIC. Plain-weave cotton fabric, bleached or dyed in the piece. Lower qualities have a smooth, bright finish. Light in weight, well adapted for sewing, has good body, is well sized and presents a neat finish. Since cambric launders very well it is popular for handkerchief linen, children's dresses, slips, underwear, and nightgowns.

CAMBRIC FINISH. A firmer and brighter finish than the muslin finish often given to cambric. The cloth is well-singed, calendered, and may or may not be a pure or back-filled cloth.

CAMBRIC, FLAT. A plain-weave, low-quality cotton cambric that is piece dyed and given a smooth, glossy luster. Texture is around 56 x 52 with yarn counts of about 40s.

CAMBRIC GRASS. Another name for the ramie plant.

CAMEL. There are two types of camel: the dromedary, or one-hump type, and the Bactrian, or two-humped type. Dromedaries, whose fibers are never used in fine fabrics, are found in Arabia, Egypt, Iran, Senegal, and Syria. Bactrians are native to all parts of Asia from the Arabian Sea to Siberia, and from Turkestan to the Steppes of Tartary, Tibet, Mongolia, and Manchuria to all parts of China. The finest fiber comes from Mongolia.

Three types of hair are obtained from camels:

1. Quality One: The "down-type" of fiber, also known as noil and next to the hide, is short, soft, and silken in feel. The fibers are beautiful light tan shades; they have good tensile strength and may be used in the natural condition or dyed dark colors. Quality One is used in high-grade fabric, which comes in tannish colors. The fibers of this quality are from 2½ inches to 3 inches long.

2. Quality Two: Beneath the outer hair of the animal there is a growth which combines the outer hair and the shorter, less coarse portion of the fleece. This grade is used in apparel fabric.

3. Quality Three: The outer hair—coarse, tough, and wiry—possesses cactuslike tipped ends and ranges in color from brownish-black to reddish brown. The fibers, which range from 4 inches to 10 inches in length, are used by natives in making blankets, tents, cord, and rope.

The camel sheds its hair in clumps and therefore is not shorn or plucked as in the case of other fleece-bearing animals.

CAMELEON. French term for the changeable effect seen in some fabrics. Two or three picks of different color are shot into the same shed to bring about the effect. Full color or mottled yarns may be used. See Chameleon.

CAMEL HAIR, CAMEL'S HAIR. Hair obtained from camels. Rather wool-like in texture, its natural color varies from light tan to brownish black. This underhair of the camel is lustrous and extremely soft, and used, either by itself or combined with wool, for coats, suits, sweaters, some blankets, and oriental rugs.

CAMEL-HAIR FABRIC. A soft, spongy, medium-weight woolen cloth made to simulate the natural color of camel's hair, although the fabric may be dyed any color. The long nap is a characteristic selling point of the goods. The better grades are very soft and light in weight. The fabric gives good warmth.

CAMEL-HAIR SHAWL. A shawl or throw made of camel's hair, considered as a luxury article which commands a good price. Today, however, the term seems to have lost its original meaning since it is used somewhat indiscriminately to describe shawls regardless of the amount of camel's hair used.

CAMELINE. See CALIMANCO.

CAMELOT BARACANE. A French decorative fabric in which the warp yarns are lower in count and bulkier when compared with the filling yarns. See BARACAN.

CAMELOT CLOTH. 1. Coarse fustian used for work clothes in Great Britain. 2. A fabric woven of cotton and wool, having a waved surface.

CAMELOTE. French for cheap, gaudy, bizarre fabrics.

CAMEOLE. A satin-weave reversible cloth usually made with rayon warp and acetate or silk filling; other combinations may be used. This rather heavy material has a different color effect on each side.

CAMEL SUEDE. A cotton cloth which resembles camel's-hair fabric; the cotton content in the fabric must be stipulated in accordance with ruling of the Federal Trade Commission.

CAMELTEEN. An all-worsted cloth made to simulate genuine camlet fabric.

CAMERA. A coarse French linen in open texture with bleached or unbleached yarn; bleached fabric is often dyed in pastel shades, usually yellow.

CAMISA. An embroidered bodice or waist with large flowing sleeves. Worn by Philippine women and by some women in the Mediterranean areas. It is the Spanish word for skirt.

CAMISIA. Name often applied to an alb. Originally this referred to the place where the Book of the Gospels was kept in the early days of the Roman Catholic Churches.

CAMISOLE. 1. A kind of corset cover, usually loose-fitting and often trimmed with ribbon and lace with straps over the shoulders. 2. A short negligee jacket for women. 3. Refers to a neckline like that of the camisole-top slip, straight above the bustline,

with shoestring straps over the shoulders.

CAM, KNITTING. A device for actuating needles in knitting. By operating on the butts of the needles or jacks, the cam positions them to the desired knitting, tucking, welting, transferring positions, and others.

CAMLET. 1. Originally a costly material made in Asia of camel's hair; later made mixed with angora wool. 2. Imitations of hard-twist woolen and worsted yarn, with an admixture of silk or goat's hair and made with a satin weave. 3. A stiff, loosely woven, nearly waterproof fabric of camel's hair or some imitation or substitute.

CAM LOOM. This loom uses cams to control the shedding action; limited to small repeat weaves, chiefly in the filling direction.

CAMP. The large sheep-grazing areas in South America set up with a feeding center for the flocks, and where the estancias are located.

CAMPAGNE, CAMPAIGNE. An old-time French narrow lace made with picot or scalloped edging; made on the pillow and used as edging.

CAMPATILLAS. Woolen dress goods in Spanish.

CAMPBELL TWILL. Also known as Mayo twill, it is any diagonal weave that repeats on 8 ends and 8 picks; examples could be a $\frac{3\ 1}{1\ 3}$ or a $\frac{5\ 1}{1\ 1}$. Used chiefly in woolen dress goods.

CAMPECHE WOOD, CAMPEACHY WOOD. This wood supplies logwood for the dyeing industry. Named for the province of Campeche, a seaport in southeastern Mexico.

CAMPOS. A Spanish clothing wool.

CAMWOOD. See REDWOOD.

CANADAS. French woolen blankets.

CANADAS REAL. The hundreds of miles of well-defined "sheep paths" made by Spanish Merino sheep who used to roam at will in that country. The Arabs introduced this method of giving sheep a "free reign" there, and it seemed to reach its peak in the thirteenth century, that greatest of centuries except for the present century. Migratory and periodic habits of sheep could be studied by animal husbandry men. The limit of the longest paths was about four hundred miles.

CANADIAN HEMP. A common North American hemp which yields a soft, fine bast fiber.

CANDIED. Sized or weighted material which shows a crystallization in some areas caused by chemical reaction of filling agents used on the cloth. It is noted sometimes when weaving

or finishing cotton, silk, or man-made fiber materials.

CANDLE-FILTER. Candle-shaped device which contains fine cambric or similar cotton cloth through which the viscose solution is forced from the spinning pump to the spinneret in order to remove the final traces of foreign matter.

CANDLEWICK FABRIC. 1. Unbleached muslin bed sheeting (also called Kraft muslin) used as a base fabric on which a chenille effect is formed by application of candlewick (heavy-piled yarn) loops, which are then cut to give the fuzzy effect and cut-yarn appearance of the true chenille yarn. Used for bedspreads, drapes, robes, and so on. 2. A soft woolen dress material made in imitation of the candlewick bedspread, with tufted patterns similarly applied.

CANDLEWICKING. A cotton ply yarn noted for its loose twist and soft feel.

CANDLEWICK SPREAD. It is made of muslin sheeting with machine-tufted motifs of soft, rather coarse, cotton yarn called candlewicking. The yarn comes in white and all colors. Distinguished by its individually spaced tufts of dots which, taken collectively, form the designs or motifs. This is the point of demarcation from the chenille-type spread, recognized by its closely spaced tufts which form continuous lines. Supposed to have originated as a handcraft in the South, the work is now done by machines. See SPREAD, CHENILLE.

CANDY STRIPES. Also known as "peppermint candy" stripes, the effect is often seen in household and beach wear.

CANE. Another name for silk warp.

CANEBRAKE COTTON. A strong Alabama cotton which has a staple of about $1\frac{1}{16}$ inches; most Canebrake brings a higher price than cotton raised in other areas in Alabama.

CANE ROLLER. Warp beam.

CAN GILL BOX. The coiler head on the gill box deposits the sliver, slub, or top into the coiler-can attachment at the front of the machine.

CANICHE. Cloth that has a curly face in imitation of the fur of the French dog (poodle).

CANILE, CANNELE, CANALE, CANELLEE, CANELE. One meaning refers to the warp or the filling effect of some satin weave, or a variation of the basic construction.

When ribs are woven into goods, the term signifies the cord effect in the warp direction, somewhat similar to the Bedford cord weave. Filling effects can be made as well, and there have been instances where the term has been applied to these constructions.

Canilé (cannelé, canalé, canellée, canelé) is made of silk or rayon yarn with two warps and one filling. One warp is single ply, which gives body to the fabric; the other is a ply warp, which makes the cord effects possible.

CANNELE ALTERNATIF. Name in the French silk industry for a horizontally striped fabric whose odd and even threads alternate to form a rib effect by the use of floats on the face of the goods held in tight formation by the opposite system of yarn. In the weave, the odd-numbered warp yarns float together for several successive picks while the even-numbered yarns form the binding, interlacing on the reverse side of the fabric. On the next float while the odd-numbered yarns form the binding with tight interlacing with the opposite system of yarn used in the fabric.

CANNELE SIMPLETE. Term used in the French silk industry for a weave with horizontal bands, cannelé. The effect is characterized by a uniform arrangement of pile warp yarns which float together to form ribs above a ground weave formed by means of a ground warp, and then, in passing together to the reverse side of the fabric, interlacing with the filling yarn, usually for one or two picks.

CANNETE. 1. A fine wide cotton cloth made with cords which run in the warp direction. 2. A single-ply schappe silk yarn is also called canneté.

CANNETILLE. Cannelé simpleté, the pile warp yarns of which, instead of forming horizontal bands, are arranged in quincunx (four corners and the center of a rectangle; arrangement of five things in those positions) above a foundation weave formed by means of a ground-warp-plan construction.

CANNIQUIN. A plain-weave, handwoven, bleached cotton cloth made in India. Texture runs about 56 x 52 with 26s warp and 30s filling yarn used.

CANOPY. A covering, usually fabric, supported on poles and set over a bed, throne or window. This overhanging is used decoratively both indoors and outdoors.

CANOTIER. A French dress goods made on a 2-up and 2-down, twill or serge weave. Used for yachting and boating costumes and outfits.

CANT. The strand of the rope.

CANTAI. An Indian cotton muslin of about 48 x 42 in texture with yarns of 40s to 50s in warp and filling.

CANTALA. A fiber compared with sisal but inferior in all respects as to fineness of fiber, strength, and usage. Color runs from yellowish-white to brownish-white. Fiber is obtained from the leaves of the plant, *Agave Cantala*. Found in the Philippines, India, Java, and Sumatra. Also known as Manila Maguey, Bombay aloe, or Cebu Maguey in quotations for water-retted, hand-cleaned cantala stock of the Philippines. Used for twine.

CANTAR. A raw cotton measure used in Egypt. A Cairo cantar is 45 pounds; Syrian cantar is ·500 pounds. The crop in Egypt is based on the cantar weight of 98 pounds; thus an Egyptian bale weighs seven cantars or about 700 pounds.

CANTON COTTON. Sometimes referred to as Canton flannel, this twill-weave material is made with low counts of yarn, 20s to 30s in the warp, 8s to 14s in the filling. The cylindrical filling is slack-twisted in order to make a good nap possible. Canton is usually dyed in the piece or may be printed for use as underwear, lining, nightwear, coverings.

CANTON CREPE. This filling crepe has a pebbly surface and is made with six threads of right-hand twist followed by six threads of left-hand twist in the construction. The filling is silk of 14/16 to 20/22 denier in size. Canton is heavier than crepe de Chine. It is made today chiefly from acetate or rayon and finds use in coat linings, dress goods, dressing gowns, negligees, pajamas, scarfs, lounging robes, and accessories.

CANTON FINISH. A dull mangle finish given cottons to produce a firm feel without shininess or harshness.

CANTON FLANNEL. Cotton cloth that is heavy, warm, strong, and absorbent; made with plain or twill weave and known for its long, soft nap effect. Used for interlining and sleeping garments. Named for Canton, China, where it was first made. The fabric, when made of cotton, must be described as such, since the word "flannel" might imply the fiber content as wool.

CANTON LINEN. A misnomer for a rather stiff fabric made of ramie. Manufactured in the Orient, it is also known as grass cloth, grass linen, Chinese linen, and ramie cloth. It is used for luncheon cloths, doilies, and decorative linens.

CANTON SILK. Broad silk term for the raw silk from southern China. Despite its softness and good luster, the silk is difficult to throw because of its hairiness.

CANTOON. A compact cotton fabric which has fine twill diagonals on the face and a napped back. A 3-up and 3-down twill weave is used and high texture in the pickage gives the fabric strength and wearing quality. Used for riding breeches and camping clothes.

CANTRECE. A bicomponent monofilament or multifilament nylon yarn used primarily in women's hosiery and apparel.

CANTRECE II. Registered trademark of E.I. duPont de Nemours & Company Inc., Wilmington, Delaware, for its controlled stretch Cantrece nylon used in hosiery and pantyhose to provide excellent fit, instant recovery, and remarkable cling.

CANVAS. Also known as Numbered Duck, this plain-weave cloth is rugged and heavy. The ply yarns used give much strength and body to the fabric. From 2-ply to 14-ply yarns are used to make the goods. It is manufactured in the gray state or natural condition, but is also dyed olive drab or khaki for the armed services. Duck and canvas are more or less interchangeable terms today. Uses for canvas include tents, wagon covers, many types of army equipage equipment, sails, mail bags, sacks.

CANVAS CLOTH. A 3-ply warp and filling yarn is used in this open, plain-weave material used as a woman's-wear dress goods, a rather spongy type of material.

CAOUTCHOUC. See RUBBER.

CAP. In cap spinning of yarn, refers to a polished cap, six to eight inches long, just large enough to fit over the bobbin or spindle. Its chief function is to prevent ballooning of the yarn as it is being spun and then wound onto the bobbin.

CAP BAR. A small metal device used on the drawing rollers of various machines used in textiles to keep the top drawing rollers in correct line with the bottom drawing rollers.

CAPE. The upright part of a loom; the breast beam of an upright loom. 2. A soft grain glove or clothing leather made from the hair of sheep skin. 3. A sleeveless garment fastened at the neck and falling loosely from the shoulder. 4. The outer garment worn by a bullfighter, often decorative.

CAPE MOHAIR. Mohair fiber raised in the Union of South Africa which compares well with Turkish and Texas mohair. Summer and winter clips are obtained from the animals, and the fibers are brown to deep brown in cast. In classification the following designations are used—Cape kid, Cape first,

Cape winter, Cape Basuto, Cape mixed, and Cape Thirds. Basuto is the same as a Cape Second. Uses include braiding, headgear, lining, certain pile fabrics in the plush group (⅛-inch or more in pile height), and for blending with wool in mixture fabrics.

CAPELLA LAYOUT. Many crossbar or striped cotton fabrics manufactured in the British Isles are made with a capella arrangement of colors to brighten the pattern, particularly in the matter of goods made for the export trade.

The following is a typical capella layout of woven colors:

Half-inch of ground color
2 picks of white
Half-inch of ground color
2 picks of white
2 picks of ground color
4 picks of white
2 picks of ground color
2 picks of white

This arrangement is repeated for, say, five times. Then two or three inches of ground color are woven in the goods. The following arrangement, the reverse of the tabulated list above, is then woven in and repeated five times:

2 picks of white
2 picks of ground color
4 picks of white
2 picks of ground color
2 picks of white
Half-inch of ground color
2 picks of white
Half-inch of ground color.

CAPESKIN OR LEATHER. Glove leather that is made from imported hair sheepskins in which the natural grain has been retained. The term should be confined to the hair sheep of South Africa.

CAPE WOOLS. General name given to wool obtained in Natal, Orange River Colony, Transvaal, Rhodesia, and Cape Colony, the states which comprise the Union of South Africa. These high-quality fleeces are in great favor in this country because of their excellent working properties during manipulation; they are much sought for use in the heavier woolens materials.

CAPILLARITY. The action of movement of a liquid into very minute pores, tubes, or channels. The absorbency of textile fibers is an example, and the importance of clean pores, free from clogging dirt or soil, is obvious. It is also the action by which the surface of a liquid, where it is in contact with a solid, is elevated or depressed, thereby resulting in capillary attraction or capillary repulsion.

CAPIURES. The lacing threads used to hold silk skeins together in a book, chiefly used for Grant-wound skeins.

CAPOT. A strong British or French cloth that is rugged, heavily fulled, and has a napped face similar to kersey and melton. It is often waterproofed or water repellent. Used for ulsters, pea jackets, other types of coating. Reworked or reused fibers are often used in the fiber content.

CAPOTE. A large, loose cloak with a hood attached; made of heavy material, it is worn by women in cold climates.

CAPPADINE. Silk waste from the inner areas of a cocoon.

CAPPA MAGNA. Used by bishops, canons, and cardinals. This long vestment is lined with silk or fur and is usually red or purple in color. The fur is either white or deep brown. It is used for assistance at Divine Office and at Mass for a prelate who is not celebrating.

CAPPED. About one bale in four in Australian wool auctions is shown with caps removed; the front flaps only, of the rest of the bales, are dropped for inspection.

CAPROLACTAM. The raw material used in the manufacture of Nylon 6, the base of Caprolan, made by Allied Chemical & Dye Corp., Enka Nylon, IRC Nylon, Phrix Perlon fibers and filaments, and fine monofilaments made in Germany. The recurring amide groups, (C-NH-), serve as the integral

$$O$$

part of the polymer chain. See CAPROLAN.

"CAPROLAN." Name for Allied Chemical & Dye Corporation's polycapramide nylon filament, staple fiber, and tow. This "deep-dye nylon" has excellent affinity for all classes of dyestuffs used on nylon, and is outstanding in affinity for the acid, direct, premetalized acid, chrome, and vat dyes. Caprolan is a Nylon 6 fiber.

CAP SPINNING. A method of spinning yarn in which the twisting and the winding are done by passing the end under a stationary cap while the bobbin revolves inside of this cap. The cap covers the entire bobbin.

Cap-spun yarn is rather wiry, harsh, and boardy since long-fiber staple, coarse in nature, is often spun on this method. Cap spinning gives higher production when compared with yarn spun on the ring, mule, and flyer systems of spinning worsted yarn. It is much resorted to in spinning on the Bradford or English system; medium and below-medium fabrics are made from the yarn.

CAPTION. Coarse waste silk raised in France; used as stuffing.

CAPUCE. French for the woolen hood or cowl worn by members of religious orders.

CAPUCHIN CLOTH. The coarse brown cloth worn by the monks of the Capuchin Order of the Roman Catholic Church. The garment consists of habit and a cape or cowl. Wool, mohair, and other hair fibers are used in making material which varies in weight in accordance with the seasons.

CARACAMI. Italian silk waste.

CARACUL. A short, curly-haired fur distinguished by its flat, open wavy curl. Chinese caracul is larger and lighter in weight than Russian caracul, which is naturally brown, black, and occasionally white. Wearing qualities, good. Judged by luster of fur and pattern. Found in Russia and China. Worn for dress. Indian lamb, also in the caracul group, comes in white, black, or gray—now being dyed in honey beige and brown.

CARACUL CLOTH. Heavy woolen fabric woven to resemble Persian lamb. Used for women's and children's coats, capes, muffs, and so on. Named for the Persian lambs found in Russia.

CARACULE. A smooth cloth that features, at certain places, knots which are made of mohair, to simulate genuine fur caracul.

CARAGUATA. This long, soft, silky leaf-fiber of the bromelia in Brazil is used for roping.

CARAVONICA COTTON. This tree cotton was originally produced by crossing a long-staple Mexican cotton with a coarse-staple Peruvian cotton. It is, at present, classed as an Australian cotton and is also raised in Egypt and Peru with much success. There are two qualities of Caravonica —a silklike fiber and a wool-like fiber. The staple is comparable with ordinary American cotton, the chief difference being that, though the fiber is white in color, the tips have a yellowish tinge. The staple may be raised from soil which has very little moisture.

CARBASUS, CARBASSUS. Ancient Latin writers used this term in reference to fine cotton muslin made in India. Also implies linen cloths of any texture made from Spanish flax (Carbassus).

CARBOHYDRATE. A compound of carbon, hydrogen, and oxygen, such as sugar or starch. It contains the elements of hydrogen and oxygen usually in the ratio of two parts of the former to one of the latter—water or H_2O. Glucose is an example.

CARBON. An elemental substance with the symbol of "C." Diamonds are pure carbon, while coal and soot are largely carbon. Carbon is found in all organic materials, such as fats, sugars, meats. Has no known solvent.

CARBONATE. A chemical salt in which the neutralized acid is carbonic acid. Soda ash is sodium carbonate. See BASE.

CARBON BISULPHIDE, CARBON DISULPHIDE. An inflammable liquid, a compound of carbon and sulphur, which is mixed with alkalicellulose in the rayon manufacturing process, to produce a gelatinous mass called cellulose xanthate, orange in color. Xanthate comes from the Greek, and while specifically meaning orange, the term is applied sometimes to red, brown, and yellow.

CARBON DIOXIDE. Colorless, odorless gas (CO_2) given off by an animal body as a waste product. Green plants use it in making food.

CARBONIC ACID. An acid whose salts are carbonate in structure. Formula is H_2CO_3. See Polycarbonate Fiber.

CARBONIZED RAG FIBERS. Those animal fibers reclaimed by carbonizing, whether wet or dry; another name for Extract Wool.

CARBONIZED WOOL. All wool contains varying amounts of chaff, dried grass, burrs, straw, and other vegetable impurities. Carding and combing will extract the bulk of this matter but not all of it. These particles must be removed before the stock will give good results.

The wool is placed in a 4 to 6 per cent solution of sulphuric acid for one hour. Drying at moderate heat, followed by baking at 90° to 150° Fahrenheit, will reduce the vegetable particles to carbon, which is dusted out. Rag wastes lose the charred vegetable matter by willowing, while the excess acid is removed by soda ash and washing.

Wool noil will remain unharmed, if the strength of the bath has not been too great, or does not become stronger during the treatment—which must be carefully judged for exact timing.

CARBONIZING. Manufacturing process to free raw wool of burrs or vegetable matter. Done by using chemicals and heat. When wool is dry, the carbonized matter "dusts off." A process also used on re-used wool.

CARBONIZING, FELT. The immersion of semiprocessed felt in a weak solution of sulphuric acid to oxidize any vegetable matter present that might tend to retard the felting process.

CARCASS FABRIC. Any basic material that is later on coated, compounded, laminated, or treated in any other manner for use in industrial fabrics. See TIRE CORD; TIRE CORD FABRIC; TIRE FABRICS.

CARD. See CARDING; CARD CLOTHING; CARDING MACHINE.

CARD BASIS. The Cotton Duck Association uses a price list to determine sales prices for the various ducks on the market today in accordance with the many widths and weights of the duck.

CARD CLOTHING. Special cloth or rubber studded with wire teeth which serve to open up textile fibers, clean them of some of the impurity, and arrange these fibers in parallel order. The fillet of the clothing is made of linen and cotton fabric.

CARD CLOTHING, TYPES OF.
1. KNEE: The bent wire teeth set in a foundation fabric which is wound around rollers on a carding machine.
2. METALLIC: The narrow serrated metallic flutes which are spirally arranged and cover the entire surface of a roller.
3. STRAIGHT: Wire teeth set in a foundation fabric which is wound around a roller.

CARD CLOTHING FOUNDATION. The heavy, strong fabric through which card clothing staples or wires are forced by a device used for the purpose. This fillet is a combination of cotton and linen, cotton and rubber, linen and rubber, and so on.

CARD CUTTING. The act of punching holes in Jacquard cards in accordance with the motif, design, or design draft, so that when the cards are set up in the loom, they will control the weaving mechanism and the pattern will be woven into the fabric.

CARD CYLINDER. That part of a Jacquard loom which supports and holds the pattern cards in position while the plungers, which control the weaving of the designs, pass through the holes in the cards.

CARD DOFFING. Stripping the sliver from the carding machine.

CARDED KNITTING YARN. A rather low-quality yarn made from short, irregular-length fibers which lie in a topsy-turvy manner. Inferior to combed yarn in all respects. Made of cotton, wool, or a blend of these, the yarn goes into hosiery and underwear.

CARDED SILK. Any of the cocoon waste silk stock that is capable of being carded and then spun into some variety of spun silk yarn.

CARDED UNION YARNS. British expression for low-quality yarns which contain cotton and wool fibers. Both fibers are carded together, the cotton provides extra strength and aids even spinning of the resultant yarn.

CARDED YARN. Made from short-staple cotton fibers which have been cleaned of most impurities by carding. Some remain as motes which are seen in carded gray cloths. Most cotton yarns are carded because bulk of cotton grown is too short for combing. Compared with combed yarn it is a fibrous, uneven yarn. Yarns generally run from 1s up to 50s.

CARD FELTINGS, FETTLINGS. British term for carding machine wastes such as strippings, matted fibers, and other wastes taken from the cards when they are cleaned in the mill. Refers to woolen fibers which are sometimes garnetted, scoured, and then carded again by being carried along by longer fibers in the mix when run through a second time in the frame.

CARD FLAT. A flat piece of material covered with card clothing held in a horizontal position on the so-called flat top type of card. The flats aid much in opening up cotton fibers, removing of some waste, and presenting the cotton in a better condition for further treatment.

CARD GAUGE. The device used to determine the distance and the setting between the several rollers on a card. Setting requires much skill, and the gauge used is a leaf, a flat steel strip gauge, or a quadrant.

CARD GRINDING. The periodic sharpening of the pressed-steel card clothing wires which serve as the covering for the various rollers found on a carding machine. An abrasive cylinder does the grinding.

CARDIGAN. 1. A form of the rib knitting stitch, modified by tucking on one or both sets of needles. For half cardigan, tuck on one set, for full cardigan, tuck on both sets of needles. Tucking thickens the fabric.
2. A sweater style, usually a 3-button coat sweater with either a V or round neck. There are also cardigan jackets made of a woolen or worsted fabric.

CARDIGAN STITCH. It is made on flat hand or flat power knitting frames equipped with two sets of needles. Half cardigan stitch is made with one bed knitting continuously, while the other bed knits and tucks in alternating order. Full cardigan is made by having the front bed and the back bed knit alternately and then tuck. The front bed knits while the back bed tucks; when the front bed tucks, the back bed knits.

CARDIGAN SWEATER. See CARDIGAN, also SWEATERS, MEN'S AND BOYS'; SWEATERS, WOMEN'S AND MISSES'.

CARDINAL CLOTH. Ecclesiastical cloth made from merino wool and given great care in finishing. This red woolen material is worn by the cardinals of the Roman Catholic Church.

CARDING. The process in yarn manufacture in which the fibers are brushed up, made more or less parallel, have considerable portions of foreign matter removed, and are put into a manageable form known as sliver. This approximates the size of a man's thumb in diameter. Carding is done by means of rollers or flats that are clothed with fine, cylindrical pressed steel wire called card clothing. See Illustrated Section.

CARDING, SPINNING, AND WEAVING, DEVELOPMENT OF. The four eras of this development follow:

1. THE FAMILY SYSTEM (to about A.D. 1100).

Under this system, carding, spinning, and weaving were carried on by members of the household for the purpose of supplying the family with clothing. This was before the days of sales, prices, cut prices, and bargains. Each class of society, from the humblest peasant to the nobleman or blueblood, had its own devices and methods of making textiles and clothing. This system was totally for home consumption.

2. THE GUILD SYSTEM (from about 1100 to about 1750).

As the world progressed and as communities became larger and cities came into being, the textile industry became a larger business than for the family alone. Better textures and fabrics were in demand. To meet this demand, it was necessary to have looms and the improved parts for these looms. The small weaver, who owned and constructed his own looms, was not able to own all of the necessary parts. Hence, he had to turn to a more prosperous weaver for his livelihood. The same applied to carding and spinning. These two phases of the industry became separated from weaving. In time, they also separated.

The guild system caused the small weaver to be driven out by the growth of organized labor and capital, particularly by the latter. Under this system, the industry was carried on by a small number of men called masters. They employed two or more men, who were called journeymen or apprentices. These masters organized the guilds on a systematic basis and controlled the manufacturing phases to a greater extent than is possible today.

3. THE DOMESTIC SYSTEM (from about 1750 to 1800).

By the middle of the eighteenth century the separation of carding, spinning, weaving, and other branches of the textile industry was an accomplished fact. The rural communities increased in textile work. When the rural districts took up textiles, the guild system and masters began to decline in the power once wielded. While the work was still carried on in the master's house or shed, he now began to receive his raw material from the merchant, and disposed of the finished goods to a middleman who looked after the demands of the various markets. The economic laws of supply and demand, production, distribution, and consumption were at hand. Raw material took its place with other factors.

4. THE FACTORY SYSTEM (from about 1800 to present time).

Necessity is the mother of invention, and as time went on, the factory system just had to come. The factory is a place where goods are produced, by power, for commercial purposes and use. Following the invention of the steam engine, the factory system was an actuality. No record has been found that shows that this system was in vogue prior to this invention.

English, Irish, Scotch, and Welsh spinners and weavers became very skillful, and with many English inventions during this incipient stage in the factory system, the production of yarn and cloth increased. By the mechanical arts, one man could do the work that formerly was done by ten, twenty, or more men. Water and steam power replaced manual labor. This caused large-scale production by combining capital and machinery. This resulted in what is now the factory system—the product of the Industrial Revolution.

Prior to the factory system, there was no reason why any industry should be centered in one particular district. With the Industrial Revolution an accomplished fact, greater subdivision of the textile industry was necessary. Each unit became, to a greater or lesser degree, localized. Geographical and raw material factors had to be considered. Suitable areas of a country had to be taken over for this or that phase of the industry to which it would be best suited.

Old-time textile areas that are still great were established because of water power, rivers, accessibility to markets, and natural positive factors.

CARDING ACTION. This occurs on a card when two surfaces covered with card clothing pass each other at varying speed with the tips of the one roller acting against those of the other roller. The action combs the fibers and causes them to lie parallel to one another. See Illustrated Section.

CARDING BEATER. Used on cotton pickers, it is made up of three wooden lags fastened to the beater arms. Sharp steel pins of lags, in spiral arrangement and of varying length, project from the lags. Also known as the Kirschner beater.

CARDING DRUM. The large, rapidly revolving cylinder on the card, covered with millions of wire teeth, that picks up or "pulls out" the fibers and, working in conjunction with the other rollers of the frame, combs the fibers parallel and removes small, minute particles of dirt, foreign matter, and knotted stock.

CARDING ENGINE. The true name for a carding machine.

CARDING LEATHER. A particular type of leather used on carding machines in the manufacture of textiles. It lies flat against the beds of the cards, and the teeth have to be forced through it by a device made for this purpose.

CARDING MACHINE, COTTON. The machine used in the manufacture of cotton textiles which receives the cotton in lap form as it comes from the finisher picker machine. The cylinder, and the revolving flats, arranged in an endless chain, parallel the fibers, remove great amounts of motes, shives, unripe seeds, and other impurities. The sliver as it comes from the doffer roller in a weblike formation is then led to the coiler attachment, condensed to a sliver form, and deposited into the coiler can, which rests on a revolving plate at the delivery end of the frame. There is no twisting of the fibers in carding, and the draft will range from 90 to 120. See Illustrated Section.

CARDING WOOL. Term used in woolen manufacture. Fine wool, of 1¼-inch staple, and coarse wool, of 2-inch staple, may be carded. The term signifies that the stock is suitable only for woolen yarn manufacture.

CARD LACING MACHINE. A type of sewing machine equipped with a series of needles, shuttles, and cords. The Jacquard cards are stitched together at the end and in the middle, in a firm manner, and when the lacing is completed the cards are then tied into an endless set. They are run over the cylinder of the Jacquard loom and govern the filling pickage of the fabric so that the motif will result from the interlacing with the warp ends in the machine.

CARD PUNCHING MACHINE. A machine which perforates the cards to be used in weaving Jacquard designs; these punched cards control the motif in the woven fabric.

CARD SLIVER. See SLIVER.

CARD STRIPPING. The removal of short, imbedded textile fibers from the pressed steel card-clothing used in carding machines. A small-diameter tooth-clad roller is used for the task.

CARD WASTE. The wastes of all types taken from a card—fibers, shives, motes, dirt, strips, and the rest. The cylinder, doffer, and the revolving flats on a cotton card give the most waste.

CARD WASTES, TYPES OF COTTON.

1. CYLINDER STRIP WASTE: It is removed from the card cylinder by vacuum or roll stripping at the end of the stripping cycle. This strip is chiefly normal-length staple fiber which has become embedded in the clean card clothing when the machine is started after stripping. The strip also includes short fibers and trash which accumulates during processing of the fibers.
2. DOFFER STRIP WASTE: It is obtained from the doffer roller at the end of the stripping cycle; comparable with cylinder strip stock. Cylinder and strip wastes are combined and sold as vacuum strip.
3. FLAT STRIP WASTE: Fibers and trash collected in the carding action between the cylinder and the card flats. Much usable fiber is contained in the waste which is considered to be the most valuable of all card wastes.
4. FLY WASTE: Composed of short fibers that are thrown out between the opening of licker-in and cylinder screens, it is light and cleaner than other card wastes. In practice, fly and motes are combined usually as one type of waste to facilitate cleaning beneath the card without attempting to separate them.
5. MOTE WASTE: This is the mass of heavier type waste found underneath the licker-in roller. Composed of leaf, lint, seed, fragments of seeds, and trash, it is removed by the opening and cleaning action of the licker-in and mote knives.
6. REWORKABLE WASTE: It comprises pieces of picker lap stock removed in starting a new lap and running out an old lap, short sliver lengths, and the soft roll of fibers formed by the doffer comb when it is started.
7. SCAVENGER OR CLEANER WASTE: This is collected by the revolving flannel-covered clearer roll at the small opening between the licker-in cover and the feed roll. It consists chiefly of rather short fibers that are carried around by the air set in motion by the licker-in roll.
8. SWEEPS WASTE: General term for all wastes collected and swept from the floor around the cards. It is composed chiefly of lint but may contain much foreign matter of vegetable and nonvegetable nature.

Reworkable and sweeps wastes is a problem of mill management wherein proper training for picker tenders and card tenders will pay off. The other six types of waste are controlled chiefly by mechanical changes and in modifications of the card.

CARD WINDING MACHINE. The machine used to wind short lengths of yarn or thread onto a small card for retail sale. Used for darning, mending, gathering, sewing, and other purposes where small quantities are needed.

CAREER APPAREL. Apparel of good to excellent quality made to provide long wear performance without losing too much of its freshness or neatness. Apparel in this category should last for at least one year to eighteen months, if properly cared for. Depending on local conditions the garb may come in two or more combinations so as to allow for cleaning, pressing, washing, etc. Ideal for airlines, banks, car-rental agencies, insurance companies, public utilities, transporatation companies, and comparable industrial and service companies; a "white collar type" of apparel.

"Blue collar apparel" may also be uniformed but cannot be classed, strictly speaking, as career apparel because of the nature of the work. It is used by gas station personnel, in manufacturing plants of wide variety and includes the "work and wear" artisans. This garb does not seem to have the serviceability of the apparel used in the "white collar types," as to cleanability, wear and performance, creasing, etc.

CARGAN. A Belgian casein fiber.

CARISEL. Coarse, plain-woven cotton or jute cloth used as foundation fabric in making carpets. Textures are low, and the cloth comes in many widths.

CARISOL OR CRESEAU. Openwork canvas used as embroidery foundation in France.

CARLE HEMP. Male stems are known as fimple while female stems are called carle; comes from the hemp plant, Cannabis sativa. Carle is an Italian hemp.

CARMAGNOLE. A jacket as worn by the French Revolutionists around 1789. The term also implies an entire garment including wide black pantaloons, bright-colored waistcoat, the typical high red cap, etc.

CARMELINE. A medium grade of vicuna wool used in France.

CARMELITE CLOTH. Named in honor of the Carmelite Order of the Roman Catholic Church. Plain-weave, low-texture, woolen cloth that is given considerable fulling. Somewhat resembles woolen bunting. Used as garb.

CARMINE. 1. Coloring matter from cochineal which consists mainly of carminic acid, a rich purplish-red. 2. As a color, it is crimson in hue, has high saturation a l low brilliance; higher than cerise in saturation.

CARNABY STREET. This street, now known throughout the fashion world, came into much prominence in 1965 with the arrival of "mod clothing, fashion, and style." Only two blocks in length, it is as well known as the famous Saville Row, situated in London's West End. The Beatles and Carnaby Street introduced items such as bell-bottom trousers, denim and comparable fabric jeans, wild looking shirts in bizarre prints, scarves in wild colors, boots, and several types of jackets, etc. Its impact on clothes and apparel has been tremendous in the first real change in male apparel in the last ninety-five years, or since the Franco-Prussian War in 1870.

CARNAUBA PALM. A palm leaf fiber whose botanical name is Corypha cerifera.

CARNEOUS. Flesh-colored; applied to sericulture or raising of silkworms.

CAROA, CRAUA, CROA, COROA. This Brazilian plant yields a fiber that can be used for suiting and coating in tropical countries, rugs, paper, light rope, and twine. The fibers mix well with cotton and are worked on the cotton system of spinning. Compared with jute, caroa is three times as strong, and fabric, sacking, or twine made from it is about half as light as similar articles made from jute.

CAROLINA PRIDE COTTON. An early-maturing South Carolina cotton which produces a 1-inch staple and a lint-yield of about 31 per cent. Also known as Early Carolina, Extra Early Carolina, South Carolina Pride.

CAROLINAS. Low-quality ginghams and comparable cotton cloths used in Colombia and neighboring countries in northern South America.

CAROLINE. French serge made on eight ends and eight picks to the repeat.

CAROSEL. A type of dish-toweling made by the Textile Division of UniRoyal Inc., Winnsboro, South Carolina; it is made of 80 percent cotton and 20 percent asbestos which contributes to absorbency and polishing properties.

CARPEL. The sections of an empty cotton boll, or hull, which separate the cotton locks in the boll.

CARPET. A heavy, ornamental floor covering and the fabric used to make it. It covers in totality an entire floor or nearly so. The term comes from the Latin "carpere" into Middle English "carpete" to the present day English "carpet." The Latin spelling implied a plucking of wool or a carding of wool fibers; the connection being that for centuries wool has been used in making carpets. See Rug.

CARPET, CINEMA PILE. British expression for a stout Wilton carpet with a very thick pile to withstand traffic in public places such as hotels, museums, offices, theaters, etc. Made with around 18- tufts per inch, the rug usually has a motif with floral reliefs on a suitable dark ground.

CARPET, CORD. See Haircord.

CARPET, CUSTOM TUFTED. One in which the pile yarns are tufted with hand labor by hand machines or by a narrow width tufting machine.

CARPET, DOUBLE-BACK. A secondary backing used on floor-covering in which the backing is adhered to the back of tufted, and in some instances, knit or woven carpet. It is an actual reinforcement to add strength and increase dimensional stability to the carpet. See Dimensional Stability.

CARPET BACKING. The backing for a floorcovering irrespective of its construction. *Primary Backing* is the material to which the surface yarns are attached. Used for this purpose are cotton, jute, kraft cord, woven or nonwoven manmade fiber materials. *Secondary Backing*, also known as *Double Backing*, is any material laminated or otherwise attached to the primary backing, such as a cushion of foam, jute, scrim, and woven or nonwoven manmade fiber material. *Jute Backing* is much used in primary backing, especially in tufted carpet backing. *Polypropylene Backing* is used mainly as primary carpet backing. *Ruber Backing* finds use only in secondary backing whereby it is made to adhere to a primary backing of jute, polypropylene or other materials used for this purpose. The better quality carpeting requires the use of a secondary backing.

CARPET BACKING TRADEMARK NAMES IN MANMADE FIBER PRODUCTS. Utilized in the merchandising of carpet backing made from manmade fibers, each name is followed by that of the manufacturer, the form of the mater-

ial and the special properties or specific uses:

All of the materials are based on polypropylene. Some are woven of monofilament, extruded ribbon yarns, or slit film, while some are nonwoven or spun-bonded sheets.

Amco, American Mfg. Co., extruded ribbon.

Dawbac, Thiokol Chemical Corp., woven extruded ribbon fabric, primary.

Kynol Novolac, (CA-0001) Carborundum Co., woven, primary.

Loktuft Duon, Phillips Fibers Corp., nonwoven, secondary backing.

Loktuft Primera, Phillips Fibers, nonwoven primary backing.

Nofray, Enjay Chemical Co., Ribbon Fabric Division, extruded monofilament, woven fabric, primary.

Poly Bac, Patchogue Plymouth Co., woven ribbon primary backing.

Poly Bac FLW, Patchogue Plymouth, woven, ribbon, primary.

Pro-Tuft, Bemis Co., Inc., extruded ribbon, woven, primary.

Typar, E. I. DuPont de Nemours & Co., spunbonded continuous filament sheet for primary backing.

WeyBac, Moultrie Textiles, slit film, woven, primary.

CARPET BAG. Reminiscent of Civil War days, this carry-all type of bag was actually made of carpet strips.

CARPET BEAT-UP. Used in connection with the weaving of Axminster, chenille, and other carpets not woven over wires, it is the number of tufts per inch of length in the weaving of the carpet. The term is synonymous with "wire" used in weaving Brussels and Wilton carpets.

CARPET BEETLE. The small red, white, and black beetle, *Anthrenus Scrophulariae,* which in larva condition wreaks havoc with any woolen goods. There is also another type capable of doing just as much damage, the black bettle, *Attagenus piceus.*

CARPET BINDING. Narrow tape made of wool or cotton to bind the edges of all types of floor coverings and carpets.

CARPET BINDING YARN. Weft yarn carried across the loom by a shuttle (in Axminster by a needle thrust) alternating with the filling yarn, usually cotton or jute.

CARPET CHAIN WARP. Two cotton yarns running warpwise of fabric and drawn by heddles alternately over and under the weft binding and filling yarns. Inserted by shuttles in tapestry, velvet, Wilton, and chenille weaves, and by a needle thrust in Axminster.

CARPET FILLING YARN, WEFT

FILLING YARN. This yarn is carried through most looms by a shuttle (Axminster by a needle thrust) alternating with the binding yarn; usually made of cotton or jute.

CARPETING, LOW ROWS IN. Rows of very low pile height which extend across the carpet width. Often resorted to in running-out the final portions of face yarn on the spools as in the case of Axminster loom weaving. See Axminster.

CARPETING, NEEDLE LOOM. A nonwoven, nonpile floor covering with a feltlike face effect. Bases such as burlap, cotton, plastic, or rubber are bonded and covered with batts, blizzards, laps, or webs of loose fiber stocks by the needles, which are arranged so that they, with their barbs, cause the fiber tufts and matts to become firmly imbedded in the base fabric as these needles swing into their up-and-down action.

CARPETING TERMS, CONCISE BASIC DEFINITIONS OF.
Axminster Carpet: A machine-woven carpet in which the filling-wise or weft-wise rows of pile are inserted during weaving according to a predetermined arrangement of colors. There are four main types of Axminster weave, namely - Spool, Gripper, Gripper-spool, and Chenille. 1. *Spool Axminster:* A carpet in which the yarn for each weft-wise row is wound on a separate spool according to the design or pattern. The tufts are severed from the yarns presented at the point of weaving after insertion in the backing structure. 2. *Gripper Axminster:* A carpet in which the tufts of yarn are inserted at the point of weaving by means of "grippers." The colors are selected by Jacquard-operated carriers which present the appropriate ends of yarn to the "grippers" before the tufts are severed from the yarns. 3. *Gripper-Spool, Spool-Gripper:* This type of Axminster is a carpet in which the yarns for each weft-wise row are wound on a spool as for Axminster weaving. The tufts severed from the yarns are inserted at the point of weaving by "grippers" as in Gripper-Axminster weaving. 4. *Chenille Axminster:* Descriptive of a carpet that has a pile of chenille weft. See Chenille Yarn.

NOTE: Many trade names, by force of long usage, have acquired definite significant meanings of some kind in the minds of the consuming public. White the names, Axminster, Brussels, and Wilton, as applied to carpets may have referred originally to the place of origin, it should be noted that this geographical significance has been changed gradually into one which now implies a grade, method, or quality of manufacture.

Brussels Carpet: A loop-pile carpet woven over an unbladed (tipless blade) vertical, flat (elliptical) wire inserted on edge.

NOTE: The weaving is carried out on a Wilton loom and the carpet is therefore often referred to in the industry as a Brussels Wilton.

Brusselette Carpet: A ribbed-type carpet woven from a loosely tensioned, coarse warp and from a fine chain. See Carpet Chain Warp.

Wilton Carpet: A woven carpet in which the pile threads run continuously into the carpet and are treated as an integral part of the weaving process, being raised above the surface of the backing to form a pile by means of wires, hooks, or by being stretched between two backings (face-to-face weaving). After being woven, the pile may be left as a loop, or cut by a bladed wire or the separation of the two fabrics in the case of face-to-face weaving.

Wilton, Figured: It is usually made on a Jacquard loom and presents a motif obtained by the use of from two to five frames, each of which shows a different color. Additional colors may be obtained by substitution (planting) of colors in any frame. This type of carpet is sometimes known as the carpet of hidden value because of its unique, intricate construction.

Wilton, Mottled or Stippled: Similar to Plain Wilton, but woven from plied yarns, folded from singles of different colors.

Wilton, Plain: It is woven face-to-face on a Jacquard loom, or on a tapestry loom and there is no surface design of effect in the motif. It is normally of a single color which, if cut-pile, may be described as a "Plain Velvet." A variation uses hard-twist yarns.

Carpets, Loop Length (Pile Structures) In: The length of yarn which forms one complete loop, and to include the portion that is held in the backing.

Carpet, Pile: The tufts or loops of the surface fibers or yarns which project upwards from the base or the backing of the carpet to form a non-matted surface.
1. *Loop Pile (Uncut Pile):* A pile whose fibers or yarns are caused to form loops during the manufacture of the fabric.
2. *Cut Pile:* A pile surface consisting entirely of severed ends of fibers or yarns.
3. *Curl Pile:* A curled pile, cut or uncut, made from specially prepared yarn.
4. *Sculptured or Carved Pile:* A pile in which a pattern is created by having areas of different height or by omitting the pile effect in certain areas.
5. *Textured Pile:* One in which the surface character or effect is varied. An example is to have areas of different characteristcs, by a combination of loop and cut pile, etc.

Mat, Floor: Carpeting that is normally less than 22½ inches in width and with an area of less than 7½ square feet.

NOTE: The area mentioned above is calculated on the maximum length and width of the mat irrespective of the shape.

Rug, Floor: A collective term for pile floor-coverings of small size.

NOTE ONE: Floor rugs may either have the normal carpet construction or have a deep pile, with or without a supplementary attached backing. In commerce, floor rugs are generally supplied up to 30 feet square in area.

NOTE TWO: In the United States, this term applies to "carpet squares" and the equivalent term in the United States is "Scatter Rug" or "Throw Rug."

Pile, Unit of: A length of pile yarn which protrudes above the highest point of the backing of a carpet.

Pile Root: The fiber, fibers, yarn, or yarns from either a particular tuft or two connected tufts, which are contained in the anchoring structure.

Tuft: A "J", "U", or "W"-shaped length of yarn, the leg or legs of which form the pile in the carpet.

Tuft Length: The distance between the extremities of a tuft, after removal or straightening.

Tuft Row: A row of tufts which run between selvage edges in a carpet.

Courtesy of: J.L. Carter, Secretary to Federation of British Carpet Manufacturers (1960).

CARPET LOOM FRAMES. Trays or creels holding spools of surface yarn in two to six levels back of the Wilton loom. One strand of yarn is lifted into position by the Jacquard mechanism to form the design on the pile surface while the other yarns, one to five in number, are woven dormant in the warp direction.

CARPET MOTH. The larvae of a carpet bettle, larger than the ordinary clothes moth, which feeds on woolen goods.

CARPET PICK. Refers to the filling yarn in making carpets and is determined from the number of reed spaces in the loom and may denote the total number of loops or tufts in a standard 27-inch carpeting.

A pitch of 256 signifies 256 reed splits or about 9½ ends per inch. One loop or pile is often denoted as a point, and the number of points per square inch is equal to the number of wires times the pitch.

The number of filling picks considered in reference to the pile tufts or loops is called the shot. Thus, a two-shot carpet is one that has two filling picks or yarns to each row or pile loops; a three-shot carpet would have three filling yarns to each row of pile tufts, and so on.

Pick is also applied to the filling yarns thrown through the shed of the loom in a crosswise direction between the warp ends. The number of picks per inch indicates the compactness of the weave texture. Fine quality Wilton will have three shots times 13 wires or a total of 39 picks.

CARPET PITCH. The number of warp yarns per inch crosswise on the loom. It is usually stated in relation to a 27-inch width or 3/4 width. Standard pitch for Wilton carpet is 256; Axminster, 189.

CARPETS, TYPES OF WOVEN.

TYPES	CHARACTERISTICS	USES
CHENILLE: Custom-order chenille can be specified in a wide range of quality and price. It has been woven to copy some of the finest and rarest Oriental creations.	The striking characteristic of custom order chenille is its heavy woolen back. This makes the fabric almost a complete animal fiber product. The heavy cushion-back will guarantee greater wear to the same amount of surface yarn.	The chenille weave is adaptable to any and every need. Any type of yarn, any width to thirty feet seamless, any shape and coloring, any design, any density of pile and in one of four depths of pile, give an architect a freedom of choice.
WORSTED WILTON: Wilton is recognized as a luxury fabric. The finer and more expensive worsted yarn grades provide a detail and delicacy in design, through the use of the Jacquard pattern control, not possible to obtain in any other of the standard types.	The surface yarn buried in the body of a Jacquard Wilton weave (usually seen through the back) and its consequent sturdy construction are its outstanding characteristics. The use of worsted yarn provides a delicacy of design and permits frequent and comparatively harsh cleaning.	In Worsted Wilton each fiber in the face yarn is tied in to the back construction. This makes it particularly suitable for dining rooms where any fluff would be objectionable; for hospitals where cleanliness is paramount; for Pullman cars where frequent cleaning is necessary.
WOOLEN WILTON: Woolen yarn, heavier and coarser than the worsted, provides a luxury feeling under foot coupled with design detail and an extremely sturdy foundation construction. Expansive rugs often provide the correct installation for large lobby or foyer.	Compact in surface yarn, stanch in foundation and deep in pile, better qualities of wool Wilton are distinguished for their splendid wear value under severe traffic. Exceptional wear can be met with the use of a tightly twisted Saxony type of surface yarn.	Wool Wilton can be chosen advisedly for all the heavy traffic positions. Particularly severe wear conditions should be met by the use of the tightly twisted yarn known to the trade as Saxony. This type can also be woven economically in lesser yardages.
AXMINSTER: The Axminster construction leads in yardage production in the U. S. A. Unlimited in use of the number of colors, it fits perfectly into the middle cost bracket in any requirement for public or residential use.	Distinguished by the double row of weft binding and filling yarns inserted by a needle thrust (easily noted on the back), Axminster can be rolled lengthwise but not crosswise. The better grades provide deep pile and closeness of weave that give them superb luxuriousness.	Axminster is woven in so wide a range of qualities that it can be adapted to almost any requirement in the middle price bracket. It does not compete with the Wilton or chenille weaves for heavy duty in public areas. It is the best type of carpet for silence and a sense of luxury.
VELVET: The velvet weave is the simplest form of carpet construction. The use of razor-bladed pile wires cut the surface yarn loops, giving the velvet-like face and the name for this construction. Better qualities serve many requirements with deserved success.	All the surface yarn is doing its full duty in the velvet as it is held firmly in the back construction and it is not buried too deeply in the fabric. The usual construction is a tightly woven pile of comparatively short length intended to give maximum service for the investment.	Velvet can be used where traffic is moderate or where there are definite budget limitations. Where there is a desire to change the decorative scheme occasionally, as in supper clubs, neighborhood theaters, salesrooms, and the like, velvet can be recommended with confidence.
TAPESTRY: The tapestry weave is formed by uncut surface yarn loops over round pile wires in the same simple loom operation as the cut pile Velvet. It is often referred to as a hooked type because it simulates home hand-hooked products.	Unusual wear is assured from the uncut loops in this tapestry and hooked form. The use of heavy yarn will furnish a depth of pile and also allow for variety in the height of the loops to form special texture effects.	The uncut loop tapestry and hooked effects give a longer wear value in the same locations but will often lack the resilience and sound absorption found in the cut pile fabrics. There is a growing interest in the use of high- and low-pile novelties.

CARPET SETT. The number of surface pile-warp units that run filling-wise in one inch of the fabric. Other standards may be used depending on where the carpet was made.

CARPET STAIN REMOVAL ON MANMADE FIBER CONSTRUCTIONS. If detected at once, absorb or blot as much of the area as possible. Grease and oil stains should be treated with a non-flammable drycleaning liquid but carbon tetrachloride, benzene, gasoline, or lighter fluid should not be used. The universal solvent, water, may remove many types of stains, and others disappear by the use of a small amount of detergent-vinegar compound. About one teaspoon of a mild detergent, devoid of bleach, and one of white vinegar in a quart of warm water should suffice.

It should be borne in mind that excess cleaning fluid should be blotted as soon as possible, followed by the use of a layer cloth which contains clean, white absorbent ingredients, followed by natural drying. Periodic shampooing of carpets is suggested once or twice a year.

CARPET STRETCHER. A device for stretching carpets tightly. Several kinds are in use, one of which consists of several sharp teeth attached to a knee pad. The worker sticks the teeth into the carpet and pushes on the pad with his knee to draw the carpet tightly against the floor.

CARPETTE. Low-grade, twill-woven bast fiber bagging made in France and used as container for grease wool when gathered or shipped.

CARPET TEXTURE. Texture in this meaning refers to the surface effect and appearance of the article. There is a host of textures applicable to carpets such as: coarse, compact, firm, high-pile, low-pile, mottled, plain, plush, rough, scalloped, shaggy, lustered, shiny, smooth, uneven-pile, velvet-like, etc.

CARPET THREAD. A very tough, durable, waxed, ply thread used in the carpet trade in carpet-binding work and for sewing seams.

CARPET WARP. A 4-ply, strong cotton cord often used as the warp in rag and other types of floor coverings.

CARPET WEAR TESTER. When in operation, the carpet testing machine submits a circular sample of material to a wearing action through the use of leather abrasive surfaces. The leather surfaces are mounted on a set of wheels, one driving wheel and one braking wheel. During the test the wheels produce a circular track on the face of the specimen and set up a wearing action through pressure and friction which duplicates normal wear over a period of time. The loss of thickness produced by the action determines the results obtained by the test.

CARPET WIRES. Strong, thin metal rods or strips inserted underneath the pile warp yarns during weaving to form loops which are bound-in by the weft of filling.

On the withdrawal of a tipless, round, or elliptical wire or blade, an uncut or loop pile results. A tipped wire or blade cuts the loops when it is withdrawn and forms a cut-pile effect.

Wires still find use in the hand weaving of velvet and these have a slot along the upper edge; the knife or trivet which is guided by the slotted wire is drawn by the weaver across the loops to produce a cut-pile effect.

CARPET WOOL. Any wool that cannot be classed as carding, clothing, or combing wool. It is the poorest of the four major types of wool. It cannot be combed and is often difficult to card. The wool is much used in carpets, rugs, cheap boys' clothing, Mackinac and windbreaker fabrics, and in low-priced apparel for adults. All carpet wool used here is imported because the manufacturers in this country have caused the wool growers to elevate domestic carpet wool to the point where most of it, because of scientific crossbreeding, is now used in making fabric for the apparel trades.

Some popular foreign carpet wools much used here include Aleppo, Awassi Karadi, Buenos Aires, Cordova, Joria,

SOME MAJOR CARPET CONSTRUCTIONS

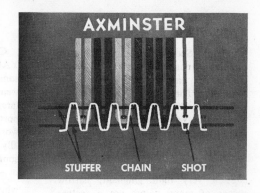

In the *Axminster* weave each pile yarn is inserted independently, as in hand-tufted carpets of the Orient. This permits infinite variation of color and pattern. Patterned carpets using many colors in complex designs are Axminsters. Almost all of the yarn appears on the surface, and the pile is cut except in a few special weaves. The carpet is heavily ribbed as a result of the double shots that hold the tufts to the stuffer yarns with the chain bind.

Usually sizing or a latex compound is applied to the backing to lock the tufts. Varying pile heights are possible.

Chenille is made by two weaving processes. First the pile yarns are woven in a "chenille blanket" that is cut into long, furry, caterpillar-like strips. In the second weaving step, the strips of pile yarns are woven into the base of the carpet. The carpet base is made of heavy, thick wool yarn woven in the same operation that attaches the pile to it with the "catcher threads." Chenille carpet is thick and soft. It can be woven in a wide range of patterns and in any color, shape or size up to thirty feet wide. Is usually custom-made.

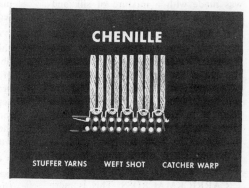

In the *tufting* construction, the pile yarn is needled through a prewoven backing fabric, usually made of jute, then firmly locked by a latex backing compound.

Hundreds of needles on the wide-width machines turn out rich, deep-pile carpets at high-speed production.

Though formerly limited to solid color or either cut or looped pile, tufted carpets can now be made in a variety of color combinations in varying heights for appealing and attractive motif and textural designs.

In the *velvet* weave pile yarns are seen on the surface at all times. As indicated by the dotted lines above the tufts, the pile may be cut or looped. New techniques make possible a wide range of textural effects, including tight frieze twists or pebbly surface and multilevel looped textures.

The "shot yarns" actually bind the pile yarns to the "stuffer yarns," which act as a structural foundation for the carpet. The entire construction is locked together by the "chain yarns."

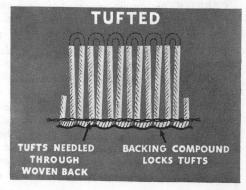

The *Wilton* uses up to six different sets of yarn to form the pile in this "rug of hidden values." When it is desired, each set of yarns can be a different color. The "hidden-value yarns," when not drawn to weave on the face of the carpet by the Jacquard loom upon which Wilton is made, are buried deep in the body of the carpet. Thus, this gives a cushion effect that provides luxurious feel and comfort.

Wilton weaving makes possible the modern carved effects of high and low pile effects. The carpet pile may be cut to give a "plush effect," or looped as shown in the picture.

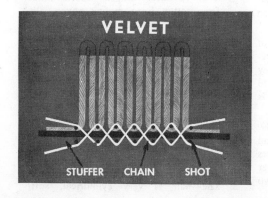

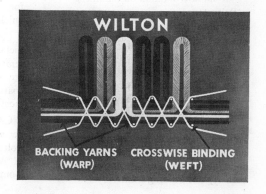

Kandahar, Scotch Blackface (the most popular carpet wool used in this country in the carpet trade), Tibet, and Vicaneer. These wools may have a price range from about forty-five cents a pound up to sixty cents a pound.

CARPINCHO. See GLOVE LEATHER.

CARRADORS. Cloth made of Indian cotton and sold chiefly in India. Simulates a very light gingham; narrow stripes of many colors are a feature of the fabric.

CARREAU. French for check.

CARREL. Popular in the sixteenth and seventeenth centuries, this cloth was made with a mixture of silk and worsted or silk and linen yarns.

CARRIAGE. 1. The movable part of the mule spinning frame which goes from the headstock of the machine to the end of the outward run, a distance of several feet. The carriage holds the spindles, faller wires, gears, and so forth. 2. In flat knitting it is the sliding frame which sets above the needle beds, and holds the cams and yarn guide in order to carry them along in their action.

CARRICKMACROSS. This is more closely allied with embroidery than it is to lace. It consists of a pattern cut in cambric and then applied to a net ground. Brides or bobbin-made sprigs are not a feature of Irish lace.

CARRIER. An organic compound of the "swelling agent" type used in the dyeing and printing of polyester hydrophilic (water-absorbing) and certain other manmade fibers of the hydrophilic type. The ideal carrier is one which disperses readily in order to permit or promote dye up-take by the fibers at lower temperatures than would be possible without its use. After it has achieved full fixation in fixing or dyeing the aforementioned fibers under less than optimum conditions, the carrier can be removed easily following coloring. The use of a carrier is important under certain conditions of steaming to give the fastness requirements desired, as well as the fact that costs are lowered because of the speedier fixation on the fibers.

Polyester carriers are emulsions or dispersions of biphenol, ortho-phenylphenol, trichlorbenzene, benzoic acid esters, etc. Some disadvantages include possible toxicity (poisonous), fumes, harm to lightfastness, and difficulty in handling. Costs should be well-checked prior to usage.

CARRIER, YARN. A device on a knitting machine to feed yarn to needles or other loop-forming elements. The construction of the carrier varies for each type of knitting frame.

CARRIER FIBER, CARRIER YARN. A fiber or yarn used to support some other fiber or yarn in spinning or weaving. The support fiber or yarn is later on dissolved out from the supported material. Used in burnt-out work, lace manufacture, and occasionally for woven or knitted fabrics of some particular structure.

CARRIER ROD. The device on which yarn carriers in a full-fashioned knitting machine are mounted.

CARROT. To brush furs with a solution of mercury and nitric acid. The treatment opens the sheaths surrounding each fur fiber and permits the matting or felting of the fibers in subsequent operations.

CARROTING MACHINE. A machine for carroting fur to prepare the fibers for felting. The machine consists of a storage tank, a power-rotated brush, and a table. The skins are pulled across the table beneath the brush, moistened with solution that drips from the storage tank faucet, moistening and working the fur fibers.

CARR'S MELTON. The fine, high-grade meltons made by Carr, Son, & Company, Ltd., of London; the acme of perfection in this face-finished fabric.

CARSEY. Kersey, at one time, was spelled this way in Britain.

CARTHAGENA. West Indian staple raised from American cotton seeds; it has rather long staple.

CARTHAMUS. Safflower, an annual plant raised in southern Europe, Egypt, and Asia, known for the red dye product taken from its flowers.

CARTHENI. A traditional Welsh blanket made with bright and pastel colorings. Used also as a bedspread, the fabric is fringed, well woven, made of good quality wool. The weight ranges from four to five pounds.

CARTISANE. Guipure or passementerie made with fine silk or nylon and strips of parchment that are covered with gilt.

CARTRIDGE CLOTH. Made originally from silk cloth to hold powder charges for big guns, silk noil is ideal for cartridge cloth since it burns quickly and completely.

CARTRIDGE TUCKS. A series of tucks arranged in the material to resemble a military cartridge belt. They are used to give a military effect to coats, skirts, sleeves, etc. The effect is most pronounced in times of war.

CARTRIGHT, EDMUND. In 1789, he applied power of the Watts and Bolton Steam Engine to the machines of Arkwright. He invented the power loom and the combing-machine—two

of the greatest contributions to the textile industry. Incidentally he was a great friend of Robert Fulton and gave the latter many valuable ideas for his steamboat.

CASCADE WASHER. A laundry wash-wheel built on the cascade principle, which provides for a continuous rolling lift and drop of the goods with a waterfall or cascade-like expression of the detergent bath.

CASEIN. A noncrystalline solid, light straw in color, and having a faint, rather pleasant odor. It is the protein obtained from skim milk. Lanital and Merinova are examples of textile fibers made from it.

CASEIN FIBER. Synthetic protein fiber made from casein, which is precipitated from skim milk. Lanital was the first casein fiber to appear in the trade, an Italian product. When cut to staple length, the fiber has many of the properties of wool. Fibers made from a base of condensed milk, evaporated milk, or skimmed milk are: 1. Germany, Triolan; 2. Holland, Lactofil, Casolana; 3. Italy, Merinova; 4. Belgium, Lanital.

CASEIN PLASTIC. Milk curd and formaldehyde make this plastic which has been in use since the turn of the present century. Except for the fact that this plastic tends to warp out of shape when placed in water, it makes an ideal substance for beads, buckles, buttons, and trimmings. It has high luster and is not injured by dry-cleaning fluids. Commonly known as Galalith or Galorn, it is mixed with wool for making felt hats, pillows, and upholstered furniture stuffing. It is also blended with the major textile fibers for women's winter dress goods, and for socks.

CASEIN WOOL. See CASEIN FIBER.

CASE LEATHER. See BAG LEATHER.

CASEMENT CLOTH. 1. An English fabric made of combed cotton yarn, heavier than lawn, and made of plain weave. Small fancy weaves are sometimes used for this dress goods which may be white, colored, or printed.

2. A sheer drapery fabric made from cotton, linen, mohair, rayon, silk, or mixture yarn. Common weaves are used to make the goods, which come in white; light, dark, or neutral shades are also produced. The material is used for window-length curtains, screening purposes, and as a backing for heavy drapery fabrics of the decorative type.

CASHMERE. 1. The finest cashmere goat is raised in Tibet, the Kashmir province in northern India, Iran, Iraq, and southwest China. Cashmere is more like wool than any other fiber. The hair is very cylindrical, soft, strong, and silken. True cashmere, which is brownish in color, ranges from 1¼ to 3½ inches in length. The long coarse outer fibers are from 3½ to 4½ inches long. The fiber diameter is about 1/1600 inch.

2. The cloth was first made from the downy hair of goats of the Vale of Kashmir. Indian commercial cashmere cloths are found in overcoatings, suitings, and vestings. Cloth is made of fine wool that may be mixed with hair fibers. Soft finish is noted in the fabric. In all-hair fiber cloth, the material is made into the famous, well-known, highly desirable Indian shawls.

CASHMERE, COTTON. Soft-woven cotton cloth of Great Britain which simulates the all-cashmere or wool-cashmere fabrics. A 2-up, 1-down twill is used as the weave, and the cloth may be printed in imitation of the more expensive materials.

CASHMERE, DOUBLE. A cashmere or some other specialty fiber fabric made with the cashmere twill (2-up and 1-down) on the face, with the back made of plain weave of good texture.

CASHMERE, SILK OR RAYON. A silk or rayon fabric made on a 2-up and 1-down, right-hand twill weave and given a soft, cashmere-like finish.

CASHMERETTE. 1. Spun silk or rayon warp and woolen filling are used to make this twilled dress goods. 2. A lightweight cotton flannel made on a twill weave and given a nap to simulate cashmere fabric.

CASHMERE TWILL. The 1-up and 2-down, filling-effect, right-hand twill weave.

CASKET, COFFIN LINING. When made of rayon it is a good quality fabric with medium to high texture. Also known as undertaker's cloth, some grades are made of wool, wool waste, cotton and wool, or mixture fabric.

CASOLANA. A Dutch casein fiber.

CASSIMERE. Broad term for a large and popular group of fancy worsteds and some woolens used for suitings and trouserings. Plain-, twill-, and fancy-weave effects are used to make checks, chain-breaks, plaids, and stripes observed in the goods. Cassimere is said to be a serge with a pattern or design in it. Given a clear finish. The term is sometimes used for worsted fabrics which cannot be placed in some other classification.

CASSIMERETTE. A cheap grade of cassimere suiting.

CASSIMERE TWILL. Another name for a 2-up and 2-down twill weave. In other words, it is an even-sided, four-harness twill construction.

CASSINET. A cotton warp and wool or worsted filling cloth made to simulate cassimere worsted used for men's suiting. Made in lighter weight than cassimere, it is used as a dress-goods fabric.

CASSINETTA. An all-cotton type of cassinet, a low-grade trousering made in colored stripe effect. Fine cotton warp and yarn-dyed filling are used. Material is given a light fulling, and calendering. Made on a 3-up and 1-down, right-hand twill weave.

CASSOCKS. 1. Loose hip-length jackets introduced in the 16th century on the Continent and the British Isles. 2. A loose fitting topcoating or overcoating called a gabardine, made with rather wide sleeves; a contemporary of the foregoing jacket. Worn by religious and lay men in church services. Both were forerunners of the present day suit jacket and topcoating made of gabardine, covert, whipcord, and similar materials. See Mandeville, Schaube.

CAST. A coarse, irregular, low-quality wool fleece.

CASTALOGNE. A fine woolen blanket made in France and Spain.

CASTELLAMARE COTTON. An Italian cotton developed from American seed and consumed in Italy.

CASTING-OUT. Rigging or inactivating some of the pattern control hooks on a Jacquard loom; putting control hooks out of action when the motif or design does not require their movement at all or at some particular time during the weaving.

CASTLE, IRENE AND VERNON. The Castles, Irene and Vernon, were known as The International Ballroom Dancers and were the toast of the World War One era. Vernon Castle became an officer in the Royal Air Force of Great Britain, and was killed in an airplane accident in Fort Worth, Texas, in 1918, where he was training American pilots. The Castles had a great impact on American life during and even after the war, when, despite Vernon's death, the team's influence lived on.

Irene Castle revolutionized ballroom dancing and women's fashions. She is remembered for her Dutch lace cap, her flowing, wide-brimmed hat, Scottish Glengarry cap, as well as the "black velvet headache band," and the ankle-length gown. She also brought in the slim boyish figure to the world of fashion, which spelled the end of the lush silhouette that had held sway since the Gay Nineties, as typified by the famous Lillian Russell, Nora Bayes, Blanche Ring, and others of the era. Because of Irene Castle's boyishness she was the first performer to go without a girdle.

She also introduced bobbed hair, and the Croquignole, a permanent wave which was achieved by winding the hair around rods and then giving it a heat treatment. Croquignole comes from the French word meaning "crunch." This innovation took the feminine world by storm and enjoyed great popularity for many years.

In their dancing the Castles introduced the Castle Walk, the Brazilian Maxixe, the One-Step, and the Tango. Their interpretations and personal charm won them so much world favor that the couple would receive one thousand dollars for a one-night appearance, a goodly sum for a few hours work, especially in those days.

CAST OFF. Knitting term for the finishing off of work in any of the work or operations needed to finish an article.

CAST-OFF POSITION. The position in the knitting cycle where the needle is retracted to its lowest point, allowing the new loop to be drawn through the old loop and then casting the latter over the head of the needle hook.

CAST ON. The initial placing of yarn upon a knitting needle to form stitches to make fabric.

CASTOR. 1. Heavily fulled, smooth-finish broadcloth which gives excellent wear because of the high-quality yarn used in warp and filling. An overcoating of the formal, dressy type. 2. Hair-sheepskin or goatskin leather that has been suède-finished on the grain side.

CASTOR OIL. A viscous fixed oil, pale yellow or colorless, extracted from the seeds of the castor oil plant, Ricinus. It is used in the manufacture of sulphonated oils, as a lubricant.

CAST OVER. To bring yarn over the needle and around it, in knitting.

CASTRAVANE. Raw silk from the Levant used for braiding.

CASTULI FIBER. Bast fiber obtained from the musk mallow and used in the Philippines for cordage.

CASUAL LABOR. Individuals who are employed for short durations, usually each time by a different employer.

CATACAOS COTTON. A Peruvian tree cotton.

CATALICTIC. The chemical action which one substance produces upon another without undergoing any change itself.

CATALONIA LACE. Spanish lace originally from the Catalonia region, which features black and blonde silk laces. Today, the term is applied to lace of fine Cluny character.

CATALYST. A substance that changes the speed of a chemical action without being altered permanently itself. In sulphur dyeing, for example, the action of sodium sulphide is catalytic since it does no actual dyeing, but causes the dyestuff to have increased affinity for the goods. The use of salt in direct dyeing will aid the dyestuff to go onto the material—another example.

CATANIA. British decorative fabric made with a warp-effect satin weave ground enhanced by brocade effects on the face of the goods. Two-ply cotton is used for colored striping in the warp while the filling may be made of rayon, acetate, etc. The filling forms the motif on the goods. Warp texture in this goods is very high and varies with the type of material desired by the designer.

CATAWBA COTTON. A South Carolina cotton which has a 1-inch staple and gives a lint yield of about 35 per cent.

CATCH BAR. Device on a full-fashioned knitting machine to move the dividers forward in simultaneous action after the sinkers have been impelled forward.

CATCH CORD. A cord or wire used in weaving some fabrics. It is located near the selvage edges and is later withdrawn from the material. It may serve to form a loop or picot selvage edge, or to catch thick, extra filling yarns which are later clipped off and should not weave in with the regular selvage.

CATCHER-THREADS. In Axminster carpet weaving of the chenille type, this term refers to the attaching of the chenille or caterpillar fur to the backing structure of the carpet.

CATCH STITCH. A backward cross-stitch used when fabric is too heavy to turn down twice.

CATECHU. Same as GAMBIER.

CATENA FIBER. A white bast fiber obtained from a species of the Heliocarpus tree in Mexico; used for cordage.

CATERPILLAR THREAD. One which breaks or curls around the unbroken part of the thread. It is caused by a weak place in the yarn catching in a guide eye or reed.

CATGUT GAUZE. Made by a special method in gauze or leno weaving whereby there is a double crossing of the warp ends between the picks, so arranged that the crossing spreads are held in place by the filling, always on the same side of the standard warp ends.

CATGUT LINEN. Hard-spun, tightly twisted yarn is used to make this open, plain-woven linen cloth used for embroidery purposes.

CAT HAIR. It comes in many colors and has good luster; it is from 1 cm. to 2 cm. in length. The hair is used as "filler-in" fiber in some dress goods.

CATH-DATH. The battle colors of a Scottish clan.

CATIFA. Spanish term for Oriental floor covering of high quality.

CATION. A positively charted ion in a solution which tends to migrate towards the cathode under the influence of an electric field. Cationic materials should not be used with cationic soaps or other materials that are strongly anionic in nature.

The use of the word, cationic, has developed in recent years for several reasons. Many cationic materials have been found to be definite in mildew-proofing value since they inhibit the growth or mold of bacteria. Cationic softeners are now used widely in the textile industry.

Perhaps the latest widespread use of the word is in connection with the acrylic and modacrylic fibers. Basic dyes are commonly used to color some of these fibers, and since these dyes are cationic in nature, many persons have not referred to them as a cationic dye for the fibers.

Because these dyes are cationic in nature, it is most important to be certain that no anionic materials are present in the dye bath. It is also important to be sure that an anionic or detergent is not used in the scouring of the goods prior to dyeing. A prescour of the fibers that are to be dyed with basic dyes is best carried out with the use of a nontoxic detergent. Cations are nontoxic and bland to the human skin.

CATIONIC DYES. Basic dyes which color acrylic fibers in medium and dark shades. These dyes have superb wash fastness properties. The dyes are dispersed in aqueous solution to produce a colored ion that is positively charged. A basic dye, for example, is a cationic dye characterized by substantivity for tannin-mordanted cotton.

CATIONIC SOFTENER. Any of a group of softeners applied to knit or woven goods. It has replaced the use of soaps or emulsified and sulphonated oils. A softener of the cationic type may not be entirely durable and resistant to washing and drycleaning but it is an improvement over the agents formerly used. It does, however, stand up well in its affinity for certain fibers which accounts

for their growing use in fabrics or garments that are laundered and drycleaned. It should be kept in mind that these surface-active agents may have some negative effect in washing and in the light-fastness of the dye used. Light shades and white may take on a slightly yellowish tint if the union of the ingredients is not well-nigh perfect.

CATS-AND-DOGS. Miscellaneous clothing merchandise of more or less doubtful value.

CAT'S EYE. Flecton, a fiber that reflects in darkness, is used in various ways for motif in this fabric which was a trade-mark name of William Skinner & Sons, New York City and is a unit of Indian Head, Inc., New York City. See Flecton.

CAT STITCH. See CATCH STITCH.

CAUCASIAN RAMBOUILLET. A Soviet breed of sheep developed by crossing American Rambouillet rams with Russian Merino ewes. The fleece has the length and fineness of Rambouillet, and the fiber density of the merino. Staple is three to four inches, and the wool scours out to about 35 per cent. Fleece weight ranges from about 18 pounds to around 25 pounds.

CAUSTIC. The hydroxide or hydrate type of alkali. Commonly known as caustic soda or lye. When used as a builder, this alkali is destructive to cotton and will discolor the goods. Rinses with difficulty. Caustic is much used in kier boiling to digest and destroy cotton-seed motes, shives, etc.

CAUSTICITY. The amount of free alkali (hydroxide) freed when alkaline salts are dissolved in water.

CAUSTIC SODA. Formula is NaOH. It is a white, crystalline solid readily soluble in water. It is used in mercerizing cotton, printing of indigo, vat dyeing and soap manufacture and is an important chemical in the making of man-made filaments. Caustic soda will destroy animal fibers such as wool or silk; it has little effect on vegetable matter like cotton or flax.

CAUSTIC SODA CREPE. A blistered, puckered, or crepe effect applied to the usual run of cotton fabrics used for summer dress goods. Applied directly to the goods, or by the use of a resisting agent and then the caustic, it will be the caustic-treated areas that will shrink and allow the untreated areas to blister. Striped patterns, as in plissé, are the most popular.

CAUSTIC, SODIUM HYDROXIDE. A very strong alkali commonly known as caustic soda or lye, it rinses with difficulty. When used as a builder it can be destructive to cotton and will discolor goods when they have not been fully rinsed. Caustic is used in kier boiling to digest and destroy cotton-seed motes, shives, etc.

CAVALLEYS. Panamanian Indians made this dyed cotton cloth in the eighteenth century. The British bought the fabrics for use as tablecloths, counterpanes, and coverlets.

CAVALRY TWILL. A strong, rugged cloth made with a pronounced raised cord on a 63-degree twill weave. Woolen or worsted yarn is used. The weaves used for cavalry twill and elastique are the same, and there is no set weave for either fabric. The weave may vary according to the size of the yarn used and the fabric weight per yard. Cavalry twill is the original name; elastique is a United States government term used very likely because of the different texture of the alternating picks which give the fabric more elasticity and properties and characteristics resembling knitted fabric. Cavalry twill has the coarser rib effect when compared with elastique, which has a smoother effect and feel. The cloth is also made in spun rayon. Used for riding habits, ski wear, sportswear, uniform fabric. See Illustrated Section (Fabrics 30).

CAVINGS. Term used in flax which implies the rejects which arise from the bottom riddle of a roughing-out machine. Cavings are essentially rough bits of broken straw along with some end roots of the flax. See ROUGHING FLAX.

"CAVITOMA". A cellulose-destroying micro-organism that causes deterioration of cotton. Producers, ginners, manufacturers, and finishers of cotton goods are concerned with this parasite. Tests made have revealed the existence of a low-reducing sugar content and pH values of 8 to 9.5 of the readily water-extractable constituents. The term has been coined by Dr. L. T. Hall and Mr. J. P. Elting of Kendall Mills, Inc., Paw Creek, N. C.

CAVLAN. A soft, all-nylon surface, foam-cushioned stretch fabric with the appearance of leather for use in the upholstery field. It is made with a knit surface of Caprolan nylon of Allied Chemical Corporation, while the fabric is made by Guilford Mills, Guilford, North Carolina. The material combines the practical advantages of leather and vinyl in that it is easy to clean, has a fully breathable surface for all-weather comfort, offers easy application to furniture because of its stretch characteristics, and exceptional seating geared for comfort because of the foam core construc-

tion. The backing is of nylon.

The leather appearance is obtained through a combination of printing and embossing which provides authentic motif and textured definition. Cavlon does not ravel and it may be sewn to within one-eighth inch of the edge without risk of seam slippage.

CAYENNE. Unbleached French linen cloth made in low textures.

CCC-T-191A. The following is the Laboratory Wash Formula for predetermining shrinkage of washable cotton and linen fabrics in accordance with Federal Specification CCC-T-191a Wash Test Method:

SAMPLES: 20 inches by full width of cloth. Mark off three 18-inch measurements, in both warp and filling directions.

EQUIPMENT AND MATERIALS:
Small Reverse Wheel, cylindrical (20-inch wheel).
Use a standard load—three pounds dry samples.
Water to be fifty times the weight of the goods.
Soap—good grade laundry soap to give running suds. (Add additional pieces of cloth to samples if necessary to make standard load).
Cloth should be well covered by water.

PROCEDURE:
1. Place samples in wheel and start wheel.
2. Turn on water and steam.
3. Run water in to proper level—add soap.
4. Turn off steam when water boils—approximately 212° F.
5. Run wheel forty minutes from the time started.
6. Draw off water. Do not stop wheel.
7. Fill wheel to proper level with water—bringing temperature to 140° F.
8. Run for five minutes.
9. Draw off water.
10. Fill to proper level—bring temperature to 140° F. Run ten minutes.
11. Drain off water while the wheel is running and run five minutes without water. Total time is sixty minutes, wheel running continuously.
12. Remove samples from wheel—squeeze, do not wring. Spread out and dry on screen or ventilated surface.
13. Dampen with spray dampener—allow samples to condition for five minutes.
14. Press on press machine or by hand iron—by raising and lowering iron—do not slide the iron.

INFORMATION REGARDING WASH WHEEL:
1. Speed of wheel (when not run-

ning in one direction) about 35 r.p.m.
2. Reversals of direction of rotation—every eight or nine minutes.
3. Keep belts tight in order to prevent slippage.
4. Water, steam, and drainage connections should be so arranged that the wheel can run continuously during the test.

CEBA COTTON. A fine, silky cotton obtained from tree of this name found in Mexico.

CEBU HEMP. A grade of Manila hemp.

CEBU MAGUEY. See CANTALA.

CEDILLA NYLON. Registered trademark of Celanese Corporation of America for its crimped nylon known for its ease-of-care, luxuriant hand, and quality in warp-knitted fabrics. Delivered to knitters on tricot beams this textured yarn adds softness, bulk, opacity, and smoothness to tricot lingeries and printed tricot outerwear.

CEGLIN. Alkali soluble cellulose ethers are the base for this set of five textile finishes produced by the Sylvania Industrial Corporation, now a unit of the American Viscose Division of FMC Corporation. Cottons and rayons, treated with the proper finish, will be improved since the treatment reinforces each yarn to the degree that each fiber is fast even to kier boiling. Each of the five types of finish has a different viscosity and each is intended for different and specific work. The product comes in dry form or in solution.

Ceglin may be applied prior to boiloff, during mercerization, before or after dyeing, or as a final finish. Curing, or aging at high temperatures, is not necessary.

Dependent on the type of finish resorted to, the following features are observed: durability of finish, improved hand, reduced shrinkage, longer wear, linen effects, fabrics free from lint or fuzz, better dispersion and binding of colors; crisp, medium, or soft hand, abrasion resistance, and increased tensile strength are also noted.

CEIBA. Used for stuffing, it is a yellowish, silky, seed hair of the South American bombax tree.

CELAIRESE. A successful replacement for other materials which for years have been used as filler for bathrobes, bedspreads, card-table covers, comforters, jackets, pillows. This product of the Celanese Corporation of America is a natural insulator; it launders or dry-cleans very well, and since it is free from foreign matter it remains clean and unaffected by atmospheric conditions or perspiration. Celairese is available in two colors, permanent pure white and a natural black which is inherent in the fiber.

CELANESE. The registered trademark of the Celanese Corporation of America, used to designate its textile and other products. The Celanese Corporation is the largest producer of yarns made by the cellulose acetate method. One of the important characteristics of acetate yarn is low moisture absorption, which means speedy drying and resistance to wrinkling, mussing, shrinking, and stretching. Since acetate yarn is thermoplastic it can be shaped and set by controlled heat and pressure, thus permitting moiré markings and pleats in finished garments.

Acetate fibers, unlike the natural fibers, are born white and remain so. They are naturally resistant to mildew, mold, and silverfish, and are nonirritating to the skin.

Certain characteristics set Celanese fabrics apart from others. Some of these features include retention of body in damp climates, easy application of dyestuffs, drapability, dimensional stability and ease in care of the fabrics.

CELANESE CORPORATION. Licensed trademarks of Celanese Corporation show that the Fibers Marketing Division of the company markets a goodly number of products. The Licensed Program follows; all are registered trademark items:

Arnel: Triacetate fiber for men's and women's apparel and home fashions.

Celabond: Bonded fabrics backed by Celanese acetate tricot.

Celacloud: Acetate fiberfill for apparel, sleeping bags, mattresses, etc.

Celafil: Acetate fiberfill (Type K) for pillows and comforters.

Celaire: Acetate/nylon yarn for upholstery fabrics and carpeting.

Celanese Nylon: Nylon for knit or woven apparel.

Celara: Knit fabrics made with textured acetate.

Celustra: Jersey knit fabric of triacetate yarn.

Chifonese: Sheet curtain fabric which contains acetate.

Clairanese: Drapery fabric which contains acetate.

Durel: Polypropylene for carpets.

Fortrel: Polyester fiber for apparel, home furnishings, industry.

Fortrel Fiberfill: Polyester fiberfill for apparel, pillows, sleeping bags, etc.

Fybrite: A fabric which contains Fortrel polyester with anti-static properties and which resists soil redeposition.

Multicord: Drapery fabric which contains acetate.

Permanese: Sheer curtain fabric of solution-dyed acetate.

Prospector: Sharkskin-type fabric of triacetate fiber; has filament warp and spun filling.

Safeguard Seal: An acetate tricot fabric of 5.75 yield or heavier. Licenses for both fabric producer and garment manufacturer.

Starset: An acetate fabric.

Sundance: Knitted marquisette curtain fabric of Fortrel.

Tricocel: An acetate tricot of 5.5 yield or heavier. Licenses for both fabric produce and garment manufacturer.

CELAPERM. A color-pigmented acetate yarn with "sealed-in" color. Fabrics colored with Celaperm come in a wide range of colors and are claimed to be lightfast, washable, drycleanable, and to withstand perspiration, gas fading, crocking, and sea water.

Colorfastness is unexcelled by conventional dyeing of any fiber, natural, man-made, or synthetic. Many different colors may be used in one fabric by the use of Celaperm. Through the addition of white, or thick-and-thin yarns, the color stylist has a very wide range in which to work. The term is a registered trade-mark of Celanese Corporation

CELARA, CELABOND. Celara is Celaperm solution-dyed acetate filament yarn for texturing; provides aesthetic and economic advantages to a variety of men's and women's double-knits, and warp knits. Celabond is the quality controlled trademark for fabrics bonded with Celanese Acetricot which have to meet the rigid performance tests as per specifications.

CELASTIC. A patented liquid which, when applied to fabric, first softens it to facilitate molding to shape, and when dry stiffens the fabric to preserve that shape. The liquid is used in preparing fabric for use in box toes of shoes.

CELATOW. Acetate tow sold under the trade-mark of the Celanese Corporation of America.

CELCON. This plastic is made from trioxane, a formaldehyde derivative, and an unnamed by-product of petroleum. It is classified chemically as an acetal copolymer. Celcon has all the qualities of high-strength engineering plastic including hardness, stiffness, dimensional stability, light weight, and resistance to abrasion and environmental attack. It may replace metals for use in die-cast zinc, aluminum, brass, and steel. This product of the Celanese Corporation of America in its advantages has lower cost, improved versatility in design, lowered weight, and elimination of some finishing and assembly procedures.

CELCOS. A man-made fiber which contains acetate with a large percentage of viscose rayon. The first yarn in this field which combines set proportions of acetate and viscose rayon in a single fiber.

CELERINA. A term applied to fancy woven Swiss voiles.

CELLOPHANE. Transparent cellulose sheeting made in the same manner as viscose yarn except that it comes in the sheet form. The sheets resemble metallic threads and do not tarnish as in the case of gold, silver, and aluminum threads. Cellophane is smooth, odorless, strong, and light in weight. Uses of the film yarn product are for curtains, hangings, shade cloth, belts and braids, fringes and lacing. In conjunction with other fibers, cellophane is used in the clothing and dress trade, and for decorative fabrics.

Other uses of cellulose derivatives are: celluloid, toys, nonflammable film, dope for airplane wings, thermoplastic materials, lacquers, and finishes for automobiles, artificial leather, smokeless powder.

CELLOPHANE, CHARACTERISTICS OF:

1. DIELECTRIC PROPERTIES: When dry and free from moisture, Cellophane has excellent dielectric properties and may be used as insulating material.

2. GREASEPROOFNESS: Cellophane is 100 per cent greaseproof and oilproof.

3. HYGROSCOPICITY: When exposed to high humidity, Cellophane will absorb moisture and swell; exposed to low humidity, the reverse is true.

4. MOISTUREPROOFNESS: Moistureproof Cellophane is the plain product specially processed to make it highly resistant to the penetration of moisture in the vapor phase. Moistureproof Cellophane prevents the penetration of water-soluble odors.

5. ODORPROOFNESS: All Cellophane greatly retards the penetration of odors.

6. PHYSICAL PROPERTIES: Cellophane burns in air similar to paper; it is not explosive and does not disintegrate in water. Plain Cellophane ranges from .00088 to .0016 of an inch; moistureproof Cellophane from .0010 to .0017 of an inch.

7. TRANSPARENCY: This is the outstanding characteristic of Cellophane. It is even transparent to ultraviolet light.

CELLOPHANE-COATED FABRICS. Cotton fabrics of various suitable types, piece dyed and then laminated on one side with Cellophane for use in curtains, garments, lamp shades, etc. See CELLOPHANE.

CELLUCORD YARN. This yarn can be woven with cotton, wool, jute, viscose rayon, acetate, nylon, and the other man-made or synthetic fibers. It can also be knitted, braided, or bonded, and there are many applications for the product in industry—automobile seat covers, upholstery, furniture webbing, belts and belting, matting, shades, screens, welting, cable wrap, hampers, and handbags, among others.

Tensile strength, depending on the size of the yarn, varies from 6½ pounds up to 200 pounds. This pliable plasticized yarn is a product of the Cellucord Corporation.

CELLULAR CLOTH. 1. A porous leno-woven, cotton cloth made in England and used for underwear. 2. Broad term for openwork or porous fabrics without regard to weave or material. 3. A thin, openwork cloth used for shirts and blouses in France, Australia, and the East.

CELLULOID. Made from a compound of guncotton and camphor, it is used to imitate coral, ivory, tortoise shell, and so on. Collars, belts, and novelties may be made from it.

CELLULON. Made of celluloid on the principle of rayon staple fiber, it is spun on the cotton system.

CELLULOSE. A substance which constitutes the chief part of the solid framework of plant life such as cotton, flax-linen, paper, rayon, etc. In its pure state it is a white, shapeless, amorphous mass. It is a carbohydrate ($C_6H_{10}O_5$) taken x or n times of the same percentage composition as starch. About 95 per cent of cotton is cellulose. It is soluble in Schweitzer's Reagent and zinc chloride solution but not in any of the common solvents such as water, alcohol, or ether. The chemistry of cellulose is very complicated. Cotton minus its water content gives cellulose, which finds use in making nitro-cellulose from which guncotton is made, pyroxylin, cellophane, collodion, and other commercial products. One of the greatest products made from cellulose base is the man-made fiber group of textile yarns—viscose rayon, cuprammonium, nitro-cellulose, and acetate. Cotton linters or hemlock, pine, or spruce chips, all vegetable matter, are used as the base for these yarns.

CELLULOSE ACETATE. Filaments made of an acetic acid ester of cellulose which has been coagulated or solidified from the spinning solution; a type of man-made, cellulosic fiber which is a compound of cellulose and other chemicals.

CELLULOSE ACETATE, PRIMARY. The product of the acetylation of cellulose prior to any hydrolytic treatment (ripening) has been applied. Primary cellulose acetate contains sixty per cent or more of combined acetic acid.

CELLULOSE ACETATE, SECONDARY. The result of hydrolysing or ripening a primary cellulose acetate. The ripening in the commercial manner is carried usually to the point of solubility in acetone.

CELLULOSE ACETATE FLAKE. Also known as Flock Cellulose or Flake Cellulose, it is an impalpable powder of cellulose used for flocking and as a filler for molding powders. It is considered a secondary acetate substance used in the manufacture of acetate.

CELLULOSE ACETATE PRECIPITATION PROCESS. The expulsion of cellulose acetate from the acetylation solution. Water is the usual precipitant used and is added in the form of dilute aqueous acetic acid.

CELLULOSE DERIVATIVES. They are defined as compounds in which cellulose has reacted with an alcohol. These derivatives are classified as follows:

1. CELLULOSE ESTERS:
   A. Inorganic:
      a. Nitrate (Nitrocellulose).
   B. Organic:
      a. Acetate
      b. Propionate
      c. Acetate propionate
      d. Acetate butyrate

2. CELLULOSE ETHERS:
   A. Soluble in Organic Solvents:
      a. Ethyl Cellulose
      b. Benzyl Cellulose
   B. Soluble in Water or Organic Sodium Hydroxide:
      a. Methyl Cellulose
      b. Sodium Carboxymethyl Cellose
      c. Hydroxyethyl Cellulose

CELLULOSE DIACETATE. Theoretically a compound of cellulose and acetic acid containing 48.8 per cent of combined acetic acid; not a commercial product. The term is applied loosely to a secondary or acetone-soluble cellulose acetate which contains about 2.4 acetyl groups per glucose unit.

CELLULOSE ETHERS. A finishing material for yarn or fabric used in lieu of starch. A brand name for methyl cellulose, carboxymethyl cellulose and comparable compounds.

CELLULOSE-FROM RAW MATERIAL TO CELLULOSE ROLLS SHIPPED TO FIBER PRODUCERS. Cellulose, for the textile industry, is obtained from cotton linters or trees such as hemlock, spruce, or pine. Today, however, the choice falls to pine trees whose span from planting to maturity for use in the manufacture of acetate and rayon is about twenty-eight years. These, logs, after harvesting, are sent to the "log mill" where they are stored until ready for use. The logs are cut into twenty foot lengths, the bark is removed by hydraulic pressure, and the stock is now ready for chipping. The chipping is done by a large revolving disc which has a series of blades whose function it is to reduce the logs into chip forms an inch or so in size.

The wood chips are then set to a digester for conversion into unbleached pulp form. A series of bleaching treatments comes next and its purpose is to bleach the stock, remove impurities, and cause the matter to become white in shade. At this point selective purification, which depends on the terminal use to be made of the cellulose, occurs.

The pulp is then made into long, fibrous sheets about one-twentieth of an inch thick. After cutting to proper size, this stock resembles desk blotters in size and shape. This mass is composed of millions of tiny fiber stock which has a length of about 1/10th of an inch. The "blotter stock" is now purified cellulose. It is dried thoroughly, wound into rolls or some comparable form, and then shipped to the fiber manufacturers.

CELLULOSE IMAGO PRINT. This method of printing is used when it is desired to obtain white on white or an opaque effect on white or pastel ground. The cotton fabric is printed with a cellulose and pigment solution to give the desired result.

If the proper pigment is used the material will withstand washing and is considered a permanent washable print. Consumers should read the labels found on garments for definite information with regard to laundering and dry cleaning.

CELLULOSE, REGENERATED MODIFIED. Cellulosic fibers modified permanently by chemical means. Cellulose acetate and cellulose triacetate are examples.

CELLULOSE TRIACETATE. Compound of cellulose and acetic acid which contains 60 per cent or more of combined acetic acid. Theoretical cellulose triacetate contains 62.5 per cent of combined acetic acid.

CELLULOSE XANTHATE. The viscous mass resulting from mixing carbon bisulphide with alkali-cellulose crumbs in the manufacture of rayon.

It is orange in color.

CELON. Product of Courtaulds, Ltd., Great Britain, it is the nylon fiber of this company.

CELTA. A French yarn made by the Rhodiaceta Company in France and Switzerland. Made in bright, continuous filament, acetate or rayon, the yarn has a hollow filament formation that is supposed to give greater bulk because of the hollow core.

CELTAFLAM. Comparable with Celta except that it is made in a thick-and-thin type yarn. Manufactured in France and Switzerland by Deutsche Rhodiaceta, A.G., Freiburg, West Germany. See CELTA.

CELTALAN. A hollow-filament viscose rayon staple fiber. See CELTA.

CELTIC WEAVES. Twilled basket weaves are sometimes known by this name.

CENTER, CENTERED TIE. The point tie: harness tie used in weaving.

CENTER DRAW SCOTCH FEED. This intermediate wool card forms the web from the breaker card into a narrow ribbon-like formation, and feeds it by means of an endless lattice apron to the feed rolls of the next card. Here it is lowered and deposited as a lap by the use of a horizontal oscillating motion.

CENTER FIBER. The main vein of the leaves produced in bobbin lace.

CENTER FILLING FORK. Filling stop-motion forks that are located in the middle of the race plate of the loom, rather than near the shuttle boxes on the one side of the loom, as is often the case. The center-fork method will operate on every pick placed in the shed; the side-fork method operates every two picks.

CENTER SHEDDING. Prior to the opening of the shed for actual weaving, all the warp ends form a straight line. When the loom is in action those ends which form the top shed rise and those which form the bottom shed are lowered; thus the shuttle can easily pass between the raised and lowered sets of yarn. Also known as split reed.

CENTER STITCHING WARP. An extra warp used in weaving double-cloth fabrics to bind or stitch the two single fabrics together. The arrangement of the binder warp causes the ends to weave under the back warp and over the face warp according to some set weave plan. Since the stitching warp is usually finer than the warps used for the face and back of the cloth the latter tend to cover up the former and prevent their being observed on the face or back of the goods. Melton, kersey, beaver, broadcloth, chinchilla and other face-finished fabrics are woven in this

manner.

CENTIGRADE. A thermometer on the scale of which the interval between the two standard points—the freezing point of water and 100°, the boiling point of water—is divided into 100 parts or degrees.

CENTRAL HIRING HALL, AIRING HALL. A location used by unions to gather together their members for referral to jobs with companies with which they have closed-shop agreements. Used chiefly in casual and seasonal trades.

CENTRIFUGAL SPINNING. See POT SPINNING.

CENTRIFUGAL POT, CENTRIFUGAL BOX. A pot or box which combines the process of spinning and twisting synthetic filaments. The number of revolutions per minute ranges from 5000 to 6000. Provision must be made for even balancing and for resistance to acids in the bath.

CENTRIFUGAL EXTRACTOR. Same as Hydro-extractor.

CENTRIFUGE METHOD. It is used when two materials of different densities are rotated at high speed and thereby separated from each other.

CEPKEN. The bolero-type jacket worn by males in Turkey and adjacent areas. It is profusely embroidered and very colorful.

CERE, CIRE. Originally the term ceré or ciré meant English shroud fabric which had been given a "wax treatment." Other names were cerement and sear; these are, however, superseded by the term ciré. The treatment, nevertheless, is still the same as in the original, and it is much used on silk, manmade, and synthetic fabrics, to impart a smooth, lustrous effect and hand. There is the tendency of some ciré fabric to become "heavy" if the body of the goods is in any way substantial. Used chiefly in evening wear.

CERECLOTH. A linen fabric more properly called a chrismale. It is waxed on one side and should be spread upon the entire top, the mensa, of an altar before before the altar cloths are laid as long as any traces of the holy oils remain on the surface of the altar after its conscration.

CEREX. Spunbonded fabric made of nylon and having recoverable stretch properties. The first fabric of its type, it is claimed to be the most flexible fabric on the market today. Uses include backing for urethane and rubber-coated fabrics, gas and liquid filters, construction applications, and in awnings, dust coverings and packaging, as well as in apparel and home furnishings.

Features of Cerex include practically

any degree of softness, hand, bulk, dimensional stability, pliability, softness, and excellent stretch. It has high heat stability and can withstand, at present, two or three washings. It is a product of Monsanto Textiles, Inc.

CERISE. A cherry-like color; specifically, a color which is red in hue, of very high saturation and low brilliance. Bluer than claret and much bluer than cherry.

CERTIFICATION. Recognition by the National or a State Labor Relations Board that a union has been duly selected by the employees as the execu-made with two-ply yarn in both directions. Identified by the weave used— 2-up and 2-down broken twill, two ends of right hand and two of left hand; repeated on four threads each way.

CHAIN COTTON. Trade name for Brazilian cotton.

CHAIN DRAFT. The outlined plan on design paper that gives instructions so that the draft or loom chain may be built by the chain builder in the weave shed. This chain controls the raising and lowering of the harnesses as the cloth is being woven. The draft is made with the principle in mind that "All ends that weave alike should go on the same harness."

CHAIN-DYEING. A method of dyeing yarns and fabrics of low tensile strength. Fabrics are tied end-to-end and processed through the dye bath in a continuous process.

CHAINE. French term for warp.

CHAIN LACE. Synonymous with tambour. See TAMBOUR.

CHAIN LOOM. Synonymous with a dobby loom since the design in the fabric is governed by the chain located at the side of the loom near the head motion.

CHAINS, COTTON. Cotton warps which have been made up in rope form and linked into a chain form, often called warp-linking.

CHAIN STITCH. A basic stitch, sixth in importance in the art of sewing. It is made by connecting loop stitches forming links as in a chain. It is much used in embroidery. In crochet work, the stitch is made by catching the thread around a hook and pulling it through a thread loop. Repeating the process, over and over again, results in the chain stitch effect.

tive bargaining agent with the company.

CEVENNES. The best grade of French raw silk is Cévennes. This white silk is used in the manufacture of silk lace made in Bayeux, Caen, and Chantilly, France. It was first made, however, in the Cévennes region, and the name still clings.

CEYLON. 1. Maltese laces have been made in this city in India for a very long time. 2. An English shirting and blouse fabric made from a mixture of cotton and wool. Popular in the Straits Settlements.

CEYLONETTE. British blouse and shirting fabric made of 20s warp and 12s filling. The texture is about 60 x 50, and the material comes in the white or can be dyed or printed.

CHADDAR. 1. Hand-woven Indian fabric made in cotton from plain, twill, and other small repeat weaves. Used for sheeting and dresses. 2. Indian shawls made of wool and hair fibers with woven figures set in the ground construction. 3. British material that is semi-bleached and identified by a solid color or border along one selvage edge. Classed as an export fabric; used chiefly as loincloth.

CHAFED YARN. Yarn which has become weak from friction or abrasion. Caused by over-filled filling bobbins in the shuttle, poorly twisted yarn, uneven yarn, yarn slippage on the warp beam, and so on.

CHAFE MARKS. Broad term applied to fabrics which, when wet, cause some of the fibers to loosen and give a chafed appearance, noted chiefly in silks and rayons.

CHAFER FABRIC. This special duck is often made with looped selvages, is practically square with regard to construction, and is used in the manufacture of rubber-tread tires. The ply in both warp and filling yarns ranges from two to six, and the fabric weight runs from 8 ounces to more than 16 ounces per square yard. Widths range from 40 to 60 inches. Also called bead fabric.

CHAGIN. Cotton bookbinding cloth.

CHAGNAR FIBER. A strong leaf fiber of the Argentine used for bags, cordage, hammocks.

CHAGRIN. 1. A cotton book cloth made in England. 2. A narrow silk fabric given a pebble finish to simulate leather. 3. A narrow braid made of silk, rayon, or metallic threads.

CHAIL. A printed cotton native to India. Called Chits if detached figures are printed on the goods, and if colored with coin dots or spots like bandanna the term Bhandu is given the product. See BHANDU.

CHAIN. 1. The warp in carpet weaving. 2. Hanks or skeins of yarn linked or tied by soft string or twine prior to bleaching. 3. See CHAIN DRAFT; HARNESS

CHAIN.

CHAIN BOUCLEE. Part of the macramé which is made by knitting two threads into a cord formation. See MACRAME.

CHAIN-BREAK EFFECT IN CLOTH. Also referred to as woven over-plaid, filling-break, and weave-break in filling; a very broad term. The effect is sometimes observed on clear finish worsteds. It is controlled by the "breaks" made in the weave-chain on the loom when the cloth is being woven. These box-effect breaks are made purposely to add to the effectiveness of the design. They are clearly seen in the cloth pattern on examination. J. E. Sohnne, a textile manufacturer of Burtscheld, Prussia, is supposed to have originated this type of design for the trade.

CHAIN CLOTH. Used for filter fabric, this compact, heavyweight cotton is

CHAIN STORES. These follow:
Apparel - Diana Stores, Grayson Robinson, Lane Bryant, Mangel, Miller-Wohl.
Automobile Variety Stores - Gamble-Skogmo, Western, White.
General Merchandise - W.T. Grant Co., Inc.; Interstate Stores, Inc.; Mercantile, Inc.
Grocery Stores - Acme Company, Inc.; Grand Union Stores, Inc.; Kroger Stores, Inc.; Safeway Stores, Inc.
Mail Order Stores - Montgomery Ward & Company, Inc.; J.C. Penney & Company, Inc.; Sears Roebuck & Company, Inc.; Spiegel Company, Inc.
Men's Wear - Bond Stores, Howard Co., Inc.
Shoe Stores - Edison Brothers, Inc.; Kinney Company, Inc.; Melville Shoe Co.
Special Lines Stores - Gordon Jewelry Company, Inc.; E.F. MacDonald Company, Inc.; Reliable Stores Corporation, Sterchi Brothers Stores, Inc.; Sperry & Hutchinson Company, Tandy Corporation, Wickes Corporation.
Variety Stores - Cunningham Drug Stores, Inc.; Jack Eckerd Corporation, Fishman Stores, Inc.; Franklin Stores, Inc.; S.S. Kresge Company, Inc.; McCrory Corporation, G.C. Murphy Company, Inc.; Neisner Brothers Company, Inc.; J. J. Newberry Company, Inc.; Peoples Drugstores, Inc.; Thrift Drugstores, Inc.; Walgreen Company, Inc.; F.W. Woolworth Company, Inc.; S. H. Kress Company.

CHAIN TWIST. A two-ply yarn twisted with a third yarn in reverse twist.

CHAIN WARP. Containing fewer ends when compared with a ball warp. The warp ends are made into a chain form in order to do the dyeing and sizing in the most advantageous man-

ner.

CHAIN WEAVE. Effect noted on clear-finish worsteds of staple variety. Chain breaks in cloth are purposely made in the construction of the cloth, and they work very well in finished appearance of the material. Clearly seen when examining the cloth. John Erckens Sohnne, textile manufacturer of Burtscheld, Prussia, is given credit for revealing this novelty type of design to the trade.

CHAIN YARN. A novelty yarn composed of a thick, soft yarn, twisted with a finer count of yarn that has ordinary twist, and then plied with a third, and finer, yarn, in reverse direction.

CHAIR WEB. Narrow woven fabric used to support upholstery springs in furniture. Woven in widths from 2 inches to about 3½ inches. Cotton, jute, hemp, and flax are used in varying combinations to make the web.

CHAKHI. Silk warp and cotton filling are used in this Egyptian fabric made on a warp-effect construction, either twill or satin.

CHAKUWALLA. Indian term for one who draws samples of cotton from bales which are to be compared with accepted samples at time of contract.

CHALICE LOOK. A silhouette whose feature is the accent on widened-shoulder-to-tapered-waist and molded hip. Suggested by the full-bodied goblet on a flutelike stem.

CHALINET. Another name for challis.

CHALK FINISH. It is applied to certain cottons, acetates, rayons, and silks to provide dullness and added weight; is not durable. Thick, thin, and medium starches of corn, rice, wheat, etc., or talc, China clay, alum, blanc fixe, etc., are used as the filling agents. Fabrics that may be given the finish include shirting, cambric, lawn, organdy, pajama cloth, lingerie fabrics, etc.

CHALKS. Cotton quotations listed in the box-chart "squares" by the use of chalk on the board in cotton exchanges. Chalks list the futures market prices of cotton.

CHALK STRIPE. Stripes in men's and women's wear suiting fabrics that resemble a chalk line; usually made in good harmony or contrast with the body color of the goods. See Illustrated Section (Fabrics 24).

CHALLIS, CHALYS. 1. Soft, lightweight woolen cloth made of plain weave. Is of medium construction. May be dyed or printed. Used for women's and children's dress goods, comforters, counterpanes, Kimono cloth, robes and spreads. The cloth is inexpensive. Originated in England about 1830. The fabric is made in cottons and from hair-fiber yarn. One of the most popular types of this material made from silk warp and worsted filling.

2. Challis is also a spun rayon fabric made with plain weave. Printed to simulate woolen or worsted challis. Durable, launders well, and drapes in satisfactory manner.

CHALWAR. The baggy trousers worn by Turkish and Balkan women. When spread-eagled they look like a pillowcase with funnels at either side for the feet to go through. Used at the present time for at-home wear.

CHALYS. See CHALLIS.

CHAMARRE. French for embroidery or lace.

CHAMBERS COTTON. A late-maturing South Carolina cotton which has a 1-inch staple and lint yield of about 32 per cent.

CHAMBERY. French dress goods, Chambéry is made from silk or rayon warp and worsted filling in a small twill-weave effect.

CHAMBORD. Woolen mourning cloth that may contain cotton, rayon, or silk fibers. The cloth has a ribbed appearance; the size of the ribs varies in diameter.

CHAMBRAY. A smooth, durable cloth made of a dyed warp and unbleached or white filling, featured by an all-white selvage. It is made of carded or combed yarn, and is somewhat on the order of gingham. Plain weave or dobby designs on a plain-weave ground are the constructions used to make this material, which is one of the most popular staples in the cotton trade.

The cloth, which is much used for shirting, shorts, and dresses, is often made with an end-and-end arrangement; the warp plan is made up of alternate ends of colored and white yarn instead of being all one color. This same effect is used in broadcloth and madras shirting. Chambray is made with a texture of about 80 x 76, or may be constructed with a square pick count. Cheaper cloth is used in children's dresses. This sturdy cloth is attractive either in plain or mottled effect, is easy to manipulate into a garment, wears very well, and gives good results in laundering. See Illustrated Section (Fabrics 14).

CHAMBRAY, IMITATION. Sized warp yarn in this fabric will take on the dye readily in the cold-water dye solution used; the filling with the wax still in it repels the dye or is only affected slightly. Dyeing is done in the gray goods state. Not always a satisfactory dyeing, which does not begin to compare with regular chambray, the material finds use in some print cloths. boys' shirtings, some sheetings, and work clothes.

CHAMELEON. A three-tone effect given sometimes to faille, taffeta, poplin, and comparable cloths made of silk or man-made fibers. Named for the chameleon — the lizard that changes his colors. Single-warp yarn is used along with two differently colored filling yarns for the effect. Another method used is a filling yarn made up of two individual yarns of varying color and with little twist in the plying of these yarns. Textures are about 96 x 48, twice as many ends as picks per inch in the pick count. See Cameleon.

CHAMMARRER. French, meaning to use gaudy, multicolored, or wild-effect trimmings.

CHAMOIS. 1. Leather which has been made from the flesh split of sheep or lamb skin and given a suede finish. The grain is removed by frizzing which implies working the hair into small crisp curls or minute tufts. 2. Antelope or chamois provides this leather made from the skin; a rare type at present. 3. General name for any soft, pliable leather. See Chamois Leather, Kip, Kipskin.

CHAMOISETTE. A fine, firmly knit cotton glove fabric which has a very short and soft nap. The napping is done by the emerizing process. The material is an imitation of chamois.

CHAMOIS FABRIC. Cotton cloth that has been napped, sheared, and dyed to simulate chamois leather. The material must be designated as "cotton chamois-color cloth."

CHAMOIS LEATHER. This soft leather was first made from the skins of the Alpine antelope, or chamois, now practically extinct. At present, it is made from the fleshers or the underside of sheepskins, oil-dressed, suede-finished, and used chiefly for cleaning and polishing purposes, as well as for gloves.

CHANDAR. Unbleached, bleached, dyed or printed cotton cloth, imported by India, is known by this term.

CHAND-DAR. Cashmere shawls of India made with a border and with central figures developed in the weaving of the material such as sprigs, flowers, circles, etc., alone or in combination. Also called Chantadi-dar, these shawls are expensive and classed as luxury items.

CHANDIN, CHANDI. Inexpensive plain-woven cotton fabric used in India for ceiling drapes, curtains, etc. Texture is about 44-square with 40s to 46s yarns used in the construction.

CHANEL, GABRIELLE BONHEUR. She was born on August 19, 1883 near Issoire in the Auvergne, a drab mountain area in South Central France. This great couturiere who became a legend in her own time, died at the age of eighty-seven in the Ritz Hotel, Paris, France, on January 10, 1971. Ranking with Madame Pompadour, Marie Antoinette, and Princess Eugenie in the fashion world, Chanel was the creator while the others were only the wearers of creations made under their personal supervision.

Always gifted with a needle and thread, Chanel started out in Deauville but in 1914 set up a millinery shop in Paris which was to be her headquarters throughout her career. Eventually she turned from millinery to women's clothing and was on her way to a multi-faceted business. By the early 1920's until the time of her death, a span of 50 years, Chanel had four businesses - her fashion house, a textile business, perfume laboratories, and a costume jewelry concern, and employed 3,500 persons.

Following is a digest of the highpoints of "This Spirit of the 20th Century:"

1916: She was the first designer to use jersey fabric and it was such a sensation with the affluent woman that her enterprise was known as "The Jersey House." She introduced a sport suit trimmed with velvet, and her "poor-girl-look" became popular following World War I.

1926: She persuaded women to shed their corsets, bob their hair, be comfortable in tweed suits with jersey blouses, and make use of strings of pearls.

1931: Chanel came to the United States in a coat that is still popular today, the all-wool or wool and hair fiber content which provided warmth and looked well. She also unveiled her silk chiffon evening gown, a sensation enhanced by its excellent soft drape and flowing effect which added much to the femininity of the wearer.

1937: Chanel continued to use jersey as a prime favorite, along with her broad-brimmed Breton sailor hat.

1940: She began a retirement which lasted but 15 years. She left the field with the lasting mark of the tailored look enhanced by the use of jewelry.

1954: Chanel became active again and it was reported that she wanted to bolster lagging sales in her perfume business. She went to work with great agility and came out with her navy blue suit and white shirtwaist, made of cotton, silk, or linen. She called this effort her lucky number - Number Five, a number that is a household word today when it comes to perfume. Her return was widely acclaimed.

1964: The Chanel suit to be worn with a striped blouse, and priced at $185.00, was taken from her original creation which sold for $1,000. Chanel also looked into the properties of manmade fibers and began to use these materials heavily, both alone or in blends. Nylon, polyester, and acrylic fibers, alone or blended, made their debut and received marked attention from the buyers at her showings. In 1967 she began the use of vinyls with good results.

1970: This was the year of the great decision; were dresses to be the mini, the maxi, or the midi? Always the non-conformist, Chanel maintained the mid-knee hem and never advocated any extreme length, be it too short or extremely long.

Chanel's passing marked the end of an era and career where she had been The Queen of Fashion for fifty years. Some of her lasting innovations include bell-bottom trousers, collar and cuff sets, cardigan jacket, use of handbags, box jacket, gypsy skirts, pea jackets, rope-like necklaces, slim-back pumps, trench-coats, turtleneck sweaters, and of course, her famous Chanel Number Five perfume. Most of the foregoing items were revivals of earlier times but she brought them back into favor. Chanel had not only ideas but also tools to work with and gained astronomical heights in her great career. Throughout her life it seems that there was nothing she ever missed. At the time of her death, she was reputed to be worth about $15-million. Her companies, at the time of her death, were reputed to be doing about $160-million annually. Though Chanel has left the fashion world. The House of Chanel at 31 rue Cambon in Paris still stands six stories high.

Courtesy of The New York Times Company, Inc. Reprinted by permission.

CHANGEABLE. Color or certain types of finished fabrics which present different casts, shades, tones, or hues as the rays of light strike the goods from various angles.

CHANGEABLE SILK. See SHOT CLOTH.

CHANGEABLE TAFFETA. This cloth effect is made possible by the use of yarn-dyed warp which will contrast well with yarn-dyed filling. For example, a red warp with a gray filling should give the effect, which is enhanced by the typical taffeta finish.

CHANGE GEAR. Found on a great many machines, it can be removed and replaced easily by another gear. A change gear is used on machines to increase texture of fabric, weight, length.

CHANTILLY. White lace of this name closely resembles lisle; a thick silken cotton yarn outlines the pattern. Black silk Chantilly made its appearance about the middle of the eighteenth century. It was characterized by fine ground and an elegance of floral festoon motif. The silk laces made in natural color are known as Blonde, and the term is now accepted as applying to silk lace only. Black Blonde is the name for black silk Chantilly. The introduction of machinery and the machine age have done much to kill the handmade industry in Chantilly, as well as in other centers known in the history of the lace trade.

CHAPARRAL YUCCA. A California bast fiber about three feet long with properties comparable with those of henequen.

CHARACTER. The requisite properties and characteristics that go to make a first-class textile fiber. See COTTON FIBER, CHARACTERISTICS OF.

CHARARA COTTON. A minor Egyptian cotton used in home consumption.

CHARDONNET, COUNT HILAIRE DE. At his home in Besançon, France, this great benefactor of the human race used the extract of mulberry leaves to build up an artificial silk, now known as rayon.

He commenced his experiments in 1884, and in 1889 he displayed his synthetic materials at the Paris Exposition. Chardonnet began his work under the tutelage of Louis Pasteur, the savior of the silk industry. His scientific research lasted for thirty years. The first patents were taken out in 1884; by 1891, Chardonnet began the commercial manufacture of his product by the nitrocellulose method.

Nitrocellulose rayon was made in this country in Rome, Georgia until 1934. The viscose and cuprammonium (Bemberg) rayons caused it to pass into oblivion. It is no longer made anywhere in the world.

CHARGE, ELECTRICAL. Applied to detergency, it represents the electrical characteristics of the goods being washed, detergents, and detergent-dirt complex.

CHARKANA. Small checks of four ends and four picks are used to make this Indian muslin of all-cotton or of cotton and silk. Some of the fabric is now made with a larger check effect.

CHARKAS. The hand spinning wheel of India; it is estimated that 50 million of these wheels are used there today.

CHARMANTE SATIN. A British twilled silk cloth whose face is a 2-up, 1-down twill with the back made from a 12-shaft satin weave with a base of 5 or 7. Hard-twist crepe yarn is used in the warp, while the filling has little or no twist (zero twist). It is woven one face pick, one back pick.

CHARMEEN. A very high-quality, compact-texture, worsted dress-goods cloth used in women's wear. Dyed in all colors, this distinctive twill-weave fabric is used for conventional, tailored ensembles. Charmeen resembles French serge to a marked degree.

CHARMELAINE. A high-quality dress goods for women's wear made from a 1-up and 2-down twill weave, to give a fine rib appearance on the face of the goods. The back of the material is very smooth. Rayon, silk, or high-quality worsted yarn may be used for the warp; filling is always worsted.

CHARMEUSE. A staple dress silk made on the eight-end satin weave using a 70 to 80 reed. There are four ends of two-thread, raw organzine per dent. The filling is either Schappe or spun silk, in singles or two-ply. The cloth is finished at forty inches, and the pickage ranges from 80 to 100 per inch. Charmeuse is soft in feel, drapes very well, and is a leading fabric for evening wear. It comes in black, white, colors, and prints.

CHARMOISE. A French breed of sheep developed from crossing Romney Marsh rams with native French ewes. The white fleece weighs from about 6 to 7 pounds.

CHARTREUSE. This greenish-yellow color is of high brilliance and ordinary saturation.

CHARVET SILK. Made from a diagonal rib weave, this soft, dull tie-silk, made in stripe effects, drapes very well.

CHASE. The extent of the traverse of the winding faller on a mule spinning frame.

CHASED FINISH. From four to sixteen layers of cotton cloth are "threaded" so that they will pass between the chasing rollers of the machine at the one time. The goods will have a deep grain luster rather than a top shine, unlike the flat, shiny appearance noted in calender-finished material. Chased finish is an imitation of beetled effect, is not permanent, and disappears with laundering. See CALENDERING; BEETLING.

CHASE LENGTH. Term used in packaging to imply the package itself wherein the length of the chase is measured along its surface, and not by its projection on the package axis. The term is also used where attention is centered on the yarn of which the package is composed, implying the actual length of yarn that is wound on in one complete traversing cycle.

CHASUBLE. The outer vestment worn by priests and bishops at Mass, distinctive sacrificial and priestly garment in the Roman Catholic Church. It is 46 inches by 30 inches, with rounded corners, hanging from the shoulders. It is symbolic of all-covering charity and the yoke of Christ.

CHATEE. Indian term for jute fabric or gunny sacking.

CHATELAINE BAG. Small bag, knitted, beaded, or of leather or fabric, suspended from the belt.

CHATOYANT. French expression for changeable, iridescent, or shot-about effect as noted sometimes in faille, taffeta, poplin, etc.

CHAYA. An East Indian plant root which yields a durable red dye similar to madder.

CHECK. A small pattern woven in or printed onto a cloth. Glen, gun-club, hound's-tooth, shepherd's checks are examples. See Illustrated Section (Fabrics 26 and 39).

CHECK, TURN-BACK. English cotton export cloth which has a check arrangement in the center while the border is made with solid color. Much used in India.

CHECK, TWO-AND-TWO. A check effect in which both warp and filling yarns are arranged with two yarns of the one color alternating with two threads of some other color, black, or white. The same plan is used in the filling as it is woven into the fabric. Made on plain weave.

CHECK-BACK. A plaid-back.

CHECK CANVAS. Used for embroidery purposes, this open-mesh fabric is made in a two-and-one alternating yarn arrangement to produce small checks.

CHECKERBOARD WEAVE EFFECTS. Under this caption, twill and satin weaves are used to give checkerboard, oblong, square, and other effects in certain fabrics. These repeats of pattern are quite large for a single repeat as to the number of threads each way in the design. Weaves used for this type of fabric designing include braided twill, bright-and-dim satin, clear-break in satin, checked broken twill, checked pointed twill, double twill effect, entwining twill, fancy entwining twill, figured pointed twill, twill rib, etc. All of these weaves do not require many harnesses in the loom; many can be made on fewer than 12 harnesses, and,

in many instances, only 8 shafts are necessary for the construction throughout the fabric.

CHECKERWORK. Any design in which the general effect is that of equal squares arranged in some alternating layout of different colors.

CHECK LIST, PIECE GOODS —BUYERS' AND MANUFACTURERS':

1. Name of Cloth . . . .
   Range of colors . . . .

2. What Season?
   a. Fall . . . .
   b. Winter . . . .
   c. Spring . . . .
   d. Summer . . . .

3. What price range? . . . .

4. Raw Material
   a. Warp is . . . .
   b. Filling is . . . .

5. Construction
   a. Weave? . . . .
   b. Texture-ends and picks per inch
      . . . .
   c. Is the texture high, or low, or medium? . . . . . .
   d. Weight in ounces per yard?
      . . . .
   e. Finished width? . . . .

6. Methods of Coloring
   a. Is cloth dyed, printed, or in the white? . . . .
   b. If colored, what method was used? . . . .

7. Finish of the Material
   a. What type of finish has been applied to cloth? . . . .
   b. Is the finish permanent or temporary? . . . .

8. End Uses
   May be used for . . . .

9. Working Properties of Cloth
   a. Handle or feel? . . . .
   b. Drapability? . . . .
   c. Hold crease? . . . . . .
   d. Shine with wear? . . . .
   e. Clinginess? . . . . . .
   f. Sagginess? . . . .

10. Manipulation
    a. In cutting? . . . .
    b. In fitting? . . . .
    c. In sewing? . . . .

11. Launderability
    a. Easy or difficult to launder?
       . . . .
    b. Will cloth have tendency to shrink? . . . .
    c. What is the effect of laundering on the finish? . . . .

12. Cleaning

a. Will it be necessary to have the cloth dry-cleaned after usage?
   . . . .
b. If so, will the fabric clean well?
   . . . .

13. Cost
    What is the estimate of the cost per yard of cloth based on a . . . . inch width?
    $ . . . .

14. Fashion Check
    a. Staple . . . .
    b. Classic . . . .
    c. High fashion . . . .
    d. Comment . . . .

15. Selling points for advertising and sales staff . . . .
    . . . .

16. Additional comments . . . .
    . . . .

CHECK MUSLIN. Muslin made with cord yarn used in warp and filling to produce check effect; may simulate barred dimity.

CHECK-OFF. Arrangement under which a company automatically makes deductions of monies due a union from the pay of each union member in its employ. The money is turned over to the union.

CHECKS. These cloths belong to the gingham family but differ in that the design is even-sided, and usually one color and white are used in the pattern, although more than one color may be used. The counts of yarn run from 30s to 100s, cotton warp and filling.

A typical pattern for a check might be 12 ends of red, 12 of white, 12 of blue, 12 of white for one repeat.

Checks are used in aprons, dress goods, decorative cloths. There are woolen and worsted checks (which are usually referred to as "gun clubs"), velour checks, and other attractive names.

CHECKS, HOMESPUNS, AND TWEEDS, STANDARD SCOTCH. The National Association of Scottish Woolen Manufacturers, Edinburgh, Scotland, gives the following list of standard checks, homespuns, and tweeds:

Ardtornish	Gordon
Arndilly	Highlanders
Ballindalloch	Hay or Dupplin
Balmoral	Invercauld
Brooke	Invermark
Bateson	Kinlochewe
Black Watch	King's Own
Benmore	Lochmore
Corgach	Mar
Carnegie	Minmore
Carnousie	Minto
Dacre	Pitgaveny
Dalhousie	Poltalloch

Erchless   Seaforth
Fannich   Strathspey
Glengarry   Strathmashin
Glenfeshie   The Kintail
Glenurquhart   Wyvis
Glenmorriston   Welsh Guards

CHEESE. 1. A roll of yarn made according to some plan and made ready for winding on the warp beam. 2. An indefinite length of yarn built up on a paper or wooden tube in a form which resembles a bulk cheese.

CHEESECLOTH. Narrow cheese-cloths are under 36 inches wide; wide cheesecloths may be finished up to 55 inches wide. The cloth is loosely woven, thin, light in weight, open in construction. Carded yarns are always used. When the cloth is finished at 36 inches, it is called tobacco cloth.

Textures range from 32 x 32 to 48 x 48. Warp yarns are 28s to 30s, while filling yarns range from 39s to 42s. The cloth runs from 6 to 14 yards to the pound.

In the gray the cloth is used for covering tobacco plants and for tea bags and wiping cloths. Applied finishes include buckram, crinoline, and wigan. Uses of finished cloths include curtains, bedspreads, bandages, bunting, dust cloths, sign cloths, label fabrics, hat linings, surgical gauze, fly nets, theatrical gauze.

CHEETHAM, DAVID. The inventor of the coiler can attachment which receives finished sliver from the calender rollers of the carding machine.

CHELAIS. A checked or striped border features this plain-weave, Indian cotton fabric that is used as loincloth and scarf fabric. See DHOOTIES.

CHELATING AGENT. Any compound that will inactivate a metallic ion by making the metallic ion an integral part of an inner ring structure.

CHELATION. Compounds which have a ring structure formed by hydrogen bonding in which two electronegative atoms are joined by a hydrogen atom. See ATOM, HYDROGEN.

CHELATION. From the Greek word, kelos, meaning "claw." A chelate is a claw which holds a metallic ion inactive in solution. Chemically speaking, chelation is a chemical reaction in which polyvalent metallic ions are reacted with organic reagents (chelating agents) to chemically inactivate these polyvalent metallic ions in the form of an extremely stable, water-soluble chelate.

CHELEM. A type of Yucatan sisal. See SISAL.

CHELOS. Plain-weave, calico shirting printed with checks, tartans, etc., for use in the East Indies and India.

Texture is about 64-square with yarn counts about 36s or so.

CHEMBACK. A strong carpet tufting medium perfected by Monsanto Textiles, Inc.; a lightweight primary tufting material which consists of a nylon scrim encased in a polyurethane foam. The product runs to about 4.0 ounces per square yard and is one-eighth of an inch in thickness. This medium is ideal for use in better quality area rugs, bath mats, and carpetings.

Chemback is characterized by high-speed operation, a very fine tuft pile bind, complete resistance to rot, mildew, moths, carpet beetles, silverfish, and other insects. Features of the backing include a lush depth underfoot, superior coverage, compressibility and resistance to deformation because of the cushing effect of the backing; long lasting loft and resilience. It also possesses exceptional wear life and durability; increased uniformity when compared with similar products on the market. Other features are attractive surface pile effect and excellent insulating properties.

At present, Chemback comes in two shades. 1. Neutral gray is intended for tufting with yarn dyed to medium and dark shades. 2. Natural or white shade is for use with pastel colorings. Natural Chemback is best to use when dyeing after tufting in articles such as area rugs, bath mats, et al. Conversion of a tufting frame from jute to Chemback is no more difficult than switching from lot of jute to another.

CHEMIC, CHEMICK. A chlorine bleach.

CHEMICAL COTTON. A term sometimes applied to purified and bleached cotton linters. Used as a source of cellulose in the manufacture of many products, such as different types of rayon, nitrocellulose lacquers, explosives, and others.

CHEMICAL ELEMENT. A primary substance which cannot be decomposed into other substances.

CHEMICAL FINISHES ON FABRICS, MAJOR:

1. BLEACHING: Natural fiber color and other impurities and discoloration that have been picked up during the manufacturing procedures are removed so as to prepare the goods for dyeing, printing, and the various finishing operations. Although wool, worsted, silk, linen, acetate, and rayon are usually bleached in the yarn condition, the finisher may bleach fabrics made of these fibers. Cotton is usually bleached after weaving. The chemicals and the methods used to bring goods to the white vary for each fiber, and it becomes nec-

essary to control the goods at all times in order to prevent possible weakening of the material.

2. MERCERIZATION. This is the simplest method of providing luster to cottons and linens. Gray goods are mercerized by immersion in a specially prepared solution of caustic soda at usually 25 degrees to 45 degrees strength, Twaddle thermometer; and at room temperature, a controlled temperature. The cloth is then washed, neutralized, and rinsed. The action of the chemicals, heat, and tension actually increase the strength and luster, and the absorbency of dye by the fiber.

3. CRINKLED OR PUCKERED EFFECTS: The most satisfactory of the nonwoven crickled or blister effects is obtained by printing caustic soda paste onto the goods according to the planned design. When the material is washed, the part to which the paste has been applied will shrink and cause the untreated areas to pucker.

Another method involves the use of the caustic resistant paste and the cloth is then immersed in a caustic soda solution. The uncovered area in the goods will shrink and then produce a crinkled effect. Plissé fabric finish is applied in this way, but it is nondurable.

CHEMICAL FINISHING. The use of chemicals in some form for the following purposes or types of finish: absorbency, antiseptic, antistatic, bleaching, colorfastness, crushproofing, dry-cleanable, durable, filling, flame resistant, glazing, impart crispness, improved drape, improved hand, inhibit gas fading, light fastness, lintless, lustrous, mercerized, mildew-resistant, mothproof, odorless, permanent, plissé, porosity, preserved, shrinkage resistant, slip-resistant, stain-resistant, stretch- and sag-resistant, softening, spotproofing, stiffening, wash fastness, waterproof, water-repellent, wilt-reducing, weighting—and more.

CHEMICALLY MODIFIED COTTON. When cotton is treated with chemicals so that the structure of the cotton is changed permanently, the cotton is said to be "chemically modified" or "chemmod." The latter term is obviously a contraction of "chemically modified." The purpose of such modification is either to add a new characteristic, such as permanent crease resistance, or to increase a regular characteristic, such as absorbency.

CHEMICALLY REACTIVE DYES. See REACTIVE DYES.

CHEMICALS, BODY. In 1936, during the Depression, a professor in chemistry in Northwestern University, Evanston, Illinois, stated that the value of the chemicals in the human body were worth ninety-eight cents. His breakdown follows: Carbon, 65 percent; Oxygen, 18 percent; Hydrogen, 10 percent; Nitrogen, 3 percent; Calcium, 1.5 percent; Phosphorous, 1.0 percent with traces of sulphur, gold and silver for a total of 1.5 percent to give the total of 100.00 percent structure total chemicals in the body. Professor Donald T. Forman of biochemistry in the Medical School of this university, stated that in 1969, the value had risen 257 percent in value and the body chemicals now have a value of $3.50.

CHEMICKING. Cotton goods are run through a dilute solution of bleaching powder, or chloride of lime, in a washing machine, to permit the bleaching powder to act on the natural coloring matter. This is destroyed by chemical reaction, to give the bleach.

CHEMISE. The "easy-going type" of dress, cut slimly and with no definite waistline in sight. It drops from the shoulder, must fit well at the bosom and hips although it ignores the waist completely. Usually worn short for effectiveness and sometimes referred to as a "shift."

CHEMNYLE PROCESS. Used to dye products made from filament nylon. Washfastness, improved lightfastness, and elimination of streaks are features of the process owned by Monsanto, Inc., New York City.

CHEMSTRAND FRN NYLON. Registered trademark of Monsanto, Inc., New York City, for its nylon tire yarn made specifically for aircraft, automobile and truck tires which shows a more than 100 per cent increase in the fatigue-resistance factor over tires used in the past. The product provides a higher percentage of tire suitable for retreading as well as an increase in the number of times a tire may be retreaded.

CHEMURGIC. To work witn chemicals—usually applied to farm products raised as raw materials for industry. A great chemurgic crop is cellulose, which is used in industry and not for food. This chemical grows and makes an ideal raw substance for use in world economy. See CELLULOSE.

CHENE. Warp yarn printed prior to being woven into cloth.

CHENILLE. A cotton, wool, silk, or rayon yarn which has a pile protruding all around at right angles; simulates a caterpillar. (Chenille is the French word for caterpillar.) The yarn is used as filling for fancies, curtains and carpets, embroidery, and fringes. It is woven in gauze weave with cotton or linen warp and silk, wool, rayon, or cotton filling. The warp threads are taped in groups, and the filling is beaten in very compactly. After weaving the fabric is then cut between the

bunches of warps, and the latter twisted, thereby forming the chenille effect. Chenille carpeting is rather expensive and luxuriant. See Illustrated Section.

CHENILLE AXMINSTER. A cut-pile carpet, made by binding printed chenille yarn, from side to side, to the foundation. See Illustrated Section.

CHENILLE FABRIC. Made from any of the major textile yarns for the warp with chenille filling and used in the millinery trade. Should not be confused with tufted effects obtained without the use of true chenille filling. The word is French for caterpillar, and the fabric shows the hairy effect.

CHENILLE SPREAD. See CANDLE-WICK FABRIC.

CHENILLE SWEATER YARN. This novelty yarn has body surface and is made from most major textile fibers in staple form alone, or in a combination of these fibers. Used chiefly for decorative purposes.

CHENILLE VELVET. One, which because of the use of chenille filling or weft, has the appearance of a double-fabric material. See CHENILLE, CHE-NILLE FABRIC; VELVET, DOUBLE.

CHENILLE YARN. 1. This yarn has a fuzzy pile effect, which protrudes from all sides and reminds one of a caterpillar, the French word being chenille. It is cut from woven chenille weft or filling fabric, an actual woven material that is cut in order that it may be used for weft or filling in the weaving of a chenille rug. Made from all major fibers at present, it also finds use for embroidery, fringes, tassels. 2. Fabric made from the yarn is called chenille. 3. A worsted bouclé yarn used in the knitting trade, not to be confused with the doup-woven, cut chenille yarn used in the manufacture of rugs and carpets.

CHEQUER STITCH. A stitch used in Honiton bobbin lace for small motifs of fruits, flowers, etc.

CHEROLEE. An Indian cloth of plain weave enhanced by stripe effects. Texture is around 50-square.

CHERRY. A bright-red color, specifically a color, yellowish red in hue, of high saturation and low intensity.

CHERRY CLUSTER COTTON. An early-maturing, small-boll South Carolina cotton which has a 1-inch staple; lint content is about 32 per cent.

CHESHIRE PRINTERS. Superior quality when compared with Burnley Printers. Finished at a width of one yard with cut lengths of about 125 yards. See BURNLEY PRINTERS.

CHESSBOARD CANVAS. An embroidery canvas made with white and colored check effect; squares are one inch or so in size. Plain woven with double picks used in the filling.

CHESTERFIELD. 1. Named for Philip Dormer Stanhope, the fourth Earl of Chesterfield, the coat was single-breasted with a fly front and plain back which had a center seam, notched lapel, and a velvet collar. This eighteenth-century popular coating is now made in all colors and is used for overcoating adapted into tailored coatings for women's wear. The term also refers to a four-button, cutaway coat in which the top button only is used for fastening purposes.

2. A single-breasted, fly-front overcoat of medium length, having a plain back with or without a center seam.

3. A single-breasted cutaway frock coat for stout men, usually made with four buttons, the top one only used.

CHESTING. Cotton finishing operation used to give fabric a lustered, thready effect. The cloth is wrapped in a mass form around the calender bowls rather than around an independent batch roller.

CHETEE. Indian term for cotton chintz.

CHEVENING. One of the initial methods for manufacture of machine lace. Also implies "clockwork" in hosiery; a British term.

CHEVILLIER. French term used in Britain for a finishing that provides mellowness and luster to dyed silk yarn by twisting and winding under pressure. The product is called Chevilled Silk.

CHEVIOT. Rough woolen suiting and overcoating cloth. Similar to tweed in construction. Name is derived from the fact that hardy wool from the Cheviot Hills of Scotland is used in making the cloth.

Today the cloth is made from a plain or a twill weave. Many other cloths use Cheviot wool but are not classed as Cheviot cloth. True Cheviot is very rugged, harsh, uneven in yarn, does not hold the crease and sags with wear. It is a good "knock-about" cloth and ideal for sports. May be piece-or stock-dyed and has the tendency to shine with wear. In quality, material ranges from low to high, and it is made on hand or power looms. A genuine British fabric. See also CHEVIOT, TWEED, AND HOMESPUN CLOTHS.

CHEVIOT BRITCH. Classed by itself, in contrast to britch wool from other Luster wools—Lincoln, Leicester, Cotswold, and Romney Marsh.

CHEVIOT FINISH. A popular finish that has come into its own in recent years. Shetland finish is on the order of a cheviot, but it is softer and better in quality of wool used. The cloth is called Shetland. There are many cloths that seem to be on the borderline between Cheviot and Shetland, and, at times, the names are interchangeable and used indiscriminately.

Cheviot finish is on the order of the undressed type of finish. Grades of the fabric vary because of the several types of basic stock used: Cheviot, Lincoln, Leicester, Cotswold, or Romney Marsh wool.

CHEVIOT SHEEP. A medium wool obtained from hardy sheep able to withstand rigorous climate. Originating in the Cheviot Hills of Scotland and grown for centuries there, as well as in Northumberland, England, the staple length is about 4 inches, and the fleece weighs from 6 to 8 pounds. Cheviot are much used in cross-breeding in the British Isles, with Border Leicester or Lincoln sheep for market lambs. Shrinkage is about 35 per cent. See Illustrated Section.

CHEVIOT SHIRTING. Similar to Oxford shirting, except that in the former there are small motifs in the colored stripings in the warp direction. These shirtings are rather heavy whereas most shirting of today is lightweight; 2/40s warp and 1/10s fillings are used. The filling is bulky, loosely spun, and twisted. The shirts soil readily and have declined in popularity since the advent of broadcloth. Efforts are made periodically to revive this shirting but with little success.

CHEVIOT, TWEED, AND HOMESPUN CLOTHS. Strictly speaking, original tweed cloth showed warp and filling, stock dyed and of the same color. There is a wide range of color used in all three cloths. While a homespun should be made with a plain weave and a Cheviot with a twill weave, there is much confusion as to just what is a homespun and what is a tweed, in the trade today. Homespuns are sold for Cheviots and vice versa. In the mill, however, a plain-weave cloth of the usual characteristics is called a homespun, and a twill-weave cloth would signify Cheviot or tweed.

Homespun, as a tweed, is the heaviest tweed in weight per yard. It has the salient features noted in genuine tweed. In the trade today, the belief seems to be that homespun is very coarse, rather irregular and of low texture. The lighter cloths in this group are called tweeds.

The center of this cloth industry, in the olden days, was along the banks of the Tweed River which separates Scot-

land from England. Prior to the Industrial Revolution the material, from raw stock to finished cloth, was made in the home—shearing of the sheep, sorting, mixing, carding, spinning of yarn, dyeing, and weaving. From about 1750 the factory system began to replace the home system. The result was that most of the cloth was now made on power looms that were coming into use.

Despite the great rise of powerloomed cloths, handwoven Cheviots, tweeds, and homespuns are still in good demand. They bring a good price. Incidentally, there is a good psychology in advertising homemade materials and articles. The better store features this end of the trade very much. This is why the old home industry still carries on and is flourishing in some of the more remote sections of the world.

CHEVIOT WOOL. Originated from the sheep raised in the Cheviot Hills of Scotland, and now raised all over the world. It is of the luster type which reflects the light's rays, thereby making it ideal for Shetlands, Cheviots, homespuns, tweeds, and herringbones. Staple is from 3 to 4 inches to 12 or 14 inches.

CHEVREAU DE SOIE. Trade name for a piece-dyed grosgrain silk made with crepe filling in the construction.

CHEVRETTE. Lime-processed hair obtained from Angora kidskins.

CHEVRON. Another name for herringbone, as well as for a French serge which is made on eight ends and four picks in a small broken-twill effect. The design resembles the army chevron. The cloth is used in woolen and worsted suiting and topcoating.

CHEVRON STRIPE. Wide herringbone effects are known by this term.

CHEVRON WEAVE. A twill weave on the order of broken twill or herringbone construction. Strictly speaking, the weave is a small repeat effect of a pointed twill weave, wherein the righthand and the lefthand series of threads come to a point rather than forming in the so-called "breakline" effect noted in broken twills.

CHIFFON. A plain-weave, lightweight, sheer, transparent cotton, rayon, or silk fabric made with fine, highly twisted, strong yarn. Chiffon is often used as a "drape over silk or rayon." The fabric is difficult to handle but drapes and wears well. This stately or conventional fabric is very durable despite its light weight. It is not a material for everyday wear, and must be laundered with great care.

CHIFFON BATISTE. The name for sheer batiste made of wool or worsted yarn. Used as dress goods, this cloth comes in colors, and in black and

white.

CHIFFONETTE. The sheerest of all chiffon fabrics.

CHIFFONIZED. A finish used in Great Britain and on the Continent, applied to velvets made of silk and wool in which the lustrous pile is given a crushed, dull-surface effect.

CHIFFON LACE. Chiffon made with silk or nylon lace which has been given very high twist to provide sheerness, strength, and wear.

CHIFFON NET. Silk or nylon net used as lace, chiefly in the British Isles.

CHIFFON SWISS ORGANDY. A fine fabric whose texture counts from 140 to 160, and has the same type of finish and cleaning properties as Swiss organdy. The fine yarns are conducive to the softness and delicacy of the material. Skilled techniques are vital to the finishing of the goods, and they are finished only in commercial quantities in Switzerland.

CHIFFON TAFFETA. A good, lightweight taffeta, soft in feel and lustrous in finished appearance. Used for evening gowns, blouses, dresses, and suits.

CHIFFON TWIST. Single raw-silk threads which receive from 50 to 65 turns of twist per inch. Used in chiffon, mousseline de soie, and veiling.

CHIFFON VELVET. Similar to woolen broadcloth but is lighter in weight, ranging from 7 to 10 ounces per yard, Broadcloth will run from 10 to 16 ounces, or slightly more, per yard. Chiffon velvet has a smooth feel, excellent finish, and is one of the better quality cloths in demand.

CHIFFON VELVET, WOOLEN. The same in construction as bettergrade broadcloth but much lighter in weight. The cloth runs from 7 to 10 ounces in weight per yard, has a fine, soft feel and will give excellent wear, since the material is made of high-quality stock.

CHIGNON. Knot or twist of hair, natural or artificial, worn at the back of the head, high or low.

CHIKAN. A fine, embroidered cotton muslin used in India. This fabric is very light, on the order of some zephyr fabrics made of cotton.

CHIKTI. A soft, but strong and lustrous, bast fiber raised in India which has the same uses as jute; chiefly cordage, matting, etc.

CHIKUN. An Indian nettle bast fiber raised in India and used for native clothing.

CHILDREN'S WEAR, BREAKDOWN OF. 1. Babette: This includes

the infant of three months, the small size for a baby of six months, and the medium and large size for a youngster about one year old. Infant's and baby wear go until the walking age and come in sizes 1 to 3, with 3X listed as a transition size.

2. TODDLER: The sizes are 1, 2, and 3-year with sometimes 4 and 4-Tall included. These sizes cover children who walk but are not more than three years old. Featured are short waistlines, and allowances made for children with a protruding stomach or the excessively stout types. The dresses are short and should cover the diaper panties.

3. CHILDREN'S: The sizes are 3 through 6, with 6X for the tall size six. It covers youngsters three to six years old, the nursery-school and kindergarten types. The child at this stage is taller and thinner than the toddler. The waistline is still not defined clearly, but dress shapes create an illusion of waistline with full skirts and fitted bodices.

4. GIRLS: Includes sizes 7 through 14, although there seems to be the tendency to do away with the latter size since these girls wear sub-teen sizes unless they are quite heavy in weight. Covering the elementary school group, seven to eleven years, the waistlines are defined, with some appearel manufacturers catering to either the slim types or the heavier types. There is no bust development considered at this stage, not even in the larger sizes.

5. SUB-TEEN: Sizes eight through fourteen, the junior-high-school group aged twelve to fourteen. There is a slight bust development, and waistlines are defined although still not as clearly as in the case of the true teen-age figure. Bodices are longer waisted than the sizes used in the girl's group but shorter than the teen-age group. Slight hip development is cared for in manufacture.

6. TEEN-AGE OR JUNIOR: This span covers sizes 7 through 13, and some manufacturers even go a size 5 or a size 15. Since the inception of the sub-teen size range, teen-age clothes are practically the same as for the so-called juniors. The age group covers thirteen years to sixteen years, and waistlines are defined clearly, and there is a smaller bust that is high and rounded. Hips are fuller in this group. Even to the actual styling, one may consider a teen-age garment equivalent to the young junior-age. The word, teen, is obsolete since the youngsters in this age group now prefer terms such as Junior Miss, Miss Junior, Junior Deb, and Young Junior, because they imply more sophistication than the common term, teen or teen-age.

CHILLI, CHILLO. Coarse, low-count, plain-woven, dyed cotton cloth made in Britain and exported to many parts of the world, chiefly to West Africa.

CHILVER. A yearling ewe.

CHIMAYO. The several tribes of Indians in the American Southwest made this woolen blanket identified by the crosswise stripes, chiefly in black, blue, red, and white. Much of the fabric is now made on power looms in eastern woolen mills.

CHINA BALL. Northern Chinese wool is combed or pulled from the sheep's back and rolled into balls.

CHINA CLAY. This soft, rather greasy weighting agent is used to add weight to fabrics, and to serve as a filler in certain materials, especially in low-count goods. The clay has an earthy odor and should be devoid of gritty matter when ready for use. It is plastic because of its great power of moisture absorption.

CHINA COTTON. A type of short-staple cotton from China that is harsher than American cotton. Because of its harsh wiry nature, it is used in mixtures for part-wool blankets, hosiery, and so on.

CHINA GRASS CLOTH. A plain-woven, Rhea, ramie, or China grass fabric which comes in many qualities and widths; somewhat resembles linen cloth and is used for small tablecloths.

CHINA GRASS, RHEA GRASS. The un-degummed form of ramie shipped from China. The fiber is obtained from the stalk and outer part of the plant.

CHINA HEMP. The *Canabis gigantes* provides this so-called giant Chinese hemp which grows to a height of twelve to twenty feet.

CHINA JUTE. See CHINGMA.

CHINA SILK. A very soft, extremely lightweight silk made in a plain weave, used chiefly for linings. Irregularities of threads, caused by the extreme lightness and softness of China silk, are characteristic of the fabric.

CHINCHILLA. The name of a rodent whose fur is mixed with other textile fibers in making cloth of high quality. The cloth of today does not resemble the pelt of the animal. The knotted face, modern overcoating takes its name from the town of Chinchilla, Spain. The present-day type of chinchilla cloth was first made here. The product is made into coatings, uniform cloth, and livery wear.

Chinchilla fabric is made in double and triple constructions. Cotton warp may be used because of its twist property. Cotton can be used because, in the cloth construction, it will not show on the face or the back of the material. The nubs on the face are made by the Chinchilla machine. It attacks the face of the cloth, and causes the long floats used in the construction to be worked into nubs or minute balls. The length of the floats is usually five or seven. Chinchilla is a pile cloth and may be piece, stock, or skein-dyed. Weaves, other than the filling to be floated, are usually satins. They aid in bringing about the best possible appearance of the cloth. The fabric is one of the "cycle group" and comes into prominence about every seven or eleven years, and for a year or so is a genuine leader in the trade. See CHINCHILLA CLOTH FINISHING.

CHINCHILLA CLOTH FINISHING. This heavy, woolen cloth is used for cloaking and overcoating; its chief characteristic is its nub finish. The cloth has three fillings and sometimes more; two fillings can be and are sometimes used, however, depending on the weight desired in ounces per yard. The material is heavily fulled, napped, and whipped; the nap brushes up the fibers while the whipping causes them to stand erect when the cloth is placed in the finishing machine.

The goods are fastened down to a bottom-bed plate on the rubbing machine. This machine measures six feet by eight feet. The top bed plate, which has a very rough surface, is let down and begins to work in a reciprocating motion to provide the nubbing. The nubs are worked into position since the cloth has long filling floats of stuffer and wadding picks which are held in place by the basic warp and filling construction. The fibers are actually curled into chinchilla nubs. The rough surface of the bed plate will pick up the fibers that were erect, and the agitating and rubbing actions make the finish possible.

CHINE. From the French, meaning speckled or variegated. The textile interpretation is mottled, shot-about, or speckled effects on some fabrics. Warp-printed bed coverings and summer dress goods, for example, use this effect. The bright blotches or areas on the warp yarns become subdued when they interlace with the filling to make the goods.

CHINESE COSTUME. See Costume, Chinese.

CHINESE, RUSSIAN COTTONS. About 20 per cent of the world cotton comes from China and Russia. The fiber is inferior, less than 1 inch in staple, harsh, irregular, and can be spun only in low yarn counts. Much research and experimentation will be needed to improve the stock. Used in low-quality fabrics, hosiery, part-wool blankets, and all-cotton blankets.

CHINESE JUTE. See ABUTILON, CHINGMA.

CHINESE LINEN. See CANTON LINEN.

CHINGMA. Member of jute family obtained from the inner bark of the plant of this name. Also known as Chinese or China or Tientsin jute, comes from China, Korea, and Japan.

CHINO FABRIC. An all-cotton fabric made with a twill weave, very popular for summer wear in the armed forces. Combed two-ply warp and filling are used in the construction of the goods, which are dyed olive-drab. The fabric is mercerized and Sanforized.

CHINOISERIE. A fashion detail in designs and ornamentations which originated in France and was prevalent in the textiles, furniture, glassware, painting, sculpture, etc. of 18th century Europe. The motifs used were easily recognized by the standard Chinese patterns employed. Textile fabrics with this type of pattern were of high quality, brilliant color as to harmony and contrast, appealing in hand, and made from lush materials as in the case of brocades, brocatelles, damasks, some dress silks, etc. See Antique, Baroque, Rococo.

CHINTZ. Glazed cotton fabric often printed with gay figures and large flower designs. Named from Hindu word meaning spotted. There are several types of glaze: the wax glaze and the starched glaze are both produced by use of friction or glazing calenders. (Will wash out in laundering.) The only durable glaze is a resin finish, which will withstand washing or dry-cleaning. Unglazed chintz is called cretonne. Used for draperies, slipcovers. Lately it has been used for summer dresses.

CHINTZAH. A good quality of waste silk of various types.

CHINTZING. See PLANTING.

CHIQUE-CHIQUE. A lightweight leaf fiber obtained in Venezuela that is strong, durable, and tough. This bast fiber is used in brooms, brushes, cordage, matting, ropes, etc.

CHIQUE SILK. A low quality French silk used for sewing thread.

CHIRIMEN. A Japanese silk crepe used for blouses, dress goods, and kimono cloth. Comes dyed or printed.

CHIRIPA. A square of colored fabric or a blanket for added warmth, used by the cowboys in Argentina. The fabric is wound around the waist and legs and is fastened by a belt made of silver or some

other metal. It is a mark of distinction in the dress of cowboys.

CHITON. A gown or tunic used by the nations known to the student of Ancient History, prior to the B.C. days in history. Its use actually lasted until around 100 B.C., and it then faded into oblivion. It was made up of rectangular pieces of goods draped or wrapped around the body without any cutting or sewing done on the materials. This long lasting garment was in vogue for many centuries and was knee-length for males, ankle-length for females. A Doric chiton, for example, was made of wool while one used by the Ionic peoples was made of linen. Linen, a loose fitting fabric, was popular and much used when the article was made with folds. It was often worn as a blouse, tucked in and held in by a belt or cord. See Toga Rosa, Tirta.

CHITRA. East Indian term for mottled, spotted, or variegated cloth. This printed material was the forerunner of present-day calico and chintz, which are now individual textile cloths.

CHITRANG FIBER. A bast fiber obtained from the large leaves of the *Sterculia Wigtii* in China and India. Used for cordage.

CHITS. Good-textured, plain-weave cotton calico made in India; printed with detached motifs.

CHLAMYS. A short, high quality woolen fabric made into mantles and worn by males in the halcyon days of Greece, Rome and contemporary nations; actually what is called a cloak at the present time. The word is a basic Greek term implying a covering for the body. It was often rather short in length and was held in place by fastening it on one shoulder. See Chiton, Himation.

CHOCOHURSTLE OR GUAMERO. A pineapple bast fiber native to Mexico; used for domestic clothing.

CHOLET. French term for fancy colored or novelty handkerchiefs. A lightweight, unbleached, and unsized French dress goods; when woven with stripes, known as Cholet Stripes.

CHLORATE. A salt representing a higher state of oxidation than chloride. Chlorates give up oxygen when treated with a strong acid, but they have no real commercial value in bleaching procedures.

CHLOREGAL D. Used to control the felting shrinkage on wool, it is an acid wet chlorination treatment developed by Ciba-Geigy Corporation, Greensboro, N.C. 27409.

CHLORIDE. A chemical salt representing a union of hydrochloric acid with a metal. Ordinary salt is sodium chloride.

CHLORIDE OF LIME. Bleaching agent made by the action of chlorine gas on slaked lime; bleaching powder.

CHLORIDE OF SODA. Sodium hypochlorite.

CHLORINATED WOOL. Chemically treated woolens whereby shrinkage is decreased and dyeing properties increased, especially in the case of fabrics that are to be printed.

CHLORINE. An elemental gas known chemically as halogen and an important oxygen releaser from water; it plays an important part in bleaching operations and compositions.

CHLORINE, AVAILABLE. The chlorine-equivalent of the oxygen available for oxidation or bleaching. A positively misleading term commonly used to evaluate the oxidizing power of hypochlorite bleach.

CHLORINE ON COTTON, ACTION OF. The action is carried out by treating the sample for one hour in a cold solution of chloride of lime at $1\frac{1}{2}'$ twaddle. The reaction shows that: $2CaClO$ plus $2H_2SO_4$ gives $2CaSO_4$ plus $4HCl$ plus O_2. The oxygen molecules do the actual bleaching.

CHLORINE RESISTANT FINISH. Any finish which does not retain chlorine used as a bleach in the laundering process is said to be chlorine resistant. It is desirable that finishes be chlorine resistant, for otherwise, upon ironing, the goods become tender, and, if white, will turn yellow.

CHLORINE RETENTION. The tendency of nylon and other fabrics to retain certain and varying amounts of chlorine when bleached with chlorine bleaches; due to resin finishes or treatments. On pressing or heating the fabric, this retained chlorine will often cause degradation and/or discoloration.

CHLOROFORM. Colorless, volatile, sweetish compound formed by distilling alcohol or acetone, water, and chlorinated lime, or by distilling chloral with alkalies. This organic solvent is used to distinguish cellulose tri-acetate from di-acetate and mono-acetate. Tri-acetate is soluble in chloroform but insoluble in acetone.

CHOCOLATE. This color of dark reddish brown has low saturation and low brilliance.

CHOICE WOOL. Usually the third-best quality of wool from a fleece; comes from the middle of the sides.

CHOLESTEROL. A fatty monatomic crystalline alcohol derived from bile and present in most gallstones. This is a chief constituent of the grease in wool fleeces.

CHOLI, CHOLEE. A short-sleeved bodice or short blouse, not reaching to the skirt, low at the throat, and usually made of cotton. Worn by Hindu women.

CHOM FIBER. A strong, silken leaf fiber of the wild pineapple found in Yucatan, Mexico.

CHOPPER. The operative who lays the paper patterns made by the cutter onto the cloth, does the marking, and chops or cuts the material.

CHOPPER BAR. Found on a Raschel knitting machine, it is a solid steel bar which is set between the guide bars, swings with them, and has an up-and-down action. Its function is to take certain laps between the needle latches in order to have the yarns incorporated into the fabric without actually being knitted-in.

CHOPS, CHOP MARKS. Used by the Chinese and Japanese when silk bales are shipped. Each reeler has his own chop mark or trade-mark. By these it is possible to distinguish good silk from poor silk. Most silk, however, runs fairly uniform. The neatly designed, printed chop marks or labels are found on all silk bales.

Many chop marks have individual Chinese or Japanese pictures or emblems. Each chop has its own name, such as "Pagoda," on which there is a picture of a pagoda and the name of the reeler, as well as all other essential data pertinent to the silk in the bale. There are a great many different chops in use today.

CHOQUETTES. Silk cocoons in which the worm has died.

CHOU. (French for cabbage.) Soft, cabbage-shaped rosette knot of velvet ribbon; used decoratively on women's dresses.

CHROMA. 1. Some definite color, such as red, blue, or green, as apart from black, white, or gray. 2. The purity of color with regard to freedom from any neutral cast. Intensity and saturation are often used in the same sense as chroma.

CHROMASCOPE. A device or instrument used to obtain optical effects of color.

CHROMATE PROCESS. Coloring of fibers, yarns, or fabrics in a dye bath which contains a suitable chrome dye together with ammonium chromate, thereby forming a dye-chromium complex that is bonded into the fibers.

CHROMATIC. Linked with color, it implies a full or high color used in textile design; interchangeable with the word "color."

CHROMATIC DYEING. This method, introduced in 1971 by B. Thies of Coesfeld, West Germany, combines the advantages of hank and package dyeing. In the system, large muffs of low density are wound on special winding frames, covered with hose, and placed on carriers holding perforated spindles. The muffs are dyed in a horizontal machine of special design at temperatures up to 280° F., and static pressures up to 57 pounds. Dyed yarn can be unwound at speeds up to 650 yards per minute.

CHROMATICS. Colorimetry which embraces color hue and color saturation.

CHROMATOGRAPH. A device for the production of composite color tones by the use of particolored disks.

CHROME. Bichrome sodium dichromate, NaC_2O_7; potassium dichromate, $K_2Cr_2O_7$. Chromes are oxidizing agents that can be used as mordanting agents, and as stripping agents with sulphuric acid.

CHROME DYES. Dyestuffs in this group are known as mordant colors; that is, a compound is used to set the dye on the fiber and to improve the property of fastness of color. The mordant used is usually chrome salts, which give the dyestuff its name.

There are three basic methods used to apply the dye: 1. Top chrome method. 2. The meta-chrome method. 3. The bottom chrome method. In the top chrome method, the dye is first applied to the yarn or fabric and is then fixed with the mordant. In the meta-chrome method, both the dyestuff and the mordant are applied to the dye bath at the same time. In the bottom chrome method, the mordant is applied first, with the dyestuff being added later on.

CHROMEFLEX. A nontarnishable aluminum yarn laminated with Mylar synthetic plastic, a trade-mark of Metal Film Company, Inc.

CHROMSPUN. Trademark for color-locked acetate yarn of Eastman Chemical Products, Inc., New York City. The coloring agents are introduced at the solution stage before the fiber is actually formed by extrusion. Chromspun is highly resistant to all known fading hazards and its major uses are in bedspreads, draperies, and linings. In apparel, Chromspun is used in swimwear fabrics, linings, and patterned double knits where color fastness is also important.

CHROME TANNAGE. Chrome is the mineral-agent method chiefly used in tanning at the present time. The processes used differ to some degree, but all of them employ one or more salts of chromium. Chrome sulphate and bichromate of potash or soda are very popular bases. Chrome tanning is used for tanning practically all the shoe upper leather made in this country, such as kid, calf, and side upper leathers.

CHROMIUM FLUORIDE. A chemical compound used as a mordant to act with the dyestuff in order to produce lasting color in woolen goods. See MORDANT.

CHROMOPHORS. A molecular group necessary to have a body capable of forming a dyestuff.

CHROMSPUN. Trade name for Eastman's made-in-the-color acetate yarn and staple fiber. The coloring agents are introduced at the solution stage, before the fiber is actually formed.

CHRYSALIS. The stage of growth of the silkworm that is encased in the cocoon. It is destroyed when the cocoon is placed in sulphur fumes, which kill the worm so that the filaments will be easier to reel in the reeling basin.

CHRYSOTILE. Another name for the greenish-yellow asbestos fiber. This silicate of magnesia product is classed with the other asbestos fibers—amosite and crocidolite.

CHUBUT WOOL. Dry, black wool raised in southern Argentina, in the higher qualities will spin from 64s to 70s. It contains much loose foreign matter.

CHUCHAO. Bast fiber raised in Ecuador and Peru. Runs from 3 to 5 feet in length. It is finer and more flexible than henequen, is lustrous, and has good strength when properly cleaned. Used chiefly for cordage, sacks, twine.

CHUCUNCI FIBER. A hard, rough sisal fiber native to Yucatan.

CHUDDER (CHUDDAR, CHADAR, CHUDDAH, SHUDDAR). 1. Arabian cotton cloth made of plain weave featured by wide blue or black stripes in the warp direction. Narrow filling stripes of white appear in a sequence of four bars at the ends of the material which is made 100 inches long and about 40 inches wide.

2. Hindu language term applied to brilliant bright green color observed in billiard cloth, a very high grade and expensive fabric.

3. East Indian shawl fabric made of goat's hair or wool; it has woven figures on a solid background.

4. East African term for semi-bleached cotton cloths made in India; used as loincloth.

CHUKKER, CHUKKER SHIRT. A popular polo shirt made with open neck and short sleeves. The cloth is made of cotton, silk, synthetic, or mixture yarns. It comes in colors, in printed effects, and in white.

CHUNA. Descended from the old-time Spanish Merino sheep in South America, this type is known for its long fibers in the shorn fleece.

CHUNCU FIBER. Bast fiber from the caladium tree of Peru.

CHUNDARI. 1. A silk dress goods made in India. 2. An Indian cotton fabric colored by the dip-dye or tie-dye method to give it a mottled appearance.

CHURCH BRAID AND LACE. A needle lace first made in Italy in the seventeenth century and used for vestments and other church fabrics. Biblical scenes are stitched into the base fabric for embellishment. The braid, now made of silk or nylon in plain or fancy constructions, is interspersed throughout with metallic threads for decorative purposes. Church braid and lace is now made in many centers all over the world—monasteries, homes, convents, missionary centers, etc.

CHURN. See XANTHATING CHURN.

CHURRO. A long, harsh Spanish wool.

CHUTE FABRIC. Brief expression for any and all types of parachute fabric, used now for a host of purposes.

CICIATOUN. Popular in the Middle Ages, this gonfalon or small flag was fastened to the poles of lances. Usually made of silk and embroidered, the fabric was also used for cloaks.

CIDER-PRESS CLOTH. A rather heavy, open-mesh cloth with low texture, 10 x 10. Coarse-ply yarns are used.

C.I.F. COTTON. Standardized cotton bought according to sample, which is to be delivered at some specified rate. Invoice months are stipulated when the contract is drawn up; the seller pays the cost, insurance, and freight to the port of entry in some foreign country.

CIGAIE. General term for high-quality wool along the Danube River area.

CILANA. This is a permanent crepe effect on plied-yarn Swiss voile, or on the full-type voile.

CILAPERL. The name for a partly chintzed-surface Swiss cotton which has a blistered effect.

CILASILK. A registered trade-mark to describe a Swiss batiste which has a silky hand and permanent luster.

CILATEX. Washable Swiss cotton chintz that has a permanent finish.

CILICE. A haircloth undergarment worn by several orders of monks throughout the world; comes in brown and black.

CILICIUM. Literally cloth of hair.

It is a penitential garment, a hairshirt, sometimes worn next to the skin, especially by certain religious orders of the Roman Catholic Church.

CINCH. A wide belt which pulls in the waist.

CINCTURE, GIRDLE. A cord, 12 to 14 feet long, with tassels at each end, used to bind the alb at the waist when a priest is vesting for Mass. It is usually white but, properly, should be the same color as the vestments. It may be of any material, but that of prelates is made of silk. See Alb.

CINQ TROUS. A five-sided mesh ground lace first made in France.

CIRCASSIAN. Dress-goods fabric of cotton warp and wool filling made with some type of diagonal-weave effect. Comes in black, white, and colors.

CIRCULAR. A flared edge, commonly used on the lower edge of skirts, dresses, gowns, and so on. Garments designed with circular lower edge usually are finished with a narrow hem at the bottom.

CIRCULAR BOX LOOM. It is used in Great Britain and on the Continent; its features include a cylindrical shuttle-changing mechanism capable of holding six shuttles, which can be rotated in clockwise or counterclockwise directions to bring the desired shuttle in line with the raceplate of the loom.

CIRCULAR KNIT HOSIERY. Fabric for hosiery knit in a tubular formation, and shaped by varying the tension at the various parts of the stocking. No seam is necessary, but a mock seam may be introduced to simulate full-fashioned hosiery. This type of seam can be recognized since it does not extend into the welt or sole areas of the article.

"Mock fashioning marks" are introduced sometimes to imitate full-fashioned hosiery, and they also can be easily recognized, since they appear as a small hole (tuck stitch) rather than as a raised mark as in the narrowing. Full-fashioned hosiery is the better-fitting stocking when compared with the circular or seamless type of stocking, because of the method of construction.

CIRCULAR-KNITTED. Fabrics or garments knitted in a circular or tubular form so that they are seamless. Later a garment may be shaped by careful cutting. Imitation seams and fashion marks are sometimes added for effect.

CIRCULAR KNITTING MACHINE. A knitting machine that produces tubular fabric made from either one of two sets of needles. It may be of hand power or machine power, and the fabric may vary from about one inch up to several feet.

CIRCULAR RIB MACHINE KNITTING STITCH. Characterized by lengthwise or warp ribs caused by the wales alternating from face to back on the goods, and referred to as a 1 x 1 rib. If every two wales alternate, the stitch is called a 2 x 2 rib stitch. See Circular Knit Hosiery, Circular-Knitted, Circular Knitting Machine.

CIRCULAR WEB. Tubular fabric made on knitting machines, then cut and sewed to make garments.

CIRE. See CERE.

CIRRASOL PT. A registered trademark soil release product of Imperial Chemical Industries, New York, Ltd. It came into the market in 1964 and is applicable to all weights of fabrics in which the system is workable; used on both precured and postcured fabrics; is not a soil repellent but is a full-fledged releaser of soil and combats soil deposition through static. It can take forty washings without degradation to the article. The product is ideal for 100 percent polyester materials and polyester/cotton blends such as those found in sheeting and shirting, etc.

CISALFA. An Italian product of viscose rayon fibers with 3 to 5 per cent casein incorporated to give it wool's dyeing properties.

CISELÉ. In speaking of velvet this is a motif formed by cut and uncut pile when the cut pile is raised by the method of weaving above the uncut portions in the motif or design. Italian, soprarizzo, casellato.

CISELE VELVET. Velvets in which the loops of yarn or thread formed on the surface by the pile warp ends are both cut and uncut so as to achieve the motif. In France there is a distinction between velours ciselé and ciselé velvet (velours broderie) in which the former has the cut pile higher than the uncut pile, while the latter will show the cut and the uncut pile effects of the same height.

CITAMCI FIBER. Low-grade sisal from Yucatan.

CITRINE. A color which resembles that of a lemon; of medium brilliance and saturation.

CITY CROP. Sundry cotton samples found in the office of the broker in the "cotton cities" of the South; a collection of odds-and-ends samples that have accumulated in the office.

CIVET CAT. A soft, fluffy fur with rich, black top hair interspersed with white markings.

CIVONA. Du Pont trade-mark for its hollow filament rayon yarn.

CLAN. (Gaelic Clann.) A tribe or number of families among the Highlanders of Scotland bearing the same surname, descended from a common ancestor, and united under a chieftain.

CLAN PLAID. Any plaid in the true colors of some particular Scottish clan such as Cameron, Campbell, MacPhee, MacDonald.

CLAN TARTAN. Tartan of a pattern worn by a particular clan.

CLARET. A claret wine color which is red in hue, of high saturation and low brilliance. Sometimes known as Bordeaux, the city in France noted for claret wines.

CLARK'S DIRECTORY OF SOUTHERN TEXTILE MILLS. Includes all mills in the South from Maryland and West Virginia through Texas. Contains list of mills, addresses, telephone numbers, all officials, chief products and other specific information pertinent to every company listed.

CLARTE. French for the clear surface finish on a cloth.

CLASSER, COTTON. The cotton expert who actually classifies raw cotton for color, grade, quality, staple length, tinges, and other characteristics. Assets the classer should possess are keenness of eyesight, fine sense of touch, and years of actual experience.

CLASSIC. Any wearing apparel in such simple, good taste and so becoming to most people that it continues in style despite changing fashions.

CLASSIFICATION. 1. Sorting, grading, or classifying raw materials, yarns, fabrics, finishes, weaves, and so on. 2. Used with regards to finish according to type such as Durable Press, Crease-Resistant, Pure, Starched, Starchless, etc. 3. Pertinent to the Laundry Industry the term means the separation of soiled garments prior to washing according to the degree of soil, dirt, grime. Attention is usually given to the color of the respective articles.

CLASSING. The sorting of various textile fibers for quality, color, tinges, staple length, fineness, foreign matter, and so on.

CLASSY COTTON. Facetious term for cotton which rates well, devoid of imperfections.

CLAY, CLAY DIAGONAL, CLAY SERGE, CLAY WORSTED. A staple worsted made on a 3-up and 3-down, right-hand twill, a weave made popular by J. T. Clay, a leading textile manufacturer in Rastrick, Yorkshire, England.

The cloth has a low texture, is piece-dyed, and runs from 12 to 18 ounces per yard in weight. The fabric, which has a harsh, boardy feel, gives good service which is enhanced by the rather shaggy finish applied. The yarn is beardy in feel and appearance, and is given good, hard twist.

CLEANER. One who cuts loose threads from the seams of a finished garment and cleans spots with a cleaning solution. An operative handles the garment before the examiner.

CLEANING AND BLENDING FEEDER. See AUTOMATIC FEEDER.

CLEANING AND SCOURING. Applied to woolens and worsteds, these two operations may be more or less combined. The purpose of the operations is to rid the material of all oil that was added to the stock in blending, oiling, and mixing operations, as well as stains, dirt marks, and other unclean areas which are frequently seen in cloth. They are difficult to avoid because of the great number of operations that wool undergoes from raw stock condition to the gray goods state. The handling of the goods by many operatives is also the cause of many stains.

Sizing is also taken out if any has been applied to the yarn in the warping operation, in order to aid the warp yarn in weaving.

The cut of cloth, having been placed in the fulling mill or machine, has had its ends sewed or tacked together, after being run through two large eyelets in the machine. This is done so that perhaps a 60-yard cut of cloth could be made endless and cut down to one-half the original length dimension—a cut of cloth that is now endless with two 30-yard circumferences.

The fulling mill bath is made up of hot water and soap, and there may be some other ingredients added. This bath causes the cloth, when it is fed into the milling liquor, to become very wet. The length of time the cloth is in the mill varies from one-half hour to several hours, dependent on the cloth in question. Scouring, rubbing, friction and pounding cause the felting and shrinking-in.

CLEANING BARS. See GRATE BARS.

CLEANING, LAUNDRY. The processes used to remove dirt, grime, soil, etc., from fabrics or garments.

CLEANING TRUNK. Device, vertical or inclined, and made of metal or wood; it carries cotton along in its course by air current. The action allows the removal of much loose foreign matter in the initial or auxiliary treatments in cotton yarn manufacture.

CLEAN PILE YARN. Pile yarn, which has lost its fats and sizing agents by chemical treatment. Also implies yarn that has been conditioned prior to

testing it for some reason.

CLEAN-UP PERIOD. Time allowed employees at the end of the work day to remove grime and dirt accumulated while they were on the job.

CLEARANCE. The contraction of silk, synthetic, or man-made yarns when twisted or thrown.

CLEARER. Device by which slubbing, drawing, roving, and spinning frames collect the lint bound to accumulate in processing cotton into yarn. Clearer cloth, set on a rolled or flat surface and in contact with the rollers, gathers the lint.

CLEARER BOARD. Felt or clearer cloth set in a flat board, which is set on top of the drafting rolls of a spinning frame. Tends to keep the rollers clean so that production will not be impaired. A small felt-covered roll collects the waste when an end breaks; the action is frictional.

CLEARER FABRIC. A dense, thickly napped woolen flannel used to cover clearers on various textile machines.

CLEAR FINISH. A finish for cloth in the woolen and worsted trade—one in which no nap or fuzz remains on the face of the goods. All protruding fibers have been removed, because of the operations that the cloth is subjected to in this finishing; the warp and filling are plainly seen. This finish is given to fabrics where the weave is an outstanding characteristic. Clear-finish fabrics have the tendency to shine with wear, but hold the crease very well.

Examples are cassimere, charmeen, covert, diagonal worsted, garbardine, serge, poiret, tricotine, elastique, twill cloth, twillcord, whipcord.

CLEARING. The rinsing and washing of dye from the unmordanted areas in printed calico and similar cloths.

CLEARING YARN. Removal of any and all types of blemishes and imperfections from the body of the yarn.

CLEAR NOIL. Wool or worsted noil devoid of all vegetable matter.

CLEAR TOP. Worsted top devoid of kemps, neps, specks, and so forth.

CLERICAL COSTUME. See Costume, Clerical.

CLEW. A ball of yarn, any type.

CLING. See DRAG.

CLIP. 1. Wool taken from sheep after one season's growth. 2. To cut with shears or scissors in order to separate material or to relieve tension.

CLIPPED-SPOT FIGURES, CLIP-SPOTS. Small embroidered effects noted on dress goods, of the dotted Swiss variety, and curtains. These dots are produced by either a lappet or swivel loom.

Lappet looms make the effect by the use of an extra warp; swivel looms by an extra filling.

The long floats between the interlacing of the spots with the body of the cloth are clipped off so that the finished fabric will show more or less brilliant spots of color on a plain background. The use of flock dots on cloth has done much to lower the yardage produced by swivel and lappet looms. Lawn, voile, and organdy are often made with clip-spots and used for curtaining, hangings, and summer dress goods. See Illustrated Section (Fabrics 61–64).

CLIPPING. 1. Sheep shearing. 2. Term sometimes used pertinent to a sheep fleece.

CLIPPINGS. 1. Waste materials from tailors' clippings to house-clippings. They usually find their way to a shoddy mill and are ultimately used in making manipulated cloth from fibers obtained from discarded apparel. 2. Also known as Peddler's Wool, it is the poorest quality fiber taken from a sheep fleece.

CLOAK. A loose outer garment or wrap worn by men and women. The name is derived from the French "cloche," meaning bell. Many cloaks are bell-shaped.

CLOAKING. The heavier woolen fabrics are used to make cloaks of any description. Fabrics in this group would be melton, kersey, beaver, heavy broadcloth, covert, Cheviot, homespun, tweed, and others.

CLOCHE. Bell-shaped crown headgear, worn by women. The brim of the hat may be even but turned down to suit the wearer. Also known as cloche is the type of bell-shaped hat which has a short brim front and back with the sides somewhat wider.

CLOCKS. Decorations on the side of hosiery put in by hand embroidery or machine operation. Recent improvements enable the machine to put in the clockwork at the time the stocking is made.

CLOISTER FABRIC. A lightweight drapery fabric on the order of monk's cloth.

CLOKY. The small, figured motifs used in fancy piqués. The word comes from the French "cloqué," meaning blistered or puckered.

CLOQUE. Blister-type cloth made in double-cloth construction from some of the major fibers.

CLOQUE ORGANDY. An interchangeable term with Swiss crepe organdy.

CLOSED SHOP. That union status agreed to by a company in which union membership is required as a condition of initial and also continued employment.

CLOSE LEAF MOTIFS. Leaf designs in bobbin-lace such as Honiton in which the bobbin-made sprig effects are totally covered by cloth stitching to fill the leave areas.

CLOSE-OUT. Reduced merchandise for quick sale.

CLOSE SHED. A type of shedding action which causes the warp ends to come together in a straight line after every pick is woven in the fell of the cloth. There are two types of this shed —the center, or the bottom. If the ends meet together at the bottom of the shed, it is a bottom shed; when they meet in the center, it is a center shed.

CLOSING. Low-count cottons which have been treated with a sizing or filler-in mixture to decrease the small areas between the interlacings of the warp and filling yarns. The fabric is given a careful calendering to flatten the yarn enough to close up the open spaces.

CLOSING MACHINE. It lays and twists strands or yarns into a rope form in the manufacture of rope.

CLOTH. More or less synonymous with cloth are the terms fabric, goods, stuff, and material. Cloth has to be made from some raw material, constructed by weaving, knitting, plaiting or braiding, or by an interlocking of fibers to produce felt fabric. The product may or may not be colored and most fabrics are given some sort of finish. Goods not given a finish are often called "loom-finished," since they are "finished" when taken from the machine.

Cloth is used chiefly for innerwear and outerwear; other uses range from decorative materials to heavy industrial fabrics.

CLOTH, MACHINE PINKING OF. This is done by a pinking machine which cuts swatches of cloth for the trade. The feature of the machine is that it gives a wavy or scalloped edge to the goods to prevent raveling of the edges. Pinking may also be done by hand-pinking shears.

CLOTH, PARTS OF A PIECE OF.

1. FIBER: The smallest unit in a woven, knitted, braided, or felt material. Fibers are also used to make felt material.

2. FILAMENT: A long fiber that may be indefinite in length as in man-made filaments.

3. YARN: This is made up of twisted fibers or filaments and can have considerable strength and length.

4. PLY YARN: Two or more yarns that are twisted or plied together to make one yarn.

5. CLOTH: This is made from yarn in three ways:

I. Woven cloth is made from two systems of yarn or thread which interlace at right angles to each other; serge, homespun, damask.

II. Knitted cloth is made from one system of thread or yarn which interloops, a loop within a loop; hosiery, jersey, sweater fabric.

III. Braided or plaited material is made from an interlacing of one yarn only. The yarn may be made to interlace at any angle; lace, veiling, shoe lace.

Felt is not made from yarn; it is made from a mass of fibers that are interlocked and made into a material by means of heat, pressure, moisture, pounding and rolling, hot water, and other methods.

6. THREAD: It is used in sewing materials and is a ply yarn of some special nature. This ply thread is given a high number of turns of twist per inch. It is often waxed, coated, or treated in some way for a particular use in order to work smoothly and well. Ply yarn, such as automobile tire fabric, may have a ply of nine, ten, or eleven. See NONWOVEN FABRIC.

CLOTH, POSSIBLE DEFECTS IN. The following will show the number of possible defects that may be found in woven goods:

1. Barry or barre marks.	25. Oil stains.
2. Bleeding colors.	26. Overwidth.
3. Broken pattern.	27. Reed marks.
4. Broken ends or picks.	28. Rolling selvage.
5. Cloudy goods.	29. Section marks.
6. Cockled cloth.	30. Shear marks.
7. Coarse ends or picks.	31. Shiners.
8. Creases.	32. Skipping.
9. Crocking.	33. Shuttle marks.
10. Cut listing or selvage.	34. Slugs.
11. Dead colors.	35. Specky goods.
12. Double picks.	36. Sluff-offs.
13. Ends out.	37. Sand roller marks.
14. Floats.	38. Start-up marks.
15. Hair in filling-fuzziness.	39. Thick stripes.
16. Harness skips.	40. Thin stripes.
17. Hitch backs.	41. Tender goods.
18. Holes.	42. Tight picks.
19. Kinks.	43. Tight selvages.
20. Loose picks.	44. Torn selvages.
21. Loose selvages.	45. Uneven cloth.
22. Mispicks.	46. Washer wrinkles.
23. Mixed filling.	47. Weaving over or under.
24. Narrow width.	

48. Weaving
slack.

49. Wrong
draws.

50. Uneven dou-
ble and twist.

CLOTH BEAM. The roll at the front of the loom around which the woven fabric is wound. The cloth beam, on a true working size hand loom, is usually underneath the breast beam or knee beam, as it is commonly known, and in front of the line of lams.

CLOTH BOLT. The length of the woven cloth as it comes from the loom, or the length of the material as used in the trade. Woolens and worsteds are finished at the following length—55, 60, 72, 80, 85, 90 or 100 yards, the firms usually specifying the length in cutting-up of the goods.

Cottons are usually finished at lengths of 40 and 45 yards.

Silks and rayons are finished at about 40 yards in length.

CLOTH BUYER. He should have a knowledge of the raw material, construction, color, and finish of the fabrics he buys. The raw material for the cutting-up house is the finished fabric in cut or bolt form. Cloth should be judged for certain working properties —handle or feel, drapability, crease-resistance, shine with wear, clinginess, sagginess, etc. Manipulative properties are important in knowing how to cut, to fit, and to sew and trim the garment.

CLOTH CONSTRUCTION, TEXTURE, PICK COUNT. The number of warp ends and filling picks per square inch in a woven fabric. For example, a 92 x 68 cloth would mean that there are 92 ends and 68 picks per inch in the construction.

CLOTH CUTTING MACHINE. A machine for cutting numerous layers of cloth simultaneously. The machine frame, mounted on casters or runners, houses an electric motor, and a rotary or reciprocating knife; the latter cuts the material as the machine is pushed over the cutting table through the material.

CLOTHES. A broad, general term to designate all fabric articles used in the manufacture of all types of apparel and garments.

CLOTHESLINE. A braided or twisted cotton rope, put up in fifty-foot and one-hundred-foot hanks, and used for hanging clothes for drying. When braided, the construction is similar to sash cord in the better qualities, and of less dense construction in the lower-price varieties. When twisted, it is made in a cable construction, usually in $\frac{3}{16}$- and $\frac{1}{4}$-inch diameter sizes. Weights range from 15 to 22 pounds per dozen

hundred-foot hanks, the variance being dependent on the grade or quality construction of the clothesline. Also made with nylon, "Dacron," "Orlon," and some plastics.

CLOTHES MOTHS. Any of a group of moths which feed upon animal fiber fabrics, feathers, furs, etc. *Tinea pellionella* is the most common type in this country.

CLOTH FINISH. 1. Same as face finish or dress finish on woolens. 2. A raised or napped finish on some rayon fabrics.

"CLOTH FINISHING." Term used in woolen and worsted finishing which implies that the cloth can be brought back to its natural or desired finish as it was prior to sponging.

CLOTH FOLDER. A machine for folding lengths of cloth into a convenient form, usually yard-long folds.

CLOTH HALL. A meeting place popular in Europe from the days of the Hanseatic League to about the end of the eighteenth century, used for buying, selling, and exchanging textiles, chiefly woolen cloths. A town of any size had its cloth hall, as it does the city hall of today. Several halls were established in England in the early eighteenth century—Halifax, Wakefield, Leeds, Huddersfield, and others. The rise of the factory system more or less sounded the death knell of the importance of the cloth halls. Social, political, and economic changes lessened their importance as well.

CLOTHING, THE. Name given to the formal admission of a candidate to a religious order at which time he is solemnly clothed in the habit of the particular order.

CLOTHING LEATHERS. The term covers the material used for leather coats, breeches, and hats. Coats are made chiefly from sheepskins, tanned either with or without the wool. Short-wooled skins are called shearlings.

Clothing leather includes jerkin leather, which is made of sheepskins, wholly or in part vegetable-tanned. Garments of this type are ideal, in wartime, for sleeveless leather coats worn by various groups in the armed services.

The finer sheepskin garment leathers, both grain and suede, are tanned with chrome, alum, or a combination of the two. Cattle hides and horsehides are also used for clothing leather, especially for heavier garments worn out of doors by workers for protection against the elements. Windbreakers and other sportswear garments use suede sheepskins and fleshers. Buckskin is used in riding breeches.

CLOTHING TWILLS. Fabrics made chiefly from the three-leaf twill and

comparable constructions.

CLOTHING SIZES.

MEN'S CLOTHING SIZES

Clothing and shoe sizes are not standardized throughout the world. Use the following chart for approximate size relationships.

SHIRTS

AMERICAN	ENGLISH	EUROPEAN
14½	14½	37
15	15	38
15½	15½	39
16	16	41
16½	16½	42

SWEATERS

AMERICAN	ENGLISH	EUROPEAN
SM	34	44
MED	36-38	46-48
LARGE	40	50
X LARGE	42-44	52-54

SHOES

AMERICAN	ENGLISH	EUROPEAN
7	7	40
7½	7½	41
8	8	42
8½	8½	42
9	9	43
9½	9½	43
10	10	44
10½	10½	44
11	11	45
11½	11½	45

HATS

6¾	6⅝	54
6⅞	6¾	55
7	6⅞	56
7⅛	7	57
7¼	7⅛	58
7⅜	7¼	59
7½	7⅜	60

WOMEN'S CLOTHING SIZES

AMERICAN	ENGLISH	EUROPEAN
4-4½	2-2½	34
5-5½	3-3½	35
6	4	36
6½	4½	37
7-7½	5-5½	38
8	6	38½
8½	6½	39
9	7	40
9½-10	7½-8	41

DRESSES AMERICAN	SUITS EUROPEAN
10	40
12	42
14	44

16	46
18	48
20	50

STOCKINGS

AMERICAN	EUROPEAN
8	20¼ (0)
8½	20½ (1)
9	22¾ (2)
9½	24 (3)
10	25¼ (4)
10½	26½ (5)

CLOTH MEASURE. The yard is 36 inches, the quarter is 9 inches, and the ell is 45 inches. The old English measure was ¹⁄₁₆ yard, or 2¼ inches.

CLOTH MULBERRY. See PAPER MULBERRY.

CLOTH OF GOLD. A cloth which, through the ages, has been referred to as having gold threads, strips of gold, or gold twisted with other textile yarns. Gold has been used in tapestries, brocades, brocatelles, and other expensive fabrics, many of which now repose in museums and salons.

CLOTH OF SILVER. The use in decorative fabrics of silver threads, silver strips, or threads in which there is some silver content. See CLOTH OF GOLD.

CLOTH OF STATE. Fabric spread over a throne or seat to serve some dignitary, official, or high ecclesiastical personage. Also called baldachin, baldaquin, baldakin.

CLOTH PAPER. See PRESS PAPER.

CLOTH PRESS. The machine used to remove creases, wrinkles, and such, in the finishing department of the mill. Action is by heat and pressure.

CLOTH ROLLER. The roller upon which the cloth that has just been woven is wound. The cloth relief sets under the breast beam which is next to, or near, the sand roller; the latter roller is also under the breast bream. A small guide roller is also present to aid in winding the cloth properly.

Woven cloth, after leaving the sand and guide rollers, winds onto the cloth roller. When a sufficient number of yards has been woven, the cut of cloth is taken from the loom. This is taken to the Percher, usually an experienced weaver, who marks with chalk all the blemishes that have been made in the weaving, both avoidable and unavoidable. All places where the chalk marks show defects have to be remedied in the sewing-and-mending department of the dry-finishing department in the mill.

CLOTH THICKNESS, MEASUREMENT OF. The General Electric Company, New York Division, has developed an instrument that will measure cloth thickness by means of radioactivity.

The material is bombarded with beta rays (electrons). The number of beta rays that pass through the material is measured, and from this it can be determined how much the material varies from the desired thickness. The instrument, similar to the one used to measure cosmic rays, radiates beta rays by radiation from a pinhead-size grain of strontium 90, a radioactive isotope.

CLOTH-TREE. See PAPER MULBERRY.

CLOTH VACUUM EXTRACTOR. The machine which removes excess moisture from goods. Suction pipes connected with a vacuum pump take out the excess as the cloth is run through the machine.

CLOTH WEIGHT. 1. Ounces per yard for woolens, worsteds; ducks, canvas, and other heavy industrial fabrics. 2. Yards to the pound for cottons, linens, man-made and synthetic fiber fabrics. 3. Ounces per square yard for man-made and synthetic fiber materials. This weighing method is popular on the Continent, in Great Britain, the United States, and Canada. Its popularity seems to be on the increase. Some large plants use a line of demarcation on fabric weights. They may sell cloth that weights less than 4, 6, or 8 ounces per yard on the yards-per-pound plan, and fabrics that are above this line are sold on the ounces-per-yard basis.

CLOTH YARD. Lineal length of 36 inches, irrespective of fabric width.

CLOUD YARN. The combination of a finely twisted yarn with a coarse, soft yarn or thread which is retarded in order to give thick, thin, and bare effects; a mottled or cloudy effect results when this yarn is woven into fabric.

CLOUDY GOODS. Material that is off-shade because of uneven, faulty dyeing. The cloth has a clouded or mottled appearance when the light's rays strike it. Poor penetration of dyestuff, specks, streaks, and cakiness cause cloudiness.

CLOUDY WEB. Cotton sliver which has thin places caused by uneven carding.

CLOUDY WOOL. Tinged or discolored wool that may be seen in some areas of a fleece. Climatic conditions have much to do with this cloudiness.

CLOVE. British term for measuring wool—7.7 pounds to the clove.

CLUB BOWTIE. A straight-cut bow tie used in evening wear. White is used with a tail coat and midnight blue or black with dinner jacket.

CLUNY LACE. A coarse-thread bobbin lace of silk and cotton that shows a close-stitch pattern made with an open ground. Used in curtain and trimming trades. Cluny is a luxury lace that is very durable and beautiful in appearance. Wheel effects feature the design.

CLUPAK. Trade-mark of Clupak, Inc., for its nonwoven stretchable paper fabric invented by Sanford Cluett of Cluett, Peabody & Company, Inc.

CLUSTER, SPLINTER. The clinging of two or more staple fibers to one another causing a hard or stiff cluster which has to be pulled apart prior to any further processing. A rather common occurence in certain fabrics whose construction makes this clinginess possible.

CLUSTER FRINGE. A fringe or a narrow fabric in which the lengths of the threads in the skirt are finished off to give a saw-toothed effect. See FRINGE.

CLUTCH. Device which determines how the cylinder of a knitting frame is driven.

CMC. A water-soluble cellulose gum which possesses many properties of water-soluble starches, gelatins, and gums, as well as those qualities found in processed or synthesized hydrophillic colloids. Acts as an emulsifying agent in oil-in-water emulsions and actually protects the emulsion. Product of Hercules, Inc., Wilmington, Delaware.

COACH HIDE. A dyed, matt-finished, full grain, boarded leather that has been vegetable tanned from a cattle hide.

COACH LACE. Originally implied trimmings used on carriages, coaches, hacks, stage coaches, etc. Now means narrow woven fabrics of many types used for automobile "trim."

COAGULATE. To close, contract, or consolidate into a smaller mass. Example is the boiling and solidification of egg white.

COAGULATING BATH. An acid solution, usually sulphuric acid, that hardens viscous fluid into cellulose filaments as it is extruded from the minute spinneret holes into the bath; used in the manufacture of rayon.

COALESCE. When two small drops of oil run together to form one larger drop they are said to coalesce. In a good emulsion, oil-drops should not coalesce in this manner.

COAL TAR. Derived from coal, it is a crude mixture which includes a valuable organic chemical used in making dyes.

COARSE. Mill parlance when lap, sliver, slubbing, roving, or yarn accidentally run double.

COARSE BOBS. Old-time British expression for cable net. See CABLE, etc.

COARSE ENDS. Ends that are too irregular in diameter or have too much foreign matter in them to make a smooth, uniform yarn.

COARSE PICKS. Picks that are faulty and show up to poor advantage in the body of the cloth.

COARSE TOW. See FLAX FIBERS, INFORMATION ON.

COARSE WOOL. The common and braid types, 36s to 44s, and low quarter-blood wool of about 46s. Also called Low Wool.

COAT. A form of outer garment, chiefly one worn by men, covering the arms and upper part of the body.

COATED FABRICS. As the name indicates, they are fabrics coated with some substance to make them impervious to water or other liquids. The uses are numerous, and the coating substances or materials include oil, pyroxylin, rubber, resins, melamines, plastics. Coated fabrics include oilcloth, koroseal, fabrikoid, imitation leathers.

COAT FRONT. Trade term for a built-up stiffening or shape-retaining interlining for the fronts of coats, made of stitched layers of haircloth, felt, and canvas.

COATING. 1. Tailoring term for all fine woolen or worsted fabrics especially suitable for dress coats, such as broadcloth, crepe, unfinished worsted, vicuna, refines, etc. The term is also applied to overcoating. 2. Any fabric used as a coating. 3. The application of some material which is used to coat textile fabrics such as oilcloth, rubberized fabric. Lacquer, oil, resin, synthetic resin, linseed oil, cork, and plastics are among the various coating materials used.

COATING VELVET. A medium to heavy silk, acetate, or rayon pile velvet with a cotton back in the average types. Quality, texture, weight, and price vary to marked degree.

COAT OR SUIT, WELL-MADE, POINTS TO LOOK FOR.
1. OUTER FABRIC: It should be firm enough to allow for good tailoring and checked for pre-shrinking and color-fastness.
2. TRIMMING: Quality trimming should be used, and buttons should be satisfactory and well sewn to the material.
3. INTERLINING: Hair canvas should be used in preference to "deadweight" cotton, hopsacking, percaline, or burlap. The hair canvas should be resilient. The interlining should be checked for crease-proofing, wrinkle-proofing, crush-proofing, and pre-shrunk fabric should have a set-finish.
4. TAILORED: The back of the waistline should be properly taped to prevent stretching; lining should be hand-

sewn, and the interlining correctly sewn in and taped at the edges.

The lapel should have a soft, smooth, pleasant roll and lie crisp and flat.

The collar should be turned in so that it fits the neck without a bulge. Armholes should be reinforced to keep their shape. Sleeve cuffs should be reinforced at the wrist. Good quality shoulder pads should be used and firmly tacked into place.

Pockets should be well reinforced to withstand wear; the back section of the pocket should be faced with the suiting fabric. If patch pockets are used, attention should be given to the manner in which they curve to conform to the body shape.

Buttonholes should be accurately and carefully made. Jacket hems should be even. Hems should be such that allowances can be made for lengthening. Seams should be treated to prevent raveling.

COBBLERS. Dyed pieces of goods which have been returned to the dyers because of faulty dyeing or finishing.

COBBLING. British expression for fabric that has been redyed for some reason, usually inferior first dyeing.

C.O.B. CLEANING TRUNK. (Cleaning. Opening. Blowing.) A specially made cotton cleaning trunk used to cleanse fibers that contain large amounts of dirty, clumpy cotton. Vibratory action is the feature of the machine, which has a set of grid bars through which wastes fall into receptacles.

COBURG, COBOURG. Dress goods and lining cloth made on a 2-up and 1-down twill or on a 2-up and 2-down twill, right-hand direction. This cotton warp and worsted filling cloth is piece-dyed or printed.

COBWEB COTTON. Late-maturing, large-boll Mississippi cotton with fiber length of 1¼-inch to 1½-inch; this fine, silklike cotton has lint content of about 29 per cent.

COCHINEAL. The female insect, *Coccus cacti*, found in Central America and Mexico, furnishes the base for this brilliant red dye. It is applied to wool on a mordant basis, thus, chromium will give purple; aluminum, crimson; iron, purple; copper, claret; tin, scarlet.

COCHRAN COTTON. A Georgia cotton of 1¼-inch staple and lint yield of about 32 per cent. Also known as Cochran Extra Prolific, Cochran Short-limbed Prolific.

COCKING. Tailor's term for critical inspection of finished garments for discovery of mistakes—derived doubtless from an affected manner of squinting or "cocking the eye" on the part of the zealous examiner.

COCKLE BURR. The Xanthium burr that is about one inch long, found in sheep fleeces. This infestation gives much trouble in manipulating a fleece.

COCKLE, COCKEL. From French "coquelle," meaning cockle shell. Name is given to a distorted or shriveled effect on fancy clothes. This is a result of uneven scouring and fulling in finishing. Cockling may also be caused by improper tension on yarn in weaving, or lack of uniform quality in the raw material used. Several novel ideas have been advanced for the correction of this detriment to cloth.

COCOA MATTING. Coarse matting made from the coconut fiber, coir.

COCONUT OR COCOANUT FIBER. See COIR.

COCOON. A covering of the silkworm made up of a single filament. When the worm breaks through the covering, a moth is produced. The shapes of the cocoon will vary; peanut-shaped cocoons give less silk than the oval or round. The original Japanese cocoons were peanut-shaped. European and Chinese cocoons were round. Japanese and Chinese cocoons are white in color while the Italian and some other European types are golden yellow.

The silk, on being boiled-out, loses any cast or shade that it may have had and becomes very white. The range of filament is from 300 to 400 yards up to 1,400 or 1,600 or more yards; about one third, however, of the entire length of the filament is easily reeled.

Cocoons are sold in the fresh, stifled, or dried condition. In Japan, most cocoons are sold in the stifled condition since the pupa, when changed to a moth, pierces the cocoon and causes the filament to be known as waste silk. The pupa must be killed within two weeks after the cocoon is developed.

The preservations in silk cocoons show that the grower will obtain about 87 per cent good quality, 9 per cent in douppioni and a 4 per cent total loss because of irregularities. About 1 per cent of the crop is used in Japan for making eggs on cards. These breeding stocks are pierced by the moth and cannot be used for reeling purposes.

Assorting and boiling of the cocoons is carefully done by means of steam vapor which assures even temperature at all times. Two systems of boiling are used: 1. Boiling the cocoons as done by the reeling operative. 2. Boiling by specially trained help in the Boiling Division in the plant.

COCOON, CHOKED. One in which the chrysalis is dead.

COCOON, SILK, FACTS ABOUT.
1. There are two glands along the underside of the silkworm's body, from

head to tail, known as silk ducts. These glands terminate in a tiny hole in the mouth, known as spinneret, from which the silk thread is spun.

2. In the last segment of the caterpillar there are two minute bags which contain the gummy fluid called sericin.

3. When the silkworm begins its spinning task, two fibers are emitted from the silk ducts and are covered by the silk gum or sericin from the sacks before they come out from the mouth.

4. As the liquid is emitted by the silkworm it solidifies on contact with the air.

5. A separate filament is called Brins.

6. The two filaments are cemented together by silk gum or sericin.

7. Solidified filament is called silk or Fibroin.

8. The two filaments joined together produce what is known as the cocoon thread or Bave.

9. The moth dies within two days after the eggs are produced. Each moth and tray of eggs is numbered and indexed. Only a portion of the total number of cocoons is used for breeding purposes. The great majority of cocoons are placed in a hot, dry room, and this heat causes the chrysalis in the cocoon to be stifled or stoved.

See Illustrated Section.

COCOON CHIQUE. See COCOON, CHOKED.

COCOON FOIBLE. Weak, loose, irregular cocoons which are cold water treated to prevent tangling of the filament.

COCOON POINTUS. Cocoons with "pointed tips or ends" are usually weak, thereby causing considerable breakage in silk reeling.

COCOONS, GREEN. Fresh or unchoked cocoons. The term should be avoided except when it refers to cocoons of a green color.

COCOONS OUVERTS. In French means "open cocoons." In the United States known as pierced cocoons.

COCOONS TACHES. Diseased, rotted, or spoiled cocoons which give off a bad odor; really lousy cocoon and/or lousy silk.

COCOS FIBER. See COIR.

COCUIZA FIBER. Strong, smooth bast fiber raised in Venezuela and used for bags, ropes, twine. Known as Fique in other areas of tropical America.

CODILLA. Coarse waste matter removed from flax and hemp during scutching.

COFFIN CLOTH. Black-dyed material made of cotton warp and wool filling for coffin interiors.

COGWARE. On the order of frieze,

this fifteenth-century material made in England was popular with the poorer classes. Used as apparel.

COIESCO. Tissue made from fatty membrane and the subcutaneous tissue left over from dressing of skins for tanning. Conversion of the glutinous fiber from the inner side of the hide is obtained by the ordinary leather-tanning process. When tanned, the inner hide is treated at the correct pH to permit the fiber to resist deterioration. It is then dried, and a spongy mass is obtained in the form of an aseptic tissue which can be carded. Made in Italy, the resultant fibers are 3 to 4 microns in diameter and suited for felting purposes or as a filling for blended materials.

COIF. A close-fitting cap, usually of soft, white fabric with much variance in style. Uncertain as to origin, it is known that it was born in the early Middle Ages. In those days it was worn as a hood-like white cap with extended sides tied under the chin; also, the name of a metal skull-cap worn under a hood or covering of mail.

By the 16th century the coif was worn under caps or as a cap by itself. In the last century it was worn under a wig as an inner skull-cap by English barristers and judges and this style still prevails. Brittany has been partial to the coif for many centuries. Ornamented with hand embroidery and worn under the hat or by itself. Also spelled quoif. The coif, of course, is worn by nuns of the various orders of the Roman Catholic Church and has been for many centuries.

COIL. Pertinent to false-twist stretch yarn, it is the spring-like formation observed in yarns of this type.

COILER. The arrangement by which card sliver is coiled into the coiler can, after the sliver has been taken from the calender rollers and led through the trumpet, which is located at the top of the coiler arrangement.

COILER CAN. Also known as a roving can, this upright, cylindrical fiber composition or metal can receives the sliver or slubbing as it comes from the delivery end of the machine involved. The stock is fed to the revolving can by means of the coiler attachment. The can revolves on a circular metal base and neatly winds the stock in coil form as it enters the device. A new can replaces the full one when total coiler yardage has been delivered.

COILING. Extracting neps and fibers below a pre-determined length from cotton sliver and straightening them into a parallel formation. See Coiler, Coiler Can, Coiling Head, Drafting.

COILING HEAD. A device placed in front of carding, combing, and drawing machines that deposits the sliver, as it comes from the delivery end of the particular machine, in even coiled layers in tall cylindrical cans.

COIN DOTS. The small to large circles, or polka dots, seen on some printed dress goods.

COIN MINIFOAM. An ultra thin polyester urethane that is adhesive-bonded on both sides to join two fabrics together permanently. Light weight and bulk are added which provide stability and improve shape retention. Used on loosely woven and unstable woven goods and knitgoods. The foam interior combination with Coin adhesive assures a washable bond which formerly was a problem in many laminating materials. Used in children's wear, coating, rainwear, jackets, sportswear, outerwear and women's suitings. Knits bonded to it apply to the dress, suit and coordinate markets. Registered trademark of Coin International, Inc., New York City.

COIN STANDARDS FOR BONDED FABRICS. Coin Sales Corporation, New York City, is the licensee to many companies for its Coin (registered trademark) Standards. All features of the Collins & Aikman Certifab (registered trademark) are included. Coin Standards are used for the effective bonding treatments developed by Coin Sales Corporation for use in the United States and for foreign licensees in carrying out its Quality Assurance Program. These standards are expressed in terms of *Peel Bond Strength,* both wet and dry. This strength is the basic factor used to measure quality and the durability of the bond. Tests are done on the Scott Model X5 Tensile Strength Tester; Scott Testers, Inc., Providence, Rhode Island.

COIR. This fiber comes from the outer husk of the coconut and may attain a length of ten inches. It is rough, uneven, and straggly; the strength is variable. The coarsest stock is used to make brushes, the longer fibers find use in rope and cocoa matting while the short, curled fibers are used in the upholstery trade and in packing material. Coir is not affected by salt water, but it is not as strong when compared with Manila rope.

COKER 100 COTTON. A wilt-resistant cotton staple of good yield and uniformity. Strength of fiber ranges from weak to very good. Used to spin yarns from 22s to 36s.

COLBERTAN, COLBERTEEN, COLBERTINE. An open type of network lace with a square background.

Named for Jean Baptiste Colbert (1619–1683), the famous prime minister for the French king, Louis XIV (1643–1715). It was Colbert who made the famous statement that "The fashion of lace is to France what the mines of Peru are to Spain." He established the first school for lace making at Alençon, France and set up the Royal Lace Factories there.

COLD PIG. Distressed merchandise returned to the consignee.

COLD PRESSING. Woolen and worsted fabrics are often pressed without the use of heat as a final treatment after hot pressing. Also known as cramping.

COLD TEST FOR WOOL. Sometimes used to determine shrinkage, scoured wool is weighed when cold after it has been allowed to absorb natural moisture during the cooling period.

COLDWATER SHRINKING. See CRABBING, SPONGING, LONDON-SHRUNK.

COLLAR. A sectional part of a garment that sews to the neck-edge to form a decorative effect. When attached it forms part of the garment and is usually of the same material as the dress or blouse. When used separately it is usually of contrasting material and can be detached for cleaning.

COLLARETTE. A small collar of lace that is attached to some types of knitted garments.

COLLAR LEATHER. This subdivision of harness leather is made from very light cattle hides in full thickness, or of cattle-hide splits. It is used for covering horse collars.

COLLAR TWINE. A coarse, low-priced grade of cable thread used in the British Isles.

COLLAR VELVET. A short, compact, thick velvet material used for collars in dressy coatings of the formal type.

COLLATERAL COTTON. That staple bought at a low price to sustain average in the bank account.

COLLECTIVE BARGAINING. The process by which representatives of a company, and of its employees, discuss and negotiate the various phases of their relationships with the view of arriving at a mutually acceptable labor agreement.

COLLODION. A solution of guncotton or pyroxylin in ether and alcohol. It is deposited as a film on the evaporation of the ether.

COLLODION SILK. Formerly implied nitrocellulose rayon, the de Chardonnet type of rayon, now obsolete.

COLLOID. Any substance which is very finely divided and dispersed into ultramicroscopic particles. These are invisible to the naked eye. A textile fiber can have a colloidal system, which is a mass of colloidal particles held together by different forces. A colloid substance will not crystallize.

COLLOIDAL, ALUMINA. A pilling inhibitor much used on knitwear.

COLLOIDAL SOLUTION. A dissolved substance that is present in a solution in particle or granular form from 1 to 100 millicrons in size. This is an interim step in the determination of the characteristics of a true solution as compared with the suspension material, since there is an absence of settling-out in this type of solution.

COLLOID MILL. A machine that grinds lumps from semiliquid dye.

COLONIAL WOOLS. Originally meant the British colonial wools from Australia, Tasmania, New Zealand, and South Africa. The term now includes wools from other British colonies or mandates, as well. The merino types are 60s or better, while the crossbred types are below 60s.

COLOR. The sensation resulting from stimulation of the retina of the eye by light waves of certain lengths; any coloring matter; dye; pigment; paint. See also COLOR CIRCLE, COLOR, COMPLEMENTARY; COLOR, CONDENSED FORM OF PROPERTIES AND CHARACTERISTICS; COLOR IN PATTERNS.

COLOR, COMPLEMENTARY. This is the opposite of any given color, and is found in several ways. If the given color is a primary, the complementary is determined by mixing the other two primaries. The complement of any secondary color would be the remaining primary.

All colors possess the property of calling upon their complementaries, on whatever color is placed next to it. This is the property which causes many colors and color schemes to become hazy.

In textile work, complementaries are difficult to use. Care must be exercised in using the property of colors to call upon their complementaries, sometimes known as simultaneous contrast. If the eye is allowed to rest for a span of time on a spot of color, and then is cast upon a blank sheet, the color would appear in the color of the complementary of the original color.

COLOR, COMPLEMENTARY HARMONY IN. A pleasing combination of complementary colors. One of the two must be used in larger areas than the other, and the colors must differ in value and intensity. They must not clash.

COLOR, CONDENSED FORM OF PROPERTIES AND CHARACTERISTICS OF.

1. COLOR: A property of light that causes bodies to have a different appearance to the eye.

2. COMPLEMENTARY COLORS: Those which, when mixed, produce a neutral gray.

3. COOL COLORS: Those related to snow, ice, sky, foliage—blue, green, violet.

4. INTENSITY: The changes from a bright to a neutral color.

5. PRIMARY COLORS: Red, yellow, blue. Pigments of these colors may be mixed to make many other colors.

6. SECONDARY COLORS: Green, orange, violet. Each of these is obtained by the mixing of two primaries.

7. SHADES: Dark tones of a color. Adding black will produce a shade. Adding the complement of the color to any standard color will produce a shade.

8. STANDARD COLORS: The six colors of the rainbow.

9. TINTS: Light tones of a color. Adding water to a color will give a tone.

10. VALUE: The relative amount of a color contained in different colors. The lightest or most luminous colors are spoken of as having the highest value.

11. WARM COLORS: Those related to heat, sunlight, and fire—red, orange, yellow.

COLOR, NEUTRAL. One in which there is no decided hue, but in which gray or some shade of blue predominates, as in sand-color, taupe, gunmetal, putty, beige, and some others.

Color,   Some Psychological Connotations of.

RED, DARK PURE	Love, amiability, strength.
RED, MEDIUM	Health and vitality, strength.
RED, BRIGHT	Passion, heat, warmth, vigor, strength.
RED, DARK GRAYED	Evil, slinking, cunning, slyness.
PINK, STRONG LIGHT	Femininity, festiveness.
PINK, PURE MEDIUM	Delicacy, innocence.
PINK, GRAYED LIGHT	Daintiness, lightheartedness.
PINK, GRAYED MEDIUM	Frivolity.
ORANGE, STRONG DARK	Ambition, glowing warmth, strength, flame.
ORANGE, STRONG MEDIUM	Enthusiasm, zeal, determination, interest.
ORANGE, STRONG LIGHT	Intensity, seriousness, excitement, vigor.
BROWN, DARK MEDIUM	Utility.
BROWN, LIGHT MEDIUM	Maturity, full-grown development.
YELLOW, STRONG LIGHT	Inspiration, thoughtfulness.
YELLOW, MEDIUM	Prudence, goodness, joyousness, clarity.
YELLOW, LIGHT MEDIUM	Wisdom, attention, sagacity, gaiety, lightness.
YELLOW, DARK MEDIUM	Love of humanity.
GOLD, STRONG LIGHT	Glamour, distinction.
GOLD, MEDIUM	Luxury, glory.
YELLOW-GREEN, LIGHT STRONG	Freshness, cheerfulness, smiling.
YELLOW-GREEN, LIGHT MEDIUM	Youth, youthfulness.
GREEN, LIGHT STRONG	Vitality, vigor, activity.
GREEN, STRONG MEDIUM	Sociability, friendliness, peacefulness.
GREEN, MEDIUM	Frankness, practicality, serenity, coolness.
GREEN, GRAYED MEDIUM	Innocence, naïveté, serenity, restraint.
BLUE-GREEN, STRONG LIGHT	Restlessness, instability, wandering.
BLUE-GREEN, STRONG DARK	Longing, nostalgia, memories, sedateness, quiet.
BLUE-GREEN, MEDIUM LIGHT	Calmness, repose, tranquillity.
BLUE-GREEN, GRAYED LIGHT	Placidity, stillness, soothingness.
BLUE, STRONG MEDIUM	Idealism.
BLUE, DARK MEDIUM	Sincerity, devotion, honesty.
BLUE, GRAYED MEDIUM	Kindness, gratefulness.
BLUE, LIGHT MEDIUM	Tranquillity, quietude.
BLUE-PURPLE, STRONG LIGHT	Sternness, frigidity, formality.
PURPLE, STRONG LIGHT	Magnificence, greatness.
PURPLE, LIGHT MEDIUM	Fragility, softness.
PURPLE, DARK GRAYED	Royalty, seriousness.
PURPLE, MEDIUM	Poise, individualism, distinctiveness.
WHITE	Purity, cleanliness, virginity, spotlessness.
BLACK	Mourning without hope, dignity, formality, sadness, melancholy.

COLOR, TERMS USED IN THE STUDY OF.

Achromatic Colorant: Hueless, such as black, white, or gray.

Analogous Colors: These are related closely and possess a common property such as bluish-green and greenish-blue. The tendency when used in striped materials is to separate and increase the color difference between them. Since these colors are one step removed from each other, it is important in striped effects to have them related.

Chromatic Colorant: Having hue, such as red-yellow, blue-yellow, etc.

Color Accent: A bright or vivid color or colors used sometimes to dress up or improve dark, otherwise unattractive clothing ensembles.

Colorimetry: The testing of a color or dyeing compound by comparison with color solutions.

Color Schemes: These are:

a) Monochromatic or One - Color Harmony: The use of one color in varying degrees of intensity and value; light blue, medium blue, dark blue.

b) Harmony: An agreeable combination of colors, all related to one another.

c) Complementary Harmony. A pleasing combination of complementary colors. One of the two could be used in larger areas than the other; the colors might show a difference in value and intensity; and there should be no clashing.

Complementary Color: The opposite color to a given color; it is found in several ways: If the given color is primary, the complementary is obtained by mixing the other two primaries. The complement of any secondary color would be the remaining primary.

All colors have the property of calling upon their complementaries, in whatever colors are placed next to them. This is the property which causes many colors and color schemes to become hazy or mottled. Complementary colors, in brief, are those which, when mixed, produce a neutral gray.

Cool Color: Any color related to foliage, ice, sky, or snow, such as blue, green, violet.

Hue: The attribute of color, determined by the dominant wave length or predominant wave lengths of the stimulus, which distinguishes one color from another—red, yellow, blue, green, et al.

Intensity: Refers to the brightness or the dullness of a color; corresponds to saturation, or the purity of hue that a surface can reflect. When red is all red it is said to be in full intensity. When black, white, or gray is used in the color, there is a neutralization or a reduction in the intensity.

Neutral Color: One in which there is no decided hue but in which gray or some shade of blue predominates, as in sand color, taupe, gunmetal, putty, beige, and some others.

Primary Colors: Red, yellow, and blue; pigments of these colors may be mixed to make many other colors.

Saturation: Also known as chroma, intensity, purity. It is the strength or purity of a color, intense or bright, subdued or grayed. If the color is as brilliant as possible, it is known as one of saturation or strength; if subdued or grayed, it is dull, weak, and low in intensity.

Secondary Colors: Green, orange, and violet, each of which is obtained by the mixing of two primaries.

Shade: The dark tone of a color. Adding black will produce a shade. Adding the complement of the color to any standard color will produce a shade.

Standard Colors: These are the six colors of the rainbow.

Tertiary Colors: Olive, citron, and russet, each of which is obtained by mixing of two secondary colors.

Tint: A hue plus white.

Tone: A hue plus black.

Value: Also known as "lightness" or "darkness." Proportions of colorants or variations of lightness or darkness with reference to a gray scale. Value encompasses shades, tints, and tones.

Warm Color: One that is related to heat, sunlight, and fire: red, orange, yellow.

COLOR, THE THREE PROPERTIES OF.

1. HUE: The quality that distinguishes a color from other colors. This hue or tone is given a designated name such as red, blue, green. Hue and tone are often considered interchangeable.

2. VALUE: Luminosity of a color with regard to its lightness or darkness. The degree of lightness or darkness is

the value. If the color is dark, the value is low; if light, the value is high.

3. SATURATION, CHROMA, INTENSITY, PURITY: The strength or purity of a color, intense or bright, subdued or grayed. If the color is as brilliant as possible, it is known as one of saturation or strength; if subdued or gray, it is dull, weak, and low in intensity.

COLOR TONE. Pertains to the quality of color as the shade, hue, or degree of color, as a deep "tone" of red. Any modification of a color in brilliance or saturation.

COLOR TROUGHS (ALSO, BOX TROUGHS): Copper boxes or containers on a printing machine used to hold the color that is fed to the print roller. There will be as many color boxes as there are rollers in action on the machine.

COLOR ACCENT. A bright or vivid color or colors sometimes used to dress-up or improve dark, otherwise unattractive clothing ensembles.

COLORADO RIVER HEMP. This fiber grows wild in Colorado. It is a very strong, long, white, ribbonlike fiber and is also known as wild hemp.

COLOR ANALYSIS. See SPECTROPHOTOMETER; COLORIMETER.

COLOR AND WEAVE EFFECT. Two or more colors in a fabric pattern brought about by the combination of the weave and color but rather apart from either the method of coloring or the weave. Examples would include some plaids, overplaids, Glen plaids, Bannockburns, iridescents, changeables.

COLORANT. Any coloring matter such as a pigment or dye.

COLORAY. Product of Courtaulds North America, Inc., which is produced by the inclusion of colored pigments in the fiber prior to extrusion. The fiber is supplied in staple for and is widely used in the apparel and home furnishings markets.

COLOR BLIND, COLOR BLINDNESS. Partially or totally unable to distinguish colors. Partial blindness is known as dichromatism, total blindness as achromatopsia or monochromatism.

COLOR BOND. A trade name applied exclusively to the oil-in-water resin-pigment dyeing method developed by Dan River Mills, Inc. The term is also applied to fabrics dyed by this process.

It is permanently fast to sunlight, washing, dry-cleaning and atmospheric gases, and gives uniformity in shade and added wear to the fabric. Applicable to cotton, viscose, acetate, nylon and other man-mades and blended fabrics.

COLOR CARDS. Folders, sample

sheets, booklets, catalogues, and so on used by concerns to advertise their color lines in fabrics, garments, and other goods.

COLOR CIRCLE. Sometimes known as the chromatic circle, it is the arrangement of the colors of the spectrum in a ring formation, around which each color gradually blends into its related hue.

COLOR DOCTOR. The blade on a printing machine which scrapes off excess color paste from the roller prior to its coming in contact with the fabric to be printed. Excess dye backwashes into the color box.

COLORED COTTON. In the strict sense any cotton that is not white in the natural condition; may be brown, ecru, buff, off-cast, tinged, etc.

COLORED LISTING. Fabric woven with colored selvage ends to distinguish it from the body of the cloth. Some firms weave their fabric with colored selvages for identification or trade-mark purposes.

COLOR EFFECT. See COLOR IN PATTERNS.

COLOR FASTNESS. The determination as to whether a color is fast to a number of standard tests used for the purpose. Yarn or fabric may be tested for fastness to color fading, spotting, or staining. Some of the tests employed include fastness to crocking, color bleeding, dry-cleaning, laundering, sunlight, perspiration, ironing, pressing.

COLOR HARMONY. The pleasing effect which comes as a result of correct blending of colors. It is a study in itself, and must be mastered by designers, stylists, fashionists, and fashion copywriters.

COLORIMETER. 1. An apparatus which estimates the percentage of coloring substance in a given solution; used in quantitative chemical analysis. 2. An optical instrument for measuring color intensity. It makes use of a system of prisms and lenses which places a lighted field of reflected color from the sample, side by side with one from a known standard of the same shade. In the laundry trade it is much used to evaluate and standardize blue.

COLORIMETRY. Testing of a coloring or dyeing compound by comparison with color solutions.

COLOR INDEX NUMBER. The listing of dyes as published annually by the Society of Dyers and Colourists in its Index, and The American Association of Textile Chemists and Colorists (AATCC), P.O. Box 12215, Research Triangle Park, North Carolina, 27709.

COLOR IN PATTERNS, COMPLEMENTARY. When used, in a pattern, each color tries to intensify the other one. These complementaries are used in a pattern where each color has the same width of stripes, and tone; if the colors are the same, it is noted that a hazy, blurred appearance will result. This is because each color has some influence on the other.

The best way to use complementaries is to have one darker than the other, and not have the stripes of equal width.

The use of a black or white stripe to separate the two complementaries will prevent their acting upon each other. Colors of this group are used in the loudest and gaudiest patterns. They attract the eye for a time, but people usually tire of them very soon.

COLORS IN PLAID, COMPLEMENTARY. This involves two complementaries crossing each other in the fabric. In this respect, each color appears to be gray, and this will tend to give the entire pattern a hazy appearance. To avoid this unpleasant effect, the complementaries, stronger in color, must be such that they will offset the smeared appearance, and give good contrast in the tone between them. Reds and greens give the most trouble since they readily take on the same tone.

COLOR LAKE. The insoluble combination of a mordant and a dyestuff that has been fixed on the fiber, such as tannin with basic dyes on cotton, or chrome with a mordant on wool.

COLOR MATCHING. Reproducing color so that it will match with the standard color sample. Matching is done on fiber, yarn, and fabric.

COLOR MIXER. A color wheel or color top made with dovetailing colored disks which will show differently colored sectors, which when rotated rapidly will blend into a circle of even, uniform color.

COLOR PASTE, STOCK. One with high concentration of color in it.

COLOR REMOVERS. Commerical color removers, generally speaking, are safe for use on all major textile fibers. Be sure, however, to read directions on labels. If possible, test the product prior to use on the distressed area. If there is a decided change in color rather than fading, the original color may be restored by rinsing at once and then drying the item in the air. If fading results, it is not possible to restore the original color. Not to be used in metal containers.

COLOR RESIST. An application made on cloth by the addition of selected nonreducing colors which are mixed with the white resist agent used. Resists on basic colors, for example, may include British gum, salt, soda,

tartar emetic; all white resists.

COLOR ROLLER. Used in cylinder or direct printing, it is usually a copper roller about 15 inches to 36 inches in circumference. This roller is fitted onto a steel mandril in the printing machine; its purpose is to transfer a particular color to the material, and that portion of the color motif or pattern is engraved or etched on its surface.

COLORS, ANALOGOUS. These are related closely and have a common property, such as bluish green and greenish blue. The tendency, when used in striped materials, is to separate and increase the color difference between them. As these colors are one step removed from each other, it is important, in striped effects, to have them closely related.

COLORS, CHROMATIC. The hue colors such as red, yellow, and blue in contradistinction to the achromatic colors such as black, slate, gray, and white.

COLOR SCHEME. Applied to the ensemble and the accessories worn by an individual.

COLOR SCHEMES, TYPES OF.

1. MONO-CHROMATIC OR ONE-COLOR HARMONY: The use of one color in varying degrees of intensity and value; light blue, medium blue, dark blue.

2. HARMONY: An agreeable combination of colors, all related to one basic color.

3. COMPLEMENTARY HARMONY: A pleasing combination of complementary colors. One of the two must be used in larger areas than the other, and the colors must differ in value and intensity; they must not clash.

COLOR-SEALED. A trade-mark of E. I. Du Pont de Nemours & Co., Inc., for solution-dyed-filament acetate yarns.

COLOR SHOP. A room in which printing colors are mixed from standard or base colors and prepared for printing.

Colors in Four Languages.

ENGLISH ANGLAIS ENGLISCH INGLÉS	FRENCH FRANÇAIS FRANZÖSISCH FRANCÉS	GERMAN ALLEMAND DEUTSCH ALEMÁN	SPANISH ESPAGNOL SPANISCH ESPAÑOL
Amber	Ambre	Bernstein	Ambar
Apricot	Abricot	Aprikose	Albaricoque
Ashes	Cendreux	Aschgrau	Ceniciento
Bamboo	Bambon	Bambus	Bambú
Brick-red	Brique	Ziegelrot	Ladrillo
Black	Noir	Schwarz	Negro
Blue	Bleu	Blau	Azul
Brown	Brun	Braun	Café
Buttercup	Bouton d'or	Butterblume	Amargón
Canary	Canari	Kanariengelb	Canario
Cherry	Cerise	Kirschfarbig	Cereza

ENGLISH / ANGLAIS / ENGLISCH / INGLÉS	FRENCH / FRANÇAIS / FRANZÖSISCH / FRANCÉS	GERMAN / ALLEMAND / DEUTSCH / ALEMÁN	SPANISH / ESPAGNOL / SPANISCH / ESPAÑOL
Chocolate	Chocolat	Schokolade	Chocolate
Chamois	Chamois	Gemse	Gamuza
Coffee	Café	Kaffee	Café
Copper	Cuivre	Kupferfarbig	Cobre
Coral	Corail	Koralle	Coral
Corn	Mais	Korn, Mais	Maiz
Cream	Crème	Rahmfarbig	Crema
Dust	Poudre	Staubfarbig	Polvo
Emerald	Émeraude	Smaragd	Esmeralda
Fawn	Faon	Rehfarbig	Cervatillo
Flesh (color)	Couleur Chair	Fleischfarben	Color carne
Garnet	Grenat	Granat	Granate
Gold	Or	Gold	Oro
Gray	Gris	Grau	Gris
Grass (color)	Vert d'herbe	Grassgrün	Hierba
Green	Vert	Grün	Verde
Indigo	Indigo	Indigoblau	Añil
Ivory	Ivoire	Elfenbein	Marfil
Ivy (color)	Vert-de-lierre	Efeugrün	Hiedra
Lavender	Lavande	Lavender	Espliego
Leather	Cordoue	Leder	Córdoba
Lemon	Citron	Zitronengelb	Limón
Lichen	Lechen	Moosgrün	Liquen
Lilac	Lilas	Lila	Lila
Maroon	Marron	Maron	Castaña Marrón
Mole	Taupe	Taupe	Topo
Natural	Naturel	Natürlich	Natural
Navy (blue)	Bleu marin	Marineblau	Marino
Oak-green	Chêne	Eichengrün	Verde-roble
Olive-green	Olive	Olivengrün	Verde-olivo
Orange	Orange	Orangegelb	Anaranjado
Orchid	Lila-clair	Orchidee	Lila
Peacock-blue	Bleu-paon	Pfau	Pavón
Peach	Pêche	Pfirsichfarbe	Melocotón
Pea Green	Vert-clair	Erbsengrün	Verde-claro
Pearl	Perle	Perle	Perla
Pine Green	Pin-vert-foncé	Föhrengrün	Verde pino
Pink	Rose-clair	Rosa	Rosado
Plum	Prune	Pflaume	Ciruela
Purple	Pourpre	Purpurfarbig	Morado
Red	Rouge	Rot	Rojo
Rose	Rose	Rosenfarbe	Rosa
Ruby	Rubis	Rubinfarben	Rubi
Saffron	Safran	Safrangelb	Azafràn
Sand	Sable	Sandfarben	Arena
Salmon	Saumon	Lachsrot	Salmón
Silver	Argent	Silber	Plata
Sky-blue	Ciel-bleu	Himmelblau	Azul-celeste
Smoke, Smoky	Fumeux	Rauchig	Humo-plumo
Straw	Paille	Strohfarbig	Bagatela
Strawberry	Fraise	Erdbeerfarbig	Fresa
Sunflower	Tournesol	Sonnenblume	Girasol
Sulfur	Soufre	Schwefelfarbig	Azufre
Tobacco	Tabac	Tabak	Tabaco
Tomato (red)	Tomate	Tomate	Tomate
Topaz	Topaze	Topaz	Topacio
Turquoise	Turquoise	Türkis	Azul-turqui

COLORS IN PLAID, COMPLEMENTARY. This involves two complementaries crossing each other in the fabric. In this respect, each color appears to be gray, and this will tend to give the entire pattern a hazy appearance. To avoid this unpleasant effect, the complementaries, stronger in color, must be such that they will offset the smeared appearance, and give good contrast in the tone between them. Reds and greens give the most trouble since they can take on readily about the same tone.

COLORSPUN. Registered trademark of the FMC Corporation, American Viscose Division, for its solution-dyed yarn, filament or staple, acetate or viscose.

COLOR STRIPPER. A broad term to imply the use of one or more chemicals to completely remove color from an article so that it may be redyed; an agent that will correct dyeing defects after the run has been completed and examined or an agent that will possibly lighten a shade that has come out too heavy in cast. See Stripping.

COLOTAN. A species of the Cadillo or Urena bast fiber. Se CADILLO.

COLTHORP PRIDE COTTON. A large-boll, small-seed, late-maturing Louisiana cotton of about 1-inch staple; lint yield is from 28 per cent to 30 per cent.

COLUMBIA COTTON. An Uplands variety cotton with staple length of $1\frac{5}{16}$ inches.

COLUMBIA SHEEP. A medium wool of this country originating in Idaho. The fleece weighs about 11 pounds; this long staple wool sorts to 1/4 blood. Shrinkage is about 50 per cent.

COLUMELLA, LUCIUS JUNIUS. His book, *De Re Rustica,* is the best book on sheep from antiquity, and many of its principles, methods, and suggestions are still used wherever sheep are raised. Columella was a Roman who lived in Cadiz, Spain. His estates were in and near Cordoba. In A.D. 50, during the reign of Claudius, he crossed Tarentine rams with native Italian and Spanish ewes. He understood crossbreeding. When he crossbred North African rams with native ewes he laid the foundation for the present Spanish Merino breed of sheep, known all over the world.

COLVIN DOBBY. A loom equipped with a system of levers, in lieu of harnesses, where several shedding arrangements are necessary; a type of dobby loom.

COMB. Set with a number of bars clothed with fine, steel needles or teeth, the machine removes short, un-

ENGLISH	FRENCH	GERMAN	SPANISH
ANGLAIS	FRANÇAIS	ALLEMAND	ESPAGNOL
ENGLISCH	FRANZÖSISCH	DEUTSCH	SPANISCH
INGLÉS	FRANCÉS	ALEMÁN	ESPAÑOL
Violet	Violette	Veilchenblau	Violeta
White	Blanc	Weiss	Blanco
Wine	Vin	Wein	Vino
Yellow	Jaune	Gelb	Amarillo

Color Uses, Some Comments on.

DISGUISE: Observed in "allover motifs" or in patterns on fabrics which conceal or cover up possible flaws or defects in the fabric used. All fabrics should be examined very closely. Note the hand or feel, hold it up to the light and study the texture well.

IDENTIFICATION: Symbols of color apply to many holidays during the year, such as red and green at Christmas, purple and yellow at Easter, orange and black for Hallowe'en.

INTEREST: Certain colors affect us in varied and different ways, either pleasing or displeasing, satisfactory or annoying. Color interest is often intriguing and requires much attention in appraising its values and effects.

DECORATION: Color schemes, casts, shades, tones, tints, and hues, as well as full colors, all have their place in our daily lives—at business, in travel, in the home, in apparel.
Some homes have a soothing, calm, serene color scheme; others may be such that the color scheme and decor are annoying, even very disturbing, or very uninteresting. Contrast and harmony in color or colors should be truly effective and developed in a sane, thoughtful manner. Color variety should always be "in good taste." The word "taste," however, may be somewhat difficult to understand or to define. Thus, sound judgment should prevail at all times in dealing with color.

VARIETY: Color, or colors, do make us "look different." Color can be the spice of life in many instances. A change of color, so to speak, often helps all of us. And color variety should be in good taste and well balanced as to details.

COLOR SELLS FABRICS AND GARMENTS: If the color or color scheme is one that is not satisfying or desirable, we will, psychologically, become annoyed and discard its use. An ensemble can often be very attractive except for one item—often an accessory—which may spoil the entire attire and comeliness of the wearer. Contrast and harmony should be in good balance and taste to be really worthwhile and appealing.

WE LIVE WITH, AND IN, COLOR: Color is always with us, around us, and it has much effect upon our feelings, whims, desires, satisfactions, and even our annoyances. Color can make or break any mode, dress, or garment. It may be refined, conservative, inviting, bizarre, wild, outlandish, serene. And, of course, color does much or can do much for the complexion, since both are closely correlated to each other, also for the profile, form, or silhouette. Color can also do very little for us, and in fact, might do us harm.

desirable cotton fibers, takes out some remaining foreign matter, and delivers a sliver in which remaining fibers are of the same approximate length. Used only for the better grades of cotton yarns. See COMBING.

COMBAT CLOTH. Trade-mark for an all-nylon material much used in athletic contests where body contacts seem to abound—football, basketball, hockey, baseball, softball, and such. This very durable fabric comes in bright colors which are fast to washing, cleaning, and sunlight. Combat cloth absorbs very little moisture and dries rapidly. The goods are set in the finishing and garments of the material will keep their original size in washing or dry-cleaning.

Weighing only 5½ ounces per yard and having excellent body, the cloth far exceeds in tensile strength and abrasion resistance any rayon and cotton fabrics thus far developed for athletic use. Not affected by moths or mildew. When wet, the material is slippery and therefore is ideal as a "wet-game-pant," since it maintains its strength and is difficult for tacklers, in football, to hold when wetted by rain.

Uses include football pants, basket ball and softball uniforms, hockey pants, swimming trunks and other instances where a lightweight, extremely durable material is desirable. Made by William Skinner & Sons.

COMB BOX. The cast-iron container for the bearings for one end of the doffer comb on a cotton card; bearings should always be well lubricated in order to give correct oscillating action to comb as it strips weblike fleece of cotton fibers from the doffer roller near the delivery end of the card.

COMB CIRCLES. The three combing circles on the Noble comber. There are two inner circles about 18 to 20 inches in diameter while the outside or large circle is about 44 inches in diameter. The two inner circles work inside the large one on the principle of a differential arrangement. Each circle is set with fine steel combing pins which do the actual combing of the fibers. See Illustrated Section.

COMBED TWILLS. Twill weaves derived from combining two ordinary twills in an end-and-end, or in a pick-and-pick sequence.

"COMBED-WORSTED" KNITTING YARN. It is made of good stock, uniform in all respects, with fibers of the same length; all undesirable fibers have been removed from the yarn in processing the wool. The yarn is used chiefly in knitted hosiery and underwear for use in cold weather.

COMBED YARN GOODS, COTTON. Fine quality cotton goods made of combed yarn instead of carded yarns. In recent years there has been a greater demand for combed-yarn fabric because of the higher economic standards of living and greater purchasing power. Organdy, voile, dimity, and a host of other fine cottons are examples of combed yarn goods.

COMBED YARNS. Those made from fibers that have been both carded and combed in process of manufacture from raw stock to finished spun yarn.

COMBER. A type of carding machine that performs fine work, especially used for high-quality yarns. In converting the ribbon laps from the ribbon lapper machine into sliver, it brings the fibers of cotton parallel, cleans out the impurities, and extracts a large proportion of the short fibers. See Illustrated Section.

COMBER CYLINDER. The main combing unit in the Heilman comber for the French system of combing. The half-lap and the segment are attached to this foundation cylinder.

COMBER SLIVER. The loose, untwisted strand or ropelike form of cotton fibers produced by the combing machine from stock taken from the delivery end of the ribbon lapper machine.

COMBINATION. A term which may refer to yarns or to fabrics. 1. A combination yarn may be composed of two or more yarns having the same or different fibers or twists; one yarn may have a high twist, the other little or no twist; i.e., one may be viscose, the other acetate yarn. 2. A combination fabric is one which employs the above yarns: mossy crepes, romains, alpacas, and such.

COMBINATION ACETATE OR RAYON YARN. A standard twist yarn is plied with a crepe-twist yarn for use in certain crepe-effect fabrics such as sand crepe, alpaca crepe, moss crepe, and so on.

COMBINATION STITCH. A back stitch combined with two or more running stitches. It is used whenever more strength is required than could be had by the plain running stitch.

COMBINATION-TANNED. Tanning by two or more agents such as chrome and bark.

COMBINATION YARN. One that is made of two or more different single yarns that are twisted together. The single yarns may be of the same stock, and one single yarn may have higher twist per inch than the other; or the singles may be composed of two different stocks, such as one of cotton and one of worsted.

COMBING. A method of treating cotton, worsted, and certain other fibers in the comber machine. The process removes all fibers below a certain staple length; it combs those that are to be retained and sets them in a uniform, parallel order ready for further manipulation. Combing takes out practically all foreign matter such as dirt, neps, shives, and other minute particles.

Combing is vital for the manufacture of fine yarns, and it can be done to coarser yarns when high quality is necessary. Combing, however, as mill costs run, is rather expensive because the percentage of waste is high. It is resorted to only in the case of high-grade yarn for the better fabrics on the market today. See Illustrated Section.

COMBING, COMMISSION. A mill that combs worsted tops for another mill on a commission basis; popular method in French combing in this country. See Illustrated Section.

COMBING, DRY. The combing of worsted fibers in which no oil or emulsion treatment was given to facilitate the movement of the fibers in manipulation.

COMBING-IN-OIL. Worsted top that is combed with a certain amount of oil emulsion being added in the operation. From 3 to 5 per cent of the emulsion is used and the work is done in the backwashing machine.

COMBING INVENTIONS. Despite the fact that Edmund Cartwright invented the first combing machine in 1789, it was forty years later before the machine had genuine value. Other inventors of combing machines were: Heilman, Donisthorpe, Lister, Noble, and Holden. The most important of this group was Joseph Heilman, an Alsatian. Watching his daughters comb their hair gave him the idea of his machine. He saw them draw out their hair full length between their fingers —a "separation of the top from the noil" in worsted parlance. Heilman, in 1830, perfected his machine, which was based on the nip idea of combing. This is important in German, French, and Belgian systems of combing today. The use of high-grade wool to be used for worsted purposes on his machine did away with more than an average amount of noil and other waste, to obtain more top fibers. Heilman's machine is of the upright type.

COMBING METHODS. Long, medium, and short combing wools are found in the market. They are manipulated in the following manner:

1. LONG WOOL is combed on the Lister or square knit comber. This takes care of wool used for worsted stock, ranging from 8 to 12 inches in staple length.

2. MEDIUM WOOL is combed on the Noble or circular comber. The length of stock combed this way ranges from 2 to 5 inches, and a little longer.

3. SHORT WOOL uses the upright French or Heilman comber. The comb may be single or double nipped. The best combing is done on this machine, as it cares for stock that ranges from 1½ to 6 inches in length. This type of wool is superior to all other length wool. Much of it is called baby combing wool and it is used for the best of worsted. See Illustrated Section.

COMBING ROLL. See PIN CYLINDER.

COMBINGS. A term used in wool sorting which shows the number or grade location of the wool on the sheep fleece, the quality and the grades to which the fibers may be spun in the worsted system of spinning, which uses the standard of 560 yards of yarn in one pound of a number-one worsted yarn. See table below. See also Illustrated Section.

COMBING TARE. Ratio of top to noil, in percentage terms, in worsted top combing.

COMBING WOOL. The fibers of wool from 1½ to 6 inches long used in worsted yarn. The stock is more desirable and more expensive than clothing wool. Combing wool fibers are of the same approximate length, whereas in clothing wool they are of variable length and usually shorter than combing wool fibers. Combing wool has the more parallel fibers, less foreign matter, greater serrations, and in every other respect is superior to clothing wool. Combing wool, when it is a finished worsted yarn, goes into a higher type and more expensive piece of material than does clothing wool. See Illustrated Section.

COMBING WOOL, METHODS OF.

1. LISTER, SQUARE-KNIT: Takes care of fibers from 8 inches to 12 inches long that are to be used in worsted yarn, a so-called preparing method.

2. NOBLE CIRCULAR: Combs fibers that range from about 2 inches up to 6 inches. This comb takes care of the so-called short wool fibers to be used for worsted on the Bradford or English system of combing.

3. HEILMAN OR FRENCH: Stock

about 1 inch staple up to a 5 or 6 inch staple is combed on this French method of combing. This is the only one of the three methods that can comb baby combing wool.

COMBINING. A broad, general term used when textile materials are laminated and bonded with adhesives such as glue, latex forms, etc. Laminated or combined fabric, with leather, paper, foam rubber, etc., now form an important segment of the textile and allied industries. Some belts, foundation garments, collars, handbags, luggage, shoes, and slippers are made this way— textile fabric bonded with the non-textile product. See LAMINATE.

COMBOYS. British colored goods which are woven with two threads as one in the body of the fabric. The border is woven with four double ends crammed into one reed split. A comboy layout might be: warp and filling of 26s to 32s yarn, 44 to 50 picks per inch. Warp texture will vary from 100 ends or more per inch. A 56 to 64 reed is used in weaving the goods.

The cloth has a capella woven in it; one half is put in at the beginning of the comboy and the other half at the end, thereby making the capella into a heading, the checking being woven in the center of the goods. See CAPELLA LAYOUT.

COMBUSTION, HEAT OF. Applied to a substance it is the number of small or large calories of heat evolved during the combustion of a gram or a kilogram of the substance. Using the English system of weights and measures, it is the number of British Thermal Units of heat evolved during the combustion of one pound of the substance. See B.T.U.

COMB WARPER, COMB SLASHER. A series of upright metal pegs which separate the individual warp ends and then guide them onto a beam in correct, picked-out pattern form.

COMEBACK. One interpretation refers to wool which shows a greater staple length than was expected. The other meaning implies the increased staple length as the result of careful crossbreeding of sheep. Hence, the

effort made to increase fiber length is the chief reason why there is so much crossbreeding in the sheep world today, since the fiber quality is also improved.

The theory of comeback is that a 3/4-blood ram, crossed with a 3/8-blood ewe, will give an approximate half-blood stock; thus, the 3/8 stock has been improved and the fiber length increased.

A remarkable result of crossbreeding in this country is shown in the rapidly decreasing amounts of carpet wool grown here. This is the poorest of the four types of wool, combing, clothing and carding wools being the others. By the improved scientific methods of raising wool, the carpet stocks have been so improved that they have graduated into the clothing and carding classes. With this decline of carpet wool, it is necessary to import this low-grade fiber in increasing amounts from other wool centers.

COME CLEAN. A registered trademark of Klopman Mills, a division of Burlington Industries, New York City. This soil release product appeared in January, 1967 and can be applied to fabric weights in which the process works and can be used on precured and post-cured materials, is not a soil repellent but is a soil releaser. At present there does not seem to be advantage or disadvantage in the capability of combatting soil redeposition alone or through static that may be created. It is particularly used for tablecloths, decorative fabrics, shirts, dressgoods, slacks and some women's wear items.

COMFORT AIR CONDITIONING. The method by which simultaneously the temperature, the moisture content, and the movement and the quality of air in enclosed air spaces intended for human occupancy may be kept within the required health limits.

COMFORT, COMFORTABLE, COMFORTER. A quilt or covering made with a layer of wadding or stuffing; the surface fabric may be silk, cotton, acetate, rayon, or other material. Some of the articles are quilted, knotted, padded, or tied to produce the desired effect.

COMMERCIAL DYES. Applied to

direct colors which, in most instances, are not fast to light and washing.

COMMERCIAL MATCHING. When a color is dyed within acceptable tolerances.

COMMERCIAL MOISTURE REGAIN. An arbitrary figure formally adopted as the regain used in calculating the commercial or legal weight of shipments or deliveries of any specific textile material.

COMMERCIAL STANDARD-MOISTURE REGAIN. An arbitrary figure adopted formally and used to calculate commercial or legal weights of shipments and deliveries of textile materials. The figure to be used will depend on the fiber or fibers as to content in the particular yarn or fabric.

COMMERCIAL STANDARDS. The U. S. Bureau of Standards issues Commercial Standards which are not laws, but have great importance because these are "recorded voluntary standards of the trade." They are usually referred to by number.

COMMISSION MERCHANT. One who sells textiles for a large area or district. This area may be a city, county, state or several states, depending upon the local conditions. The agent may be an individual or a firm who sells the article in his own name or in the name of some mill, domestic or foreign. The commission unit has the power of possession, management, control, and disposal of the goods in question. The merchant works closely with apparel houses and department stores.

COMMISSION OR JOB FINISHER. A concern which colors and finishes textile goods for a certain price per yard. Full instructions, including shipping data, are supplied the finisher by the converter.

COMMISSION WEAVER. The owner of a small mill, generally, who weaves material on a commission basis. The commission weaver rarely buys the raw stock on his own account for weaving or other purposes.

COMMODITY FIBERS. 1. The prices quoted daily in the business sections of major newspapers on the following textiles — Middling Cotton, one inch staple on per pound basis; Print Cloth, 64 x 60, 38½ inch width on per yard basis, and on a 78 x 78 texture in a 48 inch width on a per yard basis; Silk, "30-32," in Grade A Classification on per pound basis; Wool per pound; Worsted Tops per pound basis (5,000 pounds make a single contract when selling). 2. The selling by the manufacturer of his product as a nameless commodity rather than using the

COMBINGS

NUMBER	FROM	FLEECE	GRADES OR COUNT
First	Sides and shoulders	Fine	66s to 70s
Second	Back and across the loins to the neck	Fine medium	64s to 66s
Third	Sides and shoulders	Medium average	60s to 64s
Fourth	Sides and shoulders	Average strong	58s
Fifth	Sides	Strong	56s
Sixth	Lower part of thigh, belly, rump, shanks	Poor	Low counts of warp or filling yarn

particular brand name of the product. A goodly amount of manmade fibers are sold in this manner for some particular purpose by the purchaser of the fiber in question. Many other industries sell their wares in this manner to varying degrees.

COMMODORE. Heavy cotton drill used in maritime circles.

COMMON GINGHAM. The ordinary plain-weave, starched gingham fabric noted for its great variety of color design in both warp and filling.

COMMON TWILLS. 1. The 2-up and 2-down twill weave, right- or left-hand as to direction, and made at 45-degree twill angle.

2. Weaves such as the 2-up and 1-down, the 1-up and 2-down, 2-up and 2-down, 3-up and 1-down, 1-up and 3-down, and so on, are often spoken of as being common twills.

COMPACTING. The "texture" imparted to a fabric made from thermoplastic fibers or filaments. The heat and pressure used in the process provides shrinkage to the goods thereby providing a bulked, crepe-like hand. The effect and treatment is permanent.

COMPANIES AND CORPORATIONS IN TEXTILES AND APPAREL, SOME MAJOR. An alphabetical listing of some of the major, outstanding companies and corporations in textiles and apparel follows:

Apparel Companies-Stores, Some Major: These follow:
Bobbie Brooks, Inc.
Botany Industries, Inc.
B.V.D. Corporation
Cluett, Peabody Co., Inc.
Eagle Clothes, Inc.
Farah Mfg. Co., Inc.
Genesco, Inc.
Hart, Schaffner & Marx.
Hat Corporation of America.
Interstate Department Stores.
Koret of California (Kora-corporation.)
Jonathan Logan Co., Inc.
Londontown Mfg. Co.
Manhattan Industries.
McGregor-Doniger
Munsingwear, Inc.
National Bellas Hess
Palm Beach Co., Inc.
Phillips Van Heusen
Richman Brothers, Inc.
Russ Togs, Inc.
Siegel (Henry I).
Spartan Industries
Levi Strauss & Co., Inc.
V.F. Corporation
Villager Industries, Inc.
Warnaco, Inc.
Wayne Gossard, Inc.

Buying Offices, Some Major. Allied Stores Marketing Corporation, Arkwright, Inc.; Associated Dry Goods Corporation, Associated Merchandising Corporation, Frederick Atkins, Inc.; Independent Retailers Syndicate, Inc.; Kirby, Block Co., Inc.; Felix Lilienthal & Co., Inc.; Mercantile Stores, Inc.; May Department Stores, Inc.; McGreevey, Werring & Howell Co., Inc.; Mutual Buying Syndicate, Inc.; O'Shaughnessy, Drewes & Klein, Inc.; Wm. M. Van Buren, Inc.; Youth Fashion Guild, Inc.

Chain Stores, Some Major.
APPAREL: Diana Stores Corporation, Lane Bryant, Inc., Mangel Stores, Inc., Miller-Wohl Co., Inc.; MAIL ORDER HOUSES: Aldan Stores, Inc.; J.C. Penney & Co., Inc.; Sears Roebuck & Co., Inc.; Spiegel Co., Inc.; VARIETY STORES: Cunningham Drug Stores, Inc.; Jack Eckard Corporation, Fishman Co., Inc.; Ben Franklin Stores, Inc.; Gamble's (Gamble-Skogmo, Inc.;) S.S. Kresge Co., Inc.; S.H. Kress & Co., Inc.; McCrory Corporation, G.C. Murphy Co., Inc.; Neisner Brothers Co., Inc.; J.J. Newberry Co., Inc.; Peoples Drugstores, Inc.; Thrift Drugstores, Inc.; Walgreen Co., Inc.; F. W. Woolworth Co., Inc.; Zayre Corporation.

Chemical Companies, Some Major.
These follow:
Althouse Division of Crompton & Knowles Corporation
Apex Chemical Co., Inc.
Arkansas Chemical Co., Inc.
Atlas Chemical Industries.
BASF Corporation
Bradford Dyeing Association, (USA).
Chem-Mark, Inc.
CIBA-GEIGY
Dexter Chemical Co., Inc.
Eastman Chemical Products, Inc.
Enjay Chemical Co., Inc.
GAF Corporation

W.F. Fancourt Co., Inc.
Francolor, Inc.
Hart Products, Inc.
Hilton-Davis, Inc.
Hooker Chemical Co., Inc.
ICI (Organics) Inc.
Olin Mathieson Chemical Corporation
Minnesota Mining & Manufacturing Co., Inc.
Nopco Chemical Co., Inc.
Pennwalt
Quaker Chemical Corporation
Raytheon, Inc.

Rohm and Haas Co., Inc.
Sandoz, Inc.
Scholler Brothers, Inc.
Solvol Chemical Co., Inc.
Standard Chemical Products, Inc.
Stauffer Chemical Co., Inc.
Tantatex Chemical Corporation.
Verona Dyestuffs of Verona-Pharma Chemical Corporation.
Wica Chemicals, Inc.
Witco Chemical Corporation.

Machinery Companies For Textile and Allied Industries, Some Major.
Barber Colman Co., Inc.
Birch Brothers, Inc.
H.W. Butterworth Mfg. Co., Inc.
Cocker Machine & Foundry Co., Inc.
Crompton & Knowles Corporation
Davis & Furber Co., Inc.
Foster Machine Co., Inc.
Walter Kidde & Co., Inc.
Leesona Corporation
International Rockwell Corporation - Draper Corporation, American Textile Machinery Works, and Wildman Jacquard Company.
Parks & Cramer Co., Inc.
Proctor & Schwartz, Inc.
Prodesco, Inc.
Saco Lowell Company of Maremont Corporation
Scott & Williams, Inc., and Whitin Machine Works of White Consolidated Industries.
Scovil Manufacturing Co., Inc.
Singer-Cobble, Inc.
The Singer Company, Inc.
The Torrington Company, Inc.
Turbo Machine Co., Inc.
Union Special Machine Co., Inc.
U.S. Textile Machine Co., Inc., of Dynamics Corporation of America.
Warnaco, Inc.
Warner & Swasey Co., Inc.
West Point Foundry and Machine Co., Inc.
Willcox & Gibbs, Inc.

Nonwoven Products, Some Major Manufacturers of. These follow:
Albany Felt Co., Inc.
American Felt Co., Inc.
Chatham Mfg. Co., Inc.
Chicopee Mfg. Co., Inc.
Curlator Corporation
Dexter Corporation
Dry Corr Felt Co., Inc.
E.I. duPont de Nemours & Co., Inc.
Gustin Bacon Co., Inc.
The Felters Company, Inc.
B.F. Goodrich Co., Inc.
Huyck Corporation
Internation Paper Co., Inc.

Johnson & Johnson
Kem-Wove Industries, Inc.
The Kendall Co., Inc.
Kimberly, Clark Co., Inc.
Lowndes Products, Inc.
Ludlow Corporation
Minnesota Mining & Manufacturing
  Co., Inc.
National Felt Co., Inc.
Norton Company, Inc.
Ozite Corporation
Pellon Corporation
Phillips Fibers Co., Inc.
Raybestos-Manhattan Co., Inc.
Riegel Paper Company, Inc.
Scott Paper Company, Inc.
Standard Cotton Products, Inc.
Standard Felt Company, Inc.
Stearns & Foster Co., Inc.
St. Regis Paper Co., Inc.
Tenneco Chemical Co., Inc.
Troy Mills, Inc.
West Point-Pepperell Co., Inc.
Union Wadding Co., Inc.

Notions and Trimmings. Bailey,
Green & Elder Company, and Franken
Trim, Inc.; (both companies in the
Lyntex Corporation), Blumenthal &
Co., Inc.; Sol Kahaner & Brother, Inc.;
(Unit of Willcox & Gibbs Co., Inc.9;
Streamline Buttons, Inc.

Retail Department Stores, Some Major.
These follow:
Abercrombie & Fitch
Abraham & Straus
Adam, Meldrum & Anderson-Buffalo
Addis Co., Inc. - Syracuse
Alexander's Stores
B. Altman & Co., Inc.
Arnold Constable
L.S. Ayres - Indianapolis
Bamberger's, Inc. - Newark
Bergdoff Goodman
L.L. Berge - Buffalo
Best & Co., Inc.
Bloomingdale's
Bon Marche - Seattle
Bonwit Teller
Broadstreet's
The Broadway - Los Angeles
Broadway Hale Stores, Inc.
Brooks Brothers
Bullock's - Los Angeles
Burdine's - Miami
Capwell's - Oakland
Carson, Pirie & Scott, Inc.
Chappell's - Syracuse
Cherry & Webb - Providence
Crowley-Milner - Detroit
Davison's - Atlanta
Dayton's - Minneapolis
Denver Dry Goods Co., Inc.

Dey Brothers, Inc., - Syracuse
E.W. Edwards - Rochester
Emporium Capwell
The Emporium - San Francisco
Filene's - Boston
Foley Brothers, D.G. - Houston
G. Fox - Hartford
Franklin Simon
Julius Garfinckel - Washington
Gimbel Brothers
Hahne & Co., Inc. - Newark
Halle Brothers - Cleveland
Haspel Brothers - New Orleans
The Hecht Company, Inc.
Hochschild Kohn - Baltimore
Joseph Horne, Inc. - Pittsburgh
J.L. Hudson Co., Inc. - Detroit
Gilchrist's - Boston
Jordan Marsh - Boston
Joske's - San Antonio
Kaufman's - Pittsburgh
King's Department Stores, Inc.
Korvette - Spartan Industries
LaSalle-Koch - Toledo
Lazarus - Columbus
Lit Brothers, Inc. - Philadelphia
Lord & Taylor
R.H. Macy & Co., Inc.
I. Magnin
Maison Blanche - New Orleans
Martin's - Brooklyn
Marshall Field & Co.
May Department Stores, Inc.
McCurdy's - Rochester
Meier & Frank, Inc. - Portland
Miller & Rhoades - Richmond
Neiman - Marcus
Ohrbach's
M. O'Neil - Akron
The Outlet Company, Inc., Providence
Peck & Peck
H & S Pogue - Cincinnati
Rich's - Atlanta
Richard's - Miami
Robinson's - Los Angeles
Roos/Atkins - San Francisco
Saks Fifth Avenue
Sanger Harris - Dallas
Shepard's - Providence
Shillito's - Cincinnati
Sibley, Lindsay & Curr - Rochester
Strawbridge & Clothier, Inc.
Stewart's - Baltimore
Thalheimer's - Richmond
Unishops, Inc.
Wallach's, Inc.
John Wanamaker
Woodward & Lothrop

*Textile Companies, Some Major (other
than the So-Called "Big Sixteen").*
These follow:
Abney Mills, Inc.
Adams-Millis, Inc.

American & Efird, Inc.
American Felt Co., Inc.
Avondale Mills, Inc.
Bates Mfg. Co., Inc.
Beaunit Corporation
Belding Heminway, Inc.
Bemis Co., Inc.
Berkshire Hathaway
Bibb Mfg. Co., Inc.
Bigelow-Sanford, Inc.
Blue Bird Silk Mfg. Co., Inc.
Blue Ridge-Winkler Textiles, Inc.
Wm. Carter & Co., Inc.
Chadbourn, Inc.
Chatham Mfg. Co., Inc.
Chicopee Mfg. Co., Inc.
Clark-Schwebel Fiber Glass Cor-
  poration
Deering Milliken Co., Inc.
The Duplan Corporation
N. Erlanger Blumgart Co., Inc.
Erlanger Mills, Inc.
Erwin Mills, Inc.
Fruit of the Loom, Inc.
Fulton Cotton Mills, Inc.
Gerli & Co., Inc.
Glen Raven Co., Inc.
Graniteville Mills, Inc.
Greenwood Mills, Inc.
Hanes Corporation
International Stretch Products, Inc.
Iselin-Jefferson Co., Inc.
Frank I & Sons, Inc.
Johnson & Johnson
The Kendall Co., Inc.
Klopman Mills, Inc.
Boris Kroll Jacquard Looms, Inc.
Leslie Catlin & Co., Inc.
Liberty Fabrics of New York, Inc.
Ludlow Corporation
Johns Manville
Metlon Corporation
Mount Vernon Mills, Inc.
Munsignwear, Inc.
Opelika Mfg. Co., Inc.
Owens-Corning Fiberglas Corpora-
  tion
Ozite Corporation
Pacelot Industries, Inc.
Philadelphia & Reading Co., Inc.
Philip Wick, Inc.
Reeves Brothers, Inc.
Schwarzenbach-Huber Co., Inc.
Southern Weaving Co., Inc.
Stonecutter Mills Corporation
Textiles, Inc.
Thomaston Mills, Inc.
Tioga Textiles Co., Inc.
Troy Mills, Inc.
Van Raalte Co., (Cluett, Peabody &
  Co., Inc.)
Wyandotte Industries, Inc.

Textile Corporations, The "Big Sixteen." These follow:
Burlington Industries, Inc.
J.P. Stevens & Co., Inc.
United Merchants & Manufacturers
Kayser Roth Corporation
Indian Head, Inc.
West Point-Pepperell, Inc.
M. Lowenstein & Sons, Inc.
Cannon Mills Corporation
Dan River Industries
Cone Mills Corporation
Springs Mills, Inc.
The Kendall Company, Inc.
Mohasco Industries
Fieldcrest Mills, Inc.
Collins & Aikman Corporation
Reigel Textile Corporation

Yarn and Thread Producers, Some Major. These follow:
Allied Chemical Corporation
American Cyanamid Co., Inc.
American Enka Corporation
American Thread Co., Inc.
Athens Throwing Co., Inc.
Atwater Throwing Co., Inc.
Avisco/FMC Corporation
Belding, Heminway-Corticelli Co., Inc.
Caron Spinning Co., Inc.
Celanese Corporation
Coats & Clark, Inc.
Courtaulds North America
Dixie Yarns, Inc.
Dow Badische Co., Inc.
The Duplan Corporation
E.I. duPont de Nemours & Co., Inc.
Durene Association
Eastman Chemical Products, Inc.
Fair Haven Mills, Inc.
Fairtex Corporation
Ferro Corporation
Fiber Industries, Inc.
Firestone Synthetic Fibers & Textiles, Inc.
B.F. Goodrich Co., Inc.
Goodyear Tire & Rubber Co., Inc.
Heberlein Patent Corporation
Hercules, Inc.
Hoechst Fibers, Inc.
Lily Mills Co., Inc.
Madison Throwing Co., Inc.
Johns Manville Co., Inc.
Clarence L. Meyers & Co., Inc.
Monsanto Textiles, Inc.
National Spinning Co., Inc.
Owens-Corning-Fiberglas Corporation.
Phillips Fibers Corporation
Polymer Industries, Inc.
PPG Industries
Reeves Brothers, Inc.
Southern Lus-Trus Corporation
Textured Fibers, Inc.

Thiokol Corporation
Union Carbide Corporation
UniRoyal, Inc.
Universal Textured Yarns, Inc.
Wellman, Inc.
Whitaker Co.. Inc.

COMPANY UNION. A labor organization formed, financed, or dominated by the company in which the members are employed.

COMPANY-WIDE BARGAINING. Collective bargaining by representatives of a company, and of its employees, in all plants of the company with the view of arriving at one mutually acceptable agreement to cover all plants.

COMPARISONS BETWEEN COTTON AND LINEN.

COTTON:	LINEN:
Absorbs moisture slowly	Absorbs moisture quickly
Less sensitive to chemicals	Sensitive to chemicals
Short fiber—½ to 2½ inches	Long fiber—few inches to 40 inches
Soils rather easily, fuzzy fiber	No fuzziness, does not soil quickly
Soft fiber	A natural stiff fiber
Dull fiber	Has natural luster
Moisture content 7 per cent	Moisture content is from 8 per cent, upwards
Dyes readily	Great care has to be exercised in dyeing
Remains white in caustic soda	Turns yellowish in caustic soda
Convolutions are counterclockwise	Convolutions are clockwise
Fiber tip is fuzzy	Fiber tip is string-like
Ribbonlike in structure	Resembles bamboo in structure

COMPARISON SHOPPER. A department store employee who checks up on other stores.

COMPATIBLE. Capable of being used in conjunction with other materials without loss of valuable properties.

COMPATIBLE DYES. Refers to dyes that have been mixed together and behave in the dyeing operation as a homogeneous coloring compound.

COMPENSATOR, KIDDE. This quality control device on circular knitted swimsuit fabrics maintains an accurately controlled tension on the rubber-yarn feeds in fabrics of this type.

COMPENZINE. A three-ply yarn composed of a single untwisted yarn and two tightly twisted yarns. When given a few turns or twists per inch, usually from four to six, the single, loose yarn will pucker or crimp thereby giving a nub or slub effect comparable with the average crepe yarn found in silk.

COMPLEXING AGENT. Any compound that will inactivate a metallic ion.

COMPLIANCE. 1. The elongation produced by any load on textile fibers when testing. 2. Opposite of stiffness, it implies the sensation noted when fabrics are squeezed in the hand.

COMPOSITION CLOTH. Cotton or linen duck or canvas which has been treated to make it waterproof. Used for bags and coverings.

COMPOSITION DOT. See FLOCK PRINTING.

COMPOUND. Substances composed of two or more elements. The atoms of these elements are held together in compounds by electrical forces in the outer areas of their structure.

COMPOUND, CHEMICAL. The substance formed by chemical union of two or more elements. It differs from a mechanical mixture which is a mixture of two or more compounds. An example of a chemical compound is Table Salt: Sodium chloride.

COMPOUND, DIFFERENTIAL MOTION. The bobbin on a fly or roving frame may have at the beginning of the winding any desired speed. The entire speed of the bobbin should be thought of as being in two parts—the first bobbin speed is equal to that of the flyer while the second is the excess speed, and this will vary as the bobbin size increases. Thus, it is necessary to have both parts of bobbin speed come from two different sources thereby making control and regulation easier to handle. Before reaching the bobbin, however, the power from the two sources may be combined.

The mechanism to control speeds is known as the differential motion which, because of an epicyclic train of gears of various speeds, it is possible to keep a constant winding speed while the circumference of the bobbin is constantly increasing as the stock winds onto it. The British call this complex, intricate action the "box of tricks."

COMPOUND FABRICS. Those which have more than one warp and one filling in construction. Tubular cloths are included in the term. Examples include Frenchback, pillow casing, mail-bagging, suspendering, and apparel fabrics on the order of beaver, melton, kersey, broadcloth, plaid-backs, chinchilla.

COMPOUND SHED. A type of shed in a loom arranged so that when an end is to remain in the bottom shed for more than pick, it will lie dormant in the bottom. Ends that are in the top shed on one pick and are to remain there for the next pick are lowered only halfway and then carried back to the top section of the shed.

COMPOUND TWILLS. A construction that combines two or more combinations of weave in the pattern—twilled baskets, braided twills, entwining twills, etc. Each weave is distinctive in the construction of this type.

COMPRESS. A modern warehouse which uses high-powered presses to make high-density, standard cotton bales from gin bales.

COMPRESS BALE. See BALE, BALES, AMERICAN COTTON.

COMPRESSIBILITY. The ease in squeezing a fabric; this may be soft or hard, high, or low.

CONCENTRATE. To intensify or make a chemical "strong," by removing a diluting or adulterating substance. Examples are concentrated acids such as hydrochloric, nitric, sulphuric, and concentrated ammonia.

CONCENTRATION. The strength of a particular solution. It can be reported in terms of percentage, grains per gallon, or other measures.

CONCILIATION. Third-party attempt to reconcile the differences that exist between a company and its employees, and their union.

CONCORDIA WOOL. One of the best of South American wools, it is shipped from the city of this name in northern Argentina. Some Uruguayan wool is also shipped from this port.

CONDENSATION. The separation of water from milk is the evaporation of one constituent from a mixture of materials, really the opposite of condensation. For example, water is evaporated from a wet towel while water is condensed from hot air moisture on a cold towel or cold wall. Many types of plastics are made by condensation. In this action, it is not the separation as in taking water from milk, but is the actual splitting off the oxygen from one compound and the OH from another compound. The O and the OH unite to form water. Water does not become present until actual condensation takes place. After one chemical has lost its O, and the other its OH, the two molecules can then unite by combining their terminals that are now left "hungry" for a partner.

Incidentally, the "two compounds" can be molecules of the same chemical structure as long as that structure has terminals which can lose either the O or OH radicals.

CONDENSER. See OPENER, COTTON; OPENER PICKER.

CONDENSER AND GAUGE BOX. See BREAKERS, COTTON.

CONDENSER CARD. The last card in a set of wool cards. It is equipped with a tape condenser device at the delivery end so as to deliver the stock in a roving form ready for spinning. See Illustrated Section.

CONDENSER COTTON YARN. Cotton yarn which has less than the normal number of turns of twist per inch is passed through water and then given the number of turns it should receive on the twister. The yarn may be singed prior to the second twisting. The yarn is not as even and strong as a two-ply yarn, but is superior to ordinary single-twist yarn.

CONDENSER SHEETING. A sheeting with condenser filling in it, a softly spun, rather bulky filling with counts as low as 5s to 10s in cotton count. This yarn has good coverage but may contain varying amounts of waste matters.

CONDITION. Implies the amount of moisture in cotton; air-dry condition per cent is 6.66 and the maximum amount hygroscopic water per cent is 20.99.

CONDITIONER GILL BOX. In the combing-in-oil method of combing worsted top, there is a box or container set into the machine to hold the emulsion through which the top passes in the gilling-drawing operations. An immersed fluted roller guides the stock through the emulsion when the box is in action.

CONDITIONING. Determination of the true or basic weight of fibers or fabrics by the standard percentages allowed with regard to moisture content. The term also implies the restoration of moisture lost during manipulation or manufacture to fibers and fabrics.

CONDITIONING, FIBER WEIGHT IN. In the conditioning of various textiles that contain oil, it is realized that the oil may become volatile. This would impair the accuracy and repeatability of the conditioned and boil-off tests. To offset this, the fiber test has been developed.

The test is a combination of the conditioned weight and the boil-off tests. For example, a 200-gram sample of raw silk could be made up, tested, and reduced directly in the one operation to the clean, dry fiber. This fiber weight can be mathematically built up to any desired moisture and boil-off content for contractional buying and selling. See Illustrated Section.

CONDITION WEIGHT. Oven-dry weight from the conditioning oven of fiber, yarn, or fabric plus the standard commercial moisture regain added to the dry weight.

CONDUCTING TRUNK, TUBE. A cylindrical, metal tube or trunk, a foot or so in diameter, used to convey cotton from one source to another.

CONDUCTIVITY. Ability to carry electric current.

CONE. 1. The bobbin upon which yarn is wound prior to weaving. 2. A package of yarn wound into a suitable or convenient shape. 3. A tapered cylinder of cardboard, metal or wood around which yarn is wound. 4. An unblocked hat of any shape.

CONE DRAWING. Drawing worsted fibers through machines which are equipped with cones to control major actions; delivers a soft, even slubbing which produces uniform yarn.

CONE DUSTER. A machine used in manipulating wool which beats out loose, foreign, and mechanical matters from the stock. This rugged frame beats the stock by means of a cone-shaped, rotating cylinder against a screen situated underneath.

CONE WINDING. Winding yarn or stock from skeins to paper cones.

CONFEDERATE DYES. During the War Between the States, 1861-1865, cloth was colored with dyes made from bark, berries, leaves, and various plants that grew in fields and forests. Myrtle bushes yielded Confederate gray; the well-known "butternut brown" much used in dyeing uniforms, was obtained from walnut hulls; blue came from indigo plants; brown from oak bark; yellow from cocklebur leaves; black from sumac berries; green from hickory and alum; orange from sassafras, and red from poke berries.

CONGO CLOTH. Trade name for a spun rayon cloth of suiting weight. Usually made in 36-inch width, it is used for men's and women's summer suits, beachwear, ties, and other articles.

CONGO RED. The first artificial dyestuff that would dye cotton directly; discovered by Boettigen in 1884.

CONGRESS CANVAS. Cotton, linen or wool are used to make this plain-weave cloth used for embroidery purposes; ply yarn is used, and the material is quite porous but is very strong.

CONING. Pertinent to textured yarn it is the winding of the yarn onto a cone or some comparable device. See Cone Winding.

CONNAUGHT CLOTH. Cotton embroidery cloth made on small-repeat basket weave.

CONNAUGHT YARN. A loosely twisted, fine woolen yarn of Ireland.

CONSIGNING WOOL. A wool marketing term which is widely practiced when prices at shearing time are not to the liking of the wool grower. The wool is shipped to wool dealers or co-operatives, in the hope that prices may advance before the wool is sold.

CONSTITUENT. A component part referred to usually in the composition of soap powders, etc.

CONSTITUTION CORD. Heavy cotton fabric which has the broadest cord or wale used in fabric construction. Of the corduroy family of fabrics, the repeat is on 12 threads each way, and eight harnesses are used in the loom to weave the material. A layout for the goods might be 42 inches in the reed, 31 inches finished with as many as 300 picks to the inch. Warp counts vary; 16s to 20s yarn used for the filling. The reed and filling vary in that alternate pile picks are securely bound in the cloth to give firmness. The cord or cable effect is brought about by floats which appear some little distance from each other.

CONSTRUCTION. See FABRIC CONSTRUCTION.

CONSTRUCTION LINE. The style lines of a garment, so named because of the need for sewing or constructing the parts together to make a whole.

CONSUMER GOODS. Economic goods that directly or indirectly satisfy wants of human beings, such as food, clothing, shelter, transportation, fuel, tools, accessories, adornments.

CONTACT STAIN. A stain acquired by transfer from one material's touching another article being washed which is giving up color, or staining substance, at the time.

CONTINENTAL COMB. The Heilman or French comber is known by this name.

CONTINUOUS CARD STRIPPING. An automatic method of stripping or cleaning the clothing wire on card rollers while the machine is in action.

CONTINUOUS DYEING. A method of dyeing used whenever long yardages are involved, whereby the goods proceed in an uninterrupted chain from one step to another. Thus, better control is obtained over wetting-out, tension, temperature, bath density, penetration, etc. Many defects such as streaks and shading are minimized.

CONTINUOUS FILAMENT. Regenerated, cellulose derivative or synthetic filament manufactured in a continuous filament form as distinguished from all natural fibers except raw silk,

which have a short staple or length. See Illustrated Section.

CONTINUOUS FILAMENT RAYON YARN. Yarn formed by twisting two or more continuous rayon filaments into a single, continuous strand. See Illustrated Section.

CONTINUOUS SPINNING. This method, developed to speed up the processing of viscose rayon yarns and to eliminate repeated physical handling, results in highly uniform, top-quality yarns with a minimum of defects. The yarn proceeds continuously in streamlined fashion from one treatment to the next without interruption, so that the whole process from the spinneret to the finished twisted yarn takes only a few minutes.

CONTRACTING. Applied to the practice of selling wool prior to its being shorn from the sheep—on the sheep's back. This method of wool marketing is of more importance and broader usage when the demand for wool is strong.

CONTRACTION. Shortening or any decrease in the size of fiber or fabric.

CONTRO. The rounded latex and cut-rubber threads used as a cord and also wrapped with cotton, rayon, silk, or other material, in manufacture of elasticized fabrics. Product of Firestone Tire and Rubber Co.

CONTROL, ALKALI. A physical influence exerted upon the active alkali in solution by certain colloidal elements, whereby fiber and color damages are minimized. Found in soap and detergents.

CONTROL CHAINS. These are used on circular and flat-bed knitting machine equipment of the cylinder and dial type to control machine movements, changes in the stitch, pattern length, color and shape. Essentially, there are two types of chains:

1. Those which control the mechanical movement of the patterning unit.

2. Those which govern actual fabric construction.

As many as seven chains may be used in the flat-bed links and links machine. Three of the chains have direct association with the perforated metal card-patterning unit—moving the Jacquard bar, turning the Jacquard cards, and collecting the jacks. The remaining four chains may relate to stitch setting, color changes, and racking of the needle beds. Each of the links in each of the chains performs a different operation. For example, in the chain which controls the stitch setting the first link may determine whether the stitches are to be set close, medium, firm, or tight.

CONVENT CLOTH. Use is obvious.

The cloth is made of crepe weave to give it a pebbled effect. Light in weight, it is made of wool warp and silk or rayon filling. A piece-dyed fabric.

CONVENTIONAL TWIST. Relative to stretch and textured yarns it means that twisting, setting, and untwisting are done in three stages. Developed by Heberlein Paten Corporation, New York City, and High Point, North Carolina, and Wattwil, Switzerland.

CONVERTED FABRICS. Print cloth, cheesecloth and tobacco cloth form the three basic cottons for conversion into finished goods. Converting embraces bleaching, dyeing, printing, mercerizing, and a host of other treatments to make the commercial fabric of value.

Some converted goods retain the name applied to the gray goods—as broadcloth, chambray, dimity, poplin, sateen. Other goods take on a new name because of some particular type of treatment in the finishing which characterizes the fabric—as Canton flannel, chintz, domett, nainsook, percale, silence cloth, soisette.

CONVERTER. A person or a concern handling gray goods from the loom. The converter gives instructions for the type of finish desired, as well as all other pertinent data, from the time the goods leave the loom until sent to consignee.

The converter must be aware of business trends at all times so as not to be caught short or be burdened with distress merchandise. He, at times, has to create his own market or outlet for the goods.

CONVERTIBLE COLLAR. A straight collar applied to the normal neckline without use of a raised neckband, or with an extremely low neckband, and which may be worn opened or closed. In men's garments it is characterized usually by long points; much used in sports attire.

CONVOLUTIONS IN COTTON. The spiral, ribbonlike effects observed when cotton is viewed under the microscope. Sometimes referred to as "turns of twist." Cotton may have from 150 to 300 of these convolutions per inch; the greater the number, the finer will be the cotton and the higher the count of yarn when manipulated. See Illustrated Section.

COOK COTTON. A large-boll, late-maturing Mississippi cotton which ranges from 1⅛ inches to 1⅜ inches: lint yield is about 28 per cent.

COOL COLORS. They imply pastel shades, with the possible exception of red, which are popular for summer dress goods; much used in cottons and rayons.

COOL DOWN. The cooling of a high temperature washing load either during washing or after drying in order to prevent the setting of wrinkles during the tumbling action.

COOL-OFF PERIOD. The time following the termination of the drying cycle on a washing machine when tumbling continues with heat no longer entering the dryer. Obviously, this reduces the temperature of the goods being treated.

COOMPTAH COTTON. A weak, brownish-tint cotton raised in India and noted for its foreign matter which gives the staple an unclean appearance. Spins to low-quality yarns of 14s or thereabouts from a ¾-inch staple.

CO-OPERATIVE WOOL MARKETING. A method used in about ten major wool-growing states in this country whereby the growers associate to sell their wool co-operatively through a single agency. Most of these local marketing associations are, in turn, members of the National Wool Marketing Corporation, Boston, Mass., to which they consign their wool for sale. Upon receipt of the wool, the Corporation advances money on account and the local organization, in turn, distributes these partial payments to its member growers. Incidentally, Boston is the major wool port and center of activity in wool dealings.

COOSONG, COWSONG. This plain weave, cotton cloth is dyed black and used in the Far East. Pick count is around 80 x 60.

COP. 1. A paper tube upon which thread or yarn is wound. 2. Thread or twine wound into the shape of a hollow cylinder. 3. Filling yarn wound upon a cone-shaped paper tube, carried through the warp shed by the shuttle.

COPANG, COPING. Woolen and worsted fabrics on the heavy side that come in various weaves and colors. Used for men's wear these fabrics may vary as to quality and texture.

COP-CHANGING LOOM. One equipped with an automatic changing device for the filling. The run-out bobbin or cop is ejected from the shuttle and a full, new bobbin is automatically set into the shuttle without causing the loom to stop for the filling change.

COP-COP-YARN. British expression for ply yarn made up of varying colors, qualities and weights of one-ply yarns.

COP-DYED. Yarn dyed in cop form, for use in checks, ginghams, plaids.

COP-DYED SHADY-FILLING YARN. Yarn with shaded effect caused by poor penetration of the dye onto the yarn. Several things may cause the effect such as improper

paper tubes or bobbins, poor winding, irregular yarn tension, and taut winding.

COPE. A full length, liturgical vestment used at benediction and in other liturgical blessings and processions of the Roman Catholic Church. The cope varies according to the function and consequently may be made with any of the liturgical colors. It is rather heavy in weight, made of silk or rayon in compact texture, and can be cleansed.

COPENHAGEN BLUE. This color is low in brilliance and saturation.

COPOLYMER. A mixed or hetropolymer of giant size formed when two or more unlike monomers are polymerized together.

COPOLYMER TEXTILE FIBERS. They are man-made fibers made from copolymers of vinyl of vinylidene compounds and whose chief component makes up 85 per cent or less of the whole, or which consists of more than two compounds. Fibers made with copolymers having more than 85 per cent of the chief component are regarded as fibers of this compound. Dynel made by Union Carbide Corporation, is a staple fiber of a copolymer which contains 60 per cent vinyl chloride and 40 per cent acrylonitrile. It was first produced in 1949; classed as a Modacrylic Fiber.

PeCe-Faser, also a copolymer product, is made in filament form and in bristles. The combination used is 85 per cent vinylidene chloride, 13 to 14 per cent vinyl chloride, and 1 to 2 per cent acrylonitrile. Made by VEB Filmfabrik AGFA, Wolefen, Kreis Bitterfeld, Deutschland (DDR) in Republic of West Germany.

COPPERAS, GREEN VITRIOL. Ferrous sulphate.

COPPER COLOR. Reddish redyellow hue with medium brilliance and saturation.

COPPER ROLLER. A copper roller used to print fabric in which the design or pattern is engraved, etched, or gouged from the roller. The motif is filled with color paste and pressed against the cloth at the point of contact leaving the colored effect. There must be a roller for each color used in the design.

COPPER SULPHATE. Known as blue vitriol and bluestone, $CuSO_4 \cdot 5H_2O$. It is used as an oxygen carrier in aniline black dyeing; for after-treating direct and sulphur dyes on cotton to improve the fastness; and in single baths for logwood dyeing on wool.

COPPING, QUILLING. Winding yarn from a cone, bobbin, tube, or cheese into a cop formation.

COPTIC CLOTHS. See COSTUME,

COP WINDING MACHINE. The frame that winds yarn into small, headless, coreless, cigar-shaped cops or packages.

COPYRIGHT. Protects descriptive or ornamental messages or texts that are included on or with a particular product, textile, or otherwise. The Register of Copyrights in Washington, D.C., grants copyright protection for 28 years; renewal for a second 28-year period may be obtained.

COQUEIRO DE BALA. Brazilian term for the coir or coconut fiber.

COQUILLE. French for handmade laces which feature fan or shell edgings.

COQUITA FIBER. A strong bark fiber obtained from *Jubaca spectabillis*, a palm tree in Chile. Used for making cables and ropes, the product compares well with hemp in its durability.

CORA, CORAH SILK. A name given to an East Indian handkerchief fabric which is featured by a colored motif on a creamy white background. The silk is durable and launders well.

CORAH GRASS. A bast fiber raised in India and used in matting.

CORAL. A color which is yellowish red in hue, of high saturation and medium brilliance.

CORALINE. CORALLINE. An Italian needlepoint lace that is rather heavy and uses a coral-like motif in the flatpoint work.

CORAM. A rugged, bleached linen fabric used in Germany; filling yarn is finer than warp yarn in this twillweave material.

CORAVIA. A strong, lustrous, rather smooth bast fiber obtained in British Guiana and used for bowstrings, cordage, nets, twine, etc.

CORD. 1. When two or more ply yarns are twisted together they are sometimes known by this term. 2. Also known as the cordonnet, it is the raised, puffed or padded area in a motif in needlepoint lace. 3. Referred to as a wale, the term is used in certain fabrics made with a raised or corded effect —as Bedford cord, bengaline, certain transportation fabrics, Ottoman, piqué, officer's belt webbing, Russian cord shirting. 4. Short for corduroy. 5. Decorative woven fabric or braid used in the home, on epaulets worn by military officers and for regimental and other citations.

CORDAGE. A general term which includes banding, cable, cord, rope, string, and twine made from fibers. In present-day meaning cordage refers to the product made from abaca (manila), cantala, henequen, palma, phormium, or piteira. In addition, Dacron and nylon are now popular in the manufacture of some cordage. Nylon is used in mooring ropes since it has the property of desirable stretch; Dacron is popular but has less stretch than nylon. A nylon cordage is popular among boat painters since it is made so that it floats and supports the flooring upon which the painter stands. Filament nylon rope is as long as the rope itself and the number of filaments in a rope varies with the diameter of the article. There is also a spun nylon and a spun Dacron cordage which finds much use in maritime circles.

CORDAGGIO. Third and fourth grades of Naples hemp. See PAESANO.

CORDAL. A coarse French canvas made from bast fiber tow and used for aprons.

CORDALINE, CORDELINE. Some fabrics that have a strong selvage attain this strength by the use of silk, linen, or nylon yarns which are set in to give a corded effect. Noted chiefly in certain silks.

CORDAT SERGE. An all-wool fabric that is heavily fulled and milled, and used as work clothing in France; really a heavy serge fabric with several grades or qualities available.

CORD BRAID. A round braid which has a core running up the middle of the article.

CORD DE CHINE. Merino wool warp and silk filling are used in this lightweight dress goods. Plain weave is used, with two ends weaving as one to produce a fine but distinctive cord effect in the vertical direction.

CORDE. French for cord, rope, thread, or strong yarn.

CORDED. Plain-woven goods which show stripes made by thick cord ends spaced according to some plan or motif. Cord ends for the effect in the warp are usually woven from an extra beam known as the cord beam. The effect is also possible in the filling direction, as noted in bengaline, grosgrain, Ottoman, and heavy faille.

CORDED PIPING. It is used as an edging on bathrobs, beachrobes, bedspreads, slip covers, and other articles. It is made by inserting the cord between a narrow bias strip and stitching it securely in place. It is then applied to the edge of the garment the same as plain piping or it can be included in the seam. Corded piping comes in various colors and thicknesses.

CORDED TUCKS. Tucks which have a cording enclosed between the folds. It is used as a style effect whenever tucking is the outstanding feature of the style.

CORD EFFECT. Rib effects in the warp direction on cloth are called cord; filling-direction rib effects are referred to as rep or repp.

CORDELAT. A French woolen made on a small twill weave and given a finish to simulate flannel. See MOLLETON, FLANNEL.

CORDELLA. A handmade lace made with net ground and motifs outlined with heavy thread.

CORD FABRIC. In reality, this is not a fabric but merely an interlacing of about 26 ends of cable yarn with two to six single-ply yarn filling picks per inch. This loose netlike construction is run into the rubber solution in the manufacture of automobile tires. Incidentally, the number of layers of cord fabric determines the ply of the tire.

CORDING FOOT. A one-sided, sewing machine presser foot. It is used when sewing close to an edge whenever a cord is used.

CORDON. A decorative cord, lace, braid, or insignia used on costumes for embellishment and fastening purposes.

CORDONCILLAS. Low-quality, plain-weave cloth worn by the Indians of Central America; comes in the natural or in the bleached condition.

CORDONNET. 1. Crochet, knitting, or embroidery silk or nylon yarn composed of three threads. Each thread is made up of four to eight filaments of Z-twist, and the three threads are then plied together with S-twist. 2. Originally the term was applied to Alençon lace, in which the raised outer edge of the material was made of horsehair that was entirely covered by stitching. If this outer edge was ornamented with loops, it was called couronné (crowned).

CORDON YARN. A knitting yarn made from a cotton yarn plied with a low-grade woolen or wool-waste yarn.

CORDOVA. Long, coarse Argentine wool used mostly for carpet stock.

CORDOVAN LEATHER. Named for Cordova, Spain, the term now implies the leather made from the shell of horse butts. The rear portion, incidentally, begins about 24 inches from the tail. Cordovan is used for shoe uppers and leather puttees. The leather is nonporous and long-wearing.

CORD STITCH. A novelty needle stitch used in lace manufacture made by interlacing or intertwining one thread around another.

CORD STRIPES. Plain-weave derivation cloths in which a cord or a rib is used in the pattern, very often a two-beam warp construction. Examples include some dimity, Cheviot shirting, summer suiting fabric, Russian cord shirting.

CORD TIRE. Types of tire in general use consisting of built-up layers of rubberized cord plies covered with a breaker strip and thread rubber, and having a rubber-covered steel cable built in at each side where the tire fits onto the rim.

CORDURA. Formerly a rayon-process yarn with great strength, used for tire cords. It is now the registered trademark for industrial nylon fiber and twine. Product of E.I. duPont de Nemours & Co., Inc.

CORDUROY. A cut-filling pile fabric made of cotton which has hardwearing qualities. When woven with a plain-weave back the fabric is known as a "tabbyback" corduroy; with a twill weave back it is called a "Genoa-back" corduroy. This cloth is woven in about the same manner as velvet except that the pile-filling picks are bound by the warp yarns to form straight lines of floats thus producing the ribbed surface effect in the finished material. Velvet, however, is a warp-pile cloth.

There are several types of corduroy—fine reed for pinwale fabric, eight-shaft corduroy, thickset, wide wale, constitution, cable, etc. The cloth, which can now be made from fibers other than cotton, usually is made with one warp and two fillings. One filling weaves tightly to form the body of the goods, while the other one weaves with the warp for a short distance and then floats over the next three, four or more picks so that the face of the cloth, when finished, will give the appearance of a filling rib construction.

Cutting of the filling pile yarn is done after the length, bolt, or "cut" has been taken from the loom. Preceding cutting, a solution of glue is applied to the back of the fabric to prevent the filling pile yarn from being pulled out during actual cutting.

The floats of filling yarn are cut through the center by means of a series of split needles and sharp circular steel disks which extend for the width of the goods. Each split needle has its respective disk inserted in an upright position, and in the action the disk, guided by the split needle, cuts the pile yarn thereby making the "rounded-bush" effect observed in the material.

The needles fit under the respective groups of filling pile yarn and raise this yarn, thereby allowing each needle to raise its yarn group so that the circular disk can do its cutting to perfection.

The glue used to prevent drawing out of the filling yarns is then removed. The face of the fabric is then subjected to a series of brushings (wet and dry), singeings and waxing operations to give filling pile the form of a velvet-like cord in the vertical direction.

Novelty corduroy may have its rib lines (hills and dales) in both warp and filling directions.

Uses for corduroy include aviation coats, breeches, coatings of several types, hunting apparel, evening wear, slacks and trouserings, slip covers, headgear, etc. See CORDUROY WEAVE, VELVET, VELVETEEN.

CORDUROY WEAVE. One type of weave could be completed on 9 picks and 6 reed dents with the use of five harnesses in the loom. The structure could be: 68 warp ends of 2/28s cotton yarn per inch. Two hundred and thirty-four filling threads of 1/16 cotton yarn per inch—raw from the loom.

The "float filling ends," those that float over 6 warp ends, are cut after weaving and form plush warp-wise cords. The filling yarn is composed of a fine soft-twist yarn, and the tufts are beaten-up and brushed in the finishing in order to open up the cut ends of the filling. The material is often waxed and singed to remove any long, protruding fibers.

CORD YARNS. When six, eight, or more yarns are plied or twisted together they are known as cord yarns. Uses include duck, canvas, tire fabrics, webbing, conveyer belting.

CORE YARN. A yarn in which one type of fiber is twisted around a previously spun yarn—usually another type of fiber. The previously spun yarn constitutes the core and is concealed by the outer layer of the wrapped fiber.

"CORFAM". A manmade "breathable shoe-upper material for use in high fashion shoes." Following two hundred man-years of research by Du Pont, this poromeric material is neither plastic nor coated fabric but a complex, interrelated chemical structure that varies in character within its own composition, allowing it to breathe freely and wear well while flexing easily. It is noted for its ease of care, scuff and abrasion resistance, indifference to weather, colorfastness, lightness of weight, and shape retention. It comes in continuous lengths and is supplied in rolls of smooth surface, textured grain, or napped surface, soft to the touch. "Corfam" was made in Old Hickory, Tennessee, and is a registered trademark. On March 16, 1971 du Pont announced its discontinuance of

this product and that production would be terminated near the end of 1971.

CORFU LACE. A coarse lace used locally and named for this city in Greece.

CORING. Removing of samples of fiber from a bag or bale of wool. These samples are tested in laboratories for determination of the yield or clean content.

CORK CARPETS. Made of cotton or jute yarn, this coarse, plain-weave material has a layer of ground cork cemented over it.

CORK LACE. Originally a lace made only in County Cork, Ireland. Now a term used for Irish lace in general.

CORKSCREW CLOTH. This worsted staple used for suiting, coating, and spat cloth is made from a twill-rib weave. The construction is such that warp threads appear only on the face of the goods. The term is a misnomer and its derivations are doubtful. The twill weaves used are called corkscrew weaves to distinguish them from other combination twill effects. The cloth has high texture, is compact, and has a slight nap which is the result of considerable fulling and felting of the goods prior to napping. Cotton filling is often used in the fabric construction.

CORKSCREW, HEAVY. Ends that are found in silk yarn, and are about twice the diameter of the ordinary thread being used. They will cause much trouble unless removed. See CORKSCREW YARN.

CORKSCREWS IN RAW SILK. Places where one or more cocoon filaments are longer than the others and give the spiral effect of a corkscrew.

CORKSCREW TWILL FABRIC. A fabric made from any of the major fibers, and having a pronounced diagonal twill line which tends to obliterate the filling yarn altogether. Wales in the cloth may be narrow, medium, or wide.

CORKSCREW TWIST. A place in yarn or cord where an uneven twist gives a corkscrew appearance. In heavy silks, corkscrew twists are often more than twice the diameter of the yarn used and cause much trouble unless removed.

CORKSCREW WEAVES. They are made from low-angled twill constructions. Dependent on the type of weave used, the angles may run 27, 20, or 15 degrees. The minimum number or harnesses that can be used is five, and the maximum number is thirteen.

CORKSCREW YARN. 1. Made by twisting two ends of unequal thickness together for some particular effect in a cloth. 2. A yarn made by twisting

two yarns together at an uneven rate on the twister. 3. Yarn made by twisting two yarns of unequal twist. 4. Yarn made by twisting two ends in the opposite direction. 5. Ply yarn in which one of the singles has worked loose or slack and has twisted itself around the taut end or ends; gives the appearance of a corkscrew.

CORNSTARCH. Maize is the base for this starch used in finishing fabrics; has a harsh feel, gives a thick paste and does not become watery after long boiling.

COROJO. A West Indian palm tree which yields a strong bast fiber whose full name in "Pita de Corojo." Used in local consumption for rope, twine, bagging, and other purposes.

COROMANDEL. Coarse, plain-weave cotton cloth made in England for the African trade.

CORONATION CLOTH. Originated in England and was first seen at the Coronation of King Edward the Seventh. In wool and unfinished worsted suitings of solid, ground staple colors, it is a cloth upon which there are single-thread stripes, or decorations that run lengthwise. The stripes are about one inch apart and a gold or tinsel yarn is used.

The "Queen's Mourning"—black cloth with a white hairline—was a contemporary cloth. A variation of Coronation cloth was noted in this country some years ago. The fancy yarns were red, white, and blue, and the fabric was known as "Inauguration cloth."

CORONIZING. A finish given some glass textiles to provide mellowness, soft hand, good draping qualities, and wrinkle resistance. This resin finish which is applied at very high heat is a trade-mark name of Owens-Corning Fiberglas Corporation.

COROSAL FIBER. A strong fiber obtained from the leaves of the tree of this name. Raised in Cuba and Central America, the fiber is used for cord, matting, rope. Also known as corojo and coyol.

CORRECTED GRAIN. See SNUFFED FINISH.

CORRIEDALE. A new breed from New Zealand in which the wool and mutton qualities are highly valued in Australia, America, and Japan. The fleece weighs about 12 pounds and sorts from 3/8 to 1/2 blood. Uniformity of the clip is a problem with this stock, which shows a shrinkage of 50 to 55 per cent. Quality is in the 58–60s range.

CORRIENTES, CORRIENTIES. Name for this province in Argentina, this crossbred wool runs from 50s to 56s quality. Harsh in feel, it is however, a rather springy type, thus making it ideal as a knitting yarn.

CORRODE. A chemical action which involves a change in the surface of a metal, such as rusting.

CORROSIVE. Chemical agents on cottons and linens which cause a destruction of the fabrics. Corrosive action may be found in household preparations in certain medicines and pharmaceuticals.

CORSET. A close-fitting, reinforced undergarment, reaching from the bust to below the hips, worn by women to support the body or mold the figure.

CORSET OR BRASSIERE CLOTH. Rugged, strong cloth, high in tensile strength and often made in Jacquard motifs. This well-textured fabric is finished in colors that range from pink to flesh. Some fabric is made with small, intricate designs on dobby or swivel looms. Uses are for corsets and brassières; cotton, rayon, Orlon, and nylon yarns may be used. Coutil is often referred to as corset cloth, but is usually lower in price and in texture.

CORSET OR FOUNDATION BROCADE. Usually a cotton cloth made with a warp-effect satin weave, mercerized, and has small Jacquard effects in it. The filling yarn may be rayon, nylon, etc., since the effects obtained may show to better advantage than in all-cotton fabric. The effect comes as the result of the floats in the satin weave being arranged to give the desired motif. Known in the trade as "pick-and-pick brocade" the filling is one pick of white and then a pick of flesh or pink color. Textures range from 100 to 160 in the warp and from about 100 to 140 or higher in the filling. Some of this fabric can be made on dobby looms; cut or bolt lengths are around 50 to 60 yards long.

CORSICAN WOOL. A fairly good wool raised in Corsica which varies in color from gray to brown to black. Used for carpeting.

CORTEX. The major fibrous structure of animal fibers.

CORTICAL CELLS. These make up the outer or investing layer of animal fibers. See CORTEX.

CORTOLON. A stretch nylon yarn made by Courtaulds, Ltd., England.

CORUNNA STRIPES. British term for lightweight cottons made with plain stripes an inch or so apart.

CORVAL. This white staple fiber, like other cellulosic fibers, is resistant to acids, bleaching agents, scouring and laundering agents, and common solvents. Corval fabrics do not degrade quite as readily as other cellulosic fabrics in soil burial tests; they still, however, have low resistance against rot and mildew attack.

Corval found use, when blended with other fibers, in knitwear, and woven goods for apparel. It is no longer on the market.

COSMOS FIBER. Continental term for a waste fiber obtained from flax, hemp, and jute rags; used as substitute wool fiber.

COSMOS YARN. Yarn made from the waste of hemp, jute, linen.

COSSACK STYLE. Waist-length jacket made with a straight front closure from the neck to the bottom and with a turn-down collar similar to a regular shirt collar.

COSSAS. Indian cotton cloth, plain woven, which comes in many grades; texture is around 56 x 60 with about 44s yarns used. When spelled COSSAR, the term means a coarse, printed cotton material.

COST OF LIVING. The amount of money an individual must spend to maintain a given standard of living.

COSTUME, AMISH. Peculiar to the Pennsylvania Dutch Country, it is worn by the Amish, Dunkards, and Mennonites. When worn by women, the garb consists of a plain habit consisting of a skirt, basque, and bonnet, usually in black and other somber colors. These garments are tied on since they are devoid of hooks and eyes, fasteners, zippers, et al.

COSTUME, BULGARIAN. Worn by peasants for centuries, this costume includes oriental types of embroidery, alike on both sides, and executed on coarse linen garments in flat stitches of gold, silk, or silver threads. The effect has been modified so that it is even used today in bright-colored accessories, household furnishings, and for some blouse effects.

COSTUME, CHINESE. Baishin is a sleeveless vest worn by men and women. Hsieh refers to the fabric or satin slippers worn by Chinese women; if made of fabric it is highly embellished with embroidery. Chang Shan is the long gown worn by Chinese men and Ma Qua is the jacket worn over the gown, usually in black or some very dark color. Shan is the jacket while Koo means the trousers worn by the Chinese and the combination is comparable with our pajamas.

COSTUME, CLERICAL. According to Roman Catholic canon law, the ordinary dress, that is suits, coatings, etc., of those in major and minor orders is black. With special permission white may be used in certain missionary areas and countries. Dress also includes the Ro-

man collar and cassock.

COSTUME, COLONIAL. Applied to the strictly characteristic dress of the Colonial Period in the United States from 1607 to 1776. Styles covered by the term include English Cavalier, Puritan, Quaker, and Restoration, worn in the different colonies between these dates. Speaking in a more general way, the costume in the late 18th century was known for the looped-up full skirt, quilted petticoat, tight bodice, and low neck. It was adorned with laces, puffs, and ruffles, and worn with powdered, high hair dress. The so-called Colonial shoes, still popular at times, are low-cut and embellished by use of a buckle.

COSTUME, EGYPTIAN. The characteristic dress of the Egyptian male was for many centuries a white linen loincloth and/or the short skirt. The narrow, ankle-length tunic and long mantle featured the garb for females. Also used were wigs of human hair or wool, often surmounted by elaborate headdresses, wide circular collars of beads or fabrics; and rich jewelry. Fabrics of linen and wool either in pure white, brightly colored motifs, or a single color were favored. Perfumes and cosmetics, particularly coloring around the eyes, eyelash treatment effects, etc. were greatly used by the Egyptian women.

COSTUME, ELIZABETHAN. Type of dress worn during the reign of Queen Elizabeth I, Queen of England 1558-1603. Born in 1533, a daughter of King Henry VIII and his second wife, Ann Boleyn, Elizabeth was the last of the Tudor line in England. Features of the clothing worn during the period of "The Virgin Queen" were wide skirts of rich fabrics, made mainly in Italy, France, and Spain, worn over the farthingale; low narrow corseted waistlines, with a pointed stomacher; low necklines; large, wire-supported ruff; and full, slashed and puffed sleeves. The Mary Stuart cap was the last word in headgear. See Farthingale, Mary Stuart Cap.

COSTUME, HISTORY OF.

OUTLINE

1. INTRODUCTION.
2. HISTORY OF COSTUME.
   I. Oriental Period: Egyptians, Assyrians, Persians, Hebrews, 3000 B.C. to the Caesarean Era.
   II. Classical Period: Greeks, Romans, 1500 B.C. to A.D. 476.
   III. Germanic Period or Gallo-Roman Period: 500 B.C. to A.D. 476.
   IV. Franco-Merovingian Period: 476 to 752.
   V. Carolingian Period: 752 to 987.
   VI. Capetian Period: 987 to 1328.

Man, in many ways, is the great exception in the realm of living creatures. Among most of the other genre, through no desire on their own part, the male of the species is the gaudier or has the more elaborate adornment since he, instinctively, is the aggressor in the race for "boy gets girl." For *Homo sapiens,* perhaps because he is a thinking man, the situation has been reversed since the beginning of civilization.

True, there have been times when the male has worn pastel shades of elaborate materials, lavishly embellished with laces and embroidery, but his wife has always out-glamoured him. Then the pendulum would swing to the other extreme, and male attire would become as drab as that of Jenny Wren. Today, once again, the male is breaking out of his chrysalis and is attempting to emulate the butterfly—at least in what he dons for sportswear.

THE HISTORY OF COSTUME may be traced through various ages or periods in world history. The first garb worn by men was made of animal skins. This was followed, in due course of time, by the use of pressed or felted goat's hair and sheep's wool,

in the colder areas of the world, while fabrics of linen, silk, and cotton provided body covering for those who dwelt in the warmer sections. Sometimes the body and/or fabrics were stained by leaves and berries.

In colder climates, dress shape was of the pelt hung from the shoulders over the body; the various parts of the skins were held together by strips of tough skin and muscle.

In the warmer sections, the first garments consisted of a cloth made of grass or reeds, or of linen or cotton suspended from the hips to the knees. A belt or girdle was used to hold the material in place.

The women of the colder areas often wore, in addition to the foregoing, a fur or leather jacket or covering for greater warmth. In the warmer areas, women were addicted to long, flowing garments for greater comfort.

As time progressed, the dress of early civilizations began to express the spirit, temperament, customs, and traditions of the various peoples or tribes. The three earliest eras in the history of costume may be classed as Oriental, Classical and Germanic.

THE ORIENTAL PERIOD: This is represented by the dress of the Egyptians, Assyrians, Persians, and Hebrews. The Egyptians apparently contributed more to the history of costume than the other three nations. This period began with the Old Kingdom, which flourished in the years 2830–2530 B.C., coinciding with the development of stone architecture, and ended with the Byzantine-Coptic Era, A.D. 395–638. This span of time included the following: the Middle Kingdom Period; the New Kingdom Period; the Late Period, which included the building of Carthage; the Persian Era; the Ptolemaic Period; and the Roman Period, ranging from about 30 B.C. to A.D. 395. The Christianization of Egypt and the Age of Cleopatra, 69 to 30 B.C., are included in the Roman Period.

Using the Egyptian mode of dress as the example, it would appear that the people wore much linen fabric which was draped in a long, circular effect to cover the lower half of the body. Fabric lengths varied, and the folds in the cloth were the forerunner of the skirt of today. Another item of apparel at this time was the triangular, short, plaited petticoat which was a forerunner of the present-day kilt worn by the Scots.

Later on in the Egyptian Era, men and women wore over this skirt effect a loose, flowing garment which extended from the neck to the feet. Higher-textured linens and cottons ap-

peared in due time and these materials were worn by the higher castes. Loops of fabric, belts, or girdles, and draped folds became popular. Ornamentation and soft collars made their debut in the latter part of the Oriental Period.

THE CLASSICAL PERIOD: Includes the dress of the Greeks and the Romans. The period began with the Pre-Hellenic Era, 2800–1200 B.C., and lasted through the Homeric Era into the Persian Wars and the conquest of Greece by the Romans, 146 B.C., and terminated with the age of Aristotle, 384–322 B.C.

The Greeks had plain, simple tastes in apparel and did not adopt any of the highly colored and embellished costumes of the Oriental nations. The dress of the Greeks consisted of a garment made of a rectangular piece of fabric which was measured to be both twice the height and the width of the body. The cloth was folded and allowed to drape from the left shoulder where it was fastened at first by a thorn and later on by clasps, pins or buttons. A broad cloaklike piece of fabric was worn in loose fold form by men of higher rank.

The clothing of men and women was about the same except that the latter wore theirs in somewhat looser form and with more grace. White cotton or linen fabric was the favored fabric but, as time went on, purple and gold colorings became prime favorites.

The Roman costume was on the order of the Grecian attire and at first consisted of a single garment, called a tunic. The men, in time, adopted the loose garment known as a toga which was thrown in folds about the person. Many women also wore comparable attire plus a shawl which was large enough in measurement to cover the entire body.

In the halcyon days of the Romans, during both the Empire and the Republic, clothing was considered expensive and those who could afford to do so went to extremes with woolen, fine cotton, linen and silk fabrics, all of which were elaborately trimmed. Jewelry and personal ornamentation were favored by women of the times.

THE GERMANIC PERIOD may be also known as the Gallo-Roman Period, the third major period in dress attire. The period began with the first appearance of the Gauls around 500 B.C., and may be said to have ended around the year A.D. 450. That part of Europe which is now France was formerly known as Gaul, and it was conquered by the Romans under Caesar in 51 B.C. The hordes of Franks crossed the Rhine into Gaul in A.D.

276, and the French Kingdom was set up by Clovis in A.D. 486.

The Romans introduced their customs, manners, traditions, and dress to the Gauls with some modifications. Gallic women, after the conquest, wore many and elaborate costumes. Wealth may have been estimated by the number of costumes owned by the individual.

The high points of the era in women's wear included the following:

1. The tunic reached to the ground and was gathered by a belt or girdle at the waist; a band was used to adjust it to the bosom. The garment fell in folds, and only the top of the footwear could be seen.

2. Boneless corsets supported the bosom.

3. Some women wore a chemise of cotton, linen, or silk, often scalloped around the edge.

4. Embroidered aprons made their debut, and a veiling or mantilla was used to cover the face or to serve as a scarf for the head.

5. Plain and embroidered handkerchiefs came into vogue, and there was considerable use of the narrow fabric now known as ribbon.

6. Women went in for much coloring and design in dressing gowns and robes of various types. Ceremonial robes were very vivid with color and embroidery.

THE FRANCO-MEROVINGIAN PERIOD, A.D. 476–752: Rome, as an empire, fell in A.D. 476, and Clovis, as previously stated, established the French kingdom ten years later. The Germanic tribes of Franks, Vandals, and Goths established themselves after the collapse of the Roman Empire. Clovis, a Frank, made Paris his capital. He did all he could to stifle everything Roman, particularly in dress. Frankish women wore a long black gown with an opening for the head and slits for the arms. A girdle held the gown in place; arms and the bosom were mostly uncovered. A piece of cloth was wrapped around the man's body, and it was fastened over the right shoulder. The use of color, embroidery and splendor in dress was very slow in progress among these peoples.

In the latter part of the era, knee-length trousers, tunics held at the waist by girdles, leggings, strapped shoes, short mantles or cloaks, and hoods or small caps made their appearance.

THE CAROLINGIAN PERIOD, 752–987: Two of the great historical happenings of the era were the reign of Charlemagne and the Treaty of Verdun. The Kingdom of the Franks was now well established, and time could be given to other than martial mat-

ters. Dress became more elaborate and richer under the kings of the era. Men wore a short linen tunic, which was worn under the well-known woolen tunic. Matching embroidery was much used on long, flowing sleeves. Precious stones and girdles of gold and silver came into popular favor. Fabrics were made of better texture, and the surface effect was improved on wool, silk, linen, and cotton.

THE CAPETIAN PERIOD, 987–1328: This included the Crusades, travels of Marco Polo and the rise of Gothic art. To about 1100 the era is often known as the Feudal Period. Clothing of this era, chiefly that worn by women, was form-revealing. Complete neck coverage was popular, while the long tunic was fastened at the waist and closed at the wrist.

Following the First Crusade, 1095, kimono sleeves made their appearance. A type of stocking began to replace the time-worn legging. The stocking was made of fabric cut to fit the leg. Shoes were of the pointed type while hats appeared square in shape; mantles became longer and cumbersome. Men appeared in short trousers, forerunner of the modern knickerbockers; these were worn underneath the long linen tunic and the outer tunic which was unlike the type worn in prior centuries.

It was during the latter part of this period that the bliaud or transformed tunic made its appearance. The bliaud had fullness in the skirt caused by the use of gores at the sides of the garment. Veils were used to partially conceal the flowing hair which was in vogue at the time.

HISPANO-MORESQUE PERIOD, 711–1500: The Saracens conquered Spain in 1711. Of all Islamic textiles, those woven in medieval Spain ranked foremost in interest today. Sericulture seems to have been unknown in Spain before the Mohammedan conquest— yet, shortly afterwards, great quantities of raw silk were brought into Spain, and it was not long before Spanish silks were in great demand throughout Europe.

The creation of the Western Umayyad Caliphate led to new and friendly relations with Syria, and from this came a great exchange of ideas, commerce, goods, and fashions. The tiraz, a fine gauzelike fabric, became popular, and much of it was produced on Spanish looms. Elaborate tapestry borders were woven in silk and gold threads. By the ninth century Spain was making good strides in silk manufacture.

Although there are many Hispano-Moresque fabrics designed with animal

motifs, and some few with designs of the human body, on the whole the textile design of this era seemed to be limited to geometric and arabesque motifs, which predominated in all Moorish crafts. Their appeal is due largely to the jewel-like quality of the colors. Many silks were made with gold or silver threads interspersed throughout the fabric.

The thirteenth century, often referred to as "The Greatest of Centuries," brought out in Spain a wide variety of the star and lacéria motifs which predominated. In the fifteenth century, while still elaborating horizontally striped geometric patterns, there arose the idea of combining these with Kufic inscriptions in bands or cartouches. This led to the Mudejar style in which there was a clever blending of Gothic and Moorish motifs.

This style survived the Fall of Granada in 1493, while the pure Moorish style found a last nostalgic expression in certain fabrics woven in Morocco in the sixteenth and seventeenth centuries.

In the sixteenth century the Spanish were influenced by the doleful, gloomy Philip II. Somber dignity and conservativeness of line and color were in vogue during the last half of this century. Black velvet, considered an item of great smartness, was favored among the courtiers. Pins, a Spanish invention, were put to use. This time is known as the Age of the Spanish Cloak. It was of the usual shape, semicircular, short-waisted or hip-length. For travel or for older men, it was cut long to the ankles. The collar was rather wide and rounded over the top. Muffs became fashionable for women.

Thus, after eight centuries of rule by the Saracens, little by little the Spaniards regained their country, but the Moors, who possessed a much higher culture, had left an indelible influence on their living, art, customs, manners, and dress. They gave to Europe the ruche, the ruff, the short cape, and the corset; the hoop, the bombast style of the padded doublet and trunk hose, followed by the unpadded trunks or breeches. Silk-knit stockings were a Spanish invention and for many years the Spanish hosiery surpassed that made elsewhere.

THE MIDDLE AGES, 1100 to about 1600: Also known as the Moyen Age. Various historians have taken different views as to when it actually began. The usual dates seem to be from the Fall of Rome in A.D. 476 to either 1500 or 1600. Thus the Franco-Merovingian, the Carolingian, and the Capetian are really a part of the Moyen Age. Considering the year 1100 as a beginning for the purposes of costume design, the changes of major import up to about 1550 include the following:

1. The tendency to overdress; women wore long, tight-fitting robes and gowns with a decorated band or collar. Large hoods to which were attached flowing veils were very popular. Women wore external corsets made of silk with elaborate decoration interspersed throughout.

2. Fancy headdresses and accessories were very common.

3. Sleeves were slashed at the shoulder to reveal undergarments. Furs and velvets were worn indoors for warmth.

4. Clothing for men was elaborate—breeches, coats, shoes, and stockings, greatcoats. Long sleeves were in fashion for men.

5. All garments were stiffly padded and were hot, uncomfortable and cumbersome.

6. People in the warmer nations wore loose, flowing dresses made of soft-textured fabrics featuring wide sleeves, square necklines, and girdles at the waist.

The so-called Middle Ages are looked upon today as the springboard for present-day costume design, fashion, and style. As a carry-over from this period to present-day style, the following will prove the point: Today's use of the close-fitting bodices which follow the natural lines of the figure to the hips and are held close to the figure by a band or belt of some sort. In addition, we find the free use of embroidery, the use of a girdle, and the revival, periodically, of a great many of the favorite fashions taken from the era of the Middle Ages.

ITALIAN GOTHIC, 1100–1300: At this time, the bliaud, the full over-tunic of the men, had shortened to the knees and by the latter part of the eleventh century young men wore them "shockingly short." The tunic hung straight or belted, with a skirt of only a few inches below the waist. Hip-length stockings or tights were worn, of bias material, usually red, and with gold and jeweled garters, accompanied by soft leather shoes.

Both sexes wore sumptuous, loose, full mantles. The feminine tunic invariably had a train, and many attempts were made to regulate its length. Early in the fourteenth century there was a new style of feminine robe which brought about a second advent of the corset. (The first use of the corset was in prehistoric Greece.)

FLEMISH TEXTILES AND GERMAN GOTHIC EFFECTS, 1150–1500: Weavers and fabric fullers were in business in Ghent by the tenth century. Flanders was thoroughly Gothic in influence in the fourteenth and fifteenth centuries. Features included the long tunic, slashings, puffings, starched fabrics and the use of steel needles.

By the fifteenth century the best woolens in the world were produced in Flanders. North of the Alps there was a great impetus in textile art. Linen damask tablecloths and napkins to simulate silk damask came in vogue. The flax-growing regions of Saxony, Flanders, and northern France profited from this rise in linen cloths. Holland was to profit in due time.

A special style of design was evolved, possibly by borrowing from the early woodcuts of the Flemish and German schools. The subjects were chosen chiefly from the Old and New Testaments, and often resembled the woven orphreys of Florence. Armorial devices and trophies, sometimes accompanied by lengthy inscriptions, were woven to the taste of patrons.

Red, blue, yellow, black, and white, along with metallic colors were favorites from the standpoint of color and motif, the reds running from pink to deep crimson and bright scarlet.

Cloaks were richly lined and turned back to show the lining of the garment. Decoration, in open-work braid effect, was applied along the seams of the underarm, the sleeve, and breeches. Silver brocade and satin fabrics were used by the upper classes.

It is interesting to note that during the Middle Ages women's arms were never bare. In the fourteenth and the fifteenth century, low necks and very bare shoulders were the vogue, but it was rigid rule that the arms be covered. In the fifteenth century, cuffs concealed the hands to the second knuckle of the fingers while, at the same time, décolletage was hardly above the waistline.

The Italian Gothic Era ended earlier than in other countries of Europe, about 1300. The Renaissance was slower to spread in Flanders and Germany because they were hostile to anything that had a Roman tinge.

THE RENAISSANCE, from about 1475 to 1600: There is little doubt that the latter part of the Moyen Age and the Renaissance intermingled to a considerable degree. There seems to be no exact line of demarcation. Modern fashion is said to be taken mainly from this great era in world history.

In Italy, where this "rebirth of culture" began, it should be kept in mind that art reached the Golden Age under the patronage of the de Medici, Borgia and other reigning princely families. The paintings and sculpture, mostly religious, by such men as Da Vinci, Titian, and Michelangelo, have left us a remarkable picture of the fashions, both male and female, prince and peasant; while the writings of men like Dante and Machiavelli have done much to give some impression of the daily life of the time. The influence of the Italian Renaissance ultimately spread to other European countries, led to the Reformation and an interest in the Humanities, and culminated with the Elizabethan Era in England.

Three historical events of the era, in France, were the Field of the Cloth of Gold, 1520, the Massacre of St. Bartholomew, 1572, and the Edict of Nantes, 1598. This was the era of Rabelais, Clouet, Ronsard, and Montaigne. It was the time of other world luminaries who have been given historical posterity—Francis I, King of France (1515–1547), the Father of the Silk Industry in France, who established the industry in Lyons, Paris, and other French centers, where it is still flourishing; the age of Anne of Brittany, Catherine de Medici, her daughter-in-law, Marie Stuart, her niece Marie de Medici, Mme. d'Estampes and Diane de Poitiers. Each of the foregoing women still has an influence on present-day fashion and style in the women's wear field.

Historically, this was also the era of the Reformation and Counter Reformation, the era of Luther, The Council of Trent, The Peace of Augsburg, Zwingli, Calvin, Henry IV of France, Henry VIII of England, Queen Mary of England, the daughter of Henry VIII and Catherine of Aragon, Queen Elizabeth, Pope Gregory XIII, Cesare Borgia, St. Ignatius of Loyola, Erasmus and a host of other great figures, men and women, too numerous to mention here.

Some of the outstanding contributions to fashion and style of the era which have influenced present-day attire include:

1. The pourpoint, full-skirted doublet which retained its broad neckline and was cut with a full, knee-length skirt held in at the waist by a sword-type belt.

2. Sleeves were long and roomy, and slashed to permit rich and colored linings to be pulled out between the slashes.

3. Jeweled pins and other costume jewelry were used to add color to the ensemble.

4. Women wore sleeves to the elbow, loose and richly ornamented. The waist was long and pointed. Large skirts were gathered at the waist and trimmed around the bottom with embroidery, often raised, slashed, or cut to show a petticoat of rich fabric. Incidentally, the overskirt and sheer embroidered underskirt of today are

taken from this idea.

5. Catherine de Medici introduced the ruff collar worn at the neck. She was the widow of Henry III, King of France, but was of Italian birth. Thus, it seems only natural that she should have had such a great influence in the fashions of France. Catherine de Medici had a sixth sense when it came to fabrics, and she relied on her native Italy for the importation of the most exquisite materials from that country to make the French people the best dressed in the world at this time, an era of extravagance in dress.

6. During the reign of Henry VIII, King of England, men's dress reached the acme of elaboration and embellishment. The use of plain and untrimmed frills at the neck and the wrists came into vogue, and the general effect seemed to make the lower part of the body rather broad.

7. Mary, Queen of Scots, has given to posterity the well-known Mary Stuart collar.

8. The hoop skirt came into being during this era of lavishness. Stiff cottons were used chiefly to obtain the effect. The long-waisted, pointed bodice effect was also introduced, and it is still popular, at times, in women's dress today.

Louis XIII, 1610–1643, of France, and his Contemporaries, James I (1603–1625) and Charles I (1625–1649), Kings of England, whose reigns are sometimes referred to as the Stuart Period, made the following contributions to the history of costume:

1. The picturesque costumes of the Cavaliers of England and the Mousquetaires of France. Broad velvet hats became the rage. Adorned by an ostrich plume, they were worn over the face of the wearer who usually sported a pointed beard and long, curly locks.

2. Falling, unstarched ruffles of lace and embroidery were favored; shoulder widths were increased by curved epaulets. An ornamented belt supported the sword.

3. Breeches were loose and tied at the knee by means of ribbon. Long gantlets and a short cloak, trimmed with lace and with silk lining, completed the ensemble.

4. "Slashed garments" seemed to be more or less the order of the times, breeches, shoes, skirts, gowns—all were slashed to bring out varying effects.

5. Frilled skirts, tight at the waist, were worn over rich fabric used for petticoating; hips were padded with whalebone or steel.

6. Ruffs were popular with both men and women. Wide-brimmed hats were worn by the men. Overcoats had snug-fitting sleeves.

7. Velvets, damasks, brocades, brocatelles, and other silk fabrics were eagerly sought for by the affluent people of the times.

Louis XIV, 1643–1715: His wife was Maria Theresa of Austria. Known in history as "Le Grand Monarque," he was the son of Louis XIII and he warred with England, Austria, and Spain. The period was one of exaggeration in style; men wore wigs and large, round castor hats trimmed with feathers. The tight-fitting body garment had increased in length and was decorated with gold lace or comparable material. It was buttoned from the neck to the waist. The coat was made without collar or lapel and was open at the neck to show the waistcoat. A lace cravat was carelessly knotted around the throat.

Coat sleeves were rather loose and were turned up so as to be rather short and thus show ruffled shirt sleeves of fine cambric material. Breeches were made of moderate width and were tied at the knees with ribbons. Low shoes replaced high shoes, and gold or silver buckles were in great favor. Toward the end of the period, men's dress did become simpler and more comfortable but elaborate trimmings still held.

The corsage of the women was of the décolleté variety; the bodice was rather pointed and sleeves were made of shorter than elbow length with long folds of lace. Long gloves became fashionable. Skirts were full, rather simple, short in the front and with fullness given at the sides and the back by the use of an overskirt open at the front. The hairdressing of men and women was about the same. The simply arranged curls about the temples which had been fostered by Ninon de l'Enclos were superseded by elaborate headdresses composed of lace, ribbons, and flowers wired to great height and introduced by one of the king's favorites, Mlle. de Fontanges. Muffs were worn by both men and women. Court plaster was used as a "beauty mark." Gloves of kidskin or net replaced the ill-shaped leather gloves of the prior period. The draped bustle was extensively used by women of the day.

France, after the Renaissance had run its course, made a definite move to become the art center of the world. Kings, queens, nobility were all interested keenly in developing things artistic. Textiles received their share of attention. The first great patron of art after the Renaissance was Louis XIV. He fostered many establishments devoted to fine fabrics; his patronage of the Gobelin family was outstanding. He sought skilled textile workers not only from France, but from other countries as well. Louis was very desirous of obtaining expert weavers and encouraged other patrons to do the same.

While the characteristic motif of the Renaissance Period was the repetition of the acanthus plant, the ornament for the capital of a Corinthian column, and vases, the age of Louis XIV brought a refinement of this with motifs of scroll effect in a masculine strain that was classic and serious.

ENGLISH COMMONWEALTH, 1649–1664: It should be recalled that, with the advent of the Commonwealth in England under Oliver Cromwell, the era of John Milton, simplicity ruled and a rigid regime resulted. Because of the religious belief and the revolt against the ornateness of the first Stuart Period, bright colors, embellished materials, fancy cuts in both men's and women's wear, and elaborate hair-dos were banished by law, as were all forms of entertainment and their concomitant fancy dress.

Women wore gray or black, tight-waisted dresses relieved by a white triangular kerchief and tight gray or white bonnets. The men wore gray or black knee breeches with silver buckles, three-quarter length matching coats with white circular collars, and stovepipe hats with narrow brims. They cut their hair, which gave rise to their nickname of "Roundheads."

Silver buckles were worn on the front of these hats while similar large silver buckles adorned their sturdy shoes. It was this type of Puritan garb that came to the New World with the Pilgrims and may be still seen, to some extent today, in the clothes of the Shakers, Mennonites, Amish, and other such sects. We also still see reversions to some of these styles in contemporary fashions.

Louis XV, 1715–1774: He was the king who ceded Canada to England. His Queen was Marie Lecinska. Men's dress retained the knee breeches, the long coat, the doublet and the wig from the period of Louis XIV. These, as time went on, were modified considerably. The skirts of the coat, with pleats at the sides, became fuller and were held out from the body at the sides and the back by the insertion of stiffened materials and whalebone. Both coat and waistcoat were of low-neck cut and revealed the soft, lacy finish of the shirt. Lace ruffles were still conspicuous. Wigs died out by about 1740. Men dressed their hair in a few long curls which fell down the back of neck only, and a black ribbon was used to hold the queue in place.

In women's wear, the draping and lifting of the skirts brought out a silhouette that was broad and broken.

The panier or hoop-skirt effect was much in favor; the draped bustle remained in fashion and was greatly used.

Mme. de Pompadour, the power behind the throne, introduced the combed-back hair style. Bodices were of the décolleté type and were trimmed around the edges with small floral motifs. The paintings of Watteau and the printed cambrics of Oberkampf exemplified the trends of the times. Silk, flowers, fur, gauze, lace, and ribbon were extensively used on skirts and gowns for formal wear. Fabrics were rich in texture and motif and truly represented this era of frills and extravagances.

Louis XVI, 1774–1793: Born in 1754, this grandson of Louis XV was king of France from 1774 until guillotined in 1793. His queen was Marie Antoinette. Men's attire during his reign did not undergo too radical a change from the time of Louis XV.

Coats were cut away at the bottom, skirts lost much of their fullness and flare, while the coat sleeve was made longer and fitted closer to the wrist. High heels became passé, and the tricorne felt or velvet hat became popular with the cocarde or cockade of ribbon, which replaced the feathers formerly in style. The redingote became a favorite with its long swirling skirt effect, long tight sleeves, and shoulder cape effect.

In women's wear, the dress was full, comfortable and loose-fitting. It hung from the shoulders with the back fullness caught into a deep box pleat from the neck to the waist. The polonaise was another favorite dress. This was a one-piece dress with a close, tight waist; the usual short sleeves and a skirt which was draped at the sides into the shape of two broad wings while a third, and somewhat larger, one was at the back. Silk stockings and satin slippers were always shown to advantage.

Flounce effects became extremely popular. The figure became narrower, and the bust and the bustle were exaggerated toward the end of the period.

The years 1789 to 1793 in the reign of Louis XVI are known as the Era of the French Revolution. These few years wrought a complete change in France; art, design, weaving, fabrics, all went through drastic changes. This great turning point in the history of the world is still felt and has done much to promote modern ideas in fabrics and apparel. Simplicity in dress replaced the extravagance, show, and formality of the kings. Men began to wear long trousers in dull and somber colors which were known as "sans culottes" ("without breeches"—i.e. forerunners of the present-day lady's culottes or pedal pushers). Long great coats, cutaway coats, and dark hats also came on the scene. Clothes of the time were arranged poorly, fitted badly, and were form-concealing.

Women of the day wore simple, short-waisted dresses, with a kerchief around the neck which was crossed over the bosom and knotted at the back of the waist.

Directoire Period, 1795–1799: Following the French Revolution there was a three-year span known as the First Republic, 1792 to 1795. English sailors' trousers inspired the new style for men which decreed that these garments reach halfway between the knee and the ankle. By 1793, the trouser reached to the shoe top. Russian boots came into favor. Women's silhouettes were broad and broken, and the exaggeration of the bust made its appearance. Hoops were discarded but hairdressing received much attention. The First Republic was a time of uncertainty and chaos.

The Directoire reverted to the revival of Greek fashion and style. Sheer, transparent materials became popular with women; trailing skirts were slit from the hem to the knee; some were even slit to the waist. Women had their hair cut to current style and took to wearing wigs. The Directoire coat for men came into being; it had a short front with cutaway lines. The period was one in which the economic living standards were low because of the heavy costs of war. Accessories, however, were important.

Consulate Period, 1800–1803: The atrocious fashions and styles of the Directoire Period were abolished, and simple plain clothes, in which white was the favorite color, came into favor. It was the influence of the so-called Neo-Classicists which prevailed. Women wore tunics of color and texture at variance with the foundation dress. Satin, muslin, velvet, and lace were the favorite materials worn. Tunics were not made with any regularity as to length.

Empire Period, 1804–1814: This was the era of Napoleon, Josephine de Beauharnais, and Marie Louise. Napoleon had absolute control, and the period is noted for its poor taste in dress, culture, and manners. Greek fashion prevailed with the short-waisted effect which received the name of Empire Fashion. Gowns and dresses were long, simple in cut, while the waist was very short and very low and plunging in effect. Headgear of all types was ugly, large, off balance and profusely trimmed with artificial flowers. All told, the period was somber, dull, and listless.

American Colonial and Post-Revolution Periods: The periods from that of Louis XVI through that of the French Empire correspond roughtly with the Georgian Period (1714–1820) in England, and our own late Colonial and Post Revolutionary Periods. What France dictated, the rest of the fashionable world copied, whether one lived just across the border or Channel or amidst the hardships of the New World. Milady and her spouse waited anxiously for the latest fashion magazines from Paris and had the garments copied, even though the style might be inappropriate to the climate or the other exigencies of life in the Colonies.

The clothes of the Cavaliers in the Virginia Colonies lacked nothing of the elaborateness of their homeland brothers. Other colonists, however, like the Pilgrims in New England and the Dutch in New Amsterdam, had brought their own styles along so that when the various groups met and mixed, some modifications resulted and many of the unnecessary furbelows were eliminated. Simple homespuns and printed fabrics replaced the rich silks, satins, and brocades, and dress, too, became simpler.

French Restoration Period, 1814–1830: At this time in France, the styles were a carry-over from the Empire Period—long shoulder effects and large sleeve effects which ended at the elbow. Hoops were in favor, and these distorted the form and silhouette. Short, full skirts were the order of the day. Hair was worn parted in the center with long curls at the sides of the head.

The effects of the Industrial Revolution were now being felt and machine-made materials caused the attire of the more affluent people to be easily and readily copied or pirated. Then, as now, changes were frequent because fear of obsolescence seems to be the psychology of the female mind in fashion and style, and anticipation seems to prevail over realization. Changes were the order of the day.

The period, however, marked the end of the frills of the prior periods in men's wear; gone forever were satins, lace effects, powdered wigs, and so on.

Around 1820, the corset returned to favor, thereby causing the waistline to become smaller. Broad belts came into prominence. The large sleeve effects were held from the arm by boning or padding, and gloves became very popular, either colored or white.

Louis Philippe, 1830–1848: Known as the Romantic Period, this era saw the advent of the bertha collar, the scarf, and the small shoulder cape to accentuate the long drooping shoulder which was the last word in fashion appeal in women's wear. Low, straight-cut necklines were used in evening wear, and these tended to give a broad effect to the wearer. Skirts were wide at the bottom, and the hem was several inches from the ground; only the shoes or slippers were revealed by the skirts of the day. All types of flounces, ruffles, and tucks were in vogue.

In men's wear some of the features of the times included the wearing of two vests, one short and one long; starched shirts with high collars, small ties, tight pantaloons which were long and strapped in gaiter fashion under the shoe, as well as the introduction of the corset or basque to make men's waists slender. The short jacket and the chimney-pot type of hat were in style.

SECOND REPUBLIC PERIOD, 1848–1852: Costumes of this period were a continuation of the Restoration Period and the Louis Philippe Period with some modifications. These included longer shoulder lines and smaller waists. Black lace became extremely popular, and black velvet bands for the wrist and throat also were in demand.

SECOND EMPIRE PERIOD, 1853–1870: The days of Napoleon III and of the famous Eugénie, 1826–1920, and the Empress of France from 1853 to 1870. Her real name was Eugénie Marie de Montijo de Guzman. Under the direction of Empress Eugénie, many changes took place in fashion and style. A new era came into existence. Extravagance seemed to become the keynote. Worth, the famous fashion house of France, still in existence, made the clothes for Eugénie. Soft shades of blue, gray, mauve, and sapphire blue were color favorites, while tulle, gauze, and laces were favorite materials. Long, full skirts with many flounces were held out by hoops. Startched and ruffled petticoats were also in style. Tight, pointed bodices, buttoned to the neck, had small turndown collars. Sleeves were set in a low armscye and were long and tight or bell-shaped with lace and muslin undersleeves. Off-the-shoulder necklines and short puff sleeves were used in evening wear. Accessories included small bonnets, lace mantillas worn as shawls, and lace gloves. Incidentally, in the 1930s, the Empress Eugénie hat with its side plume was revived and achieved great popularity for quite some time.

It was during this period that the bathing suit was introduced. From the late years of the seventh century, the bustle was revived; and it soon trans-formed the entire silhouette.

MID-NINETEENTH CENTURY IN AMERICA: After the War of 1812, American styles, while still influenced by Europe, took on a flavor all their own. Publications like GRAHAM'S MAGAZINE and GODEY'S Lady's Book contained the fashions now worn by the ladies of the young Republic. With the establishment of long trousers and duller colors for men, their fashions have remained static until the present time when some bright notes are being added by the Hollywood and Hawaiian influences on sports and evening wear.

In the early 1830s, the lady's silhouette was still quite extravagant, but it softened into a bell shape in the '40s and early '50s, with the use of sloping shoulders, tight waistlines and full skirts made of silk, satin, velvet, woolen cloth, muslin, and cambric. The rural and pioneer women created more practical styles that conformed more closely to the figure and made much of printed cottons.

In the late 1850s, the hemline opened to its widest with the help of crinoline and the hoop, while the waistline was kept small enough for a man to grasp it in his two hands, and the sleeves were made full, going to three-quarters or wrist length.

Because of the War between the States, women's styles varied throughout the country, but certain basic changes were noted in the early '60s, primarily in shrinkage of the hem's circumference from 17 to 20 yards of cloth to 10 or 12 yards, and the slimming and simplification of the sleeves which were now wrist length and sometimes had an epaulet effect.

Black was considered elegant for cloaks, both in summer and winter. Bonnets, which had been worn on the back of the head, were replaced by flatter hats, that were tied under the chin. By the late '60s, further modification of the hem led to extravagant trains, a belt line and sashes were introduced, and there was a trend to have the entire garment of the same color and material. Hair styles began to be more elaborate, with curls and/or chignons being added. As a result, the hat or cap practically disappeared, and was replaced by various types of ornaments which were interlaced in the hair-dos. Dress materials ran the gamut of all types, while costly furs were also used.

THIRD REPUBLIC OF FRANCE, 1870 to present time: With Paris and Lyons, and later on, New York and Hollywood, all being centers of fashion and style, apparel and clothing from this time forward have seen many changes in women's styles. Some of the changes early in the period included the skirt, made plain and pulled back by a cord to insure snugness in the front, much ornamentation on dresses, the demise of the hoop, and greater freedom than was formerly the case. Taffeta came into its own in favorite shades of blue, green, yellow, and magenta; black was also in favor for some occasions.

Tight bodices were set off with jabots of lace, and the polonaise, a waist and an overskirt in one piece, became popular. The mannish tailored suit, made in somber colors, also made its debut. Dolman sleeves were used on jackets and coats. Small headgear, pleated fans, and fancy parasols were popular accessories.

In men's wear, from about 1870 to the present time, there has been comparatively little change. The French Revolution dealt a serious blow to fashion in men's apparel in so far as the lavish tastes prior to the Revolution were banished, and they have not returned. Present-day men's wear may be said to be a carry-over from the days of the early '70s in France.

AMERICAN FASHIONS COME OF AGE, 1875 to present date: Styles in America were already looking back and copying those of the Colonial Period as the country prepared to celebrate its centennial in 1876. Instead of the side panniers, however, the back bustle was introduced. Waistlines were higher, and skirts hung to the ground.

Hair styles became even more elaborate, while hats became smaller with an even wider variety of trimmings. At this time, too, coats and jackets became very tailored, often in dramatic contrast with the elaborate and trained skirts.

In the 1880s, the silhouette changed greatly so that the figure was revealed. Women were not expected to be active, so skirts were narrow at both the knee and the hemline, which frequently had several rows of ruffles protruding from it. An even wider variety of materials and colors was used. Bathing "dresses" began to appear, and the corset took on great importance because it held the figure tight and nipped in the waistline to conform to the dictates of fashion.

The "Gay Nineties" was characterized by what came to be known as the "leg o' mutton" sleeve and skirts with fullness in the back. Bonnets were smaller and flatter, while hats were wider in the front and turned up behind. Side plackets appeared in dresses, and the first dress was specially designed for sport-bicycling. Then, as now, the theater influenced style, and the Juliet cap and Flora Dora parasols, among other items, gained great popularity. As "Society" emerged, so did styles change again, and the 1900s saw the return of the back bustle with skirts ending in elaborate trains.

Emphasis was given to the bustline by ruffles and jabots. Embroidery was a favorite pastime, so its product appeared on both lingerie and outerwear. Accessories became important and the earliest discussions of maternity wear were printed. A new century for women's wear had dawned.

The past fifty years have seen some drastic changes in styles, but they have not been as frequent as heretofore. Artists such as Charles Dana Gibson and Howard Chandler Christy "created" the fashions at the beginning of the century. The advent of the automobile introduced the duster, and the hats with long veils. The topheavy "hair-dos" and the hobbled skirts of 1912–1914 changed quickly when women were needed to do their part in World War I. Skirts became shorter and fuller because of the need for greater mobility.

Home-knit sweaters and skirts became popular, while middies and bloomers became the approved thing for gymnasium and outdoor sports activities. This, in turn, led to the rise of the "flapper" and her own peculiar uniform of mannish clothing, felt hat, and open galoshes. The teen-ager was asserting herself as a result of the greater freedom for women. This period, too, saw the introduction of man-made synthetic fibers, and attention was given to molding the figure rather than confining it.

One of the most drastic revolutions to hit the fashion world came with the "Roaring '20s." Everything changed. The hair was cut in mannish style, the figure was flattened to a sexless silhouette, waistline and hemline almost met, the one being lowered too far while the other rose to the knees. All wore the same styles, whether they were becoming or not. All sorts of make-up were worn. Good taste had fled. True, outfits were designed specifically for every activity of milady, but all along the same basic pattern. Such a trend could not last.

The only bright spot was in hosiery, with the change from black to beige and tan, and from cotton to silk.

Rayons began to appear in hosiery colors that seemed to go well with the ensemble. Fortunately, the age of nylon was just around the corner.

The 1930s saw a return of artistic taste. Because of the depression, women took to making their own clothes because dress materials were so low in price. Then, ready-to-wear garments also fell in price. Hemlines dropped a bit here and there, until they straightened out to a more graceful length, where they have remained with slight variations, such as a plunge with the "New Look," until now. Slide fasteners came into use as did a limitless variety of materials. A greater individuality appeared, influenced by world events.

And then World War II began. This froze styles and cut the amount of material to be used in each garment. Skirts were short because of the lack of fabric, and the era became a period of static, inartistic style. Shoulders were padded, flattering only the slender youthful figure. Old and young, slim and stout, all wore exactly the same things.

After the shortages caused by the war had been overcome, the late '40s saw a rapid swing away from the frozen, too-short skirt and the too-wide shoulder. Skirts became very long and full, hips were padded, and the bustline was emphasized. Garments were designed for ease of motion and comfort. The "New Look" from Paris arrived.

Today, the Colonel's Lady and Rosie O'Grady both can look equally smart and stylish, for both wear clothes designed by New York, Paris, or Hollywood designers. The use of nylon and other new textile fibers and fabrics has inspired many new styles so that each may have what is becoming to her. The influence of Hollywood is noticeable.

Since the flapper first declared her independence, more attention has been paid to fashions for the young. For countless centuries children were simply miniature adults—whereas during the past thirty years, all this has changed and there are specialists designing for the different age groups.

Particular attention is given to the teenager with her constantly changing proportions, and there are several fashion magazines geared to her needs. Today, if she will, the adolescent can look and feel as comfortable and stylish as her mother. Unfortunately, however, she has developed a uniform of her own — her brother's plaid shirt worn outside of her sloppy blue jeans with their turned-up or shredded bottoms.

For the last few years her brother copies her fashion and style and vice versa. With the tremendous explosion in non-conformity in clothes it is difficult, at times, to distinguish the boys from the girls. Father as gotten away from the rather drab and dull colors, thanks to Hollywood and the clothes designers, many of whom claim there is no more fashion and style and "that anything goes." And it is difficult, as well, to distinguish the men from the boys. Designing, fashion and style have really gone awry and the quick, everchanging modes and moods in clothes seam to bear out this statement. What the future History of Costume will be, no one can make any forecast at all. One person's guess is now as good as another's.

REFERENCE: *Mode in Costume,* R. Turner Wilcox, 2nd edition (New York, Charles Scribner's Sons).

COSTUME, JENNY LIND. This included a fitted bodice with off-shoulder neckline, and bell-shaped hoop skirt often decorated with three graduated ruffles of lace, in the styles of the Civil War Era. Named for Jenny Lind "The Swedish Nightingale," the famous coloratura soprano, 1820-1887.

COSTUME, LOUIS PHILLIPE ERA. Known as the "Citizen King" of France from 1830 to 1848, women's fashions took on a new look with the introduction of the wide, drooping shoulder accentuated by a cape, bertha, or scarf. Plaits, ruffles, and tucks became the vogue in attire. Skirts were wide and banded in a variety of ways, the straw hat became popular with its embellishments to add to the silhouette.

COSTUME, MEXICAN. Derived from a combination of Aztec and Spanish fashions, women's costumes included the loose, full skirt with a starched, lace ruffle; the short, sleeveless cotton blouse, and the starched, lace headdress. There was also the Spanish full skirt worn with a mantilla and the high comb in the hair. Silver and precious and semi-precious stones were made into jewelry by the Indians and worn by men and women.

Men's garb were the white or dark trousers and short black coat, often highly embroidered. The ruffled shirt and serape became stock in trade with the Mexicans. Many of the foregoing are quite popular in today's styles for men and women. Brown was the most commonly used color.

COSTUME, NAPOLEONIC. Napoleon Bonapart, 1761-1821, unveiled new vistas in attire. Some of these were tight kneebreeches, the square-cut waistcoat, the coat which was cut away from above the waistline in front to the tails in the back; the high-standing, turnover collar with wide revers, the knee-high boots, and the famous cocked hat.

COSTUME, PURITAN. Named for the Puritans who came to our shores in the early 17th century. They had austere, stern, and strict religious principles which were noted in their attire. Women wore a close bodice, long, full skirt over a homespun petticoat, a white apron, kerchief, and cuffs. A dark hood or broad hat was used. The men wore plain dark colored coatings, knee breeches, bulky stockings, the long cloak, broad-brimmed, high crowned hat, and shoes adorned by a buckle. Colors were very dull and somber, predominately black, brown, dark gray, and dark blue.

COSTUME, QUAKER. Effected by the Quakers who were among the early settlers in this country, features of women's wear included the plain, simple basque-type dress usually gray in color; the gathered skirt and long apron. The short-sleeved bodice with white under-sleeves and shoulder apron were also parts of this attire. Ruffled caps and a soft hood were worn over the cap when outside the home. Stiff beaver hats, and then the stiff poke bonnet, succeeded the cap. This type of attire was in vogue for more than two hundred years, ending in the 19th century. Men's wear may be compared with the attire of the Puritans, Pilgrims, and the Dissenters of the same period although the latter styles did not have nearly the longevity of the Quaker garb for men.

COSTUME, REGENCY. This short-lived period was during the regency of Louis XV and covered the years 1715-1723. The period became known as "The Era of the Salon." Women's wear featured dresses of lightweight fabrics, basque bodices, pagoda sleeves, and enormous panniers. Incidentally, English dress of the same era showed long, straight skirts, high waists with a low neck and pelisses, outer garments lined or trimmed with fur or a long cloak with slits for easy arm movement. Bonnets and shawls were by now staple items of apparel.

COSTUME, RESTORATION. The restoration period followed the downfall of Oliver Cromwell in 1660 and lasted for the next twenty-five years. With the return of the Stuart reign the use of the straight or looped-back skirt came into being along with the deep, open neck effect, and short sleeves that were slit from the shoulders. The styles were decidedly different from the dull, somber apparel of the Cromwellian Period from 1640-1660.

COSTUME, RUSSELL, LILLIAN. The never-to-be-forgotten form-fitting gown and train, set-off by the enormous hat with plumes; worn by Lillian Russell. See Russell, Lillian.

COSTUME, SCOTTISH. The national dress of the Scots prevailed in this attire. Women's dress was given little attention with cloth bodices, skirts, and the basic tartan shawl, all that one can say about it.

Men's wear, however, has many features, among them the tartan kilt which is a full, plaited, skirt-like garment fastened by a belt around the waist and ending at the knee. The waistcoat, short in type, is made of velvet or any other suitable fabric; a folded plaid is worn over the left shoulder and fastened with a large brooch. Stockings are fastened below the bare knee. The Tam-o-Shanter with its basic ribbon streamers is decorated with a brooch, a feather, or both. The sporran, a large purse, usually made of fur, is worn suspended from a belt at the front of the kilt below the waistline. Incidentally, in World War I, the Scottish regiments which were called "The Ladies from Hell," were also known as "The Skirted Soldiers."

COSTUME, SECOND EMPIRE. This French period covered the years from 1852 to 1870, the time of the Franco-Prussian War. Women's wear featured the broad silhouette with close bodice and small waistline; the bouffant skirt was flounced and ruffled. Much attention was given to the neck and bosom with the decollete effect, the bertha, and the fichu. Pagoda sleeves, a heavily trimmed bonnet, and a mantle or shawl rounded out the well-dressed female of the era.

COSTUME, TYROLEAN. In this fascinating garb there is the full skirt worn over several petticoats, an embroidered apron with embroidered basque or laced bodice, the simple blouse, and the kerchief. Men's wear features the well-known felt or fur headpiece with its brash and/or tassel, the bright, embroidered woolen vest, and bright colored, embroidered suspenders. To match the jacket, there are long trousers or knickerbockers, or the well-known lederhosen made of leather.

COSTUME, VICTORIAN. Style of dress named for Queen Victoria (1819-1901), monarch of Great Britain and Ireland (1837-1901) and Empress of India (1876-1901). There were not any outstanding features in this period which is known for its listlessness, lack of innovation, and cumbersome attire for women.

Wide hoop skirts were caught up and flounced; basques, berthas, and long sleeves were prominent, and a great deal of luxurious and rich fabric, especially silk, was wasted in the attire of milady. Toward the end of Victoria's reign narrower skirts came into being. These were drawn up over the ever-present bustle at the back. Tighter fitting jackets, atrocious poke bonnets, and shawls completed the general attire.

COSTUME VELVET. Name given

to the heavier dress velvets which may be made with a silk or rayon pile and a cotton back. The better grades of the cloth are woven with a mercerized cotton pile. While extensively used for theatrical costumes, it has, of late, been used for skating or sport suits and is often substituted for corduroy in the manufacture of the better grade and higher types of sport clothes and skating costumes.

COT. That part of the drawing roll set-up on various cotton machines known as the boss is covered with a cot of cork, leather, or some other suitable material.

COTE DE CHEVAL. A corded cloth of France used as riding habit material and uniform cloth for officers. Côte means ribbed or lined, cheval means horse; hence the cloth has a grosgrain effect, broken at intervals with a short step to produce a striped appearance that is slightly rounded, and may be compared to the ribs noted on the horse.

COTE-HARDIE. In the 15th century, the upper classes dressed in a snug-fitting, low-necked tunic which was buttoned down the front and worn over the jupon or gipon. The less affluent wore its counterpart, the Cote-Hardie, which was a loose fitting garment, devoid of buttons and had to be put on over the head. The edge of the item was often of the sawtooth variety which presented rather singular effects. Its span of life was in the 14th century but some variations are still used to the present day. Tight-fitting sleeves from wrist to elbow and then flared to the shoulder were also features of this item. The Cote-Hardie were very long and wide and in some cases even extended to the knees. In the last quarter of the century a collar attachment was devised. All told, a very cumbersome garment. See Jupon, Tunic.

COTELE. A French term for bengaline made from a silk or rayon warp and worsted filling which is given hard-twist. Used for lightweight coating.

COTE MENUE. French fabric on the order of serge and made with a repeat of 10 ends and 5 picks. The cloth has a cord or rib effect in it.

COTENTIN. A hardy sheep raised in France which has a white fleece that runs around seven pounds, when shorn.

COTE PIQUE. Made with a piqué construction to present a cord effect, that French serge fabric is piece-dyed solid colors. The weave repeats on 8 ends and 8 picks.

COTELINE, COTELAINE. Fine rib stripes set-off this lightweight, French muslin that may be dyed or printed and comes in many grades, widths, and cut lengths.

COTHA MORA. Frieze fabric made for centuries in Ireland, for overcoating. Still very popular.

COTON. French for cotton.

COTONINE. French for a very strong, stout sailcloth made of cotton warp and hemp filling.

COTRON. Trademark of FMC Corporation, American Viscose Division for a fabric made of cotton and Avisco rayon. Fabrics of this sort show rich luster, luxurious hand, improved drapability, better light fastness, and a finer definition in printed motifs. Resinated Cotron fabrics compared with resinated all-cotton materials, show a greater strength after repeated launderings, and improvement in strength retention after repeated launderings with chlorine bleach.

COTSWOLD. The big-bodied sheep native to Gloucester County, England. One of the Luster wools, it is a hardy animal, has its wool in loose wavy ringlets somewhat on the order of Angora fleece. Its quality runs from 40s to 44s, and staple ranges from 8 to about 14 inches. Rather crisp in feel, the fleece ranges from 10 to 14 pounds in weight. See LUSTER WOOLS. See also Illustrated Section.

COTTA. A white vestment with full sleeves reaching just below the elbow, and its hem descending just below the hip line. This type of surplice is worn by priests over their cassocks and by acolytes and altar boys. See Surplice.

COTTAGE STEAMER. A type of sealed cylindrical chamber wherein print colors are fixed on the material by the action of live steam, either at atmospheric pressure or up to 10 pounds gauge pressure.

COTTE. 1. A close fitting garment tunic-like in effect which has sleeves, is usually hip-length, and is laced, or buttoned down the front. Also called côte-hardie. 2. French for coat, jacket, short petticoat. 3. The cotte historiée was an heraldic costume or coat embellished lavishly with fur such as ermine or marten. Satins and velvets embroidered with gold leaf or silver leaf and then made more luxurious by the use of enamel or powder in brilliant colorings. The cotte was used in the Age of Chivalry in the fourteenth and fifteenth centuries.

COTTED FLEECE. One in which the fibers are matted, tangled, and very irregular. Caused by the poor health of the sheep or may be due to lack of nourishment. An absence of yolk and suint are noted in fleeces of this sort.

Cotted fleeces are inferior, harsher, more irregular and kempier when compared with first-run fleeces.

COTTON. A white, brownish-white, or bluish-white, soft, fibrous substance that surrounds the seeds of certain plants of the mallow family, called Gossypium. Cotton is the most important and versatile fiber known to mankind. It is used in inner wear, outerwear, accessories, decorative materials in the home, and in industry.

Cotton may be used to make cheap cheesecloth, tobacco cloth, or print material. It may be used to make fine drawnwork materials whose price may run into hundreds of dollars in value. Fine cotton work is produced in Europe, where most of it comes from the religious schools in which the manipulation of cotton yarn, thread, and cloth has been taught for centuries.

The United States now produces about 35 per cent of the world production; India is the second largest producer of the fiber. Brazil, Egypt, Central America, China, Mexico, and Peru are other noted producing areas.

In this country there is about twelve times as much cotton used per year as scoured wool. There is about three times as much cotton cloth produced annually, on a square yard basis, as all other textile cloths combined.

Only 15 per cent of the available cotton raising area is used for this purpose; hence, the supply can be readily taken care of by increased demands of industry. It has been said that cotton is truly a miracle fiber—it is older than recorded history; it is mothproof without treatment; it does not store up static electricity; and it does not melt. It will not vanish under chemical fumes as you walk down the street; it can be dyed any shade and can be made colorfast. Cotton can be treated so that it will not shrink, and it can be treated so that it will not wrinkle. And, the styling of cotton fabrics is always very good and one of the major reasons as to why cotton is often known as the "universal fiber of the textile fiber kingdom." See Illustrated Section.

COTTON, ACETYLATED (PA). A treatment which uses acetic anhydride to improve the resistance of cotton to acids, heat, and rot. Woven fabric of the product is used as covering for calender rollers, press rollers, etc.

COTTON, AMERICAN. See Cottons, American.

COTTON, AMINIZED (AM). When cotton is treated with aminoethyl sulphuric acid greater dye receptivity and chemical reactivity become apparent. Fiber, yarn, or fabric becomes faster to light and laundering and reacts more readily with the various chemical treatments applied in pro-

cessing.

COTTON, ARIZONA. Cotton raised in Arizona, New Mexico, Southern California, and Egypt is the best in the world, with the exception of Sea Island which is negligible in production when compared with these staples. Known also as Western or irrigated cottons, they have undergone much research, development, and improvement. Natural conditions have had much to do with their progress. They have been raised for about 150 years under supervision since at this time there was an exchange made between Arizona and Egyptian merchants of their native seeds. Both areas have profited well from the exchanges.

Arizona cotton is raised in the Salt River Valley and the Yuma Valley, in Arizona, and in the Imperial Valley of Southern California. There is a constant increase in annual acreage. Arizona cotton is classed with the Egyptian cottons, Mitafifi and Jannovich in the brownish tinge, and with the famous Sakellaridis white staple.

The Department of Agriculture, and the Bureau of Standards, have done much to give Arizona cottons the position they hold today. College Experimental Stations have also contributed to a great degree. The production, which is for high-quality staple, gives a cotton that commands a good price. The fibers go into the very best of cotton yarns used in the superior types of cotton materials—broadcloth, poplin, dimity, shirting, organdy, voile, etc.

The first American-Egyptian strain, after the turn of the century, was Yuma cotton, first raised in the Salt River Valley and in the Imperial Valley, in 1911. By 1919, this had been displaced by Pima cotton, which was a leader until about 1943.

At that time, S x P, a cross between Egyptian Sakellaridis and American-Egyptian Pima, became popular, and is now the only type of American-Egyptian in commercial production in this country. Since 1943, this staple has given way to Amsak and Pima 32. Amsak was the result of crossing S x P with Sakellaridis.

Pima 32 is the result of crossing S x P, Pima, and Giza 7, an Egyptian type. It was first raised in 1948 on a commercial basis. At the present time, Pima 32 has almost completely replaced S x P, and only a negligible amount of Amsak is produced.

Pima S-I is now in commercial production, and it compares well with Karnak, Amsak, and Pima 32.

The future of American-Egyptian cotton will depend upon the relation of its price with that of imported Egyptian cotton, and upon whether the quality characteristics of Amsak and

Pima 32 are good enough to offer serious competition to the famed Egyptian Karnak.

Incidentally, the Peruvian cotton, Tanguis, may be classed for quality with the foregoing cottons. Its length and color make it outstanding, it has a staple of 2 inches to 2½ inches, and a very clear, bright white cast. The production ranges around 1500 bales, at 500 pounds per bale, per season.

COTTON, BA. A durable flame resistant application to cotton in which a vinyl type monomer (bromo-alkyl allyl-phosphate) application is followed by heating the presence of a peroxide to cause polymerization.

COTTON, BUYING POINTS OF.

1. GRADE: The appearance of the cotton as to cleanliness, freedom from leaf, chaff, stains, dirt, and so on.

2. STAPLE: The average length of

the bulk fibers, 1½ inches, etc. Staple also implies whether the cotton is harsh, crimpy, weak, strong, substantial, and so on.

3. IMPURITIES: The amount of sand, grit, and other ordinary impurities that are met in dealing with the stock.

4. DAMPNESS: The determination whether the cotton has more than 6 or 7 per cent of dampness, the usual amount. Weather conditions will cause

COTTON

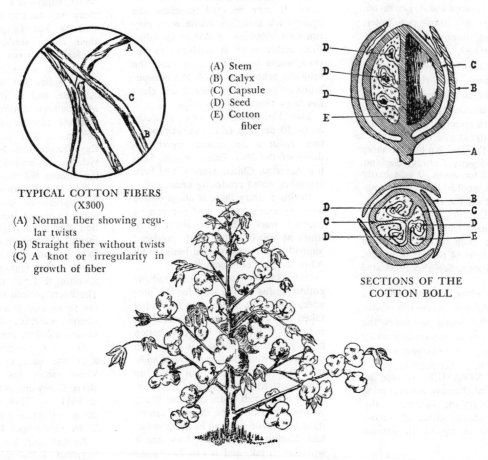

(A) Stem
(B) Calyx
(C) Capsule
(D) Seed
(E) Cotton fiber

TYPICAL COTTON FIBERS
(X300)

(A) Normal fiber showing regular twists
(B) Straight fiber without twists
(C) A knot or irregularity in growth of fiber

SECTIONS OF THE COTTON BOLL

AMERICAN UPLAND COTTON SHRUB (AFTER DODGE)

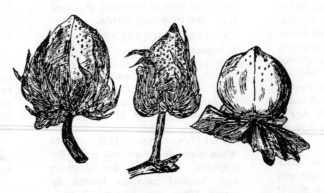

COTTON BOLLS

Reprinted by permission from "Textile Fibers", fourth edition, by Mathews, published by John Wiley & Sons, Inc.

the moisture content to vary, and this point has to be closely watched.

5. TINGES AND OFF-SORTS: These may spoil a lot of cotton, intended for some particular use. They are caused by the plant falling on the ground because of rain, wind, sand storms, and such.

6. OTHER POINTS: The fineness of fiber, amount of waste, feel, freedom from seeds, short and immature fibers, strength, cracked seeds, brightness, and comparison with other known qualities.

COTTON, CARBOXYMETHYL (CM). Two distinct forms are taken on when cotton fiber, yarn, or fabric is carboxymethylated by treatment with monochloroacetic acid followed by treatment with strong sodium hydroxide. One reaction is that a modified fabric is produced which has a built-in, starched effect; increased water absorbability, and greater receptivity to crease-resistant treatments when compared with ordinary fabric.

The other result is obtained by treating with a higher concentration of monochloroacetic acid-sodium hydroxide which results in a retention of 80 per cent to 100 per cent of original strength, and which becomes soluble in ordinary tap water.

COTTON, CHARACTER AND FINENESS OF. Spinning of cotton depends on the strength, length, fineness, and amount of twist in the individual fiber. Cotton fibers consist almost entirely of cellulose, plus a small amount of coloring matter. The waxy or fatty matter ranges from 4 per cent to 7 per cent.

COTTON, CHEMICAL FORMULA OF. This is $C_6H_{10}O_5$, taken n times. The n is what makes cotton capable of taking high twist, as well as being spun into fine yarn counts. The fiber has a long series of spiral twists which extend the length of the staple. The twists vary with the several types because of the effect on the chemical structure on these turns. Sea Island has 300 per inch; Egyptian, 230; Brazilian, 210; American Peeler, 190; Indian, about 150.

The lint and staple of Egyptian cotton is the most regular in length and diameter.

Cotton, which comes under the carbohydrate group, is closely akin to the following:

1. Monosacharoses: Pentose is an example ($C_6H_{10}O_5$).

2. Hexoses: Glucose, grape sugar, and dextrose are examples—$C_6H_{12}O_6$.

3. Disacharoses: Cane sugar is an example—$C_{12}H_{22}O_{12}$.

4. Polysacharoses: Cellulose, starch, and glycogen—$(C_6H_{10}O_5)$ x—are examples.

COTTON, CHLORINE ACTION ON. $CaOCl_2$, chloride of lime, is used as a common bleaching agent. Chloride of lime in solution is known as Javelle water. When a weak solution of sulphuric acid is added to the lime bath, chlorine is liberated and combines with water to liberate oxygen, which does the actual bleaching.

COTTON, CM. Conversion to this kind of cotton is done by treating cotton with monochloroacetic acid and then with sodium hydroxide. There are two types: 1. The "stiff or starched" variety, capable of absorbing more water than straight cotton. This type finds use in crease-resistant fabrics. 2. As a "builder cotton," it is used as a temporary yarn in producing materials from which the undesirable yarn is easily removed, usually by water.

COTTON, CURLY. Same as stringy cotton.

COTTON, CYANOETHYLATED COTTON (CN). An acrylonitrile treatment developed and perfected in the Institute of Textile Technology, Charlottesville, Virginia. The product increases resistance of cotton to heat and rot, and improves receptivity of dyes to the fiber. See AZOTON.

COTTON, DECRYSTALLIZED. Low crystallinity of cotton is brought about by treating it with anhydrous liquid ethylamine. The reduction in crystallinity is about 30 per cent, and it improves fiber toughness, increased extensibility, higher absorbency, and higher dyeing capacity.

COTTON, EGYPTIAN. High-grade, long-staple cotton grown in Egypt, mainly in the Nile Valley. The stock is not as long or as fine in diameter as Sea Island cotton, but the amounts produced annually make it one of the outstanding world cottons. Egyptian has less waste than Sea Island. It is ideal for lace, thread, tire cord, etc.

All Egyptian cotton has good strength and is ideal for mercerizing, gassing, and other finishing operations. It has a diameter of about .0007 inches and works well with wool, as well as with other fibers. The average color or cast of the cotton may be classed as ecru. Bleaching properties are splendid, and excellent whites are readily obtained. Fabrics that Egyptian cottons are used for include batiste, broadcloth, curtaining, organdy, dimity, lawn, longcloth, and voile.

Egyptian cotton depends on the Nile River for proper irrigation and nutriment. Its planting, cultivation, and picking compare with the methods and times used here. Planting is done in March; picking is at its peak in September, with a second picking in October. The land is irrigated after the second picking, and a third crop is obtained in November. The first two pickings are superior to the last.

WHITE EGYPTIAN COTTONS: Sakellarides is a choice Egyptian cotton. Its staple is from 1½ to 1¾ inches. While it does not have all of the genuinely fine characteristics of Sea Island, and does not mercerize quite as well, it does have good strength, dyeing and printing characteristics in affinity to dyestuff and in the handle and feel of the finished goods. This cotton makes up approximately 50 per cent of Egyptian production.

Abassi is strong, fine, and silken, and nearly white in cast. The staple is from 1½ to 1⅝ inches. This stock is used for counts of 100s and better, and it is superior to brown Mitafiffi in all respects, though Abassi and Mitafiffi are used in similar materials.

Another leading white staple is Gallini, which is comparable with brown Ashmouni, and, like it, has declined in popularity as other staples have received greater favor. Years ago Gallini held the same position in Egypt that Sea Island held here.

BROWN EGYPTIAN COTTONS: Mitafiffi is light brown in color and considerably darker in cast than Sakellarides. The staple is from 1¼ to 1½ inches. The fiber is used to make yarn counts that range from 70s to 100s.

Ashmouni and Bamia are two well-liked staples. Both are darker than Mitafiffi, and the latter ranks just behind Mitafiffi in all respects. Both cottons have long staples, are soft in feel, silken in nature, and strong; they run, however, rather high in lint percentage. This may at times be as much as 30 per cent. Ashmouni has declined in popularity in recent years because of the fact that no staple over 1 inch is now produced. Longer-staple cottons have replaced it.

Other prominent Egyptian cottons include Dandara, Jumel, Karnak, Maarad, Maco, and Menoufi. The comparatively new Giza strains have come to the fore, and being of major importance, should soon replace some of the older types raised in Egypt. Extra long staples are Giza 45, and Giza 58. Medium long and long staples (up to 1⅜ in length) include Giza 66, Giza 67, and Giza 69. Cooperative marketing of cotton began in 1965 and fifty percent of the crop, 140 to 170 million pounds, is exported annually.

COTTON, FIRST AND SECOND LYE BOILS ON. They consist of thorough boiling of the goods in a lye solution that is made of soda ash and resin soap. The soda ash combines with the free fatty acids to form soda soaps that are removed by washing.

The first boil takes several hours. The solution requires about 2 per cent of soda ash and 1 per cent of resin figured on the weight of the material. The resin forms what is known as resin soap with the caustic alkali, which has a very strong action on some of the impurities in cotton. Following the first boil, all traces of the resin are removed by the second treatment, which does away with the possibility of yellowish stains that may appear in the goods. The goods are thoroughly washed, and any tint is later removed by chemicking if the cloth is to be dyed a light shade.

COTTON, LEAD CHROMATE TREATED. Cotton tobacco shade cloth is treated with lead acetate and then with potassium or sodium bichromate from which a yellow chromate pigment is deposited onto the fabric. This action screens out the sun's rays and extends the life of the fabric to three times that of similar untreated cloth.

COTTON, POTASSIUM IODIDE TEST FOR RIPE. A solution of iodine in potassium iodide will give a rich, dark, yellowish brown color to the cotton, if it is ripe and ready for picking. If the fibers are not ready, a yellowish color will remain.

COTTON, PROPERTIES OF.

PHYSICAL CHARACTERISTICS:

1. MICROSCOPICAL APPEARANCE: A flat ribbonlike fiber which has from 150 to 300 natural turns of twist per inch.

2. LENGTH: ½ inch to 2 inches or slightly longer.

3. DIAMETER: .0005 inch to .0009 inch.

4. COLOR: Ordinarily white, may be cream colored or tinted brown.

5. LUSTER: In untreated condition has no pronounced luster.

6. STRENGTH: Intermediate between silk and wool. The single fiber will sustain a dead weight of 2 to 8 grams. Strength is temporarily increased when wet, and decreased when abnormally dried.

7. ELASTICITY: Not nearly as elastic as silk and wool. Spiral twists make it apparently more elastic than linen.

8. CONDUCTIVITY OF HEAT: Better than silk or wool, not as good as linen.

9. HYGROSCOPIC MOISTURE: 6 per cent to 7 per cent.

10. CAPILLARITY AND PENETRABILITY: It has capillarity because of its tubular structure.

11. FIBER COMPOSITION: Formula is $C_6H_{10}O_5$, n or x times. Cellulose content varies from 90 per cent to about 96 per cent, water from 5 per cent to 8 per cent, natural impurities from 4 to 6 per cent.

CHEMICAL CHARACTERISTICS:

1. EFFECT OF LIGHT: Loses strength.

2. MILDEW: Pure cotton is not attacked readily. Sized or treated with starches, flours, and gums in presence of dampness will be affected by mildew.

3. HEAT: Withstands high temperatures well. In dry atmosphere, it can be heated to 300° F., without injury. At 475° F., the fiber will turn brown and burn.

4. WATER: Boiling water does not affect the fiber.

5. MINERAL ACIDS: Concentrated acids such as hydrochloric, hydrofluoric, nitric, and sulphuric will destroy the fiber. Cold dilute acids will not injure the fiber if washed out or neutralized. Dilute solutions, 3 per cent or less, of these acids, if allowed to dry, cause the fiber to become tender, and in time will destroy cotton.

6. VOLATILE ORGANIC ACIDS: With formic or acetic acids there is no detrimental action.

7. NON-VOLATILE ACIDS: Oxalic acid will cause a high loss in tensile strength; a low loss with tartaric acid. Citric acid will tender the fiber, if not removed, and especially if heat is applied.

8. STRONG ALKALIES: With caustic soda, soda ash, there is no injury, even if concentrated, and even if the heat is applied when the oxygen is excluded. Concentrated solutions will mercerize cotton if it is under tension; otherwise the cotton will shrink.

9. WEAK ALKALIES: No injurious effect upon the fiber.

10. OXIDIZING AGENTS: Potassium permanganate, for example, will destroy cotton if not controlled.

11. METALLIC SALTS: Cotton has practically no affinity for metallic salts.

12. AFFINITY FOR DYESTUFFS: Less than that of silk and wool.

13. DYEING: Cotton is dyed by direct dyestuffs, sulphur dyes, basic dyes with a mordant, by coloring matter developed in the fiber, and by vat dyes.

14. BLEACHING AGENTS: Chlorine bleach or hypochlorites, when in cold, dilute solution will not injure the fiber. The bleach used, however, should be removed carefully since heat and concentrated solutions will destroy the fiber.

15. OTHER OXIDATION BLEACHES: Hydrogen peroxide, sodium perborate, or potassium permanganate will not injure cotton, if properly controlled.

16. REDUCTION BLEACHES: Sulphurous acid (sulphur dioxide plus water) or hydrosulphites will cause no injury, if controlled.

COTTON, PA. The "PA" signifies "partially acetylated" and this condition is arrived at by treating the fiber with acetic anhydride in an acetic acid bath. It has the appearance and hand of ordinary cotton, is odorless and non-toxic. PA cotton can resist heat at much higher temperatures than ordinary cotton. At 250° C, the latter loses one-third its strength in three minutes while the former holds on to its strength for about 25 minutes. This modified cotton gives good to excellent service against mildew, rot, and other degradations more or less peculiar to the cotton fiber.

COTTON, PROPIOLACTONE (PL). Dye receptivity on cotton comes as the result of treating it with propiolactone.

COTTON, RING SPINNING OF. Final drafting, twisting, and winding takes place in the ring frame. The roving is taken from the speeder frames, and placed in a creel. Two ends are fed into the machine; they are drawn through three lines of fluted rollers. This is known as double rove spinning. The rollers are set at an angle of about 30 degrees in order to insure uniformity of twist, which on this machine is high when compared with the amount given by the speeders.

At the fibers emerge from the front rollers they are drawn and twisted through a yarn guide over the spindle, pass through the traveler on the ring, and then proceed to the bobbin for winding.

Tension on the yarn bobbin is regulated by the weight of the traveler placed on the ring, and it should be such that the yarn will break if it runs through singly. However, the tension should not be too great since it may break the yarn or cause the ends to become slack, causing them to snarl.

Twist is put in by the spindle traveling faster than the amount of stock delivered by the front rollers.

The yarn count or number that may be spun is regulated by the hank number or size of the roving in the creel. For example, suppose a 40s yarn is desired. The roving in the creel is, say, 8 hank; this, when doubled, gives four-hank roving. 4)40(10. This demonstrates the fact that a draft of ten is necessary with an 8-hank roving in the creel to insure a 40s yarn from the spinning frame. The spindle speed for this count is about 6500 r.p.m.

Twist would be about 19 turns per inch. For finer yarn counts, the speed and the twist are increased; for coarser sizes, they are decreased. See Illustrated Section.

COTTON, SEA ISLAND. The romance cotton of the United States. It was first grown on the islands along the Southern coastal area—Saint Helena, Edisto, Port Royal, James and John of South Carolina, Saint Simeon, and Cumberland off Georgia, and many of the smaller islands.

The first crops came into notice around 1790, at the time that much thought was being given to ginning of cotton. As the years rolled by, and mainland cottons supplanted Sea Island staple, the interest waned. The cost of raising and transportation could not compete with the cottons that were more adjacent to markets. By 1928, this cotton had vanished from America because of the economic conditions entailed in raising the staple. The decline of this cotton is noted from the following tabulation:

1917: 125,000 bales.
1922: 2000 bales.
1926: 100 bales.
1927: 12 bales.

Other cottons have been developed that are supposed to be just as good, and they can be raised at much less cost. The background and tradition, however, of Sea Island cotton has always remained dear to the heart of the Southern cotton planter.

Sea Island cotton, as an American commodity, was dormant until 1934. In that year, a cotton merchant in Providence, R. I., received 15 bales of Sea Island cotton in a consignment. Being familiar with the market for extra long Egyptian and Arizona cottons, he deemed it worthwhile to try to bring the staple back to its former prestige in the annals of American cotton raising. A friend experimented with the bales on hand in Florida; the results were gratifying. In two years a little over 500 bales were in production. Since 1943, however, less than 100 bales have been raised in a single season. The Bureau of Agricultural Economics, U.S.D.A., report shows that the price average was 44.8 cents, the last year that price quotes were given.

Sea Island is raised successfully in Mexico, the Central American countries, and the northern areas of Colombia and Venezuela. The staple is used in commercial yarns that range from 100s to 140s, upwards. Counts of 300 have been spun for experimental and exhibition purposes. These fine yarns are used in the best grades of organdy, voile, batiste, and handkerchief linen. The strength and twisting properties of the staple are of the best. It has a range of one to two inches in length, and when below 1⅛ inches has to compete with "long staple" Uplands. The average staple range is over 1½ inches. Sea Island is silklike in feel, smooth, and gives the best of results when manipulated.

COTTON, SULPHURIC ACID ON. Concentrated acid causes cotton to swell and become a gelatinous mass, from which water precipitates a starchlike body known as an amyloid. This is a fundamental part of many compounds such as alcohol, fusel oil, and similar compositions. It comes from amyl, C_5H_{11}, is found only in compounds. If the cotton is allowed to remain for some time in the sulphuric acid, it dissolves.

Incidentally, parchment paper is produced by the brief action of strong acid on paper whereby a layer of amyloid is formed on the surface.

COTTON, TAR STAINS ON. Tar is used to mark the ends of bolts of cloth for identification purposes; carelessness in its use will allow it to seep through to other parts of the cut. The stains are not soluble in any bleaching compound, but may be removed by some solvent such as turpentine or benzene.

Marks can be made on cloth, in transit, by tarpaulin covers used to protect material from the elements. These stains should not occur if the pieces are handled carefully.

COTTON, THPC. A crease, flame and tar resistant applied to cottons in which a monomer of the condensation type known as THPC is used in conjunction with methylolmelamine.

COTTON, VOLATILE ACIDS ON. Hydrochloric and acetic acids will evaporate without doing any damage to the goods. Quick drying is more destructive than slow. The amount of tendering will depend on temperature and the speed of the drying operation.

Tendering also occurs when the goods are treated with salt solutions that are used in sizing and finishing—chlorides of lime, iron, and magnesium. When these salts dry, they decompose and form an acid which affects the cloth. If the acid is strong enough, the cotton will be destroyed, and on drying a white powder known as hydrocellulose is formed. This action is the one that is used in the separation of vegetable fibers from animal fibers in materials. Animal fibers are unaffected by the action.

COTTON, WANNAMAKER. Clemson Agricultural College, Clemson, South Carolina, developed this popular staple which runs from 1-inch to 1½-inches, and is uniform and strong.

COTTON, WHITE SOUR ON. Cloth, after being washed well in water, is run through an acid bath which completely destroys any bleaching powder that might have remained on the goods, and completes the bleaching. Either hydrochloric or sulphuric acid is used.

COTTONADE. Cotton suiting made to simulate worsted cassimere for men's trousers and suits. It is dyed in dark shades and is designed like worsted goods. Cottonade gives good service and is an ideal suiting fabric for the lower-priced trade in warm climates. Much of the goods are used in the south, and in South American and South African trade.

COTTON AND WOOL MIXTURES. Plain, twill and some fancy-weave materials made of two or more different yarns. The warp and filling may be different yarns, or the individual yarn may be a blend of these fibers.

COTTON-BACK SATEEN. Cloth, made in silk and rayon mills, single in construction and with good body. When made on a 5-shaft satin weave, it is called sateen; when made on an 8-end satin weave, it is known as a Venetian.

The material is finished in special widths which range from 26 to 58 inches; textures vary from 64 x 48 to 190 x 72. The use of the goods determines the texture. Cotton-back is now dyed in all colors.

This acetate, nylon, or rayon warp and cotton filling cloth is much in demand since it is used for blanket binding, comfortables, corset covering draperies, dressing gowns, bedspreads, bloomers, brassières, mattresses, pajamas, parasols, pillows, ribbons, shoe uppers, slips, suit lining, trimming, ticking, underwear, umbrella fabric. The fabric has high luster on the face while the back is dull.

COTTON BAGGING. Material made of jute, used for baling cotton.

COTTON BATTING. See BATTING.

COTTON BLEACHING. The first treatment is to chemick the goods in a dilute solution of bleaching powder or chemick in a washing machine. The cloth is then squeezed and piled in a heap so that the bleaching powder may do its work—the removal of coloring matter or pigment in goods.

The bleached goods are then washed well in water to remove traces of bleaching powder. Acid is used to counteract the alkaline action; the usual bath contains hydrochloric or sulphuric acid. This part of the procedure is called souring.

A good bleach may be judged by comparisons made with other samples. Well-bleached cloth should be pure white. Cloth that has the characteristic yellow tinge present may lose this cast by a careful blueing treatment. Ultramarine or Methyl Blue is used in the blue bag, in ordinary water at a strength of 1/200 to 1/300 of 1 per cent.

Well-bleached cloth should be free from waxy and fatty matter and bodies, lime, acid, and bleaching powder. If any acid or bleaching powder remains in the goods disintegration will soon set in.

COTTON BALES

TYPE:	DIMENSIONS:	WEIGHT:
1. American	54 x 27 x 27 inches (variable)	500 lbs. over-all, 478 lbs. legal
2. Brazilian	50 x 20 x 16 inches	250 lbs.
3. Egyptian	50 x 20 x 30 inches	700 to 730 lbs.
4. Indian and Far East	50 x 20 x 16 inches	400 lbs.
5. Mexican	53 x 33 x 46 inches	500 lbs. approximately.
6. Peruvian	45 x 25 x 20 inches	200 lbs. approximately.

COTTON BREAKER. The bands on the bales are cut by shears and, after the burlap is removed, the stock is opened up and thrown directly from the bale into the cotton breaker. This machine starts the cotton through the many processes necessary in manipulation. The stock is usually blown through large pipes from the room, in which the bales have been broken, to where the openers are located. The functions of the openers are to free the cotton from as much dirt as possible; get rid of the leaf, chaff, pod, and so on, which may have clung to the fiber even in the cotton's passage through the gin, in both the first- and second-time ginning.

The openers also roll the cotton into a manageable lap form or condition so that it may be easily handled.

COTTON CARD, REVOLVING FLAT. The purpose of this machine is to cleanse the cotton, lay the fibers parallel, condense them into a sliver form about the size of a man's thumb. The action of the card is that of what might be termed a rough combing. The draft on the machine is from 90 to 120. The lap from the finisher picker is fed into the card. This is 40 inches wide and weighs 40 pounds. The sheet lap that is fed in weighs from 12 to 16 ounces per yard; the sliver delivered weighs 40 to 60 grains per yard.

The course of the cotton through the machine is as follows: from the feed rollers, it goes to the licker-in, a saw-tooth, revolving roller that loosens the fibers and passes them onto the cylinder. Here, the fibers are laid straight, by passing between the fast-revolving cylinder, which is covered with fine wire known as card clothing, and revolving flats that are covered with steel wire or clothing. The cylinder goes from 450 to 900 r.p.m.; the flats from 4 to 7 inches per minute. The flats are studded with wire that is ten numbers finer than that of the cylinder. Actual carding occurs only between the flats and cylinder; all other rollers are of auxiliary nature. The doffer, the next roller in order, receives the cotton from the cylinder, carries it around for a half-revolution, and then loses the fibers by means of the doffer blade. This saw-tooth-edged comb or blade

has an oscillating motion that takes the fibers cleanly from the doffer. The 40-inch, diaphanous web is condensed, after leaving the doffer knife, by two 3-inch calender rolls and a small funnel or trumpet, through which the web enters to be condensed into a rope form. This sliver form is then passed upward into the soiler-can attachment and is led into the revolving coiler-can as carded sliver. See Illustrated Section.

COTTON CLASSER. The United States Cotton Standards Act of March 4, 1923, decreed that a classer was a person who obtained a license to classify cotton and be able to certify to the description of cotton in accordance with the official cotton standards as set by the Department of Agriculture. The classer is interested chiefly in the grade, staple length, and all aspects of the character of the cotton in question.

COTTON CLOTH, TYPES OF.

1. GRAY CLOTH: Unbleached material as it comes from the loom. Greige refers to yarn-dyed shirting and kindred fabrics from the loom.

2. CONVERTED CLOTH: That which has been bleached, printed, or dyed after being taken from the loom.

3. COLORED WOVEN CLOTH: Yarn or skein-dyed cloth.

COTTON CLOTHING, USES OF COTTON IN.

1. ACCESSORIES: Handkerchiefs, belts, gloves.

2. ATHLETIC: Bathing suits, robes, uniforms.

3. COATS: Jackets, jumpers, top, rain.

4. COSTUMES: Carnival, party, theatrical.

5. DRESSES: Evening, house, school, sport.

6. FOUNDATION GARMENTS: Brassières, corsets, girdles.

7. HOISERY: Dress, sport, work.

8. INFANTS' WEAR: Bibs, diapers, wrappers.

9. SHIRTS: Business, dress, sport, work.

10. SLEEPING, LOUNGING: Coats, gowns, pajamas, robes.

11. SUITS, PANTS: Overalls, slacks, summer suits.

12. UNDERWEAR: Shirts, shorts, slips, union suits.

13. UNIFORMS: Industrial, military, professional.

COTTON COMBING MACHINE. A machine which prepares the ribbon lap stock for spinning into fine yarn by removing short fibers, foreign matter, dirt, neps, and so forth, and by straightening the remaining fibers into a parallel arrangement.

COTTON CONDENSING. The dividing of the wide sheet of cotton fibers that have been taken from the doffer roller on the carding frame into a number of narrow ribbonlike strands which, when acted upon by the leather belts and rollers of a condenser, are formed into loose heavy strands called roving, ready for spinning. Roving, incidentally, means stock which is one step removed from being spun yarn.

COTTON DISEASES. Both plant and boll are susceptible to disease. Plants are affected by fungus, microscopic worms, or improper nutriment-anthracnose, root rot, rust, wilt, and other troubles. The boll is affected by the boll weevil, pink bollworm, leaf worm, cotton flea hopper, cotton louse, and others. Havoc wrought by disease often runs into hundreds of thousands of dollars.

COTTON DRAFTING, SOME SYSTEMS OF.

Le Blan-Roth System: This method of drafting is done with a single apron whose purpose is to obtain continuous contact with the stock along the length that is subject ot the drafting action. The apron is driven from the back roll, its regular movement being insured by the manner in which the back roll surface is cut. The tension supplied by the tension roll and the pressure applied to the top back roll are sufficiently heavy to extablish the necessary grip needed to draw the roving forward from the creel and for definite drafting purposes.

The apron is supported by a smooth metal plate over which it slides, the light roll resting on the apron as it passes over the plate. The control rolls which under suitable conditions may be less than one-half inch in diameter, are held in position and are separately adjustable by cap nibs. The control rolls, which keep the roving and apron in continuous contact, exert pressure which accounts for the fiber control and resistance to drafting.

There is a slight difference in the control exercised when a strand of cotton is drawn over a flat surface. In the former method, fibers, which are longer than the setting distance, are drawn over a convex surface, setting up an additional binding and retarding force among the fibers in the strand. This is absent in the latter case.

The object of the back light roll is to supplement the control exercised by the front roll. This permits any length fiber to be drawn forward by the front rolls without any detrimental disturbance to the stock as a whole.

The arrangement allows the use of either one or two light top rolls, the weight, diameter, and surface character all of which may be varied according to requirements. All the top rolls are carried by adjustable cap nibs which facilitate adjusting the setting distance to suit varied staple length and other conditions. The fact that only the top control rolls require adjustment for setting purposes is an important advantage.

The top clearer can be placed in good working position on the front and back rolls, being well clear of the light middle rolls, the under-clearer being placed in the usual position.

Casablanca System of Cotton Drafting: This system uses the double apron arrangement in its work. It is one of the earliest, if not the first, of the modern, modified drafting arrangements. The system differs from the single-apron method and the floating toproll system in that the stock, which follows a straight path through processing, is controlled by a pair of flexible leather aprons. These aprons carry it forward under pressure which varies from a definite nip at the back to almost zero at the front.

Pressure is applied to the top apron roll by a saddle which is weighted from the front in order to obtain sufficient grip to exert a brake draft or, if required, to release some of the binding effect of twist. As the strand of cotton passes through, it is subjected to slight pressure between the aprons which carry it forward, exerting an effective control on the displacement of the fibers, and restraining any undesirable movement until they are individually seized by the nip of the front pair of rollers.

Sefton and Lee System of Cotton Drafting: This method uses three pairs of drafting rolls, the top-center one being a petented roll. It consists of a spindle approximately 5/8 inch in diameter at the center and turned down at the ends allowing shells of similar diameter in the center boss

or driving part to fit quite loosely. The shells and center boss are connected together by a single leather cot drawn over and secured to both.

By these means, the shells are rotated by the spindle, the leather-covered shells resting on the fluted surface of the bottom rolls, the flutes of which are cut across the full width.

The contact between the fluted bottom roll and the leather-covered boss insures definite driving of the top-roll spindle, and as the weight of the spindle does not affect the pressure between the shells and the bottom roll, adequate weight can be obtained for satisfactory driving purposes. Being of flexible nature, the shells move eccentrically relative to the axis of the spindles and rest on the bottom roll. The amount of clearance between the shells and the spindle should, without being excessive, be sufficient to allow the shells to work freely and exercise pressure without interference, but at the same time prevent, as far as possible, undesirable eccentricity of movement. This roll represents an attempt to combine definiteness of driving with very slight pressure on the roving stock.

COTTONETTE. Low-priced dress goods made of one-third wool and two-thirds cotton. Covers a number of fabrics found in the trade today.

COTTON FABRIC USES, THE UNITED STATES GOVERNMENT LIST OF. The Department of Commerce, in a publication covering this subject, has issued the following list of uses for cotton fabrics, and it should prove of great value to the student, engineer and layman:

ABRASIVES (Emery cloth, etc.): Cheesecloth, drill, duck, jean, Osnaburg, sheeting, tag cloth, and twills used for backing.

ADHESIVE PLASTER: Cheesecloth, crinoline, moleskin, sheeting, muslin.

ADVERTISING: Batting and wadding, bunting, cambric, cheesecloth, drill, duck, felt, flannel, imitation leather, lawn, muslin, oilcloth, Osnaburg, print cloth, ribbon, sheeting, tapes of many kinds.

AIRCRAFT: Airplane and balloon fabrics as covering, duck for propeller blades (impregnated and compressed) and airplane socks (field guides as to velocity of wind at time of landing). See also list under AUTOMOBILES.

APRONS, HOUSEHOLD, and so on: Butcher's linen, chambray, chiffon, crepe, cretonne, dimity, duck, drill, flannel, lace, gingham, madras, muslin, Oxford, percale, plaid, prints of many

types, sheeting, ticking, tapes, braids, fringes, voile.

ARMBANDS, GARTERS, SUSPENDERS: Braids, elastic cord, elastic fabrics, hickory cloth, webbing, felt for brassards.

ARTIFICIAL FLOWERS: Buckram, crinoline, drill, cotton-back duvetyne, imitation leather, muslin, nainsook, organdy, print cloth, sateen, cotton-back satin, sheeting, soisette, tulle, velours, cotton-back velvet, velveteen.

ASPHALT CASES: Shredded cotton as binder.

ATHLETIC AND SPORTING GOODS:
BATTING: In padding boxing gloves, for shoulder pads, mattresses.

DUCK: For backstops, and bags in golf, baseball, volley ball, golf targets, kayaks, stretchers, creels, shell bags, shinguards, and protectors of many types, surfboards.

ELASTIC FABRIC: For supports, gores in apparatus.

NETS: For use in tennis, basketball, lacrosse, as backstops, etc.

TUBING: For covering golf club heads, and other athletic supplies.

WEBBING: For use in uniforms and straps of various types.

ATHLETIC UNIFORMS: Batting, duck, holland, jersey cloth, khaki cloth, nainsook, Oxford, rep.

HUNTING SUITS: Bedford cord, corduroy, duck, hickory cloth, imitation leather, jean, jersey cloth, khaki cloth, moleskin, oilcloth, rep, rubberized fabric, waterproof fabric.

SHIRTS: Broadcloth, cotton burlap, cottonade, crash, denim, drill, duck, hickory cloth, holland, jersey cloth, hose.

TICKING: For use in mattresses.

AUTOMOBILE CURTAINS AND TOPS: Imitation leather; rubberized and waterproof fabrics. See also list under DRAPERIES.

AUTOMOBILES: Awnings, upholstery, tires, straps, luggage, trunks, roofing, automobile curtains and tops, cleaning cloths, cushions, pillows, electrical supplies, gaskets, gears, linoleum, shock absorbers, transmission, and brake lining.

AVIATION: Airplane fabrics for wind indicators; duck for field markers and roof markers; tarpaulins for protection of unhoused planes. See AIRCRAFT.

AWNINGS, CANOPIES, BEACH SHADES, ETC.: Awning stripes, denim, drill, khaki cloth, Osnaburg, sheeting, tapes, ticking, braids, cord, fringes, tape, and webbing for trimming.

BABY CARRIAGES: Batting, bedford cord, braids, corduroy, cords, elastic cords, fringes, tapes and laces as trimmings, imitation leather; oilcloth, waterproof fabrics.

BACKING (Shoe leathers): Duck; sheeting.

BAGGING (Baling): Baline, cotton burlap, Osnaburg.

BAGS: Canton flannel for jewelry, silverware bags. Cheesecloth for bags for dyes, herbs, spices, and tea. Crash for work bags, seed bags. Crepe for household bags; cretonnes, ginghams and muslins for laundry, shopping, work, clothespins, wardrobe. Denim and drill for clothes, shoes; for bean-bags and bags for coin, gold; duffle bags, dunnage and sea bags; mailbags; bags for masons' tools, news, and miners (coal, ore and dirt); nose bags; vacuum-cleaner bags; cotton-picking bags; shell bags.

Osnaburg for bags for fertilizer, grain, lime, nitrates, salt, seed, soap, starch. Sateen for clothes-, hat-, and shoebags. Sheeting for bags for clothes, silverware (napped), shoe, feed, grain, salt and bags for sugar (lining in jute bags); waterproof fabrics for bathing-beach bags.

BANDAGES: Sheeting, muslin, narrow fabrics, cheesecloth, gauze.

BASES (Protectors against scratching): Baize, felt.

BASKETS: Duck.

BATHING SUITS: Knit goods, sateen, satin with cotton-back.

BATHROBES: Blanket cloth, corduroy, éponge, flannel, ratine, terry cloth.

BATHTUBS, BASINS, BUCKETS: Duck, waterproof fabrics.

BEACH BAGS: Terry cloth, prints.

BEACH PADS: Awning stripes, duck, imitation leather, batting, rubberized fabrics, waterproof fabrics.

BEACH ROBES AND COSTUMES: Basket-weave fabric, beach cloth, brocade, chambray, corduroy, crash, crepe, cretonne, duck, gingham, lawn, madras, moire, muslin, Oxford, piqué, plush, pongee, poplin, ratine, sateen, cotton-back satin, seersucker, soisette, terry cloth, cotton-back velvet, velveteen, Venetian.

BEADS (Tire): Enameling duck, sheeting.

BEDSPREADS: Cretonne, damask, dimity, flannel, gingham, Jacquard fabric, muslin, organdy, pongee, poplin, print cloth, sateen, cotton-back satin, seersucker, embroidery braids, fringes and lace for trimming.

BEE VEILS: Muslin.

BELTING AND CONVEYERS: Braids, drill, duck, Osnaburg, scrim for starch aprons in laundry machinery, sheeting, tapes, triple fabric, woven belting.

BELTS (Men's and women's): Artificial leather, braid, cord, oilcloth, webbing.

BIAS BINDINGS: Cambric, lawn, percale, twill.

BIBS (Baby): Basket-weave fabric, batiste, broadcloth, cambric, crash, crepe, dimity, gingham, madras, muslin, oilcloth, pajamas checks, piqué, pongee, poplin, rubberized fabrics, terry cloth, swiss.

BINDINGS: Braid, cambric, duck, lawn, muslin, nainsook, print cloth, sateen, tape, thread, webbing.

BLANKETS: Blanket fabric.

BOATS AND CANOES: Duck for collapsible boats, canoe covering, sails. See also lists for MARINE SUPPLIES, AWNINGS, UPHOLSTERY, CUSHIONS, SPORTING GOODS.

BOOKBINDING: Book fabric, buckram, cheesecloth, drill, duck, imitation leather, oilcloth, Osnaburg, percaline, print cloth, sheeting.

BOOKS: Muslin, sheeting, print cloth.

BRASSIERES, CORSETS, GIRDLES: Batiste, calico, cambric, coutil, drill, duck, elastic fabric, Jacquard fabric, jean, lace, cotton-back satin, sateen, sheeting, tape, webbing.

BRIDGE AND TUNNEL DODGERS: Cord, duck.

BROOMS, BRUSHES AND WHISKS: Duck, sheeting, twine, velveteen.

BUFFERS: Cheesecloth, denim, duck, felt, flannel, Osnaburg, sheeting. See list for ABRASIVES.

BUILDING TRADES: Listed under DROP CLOTHS, TARPAULINS, FLOOR COVERING, ROOFING, WALL COVERING, WEATHER STRIPPING.

BUTTONS: Practically all fabrics that are used for women's and children's wearing apparel.

CAPS: Men's and boy's caps of beach cloth, Bedford cord, buckram, corduroy, crash, eiderdown, elastic fabric, felt, hickory cloth, holland, khaki, madras, covert, plush, poplin, rep, rubberized fabric, serge, suede, terry cloth, waterproof fabric, tape and webbing. Babies' caps of lawn, lace, mull, muslin, organdy, outing flannel, piqué satin. Boudoir caps of batiste, broadcloth, calico, cambric, chambray, gingham, Chantilly lace, chiffon, crash, crepe, cretonne, lace, lawn, marquisette, muslin, netting, piqué, pongee, ribbon, sateen, scrim, soisette, voile. Interlining and lining for caps are made of canton flannel, cotton-back satin, flannelette, sateen, suede fabric. Yachting caps of duck.

CARCASS (Tire): Duck.

CARD LACE (Loom): Twine, cord.

CASES (Gun, level, rod): Duck, drill, imitation leather, sheeting, tape, thread. Waterproof fabric for lining: Flannel and napping sheeting.

CASKETS: Lining of braid, broadcloth, brocade, flannel, casement cloth, charmeuse, chiffon, crepe, eiderdown, fringe, longcloth, moire, muslin, nainsook, net, organdy, piqué, pongee, poplin, scrim, soisette, suede fabric, terry cloth, Venetian, velours, velveteen. Batting is used for padding, and casket cloth for covering.

CHAFER STRIPS (Tire): Square-woven fabric.

CHAIRS AND COTS (Beach and porch chairs, stools, army cots, etc.): Awning stripes, cotton burlap, duck, Osnaburg.

CHUTES (Fire escape, feed, water): Plain duck, coated duck.

CLEANING CLOTHS: Mops of drill, cheesecloth, knit goods, tape, twine, webbing. Pot cleaners of tinsel yarns. Polishing cloths of cheesecloth, drill, duck, sheeting suede fabric.

COATS, WOMEN'S: Beach cloth, broadcloth, brocade, Cheviot, corduroy, crepe, drill, duck, duvetyne with cotton-back, flannel, hickory, jean, jersey cloth, khaki cloth, moire, plush, serge, velvet with cotton-back, velveteen.

COLLARS, MEN'S: Bedford cord, broadcloth, longcloth, madras, muslin, print cloth and comparable fabrics for shirting and collar material, tape, and webbing for binding.

COMFORTABLES AND QUILTS: Coverings and linings of cambric, challis, cotton-back satin, drill, duck, holiand, marseilles, muslin, sateen, sheeting. Fillers use batting and wadding, linters, wastes.

CORNUCOPIAS: Sheeting.

CORSETS AND GIRDLES: Basket-weave fabric, brocade, coutil, elastic fabric, lace sateens, tape for binding, twill.

COSTUMES, CARNIVAL AND THEATRICAL: Batiste, batting broadcloth, bunting, cambric, calico, cheesecloth, chiffon, corduroy, crash, crepe, cretonne, crinoline, drill, duck, flannel, gingham, jersey fabric, knit goods, marquisette, mull, muslin, nainsook, organdy, percale, piqué, pongee, poplin, ratine, ribbon, sateen, cotton-back satin, seersucker, serge, sheeting, soisette, swiss, terry cloth, velours, velveteen, voile, webbing.

COTTON-PICKING SACKS: Listed under bags.

CURTAINS: Basket-weave fabric, bobbinet, bunting, cheesecloth, chiffon, crash, fringe, lace, lawn, marquisette, muslin, net, Osnaburg, scrim, soisette, swiss, tinsel, several types of novelty yarns.

CUSHIONS AND PILLOWS: Ticking—awning stripes, cambric, cretonne, damask, denim, drill, duck, muslin, organdy, print cloth, cotton-back satin, sheeting. Cushion and pillow covering —awning stripes, basket-weave fabric, beach cloth, broadcloth, brocade, cambric, calico, chambray and chambray gingham, charmeuse, Chantilly lace and net, chiffon, corduroy, cottonade, crepe, damask, denim, duck, duvetyne, fringe, gingham, Indian linon, Jacquard fabric, jean, khaki cloth, lawn, longcloth, cadras, marquisette, moire, moleskin, muslin, nainsook, novelty yarns of many varieties, organdy, pajama checks, pin checks, plush, pongee, poplin, print cloth, ratine, rep, ribbon, sateen, scrim, seersucker, soisette, suede, swiss, tapestry, terry cloth, velours, velvet, Venetian, voile. For pillow cases—broadcloth, pongee, Indian linon, muslin, print cloth, sheeting.

DAUBERS: Twine.

DESKS: Duck for backing of roll-top desks; imitation leather and linoleum for covering of desktops.

DOCTORS' AND ATTENDANTS' UNIFORMS: Beach cloth, broadcloth, butcher's linen, cambric, duck, muslin, sheeting.

DOG NETS: Sash cord.

DOLLS: Batting, batiste, bird's-eye, broadcloth, cambric, charmeuse, challis, cheesecloth, corduroy, cottonade, cotton waste for filler, crash, crepe, cretonne, damask, denim, dimity, duck, duvetyne, embroidery, felt, flannel, gingham, holland, imitation leather, Jacquard fabric, jersey cloth, lace, lawn, muslin, nainsook, net and netting, novelty yarn, oilcloth, organdy, Oxford, pajama checks, percale, pin checks, piqué, plaid, plush, pongee, poplin, print cloth, ratine, rep, ribbon, rubberized fabric, sateen, cotton-back satin, scrim, seersucker, sheeting, soisette, stockinet, swiss, terry cloth, thread, tufts, velour, velveteen, Venetian, voile.

DRAPERIES: Basket-weave fabric, beach cloth, cambric, casement cloth, corduroy, crepe, cretonne, damask, drill, duck, etamine fringe, gingham, hammock fabric, Jacquard fabric, marquisette, momie cloth, moire, muslin, net, Osnaburg, plush, poplin, sateen, cotton-back satin, sheeting, soisette, tobacco cloth in printed effects, tapestry, tarlatan, terry cloth, velours, cotton-back velveteen, voile.

DRESS GOODS AND DRESSES, GENERAL: These include practically every type of cotton fabric, from the very fine sheers to the coarse, heavier grades of materials. The basic weaves used are plain, twill and satin. Derivations of the plain weave are also used as in the case of seersucker, chambray, crepe, dimity, gingham and madras. Other small repeat weaves are also used—herringbones, baskets, double satins, ribs, twilled baskets, etc. Fancy designs are often a feature of some of these dress-goods materials. Knitted fabrics are also used in this category. The construction, yarn count, texture, surface-effect, pattern, and fin-

ish of the various fabrics determine largely their end-use.

DRESS SHIELDS: Cambric, rubberized fabric.

DROP CLOTH: Drill, duck, Osnaburg, and sheeting are used by painters and other artisans to protect floors and furniture.

EAR MUFFS AND PROTECTORS: Outing flannel, cotton-back velvet, velveteen, braid, thread.

ELECTRICAL SUPPLIES: For use as insulation upon magnets, armatures and wires, the following fabrics are used: Braid, drill, duck, muslin, Osnaburg, print cloth, sheeting, tape for cable identification, tubing, as well as twine.

END CLOTHS (Bleaching and dyeing): Drill, print cloth, sheeting.

EYE SHADES: Duck, drill, sheeting, imitation leather.

FANCYWORK AND EMBROIDERY: Basket-weave fabric, broadcloth, cretonne, chiffon, crash, damask, dimity, flannelette, gingham, jersey cloth, lawn, madras, muslin, nainsook, net, Oxford, pongee, poplin, sateen, swiss, sheeting, sponge fabric, terry cloth, voile, cotton-back velvet, velveteen.

FARM USES: See lists under HUSKING GLOVES, HAY COVERS, WINDBREAKS, BAGGING, HARNESS, TARPAULINS, WORK CLOTHES.

FILLER (Shoe sole): Felt.

FLAGS: Bunting, print cloth, sheeting, tobacco cloth, tape, fringe.

FLAPS (Tire and splash): Osnaburg in a twill weave, sheeting, and flannel are used for tire flaps; imitation leather is used for splash flaps.

FLOOR COVERING: Duck, covert, felt for soundproofing and insulation, linoleum, Osnaburg, sheeting, terry cloth, webbing and braid for trimming oilcloth.

FOUNDATIONS ON UNPLASTERED WALLS FOR PAPERING: Cheesecloth, tobacco cloth.

FUMIGATION (Citrus fruit culture): Duck.

FURNITURE, CAMP: Drill, duck, awning stripes.

GASKETS: Duck, felt, sheeting.

GAS MANTLES: Knit goods.

GEARS: Drill or duck in layers, impregnated and compressed.

GLOVES: Canton flannel, drill, flannel, jersey cloth, knit goods, lace, tape, suede fabric, tubing, webbing.

GRASS CUTTER (for lawn mowers): Duck.

HAMMOCKS, GARDEN SWINGS: Awning stripes, braid, cord and cordage, denim, duck, fringe, hammock cloth, netting, tape, webbing. See also list for AWNINGS.

HAMPERS: Canvas.

HANDBAGS: See list for POCKETBOOKS,

PURSES, AND HANDBAGS.

HANDKERCHIEFS: Batiste, chiffon, gingham, longcloth, marquisette, muslin, nainsook, organdy, pongee, print cloth, soisette, swiss, voile.

HARNESS: Cordage, duck, tape, webbing. Collar facing and pads use awning stripes, chambray, denim, drill, duck, felt, print cloth, sheeting, ticking, webbing. Saddles used duck, felt, imitation leather, oilcloth, Osnaburg, webbing.

HATS: Men's hats use military cord, duck, felt, imitation leather, khaki cloth, netting, oilcloth, ribbon, rubberized fabric, sateen, cotton-back satin, webbing. Women's hats use braid, buckram, chiffon, cord, crepe, haircloth, holland, imitation leather, khaki cloth, lace, moire, netting, sateen, cotton-back satin, tarlatan, terry cloth, velours, velvet, voile, velveteen, waterproof fabric.

HAY COVERS: Duck.

HEDDLES FOR LOOMS: Twine.

HEEL PADS AND CUSHIONS (Shoes): Flannel, felt.

HEELS, ORTHOPEDIC: Duck.

HOSE (Fire, Garden): Drill, duck, Osnaburg, sheeting, triple cloth, tubing.

HUSKING GLOVES: Drill, flannel.

ICE-CREAM CONTAINERS: Duck serves for covering and liner.

IMITATION LEATHER: Drill, duck, jean, moleskin, nainsook, Osnaburg, sateen, sheeting.

INFANTS' WEAR: Basket-weave cloth, broadcloth, cashmere, chiffon, crash, eiderdown, flannel, flannelette, fleece, gingham, Indian linon, jersey cloth, knit goods, lace, muslin, nainsook, organdy, pin checks, piqué, pongee, poplin, ribbon, sateen, cotton-back satin, serge, swiss, velours, velvet, velveteen, voile.

INNERSOLES FOR SHOES: Buckram, felt, duck, and Osnaburg for re-inforcing.

INSULATION, ELECTRICAL: Cambric, muslin, sheeting, print cloth.

KIMONOS: Basketweave fabric, beach cloth, brocade, chambray, corduroy, crash, crepe, cretonne, foulard, gingham, lawn, madras, moire, Oxford, muslin, piqué, plush, pongee, poplin, ratine, sateen, cotton-back satin, soisette, swiss, velours, cotton-back velvet, velveteen, Venetian.

KITES, BOX: Muslin, sheeting.

LABELS, MARKERS, TAGS: Cheesecloth, imitation leather, oilcloth, print cloth, rubberized fabric, sheeting, tape, webbing. See also list under ADVERTISING.

LAMP SHADES: Basket-weave cloth, braid, broadcloth, brocade, Chantilly lace, lace and net, chiffon, chintz, cord, crash, crepe, cretonne, dimity, embroidery, fringe, gingham, holland, lace, lawn, marquisette, muslin, nainsook, net, novelty yarn effects, organdy, pongee, print cloth, sateen, cotton-back satin, sheeting, soisette, swiss, tapestry, tinsel yarn, voile.

LEGGINGS: The men's types use drill, duck, khaki cloth, and corduroy for facing. Children's leggings use canton flannel, corduroy, eiderdown, velours, cotton-back velvet, velveteen.

LIFE PRESERVERS: Drill, duck, sheeting, tape.

LIGHTERS, CIGAR AND CIGARET: Absorbent cotton, imitation leather, wicking.

LININGS: Alpaca, baize, beach cloth, beaver fabric, brilliantine, brocade, buckram, calico, cambric, chambray, charmeuse, cheesecloth, chiffon, chintz, cottonade, crepe, crepe de Chine, crinoline, domett, drill, duck, duvetyne, eiderdown, flannel, foulard, gingham, Indian linon, jean, knit goods, madras, moire, moleskin, moreen, mull, muslin, net, organdy, Osnaburg, Oxford, percale, percaline, piqué, plush, pongee, print cloth, rayon alpaca, sateen, cotton-back satin, scrim, serge, sheeting, suede, silesia, soisette, swiss, tarlatan, ticking, twill, velveteen, cotton-back velvet, velours, Venetian, voile, wigan.

LINOLEUM: Cotton burlap, Osnaburg.

LUGGAGE FOR BOXES, TRAVELING BAGS: Canvas, duck, imitation leather, and oilcloth are used for the body. For protecting purposes the following fabrics are used: brocade, burlap, cretonne, damask drill, duvetyne with cotton backing, hickory cloth, moleskin, poplin, ratine, sateen, sheeting, tarlatan. Linings and interlinings use broadcloth, brocade, buckram, cambric, charmeuse, cheesecloth, Cheviot, chintz, cottonade, cretonne, denim, drill, duck, flannel, gingham, hickory cloth, jean, moleskin, Osnaburg, plush, sateen, sheeting, velours, cotton-back velvet, velveteen. See also list under TRUNKS.

MACHINERY: See lists for AUTOMOBILES, BELTING AND CONVEYORS, ELECTRICAL SUPPLIES, GASKETS, GEARS, PACKING, TRANSMISSION, AND BRAKE LINING.

MAPS, CHARTS: Cheesecloth, duck, muslin, print cloth, sheeting.

MARINE SUPPLIES: Batting and wadding and waste for calking; duck for boat covers, clothing caps, boat fall tub covers, fenders, hatch covers, mast collars, sails and sea drags. See lists for HAMMOCKS, LEGGINGS, LINOLEUM, MATTRESSES, FLOOR COVERINGS, MACHINERY, TARPAULINS.

MATTRESSES: Fillers use batting and wadding, linters, waste, felt. Ticking, covering and trimming use braid,

chambray, cord, cretonne, drill, denim, duck, muslin, print cloth, sateen, cotton-back satin, sheeting, tape, ticking, tufts, webbing.

MEAT COVERING: Cheesecloth, drill, Osnaburg, sheeting, stockinette.

MEDICAL, SURGICAL AND SANITARY SUPPLIES: Sheeting and muslin serve as the base for backing for adhesive plaster; batting and wadding are used for absorbent cotton; cheesecloth, duck, and gauze are used for bandages.

Coutil, elastic cord, and elastic fabric, tape, and webbing find use in many types of supporters. Elastic banding and hose are used in the medical field.

MILK-CAN JACKETS: Duck is used as a covering and liner.

MINING: See lists for VENTILATORS, BAGS, WORK CLOTHES.

MUSICAL INSTRUMENTS: Felts for pads in pianos, wind instruments; webbing in pianos.

NAPERY: Broadcloth, crash, crepe, damask, gingham, pongee, sheeting.

NECKWEAR, MEN'S: Beach cloth, crash, damask, flannel for lining, knit goods, pongee, print cloth, sateen sheeting, velveteen.

NECKWEAR, WOMEN'S: Basket-weave fabric, batiste. braid, broadcloth, brocade, chiffon, corduroy, dimity, drill, duck, cotton-back duvetyne, flannel, fringe, lace, lawn, marquisette, moire, mull, muslin, net, novelty yarn effects, organdy, pin checks, plaid, pongee, poplin, ratine, ribbon, sateen, cotton-back satin, soisette, swiss, terry cloth, velours, velvet with cotton backing, velveteen, voile.

NIGHTGOWNS: See list for PAJAMAS AND NIGHTGOWNS.

NURSES' UNIFORMS: See list for DOCTORS' AND ATTENDANTS' UNIFORMS.

OILCLOTH: Cheesecloth, drill, duck, muslin, print cloth, sheeting.

OVERALLS: Denim, drill, duck, dungaree, Cheviot, cottonade, covert, hickory cloth, jean, khaki cloth, sheeting, ticking. Webbing and tape are used in trimming.

OVERSHOES: Canton flannel, cheesecloth, drill, duck, flannelette, fleece, knit goods, moleskin, muslin, print cloth, sateen, sheeting, webbing.

PACKING, MOTOR AND PUMP: Asbestos fabric, Canton flannel, cheesecloth, drill, duck, muslin, Osnaburg, sheeting, wadding, waste, yarns. These are used in plain or impregnated forms.

PAJAMAS AND NIGHTGOWNS: Basket-weave fabric, batiste, broadcloth, cambric, chambray, chiffon, crepe, dimity, flannel, flannelette, gingham, knit goods, madras, nainsook, Oxford, organdy, pajama checks, percale, pongee, print cloth, sateen, soisette, voile.

PAPER, PACKING AND COVERING REINFORCED: Cheesecloth, thread, and twine are used as re-inforcement upon a paper background, usually waterproofed.

PILLOWS, GARDEN: Bathing, imitation leather.

PIPE COVERING: Muslin, sheeting, duck, Osnaburg.

POCKETBOOKS, PURSES AND HANDBAGS: Basket-weave fabric, brocade, Chantilly net and lace, corduroy, crepe, cotton-back duvetyne, fringe, Jacquard fabric, madras, moire, moleskin, plush, poplin, ratine, ribbon, sateen, suede fabric, tapestry, terry cloth, velours, velvet, velveteen.

POCKETS, LOCKER: Drill, duck, muslin, sheeting.

PONCHOS: Waterproof fabrics of many types, rubberized materials.

POWDER PUFFS: Knit goods, plush, suede fabric, velours.

PROTECTORS, ATHLETIC BODY: Batting and wadding, drill, duck, khaki cloth.

RADIO: Felt for soundproofing purposes in studios, silence cloth for instrument base pads, and tapes and braids for head sets. See list for ELECTRICAL SUPPLIES.

RAINCOATING, RAINCOATS: See WATERPROOF FABRICS, RUBBERIZED FABRICS.

RE-INFORCED USE FOR TIRES: Square-woven fabric.

RESTRAINT APPARATUS: Duck is used for sheeting of various types and textures for sheets, strait jackets, and similar articles.

ROBES AND WRAPS: Brocade, crepe, cotton-back duvetyne, Jacquard fabric, knit goods, marquisette, moire, net, lace, novelty yarn effects, plush, cotton-back satin, serge, tapestry, cotton-back velvet, velveteen.

ROLLERS FOR TEXTILE FINISHING MACHINERY: Duck in compressed layer formation.

ROOFING AND DECK COVERING: Drill, duck, waterproof fabrics.

RUBBERIZED FABRICS: Cambric, cottonade, drill, duck, cotton-back duvetyne, jean, lawn, Osnaburg, print cloth, sateen, sheeting, ticking.

RUGS AND CARPETS: Fringe, twine, webbing yarn.

SAFETY DEVICES: Cord for nets, duck for life belts and preservers, fire nets, and chutes.

SCARFS: Basket-weave fabric, beach cloth, brocade, cambric, chambray, Chantilly lace, chiffon, crepe, cretonne, damask, dimity, flannel, fringe, lawn, madras, moire, organdy, plaid, pongee, print cloth, ribbon, cotton-back satin, soisette, suede, velours.

SCENERY, THEATRICAL: Drill, duck, netting, Osnaburg, sheeting, cordage, rope, twine.

SCREENS AND PARTITIONS: Airplane fabric, awning stripes, basket-weave cloth, beach cloth, broadcloth, brocade, cotton burlap, casement cloth, corduroy, cottonade, crash, damask, drill, duck, duvetyne with cotton-back, fringe, gingham, hickory cloth, holland, Jacquard fabric, khaki cloth, marquisette, moire, momie cloth, muslin, Oxford, pongee, plush, poplin, ratine, sateen, sheeting, tapestry, velours, cotton-back velvet, velveteen.

SHIRTS: Airplane fabric, balloon cloth, basket-weave cloth, Bedford cord, broadcloth, Cheviot, cotton crepe, dimity, domett, drill, éponge, flannel, khaki, madras, marseilles, moleskin, Oxford, percale, pin checks, piqué, pongee, soisette, swiss, wigan.

SHOCK ABSORBERS, SNUBBERS: Webbing.

SHOES: Brocade, drill, duck, print cloth, cotton-backed satin, sateen, terry cloth, cotton-backed velvet, velveteen for shoe uppers.

Duck is used for heel stays while eiderdown and felt are used in innersoles. Duck and Osnaburg are used in innersole reinforcing and duck, drill, sheeting and flannel are used for lining. Haircloth and netting find use for interlining, buckram for reinforcing and stiffening of shoe tongues. Drill is used to reinforce seams and as underlay for eyelets, buttons, buttonholes and tips. Flannel and sheeting are used as underlay for tips while narrow fabrics of various types are utilized to reinforce seams. Shoe trimming is cared for by narrow tape, beaver cloth, brocade, and duck. Osnaburg is used to line rubber shoes and elastic fabric is used for goring; drill, felt, and flannel are used in heel pads for which wadding is used for build-up. Duck and sheeting find use for backing-up the upper fabrics used in shoes and also support thin leather often used in shoes. Felt serves as filler between the innersole and the outersole.

SHOWER CURTAINS: See lists for WATERPROOF FABRICS, RUBBERIZED FABRICS.

SHROUDS: Batiste, brocade, broadcloth, crepe, lace, longcloth, moire, muslin, net, plush, pongee, sateen, soisette, swiss.

SILENCE CLOTH: Baize, felt, molleton.

SMOCKS: Broadcloth, brocade, calico, crash, crepe, cretonne, duck, gingham, lawn, longcloth, moire, muslin, percale, pongee, poplin, print cloth, sateen, sheeting, soisette.

SNUBBERS: See list for SHOCK ABSORBERS.

SPORTING GOODS: See list for ATHLETIC AND SPORTING GOODS.

STENCILS FOR WALL DECORATIONS: Lace.

STRAINERS, FILTERS, PRESS CLOTHS: Cheesecloth, drill, duck, sheeting.

STRAPS: Duck, ticking, webbing.

SUITS, MEN'S: Flannel, serge, tropical cloth.

TABLE COVERINGS (Runners, Sets, Doilies): Basket-weave cloth, beach cloth, broadcloth, cambric, chambray, chiffon, crepe, cretonne, damask, dimity, embroidery, flannel, gingham, knit goods, lace, lawn, madras, organdy, Oxford, piqué, pongee, sateen, cotton-back satin, sheeting, sponge cloth, velours, voile. As silence cloth, asbestos fabric, felt, flannel, imitation leather, oilcloth, plush and velvet made with cotton-back are used.

TANKS, EXHIBITION, SWIMMING: Duck.

TAPES: MEASURING: Narrow fabric, print cloth, sheeting.

TARPAULIN: Drill, duck, Osnaburg, sheeting.

TENTS: Awning stripes, cordage, denim, drill, duck, Osnaburg, serge, sheeting, tape, webbing. See list under AWNINGS.

THEATRICAL GOODS: See list for ARTIFICIAL FLOWERS, COSTUMES, DECORATIONS, SCENERY, TANKS.

TIRES: Tire cord and cord fabric are used for the carcass while square-woven fabric is used for valve pads, chafer strips, carcass and reinforcement. Doup or leno-woven fabric is used for breakers, and enameling duck and sheeting are used for beads.

Flannel and Osnaburg made with a twill-weave construction are used for flaps, with duck, imitation leather, oilcloth, rubberized and waterproof fabric used for tire covers. Tire-repair material consists of duck and holland.

TOILET KITS: Canton flannel, crepe, cretonne, damask, denim, duck, imitation leather, jean, plaid, poplin, rubberized and waterproof fabrics, sateen and sheeting.

TOWELS AND WASHCLOTHS: Dish towels: Cottonade, crash, damask, glass cloth, Osnaburg. Bath towels: Novelty yarn effects, sponge cloth, terry cloth. Washcloths: Knit goods, sponge cloth, terry cloth. Face towels: Crash, damask, huckaback, knit goods, lace, novelty yarn effects. Tapes are much used in trimming towels and washcloths.

TOW LINES, AUTOMOBILE: Webbing.

TOYS: Absorbent cotton, airplane fabric, alpaca, awning stripes, baize, balloon cloth, basket-weave cloth, batiste, batting, beach cloth, broadcloth, brocade, calico, cambric, chambray, Chantilly lace, cheesecloth, chiffon, chintz; cord, rope and twine; corduroy,

cottonade, crash, crepe, cretonne, crinoline, damask, denim, diaper cloth, dimity, drill, duck, duvetyne, elastic fabric, felt, flannel, gingham, gauze, hickory cloth, Indian linon, Jacquard fabric, jean, jersey cloth, khaki cloth, lawn, longcloth, madras, moire, moleskin, muslin, nainsook, narrow fabric of many types, oilcloth, organdy, Oxford, pajama check, percale, piqué, plush, pongee, poplin, print cloth, ratine, rep, ribbon of many varieties, sateen, cotton-back satin, seersucker, scrim, sheeting, soisette, stockinet, swiss, tapestry, terry cloth, ticking, velours, cotton-back velvet, Venetian, voile, waterproof and rubberized fabrics, webbing.

TRANSMISSION AND BRAKE LINING FOR AUTOMOBILES: Webbing.

TRIMMINGS FOR WOMEN'S WEAR APPAREL AND ACCESSORIES: Basket-weave cloth, bobbinet, braid, broadcloth, brocade, chiffon, corduroy, crash, crepe, cretonne, denim, drill, duck, cotton-back duvetyne, elastic fabric, flannel, fleece, gingham, Indian linon, lingerie checks, longcloth, marquisette, moire, muslin, net and lace, organdy, pin checks, pongee, poplin, ratine, ribbon, cotton-back satin, sateen, scrim, seersucker, sheeting, soisette, swiss, tapestry, terry cloth, velours, cotton-back velvet, velveteen, Venetian, voile.

TRUCKS: Duck, webbing for straps and trimming, and cretonne.

TRUNKS: Cheesecloth, chintz, cotton burlap, drill, duck, felt, gauze, hickory cloth, imitation leather, jean, moleskin, muslin, sateen, sheeting, tape, ticking, tufts, cotton-back velvet, velveteen, waterproof and rubberized fabrics, webbing.

TYPEWRITER RIBBONS: Cambric, sheeting, tape.

UMBRELLAS AND PARASOLS: Awning stripes, broadcloth, cretonne, duck, fringe, gloria goods, muslin, print cloth, sateen, serge for covers, sheeting, umbrella gingham. See also list for WATERPROOF AND RUBBERIZED FABRICS.

UNDERWEAR: Women's: Airplane fabric, braid, basket-weave fabric, batiste, broadcloth, brocade, cambric, Canton flannel, cashmere, crepe, charmeuse, chiffon, dimity, elastic fabric, flannelette, fleece, gingham, Indian linon, knit goods, lingerie checks, longcloth, madras, muslin, nainsook, net and lace, Oxford, pajama checks, pin checks, poplin, pongee, swiss, tape, voile. Men's: Airplane fabric, balbriggan, batiste, broadcloth, dimity, flannelette, knit goods, longcloth, madras, muslin, nainsook, Oxford, print cloth, seersucker, sheeting.

UNIFORMS, MILITARY: Butcher's linen, chino, dungaree, duck, gabardine, khaki cloth.

UPHOLSTERY: Filler: Batting and wadding, felt, linters, waste. Trimmings: Braid, lace, embroideries, twine, webbing. Covering: Armure, Bedford cord, brocade, broadcloth, cambric, charmeuse, Cheviot, cretonne, corduroy, crinoline, damask, denim, drill, duck, haircloth, imitation leather, Jacquard fabric, moleskin, momie cloth, muslin, print cloth, Osnaburg, plush, rep, tapestry, sateen, sheeting, velveteen, Venetian. Slip Covers: Alpaca, awning stripes, cambric, chambray, crash, cretonne, chintz, denim, drill, duck, gingham, Indian linen, muslin, sateen, sheeting.

UPPERS FOR SHOES: Brocade, drill, duck, print cloth, sateen, cotton-backed satin, terry cloth, cotton-back velvet, velveteen.

VALVE PADS FOR TIRES: Square-woven fabric.

VENTILATORS FOR SCREENS: Cheesecloth, duck for air ducts, print cloth, scrim, sheeting.

WALL COVERINGS NOT DRAPERIES: Armure, brocade, cotton burlap, cheesecloth, damask, duck, momie cloth, muslin, oilcloth, print cloth, Osnaburg, sheeting, tapestry. Used plain, impregnated, coated with paint, or in combination with other materials.

WASHCLOTHS: Listed under TOWELS.

WATERPROOF FABRICS: Airplane fabric, balloon cloth, denim, drill, duck, gabardine, jean, moleskin, muslin, sateen, serge, sheeting.

WATER WINGS: Rubberized fabric, waterproofed fabric.

WEATHERSTRIPPING: Batting and wadding, felt, sheeting, webbing, yarns for particular use.

WHIPS: Braid, imitation leather, oilcloth, sheeting, webbing.

WINDBREAKS: Duck.

WINDOW SHADES: Cord, duck, fringe, holland, imitation leather, oilcloth, print cloth, sheeting, tape, tobacco cloth, waterproof fabric.

WINDSHIELDS FOR MOTOR CYCLES: Duck, khaki cloth.

WORK CLOTHES, MEN'S: Bedford cord, corduroy, crash, denim, drill, duck, dungaree, jean, jersey cloth, Oxford, rep, sheeting, swansdown, ticking.

COTTON FELT. An undyed cotton cloth, heavily napped on both sides. Serves as silence and preserving cloths under table covers.

COTTON FERRETS. British expression for inexpensive bindings and unsized tapes, usually colored black or gray.

COTTON FIBER, NATURAL TWISTS OR CONVOLUTIONS PER INCH IN THE.

TYPE OF COTTON	MIN. PER INCH	MAX. PER INCH	AV. PER INCH
Sea Island	240	360	300
Egyptian	175	280	228
Brazilian	158	260	210
American-Orleans	144	240	192
Indian-Surat	120	190	155

In general, the finer the fiber the greater will be the number of twists per inch. Reversal in twist is an additional advantage in cotton spinning because it increases the locking action among the fibers. See Illustrated Section.

COTTON FIBER, WEIGHT OF AMERICAN. It varies from 2 to 6 micrograms per inch, with an average of 4.5 micrograms per inch. A 2-microgram fiber, which is the fine and light fiber, is equivalent to 0.7 denier and the 6-microgram fiber is equivalent to 2.1 denier; the 4.5 microgram average, 1.6 denier. It is for this reason that a 1.5-denier rayon staple fiber should be used in mixtures with cotton. The size seems to match well with the size and weight of the cotton fiber.

COTTON FLANNEL. See FLANNEL, FLANNEL FINISH; FLANNELETTE, COTTON.

COTTON FOULARD. Cotton fabric made to simulate silk foulard.

COTTON FUTURES. They are contracts to deliver cotton, of a designated grade and staple, at some future time. This is often done after the contract has been placed. In this event, the seller does not own any cotton, but assumes a risk of being able to purchase and deliver the cotton in question, to the consignee at the specified time. There is no futures market in Sea Island cotton; it is bought outright on contracts to give the purchaser so many bales per month, until the contracts expires.

COTTON GIN. See GIN.

COTTON GOODS, ACID ACTIONS ON. Cottons, when treated with concentrated acids, are generally injured. Temperature and the time allowed for the action to take place have an effect, as well.

AMMONICAL COPPER SOLUTION: This dissolves the cotton completely but does not affect animal fibers such as wool and silk. If run through the solution rapidly, and then quickly dried, the cotton will not dissolve but will swell into a jelly-like mass. This is the Willesden Method of treating cotton goods. Care and judgment must be used in the determination of proper-strength acid to use if it is to be employed in some finishing operation.

SULPHURIC ACID: This causes the fibers to swell at once. If the solution is diluted quickly with water, a compound or body is formed which is known as an amyloid—the fundamental part in many compounds such as alcohol and fuse oil. Amyloids occur in compounds only and are derived from C_5H_{11}.

If the cotton is allowed to remain in the acid for a longer time, it is usually destroyed.

NITRIC ACID: Goods treated with acid and then heated will rapidly disintegrate.

NITRIC AND SULPHURIC ACIDS: Taken together, they are not detrimental to cotton. However, when applied separately to the goods, the latter acid seriously affects the material.

In combination, the acids do not dissolve cotton any quicker and they form a new compound which has great commercial value. This is nitrocellulose, which is explosive and inflammable, and goes under the common name of guncotton.

DILUTE MINERAL ACID: When used cold, it has little effect. However, if the cotton is treated with the acid and it is not removed by washing, the material will disintegrate in time, as the acid becomes stronger through the evaporation of the water present.

ORGANIC ACID: It can be used on cotton without any harmful effect, but nonvolatile organic acids, as oxalic, if allowed to dry on the fiber at high temperatures, will cause tendering.

COTTON GOODS, ACID TENDERING OF. The goods should be boiled in water. A solution of methyl orange is added to this bath. If the material is tender, the water will turn red. If no acid is present to weaken the goods the water will remain orange in color.

COTTON GOODS, ALKALI TENDERING OF. The material is boiled in water, and then a solution of alcohol or phenolphthalein is added. If the stock has been tendered by some alkali, the water becomes a reddish color.

COTTON GOODS, BLEACHING POWDER PRESENT ON. The cloth should be soaked in water to dissolve any bleaching powder that may be present. A solution of iodide of potash is added to the water bath. If bleaching powder is present, a blue color will be observed, otherwise, there will be no color change.

COTTON GOODS, OIL STAINS ON. The result of careless handling of the goods through the mill. Faulty weaving will likewise cause these marks. If the stains are not too severe, they are permitted to remain in the goods until the bleaching operation. Large stains are taken care of by oil remover.

Stains that are allowed to remain in the material will spoil the goods because oil seems to have more or less affinity for dyestuff.

Mineral oil stains are not removed in bleaching. They should be cared for by the use of a solvent. This type of stain must be removed with care, since they will show to marked disadvantage in cloth, whether in the white or in the dyed state.

COTTON GRADING TABLE, UNITED STATES.

1. Middling Fair.
2. Strict Good Middling.
3. Good Middling.
4. Strict Middling.
5. Middling—all grades of cotton are compared with this type.
6. Strict Low Middling.
7. Low Middling.
8. Strict Good Ordinary.
9. Good Ordinary.

There is a more rigid grading of the cotton than the above table. Sometimes, in large cotton mills, where many grades and varieties are used, it is necessary to grade the cotton very closely. The plan used is to divide the above table into twenty-seven distinct grades. Each of the grades in the above table is divided into three parts. For example, Good Middling, in the rigid grading method, would be classified as High Good Middling, Good Middling, Low Good Middling.

COTTON GRASS. It comes from the fruit of the reed mace and is used for wadding or stuffing in upholstery.

COTTON GRAY WASH. An optional treatment. It consists of passing material that has come from the singe house through water, and allowing it to remain on the floor overnight. This softens the starchy matter that is present in the sizing and allows fermentation which changes the starch into a sugary substance that is soluble in water. Thorough washing follows the treatment.

COTTONIN. A Russian substitute for cotton, made from Kendir fiber subjected to a chemical treatment to make it simulate cotton.

COTTON INCORPORATED. Representing the cotton producer, Cotton Incorporated takes care of the marketing sales functions as well as research on and off the farm. It has no affiliation with any other cotton organization or governmental agency. It is the successor to Cotton Producers Institute with offices in New York City; Raleigh, North Carolina; Dallas, Texas; Washington, D.C.; and Los Angelese, California.

COTTON INSECTS. These pests include among others the boll weevil, pink bollworm, cotton flea hopper, cotton louse, and leaf worm.

COTTON, IRON RUST STAINS ON. These are caused by wet goods coming in contact with iron before or during bleaching. They are detected and distinguished from all other stains by moistening the goods with weak hydrochloric acid, followed by a weak solution of yellow Prussiate of potash, which causes the stain to turn blue.

COTTONIZE. Reduction of some of the major bast fibers to a staple length of cotton—from ½ inch to about 2 inches.

COTTON LINTERS. Short-fiber stock that is used to make absorbent cotton, guncotton, rayon, celluloid, and other products from cotton and its seed. Linters are not used to make cotton yarn. The fibers are obtained from second-time ginning of the cotton. First-time ginning is done in the plantation areas at the community gins.

Linters come in a brown sheet form and cost only a few cents per pound. Their greatest use is in making rayon for which they serve as the base. When treated with strong acids, linters form the basis for guncotton which is used for explosives. The term should not be confused with lint.

COTTON MANUFACTURE. The processing of cotton from field to fabric follows:

1. PREPARATION: Testing of the soil for planting and cultivation. Begins in early January and completed by the first of March. Frost and other climatic conditions are given consideration.

2. PLANTING: Begins about the middle of March to the middle of April; by this time all planting is completed.

3. PICKING: May begin in most southerly sections in July. "First bales" come in during July. Picking lasts until early September. Three crops are usually obtained, and it is often early December before final picking is consummated.

4. GINNING: Separation of fiber from seed; one third of the weight is cotton fiber, other two thirds, seed and foreign matter. First-time ginning occurs on the plantation or at the "community gin."

5. DE-LINTING, SECOND-TIME GINNING: Done in the large cities of the South—to separate the short fibers not taken off seeds in the first-time ginning so that they may be used in industry. These short, brown fibers are known as linters.

6. BALING: Compressing of cotton into bale form. It is wrapped in burlap. Average American bale weighs about 500 pounds, and the dimensions are usually 54″ x 27″ x 27″. Legal bale weighs 478 pounds.

7. BREAKING, PICKING: In the mill the picker machines break up lumps and clods of cotton. Loose waste matter is removed, as well, by the revolving, tumbling action of the breaking machines. Cotton comes from the finisher-picker in lap form, 40 inches wide, and about 40 pounds in weight.

8. CARDING: Cleanses the fibers and disentangles them to considerable degree. Changes the bulk, raw stock into a sliver which is a loose rope-form of fibers about the size of a man's thumb. Sliver will weigh from 40 grains to 60 grains per yard. Twist is not applied in carding of the fibers.

NOTE: Carded cotton goes from the card directly to the drawing frame and skips the sliver-lap machine, ribbon-lap machine, and the comber frame.

9. COMBING: Completes the cleansing of the cotton and removes the short fibers known as noil. Combing puts the long, choice, desirable fibers into a silken sliver. The sliver-lap machine and the ribbon-lap machines have aided in the auxiliary work.

10. DRAWING: Carded stock is run once or twice through the drawing frame in sliver form to double and redouble the cotton. Combed stock is run from two to six times through the drawing frame to increase the doublings and redoublings.

11. SLUBBER, ROVING FRAMES: These condense the sliver into slubbing form. The diameter of the slubbing is about the size of a lead pencil. The roving frame still further condenses the slubbing into roving, which may be compared in size with the lead in a pencil. Roving also signifies a form of fibers that have been drawn and twisted in order to be made ready for spinning into yarn. Roving is one step removed from finished, spun yarn.

12. SPINNING: Cotton is spun into yarn on the mule frame or the ring frame. Drawing, twisting, and winding are the three chief operations of either machine. Yarn is the final product of spinning which is the result of all of the foregoing operations.

13. CLOTH MANUFACTURE: This includes weaving fabric on the loom, making knitted cloth on a knitting frame, and the manufacture of braided or plaited material on braiding, lace or similar machines. Hundreds of materials are produced by each of these three methods of making commercially valuable products.

14. FINISHING: It may be said that "all cloth is made in the finishing." A permanent or temporary finish may be given to fabrics. Finishing includes all the treatments given cloth after it

leaves the loom in the so-called gray goods condition.

COTTON PICKER. 1. One who picks cotton in the field by hand. 2. A machine, one of the greatest inventions of all time, perfected by John Rust and his younger brother, Mack, in 1933. The machine was first tried out on a cotton field at the Delta Experiment Station, Stoneville, Mississippi. From 1949 on, the farm-implement business fairly exploded with these autmatic pickers. Allis Chalmers Co., Inc., International Harvester Co., Inc., and the John Deere Company, Inc., manufactured the machines and by 1952 over 2 million bales were harvested by their use. Incidentally, down through the ages, more than four thousands attempts were made to perfect the cotton picker machine. Ninety-five percent of the present American crop is now harvested by machine. See Cotton Picker or Scutching Machine.

COTTON PICKER OR SCUTCHING MACHINE. This is often referred to as the opening picker machine. From the mixing room, the cotton is fed to the opener by means of a chute, which is even with the floor of the mixing room. The reason for this is to expedite the work.

The cotton comes down the chute to the hopper feed, which helps to break the clumps by means of a revolving, spiked cylinder over traveling, spiked lattices. From the hopper feed, the stock is delivered to the porcupine, a spiked cylinder about 40 inches in diameter. It travels at a speed of about 500 r.p.m. This cylinder breaks up the cotton, with the help of bars that are underneath it. Through the openings between the bars, all types and kinds of loose, foreign matter drop into a receptacle, which, when filled, can be cleaned.

If too much cotton falls through the bars, they may be closed or the spaces can be made smaller.

The cotton is then drawn to the cages by means of a fan, placed under the machine. If there is not sufficient draft, this may be regulated by means of dampers on the opener side.

The cotton passes between the cages to the calender rollers, where it is condensed by its passage between these rollers. The last roller on the machine, the lap roller, winds the cotton into a web or lap form.

COTTON PLANT. See COTTON; also COTTON, PROPERTIES OF.

COTTON PONGEE. Staple fine combed cotton which has very high luster, mercerized and Sanforized. Ideal for underwear and light outer garments. See PONGEE.

COTTONS

NAME:	STAPLE LENGTH:	GROWN IN:
Sea Island	1½ to 2 inches	Florida, Mexico, Central American nations
Egyptian	1¼ to 1¾ inches	Egypt
Arizona	1¼ to 1¾ inches	Arizona, New Mexico, Southern California
Uplands	¾ to 1¹⁄₁₆ inches	Carolinas, Tennessee, Louisiana, Alabama, Mississippi
Peruvian	1¼ to 1½ inches	Peru, Arizona
Indian	½ to ¾ inches	India and adjacent areas
Chinese	½ to ¾ inches	China, Korea, Japan

See also Illustrated Section.

COTTON QUOTATIONS. This is governed by Middling Cotton of the United States on the futures exchanges of New York and New Orleans. The 15/16-inch staple is taken with qualities being above or below. Quotations are in terms of a point, 1/100 of a cent.

COTTONS, AMERICAN. World War II may be taken as the dividing line between the old-time American cottons and the newer concept of these staples. In 1928, for example, there were about 600 varieties raised, while today about 30 improved staples are used for the entire crop. Acre-yields have increased about 24 per cent in the past 15 years. Machines have taken over much of the old hand and mule power since 1939. At that time only a few mahcines were in use, whereas at the present time 10,000 pickers and close to 20,000 strippers are used to remove cotton from the fields. This pace is advancing constantly.

Much of our cotton is now grown in irrigated, high plains and delta areas. Greatest progress in staple improvement occurs in the Southwestern and West cotton belts. A different but improved type of cotton farming is developing in the Southeastern area.

Before World War II, the prominent staples included Benders, originally raised along the banks of the Mississippi River; Canebrake, an Alabama cotton; Durango, from the Imperial Valley of California; Peelers, of the delta area; Gulf from the lands that border on the Gulf of Mexico and also raised in the Mississippi River basin; Meade, the cotton that superseded Sea Island cotton; and Texas, raised in Arkansas and Oklahoma as well as in Texas.

With the demise of these cottons, newer strains have come into being which have proved their worth and made possible the cutting down from several hundred types to the 30 or so now used. Uplands, of course, still prevails and holds the same high position that it held before the War.

Compared with the old staples, the fiber of today is greater in length and strength, both of which make for easier processing, improved yarns, and better fabrics. Length and strength are now the two main factors used by breeders in making selections and crosses in varietal improvements.

The following will show the principal staples raised in the cotton areas today:

1. SOUTHEASTERN AREA: Includes those cottons raised in Virginia, the Carolinas, Georgia, Florida and Alabama. Cottons from Illinois, Kansas, and Kentucky are also included in this grouping at times.

Cottons: Acala 5675, Coker 100 Wilt, Empire WR, Sealand 542, Stonewilt 6, White Gold, Wilds.

2. DELTA AREA: Includes cottons of Missouri, Arkansas, Tennessee, Mississippi, Louisiana.

Cottons: Bobshaw 1–819, Coker 100 Staple, Delfos 531C, Delfos 651, Delfos 9169, Deltapine 14, Deltapine 15, Stoneville 2B.

3. SOUTHWESTERN AREA: Raised in Texas and Oklahoma.

Cottons: Acala 893, Hibred, Lockett, Macha, Mebane, Mebane 140, Northern Star, Oklahoma Triumph, Paymaster, Rowden 41B, Stoneville 62.

4. WESTERN OR IRRIGATED AREA: Grown in California, Arizona, New Mexico.

Cottons: Acala Mesa, Acala P18C, Acala RB, Acala Santan, Acala 4–42.

5. AMERICAN UPLANDS COTTON ACCORDING TO WHERE GROWN: Uplands is the standard staple raised here and all other cottons are compared with the fiber, in classification:

TYPE:

Hibred, Lockett, Macha (Texas).
Rowden (Arkansas).
Coker 100 Wilt (S. Carolina).
Deltapine, Deltapine-Fox (Mississippi).
Empire Wilt (Georgia).
Acala 4–42 (California).
Stoneville 2B (Missouri).
Acala 1517 (New Mexico).

The first record of cotton improvement goes back to 1806, when a superior Mexican cotton was acclimatized to conditions in Mississippi. The United States Department of Agriculture began cotton improvement in 1867, and expansion, co-ordination, and research have continued to the present day. Research is under the auspices of the Bureau of Plant Industry, Soils, and Agricultural Engineering in conjunction with other agencies of the Department and the experimental stations of the 14 cotton states. The research includes cotton breeding, genetics, improvement of cultural and harvesting practices and ginning methods, and regional studies of the effects of variety and environment on fiber and spinning properties.

From 6 to 10 years are needed to breed, stabilize, and develop an improved variety or strain of cotton so that it may be raised on a large production basis. Today, there are objective methods and improved devices for measuring structure, maturity, and fineness of the cotton fiber with a concise degree of precision. One of these methods is the X-ray diffraction pattern whereby it is possible to determine fiber structure evenly in badly weather-damaged cotton.

The Southern Regional Laboratory, Baton Rouge, La., uses a binary dye mixture to indicate the proportion of thin-walled fibers in a sample. Mature thick-walled fibers take one of the dyes while the immature or thin-walled fibers dye the other hue.

The Fiber Laboratory at the University of Tennessee has developed the Areolometer which measures fiber fineness through a surface area determination that is much more rapid than the weight-per-inch method formerly used. See COTTON, ARIZONA; COTTON, SEA ISLAND. See also Illustrated Section.

COTTONS, POLISHED. These are characterized by a high or a subdued surface luster. Thermosetting resins are united with the cotton fibers to make this luster durable. After the resins have been applied, the cloth is mechanically "buffed" until its surface has a deepseated, subdued luster or a highly polished glaze as in chintz. The resins stabilize shrinkage within two per cent. These fabrics are wrinkle-resistant, shrink-resistant, have ease of washing, and are quick to dry. They may be washed either by hand or machine, or by hand in lukewarm water with mild soap. Chlorine bleaches should be avoided. Used in dress goods, swim wear, separates, lounge wear, men's and boys' shirtings. Lawn, percale, and sateen are ideal examples of polished cottons.

COTTONS, WRINKLE-RESISTANT.

The term "wrinkle-resistant" on a tag identifies a group of modern cottons which have been treated chemically to maintain a smooth appearance. They wrinkle less than untreated cottons. Wrinkles that might occur hang out overnight. There is only a slight degree of difference between these cottons and those termed "wash-and-wear." Wrinkle-resistant cottons generally need some pressing after laundering, but the amout of ironing needed is so greatly reduced, and can be done so easily and quickly, that these cottons offer major time-saving advantages as well as lasting neatness. Wrinkle resistance is achieved by passing the cotton cloth through a chemical bath which contains a resin. The material is then baked in heat chambers to fix the chemicals into the fibers in the yarn in the fabric. This, in a sense, gives each fiber a "memory," so that when creased or bent it "remembers" to return to its original shape, thus smoothing out the wrinkles.

COTTONSEED. Two thirds of the weight of cotton prior to ginning consists of the seed, which is separated from the lint cotton during actual ginning. The seed, oval in shape and from ¼ to ½ inch in length, is covered with a very tough hull.

Some types of cotton come clean after ginning while others retain the short-fuzz linters. First-time ginning occurs on the plantation or at the community gin; second time ginning or delinting takes place in the cotton cities of the South.

The chief by-products of cotton approximate the following: linters, 15 per cent; cake and meal, 30 per cent; hulls, 40 per cent and cottonseed oil about 15 per cent.

Approximate estimates as to what one ton of cottonseed will produce are lint, 30 pounds; meal, 675 pounds; hull, 950 pounds; oil, 40 gallons.

The seeds of cotton, up to shortly after the turn of the century, were not thought to be of much value. Today the business done in cottonseed and its conversion into valuable products runs into millions of dollars annually.

COTTONSEED, USES FOR.

1. CAKE AND MEAL:

Stock feed: For cattle, hogs, poultry, sheep.

Fertilizer: Field crops, gardens, lawns.

Miscellaneous: Dyestuffs, food for human beings.

2. OIL:

Food: Fats, margarine, oils.

Coated fabrics: Artificial leather, linoleum.

Soaps, Cosmetics: Creams, lotions, soaps.

Miscellaneous: Explosives, medicines, paints.

3. LINTERS:

Bedding: Comforts, counterpanes, mattresses, quilts.

Cellulose: Base for acetate and rayon, cellophane, explosives, films, lacquers, plastics.

Upholstery: Automobiles, furniture.

Yarns: Cordage, mops, wicks.

Miscellaneous: Absorbent cotton, batting.

4. HULLS:

Cellulose: Acetate and rayon, explosives.

Furfural: Plastics, synthetic resins.

Packing, stuffing: Baseballs, insulation.

Stock feed: Bran, roughage.

COTTONSEED HULLS. They make up about half the weight of ginned seeds. This crushed outer covering of the seed is taken out at the oil mill. Used chiefly for cattle fodder.

COTTONSEED MEAL. Cotton cake is ground after the oil has been taken from the seed. A greenish-yellow powder, rich in nitrogen, is obtained, which is used for fertilizer, cattle feed, and other purposes.

COTTONSEED OIL. This valuable cotton by-product is pale yellow in color, almost odorless and tasteless, and oily in substance. It is much used in the manufacture of cooking and salad oils, fats, and margarine, and serves as the oil used in the lower-priced cans of sardines.

COTTON SHELL. British term for fragments of the hulls and kernels not taken out in the first or second-time ginning of the cotton. This waste is found in yarn after the fibers have been manipulated.

COTTON SLED. See COTTON STRIPPER.

COTTON'S PATENT FULL-FASHIONED KNITTING MACHINE. A machine patented by William Cotton, Loughborough, England, in 1864. Remarkable in that his technique of knitting has not been modified to any substantial degree to this day. The machines have changed from Cotton's original four-section type, to six, eight or ten knitting sections. The gauges range from 15 to 27 in the outerwear knitting field while the number of needles used would be ⅔ of the gauge or equivalent to 1½ inches. Thus, a 21-gauge frame would have 14 needles to the inch. The crosswise measurement of the needle bar is about 30 inches.

COTTON SPECIES. The main cotton species are:

1. *Gossypium hirsutum*, source of American Uplands cotton.

2. *Gossypium barbadense*, includes

Sea Island and most Egyptian cottons.

3. *Gossypium herbaceum,* includes Asiatic and Indian cottons.

COTTON STAPLE. See COTTON FIBERS, CHARACTERISTICS OF; STAPLE.

COTTON STRIPPER. A machine sometimes used to harvest cotton; has a series of closely spaced fingers through which the plans project as the stripper passes over the row of shrubs. All matter that clings to the boll, as it is plucked, is carried along with it.

COTTON SUITING. See COTTONADE.

COTTON SYSTEM. The method of manufacture of cotton from raw material into yarn. With some modifications, the cotton system is now employed for the manipulation of other major textile fibers from raw stock to yarn condition. The gamut of machines in the cotton system include bale breaker, picker, card, sliver lap, ribbon lap, comber, drawing frame, slubber, intermediate frame, roving frame, ring or mule spinning frames. The cone winder, twister, spooler, and warper take care of the yarn after it has been spun and is to be made ready for weaving.

COTTON TAFFETA. Belongs to the poplin-rep fabric family and is used for slip covers or upholstery fabric. The filling-wise cords may vary in size to give a rather fancy effect.

COTTON TREE. Refers to *Gossypium arboreum* and includes staple raised in Arabia and Ceylon. The tree-like plant has a height of 12 to 18 feet, the fibers are greenish in cast and rather coarse; the flowers are purplish.

Gossypium religiosum is native to India. The perennial plant lasts from five to six years while staple is fine, silken and of good length; unfortunately, however, little of the type is produced when compared with other world staples. In fact, it is never used as a field crop. Its cultivation in India is likely more ancient than that of any other nation.

COTTON TROPICAL. Made to simulate tropical worsted, this lightweight fabric is made from stock-dyed blends and comes in plain or striped patterns.

COTTON WARP, COTTON-WARP UNION. Staple or fancy cloths made with cotton warp and animal fiber filling. "Cotton-warps" can stand more friction, chafing, and tension than animal fibers; hence, their use for some particular purpose. The use of cotton warps is an economic measure, and some woolens and worsteds do not call for any type of yarn better than these warps.

COTTON WASTE. Lint and other yarn refuse which accumulates during the manufacturing process. The softer parts are used for padding, and the harder, coarser pieces for paper manufacture. Waste from the carding machine is used by some mills. Varying percentages are mixed with regular cotton in making part-waste Osnaburgs and other materials.

COTTON WASTES. In the conventional methods of spinning cotton yarn, a rather substantial amount of fiber put into process never actually gets into the yarn during spinning. It is taken out either unavoidably in the cleaning processes, or intentionally because of it being shy in staple length as the manipulation progresses from machine to machine in sequence. It is called waste, but actually it is not a true waste because it is not really wasted but is used in the spinning of other yarns or in some other form of processing into a product.

The approximate world consumption on an annual basis is two-billion pounds of cotton waste out of a total of 12-billion pounds of cotton fiber. The disposition by marketing or sale of this material is of vital importance to the cotton manufacturing plant, and is one of the decisive factors in the success or failure of a textile mill. From 15 per cent to 20 per cent of the mill's raw cotton becomes what is known as cotton waste. Some of this waste is put back into production by the mill itself, generally speaking; however, other waste fiber is sold directly, or by sale arrangement, to the waste merchant specialists who work on a commission basis.

Waste is graded according to quality, from floor sweepings and picker motes through grades of fly wastes, card strippings, and comber frame noils. Another angle in the thought that the term, waste, is a misnomer, is that the waste from a high-grade premium cotton may well be, and often is, of better quality than new cotton fiber of an inferior quality.

Waste is divided into two main groups, spinnable and nonspinnable. The types not suitable for spinning include sweepings, picker wastes, and thread wastes. The latter is sometimes placed in the spinnable class by being broken back to the fibrous condition by the garnetting or hard waste machines. When left in the twisted condition, thread waste is used in wiping, cleaning, and packing. Spinnable cotton waste is often mixed with new fiber stock such as cotton, wool, and the various man-made fibers. These yarns are used in weaving and knitting of many fabrics, and the identity of the waste is lost in the finished material.

There are many items made entirely from cotton waste such as mops and mop yarns, cordage of many varieties, filler cords, and core yarns. Thus, many millions of pounds of cotton waste eventually become ingredients in whole or in part of a wide variety of products. See COTTON WASTE, WASTE MACHINES.

COTTON WAX. This waxy or resinous matter, which amounts to about 1 per cent, makes the fiber water-repellent. This coating of the fiber is removed in boiling-out the stock, yarn, or fabric.

COTTONWOOD. The fibrous bark from the tree of this name is used by American Indians for cordage, rope, twine, and very coarse, rough garments for use as shirting and trousering.

COTTON WOOL. Archaic term for regulation staple cotton used in the textile industry.

COTTON-WORSTEDS. Cloth made of cotton warp and worsted filling in imitation of an all-worsted fabric. Much used in men's and women's dress goods.

COTTON YARN MEASURES.
1. 54 inches equal one thread, the circumference of the warp reel.
2. 80 threads equal one lea.
3. 1 lea equals 120 yards.
4. 7 leas equal one hank, or 840 yards, the standard yardage in one pound of a 1s cotton yarn.
5. 1 bundle equals 10 pounds.

COTTS. Brittle, kempy parts of a sheep fleece caused by a diseased sheep or one that has not grazed properly.

COTUL. A British moss which serves as the basis for brown dyes used in coloring Harris Tweed.

COUCHING. A type of embroidery work in which a motif is developed by the use of threads, cords, etc., laid upon the surface of a material and secured by fine stitches, couching stitches, drawn through the material. Couching is either raised or flat, and it is named according to the direction of the securing stitches—basket, diamond, and others.

COULIER MOTION. A reciprocating motion which provides motive force to operate the slur cams and friction boxes on the Cotton's Patent full-fashioned knitting machine.

COUNT. The size or the number of a yarn, based on the relation between length and weight of the yarn in question. The term also means the number of warp ends and filling picks per inch in a woven fabric, the construction or the texture; the number of wales and courses in a knitted material. Yarn count is based on the number of fixed lengths per standard weight or on the number of fixed weights per standard length. In the former, coarse yarns have low numbers and fine yarns high numbers as in the case of the natural fibers with the exception of silk. In the latter instance, the coarse yarns have high numbers while the fine yarns have low numbers. Observed in silk, the man-made, and the synthetic fibers and filaments.

COUNTENANCE. The French name for a muff which was supposed to add poise, dignity, or bearing to the wearer: thus, to improve the countenance or configuration of the individual wearing the article. Popular toward the end of the sixteenth century.

COUNTER. See SATIN WEAVES.

COUNTER-CHANGE CHECKS. Material in which the adjacent checks vary in color or in weave.

COUNTERPANE. A cotton bedspread or coverlet of the raised pattern variety; somewhat on the order of Marseilles.

COUNTERSHAFT. An intermediate shaft driven by the main shaft to transmit motion to machinery.

COUNTING GLASS. Same as PICK GLASS, PICK COUNTER, LINEN TESTER.

COUNT OF CLOTH. The number of ends and picks per inch in a woven fabric as counted by an individual. If a cloth is 64 x 60, it means that there are 64 ends and 60 picks per inch in the fabric. A cloth that has the same number of ends and picks per inch in woven goods is called a square cloth— 64 x 64. Pick count is the term that is synonymous with texture and counts of cloth, in speaking of cloth construction. See Illustrated Section.

COUNTRY CLOTHS. British term for fabrics and mattings made by African natives from grasses, cotton yarns, etc.

COUNTRY DAMAGE. Damage done to cotton on the outside of bales during transit after leaving the baling press.

COUPE, COUPE'. From the French, meaning to cut. The term implies a cut or span of fabric from the Schiffli embroidery machine. The cut will range between ten and fifteen yards in length, two cuts equal "a machine of goods."

COUPLED DYES. Used for fast browns on cotton, these dyes are applied after a suitable substantive color has been applied to the goods. They serve as a developer to couple or combine with a diazotized base, usually paranitraniline. See DIAZOTIZING.

COUPLING. See JACQUARD HARNESS.

COUPLING PROCESS. The application of an organic compound to a fabric which has been dyed to produce an insoluble color on the goods.

COUPURE. French for "cut

through." The cloth is a cashmere, cut so that the lines cut through show the twill in the lengthwise direction of the cloth.

COURATARI FIBER. Native to many parts of South America, this bast fiber is used for blankets, clothing, and coverings.

COURLENE. Olefin fiber of the polyethylene group made by British Celanese, Ltd., United Kingdom. Made on the extrusion method, molten polyethylene at 300° C is forced through spinnerets and jets of plastic are cooled in air or water on emergence. The solid filaments are stretched and then set at an elevated temperature. It comes in monofilament and the spun-dyed yarns are known as Courlene-Duracol.

COURLENE X3. A range of high density polythene monofils which are used in a number of ways, such as in production of plastic floor matting, roping, netting, and twine, deck chairs, awning and blind fabrics, woven filter fabrics, and knit filters, In braid formation it is used on the outside of cables and vacuum hoses. Also used as screen fabric, radio and television "speaker fabrics." Registered trademark of British Celanese, Ltd., Great Britain.

COURNOVA. Polypropylene monofilaments used in the cordage field and in filter fabrics. Includes stiff fabrics and knitted scourers as used in the kitchen, bale twine, as well as automobile upholstery fabrics, and straw type yarns. The term is a registered trademark of British Celanese, Ltd., Great Britain.

COURONNE. The small loops on the outer edge of a cordonnet. See CORDONNET.

COURPLETA. Made by Courtaulds, Ltd., England, this tri-acetate fiber comes in bright and matt continuous filament, matt tow, and staple fiber.

COURSE. A series of stitches or loops that run crosswise in knitted fabric, corresponds to the filling in woven goods.

COURSE, KNITTING. A series of adjacent loops which form a horizontal line across the knitted fabric. Small horizontal stitches mean that more yarn has been used which results in a finer fabric, greater elasticity, and longer wear.

COURSE COUNTER. A device for registering the number of courses knitted, and then stopping the knitting machine when the desired number of courses has been knitted.

COURTAULDS NYLON. Type 6 nylon made by Courtaulds North America, Inc., in both monofilament and multifilament types. The yarn is available up to 100 denier and is satisfactory for most

textile uses.

COURTELLE. Made by Courtaulds, Ltd., England, this acrylic fiber is creamy white in color and of low density. There are two types—standard and high shrinkage.

COURTE POINTE. French term for piqué or printed cotton quilting stuffed with cotton wadding. Novelty braided edges often feature the article.

COURTOLON X10. Courtaulds, Ltd., England, makes this bulked nylon stretch yarn; application of heat is used in the treatment to achieve the effect.

COURT PLASTER. Thin silk, cotton, or nylon that is treated on the one side with medicated glue to adhere to the skin or bandage. Made in white, black, pink. The "beauty patches" of Colonial days were made of court plaster.

COVINAIR. Various types of knitgoods made of viscose rayon sold under the trademark of Industrial Rayon Company, Inc., a division of American Cyanamid Company, Inc., Wayne, New Jersey.

COVINGTONE. Trademark for several qualities of viscose rayon fabric manufactured by I.R.C. Division of American Cyanamid Company, Inc., Wayne, New Jersey.

COURTRAI FLAX. Flax that is retted in and around the city of that name in Belgium, located on the small but famous Lys River. The best retted flax comes from this area since the chemical action of the river is different from that of any other body of water in the world. Flax from all over the world is sent there for superior retting. There is also much tank retting carried on in this section with water taken from the river. Chemists have never been able to find out what there is in this noted stream that other waterways do not possess. Much work, research, and experimentation have been done on this problem, but, as yet, nothing of a positive nature has resulted.

COUTIL. The French term for drill. The material is made from a threeharness, warp-face, herringbone twill. This strong fabric, which is woven compactly, is usually higher in count and heavier than jean cloth. Some coutil is made with stripes or figured effects. The yarns used are about the same as those found in medium weight sheeting. Uses: drop curtains, corsets, brassières, surgical belts, draperies, ticking, work clothes, linings, sportswear, and suit banding for use in tropical countries.

COUTURE. French for the dressmaking or tailoring to the more exclusive trade. The meaning of the term through the French, "haute couture" (fine tailoring) has become dignified to the extent that it now signifies any outstanding dress-designing establishment, usually located in Paris, Hollywood, or New York. Most coutures are owned and operated by the couturier or couturière.

COUTURIER. A male designer of women's clothes for exclusive stores and shops.

COUTURIERE. A designer of women's clothes of the expensive type.

COVER. When fabric is well woven and gives a "full," evenly distributed appearance to the goods.

COVERED RUBBER YARN. A rubber core yarn.

COVERED YARN. A thread that partially or completely covers a core or heart yarn in a thread.

COVERLET. 1. A hand-woven bed covering made by hand weaving, crocheting, knitting, overshot work, and so forth. 2. The topmost cover of any type used on a bed.

COVERT. Twilled, lightweight overcoating cloth. Usually made of woolen or worsted yarn with two shades of color, say, a medium and a light brown. This cloth was first used as a hunting fabric, and its name is derived from a similar term in connection with field sport. Covert is rugged and stands the rigors of wearing very well. Highly desirable cloth and gives smart appearance to the wearer. The material is a staple stock-dyed fabric. Covert is also made in cotton or rayon, spun rayon, wool and spun rayon. The speckled effect is a characteristic of the goods. Used for coats, raincoats, riding habit cloth, sportswear, and suits. See Illustrated Section (Fabrics 27).

COVERT, COTTON. Made of single yarns with mock twist (half white, half black or blue, etc.) which give a flecked or mottled effect of a two-ply woolen covert yarn. Warp twill weaves are used to make the fabric. It is the lowest cost fabric of good weight for work clothes. Some of the lighter weights find use in shirting.

COVERTING. A little-used term which covers the finishing of cotton gray goods into finish cloth; contraction of converting.

COW CATCHER. A salesman who hogs all the customers.

CO-WE-NIT. Registered trademark of Karl Mayer & Cie., Maschienfabrik, Tailfingen, Wurttemberg, West Germany, for its Raschel knitting frame in which the guide bars have twice the gauge of the needle bar. The supply threads which are laid in warpwise or vertical direction stabilize the fabric and increase the elasticity in the desired direction.

CO-WE-KNIT FOR COMBINED WEAVING AND KNITTING. This process and production emanates from Sunbeam Wolsey of Ireland, in the Midleton Worsted Mills, Ltd., of this company. This process labeled as "combined weaving and knitting" makes fabric six times faster than woven goods yet provides a "woven-look." This development in warp knitting on raschel principles lowers production costs by about 75 percent, and is capable of making 20 to 30 yards a minute. The machine which makes the goods is produced by Karl Mayer Gesellschaft, Oberthausen, West Germany. The agent for the company in the United States is Mayer Textile Machinery Corporation, Clifton, New Jersey.

In the framework of the knit structure, visibility is only on the back or reverse side of the material. The face shows interlacing of warp and welt in a wide range of woven fabric surfaces. The raschel machine is now able to use spun yarns for outerwear, and fabric weights run from 5.5 ounces up to 12 ounce per yard fabrics.

On this machine, Sunbeam chiefly uses Australian 64s merino wool, a few crossbreds of 50s, and some New Zealand wool. At present, the prices for the machine range from $6,250 for the 2,500 pound, 65 inch, slow-speed frame; to $8,750 for the 3,500 pound, 124 inch model, installed in the plant.

COW HAIR. Fiber used in coarse carpet yarns, blankets, and cheap felted goods. The industry centers in Siberia. The hair, which is from 1½ to 5 cm. in length, is classed in the following manner:
1. Thick, stiff, beard hair.
2. Soft, fine, beard hair.
3. Very fine, soft "wool hair."

COWHIDE LEATHER. Made from the hides of cows, although the term is applied loosely to characterize any leather tanned from hides of animals of the bovine type.

COWL. 1. The hood worn by monks of religious orders. Within recent years cowls have become popular in fashionable attire for evening cloaks and wraps. 2. The nightcap worn by Scottish folks is known by this name. 3. See COWL NECKLINE.

COWL NECKLINE. A soft fold or drape of material at the front neckline.

COWTAIL. A very coarse fleece more like hair than wool, poor in grade and working properties.

COX ROYAL ARCH COTTON. Early-maturing Georgia cotton which has a staple of about 1 inch and a lint yield of about 32 per cent.

CRAB. A hand device used to stretch carpet a trifle in a small area where a knee kicker or a power stretcher cannot be used. See Crabbing, Crabbing Machine, Knee Kicker, Power Stretcher.

CRABBING. Process used after excess moisture is taken from cloth by the hydro-extractor or whizzer. In the hydro-extractor, the circumference plate of the machine is perforated with a great number of holes, which in the revolving action of the cylinder, through centrifugal force, take the water from the cloth. A drain pipe takes off this excess. Whizzing takes only a few minutes and the great number of revolutions per minute of the perforated cylinder leave the cloth in a fairly dry condition. The extractor is filled solidly with the yarn or cloth that is to lose this excess water and moisture.

Following this operation, the cloth is stretched to its full width for further treatment, and now crabbing performs the function of "setting cloth." Crabbing also "loosens" the goods. The material is run over a cylinder roller series to prevent wrinkles. The cylinders are immersed in hot water, and the cloth rotates for about fifteen minutes. The cloth, after an hour or so, is returned to the setting bath under a boiling pressure. This gives the required setting. Sometimes, hot and cold baths are alternated in the process, dependent on the particular conditions.

CRABBING MACHINE. The roller-equipped machine used to crab woolens and worsteds, by running cloth in a hot water bath followed by a cold water bath. The operation may be repeated more than once. Its purpose is to set the yarns in the material and to prevent ordinary shrinkage. See CRABBING.

CRACK. 1. A blemish in cloth caused by a mispick; runs in filling direction. 2. Taffeta and other fabrics which may have been improperly treated in finishing may crack, or split, because of slow chemical action upon the yarns.

CRACKERS. British expression for cotton yarns which contain minute bunches of foreign matter such as short fibers, motes, shives, slubs, etc. Found more in ring spun yarn than in mule spun yarn.

CRADLE. The rods that support the set of cards on a Jacquard loom. Also implies the device used to guide and support the leather bands on some long-draft spinning frame.

CRAFT UNION. A labor organization, the membership of which is restricted to individuals who possess or work at a specific skill or trade—such as diemakers, carpenters, electricians, spinners, weavers.

CRAMMED. 1. Cloth with lines in the warp direction caused by faulty reeding which may have come from swollen dents in the reed. 2. Another name for cockled fabric. 3. Cloth with a higher warp or filling texture than it is supposed to have. 4. Crammed stripes are purposely set in some fabrics for effect, as in shirtings, and handkerchief borders. It is done by cramming more than the usual number of ends in the particular reed splits which will guide the yarn into the material. If a filling-crammed motif is desired, an arrangement can be made to have the take-up motion stop on certain picks to give the effect.

CRANE. In 1775, this knitter of Nottingham, England, developed the warp knitting frame. In this machine there was a thread for every needle instead of a single thread for all the needles. Practically any kind of thread could be used on the machine and his findings showed that the warp threads acted as pillars upon which the traversing threads could be carried. His work was improved upon by subsequent lacemakers in the manufacture of machine-made lace.

CRANK. A device for causing rotation of an axis for converting rotary action into reciprocating motion.

CRANKSHAFT. A shaft that bears one or more cranks. The crankshaft on a loom, for example, changes the circular motion of the driving pulley into the reciprocating motion of the lay of the loom. See CRANK.

CRANKY CHECKS. Colored-cotton woven goods distinguished by solid lines which show in the warp or the filling, or in both. The effect is caused by the warp thread arrangement and the lifting of the harness shafts. Many novel effects are possible in this dress-goods and shirting fabric.

CRAPAND. French for mispick in weaving fabric.

CRAPE. A sheer, lightweight black worsted worn by the clergy. When used in dress-goods trade the fabric comes in all colors and white.

CRAPONNE. A cheap, stout thread used for furniture guipure. See GUIPURE.

CRAQUELLE. Also known as coffinnet, this cotton machine-made lace has an irregularly shaped net which has the outline of a coffin.

CRASH. Cloth made from cotton or linen, or from combinations of these fibers. The material is rugged, substantial in feel, comes in white or natural shades. It may be made with stripe effects as in toweling, suitings, doilies,

decorative cloths. Other uses of crash include dresses, cap cloth, summer coatings. The yarn is strong, irregular, and smooth. The fabric is of fairly good texture. Fiber content must be declared.

CRAVA-CLEAN. The Cravenette Company, Inc., a division of Crown-Metro, Inc., Providence, Rhode Island, owns this registered trademark product. This soil release method produces a soil release finish, imparts a durable press, and is applied in a one-bath treatment on precured or postcured finishes. The product also imparts anti-soil redeposition as well as anti-static properties, and is effective on all types of manmade fiber blends, 100 percent cottons, and rayons.

CRAVAT. A mercenary regiment of Croatians serving in the French army around 1650 is responsible for this term. The soldiers were called Cravates by the French and were recognized by long strips of woven or lace fabric tied around the neck and hanging loosely on the chest. Upon the approval of Louis XIV, the style became very popular in France and spread elsewhere in due time. This decoration, before the advent of neckties as we know them today, also "covered the heart" and facetiously was said to be a covering and protection of the heart. The term also is a name for the four-in-hand necktie of today.

CRAVENETTE. A finishing process that is nearing the century mark in usage. This product makes fabrics waterproof, rainproof, and spotproof. The name is now a registered trademark of The Cravenette Company, Inc., a Division of Crown-Metro, Inc., Providence, Rhode Island. The name was coined by a Bradford, England, manufacturer, and finisher named Wiley who named it for the street in which he lived, Craven Street. The term is now applied to waterproof or water resistant fabrics in the United States regardless of their nature; the proper name of the cloth, however, not being changed by the application of the process to them, in accordance with a decision of the United States Custom House Service.

CRAWFORD COTTON. An early-maturing South Carolina cotton which has a staple of 1 inch to 1⅛ inches; lint yield is about 32 per cent.

CRAZY QUILT. A quilt made by sewing a great number of odds-and-ends pieces together to form a covering or quilt. The pieces used in the ordinary quilt vary in size, shape, color, material, and design. The finished product shows unique design and color contrast, and may or may not have fancy stitching which would enhance the appearance of

the article. Discarded apparel can be used to advantage in quilt making.

CREAM. A very light yellow, ivory, or cream-color.

CREAM, ECRU DAMASK. Napery fabric that is given a cream or ecru color-effect either by the use of natural color of the yarn, or by bleaching and dyeing to shade.

CREAMED LINEN YARN. Flax yarns which have been boiled and then bleached with bleaching soda; there is a 10 per cent to 12 per cent loss in weight from the treatment.

CREAM OF TARTAR. Potassium bitartrate, made by purifying argol.

CREASE LINE. A tailoring term. 1. Line along which a coat collar is folded. 2. Place where a lapel or revers is turned. 3. Horizontal line in the center of trouser legs, front and back. 4. Place where any crease may be considered necessary or fashionable.

CREASE RESISTANCE, CRUSH RESISTANCE. The property of a fabric which enables it to resist wrinkling or mussing. Chemicals, usually resins or synthetic resins, are used to provide resistance to washing and dry-cleaning. Effectiveness of the resistants depends on the chemicals used, method of application, and the handling of the goods. Durable treatment for resistance causes wrinkles to come out either immediately or after hanging for a short time.

CREASE-RESISTANT-FINISH. Also referred to as the CRF Finish, it is chiefly applied to cotton-polyester blends which contain a small amount of resin to produce an appealing hand to the goods and a moderate degree of wrinkle shedding. In rayon blends, a high degree of resin is used to give a desirable hand and proper wrinkle shedding qualities.

CREASES. Caused by uneven tension and tautness on the cloth as it goes through the wet and dry finishing departments of the mill. They have to be combated in the finishing of cloth in order to make the material appealing to the eye. Washer wrinkles are most difficult to remove.

CREASE SHEDDING. Fabrics which have been treated to give them greater recovery from creasing than they have in their normal condition. Preferred in some countries to crease resistant, which may mislead the consuming public and does not seem to describe correctly the effects of the process applied.

CREEKS. Old name for cotton raised along the minor tributaries of the Mississippi and smaller rivers in the deep South. The staple was softer when compared with Rivers cotton of this area.

CREEL. Device used as a spool rack for winding warp. Also used to hold warp ends for a sectional beam.

CREEP. Deformation in fabrics under set conditions in which the time element and load element are important factors.

CREEPER. An endless moving apron on some textile machines.

CREEP RECOVERY. Gradual recovery of form after removal of stress.

CREOLE. The Dominican Republic raises this sheep, believed to have descended from Lincoln sheep of Great Britain.

CREOULA, CRIOULA COTTON. A Brazilian tree cotton noted for its glossiness. Staple is from ¾ inch to 1¼ inches and three, four, or five crops may be obtained. Also known as Maranhao, Maranham, Mindo.

CREPAGE TESTER. A device to measure contraction in yarn under controlled conditions for denier size, twist, throwing oil, weave formation, etc.

CREPE. A broad term given to various fabrics generally recognized by a crinkled, puckered, or pebble-effect surface.

Alpaca crepe is a soft, dull-finished acetate, rayon, or silk fabric made to simulate wool crepe. Fiber content must be declared. Alpaca crepe contains no alpaca fiber at all.

Bark crepe simulates the bark of a tree and comes in several effects.

Crepe-back satin or satin-back crepe is a reversible fabric. Alternating hard-twist yarns give the back of the goods its dull effect. Unless all silk, fiber content must be declared.

Crepe de Chine in present-day use is a light, sheer flat crepe. Unless of silk, fiber content must be declared.

Crepe Marocain is really a heavy canton crepe of dress weight.

Crinkle crepe, sometimes called plissé, is a thin, blister-effect cotton which needs no ironing.

Faille crepe is smooth, dull and has a richer surface effect than crepe de chine. Fiber content must be declared if not made of all silk.

French crepe is made of right-hand or left-hand twisted yarn or both, 100- to 150-denier is the usual size yarn used to make this rugged, well-wearing fabric. The term, French crepe, is given to this fabric when it has been pigmented, a very popular crepe today. Excellent draping qualities but may shrink if not laundered carefully.

Georgette crepe is a dull-textured, sheer material with a pronounced crepe surface-effect brought about by two threads of right-hand twist followed by two threads of left-hand twist in both warp and filling.

Lingerie crepe or French crepe, since it is no longer given embossing to produce the effect, is really not a full-fledged crepe texture today. Now made of silk, acetate, rayon, or nylon.

Matelassé crepe gives a quilted effect since it is made in a double cloth construction and specially finished.

Mossy crepe or sand crepe is a fabric which presents a fine moss or sand effect on the face of the goods.

Mourning crepe is a dull black fabric which may or may not be given a moiré effect. A pronounced crepe weave enhances the final effect.

One-hundred-denier crepe is one made of 100-denier viscose yarn in the same manner as that used in constructing and weaving flat crepe.

Romaine crepe is a semi-sheer type of the heavy side and comparable with alpaca crepe.

Rough crepe is any heavily textured crepe material made on the two-right and two-left plan with regard to twist in both the warp and the filling.

Wool crepe is any type of crepe fabric made with a crepe weave in which the yarns used in the warp are kept rather slack. Textures vary considerably in wool crepe.

See Illustrated Section (Fabrics 18, 19).

CREPE, COTTON. This lightweight cloth is made with a crepe weave, and the yarns used have crepe twist in them to give the pebble or crepe effect. Some of the lower grade fabrics receive their crepe effect by treatment with caustic soda which gives the puckered or blistered effect. Much of this material is printed and finds use in bedspreads, blouses, counterpanes, dress goods, kimonos, bathrobes, and lounging robes.

CREPE, WOOLEN. Originally a mourning cloth that showed a crimped appearance in fine silken material which got its derivation from the Latin term, "crispus." This means curled. The cloth, when black, is much used in clerical circles. Light in weight, strong and well constructed worsted material. It is of superior quality and is made with a minutely wrinkled surface to simulate silk or rayon fabric of crinkled effect.

CREPE AND FANCY CREPE COTTONS. They are lightweight dress goods that may have a crepe, crinkled, granite, or pebble effect. The use of crepe yarns and the weave makes the effect possible. Most of the cloth is washable and the effect is not lost because of the yarns used in construction. The cloth comes in white or may be dyed or printed. There is a wide range in quality and price.

Balanced crepe has two ends of regular and two of reverse, crepe-twist yarns in warp and filling. This arrangement may be increased, if desired.

Box crepe for filling uses ordinary warp yarns, but the filling is of crepe twist. The arrangement is two regular and two reverse twist, or more. A 4 x 4 plan is much used.

Filling crepe uses ordinary warp yarn combined with an all-regular crepe twist filling yarn.

Warp crepe uses two regular and two reverse, crepe twist yarns. The filling is ordinary yarn. Another method is as follows: all regular crepe twist in the warp with ordinary filling yarn.

Matelassé crepe shows novelty designs that usually give an all-over blister effect. Again, it may be a distinctive crinkly stripe effect that runs in the warp direction. These crepes are formed by interlacing crepe twist yarns with ordinary yarn in both warp and filling, or in the latter only. The weave is a small dobby design, and the cloth is woven on a box loom.

When finished, crepe yarns will pucker up those parts of the cloth woven with ordinary yarn to form the regular blistered or padded effects throughout the material.

Uses of crepe cloths are as follows: boys' suits, slacks, slip covers, summer clothing, many types of dress goods, bedspreads, and pajamas.

Cloths in the crepe family include balanced crepe, matelassé, box crepe, mommie crepe, embossed crepe, granite effects, plissé, pebble crepe, seersucker.

Crepes are finished anywhere from thirty to forty inches wide. Carded or combed yarns may be used.

CREPE-BACK SATIN, SATIN CREPE. Satin weave with a crepe-twist filling used in this silk or rayon cloth. As the fabric is reversible, interesting effects can be obtained by contrasting the surfaces. Used for dresses, blouses, linings.

CREPE CHARMEUSE. A rich filling, dull luster, piece-dyed silk that has glove-like smoothness. Grenadine silk is used for the warp while the filling is of crepe-twist yarn. Charmeuse lacks the stiffness and body characteristics of satin, but it clings and drapes very well to fall into graceful folds to give a smart appearance to the wearer. The fabric is dyed in all colors and is used for dresses, waists, evening wear, and lining in expensive evening wraps.

CREPE-CREPE. This fabric has a pronounced crepe effect because of almost excessive twist given the yarns used; the warp has more twist than the filling. May be made with cotton, acetate, rayon, nylon, silk, etc.

CREPE DE CHINE. A raw silk cloth reeded in the loom at about 4/50/2, which means that there are four ends in each of the 50 reed splits, and that each of the four ends is a double thread, a total of 400 ends per inch in the texture.

Filling texture ranges from 60 to 80 picks of 2 or 3 thread, 20/22 denier with 60 to 65 turns of twist per inch. A plain weave is used to make the fabric, which is soft and more or less lustrous. Used for blouses, dress goods, evening wear, skirting, underwear. The material is form-fitting since it is a line-revealing fabric. This fair-to-excellent quality staple is dyed or printed. It is easy to manipulate, launders well, and gives good wear.

Differs from Georgette crepe in the following manner: In crepe de Chine, the filling is woven with two picks of left-hand twist yarn; in Georgette this so-called "two-and-two" arrangement is in both the warp and the filling, thereby giving the material a harsher, crinklier feel and appearance. In crepe de Chine, ordinary raw silk warp is used with the result that the material is softer and more lustrous when compared with Georgette.

CREPE DE CHINE, SPUN. A silk cloth of Japan made with spun-silk warp and thrown-silk filling. Features of the fabric include soft hand, considerable luster, good washability, and low price. The cloth, incidentally, is sold by weight.

CREPE DE CHINE TWIST. Tram is given from 30 to about 75 turns of twist per inch. When this filling yarn is used in this manner, from 3 to 6 raw singles are combined and receive from 50/55 up to 60/65 turns per inch. These are the average twists, but can be varied depending upon the conditions at hand.

CREPE DE DANTE. A fancy crepe fabric made of silk or rayon and wool warp, end-and-end arrangement; the same yarns are used in the filling with two picks of rayon or silk alternating with two woolen picks.

CREPE DE LAINE. The latter word is French for wool. The cloth is a thin, lightweight dress-goods fabric, made with plain weave, or a crepe weave. Material is of the sheer variety.

CREPE DIANA. A crepe fabric made of cotton and silk; used for dress goods.

CREPE FAILLE SUBLIME. Any silk cloth of the heavy grosgrain type in which the filling yarn is given high twist to bring about the characteristic heavy rib effect.

CREPE FINISH. Refers to the crinkled, uneven, sand-effect or granite-effect with regard to the surface appearance in textile fabrics. Crepes are produced by twist variations in the yarns used, novelty weaves, chemical treatments, or by pressing. Most crepe effects are lasting except in the case of the pressing treatment which is not impervious to stretching, removal by water, heat, dry-cleaning treatments, etc. Crepes have to be handled with care since there is always the possibility of stretch when the fabric is damp or wet.

CREPE GEORGETTE. See GEORGETTE CREPE.

CREPE JERSEY. A light to medium weight woven or knit material with ribs in vertical direction. Usually made of silk or rayon and is piece-dyed. Used for dresses and underwear.

CREPELINE. A lightweight silk or rayon dress-goods fabric made to simulate crepe de Chine and made of all silk or all rayon warp and filling.

CREPE LISSE. Lightweight, sheer silk or rayon crepe stiffened slightly and given a glazed finish. Crepe yarns are used with the warp having slightly less twist than the filling yarn, the result being crepe lissé.

CREPELLA. Wool dress crepe sold under this trade name.

CREPE MAROCAIN. This heavy Canton crepe of dress-goods weight is made of rayon or silk warp and rayon or cotton filling. Proper crepe twist is an important factor in production of the fabric. Filling yarn is much coarser when compared with the warp yarn used and it gives a cross-rib effect in the goods.

CREPE METEOR. A satin-weave construction is used on the face of this fabric while the back is made of a 2-up and 2-down twill weave. Light in weight, the filling arrangement is the same as that used in Georgette crepe. The cloth is soft in feel, drapes very well, and gives good wear. Comes in light shades and colors, launders well, and is easy to manipulate. Made with silk or rayon yarn.

CREPE MOSSEUX. A voile that is made from plied yarn, given a shrink-proofing treatment, and noted for its high absorbency with an opaque effect, and a delustered surface effect.

CREPENETTE. 1. An all-silk pongee-type cloth made with crepe effect; dyed in solid shades for dress goods. 2. Any cloth that is given a crepe twist without the use of crepe-twist yarns; usually made of cotton.

CREPE ONDOR. The registered trade-mark for a creped organdy which has a permanent finish brought about by chemical means. It varies in softness and crispness and contains partially transparent and opaque areas. The cloth is often given multi-colored printed motifs. Ondor is an original Swiss invention.

CREPE OR CHIFFON TWIST. A thrown raw silk given anywhere from 20 to 100 turns per inch and used for chiffons and certain crepes.

CREPE PLISSE. See PLISSE.

CREPESET. Trademark name of American Enka Corporation for a nylon crepe yarn which in fabrics affords softness, beauty, richness and appealing hand. An easy-care type of yarn in which the crepe pebble-effect is built into the yarn. Ideal for blouses, dressgoods, lingerie, and sleepwear.

CREPE SIZING. Application of size to continuous filament yarns intended for twisting with crepe twists.

CREPES, VARIOUS TYPES. The word "crepe" is a much-used term. It is applied to all of the major fibers when the material has some sort of a crepe effect. There are crepes in cotton, wool, worsted, rayon, acetate, silk, linen, and other materials. All of the crepe cloths are made from the well-known "crepe weave." Some silk crepes are Chenette, de Chine, Diamond, Jersey, Faille, Sublime, Georgette, Lease, Lissé, Meteor, Crepenette, Crepon, Crinkled Crepe, and so on. See CREPE; see also CREPE AND FANCY CREPE COTTONS.

CREPE TWALLE. A group of twalle, pigmented taffeta fabrics, in which voile twist is used in the filling, of the type 104 x 72 made of all viscose filament rayon, and of the type 150 x 94 made with acetate filament warp and viscose filament rayon filling. These fabrics are full in hand, of firm body, and have good draping quality.

CREPE TWIST. Yarn that is given a high or very high number of turns of twist to the inch to be used in crepe fabrics. This yarn is harsh, crimpy, wiry and has to be watched carefully for excessive shrinking when the fabric is being finished.

CREPE WEAVES. A derivation of the plain weave, they are made with certain raisers left out of the construction according to some plan. Small floats of 3 or 5 add to the crepe effect, enhanced by the use of crepe yarn. Regular lines are missing in crepe fabrics.

CREPE YARN. One with more than the usual number of turns of twist to the inch. Single or ply in construction, they are used in certain types of hosiery, and in a host of crepe fabrics. Crepe yarn gives a rough, pebbled, or granite effect to material.

CREPINE. 1. Fringe with a wide head of network. 2. Colored French silk fabric with small dot or coin effects.

CREPOLINE. Made of lustrous crossbred wool warp and filling, or with a mohair warp, this 2-up and 2-down warp rib material is constructed so that it gives a crepe effect; this is made possible by "breaking" the warp rib effect. Roxano is another name for this cloth, not popular within recent years.

CREPON. Of the crepe group of cloths but stouter and more rugged than the average crepe. The effect is obtained by the types of yarn used to make the cloth. One way is to use yarn of right- and left-hand twist according to some plan or motif; another method is to use yarns with varying twists so that the looser twisted yarns used will give the crepe effect. Taken from the idea of silk yarns used in making Georgettes and crepe de Chines. Made of rayon, silk, rayon and wool, rayon and worsted.

Durable, drapes and launders well. Crepe yarns, however, may shrink, hence care should be used in laundering or dry cleaning.

CRESCENT. A motif used in lace in which the crescent shape in the design is surrounded by raised cordonnet.

CRESHI. Italian dress goods material made with silk warp and woolen or worsted filling, or vice versa.

CRESLAN. Originally called X-51, then X-54, and now Creslan, this is a trade-mark of the American Cyanamid Company for its acrylic fiber which comes in staple and continuous filament. It is known for its great bulkiness without added weight, good color, and ease of dyeing.

CRESLAN ACRYLIC FIBER, TYPES OF. These are used in carpeting:
Type 83 - Basic-dyeable, it is ideal for single-color piece-dyed effects for use with Types 84 and 85.
Type 84 - Acid-dyeable, it is intended for use with Types 83 and 85 to give sharp and distinctive cross-piece-dyed effects. For example, when in the same dyebath at the same time, Type 84 can be dyed a brilliant red while Type 83 is being dyed a deep blue. There is no bleeding nor migration of color.
Type 85 - This is a tone-on-tone variant of Type 83. If, for example, the stylist desires two tones of blue to blend with a deep red in a cross-dyed line, he will use Type 83 for the darker blue, Type 85 for the lighter blue and Type 84 takes on the red color.

CRESLAN T98. Product of American Cyanamid Company, Inc. Emphasizes fibrillation (splitting or cracking) of the fiber to impart bonding properties similar to the cellulose fibers used for paper demanding wet and dry strength, dimensional stability, resistance to acid, heat, sunlight, micro-organisms, low moisture content, and electrical properties. Finds use in mats, filters, and in electrical fields.

CRETE. Lace of the loose bobbin variety made in Crete. The designs are generally geometrical, and the ground is colored silk or flax, with a colored chain stitch along the edge; gives a gay effect. In the upholstery trade today the term Crete applies to a lightweight curtain material.

CRETONNE. Used for beach wear, bedspreads, chairs and swings, coverings, curtains and hangings, hammocks, interior decoration, pillows and slip covers, the material is a staple cotton always in demand. Quality and price vary considerably in this plain- or twill-weave cloth. Cretonne is finished from 30 inches to 50 inches wide.

Osnaburg is the basic material for cretonne, whose background is often of such a nature that the entire surface is covered with design. Much foreign matter is seen in cretonne, but it is not considered detrimental to the cloth; in fact, it seems to add to the appearance and tone of the finished material.

Printed cretonne, despite the brightness of some colors and patterns, has no luster. Generally speaking, the cloth is finished in the gray state.

This genuine household fabric is strong, stout, and substantial and gives good wear. Warp counts are finer than the filling counts which are spun rather soft and loose. Designs run from the conservative to the more or less wild, shot-about effects.

CRETONNE, REVERSIBLE. Actually a register or duplex printed cloth which may or may not have the same motif on each side of the material.

CREVA. A type of drawnwork made by the Negroes throughout Brazil; it is a rough copy of Italian drawnwork.

CREWEL. A loosely twisted, fine two-ply thread used for embroidery and edging work.

CREWELWORK. Crewel is the Old English word for wool, and the type of work known as crewel is centuries old. It was extremely popular in Great Britain during the reign of Queen Elizabeth I (1533–1603), the daughter of Henry VIII and Anne Boleyn and whose reign was from 1558 to her death in 1603. Crewel still has waves of popularity throughout the world. In this embroidery technique the design is made on tracing paper. Holes are then punched through the paper outlining the motif. This is then transferred to the fabric by dusting colored powder across the openings. The needleworker then stitches the pattern by hand onto the fabric. Motifs may be daisies, geraniums, strawberry plants, pineapples, etc. This handwork is expensive even today. Machine work such as that done in India is less costly.

CREWEL YARN. A slackly twisted worsted yarn that finds use in embroidery and fancywork.

CREW NECK. A round neckline that fits closely around the base of the throat, as in polo shirts and sweaters. This differs from the turtle neck, a high turned-over collar that clings to the throat, and from the boat or bateau neck which, though close to the neck in front and back, extends in elongated points to the shoulder seams at each side following the curve of the collarbone.

CRIMP. The natural waviness found in wool fibers. Uniformity of waviness indicates superior wool, a decided asset. The more the crimp, the finer is the wool.

In a material, crimp is the difference between any two points in the yarn as it lies in the fabric, and those same two points after the yarn has been removed from the cloth and straightened, expressed as a percentage of the distance between the two points as the yarn lies in the goods. Woven or crimp length of yarn and straightened length are determined in analyzing cloth. They are essential in figuring the take-up of the warp in weaving, the reed width, and shrinkages.

Crimp in yarn is caused by the warp ends bending over and under the filling picks and by the compactness of the goods as governed by the pickage used in weaving the material.

CRIMP FABRICS. Sometimes used to describe crepon, blister fabric, soufflé effects, and (incorrectly) seersuckers and plissés.

CRIMPLENE. A product derived by texturing a smooth filament to do away with slipperiness and slickness. First done on polyester filament by Imperial Chemical Industries, Ltd., England, in 1959. Incidentally, the name is not derived from the fact that in the process the filament becomes crimped or textured but it takes its name from Crimple, near Harrogate, Yorkshire, England, the headquarters of Imperial Chemical Industries Ltd. The term, Textured and Set, is applied to filaments which have these crimped porperties, created by the use of heat treatment.

CRIMP METHOD OF FINISHING CLOTH. It is done by the use of a gum-resist agent that is printed onto the material. Steaming follows, and the cloth is then run through a cold, concentrated solution of caustic soda. This will give the plissé finish, a popular crinkled or blister effect, but not permanent. It is the untreated areas that provide the blister effect.

Seersucker, a permanent finish, is a two-beam job in the weaving. One of the beam warps will provide the crimp effect, while the other warp forms the flat, base construction in the goods. It is made with cotton, rayon, acetate, nylon, and other materials.

CRIMP ROLL. A full-width fluted roller used to bring fabric to its full width devoid of creases or wrinkles.

CRIMP STRIPE. The stripe effect in plissé or seersucker.

CRIMSON. A color of deep crimson with a tinge of blue, but lighter than purple. It has low brilliance and high saturation.

CRIN. French technical term for monofilaments of viscose or cuprammonium rayon.

CRINKLED CLOTH. Another name for seersucker or plissé-finish cotton goods. See SEERSUCKER, PLISSE FINISH.

CRINKLED WOOL. When treated with caustic soda under correct conditions wool has the tendency to become wavy or crinkled.

CRINOLINE. A heavily sized, stiff fabric used as a foundation to support the edge of a hem or puffed sleeve. Also used as interlining, in the millinery and bookbinding trades, and to give fullness to skirts. First made of linen and horsehair and used to support hoop skirts. Usually comes in black, white, or brown.

CRIN SILK. 1. French term for horsehair. 2. The heavy substance obtained from the glands of silkworms.

CRIOLLA. A sheep that dates back to the days of the Conquistadors in Central and South America. Unimproved since that time, it is now found in the Andes Mountain areas, and much of it is raised on the Argentine plains. Kempy and straggly in nature, the fiber is used chiefly in the carpet trade. The wool not exported from Argentina is used in mattresses.

CRISP. 1. Crepe was originally known by this term in Great Britain. 2. A fine, high-textured British linen.

CRISPER. A finishing machine used in woolen mills to curl the pile in imitation of chinchilla fabric and other cloths made to simulate fur fabrics.

CROCHET. See CROCHETED MATERIAL, CROCHETING.

CROCHET COTTON YARN. Cotton yarn for the crochet trade, which is made by doubling the individual fibers that make up the yarn in the one direction, and then combining the resultant yarns into a ply condition by twisting in the opposite direction to prevent raveling. Sometimes, another doubling or ply may be given, and this would be in the same direction as the original twist given to the fibers in the single yarn. This thread is very strong and durable.

CROCHETED MATERIAL. Crocheting is a method of working interlocking loops or stitches with a hook, forming a strong, long-wearing fabric. Examples are bedspreads, coats, dresses, doilies, hats, narrow-strip work, laces, tablecloths, and rugs.

CROCHETING. Separate loops are thrown off and finished by hand successively with a special hook. In knitting, the entire series of loops that go to form one length, round or circumference are retained on one or more needles while a new series is being formed by a separate needle. Crocheting may be done by hand or by machine.

CROCHET KNIT. Resembling hand-knitted fabric, this machine-made tie fabric will give a large, loose, yet firm knot. Much crochet-knit fabric is made of mercerized cotton.

CROCHET LACE. This type of lacework was introduced into Ireland about 1820. It is recognized by the crochet stitch, and this is often used to simulate reticella and Venetian point materials. The work is done with a hooked needle, and completed articles are often referred to as "Nun's work," since so much of the work is done in convents and parochial schools throughout the world.

The name is derived from the French, crochet (crook, crooked) and the old Danish, krooke (hook).

The distinguishing mark of Irish crochet stitch is that it is followed in every thread in the product. At times, the crochet is known as raised rose point, or Point de Trico. The term Honiton crochet is also used, but this seems to indicate the character of the motif rather than the technique. The flat variety of the work is referred to as Baby Irish, as apart from the raised or "heavy" types.

The manufacture of Irish crochet, however, is not confined solely to Ireland. The Syrians in this country, and the peasants of practically all European nations and Balkan States, can perform good work in this art.

CROCHET-LOOK FABRIC. Applied to woven fabrics which take on the appearance of knitted or crocheted constructions. Cloth in this category has a loose, low-texture, open weave which affords a delicate lacy appearance. Popular staple in some women's coatings and dressgoods.

CROCHET YARN. Yarn made from any of the major textile fibers and used for crochet purposes. Doubling, redoubling, S-twist and Z-twist are features of this type of yarn, which must be strong, durable and impervious to raveling.

CROCIDOLITE. A silicate of iron product which is bluish in color and found in Africa. It is one of the asbestos group of fibers, the others being amosite and chrysotile.

CROCK. Etymology undetermined, but probably a simple colloquialism. That undesirable property of a dyed cloth by which the coloring matter rubs off the fabric and smudges or soils other materials with which it comes into contact. This fault is usually traceable to imperfect dyeing, either in regard to the method employed or the inadaptability of the dyestuff.

CROCKING. Excess coloring matter which rubs or chips off material because of improper penetration or fixation by the dyestuff.

CROCK-METER. An apparatus designed to measure, under standard test and procedure, the degree of fastness to crocking of dyed fabrics. The device measures the resistance of a colored surface to rubbing or stroking against an uncolored surface. The instrument may be used under both wet and dry conditions.

CROCUS. A coarse canvas formerly used in England for packing purposes.

CROFTING. Term used in the British Isles for bleaching bast fibers.

CROISE. French for crossed or twilled. The term indicates that the warp threads cross each other on the back of the goods to form a twill effect; noted in velvet and other pile fabrics.

CROISE SILKS. Croisé, in French, means crossed. Made in small twills such as a three-harness twills, fine twilled fabrics find use in dress goods and some suitings. The application of croisé in materials of this group signifies that the cloths show fine "cross-line effects."

CROMMELIN, LOUIS. In the eighteenth century, this expert linen weaver, who fled France to Ireland, made several improvements in the handling and manipulating of flax fibers. His work has had much to do with the position that Ireland holds in the industry to-day.

CROMPTON, SAMUEL. He invented the mule frame in 1779 by further developing the ideas of Hargraves and Arkwright. The mule frame today is one of the greatest and most phenomenal of all machines. It is composed of twenty to thirty thousand distinct parts and is absolutely self-acting. As many as 1400 ends of yarn may be spun at one time.

Crompton, a fellow townsman of Arkwright, was born in 1753 in Firwood near Bolton and died in 1827. When he was sixteen he learned to spin on Hargraves's frame, and at twenty-one he was already making improvements on it. He sold his invention of the mule for 106 pounds—it was worth a fortune, but he let it slip through his fingers. He was poor, weak, shy, and retiring in disposition, shrinking and of nervous temperament. He lacked practical knowledge in a world of men, so necessary since the Machine Age is with us, in business. In 1812 he got 5000 pounds from the English Government for his machine and had given work to 70,000 spinners, 150,000 weavers and 5,000,000 spindles. His combination of Arkwright and Hargraves reminds us that:

*The forces of nature could not further
    go;
To make a third, she joined the other
    two.*

CROP. 1. Also called Crooping, it is an English term for shearing fabric. 2. A side of leather with the belly cut off, retaining both the head and the shoulder.

CROSS. The crossing-in of threads of either or both ends of the warp; the arrangement holds the warp threads in place and prevents gnarling, tangling and winding. Situated between the two lease rods or lease sticks and between the whip roll and the harnesses.

CROSS AND BEVAN. During the years 1890–1894, these scientists tried many experiments to obtain synthetic fibers. One of their efforts which bore fruit was to use ammoniacal copper oxide to dissolve cellulose. From this finding, the cellulose acetate method of making synthetic filaments was developed later by other scientists.

In 1895 they developed commercially what is known today as viscose. However, viscose was not fully developed until 1903. In 1898 Stearn improved on their methods, and within five years viscose was actually on the market.

CROSS-BAND. British term for a type of twist in yarn; the same as S-twist.

CROSSBAR DIMITY. Fabric of this name made with cords in both warp and filling to give a windowpane or crossbar effect.

CROSS BORDER. See BORDER TIE.

CROSSBRED WOOLS. In this country they are obtained from breeding a long-staple sheep with a short one. Much crossbreeding is done all over the world. Several new types and qualities of wool have resulted from sheep crossing and there are now approximately 200 crossbreeds that have been developed from the forty distinct breeds extant today. See Illustrated Section.

CROSS-DYED CLOTH. Various animal fiber cloths that have some vegetable fibers in them are cross-dyed. A cloth might have a cotton warp and a worsted filling. The cotton yarn is dyed prior to weaving, and the animal-fiber yarn worsted requires a dyestuff of different chemical composition than the cotton. The cloth as it comes from the loom would show a dyed cotton warp and an undyed worsted filling. The cloth is then dyed in a vat, and the worsted stock is colored, cross-dyed.

Another meaning of cross-dyeing implies the multi-colored effects produced in cloths whose fibers possess varying or different affinities for dyestuff. Much man-made fiber cloth is dyed this way; for example, a viscose warp and an acetate filling fabric would often be cross-dyed to obtain pleasing color effects. At present, a popular method of dyeing.

CROSSING WARP. Mill term for warp threads in leno, lappet, and gauze weaving which actually cross from one side to the other of the straight or foundation yarns in the warp.

CROSSLAND COTTON. Peterkin cotton.

CROSSOVER. A fabric in which horizontal or crosswise stripes are produced by the filling yarns. The stripes may be colored and the weave used to make them may be different from that used in the body of the goods. The effect may be obtained in leno or doup weaving, on dobby looms, or by plain looms. This British term is rarely, if ever, used in the United States since it seems to be too broad in its meanings. See CROSSOVER LENO or DOUP.

CROSSOVER LENO OR DOUP. A lightweight fabric of cotton or nylon that is quite porous since it is made on the leno or doup method of weaving. Used for curtains the fabric is used chiefly in Far Eastern markets. Textures are around 48 x 30, and the yarns used, in cotton, are 44s to 50s. The term is used in Great Britain but is not in popular use in the United States.

CROSS PLATING. In rib-knit fabrics it is a reversal of the positions of the yarn within all the stitches contained in certain courses. A plated fabric will show one color on the plain wales and another color on the rib wales. A reversal of positions for a number of courses will produce a check effect in two colors. This is cross plating.

CROSS REELING. Traversing yarn during the reeling to form a diamond-shaped crossing to cause the skein or hank to become firmer, and to facilitate unwinding.

CROSS SECTIONS OF MAJOR TEXTILE FIBERS, MICROSCOPIC.

COTTON: Appears as a flat, ribbon-like band, more or less twisted on its longitudinal axis. Twist of the fiber is not continuous in the one direction; cell walls are thick; lumen breadth is much thicker than the cell wall; between thickened edges, the fiber shows finely granulated surface. Diameter is uniform for three-quarters of its staple length, then it tapers to a point where it is cylindrical and solid.

FLAX/LINEN: Cylindrical tapering to a sharp point; cell wall is so thick that the lumen actually appears as a thread; fine cross-lines at intervals give the appearance of joints or nodes, sometimes intersecting like the letter, X.

WOOL: Epidermal scales are observed on the surface in an irregular formation. The three parts of the fiber noted under the microscope show the medulla or marrow in the circle center, the cortical cells, and the outer surface of epidermis or scales.

SILK: Under the microscope it shows a double fiber, split into two parts, clearly imbedded and flat in appearance.

THE MAN-MADE FIBERS UNDER THE MICROSCOPE:
ROUND, OR NEARLY ROUND IN APPEARANCE:

ACRILAN—May also show a bean shape.

CRESLAN—Some showing of a mixture of round, bean, and squat dog-bone.

"DACRON"

FORTISAN-36

KODEL

NYLON 6, NYLON 66, and CAPROLAN.

POLYETHYLENE—May also have special shapes.

POLYPROPYLENE—May also have special shapes.

RHOVL—Some with one or both sides indented slightly.

SARAN—May also come in special shapes.

Vycron
Zefran

LOBED: Fibers in this category have cross-section dimensions that extend not more than halfway from the margin to the center, and the rounded lobes or sinuses.

Acetate. Arnel—More serrated than Acetate. Fortisan, Regular.

SERRATED: Scale effect.
DOGBONE:

"Orlon"—Except Type 21 which shows a compressed dogbone with one end mushroomed outwardly, along with some irregular lobed.

Verel

MULTIFORM:

Dynel—Irregular crullerlike to Y shapes, to the closed half doughnut.

Vinal—Elongated string bean to horseshow appearance with a pronounced skin-core effect.

In the Longitudinal View the fibers with round cross sections appear rodlike. The lobed, serrated, dogbone, and multiform fibers appear in striated formation, or will show twists or contour lines.

CROSS-STITCH. A basic decorative stitch used in the art of sewing. It is made by one stitch crossing over another to form an X resulting in a perfect square. It is used on children's garments, dresses, and linens.

CROSS WEAVING. Gauze weaving consists of one thread partially crossing around another thread, and with one pick in each shed; usually called marquisette. Leno weaving, another example of cross weaving, is a combination of the gauze and any other weave; thus, both gauze and leno weaving are known as cross weaving.

CROSS WIND. The winding of yarn on a bobbin with a short cross traverse.

CROSSWISE FOLD. The fold or crease of a fabric formed by folding the material crosswise. When folded, the selvages on the same side meet each other.

CROTAL. A general name for several kinds of lichen that grow on the rocks, used for producing color dyes for the homespuns of northwestern Scotland. Other native dyeing agents, from which a fair range of blues, purples, reds, browns, greens, and yellows are obtained are alder bark, heather ragwort, wild cress, blueberry, and dandelion.

CROWFOOT. 1. The so-called four-shaft satin weave; in reality, this weave is a 1-up and 3-down, broken-twill weave with two ends to the right and two ends to the left. 2. A name for the regular five-end satin weave made with

a counter or base of two or three. 3. Certain small defects in cloth which are caused by poor yarn.

CROWN. The underside of the foundation fabric through which card clothing wire is inserted; the connecting part of the teeth in the clothing. See Illustrated Section.

CROWSFEET. Wrinkles found in finished goods after folding; very difficult to remove, at times.

CROYDON FINISH. British method of finishing cottons so as to give them a threadlike appearance. The process includes hot-water mangling, light drying, calendering, beetling, and pressing.

CROYDONS. British cottons of various types which have been given the Croydon or threadlike finish. Much of the fabric simulates linen fabric of better quality.

CRUA. See caroa.

CRUMB. A picayune buyer or a petty individual.

CRUMBS. The shredded particles of alkali cellulose used in the manufacture of viscose rayon. Crumbs are obtained by disintegrating the cellulose sheets which have been soaked in sodium hydroxide. See shredding.

CRUSHED LEATHER. That which has the natural or artificial grain or design smoothed by rolling, plating, or some similar process in such a manner that the outline of the grain or design is preserved.

CRUSHED PLUSH. It is regularly woven as plain pile fabric, the content of the pile being either rayon or mohair, usually the former. The designs in crushed plush simulate fur-bearing animal skins such as Krimmer, Caracul, Muskrat, Kerami, and they are obtained in the finishing process, either by hand-effecting, by whirling with machines, or by stencil designs. Such fabrics are definitely used as imitation furs and can be made into full-length garments, jackets, evening wraps, or can be used for trimming of collars and cuffs. Also, effects are put into this type of plush for use in the toy trade to simulate fur-bearing animals.

Crushed plush with mohair pile basis is simply crushed without any attempt at symmetry or design. It is used for furniture covers and draperies of an occasional nature, and for show-window decoration.

CRUSH- OR CREASE-RESISTANT FINISH. Finish on cottons, linens, velvets, and some rayons, made possible by the use of synthetic resins, melamines, etc. If properly done, this finish should withstand washing and drycleaning.

CRUSH-RESISTANT. Name given to pile fabrics which have been treated chemically to make them resist creasing, crushing, and marking. The term also implies that the fabrics so treated will recover from the effects of pressure, friction, and moisture.

CRUSH-RESISTANT, CREASE-RESISTANT FINISH. Finish on cottons, linens, velvets, and some rayons, made possible by the use of synthetic resins, melamines, etc. If properly done, this finish should withstand washing and drycleaning.

CRUTCHINGS, DAGGINGS. Wool fibers with insects, pests, possible vermin, dung, and fodder removed from sheep a month or so prior to the final shearing. This culling treatment improves the fleece, allows the growth of new wool, and relieves the sheep of excessive burden.

CRYSTAL. 1. A physical shape or form of matter, invariably conforming to a certain geometrical formula. 2. Trade name for a process of the Bellman Brook Bleachery for a permanent finish designed to give a supple hand and smooth, crystalline luster and transparency to organdy.

CRYSTALLINE. A compound which takes the form of one or more types of crystals. Noncrystalline matter is called amorphous.

CRYSTALLINE RATIO VERSUS AMORPHOUS RATIO. Many positive properties of textile fibers depend on the fact that they are made up of regions whereby long molecular chains are arranged in an orderly or crystalline formation and in a conglomerate or amorphous manner. These regions have no real line of demarcation and some chains may pass through more than one region. Thus, an approximate ratio of these component regions is referred to as the crystalline-amorphous ratio. Amorphous means the absence of crystalline substance, a formless substance. The greater the degree of crystallinity in a fiber, the greater will be its strength and the lower its regain, generally speaking.

CRYSTALLINITY. Refers to the degree of packing of molecular chains, such as in cellulose, where, for example 40 percent of the fiber is packed tightly and known as crystalline areas.

CRYSTAL YARN. A shiny, strawlike, very lustrous form of acetate or viscose yarn used in the manufacture of simulated straw fabrics. It is also interwoven in materials for decorative effects and can be used in lustrous embroideries.

C.T.U.: Chemical Tendering Unit, originated by the Cowles Detergent Company, Cleveland, Ohio, which expresses the degree of chemical attack in the fluidity method for determination of the degradation of a fabric. The method is based upon the rates of flow of solutions of cellulosic fabrics in cuprammonium solvent, as determined by the viscometer.

C-TYPE MERINO. A Merino sheep classification used in this country. Sheep of this type are larger in stature when compared with A-Type and B-Type. Few folds are noted in this type and for mutton purposes it is the best of the group. The heavy, 3-inch staple fleece is the best stock raised in America. Also known as Delaine merino or smooth merino, the fiber is fine, heavy in the number of serrations per inch, soft, strong, and it possesses the best of spinning properties and characteristics. For a wool of this classification the shrinkage in scouring is rather low.

CUBA BAST. It is used in wrapping cigarettes and in packing cigars.

CUBAN JUTE. Not classed as a "true jute," this bast fiber is coarse and strong; used for cordage and bagging.

CUBA WOOD. Same as fustic.

CUBI. Term used by the Indians of the American southwest for aromatic sumac used to make baskets which will hold water.

CUCULUS. A type of hood introduced by the Greeks that could be attached to a cloak or used as a separate item of headgear; forerunner of the present day hood, cowl, or headcovering used in the attire of monks and brothers in some Orders of the Roman Catholic Church, as well as in academic gowns. See Hood, Pileus, Tunic.

CUDBEAR. A purplish red dyestuff, similar to archil, made from lichens. Archil and cudbear are synonymous terms. The name is a contraction of the discoverer of this lichen, Dr. Cuthbert Gordon.

CUFF. Primarily an attached or detached lower section of a sleeve. When attached it forms a trimming which is usually of the same material; however, a contrasting combination may be used. When detached, it is made chiefly in contrasting material and is removable and may be supplemented by other cuffs. Cuffs are also used on men's shirt sleeves and trousers.

CUFF LINKS. Type of jewelry used to close buttonless shirt cuffs.

CUIT. Silk with all of the silk gum or sericin boiled out. Also known as bright silk. Cuit may range from 10 per cent in the case of Tussah silk up to about 25 per cent in the best qualities of Japan and Italian silk. The word means "boiled" in French, and in our language implies that all of the sericin

has been removed or boiled away from the fiber or filament. The term is also used in speaking of the "cutting" of grease, yolk, and suint from wool fibers in the scouring operation.

CULL. Any lamb or sheep that does not come up to expectations; a substandard sheep taken from the stud group.

CULLODEN. The battlefield near Inverness, where the Duke of Cumberland defeated Prince Charles Edward Stuart, Pretender, in 1746. It was after this tragic defeat that the wearing of the Highland dress was proscribed for thirty-five years. Culloden, in consequence, did more than anything else to cast a glamour over tartans and preserve them for later generations.

CULOTTE. Also known as a divided skirt, it is an informal trouser which has full leg portion to simulate a skirt. It is used for sportswear.

CUMBI, CUMBRI. Fabric made from alpaca fibers obtained in Bolivia and Peru. The fabric may vary in quality because of the grade of hair fiber used and the weaving of the goods. Used by the natives for apparel.

CUMMERBUND, KUMMERBUND. A shawl or wide ribbon, usually worn around the waist or wrapped around the body. Most often worn with summer formal wear. Wide ribbons sometimes worn by diplomats and state functionaries at formal occasions are known by this name. Their ribbon is worn diagonally on the chest.

CUMULOFT. Textured nylon filament of Monsanto Company, Inc., used especially in the floor-covering trade.

CUNILATE. A powerful mildew inhibitor that is used when material is to be subjected to the most drastic conditions, as in contact with earth. There is a disadvantage of this inhibitor in that it may give a slight discoloration to the material which is grimy or embedded with dirt.

CUPIONI. Machine-made slubbed Bemberg rayon yarn sold under the trademark of Beaunit Fibers, Division of Beaunit Corporation, New York City. It comes in long thick uniform slub form, in uneven slub dimensions, and in thick slub formation. Simulates douppioni silk yarns.

CUPRALAN. A German viscose product chemically modified to increase affinity for acid dyes.

CUPRAMA. A rayon staple fiber, wool-like in characteristics, and made from a cellulose base. It is made in 2- to 20-denier sizes, and staple cuts range from $1\frac{9}{16}$ inches to 6-inch lengths. Cuprama can be dyed naturally and much of the product is now dope-dyed or solution-dyed. Product of Farben-

Fabriken Bayer.

CUPRAMMONIUM. The second method in historical order, of making rayon. The product is a regenerated pure cellulose (solid-to-liquid-to solid). Generally referred to as Bemberg Rayon. Registered trade-mark of Bemberg Industries, Inc., New York City.

CUPRAMMONIUM RAYON. Filaments produced by solidifying the cellulose dissolved in a solution of copper oxide in ammonia. See Illustrated Section.

CUPRAMMONIUM SOLUTION. A solution of copper and ammonia used in the manufacture of rayon that, when mixed with cotton linters, forms a spinning solution comparable with viscose solution.

CUPRESA. A continuous-filament cuprammonium rayon yarn which comes in denier sizes ranging from 25 to 150 denier. It can be dyed naturally and much of it is now dope- or solution-dyed. Product of Farben-Fabriken Bayer.

CUPROFINO. Trademark for a filling yarn which produces fabrics that combine a silk-like shantung appearance with durable press properties, made by Bemberg Industries, Inc., New York City. The silk-like appearance is obtained by incorporating a Bemberg cuprammonium slub rayon for the silk-like hand with a polyester filament or a spun yarn. Through a special process by which the Bemberg yarns can be combined with any other filament or spun yarn, the polyester and rayon filaments are permanently combined in a single, textured rayon. Interesting cross-dyed effects may be obtained by the use of this yarn.

CUP SEAMING. In the assembly of full-fashioned sweaters and sweater shirts, the term is not a cross between sewing and looping but is the joining of two pieces of knit fabric, joined selvage to selvage, by the use of the chain stitch. It is different from looping in that the seaming is done irrespective of the fabric loops. There is no attempt, as in looping, to join fabrics on a one or more loop to loop basis.

The cup seaming stitch is elastic and taut, neat and flat in appearance. Compared with seams made on other types of sewing machines, the cup seam is superior from an aesthetic standpoint. Basic elements of the cup seaming machine are the two revolving feed cups, from which the machine obtains its name, the needle, looper, threader, and the uncurler which helps to alleviate edge curl on fabrics.

CÚRAUA. See CAROA.

CURING. Setting of a chemical, plastic, or resin in or on textile materials, usually obtained by heating.

CURING CHAMBER. Any type of drying equipment in which 300 degrees F. and over can be obtained. The chamber may be of the loop, roller, or enclosed-frame type.

CURL. Usually associated with textured filament yarn, it refers to the conformation in the yarn; also used with regard to the edge-crimping process in manufacture of textured yarns. See Edge Crimping.

CURL PILE. Two types of yarn are used to make this fabric—one of high take-up, the other of normal take-up. When the fabric is finished the foundation yarn will shrink to give body to the goods, while the high take-up yarn will form kinks or curls on the face of the goods. The floats, when the cloth has been finished, simulate the skins of some animals, such as astrakhan. See CRISPER.

CURL YARN. Short name for bouclé yarn.

CURLY COTTON. Cotton which is stringy in nature; also called Stringy Cotton.

CURON. A multicellular plastic (not rubber) foam material. It is featherweight, yet very durable, has a spongy hand and a unique sparkle caused by millions of open and closed cells. The result of an exclusive formula, Curon is made by blending chemicals which are "baked" in giant size "loaves"—usually 60 feet long, 15 inches high, and of varying widths. These are then sliced into any desired thickness from $\frac{1}{16}$ inch to $5\frac{1}{2}$ inches, depending on end-use. Curon has superior insulation against both dry and moist cold or heat; will not mat or bunch, shrink or stretch; does not support mildew, bacteria or fungus growth, is nonallergic and nontoxic, and, used as outer shell laminate, eliminates need for separate interlining. Curon can be laminated to any fabric irrespective of fiber content. Registered trade-mark of Reeves Brothers, Inc., New York City.

CURON-IZE PROCESS. The bond strength of the process approaches, and usually surpasses, the strength of Curon itself. Curon resists cleaning fluids, water and washing compounds, and is not affected by steam ironing. The process causes Curon to combine well with all types of fabrics and plastic films (vinyl should contain a polymeric-type plasticizer). The Curon-ize bond remains flexible and does not harden with age, and there is no "strike-through" on fabrics or on thin sections of foam; no color is added. Products are odorless

and do not support bacteria life which causes odors. The process does not affect resilience of Curon foam, and the end-product will not wrinkle permanently or crease because of handling, use, or folded storage. Product of Reeves Brothers, Inc., New York City. See CURON.

CURRAGH. Another name for Irish point lace. Owing to the fact that many of the needle-point laces of Ireland are made at Curragh schools, the term is frequently used indiscriminately in speaking of many types of Irish lace.

CURRATON FIBER. A strong Brazilian fiber obtained from the leaf of the wild pineapple.

CURRYING. A secondary process of finishing leather after tanning for particular end-uses.

CURRY WOOL. Britch wool more like hair than wool and of very little value.

CURTAIN. An adjustable draping or covering, hanging loosely.

CURTAIN FABRICS. These include sheers such as scrim, organdy, voile, net, marquisette, dimity. Also include heavier fabrics such as cretonne, chintz, Stafford fabric, novelty curtain goods.

CURTAIN GRENADINE. See MADRAS.

CURTAIN MADRAS. See MADRAS.

CURVED TWILL. Waved effects obtained by combining reclining and steep twills with a forty-five-degree twill. Used in mackinac cloth, dress goods, and upholstery fabric.

CUSHION-BACK CARPET. One which has a cushion or padding as an integral part of the backing used in the product.

CUSHION DOT. A brushlike dot used in marquisette and similar fabrics; larger and puffier than the ordinary polka dot, it is made by one or more roving yarns which are woven into the fabric and then sheared or cut close to the surface.

CUSHION LACE. Synonymous with pillow lace.

CUSHION-SOLE. Hosiery with a reinforced sole of uncut terry loop surface. Much used by the Armed Services in World War II, and now used in some civilian styles.

CUSIER SILK. A strong sewing-silk thread made of two or more raw silk singles given Z-twist and then given reverse or S-twist to provide further strength.

CUSTOM-MADE. Made or done to order, as custom-made clothes.

CUT. 1. A bolt or length of fabric as it comes from the loom or in the finished state; most woolen and worsted

cut lengths run from 60 to 70 yards. 2. The standard of 300 yards to one pound of the Number 1 cut wool yarn; also known as Philadelphia cut system. The run system has 1600 yards in one pound of the Number 1 yarn and is also known as the Boston system for wool yarn counts or sizes.

CUT, KNITTING. Number of slots or cuts per inch in a flat needle bed on circular cylinder.

CUT, NEEDLE. The number of needles to one inch of the circumference of the cylinder in a circular knitting machine. See CYLINDER.

CUTAWAY COAT. Introduced by country gentlemen and British nobility during the Industrial Revolution in England, this coat with its "cut-away" in the front to free the knee action of the wearer, became a mark of distinction. Factory workers wore this coat to distinguish themselves from the workers in their mills. The buttons at the back of the coat allowed one to loop the tails and therefore afforded more freedom when riding. The "skirt" tapered off from the front waistline to the coat-tails.

CUTCH, CATECHU. A resinous astringent and tanning extract prepared from the wood of various Asiatic and East Indian plants, chiefly the *Acacia catechu*. The dyestuff is used to dye browns on cotton, and it also serves as a mordant. Also known as cashoo, Bombay cutch, gambier.

CUT CHECKS, CUT STRIPES. Fine lines, or dales noted in stripe and check effects made by two ends, or two ends and two picks, weaving opposite to each other to give clear cut-effects. The effect can be made on single or double cloth fabrics.

CUT CRIMPED RUCHE. One in which the filling has been passed through a crimping machine of some sort.

CUT-EDGE FABRIC. This term applies to acetate material, thermoplastic in nature, which is cut with highly heated blades or knife discs. The heat and knife pressure cuts the fabric cleanly and causes the edge of the fabric to fuse at once. Examples of cut-edge include ribbon, flags, and cloths such as faille, taffeta, and satin.

CUT-FIT-TRIM. The essential operations necessary to make a complete garment ready for the consuming public, the ready-to-wear trade. Also called Cut-Make-Trim.

CUT GOODS. 1. Trade term for hosiery knitted on a round knitting machine, the tubular, unshaped product being cut into required lengths, footed, shaped, etc., by cutting out and adding other pieces as needed; the cheapest process of manufacture. 2. Piece goods cut to definite lengths for some particular purpose.

CUT HOSE. Made by cutting the material from knitted fabric. The foot is knitted on and the stocking is then seamed to complete the article. Mesh hose is often spoken of as cut hose.

CUT IDENTIFICATION MARKS. Woven goods are marked in the loom as one weaver finishes his shift and another weaver takes over. These marks may occur anywhere throughout the cut of fabric being woven. Some symbols distinguish between day weavers and night weavers, as DW and NW. W1, W2, and/or W3 may be used if the plant is on three shifts.

Incidentally, the end of each woven cut is also marked, with some characteristic symbol, because many cuts of warp yarn are made when the warp is finally dressed and ready for mounting in the loom and weaving. Woven cut lengths will vary in length in accordance with the policy of the mill—a 40-yard cut, 60-yard cut, etc.

CUT LINE. See LINE.

CUT LINTERS. 1. First-cut linters are the short fibers removed in partially delinting the seed by making a light cut; ranges from 20 to 50 pounds per ton of seed. 2. Second-cut linters are taken from the seed on the second run through the delinter; total linters cut may run from about 30 pounds to 200 pounds per ton of seed.

CUT LISTING, CUT SELVAGE. Listing or selvage that is cut, torn, or broken. The defect occurs in the weaving of the goods or in the shearing of the material in finishing. The weaver is often to blame for this type of work, since some believe that the selvage is not a very important part of woven cloth. Of course, automatic looms equipped with warp drop wires will prevent faulty selvages. Breakages should be remedied at once since if they are allowed to go it is likely that adjacent selvage ends will soon become broken.

Another meaning of the term implies selvage that is purposely cut to give two single fabrics. This would apply in double pile weaving and in weaving cloths to give "double the reed width." This cutting occurs at or near the breast beam of the loom and is governed by the cutting knives used for this purpose.

CUT-MAKE-TRIM. Actually the old-time Cut-Fit-Trim, meaning the entire process of manipulating textile cloth. Includes cutting patterns, making the garment, and all the final operations and decoration on a finished garment, including buttons, and other finishing-off tiems to make the complete garment ready for

sale. See Cut-Fit-Trim.

CUT MARK. See CUT IDENTIFICATION MARKS.

CUT MARKS. These are caused by an incorrect viscosity of the dye being used to color the fabric, whereby repeating or spread-out cut marks appear in the goods.

CUTOSE. 1. In a human being, film found underneath the outer layer of skin. 2. It is a transparent film which is found in plants. In speaking of bast fibers in conjunction with pectose and vasculose, cutose is the gum which cements the fibers. The cutose and vasculose are removed by boiling in caustic alkalies and soap under pressure. The pectose is then removed by washing. The amount of decortication in these fibers amounts to about 2 per cent and the amount of degummed fiber to about 1 per cent.

CUT-OUT. When a group of knitting needles fails to catch the yarn, thereby causing the fabric to be cast off the machine.

CUT PRESSER. A device on a spring beard needle machine which closes only certain needle hooks. The presser is used in both warp and weft knitting machines.

CUT RUBBER YARN. The original core yarn cut into size from a rubber sheet form. Its uses are about the same as those of Lastex.

CUT RUCHE. One that has been woven in double width and then is cut down the middle.

CUT STAPLE. The same as rayon staple fiber, it is the mass of rayon filaments which have been cut to short and uniform lengths. Staple stock may be cut as short as the cotton fiber or as long as the longer wool fibers. When these short rayon fibers are spun into yarn, in the same manner as cotton or wool, the product is known as spun rayon yarn.

CUT STAPLE, COTTON. Cotton that is cut in the ginning operation because of the excess moisture in the cotton, which causes it to cling to the saws of the gin. Excessive feeding of cotton to the gin will also produce a cut staple that reduces the spinning value.

CUT STOCK. This refers to the bottom stock for shoes, such as soles, taps, lifts, blocks, and strips that are cut from sole leather.

CUT STOCKING. A stocking made from pieces of knitted fabric cut to the particular shape and sewed together.

CUT STRIP TEST. The use of 1-inch width fabric, usually heavy or sized material, to determine the breaking strength of the goods. (See BREAKING

LOAD, BREAKING STRENGTH.) No raveling is allowed in this test.

CUTTER. 1. A person employed in the wholesale garment industry where specific work is cut out on garments in single or quantity lots. The cutter piles layers of material, one upon the other, then places the marker or layout of the pattern on top of the layer of goods and proceeds to cut around the outline of the pattern with the electric cutting knife or shears.

2. The operator in tailoring who prepares the measurements and patterns for the chopper.

3. In the ready-to-wear clothing business, the cutter lays out the pattern on the cloth, cuts the material, either by shears, electric cutting machine, or long knife, corresponding to the chopper of the merchant tailor.

4. The operator in shoe manufacturing, who lays out the patterns on the leather and cuts therefrom the vamps or other parts of the shoe.

CUTTER, LINING, AND TRIMMING. The work may be done by hand with shears or a short knife, while machine work is performed by either the round-knife machine or the up-and-down machine. The task of the worker is to cut out lining and interlining fabric from single or multiple layers of cloth. He should be able to make the outlines for the cutting work to be done on the top layer of goods at hand; should also be able to spread or lay out the material in satisfactory manner.

CUTTHROAT. A price cutter.

CUTTING. 1. Shearing or cropping fabrics. 2. The cutting of floats in pile fabrics, either on the loom or after the goods have been taken from the loom, as in the case of corduroy.

CUTTING MACHINES. There are three types used in the apparel field— round knife, up-and-down knife, and the band saw. The machine cutter operates or guides the moving knife or blade of the power cutter along the pattern lines to be cut, whether on single or multiple layers of material. The cutter should also be able to spread or lay-up layers of fabric, to arrange the pattern on the goods, and then to outline with chalk.

CUTTLING. 1. Folding fabric down the center with the face inside, selvage to selvage. 2. Giving wool fabric, following fulling, milling, scouring, etc., a chance to lie dormant so that the goods may recover from these rather rough treatments.

CUT VELVET. A fine, knife-cut material that is popular in the silk trade. The term is also applied to a type of carpeting. Mirror velvet is one in which the pile has been ironed down. Uncut velvet is cloth in which the looped pile of filling face has not been cut.

Wire velvet is material which, in weaving, was subjected to a series of wires in the loom. Each wire is under the pile warp, and when it is withdrawn, causes the face of the cloth to have regular rows or loops across it. These must be cut, if it is desired to have a cut pile fabric.

CUT WOOL. The standard of 300 yards to one pound of the #1s yarn; known as the Philadelphia system of figuring woolen yarn counts. Run Wool uses 1600 yards in one pound of the #1s yarn, the Boston or New England system.

CUTWORK. Fancy work in which ornamental figures are made separately and then set into a ground material which has been cut so as to insert the figures.

CUT YARN. Any yarn that is cut or definitely not regular in all details despite the fact that, at times, the yarn may appear to be perfect.

CYANA. A prefix of American Cyanamid Co., for a family of textile finishes including Cyana Purifying Finish, Cyana Permel Plus, Cyana Shrinkage Control, Cyana Wash-and-Wear, Cyana Water-Repellent.

CYANOETHYLATION. This process modifies cotton by reaction with acrylonitrile to obtain a new fiber material resembling cotton with properties of improved resistance to wear, heat, rot, and chemical attack when compared with cotton. Greater strength and better dye receptivity are also features of cyanoethylated cotton.

CYCLE, WASHING. The entire series of operations, from beginning to finish applicable to cleansing goods in washing machines. Various names are applied to each cycle, many of them relative to laundering conditions, such as - Delicate Fabric Cycle, Regular, Short, Wash-and-Wear, etc. Some of these phases include Dry Cycle, Fill, Soak, Spin, Rinse, Wash, etc.

CYLINDER. A slotted cylindrical housing for the needles used in a circular knitting machine. The cut of the cylinder is the number of needles in one inch of the circumference of the cylinder. See also CYLINDER, CARD; CYLINDER, SPINNING FRAME; JACQUARD CYLINDER.

CYLINDER, CARD. The main roller on the revolving flat card; it is 40 inches wide and has a 50-inch outside diameter. This shell is completely covered with card clothing wound spirally on the surface. Mounted at each end on a spider, there is a center shaft

which runs through it so that the tips may rest easily in the bearings. Cylinder speed is about 160 r.p.m.

The three main rollers on the card are the taker-in, cylinder, and doffer. Actual carding occurs only at the points of contact between the revolving flats and the cylinder clothing. The cylinder presents its carded stock to the doffer roller after the action involving the flats.

CYLINDER, JACQUARD. See JACQUARD CYLINDER.

CYLINDER, SPINNING FRAME. About 6 inches to 8 inches in diameter, this hollow, sheet-metal drum or cylinder extends the full width of the frame. Its function is to support the spinning bands, which cause the spindles to revolve.

CYLINDER PRINTING. Same as roller, direct, or calender printing.

CYLINDER SCREEN. The screen that is set below the card cylinder on a carding machine, to receive dirt and all types of other matter as it drops from the cylinder and from the adjacent rollers.

CYNARA CREPE. This dress-goods material is made from filament yarns of acetate and rayon plied together.

D

DA, DHA. See KENAF.

DABBIDAR LUNGI. Worn by Mohammedans as a turban, this carefully hand-woven fabric is made with high counts of cotton and acetate or rayon.

DABBING, DABBING BRUSH. This device on the Noble or circular comber presses the worsted fibers into the comb-circle pins. Set with high-grade bristles, the brush has a quick up-and-down motion when it functions. The stock is therefore set into suitable plowth-action position for drawing-off or drafting. See PUNCH BOX.

DACCA MUSLIN. This famous Indian muslin has never been equaled for texture, feel, beauty, and quality; textures range about 100 square. The soft, fine Dacca cotton of Bengal is used to make the fabric.

The cloth may be hand-loomed or on power looms. Dacca differs from fine English muslin in that the latter has stripes or minute check designs in it.

DACCA SILK. An untwisted silk thread, originally used for embroidery purposes in India.

DACEY. A Bengalese race of silkworms, native to India, which produce eight broods a year.

DACROLON. A lightweight, synthetic coated fabric used in Arctic regions for radar shelters. It was developed by the Air Force Research and Development Command in conjunction

with DeBell & Richardson, Inc. The fabric is "Dacron"-coated with Hypalon, a chloro-sulphonated polyethylene elastomer. Properties consist of high strength, resistance to sunlight and ozone ageing, and electrical characteristics that allow transmission of microwave energy to and from targets.

"DACRON." Trade-mark name for the man-made polyester textile fiber produced by E. I. du Pont de Nemours & Co., Inc. Formerly known as Fiber V, it was first developed in England under the name of Terylene, and the American rights were obtained in 1946.

"Dacron" is a condensation polymer obtained from ethylene glycol and terephthalic acid. It is not related to or connected chemically with nylon or the acrylic fiber "Orlon."

The properties of "Dacron" include high-tensile strength, high resistance to stretching, both wet and dry; good resistance to degradation by chemical bleaches and to abrasion. Fabrics made of the fiber in filament or staple form indicate excellent resilience and resistance to wrinkling, easy laundering and quick drying, and they can be heat-set. The fiber has good electrical insulation properties and is not weakened by fungus, mold, or mildew.

The continuous filament yarn finds use in V-belts, curtains, dress fabrics, high-pressure fire hose, men's shirtings, and sewing threads. Staple fiber stock of "Dacron" is ideal for mixing with wool in men's and women's wear suitings; also in dress fabrics, knitted wear, and washable woven sportswear items. See Illustrated Section.

"DACRON" AND NYLON IN MIXTURE WITH COTTON, IDENTIFICATION OF. The test solution follows—American Cyanamid Company:

1. 50 mg. Calcocid Yellow.
2. 50 mg. Calcosyn Sapphire Blue 2GS, concentrated.
3. Dissolve in boiling water and dilute to 500 ml.
4. Add 100 mg. glacial Acetic Acid.
5. Add 5 grams Cyanatex Dyeing Assistant, EM.
6. Boil a sample of the material for three minutes in an appropriate volume of the test solution.
7. Add 2% Formid Acid (90%) on the weight of the material.
8. Rinse in hot water.
9. Results: Cotton remains undyed, "Dacron" dyes bright blue, Nylon dyes dark green.

"DACRON" COLOR - SEALED BLACK STAPLE and TOW. Ideal for style flexibility in apparel and home-furnishings, as well as in industrial fabrics.

"DACRON" 99. A polyester filling material of Du Pont which provides luxurious softness to sleeping pillows. This fiberfill product has resilience, resistance to mildew, whiteness, nonallergic properties, and freedom from odor. It supplements the Du Pont line of conventional "Dacron" polyester fiberfill and "Dacron" 88, a new high bulk fiberfill introduced in June, 1961, for sleeping bags, comforters, and insulated apparel.

"DACRON" 99 POLYESTER FIBERFILL. A Du Pont product which has extreme softness, resilience, resistance to mildew, whiteness, is free from odor, and is non-allergic. This product supplements "Dacron" 88 Polyester Fiberfill known for its high-bulking properties and used in comforters, insulated apparel, and sleeping bags.

"DACRON" POLYESTER FIBER, TYPES OF DuPONT. These follow:

Type 26: Filament yarn that is bright, dull, or semi-dull, modified cross-section yarn, disperse-dyeable, with improved cover and aesthetics. For knit and woven apparel.

Type 35: Staple and tow that is more pill-resistant, disperse-dyeable staple for cellulosic blends in woven apparel goods.

Type 52: Industrial yarn with high tenacity for sewing thread, felts, and V-belts.

Type 54: Staple and tow that is semi-bright or dull, normal tenacity, disperse-dyeable for a wide range of apparel, home furnishings, and industrial uses.

Type 55: Filament yarn that is bright with a round cross-section, normal in tenacity, disperse-dyeable filament yarn.

Type 55 A: Filament yarn with color-sealed black round cross-section yarn for apparel and home furnishing fabrics.

Type 56: Textile filament yarn, semi-dull in shade, disperse-dyeable.

Type 57: Filament yarn with dull cast; used in home furnishings, and knit and woven apparel; disperse-dyeable.

Type 59: Semi-dull, more durable staple, disperse-dyeable, for use in apparel and industrial fabrics.

Type 61: Staple for industrial usage; has high shrinkage for industrial felts.

Type 62: Filament yarn with a modified cross-section, basic and disperse-dyeable, for bright coloration, cross-dyes (piece dyes) and improved aesthetics. Use in knit and woven apparel.

Type 64: Staple and tow that is disperse-dyeable; a pill resistant staple for bright coloration and cross-dyes for use in woven suitings blouses, knit dresses, outerwear, shirts, and slacks.

Type 65: Staple and tow for knitting or woolen system of making yarn. Pill-resistance is outstanding, basic-disperse dyeability, for bright coloration. Used in 100% and worsted-blend dresses, sport shirts, and sweaters.

Type 67: Industrial yarn of high strength designed for cordage.

Type 68: Industrial yarn of higher strength for use in tires and other industrial uses.

Type 69: Filament yarn with modified cross-section, basic- and disperse-dyeable; silk-like yarn with random slubs featured. Douppioni type for dressgoods, neckwear, and suitings.

Type 75: Industrial yarn of high tenacity, a plied-twisted yarn used for fire hose.

Type 77: Industrial yarn of heavy-denier count with spun-like properties for use in cordage.

Type 85: Staple that is pill-resistant, disperse-dyeable and has good bulk, cover and aesthetics. Used in woolen spun-blends for women's dressgoods and skirtings, and men's outerwear.

Type 89: Staple fiber that uses basic- or disperse dyes, high modulus, 1.5 denier staple in yarn count for bright coloration and cross-dyes. Used in cellulosic blends for lightweight apparel.

Type 92: Filament yarn with round cross-section, basic- and disperse-dyeable, with bright coloration for apparel fabrics.

Type 96: Bright staple with high-tenacity for use in sewing thread.

Type 106: Staple that is semi-dull, has high tenacity for fine count yarn in cellulosic blends. Used in woven apparel fabrics. Disperse-dyeable.

Type 107 W: Staple that is semi-dull, pill-resistant, disperse-dyeable, with improved whiteness for cellulosic blend knitwear.

Type 152: Staple with a spiral-crimp, bright, and disperse-dyeable for bedroom floorcoverings.

Type 160: Bright, heavy-denier staple, disperse-dyeable, used in floorcoverings.

Type 161: Bright, heavy-denier staple for carpets. Basic- and disperse-dyeable. Used with *Type 160* for styling purposes.

Type 166: Staple with bright luster, modified cross-section, heavy-denier staple for floorcoverings, disperse-dyeable.

Type 167: Staple with bright-luster, modified cross-section, heavy-denier staple, bright-luster, heavy denier staple for floorcoverings. Is cationic-dyeable.

Type 651: Staple and tow of high shrinkage, a knitwear fiber and yarn with outstanding pill resistance, basic- and disperse-dyeability for high-loft yarns. Ideal for sweater and comparable knit fabrics.

Type 655: Staple and tow, disperse-dyeable fiber for knitting and woolen-system of making yarn for woven goods, outstanding pill resistance for cross-dyeing with *Type 65* or with "Orlon" acrylic stock.

Type 692: Filament yarn, modified cross-section, disperse-dyeable; silk-like filament yarn with random slubs for use in casement cloth, dressgoods, neckwear, and suiting.

Type 809: Modified cross-section staple for unique luster in suitings, slacks and other apparel fabrics, disperse-dyeable.

"DACRON" POLYESTER FIBERFILL. TYPES OF DuPONT. These follow:

"Dacron" Fiberfill: A bonded, high-bulk fiberfill batting for use in furniture.

"Dacron" Regular Fiberfill: Special bulky fiberfill for filled products such as pillows.

Type 76 Fiberfill: Heavy-denier size fiberfill with unusual bulk and aesthetic properties for use in furniture.

"Dacron" 88 Fiberfill: Higher-bulk, spiral-crimp fiberfill for sleeping bags, mattress pads, etc.

Type 93 Fiberfill: Specially engineered fiberfill batting for use in puffy, refluffable pillows.

Type 108 Fiberfill: A fiberfill batting enclosed in marquisette fabric of "Dacron" for the "Sontique" pillow. Excellent refluffability. Comes in soft, medium, and firm aesthetics.

Type 162 Fiberfill: Spiral-crimp fiberfill ideally suited for brassiere pads.

Type 178 Fiberfill: A special bulky fiberfill for use in robes.

"DACRON" POLYESTER TYPE 52T. A bulked, heavy denier industrial yarn for fire hose warps. Regulation Type 52 is used in the filling. This Du Pont product is claimed to yield hose of 100 per cent polyester fiber which is light in weight, easy to handle, and resistant to rot and mildew.

"DACRON ROTOSET." A polyester yarn of DuPont modified to improve processing in the plant and to give improved uniformity in cloth. Finds much use in curtain trade and dress fabrics.

"DACRON" SAILCLOTH, STABILIZED. This fabric weighs 3.8 ounces per yard and is dyed with colors that are sunfast, such as transluminated red and green. Fade-Ometer tests for lightfastness show practically no change after two hundred hours exposure. The material has a sleek, multi-ton heat set finish. Product of Howe & Bainbridge, Inc., Boston, Massachusetts.

DAGGER. The device at the tip of the protector rod on the shipper side of a loom. If a shuttle does not enter the shuttle box properly, the dagger engages the frog and causes it to release the shipper handle, thereby making the loom bang off.

DAGGER FIBER. Used for headgear, this fiber comes from the dagger plant, one of the bast fibers in the yucca family. The leaves of the plant furnish the fiber which, because of the sharp points resembling a needle, have given rise to the term for it of "Adam's needle."

DAGGINGS. See CRUTCHINGS.

DAGLOCK WOOL. Unclean, low-quality wool-lock fibers.

DAGS. Wool locks that are matted with dirt, dung, etc.

DAISEE, DESHI, DESI JUTE. The terms mean local. The fiber comes from the *Corchorus olitorius,* a long-pod jute. Raised in India, and runs from brownish-gray to slate-gray in cast or color.

DAKA. A cotton muslin peculiar to the Levant area. The finer, closely textured cloth is used for turbans while the lower quality serves as garment lining.

DALA. Sheep native to Southern Norway.

DALECARLIAN LACE. Made for more than two hundred years, this Swedish lace, ecru or buff in color, is made by the peasants and used for ruffles.

DALMATIAN LACE. A narrow, coarse bobbin lace made by the peasants in Yugoslavia.

DALMATIC. A vestment worn by the religious; similar to a tunic but reaches at least to the knees. It is worn by the deacon at Mass in the Roman Catholic Church and is of the same color as the one worn by the officiating priest. It is symbolic of the "garment of salvation, the garment of gladness, and the dalmatic of righteousness."

DALTONISM. Color blindness, especially red-and-green blindness. Named

for John Dalton, 1766–1884, English chemist and physicist, the discoverer of colorblindness.

DAM. Ewe or female sheep.

DAMAGE. 1. Chemical damage is that done to fabric originating through contact with some corrosive chemical. 2. Mechanical damage is fabric damage originating through some mechanical instrument—tear, cut, hole, abrasion, etc. 3. Pinhole damage is used to describe minute, scattered holes or perforations in fabric. It may be from chemical or mechanical damage—lime bleach, sludge particles, acid spattering, heavy threads, knots wearing off, poor twisting, etc.

DAMASK. Figured fabric, originally made in silk, that came to us from China via Damascus in Asia Minor. Marco Polo, in his travels of the thirteenth century, spoke of the material and gives an interesting tale about it. Damask has been made for centuries and is one of the oldest and most popular staple cloths to be found today. Damask belongs to the group embracing brocades, brocatelles, and Jacquards. The cloth is made from cotton, linen, wool, worsted, silk, rayon, and other fibers. Used for tablecloths, napkins, towels, doilies, runners, interior decoration, wall coverings, furniture covering. Elaborate designs are possible and damask is made on the intricate Jacquard looms where it is possible to give vent to the whims of the designer of these cloths.

Linen or cotton single damask is made on a five-shaft satin weave; double damask is made on an eight-end satin weave. The cloth is beetled, calendered, and is usually grass-bleached. Very durable, reversible fabric; sheds dirt; the firmer the texture the better is the quality. Launders well and holds high luster, particularly in the linen goods. Smaller designs give a stronger cloth than designs that have long floats in the weave formation. The price range of damask is very great, inexpensive to costly fabric. Linen damask, "the Cloth of Kings," is widely imitated and cheapened. Rayon damask has about the same uses as the silk fabric.

DAMASK, MIXED. A damask fabric in which the contrast of the ground and the motif effect is achieved by the use of various weave constructions such as plain, twill, basket, satin, rib, etc.

DAMASK, TWILL. A damask in which the contrast of the ground and motif or pattern is achieved by the warp-face and the filling-face of the twill interlacing arrangement.

DAMASK SATIN. Damask in which figure effects are made on satin weaves.

DAMASK SWISS ORGANDY. One which has the appearance of a raised

pattern effect comparable with damask, the motif being frequently opaque and caused by pigment printing which is done by chemical printing methods, with the ground usually transparent. The effect can also be done with regular color printing.

DAMASK TICKING. Made with cotton warp and acetate or rayon filling, this material is made on a Jacquard loom in order to provide more or less elaborate effects in the goods. Good color harmony or contrast is a feature of this material. Used in mattresses.

DAMASQUE. Fabric effect achieved by synchronizing a printing process with plissé treatment simultaneously. Used on cottons and nylons chiefly, color application is done by use of a water-in-oil emulsion with the chemicals already combined in the liquor. Caustic soda is used to obtain the effect in cottons while phenol is used on the nylon. A crinkled effect is observed on the goods comparable with plissé or seersucker effects. Actual printing is aided by the use of colorless clears used with aluminum, bronze, gold, silver powders, et al.

DAMAS LISERE. Silk damask in which the Jacquard pattern is outlined (liséré) in gold thread.

DAMAS ROBE. Term used in the French silk industry for a weave that was popular in the last half of the nineteenth century. The weave showed effects made by the ground filling to resemble gros de Tours and certain satin weave effects. The word "robe" is used to distinguish the fabric from comparable ancient damask fabrics, many of which now repose in museums throughout the world.

DAMASSE. Damassé is a staple type of linen damask (from French "linge damassé") used for decorative purposes. See OUVRE.

DAMASSE BROCART. French term used in Britain which means "brocaded damask." Damassé is rather heavy, well-textured, and is made with silk or nylon warp with metallic yarns, such as gold or silver, in the filling. The filling gives the brocade effect; made on a Jacquard loom. Used for evening gowns and wraps, decorative fabrics, upholstery, etc.

DAMASSE MOIRE. The term damassé moiré indicates the watermarked or wavy effect obtained in finishing certain fabrics—taffeta, organdy, voile, rayon sheers, and others.

DAMASSE POINTILLE. Damask fabric is called damassé pointillé when it has large or small dots arranged in checkerboard effect.

DAMASSIN. A brocade, brocatelle,

or damask of silk or rayon in which the motif is embellished by interspersing metallic threads in the pattern.

DAMBROD DESIGN. Taken from the French word "damier," which means checkerboard, the word was then adopted by the Scots, who spell it Dambord to mean a drawing board. The term now implies rather large colored checks used in napery, some dressgoods, etc.

DAMIER. French for a large, solid square check in the pattern.

DAMMESEK. Biblical term for silk, and the Hebrew word for Damascus.

DAMP DRY. 1. Drying fabrics to the degree where they are suitably moist for ironing or blocking. 2. The moisture condition in garments or fabrics after the final spin-off of an automatic washer or a spinner washer, or as the items come from a wringer.

DAMP WOOL. Term for wool that has not been given too much attention when stored; will become discolored and take on yellowish cast. Scouring may remove the discolorization, but the fibers cannot be used in manufacture of white yarn.

DAMPING. See DEWING.

DANCOMB. The registered trademark of Dan River, Inc., for its combed-yarn twill fabric.

DANCOOL. The registered trademark of Dan River, Inc., for its 50% cotton, 50% polyester check or plaid permanent press fabric used in sportswear.

D & K. Means Damaged & Kept; denotes that the finisher accepts responsibility for defects in the goods handled by him; he agrees to accept a debit for the damaged goods that he retains.

D-AND-T DENIM. Contraction of double-and-twist. Made of solid color warp and mock-twist filling, this type of denim withstands rugged wear. It should be noted that the filling yarn used is single and not ply.

DANDY. The last roving frame in the Bradford worsted system where the drafting is done only by rollers.

DANEL. The registered trademark of Dan River, Inc., for yarn-dyed 50% cotton, 50% polyester plaid permanent press fabrics.

DANFLAIR. The registered trademark of Dan River, Inc., for its 50% cotton, 50% polyester yarn-dyed check, plaid, and striped, permanent press fabric.

DANLI FIBER. A strong bast fiber used in the Philippines; used for cordage by the natives.

DAN-PRESS. The registered trademark of Dan River, Inc., for its

exclusive 50% cotton, 50% polyester permanent press process developed in the Research and Development Division of its laboratories in Danville, Virginia.

DANSETTE. The registered trademark of Dan River, Inc., for its 50% cotton piece-dyed permanent press fabric used for shirting, dress goods, and sportswear.

DANTWILL. A registered trademark of Dan River, Inc., for its 50% cotton, 50% polyester, piece-dyed, fine line twill permanent press fabric used for sportswear.

DANULON. A nylon 6 staple produced in Nyergesujfala, Hungary.

DAO. A Philippine bast fiber used for cordage.

DARALE. A plain-weave, East Indian cotton cloth with a narrow red stripe along the selvage edges of the warp. Used in native garb.

DARDANELLES CANVAS. Named for the Straits of Dardanelles, this coarse, rugged canvas is used by the Turks for sailcloth, workclothes, etc.

DARELLE. This product of Courtaulds, Ltd., is a fire retardant rayon staple marketed for use in carpeting. All normal rayon performances are retained in the fiber.

DARI. The strong double-plain weave is used to make this rugged, durable prayer rug used in the Near East. It will withstand a great many washings and cleanings. Dari also means a twill-woven cotton tent cloth which in the heavier weights is used for carpets.

DARK COLOR. One in which the use of black has darkened the full tone effect; the opposite of a light color.

DARN. 1. To mend, as a rent or hole, with interlacing stitches of yarn or thread. 2. To sew with a stitch like darning, as in embroidery or lace making.

DARNED LACE. See LACES, HANDMADE AND MACHINE-MADE.

DARNET, DOMECK, DORNECK, DORNEK, DORNICK, DOORNICK. Doornick is the Flemish name for the city of Tournai, Belgium. In the fifteenth century, the word implied damasks made of silk and wool yarns embellished with gold threads. At present, the term means cotton damask with twill motifs used. It also includes decorative cloths and floorcoverings made in Tournai. The British refer to these carpetings as Darnex. Dornoch, Scotland, is known for its damask fabrics made there; very likely the name of this town is a derivation of the Flemish Doornick.

DARNING. Correction of defects,

imperfections, and damages in materials by thread and needle. Done in the mill and at home.

DARNING COTTON. It is made from two, three, or more two-ply cotton threads twisted together. Finer yarn of this type is called mending cotton.

DART. The means whereby surplus materials is reduced to obtain a closer fitting. The size of darts varies, depending on their position on the garment. Darts are made by stitching together two lines converging to a point. When used on the sleeve cap, they form an extended shoulder effect. When used at the underarm, shoulder, and waistline, they help to fit the bodice over the curvature of the bust.

DARTMOOR. Hardy, British Mountain sheep which, however, is raised chiefly on the moorlands at present. Rather free from kemp, the stock is about 40s quality.

DARVAN. This nytril fiber (nitrile) of polyvinylidene chloride-dinitrile was formerly made by Celanese Corporation in the United States. It was used as a blend with other fibers for use in men's and women's apparel, knitwear, pile fabrics, and industrial uses. Production ceased here in 1968. Known in Germany as Travis, the fiber did not have success and was phased out in 1970. See Travis.

DATA, INTERPRETATION OF NUMERICAL. These and comparable figures, found on labels or tickets of man-made cloth bolts, may be interpreted as follows:

1. 128 x 64. This is the pick count of number of warp ends and filling picks per inch in the woven cloth.

2. 150/40. This means the denier is 150 and that there are 40 filaments in the yarn.

3. 25/1 50/50. Viscose-acetate. This implies that the yarn size or count is a single 25s on, say, the cotton or worsted system of figuring yarn counts. The cotton standard is 840, the number of yards in one pound of a Number One cotton yarn; worsted is 560. The 50/50 means that the filling is 50 per cent viscose content and 50 per cent acetate content.

4. 30/2. This means that the count or size of the yarn is composed of two single yarns, each a single 30s to make the 30/2 yarn. The single equivalent of this yarn would be a single 15s. If figured in the cotton system, there would be 840 x 15, or 12,600 yarns of yarn in the pound.

DAVAO HEMP. Abaca is known by this name.

DAVENPORT, JAMES. The first American inventor to receive a patent for any type of textile machinery. This was in 1794 and his efforts made possible imporvements in carding and spinning frames.

Da VINCI, LEONARDO (1452-1519). This famous Italian painter, architect, engineer, mathematician, musician, scientist, and creator of Mona Lisa (La Gionconda) and The Last Supper seems to have proved that he possessed the most creative and inventive mind ever enjoyed by a human being. It may be stated that he, with his drawings, sketches, maps, etc. laid the foundation for the Industrial Revolution which occurred about two-hundred years after his death.

He conceived and brought out the spinning flyer, the spinning wheel of today, as well as what today has become the continuous spinning action of drawing, twisting, and winding. He also laid the basis for Jean Marie Jacquard's loom which came out in 1801 and was shown at the Paris Exposition at that time. Eli Whitney, inventor of the cotton gin in 1793 which revolutionized the cotton industry throughout the world also was aided by some of the Da Vinci sketches.

DAY-GLO. Switzer Brothers, Inc., owns this trade-mark for its daylight flourescent color which provides extreme brilliance under daylight or flourescent conditions. Harmless, washable, and dry-cleanable, it can be applied by spraying, in paste form, or by screen printing.

DAY SHIFT. A schedule of working hours that requires employees to work during the daytime.

DDT. Brought out during World War II, this all-purpose insecticide has become a household word and has created considerable stir in many areas. Formal name for this term is di-chloro, di-phenyl-tri-chlorethane and it has been known since the turn of the century. The United States Army Corps shortened the name to DDT around 1940. Its use has become widespread for insect killing throughout the world but it is toxic, should not be inhaled nor permitted to come in contact with the human body. It should be kept away from all textiles and garments. Chemically, this term is (ClC_6H_4)-2CHCCl$_3$.

DEADBEAT. A credit customer who does not pay.

DEAD COLORS. Decorations or designs that have been "deadened," killed, or subdued during scouring or other operations in finishing. If cotton colors, for example, have been used in woolens or worsteds, or even in blended fabrics, they can sometimes be brought back to life by the use of a mild scouring treatment. If wool colors have been used, an ammonia bath will very likely brighten the colors and tend to bring them back to proper shade.

DEAD COTTON. Immature, undeveloped, or unripe cotton.

DEAD ROLL. The hollow shell covered with emery fillet used in grinding cards; is slightly wider than the rolls on whose surface it functions.

DEAD WEIGHT. The unrelieved weight of an inert body; a burden borne without aid. Dead weight of a textile fiber, yarn, or fabric may be found by merely weighing it free from any encumbrance, either at bone dry condition or with moisture in it which would entail calculations to allow for this content.

DEAD WOOL. Wool removed from skin of dead sheep by sweating method.

DE-AERATION. Removal of all undissolved and a portion of the dissolved gases, chiefly air, from the spinning solutions before extrusion in the manufacture of man-made filaments and fibers.

DEARING COTTON. A 1-inch, late-maturing cotton which has a lint yield of more than 40 per cent. Also known as Dearing Prolific, Dearing Small Seed.

DEAUVILLE SCARF. Originating in Deauville, France, this scarf was conceived by two young French girls in 1922-1923. The girls had bought various qualities of silk pieces and had colored them by tie or knot dyeing or the batik method. These scarfs which cost the girls $1.50-$3.00 each, were sold to shops for $3.00-$6.00 and then to customers for $10.00-$20.00. In a very short time these scarfs were popular all over the world and today are still worn as scarfs, shawls, and head pieces. Deauville is still one of the leading fashion resorts in France.

DECATING, DECATIZING. Cottons, rayons, and fabrics made with both rayon and cotton in them are wound on a perforated drum equipped with a steaming and vacuum system. The cloth as it winds is laid between layers of a decating blanket. Steam is passed through the material from the inside to the outside layers and then the action or treatment is reversed. The vacuum pump takes out the steam on completion of the treatment. Decating sets the material, enhances luster, and gives some assurance against shrinkage.

Decating of woolens and worsteds is done by the dry or the wet methods. In wet decating, the pressed fabric is wound on a roller and placed in a heated boiler set up with a vacuum system. The treatment is comparable with that used for cottons and rayons and with the same results.

Dry decating affords protection to woolens and worsteds between the napping and the dyeing operations. The cloth is wound on a perforated roller which allows plenty of water circulation. The heat, moisture, and pressure exerted sets the nap on the goods and increases the luster on the fabric.

DECCAN HEMP. A soft, strong, silklike fiber found in India and Africa; used as substitute for hemp in rope making. See KENAF.

DE CHARDONNET, COUNT HILAIRE. French experimenter on synthetic materials. At his home in Besançon, France, this great benefactor of the human race used the extract of mulberry leaves, from which he gradually built up an artificial silk that is now called rayon. His experiments began in 1885, and in 1889 he displayed his synthetic materials at the Paris Exposition. Chardonnet began his work under the tutelage of Louis Pasteur, and worked thirty years in scientific research. In 1884, Chardonnet took out his first patents on synthetic fibers, and in 1891 he began the commercial manufacture of artificial silk on the method that is today still known as the Chardonnet Method.

DECHETS. Silk waste, in French.

DECOLLETAGE. The low-cut neck or yoke used in dresses.

DECOLORIZING. The bleaching of color from dyed material.

DECOMPOSE. To break up into component parts by chemical or heat action. For example, heat decomposes bicarbonate to form soda ash and free carbonic acid.

DECORATIVE FABRICS. Materials made of many designs used for adornment and decoration. They are made from all of the major textile fibers, alone or in combination. Among the decorative fabric group are art denim, brocade, brocatelle, chenille, chintz, corduroy, denim, damask, cretonne, cotton plush, lace, netting, sateen, scrim, tapestry, velours, and velvet. They are observed in curtains, cushions, evening wraps, furniture coverings, and other ornamental uses.

DECORTICATE. The separation of the woody, pithy matter from the stems of bast fibers.

DECORTICATEL. To remove the bark or outer layers on bast fibers by peeling or dissolving, by either physical or chemical means.

DECOULOURISE. A British term. The same as stripping of color from yarn, fabric, or garments in the United

States. It is done by various methods of bleaching but usually gives the stripped stock a dull, drab appearance.

DECUSSATE. French (crossed, décussaté) for the interlaced warp and filling in weaving cloth.

DEEP BUFF. See UPHOLSTERY LEATHER.

DEEP-TEXTURED FABRICS. Implies three-dimensional effects in fabrics. Depth is set into the texture by various means, such as by a combination of weaves, use of thick and thin yarns such as curls, loops, bug effects, slubs, etc., to accentuate the effect. Careful selection and color blending also have an effect in developing accentuated depth effects. Fabrics of this type require large interiors for display.

DEEP WOOL. A shafty wool with high bulkiness and density of fiber. See SHAFTY WOOL.

DEERSKIN. See BUCKSKIN.

DEERSTALKER. The two-peaked, front-and-back, hunting cap to afford protection from the sun and rain. Also known as a fore-and-after, it is the cap which has come into undying prominence since being coupled with A. Conan Doyle, the British author who created Sherlock Holmes.

DEFECTIVE. Denotes that something will show to disadvantage in wool after it has been scoured. Fire, water, dampness, and moths cause defects. Wool from sick sheep is called defective, since the working properties are greatly impaired. Texas and California wools are often defective because of burrs and excessive amounts of grit and sand.

DEFECTS, TYPES AND CAUSES OF FABRIC.

1. BROKEN PICKS: Can be caused by improper winding of filling on bobbins, cut guides, excessive tensions, improper pickage, poor quilling caused by yarn bunching, misplaced knots, loops, etc. Other causes include rough shuttle boxes, improper shuttle-boxing, weak or irregular yarn.

2. BROKEN WARP ENDS: Damaged heddles, drop wires, reed, etc.; poor sizing of the yarn; rough or chipped shuttles; irregular or weak yarn.

3. BRUISED OR CHAFED ENDS: Rough or bent heddles, drop wires or reed; filling fork wire not running true; chipped or rough-surfaced shuttle.

4. BRUISED OR CHAFED PICKS: Damage by the traverse wheel in copping; poorly handled cops, shuttle irregularity, rough or improperly set shuttle guide; filling or center fork in raceplace of the loom off-center or improperly timed.

5. CREASES: Take-up rollers not functioning as they should; tight, rolling, or improper tension on selvage.

6. FILLING BANDS: Improper throwing, faulty tensions, uneven steaming treatment, yarn mixtures.

7. LOOPED OR LOOSE FILLING: Poor tensions, poorly set center filling fork, faulty copping, overpicking.

8. MISPICK: Failure of the head motion or the pattern-chain to function properly; carelessness or inexperience of the weaver.

9. OVERBEATEN CLOTH: Improper humidity; faulty warp tension either in one or more sections or throughout the entire warp; slippages; oversizing of the warp.

10. SHINERS: Yarn bunching, catching on the loom; excessive tensions; improper shuttle tension; poor knotting on cops, shuttle spindle out of alignment.

11. SHUTTLE MARKS: Damaged shuttle, improper shedding and to include poor timing of rise and fall, smashes, improper shuttle flight, poor picker-stick timing, overpicking, selvage defects such as tautness, rolled selvage, ends out.

12. SOILED FILLING: Unclean shuttle boxes, caked waste matter, oil splashes, soiling in copping or winding yarn on filling bobbin, sheer carelessness.

13. SOILED KNOTS: Unclean heddles, drop wires or reed; sticky sizing.

14. SOILED WARP ENDS: Sheer dirt and carelessness caused by unclean equipment being allowed to function by the operator, soiled hands handling the warp, oil splashings, effects of perspiration from the hands of the particular operative.

15. START-UP MARKS: These results may appear tight or loose, bright or dim. These can be caused by poor timing and action by either the let-off or take-up motions; faulty clutch, poor loom start-up, allowing the loom to stand too long with an open warp shed, warp yarn stretching caused by long standing. Carelessness is often a cause of faulty start-up marks, as well as inexperience on the part of the weaver.

16. TEMPLE MARKS: Eccentric temple rolls, worn rolls, wrong type of rolls, too much tension or pressure, poor setting.

17. TIGHT SELVAGE: Improperly dressed warp as to tension, slippage, taut selvage, improper layout of the warp with regard to selvage weave or yarn used; poor fabric layout or construction.

18. UNEVEN CLOTH: Improper let-off or take-up action, slipping clutch, uneven sizing, uneven weave, cockling.

19. WARP STREAKS: Chafed ends, poor slashing of the warp, improper sizing, incorrect drawing-in or reeding, loose, weak or worn reed, yarn mixtures.

20. WEAK CLOTH: Reed damages and take-off attempted to cover up damages.

DEFECTS IN WOVEN CLOTH, POSSIBLE.

1. Barry or barre marks.
2. Bleeding colors.
3. Broken pattern.
4. Broken ends or picks.
5. Cloudy goods.
6. Cockled cloth.
7. Coarse ends or picks.
8. Creases.
9. Crocking.
10. Cut listing or selvage.
11. Dead colors.
12. Double picks.
13. Ends out.
14. Floats.
15. Hair in filling— fuzziness.
16. Harness skips.
17. Hitch backs.
18. Holes.
19. Kinks.
20. Loose picks.
21. Loose selvages.
22. Mispicks.
23. Mixed filling.
24. Narrow width.
25. Oil stains.
26. Overwidth.
27. Reed marks.
28. Rolling selvage.
29. Section marks.
30. Shear marks.
31. Shiners.
32. Skipping.
33. Shuttle marks.
34. Slugs.
35. Specky goods.
36. Sluff-offs.
37. Sand roller marks.
38. Start-up marks.
39. Thick stripes.
40. Thin stripes.
41. Tender goods.
42. Tight picks.
43. Tight selvages.
44. Torn selvages.
45. Uneven cloth.
46. Washer wrinkles.
47. Weaving over or under.
48. Weaving slack.
49. Wrong draws.
50. Uneven double and twist.

DEFIBERING. Separating flax fiber from the stem of the plant.

DEFLOCCULATION. Scattering or dispersion of a substance in another medium. For example, breaking by scattering and emulsifying dirt into a finely divided condition.

DEGAGE. English dégagé is from French, meaning detached, disengaged or free and easy; implies necklines in women's wear on the order of décolleté or deep décolletage.

DEGRADATION. This is one of the banes observed in textile materials in-the-white, and partially or fully colored. It is the term used when there is destruction, breaking, or damage done to the fibers either by chemical or external means. Migration or the shifting or running of colors on fabrics is also classed as degradation.

DEGRAINED LEATHERS. Suéde-finished glove leathers of imported hair sheepskin, finished on the grain side. This term is not so ambiguous as "imported suède" which is used at times to describe these leathers.

DEGREASED WOOL. Wool from which yolk, suint, and other foreign matter has been removed by the naphtha method.

DEGREASING. Any method or process used to remove yolk, suint, and foreign matter from wool. Naphtha is often used as the removal agent.

DEGUMMING. The process of the removing gum from silk, the sericin from fibroin. Boiling-out of the silk in a hot soap-bath removes the gum. The amount of gum removed will be from about 10 per cent in the poorest grades to about 25 per cent in the best qualities.

DEHUMIDIFY. To reduce by any process, the quantity of water vapor in a given area.

DEHYDRATE. To remove water in all forms from matter. Liquid water, hygroscopic water, and water of crystallization or water of hydration are included.

DEHYDRATING AGENT. A chemical action whereby water (H_2O) is removed from a compound.

DELAINE. French for "of wool." The term originally meant a high-grade women's dress goods. Today the word is used to imply a high-grade combing wool used in the best worsteds.

Delaine wool is raised in Ohio and adjacent states; one of the best wools grown here. Incidentally, Delaine wool does not necessarily have to come from Delaine sheep, a Merino type found in this country.

DELETERIOUS. A destructive action; usually refers to the action of harsh alkalies upon textile fibers.

DELFION. A caprolactam-based Nylon 6 made in filament, staple, and top forms and spun in the conventional methods of spinning. Product of Bombrini Parodi-Delfino, Italy.

DELFT. A soft, medium blue devoid of any yellowish cast.

DELINEATOR. One who writes fashion and style copy and is supposed to be able to prophesy, more or less, what the coming vogue will be in apparel and accessories.

DELINERE. Plain-woven, bleached linen cloth of medium grade used for household purposes in France.

DELINTING. Another name for second-time ginning of cotton. It is done in the large cities of the South, and not on the plantation or community gin where first-time ginning occurs. Delinted fibers are very short, brown in color, and when refined serve as a raw material in the manufacture of acetate and rayon.

DELIQUESCENT SUBSTANCES. Textile ingredients or substances which attract moisture to yarn in order to give pliability and easy manipulation when processing. Popular deliquescents are calcium chloride, magnesium chloride, glycerine.

DELIVERY ROLLS. Those sets of rollers found at the front or delivery end of various machines used in cotton manufacture. Usually arranged in pairs, they deliver the stock following drawing, drafting, doubling, redoubling, attenuating, and other processes.

DELTA. This term applies to two world cotton-raising centers. The first is the area between the Mississippi and Yazoo Rivers in western Mississippi. The staple raised here is high in all characteristics. The second embraces the triangle at the mouth of the Nile River loosely bounded by the three cities of Alexandria, Cairo, and Port Said. It is in this region that the best Egyptian cotton is raised. See AMERICAN COTTONS, OUTSTANDING; EGYPTIAN COTTONS.

DELTA COTTON. See AMERICAN COTTONS, OUTSTANDING.

DELTAPINE COTTON. It has high yield and lint percentage, good fiber length and spins very well. Uniformity ranges from slightly irregular to good; possesses average fineness with strength weak to strong. Spun from 22s to 36s.

DELUSTERING. The reduction of the natural luster found in rayon or acetate yarn or fabric. Yarns may be made with any desired degree of luster by including a finely divided pigment in the spinning solution used in the manufacture of the yarn; titanium dioxide is a popular pigment for the purpose, although other chemicals may be used.

DELUXE. Fabric that has a high, lustrous Schreiner finish. The roller used may have as many as 360 fine grooves or gouged lines per inch to bring up the luster on the goods. Often given to Venetians, linings, lingettes.

DEMEMRARA COTTON. A raw cotton from the Guianas.

DEMI-DRAP. Means "half-cloth" in French; woolen fabric only slightly fulled, sheared, and then calendered.

DEMI-LUSTER. Wool of ordinary staple, not so long and lustrous as luster wool. This wool is obtained from English breeds, such as Cotswold, Devon, Leicester, Lincoln, Romney Marsh, Roscommon, and Wensleydale. See Illustrated Section.

DEMI-MOUSSELINE. Meaning a "half-muslin," this lightweight French fabric made of cotton or linen comes plain or in stripes. Used for dress goods.

DENIER. Three methods are used to find denier yarn sizes and the yards per pound of yarn for silk and man-made filaments with relation between a given length and a given weight. These follow:

1. STANDARD YARDAGE METHOD: An official denier coin weighs .05 grams or .771618 grains. Using the grain weight as the standard here, the following formula is used to find the number of yards in one pound of a 1-denier filament yarn.

$$\frac{492.13, \text{ standard yardage} \times 7,000, \text{ grains per pound}}{.771618, \text{ standard grain weight of 1-denier}} \text{ gives } 4,464,528 \text{ yards}$$

Thus, to find the number of yards in one pound of any size denier, silk excepted, divide the yarn size into this standard. Hence, in a 150-denier yarn, there would be the following computation—150)4,464,528(27,763.33 yards in the pound. (Often called the Rule of the Seven 4's.) Silk sizes, for example, are written as a 24/26-denier. The mean number would be 25. Thus, 25)4,464,528(178,581.1 yards to the pound.

2. THOUSAND METERS-UNITS PER KILOGRAM METHOD: This is based on the weight of 1,000 meters-units per kilogram. Thus, there would be 60,000 meters of yarn in a 60-denier yarn since 1,000 times 60 gives 60,000 meters of yarn per kilogram, the English equivalent of which is 2.2 pounds.

3. GRAM METHOD: It originated during World War II and is very popular today. As noted previously, one denier weighs .05 grams. Multiplying .05 by 20 gives a 1 gram weight. Standard length used is 450 meters (492.13 yards), and 450 multiplied by 20 gives 9,000 meters. Thus, all that has to be done is to weigh a reeled skein of 9,000 meters; if the weight, for example, is 200 grams, the denier size is a 200-filament yarn. See Illustrated Section; Denier in Yarn-Numbering Systems, World.

DENIM. This fabric has a history that goes back, as far as is known, about 1,600 years to the present city of Nimes, France, where it was first known as "Serge de Nimes" and later Americanized into denim. In this country this strong, sturdy fabric was first used between The War of 1812 and The War Between the States as covering for the famed Conestoga Wagons that carried hardy pioneers across the long trails going to the West.

This staple cotton cloth is rugged and serviceable, and is recognized by a left-hand twill on the face. Coarse single yarns are used most, but some of the cloth used for dress goods may be of better quality stock. A 2-up and 1-down or a 3-up and 1-down twill may be used in the weave formation.

Standard denim is made with indigo-blue-dyed warp yarn and a gray or mottled white filling. It is the most important fabric in the work-clothes group and it is used for overalls, coats, jumpers, caps. Denim is also popular in dress goods in the women's wear field and has even been used as evening wear. Popular also in the upholstery and furniture trades.

DENSITY. 1. Pertains to the hand or handle of a fabric, the weight per unit volume based upon the ASTM standard measurement of thickness and fabric weight. Density of cloth is classed as high or compact as against low or open. 2. The weight per unit volume expressed as grams per cubic centimeter, pounds per cubic foot, or the equivalent. 3. Applied to a package of yarn to describe its over-all hardness or compactness. Density is related closely to tension since the former is the direct result of the tension that has been applied to the package.

DENT. The opening, split, separation, or space between two pressed steel wires that constitute part of the reed through which the warp ends are drawn after the drawing-in process. A #40 reed means that there are 40 dents to the inch. The number of dents per inch varies a great deal and depends on the size of the warp yarn used, and the order or plan employed in reeding.

DENTAL FLOSS, DENTAL SILK. A very smooth, specially treated silk thread used to clean the areas between the teeth. Nylon is also used.

DENTED CORDS. The placing of two or more ends in the reed, split to produce a crammed effect in the woven goods. The cords obtained usually produce a fancy effect in the fabric.

DENTELLE. 1. French term for scalloped, picot, or pearl edging on lace since it reminds one of the arrangement of "teeth like pearls." 2. Prior to the seventeenth century the words "passement" or "passementerie" meant lace. Since that time the word "dentelle" has replaced them and implies lace with scalloped edging. See LACE, etc.

DEPAINTING. Removing the paint and tar by a solvent process, from wool and noils taken from sheep so branded for identification. Known as Depitching in England and on the Continent.

DEPARTMENT STORE. Found in practically all places where there is a settlement of people, large or small as to numerical size, from the large store of the big cities to the general store found in the villages and hamlets. This store is the clearinghouse for all kinds of textile articles and meets the economic law of supply and demand. It deals with mass production, uniform sizes, and the question of retailing, the largest single industry in this country.

The greatest amount of business done in any department store is from retailing textiles and its accessories.

DEPILATORY. The compound used in wool pulling, which usually consists of sodium sulphide, sulphuric acid, and ground oyster shells, which give the lime yield necessary in the action.

DEPITCHING. See DEPAINTING.

De PLASSE, NOEL. In 1958, he discovered the method of printing now known as "the heat system of decalcomania printing of textiles." At that time, De Plasse was Director of the Dyeing Department at La-Lainiere de Roubaix, a large textile complex in the textile city of Roubaix in northeastern France, and presently known as Prouvost-Masurel. This method is also known as Decalcomania or Decal Printing. See Printing, Decalcomania.

DEPOSIT. A collection of insoluble or foreign matter in general.

DEPRECIATE. To reduce, such as the reduction of tensile strength of yarn or fabric by harsh alkalies.

DERBY. Also known as Bowler, this hat's invention is credited to Mr. William Bowler, hatter in London, England, and its popularity to the 12th Earl of Derby, famous for his interest in horse racing, particularly the English Derby, inaugrated in 1780 and still an annual event. Derby hats, however, can be traced back to the Middle Ages. The French call it chapeau melon, and in South America it is known as the chola.

This stiff felt hat has a rounded crown, narrow brim and was introduced in the United States in 1888. A dressy piece of headgear.

DERBY BACK. The smooth metal plate at the rear of the sliver lapper frame. The sliver passes over this plate on its way to the drawing rollers.

DERBY DOUBLER. The machine used to make heavy laps for the ribbon lappers. The delivered stock is then fed into the combers.

DERBY RIB. Hoisery which has six ribs on the face alternating with three ribs on the back.

DERBYSHIRE. See GRITSTONE.

DERIVATION WEAVES. Broad term for any and all weaves used today since they must be based on the three basic weave constructions—plain, twill, and satin—no matter how elaborate the patterns for which these derivations are used, including all types of Jacquard, leno or doup, and ply fabrics. Incidentally every weave known today was also known as far back as the year 1747, when a book was brought out in Berlin, Germany, which showed every type of construction used today.

DERMESTIDAE. The larval stage of this small beetle receives its nutriment from animal fibers such as wool or fur.

DERNIER CRI. French for the "last word, latest fashion." Also referred to as the "dernier mot."

DERRIES. Indian cotton dress goods about one yard wide used in local consumption. The fabric is of the yarn-dyed variety.

DESCRIPTION COTTON. That which is guaranteed to meet specified requirements in conformity with sample specifications, such as character, grade, staple, and producing location.

DESEXUALIZATION. This term was coined in 1968 and has gained favor for several reasons. Males want to look like females, and vice versa. Females wear pants and pant suits; men have long hair and flowered shirts. Youngsters, both male and female, never come out of jeans, and with the popularity of bareness, both sexes are seen in hip-huggers and midriff-showing tops. Stores and shops have become aware of the importance of this trend, and try to increase sales by catering to the "unisex" fashions with new, often "psychedelic" decor and well-versed, clever, and rather cunning salespersons who know how to appear both naive and sophisticated.

DESI. An Indian silkworm that produces two broods, the better type in November.

DESIGN. 1. The complete plan or motif in a cloth from which one repeat of the pattern may be seen and the texture counted as to the number of ends and picks per inch in the goods. See Illustrated Section.

2. A preliminary sketch, plan, or pattern for something to be made into a finished article such as a coat, dress, hat.

3. The figured arrangement or pattern in a textile material.

4. The selection and arrangement of parts, ornament, and construction to make the completed article such as a suit or ensemble.

DESIGN DRAFT. A diagram which shows the pattern, design, or motif that is to be woven into the material; it also shows the weave or weaves that are to be used in the construction—plain, twill, satin, combinations, and others.

DESIGN PAPER, GRAPH PAPER. See WEAVING.

DESIGN PATENT. Covers visual inventions, textile or otherwise. May be taken out from the Patent Office, Washington, D.C., for periods of 3½, 7, or 14 years in accordance with your preference.

DESIZING. Removal of warp sizing from gray goods in the finishing plant; enzymes are often used for the purpose.

DESIZING MACHINE. A machine in which cloth is subjected to the action of chemicals, to remove size prior to dyeing.

DESPAISSIS SILK. Cuprammonium rayon was formerly known by this name.

DESSICATE. To have the property of drying in totality.

DESULPHURIZING. The removal of sulphur from the skeins of yarn in the viscose method of making rayon and in the finishing of material.

DETACHING MOTION. The combed portions of the slubbing, top, or lap on the Heilman comber are drawn off to make a continuous strand of fibers by this action.

DETACHING ROLLS. On the Heilman comber there are three rollers—leather, steel, and brass—whose function it is to draw off the combed fibers from the rest of the lap formation, the separation of the top from the noil.

The rollers are set up in an intermittent reciprocating movement.

DETERGENCY. The act of removing soil from the surfaces by means of detergent solutions.

DETERGENCY, SEQUENCE. A new and advanced detergent scheme which involves several stages, all occurring in orderly sequence in the one bath. Used, for example, in the formulation of built soaps.

DETERGENT. A cleansing agent, usually synthetic, that resembles soap in its ability to emulsify soaps and oils. It's cleansing or purging properties rid yarns and fabrics of dirt and soil.

DETERGENT, ALL PURPOSE. One which, in addition to the organic active ingredients, has builders—mild alkaline materials—added to improve cleaning and to soften water. This type may also include anti-redeposition agents, bleaches, brighteners, and corrosion inhibitors. Designed for the family wash, they may be granular or liquid, and provide high sudsing or low sudsing.

DETERGENT, HIGH SUDSING. Any of a number of washing products which produce a goodly amount of suds when acted upon by water. See Detergent.

DETERGENT, LIGHT DUTY. Also referred to as an unbuilt detergent, this washing product is engineered for use on fine, delicate fabrics, laundry that is slightly soiled and for hand dishwashing. A brightener may be in the compound in either granule form or in the liquid itself. See Detergent, Detergent, Heavy Duty.

DETERGENT, LOW SUDSING. One of the built detergents in which the sudsing properties are controlled or reduced. See DETERGENT.

DETERGENT, NONIONIC. As its name implies, it is one whose action is devoid of positive or negative charges. The action of this type of detergent is compatible with either anionic or cationic actions and reactions. Nonionic materials do not conduct electrical charge or current and are commonly used to increase penetration, wetting action, and detergent action.

DETERGENT, SOAPY ALKALINE. A mixture of soap and one or more alkaline detergents, and containing 2 per cent to 15 per cent of anhydrous soap.

DETERGENT ACTION. The following definitions should be of value with regard to detergent action.

1. Detergent: A solution used to increase the ability of water to clean.

2. Detergency: The act of removing soil from the surfaces by means of detergent solutions.

3. Emulsifier: Its function is to stabil-

ize the suspension of water-insoluble particles in water.

4. Surface Active Agent: A chemical agent which tends to concentrate at the surface when dissolved in water.

5. Wetting Agent: A chemical agent which increases the wetability of water.

6. Synthetic Detergent: A surface active agent other than soap.

7. Builders, Alkalies, Alkaline Salts: Chemicals used to soften water, to neutralize acidic soils and to improve the detergent action of soap.

DETERGENT CLASSIFICATION. In accordance to demand they are:

1. Linen supply; very heavily soiled white work.

2. Heavy soiled white work; fast-color fabrics and garments.

3. Lightly soiled white work; all degrees of soiled fugitive colors.

DETERGENT INDEX. A measure or factor used to determine the efficiency of a detergent.

DETERGENT OPERATIONS, TEXTILE.

1. BOIL-OFF: On cottons its purpose is to remove the natural waxes, motes, pectins, and soil and to improve absorbency. The detergent must have rapid penetration and soil-removing and suspending actions.

On man-made fibers and filaments, including hosiery, the function of the treatment is to remove spinning oils, sizing compounds, and soil. Good detergent action must be present and, in some instances, leveling properties should be of the best.

2. CONTINUOUS BLEACH: On cottons the aim is to remove the natural waxes, motes, pectins, and soil and to improve absorbency. Rapid penetration is necessary for good results.

3. DESIZING: On cottons, rayons, and fabrics made from combinations of these fibers the purpose is to remove size; rapid penetration and wetting actions are important properties that the detergent should possess.

4. DYEING: On cottons the function of the detergent is to improve penetration and leveling action. The detergent should have stability to acids used. On wool the function is to provide good leveling action. Properties of the detergent should include dye-suspending action, stability to acids.

5. FINISHING: On cottons the action should provide a soft, mellow hand to the goods. Properties of the detergent used should include low titer, freedom from rancidity.

On man-made fiber goods the purpose of the detergent is to supply proper scroop. High titer and freedom from being rancid should be the chief assets of the detergent used.

6. FULLING: On wool detergent, function is to aid in the fulling treatments and in the scouring of the goods. Even lubrication is the chief asset that the detergent should have. See Illustrated Section.

7. KIER, BECK, VESSEL BOILING: On dyed cottons the purpose of boiling is to remove natural waxes, motes, pectins, and soil. Absorbency should also be improved. The detergent used should provide for rapid penetration, soil removal, and suspending action.

8. SOAPING: On cottons, rayons, and fabrics made from combinations of these fibers, the function of the detergent is to remove excess dye and to help bring the color to the proper shade. Maximum detergency action is essential in all instances.

On prints the purpose is to remove all gums and starches, and so on. Maximum detergency action is vital at all times.

9. SCOURING: On raw wool, the detergent is used to remove dirt and grease. Easy solubility and rinsability should be properties of the detergent.

On woolen piece goods and yarns, the detergent should be able easily to remove oils and soil. Oil emulsification is the chief asset for the detergent.

DETERGENT PRESSURE. Total amount of alkali present, to which must be added colloid effectiveness when dealing with a collodial detergent.

DETERGENTS, MAJOR CHEMICAL FORMATIONS IN. These follow:

Caustics: Preparations commonly contain caustic soda, (sodium carbonate), and usually found in soaps. Caustics are not nearly so effective when compared with phosphates or NTA in cleaning clothing, chiefly in areas where hard water prevails.

NTA: Initials for nitriloacetic acid, which began to find use in the late 1960's, as a chemical substitute for phosphates in detergents. In addition to being free of phosphorous, NTA was regarded as better than phosphates because of its ability to soften water and prevent redeposition of dirt and soil.

Phosphates: These are molecular combinations of oxygen, sodium, and phosphorous which have been used as major detergents since 1948. The chemical, most commonly used in sodium tripolyphosphate, softens water by neutralizing the mineral impurities and prevents dirt and soil that has been washed out of clothing from being redeposited on it.

DETERGENT SOAP POWDER. A mixture of soap and one or more alkaline detergents, and containing 25

DETERGENTS, FOOD AND DRUG ADMINISTRATION ASSESSMENT OF.
On September 15, 1971, The Food and Drug Administration, Washington, D.C., published a survey of 37 detergents out of the approximately 200 now on the market. Potential hazards in their use are based on a rating system, which follows:

1. Caution, harmful if swallowed.
2. Caution, harmful if swallowed, eye irritant.
3. Warning, injurious to eyes; harmful if swallowed.
4. Warning, injurious to eyes and skin, harmful if swallowed.
5. Danger, may cause burns to eyes and skin, harmful if swallowed.

Rating of these 37 products follows:

Product	Phosphate Content	Rating
Acme	None	4
All	Yes	2
Arm and Hammer	None	2
Balance	None	5
Basic I	None	3
Bio-D	None	3
Breeze	Yes	2
B-70	None	4
Burst	Yes	2A
Cascade	Yes	2
Cheer	Yes	2
Cold Power	Low content	Eye and skin
Cold Water	Low content	2
Concern	None	4
Controll	None	3
Crystal Clear	Yes	2
Drive	Yes	Toxic - eye and skin
Ecolo-G	None	4
Fab	Yes	4
Giant OW	Yes	5
King Kullen	None	3
Klean	Yes	5
Logic	None	4
M-W Lo Suds	None	1
Miracle White	None	3
Par	None	3
PFD	None	4
Phos Free	None	Eye and skin
Phosphate Free	None	3
Pure Water	None	3
Sears	None	1
Spring Clean	None	2
Tide X-K	Yes	Eye and skin irritant
Trend	None	2
T-Rif	None	1
Triumph	None	3
Un-Polluter	None	3

In the F.D.A. listing, Amway SA-8, without explanation, was classified as both containing phosphate and also free of it. See Detergent and all other Detergent Captions; Phosphate.

to 50 per cent of anhydrous soap.

DETWISTED. A rope or strand of fibers or filaments from which all twist has been removed.

DEVELOPED DYEING. This is usually done with dyestuffs that are substantive to cotton and rayon, wherein further treatment may be applied, such as diazotizing and coupling with phenols, naphthols, or amines to increase the fastness to washing.

Naphthol dyeings are usually considered to be those produced from a beta oxy-naphthoic acid derivative combined with a diazotized amine. Para Red is produced from Paranitraniline, diazotized and coupled with beta naphthol.

DEVELOPER. A reagent which produces an ingrain color through its action on a textile fiber. An example would be beta naphthol.

DEVELOPING AGENTS. Various organic chemicals, which, when mixed with dyestuffs or other chemicals, produce insoluble colors that are not lakes. Potassium dichromate, an oxidizing agent, is used in alizarine dyeing as a developer.

Perborate is used as a developing agent in vat colors. Beta naphthol is a developer on certain direct colors to increase the fastness, such as on Diamine Black BH to obtain a fast black.

DEVIL. 1. Facetious term applied to spur-tooth cotton picker machines. 2. The garnetting frame is also called by this name, at times. See GARNETTING.

DEVIL'S COTTON. See ABROME.

DEVON LONG WOOL. This British breed of long wool sheep is more of the mutton type than wool type. Dense, curly locks which average about 10 inches in length are a feature of this lustrous, coarse fiber which is graded at 36s. Because of its firmness and durability, the wool is a favorite in making cassimere and serge. See Illustrated Section.

DEVONSHIRE. A strong, yarn-dyed cotton material which is used for house dresses, children's rompers, nurses' uniforms, and other practical clothes.

DEVON WEAVE. British term for the weave used in ordinary huckaback or huck material which repeats on ten ends and six picks. In the weaving of the goods the warp arrangement could be two and then three ends, in alternate arrangement, weaving together as a single yarn. Drawing-in and reeding of the yarns make this plan possible. The filling picks are thrown through the shed of the loom two picks per turnover of the loom. Texture is about 60 x 30 with around 25s or 26s linen yarn used.

DEWING. Woolens and worsteds may be treated to a fine spray of water. The material may pass over brushes or rollers revolving in water to receive the treatment. Also known as damping, dampening.

DEWLAP WOOL. Those folds of wool obtained under the jaws of the sheep.

DEWOOLING. Removal of wool from skins of slaughtered sheep. May be accomplished by a lime-water soaking, by soaking in water and then hanging in closed areas in which high temperatures are used, or by painting the flesh side of the skin with a solution of sodium sulphide. The latter treatment takes from about 8 to 24 hours. At the end of the allotted time the wool fibers may be removed as easily as a man removes lather from his face when shaving. Only the tips of the treated fleeces give trouble and they are usually clipped off and are of little or no value. Also known as sliping or depilatory method of removing wool fibers from sheep fleeces.

DEW POINT. The temperature at which a vapor (water in atmosphere) begins to deposit as a liquid.

DEW RETTING. See FLAX PROCESSING.

DEXTRINE. An artificial sizing ingredient made by submitting starch to a temperature of 300° F. Used in heavy weighting of fabrics, this white or yellow ingredient contains about 8 per cent moisture content.

DEXTROSE. A sirupy liquid obtained by hydrolysis of starch with hydrochloric or sulphuric acid; the operation causes a chemical action which results in the decomposition of the starch into several components, of which dextrose is one.

DHARWAR COTTON. An Indian cotton which is fairly clean, strong, and has a creamish cast. Staple is from ¾ inch to 1 inch; spins to about 20s yarn.

DHOLLERA COTTON. A low-grade, weak, rather dirty cotton raised in India. Staple is about ⅞ inch with a lint yield of about 34 per cent. Used in low-quality filling yarn, it spins to about 20s.

DHOOSOOTIE. A heavy duck fabric used for tents in India.

DHOOTIES. The better grades of this cotton fabric are made with Jacquard or dobby patterns, poorer qualities have a group of colored ends located near the warp selvages and, in some cases, the effect is interspersed across the goods. Used as loincloth in India.

DHURRIES. Cotton carpets or rugs made in India from hand-spun yarn. There is no pile effect in the construction. Much of the cloth is made in the prisons of India. There is a wide range of color, design, and size in the rugs, which are known as Daris when made in twill-weave constructions to be used as tent material.

DIABLE FUERTE. Bedford cord, corduroy, and comparable fabrics are known by this term in South America.

DIAGONAL. Cloth that shows an oblique twill line that may run to the left or right on the face of the material. Most twill lines are 45 degrees and they go from the lower left-hand corner of the cloth to the upper right-hand corner. Steep twill lines may be 63, 70, or 75 degrees in angle. Diagonal cloths are easily recognized as the twill line is prominent. Some diagonals are made with a left-hand twill face effect. See RECLINING TWILLS.

DIAGONAL BASTING. Slanting stitches used to secure lining to the outside material; sometimes used as temporary stitching.

DIAGONAL CLOTH. A woolen or worsted dress-goods fabric in which pronounced diagonal lines abound. Used for suitings, the material is usually given a clear finish and worsted cloth of this name has high twist in the warp and the filling.

DIAL. The horizontal needle-housing in circular knitting machines of the rib and the interlock types.

DIAMINE. Any of a group of amino compounds formed by replacing hydrogen in two molecules of ammonia, with one or more basic alcohol radicals; a double amine.

DIAMOND COTTON. A variety developed from the Rio Grande type of short-staple Uplands cotton.

DIAMOND LINEN. Linen diaper fabric made in small diamond effects.

DIAMOND NET. Lace effects made in small diamond patterns.

DIAMOND POINT TOE. Noted on a full-fashion stocking, the fashioning process produces a diamond-shaped toe.

DIAMOND REELING. Cross-reeling in which the pronounced crossing of the yarn shows a series of open meshes in diamond effect.

DIAMOND STITCH. An embroidery stitch in which the stitches run diagonally at opposite directions to form small diamond effects.

DIAMOND TWIST. Two or more threads are twisted around a core or heart thread to give a chain or diamond effect.

DIAMOND WEAVES. Those weaves which form diamond or spot effects;

used in novelty dress goods, shirting, and so on.

DIAMOND YARN. A yarn made by twisting two fine threads in opposite direction around a strong core or center thread to give a novelty effect.

DIAPER. In the Middle Ages, the term meant a rich silk material first made in Ypres, Belgium. As time went on this cloth of Ypres (d'Ypres) took on a different meaning until today it now means diaper fabric—the soft, absorbent, bleached material that is often a household necessity. Four types of this fabric are now found in the market: Bird's-eye, which is made on a dobby loom, the soft plain-woven cloth used for babies' diapers, the twill-woven cotton flannel type, and a plain knit fabric with the typical characteristics.

DIAPER LAUNDRY AID. Used to control the growth of bacteria such as the forming of ammonia in diapers, it comes in liquid, powder, or tablet form. Some aids are used for soaking and washing, others for rinsing.

DIAPER LINEN. See DIAPER; BIRD'S-EYE LINEN.

DIAPHANOUS TABBIES. Term sometimes applied to marquisette, ninon, tulle, voile, and other sheer fabrics.

DIASTOFOR. A desizing agent which uses the action of enzymes to remove gums, sizes, starches, etc., from textile materials.

DIAZOTIZING. Part of a process whereby direct colors are made semifast by treating the fabric after dyeing in a solution of sodium nitrite and sulphuric acid; a developer is then added such as naphthol, naphthylamines, carbolic acid and other organic compounds for the desired effect.

Diazotizing may also be classed as an intermediate step in the production of developed naphthol or para dyeing. It is an essential step in the producing of all azo dyestuffs. The diazotized base is combined with a phenol, naphthol, or another amine in order to make the complete dyestuff.

DIBASIC. Containing two atoms of hydrogen replaceable by a base or basic radical, as sulphuric acid; said of salts derived from such an acid.

DICE, DICE CHECKS. Name comes from motifs often seen in tablecloths and dress goods. Satin or twill weaves, in warp-and-filling effects, cause the bright and dim blocks to appear in the material. Popular in the British Isles.

DICEL. British Celanese, Ltd., United Kingdom produces this continuous-filament acetate product. "Duracol" is

the name given the spun-dyd yarn. "Fluorescent High Life Colors" are filament that is spun-dyed, fluorescent shades with very high brightness for use in apparel goods. "Slubs" is the name for the thick-and-thin yarns which find use in dressgoods, including linen-like-finished goods. "KN" is the name for the crimp yarns to provide coverage in goods used for apparel, dressing gowns, scarves, et al.

DICHROMATISM. The state of being dichromatic; especially with reference to color blindness.

DICKEY. 1. A false shirt front or bosom. 2. A workman's loose jacket of coarse linen. 3. Detachable shirt or blouse front, often with a collar.

DICKEY ROLL. Found over the doffer on a worsted card, it has flexible card clothing, about one inch high, which raises imbedded fiber stock to the surface of the clothing on the doffer roller, so that it may be processed through the frame in entirety.

DICKSON COTTON. A popular cluster variety of early-maturing cotton which has a staple of 1 inch to 1⅛ inches and a lint yield of about 32 per cent. Also known as Cluster, Dickson, Dickson Improved, Dixon, Simpson.

DICOTYLEDON. A plant whose seed is divided into two lobes.

DIELDRIN. Originating in Australia and introduced in this country in 1949, this general purpose insecticide is of the chlorinated hydrocarbon type. In low concentrations it protects wool from attack by moth larvae even after prolonged washing and dry cleaning. Dieldrin exhausts easily in dyeing and other wet treatments, is durable, and the compounds using it as a base are very reasonable in price.

DIELMOTH. This product of Shell Chemical Company, Ltd., is a permanent mothproofing process; treated wool leaves no odor and color is not affected. Applied to all keratinuous materials such as carpets, blankets, piece goods, knitwear, underwear, knitting yarns, baby wools, and furnishing fabrics of many types. It is fast to ordinary washing and dry cleaning, exposure to sunlight, and resistant to wear and tear.

DIEPPE LACE. The bobbin point-type lace of the Valenciennes group made in the famous World War II town of Dieppe, France. One of the most popular laces of the 17th and 18th centuries, it is still made today. The narrow versions are known as Ave Maria lace and Pouissin lace; the wide type is called Dentelle de la Vierge.

DIFFERENTIAL MOTION. See COMPOUND, DIFFERENTIAL MOTION.

DIFFUSER. An agent which spreads or penetrates rapidly throughout a solution. It is important in detergency and blue applications.

DIGESTOR. A cooker used in the paper and pulp industry to form wood pulp by cooking wood chips with chemicals.

DILUTE. The act of weakening a solution by the addition of more water, etc. To reduce the concentration of solid matter.

DIMENSIONAL RESTORABILITY. The ability of a fabric to return to its original dimensions. A percentage figure specifies the dimensional change as found by laboratory testing. Many fabrics will shrink or stretch after cleaning or laundering. However, rayon fabrics which have been properly constructed and finished will return to their original dimensions by ordinary ironing.

A 2 per cent dimensional restorability means that while a fabric may shrink more than this in washing, it is restored to within this percentage of its original dimensions by ordinary home methods of pressing.

DIMENSIONAL STABILITY. The quality which enables a fabric or a garment to resist any type of change in measurement through repeated launderings. The generally accepted standard is that the garment should not shrink out of fit (that is, shrinkage should be less than 3 per cent) or become distorted after five launderings by the appropriate methods. Note, however, worsted trousers that run up and down with changes in relative humidity, or carpets that ripple or tear with changes in humidity, would have poor dimensional stability, without regard to laundering.

DIMETHYLANILINE. Derived from aniline, this brownish-yellow oily liquid is used in dyestuff manufacture. Formula is $C_8H_{11}N$. Dimethylamine, closely related to it, has a formula of $(CH_3)2NH$. Also used to make dyestuffs.

DIMITY. A thin, sheer cotton fabric in which corded stripes or checks may or may not be present in the pattern. Dimity resembles lawn in the white state, and may be vat printed or dyed. This popular staple is easy to manipulate, launders well, and the quality depends on the yarn and the texture used. Made of combed yarn and finished at 36 inches wide, textures range from 76 x 64 to 130 x 94. There are about nine yards of cloth to the pound. Used for aprons and pinafores, art needlework, bedspreads, curtains, collar and cuff sets, carriage covers, children's dresses, infants' wear, summer dress goods, waists, and underwear. See Illustrated Section (Fabrics 15).

DIMITY RUFFLING. A closely plaited, narrow cotton fabric used for edging.

DINGY, DINGY WOOL. A satisfactory wool except for lack of brightness or poor color; difficult to scour to the white.

DINITRILE OR NYTRIL FIBER. See DARVAN.

DINMONT. A wether sheep between the first and second shearings; the sheep between one and two years old, as well.

DINNER JACKET. An informal evening dress coat without tails; known as a tuxedo.

DIP. Generally applied to the immersion of cloth in "the blue vat."

DIP-DYED. See TIE DYEING.

DIP-DYED, INGRAIN. Hosiery made from yarns that have been dyed prior to knitting.

DIP DYEING. 1. Method of dyeing hosiery and knit goods on commercial basis. 2. Partial immersion in two or more dye baths to produce a variegated effect. See TIE DYEING.

DIPHENYLAMINE. A crystalline compound formed variously, and obtained by heating aniline hydrochloride with aniline; used in dyestuff manufacture.

DIPPED HOSE. Stockings made from natural color yarns and then dyed to desired shade.

DIRECT, SUBSTANTIVE DYES. These are applied to goods directly without the use of mordants; also known as commercial dyes. They are applicable to practically all fibers except acetate; used chiefly, however, on cellulose fibers.

DIRECT COTTON DYE. An anionic dye which has affinity for cellulosic fibers when applied from an aqueous dyebath containing an electrolyte.

DIRECT PRINTING. Printing of patterns directly onto material from rollers, usually made of copper and engraved to form the pattern on the goods when applied. Cretonne is an example of direct printing. Also known as calender, roller, and cylinder printing. See Illustrated Section.

DIRECT SPUN YARN. See SPINNING, CHEMICAL.

DIRECT STYLE. A method of printing in which one or more colors are applied to fabric and then fixed

upon the goods by ageing or some other method of application. The material is usually in the white but the method is often applied to goods already dyed.

DIRK. A kind of dagger formerly much used in the Highlands of Scotland and still worn as essential to complete the costume.

DIRNDL. A bodice dress with full, gathered skirt in which the silhouette resembles that of the pioneer women of this country. Named for similar peasant costume. Of Austrian origin.

DIRT, SOIL. Foreign substance or matter of any type: matter that is out of place.

DISCHARGE AND RESIST PRINTING, SUMMARY OF. In discharge printing, the ground is dyed a solid shade or color. The design is then printed with a discharge paste, usually with some hydrosulphite since it will give a white discharge.

If color effects are desired, the color matter is used with the discharge paste since it will not affect the color. Vat colors are often employed, since they require hydrosulphites for their reduction and, at the same time, discharge the dyed background from the goods —an ideal plan used on rayons.

To obtain a white discharge print effect on a vat print, the material is essentially blotch-printed. Discharge printed goods will show pure white or color effects which go through to the back of the goods.

In reserve or resist printing, white effects on aniline black are very effective, since excellent results are obtained; the cost is relatively low and this fast black is exceptionally difficult to discharge. In this method of printing, the goods are printed with tin salts and a gum which acts as a resisting agent. The material is then dyed. The portions of the goods which are not treated with the resist substance will take on the dyestuff. Sometimes, however, colors are added to the resist paste. These are colors which are not affected by the dyeing treatment.

Resist-printed effects may show on only one side of the material; the other side of the fabric will present a more or less solid color, generally speaking. If the fabric is rather thin or sheer, the resist effect may be seen very clearly on both sides of the material.

DISCHARGE PRINTING. Also called extract printing, this method is used for dark-colored materials which have white or colored designs. The fabric is piece-dyed, and certain areas of color are bleached or discharged, leaving white places in the goods. The

cloth is then direct-printed and some or all of the white portions are colored according to the plan. It is also possible to add a basic color to the discharge paste to produce a colored pattern. See RESIST PRINTING; DISCHARGE AND RESIST PRINTING, SUMMARY OF.

DISCOLORED WOOL. That which is stained or off-shade because of dung, urine, unfavorable weather conditions, and being allowed to remain too long in the grease condition.

DISCOUNT. The total number of points paid for a specific cotton below the quoted price for the base grade and staple. See COTTON FUTURES; HEDGING; STRADDLING.

DISCIPLINED. Bates Fabric Company of Bates Manufacturing Company owns this trade-mark for the permanent resin treatment given to cottons for wrinkle recovery in a few minutes. The treatment is effective for shrink resistance and quick drying properties, as well.

DISCOTHEQUE. This rather fantastic phenomenon was born in bizarre St. Tropez, the sophisticated resort in the Nice-Cannes area in the French Riviera, in 1963. The discotheque burgeoned in the rest of France, went to the British Isles and ultimately arrived in the United States where it has had a sensational reception. Originally the term implied a night club, private or public, where the habituees whiled away the evenings to phonographic records. In these low-lighted clubs, contemporary dance styles were exhibited.

The fashion industry soon adopted the term and the dress of this name is recognized by its low neck and short hem. Added to the ensemble were black stockings, lacy in construction, and a suitable make-up to set-off the configuartion of the individual. As an item of apparel there are several modifications and offshoots with all of these using the catchall word, discotheque.

DISCRIMINATION. A disadvantageous action taken by a company solely because of an employer's affiliation with a union, or because of his race, creed, or color.

DISC WAX. A circular disc of natural or synthetic paraffin used in winding to lubricate the yarn for proper functioning on the knitting machine.

DISEASED WOOL. Wool taken from a diseased sheep; inferior in working properties.

DISHDASHA. A long flowing shirt, reaching to the ankles, that has been worn by men and boys in Iraq and neighboring countries for centuries. The equivalent of the Egyptian gallabiyah, the dishdasha is considered by the Iraquans to be a sort of symbol, something like the three stars in the Iraq flag. Even today this ancient garb competes with trousers, with most Iraqians wearing the dishdasha except for the working classes who wear the dishdasha in their leisure hours.

Simple, low quality dishdashas sell for around two dollars; when made of fine and good textured materials prices may run as high as fifty dollars. These items take about ten days to make but tailors in Baghdad turn out the inexpensive types in around three hours.

DISHLEY. Another name for Leicester Luster sheep of England. See Illustrated Section.

DISINTEGRATE. To break up, to fall into particles, or to crumble.

DISINTEGRATING, SHREDDING. Another name in the manufacture of rayon for crumbs. In the viscose process the pulp sheets, after steeping in caustic soda, are ground or shredded by the shredding machine or pfleiderer.

DISMISSAL PAY. A lump sum of money paid by a company to an employee being taken off permanently from the payroll. It is frequently paid in lieu of an advance dismissal notice. It is the same as severance pay. It may also be paid in smaller sums at regular intervals in a manner similar to a pension, particularly when the employee whose work has terminated is close to the retirement age.

DISPERSE. To scatter finely divided particles in such a way that they are not discernible to the naked eye.

DISPERSED DYES. Dyes, mainly amino anthraquinone derivatives, are prepared for dyeing cellulose acetate by grinding in a colloid mill with soap and sulforicinoleates. These dyes are in a colloidal state, and can be dispersed readily in a dye bath. See COLLOID.

DISPERSE DYES, NONIONIC. These are "a class of water-insoluble dyes introduced originally for the dyeing of cellulose acetate (54 to 55 percent acetic acid) and applied usually from fine aqueous suspensions."

Although all commercial disperse dyes are actually slightly water-soluble under dyeing conditions, at least to the extent of 0.5 mg. per liter, their chemical and physical properties distinguish them from other dye classes (vats) which may be insoluble at some stage in the process. Originally such dyes were referred to as Dispersed Acetate Dyes. Their increased use on other fibers has brought about the use of a broader term, such as "nonionic dispersed dyes."

DISPOSABLES. Articles or items designed for or capable of easy disposal after minimal use. These articles generally are used one to five times and then discarded. The three types of disposables used at present are: 1. Absorbant articles such as diapers, hospital pads, and sanitary napkins. 2. Flat goods which are made from nonwoven products cut to shape for sheets, pillowcases, draperies, wipers, etc. 3. Apparel products.

Paper disposables were known as far back as 1872 when a trade journal carried an article on paper clothing worn in China and Japan stating that a good paper coat could be bought for ten cents, and an entire suit for twenty-five cents. Today the progressive disposables industry has two focal points. 1. Nonwoven fabrics made with supporting elements of textile fibers, chemicals and other materials. 2. Disposable soft goods whereby products are made from nonwoven fabrics combined with cellulose wadding, bonding agents, fluffed pulp or plastic film.

It should be noted that the term, "Paper Disposables" may lead to come confusion in the mind of the reader. A "Paper Disposable" is one in which paper is the chief ingredient used, but present-day disposables, generally speaking, contain little paper. The term "Nonwoven Fabrics" is more technically correct. At present, however, the terms "Nonwoven Disposables," Nonwoven Fabrics," and "Disposables" are somewhat interchangeable.

DISS. The fibrous stem of a reed-like Mediterranean grass. Uses include headgear, cordage, paper.

DISSOLVE. To melt or change from solid into liquid condition, usually to form a solution with a solvent.

DISSOLVING PULP. A specifically purified form of cellulose obtained from cotton linters or from chips of the spruce, pine, or hemlock trees.

DISTAFF. This staff, from which wool or flax was drawn in the early days of spinning, was manipulated with the spindle, and was in use until the seventeenth century. The first distaffs were fashioned like a forked twig. A cleft in the staff held the mass of carded fibers conveniently while the spinner drew out the tufts for twisting between the thumb and finger and wound the strands on the rotating spindle. The distaff is also used by those who walk and spin with a hand spindle. The spinning or Saxony wheel superseded the spindle and distaff method of spinning yarn.

DISTILL. A process of purification by evaporation and condensation of the vapor.

DISTILLED WATER. Water made pure by removal of all minerals and organic contaminants by distillation, which is the separation of the more volatile parts from the less volatile parts.

DISTRIBUTOR. See AUTOMATIC DISTRIBUTOR.

DIVIDED DRAW. Backed fabrics, double cloths, and other multiple fabrics may have two or more warps in the construction. Thus, it is necessary to provide certain harnesses for the face warp, the back warp, and possibly binder threads used in some constructions. The face warp, for example, could have four harnesses; the back warp, four more harnesses; while if the stitching was done with an eight satin weave, there would be eight shafts required, for a total of sixteen harnesses. Each construction determines the number of harnesses to be used in a divided drawing-in plan.

DIVIDER. Device used in full-fashioned hosiery to establish loops along with sinkers. The divider has been made obsolete in full-fashioned sweater knitting frames because it is not necessary for stitch formation and without its use speedier, smoother machine operation is possible.

DIVI-DIVI. The dried pods of *Caesalpinia coriaria*, which grows in the West Indies and South America; they contain 20 per cent to 35 per cent tannin and a brown coloring matter as well.

DIYOGI BLANKET. A Navajo Indian blanket made of plain weave and characterized by its bulky, loosely twisted woolen yarn. Comes in diamond and some line effects.

DJELLABA. A long, loose dress, buttoned only from the neck to waist and usually made with a hood. See Caftan, Djiba, Burnoose. Originated in Morocco.

DJIBA. Of Moroccan origin, it is a kite-shaped, slip-on garment with loose sleeves, which are cut in one piece along with the body of the garment. Usually worn by males, often with the arms inside the article supposedly to afford coller comfort to the wearer. See Caftan, Burnoose, Djellaba.

DLP 55. Propylene fiber which finds much use in outdoor furniture. Product of Dawbarn Division of Thiokol Corporation, Waynesboro, Virginia.

DOBBY. Woven on a dobby loom. Includes material with small figures, such as dots and geometric designs; floral patterns woven in the fabric, including certain shirtings, huck towels, diaper cloth, certain dress goods, drapery and upholstery fabrics. Can be dyed, bleached, or yarn-dyed in many colors. Dobby designs may be used in cottons, rayons, silks. See Illustrated Section (Fabrics 52).

DOBBY-BORDERED FABRIC. Napery fabric in which checks or stripes have a dobby-weave effect in them; sometimes will appear throughout the entire material.

DOBBY, DOUBLE-INDEX. A dobby head motion equipped with a separate index finger for each of the hooks, at top and bottom. By this arrangement one bar of the pattern chain controls two picks instead of a single pick.

DOBBY, DOUBLE-LIFT. It forms an open shed and can be run at a greater speed than single lift. In this arrangement, the harness lever can be raised by either the top or bottom hook of the dobby.

DOBBY LOOM. A type of loom on which small, geometric figures can be woven in as a regular pattern. Originally this type of loom needed a "dobby boy" who sat on the top of the loom and drew up warp threads to form a pattern. Now the weaving is done entirely by machine. This loom differs from a plain loom in that it may have up to thirty-two harnesses and a pattern chain. Is expensive weaving.

DOBBY PATTERN CHAIN. An arrangement of wooden crossbars and metal pegs or lags used to control the weaving of fabric designs and patterns. The chain is placed at the head motion side of the loom; each row of lags equals one pick in the cloth.

DOBBY WEAVES. See LOOM MOTIONS, MECHANICAL; LOOM AND WEAVING.

DOCKING. Lambs, which are usually born in the month of April, are docked by having their tails cropped, their ears nicked, their backs daubed with paint for identification purposes, and if male sheep their sexes are revised. All of this work is done with exacting precision in a very short time.

DOCTOR BLADE. Sometimes known as the color blade, it is a sharp steel blade which extends the width of a printing machine. Its purpose is to remove excess color on the etched surface of a roller used in printing textiles; prevents smudging, mottling, or spotting.

DOCTOR KNIFE. A scraper blade which removes excess dyestuff from a roller, such as that used in cloth-printing machine.

DOCTOR STREAKS. The metal blade known as the doctor knife on a printing machine will sometimes fail to scrape cleanly, the excess color from the engraved print roller prior to its coming in contact with the cloth to be printed. When this occurs, streaks of unwanted color will appear in the goods.

DODDS. Wool cut from the tail of the sheep.

DODOT. A type of kain used only in court circles. It is draped in a number of ways around the body of the wearer. See Kain Kapala, Kain Pandjang. Sarong.

DOESKIN. Used for trousering, broadcloth coating, waistcoat cloth, and riding habit fabric. The material is of fine quality, medium weight, smooth face finish, compact, and is made of wool. There are few points of similarity between this cloth and a buckskin. A five- or eight-harness satin weave is used and the yarn employed is of high count and twist. A dress finish and slight nap are features of the finished garment.

Rayon fabric of this name is a twill-woven cloth napped on one side; some of the fabric is made from a small satin-weave repeat. Used for coating, suiting, and sportswear, it gives good service.

DOESKIN FINISH. Dense and felt-like finish for certain woolens which is achieved by drawing the fibers to the surface, and straightening and combing them in one direction. The finished fabric is covered with a short nap which hides the weave entirely. Used on such fabrics as flannel and billiard cloth.

DOFFER. 1. In a loose sense, any roller whose function it is to remove stock from another roller. See Illustrated Section. 2. One who removes filled bobbins from the various machines in the mill.

DOFFER BEATER. 1. It is situated near the top of a lifting apron on certain textile machines of the opener type, and is a small, metallic roll fitted with at least four transverse strips of rugged, stiff leather. The beater is set on the opposite side of the pin cylinder and its purpose is to take off stock that has been left on the apron by the pin cylinder. Other names for this beater include doffer roll, stripper roll, pin apron stripper. 2. Found chiefly on automatic feeding machines, this toothed roll is set near the top of a lifting apron. This beater, in revolving, removes cotton or other fiber from the apron, and sends it forward through the passage set up to receive the stock.

DOFFER BONNET. The curved metal plate which covers the upper surface of the doffer roller on the card.

DOFFER COMB. Also known as the doffer knife. This saw-toothed, oscillating blade removes fibers from the surface card clothing of the doffer roller on a carding machine in web form, which is then condensed into a sliver form. See Illustrated Section.

DOFFER KNIFE, BLADE. See DOFFER ROLLER.

DOFFER ROLLER. This 27-inch diameter roller, next in size to the card cylinder, receives the carded fibers from the cylinder at the point of contact between the two rolls because of the excess speed of cylinder over doffer. The carded fibers are actually laid, by the cylinder card-clothing, on that of the doffer.

The doffer carries the cotton on its card-clothing surface for about one-half revolution where it presents the stock to the doffer knife or blade. This is a saw-tooth, oscillating bar which strips the full width of fibers from the doffer and allows the cotton to pass to the trumpet device and two calender rolls. The former condenses the web-like formation into a sliver so that it may then be fed to the coiler can at the delivery end of the machine. See Illustrated Section.

DOFFING. 1. Stripping the sliver from the carding machine. 2. Removal of a filled coiler can from the front of the card to make room for a new one to be filled with card sliver. It is done without stopping the machine. 3. Removal of full bobbins from the various machines that use them; quickly replaced with empty bobbins upon which the slubbing or roving may be wound. See Illustrated Section.

DOFFING CYLINDER. A pressed-steel wire drum or cylinder covered with card clothing, which strips the cotton in a light film form from the card drum or roller. The doffing comb, in turn, strips the stock from this roller.

DOFFING DRUM. A revolving cylinder on a card. It is covered with card clothing, which removes the cotton from the card rollers or card flats, and further cards the fibers.

DOFFING TRUCK. A rectangular-shaped box mounted on casters, used for transporting bobbins, quills, and spools between machines or departments of the mill.

DOFF, TO. Removing full bobbins, cops, cones, and so forth, from a machine such as the roving frame or spinning frame. Full bobbins are immediately replaced by new or empty ones so that production may continue.

DOG. 1. The catch that fits into the teeth of the ratchet to keep the beam from turning while weaving; another name for dog is pawl. 2. An undesirable piece of merchandise.

DOG-EARING. Cloth which has the

tendency to curl or roll up diagonally from a corner at the end of the piece or cut.

DOGGY WOOL. Wool which is more or less devoid of loftiness, springiness, and other positive qualities expected to be found in good commercial fleeces; an inferior wool caused by one or more properties or characteristics being deficient.

DOGS. 1. A very low-quality raw cotton. 2. Devices on circular knitting machines to keep dial and cylinder in correct relation to each other. Failure of the dogs to work correctly causes "dog-line effects" on the fabric. Knitting machine design today endeavors to do away altogether with dog units.

DOGSKIN. A heavy filling plush in which the pile effect is of mohair yarn. Made in a variety of effects, the cloth resembles the skin of a dog.

DOGSTOOTH. Not to be confused with Houndstooth, this 2-up and 2-down twill woolen fabric has the warp and filling arrangement of four light yarns followed by four dark yarns. The effect which produces a star motif is now better known as the Shepherd's Check, the forerunner of many of the popular Scottish District Checks. See SHEPHERD'S CHECK OR PLAID; CHECKS, HOMESPUNS AND TWEEDS, STANDARD SCOTCH.

DOILY, DOYLY, DOYLEY. 1. A small, matlike napkin, for use under dishes on a table. 2. A small ornamental napkin or short runner. (Plural usually doilies.)

DOKRAH. Loosely packed Indian cotton bales which, when sent to the shipping ports, are compressed and rebaled. Dokrah bales average about 200 pounds.

DOLE. A group of rayon skeins; there are from 10 to 20 doles in a rayon bundle of 10-pound weight.

DOLLIE. A flat truck of suitable size used to move heavy objects from one place in the plant to another. Much used in shipping department, weave shed, and finishing department.

DOLLY. A wooden device which agitates or beats cloths in the washing process. British term.

DOLMAN. 1. A jacket worn as a cloak by Hussars. 2. A capelike wrap or coat with the Dolman sleeve. 3. A long outer garment with close sleeves, open in the front.

DOLMAN SLEEVE. A sleeve fitted smoothly into the armhole, and large enough to extend almost to the waistline. It gives a capelike outline, and is often held snugly at the wrist.

DOLLY VARDEN. Applied to a cos-tume consisting of a dress with tight bodice; short, quilted petticoat; flowered chintz panniers; and a large, drooping flower-trimmed hat as worn by Dolly Varden, a character in "Barnaby Rudge," written by Charles Dickens, famed British novelist, 1812-1870.

DOMESTIC. 1. Ordinary cotton goods such as unbleached muslin sheeting or print cloth. 2. General term to cover household fabrics such as blankets, sheeting and pillowcasing, towels, washcloths. 3. American-made carpets and rugs as distinguished from those made in other countries, especially those known as Oriental rugs. 4. Fabrics made in this country from the major textile fibers as distinguished from those made in the British Isles or on the Continent —covert, serge, cassimere, melton, kersey, beaver, broadcloth; organdy, voile, dimity, and others.

DOMESTIC ORIENTAL. See SHEEN-TYPE RUG.

DOMESTIC PULLED WOOLS, TRADE CLASSIFICATIONS OF.

AA: 64s and better, very fine, usually short or of average combing length; produced the year round.

AA COMBING: 64s and better, fine staple; produced during winter months.

A COMBING: 60s and 64s staple wools; produced during winter months.

A LAMB: Fine and ½-blood lambs' wool; produced during summer months.

A SUPER: ½-blood, short combing length; produced mostly during fall months.

B COMBING: ⅜-blood staple wools; produced during winter months.

B SUPER: ⅜-blood lambs' wool; produced during summer and fall months.

C COMBING: ¼-blood and coarser, good combing length; produced during winter months.

C SUPER: ¼-blood lambs' wool, short combing length; produced during summer and fall months.

LB: High ⅜-blood, good average to short French combing; produced during fall months.

DOMESTICS. 1. English term for plain-weave cotton cloths which vary in quality. Average texture is about 60 ends of 24s warp and about 60 picks of 36s filling yarn. The gray goods are finished in several different effects. 2. A broad term for household goods such as blankets, bedcoverings, towels, pillowcases, sheets, curtainings, etc. 3. A broad term for shirting fabrics made in the United States.

DOMESTIC WOOL. 1. In this country, wool obtained east of the Mississippi-Missouri River. Also known as Fleece, Farm, and Eastern wool. 2. When applied to wools of the world it means all wool raised here, as against those raised in any other world area. 3. May imply those wools raised east of the Rocky Mountain areas and raised under farming conditions.

DOMETT, DOMET, DOMETT OR DOMET FLANNEL. Made of plain or twill weave, this generally white fabric has a longer nap than that noted on flannel; the names, however, are often interchangeable. Soft filled yarns of medium or light weight aid in obtaining the nap. The term domett also implies outing flannel. See OUTING FLANNEL.

DOMINANT HARMONY. Different values and degrees of the same color in a fabric—for example, one with three shades of brown. This type of coloring is popular at times and may have an air of distinctiveness; it is, however, monotonous and drab-looking in many garments.

DOMINICAL. The linen cloth or veil formerly worn when attending divine service, still used in Italy. This lightweight material serves also as the communion cloth used at the communion rail in churches.

DONEGAL CARPET. Hand-knotted, heavy-structure, good-quality carpets made on upright looms in and around Donegal, Ireland. The construction is 8 threads of two-ply, 8 skeins warp per inch and two-ply, 5 skeins filling yarn per inch. The pile filling is three-ply, 3 skeins tied in Ghiordes knot. The tufts are about 2 inches long to give a pile of little more than ½ inch with 16 tufts per square inch.

DONEGAL TWEED. 1. A plain weave or a herringbone weave tweed that was originally made in the county of this name in Ireland. The fabric is popular rough-and-ready material which does not possess high texture. 2. Tweed made in the British Isles on power looms; Yorkshire mills provide the yarn for the material, which is dyed and finished in Donegal. 3. Any material which is made in imitation of original Donegal. Most of the fabric today is made of plain weave. See HOMESPUNS AND TWEEDS.

DONGOLA. Rarely made today: a combination-tanned goat, sheep, or kangaroo skin.

DONSKOI. Trade name for southern Russian wool that is used for carpets.

DOPE. A pyroxylin, nitrocellulose base used in combination with color as a coating for fabric to make it impervious to air, water, or both. The term is used in many industries for any of several liquids applied to materials.

DOPE DYEING. This is a development from World War I when the term "dope" was used to imply the coating or covering for airplane wings. This dope was a solution of cellulose acetate, the forerunner of present-day acetate. The term today, pertinent to dyeing, is used in the following sense: after the solution used has been prepared and filtered for purification, dyes are introduced into the solution. The solution is then extruded through spinnerets, and then dried in the usual manner. Thus, the color used has become a corporate part of the filament itself, caused by the color and the fiber bonding together.

Much skill has to be used by the dyer in determining how much dye to place in the compound in order to achieve the desired shade; only experienced dyers can do the work to commercial satisfaction.

Also known as "solution-dyed" and "spun-dyed," the method has met with acclamation in the trade, wherever used. Dope-dyed cloths have splendid fastness to light, the colors are genuinely good and attractive, and the colors are not washed out in laundering. The method is ideal in plaids, checks, stripes, and in solid colors. In dope-dyed fabrics it is practically impossible to remove the color should it be desired to redye the goods.

DORI. An Indian-made rope used in pitching tents.

DORIAN STRIPES. Much used in India, this British-made cotton cloth has crammed stripes that are not in color. The foundation of the material is plain weave, while the stripes are made of satin weaves.

DORNIC. Spelled with many variations, it is a rugged, strong linen fabric that was figured or designed with a variance of motifs, ranging from bird's-eye diaper fabric to damask. Dornic is the Dutch spelling of Tournai (Tournay) in western Belgium, where the material was first made.

The term should not be confused with Dornic Hangings, which were made with woolen yarns only. Dornic was rather popular in England in the sixteenth century, where a plant was in operation in Norwich to make the material.

DORSAL VESSEL. In a silkworm, it is the heart, extending from one end of the body to the other, just under the skin of the back of the worm.

DORSEL. Also called Dorse and Dosel, it was a woolen fabric used for hangings, curtains, and drapes during the later years of the Middle Ages in the British Isles and on the Continent.

DORSET CLOTH. A low-grade, plain-woven British fabric made with two-ply cotton way and irregular wool "bump-filling."

DORSET DOWN. A medium-grade British Down breed which gives a wool shrinkage, when scoured, of about 45 per cent. See Illustrated Section.

DORSET HORN. Originally from Dorsetshire, England, this now widely distributed type of sheep produces a medium-quality fiber. This active, strong sheep gives a fleece of from 6 to 8 pounds, satisfactory for a 48s to 56s quality yarn. Staple is about 3 inches long and it is noted for its whiteness and crispness. Unlike other breeds of this type, the animal has long spiral horns. The hornless type, developed in England, is called Dorset Down.

DORURE. French for gold braid, decoration, plaited trimming, and so on.

DOT. A small circle used for embellishment on textile fabrics. It may be woven into cloth on the swivel, lappet, or clip-spot method; it can be printed onto cloth by the flock-dot method, or the dot may be achieved by the resist and discharge methods of printing. Effective in many types of dress goods.

DOTTED SWISS. A fabric first made by the cottage hand-loom weavers in and around Saint Gall about 1750. The fabric is still made by some of the descendants of these weavers at the present time. The hand-woven cloth has a set width of 32 inches.

There are now several types of the cloth, with varying weaves and pattern effects made at present, from the single and multicolored dot motifs placed regularly or irregularly on the material to combinations of dot effects with yarn-dyed patterns with solid grounds and drawn-thread work, and to the more intricate motifs and effects.

The hand-loomed fabric is made on a loom which has a swivel attachment to tie in the dots or designs on the back of the cloth. Hence, there is a frequent reference to "hand-tied dots" in conjunction with the dotted Swiss. A great deal of the present-day fabric is, of course, made on power looms.

DOUBLE. 1. Hosiery that has been reinforced and made stronger for better wear at the toe and the heel. Doubling makes a double thread that can be easily distinguished from the body of the hosiery. 2. To twist two or more yarns or threads on a spool to produce a ply yarn or ply thread.

DOUBLE AND DRAFT. To make uniform, and to average the stock being manipulated to produce finished yarn. Doubling is the feeding of two or more slivers, slubbings, or rovings into a textile machine. Doubling offsets drafting, since it is necessary to double up on the feeding-in end of the frame to balance the draft which draws the fibers among

themselves. Without doubling of stock, yarn could not be produced.

Excess speed of the front rollers over the carrier and back rollers makes fiber drafting possible. Twist is added in processing to sustain the fibers in their form such as sliver, slubbing, roving. These forms cannot be drafted to the point where they will collapse and be unable to sustain themselves. Doubling up on the stock fed into the machine takes care of this end of the work.

DOUBLE-AND-TWIST. This occurs when two ends are twisted together to make a thread. It differs from ply thread in that the double-and-twist thread is single, whereas in the ply thread there are two or more complete yarns plied together and used as a single end. Double-and-twist is a form of mock twist where the thread appears to be actually twisted and plied, but in reality is not. Double-and-twist is made in combination of two or more colors and is used in Bannockburn, salt and pepper effects, and in some Drummond worsteds.

DOUBLE ATLAS FABRIC. A warp-knit fabric which is made by having two sets of yarn make single-atlas traverses, course by course, in opposite directions. See SINGLE ATLAS FABRIC.

DOUBLE BEATING. Two successive beats of the reed are made in pressing heavy or bulky filling into its component place in woven cloth; resorted to in weaving carpet and Turkish toweling. An attachment placed between the sley and the crankshaft causes the action.

DOUBLE BOSS RAIL. Some makes of roving and spinning frames are built so that two or more ends are delivered from the one set of delivery rolls. Hence, the drawing rolls have two or more boss arrangements.

DOUBLE-BREASTED. A coat or jacket effect which shows the overlapping of the one front over the other front; the effect has a double set of buttons but one set only is used for buttoning purposes.

DOUBLE-CARDED. Cotton yarn made from stock that has been twice carded.

DOUBLE CARDING. A system of carding in which the stock is carded on a breaker card. The cotton is then formed into a group of slivers, and made into a lap formation which is then run through a finisher card, a second carding operation. See Illustrated Section.

DOUBLE CLOTH. Cloth with two warps and two fillings. Cloths with one warp and two fillings or with two warps and one filling are sometimes classed as double cloth. In double cloth the two cloths are woven, one on top of the other, and are held together by the manner of stitching in which certain threads, at specific times, show on the face or back of the cloth.

There are two methods of stitching: raising the back-warp thread over face pick, next to a raiser of the back warp and between two raisers of the face warp, or between a raiser and sinker of the face warp if it cannot be such that the thread will weave neatly between the two face-warp ends.

The second method is to lower a face warp end between two sinkers of the back warp and next to a sinker of the face.

Double-cloth materials of two or more warps and fillings are: beaver, bouclé, chinchilla, belting and webbing, kersey, melton, Montagnac, Saxony, Whitney, Worumbo. There are others. See Illustrated Section (Fabrics 43 and 44).

DOUBLE COMBING. The manipulation of worsted combing stock a second time, the purpose of which is to take out any remaining noil not extracted during first-time combings. Resorted to when fine, high counts of worsted yarn are desired. The term also implies the combing of cotton fibers twice in the comber to insure greater uniformity and evenness to the yarn; used when making yarns of 100s, upwards.

DOUBLE-CYLINDER DOBBY LOOM. If it is desired to weave a pattern that contains a great many picks in the repeat, a large number of bars must be built for the pattern picks since, even on the double index dobby, one bar represents only two picks, and when patterns of several hundred picks are woven, this becomes a matter of considerable importance as a long chain always requires much time in building.

Additional strain is also placed on the dobby by the use of a long chain since the chain must be supported to a certain extent by the cylinder.

When a pattern consists of but one weave it is difficult to overcome this defect, but it frequently happens that a pattern consists of two weaves, one of which is repeated many times before the next weave is brought into play. For example, in weaving handkerchiefs and mufflers, the center consists only of a plain weave repeated a number of times and the border has another weave which may also be repeated a number of times.

To overcome the difficulty of building long pattern chains, the double cylinder dobby is largely used. The pattern chain for one weave is placed on one of the cylinders while the pattern

chain for the other weave is placed on the second cylinder. Since it is possible to send either cylinder around as many times as there are repeats of the weave before changing onto the other cylinder, it is possible to build only one repeat for each weave, providing that the number of bars in one repeat is sufficient to go around the cylinder; if the repeat has less bars, a sufficient number of repeats must be built to encircle the cylinder.

Dobby motions are built wtih a capacity of from sixteen to twenty-four up to thirty harnesses. The sixteen-harness motions are used the most, whereas twenty- and thirty-harness motions are used for the more complicated weaves and novelty effects.

DOUBLE DAMASK. Table damask made with an 8-shaft satin weave. Single damask is made with a 5-end satin.

DOUBLE-DYED. Dyed twice; thoroughly impregnated; said also of mixed goods dyed once in a cotton dye and once in a wool dye, or otherwise, as the case may be.

DOUBLE ENDS. 1. Two warp ends drawn through the same heddle eye and reed dent or split thereby causing the ends to weave as a single end; rather common in weaving matting fabrics. 2. A defect caused by faulty drawing-in or reeding, thereby making a blemish in the cloth known as taped ends or flat. See Illustrated Section.

DOUBLE-FACED, DOUBLE-FACED FABRIC. A cloth in which either side may serve as the face of the goods, a reversible. Examples include double-faced satins of several types, rib-backed canton, satin-canton.

DOUBLE-FACED SATIN. Made with silk or rayon yarn, the cloth is made with two sets of warp yarn and one system of filling in order to present a satin face on either side of the goods. Both warps interlace according to some weave motif with the filling. Good quality yarns are used, since the fabric commands a good price.

DOUBLE FILLING FLAT DUCK. See DUCK; DUCKS.

DOUBLE HOSIERY. That which has been reinforced at the heel and toe, thereby making a double thread effect; this will distinguish it from the body of the hosiery.

DOUBLE KNIT. Knitted with double stitch, giving a double thickness to the fabric. See Illustrated Section.

DOUBLE-KNIT KNITTING FRAMES. The frame or machine used to make double knit fabrics, in rib-Jacquard or non-Jacquard motifs. The rib effect differs from the non-Jacquard effect in that the former is capable of exceeding a

repeat of pattern in the length of more than one machine revolution.

Non-Jacquard frames are of two types: 1. Those used for restrictive purposes. These frames have two cam tracks in both the cylinder and the dial with separate cam controls for each track at each feed. 2. Those used for extended purposes. Extended purpose machines have two separate needle tracks in both the cylinder and the dial which work in conjunction with the long and short, of the high and low butt needles.

DOUBLE-KNITTED PLAITED FABRIC. Material made from two or more systems of yarn of different stock. The face of the cloth will show the one material on the face of the cloth, while the other side of the fabric will show the other type of yarn. This effect is seen in sweaters. The cloth is medium or heavy in weight.

DOUBLE LOCK SEAM. Machine seaming used on lingerie and other ready-made garments. See SEAM, STITCH; STITCHES, TYPES OF.

DOUBLE-MILLED. Sheared twice.

DOUBLE PICKS. Defect caused by two picks having worked into the same warp shed in the weaving of the cloth, thus making a sort of rib-effect in the filling direction. The defect is quickly seen when the goods are perched or examined. Double picks occur often when the weaver begins to weave on the loom after fixing some flaw or blemish, or changing shuttles. Carelessness on the part of the weaver causes most of the double picks found in woven goods.

DOUBLE PILE. Any fabric with pile or heavy nap on two sides, as double plush, double-faced canton flannel.

DOUBLE PLAIN CLOTH. Made from a weave of that name which employs two warps and two fillings in the construction. It is used in striped cloths where the stripings interchange according to some plan or motif.

DOUBLE PLUSH. 1. A cloth with a plush pile-effect on either side. See Illustrated Section. 2. A knitted fabric with two face yarns and a backing yarn which is napped.

DOUBLE PLUSH WEAVING. The weaving of fabric, face-to-face, that is later cut in the loom, one material being taken from the loom at some particular point, and the other one taken from another part of the loom after the two cloths have been separated. A blade goes through the shed, a few inches in front of the reed, which cuts the warp in order to produce the two pile cloths. Looms which make this type of fabric have two shuttles passing through the loom shed at the same time; one shuttle is for the top shedding action, the other one takes care of the bottom shedding action. See Illustrated Section.

DOUBLER. 1. The machine used for doubling spun yarn from the mule frame, cop, flyer, or ring-spinning machines. 2. The British term for a twister.

DOUBLE RIBBON. Ribbon which has a design on both sides of the goods; may be used as a reversible.

DOUBLE RIB GIN. A type of gin that will gin half-opened bolls or those which are still closed; cotton obtained in this manner is called bollies.

DOUBLE ROVE. Combing two rovings from the roving frame and feeding them into the spinning frame as one roving, to obtain a single yarn.

DOUBLER WINDING. Winding two or more threads in parallel and uniform tension for subsequent twisting on the next machine.

DOUBLE SATIN. 1. Some double cloth overcoating is made by the use of a 5-shaft satin weave in the face and back construction. A satin weave is often used in combination with plain or twill constructions in making overcoating fabric; when thus used the satin weave is the one which does the stitching in the face and back cloths. Examples are melton, kersey, beaver, broadcloth, mackinac fabric.

2. The use of a 5-end or 8-end satin weave in dress goods and napery cloth to give bright and dim effects in the material. The bright effect may be made by using a warp-effect of the satin weave while the dim effect would be obtained from using the filling-effect construction of the same weave. Cloth thus made usually has block or checkerboard motifs.

DOUBLE SATIN DE LYONS. Both sides of this satin fabric are given a luster or glossy finish.

DOUBLE SERGE. Made of two warps and two fillings. Heavier than other worsted serges. Cloth is clearfinished, dyed in the piece, and runs from twelve to twenty ounces in weight. The cloth is not in demand as formerly, because people do not dress as warmly as they used to years ago.

DOUBLE-SOLED. Term for shoes made with extra-thick soles.

DOUBLE-SPUN YARN. Yarn that has been given two twisting operations, both in the same direction. Twist is S-S or Z-Z. Used in some crepe, hard-spun, and voile yarns.

DOUBLE-STITCHED. An edge or seam finish obtained by stitching twice in parallel rows of stated width, as "¼-inch double stitch."

DOUBLE-STITCHED SEAM. Same as cord stitch, but stitched twice and with a larger underlay or outlet for the second row of stitching. Also called lap stitch.

DOUBLET. The forerunner of the waistcoast or vest; it was a short outer garment, with or without sleeves, fitting the body. Popular in the fifteenth to seventeenth centuries.

DOUBLE-THROW YARN. Yarns made from a number of single yarns twisted together to give a double yarn.

DOUBLE, TO. The process of doubling or twisting two or more yarns into an individual-ply yarn. It is done on the twister frames in the mill. The yarn is usually twisted in the opposite direction of the single yarns that were used to make the ply or double yarn.

DOUBLE-TOP. The welt of a full-fashioned or seamless stocking.

DOUBLE TWILL WEAVE. A large repeat weave in which the pronounced twill that goes in one direction is intersected by twill lines that go in the opposite direction. The long, uninterrupted twill line in the fabric is usually the right-hand twill line.

DOUBLE TWISTER. Ring twisting frames, when used for throwing silk or rayon yarn, are often known by this name.

DOUBLE WARP. Two-ply fabric made in the British Isles is often referred to by this term.

DOUBLE WARP LININGS. Garment linings made of two-ply warp yarn of cotton, wool, acetate, or rayon.

DOUBLE WEAVE. A cloth woven with two systems of warp or filling threads so combined that only one is visible on either side.

DOUBLE WORK. Knitting term for the use of two threads together instead of one, and for the fancy effects so produced.

DOUBLE WORSTED. An old English staple worsted, finished at 45 inches.

DOUBLE-WOVEN PILE FABRIC. See LOOM AND WEAVING, DEVELOPMENT OF.

DOUBLING. Feeding two or more slivers, slubbings, rovings, or yarns into some textile machine. Doubling offsets drafting, as it is necessary to double-up on the feeding-in end of a machine to offset and balance this draft, which draws out the fibers. Without doubling, it would be impossible to make yarn.

DOUBLING MACHINE. A machine used for folding cloth to one half or one fourth of its original width and winding it onto a belt or cylinder.

DOUILLON. French for the very inferior wool grades.

DOUKALA-ABDA. Moroccan sheep, noted for its white fleece, which weighs about four pounds.

DOUP. In a loom, one of the vertical members of a harness through which is passed a warp end; the purpose is to change the horizontal as well as the vertical position of the warp in the pattern of the weave. See Illustrated Section (Fabrics 60).

DOUP EDGE. Split goods or ribbons which are woven several widths together are joined by the use of the doup, leno, or gauze weave with a doup edge to prevent raveling.

DOUP END. The thread or threads that actually cross in weaving the cloth. Also called crossing thread or whip thread, it is placed on the skeleton harness, while the base thread formation weaves on the standard harness.

DOUP NEEDLE. Same as the steel doup heddle used in doup or leno weaving.

DOUPPIONI OR DOUPION. Silk thread made from two cocoons that have nested together. In spinning, the double thread is not separated. The yarn is uneven, irregular, and diameter is large. It is used in cloth of this name as well as in pongee, nankeen, shantung and other cloths where this type of yarn is desirable. The material is of the "hit-or-miss" variety, and in some instances appears to be just so many ends and picks woven into a cloth.

DOW BADISCHE ACRYLIC 100. Based on acrylonitrile, a solution of the polymer is extruded and the resulting tow is then stretched, crimped, and cut. When melted, it leaves a hard black bead. Sticking temperature is 490° F. After being treated with direct and neutral premetallized dyes, it can be dyed with naphthol, sulfur, and vat colors. It has fair resistance to alkalis and the effect of other chemicals is rated as good. Unaffected by common solvents and resistant to mildew and moths. Uses include knit and woven apparel, pile fabrics, blankets, and floorcoverings; industrial items such as fender cloths, belts, filters, and chemically resistant cloths. Product of Dow Badische Company, Inc., Williamsburg, Virginia. See Zefkrome, Zefran.

DOW BADISCHE ACRYLIC 200. A copolymer based on actylonitrile, a solution of the polymer is extruded and the resulting tow is stretched. Sticking temperature is 420° F. Dyeable in complete ranges with cationic and disperse dyestuffs. Good resistance to acids and fair resistance to alkalies. Good resistance to other chemicals. Insoluble in common solvents; excellent resistance to mildew, carpet beetles, moths, and other micro-organisms. Uses include knit and woven apparel, pile fabrics, and floorcovering. See Zefkrome, Zefran.

DOWLAS. A low-priced sheeting or roller toweling made from a half or full bleach cloth of linen warp and cotton and linen filling. It comes in three widths—39, 46, and 56 inches.

DOWN. The soft, fluffy filaments grown under the feathers of ducks and other waterfowl. Used for pillows, quilts, paddings.

DOWN, DOWN SHEEP. Various types of medium-wool sheep raised in the rolling hill country or "Downs" of southern England. Sheep in this group include Dorset, Oxford, Shrophire, Southdown, Suffolk. See Illustrated Section.

Down breeds have been bred chiefly for mutton and they are of the sturdy type. They are not sufficiently hardy for regular range territory in this country, but they are popular in the farming areas east of the Mississippi River, where they are kept in flocks.

DOWNPROOF. Closely woven fabric which cannot be penetrated by down is termed downproof. Materials such as pillow ticking are down-resistant, and are used to cover pillows, comforters, etc.

DOWN-RIGHTS. Woolsorting term which implies wool from the lower parts of the sides in the fleece form. See Illustrated Section.

DOWN TREE. The corkwood tree of Central America and the West Indies yields thick cotton-like fibers obtained from the seeds.

DOWN TWISTER. The ordinary cap or ring yarn-twisting frame.

DOWN WOOL. This wool ranges between the length and the coarseness of long wools and the shortness and fineness of the fine wools. Fiber length is from 2½ inches to about 4 inches and the quality is from 56s to 60s. The wool has little luster. Lacking in mill properties, the stock is lofty and resilient, thereby making it ideal for knitting yarns.

DOWNY WOOLS. Those which are soft to the feel or hand.

DOW TEXTILE SOLVENT SYSTEM. To control shrinkage of woolen, worsted, and blended fabrics, this system uses a chemical stabilization resin and eliminates cold water and steam techniques. The method continually treats piece goods with a solvent soluble resin using

chlorinated solvents as the carrier. Fabrics which have been given the treatment have a residual shrinkage of one-half to one percent, compared with three to four percent, plus residual shrinkage, common with conventional cold water shrinking. The system also provides controlled fabric hand, especially in wool/polyester blends. Ballooning or puckering is prevented by hygral (moist or wet) expansion control or fabric stability at various humidities and temperatures. Product of Dow Chemical Company, Inc., Midland, Michigan.

DRAB. 1. A dull, lifeless yellow-gray color. 2. Cloth, usually khaki in color, is also called drab.

DRABBET. 1. A coarse, drab, English linen duck. 2. An unbleached linen cloth.

DRAB CLOTH. A thick, heavy and strong gray cloth, generally made with twill weave. Tinted yarns of a dull brown shade are sometimes used. The term also implies a 3-shaft drill cloth, dyed drab and used for corset-making and pocketing. A typical fabric layout would be: 80 ends of 16s warp and 60 picks of 14s filling per inch in woven goods which are finished at a 32-inch width. (*Textile Mercury*, 1936):

The term, Drab, originally synonymous with Drap Cloth (drap meaning French word for cloth) was applied to a kind of hempen linen or a sort of woolen material. The material was of a natural dyed color. Drab color, as a term, was applied to cloth which was drab in shade. Much used in drab breeches, around the 1820s. (From the *Oxford Dictionary*.)

DRAFT. 1. The extent to which raw stock, sliver, slubbing, and roving are drawn-out or lengthened by the pickers, card, drawing frame, slubber frame, fly frame, roving frame, spinning frame, etc. For example, a draft of five on any machine implies that the stock has been drawn to five times its original length. It does not mean that the fibers have been actually drawn or stretched.

2. An outline of the dress model form on the flat, with the style lines of a garment designed within. A draft shows the style lines, positions for flares, pleats, seams, fullness, etc.

3. The directions for weaving, usually plotted on cross-section or design paper, to give the correct drawing-in or threading plan to be used in drawing the ends through the heddle eyes.

4. In hand weaving, draft shows the tie-up of the harnesses and the treadling action to be followed.

DRAFT, ACTUAL. The ratio between the weight of the feeding-in stock

on a machine and the weight delivered at the front of the particular frame. All wastes must be figured prior to determination of the actual draft on any machine.

DRAFT, CONDENSING. A process by which fibers on the doffer frame are condensed into a shorter length than they occupied on the cylinder roller. It is actually the reverse of draft but this massing of fibers derives its name by analogy.

DRAFT, FIGURED. The ratio that exists between the surface speeds of the back rollers and the front rollers on machines, based on a unit length of stock being fed into the frame.

DRAFT, MATHEMATICAL AND MECHANICAL. The weight of the stock fed into a machine divided by the weight delivered is called mathematical draft. Thus, if one yard of stock weighs 5 ounces as it enters a machine and weighs 1 ounce per yard on delivery, the mathematical draft is five.

If a #2s roving is fed into a machine and a #10s is delivered there would be a mathematical draft of 5. 2)10(5.

A textile machine drafts only the regular fibers and not the waste; hence, the mathematical draft is greater than machine draft.

Mechanical draft on a machine is the ratio of the surface speed, where waste is removed, between the feed and the delivery; and this is then divided into the draft constant, to give the proper toothed gear to use.

The following problem shows the difference between mathematical and mechanical drafts:

A 10-ounce lap is fed into the machine, there is 1 ounce of waste, and a 1-ounce lap is to be delivered.

Subtract the amount of waste from the amount fed, and then divide by the weight delivered, to obtain mechanical draft. 1)10(10, mathematical draft. Ten minus 9 is 1. 1)9(9, the mechanical draft.

When twist is inserted, the mechanical draft will be greater than the mathematical draft; when waste is removed the mechanical draft will be less.

DRAFT, TENSION. A figured machine draft to counterbalance sag or stretch that might occur when fiber stock is being drafted and attenuated.

DRAFT, TOTAL. This may be defined as the draft throughout all processes in the entire mill—from bale to finished yarn. If the weight of a bale of fibers in the compressed condition and the few resultant fibers in spun yarn are considered, it can be seen that the total draft would be very great.

Any machine between the bale

breaker and the finished yarn state is considered as an intermediate machine, and would therefore be an intermediate draft point between the first and the last machine in the line-up.

DRAFT, TOTAL MACHINE. Each machine in a plant used to aid in the manufacture of yarn is set up mechanically to do a certain amount of drafting to the fibers. Thus, each machine, in itself, performs total draft. Every machine has what is known as the "breakdown." The total draft of a machine is broken down into intermediate drafts between the various parts.

DRAFT CONSTANT. The minimum or the maximum draft possible on a machine; it is obtained by leaving out the draft gear in the calculation. Maximum draft constant is called Divident, and this maximum needs but one division to learn the size of the draft gear necessary. Minimum draft is known as the draft constant factor, and this needs one multiplication to find what the draft will be.

DRAFT GEAR, DRAFT CHANGE GEAR. It is located on textile machines between the feeding-in of stock to the machine and the delivery point. Machines are so built that the gear may be changed easily without altering the machine set-up. This change gear usually controls the amount of stock to enter a frame and it can be easily seen, therefore, that if the stock feed is lower, the draft would be higher, or vice versa.

The draft change gear is usually a small pinion-type gear.

On the same shaft with the draft gear on a spinning frame or fly frame is the crown gear, sometimes known as the drag gear, as is the case on a mule spinning frame.

DRAFTING. The drawing of fibers, that may be in some sort of rope form, among themselves to make the stock take on more the appearance of yarn. Excess speed of the front rollers of the machine in question, over the carrier rollers and the back rollers, makes drafting of textile fibers possible.

Twist is added in drafting to sustain the fibers in their form-sliver, slubbing, roving. These forms must not be drafted to the point where the fibers will collapse and not be able to sustain themselves. Doubling-up on the stock fed into machines takes care of this end of the work.

DRAFTS, INTERMEDIATE. These are parts of the total draft on a machine and when multiplied together will give the total draft of the frame in question. For example, on a spinning frame under the conventional system of drafting there are but two intermediate drafts, the product of which furnishes

total draft. The following sketch shows conventional drafting with three sets of drafting rollers:

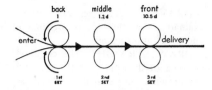

Consider that two ends are being fed to the machine—doubling of two. The first intermediate draft, between the back and middle rollers, is known as back or break draft. It is about 1.2. The second intermediate draft occurs between the middle and front rollers and is about 10.5. Thus, total draft would be calculated by multiplying 1.2 x 10.5 for total draft of 12.60.

There are different types of intermediate drafts under various names:

FIRST BREAK DRAFT: This is usually low and serves the purpose of arranging the fibers for the next intermediate draft.

ATTENUATING DRAFT: Its purpose is to arrange the fibers almost to the limit draft that the machine can produce. Machines are built for the fibers and the fibers are not made for the machines.

On a card, for example, the draft, at times, may run as high as 800 or more between the feed rollers and the licker-in roller. In other words, one inch of stock may be opened up to over 800 inches in total length.

CONDENSING DRAFT: Its purpose is to gather the fibers into some suitable form for further treatment. On the card, for example, after passing between the revolving flats and the cylinder, the cotton fibers are opened up to such a degree that they must be brought back into a form so that it may be handled by the machine. This is done by condensing the fibers into a web between the cylinder and doffer rollers on the frame. In other words, the draft at this point is known as condensing draft and is very low, usually below one; three or four inches of fiber stock are condensed into one inch.

Condensing draft increases the weight per yard of the stock; attenuating draft decreases the weight per yard of the fibers delivered.

TENSION DRAFT: Its purpose is to hold fibers in position for final drafting. It is usually found in the feeding arrangement on the card and also at the delivery end of this machine. It is also applied to the web between the front rollers and the tension rollers on a drawing frame and on combers and fly frames.

FALSE DRAFT: This is the result of improper setting of some part or parts of a machine; as a result, the draft desired will not be obtained.

LONG DRAFT: This refers to modern machinery in which the machines have extra equipment applied in the drafting arrangement for the purpose of obtaining greater draft than would ordinarily be expected.

DRAG. 1. The ability of a bobbin to resist being drawn around by slubbing, roving, or yarn. Drag is controlled by the size of the washers used which are set under the bobbin in the machine. Worsted open drawing relies greatly on this principle. 2. In passing judgment on the quality of a cotton, a group of fibers are held in one hand and pulled apart or "broken" by the fingers of the other hand. This action gives the cotton classer much information about the staple stock.

DRAKE CLUSTER COTTON. An early-maturing Uplands cotton of 1-inch staple and lint yield of about 32 per cent; a development from Peerless cotton.

DRAKE REDSPOT COTTON. Although of good whiteness some Drake cotton has reddish spots interspersed throughout the staple.

DRALON. Acrylic filament, staple, and tow manufactured by Farbenfabriken Bayer A.G., West Germany. "Dralon HB" is the name for the high-bulk staple; "Dralon Continu" is the filament product, and "Dralon Neu" signifies the acrylic staple with improved dyeability. One of the great uses of Dralon is in the headgear industry as an effect fiber, and it is ideal for blending with fur fibers used in the hat industry.

DRAMMAGE. The weight in drams of 1000 yards of rayon or silk filament; used as a measure of yarn size determination.

DRAM SYSTEM IN SILK. A dram is $\frac{1}{16}$ ounce. The Dram System is used to find the counts of thrown silk. It is based on the weight in drams of 1000 yards on the basis of 256,000 yards, the number of yards of silk in a #1 Dram silk.

If 1000 yards weigh 4 drams, the count or number is known as a #4 Dram silk.

Divided by any dram weight, 256,000 will give the number of yards in one pound of the silk in question.

DRAP. The French equivalent for the English word "cloth" or "stuff," and generally applied to fabrics of wool or silk.

DRAP D'ALMA. A cloth deriving its name from the French for a fabric of small twill repeat. This silk fabric is light in weight, comes in white and colors, and is used for dress goods.

DRAP DE BERRY. Named for a town in France, it is a woolen fabric noted for its draping qualities.

DRAP DE LYON. A name from the French for "Cloth of Lyons." A plain woven silk or rayon fabric that is rich in quality. The cloth has been famous as a staple silk material in the Cloth Halls of the continent since the Middle Ages.

DRAP DE SOIE. French for Cloth of Silk. A skein-dyed or piece-dyed silk fabric made on a small twill weave. The fabric is rather heavy in weight, and is now made with rayon.

DRAP D'ETE. French meaning is "cloth of summer." Used for evening wear and very popular with the clergy. Material is a thin-staple woolen or mixture fabric that has a fine twill weave with high counts of yarn used. Is rather expensive.

DRAP D'OR. French for Cloth of Gold which is used in evening wear, pageantry, stage, and interior decoration.

DRAPE. The manner in which a fabric falls when hung or placed on a form, frame, or manikin. Stiffness or draping quality is now measured by the Drapeometer. Draping will readily show if a material is to be used in a form-concealing or a form-revealing garment.

DRAPER. English term for a custom tailor. A skilled dressmaker or designer who fashions clothes in an expert manner, taking into consideration the silhouette, draping qualities of the fabric, and the cut-make-trim of the garment. The term originally meant one who sold cloth by the piece.

DRAPER, APPAREL. One who drapes muslin for pattern and then adjusts the cut cloth to the figure or model. The draper must possess a feeling for line and form which is absolutely necessary, in addition to a knowledge of the workability of fabrics.

DRAPERY. 1. English term for fabrics and materials made of wool. 2. Broad term for various materials used for general decorative purposes. Draperies are usually hung loose and fall into folds.

DRAPERY FABRIC. Decorative material, curtains, and hangings are known by this term. The material is made of silk, rayon, cotton, and union construction such as a cotton warp and a rayon or wool filling. Many materials use Tussah silk for filling since it adds to the softness and beauty. Durable and gives good service; comes in all weights and there is a wide range of pattern used.

DRAPING. Arranging cloth in folds so that it will hang well.

DRAPS CROISES. French for woolen or worsted fabrics made in twill effects.

DRAVES TEST. A scientific test for evaluating the efficiency of wetting-out and penetrating agents.

DRAW, STRAIGHT. The commonest type of drawing-in draft; the ends are drawn-in in straight or direct sequence from the first to the last harness in the plan.

DRAW BOX. There are three pairs of drawing rollers and one pair of calender rollers at the delivery end of a Heilman comber. These rollers combine and condense all the slivers being delivered into a single sliver.

DRAWBOY. 1. The boy who manipulated the harness cords on the old-time draw loom. 2. That part of a power loom that controls the harnesses, springs, harness cords, nogged jack, and such.

DRAWBOYS. Any of a host of fabrics made prior to the invention of the power loom in the eighteenth century. These fabrics were figured with all types and kinds of motifs and made on the "Drawboy Looms." These looms required the aid of a boy to operate the warp threads in the loom.

DRAW-DOWN. The amount of stretching given to man-made filaments between the spinneret or spinning jet and the godet or feed roll.

DRAWER-IN, AUTOMATIC. A machine that automatically draws successive warp ends from a filled warp beam through the drop-wire eyes, the empty heddle eyes of the harnesses, and the dents or splits in the reed. See Illustrated Section.

DRAW HANDLOOM. A type of loom which differs from the so-called heddle loom by the substitution of the comberboard for the heddles of the figure harness which enables each warp thread to be controlled individually and permits the automatic repeat of the motifs for the width of the fabric. The leashes which are suspended from the comberboard are operated independently, or in groups through a series of cords which are in turn, operated by a drawboy. A forerunner of the present-day Jacquard loom.

DRAWING. 1. Holding at one point or end and pulling at the other end, thereby increasing the length of the mass of the textile fibers and decreasing the diameter of the ropelike form of these fibers. 2. The product of the carding machine is in the form of a sliver which may be somewhat uneven. In order to offset this unevenness, the

product of from 8 to 20 cards is placed alongside a drawing frame, and after being processed by this frame, the resultant doubled and redoubled sliver form is made even and uniform.

DRAWING FRAME. Its purpose is to make the fibers uniform and parallel. There are usually four lines of drawing rollers which operate at an over-all draft of about six. There are six card slivers fed to each delivery, so that, generally speaking, the drawn sliver is about the same diameter as a single sliver fed into the frame. Thus, for example, a four-time drawing would show 6 x 6 x 6 x 6 for a total of 1,296 doublings. Cotton—depending on the stock used and the purpose for which it is being spun—may be run from two to six times through the same comber to increase the number of doubling and improve the ultimate product. See Illustrated Section.

DRAWING-IN. The actual drawing-in of warp ends from the warp beam, lease rods, through the heddle eyes on the harness frames, and then through the reed splits of the reed of the loom. A plan has to be followed so that the actual weave from design paper will be produced in the woven cloth.

DRAWING-IN FRAME. The framework or stand used to hold a beam of warp ends, harnesses, and reeds so that the yarns of warp may be easily drawn through the proper heddle eyes and correct reed splits. A drawing-in hook is used to draw in the ends in correct order. See Illustrated Section.

DRAWING-IN HOOK. A straight or curved hook used to draw-in the warp ends through the correct heddle eye and proper reed split in the loom.

DRAWING OUT. See DRAFT.

DRAWING ROLL CLEANER. A pad of felt or similar material that is attached to the underside of the cleaner box cover, which serves to take away dust, lint, and other particles that collect on the drawing rollers as they draw out and draft the sliver or roving fibers passing between them.

DRAWING ROLLERS. Two or more pairs of rollers, each of which rotates at a higher speed than the preceding pair, in order to draw the fibers among themselves or attenuate the sliver, slubbing, or roving passing between them. Rollers may be covered with leather, paper, cork, or other material.

DRAWING SLIVER. Sometimes called draw sliver, it implies the loose, untwisted rope form of cotton fibers which is the product of the drawing machines. See Illustrated Section.

DRAWING STITCH. A method of making an edge-to-edge join or a seam without a lap, a stitch being taken through one side, then drawn over and down under and up through the other side, and so on; usually employed in joining collars to coats.

DRAWLOOM. The old style loom superseded by the power loom. After the designer completed his pattern, the harnesses were raised and lowered by the drawboy who raised them in accordance with the drawing-in plan.

DRAWNWORK. The actual drawing-out of certain threads in a fabric to produce ornamental, open-space ("hand-drawn") work that enhances the beauty of the material. Drawnwork is an ancient European art developed in convents and in convent schools. It is used for decorative purposes, in the making of altar cloths, tablecloths and covers, handkerchiefs, doilies, scarfs and shawls. When seen on finished cloth the effect may simulate or resemble that observed on lace.

DRAWN YARN. Extruded yarn which has been given a drawing or stretching treatment to provide orientation of the long-chain molecules which make up the yarn, in the direction of the filament axis. Further stretching causes the yarn to take on elastic extension as compared with the plastic flow of undrawn yarn.

DRAW RATIO. The ratio of draw-roll peripheral speed to the feed-roll peripheral speed; in contradistinction to the stretch ratio which is the ratio of undrawn yarn denier to the denier of the drawn yarn.

DRAW THREADS. Auxiliary threads which extend lengthwise from a web of band lace, and connect together the adjacent edges of the bands. When the lace web has been finished, these threads are readily removed to separate the bands of lace.

DRAX. A water-repellent finish applied to cotton and rayon; it also has dirt- and stain-resistant properties because of the wax it contains. It is non-flammable, resists perspiration, adds durability, and requires less severe laundering. The handle, color, or porosity is not impaired; the treated garment is harmless to the skin.

Drax is a stable, aqueous emulsion of waxes, aluminum salts, and emulsifying agents which penetrate the fibers. The process follows conventional methods and is followed by drying at the highest temperature permissible for the fabric. Product of S. C. Johnson & Sons, Inc., Racine, Wisconsin.

DRESDEN SILK. Silk fabric embellished with small floral motifs.

DRESS. 1. Garments and articles of apparel and the art and science of wearing them by human beings; chiefly outer attire.
2. A particular type of raiment for some festive, formal, or other social event.
3. Outer garment worn by women and children; cut in one or more pieces, the garment is fastened at the waistline, and a belt may or may not be worn with it.
4. A distinctive manner of dressing—the contrast between the garb of a cowboy and a white-collar worker, a Spanish peasant and a Chinese peasant.
5. In the broader sense, dress consists of hat, coat, jacket, trousers or dress, and all other items which go to make up the well-dressed man or woman.

DRESS, A-LINE. One shaped from narrow shoulders to the gently-full hemline in the form of a capital A, and without gathers or pleats.

DRESSED FLAX. See FLAX PROCESSING.

DRESSED LINE. Flax that has been thoroughly hackled. See HACKLING.

DRESSED LINEN. See FLAX FIBERS.

DRESSED PILLOW. A pillow used to make lace; it is fully arranged with bobbins, and pins for manipulation.

DRESSER. See DRESSING; WARPER; WARPING.

DRESSER LINE. See CUT IDENTIFICATION MARKS.

DRESS-FACED. A term sometimes given to woolen cloths, such as doeskin, broadcloth, beaver, having a slight nap.

DRESS FACE-FINISH. Another name for face-finish fabric, such as beaver, broadcloth, chinchilla, kersey, melton, Saxony, Worumbo, some broadcloth, and so on.

DRESS GOODS. Specifically, fabrics used for women's and children's wear. This term is very broad and is sometimes used to cover other uses for textile materials.

DRESSING. 1. Sizing applied to yarn or cloth to add weight, smoothness, strength, or firmness. 2. Preparation of a warp for weaving in the loom; expression used chiefly in the preparation of woolen and worsted warps. 3. A mixture of size, starch, gums, China clay, etc., for stiffening. 4. The preparation of spun silk by combing and recombing until the stock is separated into a set of different lengths known as drafts.

DRESSING TIME. The allowance time for employees to change into and out of their street clothes for their special working clothes.

DRESS LINEN. Plain-weave cloth in which quality depends much on yarn and texture used. Comes in white, or is dyed or printed. Popular for summer wear. Launders well, wrinkles but is serviceable, durable, gives cool appearance to wearer.

DRESS STYLES. These follow:
1. BASIC DRESS: A simple classic-type dress which can be given variety easily by wearing it with different decorative accessories at different times. It is a self-trimmed dress made with tucks, folds, drape, or trapunto trim. It may have inconspicuous contrasting fabric trim of the same color as the garment. A basic dress excludes, however, the following: shirtwaist style, contrasting-color trim in beading, lace, or sequins.
2. CLASSIC DRESS: A type of dress in such simple good taste that it is really becoming and continues in good taste despite the ever-constant changes in fashions in dresses for women.
3. COATDRESS: A tailored dress, usually fitted, with coat type of front having a button- or a fly-front closure from neck to hem. It is adaptable to simple housedresses, sports dresses, street dresses, and to even semiformal dresses that are popular in fabrics such as faille, taffeta, etc.
4. DAYTIME DRESS: It is less elaborate than an afternoon dress, and is less severely tailored than the business-type dress, and is made usually of a finer type of fabric. It may have self-material or a contrasting type in the trim. Suitable for town, luncheon, informal wear.
5. HOUSEDRESS: Used chiefly for morning wear around the house. Usually made of gaily printed washable cotton fabric, or of some suitable blended fabric in which cotton serves as the base fiber used. It is styled in a simple manner with a button- or a zipper-front closure so that a person may slip into it easily and quickly. Trimmed with bias fold, rickrack, etc. A wraparound dress, strictly speaking, is not considered to be a housedress in the trade. Housedresses, because of their great use and the satisfactory price, are sold in lots of a dozen; higher-styled dresses are sold as a unit or single item.
6. SHIRTWAIST DRESS: A one-piece tailored dress with the bodice like a shirtwaist, buttoned in the front to the waist. Often tucked, and usually belted.

7. WRAPAROUND DRESS: A semifitted coat type of dress which "wraps around the body" with a wide lapover at the front or the back of the closing. Ties and/or a button belt are attached to provide the closure.

DRESS WORSTEDS. Group of fine, face-finished staples used for formal and evening wear.

DRESSES AND SKIRTS, SOME MAJOR TYPES OF.

The word "silhouette," when applied to apparel, means the outline or contour of a figure or costume. The new silhouette of any fashion season means the general contour in fashion at the particular time, with special reference to length and width of skirt, shoulder width, etc., in contrast to the popular and accepted silhouettes of the previous season. The silhouette, a profile shadow projected on a reflecting surface, or the outline of a person or object filled in with color, solid or otherwise, became a popular word in Paris around 1759, associated with M. Étienne de Silhouette, who was minister of finance in France.

The origin of the word "Shirt," which is linked to the word "Skirt," is probably the Scandinavian root *skar*, which means "to cut off," and is applied to a garment that reaches to the area of the waist. The Icelandic word for a short garment is *skyrte* and the Danish word is *skiorte*, both derived from *skar*. Thus, it may be gleaned that a shirt is for the covering of the upper part of the body while a skirt serves the same purpose for the lower part of the body.

See PRINCESS, SHEATH, SHIFT, SHIRTWAIST, VARIATIONS OF SKIRTS (illus.).

PRINCESS: This very popular dress features the following high points: (1) It is created by seaming and dart effects. (2) Vertical seaming, which begins at the neckline-armhole-shoulder area, crosses the point of the bust and continues downward to the waistline, hipline, or hemline to constitute what is known as the "princess line." (3) The amount of snugness or ease to a princess-line fit is determined by the degree of shaping used on the seams. (4) Princess-line garments may be pencil-slim or fuller than a circular skirt. (4) The amount of flare used to create the varied princess silhouette is added to the basic body contour fit. (5) Flare may be added at any level of the garment: under the bust, at the waist, on the hipline, from the knee. This creates a dual silhouette, as noted, for example, in the empire-princess type of garment.

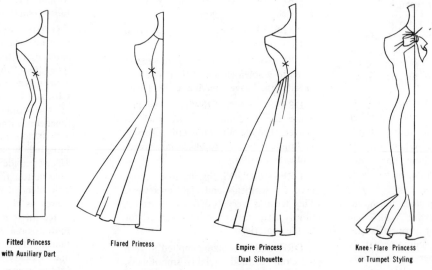

Fitted Princess with Auxiliary Dart   Flared Princess   Empire Princess Dual Silhouette   Knee·Flare Princess or Trumpet Styling

Sketches courtesy Edmund Roberts, F.I.T., New York City

SHEATH: A woman's dress made with the following high points: (1) It is always made with the vertical dart fit. (2) The vertical darts are used in single or multiple (group) darts. (3) The sheath can also be used in combination with a horizontal dart. (4) It may or may not be fitted to the contours of the figure. (5) The amount of the "dart pick-up" (depth of the dart) creates the ease or lightness of a sheath. Thus the sheath may be described as a type of slim garment, with or without a waistline seam, which is fitted rather snugly to the figure. *See* SILHOUETTE.

SHIFT: This "no-fit" dress features the following points: (1) Only the horizontal dart fit is used in this type of dress. (2) The shaping (if any) flare and the fall of the garment are directly controlled by the amount of the "dart pick-up." (3) Shifts which hit the hipline level are called "pullovers" or shells" and are controlled and constructed on the same lines as dress-length shifts.

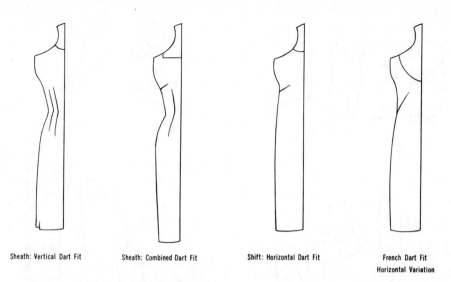

Sheath: Vertical Dart Fit   Sheath: Combined Dart Fit   Shift: Horizontal Dart Fit   French Dart Fit
                                                                                                           Horizontal Variation

The shift is a garment that hangs loosely from the shoulder or is semifitted, and has no definite waistline. There are several modifications, as noted above, and generally speaking it is not very attractive on the wearer and often reminds one of a man's long shirt. The sides of the garment are often slashed for effect, with the slashes running from short to considerable length.

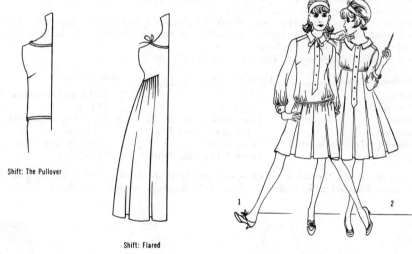

Shift: The Pullover

Shift: Flared

Two Very Popular Shirtwaist Styles of 1960's

1. The dropped waistline, which shows the influence of the 1920's.
2. Empire waistline, raised.
Note that all the components of the shirtwaist dress are featured in each sketch.

SHIRTWAIST: This type of dress is truly a concept of American designers and it is continually adapted and adopted by Continental designers. The shirtwaist was conceived and perfected by the creativeness of "Seventh Avenue" in New York City.

It was originated about 1893, it reached great heights in 1905, and has been a staple item in the apparel field ever since. It is in every woman's wardrobe, even to the present time. The popularity of the shirtwaist dress took on further impetus in the early 1960's, and it gives promise of marching along into the twenty-first century with a one-hundred-year heritage of styling, taste, and excellent fit, since it seems to be one of the few styles in female attire that is exceptionally well suited to the figure.

The shirtwaist dress is made up of seven component parts: (1) Back-shoulder yoke. (2) Bloused back-bodice. (3) Semifitted bloused front bodice. (4) Convertible collar. (5) Tab front closing. (6) Easy fit or full skirt, which is often pleated or in circular-type flare. (7) Shirtwaist mounted into an armscye always cuffed or banded (full at the wrist when long).

Note: The Tab Closing is the most positive "pure feature" of a real or genuine shirtwaist dress. The tab is a closing which is cut or slashed into an area of the garment where no seam is located. This slashing is a tailored quality or "classic touch" observed in shirtwaist styling.

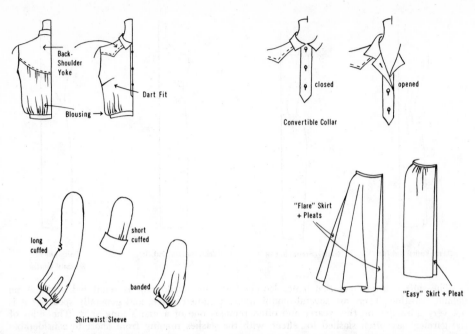

The American shirtwaist style no longer reflects the uniform of an office-girl worker. It is now used for all occasions—office, patio, at home, cocktail hour, dinner gown, golf and other sports apparel, evening gown, house dress, etc.

Practically any and all fabrics are suitable for shirtwaist styling. The ingenuity, deftness, élan and éclat of the designer determine whether or not his product is to be merely a fad or a good winner in the field of fashion.

Some popular fabrics used in the shirtwaist dress:

EVENING GOWNS	COCKTAIL DRESSES	SPORTSWEAR
Satin	Chiffon	Linen and simulated linen
Brocade	Organza	Denim
Lamé	Douppioni—true silk or	Gingham, broadcloth,
Matelassé	manmade fiber fabric	madras, etc.
Moiré (taffeta, faille, etc.)	Wool crepe	Piqué of any type
	Beaded knitwear fabric	Seersucker

As to price range, the shirtwaist dress may run from the $6.95 range in the bargain basement to around $1,200 in the exclusive salons of the leading couturiers and stores.

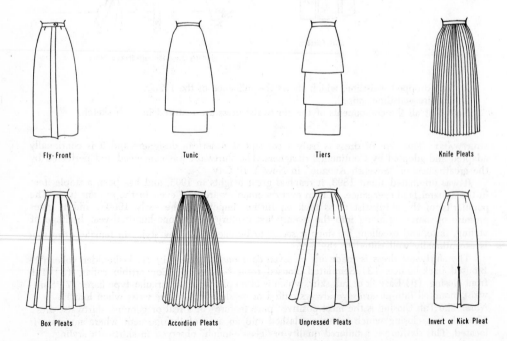

DRILL. A durable cotton fabric of relatively low count, coarse yarn, and medium weight. Most of the drill made today uses a 3-harness, warp-face, left-hand twill weave; other comparable constructions, however, are used. Carded cotton sheeting yarn is used and textures and weights vary considerably, depending upon the terminal use of the material. When dyed, drill may be known as khaki, herringbone, silesia, ticking, or by other names. Since the term drill denotes the purpose for which the cloth is to be used, and not the weave, as might be supposed, some fabrics of this name are made with a small satin weave.

DRILL, WIDE INDUSTRIAL. It is made on a three-leaf twill, left-hand, and in warp-effect. Finished at about 59 inches, the texture is 68 x 40, and there are about two yards to the pound. 14s warp and 20s filling are used in the fabric which serves as a basis for coated textiles.

DRILLETTE. A five-harness gray-goods cloth made in England which varies in quality. This lining material is much used in South America.

DRILL WEAVE. Name given to a 3-harness, warp-face twill weave; the 2-up and 1-down twill-effect.

DRIP-DRY GARMENT. Also known as a minimum care garment, it is one which cannot be completely laundered automatically since the fabric or finish cannot withstand spinning, wringing, or squeezing.

DRIP-DRYING. Allowing water to drip and evaporate from clothes which have been removed from the rinse water without spinning, wringing, or squeezing.

DRI-SMOOTH. A resin chemical finish that gives cotton fabrics the ability to be worn without pressing after washing. Product of Cranston Prints Works Company, Cranston, Rhode Island.

DRIVING CYLINDER. See SPINNING TAPE.

DROGUET. A brocade material made with silk or schappe silk warp and cotton, acetate, or rayon filling. Several colors of filling may be used to brighten the goods. At present, the word implies fabrics with brocade motifs made from cotton, silk, wool, etc., with regard to fiber content.

DROMEDARY CAMEL. See CAMEL.

DROP BOX. See BOX LOOM.

DROP MATCH IN CARPETING. This occurs in a carpet when the motif or pattern is dropped in the next combining width of the carpet to keep the design in conformity with the wishes of the designer.

DROPPERS. See DROP WIRE.

DROPPING. The slashing and stretching of fur to make the skins longer.

DROPPINGS. Wool fibers and particles cast out by the various rollers on the card, such as strippers, workers, main cylinder, fancy, and doffer rollers.

DROP STITCH, DROPPED STITCH. A defect in knit fabric which may result from a defective needle, improper stitch setting, or other similar causes. Drop stitches also may be purposely introduced in knit goods to obtain a desired motif or pattern effect.

DROP WIRE. A flat piece of metal, with a hole in it, through which the warp end is drawn. The wire will drop and, from an electric-current contact, will stop the loom when the end through which it was drawn breaks. See Illustrated Section.

DRUGGET. A printed and felted fabric made from any number of textile fibers and used for floor covering. This heavy fabric comes in all sizes and in brilliant designs. Stencil print motifs are very popular on these rugs, which originated in India and are widely used in the United States.

DRUID. A priest of religion among the ancient Celtic nations in Britain, Gaul, and Germany. Weaving in Scotland dates from druidical times.

DRUID CLOTH. A fabric in the monk's cloth group but very coarse in structure and feel. See MONK'S CLOTH.

DRUM. See SPINNING TAPE.

DRUMMOND WORSTED. A plain Oxford worsted, twill-woven with one end of black and one of one or two shades of gray or white, both twisted and then alternated. The filling arrangement is the same as the warp plan. The fabric originated with a firm of English weavers who introduced the pattern.

DRUM PRINTING. Velvet and tapestry rugs have their colors placed on the yarn by a mechanism that supplies all of the colors in the motif. The surface threads thus colored are arranged to feed into the loom in such a way that the pattern appears as the yarns are woven into the web in proper position to carry out the motif and color effect as laid out by the designer. There are 576 squares or blocks on the printing drum for figured velvet weaving. See Illustrated Section.

DRUM WINDING. Used essentially for colored yarn, it is the winding of yarn from bobbins, cops, or hanks onto warper's bobbins.

DRY. To separate or remove liquid or vapor from another substance. The liquid may be water, but the term is also used for the removal of liquid or vapor forms of other substances.

DRYCLEANER, PROBLEMS FOR THE. The drycleaner is confronted with many problems not generally understood by the customer. Some of these follow:

1. *Bleeding:* On leather trimming, buttons, the possible migration of color.

2. *Discoloring:* Noted especially in fiber-blended fabrics and on certain garments depending on the color used. Fading entails sun fading, colorfastness, excessive washing, and action of some detergents on the fabric. Pressing some articles too heavily or too long may produce a shine in the seams and in other parts of the garment where there are double folds.

3. *Shrinkage:* Rubber yarn in garments may cause undue shrinkage, as well as possible stretching that may become difficult to overcome. Bonded fabrics often give much trouble such as foam deterioration, while quilted articles may have faulty or poor stitching.

4. *Stains:* Determination of the particular stain area is often difficult for the drycleaner to solve. If the drycleaner knows the type of stain he will then know whether to use a solvent action, or a chemical absorbent or detergent action. Some stains require use of digestion or lubrication methods. Beaded trimming also gives much trouble on garments.

5. *Wrinkles:* Noted much in leather and vinyl articles in apparel, as well as in garments which have much detail work.

6. *Holes:* These are always a bane to the drycleaner, especially the so-called "mystery holes."

DRYCLEANER, RESPONSIBILITIES OF THE. He is responsible for: 1. Redeposition of soil which results from discolored fabric. 2. Removal of stains as a result of spotting. 3. Holes, rips, and tears caused by mechanical damage which had not been pointed out when the garment was given to the drycleaner. 4. Change of size because of felting shrinkage or fiber swelling shrinkage in wet cleaning. 5. Damage caused by not caring for specified serviceability information.

He is not responsible for: 1. Any size change due to relaxation shrinkage. 2. Fading caused by low resistance of color to drycleaning. 3. Color loss by ordinary water. 4. Change of feel or hand which occurred by drycleaning a decorative detail when the item has been handled in drycleaning. 6. Holes which are a result of weakened fibers caused by chemicals, insects, mildew, etc. 7. Damage which results from use of a procedure suggested on labels provided by the manufacturer.

DRYCLEANING. A process used to clean fabrics which cannot be readily laundered. Organic solvents, such as carbon tetrachloride or mineral spirits, are used to remove dirt and some stains. Other stains are removed by special methods. In organic solvent cleaning two terms are used, these are:

1. *Unrestricted Terms:* Terms such as "Drycleanable," "Dryclean," and similar terms with regard to drycleanability mean that the article can be drycleaned in a machine with either a petroleum solvent or perchlorethylene and a synthetic detergent, extracted by centrifugal action to remove the solvent, deodorized in a tumble dryer, and then restored to good appearance on a steam-heated press or on steam-air finishing equipment. The solvent-relative humidity shall not exceed 75 per cent. The temperature of the solvent shall not exceed 90° F. A drycleanable product is also resistant to contact with water as required for the removal of stains.

2. *Restricted Terms:* These limit or qualify the method of drycleaning and shall be strictly interpreted according to the limited meaning — "Dryclean — do not tumble"; "Dryclean in Stoddard Solvent Only"; etc. All procedures as specified for unrestricted terms are applicable except to the extent of the limitation.

DRY-CLEANING CYLINDER. A laboratory machine which consists of a motor-driven tumbler fitted with a water-tight cover. The rotation of the tumbler will supply the necessary agitation which, together with the use of the proper testing solvents, can determine a fabric's resistance to shrinkage and its color fastness under dry-cleaning.

DRY-COMBING. The preparing and combing of worsted stock devoid of oil or emulsion.

DRY DOUBLED YARN. Name given to some yarns which are to be bleached, dyed, or sized when a full, open, or absorbent state is desired.

DRYER. Any box, chamber, or compartment used to dry raw stock, fiber, yarn, or fabric. Drying may be done with or without tension depending on local conditions. The tenter frame is an example of tension drying, while a loop dryer for yarn skeins would not require tension.

DRYER, LOOP. A drying machine for circular knitted fabric in which the cloth is looped or festooned on a series of slats as it goes through the drying area.

DRYER, PIPE. Drying circular knitted fabric over a long vertical or horizontal pipe which is set on top of heating unit usually connected to a blower. Also known as stack dryer.

DRYER, REEL. Fabric is carried on air-pervious drums which are set between high velocity air nozzles. In passing from drum to drum, air is forced through alternately from one side of the fabric to the other to assure even drying of the goods.

DRYER FELT DUCK. See DUCK, DUCKS.

DRY-FINISHING IN THE WOOLEN OR WORSTED MILL: These are operations or treatments given to cloth in which no water, bath, or moisture is applied to the goods.

These precede wet-finishing of cloth in the mill: perching, measuring, burling, specking, mending, sewing, experienced sewing. These follow wet-finishing: shearing, napping or gigging, pressing, packing, wrapping.

DRY GOODS. Marketing term for textile fabrics: cottons, woolens, rayons, laces, and the rest.

DRYING. Removal of water or moisture from raw stock, fiber, yarn, or fabric. Examples include hydro-extracting or whizzing, tenter frame drying, box or chamber drying.

DRYING, DEODORIZING. In home laundering or drycleaning, the term has three methods of approach:

1. *Tumble-Dry:* A process which uses a heated tumble-drying machine in which hot air is circulated through the load at various temperatures depending on the type of load. The time cycle of a tumbler varies according to the size of the load, load classification, temperature, the type of solvent, and equipment. A typical cycle will run from twenty to forty minutes. Tumble-drying temperatures normally applicable in this process range up to 160° F.

2. *Tumble-Cold:* A process which uses a tumbler without application of heat. The air temperature at the intake is the same as the room temperature.

3. *Air-Dry, Cabinet-Dry:* A method of drying or deodorizing in which there is no movement of the article being dried. Hot air circulates around it as it hangs in a closed area until dry. Temperatures used are the same as in tumble-dry. The time cycle extends up to several hours, depending on the bulkiness of the article in question.

DRYING, GARMENT.

1. *Drip-Drying* - Hang the article in a dripping wet state on a line until dry.

2. *Line Dry* - Following extraction of the liquid, merely hang the item on a line until dry.

3. *Spin Dry* - The article is extracted by centrifuge force and line or tumble drying follows.

4. *Tumble Dry* - Dry in hot air up to 180° F. circulating through the load for 30 to 40 minutes.

Deodorizing or drying in drycleaning is done in a heated tumble drying machine in which hot air is circulated at 160° F. for 20 to 40 minutes. Air drying or cabinet drying is a method of drying or deodorizing in which the article is stationary for several hours.

DRYING CANS. A machine used to dry material; several large heated drums, wide enough to accommodate one or two widths of cloth, are arranged in tiers: the cloth threaded through the drums contacts a large area of each drum and therefore is rapidly dried at the proper temperature.

DRYING. COMPARTMENT. Hollow box, drum, or machine that is filled with live steam, over which printed material passes so that all excess moisture may be removed.

DRYING REEL. A wheel-like mechanism on which skeins of yarn are mounted and revolved slowly for even drying. The reel is sometimes partly collapsible to allow the skeins to be slipped on or off easily.

DRY LOAD. A load of fabrics or garments which contains five percent or less moisture content.

DRY SIZING. Sizing applied to textile yarns in which the sizing is compounded with liquids volatile at temperatures below 212° Fahrenheit.

DRY-SPINNING. 1. In the spinning of acetate, the spinneret is set at the top of a tall enclosed chamber. The spinning solution emerges through the spinneret into warm air which evaporates the acetone solvent, thereby allowing the coagulation of the filaments which are gathered at the bottom of the chamber. 2. Major bast fibers, in the shorter staple lengths, below ten inches, are spun dry. Line fibers in flax, for example, are spun wet. In dry-spinning, care has to be taken that the "reach" is long enough to prevent fiber breakage in the slubbing or roving form. Flyer-spinning is usually resorted to in dry-spinning.

DRY-SPUN YARN. The coarser yarn numbers, spun on the dry method, noted in flax, ramie, jute, and hemp.

DRY TEMPERATURE. It is that

used in an oven when oven-dry weight of fibers is ascertained, i.e., 105° to 110° Centigrade.

DRY TRANSFER. Knitting term to identify products with trade-marks, data about materials used, etc. Applied by hand or automatic pressure with a hot iron.

DUAL-ACTION SCOTCHGARD. Registered trademark product of Minnesota Mining and Manufacturing Company, Midland, Michigan. Appearing on the market in May, 1967, this soil release finish has no restrictions as to weight of fabric to which it may be applied. Can be applied on both precured and postcured durable press fabrics. The product is not a soil repellent but is truly soil releasing. It combats soil redeposition and soil deposition through static, and will withstand twenty or more washings which is approximately the life of the average garment. Items which can be treated include dresses, slacks, sportswear, work clothing, and comparable types of apparel.

DUAL DISTRIBUTION. A manufacturer who owns his own stores for distribution of his wares. Examples include the so-called "Big Seven," as follows: Cluett, Peabody & Company, Inc.; Botany Industries, Inc.; Eagle Clothes, Inc.; Genesco, Inc.; Hart, Schaffner & Marx, Inc.; Manhattan Industries, Inc.; and Phillips-Van Heusen Company, Inc. The number of stores used as outlets for their products range from one company which has about 20 stores to the largest, Hart, Schaffner & Marx, Inc.; which now has over 200 stores in its chain.

DUAL UNIONISM. An attempt by one union to organize, or enroll as members, individuals already belonging to another union.

DUB. 1. The dressing or laying of teasels in place on the napping machine. 2. In making leather, the method of rubbing in a softening or waterproof mixture or dressing.

DUCHESSE. 1. A pillow lace with a fine net ground which has motifs in a raised effect, volants, etc. This standard lace is a product of the convents in Belgium. 2. A silk or rayon material with a dense warp. It comes in medium and better-grade fabric; when made of silk, organzine warp and tram filling are used. Duchesse is very lustrous, smooth in hand, and popular in women's wear, chiefly in the dress-goods trade.

DUCK. The name duck covers a wide range of fabrics. It is the most durable fabric made. A closely woven, heavy material, the most important fabrics in this group are known as number duck, army duck, and flat or ounce duck. Number and army ducks are always of plain weave with medium or heavy ply yarns; army ducks are lighter. Ounce ducks always have single warp yarns woven in pairs and single or ply filling yarns. Other names for variations of these fabrics are sail duck, belt duck, hose duck, tire duck (such as breaker, cord, chafer), wide and narrow duck, biscuit duck, harvester duck, oil press duck, wagon duck, enameling duck, boot duck, canvas and so on. Generally made of ply yarns in warp and yarns of various sizes and weights in filling. See Illustrated Section (Fabrics 21).

DUCK BELTING. Plain-weave fabric, 42 inches wide, that has a texture of about 25 x 15. This 30-ounce goods is made of 7/5s warp and 7/7s filling, carded yarn. It is used for conveyer belting.

DUCKS, ARMY. Compactly woven fabrics whose weight ranges from 7 to 12 ounces per yard, based on a width of 28.5 inches. They are of the same type as wide or number ducks but have finer yarns, higher textures, and are usually lighter in weight. Army ducks are made in 72-, 81-, and 90-inch widths for the laundry trade. When piece-dyed in summer colors they are called sailcloth. In the gray-goods condition, the fabric is used for folding chairs, hammocks, laundry bags, linings, shoe uppers, and tool kits.

Finishes used are bleached, printed, painted-awning stripe, starched, sulphur, and mineral-dyed, waterproofed. In the finished state, the fabric is used for aprons, awnings, coats, hammocks, looseleaf book covers, overalls, pup tents, slacks, tents, tropical clothing, wading pools, washable uniforms, water buckets, and work pants. When dyed khaki or olive drab, the fabric is used for army cots, gun and instrument covers, knapsacks, leggings, tarpaulins, and tents.

DUCKS, BOOT. Coated on one side, these boot ducks have a low texture and are made from ply yarns. The loose interlacing on the warp and the filling afford ample space for the rubber treatment; the ply yarns give the strength, while the untreated side forms the lining. Made in a 40-inch width, the texture is about 28 x 17; the fabric weight is about eight ounces per yard.

DUCKS, COMBED. These are made on contract only; they are constructed in plain weave with ply yarns. When bleached and given a mercerized finish, they are used for doctors' and naval officers' dress uniforms, suitings, and shoe uppers.

DUCKS, DOUBLE-FILLED, FLAT-OUNCE. Because of the ply-yarn filling used, this type is stronger than single-filled ducks. A laid warp is used in making the fabric; each pair of warp threads weaves as one thread. Sizing of the warp is an asset in weaving. Enameling duck is a member of this group. It serves as the base for coating to make oilcloth, imitation leather, etc. The wide type of this duck is called wagon-cover duck.

Those ducks made pro rata to 29 inches, 8-ounce weight, are called regular; to 29 inches, 10 ounces, heavy; to 29 inches, 12 ounces, extra-heavy.

The gray goods may be used for blowout patches, imitation leather, oilcloth bases, bookbinding, caps, folding chairs, covers, linings, and shoe uppers. Finishes applied to this type of fabric are bleached, dyed, painted-awning stripe, printed, and water-repellent. Finished goods are used for aprons, awnings, backs for looseleaf books, caps, folding chairs, overalls, trousers, washable clothing, and work pants.

DUCKS, FLAT OUNCE. They are made with single-warp yarns that are sized for weaving purposes. Two warp yarns are laid together and woven as a single end, known as laid warp or taped warp arrangement. The effect simulates, to some degree, a filling rib weave. Thus, the cloth has a flat appearance and hence the use of the term flat.

Single filling yarn is referred to as single-filled or S. F. duck. When ply yarns are used in the filling, the fabric is referred to as double-filled or D. F. duck. Duck is never woven with single warp and single-filling yarns.

The converting trade uses the following widths of goods: 29, 36, 38, and 40 inches. Special weights and widths are made for the shoe duck, enameling, clothing, and wagon-duck trades. They may be coated with rubber and pyroxylin. Some flat ducks are treated with resin, laminated, or pressed together and made into gear wheels. Quotations specify the width, weight, and ounces per linear yard without mention of the particular construction.

DUCKS, NARROW AND EXTRA-NARROW. They are made in weights similar to sail duck. The widths vary from 6 inches to 20 inches.

DUCKS, NAUGHT. Those heavier than No. 1 are called naught ducks and are designated as 1/0, 2/0, 3/0, etc. A 1/0 duck weighs 19 ounces for the 22-inch width; 2/0, 20 ounces for the 22-inch width. These ducks are made from 1/0 to 15/0, inclusive. Naught ducks from 3/0 to 15/0 are also known as biscuit ducks. The widths range from 6 inches to 56 inches.

DUCKS, NUMBER. They include naught ducks, narrow and extra-narrow ducks, sail ducks, and wide ducks. These ducks are the heaviest and strongest that are made. Carded ply yarns are always used, and since the warp yarns are strongly plied, they are not sized for weaving purposes. Maximum strength and weight is obtained by the use of multiple-ply yarns which range from two to fifteen ply for the heaviest ducks.

The strongest number ducks are usually in the gray state for utility purposes; in this condition they are naturally nonabsorbent and, in addition to the compact texture, are highly resistant to water penetration.

Uses of number ducks include armored tank liners, army cots, conveyer belting, deck canvas, felt-dryer aprons, golf bags, heavy-duty bags, hose of many types and uses, knapsacks, laundry bags, mail bags, navy hammocks, oil-press cloth, portable water tanks, sailcloth, tarpaulin, tents, truck covers, and water buckets.

Some of the fabric is made flame-resistant or mildew-resistant. Heavy ducks are usually made from 7s yarns, in varying plies: 7/3, 7/4, 7/5, up to 7/13 used for 12/0 duck. Lighter weight ducks usually employ 13s yarn of varying plies.

DUCKS, SAIL. They are number ducks made in 22- and 24-inch widths; the latter width is called English sail duck. Sail ducks are made in 2/0, 1/0, and numbers 1 to 12, inclusive. Sail and wide ducks are woven with a blue warp end near each selvage, which serves as a guide in sewing; the heavier the fabric, the farther away the blue line is woven from the extreme selvage ends.

DUCKS, SHOE. Made in a 37-inch width, these may be D. F. flat ducks or ply-yarn army-type fabrics. Firmly starched in the gray or bleached state, they are known as white-starched. Unbleached goods are called brown-starched. Textures range from 58 x 52 to 48 x 40. The chief use of this type is for shoe linings.

DUCKS, SINGLE-FILLED, FLAT. Made in two grades, A and B; the former is the better grade. Grade B is used for dark-colored fabrics which are often treated for some definite purpose. Widths vary from 20 to 90 inches; textures range from 72 x 20 up to 88 x 32. Warp yarn is 8s to 14s filling, from 5s to 12s.

Uses in the gray are as a base for coating, bookbinding, covers for box springs, gaskets, linings, sneaker shoe uppers, and upholstery. Finishes applied are dyed, printed, starched, and white. Finished goods are used for book covers, overalls, summer caps, suiting, washable uniforms, white-duck pants. These are made usually in 29- or 38-inch widths, while the textures range from 84 x 28 to 72 x 20.

DUCKS, SPECIAL. These are variations of number ducks which are made in special weight, widths, and textures for definite purposes. Examples are belt duck, dryer felt canvas aprons for paper mills, and hose duck. Belt duck is usually made in a 42-inch width; the weight ranges from 24 to 32 ounces per yard.

Dryer felt duck is very heavy, a naught-type duck; it is the widest cotton cloth made—244 inches. It may be made of all cotton, asbestos warp and cotton filling, all asbestos, or all wool. Widths begin at 26 inches and the weights vary from 48 to 58 ounces per square yard. Hose duck is usually 40 inches in width; weight ranges from 8 to 22 ounces per square yard.

DUCKS, WIDE. This type varies in width from 26 inches to 144 inches. The standard weight of all number ducks is based on No. 3 sail duck, which is 22 inches wide, 16 ounces to the running yard. For each ounce less in weight, one is added to the number; for example, a No. 4 duck would weigh 15 ounces for the 22-inch width. The ducks are made up to a No. 12 which weighs 7 ounces for the 22-inch width.

The widths of wide duck, sail, narrow, and extra-narrow ducks, whether standard or made on contract, are made pro rata to their particular weight in 22-inch sail duck. For example, a No. 6 duck, which weighs 13 ounces for the 22-inch width, would weigh 26 ounces in the 44-inch No. 6 wide duck. For ducks heavier than No. 3, the number is one less; No. 2 would weigh 17 ounces for 22-inch width; No. 1, 18 ounces for the 22-inch.

DUCTILITY. A permanent increase in the length of a yarn when elongated beyond the elastic limit. Rayon-filament yarn has a higher ductility than natural fibers.

DUFFEL. This Belgian town south of Antwerp originated a fabric known as Duffil, a low-quality woolen cloth used for blankets and cloaks. Always made in shades of gray, the material was known for its thick heavy nap. Very likely it was the forerunner of the present day duffle bag which is a sack, usually made of canvas or duck, used by enlisted personnel to hold personal possessions. See DUFFLE.

DUFFLE. British blanket of low quality, made from low-grade woolen yarn; napped on both sides.

DULESCO RAYON. The semidull rayon yarn produced by Courtaulds, Ltd.

DULL; DELUSTERED RAYON. The use of titanium dioxide under controlled conditions will reduce or eliminate altogether the natural shine, sheen, or luster that rayon has as it comes from the spinning bath during its filament manufacture. See Titanox.

DULL FINISH. A finish produced on a fabric, with or without tentering. The cloth is usually given a slight, heated calendering; the treatment is given to cloths that are to be used for lining in suitings.

DULLING AGENT. Rayon which has been treated with a certain chemical substance to give it a semiluster or a dull luster; known in the trade as pigmented rayon. Titanium dioxide and barium sulphate are used for the purpose of delustering, which is done in the acid bath when the filaments begin to form on the principle of coagulation.

DULL YARN. Rayon yarn which has a very subdued luster, usually produced by incorporating finely divided particles of titanium dioxide in the spinning solution.

DUMB SINGLES. The best of silk yarn made from cocoon filaments reeled without twist being applied; used for filling purposes.

DUMB-WAITER ROPE. Untarred cable, cord, rope, or heavy twine made of hemp.

DUMMY. A figure on which clothes are displayed; a form; a manikin.

DUMMY BUTTONHOLE. Not cut through but stitched on the surface only, for purposes of ornament.

DUMMY TRY-ON. A basted-together try-on of linings and interlinings fitted to the customer while the actual coat is being made up without the try-on or fitting. Also known as bluff try-on, it is used by cheaper tailors to save the expense of an actual try-on.

DUMPED BALES. Foreign wool bales which have been greatly compressed for shipping purposes and easier handling. The bales are about 4½ feet by 2½ feet by 2½ feet.

DUNCAN COTTON. A large-boll, late-maturing Georgia cotton with a staple of 1⅛ inches to 1⅜ inches.

DUNCHEE HEMP. A strong, elastic bast fiber found in India; used for rope and hemp substitute.

DUNDEE. The name of this well-known "bast fiber" city in Scotland. The term is given to burlap, bagging, crash, butcher linen, etc., made there. It is also the name for a smooth-textured, twill-woven woolen cloth that is soft in hand.

DUNDEE REED COUNT. The number of porters or groups of 20 splits or reed dents contained in a 37-inch reed width. This Scottish reed-count method is used for jute and linen yarn in Dundee and Aberdeen, Scotland.

DUNGAREE. Work overall fabric made of coarse cotton denim, usually blue. Originally it was used for sailors' work clothes.

DUNGING. In this finishing process for printed cottons the cloth is passed through solutions of phosphate of lime, phosphate of soda, etc., to remove excess mordant as well as to fix the mordant on the goods.

DUNG LOCKS. Heavily encrusted, matted areas caused by dung or humus around the rump of a sheep.

DUO-CHINE. Trade-mark of Kenyon Piece Dye Works for a special application of Everglaze finish, used to produce two-texture patterns combining satin and crepe textures. It is applied to satins of viscose, acetate, and nylon intended for linings, dress goods, and lingerie.

DUPLAN. The word is not a trademark name but is the name of the Duplan Corporation, the world's largest processor of textured yarns.

DUPLEX DAMASK. One in which the motif is the same on the face and the back of the material.

DUPLEX PRINTING. Printed fabric in which the face and the back are printed with equal clarity, a reversible cloth. Also called register print, the method is resorted to in printing drapery and similar fabrics. The motif does not have to be the same on both sides of the goods.

DUPLEX SHEETING. A 4-end, reversible twill weave is used in this soft-filled sheeting which is finished with a heavy nap on both sides of the fabric. Used for table felt chiefly, it comes in light weights and is napped on both sides and then sheared to give a suede effect.

DURABEAU. A combination of finishes applied to cotton, rayon, and wool, which when used together serve as a water and spot repellent, a delustrant, a body-imparting and sealing agent, and a softener. Usually applied on hosiery, the finished fabric has more luster, softer handle, better shape-retaining qualities; is water- and spot-repellent and has greater resistance to runs and snags. The finishes are all applied in the one bath at various time intervals and react on one another to form an insoluble, elastic, flexible compound within and on the fibers. It is possible to vary the amount of each reagent to obtain any desired degree of each featured result. Product of Scholler Brothers, Inc., Philadelphia, Pa.

DURABLE FINISH. One which will retain its characteristics and remain inherent, to a large degree, in the fabric through ordinary household washings, wet-cleaning, and dry-cleaning for the life of the goods.

DURABLE PRESS ARTICLES, GENERAL CARE FOR. These articles may be laundered and drycleaned if given proper care. Tumble drying is ideal provided the items are removed as soon as the tumbling cycle is completed, otherwise it may be necessary to remove bunching or crumbling by dampening or sprinkling, and then drying the item again by tumbling in a heated dryer for a short time.

If drip-drying is resorted to, it is necessary to remove the garment from the washing machine prior to spin-drying. Twisting or wringing should not be done; non-rust hangers should be used.

Bleaching is the same as that used for non-durable articles taking notice, however, of color and fiber content. Read labels well. In chlorine bleaching be sure to follow instructions noted on the container. See Permanent Press.

DURABLE PRESS VERSUS NO-IRON. Pertains to a cloth impregnated with a resin, then cured or pressed under high temperatures to provide durable crease lines or pleats that are retained and necessitate no further ironing for the life of the material. No-Iron indicates a material, made of 100 percent manmade fibers or with a blend of manmade and natural fibers, which may or may not have been treated with a resin, and then cured or pressed under heat. The fabric is smooth in surface effect and does not need ironing or pressing after laundering.

DURAMIL. A durable water-repellent, spot-resistant, and crease-resistant finish; trade-mark of Deering, Milliken & Company, Inc.

DURANGO COTTON. Cotton raised in the Imperial Valley of California. It is 1 1/16-inch to 1 5/8-inch in staple. It is silklike, strong, comparatively free from waste, is bright in cast, and has considerable natural twist.

DURASEAL. Trade-mark of the Fair Lawn Finishing Co. for a water-repellent process for the waterproofing of nylon fabrics, which is designed to withstand repeated washings and dry cleanings without losing any of its efficacy.

DURENE. Combed cotton yarns that have been plied and mercerized under the controlled quality standards set up by the Durene Association of America.

DUST CELLAR. The chamber which receives all kinds and types of foreign matter from various auxiliary machines used in preparing stock for manipulation. Fans and exhaust pipes aid in the passage of this matter to the settling chamber.

DUST CHIMNEY. Connected to a dust or settling chamber, it provides the air outlet. Care has to be exercised to prevent pressure that might cause backdraft.

DUSTER. A cotton, linen, or union cloth, more or less dustproof, which comes in cream, khaki, or brown shades. Made in short and long coats for use in offices, stores, and in the farming districts. Textures are usually rather compact. 2. Long loose coat in style of the original duster coats, used for housework or sometimes evening wear.

DUSTING, WILLOWING, PICKERING. This operation is the beating and the cleaning of the wool insofar as the removal of considerable amounts of loose vegetable matter is concerned. Dusting aids in the ensuing operations, since wool without loose, matted waste materials will naturally work easier.

Dusting is automatically done in the machine; the wool is fed into the frame by an endless feed table, passes between two feed rollers, and then comes in contact with the main cylinder. This has long, rugged spur-teeth which catch the wool and carry it through iron spur teeth located on stationary bars in the machine. The teeth are set evenly so that the teeth of the revolving cylinder will pass cleanly between the teeth on the bars. Thus, the wool receives a rather rigid racking treatment whereby the loose waste matter drops through the meshes in the machine to the receptacle under the frame. Burrs, chaff, dried grass, leaves, motes, pebbles, are separated from the fibers of grease wool. The machine, though not very large, does rugged work.

DUST-RESISTANT. Many compact-texture materials, because of pick count or finish, seem to be impervious to particles of dust. Cloths classed as dust-resistant must be well tested before the term is applied to them.

DUST TRUNK. See CLEANING TRUNK.

DUTCH CARPETING.
1. HEAVY: Plain-weave jute fabric which presents a riblike surface effect. Colored warp and heavy black filling,

only 10 to 12 picks per inch, are used in this stair carpeting.

2. Low: This is made with colored or printed warp to brighten the black filling. Fancy stripe effects are seen in this carpeting which is woven with only 6 or 8 picks in the filling.

3. MEDIUM: The same as the low type except that 10 to 12 picks per inch are used in the filling texture.

DURABLE OR PERMANENT PRESS, SOME IMPORTANT BASIC TERMS USED IN.

ABRASION RESISTANCE: The degree to which a fabric is able to withstand surface wear and rubbing. An abrasion test for Permanent Press indicates the degree to which wash-wear chemicals have weakened the fabric.

BATCH CURE: One of the two methods used in curing Permanent Press garments. This method takes care of a single batch of garments at a time in the oven. The other method is of the continuous-process type.

CATALYST: A substance which changes the speed of a chemical action without being altered permanently itself. Applicable to Deferred Cure, it is a chemical which helps to achieve cross-linking and is therefore added to the padding solution. (See Deferred or Post-Cure.)

CHLORINE-RESISTANT: Certain chemical finishes used in textiles retain some of the chlorine used in laundering. This is called CHLORINE RETENTION, and it causes a yellowing of white fabrics. When yellowing is not apparent, the finish is known as CHLORINE-RESISTANT.

COMPRESSIVE SHRINKING: Application of pressure and steam to a fabric to provide dimensional stability against further shrinkage. (See Dimensional Stability.)

CONTINUOUS CURE: One of the two methods used to cure Permanent Press garments. This method uses a moving conveyor system to process garments in a continuous line from the pressing machine into and out of the curing oven. (See Batch Cure.)

CREASES VERSUS WRINKLES: A crease is a line or mark produced in anything by folding; a fold, or furrow. A wrinkle is a ridge or furrow on a surface caused by contraction, folding, rumpling, etc. A crease is a deformation in a fabric intentionally formed by pressing. Washing and wearing a garment will remove it. A wrinkle is formed unintentionally by washing and wearing, and it can usually be removed by pressing. In Permanent Press, however, the crease is not removable and there is an absence of wrinkles.

CROSS-LINKING AGENT: A resin or chemical that reacts with the chemical structure of a fiber in order to form an indissoluble bond or link. The agent, when cured in the fabric, provides the latter with a "memory" of its cured form.

CURING: Application of heat in order to fix chemicals permanently in the goods so that there will be no further change; comparable with the curing of fish or meat.

DEFERRED OR POST-CURE: The process whereby fabrics are treated with chemical cross-linking agents that are not fixed or cured into the goods until after the garment has been made. The goods remain in a sensitized state until after the proper heat treatment has been given. Thus the curing procedure has been deferred or delayed.

DIMENSIONAL STABILITY: The quality which enables a fabric or a garment to resist any type of change in measurement through repeated launderings, actually an ability to resist shrinkage.

DURABLE CREASE: More or less interchangeable with the term "Permanent Press," it is really limited since it refers only to the property of crease retention. Permanent Press, on the other hand, points to the shape-retaining properties of the whole garment.

"FABRIC MEMORY": The characteristic or property of a fabric which causes it to have a "memory" of its original form and thereby always return to that form on release from tension, certain treatments, etc. Wool and some of the manmade fibers possess a native or inherent "memory"; rayon, for example, in returning to its original fabric length after washing, the resiliency of wool, et al. Deferred or Post-Cure fabrics have their "memory" provided by chemical finishes.

FIBRILLATION: This pertains to the lightening of shade in Deferred or Post-Cure garments after repeated washings. This is found along the crease lines and is rather pronounced at times in dark-colored fabrics or garments, caused by the fact that the crease line is more exposed to abrasion and wear, which brings some of the fibrils in the material to the surface.

FINDINGS: Auxiliary fabrics used in the manufacture of a garment-lining, pocketing, tape, waistbanding, zipper tape, et al. All findings should be treated chemically in the same manner as the shell fabric.

FLAT CURING: Curing a fabric at the mill level—in flat-piece condition.

HAND BUILDER: The use of any chemical or finish which improves the hand, feel, or surface-effect texture in a fabric.

HOT HEAD PRESS: A type of pressing machine especially designed for processing Permanent Press garments. It generates heat between 450° and 500° F., with pressure to six tons at the head, and is generally equipped with precision automatic controls.

IMIDAZOLIDONE: Prepared by the action of ammonia on glyoxal; imidazole formula is made up of carbon (52.92%), hydrogen (5.92%), and nitrogen (41.15%). Imidazolidone is a chemical compound of which one derivative finds use in the Deferred or Post-Cure Process used in Permanent Press. It is a product of Sun Chemical Company, New York City, and is trademarked as Permafresh 183. (See Deferred or Post-Cure.)

IMPREGNATION: One meaning is to fill interstices or openings with a substance; another is to charge with something infused or permeating throughout; to saturate. Treating a fabric with some finishing compound or solution can provide full impregnation of the goods in question.

PADDING SOLUTION: Any of a number of chemical solutions that can be applied by padding the goods to be treated. The solution in the case of the Deferred or Post-Cure for Permanent Press may be described by the one produced by the Sun Chemical Company, Inc., New York City. Its composition follows:

Permafresh 183	120.0 pounds
Catalyst X-4	21.5 pounds
Mykon SF (polyethylene softener)	16.0 pounds
Mykon WA (penetrant)	1.0 pound

This combination provides one hundred gallons of the solution.

PERMANENT PRESS OR DURABLE PRESS: This term is used to describe a garment that will retain its shape-retaining properties throughout its career. Features include sharp creases, flat seams, smooth surface texture and appearance on the goods, and seams which are free from puckering.

PROGRESSIVE CURING: Term used to describe the occasion when a sensitized fabric, treated for the Deferred or Post-Cure, will cure itself during storage. This method of curing means that the sensitized fabrics had to be "made up" very shortly after treatment so that the goods would not set or cure in the flat condition. Deferred-Cure fabrics can now be safely stored for several months to more than one year. (See Deferred or Post-Cure.)

PUCKERING: The furrowed or rippled appearance of seams in a conventional wash-wear garment following laundering. It is caused by sewing tension and a varied shrinkage of the fabric and the sewing thread. Quality Permanent Press garments avoid seam puckering because they are cured and fixed after careful pressing of the articles.

REACTANT: Merely a chemical finishing compound which reacts with the fiber to form a cross-linking bond.

RESIN: Any of several organic substances obtained chiefly, or exuding, from plants in a semisolid state. A resin is insoluble in water but soluble in alcohol and ether. Resins are much used on fabrics in finishing when they are to be used for wash-wear finished articles.

SENSITIZED: Refers to fabrics that have been impregnated with certain finishing chemicals, then dried but not cured. The fabric is then said to be in a sensitized condition until the proper degree of heat is applied such as that observed in the Deferred or Post-Cure Process for Permanent Press fabrics.

SOFTENER: Any of a large number of chemical compounds used in fabric finishing to give the cloth a mellow, soft, and appealing hand or handle.

SPONTANEOUS CURING: Practically synonymous with Progressive Curing. (See Progressive Curing.)

STORAGE STABILITY: The ability of a sensitized material to remain in this condition without curing itself spontaneously during storage.

TEAR STRENGTH: Allied with abrasion resistance, it is the degree to which a fabric will resist rupture or tearing. With regard to Permanent Press, a test for tear strength also aids to determine how much the fabric has been weakened by chemical treatment. The term "tenderized" describes a fabric that has been weakened by some treatment. Tear strength is related to tensile strength, which refers to the ability of a fabric to resist vertical or horizontal stress or strain. Notations are made of the point of rupture or breakage for warp and filling directions in the sample being tested for tensile strength, chiefly for the standard or comparative purposes relative to the particular fabric.

THERMOSETTING RESIN: One that can be set permanently through the application of heat; a resin that will permanently cure a fabric through heat application.

DURABLE PRESS, SOME OF THE PROMINENT TRADEMARKS IN.

BURMI-CREASE (Pre-Cure): Developed by the Men's Wear Division of Burlington Industries, Inc., it is based on the inherent thermosetting properties of fabric blends of acrylic and polyester fibers. No resins or other chemicals are used and the durable crease is achieved on hot-head pressing machines.

CONEPREST (Pre-Cure and Spray): In this pre-cure method of Cone Mills, Inc., the fabrics are treated and then completely cured at the mill level. Prior to processing the garment, its crease or pleatline is sprayed with Coneprest Solution. This produces "amnesia" in the area sprayed so that the fabric loses completely the "memory" of its cured shape. "Memory" is restored by hot-head pressing.

DAN-PRESS (Post-Cure): In this process of Dan River Mills, Inc., the application to Fortrel polyester fiber and cotton blends has been very successful. Recommended curing temperatures and time duration are: 1. 370° F. and 2 minutes; 2. 340° F. and 4 minutes; 3. 320° F. and 4 minutes; and 4. 320° F. and 15 minutes.

KORATRON (Post-Cure): Patented process for Permanent Press or Durable Press of the Koratron Company, Inc., San Francisco, California. The idea for this type of press was conceived and developed by Koret of California, a noted women's sportswear house in San Francisco. In 1961, Koret received a patent for its Deferred-Cure Process and from this development the Koratron Company was formed to market the process. The licensing arrangement calls for strict quality controls at both mill and garment manufacturing levels. The established industry standards of the American Association of Textile Chemists and Colorists, Inc., are used to measure and check performance of the end product.

NEVER-PRESS (Pre-Cure): Developed by the Men's Wear Division of Wamsutta Mills, Inc., Lyman, South Carolina, the treatment is based on fiber-blend engineering and a special resin finish. Hot-head pressing at 320° F. is used. Normal wear for one year is guaranteed by the company.

PENN-PREST: The private label trademark for garments made for the J. C. Penney Company. Garments that bear this label must maintain a just-pressed look after home machine washing and tumble drying and are tested for no noticeable loss in appearance after five cycles of home laundering. The garments may be manufactured by any of the several systems, oven curing, high-pressure steam pressing, or careful tailoring of pre-cured fabric. The only requirements are that they perform satisfactorily and that they meet the usual minimum standards for strength, endurance, and color fastness expected of any other garment in the same end-use category.

PRIMATIZED (Pre-Cure): The process developed and merchandised by Deering-Milliken, Inc., New York City.

REEVE-SET (Pre-Cure and Post-Cure): This process of Reeves Brothers, Inc., New York City, involves two curing treatments. The fabrics are cured at the mill level in the flat condition and then are additionally set through oven curing at the manufacturing level.

SHARP/SHAPE (Pre-Cure): This method of Everprest, Inc., Salt Lake City, Utah, is especially effective on stretch fabrics. It uses the special hot-head press equipment, also developed by the company.

SUPER-CREASE (Post-Cure): Trademark name for the process developed by J. P. Stevens & Co., Inc., New York City. It is based on the use of sulfone chemicals rather than on the use of resins, thereby eliminating chlorine retention and unpleasant odors. The company, in addition, has another post-cure process merchandised as SUPER-CREASE K.

DUTCH TAPE. Linen and cotton tapes are known by this term in Great Britain.

DUVETYNE. Used in the millinery trade and in women's wear. The 6-harness irregular satin weave is used, or it is possible to use a 7- or 8-end satin construction. Originally the cloth was made of cotton warp and spun-silk filling. Other combinations are used as well. Cloth ranges from 10 to 20 ounces in weight in woolen duvetyne, and is stock-, skein-, or piece-dyed. Material is face-finished to give a smooth, plush appearance. Duvetyne has a kindly feel and comes in many shades and casts of color. When the cloth is in demand it is often difficult to supply it to the trade. One of the better quality cloths. Duvetyne resembles a compact velvet; wears very well, good draping effect, soft to the feel. Spots easily.

DUVETYNE DE SOIE. A smooth, downy, rather heavy cloth made usually from spun silk, and napped to simulate plush. Made from a 6-harness irregular satin weave, the cloth is appealing to the eye and has a pleasant hand.

DUVETYNE; FELTED, SUEDE FINISHES. In the popular finishes of these types, the cloth is napped on one or both sides and is then sheared and brushed carefully in order to obtain the closely cropped nap that is characteristic of suede finishes.

DWELL. The short span of time that a harness frame remains in one position during weaving. The shed of the loom must be open for the shuttle to pass through on its way to the shuttle box at the other end of the raceplate.

DWELL-UP. British term for causing a harness frame to remain up for two or more filling picks to pass through the shed of the loom.

DWIGHT WIND. A type of warp often found on twister frames. It has a tapered top end on the bobbin.

DYBLN. Pronounced "dye-blen," this product of E. I. duPont de Nemours & Company, Inc., Wilmington, Delaware, is used on polyester/cotton blend fabrics in which the greater the amount of polyester, the better will be the color. The process, brought out in 1971, is a new colorfast dyeing and printing method in coloring textiles. It is based on a new set of disperse dyes for dyeing and printing both fibers at one time in one heat-setting step through a thermosol unit; no special equipment is necessary. The system has continuous impact with regard to developments in pigment printing which provides improved crockfastness and improved hand without the use of any resin. Other features include wet fastness for

both drycleaning and washing, along with resistance to crease abrasion. A greater range in styling is afforded by the use of Dybln.

Fabrics dyed by this method include career apparel, uniform fabrics, printed sheetings, home furnishing fabrics except, at the present time, for draperies and over-the-counter piece goods.

DYE. See DYEING.

DYE BAGS. Used in the dyeing of completed sweaters or sweater-strips made of manufactured yarns. These mesh or net bags are usually made of Raschel knitted fabric of a noncellulosic continuous filament. They may also be woven, in which a leno or doup weave provides porosity and strength to the bags.

DYE BECK. A machine used to dye piece goods. There are several types and they are known as kier, vessel, winch, and by other names.

DYE BOX. Part of dyeing equipment. See Illustrated Section.

DYE CARD. A card on which dye formulas are recorded.

DYE DEPTH. Relative lightness or darkness of dyed woven or knitted fabrics when compared with a control fabric.

DYED-IN-THE-GREASE. Some low-quality worsteds are dyed prior to the first cloth-scouring bath; used only in dark shades.

DYED-IN-THE-WOOL. Woolen stock dyed before blending, oiling, mixing, carding, and spinning. Considered as synonymous with stock-dyed, a popular method of dyeing woolen fabrics.

DYED SLUBBING. Implies worsted top which has been dyed in the top form and then recombed before further processing by subsequent machine operations.

DYE FIXING AGENT. An agent capable of reacting with a dye on a fiber to improve fastness to water or washing. It is usually applied as an after-treatment to dyes which already possess some affinity for the textile substrate and are so distinguished from mordants. See SUBSTRATE.

DYEING. A process of coloring fibers or fabrics with either natural or synthetic dyes. Dyes differ in their resistance to sunlight, perspiration, washing, gas, alkali, dust, etc., their effectiveness on different fibers, their reaction to cleaning agents, their solubility and method of application.

DYEING, HIGH-PRESSURE. A method of dyeing in which high pressure is used to force the dye bath through the material, resulting in speed of application and good penetration.

DYEING, HIGH-TEMPERATURE.

Sometimes used on thermoplastic type fibers to improve better dye penetration and depth. Acetate and Dynel, however, at the present time are not dyed by this method. There are two methods, which follow:

1. *Molten-Metal Method:* Fabrics dyed with vat dyes are guided through a U-shaped vat in which there is a molten metal alloy at temperature from 200° to 250° F. In the molten metal solution the dye is actually reduced under pressure. The metal is removed by rinsing; the fabric is oxidized, scoured and then well-rinsed. This method affords level dyeing in dense or thick-structure fabrics, and can be used in slub-yarn constructions and in embroidered fabrics where there might be difficulty to obtain matching or comparable shades in the ground and embroidered areas.

2. *Thermosol Method:* Conventional equipment is used in this method to dye fabrics at normal or regular temperatures. Drying follows the dyeing of the goods and a heat-setting treatment which lasts for less than one minute with a temperature of around 350° F. comes next. In cloths dyed in this way, fastness to machine-washing is assured. "Dacron" is an ideal fiber for this method of coloring.

DYEING, MIXED-FIBER. This method of coloring textiles is dyeing a material which has more than one kind or type of fiber in its content. Some examples of the older and popular compositions include cotton/wool; viscose rayon/acetate; linen/cotton/rayon; and cotton with most of the manmade textile fibers. Of late, much attention has been given to coloring combinations of polyester and cotton, and polyester and rayon, in blends. In addition, attention has been given to coloring fabrics which contain fibers of different strains or types and receptive to different types of dyes. Cloth in this category are labeled as 100 percent nylon, 100 percent acrylic, etc.

Any of the foregoing fabric combinations may be piece dyed in a single solid color. This is known as *Union Dyeing.* In any of the above, one fiber can be kept undyed or white while the other fiber or fibers are colored. This type of dyeing is called *Reserve Dyeing* since one fiber is reserved from actually being dyed. In addition, one fiber can be dyed a particular shade or color while the other fiber or fibers would take on another color. This is known as *Cross Dyeing.* Depending on the location or spacing of the different dyeing fibers, various designs, motifs or patterns come into being such as checks, iridescents, plaids, stripes, etc. Incidentally, this type of goods finds much favor in popular raincoatings with a cotton warp and an acetate or nylon filling.

The selection of dyestuffs is responsible for the variations in the coloring described above. Each class or type, generally speaking, has affinity for one or more types of fibers. Home dyeing colors, such as Rit or Putnam are a mixture of several classes of dye selected with the purpose of coloring any fiber the indicated shade.

The usual types of dyes used in Mixed-Fiber Dyeing are: Acid, Basic, Direct, Disperse, Reactive, Sulphur, Vat. These types may be used in myriad combinations to dye a goodly number of different manmade and natural fibers in which two or more different fibers are used. They are also used in coloring various, usually numbered, Types of the same fiber. For example, there could be a coloring of "Dacron" polyester fiber types such as Types 35, 59, and 83. Another feature in Mixed-Fiber Dyeing is that, for example, a solution-dyed black will remain black and repel other colors used to dye the goods in piece formation.

The following table of fibers and the class of dyestuff for which one has affinity for more than the one listed below:

FIBER AND THE TYPE OF DYE:
Acetate - Disperse dyes. *Acrylic* - Basic-Disperse dyes. *Acrylic-Modified* - Acid Dyes. *Cotton* - Direct-Sulphur dyes. *Nylon* - Acid Disperse dyes. *Polyester* - Disperse dyes. *Polyester-Modified* - Cationic-Disperse. *Rayon* - Direct-Vat dyes. *Wool* - Acid-Basic dyes.

Thus, from the foregoing it will be observed that piece dyeing, cross-dyeing, and union dyeing have all contributed to the present day popularity of Fiber-Mix Dyeing which combines features of all three methods of coloring textiles. Prior to the development of this method, checks, heathers, plaids, stripes, etc., could only be achieved by raw stock (fiber dyeing), or by yarn dyeing; both of which are more costly than piece dyeing and reduce inventory control.

DYEING, PACK OR PRESSURE. Forced circulation of dye liquor through packages of fibers, filaments, yarn, or fabric without the limitation of temperatures. See DYEING, HIGH TEMPERATURE.

DYEING, SOLVENT. The process of applying dyestuff from a non-aqueous solvent to a substrate, such as skeins of yarn, fabric, etc., in which the entire substrate is being colored the same or one shade. See Substrate.

DYEING, TOP-CHROME. The application of the dyestuff to a fabric, followed by a mordant treatment in the same or in another bath. Also called after-chroming.

DYEING ASSISTANT. Surface active agents, synthetic detergents, etc., which aid dyestuff to become fixed on or into the fiber by causing it to bloat or swell, thereby bringing about better color penetration and color leveling. The assistant may be a hastening agent to "speed up" the dyeing or a retarding agent to "slow up" the action.

DYEING STOCK, YARN, AND FABRIC, SOME MAJOR METHODS OF. Textiles come in many forms with regard to color or lack of color. A fabric may be in the natural color, printed, dyed, bleached to white, mercerized as in the case of many cotton materials. In addition, fabrics may receive one or more of a host of finishing treatments such as napping, shearing, felting, smoothing, moire' or watermarking, starching, sizing, glazing, calendering. Finishes may be harsh, soft, stiff, limp, mosslike, silklike, surface-finished. Coloring and finish seem to go hand-in-hand to produce some definite texture on a fabric for consumption. There are several methods used to color textiles, and each of these depends usually on the so-called local conditions.

DYEING TEXTILES. MAJOR METHODS OF.

Stock-Dyeing: This method is extremely popular for dyeing woolen fabrics since the range of color and shade is very wide. The dyeing is done after the stock used has been scoured and dried but before the spinning of the yarn and the weaving of the cloth.

The actual dyeing is done in large vats or kiers, either in small or large lots. The final color effect is obtained when the newly dyed stock is blended, oiled, and mixed and ultimately spun into yarn.

Examples of stock-dyeing include plain colors, heathers, mixes, and shades as noted in homespun, tweed, cheviot, Shetland, covert, Venetian, and other comparable suitings and coatings.

Yarn- or Skein-Dyeing: This is done after the yarn has been spun but before fabric has been made from the yarn. The yarn skeins are dyed by being placed on cross-bars or rollers to support the skeins. Usually from 24 to 40 skeins can be accommodated on each bar. Several roller bars can be cared for in the machine. There may or may not be total immersion of the yarn while it is being dyed in the bath.

Examples include gingham, striped chambray, striped denim; checks, stripes, plaids, overplaids, tartans, Glen plaids, dressgoods.

Piece-Dyeing: This is applied to fabric which is colored a single color, shade, cast, tone, hue, or tint. It occurs after the fabric has been woven in the loom and then made as nearly perfect as possible, free from all defects.

Piece-dyeing is a continuous or semi-continuous process which takes place in a dye-beck, box, kier, jig, or vessel. On jigs and continous machines the cloth is handled in the open width while on the dye-beck it is in rope form. Piece-dyeing is very popular because of the inherent flexibility from an economic standpoint. It is far more economical to weave fabric with undyed yarns and subsequently to dye the material into popular shades than to yarn-dye with the hazard that the colors may not be popular when marketed.

Examples include blue serge, brown gabardine, green organdy, black crepe, navy-blue dressgoods, purple satin.

Cross-Dyeing: A union cloth is one made up of two or more different textile fibers or yarns in the same material. Union fabrics are among the most popular to be found on the market today. Animal, vegetable, and manmade yarns or fibers are used to produce the many fabrics that are to be dyed in this manner. Examples could be a cloth with a cotton warp and a worsted filling; a cotton warp and a nylon filling; rayon warp and acetate filling; acetate warp and "Dacron" filling; worsted warp and Arnel filling.

The dyeing may be done in one or two baths, dependent upon the local conditions and the equipment available. Special dyes are needed for each type of fiber or yarn. When the dyeing is taking place, the one yarn will take on one color or shade, while the other yarn or fiber will take on another color or shade. The resultant coloring in the goods may be harmonious or contrasting in shade or cast. Much dressgoods fabric is dyed in this manner, as well as some evening-wear fabric, etc.

Dope-Dyeing, Solution-Dyeing; Spun-Dyed Fabrics: The original name for this method was dope-dyeing. It is a development from World War I, when the term "dope" meant to cover or coat the wings of airplanes; this dope was a solution of cellulose acetate, the forerunner of present-day acetate, the cellulose-derivative fiber.

Today the term is applied to dyeing in the following sense: After the solution of cellulose acetate has been prepared and filtered for purification, dyes are introduced into the solution. This solution is then extruded through spinnerettes and dried in the usual manner. The color used has become a corporate part of the filament itself, by the bonding together of color and fiber.

Only a skilled dyer can work with dope dyes, since the amounts of dye needed to achieve the desired shade will vary and only experienced dyers can produce colors of commercial satisfaction.

The method has met with acclaim in the trade wherever used. Dope-dyed fabrics have splendid fastness to light, the colors and cast are genuinely good and attractive, and they will not wash out in laundering. This manner of dyeing is ideal for plaids, checks, stripes, and solid colors. Fabrics dyed with these dyes are such that it is practically impossible to remove the color should it be desired to redye the material.

Jig Dyeing: A popular method of dyeing which is done in a jig, kier, vat or vessel. The dyeing is done in an open formation of the goods. The fabric goes from one roller to another through a deep dyebath until the desired shade is achieved.

Package Dyeing: Yarns are dyed while on cones, cakes, cheeses or in the conventional or standard layout or set-up. Gives excellent results and high production in coloring textiles.

Top- or Slub-Dyeing: This is the dyeing of fibers in a top form or slub form which is wound into a top, usually worsted, and resembles a commercial cheese in shape and size. The top has been previously carded and combed but has not as yet been spun into the yarn. The dyeing is carried out in circular machines and the pressure in the machine is very great. The entire top is dyed from the core to the outside in the treatment. Following dyeing the various colored tops are then blended to obtain some definite color shade. Top-dyeing is resorted to in coloring fibers that are to be spun into yarn for use in worsted fab-

rics. Some of the better qualities of women's wear and men's wear fall and winter suitings are colored by this method.

Union-Dyeing: This is a one-bath process as a result of which the same color or shade can be imparted to two or more textile fibers or yarns in the same piece of material. Both cross-dyeing and union-dyeing are forms of piece-dyeing in processing. Piece-dyeing is done on fabric made of only one type of yarn as to content. Union-dyeing differs from cross-dyeing in that in the former there is a single color or shade in the finished goods. It is possible, for example, to union-dye a fabric which contains "Orlon," "Dacron," rayon, and acetate — four fibers in the one cloth and in which a decided single color cast may be obtained. Union-dyeing is very popular in many types of men's wear, women's wear, and children's wear.

Vat Dyed: Cloth dyed by the use of vat dyes which are obtained through oxidation; the fastest colors known today and a very popular method in coloring textiles. Vat dyeing may be considered to be a misnomer since fabric colored with these dyes are actually piece dyed in the conventional manner.

Vigoureux Dyeing or Printing: This method of coloring embodies both dyeing and printing. It is the dyeing or printing of worsted top fibers by passing the slivers or slubbings through a printing machine which has a roller with raised bars to carry the dyestuff. The sliver is impregnated with the dyestuff when it comes in contact with the revolving raised areas on the roller that is to afford the pressure for printing the sliver areas which are to be colored onto the actual color roller. A roller with 60 percent of its surface gouged out or cut will produce a sliver with a 40-per-cent-colored area. This method is also known as Melange dyeing or printing.

Blacks, browns, blues, and greens, seem to be the most popular shades done in Vigourex printing. Following the coloring, the stock is gilled and drawn, and is then spun into yarn to be made ready for the weaving of the fabric. Vigoureux-printed fabric appears only in the better class of men's wear and women's wear in the trade. Ideal for suiting and coating for cold-weather wear.

Williams Unit: Invented by S.H. Williams of the General Aniline & Film Corporation, New York City, this is

an extremely versatile and economical machine for carrying out many operations in textile processing. It is widely used for dyeing, washing, pretreating, and aftertreating, in the many continuous processes of the textile industry.

Other advantages of the unit include insulation to prevent loss of heat, minimum need of maintenance because of the simple mechanical construction, and compactness in size.

Light and dark shades are produced easily by a continuous-process treatment. There is control and a governing of the even circulation of solutions at all times, thereby preventing preoxidation. Each unit is equipped with microset rolls. The machine is installed to specifications using five- or ten-ton pressures, and it comes in widths of 40, 50, 60, and 70 inches.

DYEING TEXTILES; MINOR METHODS OF.

HAND METHODS: Many people like to dye textiles by hand. It may be done as a hobby but there are professional hand-dyers of textiles in the trade. This art is remunerative to them, otherwise they would not be in business. There is a vast difference between machine-dyeing and hand-dyeing as to production, labor costs, and the time element. Hand methods permit a very wide range of motif and decorativeness, and the commercial value of some of the products may be considered good, with prices in some instances rather high. Handwork is practically always more expensive than machine work. The most popular methods in hand-dyeing are:

Batik-Dyeing: The design obtained in this method of coloring is not clear cut since a mottled effect is always noted. The dyer obtains a medley of coloring which presents an interesting motif. Batik originated in Java, where the genuine fabrics, even obtainable today, used four colors—indigo blue, brown, black, and yellow. Other colors are now used, along with the originals, wherever the work is done throughout the world. *Batik* means "to paint."

A motif is traced or outlined on both sides of the cloth. Melted wax is then applied to the areas where the coloring will be more or less repelled by the wax. The wax, however, will crack and allow fine vein lines of cloth to appear as the dye seeps through and penetrates into the material. After the full colored areas and the vein-line areas are completed, the fabric is then removed from the bath, rinsed, and the wax is removed by hot water or a solvent. The operation may be repeated a number of times until the full design has been achieved. Multi-colored effects result from the work, and the colors in batik are usually from light to dark.

Burl or Speck Dyeing: Many specks and other foreign particles noted in cloth during the finishing operations must be remedied; much of this matter is vegetable in origin. Some types of woolens and worsteds, because of their nature, show these specks to disadvantage, chiefly in piece-dyed materials. The percher or specker, as he examines the goods, covers these blemishes by "inking on" the spots with the correct matching ink. These inks come in all colors. In some cases they are of much benefit to a mill.

Tie-Dyeing: Also known as tie-and-dye, or dip-dyeing, this method is a very old one; it was used by hand-loom weavers of ancient times. Before the yarn or fabric is placed in the dye liquor, it is tightly tied with string or knotted at intervals. The areas not covered by the string or knots will take on the color as the yarn or fabric is dipped into the dye bath. The operation may be repeated a number of times to obtain this random method of coloring.

The dyed material upon completion will show a blurred, rather "shot-about" or mottled effect of coloring, since the colors tend to run into each other and overlap, thereby producing many varied color shades in the finished article.

The general steps used in tie-dyeing a piece of cloth:

1. Rolling the fabric into a "pig-tail" formation, and then tying certain areas of the rolled cloth with tightly wound string. Some dyers tie the cloth into a knotted formation instead of using string.
2. Dipping the cloth into the dye liquor.
3. Removing the dyed fabric and cutting away the string or unknotting the material.
4. Rinsing and handling the material. The operation may be repeated two or more times, if desired.

MACHINE METHODS.

Bale-Dyeing: A very low-cost method of dyeing cotton cloth. The material, without any scouring or singeing, is sent through a cold-water dye bath, where the sized warp yarn will have affinity for the dye. The filling will not dye since the wax in it has not been removed to admit dye absorption. Imitation chambray and a few similar fabrics are dyed in this manner.

Beam-Dyeing: A method of dyeing warp yarn prior to weaving. The warp is wound on perforated beams and the dye is forced through perforations, thereby saturating the yarn with color.

Chain-Dyeing: Used to dye yarns and cloths of low tensile strength. The lengths of yarns or fabrics are tied or tacked end to end and then run through the dye bath in a continuous operation. Production in this method may run high.

Random Dyeing: A method of dyeing yarn in which only certain areas are colored. Three methods give the result:

1. Skeins may be tightly tied in two or more places and dyed at one side of the tie with one color and at the other side with some other color.
2. Color may be printed onto the skeins which are spread on the blanket of the printing machine.
3. Cones or packages of yarn on hollow spindles may be arranged to form channels through the yarn by means of an air-operated punch, and the dyestuff drawn through these holes by suction. The yarn in the immediate area of the punch absorbs the dye and the random effects are thereby attained (see Tie-Dyeing).

Raw-Stock Dyeing: The process of dyeing fibers before the spinning of the yarn made from the fiber stock. Used chiefly in coloring wool fibers, the dyeing follows the degreasing or scouring of the fibers and drying. (See Stock Dyeing.)

Resist Dyeing: Treating yarn or cloth so that in any subsequent dyeing operation the treated portions resist the dye and do not absorb it at all.

Speck-Dyeing: Many medium and low grade woolens and worsteds have to be speck-dyed to obliterate the specks caused by vegetable matter that has remained in the cloth during the various operations from raw stock to fabric. Much of this matter is rather deeply embedded in the goods. The cut of cloth may be dyed in a cold-soap bath of direct dyes which will color the cotton very well but leave the animal fibers unscathed. (See Burl or Speck-Dyeing).

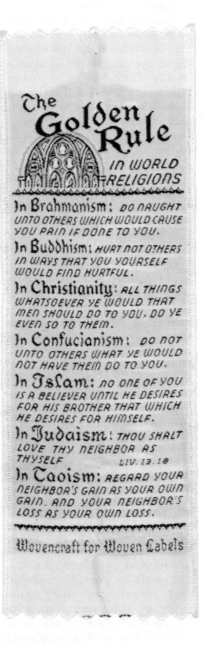

EXAMPLE OF JACQUARD WEAVING

DYEING AND PRINTING TEXTILES,
SOME BASIC DEFINITIONS USED IN.

This group of terms, in some respects, is technical. The inclusion of technical terms attempts to give the full scope of the "language of dyeing and printing" to serve the textile technologist, students in textile colleges, dyers and printers, and those scientists interested in the types of dyes used to color textile yarns and fabrics.

Most of the terms, however, should be understood and digested by students in textile courses, textile instructors, and those interested in the chemistry of textiles especially with regard to the "how" and the "why" in color application. Most of the terms will be readily recalled by students who have had science subjects in high school and college.

Attention is also drawn to "Definitions and Terms Used in the Manufacture of Manmade Filaments and Fibers" in Part Two, Unit 13, of *Natural and Manmade Fibers*, by the author of this book. This unit is a brief history of the newer manmade fibers and should be of utmost interest to the diligent student interested in the study of textiles.

The definitions for this unit follow:

ALIZARINE: Originally obtained from the madder root, but now made from anthraquinone. The word *alizarine* means "to extract."

AMINE: Any of a class of compounds prepared from ammonia by replacing one, two, or all hydrogen atoms with organic radicals.

AMINO: A prefix denoting the amino group, a combination form of amine.

ANHYDRIDE: A compound formed by the abstraction of water, an oxide of a nonmetal (acid anhydride) or a metal (basic anhydride) which forms an acid or a base, respectively, when united with water. A compound from which water has been extracted.

ANION: A negatively charged ion which is attracted to the anode in electrolysis. Any negatively charged atom, molecule, or radical. From the Greek, it means "going up."

ANODE: The positive pole of a battery or other source of current.

ANTHRACENE: A hydrocarbon found in coal tar; of importance as a source for aniline. Formula is $C_{14}H_{10}$.

ANTHRAQUINONE: A crystalline substance from anthracene or phthalic anhydride; used in the preparation of alizarine or other dyes. Formula is $C_{14}H_8C_2$.

ASSISTANT: A dyeing assistant includes surface active agents, synthetic detergents, etc., which aid dyestuff to become fixed on or into the fiber by causing it to bloat or swell, thereby bringing about better color penetration and color leveling. The assistant may be a hastening agent to "speed up" the dyeing or a retarding agent to "slow up" the action.

ATOM: The smallest particle of any chemical element that can exist by itself and retain the qualities that characterize it as that element.

AZO: A term applied to a numerous group of dyes prepared by the modifications of one general reaction—the diazo. Most direct cotton colors are of this type. Insoluble azo colors (paranitraniline red) are developed directly onto the cotton and yield very fast colors.

BATH OR LIQUOR: The solution in which dyeing, bleaching, washing, scouring, etc., takes place.

BECK, KIER, VESSEL, WINCH: A machine used to dye piece goods. There are several types of machines and they are sometimes known by other, more or less closely-allied, names.

CHELATION: A chemical reaction where a metallic ion combines with an organic substance which contains hydroxyl and carboxyl groups in suitable portions in order to form a ring structure through ionic and coordinate bonding.

COAL TAR: A black, thick, viscid liquid formed during the distillation of coal and which, upon further distillation, yields anthracene, benzene, phenol, etc. A large number of dyes and synthetic compounds are made from these basic compounds.

COLORFASTNESS: Also known as fast color, it describes fabrics of sufficient color retention so that no noticeable change in the shade occurs during the normal life of the garment. Strictly speaking, there is not any fabric that is absolutely "colorfast," but many fabrics have remarkable durability in retaining the color.

COMPONENT: A composition, constituent or ingredient which aids to make the whole compound or article.

CURING: The setting of a chemical, plastic, or resin in or on textile materials, usually obtained by heating. A curing chamber is any type of drying equipment in which 300° F. and over can be obtained. The chamber may be of the loop, roller, or enclosed-frame type.

DEPTH OF DYE: The relative lightness or darkness of dyed woven or knit fabrics when compared with a control fabric.

DIAZOTIZING: Treatment of dyed material with a solution of nitrous acid obtained by adding sulfuric acid to sodium nitrite. (See Developed Dyes.)

DISPERSE: To drive, force, or scatter as in the case of a dyestuff dispersing throughout a liquid volume when it is placed in the liquor.

ELECTRON: A minute, negatively electrified particle charged with the smallest-known quantity of electricity and having a mass approximately $1/1550$ of that of a hydrogen atom, the atom of negative electricity.

FIXING AGENT: An agent capable of reacting with a dye on a fiber to improve fastness to water or washing. It is usually applied as an aftertreatment to dyes which already possess some affinity for the textile substrate and is so distinguished from mordants. (See Substrate.)

INERT: Having no inherent power of action, motion, or resistance; a form of inaction. Some chemicals will remain inert during a reaction, method, or process.

INTERMEDIATE: Being situated or acting between two points or stages. It is a derivative of the initial material formed before the desired product of a chemical process. Examples of intermediates used to make dyes include benzene, naphthalene, ethyl alcohol, chlorine, lime, and ammonia.

ION: An important term in chemistry and physics when an electrically charged atom, radical, or molecule is formed by the gain or loss of one or more electrons. Positive ions, created by electron loss, are called "cations." Negative ions created by electron gain are known as "anions." The term also implies a fusing, or making a union, such as is often found in dyeing, between a fiber and the dyestuff used to dye it.

ISOMERIC: The word *iso*, from the Greek, means "equal," a prefix. Isomeric, in speaking of chemical compounds, means that the compound is composed of the same kinds and number of atoms, which differ from each other in the arrangement of the atoms and, therefore, in one or more properties.

JIG: The machine used to dye piece goods. Full-width material is passed from a roller through the dye bath in an open vat and then proceeds to another roller. The treatment is repeated until the desired shade is assured. Also referred to as jig-dyeing.

LEUCO: A colorless or nearly colorless soluble compound obtained in the reduction of a vat dye. Leuco means "colorless."

METALIZE: A reaction in chemistry, as in the dyeing procedures, wherein it is possible to obtain the characteristics of metal. (See Neutral Dyeing—Premetalized Acid Dyes.)

MILLING: (1) Subjecting something to the operation of a mill or milling. For example, a dyestuff that has been made into very fine granules prior to its use to dye a textile fiber or yarn. (2) Milling colors or "fast-to-milling" refers to dyes which will not bleed or fade in the wool-finishing operation on fabric known as "fulling" or "milling."

MORDANT: Much used in coloring textiles, it has the property of fixing or setting colors onto a fiber, yarn, or fabric. Especially used as a metallic compound, an oxide or hydroxide, which combines with the organic dye and forms an insoluble colored compound or color lake in the fiber. From the Latin *mordere*, and means "to bite, or to bite into."

NAPHTHOL: Either of two isomeric derivatives of naphthalene, having the formula of $C_{10}H_7OH$, and occurring in coal tar; much used in the manufacture of dyes. Betanaphthol is a crystalline antiseptic that has the same formula as naphthol and implies any of certain hydroxyl derivatives of naphthalene.

ORTHO: From the Greek, it means "straight, right, correct, upright" and is used in combination with other words. Chemically speaking, it is a prefix indicating that acid of a series which contains the most water. The expression "ortho-position," used in dyeing, means the correct position.

OXIDATION: A chemical union of oxygen with some other element or group of elements. Rusting of iron is an example. This involves the combination of iron with oxygen. Heat is released during an oxidation reaction. Burning is a form of rapid oxidation where the heat is quickly observed.

In the instance where oxygen is removed from a compound, the compound is said to have been reduced. If a compound of mercury and oxygen, for example, is heated, the oxygen is driven off, leaving the mercury in its elemental form. The compound, therefore, has been reduced.

Vat dyes, for example, are oxygen compounds which are insoluble in water. By reduction they are changed into a soluble, leuco, or colorless form, and are reconverted by oxidation into the colored insoluble state.

OXIDE: A compound of oxygen with other elements. Iron rust is an iron oxide.

OXIDIZE: To add oxygen to any material by chemical combination. Chlorine bleaching is an oxidizing action.

OXIDIZED COLOR: A dyestuff that is developed by a chemical combination to its full strength by application of certain chemicals to oxidize it.

OXIDIZER: Creates oxygen. "Rinso," for example, has sodium perborate in it, and it is the oxygen that serves as the bleach.

OXIDIZING AGENT: Any substance which can furnish oxygen to which another substance may unite. Hydrogen peroxide, for example, will bleach silk and wool because it liberates or furnishes oxygen which will combine with the dye to form a colorless product.

PAD: To impregnate fabric with dyestuff, mordant, etc.

PADDING, PADDING MACHINE: The application of dyestuff to fabric by a padding machine. It is equipped with a set of wringers that actually force the dyestuff through the material while passing through the wringers at full open width. The steam box will then develop the final color in the fabric.

This method of coloring is economical and only one application is necessary. Production is very good. Fast colors, the vat colors, are used to a great degree in pad- or vat-dyeing when large volume is wanted and production is an incentive. Some goods dyed this way include summer-wear fabric, solid-color sheeting, some curtain and upholstery cloth, and pastel-color material.

PIGMENT: The color of human hair is coloring matter and it can be bleached, dyed, or tinted. As a coloring matter in the skin, pigment cannot be removed like the color in human hair. Freckles are an example of pigment in the skin—irremovable. Applied to chemistry, it is a dry substance, usually pulverized, and when mixed with a liquid vehicle it remains insoluble.

Pigments used in textile coloring or printing are mechanically held to the fabric by a resin-binder and the goods are cured at high temperatures.

PRECIPITATE: To separate a substance out into a solid form from a solution. Curdled milk is an example.

RADICAL: An atom or group of atoms regarded as an important constituent of a molecule which remains unchanged and behaves as a unit in many reactions. Specifically, a group of atoms which act as a unit in a compound and may either pass unchanged through a series of reactions, or be replaced as though it were a single atom. Radical comes from the Latin *radix*, and means "root."

REDUCE: To take oxygen from a certain material or substance.

REDUCED COLOR: A dyestuff which has its formulation changed or reduced by chemical agents.

REDUCER: Vanished oxygen or its equivalent. Coke, for example, removes oxygen from iron ore and leaves the iron.

REDUCING AGENT: Any substance which will remove oxygen from another substance; the opposite of oxidizing agent.

REDUCTION: The process of depriving a chemical compound of its oxygen. Also, the process of decreasing the positive valence of an element by the addition of electrons; distinguished from oxidation.

SCOUR, SCOURING: In general, the cleansing of raw stock, yarn, cloth, etc., of dirt, granules, grime, grease, and a host of other possible impurities by dissolving, rubbing, scrubbing, etc., usually in some liquid which contains a detergent, soap, powder, or the like. Other suitable chemicals used in scouring, washing, and cleansing are alkalies, acids, bleaches, etc.

SIZING: The application of starch or other stiffening agent to yarn, cloth, and garments to provide a better and improved product when completely finished. For example, a size or starch applied to warp yarn increases the strength and smoothness and adds weight to the gray goods from the loom. Sizing may be applied to yarn in hank or ball form, or in the slashing or dressing frame when the warp is being made by the dressing tender. Sizes or stiffeners are much used on fabrics to enhance durability and eye-appeal to the consumer.

There are basically three main types of sizes or gums used in sizing:

1. BINDING AND STIFFENING: Sizes of casava, corn, flour, potato, rice, sago, tapioca, wheat, etc. Also, gum arabic, gum tragacanth, glucose, dextrine, Irish moss, and certain types of glues.
2. FILLING MATERIALS: China clay, talc, alum, blanc fixe, etc.
3. SOFTENING OR CONDITIONING MATERIALS: Coconut oil and some other soluble oils, glycerine, soap, tallow, waxes, etc.

STOCK REDUCTION PASTE: A printing paste used in vat dyeing that contains everything but the color. The paste and the color are mixed later on, in varying proportions, to give the desired printing paste for use.

SUBSTRATE: A substance that is acted upon by an enzyme or ferment. The term comes from the Greek and means "a stratum or layer spread or laid under another stratum or layer."

TANNIN: A natural vegetable substance much used in the preparation of dyestuffs and inks. Tannins find much use in making mordants for use in dyeing textiles. Tannic acid, for example, is soluble in water; so is tartar emetic, a white crystalline, poisonous tartrate of antimony and potassium. Both, however, will combine in a bath or liquor to form an insoluble mordant for use in dyeing textiles.

VALENCE: The property possessed by an element or radical of combining with or replacing other elements or radicals in definite and constant proportion. The degree of this property is commonly indicated by the number of atoms of hydrogen (or their equivalent) taken as a unit with which the atom or radical can combine, or which it can replace. It varies with different elements and with certain elements in different compounds. Thus, hydrogen has a valence of one, and is called univalent; oxygen has a valence of two, and is called bivalent. Carbon has a valence of four and is classed as a quadrivalent. Manganese, for example, may have a valence of two, three, or seven, etc. The word "valence" comes from the Latin *valentia*, which means "strength," or *valeo*, which means "strong."

DYE NETS. A leno or doup woven material that is made into bag containers used in hosiery dyeing to protect stockings from friction and abrasion while being processed, chiefly in machine dyeing operations.

DYEOMETER, DYE-OMETER. An intricate precision device which records continuous colorimetric or photometric measurements used to determine the strength of the dye bath as the operation proceeds to culmination. This device must be used with the utmost care.

DYER'S SPIRIT. Aqua fortis, 10 parts; sal ammoniac, 5 parts; tin, 2 parts; all are dissolved together.

DYER'S WOAD. See WOAD.

DYES. Soluble colored compounds which produce permanent colors on textiles.

DYES FROM PLANTS, MAJOR NATURAL. Many of these have been known for centuries, and several of them are still in use today:

1. ANNATO is from the pulpy part of the seeds of an Indian plant, Bixa orellana; fugitive orange-red color.
2. BRAZILWOOD is from wood of the tree Caesalpinia echinata; bright red color.
3. CUDBEAR comes from the lichen Lecanora tartarea; lilac color dye.
4. CUTCH is obtained from boiling the wood of Acacia catechu, native to India; rich brown color.
5. FUSTIC, OLD, is obtained from wood of tropical American tree, Chlorophora tinctoria; gold to yellow in color and still popular on wool.
6. FUSTIC, YOUNG OR ZANTE, comes from the powdered wood of the Rhus cotinus, a shrub-size tree of the cashew family; yellow to dark olive in color.
7. INDIGO is obtained from the plant Indigofera tinctoria; blue color.
8. KERMES is extracted from bodies of a tiny insect, Coccus arborum; red dye.
9. LAC is obtained by boiling tree incrustation produced by tiny lac insect, Tachardia lacca; bright red color.
10. LOGWOOD comes from a Central American tree, Haematoxylon campechium; gives purple on wool, blue and black on cotton, violet and black on silk.
11. MADDER comes from the roots of the plant Rubia tinctorum; red color.
12. ORSEILLE is obtained from the lichen Lichen Rocella tinctoria, found on rocks of the Mediterranean islands; reddish-purple color.
13. QUERCITRON comes chiefly from the inner bark of the black oak, Quercus nigra; brown to yellow colors.

DYES FROM PLANTS, MINOR NATURAL. The name of the dye is followed by the name of the plant it comes from:

1. BENGAL KINO TREE, Butea monosperma.
2. BABUL TREE, Acacia scorpioides.
3. BAEL TREE, Aegle mermelos.
4. INDIAN MADDER, Rubia cordifolia.
5. HENNA PLANT, Lawsonia inermis.
6. MONKEY-FACE TREE, Malotus philippinensis.
7. POMEGRANATE, Punica granatum.
8. RED SANDALWOOD, Pterocarpus santalinus.
9. SYRIAN RUE, Peganum harmala.
10. TAMARIND TREE, Tamarindus indica.

11. TULIP TREE, Thespesia populnea.

DYESTUFF. The name given to materials, solutions, or matters that color textiles. Prior to 1850, most of the dyestuffs used were animal or vegetable matter, but with the scientific progress of today many noteworthy inventions and discoveries have been introduced in the field of textile coloring. Rapid strides in dyeing have been made, chiefly in Germany, France, England, Italy, and this country.

Dyestuffs may be classed according to their origin: animal, vegetable, mineral, synthetic. The chief animal dyestuff is cochineal, which is obtained from a dried insect. This dyestuff or coloring matter is much used to color Oriental rugs in Iran, Turkey, and other centers. Cochineal may be compared with the famous shellac bug, mica.

There are many vegetable coloring matters, such as logwood (used to obtain good black on silks), madder root, quercitron, fustic, sumac, and indigo.

Many dyestuffs today are made chemically from coal-tar preparations, the so-called artificial or synthetic group. Some of the major dyes today include acid, basic, direct or substantive, vat, sulphur, indigo, and mordant.

DYESTUFFS, PROPERTIES OF.

ACETATE DYES: Good to very good in all-round fastness. Selected members have excellent fastness to light.

ACID WOOL DYES: Range from good to very good in fastness to light and washing. Much used where special fastness is not essential.

BASIC DYES: Usually of poor fastness to washing and light. Used where very bright, striking shades are necessary.

DIRECT COTTON DYES: Mostly of good fastness to light and washing, but become paler with hot soaping. Much used in coloring materials where special fastness is not necessary. It is usually possible to select dyes having excellent fastness to washing or to light but not to both.

DIRECT DYES (COTTON) DEVELOPED BY DIAZOTIZING AND COUPLING: The after-treatment greatly improves the fastness to washing but usually lessens the fastness to light.

INDIGOSAL AND SOLEDON DYES: These are merely special forms of vat dyes and they give the same colorings as vat dyes with the same fastness properties.

MORDANT WOOL DYES: Usually very good to excellent in fastness to light and washing.

NAPHTHOL OR INSOLUBLE AZOIC DYES: The same high fastness properties as vat dyes.

SULPHUR DYES: Usually very good

fastness to washing. Fastness to light ranges from moderate to good.

VAT DYES: These are used for producing colorings which have the maximum fastness to light and to washing, as well as most other influences.

DYES USED TO COLOR TEXTILES, TYPES OF. The value of color is known to all. It can "make or break" the appearance of the individual. Examination of the clothes one is wearing reveals that many colors and color combinations are present, in full color, shade, cast, tone, or tint. The application of color to textile materials may be compared with the application of cosmetics to the face of an individual, or the dyeing or tinting of hair on the human head. Dyes today come from two sources, natural and synthetic. At present over 90 per cent of the dyes used commercially are made from synthetic base. Natural sources have been used for many centuries and are still used to some extent by handcrafters such as handweavers, hobbyists in various fields, cottage industries in some of the more remote areas of the world, and tribal groups.

Natural dyes come from plant or animal substances — barks, berries, flowers, insects, kelp or seaweed, lichens, stems, and shellfish. Some vegetable sources are brazilwood, butternut, cudbear, cutch, fustic, indigo, litmus, logwood (excellent on acetate, rayon, and nylon for fast shades), madder, quercitron, saffron, sumac, and turmeric-henna.

The matter of dyeing fabrics is not easy, since the setting of color on materials, by the dyer or printer, presents many complex problems, and what will apply in one case will be totally foreign in another instance. Some dyes, for example, will color only animal fibers and have no effect at all on vegetable fibers, yarns, or fabrics. Some dyes may be able to color many of the major fibers in use today. There are many variables in the dyeing of textiles, and the dyer must be aware of all facets involved in coloring in order to present a dyed or printed material that will be suitable for some particular end use. And his results have to withstand the physical and chemical testing given to his efforts — action of acids and alkalies, crocking, colorfastness to a particular fabric from sunlight, gases in the atmosphere, perspiration, drycleaning, washing, etc.

Affinity of a dye is its readiness to be assimilated by the fiber. The lack of affinity of a dyestuff may be caused by improper chemical combination between the dyestuff and the fiber. A dye can have great affinity for woolen or silk fiber and

none at all for a cotton or nylon fiber. Fugitivity is a term used when dyed materials are not durable, such as in fading from sunlight, bleeding from washing, or fading from perspiration. Fugitivity is the opposite of fastness.

There are today between 7,500 and 8,000 different dyestuffs used in the United States, and generally speaking in all other major countries. Each of these dyestuffs has its own affinity for one or more fibers. To make some order from what would be a rather chaotic listing of so many dyes, they have been classified into groups or classes that have similar fiber affinities. Moreover, most of the dyes within each class have similar fastness characteristics. Each class of dyes may have several hundred different dyestuffs of as many colors, casts, shades, tones, and hues. By properly mixing these dyes in the dyeing operation, the dyer can produce an infinite range of colors and shades.

The matter of dyestuffs and the coloring of textiles are constantly being improved, and the strides made have been phenomenal, particularly since World War I. Much further improvement has come as an aftermath of World War II. The industry is a well-welded one, in which research, experimentation, pilot plant work, time and labor, and constant efforts for better dyes and methods are all definitely apparent.

Much is known about color today, but there is still much to be learned in this day and age of experimentation and research, and the dyeing profession is always alert to future possibilities in color, color blending, and their applications to textiles. The newer manmade fibers really compel the dyeing groups to be keenly aware of "What is new?" or "How can this be dyed better?" Give the dyer the implements to work with and the proper amount of time for research, and he is sure to come up with the answer to any of the myriad problems with which he is confronted.

TYPES OF DYES.

Acid Dyes: These are among the first synthetic dyes to be developed. Primarily for use on wool and other animal fibers, they are water soluble and applied directly with the aid of an acid, such as sulfuric acid. These dyes produce bright colors but do not provide outstanding colorfastness to wet treatment. Rated poor to fair in washing, but good in drycleaning; many of the dyes in this group, however, rate very good in fastness to light.

Acid-Milling Dyes: Like acid dyes, from similar chemical origin, they are much used in stock dyeing of wool and in the top dyeing of worsted tops to be ultimately used in worsted yarn. Milling dyes are good to excellent in fastness to light, good in drycleaning, and better than acid dyes in washing. In addition to their use on animal fibers, both acid and acid-milling dyes will dye nylon, acrylic, modacrylic, and spandex fibers. They can be used to print nylon, chlorinated wool, and silk. The manufacturing considerations and the end use of the fabric determine the type of dye to use — acid or acid-milling.

Acid-Premetalized Dyes: Like the acid and the acid-milling dyes, these are used mostly on wool. They also find use on nylon and acrylic fibers. They usually possess excellent fastness to washing, perspiration, sunlight and drycleaning. Much used in carpeting, upholstery, and suiting fabrics.

Alizarine Dyes: The vegetable dye alizarin was originally obtained from the madder root, but it is now made synthetically. It finds much use on wool and, in some instances, dyes cotton very well. The once popular turkey red on cotton is produced with alizarine dye. Resistance to sunlight and washing are features of these dyes. Used to color apparel of obvious types.

Axoic or Naphthol Dyes: Known also as ice colors, insoluble azos, or ingrain colors, they are really components rather than dyes, and are used in two separate operations — combinations of coupling components and diazo compounds:

a) The fiber is treated with one component, which does not actually dye when used alone.

b) The first component reacts with the second one to form the dye color on the yarn or fabric. This process is called "coupling" and it is much resorted to in printing motifs or designs on fabrics. They find much use in fabric printing, since they afford good to excellent results in laundering and washing. Used on cotton draperies, sportswear, decorative fabrics, tablecloths, dressgoods, and comparable materials.

Basic Dyes: The first of these synthetic dyes, derived from coal tar, was mauve or mauveine, a bright but fugitive violet dye, aniline purple. Its discoverer, Sir William Henry Perkin, synthesized the dye by accident in 1856, in England. He established the first synthetic dyestuff plant in the world. Basic dyes color animal and many of the manmade fibers directly but do require a mordant on vegetable fibers, such as tartar emetic with tannic acid. Brilliant shades result, but lightfastness and washfastness rate from fair to poor.

Basic dyes have an organic base (carbon content in the structure) solubilized with an organic acid (one in which there is no carbon element). Thus they are capable of reaction with anionic substances in a dyebath.

Newer types of basic dyes have been developed specifically for acrylic, modacrylic, and some of the polyester fibers by direct application. Bright shades result which have excellent fastness properties. Acrylic fibers colored with basic dyes are much used in knitwear, woven goods, and in carpeting.

Chrome Dyes: (See Mordant Dyes.)

Developed Dyes: These are "direct dyes" or "disperse dyes," but, because of the presence of a digest amino group in the molecule, they can be developed by after-treating to provide aimproved wetfastness. After the application as a direct dye or a disperse dye, the dyeing is diazotized and then coupled with a suitable compound such as beta naphthol. In lightfastness the rating is poor to good, depending on the particular dye used; washing is rated fairly good to good. These dyes are used on rayon and cotton when derived from a direct dye, and on manmade fibers for use in knit and woven goods when developed from disperse dye bases. (See Direct Dyes.)

Direct Dyes: These find much application on the cellulosic fibers such as cotton and rayon. Sometimes known as "application dyes" or "commercial dyes," the lightfastness rating is from poor to excellent, but because of their solubility they are not rated very highly in washfastness.

Aftertreatments are resorted to to improve lightfastness and washfastness. Ingredients used include copper salts, copperas or bluestone, copper-resin compounds, and comparable substances.

Disperse Dyes: These were developed specifically for cellulose acetate in the 1920's. Chemically, these dyes are mainly azo or anthraquinone types. There are not any solubilizing groups in this set of dyes; the coloring matter is made into a paste or finely milled powder form. They are used on nylon, acrylic, modacrylic, and polyester fibers and are ideal for printing, as well. They are much used to color apparel, hosiery, linings, dressgoods, outerwear of several types, and decorative fabrics. Colorfastness rates from poor to very good for light and washing, depending upon the fiber to which the particular dye has been applied. Some disperse dyes, especially blues and purples, will fade from exposure to imperfections in the atmosphere, commonly referred to as gas fading.

Indanthrene: A type of vat dye which produces highly resistant colors; trademark of GAF Corporation, New York City.

Ingrain Colors: (See Azoic or Naphthol Dyes.)

Mineral Colors: These, in reality, are not true dyes but are precipitated oxides or insoluble salts of chromium, iron, lead, or manganese. They are applied in a soluble form and the precipitates are formed in the dye bath by double decomposition or by oxidation. These colors are dull in appearance and are used much in color effects in awnings.

Mordant Dyes: A mordant is a substance used in dyeing to apply or fix coloring matter to a fiber, yarn or fabric, specially a metallic compound such as an oxide which combines with the fiber and organic dye and forms an insoluble color compound or lake in the fiber.

Also known as "mordant-acid dyes," or "chrome dyes," they are related closely to acid dyes. The chrome required is usually derived from sodium bichromate at some stage in the dyeing procedure. Results from the use of these dyes are rather dull when compared with those obtained from acid dyes but they are among the fastest colors used to dye wool.

Mordant-acid dyes are used to color wool, wool carpeting, nylon, silk. Silks and woolens may be printed by these dyes on the cylinder or roller method and worsted top by the Vigoureux Printing Method.

Neutral Dyeing—Premetalized Acid Dyes: Related to acid dyes except that they are produced on the basis of two molecules of dye bound to one of metal, usually chromium. The metal content improves the fastness so that they approach the fastness of mordant dyes. These dyes are usually azo compounds suitable for the coloring of woolen-union fabrics with cellulosic content in them. While good shades result from this type of dyeing, they are not as bright as regular acid dyeing colors.

They will dye all forms of wool and

other protein fibers, nylon, acrylic, and modacrylic fibers. They are ideal for blends provided dye-bath additives are used. These dyes are much used in coloring apparel fabrics. They rate fair to excellent to light, good to excellent to washing, and excellent in drycleaning.

Oxidation Bases: One of these bases is aniline dye, which is formed in the fiber by oxidation. For example, the base known as "aniline black" has been used for well over one hundred years, one of the fastest blacks known to man. Oxidation bases are ideal for dyeing fur, sheepskins, and pile fabrics, as well as for coloring cotton for a wide range of uses. Much printed fabric uses these bases in coloring.

Pigment Colors: These are based on organic coloring matter — azo compounds, metal chelates, etc. None in the group has any affinity for any fiber. They are insoluble in water and have to be fixed onto the fiber by the use of resinous binders insolubilized by a curing treatment at high temperatures. Pigment colors give very bright shades. Acetate, cotton, rayon, and other manmade fibers can be pigment-colored or -printed. These colors have a very wide range of uses — awnings, decorative fabrics, dressgoods, outerwear, shirtings, and light and medium shades of sailcloth. Rated good to excellent in lightfastness but apt to be poor in crocking or rubbing.

Pigment printing has many advantages over other methods of coloring. Practically all types of fibers and blends can be printed; there are fewer "seconds," chiefly because it is an easy matter to observe the printing results, and if flaws are found they may be remedied at once. Compatibility of colors is assured if the pigments are of the same type and have been used in the processing, thereby increasing the range of colors available.

Fixing of the color is done by a simple process of curing. Much lighter engravings, as in photo engravings, can be used with moderate pressure in the machine, affording a saving in paste consumption. No aftertreatments, other than washing or soaping, are necessary — thus a saving in steam, time, and work.

Reactive Dyes: These made their debut in 1957 and the chemical combination with the fiber sets these dyes apart from all other colorants. Reactives actually bond the color into the fiber. They give very bright shades on cottons, and can dye acrylics, nylon, silk, wool, and blends of these fibers in cross-dyeing and union-dyeing. They are much used on print-goods, and also on stock, yarn, and piecegoods, and widely used on cottons; the light and washing tests are rated from good to very good. They are fugitive to chlorine-base bleaching agents.

Sulfur Dyes: Coming into the market in 1879, they were originally made from sulfur, sodium sulfide, and sawdust. They are now made from indophenols, indamines, and other intermediates. They are insoluble in water but are solubilized with sodium sulfide and soda ash. They do not provide bright shades and their fastness properties are developed in the chemical inertness and insolubility in water. Soluble forms of sulfur dyes have been developed within recent years.

They are used to color heavy cottons, and knitwear in full and medium shades, and can be applied to stock, yarn, and piecegoods work. They also find use in printing when chrome-plated rollers are used on the printing machine. Sulfur dyes are not as fast when compared with vat dyes but the costs are lower. They are weak in sunlight except for deep shades where the fastness is rated as good. Sulfur dyes tend to be fugitive to chlorine such as that found to exist in hypchlorite bleaches.

Vat and Vat-Soluble Dyes: Natural dyeing with indigo has been known for centuries with its distinctive shades of blue. Synthetic indigo dyes came into the market in 1879. The anthraquinone groups were introduced in 1901, the water-soluble leuco esters in 1921. These dyes have been modified, but, chemically speaking, all give about the same end results as to effects and properties. Vat dyes are the fastest dyes known to man. Insoluble in water, they can be made soluble by chemical reduction. Applied to textiles, they can be returned in an insoluble form by oxidation, thereby firmly fixing the color within the fibers, a bonding-in of the colorant. They are the most resistant of any type of colorant to light, drycleaning, sunlight, washing, etc.

It should be borne in mind that vat dyeing, as such, does not exist. The dyeing is done by the conventional methods — yarn, piece, direct printing, etc. These dyes are used on cotton, and to some degree on wool. They are popular colors in work-clothes, outerwear, sportswear, decorative fabrics of many types, awnings, towelings, bed linens, etc. Light shades can also be obtained from soluble vat dyes.

NOTE: The following notations should be kept in mind on certain dyes.

Acid Dyes: Level dyeing is achieved with the use of the proper amount of sulfuric acid.

Acid-Milling Dyes: Usually applied with a weakly acidic bath.

"Strong" Acid Dyeing: Done with a 1:1 premetalized dye.

Neutral Dyeing: Done with a 2:1 premetalized acid dye which contains two dye molecules chelated with one metal ion.

Azoic Dyes: Three points should be observed:

1. The use of an azoic component.
2. The use of an azoic coupling component.
3. The use of azoic compositions.

Courtesy of Mr. Ludwig Fusser, General Aniline & Film Corporation, 140 West 51st Street, New York City.

DYE-VARIANT FIBERS. Also known as Differential Dyeing Fibers, natural or manmade fibers are sometimes treated or modified in their structure so that their affinity for colorants becomes changed in providing a lighter or darker shade, held in reserve, etc. Results depend on the particular dyes and method of application.

DYEWOOD, DYEWOOD EXTRACT. Any vegetable dye obtained by extraction from certain plants or trees, such as fustic, logwood, madder, quercitron.

DYKE. Any wall or similar enclosure in which sheep are contained; peculiar to the sheep-raising industry in Scotland.

DYLAN. Product of Stevensons (Dyers) Ltd., it denotes fabrics made of wool or blends of wool and other major fibers which have been processed by prescriptions laid down by the company. Fabrics treated with Dylan will not felt, mat, or shrink when laundered or washed by conventional methods, even in a washing machine. Natural and dyeing properties, as well as hand, are not impaired by its use.

DYNACURL. A furlike fabric that resembles Persian lamb developed by the Dynel Division of Union Carbide Corporation and the Multiplex Products Corporation, West New York, N.J. The curled chenille (caterpillar) yarn is spun with dynel modacrylic fiber. The embroidered effect is done on Schiffli frames or looms with a cotton backing fabric for support and base. Schiffli, incidentally, is comparable with hand embroidery and is used ordinarily for the ornamentation of blouses, curtains, dresses, handkerchiefs, slips, and in the manufacture of military insignia, etc. See SCHIFFLI.

DYNAMITED SILK. See SILK WEIGHTING.

DYNA-WOOL. Registered trademark of Union Carbide Corporation for its washable wool-like fabric used in low-twist blended yarns, 65 per cent wool and 35 per cent dynel. After weaving the fabric is heat-treated for stabilization against shrinkage.

DYNEL. A modacrylic staple fiber spun from a copolymer of acrylonitrile and vinyl chloride. The name distinguishes it from the older Vinyon yarns developed by the Textile Fibers Division, Union Carbide Chemicals Company, Division of Union Carbide Corporation. Fiber features include strength, warmth, and quick-drying properties, good dimensional stability, and resistance to alkalies and acids. It will not support combustion, is completely moth- and mildew-proof, can be dyed with acid- or acetate-type colors, or direct, cationic, premetalized, and some vat dyes. Dynel burns only in contact with open flame; it does not melt or drip. It is easily processed on the woolen, worsted, cotton, and silk systems in spinning. The filament sizes are 2, 3, 6, 12, and 24 denier; staple lengths are 1⅜, 1½, 2, 2½, 3½, and 4 inches. Dynel is a trade-mark term. See Illustrated Section.

DYNEL 63. Registered trade-mark of Union Carbide Corporation for its dynel with high bulking power for blending with cotton for fabrics used in winter underwear and children's sleeping wear.

DYNEL 77. Registered trade-mark of Union Carbide Corporation for a soil-resistant and resilient type of dynel used in floor-covering.

DYNEL, SOME TYPES OF.

Type 150: An uncrimped tow used to make doll's hair; crimped tow finds use in flocking fabrics.

Type 180: Standard staple and tow, bright and dull in shade.

Type 183: Standard staple and tow and having high shrinkage.

Type 197: An all-purpose filament used in carpets and rugs. Compared with the above types, it has higher elongation, better abrasion resistance, is tougher and stronger, and has lower tenacity.

DYNEL TYPE 297. This fiber, composed of 60% vinyl chloride and 40% acrylonitrile, is inherently and permanently flameproof and self-extinguishing. A registered trademark of Union Carbide Corporation, New York City, the fiber is spun with the colorant set in the solution as the fiber is being made. In acids and alkalies, even at high temperatures, there is little effect on the fiber, and in organic acids it is soluble in warm acetone and some other ketones. There is no effect from chlorine bleach, salt water, or mildew. Elongation is up to 77 percent and fiber length can be made as per instructions from the customer; moisture absorbency is 0.2% while specific gravity is 1.3. Spots and stains are easily removed by wiping with water; some will require the use of a detergent or some other common household cleaning agent. Toughness index is 0.5.

Knitting, tufting, and weaving present no problems for this fiber. Spun yarns can be handled in the same way as those made of acrylic or wool. The Type is quick drying, has excellent texture retention, good abrasion resistance, and excellent resiliency. It is used in floor-coverings of several types - durable shags, frieze, level-loop contract, plush, shear, random shear, etc. TYPE 297 is attractive, durable, gives high performance, is tough, and has excellent weatherability properties; its appearance retention is very fine, colorfastness is an outstanding characteristic, and there is excellent resistance to fire and soil.

DYNES PER CENTIMETER. A metric expression for the measurement of small forces used the same way as foot-pounds, etc.

E

EARTH FLAX. Another name for asbestos.

EASER MOTION. Used on looms which make doup or leno fabric, this motion device eases the strain of the crossing yarns at the point of intersection with the ground threads. Causes good synchronization between the standard and the skeleton harnesses and warp ends.

EASERS. Movable rods or bars used in doup or leno weaving to slacken the necessary warp threads when the doup comes into play.

EASTERN PULLED WOOL. Pulled wools obtained from the slaughter-houses of the East.

EASTERN WOOL. See DOMESTIC WOOL.

EAST IMPROVED GEORGIA COTTON. A late-maturing Georgia cotton which has a staple of 1⅛ to 1¼ inches; similar to Allen Cotton.

EAST INDIAN COTTON. This is cotton grown in the East Indies and the smaller Eastern countries. It is shipped to the English, Chinese, Japanese, and Australian markets. This cotton is inferior in all respects to American cotton, and is used for cheaper materials. The land is prepared before the monsoons; planting is done after they have passed. Much English capital is invested in these plantations.

EASTMAN "50" ACETATE FIBER. A hollow-filament yarn produced in Chromspun and Estron by Eastman Chemical Products, Inc., a subsidiary of Eastman Kodak Company. Compared with conventional forms of acetate yarns, Eastman "50" has the following advantages:

1. Better coverage with 5 per cent to 10 per cent greater bulk.
2. A crisper, firmer hand along with a fuller, smoother feel.
3. Equal or better fabric tear strength and abrasion resistance.
4. A higher, more uniform luster with more intense fabric highlights.
5. From 3 per cent to 5 per cent greater insulation properties.
6. Longer retention of fabric characteristics.

Uses include fabrics such as crepe, taffeta, crystal-filled taffeta, satin, lining, lastex fabrics for swimwear and foundation garments, tricot knitwear, and drapery fabrics.

EASTMAN 75. Registered trademark of Eastman Chemical Products, Inc., for its lofted acetate yarn.

EASTMAN ESTRON FR. Registered trademark for several fabrics made of Eastman Estron acetate yarn in which a flame resistant factor has been perfected as an integral part of the fiber or filament. This Estron FR acetate, produced in 75 and 150 denier filament yarn, is used as drapery material. In addition, sheer casement cloths and novelty weave constructions made in 100 percent FR acetate, as well as antique satins with Fr Warp and Verel modacrylic filling, come in the category of the company's FR fabrics. All these cloths are non-abrasive, dimensionally stable, flame and mildew resistant, and non-allergenic. They also dissipate static electricity and resist soiling and wrinkling. They possess excellent affinity for dyes and resist fading or deterioration by sunlight. The flame-resistant fabrics last through laundering and dry-cleaning. All have passed the National Fire Protective Association Code 701.

"EASY LIVING." The first stretch fabric group composed of "Dacron," cotton, and Lycra spandex fiber. Made in batiste, broadcloth, poplin, and in a "super-water-repellent variation." these fabrics have greater stretch power, better recovery, and a wider end-use than types of stretch fabrics produced to date. Uses range from lingerie to outercoats and jackets for skiing, and sportsclothes used in the office, at home, and for shopping. Product of Klopman Mills, Inc., a division of Burlington Industries, Inc.

ECAILLE. 1. Dobby designs feature this French silk dress goods made with fine denier, two-ply silk warp, and single ply filling. 2. A type of Brussels lace used for the ground with the pattern on the order of fish scales. 3. Spangles or sequins in a fish scale motif used to ornament certain fabrics.

ECCENTRIC YARN. Spiral yarn in Great Britain.

ECHANTILLON. French (échantillon) for a clipping, sample, swatch.

ECHETS. From the French (échevettes). Worsted hanks or skeins of yarn.

ECHEVETTES. Small silk skeins (échevettes) having a definite length, weighed to determine the actual count of the silk—the yarn number is found in the relation between the length and the weight of the skein.

ECHIZEN. The best quality of Japanese silk material.

ECOSSAIS. French word for Scotch; refers to tartan fabrics made from the major natural textile fibers, alone or in blends with the man-made fibers in union fabrics. Comparable printed materials are also known by this name.

ECOSSAISE RIBBON. A ribbon, usually silk, with a Scotch plaid motif.

ECOSSE OR TRICOT. A warp rib fabric made with about 20s warp and 40s filling. Two colors are used in the filling in alternating effect, thereby giving a two-tone effect crosswise in the material. In warp rib weaves the cord or rib goes in the filling direction.

ECOUAILLE. From the French (écouailles) for coarse wool.

ECRASE. The French term (écrasé) for crushed, as applied to leathers and textiles that may have a crushed or embossed effect; also implies puckered or blistered effects.

ECRU. A light yellowish-brown tint often applied to curtains either by precipitation of brown manganese dioxide in the fiber from weak solutions of permanganate or by actually tinting with an aniline dye.

ECRU SILK. Silk in which only the most soluble part of the natural silk gum has been removed along with the coloring pigment found in the filament.

Ecru means natural or unbleached in the textile trade. Some inexpensive odds-and-ends silk cloth is known as ecru silk.

EDGE, LENO. Formation of a set of threads that interlace in gauze weave in the body of the goods to curb any raveling when the fabric is cut in the warp direction. Usually the set of threads is duplicated and the fabric is then severed between these sets of threads.

EDGE, SEALED. The cut or raw edge of a cloth which has been treated by heat or chemical means to prevent fraying or raveling. Example would be the edges on a flag made of acetate yarn. Several repeats of a flag pattern could be printed in a wide width and then cut to size by chemical treatment whereby close examination would reveal that the edges did not have an actual selvage but did have a fine "seared edge."

EDGE BASTER. In ready-to-wear clothing manufacture, a workman who finishes the work begun by the straighteners, underbasters and edge operators, by turning in the outer part and facing (of a coat) and basting the edges preparatory to final felling and stitching.

EDGE-CRIMPING. In the texturizing process it is the heating and drawing of the filament yarn over the edge of a sharp blade, thereby creating the curl. Usually associated with AGILON of Deering Milliken Company, Inc. See Curl.

EDGE FINISH. A term applied to toweling, bought by the yard or with edges finished with hemstitching, scallops, or plain hems; the latter finish gives the best service.

EDGE OPERATOR. In ready-to-wear clothing manufacture, a workman who does only the first seaming of coat edges.

EDGES. Finishing on coats, waistcoats, and other apparel. Some edges used are: blind, bluff, braided, bound, corded, double-stitched.

EDGING. Narrow lace, embroidery work, ribbon, braiding, and so on, used as trimming on dresses, undergarments, layettes, carriage sets, etc.

EDGING, ENGLISH OR ANGLE-TERRE. A braid or cord of needlepoint edging made with one line of loops.

EFFECT YARN. Any out-of-the-ordinary yarn which is used for producing novelty effects in materials. Examples are nubs, slub effects, loops, knots, bug effects, thick-and-thin effects, fancy-colored effects.

EFFILE. Fabrics or swatches with the edges intact, not unraveled.

EGGSHELL FINISH. A dull finish created by running fabric through roll-

ers engraved with minute depressions and elevations which break up light reflections.

EGIPTO COTTON. A Peruvian cotton developed from Uplands seed; staple is about 1⅛ inches and it is used in low counts of yarn.

EGYPTIAN CLOTH. Plain-weave cotton or linen fabric featured by good texture, well-twisted yarn, and high tensile strength. This old-time staple is a carry-over from Egyptian mummy cloth and is now made in natural, white, and colored shades.

EGYPTIAN COATINGS. Piece-dyed cotton repp fabrics made in varying qualities, motifs, and widths. Textured at about 128 x 56. Stripes feature some of the goods which are exported by Great Britain to Africa and India.

EGYPTIAN COSTUME. See Costume, Egyptian.

EGYPTIAN COTTON. See Cotton, Egyptian.

EGYPTIAN FLAX. A long, coarse flax fiber noted for its reddish cast.

E.I. Appreviation used in the leather industry to imply East India or East Indian. E.I. refers to a vegetable tanned hide or kip which originated in "the Indian sub-continent" and was tanned in India. This type of hide is also called Persian. See Kip, Kipskin.

EIDERDOWN. Name derived from the soft down of the eider duck. 1. A lightweight warm fabric, napped either on one side or both. Is either knitted or woven. Used for infants' wear, negligees, etc. 2. Also a term for a down quilt. Must not be called "Eiderdown" unless made of down from the eider duck.

EIDERDOWN, TRUE. Down obtained only from the breast of the eider-duck. The term should not be used generally to describe quiltings.

EIDER YARN. Name for a softly spun, loosely twisted, cylindrical woolen knitting yarn.

EISENHOWER JACKET. Named for the late President Dwight D. Eisenhower, this jacket is an outgrowth of World War II. A very popular item of attire, it now has many variations. The original blouse jacket was 24 to 25½ inches long with a self-fabric collar, or with a knit collar, cuff, button front, separate waistband, and notched self-collar. Variations include the Hip-length, Western, or Hipster which is 27-28 inches long with a button or zipper front. Necklines vary and both self-fabric and knit collars are used.

The Parka or Whaler, ranging in length from 27 inches to 38 inches, is belted and comes with deep side vents which may snap or be zippered closed, and with different versions of hoods.

The Pullover, Poncho, or Ponderosa is like a pullover sweater and has a closed front, neck opening or placket, buttons, or zippers. It may have a hood, self-or-knit collar.

The Surcoat of 30 to 32 inch length may have a self-collar or come as a three-piece knit with the "johnny" or shawl collar. This type also is known as the Clicker and has an attached, hidden, or zippered closure, and a button-off hood.

The Button-Front Cardigan, also classed as a Leisure Coat, is comparable with the Surcoat, for this button-front model may carry sport coat details. It comes with a self-collar, knit collar, or none at all. The 32 inch type is known as the Ranch or Western Coat. It has pointed yokes, waist suppression, and bellows pleats, etc.

EIS YARN. Woolen knitting yarn, fine in diameter and given a luster treatment for glossiness. Of German origin.

ELASTIC. A rubber band, cord, fabric or thread which has springiness, flexibility, and resiliency. There are several types of elastic used in the textile trade today: lastex, cut-rubber yarn, extruded latex, filatex, rolled latex, and laton. These elastic yarns are used in belts, garters, girdles, gloves, shoes, sportswear, suspenders, etc.

ELASTIC DUCK. A very firm, starched finish used on sheeting; it is dyed black and used for coat lining.

ELASTIC FINISH SHEETING. An open-texture sheeting that is given firm starching and a flexible finish. Used for interlining, the cloth has the property of returning to original shape when pulled out or distorted.

ELASTIC FLANNEL. Knit fabric made with soft-spun woolen yarns so that it can be given a rather dense nap on the surface.

ELASTIC GORE. Elastic tape made with rubber threads and used for the sides of shoes.

ELASTICITY. The property of a filament or yarn to elongate upon application of tension, and to recover part or all of the original length upon the release of tension. Wool yarns have a natural elasticity because of the crimp in the fibers themselves. Thus, the fabric can adapt itself to body movement with ease.

ELASTICITY MODULUS. The ratio of stress in the strain within the bounds of the material's elastic limit.

ELASTICIZED. Fabrics which have elastic threads running through them, or which have been treated to provide elastic qualities.

ELASTIC LIMIT. That point where the elasticity of a material ends and ductility or permanent elongation sets in.

ELASTIC NARROW FABRIC. One that is made to provide stretch in the warp direction or in the warp and filling directions. Fabric of this type should come back to normal when released from stretch or tension. Crepe fabric is not included in this category.

ELASTIC RECOVERY. The percentage of extension recovered at once by a textile fiber upon removal of the tensile force.

ELASTIC WEBBING. Narrow fabric made with rubber or elastic threads, as noted in belts, garters, suspenders. Lastex for suiting fabric is a development from elastic webbing. It is possible to make elasticity in either direction depending on the weave used in the cloth construction.

ELASTIC YARN. A yarn possessing a high degree of elasticity. Usually consisting of a core of rubber covered with cotton, rayon, or other material. Used in garters, corsets, foundation fabric.

ELASTIC YARNS, TYPES OF. There are three types at present - bare, core-spun, and covered. Information follows:

Bare (lastrile, spandex) - Has no cover at all, no adding of cover necessary, thus keeping down costs. Manufactured by fiber chemical spinning. Bare type may be quite sheer, can be used in thin, lightweight fabrics and garments; suppleness, comfort and good hand apparent. Used for swimwear, foundation garments, sox and stocking tops, many types of apparel.

Core-Spun (spandex) - Spandex core surrounded by sheath of roving, drafted staple, etc. Core-spun, extrusion, stretch. Ply given on twister frame. Spandex is stretched about 4 times original length and a roving or a yarn is used as the sheath. Has same appearance as non-stretch fabrics. Popular in woven and knitted cloths and garments from sheers to rather heavy goods.

Covered Type (lastrile, rubber, spandex) - Surrounded or wrapped spirally with filament or spun yarn. Spandex or rubber is plied with cotton, nylon, et al., for finished singles yarn. Sheath is set on yarn in twister for ply in the opposite direction. Has greater absorbency than bare type yarns; extensibility can be controlled. Foundation fabrics, swimwear, many types of apparel, popular in sportswear.

ELASTIQUE. A 63-degree, right-hand twill weave is used to make this narrow-and-wide wale, diagonal-line fabric. Made of woolen or worsted yarn, the material tailors very well and gives excellent service. It is one of the better-quality fabrics. Fiber content must be declared in elastique. Has the same uses as CAVALRY TWILL and TRICOTINE.

ELASTOMER. A synthetic rubber product which has the physical properties of natural rubber such as high stretchability and recovery. According to the American Society for Testing Materials, an elastomer should be capable of being stretched repeatedly to at least three times its origianl length and on release of the stress return with force to its approximate original length. An elastomer is not to be confused with a stretch yarn which obtains its elasticity from some modification of a filament yarn structure.

There are three types of elastomers as per the A.S.T.M., and these follow:

TYPE	POPULAR NAME:	CHEMICAL COMPOSITION:	ASTM SYMBOL	ASTM CLASS
R	Natural rubber	Isoprene	NR	
R	SBR	Styrene/Butadiene	SBR	
R	Polyisoprene	Isoprene		
R	Polybutadiene	Butadiene		
	Butyl	Isoprene/Isobutylene	IIR	
S	Neoprene	Chlorophene	CR	
S	Nitrile	Acrylonitrile/Butadiene	NBR	SC
S	Hypalon®	Chlorosulphonated/Polyethylene		SB
S	Polyurethane	Di-isocyanate Polyester		SC
S	Thiokol®	Organic Polysulphide		SB
				SA
T	Silicone	Polysiloxane		TA
T	Polyacrylate	Ethyl Acrylate/Acrylonitrile		TB
T	Fluorocarbon	Vinylidene Fluoride/Hexa-fluoropropylene		TB

ELASTOMERIC. Used to describe the elasticity of a fiber that is a direct result of its molecular construction. Examples include natural fibers, synthetic rubber, Spandex.

ELASTOMERIC FIBERS. Based on polyurethane, the generic term for them is Spandex. They are highly elastic and find much use in stretch yarns. Coming in mono- or multifilaments they are processed as bare fibers or can be wrapped around other basic yarns such as cotton, nylon, Perlon, etc. They are light and porous and have two to three times as much retaining power as rubber, as well as being more resistant to light, cosmetics, and perspiration. Some leading fibers in this category include "Lycra" of du Pont, Vyrene of UniRoyal, Inc., Glospan of Globe Elastic Company, Inc.; and the well-known European fiber, I-Filament made in West Germany.

ELASTOMERIC YARNS. A continuous filament or spun yarn which, by virtue of the chemical structure of the fiber, is characterized by a high break elongation, a low modulus of extension, and a high degree and rate of recovery from a given elongation. (Definition includes rubber fiber.)

(Note: Definition from Section 1, of Sub-Committee B-8 of the American Society for Testing and Materials, March, 1963.)

ELASTON. A modified cellulosic staple fiber made by Svenska Rayon Ab., Sweden. Used in padding and quilting, the fiber has high permanent-type crimp, is water repellent and washable with normal detergents at a temperature of 100° to 125° Fahrenheit.

ELECTORAL CLOTH. Fine, reversible woolen goods made with a one-up and two-down filling twill weave on the face; the back of the goods shows fine ribs.

ELECTORAL WOOL. A very fine wool originating in Spain, now known by the name Saxony wool as well. This wool served as the basis for the high-quality fabrics made in woolen and worsted textile plants in Saxony, Germany. Saxony wool is the best merino stock raised in Germany.

ELECTRA CLOTH. A type of gloria goods used for umbrellas. The warp is cotton, while the present-day version uses silk or practically any of the more rugged man-made fibers for filling.

ELECTRICAL PROPERTIES. Refers to the ability to conduct electricity or to hold an electrical charge. For example, a wire can conduct electricity but a piece of hard rubber will hold a static charge. Cotton, a vegetable fiber,

cannot be used to generate a static; wool or silk, animal fibers, can generate a static charge.

Dielectric implies a substance or medium which does not conduct an electric current, as a glass or vacuum.

The dielectric strength of a fibrous material is of doubtful significance since it is dependent primarily on the air contained in the structure rather than on the fiber composition. There is little or no relationship between the dielectric strength of plastic films and those of plastic in the form of loosely woven fibers. There is evidence that surface phenomena occurring at the air-fiber interface may initiate breakdown at voltages lower than the breakdown strengths of the air. This effect, at present, is not too well understood. Source: Bell Telephone Laboratories, New York City.

ELECTRIC TAPE. High-grade Egyptian cotton is used in this quality cotton tape used in Great Britain to wind around wire for insulation purposes. Texture is around 108 x 92.

ELECTRODE. A conducting body through which the electric current enters or leaves a solution. Glass or hydrogen electrodes are used in electrometric pH determination.

ELECTROFYING. An operation used in finishing to impart high luster to high-pile knitted fabrics.

ELECTROLYSIS. A decomposition promoted by the passage of electric current.

ELECTROLYTE. A substance which, in solution, will conduct electric current.

ELECTRON. A minute, negatively electrified particle charged with the smallest known quantity of electricity and having a mass approximately 1/1550 of that of a hydrogen atom, the atom of negative electricity.

ELEPHANT TOWELING. British expression for coarse, strong cotton and linen toweling used for drawn work, embroidery, and toweling. This rough-textured material is made in huckaback effects.

EL HAMMAN. A medium-type Morocco wool.

ELIZABETHAN COSTUME. See Costume, Elizabethan.

ELK. Strictly a trade term for cattlehide shoe leather of special tanning and finish. Genuine elk is designated by the term buckskin. Smoked elk, or elk-side leather, is known in the leather trade as cattlehide shoe leather.

ELL. An old-time cloth measure of 1¼ yards, a 45-inch length.

ELLSWORTH COTTON. A late-maturing North Carolina cotton of 1-inch staple; lint yield is about 33 per cent.

ELONGATED TWILL. Implies a steep twill where the angle of the weave is more than 45 degrees, or a reclining twill where the angle of the weave is less than 45 degrees.

ELONGATION. It is the deformation in the direction of load caused by a tensile force. It is measured in units of length (inches) or in terms of percentage of the original specimen length.

ELONGATION, ULTIMATE. See BREAKING ELONGATION.

ELURA. A modacrylic fiber for wigs and hairpieces introduced in 1970 by Monsanto, Textiles Division, St. Louis, Missouri. It can be styled and managed much like human hair since it combines many of the aesthetic and performance features of human hair with the advantages of manmade fibers. Its cross-section approaches the oval cross-section of human hair and is distinctly different from that of other modacrylic wig fibers.

Elura can be permanently curled at the factory to provide highly desired convenience in wigs for wash and wear use, yet restyled easily by brushing and combing, or reset like human hair to obtain more elaborate coiffures. The superior temperature resistance of Elura offers protection from damage caused by accidental exposure to elevated temperatures, such as a blast of hot air from a kitchen stove.

Elura modacrylic is also self-extinguishing. The fiber is supplied in producer-colored form in about 18 shades of outstanding uniformity from lot to lot. Two or more shades are frequently blended for a more natural appearance and wigs and hairpieces made with such blends can reproduce almost any natural hair color.

ELVALAN. Formerly known as Elvadex, this product of Du Pont is used as an off-loom finish for dope-dyed acetate yarn and as a sizing for man-made fibers in filaments forms.

"ELVAX" VINYL RESIN. A water repellent which does not leave any odorous or oily residue; used on tents and covers. The liquid application to the protective material is absorbed completely without filling or altering the fabric. "Elvax" contributes many of the properties of a plastic without eliminating "breathability." Its natural adhesive power reduces the effect of flexing from repeated packing and unpacking. It remains flexible even in cold temperatures, and mildew is reduced by the lower water absorption of the treated yarn fibers. "Elvax" is also used to protect paper and paperboard from ice, water, grease, and scuffing. Product of E. I.

duPont de Nemours & Company, Inc., Wilmington, Delaware.

ELYSIAN. A fine grade of overcoating cloth, having the nap laid in diagonal lines or ripples, something like, but rougher than, chinchilla, and with straighter hair.

EMBAUBA FIBER. A very strong, tough bast fiber found in Brazil; used in bagging.

EMBIRA FIBER. Name given to several local bast fibers raised in Brazil.

EMBO PRINTING. Embo is really embossed and implies that fabric can be printed and embossed at the same time. The embossing roller peaks are touched with color and on contact cause the color to affix itself in the valleys of the embossed areas.

EMBOSSED CREPE. A granite or pebbled surface cloth, usually cotton print cloth, subjected to embossed calendering to give a more pronounced effect. This cloth is not launderable.

EMBOSSED FINISH. Effect produced on cloth by passing it between a series of rollers, each set having one smooth and one embossed roller. These metal rollers are heated in order to give better results. The embossed rollers have been engraved with suitable patterns, which will be reproduced on the cloth and give the appearance of a raised or embossed surface to the material. Designs may be birds, foliage, scrollwork, figures, pastoral scenes, and so on.

Embossing is applied often to thin materials, and can be used effectively on velvets and other pile cloths to bring about the desired effects. The impressions seen on some embossed cloth more or less resemble genuine Jacquard woven effects.

EMBOSSED LEATHERS. These are finished by stamping designs on the hides or skins with etched, engraved, or electrotyped plates or rollers. The effect is used on fancy pocketbook leather, upholstery, and bag leather and splits, and occasionally on shoe-upper leather. The motifs may be a simulation of the natural or conventionalized grain of skins of various animals, as well as of a purely artificial nature.

EMBOSSING. The art of producing raised or projected figures or designs in relief on surfaces. Usually produced on fabrics by engraved, heated rollers to give a raised effect. Washing, steaming, water spotting, or dampness tend to remove the design. Embossing velvet is done by pressing part of the pile flat.

EMBOSSING CALENDER SET. A calender set of two, three, or four rollers, one of which is engraved, used to emboss fabric to produce a figured or waved effect on cloth.

EMBOSSING WITH MALE AND FEMALE ROLLER. The male roller, made of steel, is so engraved that the protruding design or pattern can be pressed through a fabric into a hard paper-bottom female roller, thereby creating an indenture in the material.

EMBROIDER. To ornament textile materials by needlework which embellishes the design and appearance of the article.

EMBROIDERING FEEDER ATTACHMENT. An attachment to a power-driven sewing machine, used to embroider some fabrics with colored thread; consists of a rubber-tipped, inverted cup, in place of the regular presser foot, that, while moving back and forth automatically, can be moved from side to side by a hand screw.

EMBROIDERY. From the Anglo-Saxon word meaning edge or border. It was first used to refer to borders on church vestments. In time, the meaning implied the ornamental designs on fabric. Embroidery was done by hand until the first machine was invented by Joseph Heilman, an Alsatian, in 1828. In 1840, Rittmeyer and Volger invented an improved machine, and this is the type used today, of course with modern improvements applied.

Embroidery by machine began in the United States around the time of the War between the States. Embroidery is seen on certain silks, rayons, chiffon-type fabrics, trimmings, robes, vestments, towels, table runners, badges, curtains, flags, etc. It is always seen on fabrics or garments used for state and church ceremonials.

EMBROIDERY, EYELET. Eyelet work which is oblong, round, or square, finished by covering the edge with close overcasting or buttonhole stitches.

EMBROIDERY CLOTH. English cambric used for embroidery foundation.

EMBROIDERY COTTON. A cotton thread of varying ply, rather slack-twisted and used for decorative needlework. Some of the thread is known by the initials or name of the manufacturer, as D.M.C. or Clark's O.N.T. of Coats & Clark, Inc. (Our New Thread).

EMBROIDERY FLOSS. An untwisted or very loosely twisted thread, usually of silk, used in embroidery.

EMBROIDERY LINEN. Firmly made linen used as foundation fabric for embroidery work. See ART LINEN.

EMBROIDERY LOCK STITCH. It is used to tie in the end before or after a thread is jumped to another figure. This jump is then cut away and the lock stitch becomes a holding stitch which prevents the embroidery from raveling.

EMBROIDERY MACHINE. A power-sewing machine designed to feed and sew in any direction, as desired by the operator. The direction of sewing is controlled by means of a hand-operated crank that rotates the needle and feed mechanism.

EMBROIDERY REPEAT. Refers to the distance between the needles on a Schiffli embroidery machine. Measurement is in a French inch which is 1-1/16th inches in length. Machines today use the spacing of one French inch which is called 4/4 or four quarters. On larger patterns there is a need of spacing two needles and this is known as 8/4 or eight quarters. Other spacing is known as 12/4, 16/4, etc. depending of the size of the motif. See French Inch.

EMBROIDERY SHUTTLE LATCH. The device on an embroidery machine which controls the bobbin case in the frame.

EMBROIDERY SILK. A group of single, untwisted, or very loosely twisted silk yarns of the same size or of varying ply which are twisted slightly for use in embroidery work.

EMERIZE. A finishing operation which "sands off" excess and protruding fibers on fabrics so as to present a material which has a smooth, even nap and sheen. Emerizing is applied to high-grade worsteds, some dresswear woolens, and felt hats.

EMERIZED FABRIC. Fabric treated by a fine emery-covered roller to produce a chamois or suède effect on the surface. Some worsted fabrics, such as serge and cassimere, may be emerized to produce the characteristic effect.

EMERY. A special stone used for sharpening and polishing. It is commonly used to sharpen knives, scissors, needles, etc.

EMERY CLOTH. Cotton or linen cloth coated with fine, powdered emery and used for polishing.

EMPEROR. A 1-up and 7-down twill weave is used in this filling face-effect lining cloth made of fine cotton warp and alpaca or luster worsted filling.

EMPRESS CLOTH. Hard-twisted cotton warp and worsted filling cloth, of the rep family. Popular in the middle of the last century and brought out by the revered Empress Eugenie. The cloth was all the rage during her era. A 2-up and 1-down twill is used on the face construction. A rib weave is used for the back structure.

EMPRESS GAUZE. A fine, flower-figured fabric made in linen, rayon, or silk.

EMPTY HEDDLE. One in which a warp end is missing; caused by a broken end that has not been detected, or pieced, and then has not been drawn through the proper heddle eye.

EMULSIFIER. An agent whose function is to stabilize the suspension of water-insoluble particles in water.

EMULSION. A stable suspension of chemically inert material in a solution. Emulsions are produced by physical forces of colloidal origin.

ENAMEL. A glassy substance, usually opaque, applied by fusion to the surface of metal, pottery, etc. for ornamentation or protection. The term is applied at times to some cottons which are given a rather hard, smooth finish as noted in polished cottons. See Cottons, Polished.

ENAMELED CLOTH. Imitation leather material used in luggage, trimming for carriages, overnight bags, table covers, millinery trimming, etc. There are many qualities of this glazed-finish material based on the sheeting, drill, or other gray goods which may be used.

ENAMELED LEATHER. See PATENT LEATHER, UPHOLSTERY LEATHER.

ENAMELING DUCK. Plain-woven fabric with a laid warp and ply-yarn filling. Weight is based on a width of 46.5 inches.

ENANT. A Type 7 nylon produced in the Soviet Union, and supposed to be different from any other nylon type made elsewhere.

EN CARREAU. A square design in a fabric, may be large or small. French for "checked."

ENCRON. Registered trademark for a polyester fiber made by American Enka Corporation, Enka, North Carolina. It is made from a polymer from dimethyl terephthlate and etylene glycol. After polymerization, the polymer is extruded through a spinnerette and then chopped into chips or processed as a continuous yarn filament. Subsequent steps include stretching to provide the desired yarn properties. Production from chips is similar to that in manufacture of Enka Nylon.

Melts at 485° F., and has the following positive qualities - excellent resistance to aging, mildew, moths, micro-organisms; good resistance to most mineral acids. It is readily dissolved by concentrated solutions of sulfuric acid and disintegrates in strong alkalis.

Uses include many types of apparel for men, women, and children, including knit fabrics. Industrial usage includes cordage, dye bags, conveyor belting, filters, fire hose, laundry bags, tire cord, seat belts.

END. A warp yarn or thread that runs lengthwise or vertically in cloth. Ends interlace at right angles with filling yarn to make woven fabric.

END-AND-END. 1. A warp made from two warps by taking the ends from each warp beam in alternating order when the dressing of the warp is done. In this plan the warp threads are of the same count or size. 2. The use of two warps to make a fabric with each warp beam having a different size of yarn on it such as a fine count and a heavier count, and often of different fiber content and color, and possibly ply.

END-AND-END LEASE. The cross in which alternate successive yarns are raised and lowered.

END-AND-END SHIRTING. Broadcloth, chambray, and madras shirting with the warp layout arranged as follows: one end of color followed by one end of white in alternate order. The term also covers fabric laid out with two colors alternating. A fine pincheck effect results from the plan.

END-AND-END WARP. A warp made from two warps by taking the ends of each warp in alternating order when the warp dressing is done.

END DOOR WASHER. A laundry washwheel with eccentrically mounted inner cylinder which provides visibility of the goods and the dip throughout the process and continuous rinsing.

END-FENT. Finished fabric at either end of the cut of cloth that is not usable for the same purpose as the body of the goods. It does not necessarily imply an imperfect piece of fabric.

ENDING. Uneven dyed fabric in which the ends of the cut do not match the color in the body of the goods.

ENDOCHROME. The coloring matter within vegetable cells.

END-POINT. The final point of titration. See TITRATION.

ENDROIT. French for the face of a fabric.

ENDS DOWN. Warp ends which have broken in weaving, thereby impeding production.

ENDS OUT. Warp threads that have broken or snapped during weaving. They cause a light place in the cloth which is readily noted. Blemishes caused by broken ends are fixed either by the weaver or by the sewers in the dry-finishing department of the mill.

ENDS, STRIPPED. When one of the plies in a ply-yarn snaps or breaks, thereby causing a mat, bunch, or loop of yarn.

END-TO-END FABRIC. Broadcloth, chambray, madras, and kindred fabrics made with a warp arrangement in which the warp yarns alternate in color; a blue and white arrangement, for example, will give a fine, pinhead-check effect.

ENERGY. Defined as the ability to do work, it is better known by the things it does than by what it really is. It is called at times the force that causes motion. Potential energy is that which is hidden or stored up for some future use, such as that which is present in an electrical wire before contact is made between it and a power machine, thereby starting the machine.

Kinetic energy is that which is expended in doing work. Examples include the electricity which runs a machine; the operator operating the machine and the cutter cutting a garment are also expending kinetic energy. It can be stated, as an example, that potential energy is stored energy while kinetic energy is the energy of motion. A spring compressed shows potential energy, and when it is allowed to spring out kinetic energy results.

Mechanical energy is that expended by the machine as it operates. An example is the operation of a sewing machine, which enables one to do useful work evenly, accurately, and speedily.

ENGINEERS' CLOTH. Broad term for denims, dungarees, heavy drills, and overalls.

ENGLISH, BRADFORD SYSTEM. Method of worsted spinning in which the twist is put in continuously and the resultant yarn is wiry, harsh at times, beardy, lustrous, and rugged; the yarn does not always compare too well with worsted yarn made on the French or Franco-Belgian system of spinning.

ENGLISH, BRITISH WOOLS. Term applied to wools from Great Britain and the types represented by these.

ENGLISH ANTIQUE. A machine-made lace constructed by independent beams or bobbin-fining systems. The net has square motifs known as guipure d'art.

ENGLISH FOOT HOSE. A type of stocking with seams at the sides to join the sole to the instep. There is no seam on the bottom of the sole.

ENGLISH POINT. Like Angleterre lace. The French for England is Angleterre.

ENGLISH SYSTEM COUNT. A yarn count used in England. The count equals the number of hanks or leas per pound. One lea represents a 300-yard length.

ENGLISH YARNS. Those worsted yarns spun in oil on the Bradford or English system.

ENGRAVING MACHINE. 1. A device similar to a pantograph for engraving design or lettering in enlargement, reduction, or natural size on metal printing plates, by means of a diamond cutting point that is guided by a series of arms attached to a dummy point which is traced over the design or lettering cut into the master plate.

2. A machine used to transfer a design from a small cylindrical "mill" to a large copper roller for printing fabric. It consists of an iron frame supporting the roller rotating on a shaft, a hinged, weighted beam to hold the "mill" against the roller, with adjustable counterweight for varying pressures, and other regulative attachments.

ENKA 5,000. An improved type of Tyrex, the trade name for high tenacity rayon used in the manufacture of automobile tires. This product of American Enka Corporation has improvements in strength and fatigue resistance so essential in tires.

ENKALURE. Registered trademark of American Enka Corporation, Enka, North Carolina, for its multi-lobal, texture-set nylon yarn which is soft and silky, has luster and sheen. In knit goods where it finds much use, there is no clinging, stretch or "ride-up." Ideal in wash-and-wear fabrics in which wrinkles disappear quickly. The yarn is also used in manufacture of upholstery fabrics. The yarn has excellent affinity for dyestuff and comes in a great range of colors.

ENKA NYLON. Formerly called Nylenka, it is a nylon 6 manufactured by American Enka Corporation.

ENKA RAYON. Trade-mark of American Enka Corporation for its types of rayon—Briglo (bright), Englo (dull), and Perlglo (semidull), untrademarked names.

ENKASA. A Dutch casein product.

ENKASHEER. Registered trademark of American Enka Corporation, Enka, North Carolina, for nylon yarn used in women's hosiery. It is the first producer-textured torque nylon for stretch stockings and panty hose. Shipped as Enka Nylon, it becomes Enkasheer only after it has been made into stretch hosiery which has been tested and approved by Enka and licensed officially to carry the advertised Enka-sheer trademark on the package. See Torque Versus Non-Torque Yarns; Torque Yarns.

ENKROME. Trademark of American Enka Corporation for its rayon staple

which is ideal for taking dyestuffs. Much used in piece dyed fabrics, tone-on-tone, multi-color effects, and in cross-dyeing and union-dyeing of fabrics.

ENSEMBLE. A costume which consists of blouse, skirt, dress, and coat, harmoniously designed for the occasion. All the parts are collectively referred to as an ensemble.

ENSIGN CLOTH. Plain-woven cotton or linen cloth used for bunting and flags.

ENTER. To actually enter yarn or fabric into a dye liquor.

ENTERING PLAN. The same as drawing-in draft of warp ends according to some plan or order.

ENTOILAGE. The mesh ground in lace material.

ENTREBANDES. French for end-pieces or headings of woven cloth.

ENTRE RIOS. A crossbred wool raised in Entre Rios, Argentina. This wool rates 50s to 60s in quality and has a harsh handle, but possesses springiness, which makes it ideal for use in knitting yarns.

ENTWINING TWILLS. Ordinary even-sided twill weaves used in varying combinations of right- and left-hand twill construction to form diamond effects.

ENVELOPES. French term for canvas used as packing and containers.

ENVERS. French for the back of a fabric.

ENZYME. A catalytic substance secreted by living organisms which bring about chemical changes; such as digesting starch to cause a change into a water-soluble compound; converting sugar into alcohol. Enzymes are used in desizing. In washing and laundering, enzyme agents cause stains to be brought to a more soluble form so that they may be more easily removed in the ordinary washing process. Many stains are removed after soaking for about one-half hour; some of the more difficult ones to remove may need soaking overnight. Enzyme products come in dry, heavy duty detergents as well as in separate presoaking forms. See Detergent Action, Polyunsaturated.

EOLIENE, EOLIENNE, AEOLIAN. Dress fabric of silk warp and cotton, rayon, acetate, or worsted filling. Light in weight, it has a glossy finish, is dyed in the piece, and the weave formed shows a cross-rib effect. Texture is about 120 x 60.

EPAULET. Originally meant to hold the shoulder belt and to protect the shoulder which supports a musket, it now signifies a shoulder trimming seen

on uniforms of the military. Braiding extends downward from the padding, which rests on the shoulder of the wearer, adding to the dress uniform. Gold padding and braid are the most popular in this sort of decoration for uniforms.

EPIDERMIS. The outside surface layer of the skin in vertebrates, which consists of several layers of cells.

EPIGONATION. A lozenge-shaped ornament of stiffened silk bearing a cross or picture, worn hanging from the girdle.

EPIMINIKIA. Bands resembling the Latin maniple worn by bishops, priests and deacons.

EPINGLE. Women's suiting and dress-goods material that weighs from 7 to 10 ounces per yard. Plain weave used. Cloth is piece dyed and given clear finish. It is popular at times and is a true cycle cloth, ruled by the demands of fashion and style.

EPINGLE CREPON. Made with silk warp and two fillings—one of silk, the other of worsted. Made on a Jacquard loom, the ground is rep or poplin in effect (fine, cylindrical lines) while the motif is made by the silk warp and silk filling.

EP, EPI. A prefix that is observed in "loan words" from the Greek language. The word implies - after, at, before, near, on, over, upon. This prefix is used to form new compound words such as, in the English language, epidermis, epitome, and epoxy in which the "oxy" implies oxygen. See Epoxy, Epoxy Resin; Rayon Yarn, Carbonized.

EPINGLE FACONNE. This French faconné made with silk warp and silk or worsted filling is characterized by fine, cylindrical lines in the filling direction because of the well-rounded, uniform yarn used.

EPINGLINE. A warp-rib dress goods made of silk warp and worsted filling. The cloth has a pebbled effect and feel similar to crepe.

EPISCOPAL GLOVES. Silk gloves embroidered with a gold symbol on the back and worn at the Offertory in a Pontifical Mass in the Roman Catholic Church. They are symbolic of the power to implore God's blessing. Buskins, gloves, and sandals are in the five liturgical colors of the church.

EPISCOPAL SANDALS. Embroidered silk slippers worn by bishops and cardinals over the buskins at Pontifical Mass in the Roman Catholic Church. They are symbolic of divine protection in preaching the gospel of peace.

EPITRACHELION. A vestment corresponding to the stole of the Roman rite, this article is worn by the priests of the Byzantine rite at liturgical functions. It differs only in that the strips of cloth are fastened together from the loop at the neck to the ends and it reaches almost to the feet.

EPIZOÖTIC. A term designating a disease of widespread proportions among animals; comparable with an epidemic among mankind. Applied to silkworms that come down with various diseases.

ÉPONGE. From the French (éponge) for "spongy." Is a woolen dress-goods cloth that is very soft and spongelike. Texture is low, about 20 x 20. A plain warp and novelty yarn filling is used, or the reverse can be used to advantage. Cloth is bleached and dyed.

Rayon éponge is soft, loose, and spongy, somewhat simulating terry cloth. Novelty weaves are used in the fabric, which is used for coats, sportswear, and summer suits.

ÉPONGE, TADPOLE. An éponge cloth in which a small number of ends are used to form the ground while a looped thread is then used to produce the novelty effect; this arrangement runs for the width of the material. Other plans may be used in order to give more or less of an allover effect to the material whose surface is supposed to remind one of a tadpole. See ÉPONGE.

EPOXY. Means the containment of an oxygen atom bound to two atoms already connected, usually atoms of carbon, thereby forming a ring as in the case of ethylene oxide or epoxy ethane. Formula is H^2C (O) CH^2...n times. See Ep, Epi; Epoxy Resin.

EPOXY RESIN. Any of a group of substances derived by the polymerization from certain epoxy chemicals. Resins of this kind find much use in adhesive coatings of many types, textiles included. See Ep, Epi; Epoxy.

EQUIVALENT. Equal in one or more respects.

EQUIVALENT COUNTS. The single equivalent of a ply yarn. Thus, in a 2/36s yarn, the single equivalent would be 18s. Divide the count by the ply for the single equivalent. This term includes, as well, the number of a yarn in its own system expressed in the equivalent of some other system. For example, if it is desired to find out the count of a 40s cotton in the worsted system, the equation would be as follows:

$$\frac{40 \times 840 \text{ (cotton standard)}}{560 \text{ (worsted standard)}} = 60$$

Thus, a 40s cotton is equivalent to a 60s worsted yarn.

ERDMANN REED. A special type of reed used in weaving ondulé or waved designs. The wires are specially shaped and the reeds are raised and lowered in the loom while weaving.

ERECT PILE. This is made possible in pile fabrics by careful equalization in the height and finish to make the pile effect stand upright. Uniformity in color and appearance when the light's rays strike the material is assured if the pile construction is carefully done. As a general thing, the denser the pile, the better is the quality of the velvet.

ERILDUN. A fine, soft, elastic, resilient, and pure white merino wool raised in Tasmania. It is used only in the very best of woolen and worsted fabrics, usually for the custom trade.

ERIFON. An inorganic chemical, a solution of antimony and titanium salts, which makes cotton and rayon flame-resistant, durable to weather and laundering, and which does not change the handle or feel of the treated materials. Draping qualities, appearance, and strength are not impaired. The chemical "locks into the molecular structure of the fibers, changing them chemically but causing no change in physical properties." It adds only about 15 per cent to the fabric weight and will not irritate the skin.

A flame held to treated material will char the fabric, but the flame will not spread, and this resistance will not normally wear out or wash out during the life of the article. Because of the complications in application, Erifon is used only in textile finishing plants at present. Another product of E. I. du Pont de Nemours & Co., Inc.

ERMINE. Russian ermine, a small white animal with medium-long, straight-haired, heavy fur with long guard hair. Wearing qualities, fair. Judged by hair density and silkiness. Found in Alaska, Europe, Asia, and North America. Worn formally. Manchurian ermine comes from Manchuria and Siberia, and ranges in color from bluish-yellow to red-orange.

ERUC. Philippine fiber used for cordage.

ESCALATOR CLAUSE. The provision in a labor agreement for making upward or downward wage adjustments, or both, whenever a living standard fluctuates.

ESCALIER. 1. Ladder tape. 2. Ladder-effect lace. 3. French for staircase, and for the various types of ladder lace.

ESCAPE PERIOD. The period of time during which employees are permitted to discontinue their union membership, without loss of employment under maintenance of membership labor agreements.

ESCOBILLO FIBER. Obtained from plant of this name in Mexico, this strong, fine bast fiber, which resembles ramie, is used in making fabric.

ESCURIAL. 1. A type of Spanish sheep. 2. A heavy silk lace similar to rosepoint lace, in which the motifs are outlined with a cable edge.

ESKIMO CLOTH. A popular overcoating and mackinac fabric, usually made on a five-shaft satin weave for the face construction while a twill weave is used for the backing. About three quarters of the warp shows on the face. The cloth is made in single colors or may be brightened by the use of wide, vivid stripes which run in the filling direction in the finished garment. A long, substantial nap is seen on the goods.

ESPARTO. A fine, clear, transparent leaf fiber obtained from *Stipa tenacissima*, esparto grass or alfa, which grows in the Mediterranean region. Used for cords, carpeting, basketing and sandals.

ESTAMENE. 1. A rough-faced French woolen serge. 2. A low-texture worsted fabric made of rather rough or coarse yarn with a 2-up and 2-down twill weave. This British fabric has a napped, fibrous surface effect.

ESTANCIA. Comparable with the Australian sheep station, this small South American sheep farm is quite different from the "colonia or plantation."

ESTER. The product formed from the reaction of an acid and an alcohol involving the loss of water. For example, ethyl acetate, derived from ethyl alcohol and acetic acid.

ESTRELLA. Plain-woven British dress fabric with crepe effect. Silk warp and fine worsted filling used to make the cloth, which is picked 2 S-twist and 2 Z-twist.

ESTREMADURA. A six-ply or six-cord knitting yarn.

ESTRICH, ESTRIDGE. Fine, soft, downy hair which underlies the feathers of an ostrich.

ESTRON. Trademark for the acetate yarn of one or more esters of cellulose with or without lesser amounts of nonfiber forming materials. Eastman Chemical Products, Inc., New York City is the producer. In addition to the many uses of Estron in the apparel and decorative fields, it is used industrially for electrical insulation. The most recent developments are sunlight resistant (SLR) dull Estron and flame resistant (FR) Estron.

ESTRON, TYPES OF. This acetate fiber of Eastman Chemical Products, Inc., New York City, has the following types:

1. TYPE 10-The "Y" cross-section yarn.

2. TYPE 50-The closed "C" cross-section yarn with high loftiness, bulk, and coverage.

3. TYPE 77-Actually an improved Type 50 ideal for piece dyeing fabrics.

4. TYPE 99-The thick-and-thin type yarns of this acetate.

5. ESTRON SLR-The sunlight resistant type of yarn.

ESTRON ARILOFT. A registered trademark of Eastman Chemical Products, Inc., New York City, this filament yarn has a Y-shaped cross-section and gives a textured effect to circular and warp-knitted fabrics. It is highly receptive to dyes, provides a very full, dry hand, better than that noted in comparable fabrics made with regulation acetate. Ideal for use in women's wear fabrics.

ETAMINE. A coarse, lightweight cotton fabric that is loosely woven. It comes in white, cream, ecru, and similar shades, with or without small printed effects of floral nature. Generally used for curtaining, skirting, blouses, and waists. It is used also for overdraping to add nattiness to apparel. Within the last few years, the cloth has been made with other major fibers, alone or in combinations. Good twist is a vital asset in this material.

ETAMINE GLACE. Challis made of rayon or silk warp and worsted filling; comes plain or in attractive prints.

ETCHED-OUT FABRIC. Also known as BURNT-OUT FABRIC.

ETCHING. Engraving rollers by means of some powerful fluid which forms a coating into which a diamond-pointed needle is manipulated by the designer or operator, to cut a motif. Aqua regia, nitric, sulphuric, or hydrochloric acid is used to aid in the work.

The gougings in the roller hold the dyestuff, whose tenacity is aided by mixing gums or paste with it. As the material passes over the printing roller the dyestuff is printed onto it; as many as sixteen colors may be printed onto the fabric. Each color used must have its own color roller. The rollers may be etched with from twenty to about two hundred fine lines per inch; this etching work is very intricate and delicate. Accuracy is very important since overlapping of design must be avoided. Copper rollers give the best results.

ETCHING SILK. Twisted harder than sewing silk, it is used for outlining embroidered effects.

ETHER, ETHYL ETHER. A highly volatile, flammable liquid with a pleasant aromatic odor, used as solvent and as an inhalant anesthetic. Chemically, it is one of a class of compounds in which two organic groups are attached directly to an oxygen atom, having the general formula ROR, as ethyl ether. Highly explosive, when used in spot and stain removal great care should be used so as not to inhale the odor. Incidentally, benzene is often known as petroleum ether but its chemical structure is different.

ETHYL. The hypothetical radical of the carbon series (C_2H_5), the base for common alcohol, ether, acetic acid, and a rather large number of compounds—hydride, chloride, iodide, alcohol.

ETHYL CELLULOSE. Produced by the Dow Chemical Company, it is known by the trade name of Ethoraon. The properties impart qualities of good flexibility, toughness, and low moisture absorbency.

ETHYLENE. The diatomic hydrocarbon of olefine of the ethyl series (C_2H_4).

ETOFFE. French (étoffe) for textile material, cloth, fabric, goods, stuff.

ETOFFE DU PAYS. Means "country stuff." A coarse, gray, homespun cloth made on hand looms and used in peasant localities all over the world.

ETOILE. 1. A star design made by filling in the meshes of the net foundation. 2. A lustrous satin fabric used for dress goods.

ETON COLLAR. A folded shirt collar, usually of white linen of medium-height stand, but with a broad turn-over of nearly uniform width all around, folded at an angle; worn by boys.

ETON JACKET. A short jacket without collar or lapels, reaching only to the waistline; first worn by the boys of Eton College.

ETUN. Biblical term for linen.

EUGENIE HAT, EMPRESS. See Second Empire, 1853-1870, under Costume, History of.

EVAPORATE. To change from a liquid to a gaseous state by means of heat. For example, the evaporation of turpentine, pine oil, etc., from certain detergents on the market.

EVEN BASTING. A stitch that is used for basting seams. The stitch is the same length on both sides of the material.

EVENER DRAWING FRAME. A frame made up of several units; each section is driven separately, has its own evener motion and delivery device.

EVENER MOTION. Found on the picker machine, its purpose is to govern the speed of the feed role in accordance with the weight of the fiber stock so that it will be even and uniform when delivered to the beater.

EVENER ROLLER. See PIN CYLINDER.

EVENNESS. Evenness of the raw stock is essential in making cloth. If the raw stock varies to any marked degree, uneven yarn will result, producing poor cloth which may have to be classed as a "second," if allowed to go that far in manipulation. Streaks should not appear in cloth because of unevenness, but they are found in some cottons, some taffeta, messaline, etc.

EVEN RUNNING. Staple, uniform cotton fibers.

EVEN-SIDED TWILL. Fabric made on a twill weave which shows the same amount of warp and filling on the face of the goods, as many sinkers as there are raisers in the design. Example could be a $\frac{3}{1}\frac{1}{3}$, right or left twill. Also known as Balanced Twill.

EVERFAST. Registered trademark of Everfast Fabrics, Inc., New York City, which covers a wide range of cotton, linen, and rayon fabrics which are definitely fast in color.

EVERGLAZE. Registered trademark of Joseph Bancroft & Sons Company, Inc., a division of Indian Head, Inc., New York City, for a family of quality products. It is a guarantee to the consumer that the individual fabric is of fine quality, with durable, washable luster, controlled porosity; that it is spot, soil, and wrinkle resistant and shrinkage-controlled with 2 percent. The rigid production controls by the company insure maintenance of these quality standards by authorized users of the trademark.

EVERLASTING. A machine-made narrow cotton trimming of the French banded type; excellent wearing qualities.

"EVER-LOK." A revolutionary advance in sewing-machine stitch formation whereby this stitch is made by single thread without bobbin changing. The stitch has been incorporated into The Singer Sewing Machine Company machine, the Singer 270 Class button sewers. Unlike buttons sewn with conventional chain-stitching, "sew-through" buttons attached by this new method cannot come loose or fall off, and raveling is impossible when this stitch is used for sewing purposes.

EVLAN. Modified viscose rayon fiber for use in floorcovering purposes, particularly in carpeting. Originated in 1962, this is the most important man-made fiber in Great Britain. Properties include high extensibility and tenacity, durability, high crimp level, and good resistance to crushing. *Evlan M* is an improved version of regulation Evlan. Both fibers appear in floorcoverings from Axminsters to Wiltons to lighter weight tufted carpetings. Some of the fiber finds use in upholstery and apparel fabrics. Product of Courtaulds, Ltd., Great Britain.

EVLUX. Manufactured and marketed by Courtaulds, Ltd., London, England, it is a "deep-dye rayon" and a high crimp, heavy denier type textile fiber.

EWE. A female sheep, pronounced "you."

EXAMINER. In the mill and apparel trades, one who closely inspects and examines material for flaws, blemishes, and errors. The mill examiner is responsible for cloth which is well-nigh perfect; the apparel examiner often causes changes to be made in garments to increase their value.

EXCLUSIVE BARGAINING AGENCY. That union status agreed to by a company, or granted by the National Labor Relations Board, or similar federal or state board, in which the union is the sole bargaining agent for all employes in the bargaining unit, whether or not they are union members.

EXECUTION. Embroidery term which means the number of stitches per French inch in the blatt stitch or steils. See French Inch, Steils.

EXFOLIATION. The refined term for "lousiness" in silk cocoon filaments which have the tendency to split into their elemental fibrils during processing.

EXHAUSTING AGENT. A chemical agent that forces more and more dyestuff into action on yarn or cloth, so that the fullest value may be received from the dye in the bath.

EXHAUSTION. The ratio at any stated stage between the amount of dye or other substances taken up by the material being dyed and the amount originally available.

EXMOOR HORN SHEEP. A hardy English breed of sheep which give a thick fleece of medium-length staple stock; shrinkage is about 35 per cent.

EXOGEN. A plant which grows by additions made on the outside of the trunk.

EXOTHERMIC REACTION. Chemical reactions accompanied by liberation of heat, in contradistinction to endothermic which means heat-absorbing.

EXPANDER. A device on some machines used to keep cloth spread to its fullest width, devoid of wrinkles.

EXPANDRA. Registered trademark name for the stretch denim fabric made by Erwin Mills, a division of Burlington Industries, Inc., New York City. Known for its excellent reflex action the fabric is composed of 75 percent cotton and 25 percent texture nylon. The cloth is also Sanforized. Finds use in many types of sportswear items.

EXPANSION COMB. A type of comb which may be contracted or expanded, as the case may be, to take care of warp ends as they are being warped or slashed. This action, therefore, is of the regulating type.

EXPRESS STRIPES. This fabric is made with a 2-up and 1-down, left-hand twill on the face, and there are usually 12 ends in the pattern. The cloth has equal stripes of white and dark blue in the effect. Very rugged cloth that provides good wear, it is used for coveralls, overalls, jackets, etc.

EX-QUAY COTTON. Cotton in the ship at the dock, or quay, the French word for dock.

EXTENSIBILITY. The degree to which a fabric may be stretched. It refers to high or easy stretchability as against low- or nonstretchable textiles.

EXTENSION. The longitudinal strain or pull in a tensile strength test of yarn or fabric, expressed in terms of the original length of the specimen.

EXTENSION PER CENT. The actual elongation noted in a tensile strength test of yarn or fabric expressed in terms of the original length of the specimen.

EXTON. The trade-mark of man-made bristles used by the Dr. West Co. The bristles are derived from nylon and, by a treatment of Exton, they are made wet-proof, have springiness, and last much longer than ordinary bristles.

EXTRACTED FABRIC. Cloth made with cotton and wool or worsted yarn in warp and filling. The vegetable fiber is later extracted from the goods by chemical means, leaving an all-wool or all-worsted material that is sheer and, at times, rather porous. Acids such as sulphuric, nitric, hydrochloric, or aqua regia, at proper strengths are used for the carbonizing or extracting of the cotton content.

EXTRACTION. Removal of water from washed or rinsed fabrics or goods by draining or gravity dripping, wringing by pressure, squeezing or twisting, or by spinning controlled by centrifugal force.

EXTRACTOR. 1. A machine used to take out burrs, hulls, etc., from cotton so that it will be easier to gin. 2. A device used to extract water from fabrics, knit goods or other materials by whirling them within a rotating, perforated drum at high speed: a centrifuge.

EXTRACT PRINTING. On goods that have been previously dyed, certain portions of the original color are removed by chemicals. Another name for Discharge Printing.

EXTRACT WOOL. Wool waste that is secured by carbonizing. Vegetable and other foreign matter is removed from the stock. The carbonized wool is processed in the same manner as shoddy and mungo, and forms small, varying percentages in wool mixes. Acids are used to carbonize the vegetable matter.

EXTRA THREAD WEAVES. These are found on several types of cloth to embellish the goods with small figures or spots—lappet, swivel, clipspot, warp-float, dotted swiss, sprigged dimity, etc. The term also implies backing threads noted on some few cloths —Frenchback, backed serge, etc.

EXTRA WARP, EXTRA FILLING. The former is the ordinary two warp, one filling fabric which is made with one shuttle; commonly called Frenchback or backed fabric. The latter is a regulation one warp, two filling construction, and at least two shuttles are used to make the goods. May also be called Frenchback or backed fabric. No stitching or binding yarns are used in these constructions, as noted in double-cloth fabrics.

EXTRA WHITE COTTON. A sort of "super" white cotton when compared with cottons of the so-called white group. The lessened amount of chroma or yellowness gives the fiber a very clear white shade.

EXTRUDED LATEX. Latex is the milky juice found in certain leaves, the inner bark of branches, and in the trunk of rubber-yielding trees. The latex is forced through an orifice and coagulated in the same manner as viscose rayon to give what is known as extruded latex.

EYE. The opening or eyelet in the middle of the heddle. Sometimes called a mail.

EYELET. A small hole or perforation made in series to receive a string or tape. It is worked around with a buttonhole stitch.

EYELET EMBROIDERY. Cotton fabric punctured with eyelets or other machine-embroidered motifs. Done on broadcloth, piqué, dimity, organdy, etc.

EYELET PLATE. A crossbar attached to the end of a creel immediately in front of each row of spindles. This plate is perforated with the same number of holes as there are spindles in the row, and serves to guide the individual ends from the packages on the spindles to the warping frame.

EYELET STITCH. A jersey or rib stitch made by collective or selective transfer of needle loops to adjacent pairs of needles to produce a well-defined open-work effect.

F

FABRIC. 1. A woven, knitted, plaited, braided, or felt material such as cloth, lace, hosiery, etc. Includes materials used in the manufacture. 2. Something that has been constructed, built, fabricated, or put together. 3. The use of raw materials, construction, color, and finish to produce an article of textiles. 4. Cut lengths of fabric are shipped selvage to selvage, and face to face to afford protection in handling and transit. 5. Fabric is also known as cloth, material, goods, or stuff. Garments are made from fabrics. There are three general classes of fabrics—apparel, decorative, and industrial. See Illustrated Section (Fabrics).

FABRIC, SETT OF. British term to designate the number of warp ends and filling picks (woof and weft) per inch in a fabric.

FABRIC, WEIGHT OF. Three methods are used today to figure the weight of cloth:

1. OUNCES PER YARD: Woolens, worsteds, specialty fiber fabrics, and similar "heavy fabrics" in which man-made fibers have been blended with wool or worsted are figured by this method. Thus, an 8-ounce worsted tropical, a 14-ounce tweed, a 22-ounce coating fabric.

2. YARDS PER POUND: This method is used considerably in finding the weight of most cotton fabrics, and those made of man-made fibers. Some very lightweight materials may not weigh as much as one ounce per yard. Hence, the value of this method in figuring the weight of very light, sheer materials. Thus, a symbol such as Broadcloth—3.85 means that there are 3.85 yards to the pound of this particular material. Some of the cloths figured on this plan include wide print cloths, tobacco cloths, carded piques, poplins, broadcloths, three-leaf twills, four-leaf twills, jean cloths, sheetings, sateens, osnaburgs, drills, pebble cloths, etc.

3. OUNCES PER SQUARE YARD: This comparatively new method was introduced in France following World War II. It spread to the British Isles, other nations in Europe, then to Canada, and is now meeting with favor in the United States. Many man-made fabrics are figured this way.

Most large mills that make a wide variety of fabrics use a demarcation weight between ounces per yard and yards per pound methods. Weight demarcation limits may be 4, 6, or 8 ounces, as a general rule.

FABRIC COMPOSITION. The determination of the types, kinds, and amounts of the various fibers which may be present in a textile material This may be done by chemical means or by the use of a microscope. A few of the composition tests are:

1. The amount of vegetable fiber in an animal-fiber material—cotton in a woolen or worsted; rayon in a silk or woolen; the fibers used in a blended, mixed, sandwich blended, or composition fabric.

2. The percentage content of in-individual fibers in mixed goods.

3. Distinction and determination among fibers used in some fabrics—viscose, cuprammonium, acetate, nylon, etc. Staple stocks of these fibers are much used in varying percentages in woolens, worsteds, cottons, etc.

4. The amount of actual hair used in a woolen or worsted fabric.

5. The amount of weighting in a silk fabric.

FABRIC CONSTRUCTION. 1. The number of warp ends and filling picks per inch in woven goods; sometimes referred to as pick count or count. 2. In the larger sense the term implies the weave, pick count, yarn counts, weight per yard, type of gray goods, type of finish width, and gray-goods width.

FABRIC COUNT. The number of warp ends and filling picks per inch in woven fabrics; also called texture, thread count, pick count.

FABRIC FLAMMABILITY. The degree of combustibility of a fabric. Combustible cloth continues to burn at average or rapid rate after ignition. A slow-burning fabric, also known as one of low combustibility, is one which will burn or glow at a slow rate. Fire-retardant or fire-resistant fabric is one which, after the removal of the source of ignition, continues to burn or glow only in the area where the direct ignition was applied. Incombustible or noncombustible fabric is one that will not ignite or give off vapors that will ignite when ignition is applied.

FABRIC PORES. Extremely small capillary openings in the fiber that contract and expand with temperature changes, and become clogged with dirt. Absorbency depends upon open capillaries or pores.

FABRIC RESILIENCY. The ease with which a fabric returns to normal from deformation, in which the rate of recovery is limitless and thereby includes elasticity, which may be referred to as instant recovery. The fabric hand may be high or springy, or low or limp. Resilience may be compressional, extensional, flexural, or torsional.

FABRIC SHIFT TESTER. An instrument used to measure the resistance in a fabric to the shifting of yarns. The specimen to be tested is mounted under specific tension in a set of clamps and is then stroked by a set of rubber friction jaws. The pressure on the jaws is adjustable. The degree of distortion which occurs in the yarns of the material determines the serviceability of the fabric.

FABRIC SHRINKING GAUGE. Quality control device of the United States Testing Company, Hoboken, N. J., which consists of a template marking for the fabric prior to the test while mounted upon the pins in the machine. There is an expanding framework which expands the test fabric to its previous machine setting. A calibrated steel gauge records the shrinkage in percentage figures.

FABRIC SOFTENER. Any material or materials used to impart a soft, full hand, handle, or feel to textile fabrics. In the home laundering process, the softener is used in the final rinse to obtain a soft, appealing effect, to reduce possible static that may be present because of the fibers used in the goods, and to eliminate wrinkles. There are many household fabric softeners on the market and the housewife should always read well the directions for use.

FABRIC TAILORABILITY. The ability of a fabric to be made into a tailored garment pertinent to style. See Tailored Garment.

FABRIGRAPH. Any type of screen or stencil that is set rigid or taut on the frame used for screen or stencil printing, whether done by hand or mechanically.

FABROGRAPHY. The art and science used in processing all phases of screen or stencil printing.

FABRICS, STANDARD TYPES OF.

The following composite information is for ready reference on eight basic types of textile fabrics:

TYPE	HOW RECOGNIZED	WORKING PROPERTIES
WOVEN	Yarns interlace at right angles; warp is vertical; filling is horizontal.	Used the most; strongest cloth for inner and outerwear; drapes well; is durable unless woven loosely; is made in all fibers, dyed, printed or bleached; may be a woven design.
KNITTED	One system of yarn interlooping: a loop within a loop.	Is manufactured quickly; may sag with wear; is elastic; form-fitting; may be porous; comes in wide fabric range for innerwear and outerwear.
FELT	Made from a mass of fibers that are interlocked by heat, moisture, pressure, pounding; with stiff felt, shellac is used. Yarn is not used in felt.	Contains no system of yarn; has varying tensile strength; retains a given shape, is substantial in weight; may be rough, smooth or soft to feel; has no selvage; seldom seen in stripes; holes cannot be mended; least lustrous of the standard materials.
PLAITED, BRAIDED, AND/OR LACE	Yarns may go in any direction, one system of yarn being interlaced to obtain the effect desired.	Open work in pattern is not always durable; not easy to launder; designs are geometrically or symmetrically balanced; serviceable when given good care, as with net and lace; not suited for general use.
NONWOVEN	Web or sheet of textile-type fibers bonded together by application of narrow stripes or patterns of adhesive material or by bonding fibers through chemical activation of the surface or by heat if thermoplastic fibers are used. Yarn is not used in this fabric.	Oriented in one direction or laid and set in random manner; functional property of bulkiness; may be paperlike, felt-like, or of a woven type. Porosity comes in wide range; hard to soft texture. Will not ravel or fray, may be sewn, glued, or heat-bonded. Wide range of uses.
STRETCH	Great stretch in one or both ways; stretch yarns not easily identifiable in goods; resilient, smooth or bulky with surface appeal and good texture effects; appealing hand or feel; light, medium, or heavy in weight.	Good "muscle power"; hidden stretch dimensions; form-fitting to give ease and comfort to wearer; excellent recovery on release from tension. Filling stretch better suited to body movements than warp stretch. Very flexible. Usually made with spandex or rubber as the core yarn, which is surrounded by a sheath of cotton, worsted, nylon, etc. yarn; provides very interesting effects.
LAMINATED	Foam sheet attached to one or two fabrics; if two materials used, they are usually of different types. Usually soft, spongy hand and effect.	Provides warmth with little added weight or added bulkiness. Garments have good flexibility and are aided by laminating for better fit.
MOLDED	Molded area has greater area than its original plane from which it was drawn; this is revealed on examination of the article. Product may be fluffy, pilelike effect or a flat material.	Better fit and greater ease in movement of the body; affords more comfort to wearer. Retains permanent shape.

Some Woven Cloths: Beaver, broadcloth, brocade, canvas, cheviot, duck, cavalry twill, covert, crepe, handkerchief linen, homespun, gabardine, Jacquard, kersey, mackinac fabric, melton, muslin, organdy, percale, satin, shetland, taffeta, tricotine, tweed, voile, waffle cloth, webbing, wigan, whipcord.

Some Knitted Cloths: Baby clothes, bathing-suit fabric, jackets, jersey, mignonette, Milanese, neckwear, scarves, socks, stockinette, stockings, sweaters, topcoating, tricot-knit, tricolette.

Some Felt Cloths: Banners, blackboard erasers, felt slippers, insoles, packing, padding of many types, pennants, piano hammers, washers, all types of headgear.

Some Plaited or Braided Materials: Bedspreads, counterpanes, doilies, gauzy geometrical or symmetrical porous materials, insulation, lace, net, runners, shoelacing, trimming, veiling. Schiffli embroidery and Leavers lace machines produce all types and kinds of these products.

Some Nonwoven Fabrics: Aprons, diapers, facing material, interlinings, women's skirts, tablecloths, towels, vacuum cleaner bags, basket and casket lining, bagging and wrapping material, bed pads, covers, tissues, insulation.

Some Stretch Fabrics: Power Stretch: Athletic clothing, foundation garments, football pants, ski wear, swimwear. Comfort Stretch: Blouses and dresses, casual wear, gloves, knitgoods of several types, infants' and children's wear, linings such as for men's coatings, pajamas, shirting and sportswear, slip covers in home furnishings, undergarments, uniforms, upholstery.

Some Laminated Fabrics: Men's, women's and children's coats, jackets, and sportswear of many types; topcoating, overcoating, windbreakers; velvet, velveteen, broadcloth, corduroy, flannel, denim, poplin, etc.

Some Molded Fabrics: Effect found in better fitting effect in men's, women's, and children's outerwear garments—jackets, coats, sportswear, topcoats, overcoatings, mackinac jackets, etc.

FABRIKOID. Du Pont's trade-mark for its pyroxylin-coated and impregnated fabrics. A tough, durable, uniform film which is water resistant and washable; produced by processing the fabrics with pyroxylin. Used in upholstery, luggage, bookbinding, etc.

FABRILITE. An elastic-supported vinyl plastic upholstery built for shaping around curves without folding or pleating. The product is backed with a knitted fabric which prevents the upholstery from becoming baggy. Its resistance to cracking, scuffing, and abrasion is outstanding. A product of E. I. du Pont de Nemours & Co., Inc., used in the automotive and furniture industries.

FACE. 1. The right side of a material. 2. A piece of cloth which has one side finished better than the reverse; the side of the cloth which will appear on the outside of the garment. Cloth is shipped from the mill selvage to selvage and face to face for protective reasons. 3. In the dressmaking trade it signifies the finishing of a raw edge by the application of a fitted piece or lining of the same or some other material—braid, fur, lace, leather, ribbon.

FACED CLOTH. Fabrics which have a separate warp or filling on the back of the goods.

FACE GOODS. Materials which have had the nap raised, sheared, and then brushed down. Moleskin and doeskin are examples.

FACE FINISH. A finish given to certain goods where it is possible to give the cloth considerable fulling, milling, scouring, washing, and finishing. Felting and napping of cloth are easily accomplished. This type of finish is applied to many well-known cloths made of woolen stock, where the feature of the material is the appearance of the face of the fabric. There are two types of face-finished materials:

1. CLOSE FACE FINISH: Cloth that has received a heavy fulling, felting, and napping, and close, even shearing. This method of shearing leaves a short, croppy nap on the face, and because of the rigidity of the finishing operations, the weave and construction are entirely covered. Much of this cloth is so finished that it is impossible to see through it, even when held up to very strong light. Cloths often given this finish are: meltons, kerseys, beavers, broadcloths, certain uniform cloths, metropolitan cloth, and overcoatings on the market that have some particular trade name and are popular for only a season or two.

2. FULL FACE FINISH: This differs from the close face finish because of the fact that the finish and material seem to be "fuller" and have a greater napped surface, the feature of the cloth. Obviously, the cloth is not sheared as closely as in the close-finish cloth. Cloths that have this characteristic finish, which adds much to the selling points, are: Bolivia, bouclé, chinchilla, Montagnac, tree-bark, Saxony overcoating, Whitney, Worumbo, poodle cloth, fleece, needle point, Shetland, frieze, velour, duvetyne, ribbed and some cord-effect women's coatings, and zibeline. Most of these cloths are rather heavy in weight and quality, and prices vary.

In all face-finish materials, the weave construction and manner of stitching must be considered to obtain the desired effect. The grade of stock used and filling-float construction have to be given proper attention, so that the nap and finish of the goods will bring about the distinguishing points of the respective cloths.

FACE THREADS. Those threads of warp or filling, or both, that show on the face of multiple fabrics—double cloth, treble cloth, quadruple fabric, Frenchback, etc.

FACILITY. Trade-mark of Reeves Brothers, Inc., for a finish designed to give fabrics wrinkle- and shrink-resistance and perspiration- and acid-resistance according to U. S. Government standards. The finished fabric is washable and dry cleanable.

FACILON 1412. Made by the Facilon Division of Sun Chemical Corporation, New York City, this high strength and abrasion-resistant fabric is reinforced with 840 denier Caprolan nylon and has a thick, leather embossed protective surface of polyvinylchloride. The fabric can be used and provides excellent service in items such as wrestling tumbling mats and other types of mattings, tackling dummies, wall pads, baseball bases, etc.

FACING. Tailoring term for an underlying or overlying strip or reinforcement of material, the same as, or different from, that of the garment, as:

1. The strips along the inside of coat openings which also form the face of the lapels or revers.

2. The strips of goods inside the openings of packets so that the eyes shall not be offended by lining showing through.

3. The covering of silk laid on lapels or revers, to the edge or to the buttonholes.

4. The contra-colored cloth showing on the turned-back skirts or revers of old-time military coats.

5. The strip of cloth extending all around the inside edges of a waistcoat from neck to bottom side seam, which is sometimes of undercollar cloth for the sake of a thinner edge.

FACING LEATHER. A lightweight leather that is used to face the seams and to bind the edges of shoe uppers.

FACING, NONRIP. A continuous fabric strip sewn around the placket of the sleeve from one side of the opening to the other to prevent tearing at the placket end. Sleeve plackets may be of the one-piece continuous nonrip facing variety, or a two-piece facing will also serve the same purpose.

FACING SILK. A lightweight, closely woven rayon fabric used for collar and hem facings, linings, etc.

FACING YARN. Used on the face of fabric in plating hosiery, usually of the better grades. Opposite of backing yarn as to quality.

FACONNE. French (faconné) for fancy weave and implies small, Jacquard-effect designs in fabrics. Materials of this type drape well and give good wear. Made with silk or rayon.

FA COTTON. Fully acetylated cotton. See ACETYLATION.

FACTOR. An entrepreneur who finances a business project; accepts the accounts receivable as collateral. Some mills are financed by the factor, who may or may not continue to have an interest in the business after the plant is on a paying basis.

FACTORING. Prior to the American Revolution it can be stated that woven fabrics, generally speaking, were not made to any marked degree in this country. The mills of Great Britain were the main source of supply. Obviously shipments in transit required a long span of time, even months, and the textile plants lacked the facilities for checking credits, making collections, and did not have close contact with their sales representatives. These problems and risks were reduced and handled by financially strong, enterprising specialists here who were known as "Factors." These men offered valuable services to the mills by:
1. Recommending local sales agents.
2. Checking the credits of customer orders and guaranteeing collection of the "credits approved" receivable, and providing shipment details.
3. The handling of Customs including entry of goods into this country, re-shipping of merchandise to destination, etc.
4. Holding inventory here and making prompt shipment of "credit-approved" orders. Often the Factor attended to the packing, shipping, invoicing and billing "as agent" for his client, the mill.
5. Making financial advances to his clients. The security usually was the assigned account and/or the inventory.

As the textile industry developed after the American Revolution, especially during the years following the War of 1812 to 1837, the "Era of Good Feeling" was brought about by what is known in history as Jacksonian Democracy. The rise of the textile industry during these years was phenomenal in New England, upper New York State, and Pennsylvania, particularly in the Philadelphia area.

Factors were a strong, constructive influence in the textile industry, as well as in other fields during this era. They had experience in checking credits, making collections, and their specialized services were broadened to include sound financial guidance in management, buying and selling policy matters, as well as monetary loans for modernization and expansion.

Today, service charges by Factors are in two categories:
1. An agreed-upon percentage is paid to him by the client on sales volume for credit checking, and the Factor guarantees an approved Accounts Receivable.
2. The interest charge is based on advances only for the time outstanding at a rate somewhat above the bank rate, but the debit is revolving and/or self-liquidating by payments made by the customer of the Accounts Receivable to the Factor.
If no advances are necessary, the client's credit balance, which is left with the Factor, may earn the credit interest in question.

Factors now serve practically all major industries through the world. With the fabulous rise of International Trade, the techniques of financing imports and exports have been adapted to satisfy the changing conditions and needs of all concerned. Close cooperation with banks, here and abroad, along with bank participation have become increasingly important in facilitating the necessary credits arrangements, and if needed, the handling of foreign currency and exchange settlements. See Factoring, Commercial.

FACTORING, COMMERCIAL. This differs from Factoring in that, the customer checks his own credits and assumes full risk on collecting Accounts Receivable. The lender, the Commercial Factoring or Finance Company, offers short term advances secured by assigned Accounts Receivable. Generally, the customer is not notified of the assignment and the borrower collects the Accounts Receivable and then repays the lender.

There are also other types of loans offered by the Commercial Financing Companies. The security required and the rates that are charged reflect the risks involved and the financial responsibility of the borrower. See Factoring.

FACTORY CLOTH. Old-time term for unbleached cotton domestics.

FACTORY COTTON. Unbleached domestic cotton goods, in contrast to those which are imported.

FACTORY YARN. Coarse, unscoured woolen yarn, used for knitting hose, mittens, etc.

FAD. Pertinent to apparel, it is a fashion that is "here today, gone tomorrow." Examples might include the Nehru jacket and numerous items in women's apparel that may be easily recalled to mind. Fads cannot be considered styles since a style is a fashion which makes its appearance from time to time and reappears even after a lapse of a few years. Most fads seem to just fade away and are short-lived.

FADED DENIM. See SPORTS DENIM.

FADE-O-METER. A machine used determine the fastness or fugitiveness of colors. It does in a few hours what would take a week to do in the elements in testing for the desirability of the color. Forty hours' treatment will give results that would take many days in the sun. The sample to be tested is exposed to the light in the Fade-O-Meter, which is regulated to correspond to natural rays. Results are checked as to fastness, fairly fast to light, and not fast to light.

FADGE. Australian term for irregular packs of wool that weigh from 80 to 200 pounds.

FADING. The change produced on color by the action of any natural or artificial agent, such as sunlight, artificial light, water, abrasive.

FAG. A knot, tuft, or small unit of yarns found in coth. Used for decorative purposes, or in weaving hand-loomed rugs.

FAGA. A narrow strip or sash of silk wound several times around the waist.

FAG END. An untwisted end of rope.

FAGOTING. An open-seam stitch used to join together bands, folds, and ribbons. It forms a decorative effect and can also be done by drawing threads as for hemstitching, and catching the remaining threads together by interlacing the threads.

FAHRENHEIT. Temperature scale in which zero is the temperature of a mixture of equal weights of snow and common salt. The freezing point of water is 32° and the boiling point is 212°, both under standard atmospheric pressure. Invented by Gabriel Daniel Fahrenheit, 1686-1736, a German physicist. See °C.;

Centigrade and Fahernheit Thermometer Scales.

FAILLE. A ribbed silk or rayon cloth with crosswise rib effect. It is soft in feel and belongs to the grosgrain family of cross-rib materials. Used for coats, dress goods, handbags. Faille is rather difficult to launder well, has good draping effects, and will give good service if handled carefully. Finished at 36 to 40 inches wide. See Illustrated Section (Fabrics 9).

FAILLE COTTON. Upholstery fabric made of un-degummed silk warp and stout, two-ply, cotton filling yarn. Made of plain weave; however, because of a dense warp texture the material takes on the appearance of a rib or rep effect.

FAILLE DE CHINE. An all-silk faille; quality may vary.

FAILLE TAFFETA. Made on plain weave, occasionally on twill construction, it is crisp and stiff in feel, and has a very fine cross-rib filling effect. Made in silk, rayon, or acetate, it is used for coats and dresses.

FAILLE WEAVE. Broad name for constructions used in "faille cloths," where the material may be all silk, or of cotton warp and silk or rayon filling. Rib weaves and combinations of ribs are used to make the cloth so that the warp will entirely cover up the filling on the face and back of the goods. These weaves are used in various forms to make bengaline, hat banding, poplin, rep, staple- or novelty-ribbed silks and rayons.

FAJA. The colorful sash worn by males in Spain. See Gorro.

FAKE. A single coil of rope.

FAKE FURS. Cotton and man-made fibers are used in these woven or knitted fabrics which have periodic waves of popularity. Their effects may be conservative or bizarre. Simulations of the fur of animals such as broadtail, chinchilla, ermine, French poodle, giraffe, krimmer, mole, and pony are all well done; bizarre effects are sometimes used in exaggerated markings and fanciful colorings. Of course, fabrics and garments made of fake fur do not have the actual warmth, generally speaking, of genuine fur but the articles may be dry cleaned and made flameproof. Fake furs find use in lounging apparel, dress and sports clothes, slippers, coats, jackets, etc.

FALDA. A garment of white silk with a train. On solemn occasions, it is worn over the Pope's cassock.

FALKLAND ISLAND WOOL. Coarse wools, usually of the cheviot type, raised in the islands of the South Atlantic adjacent to the coast of South America.

FALLEN WOOL. Taken from dead sheep; inferior in all respects to fleece wool.

FALLER. An important part of the gill box that is used in treating worsted fibers. It straightens the fibers by paralleling them, takes out remaining portions of minute foreign matter, and carries the stock from the back roller of the frame to the delivery end of the machine.

There is a double set of pins on each faller; one set is slightly longer than the other one in the upright arrangement. The device extends the width of the machine and there are from 14 to 18 teeth per inch in each set of teeth or pins.

There are 18 fallers on the gill box. Twelve of them are always in action with the fibers, the other six are always out of action. They are worked by means of screw shafts and the principle of pitch. The ends of the fallers work in slots governed by the screw shaft. They are given a backward, upward, forward, and downward movement. It is only on the forward action that the pins come in contact with the fibers to aid in paralleling them. Gill boxes have a draft of about 6, which means that for every inch of stock fed in there are 6 inches delivered by the front rollers. Doubling up on ends fed into the machines offsets the drafting done on the frame.

Gilling is a rather delicate treatment that is given to the fibers, and it must be watched closely. Too much racking of fibers has to be guarded against; clogging of the pins, breaking fibers, and slippages must also be prevented when the machine is in action. See GILLING.

FALLER WIRES. Long, sectional wires on the mule-spinning frame which guide the spun yarn onto the spindle and aid in shaping the cop.

FALL WEIGHT. Medium-weight fabrics suited for fall wear.

FALL WOOL. That which is shorn in Texas and California in the fall of the year. These are the only places in the world where sheep are shorn biannually, once in the spring and again in the fall. The reasons for this are due to climatic conditions and the fact that the wool from these areas is infested with a small burr that is detrimental to the fleece and causes a reduction in the selling price. Texas, incidentally, is the largest wool-producing state in the Union; its wool is much used in this country, since it possesses many fine qualities for medium to heavy woolen fabrics. See FLEECE WOOL.

FALSE HEMP. Another name for sunn hemp.

FALSE PACKED COTTON. Cotton bales which contain damaged fibers, and all sorts of debris and matter totally foreign to the stock that should be in the bale. It is amazing when some of the things put into a bale are found when it is opened to be made ready for manipulation.

FALSE REED. This is the same as the back reed: an extra reed which is placed between the main reed and the harness in order to open up the warp lease and keep the ends straight, uniform, and under control in weaving. Gnarling and freezing-up of the ends are prevented by the use of this auxiliary reed, which is very important for good weaving of silks, ribbons, and other high-texture cloths in broad and narrow weaving.

FALSE TWIST. The major process used in texturizing filament yarns. A rotating spindle twists the yarn, then sets it in a heater-box or tube, and untwisting follows. Called by this name since the inserted twist does not become permanent. The twist, however, does remain because of the so-called "memory of the twist that was inserted in the processing." As a result, the yarn becomes torque (the movement of forces that cause rotation or twisting as in the instance of twisting cord, wire or yarn). To remove stretch, the yarn is subjected to a second heat treatment which affords stabilization and, at the same time, retains bulkiness.

FANCY. 1. In fabric, this term means that the fabric is not a year-in and year-out material with a steady demand, such as flannel, dress worsted, homespun or tweed, jersey or melton, chambray, denim, muslin, oxford, etc. It has been said "that the fancy of today is the staple fabric of tomorrow." This is not always true since many fancies never get off the ground and are soon forgotten. Fancies, however, when successful, do become staples. 2. In apparel it implies that the so-called fancy cannot always be bought in a store irrespective of what fashion and style, conservative or bizarre, happens to be in vogue. Many apparel items under this term remain only popular for a short time. On the other hand, one cannot predict the possible life span of any type of fabric.

FANCY BACK. General term for any backed fabric, the back of which differs distinctly from the face of the goods, as in the case of plaid-back overcoating.

FANCY DIAGONALS. Any fabric in which the twill or diagonal weave is a feature of the goods; several types of woolens and worsteds are made with these weaves.

FANCY DRAFT. The opposite of regular draft in laying out weaves; an irregular plan used to give some fancy effect in the woven goods.

FANCY GOODS, FANCIES. The opposite of staple goods, staples. Incidentally, the fancy of today may be the staple of tomorrow.

FANCY LEATHERS. This describes leathers, made from hides and skins of all types, which gain commercial importance primarily because of the grain or the distinctive or unusual finish, whether natural or the result of processing. Such processing may be graining, printing, embossing, ornamenting (to include gold, silver, aluminum, or other effects); or it may be any other operation affecting or enhancing the value of the leather through the production of a grain or distinctive finish.

FANCY LINE. Braided cord used for sash windows on ships.

FANCY ROLL. About a foot in diameter, this roller sets between the cylinder and the doffer on a card. Clothed with fine, pressed-steel card clothing, from 7/8 inch to 1¼ inches in length, the fancy dips into the clothing on the cylinder, and because of its excess speed, removes the carded fibers and presents them to the doffer roller. The stock is then removed from the machine by a coiler attachment. Fancies are found on all woolen cards and often on revolving flat cotton cards, especially in running low-quality stock.

FANCY SHIRTING. Broad term applied to shirting material that is usually woven in stripes or small designs with one or more colors. See SHIRTING.

FANCY WEAVES. A group of weaves that cannot be otherwise classed —braided twill, entwining twill, twilled basket, spot weaves, shaded satins, granites, quarter turns, etc. Combinations of weaves in the same pattern are included in this term.

FANCYWORK. Crocheting, embroidery, or tatting which is produced by means of a needle, hook, or small shuttle.

FANCY YARNS. Fancy yarns of many types used in hand or power weaving and knitting, crocheting, tatting, etc. They are not in the realm or confines of established staple yarns. Some of these yarns are bouclé, nub, random, Knickerbocker, bourette, slub, ratine, bug, and some of the rubber yarns. See NOVELTY YARN.

FANON. Two mozettas which are equal in all respects and worn by the Pope when celebrating Mass. These silk vestments, which are placed on the shoulders of the Pope, are usually made with closely placed ruffles which alternate in strips of gold and white. Made of silk, they are compact in texture and may be washed easily.

FARINA. This potato-starch sizing ingredient has a crisp feel and somewhat resembles salt in appearance. The moisture content of this white starch varies from 16 per cent to 20 per cent; if overboiled, it will deteriorate quickly.

FARMERS' HEDGE. One who is long on spot cotton as well as on futures cotton.

FARMERS' SATIN. Italy contributed this cloth as an imitation of the genuine silk fabric; a name for cotton or rayon lining in today's market.

FARM METHOD. A method of raising sheep in this country, used chiefly in wool-growing states east of the Mississippi River. The sheep are kept in fenced-in pastures and provided with shelters of various types as protection against the elements.

FARM WOOL. The opposite of territory wool, the term refers to wool raised on farms, in fenced-in areas, a popular method of raising sheep east of the Mississippi River.

FARTHINGALE. The hoop or framework used to extend the skirt of a woman, especially popular in the 16th century; also known as a rod or tree shoot; a single hoop mounted on a circular piece of fabric and fastened at the waist by tapes. Another meaning is a hair-stuffed cushion worn around the waist and under the skirt to provide an extension. The effect of the ante-bellum gown or dress worn by the Southern Belles is a good example of the meaning of the term. Its halcyon days were during the reign of Elizabeth I, Queen of England (1558-1603).

The French farthingale enjoyed popularity in the last quarter of the 16th century. Sometimes called "the wheel," it gave the impression that the wearer was standing inside a barrel or wheel. The skirt fastened to an outer rim and fell to the ground in a vertical manner. The Italian farthingale of the period employed the use of a whalebone wire with a tilted effect at the back. This brought about the use of a cushion or pad which gave a bustle-like effect. Outside British Court circles, where this type was most popular, the less affluent women in England used what was called a roll or "bum roll" in which a padded roll of fabric gave the wearer a sausage effect. When the authors of the times disapproved of it altogether, its life was cut short. The Spanish farthingale was the first one to come to public notice and was popular in Spain in the early 16th century. It made its debut in England about 1540-1545 and had wide appeal for fashion conscious women there. This type was an underskirt by which the extension hoops were arranged so as to give a greater or wider effect at the bottom of the dress, which, in time, became the rage of Southern Belles at a much later date in history. The forerunner of the "crinoline effect" of the nineteenth century, farthingale effects are still popular with certain circles and can be seen at various events.

FASCIATE. To be bound with a band, bandage, or fillet or to be compressed into a band or a bundle as stems grown together. See Rotofil.

FASCINATOR. Woven, knitted, crocheted, or tatted, it is a decorative headgear worn by women.

FASH. British term for clippings and other small wastes from woolen fabrics.

FASHION. The way or manner in which apparel, an accessory, or an adornment is made, without regard to prevailing styles. New fashions make new styles which are supposed to portray their general choice and acceptance by the well-dressed public. All fashions are styles, but all styles are not always in fashion.

FASHION AND STYLE. Prior to 1913, the last normal year that the present-day world has witnessed, textile mills which made men's wear and women's wear had little difficulty in keeping their looms running to supply the demands of the textile, apparel, and allied trades. What the mill decreed as to weave, construction, weight, color, finish, and types of stocks used was accepted by the buying public. Fashion and Style, in their present stature, were practically unknown before World War I.

The year 1913 was the last year of peace before the world was plunged into chaos, storm, stress, and strife by the onset of World War I, conditions from which it has not recovered to the present day. Those born after 1913 have been born in what might be termed the Age of Chaos and Uncertainty.

Following World War I, beginning in 1920, the entire scheme of things for the textile world began changing to a great degree. These changes are still taking place. At present, the acceptance of the fabrics made by mills is based solely upon the choice of the consumer, who follows the prevailing fashion as more or less decreed by fashion writers, fashion coordinators, fashion magazines, and "clothes consciousness" on the public's part.

Standards of living, as well, have had much influence on this item called Fashion, which is nothing more than a prevailing style. In other words, the textile plants began to learn that they could no longer obtain a long run on their somewhat staid, staple fabrics, and that unless they made what the consumer desired, the mills faced serious difficulties.

Thus, going back to 1913, and more particularly since 1920, the mills which make apparel fabrics, especially in the women's wear field, have found it increasingly difficult to produce goods which are of positive consumer acceptance, unless they have followed the elements and dictates of Fashion and Style.

Successful mills of today must adapt themselves to the quick, ever-changing demands of Fashion. If a plant is flexible and well managed, it should be able to produce easily and readily materials for the style markets without having fabric left on hand at the end of the season. Goods carried from season to season usually bring a lower price than the original price asked, and thus arises the problem of distressed merchandise and excessive inventory.

When one looks closely and examines this thing called Fashion, with all of its workings, ramifications, tangibles, and intangibles, one learns that Fashion is a logical element, certain and predictable. Fashion comes from the Latin factio, "a making." It can be considered as a prevalent style, or mode, in dress or attire, generally accepted by what is considered as good society at some particular time. Fashion trends are followed to a successful conclusion, namely, in the making of goods that will meet the demands of such fashion and trade trends. When wool crepes, for example, of 9-ounce weight per yard are popular and in demand for dresses, would it not be foolish for a mill to run on, say, 12-ounce "red flannel"? Likewise, when fashion, custom, vogue, or usage later on sponsors wool and some man-made fiber in the material, would it not be wise to cease to manufacture wool crepe?

This anticipation of fashion trends, when successfully carried out, will make profit for the mill, and its selling force will keep the looms humming while labor is actively engaged in continuous work.

Style may be said to be a fashion, a manner, or a way of expression in the use of this or that textile fabric—such as the popularity of covert, Venetian, gabardine, Scotch tartans and Scottish District Checks, seersucker, combination of blended fabrics, homespuns, tweeds, etc. This may be expressed by the latest fashion in coatings for women being successful in the distributive and consumer trades.

To differentiate between Fashion and Style, consider a few examples: bustles, hoop skirts, dirndl dresses, high-button shoes, powdered wigs. All of these are styles, but surely all of these are not in fashion at present. At some future time, however, any one of the foregoing may become a fashion in the cycle of apparel. At times, a trend of fashion will revive for a season or for a year or sometimes, even longer. In 1933, for example, the very popular and chic Empress Eugénie hats were a fashion, as they had been for many years in France; and from time to time they are accepted by the headgear trade and become a favorite with the consumer millinery trade.

All merchandise and fabrics are styles. Only those, however, that are in actual consumer demand are considered fashions. Style is part and parcel, or an inherent characteristic, of an object or an action. Only those styles in demand and accepted by a majority of the people at the present time are true Fashion of the day. Not all new styles marketed are accepted, and only those that are genuine become Fashion. Years ago Fashion existed as it does today, but it should be borne in mind that in the so-called good old days Fashion was not nearly the dominating factor that it is today in the ways and the standards of living.

Today, styles become Fashion very quickly, almost overnight, so it seems at times. These styles become fashion if they are in harmony with fashion trends; if they are not in harmony with other fashions they will soon expire. Some styles in fabrics not in accordance with the trends of the times are discarded by textile mills shortly after the fabric lines are opened. Years ago, different sections of the country had quite different fashion ideas. Merchandise unsalable in one section of the nation could be disposed of very quickly in some other area.

The reasons for the speedier acceptance of certain styles are obvious: scientific development and progress with fibers, old and new; advances in research, yarns, design and design development, production, dyeing, printing, and finishing have been little short of miraculous. In addition, the automobile, radio, television, talking pictures, streamlined trains, faster travel, the photogravure sections of newspapers, fashion magazines, movie shorts, and so on, have all been important in bringing Fashion to all corners of the nation and the world. People in the rural areas can drive to nearby towns and buy fabrics, clothes, and accessories that are the last word in Fashion—instead of relying on the backwoods or country store to furnish them with a dresslength of goods, the design or pattern of which might not be fashionable.

Truly, the automobile, radio, and television have done much to bring the rural population into direct and close touch with Fashion that is right up-to-the-minute. A new fashion trend soon spreads all over the nation in an incredibly short time. Any particular style which happens to become fashionable, or the "last word," develops into a piece of volume production. It is of great importance, therefore, that mills making fabrics that will be popular must know the factors and the underlying psychological principles which cause a style to become a good-selling fashion.

Mill management and good labor relations are vital factors. Fashions are a direct reflection and interpretation of the modes and the manners of living, and the thoughts of the times. Mills must be keenly aware of these reflections and interpretations. They reflect the moral, economic, religious, political, and social phases and conditions of the period.

Sports clothes play an important part in our lives today, not only in active-sports garments but in spectator-sports clothes, as well. It is the custom today to wear the proper and correct apparel when taking part in sports or in viewing sports events. Recall to mind the clothes worn for the polo game, tennis, football, college campus, fishing and hunting, beach sports, resorts for summer and winter, the cruise, etc.

It has often been stated that the higher-priced fashions in garments will probably be the fashions in the lower-priced fields the following season. This is true to some degree. Fashion and style are sought by the masses as well as by the wealthy and leisure class. Fashion permeates every city, town, village, and hamlet in the land. These groups of consumers follow Fashion and Style to the bitter end. Fashion and Style are eagerly followed all the way from the "Colonel's Lady to Judy O'Grady."

Consider for the moment the Fashion and Style for New York City. It percolates from 57th Street, the most exclusive buying area in the world, to upper and lower Fifth Avenue, to 34th Street, to 14th Street and to the Lower East Side. 57th Street with its exclusive-creation shops sets the prevailing fashions for the four seasons of the year. The other areas follow suit. And, every city, town, village, and hamlet has its Fifth Avenue and its Lower East Side, its "railroad tracks." Fashion marches on!

This series of facts bears out the impression that the people of today are more and more Style and Fashion conscious than ever before. Everyone, so it seems, wants to be dressed in correct fashion. Clothing and apparel must be correct and in keeping with the trends of the times, regardless of the price paid in many instances. Is not obsolescence, after all, the psychology of the female mind in Fashion and Style? Is not anticipation greater than realization in Fashion and Style?

Fashion surely runs the successful mills of today, whether they be making woolens, cottons, rayons, linens, silks, blends, or combinations. Textile mills, large and small, have to follow closely the fashion markets in order to keep abreast of the times. To disregard or overlook the questions and problems of Fashion and Style would be pure suicide for the textile plant.

FASHION AND STYLE, ECONOMICS OF. The marketing and merchandising of past, present and future styles which are or may become fashions. The question of raw material, construction, color, finish, buying and selling agencies, and the method of distribution to the public must be carefully considered from all angles.

FASHIONED. Shaped in the knitting process by the increase or decrease of the number of needles in action.

FASHIONING. The process of increasing or decreasing the width of knitted fabric by controlling the movement of the needles. Fashioning results in shaped, form-fitting parts—bodies, sleeves, etc.

FASHIONING MARK, MOCK KNITTING. A loop formation which differs from the main body of the fabric so as to simulate the true fashion mark in hosiery and other fashioned fabrics.

FASHION INSTITUTE OF TECHNOLOGY. Founded in 1944, The Fashion Institute of Technology and Design is a Junior College sponsored by the Board of Education of the City of New York in cooperation with the Educational Foundation for the Apparel Industry under the program of the State University of New York. Located in the heart of the garment industries at 227 West 27th Street, New York City, its present campus and buildings were opened in 1958, at a cost of

$15-million. In 1951 the Institute became a Junior College under the aegis of the State University and is empowered to award the Associate Applied Science degree. When first established, there were six professors and 100 students. At present there are 125 full-time professors and 50 part-time instructors. There are 2,500 students attending the day session and 2,000 in the evening courses.

Since its inception, F.I.T. has serviced all phases of the industry with engineers, designers, assistant designers, buyers and merchandisers, fashion illustrators and writers, designers for textile print goods, textile administrators, sales personnel, etc. The institute is the mecca for things apparel-wise and its graduates are always in demand. Its effect and influence in the garment trades is profound and it was the first college in the world to cater to these industries.

The Institute is a fully accredited member of the Middle States Association of Colleges and Secondary Schools. It receives great support from leaders in the textile and apparel industries, as well as from the various unions. Each instructor in the apparel subjects, and there are over forty in this department alone, has had at least seven years of trade experience. There is a strong textile-management department with 18 professors. There is a very close relation with industry in research, experimentation, development, fabric control, textile testing, etc.

FASHION AND STYLE, TERMS USED IN THE WORLD OF.

These terms serve as the background or core for fashion writers, department store advertising, magazine writers on all types of apparel, etc. Close examination of the writing in this field will reveal that they seem to be used over and over again, along with some slight variations.

ACHIEVED: Accomplished, gained, completed; the final garment effect ready for comment, acclaim, and criticism.

ALLURING: Pleasing, attractive, and a temptingly attractive garment, usually along form-revealing lines.

ABOUNDING: Plentifully supplied or considerable abundance, especially of the amount of fabric used in the finished article. Refers to a garment with considerable "gingerbread," or may have some allure and zestfulness.

APPEALING: To have "appearance and looks," attract attention and interest, and convey its purpose; desirable and suitable for the occasion.

BALANCE: Poise, may be a symmetrical garment that is in even order and does not border on the bizarre or the outlandish.

BEAUTIFUL: Excelling in color, line, form, silhouette, balance, attractiveness.

BEJEWEL: Ornamented or embellished as in the case of sequins and other articles used to make the article more attractive; may border on the bizarre.

BIZARRE: Singular in appearance, style or general character; whimsically strange and a type of garment that can be worn attractively by only few persons.

BUCOLIC: Of or pertaining to the countryside; rustic or rural effect.

BOUFFANT: Puffed, puffed-out, raised, blister effect, quilted; full, as in the drape of a skirt, a puffed sleeve, or quilted house gown for leisure wear.

CHIC: Natty, neat, smart, stylish; tasteful, sleek, smooth, pert type of garb.

CHARACTER: A distinctive mark or merit noted in a garment; prepossessing, having distinction and individuality; sets off the appearance of the wearer.

CONTRAST: Opposite, dissimilitude, and effective but different effect observed. Often used with regard to color contrasts, a new fashion or counter to a prevailing style.

DAINTY: Neat effect as the result of intricate or detailed work as noted on many types of apparel for both innerwear and outerwear. A chic effect.

DEBONAIR: Gentle in effect, courageous, suave, elegant, smooth, jaunty.

DEBUT: The first entrance of a new style that has become fashion and remains so for a time that is short or long in duration. The effect and silhouette have much to do on how long a style will last after its debut.

DÉCOLLETAGE: A dress or suit—evening wear—with bare neck and shoulders to provide a flimsy, low-cut effect, often a plunging neckline which may border on the daring and even seems to be "out of line."

DEFIES DESCRIPTION: Beyond actual description, sensational; must be seen to be appreciated; the "out-of-this-world" type of attire.

DELICACY: Luxuriant, graceful, refined, and a consideration of being delicate and apart from the usual order of what might be expected; the niceties of a particular garment.

DELICATE: Tender, frail, dainty, easily injured by handling; borders on the flimsy, zephyr-like type of garb.

DIAPHANOUS: Transparent, as chiffons, sheers, and comparable materials used in dresses and gowns. Sometimes referred to as the "peek-a-boo" type.

DIFFERENT: Unlike and often implies a new effect in a garment; dissimilar.

DISCOTHÈQUE: This rather fantastic, lasting phenomenon was born in bizarre St. Tropez, the sophisticated resort in the Nice-Cannes area in the French Riviera, in 1963. It burgeoned in the rest of France, went to the British Isles, and finally arrived in the United States, where it has had a sensational reception. Originally the term meant a night club, private or public, where the habituées, frustrated and otherwise, whiled away the evenings to phonograph records. In these low-lighted or candle-lighted dens of pleasure were born the frug, sired by the twist, which was also responsible for the monkey, hitchhiker, the fish, the watusi, and other forms of bodily effort.

The fashion industry soon adopted the term, and the dress of this name is recognized by its low neck and short hem; to add to the ensemble black lace stockings and a suitable make-up were adopted to set off the configuration of the individual. As an item of apparel there are several modifications and offshoots with all of these using the popular catch-all word "discothèque."

DISCREET: Prudent, conservative; a well-cared-for-effect and in good taste.

ELABORATE: To perfect or develop by labor operations embellishments for a pronounced effect. Often carried to extremes, out of the ordinary, and often used to more or less describe the so-called "new look," in some particular article of apparel.

ELEGANCE: Polish, regality, daintiness; demands a second look. May be gorgeous in effect, scintillating, commanding, and of high class, such as observed in a creation, a classic, or a haute couture.

EXEMPLIFIED: To illustrate a new departure or a new development in fashion, style, vogue, or demand with an example.

EXCITING: Stirring; attracts attention by its conservativeness or its daring effect, usually the latter. Out of the ordinary, at times fantastic.

EXPERTLY: Done in a very skillful manner as to detail, final finish, and effect in some item of apparel. Effectively completed in minute detail.

EXOTIC: Delicate, strange; or something that reveals a new departure, often on the bizarre or sensuous side. Attracts attention because of its daringness or extremes.

EXQUISITE: Dainty, delicate, neat and appealing, refined with regard to appeal, approval or taste; done in proper balance and decorum.

EYE-CATCHING: Immediately attracts optical inspection and a second glance. "Fills the eye" because of its beauty or attractiveness and may be of the breathtaking type. Brought about by color, line, form, silhouette, cut-fit-and-trim, and, at times, by revealing phases of the article.

FANFARE: Much ado, flourish, great preparation, much commotion, etc.

FAVORITE: Preferred, the best-liked, popular, the choice, "tops"; the choice from a group.

FEMININE: Female, delicate, effeminate, ladylike and without any form of masculinity in lines, cut, fit, or trim.

FIGURE-CLINGING: Form-fitting, form-revealing, alluring, exotic; especially with regard to satins and comparable materials used in evening wear.

FLIRTATIOUS: Inclined to flirt, coy, demure, "cute," and to attract attention.

FLUTTERED: Moving rapidly; unsteady, confused, wavering.

FORM-CONCEALING: To hide the figure or the shape, opposite to form-revealing. Taffeta and similar fabrics are used in form-concealing women's apparel.

FRESHNESS: Vigorous, clean, natty, neat, spotless, not blemished; often used with regard to organdies and other cottons which always seem to have a fresh appearance.

FRILLINESS: Ruffled, flounced, and may be on the fastidious side; implies too much embellishment in which excesses tend to spoil the effect of the article.

FRIVOLOUS: Trifling, petty, even silly to some of the extremes seen at times in some fashions. Also known as the "frou-frou type."

GLAMOUR: Alluring and often illusory charm or fascination; enchanting. Probably the most used and often the most abused, word in fashion and style; seems to cover a multitude of "sins of commission and omission" with reference to fashions, styles, vogues and demands, especially in women's fashions. For want of a better word, glamour is often used, since the word adroitly expresses what the writer or speaker has in mind.

GENTLY SLOPING: Inclining gradually with ease and grace, softness.

GORGEOUS: Splendid, arresting, eye-catching, regal and rich in color. Its use is often overdone when there is nothing at all that is gorgeous in the particular article. "Gorgeous" seems to have more appeal than the word "bizarre," which might describe the article in a better way.

GRACIOUS: Affable, kindly, in good taste and done with care, élan and éclat.

HANDSOME: Pleasing to the eye, graceful, liberal to some degree in fashion. A man may be handsome; a woman may be beautiful.

IMAGINATION: The power to imagine, design or develop, fanciful. The use of the mind and the senses "to create" or to develop something "new."

INTERESTING: Exciting to the point where one desires the details.

INTRICATE: Entangled or done with much dainty detail. May be complicated but effective because of the working out of the detailed effect or effects.

INTRIGUING: Done with determined effectiveness, captivating, beguiling, accomplished. An attractive garment planned with definite thoughtfulness and positive imagination.

LONG TORSO: The trunk of the body without head and hands; being long or great in linear extent.

LOOSE: Swinging or hanging detached, as in a flared or swinging skirt.

MASTERFUL: Authoritative, well done, good work and excellent execution.

METHOD: Orderly and systematic, done with care and thought, well planned.

MINIMIZED: Reduced or modified somewhat in favor of other features currently in favor in other items of apparel.

MOLDED: Shaped, formed, form-fitting in order to improve the appearance of the wearer of the article.

MOTIF: Design or pattern, period of design, planned result, effect.

NATURAL: Not artificial, inborn, done in a natural manner, gives the so-called "natural look" to the wearer.

NIFTY: One of the most used and most abused words in the field of fashion and style, extending from describing a creation, classic, haute couture, gown, frock, all the way down to what all these are—dresses. It encompasses expressions such as fine, clever, divine, smart, stylish, chic, etc. This "easy" term covers a very wide range of expressions all in favor of the article being superb in all respects. Nifty is used by fashion editors, writers, co-ordinators, buyers, and sellers, and even by operatives and the "pusher-boys" who steer their dress-carts from one door to the next one. Many items of apparel are nifty but many, as is obvious, do not seem to truly fall into that category. Ranks with "terrific," "swell," "looks like a million," "great," etc.

NOSTALGIC: Homelike, homely, to think of home; causes one to think and to philosophize, often of the good old days and the good old fashions and styles of yesteryear.

POISED: Balanced and with some dignity; bearing of carriage or poise.

RESTRAINT: Confined, sober, somber and not liberalized; checked and done with care and decorum. Devoid of flourishes and embellishments.

RICH: Done in elaborate design, a rich or regal type of fabric used in a garment, especially in evening wear.

RHYTHM: Done with confidence, balanced and symmetrical in form and shape.

SANS: French for "without," such as without a collar, etc.

SEDUCTIVE: Alluring, daring, inviting, enticing, exotic, sensual. May be an attractive garment; a good conversational word to use in fashion and style.

SILHOUETTE: Used to imply the profile or configuration—from the top of the head to the tip of the toe. May include color, line, form, shape, etc. Named after the Frenchman, Étienne de Silhouette.

SLEEK: Smooth, slinky, glossy, lustrous, alluring; clean-cut and streamlined. Applied to form-fitting and even tight-fitting attire.

SMARTEST: Done with great care and shrewdness to achieve the utmost in clever and neat results on completion of the article in question.

SOPHISTICATION: Wise, and may be an artificial disillusion. Ideas, tastes, or ways developed through education, worldliness. A change from the natural character or simplicity into what at times may develop into "nasty niceness." A sophisticated gown is one that is right up to the minute in detail, cut, and design.

STRAPLESS DÉCOLLETAGE: A garment without straps to reveal the neck and shoulders, and often the bosom. May or may not be appealing to the wearer and to the observer; usually daring and the latest item in vogue. Actually may be in good taste and, at times, in poor taste, since it does not seem to do anything for the wearer.

SUAVE: Affable, bland, easily overdone, gracious, smoothly suitable for the occasion. Often worn in a nonchalant manner and does attract attention if the garment is genuinely suited to the wearer.

SWINGING RHYTHM: A type of attire that seems to provide rhythm to the wearer; usually observed on persons "who know how to wear clothes."

TASTE: The general character, manner or style as showing perception or lack of it as to what is beautiful, desirable or well fitting with regard to apparel. Expresses the characteristics of prevailing style or fashion. In some respects it may be stated that taste is really indefinable; what one person calls good taste, another may think is atrocious. The following questions on taste are thought-provoking, in a way indefinable, and many hours could be spent on coming to a solution for each question—if that is possible:

1. Define GOOD TASTE.
2. Define BAD TASTE.
3. Is TASTE active or passive?

4. Is TASTE an activity or a quality?
5. Is TASTE dependent upon the time factor? If so, in what way?
6. Can anyone have TASTE? Can it be implanted if not already existing?
7. How is TASTE related to FASHION? To STYLE?
8. How do we account for the unevenness of TASTE?
9. GOOD TASTE is better than BAD TASTE.
10. BAD TASTE is better than NO TASTE AT ALL.
11. Analyze your own TASTE pertinent to the apparel you wear.

TIERED: Done in folds, flounces, or in a series of repeated forms. May imply one above the other, banked. Should be done effectively at all times.

TREMENDOUS: Like the word "terrific," it is much overdone in the garment industries. Implies "large," "overpowering," "powerful," "commanding." Also means "great demand." Like the words "swell" and "terrific" in American English, it is used for want of some better adjective or description in speaking of items of apparel.

FASHION KNIT. A tie fabric knitted in one piece and then stitched. The tie is fashioned down the back seam, has good resiliency, and makes a smaller, firmer knot when compared with crochet-knit tie fabric.

FASHION MARKS. Minute marks which result from the fashioning of stockings by the transfer of loops to adjacent needles; they may be observed on the calf of the leg and under the arch of the foot in full-fashioned stockings.

FAST COLOR. See COLORFASTNESS.

FASTNESS. The resistance of dyes to color-destroying agents such as light, washing, perspiration, salt water.

FASTNESS OF DYE. Property of dye to retain its color when cloth is exposed to sun, perspiration, atmosphere, washing, or other color-destroying agents. The term fastness is a relative one, as a dye may be reasonably fast to washing and only moderately fast to light. Fastness of color may be tested by standard procedures. Remarkable progress has been made in the dyeing of faster-color rayons and acetates.

FAST REED. When the reed is held securely in place in the loom—controlled by the reed cap and the groove at the back of the raceplate. See LOOSE REED.

FAT. A semisolid, yellow or white substance which forms part of the tissues of animals; contains carbon, hydrogen, and oxygen. Chemically, it is a compound ester formed by the union of organic acids and glycerine.

FATHOM. The six-foot measure used in maritime circles, the standard measurement for rope.

FATS. The natural oils that exist in plants and animals, and components of glycerine, various fatty acids which are insoluble in water and cold alcohol, and soluble in hot alcohol, ether and chloroform. Caustic alkalies will decompose fats. These compounds of carbon, hydrogen, and oxygen are whitish or yellowish in color.

FAT-TAILED, BROAD-TAILED SHEEP. Found in the Balkans, Asia Minor and Russia, these common sheep have a tail of large size that contains valuable fat, the most important product of the carcass. The fibers of the animal are coarse and kempy and are classed in the carpet grade in wool classification. Fat-rumped sheep are akin to fat-tailed sheep.

FATTY ACID. The acid component of a glyceride or, more broadly speaking, one of a series beginning with formic acid and including acetic acid and the soap acids. It is only the higher fatty acids such as oleic and stearic acids which produce colloidal soaps when combined with alkali.

FAVEURS. European term for narrow taffeta, satin, velvet, etc., used as ribbon in widths that range from about one inch up to five inches.

FAXINESS. A flax disease which causes the tip of the plant to turn red; makes retting practically impossible.

FEARNAUGHT. 1. English overcoating of the cheviot group. The fabric is heavy in weight and the filling yarns aid in obtaining the well-known shaggy-face finish of the goods. Reused and remanufactured wools are often used in the goods. 2. A machine used in opening up and mixing wool which is difficult to manipulate because of cottiness or rather long staple, as noted in carpet wools. Action of the machine is made up by the use of a large, rotating cylinder covered with hooked spur teeth which mesh with smaller rollers around the circumference of the main cylinder.

FEATHER. 1. One of the light, horny, epidermal outgrowths which constitute the external covering or plumage of birds. 2. Originally used as a writing device, feathers find much use now in clothing adornment and accessories. 3. FEATHER EDGE is another name for picot edging. 4. FEATHER EDGE BRAID is a white cotton or linen braid set off by picot work. 5. FEATHER TWILL is the same as the broken twill or herringbone weave.

FEATHERBEDDING. The practice of unions or employees limiting their production, or the amount of work to be performed.

FEATHER CLOTH. Woven or knitted woolen fabric in which little feathers are worked into the goods.

FEATHER PILLOW STUFFING. A number of types of feathers are used for pillow stuffing:

1. CHICKEN FEATHERS: The lowest in quality used as stuffing; they are stiff, hard, and the heaviest of pillow feathers. There is the tendency toward matting or batting, and there is no resilience in them unless specially curled.

2. TURKEY FEATHERS: Comparable with chicken feathers, they are mixed with duck feathers to reduce costs.

3. DUCK FEATHERS: Superior to chicken and turkey feathers, they may be colored or white, have natural resilience.

4. GOOSE FEATHERS: These have a high rating for comfort and durability.

5. DOWN: A layer of fine feathers found under the ordinary feathers on young ducks and geese. Down is much used in higher-quality pillows.

6. COMMERCIAL DOWN: This is a combination of down and stripped chicken feathers.

7. KAPOK: This is not a feather but a light, fluffy vegetable fiber used much for stuffing. It mats and dusts readily from usage. It is more expensive than chicken feathers but does not have durability.

CLEANING OF FEATHER PILLOWS: There are three main methods:

1. The feathers are removed from the ticking, placed in a pillowcase, and washed in a silk or a wool formula in a low-titer soap or a synthetic detergent. The ticking is washed in a two-suds formula.

2. The feathers and ticking may remain as received in the laundry; they are washed in a wool formula.

3. Remove the feathers from the ticking. The feathers are steam-cleaned. The ticking is washed in a two-suds formula.

FEATHERS. The plumage of birds,

differentiated as quill or stiff, strong-tail or wing feathers, and plume or long, waving feathers, they are used chiefly in millinery and the pillow trades. The kinds of feathers used mostly for ornaments are those of the adjutant, American or rhea osprey, argus, bird of paradise, chicken, eagle, egret, grebe, heron, peacock, pheasant, ostrich, swan, and turkey. The adjutant furnishes the marabou feathers peculiar to India.

FEATHERS AND DOWN. A blend or mixture in which the feathers predominate. A reverse combination is called Down and Feathers.

FEATHERS, MILLED. Those which have been chopped, crushed, ground, or stripped by some mechanical method.

FEATHER STITCH, FEATHER-STITCH. A variation of short blanket stitch. The stitch is made in groups which alternate from one side of an unmarked space to the other side; gives the appearance of a feather or branches from a main stem or vein.

FEDERAL TRADE COMMISSION EDICTS AND RULES AS DECREED BY THE CONGRESS OF THE UNITED STATES OF AMERICA. These follow in chronological order.

1. 1937: Acetate to be classed with rayon in labeling all products. Known as Acetate Rayon at this time. Effective until 1952. See 1952 below.

2. 1938: On Silk: Weighted silk could no longer be classed as all-silk, silk, pure-dyed silk or pure silk. Weighting percentages had to be on all labels, such as "silk-weighted 40 percent." A further change was decreed whereby a silk fabric dyed black could hold up to 15 percent of weighting material and still be known as a pure-dye silk. All other colors were allowed a 10 percent weighting and could be sold as a pure-dye silk. This ruling is still valid. See Weighted Silk.

3. 1939: Passage of the *Wool Products Labeling Act,* effective July 15, 1941, plus amendments on August 1, 1949, November 14, 1953, and June 20, 1964. Wool, new wool, and virgin wool can be used as true terms only to fibers which have never been manipulated or reclaimed from any other product. Other animal fibers, such as alpaca, angora goat hair, camel hair, cashmere, llama, vicuna, et al., are now to be classed as wool. See Hair Fibers, Wool.

4. 1941: Rules on Linen were promulgated and the percentages of other fibers blended or mixed with linen had to be labeled with the percentages of each fiber in the fabric marked on the labels.

5. 1952: The trade practice rules promulgated October 26, 1937, were superseded on December 11, 1951, and effective on February 9, 1952. The term, *Acetate,* was divorced from the term, *Rayon,* after a marriage of fifteen years. Acetate could no longer be known as Acetate Rayon.

6. 1952: *The Fur Products Labeling Act* was decreed. It became mandatory to use labels in which the English name of the animal which produced the fur, the amount of scrap or waste fur used in the product, and the fur's originating country were all started.

7. 1953: Interstate commerce brought forth the promulgation of *The Flammable Fabrics Act* which forbade the sale of flammable textile and apparel products used in wearing apparel.

8. 1960: *The Textile Fiber Products Identification Act* came into existence. Announced in September 1958, this rule became effective on March 3, 1960. An amendment was announced in December, 1965.

This Act covers all fibers except fiber products made from wool as per the *Wool Products Labeling Act* of 1939. A few highpoints in the Act follow:

1. Every textile fiber product must show fiber percentage content.

2. Fibers have to be listed in accordance with the generic name of the particular fiber, natural and/or manmade. Listings have to be in order of predominance. (At the present time, there are 18 generic terms for manmade fibers).

3. Labels have to be affixed to the item so that they will not fall off the article in question.

4. Fiber content of interlinings and linings must also be given, and this must be listed separately, actually the same as the decreed under the Wool Products Act of 1939.

5. Products that are imported must show the country of origin as to manufacturing or processing.

Copies of any or all the Rules and Regulations of the Federal Trade Commission are obtainable from the Federal Trade Commission, Washington, District of Columbia.

FEDERAL UNION. A local, in an industry or a craft, in which there are no existing national or international unions, which is chartered by, and affiliated directly with, the American Federation of Labor.

FEDORA HAT. In 1884, Sardou, the renowned French dramatist, staged a drama in which the heroine was named Fedora. The term became popular for a soft felt hat recognized by its crease down the middle from front to back. This type of headgear has a napped-fiber surface effect and is one of the better types of hat used today. The original Fedoras had a rather wide brim which was rolled upward on the two sides. Brims today are narrow but Fedoras are still popular in the upper-bracket qualities and prices.

FEED, KNITTING. A complete set of parts that produces a complete knitting action.

FEED APRON. An endless belt made of leather, canvas and leather, or some other suitable combination found on preparatory machines used in cotton-yarn manufacture. Used to present stock to rollers for treatment. Most feed aprons or belts are covered with wooden slats which may or may not be studded with pins or teeth.

FEEDER. Any device or arrangement for feeding stock into a machine. There are several types designed for the respective machines used in textile-yarn manufacture.

FEED PLATE. Located at the feed end of a card, it is a smooth metal plate over which the cotton lap passes before arriving at the feed rolls.

FEED REGULATOR. Used on the bale breaker, automatic feeder, and kindred machines, it is a rakelike device which keeps the supply of cotton even at all times in the hopper feed. It prevents matted or clumpy cotton from reaching the feed rollers and causing possible trouble.

FEED ROLLS. Arranged in pairs, one above the other, these rolls are used to deliver stock, in a uniform manner, to the successive rollers in the machine arrangement.

FEED YARNS, FEEDER YARNS. Yarns which are made by a fiber producer and sent to a thrower for texturizing.

FEELER FILLING CHANGING DEVICE. This will transfer a full bobbin to a shuttle before the one in action is devoid of yarn. The feeler extends into the shuttle from the side and feels the yarn on the bobbin. As it approaches emptiness, the feeler transfers automatically, with the old bobbin being cast out and the new one coming into play.

FELL. A skin, hide, fleece, or a covering of hair or wool.

FELL, FELL OF CLOTH. The few newly woven picks in fabrics which are closest to the reed of the loom.

FELLED SEAM. A seam in which the waste is turned under and stitched down to form a strong, flat junction.

FELLER. The operative who fells lining to lining, or to the cloth; usually done by hand with a blind stitch. Includes, as well, those who do one or more operations, such as felling linings at the armholes, shoulders, collar at the neck (both inside and outside of the coat). The feller also takes care of the lining at the sleeve bottom, the body lining along the seams and bottoms or corners, as the case may be, where the machine cannot do the actual catching.

FELLING MARKS. A few colored yarns woven into woolen and worsted cloth at the beginning and the end of the cut when the material is being woven in the loom; show where the one cut ends and the next one begins.

FELLING SILK. A two-ply silk yarn made with left-hand twist.

FELLING SIMILI, SIMILI BINDING. Made on a 3-up, 1-down, broken twill to give the "four-end satin effect," this mercerized cotton binding is characterized by raised selvages on the face.

FELLING STITCH. An over-and-over continuous stitch used to fasten linings onto the outer-body, to hold bindings to the edge, join under-collars to body, etc. The closeness of the stitches is regulated according to the purpose for which they are used.

FELLMONGER. One who deals in fells or sheepskins.

FELLMONGERING. English term for wool pulling.

FELT. See FELT AND FELTED MATERIALS.

FELT, SILICONE TREATED. Particularly adaptable to fashion garments such as jackets and skirts, this type of felt has the following advantages over the nontreated material—silkier hand and improved draping quality in light-weight felts; improved wrinkle recovery and better sewing properties by a decrease in needle resistance; resistance to water-borne stains and water spotting in dry cleaning.

FELTAN. Product of the American Felt Company, Glenville, Connecticut, it is a microporous neoprene runner sheeting which combines the pressability of felt with the elasticity of rubber. It has applications where nonskid friction is wanted between two dry, smooth surfaces to prevent slipping, shifting, or sliding. Feltan is used in industry as an under-layer between the floor and the company's Vibra-Mount antivibration felt pads, with, for instance, many types of business machines.

FELT AND FELTED MATERIALS.

1. FELT FABRIC: A felt cloth is made with no system of threads, but is constructed by an interlocking of the fibers of stock to be used. There is a woven felt cloth, however—papermakers' felt cloth—that is used in the newspaper presses and is made of the best wool obtainable. The nature of the uses of this fabric makes it necessary that the fabric be woven.

Felt fabric is made by subjecting the stock to be used to heat, moisture, water, pressure, and, in the case of derby hats and other stiff felts, shellac. The amount of shellac used depends on the desired stiffness of the finished material.

Leading felt products are felt hats —the most important felt item—banners, pennants, slippers, linings of many types, piano hammers, board erasers, insoles. Any and all types of stocks, wastes, etc., find their way into felt cloth.

Felt may be made of:
Camel and goat hair
China cotton
Other cottons
Cow and rabbit hair
Flocks and other mill wastes, such as card strippings, shear wastes, willow wastes
Reprocessed or new wool
Reused wool
Shoddy, mungo, extract wool
Short-staple wool noils—the most important fiber for felt

2. FELTED FABRIC: This type of woven material is also known as fulled or milled cloth. Felting, fulling, or milling is the process resorted to in order to give woven cloth a thick, compact, substantial feel, finish, and appearance. The construction of the goods is covered up and not seen when the cloth is examined. Napping and shearing may be applied to aid in making felted cloth. The effect may be produced on woolens and cottons.

Felted material runs from medium to heavy in weight. Most of it is used in outerwear during the cold months. Cloths that may be felted are flannel, cricket cloth, molleton or silence cloth; many types of overcoating, such as melton, kersey, beaver, and broadcloth; fleece coats, reefers, ulsters, and heavy uniform goods. Certain suiting and dress goods materials, robes, and blankets are felted.

The process of fulling and felting is like that of removing a spot or stain from a cloth or garment. In rubbing the affected area the cloth has the tendency to felt or mat, and the fibers to interlock. This tends to cover up the weave construction and gives the goods a felted appearance. Soap, heat, water, friction, and proper temperatures produce the felted effect seen on woven goods.

Felting covers up the spaces between the interlacings in the weave, gives compactness to the goods, and thus affords more warmth.

FELT CARPET. One that is made by felting rather than by weaving.

FELTED FABRIC. See FELT AND FELTED MATERIALS.

FELTED MATTRESS. A mattress filled with packed layers of cotton felt.

FELTER. A poorly woven area in fabric usually caused by one warp end breaking and causing other ends to break by winding around them and making them snap free. A good weaver can usually prevent extensive felters by taking remedial measures as soon as they occur.

FELT FABRIC. See FELT AND FELTED MATERIALS.

FELTING ABILITY. Wool yarns can be made to interlock under the heat and the pressure of proper finishing processes.

FELTING FINISH. Staple cotton finish given to materials by napping, brushing, and pressing under heavy pressure.

FELTING PROCESS. When exposed to moisture, heat, and pressure, wool fibers tend to tangle and mat to form a compact material. Shrinkage and fulling are early stages of this process.

FELTING PROPERTY. See FELTING ABILITY, FELTING PROCESS.

FELTING SHRINKAGE. Refers to woolen fabrics, especially knitgoods, wherein the fibers, because of action or agitation, show a definite matting or overlapping caused by the nature of the fiber structure with its serrations, scales, and natural waviness. The random, unpredictable direction that the wool fibers take under some type of pressure or treatment causes the felting. Wool is the only textile fiber that will mat or felt in a natural manner. See Relaxation Shrinkage.

FELT IS MADE, HOW.

1. WOOL: Obtained from the sheep fleece.

2. SORTING: Sheep fleeces are sorted into particular grades; from six to twenty grades of wool from the same fleece may be obtained depending upon the rigidity of the sorting and the type of fleece involved. The higher the quality of the fleece, the greater will be the number of grades sorted. See Illustrated Section.

3. SCOURING: This removes the yolk, suint, and remaining foreign matter from the wool.

4. BLENDING, OILING, MIXING: The

various grades of wool are chosen and laid down layer upon layer, each layer being sprayed with oleic oil or some other similar type of oil. After the blend has been built up, it is then torn down and the varying grades and types of stock chosen are thoroughly mixed to be made ready for the next operation.

5. CARDING: This parallels the fibers to marked degree, takes out much foreign matter that may still be in the wool, and also removes the short, undesirable fibers from the lot. Carding puts the stock in a manageable condition for further manipulation.

6. CROSSING: This operation takes the carded webs of wool, supported on lattice aprons, and feeds them to an endless lattice apron from several directions.

7. HARDENING: The first felting treatment afforded the wool is initiated at this point, when the fibers are felted by the application of heat, moisture, pressure, and vibration.

8. FELTING AND FULLING: These are effected by mechanical pressure agitation with chemical stimulus to cause the actual felting of the fibers to considerable degree.

9. WASHING: This will clean the stock and remove any soluble impurities prior to further manipulation.

10. DYEING: This is carried out in the piece-dye kettle or kier method. Water-soluble aniline dyestuffs are used to obtain standardized shades.

11. DRYING: This operation stretches the material to the proper width, and the moisture is removed by passing the felt fabric through circulating hot-air dryers under controlled conditions.

12. SHEARING: The removal of fuzzy, protruding fibers is done by the rotating blades of the shear, which work on the principle of a lawn mower. Smooth-surface fabric is the result of this action.

13. CALENDERING: The pressing and ironing of the felt under heated cylinder rollers to produce the desired finish on the fabric.

14. INSPECTING: Minute optical examination of the felt for flaws and blemishes which may be remedied or removed.

15. CUTTING: Precision die cutting of the felt into the desired size demanded by the trade.

16. TESTING: This is done in accordance with required specifications and is carried on continuously to insure the best type of product obtainable and to meet the needs of industry.

17. SHIPPING: The packaging of the finished felt product according to the desires of the customers' specifications, and the delivery to transit carriers.

FENCING. Mill ends in England.

FENTS. Short lengths of cloths classed as seconds; also used to imply end pieces.

FERRAIOLA. A short cape, attached to a cassock and reaching halfway down the upper arm. Used by the religious, both secular and order, members.

FERRET. A narrow binding tape made from major textile fibers.

FERRETTI, ANTONIO. Italian scientist who in 1904 brought out the first protein fiber, Lanital. Belgium is the only country which makes the fiber at present.

FERRIC SULPHATE. Used as a weighting agent in dyeing silk, and, to a limited degree, in dyeing cotton. It is the chief constituent of sulphate of iron. Formula is $Fe_2(SO_4)_3$.

FERRONNERIE. Certain Italian velvets of the fourteenth and fifteenth centuries were known by this term because of their resemblance to wrought iron work. The term is a contraction of the Italian word for iron, ferro.

FERROUS SULPHATE. It is used in dyeing cotton or wool black, and in indigo and alizarine dyeing. Also known as copperas, the formula is $FeSO_4 \cdot 7H_2O$.

FESTOON. 1. Any decoration that hangs in a curve. 2. A decorative wreath, formed by joining the links of a crocheted chain, that is hung from the shoulders of a knitted garment. 3. Ready-made curtains used for windows and archways, usually made of damask with more or less elaborate fringe. The fabric is draped in folds over a supporting pole.

FESTOON DRAPERY. Name for a ready-made curtain for archways or windows; usually composed of damask and a fringe and attached in graceful folds over a pole.

FESTOON STITCH. Another name for the buttonhole stitch.

FETTLER. The operator who cleans the rollers on the cards in the mill and is responsible for proper setting of the units in the frame.

FETTLING. British term for the cleaning and stripping of card clothing on woolen or worsted cards.

FETTOFLAN. A cotton cloth of plain or twill weave, raised, napped, and finished to simulate flannel.

FEUTRE. French for felted, milled, or matted. Fabric of this type is called Feutriére. Examples could be melton, kersey, beaver, Zibeline, etc.

FEUTRON METHOD IN NON-WOVEN FABRICS. American Felt Company, Glenville, Connecticut, in 1955 produced the first nonwoven fabrics consisting exclusively of man-made fibers not bonded either by resin or thermoplastically but interlocked by the mechanical means of an interlocking on a needle-loom system, followed by a felting process by the use of chemicals. Uses of the product include wet and dry filtration, high temperature oil-bearing seals, reinforcement for plastics, gaskets, oil wicking in high temperatures, thermal and acoustical insulation, base fabrics for special coatings and impregnants, and for high temperature moisture seals in street and airport lighting fixtures. The method is named for St. Feutre of Caen, France, the patron saint of the felt industry.

FEZ. Named for the city of Fez in Morocco, northwest Africa, it is a cap-like truncated cone usually made of red felt and embellished by a black tassel. Gold insignia is sometimes used for adornment. Without the tassel the cone is called a *Tarbush.*

FIBER. An individual strand, sometimes referred to as a filament. It is a slender, fine-diameter, single strand. Several fibers, however, may be combined to make them ready for spinning, weaving, and knitting purposes. A fiber usually has a rather definite set length. See Illustrated Section.

FIBER-BONDED. A registered trade-mark of the Dan River Mills, used by Dan River and also licensed by Dan River to other cotton mills for the purpose of identifying products resulting from the following patented processes: 1. A patented process for applying synthetic resins in emulsion form to fabrics for the purpose of increasing abrasion strength. 2. A patented process for the application of pigment colors and a permanent synthetic resin finish simultaneously to fabrics. 3. A trade-mark covering a patented process for making high-strength yarns with controlled resistance to stretch.

FIBER DRAG. 1. In seed cotton, it is the resistance to the separation of seeds in a lock of cotton because of the intermeshing of fibers in the lock between the seeds. 2. In lint cotton, the term implies merely resistance to separation between the fibers.

FIBER DRYER. A wire conveyor that carries wet fiber through a drying box heated by steam coils and fans.

FIBER E. A crimped viscose rayon filament yarn manufactured by E. I. du Pont de Nemours & Co., Inc. Fabric made of this yarn contracts in the finishing for use in particular end products.

How Fiberglas is made

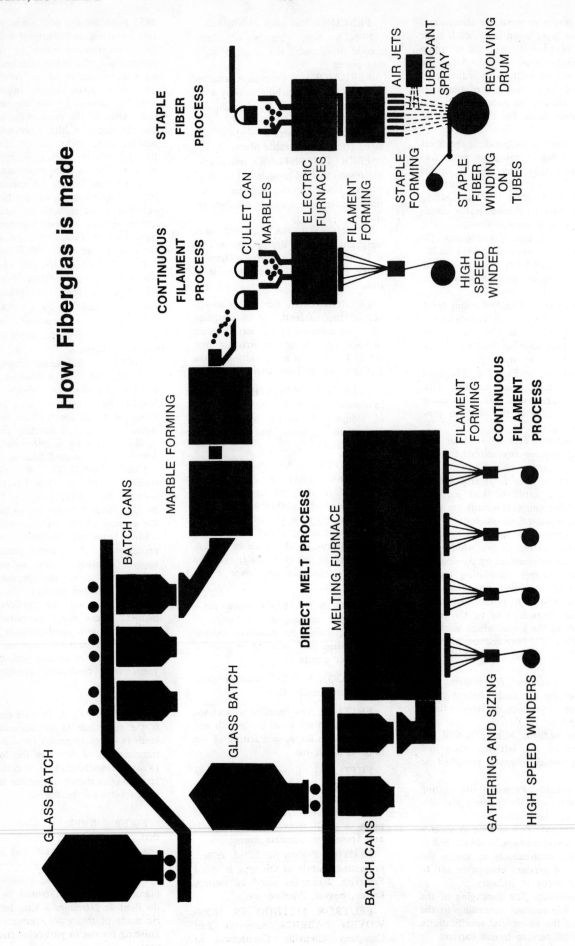

GLASS BATCH

BATCH CANS

MARBLE FORMING

GLASS BATCH

DIRECT MELT PROCESS

BATCH CANS

MELTING FURNACE

FILAMENT FORMING

CONTINUOUS FILAMENT PROCESS

GATHERING AND SIZING

HIGH SPEED WINDERS

CONTINUOUS FILAMENT PROCESS

CULLET CAN

MARBLES

ELECTRIC FURNACES

FILAMENT FORMING

HIGH SPEED WINDER

STAPLE FIBER PROCESS

AIR JETS

LUBRICANT SPRAY

REVOLVING DRUM

STAPLE FORMING

STAPLE FIBER WINDING ON TUBES

FABRIC FINISHING

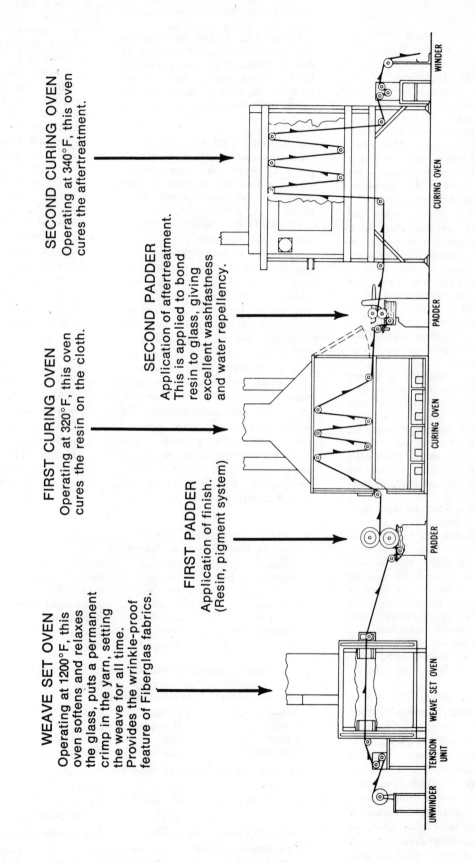

WEAVE SET OVEN
Operating at 1200°F, this oven softens and relaxes the glass, puts a permanent crimp in the yarn, setting the weave for all time. Provides the wrinkle-proof feature of Fiberglas fabrics.

FIRST PADDER
Application of finish. (Resin, pigment system)

FIRST CURING OVEN
Operating at 320°F, this oven cures the resin on the cloth.

SECOND PADDER
Application of aftertreatment. This is applied to bond resin to glass, giving excellent washfastness and water repellency.

SECOND CURING OVEN
Operating at 340°F, this oven cures the aftertreatment.

UNWINDER   TENSION UNIT   WEAVE SET OVEN   PADDER   CURING OVEN   PADDER   CURING OVEN   WINDER

Courtesy: Owens-Corning Fiberglas Corp., Toledo, Ohio 43601

FIBERFILL. Noun for manmade fibers designed specifically as filling material in apparel, comforters, pillows, sleeping bags, upholstery and similar uses. This generic term was coined by E. I. duPont de Nemours & Co., Inc., Wilmington, Delaware.

FIBERFRAX. Trade-mark of the Carborundum Company for its fiber made from molten aluminum oxide and silica. It is manufactured in both continuous filament and short lengths into a variety of forms such as batts, tapes, woven fabrics, ropes, yarns, etc. It is not sold to the consumer market, but is widely used industrially for insulation, filters, soundproofing, etc.

FIBERGLAS. Textile fibers and yarns produced from glass which, when drawn fine enough, can be woven into strong, flexible fabrics. The raw materials that are used to make ordinary glass are refined and shaped into glass marbles which are remelted and formed into more than a hundred glass filaments, simultaneously attenuated into a single yarn of minute diameter. Glass yarns have been produced as fine as 100s cotton count.

Short, staple glass fibers, ranging from 8 to 15 inches in length, are produced by striking the streams of molten glass with jets of high-pressure air or steam. This process separates the filament where required, and seals the ends of the short staple. Short-staple glass yarns have a fuzzy surface, but the continuous filament produces yarns that are smooth.

Fiberglas is resistant to most chemicals and is insoluble in organic solvents. It is affected only by hydrochloric and phosphoric acids, and by weak, hot solutions or strong, cold solutions of alkalies. It is used for fireproof clothing and draperies, for electrical insulation, and for soundproofing. It is noninflammable, nonabsorbent, mothproof, mildew-proof, and resistant to sunlight; it does not deteriorate with age. Product of Owens-Corning Fiberglas Corporation, New York City.

FIBERGLAS, BETA. This product of Owens-Corning Fiberglas Corporation is an ultrafine, pure glass fiber many times finer than ordinary glass fiber or any other fiber for that matter. Beta does not burn, is completely non-combustible, even in an all oxygen atmosphere. It will not melt until a temperature of 1,350 degrees Fahrenheit is reached. Incidentally, individual glass fibers are made by a process that draws-out batch-melted glass marbles made of silica, lime, soda, etc. through tiny platinum orifices or minuted holes, or bushings.

They can be spun into yarn, woven and sewn the same as any other textile fiber. It must have a protective substance used as a coating so that the "too-strong fibers" do not destroy one another.

FIBERGLAS AEROCOR. Made of superfine glass and about 30 times as fine as human hair, this product is lightly bonded into a fluffy blanket form for insulation, adapted for applications on the exterior of concealed ducts and for all ducts of a circular or elliptical cross section.

FIBERGLAS CURTAINS. Thin, translucent curtains which are not affected by water and strong sunlight, cannot shrink, and because of their width, do not need seams; easily cleaned.

FIBERGRASS. Product of Patchogue-Plymouth Company, Inc., Atlanta, Georgia, this is a polypropylene face yarn for use in outdoor carpeting to go along with the company's manmade fiber backing. Described as a "pol filament" yarn, the product has the hand and appearance of multifilament but a different structure. At present, it is made in heavy 5,700 denier for hard outdoor use such as in school playyards and parks, and a 3,800 denier for use in transportation areas for aircraft, boats, etc. Both possess built-in ultraviolet stability. The product provides minimized streaking and a broad multi-color range, both of which are accomplished by twisting or plying two shades into a single tufting yarn. Solution dyes are used for broadloom, mat, and rug mills.

FIBER LACE. Lace made from aloe, banana, pineapple, and similar fibers.

FIBER OPTICS. The study of the ability of translucent or transparent fibers to transmit light. Nylon, for example, is opaque in the thick state, but in sheets of a thickness of .25 inches or less is translucent.

FIBER OR YARN, UNDRAWN. Extruded fiber or yarn whose component molecules are unoriented and which show a predominant plastic flow in the first stages of stretching. Undrawn yarn, incidentally, represents an intermediate stage in the manufacture of a man-made or synthetic yarn.

FIBER PLANT. Any plant that yields a fiber for some use in textiles. Known as bast fibers—flax, ramie, jute, hemp, henequen, sisal, etc.

FIBER PORES. See FABRIC PORES.

FIBER PRODUCTS IDENTIFICATION ACT. See Man-Made Textile Fibers and the Textile Fiber Products Identification Act of June 3, 1959.

FIBER PROPERTIES, MAJOR. These follow:

1. *Physical Properties:* Abrasion resistance, capillarity and penetrability, cohesion, color or cast, composition, conductivity of heat, crimp, diameter fineness, elasticity, elongation breaking point, flexibility, hygroscopic moisture, staple length, luster, microscopical appearance, resiliency, tensile strength (dry and wet), surface texture, twist spinnability, wear resistance.

FIBER KINGDOMS, TEXTILE.
NATURAL FIBERS—ANIMAL SOURCE

Alpaca	Guanaco	Noil *	Spun silk *
Angora goat hair	Hog hair	Persian cashmere	Suri
Camel hair	Huarizo	Rabbit hair	Vicuna
Cashmere	Llama	Reprocessed wool *	Wool
Cow hair	Mohair	Reused wool *	Worsted
Extract wool *	Misti	Shoddy *	Worsted top
Fur	Mungo *	Silk	

* Classed as reclaimed animal fibers for use in textiles; obtained from discarded fabrics, apparel, tailors' clippings, wastes, etc.

NATURAL FIBERS—VEGETABLE SOURCE

Abaca	Hemp	Kapok	Ramie
Coir	Henequen	Kenaf	Sisal
Cotton	Istle	Manila hemp	Straw
Flax/linen	Jute	Pineapple fiber	Sunn fiber

MINERAL FIBERS—OBTAINED FROM THE GROUND

Asbestos	Lurex	Metlon	Spun glass
Glass fibers	Metallic	Slag wool (steel wool)	Tinsel

MODIFIED FIBERS—MODIFICATION FROM THE ORIGINAL FIBERS

Cyanoethylated cotton— acrylonitrile reaction	Mercerized cotton	Nonshrinkable wool
Immunized cotton	Modified acetate fibers— Celcos, Fortisan	Plexon
		Acetate and rayon staples

2. *Chemical Properties:* Reaction to bleaching agents, dyes, light, heat, metallic salts, mildew, oxidizing agents, to other oxidation bleaches, reduction bleaches, strong acids, volatile organic acids, strong alkalies, water, weak alkalies; swelling capacity ability.

FIBER REACTIVE DYES. See RE-ACTIVE DYES.

FIBER RUG. An inexpensive rug made with twisted cotton warp and coarse thick filling yarn made from twisted strips of paper or grass.

FIBERSET. Trade-mark of Bianchini, Ferier, Inc., for a process designed to stabilize rayon fabrics to prevent their shrinking, stretching, or sagging.

FIBER SILK. Before the coining of the term rayon, fiber silk was used to designate cloth made of "artificial silk," superseded in 1924 by the word rayon.

FIBERSTOCK. Continuous filament waste stock which has been chopped, crimped, and spun into yarn in the same manner as true staple fiber is processed.

FIBER "T." Registered trade-mark of Union Carbide & Carbon Corporation for its modacrylic fiber which has a soft hand, durability, warmth, and is quick-drying. It has good abrasion resistance, wrinkle-recovery and shape retention.

FIBERTHIN. Registered trademark of UniRoyal Fiber and Textile Division, UniRoyal, Inc., for its base fiber used in the production of high tear-resistant, lightweight, coated fabrics which are made from nylon and rayon.

FIBER TRADEMARK. This term indicates a word or words used by a person to identify a particular fiber produced or sold by him. It distinguishes fibers of the same generic class produced or sold by others. Such a term shall not include any trade mark, product mark, house mark, tradename, or other name which does not identify a particular fiber. Some examples follow:

Acele - A duPont acetate; *Arnel* - a triacetate of Celanese; *Avlin* - high modulus polyester of American Viscose; *Bemberg* - a cuprammonium rayon of Bemberg Corporation; *C-Nylon* - a nylon of Monsanto; *Caprolan* - a nylon of Allied Chemical Corporation; *Chromspun* - an acetate of Eastman Chemical Products; *Coloray* - a rayon of Courtaulds North America; *Creslan* - an acrylic of American Cyanamid Company; *Encron* - a polyester of American Enka Corporation; *Marvess* - an olefin fiber of Phillips Fibers Corporation; *Trevira* - a polyester of Hoechst Fibers.

FIBESTOS. One of the first and best-known of the thermoplastic molding compounds. These cellulose-acetate formulations produce articles which possess a high impact strength, excellent wear-resistance, a high degree of rigidity and toughness, and fairly good dimensional stability. There are over 70 standard fibestos formulations, and any one of these can be further varied to fill some specific need.

Outstanding properties include adaptability to extrusion or economical high-speed injection molding. Compression molding may be resorted to where necessary. Fibestos may be used for costume jewelry, instrument and radio panels, tool handles, cases, toilet articles, etc. The compounds are available in transparent, translucent, and opaque colors over the entire range of the spectrum, including mottles and configurations.

FIBRAMINE. A Belgian viscose product which contains 3 to 5 per cent casein to give the wool dyeing properties.

FIBRENE. Generic French term for spun rayon. Rayonne is French for rayon.

FIBRE-WEIGHT. British term for the unit by which fiber weight is measured, usually in milligrams per centimeter.

FIBRIDS. A generic term coined by Du Pont for a wholly synthetic polymer with fibrous or filmy structure, similar to beaten wood pulp, and used chiefly for bonding man-made fibers in papers. See TEXTRYL.

FIBRIL. A small or fine fiber or filament; synonymous with fiber.

FIBRILLAE. The strands or minute chain of cells forming secondary deposits.

FIBRILLATION. 1. The formation of fibrils. 2. The slitting of plastic film into yarn form. 3. When referring to silk, the term means the tendency of silk filament to split. See Exfoliation.

FIBRO. Trademark for viscose rayon staple made by Courtaulds North America, Inc., New York City. It is supplied in a wide range of deniers and lengths.

FIBROCAST. Trade-mark of Firestone Tire & Rubber Company for products of its Molded Fiber Products Division.

FIBROCETA. This is the name used by Courtaulds, Ltd., England, for their acetate-staple fiber.

FIBRO DDC. Brought out in the spring of 1968 by Courtaulds North America, Inc., New York City, this is a deep dyeing crimped rayon fiber. It is designed chiefly for the floorcovering trades and has been a factor in the development of tone-on-tone color combinations utilizing one dye bath treatment, thus providing maximum dyeing economies.

FIBROGRAPH. A device that can "read" the various fiber lengths in a sample of raw-stock fibers. Using a photoelectric eye, the device scans the sample in seconds and reports the percentages of fiber lengths.

FIBROGRAPH MEAN LENGTH. The measure of the average length of all cotton fibers longer than the mean length, expressed in terms of decimal fractions of an inch as measured on the fibrograph.

FIBROIN. The insoluble part of the raw-silk filament. The worm has two glands that contain the silk, or fibroin, which, on coming into the air, is cemented together by the silk gum, or sericin.

FIBROUS. Composed of or having the characteristics of fiber.

FICHU. Popular method of wearing a scarf, draped around the shoulders and then knotted at the bosom with the ends of the scarf hanging loose. Also implies the ruffled-drape effect on a dress or blouse bosom.

FIFTH COMBING. Wool obtained from the thigh area in grading a sheep fleece.

FIGURE. 1. A motif, pattern, design, or effect in woven goods. 2. To embellish with figures or designs.

FIGURED DRAFT. See DRAFT, FIGURED.

FIGURED WEAVES. Those capable of making some sort of motif in fabric —bird's-eye, diamond, spot, novelty piqué, swivel, clipspot, warp-float, etc.

FII POLYESTER. Produced by Fiber Industries, Inc., and marketed by Celanese Corporation of America, this material is produced from a polyment made from ethylene glycol and dimethyl terephthlate. Available in tow, staple, and filament, it has a melting point of 500° F., and a sticking point around 480° F. It has excellent strength retention after prolonged exposure to relatively high temperatures. Its resistance to sunlight, expecially under glass, is good and there is high resistance to bleaches, solvents, and most chemicals except strong bases. Used in men's, women's, and childrens' apparel, the fiber is also used in industry for items such a V-belts, fire hose, sewing thread, and tire cord. Specific gravity is 1.38.

FIBERWOVEN FABRICS

Fiberwoven fabrics, a development of the Chatham Manufacturing Company and the Fiberwoven Corporation, Elkin, North Carolina, were unveiled in July, 1964. The idea for these fabrics was conceived by Dr. Alexander Smith, a former professor at the Massachusetts Institute of Technology, Cambridge, Massachusetts. Dr. Smith did the mathematics for the project and was assisted by a physicist, a mechanical engineer, and an electrical engineer.

The batt, which is made continuously and, therefore, has no definite length, is fed into the machine in batt-fiber form in the manufacturing process, and barbed needles are manipulated into it, thereby entangling the fibers around the barbs. The barbs pick up the fibers and push them into the batt, the procedure relying on cooperating pairs of barbed needles. The top needle of the set or pair descends and pushes the loops of fiber into the batt. Then it pulls upward and out of the batt, which advances in its progress through the machine. The bottom needle of the set then comes into play and pushes the upward loop through the top loop to form a chain of entangled fibers. Thus the entire sets of needles, top and bottom, perform the work involved. About 26,000 needles are used in this machine, which is ten feet in width and approximately twelve feet in height. The needles, of course, go in two directions.

The batt can be composed of any of the major textile fibers, natural and/or manmade. It may be set up in layer formation. Any type of fiber can be used for the outside, as well as for the inside, in this "sandwich formation." For example, the outside might be wool or acrylic fiber while the inside is made up of rayon, lower in cost than wool or any acrylic. Fiber lengths may range from one to four inches in staple length, and in denier counts of yarn the range may run from 1- to 18-denier. Batts can be made by Air-Lay Equipment, Rando-Webbers, such as used in the manufacture of nonwoven fabrics, or by woolen or worsted carding machines.

A few threads, all in one direction, serve as carrier yarns for the batt, which does not have any strength. It is the needling which builds the strength into the fabric. These yarns do nothing for the fabric, and their only purpose is to aid in feeding the batt into the machine. The batt should have evenness in its structure, since the smoother and more uniform the batt, the better will be the resultant blanket or other product made by this method.

Tests show that Fiberwoven blankets provide better-balanced strength than a conventionally woven blanket. The fabrics do not have to go through the essential operations in making woven blankets—raw stock, grading, blending, oiling, mixing, carding and spinning of the yarn, and finally the weaving of the blanket. Napping on a woven blanket is done only on the filling yarn, which is soft-spun, has little twist in it, and is bulky in nature. Napping also causes the blanket to lose some strength, and as it wears down, the yarns are often observed in the structure. There is also some little loss of strength in Fiberwoven blankets, but it is uniform and as it wears down, "you see more of the same." No exposed yarns are seen.

Final results in a comparison of both types of blanket reveal that the Fiberwoven blanket provides somewhat more warmth because it has a better form of insulation, a loftier hand or feel, and gives longer wear to the consumer. Fabrics may be made heavier or lighter, stronger or weaker, harsher or softer, as the demands require. There is also less shrinkage especially when rayon, a low-cost fiber, is used; shrinkage is reduced about 50 per cent.

There are two great savings in goods of this type. Firstly, in labor requirements; it takes from 350 to 400 operatives to make one million blankets in one year on conventional textile equipment. In the same span of time the same number of blankets can be made by about 50 employees. Secondly, wastes in the manufacture of woven blankets range from around 18 per cent to about 25 per cent from raw wool to finished goods. Fiberwovens have wastes from about 12 per cent to around 15 per cent, and most of this total can be reclaimed for future usage. Their manufacture may be said to be a one-step operation from raw fiber stock to the needled blanket.

Electronics play an important part in the machinery used; each line has more than one mile of wiring, and synchronization is very important. The company has a licensing program for licensees, since the equipment is not for sale. Several items must be determined by licensees dependent upon the construction desired for production. These include needle size and shape, shape of the barbs and the barb location, angle of penetration, rate of the advance of the cloth, number of needle punches per square inch, etc.

Conventional chemicals can be used for surface treatment of the fabrics. The material stands up very well in all types of sewing. Potentials of Fiberwoven fabrics include carpet and rug backing, floor covering, trunk liners, upholstery fabrics, and other heavy goods. Embossed finishes are possible on the fabrics.

FIL. French word for fiber, thread or yarn. Some of its applications follow:

FIL AU CHINOIS: Smooth linen sewing thread (Chinese thread).

FIL DE CRIN: Heavy silk thread or yarn. See CORDONNET.

FIL D'EMBALLAGE: A very coarse thread for sewing bags, containers, etc.

FIL D'ECOSSE, FIL DE COTON: Cotton thread.

FIL D'EPREUVE: A French linen cloth made with blue and white stripes or checks.

FIL DE FLORENCE: Silkworm gut used to make fishing lines.

FIL DE JAPON: Reeled silk made from three to fifteen cocoon filaments. Each cocoon gives off two filaments cemented together by sericin or silk gum immediately after being emitted by the silkworm.

FIL PLAT: A French cotton yarn that has been bleached; used for embroidery.

FIL AU TONKINOIS: A strong, waxtreated thread used for coarse sewing.

FIL DE TRACE: This double or plied thread is used in outlining lace motifs and appliqué work.

FILAMATIC. Term used by FMC Corporation, American Viscose Division, to describe their high-speed continuous automatic process for spinning rayon filament textile yarns.

FILAMENT. 1. A fiber of indefinite length, such as filament acetate, rayon, nylon. May be miles long. 2. A single strand of rayon spinning solution as it is exuded from a spinneret orifice and coagulated in an acid bath or other medium; also true of other man-made filaments. 3. The single unit which is extruded by a silkworm in spinning its cocoon. Actually the silkworm makes two filaments at the one time, and they are cemented or glued together by the sericin, or silkgum, exuded by the silkworm in the action. Filaments are then spun into yarn.

FILAMENT COUNT. The number of individual fibers or filaments actually counted in silk, or man-made fibers or filaments. The number of filaments has direct influence on the softness, strength, pliability, and finish of the fabric.

FILAMENT RAYON YARN. Rayon yarn composed of a number of fine, continuous rayon filaments grouped together and usually given a slight twist.

FILAMENT YARN TYPES AND YARN EFFECTS, GENERIC IDENTIFICATION FOR.

1. COLOR BLEND: A technique in which two fine yarns of different colors are combined with a heavy white yarn to obtain a blending through light diffusion.
2. INTER-TEXTURED YARNS: Those in which filaments of two separate no-twist ends are combined into a single strand after dyeing or texturing.
3. MIRROR-EFFECT YARNS: These reflect a concept in yarn coloration in which a heavy white end is wrapped with a dyed fine end resulting in tinted diffusion through the strand.
4. MULTIPLEX YARNS: These are balanced plied yarns which contain ends that have been given different types of texturizing.
5. MULTI-PROCESS YARNS: Yarns to which two or more texturizing effects have been applied.
6. SINGLE-PROCESS YARNS: Those which have been bulked by only one method.
7. SPACE DYEING: A method which applies one or more colors to yarn at intervals along its length.
8. SPACE TREATMENT: Preparation of yarns in order to change the dye index at various positions along their length.
9. TRILOBULAR: Textured yarns which have trefoil cross-section.
10. WIREFORM: Generally accepted designation for filament nylon which has a round cross-section.

FILASSE. Any vegetable fiber, cotton excepted, in the manipulative stages prior to actual spinning into yarn.

FILATEX. For use on elastic yarn formed from elastic material such as rubber, rubber latex, and the like, either covered or uncovered. Patents were granted by the U. S. Patent Office, November 24, 1936, and renewed November 24, 1956, for Filatex Corporation, New York City. This elastic yarn has a round core in which the covering is cotton, nylon, or rayon and is laid on a crosswise slant so that stretch will not be inhibited.

FILATRICE. 1. French for silk floss or florette silk. 2. French dress goods made of silk warp and florette filling.

FILATURE. A place or establishment where silk reeling is carried on. Japan has about 3,000 of these places, with more than 300,000 reeling basins. Filatures will range from 50 basins up to more than 1,000. About 350,000 are employed in this part of the industry, and all but about 10,000 are females.

FILATURE CLASSIFICATION IN THE YOKOHAMA MARKET. There are 6 major grades in silk classification: 1. Grand double extra; 2. Double extra; 3. Extra; 4. Best Number One extra; 5. Best Number One; 6. Number One.

Each of the above grades may be further divided into three classes, A, B, and C. The number of mills that supply the great Yokohama market number more than 1,200. The production of the mills is considered as belonging to one of the above grades. Silk that grades lower in quality is usually consumed in domestic manufacture.

The percentages of the above grades are as follows: Grand double extra, 1 per cent; double extra, 6 per cent; Extra, 8 per cent; Best Number One extra, 16 per cent; Best Number One, 37 per cent; Number One, 32 per cent.

FILATURE SILK. That which has been reeled by machine instead of by hand.

FILE SILK. Faille silk.

FILET. 1. A lace made of different types of yarn which vary considerably in grade and quality. The motifs are made by interlacing the yarn in and out of the meshes. 2. A knotted-square net or mesh. 3. A square-mesh effect made with linen yarn.

FILET GUIPURE. See GUIPURE.

FILET LACE. A handmade-mesh linen lace, with patterns formed by filling certain squares of knotted mesh foundation with darning stitches giving a geometric effect. Designs usually found in filet lace are of foliage, fruit, animals, and birds.

Handmade filet is made with single thread, while the imitation is machine-made with ply or double yarn. The quality of the lace depends on the fineness of the yarn used. The coarser yarns produce the more inferior lace. Uses are for doilies, dresses, lingerie, neckwear, runners, and table linen.

FILIGREE POINT. The gold laces, made in the days of the "Louis Kings" in France and now museum pieces and collector's items, are simulated at present by modern versions of these priceless gems of lace. Bars of silk thread were and are used to hold the gold threads secure.

FILLED CLOTH. Fabric which has been given heavy size or starch for some set purpose—buckram, crinoline, tarlatan, bookbinding cloth, sign fabric, embroidery foundation, etc.

FILLED GOODS. Woolens which contain varying amounts of flocks.

FILLER. 1. A machine used to compress mattress filling and force it into a fabric cover. 2. A material added to a soap or other detergent which does not alter its effectiveness under the conditions of use.

FILLER CORD. A coarse, plied cotton yarn made by plying a single 1.5s and a single 2s, or slightly heavier

count of yarn. It is spun from the lower qualities of cotton wastes and is used in the manufacture of multi-wall paper bags or sacks, which in turn are used in the shipping of a wide variety of products.

The filler cord follows along the strong sewing thread in the bag manufacturing process, and bulks-out to fill the needle holes. If these holes are not filled, they would allow seepage of powdered products such as cement, flour, etc. A secondary purpose of filler cord is to help prevent the needles and thread from cutting along the perforated line of sewing. Formerly, filler cord was used on practically all multiwall bags, but of late paper filler has been substituted when the bag is to be used for coarser products such as crystals.

FILLER POINT. A retractible finger found on a full-fashioned knitting machine which picks up one or more loops to cover a needle hole resulting in the widening operation. See WIDENING.

FILLET. 1. A strip of wire clothing, 1½ to 2 inches wide, applied spirally to rollers to cover their surfaces. 2. Narrow widths of a foundation fabric covered with emery, wound spirally on the dead roll, and used for grinding.

FILLET WINDING MACHINE. The machine which winds card clothing or fillet on the various rollers found on a card. It is wound in a spiral direction.

FILLING. 1. An individual yarn which interlaces with warp yarn at right angles in weaving fabric. Also known as pick or filling pick. Filling usually has less twist when compared with warp yarn. See Illustrated Section. 2. Weft, the English term for filling, is used in this country in the hand-weaving and the carpet trades. The term, at times, is rather misleading and is often confused with woof, the English term for warp.

FILLING-BACKED SERGE. Name for Frenchback and serge made with two systems of filling yarn and one of warp yarn. Cloths of this type may be ordinary or high in quality.

FILLING BOBBIN. A tapered spindle on which filling yarn is wound. It is held in the filling battery-compartment of the loom, where it is automatically injected into the shuttle when needed.

FILLING-FACE. The face of a cloth in which the filling predominates.

FILLING FORK. This loom device for control of the filling yarn causes a loom to bang off and stop when filling breaks or the bobbin becomes spent. The fork is set in the side or in the middle of the raceplate, free of the selvages. When the filling fails to carry

through the shed, these prongs, sometimes called "the cat's whiskers," drop into a slot which has an electric contact, thereby stopping the loom. Filling picks, when running correctly, prevent the prongs from dropping into the slot, since they support the fork when the loom is in action.

FILLING FORK FILLING CHANGE ACTION. A device that transfers a new bobbin to the shuttle if the one in action breaks or runs out. In the absence of the pick going through the shed, the mechanism will engage the transfer device. The fork may be in the center of the loom, or there may be one at either end of the raceplate. Some looms are equipped with a fork at each end of the race.

FILLING KNITTING. See WEFT KNITTING.

FILLING MATERIALS. Cotton cloths are "filled" in finishing by the use of any of the following chemicals: alum, blanc fixe, China clay, talc. All of them tend to fill in the spaces between the warp and the filling of low-textured cloths such as bookbinding fabric, buckram, binding fabric, net, scrim, shade cloth, tarlatan.

FILLING PATTERN. The manner in which filling yarns of varying colors are worked into the pattern of the cloth; to be considered are the type of yarn, count and ply, color, etc.

FILLING PILE FABRIC. This cloth is formed by floating extra picks on the surface of the goods. These floats are cut in or out of the loom to form the tufts of pile. Corduroy is an example. The filling-pile yarn, appearing on the surface of a cloth, does not always have to be cut since some of the material is used as an uncut pile fabric.

FILLING REP FABRIC. This cloth is identified by its crosswise rib made possible by evenly spun, cylindrical filling yarn. The same effect is also observed in poplin and cotton broadcloth.

FILLING REVERSIBLE. Name sometimes given to napped cotton, woolen, or cotton and woolen bathrobe material. The face and back of the cloth are opposite in color scheme according to a plan or motif.

FILLING RIB WEAVE. A construction that is made in the filling direction, while the ribs or cords go in the warp direction. All filling ribs, in simple constructions, repeat on two filling picks; warp ribs repeat on two warp ends. Filling ribs include novelty shirting stripes, officer's belt webbing, piqué.

Filling ribs may have 2, 4, 6, or more picks placed in the same shed of the loom to give the repeat. Warp ribs are often termed dimity cords and are made from 2, 4, 6, or more ends grouped as one in the drawing-in and reeding of the warp in the loom. A combination of bunched ends and picks is usually called a dimity check. See DIMITY.

FILLINGS. Non-substantive and usually insoluble materials such as China clay, alum, blanc fixe, gypsum, talc, etc., added to fabrics along with starches or gums during finishing to provide added weight or to modify the appearance, hand, or mellowness of the material.

FILLING SATEEN. Cotton cloth made with a filling-effect satin weave on the face of the fabric.

FILLING STOP MOTION. See FILLING FORK.

FILLING TWIST. 1. The number of turns of twist per inch in filling yarn; generally speaking it has less turns than warp yarn. 2. See S-TWIST, TWIST MULTIPLIER.

FILLING WIND. A system used in winding yarn onto a spinning-frame bobbin. Each layer of yarn extends only a short distance and each successive layer moves slightly higher on the bobbin. The entire bobbin is wound evenly at the top, body, and heel by the up-and-down, controlled motion used in winding.

FILLING WINDER. A machine, of which there are several types, used to wind filling yarn onto a bobbin, cop, quill, or spindle so that it may be set in the shuttle of the loom and used as filling in weaving fabric.

FILM. A thin coating, layer, or membrane. A component factor in emulsification and adsorption.

FILOCHE, FILOUCHE. A French gauze-like fabric with rather large meshes; high twist, two-ply yarns are used in this cottongoods. FILOCHE is also the name of a French woolen or worsted serge made with an eight-block twill weave. Dyed in the piece.

FILOSELLE. A silk thread, inferior to silk floss since it is made from a poorer quality of fiber; used much in embroidery and fancy work.

FILO SILK. A soft, two-ply, embroidery silk thread.

FILTER. To separate a solid from a liquid by passing through a compact mass of fibrous materials which will retain the solid matter and allow the liquid to pass through.

FILTER CLOTH. A warp-effect, twill-weave fabric which varies much in weave, yarn count, texture, and weight. Finds much use in industry in the food, candy, paint, chemical, petro-

leum, and similar industries. Some filter fabric is made of cotton but, nylon, Vinyon, and Fiberglas are ideal since they are not affected by most chemicals.

FILTER PRESS. A machine used to press viscose solutions through fine cotton cloths in order to remove impurities or suspended material.

FINAL INSPECTION. As the term implies, it is the final inspection and close examination of the goods, whether it is done in the mill, the sponging and examining house, the cutting-up plant, or any other place where the goods are supposed to be perfect and free from blemishes. Final inspection cuts down the amount of poor or defective cloth, rejects, and seconds. It is the final stamp of approval given to the material.

FIN DE SIECLE. French (fin de siècle); means "the end of the century." Used specifically to indicate the end of the nineteenth century.

FINDINGS. A term applied to miscellaneous fittings, such as buttons, snaps, eyes, and ornaments, that are sewed or otherwise attached to garments and shoes during manufacture.

FINE. Used in the American Blood System of grading wool, it refers to the highest, finest, and best grade of wool. Designated in grading with a range from 64s to 80s.

FINE COTTON GOODS. Covers a host of cottons whose yarn counts vary from 35s to 80s and higher; made from carded or combed yarn, the latter being used in the better fabrics. In some fine goods a carded yarn serves in the back of the fabric while a combed yarn is used in the face.

FINE DELAINE WOOL. A fine merino wool of about 2½-inch staple used in the best worsted yarn for expensive fabrics.

FINE END. Any warp yarn that is thin or fine because one or more ply is missing; often seen in silk or rayon reeling or throwing.

FINE FRAME. A third fly frame used after the roving frame in the manufacture of high-grade cotton yarns. Also known as the speeder or the second intermediate frame.

FINENESS. Relative measurement of a yarn for actual diameter.

FINE PLAIN. Also known as "gray longcloth," the term covers combed cottons which have a texture of 170 to 200 threads per square inch. 1/40s to 1/66s yarn will give this texture, which is ideal as fabric to be finished into cambric, longcloth, and similar goods.

FINE POCKETING. A jute material made with one or two warps and one filling in a plain-weave arrangement. The cloth weighs from 15 to 17 ounces per square yard.

FINE TOW. When flax is dressed the fine tow waste obtained finds use in making coarse cloth, cord, and rope.

FINE WOOL. Implies the best grade of stock taken from a fleece in sorting wool for the several grades. It includes XX, X, or 3/4-blood wool, and sometimes 1/2-blood wool. The wool possesses the following characteristics: short fiber, the greatest number of serrations to the inch when compared with all other grades of wool, loftiness, springiness, excellent working properties, and considerable oily feel, because of the high amount of yolk present.

FINE WOOL BREEDS. Descended from the original Spanish Merino sheep, these breeds include Austrialian, Argentine, Ohio, Rambouillet, Saxony, Silesia. South African Merinos.

FINGERING YARN. A worsted knitting yarn in which the lower qualities are not combed, the noil being allowed to remain so as to give fullness to the thread. In many world centers for hand knitting the term fingering is considered synonymous with worsted yarn. A knitter, however, uses the term to mean a firm yarn for knitting socks. The origin of the term may be derived from the hand-spinning days to imply a process of passing the yarn through the fingers to obtain a straighter run of the fibers. Hand knitting and finger knitting are considered as synonymous in the British Isles.

FINGER KNITTING. Old British term still in use that implies knitting done by hand, especially hose and hosiery. See FINGERING YARN.

FINGER MARKS. Areas in some cloth, taffeta and faille particularly, where because of some flaw the irregular filling will show a light or dim area.

FINGERNAIL OR CORRECTION FLUID STAIN REMOVAL. Sponge with acetone or amyl acetate solvent. It should be noted that this treatment should not be applied on acetate, Arnel, Dynel, and Verel. Acetone will dissolve acetate content fabrics but has no effect on rayon fabrics.

FINGER PRESSING. Refers to fabrics or garments that are still moist or damp whereby the shaping of pleats, creases, lapels, ruffles, etc., are the result of pressing by use of the fingers.

FINGER RUG. Hand-loomed, cut-pile, coarse English rugs.

FINISH. A general term which covers treatment of a fabric to give a desired surface effect such as napping, calendering, embossing, lacquering. Some finishes add luster, others give a muted dull effect. Special finishes can be applied to make a fabric waterproof or crease resistant, etc. A finish often contributes much to the "feel" of a fabric.

FINISH, SEMI- OR HALF-MER-CERIZED. Cotton cloth that has been given only a weak mercerization, not fully treated.

FINISH, SOFT, MEDIUM, OR IM-PROVED. Name applied to the finish on any textile fabric in which improvements or modifications have been made to make the material more appealing in some way.

FINISHED GOODS. Cloth after passing through finishing processes.

FINISHER. One who does hand-finishing on a garment. The operation includes the sewing on of buttons, hooks and eyes, trimming.

FINISHER CARD. The third or last card in a three-set carding layout used in carding wool. By means of the tape condenser the stock comes from this card in roving form.

FINISHER PICKER. This machine is an evener frame. The laps of cotton stock from the opener picker are placed on an apron, and fed automatically to the pedal roller, beater, and then to the cages, the same as on the opener. This machine usually takes care of four laps. A draft of about five is used in order to even the weight of the laps per yard.

Pickers remove the heavier impurities by the beating, air draft, and suction arrangements on the machines. Finisher picker lap is 40 or so inches wide, and the lap weight is around 40 pounds. Carding is the next operation in sequence.

FINISHING. 1. The art and science of making materials presentable to the consuming public. Cloth is converted from the gray-goods state, as it comes from the loom, into a fair, medium, good, or excellent material ready for usage. Textile fabrics are "made in the finishing," since there has never been a perfect yard of cloth, free from defects of some sort, woven. Finishing takes care of these defects in the goods. 2. The final processing, such as bleaching, dyeing, pressing, printing, waterproofing. 3. The steps in the treatment of rayon or acetate from the time it is spun to its final form for shipment to the user—washing, stretching and drying or storing, twisting, and spooling—when cakes are not used—reeling and lacing, resulphurizing, washing, bleaching, drying, sorting and grading, packing, etc. 4. Generally speaking, the final operation in any process of manufacture.

FINISHING, COTTON. This includes the operations necessary to convert a piece of goods from the loom to the completed state. The instructions given to finishers should be carried out to the letter, and discretion, judgment, and accuracy are paramount. Some of the major finishing treatments include bleaching, chemicking, dampening, drying, dyeing, glazing, calendering, sizing, softening, scouring, stiffening, and tentering.

FINISHING MATERIALS. See FINISHING; FINISHING, COTTON.

FINISHING OPERATIONS FOR WOOLENS AND WORSTEDS.

DRY-FINISHING OPERATIONS WHICH PRECEDE WET-FINISHING OPERATIONS:

1. *Perching.* Examining cloth for all kinds of defects and blemishes while it is being run over a roller. All imperfections are marked with chalk. The perch resembles the uprights on a football field.

2. *Measuring.* Checking the actual yardage of the cut as it has come from the loom. The weaver is paid on this basis for his work—often at the rate of "so many mills per woven pick of filling."

3. *Burling.* Removal of loose threads and knots by means of burling irons, a type of tweezer. Many knots are pulled to the back of the cloth if cutting of them would make a slight hole in the goods.

4. *Specking.* The removal of specks, burrs, and other detrimental objects that might impair the final appearance of the cloth. This is usually done with tweezers or burling irons.

5. *Mending.* The darning of flaws or defects if mending is the best way to remove them.

6. *Sewing.* This includes the experienced sewers in the dry-finishing department of the mill. Ends that are out, picks that are missing, and other similar defects are actually sewed to perfection by weaving in a new end or a new pick in order to make the fabric conform to the pattern design.

When the cloth has been made perfect as to construction, it is then ready for a number of wet-finishing operations, which may be considered more or less optional, depending on the type of fabric and the finish desired.

WET-FINISHING OPERATIONS:

1. *Dyeing.* The caring for the application of color to the goods. Stock-dyed fabric is colored after scouring and before blending, oiling, and mixing of the stock being used in the material. Yarn- or skein-dyed fabric follows spinning of the yarn and precedes the weaving of the cloth in the loom. Piece-dyed fabric is colored after the experienced sewers in the dry-finishing department of the mill have completed their work. Piece dyeing would precede other wet treatments that the material will receive in finishing.

2. *Washing.* Giving the goods a thorough washing to remove dirt and possible soiled areas so that the material will be as clean as possible. Scouring may be considered as synonymous.

3. *Fulling.* Also known as milling or felting, the material is placed in warm, soapy water in the fulling mill. The goods are "pounded and twisted" to make them felt and cause the fibers in the yarns to interlock. This application of heat, moisture, and pressure, followed by a cold rinse, does much to whip the cloth into shape for future treatments. Sometimes chemicals are used to help moisten, soften, and lubricate the minute fibers so that desirable matting will result.

4. *Shrinkage.* Fulling does this to considerable degree and gives the material additional thickness and a firmer, fuller texture. Shrinkage, while it may be done by a fulling bath, can also be achieved by ordinary water baths. The longer the shrinkage treatment, the greater will be the shrinkage of the goods, with consequent increase in the strength of the material.

5. *Scouring.* This is to free the cloth from soap and other ingredients that might be detrimental to the finished goods. Scouring is comparable with the washing of the hair by an individual.

6. *Crabbing.* A treatment given to set the cloth and the yarn-twist permanently. The material is passed over several cylinders that rotate in hot water, and then immersed quickly in a cold-water bath. The goods are held firmly and tightly to prevent wrinkling. Repetition of the treatment with increased pressure results in setting the cloth and the finish.

7. *Tentering.* Its purpose is to bring the cloth to the desired width and to "straighten and level the material." A moistening or wetting of the goods occurs in order to make the cloth supple so that a uniform stretching will be possible. Tentering is done on a long machine; both edges of the fabric are held by clamps from the time it enters the frame until delivered at the front of the machine. The clamping action may be compared with the caterpillar wheel on an army tank—an endless chain that picks up the cloth, carries it along the frame and lets go of the goods as it comes from the machine.

8. *Decating, Decatizing.* This may

make them retardant or resistant to tion in conjunction with cylinder shrinking. In decating, the cloth is shrunk by winding it under tension on a perforated cylinder through which steam is passed. The treatment sometimes replaces London Shrinking.

9. *London Shrinking.* Shrinking by the cold-water method of sponging or shrinking to take out all so-called mill finish. It makes the cloth ready for the cutting-up trade, so that the finished cloth will shrink no more.

10. *Waterproofing.* Making material repellent to water. There are many processes on the market today; waxing or liquid treatments are used in waterproofing.

11. *Sponging.* A final shrinking of material to assure the apparel houses that the cloth has been shrunk to perfection.

DRY-FINISHING OPERATIONS WHICH FOLLOW WET-FINISHING OPERATIONS:

1. *Shearing.* The leveling-off of protruding fibers or nap to a uniform height, thereby giving an even surface to the goods. The shearing operation may be compared with the action of the blades of a lawn mower.

2. *Napping, Gigging, Raising.* This treatment is done by passing the cloth in a tightly stretched condition over a revolving cylinder or roller inlaid with teasels; or the roller may be covered with card clothing like that seen on a card. The wire napper uses pressed-steel wires that are from 7/8 of an inch to 1¼ inches high. The brushing treatment will cause a rather irregular napped surface that is desirable on many woolen cloths.

3. *Singeing.* The passing of cloth over a series of jets of gas flame to singe off any protruding or straggly fibers. It gives the goods a smoother, cleaner appearance. Singeing aids in giving the characteristic hard finish noted in many worsted fabrics. Both sides of a fabric may be singed, and the treatment may be compared with a person having his hair singed in the barber shop.

4. *Pressing.* A machine that presses or calenders the material to make it presentable. It gives a smart appearance to the goods and is applied to practically all materials. Pressing is done by heated rollers or drums under controlled temperature.

5. *Final Inspection.* As the name implies, it is the final inspection in the mill or in the sponging and examining house in the apparel areas. Final inspection may reveal narrow goods, poor fabric, rejects, faulty selvages, washer wrinkle marks, etc. See Illustrated Section.

FINISHING RANGE. A setup or layout of machinery for some definite purpose—Sanforized range, Williams range, etc.

FIOCCO. A broad Italian term which implies flake, staple (such as natural fiber staple and staple from the man-made fibers), tassel, tuft, clump, group, etc.

FIQUE. Similar to jute, this fiber comes from the leaves of the plant *Furcraea Macrophylla.* Raised in Southern United States, Mexico, and Central America, it produces a fiber from 3 to 5 feet long. Cabuya and Piteira are sometimes known as fique. Used chiefly in local consumption.

FIREGARD. Registered trademark of M. Lowenstein & Sons, Inc., New York City for its flame retardant finish on 100 percent cotton flannel, mainly used in flannel sleepwear for children. A sewed-in label on the article provides washing instructions, as follows:

Machine washable, tumble dry.

May be hand washed.

Use any good detergent; do not use soap.

Do not use chlorine bleach.

Commercial laundries should not use acid-sour process.

FIRE HOSE. A seamless tubular woven fabric used to convey water under pressure; comes in unlined and rubber-lined forms.

FIREPROOF, FIRE-RESISTANT FINISHES. Fireproof fabrics must be 100 per cent fireproof. If treated to prevent the spread of flame, they should be called fire-resistant. Some materials are treated with a chemical which melts at a low point and covers the goods with a nonflammable film.

FIREPROOFING. A composition which may be applied to all kinds of textile fabrics without causing deterioration in any way consists of:

Sulphate of ammonia .. ⅔ of a pound
Boracic acid .... 3 pounds
Borax-pure .... ¼ of a pound
Starch .... 2 pounds
Water .... 100 pounds

It is merely necessary to steep the material in a hot solution of the compound until it becomes thoroughly impregnated.

Another fireproofing solution is made up of: 2 parts of sublimated sal ammoniac and sulphate of zinc, 1 part in 20 parts of water. This is the Vogt Method.

Good results may be assured from steeping material in a solution which contains 5 per cent alum and 5 per cent phosphate of ammonia. This is the Siebrath Method.

The Paris Municipal Laboratory Method is as follows:

Aluminum sulphate .... 2 per cent solution

Silicate of soda .... 5 per cent solution

Mix and then immerse the material; after squeezing and drying, the aluminum silicate formed in the goods is insoluble.

FIRE RETARDANT. Fabrics chemically treated with special agents to make them retardant or resistant to fire. There is a wide range of fire retardants on the market today.

FIRE-RETARDANT FINISH. There are several methods of rendering cottons fire retardant today. Two of these follow:

First Method:
5 ounces of ammonium
16 ounces common alum
3 ounces boracic acid
3½ pounds borax
6 pints water to make up the solution

Second Method:
8 ounces ammonium phosphate
1 ounce boracic acid
4½ pints water to make up the solution

With either method, the cloth is soaked in the liquor used. These formulas may be increased proportionately to the amount required to take care of all the cloth to be immersed. Proper soaking is vitally important. If the goods are washed and laundered, the operation must be repeated.

Much fabric is now treated to make it fire retardant by means of a spray attached to a chemical container.

FIRE RETARDANT TREATMENT. Any method or process which decreases the flammability of a textile material. Tests are made to determine the amount of time it takes for a flame to be extinguished. Stop watches are used for the timings necessary for computations. The test proves whether or not the article comes up to standards. Several tests are completed so that comparisons may be made for final decision.

FIRST COMBING. Long wool taken from the sides of the sheep fleece; of choice quality.

FIRST PIECES. Long skirtings taken from wool fleeces after the broken bits have been removed.

FIRST PRESSING. The pressing of a garment prior to marking and sewing on the buttons.

FIR WOOL. Fibrous substance obtained by pounding and grinding the leaves and bark of coniferous trees.

Some of this stock is mixed with wool to make heavy Mackinac fabric.

FISHER. A medium-haired fur ranging from medium brown to dark brown in color, with guard hairs ranging from yellow-brown to deep blackish-brown. Wearing qualities good. Judged by color, thickness, and silkiness of the hair. Found in Canada and, occasionally, in Maine. For general wear.

FISHEYE. Large diamond effect that is similar in shape to the eye of a fish. Comparable with the smaller patterns noted in bird's-eye, and used chiefly for toweling, since the fabric is durable, has good absorptive properties, and is reversible. Made of linen, cotton and linen, or all cotton.

FISH NET. Wide-mesh material resembling fishing nets, used for scarfs and dress trimming.

FISHNET EFFECT. Some fabrics have an open effect, despite the fact that they have been woven. They assume the effect of a fishnet, hence, the name. The slightly hairy surface of the spun yarn in these woolen cloths seems to provide the desired textured look in use for women's coatings and some dressgoods. Fabrics in this field are usually light in weight and have an "airy look and texture."

FITCH. A medium-haired fur in light yellow, white, or brown. Wearing qualities good. Judged by silkiness of pelt. Found in Russia, Western and Central Europe. For general and dress wear.

FITSCHI COTTON. A type of Sea Island cotton which has a 2-inch staple length.

FITTER. One who can sort, match, and trim the cut garment parts and linings to proper size prior to the ensuing sewing operations. The fitter will be found in wholesale manufacture, in retail stores, and in custom-tailor establishments.

FIVE-EIGHTHS HOSE. Also known as golf hose, it is a stocking which reaches five-eighths of the distance from the ankle to the knee.

FIVE O'CLOCKS. Fine British damask table linen.

FIXING. Making dyed or printed colors fast in cloth by treating the material with chemical, such as ammonia, and steam in an ager.

FIXING AGENT. Any chemical used to render a soluble chemical insoluble in the fiber. It is used with various mordants, for example: chrome plus tartar—potassium bi-tartrate or cream of tartar are the other names for tartar, $KH(C_4H_4O_6)$.

FLACHERIE. Silkworm disease probably caused by the worm eating contaminated mulberry leaves.

FLAIKONA. Registered trademark of Beauknit Fibers, Beauknit Corporation, New York City, for its continuous filament with flat, flaky areas or slubs interspersed throughout the yarn.

FLAINE. French ticking.

FLAKE CELLULOSE. Cellulose pulp in chip or flake form.

FLAKE YARN. Yarn that is spotted by interspersed round or elongated series of lumps, nubs, or flakes. This novelty yarn is used for fancy stripings and effects in men's and women's wear, children's coating, and novelty dress goods. Other fancy yarns are: Knickerbocker, bouclé, bourette, bug, and nub.

FLAME CHECKING. Treatment of inflammable materials with particular processes to provide some degree of protection against the spread of flame if fabric or article comes in contact with flame. See "FLAMMABLE FABRIC."

FLAME CULTIVATION. A burner-gun torch flame, mounted on a tractor, is used to flow flame around the base of cotton plants to kill grass and weeds along the cotton-plant rows. Also called flaming.

FLAMEPROOF FABRIC. See FIRE-PROOF, FIREPROOFING, FLAMMABILITY TESTER.

FLAME STITCH. Also known as Hungarian Point, this ancient pattern in needlework has been known for many centuries. Today there are several versions which follow the tradition of many colors and a havd-woven appearance. The motif presents an optical illusion of movement and the desire for the so-called "bold or strong designs" seem to have brought this stitch back into some favor in home decorating circles.

FLAMMABILITY ACT OF JULY, 1972, FTC. Effective July 29, 1972, The Federal Trade Commission decreed the Children's Sleepwear Standard Act - DCC-FF 3-7. Under this Standard, garments made for the infants' sleepwear trade, such as nightgowns, pajamas, and bathrobes in sizes 0-6X shall meet requirements of a vertical fire test as described in the Standard. In the Act, the FTC initiated steps to include sizes 7 to 14, as well. One year's time to July 29, 1973, was granted to permit labeling of non-conforming garments.

The Standard requires a maximum average flame spread, as measured by the char length, of 7.0 inches and a molten drip time of less than 10.00 seconds. These standards must be met with in the original state of the fabric and after 50 launderings. Garments, as well as the fabric used therein, must meet the requirements of the Standard. See Labeling Act of Textile Wearing Apparel of July, 1972, FTC.

FLAMMABILITY TESTER. An apparatus approved by the American Association of Textile Chemists and Colorists for the evaluation of textile materials with regard to flammability characteristics by measuring the rate of burning. Under standard test procedures the results can be interpreted as to whether or not a fabric is flammable.

"FLAMMABLE FABRIC." A woven knitted, or otherwise constructed textile fabric or product made from fabric which burns at an average rate of 5 inches in less than 4 seconds, or, if it has a pile or a nap, it shows in addition ignition or fusing of the base fabric. If flameproofing is applied, it must be effective for the life of the fabric.

FLAMMABLE FABRIC, HIGHLY. To test burning quality as decreed by the commercial standards of the U. S. Department of Commerce, a flame the size of a match-flame is applied to a material for one second, to a swatch that measures 2 x 6 inches. With swatch held at an angle of 45 degrees, the spread of the flame is measured. If the flame-spread lasts less than four seconds, and the intensity of the flame is such that it sets the base fabric on fire in napped, pile, tufted, or flocked fabrics, the goods are classified as having a "rapid and intense" burning quality and are then considered dangerous and unsuitable for clothing.

FLAMMABLE FABRICS ACT. A Federal Law which went into effect on June 30, 1953. It bans the introduction or movement in interstate commerce of fabrics for clothing and apparel that are so highly flammable as to be dangerous to the consumer.

FLANDERS SHEEP. See TEXEL SHEEP.

FLANGE. Refers to the traveler which fits onto the ring of the ring-spinning frame. The flanged traveler has a speed which ranges from 4000 to about 13,000 r.p.m. in its course around the ring. Rings can be flanged on the top side or both sides.

FLANNEL. A cotton cloth, originating in Wales, that is napped on one or both sides to imitate wool flannel. It is heavier than flannelette and is often called Canton flannel. Simple twill weaves are used to make the cloth, which is featured by a soft-spun filling to give a good nap, sized warp, and a light, well-twisted warp yarn. The dull finish tends to conceal the weave. The cloth comes in blue, white, and fancy effects, chiefly in stripe form. There is considerable variance in the weight and texture of flannel. The fabric is finished from 30 to 39 inches, made of 14s to 22s yarn, with textures ranging from 48 to 62 by 48 to 58. Flannel is used for dresses, imitation serge, nightwear, outing material, shirting, skirting, and slacks.

FLANNEL, RAYON. There are two major fabrics under this term. Both cloths are made in 2-up, 2-down right-hand twill weave. One material is a 2/30s yarn construction while the other is with a 1/15s. The 2/30s is run usually with 70 per cent rayon and 30 per cent acetate. The 1/15s is run in two versions—a 50 per cent each of acetate and rayon, or a 70 per cent rayon and 30 per cent acetate. This is done to obtain different color effects. Practically all these fabrics are cross-dyed and a slight nap is provided in the finishing of the goods.

FLANNEL, WOOLEN. Lightweight, soft woolen cloth with napped surface. Dull finish conceals weave. In colors and fancy effects. Weight and texture vary somewhat. Kindly feel and handle. Shrinks much if care is not taken in laundering. Sags with wear, does not shine or hold crease. Works well.

FLANNELETTE, COTTON. A heavy, soft material that is given a napped finish. There are many types on the market. Used for pajamas, nightgowns, pocket lining, quilts, clothing, shirting. Flannelette is made in stripes, plaids, prints. Launders well and is easy to manipulate. Nap will come off in the cheaper qualities. Soft filling yarn is used so that a good nap may be assured. Generally speaking, the public uses the words flannel and flannelette interchangeably.

FLANNEL FINISH. Cotton cloth that is slightly napped on both sides to imitate wool flannel.

FLANNEL FINISHES, COTTON.
1. COLORED WOVEN FLANNELS: Glove and mitten flannel, interlining, outing flannel, oxford-gray mixture flannel, and plaid effect.
2. UNBLEACHED FLANNELS: Canton, interlining, and table felt or silence cloth.
3. CONVERTED FLANNELS: These include automobile headlining, baby flannel, duvetyne finish, diaper flannel, domet, felted flannel, flannelette, kasha cloth (flannel face and chambray-effect back), shaker, suède finish, tarnish-resistant cloth. Finished widths are 27, 30, or 36 inches.

FLANNEL TWILL. Cotton twills made with a three-shaft or a four-shaft weave. The soft-twisted, cylindrical filling is ideal for napping purposes so that flannel finish may be achieved in finishing. May be piece-dyed or woven with stripe or check effects.

FLAP POCKET. Built into the interior of a coat, jacket, or trousers; it is a flap covering the opening in the pocket; provided with a button and eyelet for fastening or closing.

FLAPPER AGE, THE. The word, flapper, comes from the Middle English and means to cause flatness by hitting, flattening, or to "slap down." The era began in England around 1910 and met with great success in the United States from 1915 to 1918 and its demise occurred in 1922. The flapper was an unruly, giddy, unconventional girl and exemplified "flaming youth" of the era. Her attire was a short skirt which gave glimpses of her knees since stockings were rolled down below the knee, her mouth rouged in the shape of Cupid's bow, a one-piece underwear garment called a "Teddy," and short hair either in stiff waves or tortured into wiry curls done by the new permanent wave machine. "Daring freedom and wildness" was an expression used to describe the flapper. Spearheaded by the popular screen star, Clara Bow, the "IT" Girl, mannish clothes became popular and the figure was really flattened to a sexless silhouette, especially in the bosom. The waistline and hemline almost met, the one being lowered too far while the other rose to the knees.

The flapper wore a cloche hat which came down over her ears, and in cold weather galoshes were open at the top. While there was a molding and confining of the figure in a rather mixed-up way, the era had one noteworthy feature which was the acceptance of silk stockings. A girl wearing cotton stockings was now thought of as just not being able to afford silk ones. People would turn around, look at her, and say, "the poor thing." Instead of the somber black stockings seen heretofore, there now arrived such exciting shades as beige, ecru, nude, and tan.

This flapper age also saw the advent of the camel hair coat, the leopard coat, and the Stutz Bearcat car. It was an era that was fantastic, chaotic, unsettled, and one that caused much comment, good and not so good. It did, however, leave a great imprint of things to come in fashion and style. Women earned the right to vote in 1920, the same year that The Jazz Age was born, and Prohibition made its debut in 1921, and the world began to change to great degree.

Some of the fashion happenings which took place shortly after the Flapper Age are as follows:

1923 - Paul Poiret, one of the great Parisian couturiers of all time, brought out his new fabric, Poiret Twill, which was made in a steep twill weave with line angles of 63, 70, and 75 degrees. His fabric was a sensation at the time; it was a worsted material of high and compact texture. He also brought in the corsetless woman, a new departure. He featured his famous East and Near East motifs in his showings for spring and summer wear, and he was influential in the promotion of the popular ensemble, aided by his superb workmanship and exquisite detail in the garments.

That same year, Gabrielle Chanel, popularly known as Coco, introduced her simple two-piece dress made of jersey fabric. She was the first to use this material. She is also known for having introduced the soft, flowing chiffon evening gown. Known as the first modern dressmaker, her styles emphasized simplicity and comfort to be enjoyed by the young as well as the not-so-young.

1927 - Premet, another French designer, unveiled his boyish-type dress known as the "Garconne."

929 - Louise Belanger, Parisian designer, showed her high-front, trailing-in-the-back dress or gown. This style became the rage for evening wear.

1930 - Paul Poiret presented his long-type dress of in-draping chiffon; it was high-waisted and embellished by many frills. This style was ideal for the slim girl.

1933 - Marlene Dietrich made modifications of Amelia Bloomer's bloomers, and pants and slacks for women have constantly gained in popularity since then and seem to be the rage in the early 1970's, the answer to the mini, mide, and maxi styles that have caused such a great concern for women.

In this same year of 1933, Joan Crawford, one of the all-time greats of stage and screen, brought in the Lettie Lynton dress from the movie "Wuthering Heights," after the book by Emily Bronte'. This was the first type of covered-up type of evening gown.

Textured stockings, country clothes, and boots made their debut around this time, and all are foremost in today's fashions.

Elsa Schiaparelli, Italian designer of the era in the United States, introduced her collarless coats, the no-neckline coat. She also favored shoulder padding and special accent on sleeves. It was also at this time when the chubby fur coat was born. It had no collar nor real neckline. These short coats were foremost for a few years and then became distress merchandise. The sunsuit also came in at this time, but did not meet with much favor and had to sustain much criticism from the female public. Shorts were still not accepted.

FLARE. The surplus materials allowed to a garment which falls in soft folds. This extra fullness forms a circular effect when spread. A flare relieves tightness in a garment and gives freedom of movement to the wearer. A style effect used on coat, cuffs, petticoats, skirts, and slips. Also means the upper portion of a stocking that has been widened or flared.

FLARE, KNITTING. Upper portion of a stocking that has been widened or flared.

FLAT. Implies that two filling picks have been woven in together in the same shed, thereby causing an imperfection in the goods. A warp flat occurs in plain cloth when the one end is missing and the ends on each side of where the missing end should be come together and give a "flat" effect in the material. A flat is a rather common occurrence in some low-quality, low-priced cottons.

FLAT BALE. The average or ordinary cotton bale delivered by the cotton gin.

FLAT BED PRESS. An ironing or pressing device used in making shrinkage tests on textile fabrics. It is so designed that it will eliminate, as much as possible, any distortion of the fabric such as might occur during the pressing of material with an ordinary flat iron. The device is supplemented with a perforated steel plate upon which the specimen to be tested for shrinkage is placed for pressing.

FLAT CHAFER FABRIC. Made with coarse single yarns in the warp and filling and similar to regular chafer fabric.

FLAT COTTON. That which has not been compressed.

FLAT CREPE. A major type of crepe in which the warp with flat yarn and the filling with S-twist and Z-twist yarn are used to make this fabric finished at about 41 inches. Denier of the warp may be 150, 100, or 75; filling is of 100-denier or 75-denier yarn. Textures range from 80 x 40 to 48 up to 150 x 76, which is a print-cloth texture.

The origin of crepe is found in the Latin, crispus, which means crimped. As the name indicates the material is comparatively flat and reveals only a slight pebble or crepe effect. The use of crepe filling imparts a soft, pliable hand which enhances drapability despite the light weight of the goods. Reed widths are from 3 to 5 inches wider than the finished width. The print-goods texture is extremely popular in the apparel trade and is used in garments such as accessories, blouses, dress goods, negligees, and pajamas. Any of the flat-crepe textures may be used in the above-mentioned garments, as well as in the lining trade.

FLAT DUCK. Light to medium-weight cotton duck made with single warp yarn which is sized prior to weaving. Two ends are drawn as one through the heddle eyes and four ends are drawn through the reed split in reeding-in. Fabric is woven in plain weave. The filling may be single or ply and is referred to as single filling or double filling. There are many more ends than picks in the texture. Uses include clothing duck, enameling duck, wagon-cover duck, and certain army equipage. Also known as flat-ounce duck.

FLAT FABRIC. 1. Term applied to fabric made on a flat-knitting machine to distinguish it from a circular-knitted fabric. 2. In the underwear trade this term is applied to plain-stitch fabrics made on a circular knitting machine (not on a flat machine). Such fabrics have a flat surface, and the term is used to differentiate them from ribbed fabrics. 3. Broad, woven rayon fabrics such as taffetas and twills, which contain only the producer's twist in the warp and the filling yarns; contrast with twisted-yarn fabrics.

FLAT-FELL SEAM. A seam that lies flat with the material, has no extension, and shows two rows of stitching. It is commonly used on tailored garments such as boys' suits, pajamas, and work clothes, or wherever a sturdy seam is necessary.

FLAT FOLD. A method of rolling cloth without doubling.

FLAT GOODS. Term used in the underwear trade to indicate cloth made on a circular-knitting machine equipped with one set of needles. The term differentiates jersey fabric from rib material. Jersey fabrics lie flatter than rib-knit fabrics, hence the term flat goods.

In the outerwear trade, the term flat means fabrics that have been made on a flat-knitting machine to distinguish them from circular-knitted fabrics.

FLAT KNIT. Fabric made on a flat-knitting machine in contrast to that made on a circular machine. In the underwear trade, the term implies a fabric or garment made with a plain stitch.

FLAT-KNITTING MACHINE. A machine in which the needles are set in a straight line and held in place by a flat plate called the needle bed. The yarn traverses from side to side in the knitting and the width is variable and can be easily set in the machine. There are three groups: 1. Latch needles are used to make the coarser fabrics such as scarfs, ensembles, sweaters. 2. Spring or spring-beard needles are used for fashioned hosiery. 3. Warp-knitting machines produce fine fabric for lingerie, dress goods, blouses.

FLAT LOCK STITCH. A flat interlocking stitch.

FLAT MACHINE. A knitting frame that has its needles arranged in a straight line and held in a flat plate called the needle bed. Knitting on this machine is from side to side. Production is not so great as on the circular-knitting frame.

FLAT-PLATE PRINTING. In this method of imprinting textiles with color, the chosen design is cut by hand into a flat copper plate, then the desired color is applied to the plate and the surface lightly cleaned, leaving the color in the grooves. When the plates are pressed firmly onto fabric, the motif is imprinted. The dye must then be put into the grooves again for the next repeat. With this method only one color can be used.

FLAT RIB MACHINE KNITTING STITCH. The carriage in this flat bed machine runs longitudinally back and forth over two flat needle beds formed into an inverted "V". In the conventional flat bed machine, the stitches come into action by being activated in an up-and-down movement in their slots or grooves by a cam system which is essentially a triangular shaped wedge. Aside from this conventional plan, the flatbed frame has three basic functions. These follow:

Stitch Transfer: In this work the carriage of the machine switches from one needle bed to another in order to provide a variety of possible stitches. Lace effects and other openings are possible by this action. It is also possible to double this method and have every sixth needle take two stitches. This is often done to make cuffs elastic or stretchable. The body of a sweater with 100 stitches and the cuffs with 120 stitches over the same given area provide elasticity devoid of any detrimental ridges at the joining of the body and the cuff.

Widening-Out: When a flat bed machine is used to make sleeves, it is possible to drop certain specified needles at the side, thereby, producing a prism-like structure without any waste. In contrast, it should be noted that in circular rib fabrics the goods would have to be cut along the side of the material in order to make the same prism or sleeve. This would give a waste possibly as high as 20 percent. *Stretch and Transfer Jacquard:* This type of flatbed machine produces cable stitches, full-fashion collars, and comparable items. Coarse or low gauge frames can make fancy sweater fabric while fine gauge frames are able to produce the cable stitch across the entire machine; when cut, the cable stitching can then be sewed onto sweaters for use as trimming. This type of knitting gives less waste than that noted in circular knitting; volume, however, is lower.

FLAT ROPE. A wire rope in which the strands in ply or cable formation are given alternating twist—S and Z. The diameter of the wire determines the amount of twisting necessary, along with the number of plies used. The roping may be held in place by soft wire. Used for hoisting and shifting cargoes.

FLAT RUCHE. It is made on a loosely constructed warp-knitted web with an uncut pile effect on one surface. See RUCHE.

FLATS. An endless belt or band of laths, each of which is clothed with card-clothing wire to work in combination with the card clothing of the cylinder of the cotton carding machine.

FLAT STITCH. A jersey or plain stitch in knitting.

FLAT-STRIPPING BRUSH. A strong, revolving brush which simulates the blades of a lawn mower. It is used to clean the teeth of the card flats which have become embedded with short fibers and "strips."

FLAT-STRIPPING COMB. A saw-toothed metal bar that extends the width of the card. Its oscillating motion and fine teeth clean the teeth of the revolving flats of the machine.

FLAT STRIPS. Short, immature, and waste fibers stripped from the revolving flats on a cotton card. This waste is wound into a lap form and is used for manufacturing rope and spindle banding.

FLAT UNDERWEAR FABRIC. See KNITTED FABRICS.

FLATWORK. Fabric material other than wearing apparel, such as handkerchiefs, napkins, sheets, and tablecloths; the term implies household linens that can be ironed on a mangle.

FLATWORK IRONER ROLLING. The rolling under of the edges of flatwork when it is passed through a chest-type ironer. This trouble is usually indicative of excessive souring, but it can also be caused by many other agents, both chemical and mechanical, which tend to develop friction. It is

frequently characteristic of only one or more lots of flatwork handled in a plant.

FLAVIN. A coloring matter extracted from quecitron.

FLAX, GRAY. Boiled-off linen yarn that has not been bleached.

FLAX, GREEN OR NATURAL. Scutched flax obtained from de-seeded straw which has not been given any intermediate treatment such as retting.

FLAX, LINE. See FLAX FIBERS, INFORMATION ON.

FLAX, LINEN. An important type of bast fiber, the plant is called the flax plant and the product is called linen. Flax is obtained from the plant stalk, which grows in many world areas. It is the oldest textile fiber known in the vegetable group and it may attain a length of about 40 inches. The name of the plant is *Linum usitatissimum.*

The plant is raised for two purposes, the fiber and the seed. The latter is known commercially as linseed, and it is used as linseed meal for animal feed, for birdseed, and in cake form in the chemical industry.

The fibers are manipulated into yarn and cloth, and the fabric is used for tablecloths, napkins, doilies, runners, crash, toweling, suiting material, twine, canvas, aprons, shoe thread, fishing tackle and nets, cigarette paper, currency and bank-note paper, and similar products.

The chief flax-producing countries are Russia, which supplies 75 per cent of the world output; Belgium, which raises the best flax in the world; Ireland, where the best workmanship is found; the United States, Holland, South Africa, France, India, Japan, China, and Asia Minor.

In this country, Oregon is the leader for fiber and seed, while Michigan, Minnesota, Wisconsin, Washington, and Kentucky are interested mainly in the seed.

Fiber flax is sown about 85 to 100 pounds to the acre. The straws grow straight to a height of 30 to 40 inches. The seed branches are seen at the top only. The Oregon fiber is high in quality and compares favorably with the well-known Belgian thread fiber called Courtrai stock.

FLAX, WHITE DUTCH. Light cast or shade flax, retted in the Scheldt and other rivers and streams in the Netherlands.

FLAX BUTTING. A machine operation which jogs the flax stalks in order to get at the root ends prior to scutching. The operation prevents considerable waste in flax manipulation.

FLAX COMBINGS. Short fibers combed out in hackling and drawing

machines, and later spun into tow yarn.

FLAX COUNTS. 1. The number of leas of 300 yards each that weigh 1 pound. Thus, 40 leas means that 40 leas of 300 yards weigh 1 pound, 12,000 yards in the pound.

2. The linen reel used to find the counts of yarn is usually 90 inches in circumference:

1 thread equals 2.5 yards
120 threads equal 300 yards, or 1 lea
10 leas equal one hank
20 hanks equal 1 bundle

FLAX CUTTER. A machine used to remove the root and top ends of flax; about 14 inches to 18 inches of choice stock remain for manipulation.

FLAX DISEASES. These include yellowing, specks of various types that cause the stem fiber to disintegrate, browning, or discoloration caused by fungus, stem breakage, etc.

FLAX DRAWINGS. A mechanical process whereby the loose flax is drawn out into a loose roving of the required thickness in order to spin the fibers into yarn.

FLAX DODDER. A parasite that winds itself around and up the stem of the flax plant with the aid of suctorial ducts. A concentration of two dodders per square metre is enough to destroy an entire crop of flax. Dodder seeds, however, are much smaller than those of the flax plant and are eagerly sought for and removed by seed cleaning machines.

FLAX DRYING. Flax seeds that are to be saved from the flax must be dried. Little Irish flax is dried because of the damp climate. Most dried flax comes from other countries that specialize in the use of the seed.

FLAX FIBERS, INFORMATION ON.

1. LINE FIBERS: Those from 10 inches to 20 or more inches long. They are used in the finest-quality fabrics and are spun on the wet method.

2. TOW FIBERS: Those fibers below a 10-inch length. They are used in the coarser fabrics and are spun on the dry system.

3. LINE YARN: This is made up of fiber cells which have narrow lumens and pointed ends. It is free from the other tissues of the stem.

4. TOW YARN: It is composed of fiber cells with narrow and broad lumens and contains the epidermal cells.

5. LUMEN: This is the hollow canal that runs through the center of the fiber.

6. CELL WALLS: These will vary in thickness and are structureless and porous.

FLAX LINEN, CHEMICAL FORMULA FOR. Bast fibers are closely related in chemical composition. Generally speaking, cellulose content runs around 75% to 80% of the structure along with varying amounts of ash, fat, gum, wax, and water.

FLAXON. A smooth, crisp, lightweight cotton cloth that simulates dimity. It comes in plain or cord effects, is white, tinted, or printed. It is used for aprons, lingerie, and infants'-wear.

FLAX PROCESSING.

1. Growing: Preparation of the soil, planting, and cultivation.

2. Pulling: The flax plants are pulled out of the ground, roots included.

3. Rippling: Removal of the seeds and leaves from the dried flax, leaving the long stalks of flax straws.

4. Bundle Ties: The flax is tied into bundles and is allowed to dry and age in the sun.

5. Retting: Rotting of the stalk except the fibers, by various methods, as follows:

a) *Dew Retting:* Retting the flax by exposure in fields to the action of dew and sunlight; requires from 4 to 6 weeks' time. This natural method of retting gives uneven results but provides the best wear. Russia uses this method.

b) *Pool Retting:* This is the most rapid natural retting method because of the excess bacteria in stagnant water which speeds up the fermentation. Requires about one week's time. The flax is placed in crates, and crate-weights are used to insure total immersion of the fibers in the murky water.

c) *Stream Retting:* Similar to pool retting, except that the flax is placed in a flowing stream which does not have as much of the bacteria which is so essential in good retting. The Lys River in Belgium gives the best results in the world. The time required is from five to fifteen days. Courtrai, the famous "Flax City" is on this river.

d) *Tank Retting:* This is done in Ireland. It is the best and the quickest method of retting, taking only about three days. Finer fiber results from this method. Another feature is that controlled temperature of the plain water used is always possible; the retting may be done at any time of the year.

e) *Chemical Retting:* This method has not yet proved to be a genuinely satisfactory method. Retting is brought about by the action of various chemicals such as soda ash, caustic soda, oxalic acid. Action is violent and uncontrollable. Much effort is being made to perfect and promote chemical ret-

ting.

6. Breaking: Following retting, the bundles of flax are removed from the water or raked from the ground. Drying follows. The stalks are subjected to a breaking action which breaks the rotted part of the stem from the flax fiber.

7. Scutching: This machine gives more rigorous treatment to the flax than the breaking rollers. The turbine machines which are used have steel rollers attached to revolving cylinders that beat out more of the woody portions of the fiber straw. The straw is fed automatically from the breaker to the turbine scutcher. The stock then comes from the machine practically clear of shives and other woody waste. A further breaking and separating of the rotted flax stem from the linen fibers follows.

8. Hackling, Combing: This combing action removes any remaining impurities and separates short-fiber "tow" from the longer, choicer fiber "line." This hand-manipulated operation consists of throwing a handful of scutched fibers over iron combs. The fibers are pulled through the teeth of the combs, each of which in succession has a progressively increasing number of teeth per unit. Several hacklings may be given the fibers. The fibers are now ready for spinning into yarn.

9. Spinning: This is the converting of the flax fibers into linen yarn; may be done wet or dry, with the former method providing the better and finer yarn. Wet spinning is done in a room with a temperature of about 120° Fahrenheit; this prevents breakages, insures fine, even, flexible yarn. Dry spinning is done under approximately the same conditions as is cotton spinning.

10. The Fabric: The weaving of fabric on the loom, hand or power, by causing the warp and filling to interlace at right angles.

11. Finishing: The major finishes include beetling, bleaching, calendering, lustering, pressing. Beetling flattens the yarns by a pounding action, thereby giving the material what is often referred to as a "kidskin feel."

FLAX RUST. A fungus which attacks flax by the emergence of small orange-colored specks, or postules, on the leaves and stems.

FLAX SEED. A flat, oily seed, brownish in color, which has several uses. Linseed oil and meal are two great by-products. The seed is used much as stock fodder. Plants that are raised for the seed are practically useless as a textile fiber.

FLAX SPRIT. Minute woody epider-

mal tissue which clings tenaciously to fiber strands.

FLAX TOW. The short, tangled, noil fibers taken from flax in the scutching operation or in hackling. Fibers less than 10 inches long are called tow, in contrast to the line fibers, which are over 10 inches in length. Tow is used to make twine and low-grade yarn. It should not be confused with upholstery tow.

FLECKED. Yarn or fabric which contains flaws of off-color dots or flecks.

FLECKED, FROSTED YARN. Applied to a blended yarn of cotton and acetate staple. Because of the method of dyeing, the acetate remains white and supplies the specks or minute frosted effects in the yarn.

FLECTON. Registered trade-mark of Minnesota Mining & Manufacturing Company, Inc., for its yarn which reflects light in the dark by means of microscopic glass beads affixed to the yarn surface. Fabrics which use Flecton include some coating, denim, poplin, snow suits, ski suits, rainwear.

FLEECE. 1. The mass of fibers taken from a sheep at shearing time. The fleece is made up of wool fibers, yolk, suint, fodder, dung, pebbles, etc. It has to be carefully sorted and scoured before machine manipulation to manufacture yarn. See Illustrated Section.

2. The name for a soft-feeling pile fabric which may be used for dress goods and lining of some coats.

3. A heavy, compact, long-napped overcoating much in use today. Interlacings are well covered by the nap. Range from low-quality to high-quality, expensive fabrics. Usually, however, the fabric is of good grade and it gives the wearer long service. The material may be somewhat cumbersome to handle in manipulation, and the nap should be well cared for by the consumer. Stock-, skein- or piece-dyed, the fabric ranges from 15 to 25 ounces per yard in weight.

4. Waste stock taken from carding machines—cotton, wool, or worsted —and made into a flat-layer form. This by-product or waste finds use in the manufacture of low-quality yarns.

5. Clip wool contrasted with pulled wool, which is obtained from dead sheep.

6. The words "fleece" and "fleecy" cannot be used unless the fiber content in a fabric comes within the wool class.

FLEECE, COTTON. The weblike sheet of cotton fibers obtained during the carding operation. The cotton enters the frame in lap form, then becomes fleecy, and finally, at the delivery end of the frame, is wound into a sliver form and led into the coiler can at the front of the machine.

FLEECED. A napped surface, usually in knit goods. The term cannot be used for a fabric not made of wool, unless the fiber content is declared.

FLEECE-LINED. Double-knit cloth in which one or both sides have a series of floats which have been napped in order to give greater warmth to the wearer. Used in "sweat-shirts" and some apparel coating and jacket fabrics. The term also implies sheep-lined coats such as used in cold climates and by aviators.

FLEECE-LINED UNDERWEAR. Made with napped surface on the back of the goods, or the part that comes in contact with the body. It is knitted on a frame that draws a long loop on the face which aids to produce the napped-surface effect.

FLEECE WOOL. The entire coat of wool taken from the sheep at shearing time by hand or power clippers. Shearing is comparable with a person receiving a haircut. It is done annually in the spring, with the exception of Texas and California wools, which are obtained in the spring and fall. Sheep from these two states are sheared biannually because of climatic conditions and because of the fact that the wool is infested with small, spiral burrs that cause the wool to be sold at a few cents a pound lower than other wools.

Because of the presence of yolk, suint, and foreign matter, which cause the fibers to become matted and stick together, the fleece may be picked up as a single piece.

Fleeces are put into burlap bags, packed, and tied so that they may be shipped immediately. Wool bags weigh from 200 to 300 pounds.

Grease merino fleeces may weigh from 16 to 22 pounds; the poorer grades will average from 6 to 12 pounds. It is interesting to note, as a general thing, that the smaller the sheep in size and weight, the better is the quality of the wool, the heavier the fleece, the more the serrations, the greater the number of fibers to the square inch, the more expensive the wool, the better the working properties, the more the yolk, the less the suint.

FLEECE, WOOLEN. Heavy, compact, long-napped overcoating much in use. Interlacings well covered up by nap. Range from cheap to expensive cloths. Stock-, skein- or piece-dyed. From 15 to 25 ounces per yard. Good-quality cloth, gives good wear. Material is often cumbersome and bulky, therefore it may be difficult to manipulate. Nap wears out in time.

FLEMISH DESIGNS AND TEXTILES. The Flemings were the forerunners of the present-day Belgians, a race which has always been a keen, sturdy, submerged group who, however, have certainly given more than their share to textiles and textile art. Full credit has never been accorded these people for their originality and integrity. They have excelled in carpets, decorative fabrics, laces, rugs, tapestries and velvets. Belgium has been aptly called the workshop of the Continent, and textiles have done much to keep her busy at all times. Flemish art and design are noted in many standard, expensive, elaborate fabrics of the present day.

FLEMISH FLAX. Flax obtained from Belgium and northeastern France.

FLEMISH LACE. See LACE.

FLEMISH POINT. Flanders needlepoint lace.

FLESH. The average color of the skin of a Caucasian; specifically, a color, red-yellow in hue, of very low saturation and high brilliance.

FLESHER. The suèdelike finished flesh side or undercut of a sheepskin, split prior to tanning. See CHAMOIS LEATHER.

FLEUR DE LIS, FLEUR DE LYS. Conventionalized flower motif suggesting the iris. A design of ancient origin, used as the royal emblem of France.

FLEUR DE SOIE. A twelve-shaft, high-quality French satin fabric.

FLEURET OR FLORET. The choicest fibers obtained from spun-silk carding.

FLEXIBILITY. The ease with which a material is bent. This may be pliable or high, stiff or low.

FLEXIBLE BEND. A set of cylindrical rollers found at each end of the cotton card. They support the endless belt of revolving flats which work with the card clothing of the cylinder to perform actual carding of the fibers. The rollers or arches are easily adjusted for best results.

FLEXIBLE REED. Specially made reeds used in doup or leno weaving where the douping ends are rather bulky. The reed is made by wrapping only one baulk with pitched cord and the other with unpitched cord.

FLEXING MACHINE. A machine used to determine the flexing qualities of upper leathers for use in shoes, artificial leathers, and comparable materials. Equipped with templates for cutting out test specimens; also adjustable for the thickness of the sample to be tested.

FLEXURAL FATIGUE. The actual flexing physical property expressed by the number of times a material can be bent upon itself through a prescribed angle prior to its rupture or ability to recover its flexibility.

FLICK. The nap on flannel and kindred materials is frequently called flick in the British Isles.

FLINT AND DAWSON. In 1786, Flint invented the point bar which was used by Leavers when he built his own machines beginning in 1813. In 1796, Dawson developed his rotary movement to machines so that the cams and wheels would move the bars and keep the warp threads at equal distances, with the cams synchronizing the wheels after the twist requirements had been met. Shortly thereafter, Brown and Copestake were able to make Mechlin net on a warp machine.

FLIPES. Cloth as it is folded over into ½- to about 1-yard lengths to facilitate inspection.

FLOAT. The portion of a warp or filling yarn that extends over two or more adjacent filling picks or warp ends in weaving for the purpose of forming certain designs.

FLOATING GLASS. The formation of a continuous ribbon of glass on the surface of a bath of molten tin which produces glass with the perfectly flat characteristics of plate glass, without the necessity of grinding and polishing, and with a brilliant finish. PPG Industries, Inc., Pittsburgh, Pennsylvania, a leader in the industry, produces the product in its Meadville, Pennsylvania, plant, opened in October, 1968, and the largest in this type of production in the world. Floating glass is used chiefly in automobiles in which from 55 to 60 or more square feet of the glass is required.

FLOATLESS PATTERN FABRIC. Figured pattern and plaid motif fabric knitted without long floats on the back of the cloth. This is essentially knit and welt fabric with a tuck or tie-in position used to anchor the floats to the back of the goods at predetermined intervals.

FLOAT PLATING. Knitting term for a plated fabric in which the face yarn is mis-knitted by particular needles to admit other yarn to show on the face of the goods.

FLOATS. Caused by an end or ends failing to weave into fabric in the manner in which they should. The loom not functioning in the proper way will also cause floats. The weaver, because of laxity in fixing ends that need attention, is another cause. Incorrect drawing-in or reeding-in can cause one or more ends to form float areas in cloth. Floats can be remedied in the dry-finishing department in the mill as a last resort.

FLOAT STITCH. Knitting stitch which occurs when a needle in a welt position passes by a yarn carrier and does not form a loop. Thus, the yarn floats tautly across the back of the goods. Usually found in combination with a plain stitch.

FLOAT WARP. An extra warp woven into the surface of fabrics to keep the pile firm and straight; much used in weaving carpets.

FLOCCULATION. To coagulate or coalesce. It occurs when an emulsion breaks and allows the dirt to settle back into the goods.

FLOCCULENT. A bulky cloudlike precipitate.

FLOCK. 1. A number of animals, especially sheep, living or herded together.

2. A lock of wool or hair.

3. Woolen or cotton waste, old rags, etc., reduced to a degree of fineness by machinery, and used for stuffing.

4. Very short fibrous particles of wool, rayon, cotton, and so on, chiefly those from shearing-pile fabrics, napped goods, etc. Sometimes wool has sufficient length to be used in blends, but it is often powderlike in form.

5. Rayon flock obtained from rayon staple or tow, as well as from the waste materials mentioned above.

FLOCK, COATING. Powdered or comminuted fibers which have been obtained by cutting or grinding, used for application on fabric, paper, wood, etc. An adhesive is mixed with the flock prior to application.

FLOCK, STUFFING. Conglomerate masses of broken fibers obtained as a by-product from any of a number of mill operations such as napping, shearing, milling, teaseling, etc. Used mainly for stuffing, padding, etc.

FLOCK, WASHED. Flock fibers obtained partly or wholly by mangling or garnetting yarn; woven, knitted, felt, felted, or other materials either old or new. Washed flock should have not less than 50 per cent wool content.

FLOCK CELLULOSE. Impalpable powder of cellulose used for flocking purposes, as well as for filler for molding powders.

FLOCK DOT. Dots or figures composed of wool (or rayon) flocks, applied, rather than woven, to a fabric with paste, adhesive, rubber cement. They are usually washable and dry cléanable, although lacquered figures may not be durable.

FLOCK EWE. The ewe in the flock as distinct from the stud.

FLOCKING FABRIC BY SPRAY METHOD. Viscose rayon staple may be flocked onto fabric, leather, cardboard, etc., to give plush, suède, and velvet effects. Known as Visca Fiber Technique, the method has been developed by Societé de la Viscose of Emmenbruecke, Switzerland.

The short-staple fiber may be applied to an adhesive backing either by spray or by an electrostatic plan. The spray method uses compressed air much on the order of spraying paint. In the electrostatic method the fibers are drawn by an electromagnetic setup onto a resin-treated surface. Suèdes are developed from an 0.5-millimeter length of fiber, while velvet is simulated from a length of 1 millimeter, and plush from a 1.5-millimeter length.

FLOCK POWDER. Fine form of flock used to embellish some fabrics by the flocking method.

FLOCK PRINTING. Application of dots to fabric by means of a gummy paste. These dots consist of wool, rayon, or cotton fibers in powder form. The effect on fabric gives the impression of small embroidery work. Metals are often used to give gold or silver effects. When metals are used the cloth is known as a metallic print. Any cloth may be given flock dotting, and this method of embellishing material has done much to cause the decline of lappet, swivel, and clipspot weaving, formerly rather popular. Flock printing also includes solid effects applied to materials; very appealing suède effects are now produced by the method.

FLOCKS. Soft, short fibers of wool thrown off by certain processes of woolen and worsted manufacture.

FLOOR CLOTH. Thin, coarse cloth made from a 2-up and 2-down twill weave. Waste woolen and cotton stocks are used to make the yarn, which is spun on the woolen system. The yarn counts range from 6s to 9s, textures from 18 square to 22 square.

FLOOR COVERING, CLASSIFICATION OF. They are divided into four general groups:

Cut Pile, Handmade: Oriental rugs.

Cut Pile, Machine-made: American oriental, chenille, Wilton, Axminster, and velvet.

Uncut Pile, Machine-made: Brussels, tapestry.

Miscellaneous Group: Grass, hooked, ingrain, linen, linoleum, punched-felt, and wool-fiber covering.

1. Genuine Oriental Rugs: They are woven by hand, and their names designate the district where they are

made, or the tribes that made them. The value of these rugs depends on the number of knots per inch, rarity and beauty, the results of dyeing, compactness of the weave and knotting. Commercial grouping of genuine orientals follows:

a) Caucasian: Baku, Derbend, Kazak, Khila, and Shirvan. The colors are few and bright, but never blood-red in cast. The designs are balanced symmetrically in squares, stars, crosses, rhomboids. These are often connected by the traditional latch-hook motif.

b) Chinese: Kashgar, Khotan, Tibetan, Yarkand. The motifs in these rugs are the key, the fret, and emblems—butterfly, dragon, and the eight emblems of Buddhism. Blue with a yellow background is popular.

c) Indian: Agra, Amritsar, Jaipur, Kandahar, Lahore, Sringar. Floral motifs are used the most. The rugs seem to lack elaboration and show much dull or dead spacing.

d) Persian: Herat, Kerman, Mosul, Saruk, Senna, Serabend. These rugs excel all others, and are copied much in power-loom weaving of rugs. A fine, compact weave is used to weave these rugs, which feature floral patterns to a marked degree.

e) Turkestan: Afghan-Kerki, Beshin, Bokhara, Khachli-Bokhara, Samarkand, and Yomut. The rugs show symmetrical simplicity in design. The basic colors used are Turanian red, natural white, yellow, and black. One color predominates always in the rug. Knottage ranges from 30 per square inch upwards.

f) Turkish: Anatolian, Ghiordes, Karaman, Konya, Kulah, Sivas. Coarse yarn is used in the rugs which have a heavy pile. Compared with Persian rugs, they are less expensive, and have brighter colors. The curves of the Persian rugs are replaced by heavy, angular lines in the motif.

2. Cut Pile, Machine-made:

a) American Oriental Rugs: Commonly known as domestic oriental, luster-type, modern, sheen, and washed. Axminster or Wilton weaves are used in the construction. The rugs are woven on power looms. They are copies of Oriental designs. Many of the rugs are treated chemically to duplicate the genuine Oriental effect. For this reason they do not always give good service.

b) Chenille: The French word for caterpillar. The material is woven on price. Despite the influx of other rugs on the market, there is always some demand for this staple covering.

c) Ingrain: The yarn is dyed prior to weaving; the warp is cotton or wool, the filling is wool. Ingrain has no pile effect; it is inexpensive, and 36 inches is the usual width of the fabric. When this width is used, the rug is bought and sold as Kidderminster.

d) LINEN: Plain weave is used in this linen warp and linen filling covering. The rug is rather durable, heavy, and lies well.

e) LINOLEUM: This is made from ground cork mixed with gums, oxidized linseed oil, and dyes. The mixture is pressed into a burlap sack and is then seasoned. There are four types of linoleum—plain, jaspé, inlaid, and printed. Linoleum is made from 6 to 12 feet wide, and heavy linoleum is ⅛ of an inch in thickness. Medium thickness is .095 inch, while standard thickness is .079 inch. Low temperature will cause the material to become brittle and possibly crack. Plain, jaspé, and inlaid, when washed, should be waxed for the sake of preservation and wear. Printed linoleum should be lacquered and wiped with a mop or damp cloth.

f) PUNCHED FELT: Felt is punched into burlap by means of a board which has an up-and-down motion. The board is set with a series of nicked pins which catch the felt fibers and carry them through the burlap on the upward motion. As the pins are on the way down, the burlap wipes off the felt fibers, thereby allowing the pins to be ready to pick up the next batch of stock to be punched into the burlap. looms; the pile ranges from ⅜ of an inch to 1½ inches in height. A filling cloth is woven and then cut into narrow strips, and then ironed. The caterpillar strips are put into another loom and combed up through a fine set of catcher warp. Four picks of filling follow each row of chenille. There is a Smyrna-rug pile on both sides of the material. See Illustrated Section.

c) WILTON: Originated in Wilton, England, they were copies of Belgian and French tapestries. Woolen or worsted yarn is put into the rug, and a Jacquard loom does the weaving. The pile is made by looping the yarn over a series of long wires; the depth of the wire regulates the depth of the yarn. As the wire is withdrawn, the one end of it, which has a very sharp blade at the tip, cuts through the top of each loop, thereby forming the velvety-pile effect. Worsted Wilton gives better service than wool Wilton. Compared with the latter, the stock is better, has more twist, a shorter pile effect, and a stiffer back. Usually, the yarn can be seen rather plainly on the back of the rug. See Illustrated Section.

d) AXMINSTER: Originally made in Acksminster, England. Spools of various yarns are placed in a continuous sprocket chain, the ends of the yarn being brought down by steel arms into a chain of cotton warp. Jute binder threads hold the wool in place, and the ends of the woolen yarns are clipped off by broad knives, and the spools are returned to their position on the chain. Axminster has woolen yarn only in the face construction. The pile varies from ⅛ to ⅜ of an inch. Axminster is moderate in price, has a good appearance, and can be made up to a width of 12 feet. It gives the appearance of a hand-knotted carpet. The standard texture is seven tufts wide, and eight rows per inch. The rug may be rolled-on in the lengthwise direction.

e) VELVET: Made of woolen or worsted yarn, the colors are printed onto the yarn prior to weaving. The wool, in the woven construction, is looped over the wires that cut the loops in order to make the pile. Velvet needs less wool than Axminister, and the rugs are inexpensive. There are no rows on the back of the goods, and all the wool is used in making the pile effect. Jute backing is used, and it is well-sized in order to make the rug lie flat.

3. UNCUT PILE, MACHINE-MADE RUGS:

a) BRUSSELS: Made of worsted yarn and has an uncut pile. The Jacquard loom is used for the pattern. The rug is made in the 2-shot construction only.

b) TAPESTRY: This rug is made of woolen or worsted yarn in the same manner as velvet rugs. It does not have the loops cut as in the case of velvet rugs. The rug is inexpensive and rather durable. Tapestry does not have the softness of a velvet rug, and the motifs are rather indistinct because of possible color bleeding. See Illustrated Section.

4. MISCELLANEOUS FLOOR COVERINGS:

a) GRASS: Plain weave is used, and grass twine is used for the warp and the filling. In the so-called grass-and-fiber rugs, the fiber is used for the warp, and the grass for the filling. The warp has cotton mixed with it to hold the twist and aid in the weaving. These rugs are reversible.

b) HOOKED: The foundation is of burlap or monk's cloth, upon which the pattern is drawn. The yarns are cotton, silk, wool, rayon, acetate, or manipulated stock, and are about ½ inch in width. Prior to the American Revolution, these rugs were very popular, but hand-loomed and power-loomed rugs caused their decline. Handmade rugs vary considerably in

FLORENCE. A lightweight silk lining fabric; usually square in texture.

FLORENTINE. 1. A heavy silk fabric, woven-figured or plain-twilled, used as waistcoating. 2. A worsted waistcoating fabric. 3. A twilled cotton cloth used for summer trousers.

FLORENTINE DRILL. A rugged warp-face cotton fabric made on a 3-up, 1-down twill weave.

FLORENTINE TWILL. Lightweight dress goods of the lustrous type. Cloth comes in waves of popularity at times. Various weaves are used, and the term holds the significance that a Florentine twill cloth must repeat on eight warp ends and eight filling picks.

FLORET, FLORETTE: One of the better qualities of spun silk, since it is obtained from the longer-staple stock. Used for fancy stripings in dress goods.

FLORET YARN. A mixture yarn of floret silk and cotton or rayon.

FLORIDA. 1. Sea Island cotton is sometimes called by this name. Florida is now the only state in the Union which raises this cotton. 2. Printed madras used in the Balkans is known by this name.

FLORIDA MOSS. The term is a misnomer and is often referred to as Spanish Moss, an incorrect term. This so-called moss is the festooned fiber growth found on long branches of trees, and it is actually a member of the pineapple fiber family. Found in Florida, Georgia, and the Carolinas, it is not a true parasite as is generally believed. Other names for it include Spanish-beard, and Long-moss.

FLOSS. A silk fiber of various types and grades not suitable for reeling. The floss must be removed before the regular filament can be reeled. It also implies the soft, loosely twisted thread used for embroidery purposes.

FLOSS THREAD. A soft linen yarn or thread used in embroidery; also called linen floss.

FLOUNCE. A section or part of a skirt either circular or straight; generally used on petticoats, they are also used on skirts which from time to time are popular when made with a flounce effect.

FLOUNCING. A wide lace identified by a straight top and a scalloped front the same as edging. It comes in widths from 12 to 54 inches. Flouncings find use in deep ruffles, or they may be gathered or pleated at the top.

FLUFFING. When drying garments in the home, this implies the removal of wrinkles without using heat in the tumble cycle.

FLOORCOVERING MANUFACTURE, TERMS USED IN.

BACKING: The back, foundation, or underside of a carpet or rug secures the pile yarns in position and affords a firm foundation. It is usually carpet rayon, cotton, jute, or Kraftcord.

In the weaving process, the backing is woven simultaneously with the pile yarn. In the tufting process, the carpet is tufted onto the broad woven fabric which serves as the backing.

All tufted carpets, as well as some types of woven carpet, are coated on the back with latex to seal in the tufts. With this type of finish individual tufts will not work loose and a clean edge can be cut in any direction. Binding is not necessary at all. Damaged or burned areas may be cut and replaced without showing a seam.

BEAM: Large horizontal cylinders or spools upon which the warp threads are wound. This warp beam is set at the back of the loom, and the warp yarn is fed off in a uniform, controlled manner as the fabric is being woven.

BINDING YARN: Filling or weft yarn carried across the loom by the shuttle. In Axminster weaving, this operation is done by a needle thrust. The binding yarn in carpet weaving alternates with the filling yarn, which is usually cotton or jute.

BROADLOOM: Carpeting that is more than three quarters (27 inches) or four quarters (36 inches) in width. A quarter is 9 inches; hence, a three-quarter carpet would be 27 inches wide. Broadloom is usually 6, 9, 12, 15, 18, up to 30 feet in width. Another meaning of the term is that of carpeting woven on a wide loom, usually 9 feet or more in width. Broadloom does not mean a type of carpeting, an actual fabric, nor a grade or quality of fabric.

CHAIN WARP: Two cotton yarns that run warpwise or vertically and are drawn by heddles over and under the weft binding and filling yarns as they are inserted, by shuttles in tapestry, chenille, velvet, and Wilton weaves, and by a needle thrust in Axminster fabric.

FILLING YARN: Weft yarn carried across most looms by a shuttle (in Axminster by a needle thrust) alternating with the binding weft yarn, which is usually cotton or jute.

FRAMES: Trays or creels holding spools of surface yarn in two to six levels at the back of a Wilton loom. One strand of yarn is lifted into position by the Jacquard mechanism to form the design on the pile surface, while the other yarns, one to five in number, are woven dormant in the warp direction.

GROUND COLOR: The background color against which the surface colors create the pattern or motif in the design.

JASPÉ: In either plain fabric or fabric with a design, irregular warp stripes of two hues of one color in the surface yarn. The same effect may be obtained by using yarns of different twist.

KRAFTCORD: A tightly twisted, plasticized yarn made from cellulose fiber of a tiliaceous plant (lime or linden tree, etc.). Used in carpet weaves as an alternate backing yarn to cotton or jute.

PICK: A shot of weft binding or filling yarn to effect a weave by interlacing with the chain warp yarns. Use of the word indicates the quality; for example, 39 picks to the warp inch means that 13 wires would be used in a three-shot construction, or $3 \times 13 = 39$.

PITCH: The number of construction units per 27-inch width in a floor covering.

PLANTING: A method of spacing spools of different colored surface yarns in frames at the back of the Jacquard Wilton loom so that more colors will appear in the design than are supplied in the full range of solid colors used. These extra planted colors are usually arranged in groups of each shade to give added interest to the motif.

SHOT: The number of weft yarns to a row of surface yarn tufts; for example, a binding and filling shot for each row of tufts would be a 2-shot construction, while adding a second binding yarn would make it a 3-shot construction, costing more material and weaving time. Tapestry, wool velvet, and wool Wilton are two-shot, Axminster and worsted Wilton are three-shot, while chenille is a four-shot construction. (See Pick.)

STUFFER WARP: Jute, cotton, or Kraftcord yarns running dormant in the fabric to provide added weight and strength.

TOP COLORS: Colors of the yarn forming the motif, as distinguished from the ground color.

WEFT YARN: Cotton, jute, or Kraftcord running crosswise, weftwise, fillingwise, or horizontally in the fabric as binding or filling. In the "wire weaves" it is inserted through the chain and stuffer warp yarns with a shuttle, and in the case of Axminsters, with a needle thrust.

WIRES: Metal wires or strips which are inserted in the weaving shed of the loom under the surface yarns to form the loops as the yarns are bound by the weft shuttle, in tapestry-velvet and Brussels-Wilton weaves.

Round, untipped wires for tapestry and Brussels fabric are withdrawn from the fabric, leaving uncut pile loops; while flat, bladed-tip wires, in the velvet and the Wilton weaves, cut the loops to form a plushlike surface of tufts.

FLUFLON. This product of Marionette Mills, Inc., uses a false twist technique for stretching or texturing continuous filament yarn. It is different from Helanca in that the twisting and the untwisting operation is carried on in a single equipment unit. In the relaxed state it is a very fluffy yarn.

FLUO, FLUOR. Chemically, a combining from fluor, indicating fluoride; used as an ingredient as in fluosilicate.

FLUOPHOSPHATE. A double salt of hydrofluoric and phosphoric acids.

FLUORESCENCE. When pigments glow for 1/10,000th of a second after exposure to light, they are said to be fluorescent. Pigments of this type must, therefore, be exposed continuously to stimulus.

FLUORESCENT DYES. They are made from inorganic dyestuffs designed to impart to textile fibers and fabrics an unusual color brightness both in daylight and under the so-called "black light" conditions. Daylight fluorscent dyes impart a brightness of shade to textile materials, under daylight conditions, that is not obtainable with the conventional dyes. The "black light" property imparts an ability to glow in total darkness when excited by ultraviolet light. Fluorescent dyes can also be used to gixe textile material an iridescent appearance.

FLUORITE. A cleavable, isometric, variously colored calcium fluoride, CaF_2.

FLUOROCARBON. An example is Teflon, manufactured by E. I. du Pont de Nemours & Co., Inc., Wilmington, Delaware. Fluorocarbon fibers have extreme resistance to acids, alkalies, other chemicals and heat. Used practically in industrial fabrics.

FLUORO-CHEMICALS. Substances in which the element fluorine is a characterizing ingredient. Some of these form a finish that makes fabrics water-repellent and resistant to oil and comparable stains. See RESIN, FLUORESCENT DYES.

FLUOSILICATE. Chemically, a salt of fluosilicate acid; also called "silicofluoride."

FLUSH. 1. Same as a float in weave construction. 2. Same as face in speaking of a warp-face or filling-face weave or fabric. 3. A short water rinse without supplies of any type being used. 4. A short water rinse to remove blood and other solids before the Break (first) Operation in laundry practice.

FLUTING. Ruffles, pleats, flutes, or comparable trimming.

FLUTING IRON. A type of laundry iron used to flute ruffles.

FLY. 1. Short cotton waste picked up around the machines in cotton manufacturing; often used with longer-staple fibers to make yarn. 2. Chaff and other light wastes found in textile mills; fly often floats in the air prior to landing.

FLY COTTON. Short, immature, neppy cotton fibers obtained in the carding operation.

FLYER. An inverted "U-shaped" device which sets on the spindle top and revolves with it. It has a solid arm and the slubbing or roving enters the top of the hollow arm, travels downward and emerges at the bottom and is then wound around the presser finger of the device. The stock, after leaving the eyelet in the presser finger, is wound onto the bobbin set around the spindle. The flyer inserts twist into the fibers and winds the stock onto the bobbin in uniform manner. The device is used on all cotton slubbers and fly frames, on flyer-spinning and flyer-twisting machines, and on many of the drawing frames used in worsted-yarn manufacture.

FLYER LEAD. Refers to slubbing and roving frames where the speed of the flyer is slightly in excess of the bobbin.

FLYER SPINNING. A method of spinning worsted yarn. The roving to be spun into yarn is fed into the back rollers, passes between the carrier rollers, and is delivered by the front rollers to the flyer. Spinning is done by means of the hollow arm on the flyer. The inverted "U-shaped" flyer sets over the top of the spindle. From the front rollers, the stock passes downward and through a hole in the top of the flyer, and emerges from an adjacent hole just below the top opening. It then passes through the hollow arm of the flyer attachment. The solid arm does not come in contact with the fibers. As the yarn emerges from the bottom of the hollow arm, it is wound two or three times around the presser finger, and then goes through an opening at the tip of the finger, where it passes onto the bobbin which fits around the spindle.

The action of the spindle, flyer, and bobbin completes the spinning in entirety. The action of the carriage on the machine insures even, uniform winding of the yarn onto the bobbin at the nose, body, and heel.

The function of the presser finger is to act as a guide, and govern the yarn in its passage through the hollow arm of the flyer to the winding on the bobbin. It regulates tension as well.

A flyer lead on the machine means that the flyer goes slightly faster than the bobbin. Bobbin lead means that the bobbin goes at a slightly faster rate of speed than the flyer. Flyer lead will give a softer yarn than bobbin lead.

Three of the four methods of spinning worsted yarn—cap, flyer, and ring—twist and unwind by friction. They may produce a rather beardy, harsh yarn that is not as cylindrical as mule-spun yarn.

FLY FRAME. A group name for the following machines used in a cotton mill: slubber, intermediate frame, roving frame, and fine frame. These machines draw, draft, attenuate, twist, and wind the fibers prior to spinning.

FLY-FRONT. A piece of material, attached by one edge and suggesting a flap, to conceal garment fastening.

FLY REED. The loose or receding reed used in looms when weaving terry towels and other warp-pile fabrics.

FLY SHUTTLE. Invented by John

Kay in 1738, it enabled the weaver to do away with his helper in weaving broad goods on looms. This was the first important thing that gradually led to the mechanistic age, and was the incentive that caused trouble, riots, strikes, and general havoc in the early days of the Industrial Revolution in England. Many men were thrown out of work by this invention, and excitement ran so high that Kay's home was sacked and burned by a frenzied mob in 1753. Robert Kay, his son, was the inventor of the drop-box loom. The fly shuttle was thrown through the shed of the loom by pulling a cord. This method is still used on hand looms. The picker-stick action on power looms throws the shuttle automatically through the loom shed, at great speed.

FLY WASTE. Short fibers and some minute foreign matter that fall through the cylinder screen on a card. Modern mills use vacuum strippers which take the card strips and other matter and deliver them to dust chambers. There is a waste of about 1 per cent or so of strippings, about ½ per cent of fly waste, 4 per cent of flat-strip waste, and 1 per cent of unforeseen loss during the carding operation.

FOAM. In foam made for textile use, air is enclosed by cell walls made of material that is sturdy enough to be durable (rubber, vinyl, urethane, etc.). If the walls form individual closed cells, the compressibility is less; if the air cells are open to each other, the structure can be pressed flat and is more flexible. The air cells form a good insulation for garment interlining. Other uses are for mattresses, pillows, furniture padding, and rug pads.

FOAM, HIGH DENSITY. A rubber compound applied in liquid form, then cured, and used to form an integral part of carpet backing. Minimum weight is 38 ounces per square yard; minimum thinkness is 1/8-inch, and minimum density is 17 pounds per cubic foot.

FOAMCRAFT. Registered trademark of E. W. Twitchell, Inc., Philadelphia, Pennsylvania, this is a fabric material of plasticized cellulose kraft knit with a layer of foam rubber cast on one side. This strong abrasion product is inexpensive and provides long wear. The yarn used has a nylon core for extra tensile and tear strengths. Now used for infant and outdoor furniture.

F.O.B. Freight collect (Freight on Board). To avoid misunderstanding it should be noted that most foreign buyers do not understand the American use of this term. When quoting abroad, F.O.B. means "Free-on-Board" and should only be used to indicate all charges paid prior

to actually being placed aboard a ship unless there is a further qualification involved.

F.O.B. COTTON. A buyer or seller who deals in spot cotton at local or country terms as to price.

FOCHETTE. This material is named in honor of Marshal Ferdinand Foch of World War I fame. It was first made on Armistice Day, November 11, 1918, and is a double tubular plain-knitted fabric whose rigidity is increased by the use of an extra yarn between the cloths in addition to the tying thread. When this binding thread is pulled out two separate fabrics are then formed.

FODEN. Cotton fabric made in both stripes and checks in which the warp has two ends running as one. The colors are usually blue and white; the former color is used for the ground, the latter for the line effects. Much used for aprons and dress goods.

FOLD. 1. Refers to the number of ply in a yarn. 2. A layer of cloth. 3. Cloth which has been doubled, such as selvage to selvage or end to end.

FOLDED YARN. English term for a ply yarn composed of several single-ply yarns.

FOLDER. Same as folding machine.

FOLDING MACHINE. There are several types of this machine in the trade used to fold piece goods in some particular manner.

FOND. The groundwork in handmade lace. The motifs are spread out over the ground, which is either a mesh effect or one composed of brides.

FOND EPINGLE. See LACES, HANDMADE AND MACHINE-MADE.

FOOTBALL LEATHER. Originally this was a pigskin leather, but it has been replaced by an embossed or printed cattle-hide leather; sheepskin has also been used to make this product.

FOOT-AND-MOUTH DISEASE. A dread disease, peculiar to animals, in which ulcers form in the mouth and in the hoof area.

FOOTCLOTH. 1. A carpet, rug, or throw. 2. Part of the caparison seen on performing horses.

FOOTER. That part of a knitting machine which makes the foot in full-fashioned hosiery.

FOOTING. 1. A lace flouncing edge which has been sewn to material. 2. An insertion of Brussels net that is 1 to 3 inches in width. 3. Repairing holes in the foot of a stocking.

FOOT ROT. An inflammatory di-

sease that may be severe enough to cause the loss of the hoof of an animal.

FOOTSTEP. A bearing used at the base of each spindle on a roving or spinning frame. Bolted to the step rail, a staggered formation is used so that even balance will result to care for each spindle in the machine setup.

FORD. This type of apparel is wearable for all types and figures and has a slightly novel treatment of some popular theme. It is a fashion with an interesting story behind it; it is becoming to young people and makes older women look and feel younger. Fords are adaptable to many occasions and are instantly and universally appealing.

FOREBEAM. The same as the breastbeam on a loom. It is situated where the weaver stands. The newly woven fabric passes over the forebeam on its way to the sand roller and the cloth roller.

FOREIGN COTTON. Cotton raised anywhere outside of this country.

FOREIGN MATTER. Any of the matter, foreign or otherwise, that affects cotton as to quality or grade.

FOREL. British term for the selvage border.

FORESLEEVE. That part of the sleeve below the elbow.

FORESTRY CLOTH. Used by the United States Government for uniform cloth, overcoatings, trouserings, knickers, shirts, blouses, etc. The cloth is olive drab in color, and it is made from a twill weave. Made of worsted, wool, cotton, mixes, etc. This cloth is used essentially in the Forestry Service of the nation but is likewise utilized by some other departments. In short, the name may be nothing more than another term for khaki cloth.

FOREST WOOL. Pine needles are treated and reduced so that they may be mixed with cotton or wool for use in coarse materials such as blankets and low-grade clothing. Known as Waldwolle in Germany, where much of the material is made.

FORMALDEHYDE. A colorless gas obtained from wood alcohol (methanol). Finds much use as a preservative and disinfectant. This formic aldehyde is an important reagent in some phases of textile chemistry.

FORMALDEHYDE TANNAGE. A method of tanning of the same type as oil tanning, and used for approximately the same types of leather.

FORMELLE. Registered trademark

of Rohm and Haas Company, Inc., Philadelphia, Pennsylvania, for its nylon hosiery fiber designed to eliminate the "bag and sag" in pantyhose. The yarn retains its stretch and recovery properties in the finished article by a unique process which enables stretch nylon yarns to be colored prior to being knit into hosiery. This eliminates the necessity of dyeing the hosiery to obtain fashion colors, a process which causes nylon yarns to lose a certain degree of stretch because of the high temperatures required for dyeing. Since the dyeing step is done away with, hosiery products have the bounce in the box that they had in the knitting frame. Multi-dimensional motifs, in these color-spun yarns, such as in Jacquards, are possible thereby creating new high-fashion items. Formelle is made in the Fayetteville, North Carolina plant of the company.

FORMER. The machine which twists the yarns into strands in the manufacture of rope.

FORMICA. Trademark for a thermoplastic used as a chemical-proof and heat-proofing covering for tables, wall panels, etc. This laminated plastic is made of synthetic resins, cloth, or paper.

FORMING TRUMPET. 1. A short, flared metal tube found at the delivery end of the card. The film of cotton fibers which extends the width of the machine is condensed and passed through the tube into the sliver can which is underneath the trumpet.

2. The warping machine is likewise equipped with a trumpet or tube at the front of the frame. The purpose of the trumpet is to gather a number of strands of yarn into a loose, untwisted rope formation when ball warping.

FORMULA. The complete schedule, say, of the applications of detergents and other supplies in finishing, laundering, etc.

FORTISAN. No longer in production, the name was a registered trademark of Celanese Corporation for their very strong yarn which was made by subjecting cellulose-acetate yarn to mechanical treatment to obtain a parallel molecular structure. Saponfication followed for a regenerated yarn which is chemically similar to cotton. Its uses included parachute fabric, core threads for tinsel conductors, shroud lines, sewing thread, and high-strength coated fabrics. See Fortisan-36.

FORTISAN-36. Registered trademark for the highly oriented regenerated cellulose (rayon) made by Celanese Corporation. No longer in production, it differed from Fortisan in that it had

higher strength and was made by an entirely new and different process which produced yarns with a high degree of uniformity and at the same time was suitable for production of heavy deniers required in industrial applications. The product had exceptional strength, high resistance to stretching under tension, and good dimensional stability. As with Fortisan, it was much used during World War II and was ideal for the used as noted in Fortisan, above. See Fortisan.

FORTREL. The counterpart of Terylene made by Imperial Chemical Industries, Ltd., London, England, and sold throughout the world under this name, with the exception of the United States, where it is known as Fortrel. This polyester fiber comes in staple and yarn forms. Terylene was discovered in 1941 by J. R. Whinfield and J. T. Dickson in the laboratories of the Calico Printers Association in Lancashire, England.

To enter the American market with Fortrel, Imperial Chemical Industries, Ltd., and Celanese Corporation of America formed Fiber Industries, Inc., a jointly owned enterprise, to sell this polyester textile fiber, comparable with "Dacron" polyester fiber of E. I. duPont de Nemours & Co., Inc., Wilmington, Delaware. The product comes in filament and staple forms and is used in blends with cotton, wool, and worsted. The plant is in Shelby, North Carolina.

Celanese Corporation, deep in the chemical field in addition to textiles, manufactures acetate and rayon fibers, Fortisan yarns, Arnel, the triacetate fiber, chemicals and plastics. Imperial manufactures dyestuffs, pharmaceuticals, fertilizers, paints, explosives, and nonferrous metals.

FORTREL ECF. A Fortrel polyester fiber engineered for the carpet industry, capable of providing lush, velvety pile effects with high strength which resists crushing and matting. It is capable of withstanding pattern walk-out, making it ideal for areas which receive heavy traffic. Since the fiber may be dyed without a carrier, this makes the fiber important to dye economies in mills. Trademark of Fibers Industries, Inc., Charlotte and Shelby, North Carolina.

FORTREL POLYESTER FIBER, TYPES OF.

Type 300: A high tenacity staple made to blend well with cellulosics.

TYPE 310: Type 300 with an optical brightener.

Type 400: A staple fiber used for general textile applications.

Type 410: Type 400 with an optical

brightener.

Type 440: A high shrinkage Fortrel staple fiber used for blending with low shrinkage fibers to increase fabric bulk.

Type 450: Ideal for nonwoven fabrics; it is a low fusion binding staple for binding fibers together.

Type 700: A continuous filament of normal tenacity for general textile applications.

Type 720: Type 700 with an optical brightener.

Type 730: A producer-textured filament for bulk and premium aesthetics.

Type 760: Continuous filament ideal for texturing.

Type 770: Continuous filament used primarily for industrial items such as core-spun threads.

Type 785: Continuous filament primarily used for industrial items such as tire cord and seat belts.

FORTREL POLYESTER STAPLES. Fiber Industries, Inc., Shelby, North Carolina, unveiled the following polyester staple variants in 1969:

Type 402: A cationic dyeable polyester staple which permits three-way blend corss-dyeing. Advantages in its use make possible greater color and styling versatility when combined with regular polyester, cotton, or rayon. Also provides brighter shades in print or in plain dye fabrics. It can also be blended with wool or used in 100% form in men's and women's knit and woven sportswear.

Type 405: A variant polyester staple fiber which provides a color styling range through deeper dyeing effects and multi-color piece dyeing when in combination with other dye variants and fiber types. Printed fabrics can be obtained in the use of Type 405 wherein the fixing of color is done by atmospheric steaming rather than by the pressure steam-setting plan. Type 405 finds use in apparel and home furnishing fabrics.

Type 408: This is a "T" cross-section fiber built to impart a sheen or gloss to finished fabrics by a greater clarity of color and, at the same time, to add greater bulk and warmth of hand than that found in circular fibers. Blended with cotton or rayon, or used alone, Type 408 is used in casual knit and woven goods.

Type 461: Engineered to virtually eliminate pilling in garments and to reduce differential wear and frosting on durable press blends, this fiber retains the desirable dyeing and processing properties of conventional polyesters. May be used alone or blended with several other fibers to provide high-bulk yarns.

Type 790: An adhesive-activated polyester yarn which can be used in a conventional single dipping process with resorcinol/formaldehyde latex dip ingredients and provides improved adhesion to rubber in making tires, hoses, and belts. Dipping can be done at lower temperatures than are necessary for the conventional polyester tire yarns, thereby retaining more strength in the cord and reducing stiffness.

FORTREL TYPE 408. This is a "T" cross-section polyester staple fiber which, when manipulated into fabrics, presents great bulk and warmth of hand, imparts a subtle sheen to finished goods, and lends a distinctive clarity of color in the motifs or patterns used in non-white cloth. It may be used alone or in blends with cotton or rayon for use in men's and women's apparel, draperies, table cloths and comparable materials. Registered trademark of Celanese Corporation, New York City.

FORTREL TYPE 765. A variant designed for the polyester market. It features a faster dyeing, disperse dyeable filament. When combined with the dyeable yarns Type 760 and cationic Type 764, it makes multi-color effects possible in piece dyeing in a single dye bath. When the three dye variants are combined with solution-dyed black yarn, four distinct shades are possible in stretch woven fabrics. Fabrics which contain only Type 765 can be printed and fixed by atmospheric steaming rather than by pressure steam setting. Used much in men's and women's knitted and woven apparel.

FORTRON. A material made with a layer of Fiberglas fabric between sheets of vinyl film, laminated under heat and pressure to form a single sheet. Properties include strength, non-absorbency, proofing against mildew and fungus, and resistance to acid, flame, and grease. Fortron will not stretch or shrink and will not crack at temperatures ranging to 30 degrees below zero. Colored and translucent types of the product are made at present. A product of Thermoplastics Fabrics Corporation.

FORTUNE. A combination-yarn material with the following layout: texture of 72 x 54 with a warp of two ends of 150-denier acetate, voile-twist, and one end of 100/150 combination. The filling arrangement has two picks of acetate of 150-denier filament, voile-twist, and two picks of 100/150 combination yarn.

FORTUNY PRINTS. A series of rich, artistic fabrics executed by a secret screen-printing process. Originated by Mariano Fortuny of Venice, the Renaissance motifs used featured the use of light colors on dark backgrounds. Some of the fabrics were stamped with gold or silver to give further vividness to the pattern. Twill or satin weaves are used in the plain constructions, while pile-effect weaves are used in velvets and velveteens for the more expensive materials. The prints have been used for evening wear, runners, upholstery, wall hangings, and other general decorative purposes. Fabric widths are 27 inches and 50 inches.

FOULARD. A lightweight silk or rayon cloth noted for its soft finish and feel. Made with plain or twill weaves, it is usually printed with small figures on dark and light backgrounds. Suitable for dresses, robes, and scarves, foulard is always a popular staple for summer-neckwear fabric.

FOULARD, COTTON. Name given to cotton fabric made to imitate popular silk material of that name.

FOULE. From the French verb fouler, to full. The cloth is made of a twill weave, is unsheared and unsinged. The face is quite uneven and rough. Much shrinking gives the face its characteristic finish. Foule is on the order of estamene but is supposed to be the better material.

FOUNDATION GARMENT. Made from silk, cotton, rayon, lastex, and other yarns. It refers to a girdle, corset, or corselet and is usually combined with bandeau or brassière.

FOUNDATION MUSLIN. Any plain muslin treated with size, starch, or gum. Examples may include crinoline, buckram, tarlatan.

FOUNDATION NET. See BUCKRAM, TARLATAN.

FOUNDATION PATTERN. Plain, basic pattern without fullness or designing lines; used for size only.

FOUNDATION WARP. Alternate term for the ground, basic, or main warp when it forms the foundation weave effect in a textile material, and when the material has one or more warps to give certain effects in the finished fabric made by fancy or flushing warps.

FOUNDATION WEAVES. All staple or novelty weaves are derived directly or indirectly from the basic weave used in weave formation—plain, twill, satin.

FOUR BUTTON LENGTH. Glove lengths are referred to in terms of buttons whether or not there are any actual buttons on the glove. A one-button lengths refers to a glove which extends one inch above the base of the thumb. This is actually a French measurement of $1\frac{1}{12}$th standard inches. A four-button glove extends up the arm for four inches above the base of the thumb, etc. When hemmed, the measurement will include the portion turned under for this hem.

FOURCHETTE. A glove term which pertains to the forked pieces or the walls of fabric which form the inside portions of the glove finger.

FOUR-FRAME BRUSSELS. Brussels carpet made with four pile warps in the construction.

FOUR-IN-HAND. The term comes from a coach drawn by two teams of horses, four in all, in a tandem formation. The four-in-hand was the type of neckwear worn by these coachmen and was adopted by the young men of England during the 19th century. It folds in a vertical direction.

FOUR-LEAF TWILL. Any twill or diagonal weave using not more than 4 shafts or harnesses per weave repeat. The most common are 3-up and 1-down, 2-up and 2-down, and 1-up and 3-down weaves.

If the cloth has the warp ends and filling picks about equal per inch in the texture of the goods, the material is called serge. If the warp texture is considerably higher than that of the filling, the cloth may be called whipcord; however, a true whipcord weave repeats on 11 ends and picks—5-up, 1-down; 1-up, 2-down; 1-up, 1-down, a 63° twill.

On the 2-up and 2-down weave with the warp and filling the same as to ends and picks per inch, the angle will be a 45-degree twill line. If the ends are increased in the texture, the diagonal line obtained will be greater than the 45-degree angle.

The 2-up and 2-down four-leaf twill is the most popular weave. The 3-up and 1-down twill is much used in army uniform cloth.

Four-leaf twills are used for a great many fabrics in men's and women's wear. They are also used to make awning fabric, bags, Boy Scout cloth, dress uniforms, hunting fabric, raincoating, sail cloth, shoe lining, slacks, and trouserings.

FOUR-LEAF TWILLS:

Serge Twill

Navy Twill
Marine Twill

Pocketing Twill. (Also made
on a 1-up and 2-down twill)

FOUR-STRANDED. A rope made of four strands and center heart.

FOURTH COMBING. Indicates the wool taken from the sides and the shoulders of an average fleece, graded to about 58s.

FOX. Black, blue, cross, gray, king, kitt, platina, red, silver, and white, found in many countries throughout the world, in a variety of colors. Wearing qualities, variable from poor (blue kitt) to good (cross). Judged by natural coloring, quality of guard hairs, and fullness of fur. Worn for informal and dress, in jackets, scarves, and occasionally in great coats.

FOXY-COLOR COTTON. Raw cotton with a reddish cast.

FOYLON. A textile and aluminum foil laminate that is porous and flexible yet has the conductivity of metal; product of Archer Aluminum division of the R. J. Reynolds Tobacco Company, Inc., and under license of Shirley Institute, Manchester, England. In its use as a heat reflective material it can cut air conditioning costs by about 20 percent. Uses include drapery lining, automobile ceiling liners, protective clothing for firemen, awnings, window shades, beach umbrellas, sports clothing, and various uses in military and space applications.

FRAME. 1. Practically any type of machine used in the manufacture of textiles, chiefly those that aid in making yarn—slubber frame, drawing frame, ring-spinning frame, etc. 2. The metal or wooden frame upon which heddles are placed or strung, particularly on a hand loom. 3. The rack or tray used in weaving certain types of carpets, such as Brussels and Wiltons. A number of these are set at the back of the loom in order to plant the proper colors for weaving.

FRAME SPINNING. Implies ring spinning. See Illustrated Section.

FRAMING. A finishing process in which the cloth is "framed" or held out as near to the finished width as possible on a clip or pin tenter frame.

FRANCO-BELGIAN SYSTEM. The same as the French system in manipulating worsted fibers into yarn.

FRANKLIN SPRING. A helical spring used in package dyeing of yarns. A knitted sock or parchment paper is set over the spring prior to winding the yarn onto it.

FRAY, FRAYED. One system of yarns may shift, slide, or slip over the other system in the woven goods to produce frayed effect. Cut and unfinished edges of fabric will also give the effect.

FRAYING. Thread or yarn slippage, usually in the filling, during the finishing operations.

FRAZIER TESTER. A hosiery-testing machine used to measure distensibility, recoverability, and stretch-endurability of women's hosiery. This apparatus provides a means for the measurement of behavior of a stocking when the upper part of the leg of the stocking is repeatedly distended in a way which subjects it to forces similar to those which occur at the knee and the garter clasps of a stocking in use. It records on a chart the relationship between the load and the circumference for each cycle of loading and unloading, and the number of cycles on a counter.

FREE ALKALI. Alkali which is chemically uncombined; in other words, caustic soda or caustic potash which has not been united with any neutralizing substance. It is a destructive form of alkali.

FREE COTTON LINTERS. Those linters that were not sold on the basis of cellulose content, but on the grades as set forth in the regulations of the O.P.A., during World War II. Chemical linters were those sold on the basis of cellulose content as determined by chemical analysis.

FREE RUN. A short period of running a loaded wheel without water or supplies after a break or a suds operation. Sometimes used on heavily soiled laundry work to speed up the removal of emulsified dirt.

FREE WOOL. Wool free from defects, especially burrs. Also means wool that has scoured to the white evenly and cleanly.

FRENCHBACK. A cloth with a corded-twill backing of different weave than the face of the cloth, which is clear finish in appearance. It is a staple worsted cloth. Back weave is of inferior yarn when compared with the face

stock. The backing gives added weight, warmth, more texture and stability to the cloth. The interlacings are covered up better than in the average single cloth. Frenchbacks can be made with little extra cost to the cloth. Fabric is usually made of two warps and one filling. It is piece- or skein-dyed, weight ranges from 15 to 20 ounces per yard. Cloth has good feel and clinginess and may be used for formal or informal wear. Backing is often cotton.

FRENCH-BACKED TWILL. A worsted or cotton-worsted suiting fabric made with a twill weave on the face while the filling is woven on the back in a satin order; a 1-warp, 2-filling formation.

FRENCHBACK SERGE. Men's-wear serge of two warps and one filling. Runs from 16 to 18 ounces per yard in weight, is piece-dyed, given clear or semifinish. Used much in winter suitings. Quality and price vary considerably.

FRENCH CAMBRIC. Neckwear made of cotton and linen content.

FRENCH CANVAS. Made about 25 inches wide and in cut lengths of 48 yards, this fabric is used for embroidery purposes. Also means a dress goods in the grenadine group. See GRENADINE.

FRENCH COMB, HEILMAN COMB, CONTINENTAL COMB, RECTILINEAR COMB. This comb handles worsted-fiber stock as short 1½ inches in staple, something that other types of combers are not able to do. Staples stock of other fibers is also well handled by this comb.

A fringe of fibers is combed, followed by a breaking away of the tuft of fibers from the fringe, combing the tail end, and delivering the slub or top formation of stock. The machine is rather small and is of the upright type.

FRENCH COMBING WOOL. Fine wool with a staple of 1½ to 2 inches; a large part of Territory-fine clip is of French combing length. The term implies stock that is ideal for "top making" as apart from staple or fine combing and Delaine wools.

FRENCH CREPE. Another name for flat crepe. See FLAT CREPE.

FRENCH CREPE YARN. Hard twisted man-made fiber yarn which does not have the usual number of crepe twist turns per inch. Given either S-twist or Z-twist, either of these twists is used throughout the fabric being made. Resultant fabric does not have the feel of cloth made with full crepe twist. Full crepe twist is about 60/65 turns per inch; thus, this yarn has around 30/32 turns per inch.

FRENCH CUFF. A shirt cuff that either

folds back or has a double thickness, closed usually with cuff links.

FRENCH DRAWING. This worsted operation gives the ultimate yarn a soft, cylindrical, and kindly feel. No twist is given the worsted fibers to make the fluffy yarn, and it is in this respect that it differs from the Bradford or English system of making worsted yarn.

Twist in the French system does not begin until the stock is actually being spun into yarn on the spinning frame. The French, because of the excellent methods produced by the Heilman method of combing, are able to comb fibers as short as 1½ inches. This makes it possible to obtain even, uniform, and cylindrical yarn on the spinning frame.

Also known as the Franco-Belgian system.

FRENCH FASHION TERMS, SOME BASIC.

A novelty	Une nouveauté
A suit	Le tailleur
Bargains	Les soldes
Coat	Le manteau
Cotton	Le coton
Cut	Découpé
Easy-to-wear	Facile à porter
Fabric	Le tissu
Jewel	Le bijou
Kimono shoulders	Les épaules-kimono
Lace	La dentelle
Original way	Façon originale
Pleated	Plissé
Printed silk	La soie imprimée
Ready-to-wear	Prêt à porter
Satisfied customer	La femme épanouie
Short sleeves	Les manches courtes
Silk	La soie
Skirt	La jupe
Supple lines	Les styles souples
Tomorrow's silhouette	La silhouette de demain
Wool	La laine
Wool jersey	Le jersey de laine
Young fashion	Une mode jeune

FRENCH FELLING. A tailoring method of holding two pieces of fabric together, such as the forepart and the facing of an edge. The parts to be joined are laid flat, edges even, right sides within. The needle is passed straight through, at right angles with the edge and close to it from underneath, upwards. The material is then turned right side out, and the edge finished with stitching as desired, the felling being intended to hold the edge and prevent raveling.

FRENCH FLANNEL. A broad term for plain or twill-woven, soft, slightly napped, wool flannel for use as bathrobes, lounging gowns, shirting, and dress goods. In some cold areas it serves as underwear. Comes in solid colors, stripes, tartans, overplaids, checks, etc.

FRENCH FOOT. A common type of foot on the full-fashioned stocking. The seam on the back of the stocking continues down the center of the sole. Fashion marks show in the sole of the stocking near the heel, and also at the toe. Fashion marks in the toe show the characteristic diamond point, the distinguishing mark of genuine full-fashioned hosiery.

FRENCH GINGHAM. See ZEPHYR GINGHAM.

FRENCH HEM. A finish made by turning the raw edges to the wrong side and catching the edge in a tuck made on the right side. This completely conceals the raw edge. It is used on the edges of fabrics that ravel and for inserting embroidery and lace bands; also used on the bottom of men's trousers.

FRENCH INCH. Used in knitting circles in the determination of glove sizes; 9.4 French inches equal 10 English inches.

FRENCH KID, FRENCH-KID FINISH. The original French kid was made in France, and, because of its distinctive finish, the term began to be applied to a special class of leathers made in other countries. The present meaning is that of leather tanned from kidskin by the alum or vegetable process.

FRENCH KNOT. It is made by twisting the thread several times around the needle; a decorative knot.

FRENCH MERINO. Name for Rambouillet, the Merino sheep of France.

FRENCH OR BAG SEAM. Stitching of the seam on the right side, one quarter of an inch wide, trimming closely to the stitching, and then turning the stitch on the wrong side for the desired width of the seam. This type of seam is used on sheer material and commonly found on such garments as blouses, children's dresses, and some undergarments.

FRENCH PERCALE. Similar to high-quality percale made in this country, it is used for dress goods; noted for its fine, appealing finish.

FRENCH PLEATING. Decorative pleats used as drapery heading. The material is gathered and then stitched in small folds at regulated intervals.

FRENCH SERGE. Very high-type dress goods with a fine, lofty, springy feel. Superior to the average run of serge and one of the best cloths on the market. Warp may be singles or doubles and filling is usually single-ply worsted. Weight runs from 6 to 10 ounces per yard. Fabric is piece- or yarn-dyed. An ideal cloth for women's wear of the better sort. The yarn is cylindrical and has the best of tailoring qualities. The best of this cloth is imported from the noted textile centers of France—Arras, Lille, Roubaix, Rouen, Turcoing, and Montainebleau. Cannot be called by this name unless actually made in France.

FRENCH SIZING METHODS ON SILK AND MAN-MADE YARNS.

1. The yarn is soaked in the sizing bath for a period and at a temperature which varies according to the structure of the fiber. It is then subjected to a first drying, followed by a more careful drying under special atmospheric conditions (which depend also on fiber structure). In this process the sizing bath is generally composed of heated linseed oil and a solvent—benzol or white spirit.

2. In the second process the yarn is first warped, then drawn through sizing rollers. The sizing may be hot or cold, and may be composed of gelatin and a softening agent, or of synthetic resins, or of soluble celluloses, or of special starches. This method is the commoner type and has been used in France since 1950.

FRENCH-SPUN YARN. This worsted yarn manufacturing method can manipulate shorter, crimpier fibers than the Bradford or English system of making yarn; the range runs from a 1¼-inch staple for one of three inches or more. French yarns are dry-spun while English yarns are wet-spun with an oil emulsion. Only a very small amount of oil is used in the former to control static electricity; applied to the sliver prior to the combing operation.

Fibers used on the French system are double-carded which is similar to carding on the Bradford method. However, the backwashing of the fibers follows the combing operation whereas it precedes the combing in the Bradford method. No oil is added in French spinning after backwashing.

The combing is done in the Heilmann comb which is capable of handling very short staple fibers. The noils in this rectilinear comber are shorter than those eliminated by the Noble or circular comber used to comb on the English system.

After combing, French system stock is then backwashed to remove the impurities gathered in processing and to improve the appearance and color. Gilling and porcupine roller drawings are then applied to the stock so as to produce an even, uniform sliver, slubbing, and roving ready for spinning on the mule frame or ring frame. French-spun yarn is soft and lofty and this results from a relative absence of twist, short and pliable fibers, and a lack of oil. Sold on a 15 per cent regain basis, the yarn is somewhat more expensive than Bradford-spun yarn.

FRENCH WELT. It is formed on two-feed knitting machines; two separate jersey fabrics in the form of a flat hem on the edge of the hosiery top.

FRESH-TEX. Trade-mark of the Cranston Print Works Co., for a cotton finish designed to render fabrics crease- and wrinkle-resistant, to control shrinkage within 2 per cent, to resist perspiration and mildew, with complete washability.

FRIAR'S CLOTH. MONK'S CLOTH. The same as Druid cloth except that a 4-and-4 basket weave is used in the construction. It is not as coarse and harsh as Druid. Used for hangings and other decorative purposes.

FRIB, FRIBS. Wool which contains excessive amounts of second cuts and sweat points.

FRICTION CALENDERING. Passing material between heated rollers, one of which has a slight excess speed over the other one, thereby creating a friction-calendering operation which adds much to the luster of the goods.

FRICTION FABRIC. Cord fabric impregnated with rubber to form a tacky type of cloth.

FRICTION TYPE KNITTING NEEDLE. It is a latch needle with a square butt, bent slightly near the butt, which exerts pressure against the trick walls of the needle cylinder and is capable of remaining in position while the cylinder is revolved at high speed.

FRIEZE. Heavy woolen overcoating with a rough, fuzzy, frizzy face. Cloth is said to have originated in Friesland, Holland. Irish frieze has an established reputation. Cloth ranges from 22 to 30 or more ounces per yard. Much used in times of war as overcoating for soldiers. The grade and quality vary considerably. The average army frieze is made of cheap stock, is stock-dyed, harsh and boardy in feel, has much flocks in it, and is not any too serviceable. A composition of frieze could be 67 per cent of three-eighths wool and 33 per cent of shoddy and reworks. Much adulteration is given the cloth, hence the wide variance as to the quality. Lightweight frieze is now made with a blend of spun rayon and wool. Double-cloth constructions are used in the overcoating material, which gives fair to good service. See Illustrated Section (Fabrics 73).

FRIEZE BOUCLE. From the French (frisé bouclé) for terry-cloth fabric.

FRIEZETTE, FRISETTE. The diminutive "ette" seemingly indicates this to be a smaller replica of a frisé. A friezette, however, is made of a flat weave, and in order to obtain the imitation of a frisé, a rep weave is used, so that when the fabric is woven, small ridges or hills are formed on the order of corduroy. It has a cut pile and is used in the upholstery trade.

FRIEZE YARN. A tightly twisted surface yarn which gives a rough, nubby appearance to the pile effect in carpets. In addition to use in plain colors, it is used to form designs against plain grounds and thus give an engraved effect in the product.

FRILALS. Borders or ornamental ribbon.

FRILL. A border or edging secured at one edge only, usually fluted or crimped like a very narrow flounce.

FRILL YARN. This spiral or corkscrew-effect yarn is made on novelty twister frames for the effect; often done on man-made filament yarn.

FRINGE. A trimming consisting of long or short projecting ends either applied or worked from the fabric itself. Usually found on curtains, drapes, sashes, uniform embellishments, etc.

FRINGE ISSUES. Provisions in a labor agreement that concern money, but are not part of the employees' regular wage rates; that is, overtime, vacation, shift differentials, etc.

FRINGE SILK. British term for a silk yarn made by twisting first to the right, and then to the left. This coarse yarn may have 14 right-hand turns in the first twisting followed by 16 left-hand turns in the second twisting, or vice versa.

FRIQUETTE. A fine machine-made lace with very distinctive, clear meshes set off by embroidering fine, neat floral motifs along the edge of the lace. One or both edges of the edges may have the embroidery work. Has considerable use for veiling and mantillas.

FRISÉ. A fabric usually woven double shuttle, single cloth, with the top pick or filling forming the loop in the goods. A wire gauge is used in each dent that runs parallel to the pile yarn. This arrangement keeps the pile yarn from falling over and governs the height of the loop.

The fabric may also be woven double shuttle and double cloth, but this gives a rib effect on the face of the material, whereas in the single cloth weaving each dent is woven offset by one pick, which gives an all-over effect on the face of the goods. The cloth is also woven on wire looms, where a round wire is thrown across the loom and the pile yarn loops over the wire. The wire forms the loop instead of a top filling end.

Patterns of cut pile and frisé can be obtained by throwing draw or round wires and cut wires. These are wires with a small blade on the edge of the wire that cuts the loops to form a cut tuft. The number of wires depends on the desired motif. Cloths of this type are used as transportation fabric by air, railroad and bus lines.

Every known type of fiber, it may be safely stated, is or has been used to make pile fabrics. The pile is usually from the fiber which is to predominate in the pattern. The pile bears the heaviest burden of wear. Rayon and mohair are widely used in fabrics of this type at the present time. The ground or backing yarns are usually made of cotton, although jute and hemp are often used in the "cotton" or very heavy furniture trade. In velvet frisé fabric, rayon and silk are popular fibers in use today.

FRISON. 1. Also known as knubs, it is the unreelable cocoon which has pulled "loose" and become matted into a thick, ropelike strand. 2. Tangled silk on the outside of the cocoon, also known as floss.

FRISONETTE. Low-quality frison.

FRISURE. 1. The thin gold or silver braiding used on service uniforms. 2. A core yarn such as cotton, silk, or nylon around which is spiraled gold, silver or other metallic threads or yarns. Much used in passementerie work such as braid, fringe, edging, etc.

FRIVOLITE. French (frivolité) for tatting.

FROCK. Supposed to be smarter or more chic than a dress, it is the principal outer garment of a woman or girl. A frock is more expensive than a dress, less costly than a gown, creation, classic, or haute couture.

FROCK CLOTH. Light grayish shades of cotton covert are sometimes known by this name.

FROCK COAT. An outer coat, a former fashion for men, usually double-breasted and having skirts reaching about to the knees.

FROCKING. Coarse cotton jean, drill, denim, dungaree, or fustian.

FROG. An ornamental looped fastening made of braid. It is used as a decorative accessory to secure pajamas, coats, cloaks, etc.

FRONT. This term is applied to horse hides to distinguish the forepart of the hide from the butt or hind portion. A half front is about a third of the entire area of the hide, and the whole front is about two thirds of the area.

FRONTAL. A lace or embroidered covering hung in front of an altar.

FRONT PLATE. The three-section, metal plate that is set between the revolving flats and the doffer roll. Its function is to prevent cotton being cast off the cylinder of the card and to control air currents. The middle plate is removable, thereby giving access to the operator so that he may strip and grind the cylinder when necessary.

FROST, ROBERT. In 1770, with his basic ideas taken from the lace machine that Jedediah Strutt had perfected in 1758, Frost produced a figure on a hexagonal mesh. In 1777 he perfected the square mesh.

FROSTING. Slight luster applied to cotton goods by the mechanical operation of sizing at low pressure.

FROTTE. From the French (frotté, rubbed) for toweling.

FROWSY WOOL. Lifeless-appearing wool with fibers more or less topsy-turvy; the opposite of lofty wool.

F.T.C. LABELING ACT OF 1972 ON PIECE GOODS. The Federal Trade Commission Rule, effective July 3, 1972 stipulates that "any textile product in the form of piece goods, made for the purpose of immediate conversion by the ultimate consumer into a finished article of wearing apparel must be accompanied by a label which closely discloses instructions for the care and maintenance of such goods. The label must be of a type that can, by normal household methods, be permanently affixed to the finished article for the ultimate consumer." The FTC exempts remnants sold over the counter in the form of piece goods in two-yard lengths or less, when not cut from the bolt or cut of cloth.

FTORLON. Made in the Soviet Union, it is a fluorine-containing copolymer with good resistance to chemicals.

FUDDY COTTON. Cotton with bunches of "dead fiber" present.

FUDS, FUDDIES. The short, oily fibers which drop from the carding machine in processing. Short cotton fibers picked up in carding and drawing operations are sometimes known by this term.

FUGITIVE. Colors that are uncertain and tend to bleed or run during a washing process.

FUGITIVITY. The lack of fastness of dyestuffs to one or more of the various color-destroying agents such as sunlight, washing, perspiration, crocking.

FUJI, FUJI-TYPE FABRIC. A popular staple fabric, characterized by a fine, cylindrical filling yarn. Textures range from 120 x 68 to 150 x 62. In the former construction the warp is made of 120/40 acetate yarn while the filling is 15/1, 50/50 viscose-acetate yarn. The latter construction is 75/20 acetate in the warp with the filling of 25/1, 50/50 viscose-acetate. The material is very

popular in blouses, children's dresses, men's shirtings.

FUKUI HABUTAE, FUKUI HABUTAI. The heaviest grade of habutae silk fabric made in Japan. Denier count is 8/10 or 10/12.

FUKUI SILK. Doubled silk yarns feature this crepe de Chine, one of the staple cloths made in Japan. Finished around one yard in width, the cut lengths are around 50 yards long. See CREPE DE CHINE.

FULL-BLEACH FINISH. In demand in cotton goods because of the desirable clear-white finish that is attractive and always in good taste. All natural coloring matter is removed by bleaching. Examples include batiste, broadcloth, cambric, dimity, lawn, organdy, voile.

FULL CARDIGAN. In this type of knitting stitch, tuck stitches are formed by both sets of needles. One set knits the plain stitch while the other set knits tuck stitches with the carriage moving in the one direction. The opposite set of needles form the cardigan stitch when the carriage moves in the opposite direction.

FULL CARDIGAN STITCH. Unlike the flat stitch, the full cardigan stitch has the same series of wales or lengthwise ribs on both sides of the material.

FULL COVER. Refers to some types of the better grade of book muslin in which an extra filling is used to add substance and body to the goods.

FULL CROSS LENO. The full leno or doup weave first used in the manufacture of this high-grade silk fabric used for nun's veiling and expensive dress goods. The skeleton or crossing yarns covered completely the standard yarns used in the construction.

FULLER. 1. One who fulls and cleans cloth in the fulling mill of the plant. 2. To goff or crimp linen with a fluting iron.

FULLER'S EARTH. A nonplastic clay used as a filler in cotton finishing and in fulling cloth. As an absorbent, it is used to remove grease, oil, and other common stains from clothing.

FULLER'S HERB. *Saponaria officinalis,* a plant used in the fulling of textile fabrics.

FULLER'S THISTLE. Also known as teasel, the botanical name is *Dipsacus fullonum;* used in napping textile fabrics.

FULL FASHIONED. A knitted fabric shaped on a flat knitting machine by adding or reducing stitches. Applied to hosiery, sweaters, etc.

FULL-FASHIONED HOSIERY. This is knitted flat and is shaped during the knitting by the inward transfer of the selvage stitches, usually two at a

time, on each side in order to provide the correct shape to properly fit the leg. Narrowings are always located at the calf, heel, and toe, and generally above the knee just below the shadow welt.

In stockings made by the single-unit method the fabric is also widened at the instep to form a heel pocket. This widening is generally over one needle at a time and may be made at the selvages when it is invisible or some wales away from the selvage, in which case a gore line is visible in the heel. The latter method provides a better-fitting stocking. The selvage edges are then joined by a seam.

FULL FINISH. The British use this term to mean that a fabric, especially woolen, has been finished on both sides. The rise of home dressmaking has given further rise to the term since many cottons and other types of dress goods are now finished on both sides providing greater manipulation possibilities and ease in matching the fabric.

FULL GAUZE. The name given to cloth of a leno weave, particularly when the crossing of the skeleton threads is plainly seen where they come in contact with the base threads of the cloth.

FULLING. A process in the finishing of woolen cloth. The cloth is dampened and beaten under heat, which causes shrinking, increases the weight, and obscures the weave of the cloth. See Illustrated Section.

FULLING MILL. The machine that fulls cloth in finishing.

FULLING MILL, STOCK. A fulling machine that takes care of entire cuts or pieces of cloth at the one time. The bath and the pounding units in the mill will shrink the goods in length and width, this depending on the number of hours the goods should be fulled.

FULLING STOCK. Pertains to the wooden beaters or mallets used in fulling cloth.

FULL-LAP STOP MOTION. Used on cotton pickers to stop the machine when the lap has reached full size.

FULL PIQUE. Knitting term implying a manner of seaming glove fingers where the raw edges of the forchettes are inside the glove and the raw edges of the finger back-and-front are outside; thus, one raw edge is exposed along each seam.

FULL, TO FULL. To treat or beat fabric for the purpose of cleaning it, and to add bulk and thickness to the material during this wet treatment in the wet finishing of fabrics. See Illustrated Section.

FULLY DEGUMMED SILK. Silk

with all gum removed from it.

FULLY TRIMMED OVERALLS.
Refers to the buckles used to adjust shoulder straps, buttons on the bib pockets where needed, and the two buttons at each side of the waist. These features are often omitted in the lower grades of overalls.

FUME FADING. Some man-made materials, especially red-, violet-, blue-, or green-dyed cellulose-derivative acetates, will react to gas fumes in the air by turning a reddish hue or shade. Found more in industrial areas where these fumes seem to prevail. May be counteracted by special resistant dyes and chemical compounds, and by frequent airings of the clothes closet. Incorrectly called, at times, gas fading.

FUNCTIONAL FINISHES, SPECIAL.
1. WRINKLE-RESISTANT: This type of finish receives much attention from the consuming public. The elasticity and the vitality of fabrics, from the finest sheers to some of the heavier weight cloths, are increased by an impregnation of the fibers with thermosetting resins which become an integral part of the fiber and, with proper care, will serve for the life of the fabric. This finish will also impart shrinkage control, and improve resistance to soil, mildew, and perspiration.

2. WATER-REPELLENT: This type of finish has had much to do with the increase and demand for fabrics. Fashion fabrics can now be styled for rain-wear or other uses where resistance to penetration of water is vital. Water-repellent finishes are treated with a protective chemical coating which does not, as in the case of waterproof fabric, inhibit air porosity. The durability of water-repellent finishes varies with the type of finish and the fabric construction.

3. MOTHPROOF: Fabric can be made unpalatable to moths by chemical treatment. One finish, guaranteed to last for the life of the garment, is applied in the dye bath. Other finishes that are less durable and unaffected by dry cleaning, are removed by washing. Mothproofing finishes are as important to the retail stocks as they are to the safeguarding of consumer goods.

4. MILDEW-PROOF: The use of sizing in finishing will cause certain types of fabric prone to attack by mildew. Chemical treatments have been devised which will render fabrics immune to deterioration by mildew.

5. DURABLE STARCHLESS FINISH: Chemical compounds are applied to cloths so as to do away with the necessity of starching after laundering. Freshness and crispness are restored by ironing. Very successful on sheer cottons, starchless finishes are relatively durable

under normal conditions of wear and usage.

6. ABSORBENT: Corsets, diapers, towels, and underwear require absorbent fabrics. Cotton, linen, acetate, and rayon materials can be processed with complex ammonium compounds which will improve moisture absorptiveness and holding qualities.

FUNGICIDE. Fungus-killing chemical.

FUNGUS. Any of a group of thallophytic plants embodying molds, mildew, smuts, etc., which form coatings on some objects, such as fabrics, certain foodstuffs, damp walls, white paints. Mildew will form on animal and vegetable fibers and fabrics, as well as on some of the man-made yarns and materials because of some of the finishes applied to them. On fabrics, the formation of fungus (mildew) is caused by the material being held under conditions of warmth and moisture. These can be very injurious, difficult to remove, and at times impossible to eradicate. There is an invisible type of fungus destruction which is impossible to detect while wearing some garments. The results will show that the article has become tender and rotted.

FUR. The soft, hairy coat which covers the skin of many mammals such as beaver, ermine, sable, fox, squirrel, etc. Its uses are obvious.

FUR, WILD. Pelts taken from animals that have been caught in traps, as apart from those raised on farms or ranches.

FUR BLEND YARN. One which contains a percentage of any type of fur fibers such as coney (rabbit fur), mink, muskrat, raccoon, etc. Other fibers in the blend usually consist of a goodly percentage of lamb's wool and a small amount of nylon. An ideal blend is 65 per cent lamb's wool, 25 per cent fur fiber, 10 per cent nylon. Yarns in this field are ideal for knitted outerwear. Spinning is done on the woolen system of yarn manufacture.

FUR CLOTH. Any deep-pile fabric made to simulate genuine fur and used in the manufacture of imitation-fur garments.

FUR FABRICS. Large class of pile fabrics of wool, spun rayon, or other fibers imitating various furs by dyeing and special finishing. Fabric can be either woven or knitted. Any variations of basic weaves are used. The fabrics are used in popular-priced winter coatings and trimmings.

FURCRAEA. Found in the tropical sections of the Americas, this genus of plants yields fibers such as cabuya, fique, piteira.

FURFURAL. A volatile liquid, yellowish in color; an aldehyde obtained from cereal bran, corn, straw, et al. It is a synthetic base used in various industries. Furfural obtained from cottonseed hulls is used with phenol to form thermosetting plastics comparable with the phenol formaldehyde group of plastics. It is, at present, used in the manufacture of nylon. Formula is $C_5H_4O_2$.

FURNISHING ROLLER. The roller that revolves in the color paste on a printing machine and transfers it to the engraved-print roller. The doctor blade scrapes off excess coloring matter so that it will not reach the printing roller. This blade is between the furnisher and print rollers.

FURNISHING WHEELS. Positively driven gear wheels used on some circular knitting machine units of Terrot, Wildman spring needle, and other types to assure even feeding of yarn to the knitting needles.

FURNITURE CORD. A ply cord used to trim upholstery. The plies are usually core yarns covered with mercerized cotton, silk, rayon, or nylon.

FURNITURE DENIM. Broad term for solid-color drill or plain-weave fabric for chair covers, furniture, etc. Some furniture, however, is covered with denim or other fabric closely resembling it.

FURNITURE PLUSH. Made of all cotton or of cotton-ground construction and mohair-pile yarn, it is a plush used for upholstering chairs and other articles of furniture. Also known as Utrecht plush.

FURNITURE TWILL. Printed cretonne used in the furniture and upholstery trade.

FURS, PIECED. Pieces are obtained from paws, tails and lighter underparts all matched and joined. These parts are taken from peltries in the manufacturing processes. When enough of the pieces of a certain kind are gathered, they are then matched, sewn into plates, and used to make garments and trimmings, such as mink chevron, mink gill, mink paw, pieced caracul, and pieced Persian lamb coatings; mink tail and silver fox tail trimmings; and pieced squirrel and squirrel-lock linings. These products, obviously, are byproducts and are not as valuable as full pelt articles nor do they give the wear of these full pelt coatings.

FUR SHADING. Gradual color change that may exist in a fur pelt; shading is simulated in fake fur fabrics in order for them to look like true fur items.

FUSE. To melt or to liquefy by heat. Acetate, for example, will fuse if the temperature is too high in pressing.

FUSED COLLARS. Especially prepared interlinings, often made of acetate yarns, which are fused to the outer and the inner layers of the collar after high temperature is applied. The fusing tends to keep the collar in shape.

FUSED FABRIC. A resilient two-layer collar or cuff fabric bonded together by an intervening solid film of cellulose binder. See TRUBENIZING.

FUSING. The melting or melting together, such as the melting of an acetate fabric by too hot an iron, or the melting of an acetate plastic with cotton cloth to make men's shirt-collar cloth stiffer. The changing of a solid into a molten mass.

FUSION POINT. The temperature at which a solid will become fluid.

FUSTET. Young fustic, Venetian *Sumach rhus cotinus;* it provides a fine orange color which possesses little permanence.

FUSTIAN. The origin of this cloth is traced to the Egyptians and the Arabs. The fossatum or walls that protected one of the Imperial Legions became the nucleus of the city of Cairo, Egypt. It was in the Fustat, or old Arab Quarter of the city, that the cloth was supposed to have been first made. Cotton and linen were used in the fabric. Today, this generic term implies a group of heavyweight, high-pickage cotton fabrics, such as beaverteen, corduroy, moleskin, velveteen. There is also a low-quality woolen fabric made on a small repeat-twill weave that periodically appears in the market.

FUSTIAN CORD. The British sometimes call corduroy and velveteen by this term. See FUSTIAN, CORDUROY, VELVETEEN.

FUSTIC. A natural yellow plant dye, used with logwood for producing black.

FUSTIC, OLD. This ancient dye produces colors which range from gold to yellow. Obtained from the tropical American tree, Chlorophora tinctoria, the dye is still used on wool.

FUSTIC, YOUNG OR ZANTE. A yellow to dark olive dye, depending on the mordant used, is extracted from the powdered wood of the Rhus cotinus, a shrub-size tree of the cashew family. Classed as an ancient dye.

FUTURES, FUTURES CONTRACT. A contract, usually in lots of 100 bales, to receive or deliver a specified amount of cotton during a specified future period on a fixed-price basis for the grade and the staple length. Rigid rules and regulations govern futures. See STRADDLING; HEDGING.

FUZZ BALLS. Loose, frayed, or nubbed fibers which form balls or pinheads when weaving the goods.

FUZZINESS, FUZZY. Hairy effect on some fabrics caused by broken fibers or filaments.

FYBRITE. Registered trademark of Celanese Corporation of America for its soil release product which made its debut in September, 1966. It can be applied to weights in which the method provides good results and is restricted, at present, to precured and 100 percent polyester fabrics. It does not repel soil but has the property of easily combating soil redeposition, as well as soil deposition through static. Ideal in home washing for life of the garment, it is used on printed dressgoods, lingerie, shirtings, 100 percent knitted polyester uniform fabric, and comparable constructions.

G

GABARDINE. Construction is the same as for cotton gabardine—a 45- or 63-degree twill. These weaves give the characteristic, single diagonal lines noted on the face of the fabric. Material is piece-dyed and used in men's and women's wear. Combination of yarn as to color and cast may be used, as in the case of covert cloth. In this event, the yarn should be skein-dyed. It is also possible to use the stock-dyed method. Because of the twist in the yarn and the texture, the cloth wears very well and outlasts similar materials used for the same purposes. Weight ranges from eight to fourteen ounces per yard; clear finish is given. Cotton yarn is sometimes found as the warp structure in the cloth.

Cotton gabardine is made with carded or combed yarn. The twill line is usually to the left if made with all single-ply yarn, and to the right when ply-warp and single-filling are used.

Gabardine made of spun rayon, a very popular staple, comes in dress and suit weights. Used for men's, women's, children's wear, sportswear, shoe fabric, uniforms, rainwear, and ski-wear. See Illustrated Section (Fabrics 28).

GABERCORD. A soft-feeling, cotton cloth made with a fine warp-face twill which shows very clearly on the face. A typical gabercord, made of 30s warp and 20s filling, would have a texture of about 144 by 60.

GAGE. See GAUGE.

GAGING THREAD. On the order of a catch cord, it is found along the selvage edges of fabric as it is being woven. It is removed later and leaves a loop selvage. See SELVAGE, LOOP.

GAIT, GATE. A term used in the English woolen trade to denote a full repeat of the draft in harness weaving. It also signifies a full repeat of the harness draft in designing Jacquard material, and means one complete row of either 8 or 16 holes in the comber-board arrangement.

GAITER. A covering for the lower leg or ankle, fastened at the side and usually strapped under the foot. 2. A shoe covering the ankle and having no opening in front, and usually elastic sides. 3. A cloth upper overshoe.

GAIT-OVER. In mill parlance, a complete repeat of pattern in a dobby design; a dobby design made on twenty ends has twenty ends to its gait-over.

GALABIYA. The long robe worn by Egyptian males. It has no collar, is closed at the front and neck opening. A waistcoat which is worn underneath it and a wide belt completes the ensemble. Vividly colored caps are usually worn with the costume.

GALASHIELS. 1. Popular Scotch tweeds made in and around this district in Scotland. 2. Scotch system for numbering woolen yarn. The standard is a cut of 300 yards, which weighs 24 ounces, so that the Number 1 yarn would have 300 yards of yarn to the pound. Also known as "gala."

GALATEA. Narrow, solid-color, or printed washable cotton in which the five-end, warp-face twill weave covers the face of the goods. This left-hand twill cloth is used for dress goods, uniform fabric, play clothes. Some printed jean fabric is called galatea. This broad term has been applied, at various times, to twill cloth, jean, and even warp-sateen fabric. A good quality English shirting of the calico type with equal blue-and-white stripes is known by this name.

GALA TWILL. Merely a 4-up and 4-down right-hand twill, straight draw in the drawing-in plan.

GALETTAME. (Galettamé.) Waste from the inner skin of the cocoon which remains after reeling.

GALETTE. 1. Pierced, fuzzy, or thin cocoon. 2. Silk yarn made from cocoon wastes of various types is also called galetté.

GALLOON. Narrow fabric of lace, embroidery or braid. Metallic threads are often used for ornamentation of the material, which is used for trimming and uniform adornment.

GALLS, GALL NUTS. Oak galls are produced by the egg of an insect, the female gall wasp. An excrescence is produced round the egg; and the insect, when fully developed, pierces a hole and then escapes. Those gall nuts which are not pierced contain the most tannic acid. The best product comes from several parts of Turkey.

GALLUSES. The early name for suspenders.

GALON. Narrow woven fabric made

with two fillings—one for the ground and the other for the filling-effect motif. The ground yarn is usually mercerized cotton yarn; the pattern yarn is metallic yarn or bright acetate or rayon.

GALWAY. 1. A coarse, thick and heavy red flannel that is woven or knitted in Ireland. 2. A thick, heavy overcoating cloth usually made with Irish wool and dyed scarlet. 3. A homespun tweed made in Ireland which finds use in suiting, topcoating, and sport coating. Some of the fabric is made on hand looms.

GAMBIER. A fast brown dye obtained from the acacia trees of India. It is marketed in a dark brown paste form.

GAMBROON. 1. Union fabric, usually of cotton and wool, used for summer slacks and linings. 2. British term for a group of fabrics made on plain or small twill weaves, and used for clothing. These cloths are union fabrics, and cotton, wool, worsted, and linen are the yarns used.

GAMMADION. An ornament that formerly had much usage in church embroideries as an ecclesiastical emblem or insignia. Its use declined during World War II. The symbols below are made from the Greek letter, gamma, being used four times in the form of a cross.

GAMSA. Made on a twill weave to resemble crepe-back satin. The warp is acetate while the filling is usually viscose rayon. This popular dress-goods fabric, which may be dyed or printed or white, gives good wear and is easily laundered.

GANSE. A narrow French edging such as braid, cord, or guimp made from several of the major fibers; chief use is in upholstery.

GANTRON. This fabric receives its energy from the ultraviolet rays of daylight and is very bright under normal daylight conditions. It is purported to be twice as bright as ordinary textiles under normal daylight conditions, and up to ten times more discernible at dusk or under overcast skies. Gantron will dry instantly since it has nonabsorbent properties.

GANTRY. From the Greek, it implies a spanning framework or bridgelike structure or scaffolding which gives support to frames, machines, etc. at various levels. In the textile industry it is applied to Jacquard looms whose parts have to be supported by the gantry principle in supporting the loom structure, Jacquard head motion, and the cut cards which make the motif possible when the loom is in action.

GARAN FINISH. A finish used on glass fiber cloth to give high wet-strength retention and other important characteristics to industrial glass cloth used in the manufacture of plastics. Owned by Johns Manville Products Corporation, Manville, New Jersey.

GARB. 1. Style of apparel, chiefly as characteristic of some office, rank, etc. 2. To array garments or the entire ensemble in a graceful, pleasing manner.

GARBER COTTON. An Alabama cotton developed from Uplands which has a ¾-inch staple and a lint yield of about 34 per cent.

GARE. Glossy, kempy fibers taken from the legs of sheep. Gare will not color evenly and much difficulty is encountered in blending and mixing it with better stocks.

GARLICK. Gorlitz in Silesia, Germany, is where this formerly popular staple linen fabric originated.

GARMENT. An article of clothing. Any individual piece of clothing worn to cover the body. It is most becoming if designed to suit the figure and the personality of the wearer.

GARMENT BIAS. Any edge which is neither a straight edge nor a true bias is known by this name.

GARMENT MAINTENANCE. Some major highpoints in garment maintenance follows:
Development of Cleaning Processing:
1. Types of soil. 2. Detergency process. 3. Solvents for soil remaoval.
Fibers and Soil Removal: 1. For cotton, chemically modified cotton, and manmade fibers.
Water Wash Process. 1. Soil removal. 2. Drying. 3. Finishing.
Drycleaning Process: Soil removal. 2. Drying. 3. Finishing.
The Future: 1. Water washing versus drycleaning. 2. Complete garment process.

GARMENT SEAMS. These follow:
1. **DOUBLE-LOCK:** A plain seam in which the seam stitches are overlaid with zigzag stitching for increased strength. The seam edges are usually pinked. A common type of double stitching on women's slips.
2. **FLAT FELL:** A sturdy, flat seam which shows two rows of stitching on one side of the fabric but only one row on the other side. In making this seam the edges of the material are stitched together; one edge is trimmed, and the wider edge is turned under over the trimmed edge and then stitched down. At times, the "full" or "trade seam" terminology is used interchangeably with the "flat fell" and may also be applied to a similar seam which shows two rows of stitching on both sides of the goods. In this latter seaming, the raw edges of the fabric are lapped over each other; the edges are turned under and in, facing each other and stitched down.

   These types of flat seaming are used on shirts, pajamas, work clothing, etc. Triple stitching is obtained by adding an extra row of stitching in the center of the two rows obtained.

3. **FLATLOCK:** Two edges of material are laid one upon the other and stitched with a broad seaming which conceals the raw edges on both sides. The right side of the seam has the appearance of four rows of closely interlocking stitches with horizontally connecting threads. This is a flat sturdy seam common in knit underwear.

4. **FRENCH FELL:** This is a seam within a seam. The edges of the fabric are plain seamed on the right side. The fabric is then turned, creased, and stitched on the wrong side in order to conceal the raw edges. This seam is used on soft lightweight fabrics. It is neat and durable. Girls' better quality slips often have this seaming.

5. **MERROW OR OVERLOCK:** A common knit underwear seam that is not flat and is narrower than the flatlock seam. The right sides of the fabric are placed face to face, and the raw edges are sewed together and then finished by overstitching.

6. **PLAIN:** This most commonly used seam shows that the right sides of the fabric are placed together and then stitched along the edge. These edges may then be pressed flat in one direction or they may be pressed open. The edges may be left raw or finished in one of several manners depending on the type of fabric being used and the grade of workmanship specified.

7. **PLAIN, BOUND EDGES:** This seam is used in tailored garments such as unlined portions of coats and jackets to conceal the raw edges. The edges may be bound together, but usually the seam is pressed open and the edges bound separately. Also referred to as seam binding.

8. **PLAIN, PINKED EDGES:** In firm fabrics that do not ravel easily, the raw edges may be pinked or notched to prevent fraying. Women's dresses of low-quality workmanship have raw seam edges. The use of pinking may vary from only the skirt side seams to almost all body seams in the better grade dresses.

9. **PLAIN, STITCHED EDGE:** Used on fabrics which ravel easily. The

plain seam is pressed open; each raw edge is turned under slightly, held free from the garment and then stitched.

GARMENT SEWING AND MENDING. Burns, missing threads, moth holes, and tears may be remedied in the following manner:

1. If the damage is too serious, the affected area should be fixed by a commercial house which specializes in the work.

2. If the blemish can be fixed at home:

Remove all straggly, loose threads in the area.

Obtain yarn to be used for the sewing and darning from the selvage or some other part of the cloth—the seam or hemmed portion.

Actually weave in the warp threads according to the pattern.

The filling pattern should then be interlaced with the respective warp threads.

Remove the excess lengths from warp and filling threads.

Dampen and press cloth well.

GARMENT SIZE. The complete uniform size specifications must be apparent at all times in order to enable all concerned to know whether the garments are correctly sized and full-cut for the manipulation into a garment. The cut, fit, and trim of a garment must conform to specifications which cannot be impeded by poor shrinking before manufacture.

GARMENTURE. Generic term for dress, apparel, ensemble.

GARNETT WIRE. The rollers on a garnetting machine to pull discarded clothing, felted or unfelted, apart so as to obtain the mass of fibers that are used over again in the manufacture of some fabrics. These rollers are clothed with rugged, sharp, saw-tooth pointed wire, also known as lag. Usually clothed in leather base, or set in wood or metal. See GARNETTING.

GARNETTING. The process of recovering the fibers from hard twisted thread wastes, rags, clippings, especially of wool. The object is to thoroughly break up the material and return it to a fluffy fibrous condition so it can be reused in blends, or in some cases alone. A garnett is used for the treatment.

GARNITURE. French for trimming.

GARTER. A band or supporting strap, usually an elastic narrow fabric, used to prevent a sock or stocking from slipping down the leg.

GARTER-RUN STOP. A specially knitted course in a stocking near the top to prevent runs from extending below the course. In circular hosiery, it is done by forming a course of tuck stitches; in full-fashioned hosiery there is an interlocking of the loops of the course to stop the run should it occur.

GAS FADING. Gaseous elements in the air may change the color on dyed acetate fabrics. The rate of fading cannot be determined. See FUME FADING.

GAS FADING INHIBITOR. Chemicals that are applied to acetate fabric to retard or prevent gas fading. See INHIBITOR.

GASSING. The process of burning off protruding fibers from cotton yarns and cloth by passing it over a gas flame or heated copper plates. This gives the fabric a smooth surface and is very necessary for fabrics to be printed and for fabrics where smooth finishes are desired. Same as singeing.

GATHERED WOOL. Wool collected from pastures, hedges, fences, and outbuildings.

GATHERING. A drawing together of a fold made by drawing it up on a thread that is run through it.

GATHERS. A fullness used for style effect on a garment. They may be used on any part of a garment and the amount of gathering varies depending on the texture of the material. Gathers at the shoulder or waist are examples.

GATING, GAITING. Adjusting looms, chiefly hand looms, so that all harnesses are at right height and proper angle.

GATING, INTERLOCK. Relationship to each other of the alternate long and short needles in the dial and cylinder of an interlock knitting frame. Because of the method of needle functioning in this type of machine, the dial and cylinder needles are set directly opposite each other. See GATING, RIB.

GATING, KNIT. Relationship of knitting needles to each other in opposed housings. See GATING, INTERLOCK; GATING, RIB.

GATING, RIB. Relationship of knitting needles in cylinder and dial so that they will work midway between each other. Thus, each dial needle in the frame is centered between two cylinder needles.

GATTINE. Old term for a mild phase of the disease known as pébrine, very destructive to silkworms in which growth is stunted and black spots appear on their skin.

GAUCHO BLOUSE. A full blouse gathered at the waistline, with full sleeves gathered at the wristband, as worn by Gauchos or South American cowboys.

GAUCHO SHIRT. See KNITTED

GARMENTS, APPROXIMATE AVERAGE YARDAGE ESTIMATES IN:

Type of Garment	Size Range			Plus/Minus Tolerance
	Junior—9 to 17 Thirteen	*Miss—12 to 20 Fourteen*	*Woman—36 to 42 Thirty-eight*	
Dresses	36″—3¼ yards	36″—3½ yards	40″—4 yards	⅛ of a yard
Ensemble (Two-piece suit)	39″—3¾	36″—4	54″—2½	¼
Suits	36″—4½	54″—2¾	40″—4½	¼
Skirts	36″—2¼	36″—2½	36″—2¼	¼
Jackets	54″—1¾	54″—1¾	54″—2	¼
Coats	54″—2¾	54″—2¾	54″—3	⅛
Capes (Long)	54″—2¼	54″—2⅜	54″—2½	⅛
Nurses Uniform (Maids)	30″—3½	36″—3⅛	40″—3¾	⅜
Aprons	36″—3¼	36″—3¼	36″—4	¼
Smocks	40″—2⅞	36″—3⅛	36″—4	⅛
Hoover Aprons (Wrap-around)	36″—3¾	36″—4	36″—4	⅛
Blouses	39″—2	39″—2	39″—2¼	(22 yards to the dozen)
Ski Suits (Jackets)	36″—2¾	39″—2¾	36″—3¼	⅛
Slacks	36″—2¾	36″—2¾	54″—2½	⅛
Snow Suits	54″—1¼ (1 to 4)	54″—1¼ (3 to 6×)	54″—1¼ plus 7 to 14 cut in dozen lots	(Children's Sizes)
Beachwear (Play Suits)	36″—2¾	36″—3¼	36″—4	¼
Bathing Suits (Full Cut)	39″—3	39″—3½	39″—3¾	¼
Bathing Suits (Knitted) (Stocking)	44″—2	44″—2¼	44″—2½	⅛

Theatrical: These will vary because of color and fabric combination.

SHIRTS.

GAUFFRE. This French term, Gauffré, means to emboss or to produce motifs such as on velvet and velveteen, to enhance the finished appearance of the goods. See GAUFRE SILK.

GAUFRE SILK, GAFFERED SILK. The first word, gaufré, implies embossed, as is sometimes applied to velvet, velveteen, ribbon, trimming, certain dress goods. A paper roller and a heated roller with embossing nipples or areas presses into the former, thereby giving the raised effect on the goods by this form of calendering. The finish is not permanent in nature, and washing will remove the traces of the motif. The word, gaffered, is the English expression used since it is easier to say than the French term.

GAUGE. A unit of measurement with several meanings:

1. The number of knitting needles in 1½ inches of the needle bed or cylinder on certain types of machines. It is derived from the original meaning in the preparation of leaded needles in 1½-inch space, in full-fashioned hosiery.

2. With regard to knitting needles, gauge refers to the thickness of the needle in the shank and the hook. The shank is not always the same gauge as the hook—a 38-gauge shank may have a 42-gauge hook.

3. In a fabric, gauge refers to the construction.

4. In spinning machinery, the term is used when speaking of the spacing of spindles in order to figure floor spacing, layouts, etc.

5. In rare instances, gauge is used to designate the courses per inch in hosiery fabric. This application, however, is meaningless as far as the actual gauge of the machine, upon which the fabrics are made, is concerned.

6. The trend, at present, is to refer to the "cut" in knitting—the actual number of needles per inch in a machine. In flat rib knitting, "gauge" and "cut" are both used, to imply the number of needles per inch in each needle bed; rib work requires at least two needle beds, either flat or circular.

GAUZANDA. A registered trademark and another name for Chiffon Swiss Organdy.

GAUZE. Made of several types of construction, 30s yarn is often used for the typical cloth. Textures vary considerably depending upon the ultimate use. The warp in gauze is carefully sized, then desized so that total absorbency is obtained without entailing loss of weaving production. This plain weave, lightweight cloth finds use in

bandages, sanitary goods, surgical dressings, etc. Fine gauze is made of 60s yarn and has about the same uses as ordinary gauze. One of the chief uses is for tea bags.

GAUZE, SURGICAL. Cheesecloth that has been sterilized after bleaching.

GAUZE WEAVE. Openwork weave of porous nature made on the principle of plain weave. Leno or doup weaving aids in securing gauze effects. There are also imitation gauze weaves used to bring out a design; marquisette, scrim, curtaining material and lace are examples of the weave.

GAW. Scotch term for thin or weak places in cloth.

GAZE. French for gauze or network.

GEAR CRIMPING. A texturing method wherein yarns are passed through the meshing teeth of two heated gears. This results in a sawtooth configuration and the process is associated with SPUNIZE, a textured yarn made of nylon, polyester, or polypropylene on the stuffer box method in texturinzing. Product of Spunize Company of America, Unionville, Connecticut.

GEAR DUCK. Any duck molded with bakelite and used in the manufacture of composition gears. Army, flat, or number duck may be used depending on the specifications at hand.

GEAR WHEEL. Any wheel toothed on the face so that it can mesh with other gears.

GEFLECT. Embroidery term which means a particular type of stitching which uses two or more movements to cover a blatt stitch. The effect provides a flat effect or surface. See Blatt Stitch.

GELATIN SILK. One of the first forms produced for what eventually was to be known as rayon. Formaldehyde was used to treat the filaments for this now obsolete method of making rayon.

GENAPPE YARN. (From Genappe, Belgium, according to Webster.) Worsted yarn is often gassed or genapped to do away with loose, protruding fibers; the yarn becomes clear, lustrous and smooth and finds use in braiding and trimming.

GENELLE. A nonwoven polymeric favric, manufactured in roll form. It has good stretchability, is stain-resistant, and can be dry-cleaned and hand-laundered. Product of The General Tire & Rubber Company, Inc., Akron, Ohio.

GENERIC. Pertains to a genus, class, kind or race; characteristic of a group as opposed to something specific. In biology, for example, the term refers to the

genus. Examples of generic names or terms include bread, acetate, rayon, salt, match, spandex, nylon, etc.

GENEROS CRUDOS. In many South American markets the term is used for any width sheeting made of cotton and bleached in the piece.

GENEVA GOWN. The black academic gown or robe that was adopted by the Calvinistic clergy in Geneva.

GENOA. Heavy lace made of aloe fiber. Sometimes called macramé.

GENOA CORD, GENOA CORDUROY. Twill-back corduroy made with a three-end or a four-end arrangement; known as "twill-ground corduroy" or "back-cloth" cord.

GENOA PLUSH. A cotton Genoa velvet or velveteen made with a 2-up, 2-down or a 1-up, 2-down twill backing. The British use this fabric which is accentuated by large floral effects, often produced by embossing. Some of this work can be obtained by the burnt-out method, as well. See BURNT-OUT.

GENOA TWILL. Another name for three-leaf or three-end right-hand twill.

GENOA VELVET. 1. Originally, a very high-textured, all-silk velvet brocade made on a satin ground construction. Large motifs were popular in this Italian fabric which was very popular in the Middle Ages. 2. A filling-pile cotton velvet made with small twill weave in the ground construction.

GENTILE DI PUGLIA. Originating from native sheep in northern Italy which were cross-bred with imported Spanish Merino sheep at the end of the eighteenth century. This breed was a contributing factor to the famous Saxony Merino breeds of Germany. One of the outstanding Italian sheep breeds, these hardy, migratory sheep give a fiber length of 2.5 to 2.75 inches. The wool is usually shorn biannually.

GENTILLE. French for a cloth blemish in weaving caused by warp ends being raised incorrectly on successive sheds, thereby forming a float on the face of the goods.

GENUS. A category or class of similar things; scientifically divided into related subordinate groups known as species; each member of a species has certain differentiating characteristics.

GEON PRODUCTS. These are used to service the textile industry and are trade names of B. F. Goodrich Chemical Company, Inc., Cleveland, Ohio.

Geon 460X6: This unplasticized latex is a compounding base and is easily plasticized. Used to impregnate heat-moldable paper, textiles, nonwoven fabrics, flame retardant filler for binders, coatings, adhesives.

Geon 590X3: A general purpose latex plasticized with DOP to provide excellent alanace of properties or ingredients used. Used as adhesives for heat-sensitive or thermoplastic substrates; binders and coatings.

Geon 590X4: This is plasticized with a phosphate ester plasticizer for flame-retardant applications. Used for adhesives, binders for textiles, papers, rug backing.

Geon 590X6: Plasticized with a phosphate ester plasticizer for flame-retardant applications which require good flixibility and soft hand. Used for flame-retardant binders, costings, and adhesives.

GEON RESIN 100-X-26. The first true polyvinyl chloride paste-forming resin to be produced in this country. This resin of the B. F. Goodrich Chemical Company is a polymer which is a free-flowing white powder with a specific gravity of 1.40; easily dispersed in plasticizer with the use of simple processing equipment. Using the resin-plasticizer formulating method, the fabricator will gain the added advantages of 100 per cent total solids; no shrinkage of mass because of loss of volatiles and thicker coatings with a single dip or pass treatment. The product is on the market in the form of a coated tablecloth fabric called Plastolyn (Columbus Coated Fabrics Corporation).

GEORGERETTE, GORGERETTE. (From French for bib or ruff.) Cambric handkerchief.

GEORGETTE CREPE. A staple, plain, or crepe-weave silk fabric, usually woven with a 40-reed or a 45-reed with two ends per dent. The warp is usually two-thread or three-thread 13/15 up to 20/22 crepe yarn twisted about 60 turns per inch. The filling is generally the same as the warp. Textures range around 80 x 70.

The warp and the filling arrangement is two ends of right-hand twist. followed by two ends of left-hand twist. This produces a pebblelike feel and crepe effect. Incidentally, crepe de Chine may use the same warp as Georgette, but the filling is softer and receives fewer turns of twist per inch. Georgette is harsher than Canton crepe.

Georgette may be white, dyed, or printed. This rugged, lightweight fabric has stiffness and body, and gives excellent wear because of its construction.

GEORGETTE THREAD. In a fabric, the yarn is laid out as follows: two ends of left-hand twist, followed by two ends of right-hand twist in the warp. The filling arrangement has two picks of right-hand twist, followed by two of left-hand twist. Twist runs from 60 to 65 turns per inch, and gives the goods a crinkled, pebbly effect that is right to the touch. Used in ladies' dress goods, waists, evening wear. Comes in white, colors, and prints.

GEORGIA CREPE. An armure fabric with either pebble, bird's-eye, grain, or small diamond motifs. It is used for dress goods in women's wear. Armure (French, armor) means a chain pebbled effect as in chain mail armor.

GEORGIA PROLIFIC COTTON. A variety of short staple Georgia cotton developed from Uplands.

GEORGINE. Not used in the United States, it does find some favor abroad. It is a lightweight georgette crepe made with mi-cuit silk yarns with the total sericin or silk gum being removed following weaving.

GERMAN MOUNTAIN. Extremely hardy sheep found in the Bavarian and Austrian Alps, as well as in Italy. The wool is straight and has a staple of 6 to 7½ inches.

GERMANTOWN. A coarse, four-ply worsted knitting yarn with a slack twist. Term must not be used except to describe yarns made in Germantown, Pennsylvania.

GERMICIDE. A chemical agent that will kill bacteria.

GERNREICH, RUDI. A daring, fantastic designer who made his name by leaving off as much as he had been putting into clothes. The topless bathing suit was his creation. Not yet fifty years old, he has been in the designing business since 1949. Before this, he was a dancer in the Lester Horton Dance Troupe.

His designs feature freedom of movement for the body. In 1954, he brought out his tank-top bathing suit, and since then has been cutting away the sides, here

GERMAN MAN-MADE FIBER TEXTILE TERMS, SOME TRANSLATIONS OF.

Aerated rayon	Hohlseide
Animal and vegetable proteins (egg white, alginate)	Tierischen und pflanzlichen proteinen (eiweiss, alginat)
Cable	Kabel
Carded	Gekrempelt
Carpet fiber	Teppichfaser
Cellulose acetate	Cellulose-acetate
Cellulose and cellulose derivatives with special treatment	Cellulose und Cellulosederivaten mit Spezialbehandlung
Chemical fibers	Chemiefasern
Colored or dyed during spinning	Spinngefärbt
Crinkled or crepe effect	Gekrauselt
Cuprammonium continuous filament	Chemiekupferseide
Cuprammonium fiber	Kupferspinnfaser
Endless threads	Endlose Fäden
Glass, Metallic	Anorganischen Rohstoffen (Glas, Metall)
Half-matt	Halbmatt
Highly water resistant	Hochnassfest
Hollow tube	Hohlfaser
Monofilament	Monofil
Of middle and high tenacity	Mittel- und hochfest
Raw material groups	Rohstoffgruppen
Regenerated cellulose	Regenerieter cellulose
Registered Trade-mark	Eingetragenes Warenzeichen
Special fiber	Spezialfaser
Tenacity, middle and high	Mittel- und hochfest
Threads and fibers of synthetic raw materials	Faden und Fasern aus synthetischen Rohstoffen
Textured, texturized yarns	Texturierte Garne
Twisted fibers	Spinnfasern
Viscose rayon, bright or lustrous	Viskose- glänzend
Viscose matt	Viskose matt
Viscose, high tenacity	Viskose- hochfest
Word reference and/or picture reference	Wort- und/oder Bildzeichen

and there, and in 1964 eliminated the bathing suit top. He was a pioneer in introducing short skirts and colored stockings. It is interesting to note that in recent seasons he has felt that fashion in women's wear has gone down so many untrammeled ways that is difficult to chart a new course.

GERTRUDE. Infant undergarment, corresponding to a slip, usually embroidered and trimmed with lace.

GHIORDES KNOT. In Oriental rugs the ends of the hand knotted pile alternate with every two threads of the warp. This produces fewer knots per inch than Senna knotting which shows a complete loop formed by the yarn to give a pile effect from every space between the warp threads. Senna construction gives a denser, thicker, and evener pile effect on rugs than the Ghiordian knot.

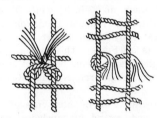

GHIORDES RUG. The original rugs woven in Asia Minor were made of wool or silk, fine in weave construction and intricate in design. These prayer rugs have a short pile tied in the Ghiordes-knot effect.

Modern Ghiordes rugs are larger in size, not quite as good in quality, and have a long, loose pile effect with some cotton used in the fiber content.

GIBSON, CHARLES DANA, 1867-1944. A great artist and illustrator, this one man stressed manners, mating habits, and morals of his era with commentary and superb sketches of the American Girl. He created a "Gibson Girl" who lasted from the early 1890's to the beginning of World War I. She was a symbol of loveliness, courage, foolishness, delicacy, and strength. She was individualistic and created considerable stir for the American woman.

The behavior and dress of the "Gibson Girl" were extremely popular for more than a generation and she has not passed into oblivion to the present time. Gibson stressed the mannish, tailored shirtwaist, wide at the shoulders and highnecked; full, long sleeves with the plaited effect over each shoulder. The wasp or semi-wasp waist effect was used to provide slimmness. He stressed the sailor hat, shallow-crowned and stiff-brimmed. This was comparable with the Breton sailor hat with its wide, turned-up brim

and the off-the-face effect with the brim lowered at the front.

Gibson also created the "Gibson Man." As his first model, he used, Richard Harding Davis, a handsome and illustrious man, and a close friend. However, it was with Gallagher, in a setting in Torresdale, Philadelphia, Pennsylvania, that Gibson produced the type of man who was handsome, chivalrous, scrupulous, and never stuffy. He did this to lesson the odds against his Gibson Girl, his heroine.

Gibson's "Girl" and "Man" are still with us in fashion and style and at times, do have some influence on present day types and modes of attire, especially among the more affluent population in America.

Gibson's work appeared on posters, advertisements, programs, trains, subways, paintings, etc. Among students of art, illustration, fashion, and style he ranks with other individualists such as Marie Antoinette, Empress Eugenie, Beau Brummell, the Castles, Chanel, Dior, etc.

GIBSON WAIST. High-necked, usually tailored, shirtwaist with long sleeves set-in with fullness and often having plait over the shoulders. Frequently seen in portraits of women done by Charles Dana Gibson, "The Gibson Girl" creator at the turn of the present century.

GIGGING. The raising of nap on fabric by drawing it across rollers that contain teasels set in frames which extend the width of the machine. The bristles of the teasels "scratch-up" the surface fibers of the goods.

GILET. Originally was a waistcoat or vest and now signifies a sleeveless bodice worn in lieu of a blouse with suit or ensemble.

GILLING. One of the operations in the combing of worsted fibers; gilling is an advanced form of carding which helps to separate the long, choice desirable fibers of the same length from the remaining short, immature or otherwise undesirable fibers. Only choice fibers may be gilled. The operation is comparable with a person combing his hair with the fine-mesh part of a comb. See FALLER, DRAWING. See Illustrated Section.

GILT LEATHER, GILT MEMBRANE. Narrow strips of leather or membrane gilded in order to be used as gold threads in damasks, brocades, brocatelles, etc. Threads of this type may be flat or wound around a core yarn. Membrane or leather can also be "silvered" to give a silver effect to the thread. French, lamelle de pellicule dorée; lamelle de baudrache dorée.

GILT PAPER. Narrow paper strips gilded for use in the manufacture of gold thread, either flat or wound around a core thread, usually cotton. May also be a "silvered thread" when a silver-colored coating is used. Used as decorative fancy yarn in certain fabrics. French, lamé de papier dorée; Italian, lamina di carta dorata.

GIMLET POINTS. The narrow, scanty, straggly ends or tips of mohair locks.

GIMMER. A young ewe.

GIMP. 1. Covering cotton or wire with silk or rayon yarn for use in embroidery, lace or trimming. 2. Narrow strip of fabric used in trimming furniture; often has a stiffening of wire or heavy cord running through it. Gimp can be used to sew buttons on clothing.

GIMP, SCROLL. A woven figured narrow fabric made with one warp and two fillings. Each set or formation of filling is made up of three gimp cords laid flat. The ground series or set projects at one edge of the fabric in order to effect a triple loop, the figure series passes through the warp and returns over the warp threads alternately thereby forming a loose scroll effect on the surface of the fabric. Plain weave is used for the warp and fabric width ½-inch to ¾-inch.

GIMP YARN. Yarn consisting of a tightly twisted center or heart yarn wrapped around by soft twisted, and usually colored, novelty yarn. Spirality in gimp is very important to bring out the effect.

GIN. The machine that separates lint cotton from cotton seeds. The full name is Cotton Engine. See SAW GIN; ROLLER GIN; WHITNEY, ELI. See Illustrated Section.

GIN BALE. Weighing from 480 to 500 pounds and having dimensions of about 54 x 45 x 27 inches, the bale of cotton as known in this country has a low density of about 12 pounds per cubic foot. Made at the gin and sometimes known as box, flat, or square.

GIN CUT. Saws of the gin often will cut the fibers and lessen the value of the staple; increases the amount of short fibers and waste. Cotton should not be ginned when damp or wet since cuts are very likely to occur.

GIN FALL. Trash and other sorts of waste remaining in raw cotton after it has been ginned.

GINGHAM. Comes from the Malayan word gingan, thence French guingan, a term used by the Bretons to signify cloth made with striped coloring. (The Malayan term means striped.) Gingham is usually made on plain weave.

Medium or fine yarns of varying quality are used to obtain the plain, check, or stripe effects. The cloth is yarn-dyed or printed, and it runs to about six yards to the pound. Textures center around 64 x 56. The warp and the filling may often be the same, even-sided, and balanced.

Gingham is strong, rather stout, substantial, and serviceable. It launders well but lower-textured fabric may shrink considerably unless pre-shrunk. Gingham has a wide range in price; designs run from the conservative type to gaudy, wild effects. Uses include dress goods, trimming, kerchiefs, aprons, children's wear, beach wear. Much gingham is made now from man-made fibers. Some ginghams on the market include chambray-gingham, nurses-gingham, Scotch, tissue, and zephyr. See Illustrated Section (Fabrics 4).

GINGHAM, IMITATION. A carded print cloth made in plain weave which is printed in designs such as stripes, plaids, checks, tartans, etc., to simulate woven gingham motifs. Has the same uses as gingham. Textures are around 60-square while the yarn count range is from 28s to 40s. Practically all the cloth is used for export, especially to South America.

GINGHAM PRINT. Material of the gingham group in which all or part of the design is printed onto the fabric.

GINGHAM TISSUE. Popular staple of the sheer type. Patterns range from the small conservative type to large, gaudy designs. Much man-made yarn is now used in making tissues. Corded effects may be noted in the cloth.

GINNING. The process of separating the lint cotton from the seed; the term also implies the other processes entailed in producing a gin bale. See Illustrated Section.

GINNING, ROLLER. The original Hindu method of ginning, still used in some world areas. The cotton comes in contact with a rough leather apron as it comes from a bin or hopper. The fibers adhere to the apron, and as the latter revolves, the fibers are drawn around the surface. Pressing against the roller is the steel doctor knife or blade. This arrangement permits the fibers to continue on their course, but will prevent the seeds from doing so.

This gin is not built for production, and poor results occur often because of the cumbersome method of separating seed from fiber.

GINNING OUT-TURN. Percentage of lint received following ginning of a cotton lot. Expressed in terms of the weight of the seed cotton, the average for American bales is around 35 per cent. The span may run from 20 per cent to 50 per cent.

GIRDLE. Women's foundation garment replacing corset. More flexible and lighter than a corset, it does not come above the waistline. Also means a belt for girdling or encircling a loose garment around the waist.

GIRL SCOUT CLOTH. A gray-green cotton fabric for official uniforms.

GIST, W. C. In 1858, this American inventor unveiled a circular knitting machine that had eight feeds and successfully made striped fabrics. Patented in England, this machine received great acclaim.

GIZA. Broad, inclusive term for cotton raised under the auspices of the Egyptian Cotton Research Board. Numbers are applied to the Giza for identification purposes, such as Giza 19, Giza 29, etc. Giza 29 is known at present as Karnak, a leading Egyptian cotton.

GLACE. 1. The term glace comes from the French for glazed. Used for a glistening, lustrous effect imparted to fabrics in finishing. 2. In leather, it is one that has a glossy grain finish achieved by glazong, ironing, plating, or polishing.

GLACES. A broad term, glacés means the luster fabrics made of fine cotton warp and rather bulky mohair filling, which affords most of the luster effect.

GLACIAL ACETIC ACID. 95 per cent pure acetic acid used in making cellulose acetate, CH_3COOH.

GLADSTONE COLLAR. A standing collar having points which flare at the sides. Worn with a wide silk scarf tie. Named for William Gladstone, the famed Birtish Prime Minister who between 1868 and 1894 served four terms.

GLANGORRA. English woolen homespun treated with antiseptics to resist disease germs.

GLANTZSTOFF. The name usually given to rayon yarn of the Vereinigte Glantzstoff Fabriken, the original basis for Bemberg yarn.

GLASS. Obtained by melting certain oxides, combinations of oxides, or other substances that yield oxides on thermal decomposition, and so cooling that it is impossible for crystallization to develop.

GLASS, GLASS FIBER. Glass is the generic term decreed by the Federal Trade Commission (March 1960) for fibers whose fiber-forming substance is glass.

The glass fiber industry promulgated its own definitions for glass, as follows:
1. CONTINUOUS STRAND: This is a drawn fiber which is obtained from a textile-type bushing.
2. STAPLE SLIVER: In present day practice this is a blown fiber, and it is produced in comparatively small amounts.

Textile Glass Fiber, incidentally, does not include the substantial poundages of blown glass wool and pack, i.e., mat for air and liquid filtration, acoustical and thermal insulation, battery mates and separators, underground pipe wrap (except reinforcing), etc.
3. CHOPPED STRAND: This means a chopped strand, roving or yarn, the staple length of which runs from ¼-inch to 3¾-inches.
4. MAT: This means the mat in any nonwoven form as made from a continuous filament, i.e., continuous strand mat (filaments bonded with a suitable binder to form a membrane) and chopped strand mat (½-inch to 3-inch strands) deposited in random formation and held in by a resin binder.
5. MILLED FIBER: This is hammer-milled yarn, roving or strand whose staple length ranges from 1/32-inch to ¼-inch.
6. ROVING: Two or more ends of untwisted strand. It includes spun strand roving (a single, continuous strand looped back on itself to give the equivalent of two or more strands) and roving for making woven roving.
7. STAPLE YARN AND SLIVER: A blown fiber and includes ribbons of generally parallel glass staple in random lengths which run from 3 inches up to 15 inches, with or without a filament yarn reinforcement, with or without a binder, and slightly condensed to an approximately uniform cross section. The poundages produced and shipped include normal sizing, but the weight of vinyl, polyester, Teflon or other types of coating is excluded.
8. YARN AND STRAND: This term covers continuous filament yarn and strand packaged for sale as such. It also includes the yarn and strand used in the manufacture of nonwoven scrim for sale as such. See FIBERGLAS.

GLASS TEXTILE. Glass that is in a suitable form for spinning or weaving. It comes in continuous filament or staple fiber form.

GLASS TOWELING. A plain-weave linen cloth with highly twisted yarns arranged with red, blue or some other color for the stripe or check effects noted in the material. Has no fuzziness or protruding fibers, launders well and gives excellent service.

Cotton toweling is a cheaper quality

and, while loose weaves are more absorbent than close ones, the wearing quality of cotton glass toweling is not too good.

GLASSINE. A thin, transparent paper usually made from sulphite pulp; used for making waterproof bags.

GLAUBER SALT. The hydrated grade of sodium sulphate often referred to as crystallized sulphate of soda. Used as a common dyeing assistant when dyeing wool, worsted, and silk to increase affinity and insure better evenness in final results. Formula is Na_2SO_4.

GLAZE. The sheen, shine, luster, or polish seen on some fabrics. It is done by friction calendering and the depth and life of the fabric or garment depends on the ingredients used. Some glazed cloths have durable finish, others will not withstand laundering.

GLAZED CHINTZ. Chintz and some tarlatan may be treated with blue, paraffin, shellac or size and then run through a hot friction roller to produce a smooth, high luster. The method will not give good results since washing will affect the chemicals used in dressing the cloth prior to roller treatment. Synthetic resins are now being used to make the glaze permanent. The fabric is brightly colored, printed or made with solid color effects. Uses are for summer drapery fabric, pillows, covers.

GLAZED FINISH. A stiff, highly polished finish given to chintz, some bookbinding fabric, and kindred materials. The cloth is subjected to a starch-and-gum treatment followed by a calender or a friction-calender treatment. The finish is not always durable. In the leather trade, it is produced by polishing the grain surface of the leather with a roller of agate, glass, or steel. The finish can also be obtained by the use of a shellac or varnish coating.

GLAZED KID, GLACE KID. A leather. Glazed or glacé kid is a product of goat and kid skins, chrome-tanned, in either black or colors.

GLAZED THREAD. A polished thread used mostly in temporary sewing.

GLAZING. Obtaining a glossy or sheen finish, on fabric or leather, by any of the conventional methods used at present - friction rollers, calendering of textile fabrics, ironing, mercerizing of cloth, plating, polishing, etc.

GLENGARRY. 1. An English tweed cloth of the homespun and tweed group. Made from woolen yarns of the "hit-or-miss" type. This fabric often admits of the use of some so-called waste stock and low-quality fibers. 2. The Inverness or cape overcoat. 3. A Scotch cap.

GLEN PLAID. "A four-and-four and a two-and-two" color-effect weave in the warp and in the filling direction of the goods. The fancy overplaid, observed in the overplaid motif, is missing in the glen plaid used in woolen and worsted fabrics for suitings and coatings.

GLEN URQUHART CHECK, TRUE. The layout for this construction made on a 2-up and 2-down color-effect weave, using black and white yarn, is as follows:

WARP: 2 white ends and 2 black ends, 15 times, followed by 4 white ends and 4 black, 8 times.

FILLING: 2 white picks and 2 black picks, 19 times, followed by 4 white picks and 4 black picks, 8 times.

GLEN URQUHART PLAID. Woolen or worsted suiting or coating material made with the ever-popular plaid or overplaid effect from two or more colors; most combinations are made of three colors at least.

Color-effect weaves based on a plain or twill weave give the best overplaids. The cloth is named in honor of the Glen Urquhart Clan of Scotland.

The fabrics are ideal for school, business, and travel since they do not have the tendency to show the dirt when compared with many other garments.

These skein-dyed cloths may be given any of the following finishes—clear, semifinish or unfinished finish.

Worsted glens run from 9 to 12 ounces in weight, woolens from 12 to 16 ounces. Overcoating cloth would be much heavier in yard weight. The material is classed as a staple and is always in demand.

West-of-England and windowpane designs resemble glens to some degree.

GLISSADE. Satin-weave cloth made in England in which the dark colors receive a polish to improve appearance; glissadé is used for cotton lining.

GLOBE. Trademark name for the rubber threads made by Globe Elastic Thread Company, Ltd., United Kingdom. In the manufacture the filaments are formed by the extrusion of latex into an acid coagulating bath. *Group A* implies the standard threads with non-staining anti-oxidant properties; *Group B* threads are the same as those in *Group A* without the non-staining anti-oxidant property. *Group C* covers the heat resistant threads.

GLOBULE. A small liquid drop.

GLOBULIN. A protein stain former that is insoluble in water.

GLORIA. A very closely woven, lightweight fabric used for umbrella covering. Generally made with plain weave, but twills and satins are also used. Originally made with silk warp and fine worsted filling; also made with cotton filling, as well as all cotton. Nylon has come into popularity as a raw material in making this fabric.

GLORIA GOODS. There are some variations of the term, gloria. These follow. 1. GLORIANA is a rather low-quality umbrella fabric made with raw silk or nylon warp and cotton filling. 2. GLORIETTA is merely a lightweight cotton gloria fabric. 3. GLORIOSA is an umbrella cloth of cotton warp and silk filling, the type of which may vary in quality. See GLORIA.

GLOSPAN. A spandex monofilament thread made by Globe Manufacturing Company, Fall River, Massachusetts. It has high resistance to aging, sunlight, perspiration, laundering and drycleaning; has good dyeability and resistance to home laundering bleaches.

GLOSS. The brightness, luster, or sheen on a material or substance, usually brought about by some treatment to give smoothness on the surface.

GLOVE. A covering for the hand with a sheath for the fingers and thumb. Made of fabric, woven or knitted, and leather.

GLOVE FABRICS. These include woven or knitted fabrics of cotton, wool, nylon, rayon, silk, etc. Tricot knit and Milanese are two popular knit fabrics used to make gloves. Work gloves are made of Canton flannel, drill, asbestos, etc.

GLOVE FLANNEL. It is usually Canton flannel made with colored ground warp with colored stripe effects.

GLOVE LEATHERS. These include the following:

1. KID: The term commonly applied to grain glove leathers from goat or lambskins of wool or hair types. The name clings to the product merely in a popular sense and is not used by manufacturers except for stock actually made of immature goatskins. The term cape is also used to designate one kind of kid gloves. In the glove industry goatskin leather is usually known as real kid.

2. NAPA LEATHER: This is a sheep or lambskin leather that is made with a chrome, alum, or combination tannage, and drum-colored. It is made from South American or New Zealand sheepskins.

3. MOCHA LEATHER: A leather that is obtained from sheepskins with a friezed finish on the grain side so that both surfaces have a suede or ooze finish.

4. PIGSKIN LEATHER: In the glove trade this leather comes from the skins of carpinchos and peccaries, and is

chrome-tanned. It is tough, durable, and suitable for both fine dress gloves and sportswear gloves. A little of this leather is formaldehyde-tanned for white dress gloves. When chrome-tanned, it is a rich yellow-colored leather.

5. PECCARY: A pig leather that comes from the wild boar in Central and South American countries. Argentina and Brazil are important sources for this leather. It is fine grained and can be shaved down to a very light weight, thereby making it desirable for ladies' fine dress and sports gloves. It is usually chrome-tanned, is washable and particularly durable.

6. CARPINCHO: This comes from a water rodent peculiar to Argentina and Uruguay. The leather is heavier than peccary and its chief use is in men's fine dress and sports gloves. Carpincho is usually chrome-tanned and is washable. In classification, it is a pigskin type of leather.

GLOVES, EPISCOPAL. Made of silk or nylon and ornamented with embroidery, these gloves correspond to the liturgical color of the vestment. They are worn up to the Offertory in a Pontifical Mass of the Roman Catholic Church. A bishop, at his consecration, is invested with gloves but they are of ceremonial use rather than essential vesture of his office.

GLOVE SEAMS. These follow:

1. HALF-PIQUE: This is a combination of the pique and the inseam. The pique seam is used for the back of the hand while the inseam is used for the palm seams thereby giving smoothness and durability. Half-pique is less expensive than full pique.

2. INSEAM: It is made by stitching glove seams on the wrong side so that when the glove is turned inside out no stitches are visible on the right side. Gives a neat, smooth seam.

3. OUTSEAM: General term to define all seams on the outside of a glove, opposite of inseam. The stitching may be done vertically along the edges of the seams in one of several ways, such as in the saddle-stitch.

When the seams are sewed so that the stitches pass over the two edges of the glove fabric, it is called an overseam. The whipstitch is typical of this type of seaming.

4. PIQUE: Also referred to as "P.K.," it refers to a leather glove seam which is made by lapping one edge over the other and stitching it on the right side. This provides a smooth, flat seam with only one cut edge visible. It is elastic, durable, and trim but rather difficult to make. Full pique seams in reference to a glove, indicates that all seams have been pique sewn. This plan is used in the best grade of gloves. The identical seam in fabric gloves is known as a kip seam. Also, the edge of the overlapping piece may be tucked under so that there is not any raw edge exposed in the kip seam.

GLOVE SILK. Finely knit silk fabric made on a warp knitting frame. Used chiefly for gloves and underwear.

GLOVE STYLES. These follow:

1. CLASP OR BUTTON: A short or medium-length glove with a fastening at the wrist.

2. GAUNTLET: A slip-on or a pull-on glove with a flared cuff. Usually about a 4- or a 6-button length. Used today only in high fashion circles.

3. MITTEN: A hand covering, usually knit, having one pocket for the thumb and one large pocket for the rest of the hand and the fingers together.

4. MOSQUETAIRE: An 8-, 12-, 16- or a 20-button length glove that is fastened at the wrist. Used for very dressy and formal wear.

5. NUN'S GLOVE: Always a black glove of 2-button length; made in silk, nylon, or cotton.

6. PULL-ON: A glove style that does not use fasteners of some type. It is made to extend above the wrist and slips on easily.

7. SHORTY: A slip-on glove or a 1- or a 2-button length glove that may be worn with long sleeves for daytime wear, or for sportswear with long or short sleeves.

GLOVE SUEDE. Made from long-staple cotton, glove suède fabric is given a soft, suèded surface and finish to simulate true chamois skin.

GLOVER'S WOOL. Wool taken from slaughtered sheep by the lime process.

GLOY. A manufactured starch sizing ingredient used in finishing textiles. It comes in a stiff jelly form and imparts a soft hand to the yarn.

GLUCOSE. A carbohydrate that occurs in many animal and vegetable tissues, blood, and sweet fruits. It is prepared by the hydrolysis of starch, cane sugar, and glucosides. Glucose is used in the precipitation bath in the manufacture of rayon, and in cloth printing. Formula is $C_6H_{12}O_6$, taken n or x times.

GLUE. Substance manufactured from gums, plus other materials, for adhesive purposes, and to paste two pieces of cloth together. In the case of some raincoat fabric rubber cement is used in the glue in treating the fabric. Fish glue is much used in the furniture trade.

GLYCERIDE. A chemical substance or fat which is a combination glycerine and fatty acid.

GLYCERIN, GLYCERINE, GLYCEROL. A polyhydric alcohol; a clear, colorless, sirupy, sweet liquid, obtained by the saponification of fats used to make soaps. Glycerin is much used as a solvent, conditioning agent, softener, in printing textiles.

GOAT HAIR. In addition to mohair and cashmere, which are obtained from goats, there are two common types known as ordinary goat hair and meadow goat hair. The hair ranges in color from white to yellow to brown or black. The fibers have some use in lower-quality fabrics.

GO-BACK. An improperly laundered piece sent back for rewashing.

GOBELIN REP. Actually a cotton rep or repp printed so as to simulate tapestry effects for use as wallcovering, drapes, etc. It is a backed-fabric since it uses two warps, one of cotton and the other of wool, and a single filling of cotton. No binding threads are used to make the cloth since it is not of true double-cloth construction.

GOBELIN STITCH. See GOBELIN, TAPESTRY STITCH.

GOBELIN TAPESTRY. Tapestry made by one of the greatest concerns in the world. Gobelin is known the world over and is a real institution in world culture. There are over 400 of these tapestries extant which have the old quality in pattern and workmanship. Some of them are worth well over one hundred thousand dollars. Beauty in Gobelin is achieved by a clever medley of colors and skilled workmanship.

The Gobelin tapestry works was founded by Jehan Gobelin, member of a Flemish family that settled in Paris in the fifteenth century. Gobelins were taken over by the French Government in 1662; since then they have become a national institution. Gobelin originally was a dyer in Rheims during the Renaissance in France. The plant is located in Faubourg St. Marcel in Paris.

Royalty and nobility eagerly bought the genuine tapestries as they became available. The last of the Gobelins died in the seventeenth century and with him the secret of the making of the vivid dyestuffs which enhanced the beauty of the products; the value of the older tapestries, therefore, was increased

The Hapsburgs bought many, some of which are so large in size that they are most difficult to hang. Walls were not of sufficient size to care for them. Museums now house many of these priceless works of art in weaving.

During World War I, the Austrians were willing to sell anything and everything, so it seemed, for relief in food, clothing, and shelter, but they would not part with the Gobelins, which would have brought them a fortune. They were sustained in this matter after the war by the Reparations Committee when there was some talk of Austria's war debt being paid off in part by giving the tapestries to the nations which had claims against Austria. Tapestries can be seen in many museums; a Gobelin, however, is a Gobelin, and no other tapestries seem to measure up to them.

GODET. 1. A piece of material, wider at the bottom than at the top, which is set into a garment for fullness or decoration. It is usually applied to skirts, sleeves, collars, and peplums. 2. A glass or plastic roller over which yarn is guided downward into the centrifugal box in viscose rayon spinning.

GODET WHEEL. The wheel made of glass over which newly spun manmade filament is wound. It is located in the revolving feed box of the spinning machine.

"GODEY'S LADY," GODEY'S LADY'S BOOK. The outstanding magazine, in the nineteenth century, on fashion, style, manners, morals, and customs. Edited by Sarah Josepha Buell Hale, a genuine contributor to American life, it may be safely asserted that no magazine of this century can cope with her *Godey's Lady Book* in influencing American thought from the social aspect.

The aim of the magazine was to "shed a beacon-light of refined taste, pure morals, and practical wisdom." Sarah Hale's outlook was akin to that of the majority of women of her era; she opposed woman's suffrage, believed a woman's place was in the home, but was a strong advocate for the education of women.

GOFFER, GAUFFER. To flute, crimp, make tucks, or raise in relief. Goffering is seen on some women's wear dress goods.

GOLD, GOLDEN. 1. A yellow precious metal. 2. Gilt. 3. Metallic yellow color of medium brilliance and saturation.

GOLD-BRICKING. Term for the limiting, on the part of unions or employees of production or the amount of work to be performed.

GOLD-DUST COTTON. Also known as Tennessee Gold Dust and King Cotton, it is an early-maturing type of

prolific Uplands with a staple measuring 1 inch to 1$\frac{1}{16}$ inches. The small bolls of this desirable cotton have lint yield cf 32 per cent to 34 per cent.

GOLDEN FLEECE. Alfonso V (1416-1458), King of Spain, in 1430 created the highest order of Spanish knighthood. The Golden Fleece. The name came from the great Spanish merino sheep industry which began when Lucius Junius Columella crossed Tarentine rams with native Italian and Spanish ewes.

The National Association of Wool Manufacturers, many decades in age, at its annual meeting in New York City confers the Award of the Golden Fleece on some outstanding luminary in the textile industry. See Culumella, Merino, Merino Sheep.

GOLD LACE. Gimp or braid that is covered with metal or tinsel thread.

GOLD OR SILVER, SPUN. Threads of gold or silver are wound around a cotton core thread in the manner of plating, to produce novelty yarn. Used for decoration in evening gowns, headgear, tunics, slipper fabric for evening wear, etc.

GOLD THREAD. Twisted gold filament or laminated thread is twisted around a core of cotton or silk yarn. The product is used for embellishment and decoration of basic goods.

GOLLER. A shoulder cape with flared stand-up collar used chiefly by German women in the sixteenth century. It protected the neck and bosom in cold weather and was often lined with fur. By the seventeenth century the goller became a part of the national dress of Germany. Periodically it comes back into vogue both here and abroad.

GOMBO HEMP. Portuguese African term for kenaf.

GOMUTI FIBER. The base of the leaves of the sago palm in Malacca yield this dark-colored, strong fiber used for cordage.

GOOD COLOR COTTON. That which is in between white and creamy casts; cotton that is too creamy is called buttery; if too white, it is called blue cotton.

GOODS. Merchandise of all types sold in textile markets, department stores, neighborhood stores. Found in every city, town, village, and hamlet in the nation. Synonymous with cloth, fabric, material, stock, stuff. Dry goods implies textile goods only.

GOODS, TYPES OF. There are several words used to signify goods in the textile and apparel fields, such as merchandise, the British term, stuff or

stuffs; and American words such as cloth, fabrics, materials, tissues for certain very lightweight fabrics, etc. Some major types of goods follow:

Dress Goods: Fabrics that can be used in women's and children's dresses; usually refers to materials bought over the counter in the department store or specialty shops. Sold in yard lengths.

Dry Goods: Materials used for clothing and furnishings as differentiated from wet goods such as liquors, oils, gasoline, etc.

Fancy Goods: Includes items such as art needlework, embroideries, stamped linens, supplies for so-called fancy work of many types. Also includes fancy weave or motif-woven fabrics-doup or leno, lappet, swivel, clipped spots, etc.

Gray, Grey, Greige, Griege Goods: Woven or knitted fabrics as they come from the loom or knitting frame before any dry or wet finishing treatments or operations are given to the bolt or cut of cloth. Greige and griege are words that originated in Switzerland, and are pronounced gray.

Piece Goods: Also known as yard goods, they are sold in the department store from the cut, bolt or piece of fabric in yard lengths. Often referred to as Yard Goods.

Wash Goods: Those fabrics and garments that may be washed in the home or in the commercial laundry. Always read labels well on wash goods.

White Goods: White materials in general with particular reference to dress fabrics. Also means finished fabrics in the white such as napery and tablecloths, pillowcases and sheets, hospital items.

Yard Goods: Same as Piece Goods.

GOODS CLASSIFICATION. In laundry practices, goods are classified according to degree of soil, dirt, and grime, and according to the resistance of the material to color and chemical attack.

GOOSE EYE. See LOZENGE TWILL.

GORE. 1. A triangular piece of fabric set into a garment to give fullness to a part, as a sleeve. 2. A short piece of elastic tape, stapled to the back of a shoe ornament, by means of which the ornament is attached.

GORRO. The red, blue, or purple stocking cap worn by Spanish Catalonians.

GOSSAMER. A very soft-feeling silk of the veiling type, characterized by a pronounced gauze effect; used chiefly for brides' veiling.

GOSSYPIUM. The generic botanical term for cotton. There are four types:

1. ARBOREAM: The perennial tree found in Arabia, China, Egypt, and India which attains a height of 15 to 20 feet, and products good cotton.
2. BARBADENSE: Native to the West Indies, the original home of the famed Sea Island cotton in the United States before the Civil War, this fiber of romance is no longer produced in this country, but is still raised in the Barbados and Central America. The plant is from 6 to 15 feet in height.
3. HIRSUTUM: This 6-foot plant is found in the southern and southwestern parts of the United States and is the basis for American cottons today.
4. HERBACEUM: A 4- to 6-foot plant native to China, Egypt, India, and Asia Minor. The famed Egyptian cotton belongs in this grouping.

GOUREUX. Short for Vigoreux; Vigoureux in Great Britain. See VIGOREUX PRINTING.

"GO-THROUGH PRINCIPLE." Applied to a Leavers machine, the frame carries the bobbin threads twice through the warp threads at the one revolution of the crankshaft of the machine. This principle increases greatly the machine production. Most of the frames used today resort to this idea which has replaced the old-time method of using landing bars.

GOTLANDS FARET. A sturdy Swedish sheep that thrives on shrubs and can withstand outdoor winter weather. Inferior in quality when compared with Continental breeds, its underhair is a detriment.

GOUTS. About the same as neps, except that they are larger and give more trouble to burlers and inspectors, they include foreign matter, wastes or matted fibers found in woven goods.

GOWN. 1. An evening dress, in all features ranking next to the haute couture, "creation," and "classic," in the most expensive women's wear apparel for evening or formal dress wear. 2. A robe worn by clergymen. 3. The robe worn when a degree is awarded to an individual. 4. The covering thrown over a person in the barber's chair. 5. A sack overcoat, raincoat, or Chesterfield. 6. A night robe.

GOWNS, SELLING POINTS OF. These include color, fabric, sleeves or sleeveless, high or low backs, necklines, trimming and hand detail work. The quality of the material used and the techniques of the operatives are vitally important.

GRAB TEST. Testing of fabrics for strength, by a controlled method in which the test is made on a machine, the important features of which are two metal jaws that grip and pull the fabric until it is ruptured. The breaking strength is recorded by a dial on the scale disk. Sample size should be 6 inches long and 4 inches wide. The averages of five tests each way, in warp and in filling, should be taken for final breakage acceptance.

GRADE. 1. The quality of relative fineness of wool. 2. Sheep of mixed blood, showing no particular breed characteristics; also applied to crossbreed sheep. 3. Means the particular quality of wool, cotton, flax, hair fibers, etc. 4. A system of scale used in classifying certain things with regard to quality, price, length, weight, size, etc.

GRADE, STRAIGHT. If a wool is graded as a 60s, for example, it should not deviate from this classing to any marked degree. Bulk grade is the expression used when there is a rather wide variation from the classed number.

GRADE STANDARDS. The U. S. Department of Agriculture has decreed the following with regard to cotton grades:

1. 32 grades for Upland cotton.
2. 5 full grades and 4 half grades for American-Egyptian cotton.

The Standard Sample Box contains twelve varieties for comparison. Each Standard Box is photographed prior to shipping as evidence of authenticity; the picture is inserted in the box when shipped.

GRADING. Classifying—or classing —for varying qualities and characteristics of some particular fiber—cotton, flax, wool, silk, etc.

GRADING, FUNCTION OF PATTERN. Pattern grading is the drafting process of diminishing or enlarging a style pattern into patterns for other sizes. The function of grading is to ascertain that this is accomplished with proper fit for the other size without changing the style sense of the original model. If the style sense of the original model gave the wearer an illusion of additional height and a slim silhouette, the same style sense must be present in the graded sizes. This sense of style and illusion is the important factor in grading; to mar it makes the grading valueless.

GRADING MEN'S WEAR GARMENTS. The popular grades range from the lowest, known as X, to 6-plus, the highest, in the following order: X, 1, 2, 4, 6 and 6-plus, the made-to-measure and custom rating. Appraisals are made according to the fabric and its properties and characteristics, style, cut, make, and trim. The lowest retail price for a complete garment is about $35.00. The fine tailored, fitted, and popular brand garments with quality fabric and trim sell from $125 up to $225. It should be borne in mind that the quality of the raw material, in this case the fabric, and the techniques of the operatives concerned usually determine the selling price of the garment.

GRADING WOMEN'S WEAR GARMENTS. The grades for coats and suits range from 1 to 5. There is no grading in, say, the $9.75 range except in sportswear (slack suit, bolero suit, vestee suit, etc.). There is an established union control over grades 1 to 5. Each grade will depend upon fabric, cut, detail, and finish.

Above grade 5, while it may be called grade 6, there is no control as to fabric, cut, style, details and finish. There is, as well, no set price; the garment may sell for well over $100, in some cases as high as $350 with some fur trimming added to the garment. Supply and demand are the two major factors in the price of any garment above grade 5. Custom work, of course, is an entirely different matter since price is no object and the individuality of style is the major consideration, plus very fine quality materials and labor.

GRAIN. Threads in the material which run parallel with the selvage. All pattern pieces laid on the material should have the grain line of the pattern running parallel with the warp or grain in the goods.

True grain is when the key threads are at right angles to each other—the warp thread or threads at right angles to the filling thread or threads.

Bias grain is where the key thread or direction, dependent on the way the material is held or laid out, runs in the diagonal direction. As a unit of weight a grain is .0648 gram or .000143 pound.

GRAIN, GRAINY WEAVES. These include crepe, oatmeal, seed, granite. Fabrics of these weaves present a pebbled surface-effect. Sand crepe is an example of cloth with a grain face.

GRAIN TRAVELER. A traveler figured on a system of numbering based on the weight in grains of a definite number of travelers. See TRAVELER.

GRAINE. Silkworm eggs.

GRAM. 15.432 grains, or .0022 pound, Troy measure.

GRAMMONT. White pillow lace used for shawls and throws.

GRAMS PER DENIER. Also written "gpd," it serves as the basis upon which the tensile strength is determined on man-made fibers, filaments, and yarns, as well as for the filament, silk. Both dry and wet strengths are given in "gpd."

GRANADA. From Italian granito and the Latin granum. In English the term means "grained or grainy." The material is a fine, face-finished cloth, made of worsted stock. Often dyed black. Broken-up appearance of the weave tends to give fabric the regular granular effect readily noted when the cloth is examined.

GRANDELLE FABRIC. A British rainwear fabric made waterproof by combining two cotton fabrics by means of a rubber sealing solution. The same or different patterns can appear on each side of the item, or the article may be plain or singled colored. Textures range from 54-square up to 64-square.

GRANDRELLE SHIRTING. It is made on the order of denim and is used for shirting. When hard, rough wear is encountered, this English fabric is made in suitable colors on a 5-shaft satin weave.

GRANDRELLE YARN. Fancy yarn obtained by the twisting of two contrasting single yarns together. It is used for novelty effects in suiting, some coating, and some shirting. Grandrelle will brighten or add luster to cloth which has a dark-colored background.

GRANITE CLOTH. Made of wool worsted, or other major textile fibers, the fabric is a fancy, irregular cloth with a pebbly, rough surface and feel.

GRANITE WEAVE. 1. A filling satin-base construction in which extra raisers are added to the interlacing points, at the top, side, above, or below. This weave comes in many effects, because of the additional raisers added to the interlacing point. 2. The small, broken effect seen on cloths made by using a granite weave. Some expensive worsted and Jacquard fabrics use the weave.

GRANT REEL. Yarn reeling in which the yarn makes definite and regular crossings which differs from the conventional yarn reel which winds the yarn in parallel formation. When done on tubes, bobbins, spools, etc., the yarn is said to be a Grant Wound Skein, or merely Grant Wound. Named for the inventor of the method.

GRASS BLEACHING, GRASSING. This is done in the British Isles for bleaching and treating linen cloth after it has been washed. The action of the elements in this grassing, or crofting, does not cause the material to decompose or disintegrate.

GRASS CLOTH. Broad term for Canton linen, rhea or China grass cloth, and materials made from vegetable fibers such as ramie, jute, hemp, etc. Many of the cloths of this name are woven by hand and are purchased in shops and bazaars all over the world. Grass cloths launder easily, iron well, but will not resist wrinkling. Used for blouses, luncheon sets, sportswear, and other purposes.

GRASS LINEN. Fine linenlike grass fabric.

GRASS RUG. This floor covering is made of "wire grass" held in place by the use of fine cotton threads. This reversible rug has a stenciled design on it. Different-colored warp ends may be used in the weaving of the material to give geometric patterns.

GRASSERIE. Disease of silkworms. It causes them to bloat, thereby stretching their skin, through which exudes a soiling liquid. The disease is not contagious.

GRASSERS. Shelly, starved, rough-necked, thin calfskins or kips.

GRATE BARS. A set of inclined, flat steel bars which form a part of the bottom of the passage between the beaters and cage sections of a picker machine. Foreign matter will drop between the bars; every fifth bar in the series is a deep one. An air current aids in getting rid of the ever-present foreign particles.

GRAVATAS. A Brazilian fiber which competes with sisal and piteira. It is used as stuffing for cushions, mattresses, and saddles. Some of it is also used for excelsior in packing. The better grades find use in the textile, rope, and paper industries. The best grade, desmoncus, is used in woven seats and chairbacks.

GRAVEYARD SHIFT. A schedule of working hours which requires employees to work during the late evening and early morning hours.

GRAVITY. The relative weight of a certain volume of a liquid as compared with an equal volume of water.

"GRAVY-PROOF" CLOTH. Treated tablecloth material whose resistance to stains is derived from a super-thin, almost invisible coating of flexible transparent plastic—so inconspicuous that only an expert can visually distinguish a treated fabric from an untreated companion. The protective layer on the goods will last as long as the fabric, and, under normal laundering conditions, will neither crack nor peel after repeated trips through the washing machine. The fabric must be hand-ironed on the untreated side. A Monsanto Chemical Company product.

GRAY. 1. Of the color of black and white mixed, and without brilliancy. 2. A gray color; any dullish whitish tint; specifically, an achromatic color which may have some brilliance but is devoid of hue and saturation.

GRAY COTTON. Gray, slate, or blue-stained cotton is known by this term.

GRAY (GREY, GREIGE, GRIEGE) GOODS. Cloths, irrespective of color, that have been woven in a loom, but have received no dry- or wet-finishing operations. Gray goods are taken to the perch for the chalk-marking of all defects, no matter how small. These blemishes must be remedied in finishing of the cloth. Material is converted from the gray goods condition to the finished state.

Dry-finishing operations may include: perching, measuring, burling, specking, mending, sewing, experienced sewing; shearing, napping, gigging, pressing, packing, wrapping, and so on.

Wet-finishing operations may include: dyeing, printing, washing, fulling, milling, scouring, soaping, shrinking, crabbing, tentering, sponging, decating, London shrinking, waterproofing, mercerizing, gassing or singeing; beetling, chasing, schreinerizing, embossing, bleaching, sizing, calendering, friction calendering, Sanforized.

GRAY OR GRIEGE YARN. Unprocessed yarn received from spinning mills to be bleached, dyed, finished or otherwise processed.

GRAY SHEETING. "In the gray" or unbleached linen sheeting.

GRAYSON COTTON. An early-maturing, prolific Uplands cotton of 15/16-inch to 1-inch staple; 34 per cent to 36 per cent is the lint yield.

GRAY SOUR. Process which in bleaching cotton, follows kier-boiling and consists of treating in a weak acid solution. Used to neutralize excess alkali and to decompose lime soaps, etc.

GRAY WASH OR STEEPING OF COTTON CLOTH. An optional treatment. It consists of passing material that has come from the singe house, through water, and then allowing it to remain on the floor or in a bin overnight. This aging tends to soften the starchy matter present in the sizing, and allows fermentation to set in. Aging changes the starch into a sugary substance that is soluble in water. When ready for further treatment, the cloth must be washed thoroughly. Diastofor or malt extract, which may have been used to change the size into sugar, is removed prior to the washing.

GREASE. Either a solid fat or a mineral mixture, the latter usually being prepared by mixing lime soap with mineral oil.

GREASE-DYEING. Process used in dyeing serges and woolens with a cotton warp without previous scouring.

GREASE SOLVENTS, NONFLAMMABLE. Perchloroethylene, trichloroethane, and trichloroethylene are nonflammable solvents that are sold under these names or under various trade names. Tricholoethylene should not be used on Arnel or Kodel.

GREASE WOOL. Wool from the live sheep with yolk and suint intact.

GREASE WOOL, CONDITION OF. Means the amount of "oil" there is in a fleece of grease wool. Oil implies the yolk and suint contained in the wool, and they are removed by scouring. The oil amounts found in fleeces range from about 30 per cent in the poorest grades to about 65 per cent in the best qualities. The more the yolk and suint present in the wool, the better will be the quality of the raw stock in working qualities.

GREASE WOOL, MARKETING OF. There are seven ways to sell grease wool to the prospective purchaser. It may be sold to:

1. A representative of the wool market, a wool expert.
2. The mill that is not located near the source of supply.
3. The mill in the locality where the wool is grown.
4. Buyers at wool auctions.
5. Buyers on the cooperative method of purchasing.
6. Users of wool by the consignment method.
7. Local dealers by growers who raise the wool as a side line.

GREATCOAT. English term for any long, heavy overcoat.

GREEK LACE. A lace developed from cutwork or drawnwork, the first needle-point lace to be created.

GREEK STRIPES. Colored cotton goods made in splits—two pieces woven together and then cut up the center. The background of the cloth is blue and the stripes may be of any desirable color. An inferior quality warp yarn is used in this heavily sized, rough-feeling cloth which the British ship to the Balkans, Asia Minor, and the Near East.

GREEN. 1. The spectrum color between blue and yellow. 2. A color in which the hue is less yellow than that of emerald. 3. A green pigment or substance.

GREENAWAY, KATE. 1. An English designer, illustrator, and writer of children's books. 2. The name for the various types of children's attire which were developed from the characteristics of the Empire Period in France, 1804-1814. This was the era of Napoleon and his wives, Josephine de Beauharnais and Marie Louise; known for its poor taste, somberness, dullness, and listlessness. Highpoints stressed by Kate Greenaway were high waistlines, frilled necks, and sleeves, and bonnets - a period of true "gingerbread" in fashion and style and cumbersome to the wearer.

GREEN COTTON. Cotton picked before maturity.

GREENFIELD TOP. British expression for man-made fiber top stock made directly from the tow stock, as from acetate or rayon tow.

GREEN FLAX. Flax which has been scutched without retting.

GREEN LINEN. Linen yarn or fabric in the unbleached or "green condition."

GREEN RAMIE. White ramie, China grass, or rhea has white on one side of the leaves; green ramie has green on both sides of the leaves; hence, the distinguishing point between green ramie and white ramie.

GREEN YARN. Undressed jute or unbleached linen yarns.

GREENS. A name for breeds of silkworms which give a greenish cast to cocoons.

GRÈGE. French for the silk thread made by reeling together the baves of several silk cocoons. Grège has no twist; the baves are merely held together by the silk gum or sericin. This type of silk cannot be used for weaving fabric except in the gum condition. Sometimes known as Nett Silk. Italian, seta greggia.

GRÈGE YARN. A strong yarn made of wool and silk combined.

GREIG, GREIGE GOODS. See GRAY GOODS.

GREIGE YARN. Unprocessed yarn received from spinning mills to be bleached, dyed, finished, or otherwise processed.

GREMIAL, GREMIALE. An oblong veil, silk or nylon, decorated with embroidery. Laid on the knees of a bishop when he sits during a Pontifical Mass in the Roman Catholic religious service. Its practical purpose is to serve as an apron to keep ashes, drops of oil, and candle wax from falling on the vestments to which it corresponds in color. A linen gremial is used when Holy Orders are conferred. It is not strictly a pontifical vestment, having been used at all High Masses. A similar lap-cloth, the mapulla, is still used by the Dominicans and the celebrant in Carthusian and calced (sandaled) Carmelite orders.

GRENADA. A cloth made of black cotton warp and some hair fiber filling. A five-harness, filling-effect satin weave is used.

GRENADE. 1. French table linen made in plain weave or small dobby loom effects. 2. A French table covering of good texture made from silk or rayon warp and woolen or worsted filling.

GRENADINE. 1. Dress-goods fabric made with leno or doup construction; hard-twisted yarns made from any of the major fibers are used. Dyed yarns are used and stripes or checks are made cramming the ends, while the open spaces in the goods are made by leaving certain reed dents empty. 2. A fabric of this name is made on a Jacquard loom which resembles a fine gauze; a harsh finish is apparent in this dress goods and neckwear fabric. 3. A dobby loom may be used to make a dress goods known by this name; the type of motif determines the use of the name. 4. A silk cord made by twisting together several twisted yarns in a ply effect. 5. A type of thrown silk. See THROWING.

GRENADINE, TULLE. A tulle made with alternating rows of black and white meshes.

GRENADINE TWIST. Organzine with hard twist to make it suitable for grenadine weaving; the twist goes from 20/18 to 60/60 and the yarn is substantial. See ORGANZINE.

GRENAI. A group of cloths in which the warp and filling are made of combination continuous-filament yarns—a full-twist viscose yarn and a normal-twist acetate. This combination is on the order of plain or novelty alpaca fabrics. Grenai fabrics are full-bodied dress-weight cloths, soft, pliable in texture and sometimes called heavy sheers.

The second syllable of the word is pronounced as ay in "say."

GRENFELL CLOTH. A closely woven, reversible, ply-yarn twill, water-repellent, windproof fabric originally used on the Grenfell Mission in Labrador. Similar to Byrd Cloth. Much used now for winter sports clothes, snow suits, rain wear.

GRESSET, GRISETTE. A low-textured, low-quality gray woolen fabric used in the seventeenth century, in the British Isles and on the Continent.

GREYFACE. A British mountain sheep developed by crossing Leicester rams and Blackface ewes, very popular in the Highlands of Scotland. The wool is coarse—about 32s—although somewhat finer than Blackface, and about 6 inches in length. Wool from these sheep is sometimes known as "Scottish cross."

GREY GOODS. See GRAY GOODS.

GREY OR (GRAY) KNIT MATERIAL. Knitted fabric that is neither bleached nor dyed. The name comes from the color of the undyed material.

GREYS, GREY CLOTH, GRAYS, GRAY CLOTH. Cotton cloths which contain unbleached yarn whether made of plain or fancy constructions.

GREX. The system used for yarn counts or sizes which employs a universal length and weight of yarn in the calculations. Ten thousand meters is the standard length while one gram is the standard weight.

GRID BAR. A cleaning mechanism found on cotton openers and pickers. Triangular in shape, a number of these bars are set close together to form an arc of a circle in order that foreign matter may drop between the bars.

GRIEVANCE. An employee's feeling of dissatisfaction, or of being treated improperly by the company or its representatives.

GRIFF. See JACQUARD LIFTING KNIVES.

GRIFFIN COTTON. An American cotton which has yielded the longest staple known, up to 3 inches. The staple is very fine and silky; the bolls are large and yield about 28 per cent lint.

GRI-GRI FIBER. A fine, soft bast fiber obtained from the palm Astrocaryum in Brazil. Used for bowstrings and nets.

GRILL, GRILLE, GRILLEE. Barred or corded effects which surround openwork areas in lace.

GRINDER, GRINDING ROLLER. Also known as the Dead Roll and the Traverse Grinder, this roller grinds the card clothing on the card.

GRINDING. Refers to the sharpening of card clothing wire on the cylinder, doffer, revolving flats or other rollers used on cards. An emery-covered roller is used for this purpose. See CARD GRINDING.

GRINDING AND MIXING. A treatment used in the manufacture of rayon whereby cellulose is made into a uniform solution from several batches.

GRIPPER FASTENER. Large snap fasteners that are clamped into cloth instead of being sewed on. Used on men's shorts, boys' dungarees, etc.

GRISSAILLE. (French for grayed.) The warp and filling of grissaillé material have contrasting black and white threads which give grayish appearance to the goods. The name is applied broadly to any grayish-colored material which does not have a definite name.

GRIS-BRUN. In French, gris means gray while brun means brown. Thus, from this has come a French woolen military uniform fabric composed of one-third of the content being a white or grayish wool and the other two-thirds made up of brown to black fiber content. The cloth is heavily fulled and milled.

GRIST. Scotch term for a standard-size rope of 1-inch diameter. It is made up of three sections, each of which has twenty yarns plied together.

GRITSTONE SHEEP. One of the oldest breeds of British sheep, native to Derbyshire and Yorkshire. Hardy and healthy, this mutton sheep yields a springy, rather fine fiber. Also known as Derbyshire. The fleece contains high amounts of black and gray fibers.

GRITTY WOOL. Dry, harsh wool which has an excess of sand and grit in it. Wool from the Dakota area is often gritty.

GRIVELE. From French for speckled, grivelé effects in woven fabric are mottled, speckled, or spotted.

GROFFER. To crimp or to plait frills for dress wear.

GROG. Any type of cloth woven "two-ends-together." Gives a basket or hop-sack effect to the fabric.

GROGRAM. Admiral Vernon, the famous English admiral of the early eighteenth century was noted for the breeches he wore made from grogram, a coarse silk and mohair fabric on the order of present day grosgrain. The breeches were instrumental in giving him the nickname of "Old Grog." Also, the Admiral signed an order which made sailors of the Royal Navy dilute their rum with water, and this mixture soon was given the name of grog. The fabric at the time was referred to in many circles as grogram instead of the correct name, grosgrain. During the reign of Queen Anne of England (1707–1714) the material was used for women's gowns for many varying social functions of the day. See GROSGRAIN.

GRONINGEN FLAX. Pale-colored, water-retted flax from Holland.

GROS, GROSSE. 1. French term for coarse or thick; applied to silk and other fabrics which are rugged, high in texture, and corded in the weave effect, usually in the filling direction. 2. Refers to a number of cross-rib materials in the grosgrain family of cloths. 3. Any heavy, rugged, substantial fabric.

GROS D'AFRIQUE. French cloth made of silk warp and cotton or rayon filling. The warp is coarse and two or three fillings of different counts of yarn are used in this plain-weave fabric.

GROS D'AFRIQUE CORDE. Used for dress goods, the cordé cloth is made of two silk warps; a single ecru silk yarn and a two-ply or three-ply silk yarn. A cylindrical cotton yarn of low-count forms the heavy cross-rib effect in the fabric.

GROS D'ALGER. A French silk fabric made with two sets of warp and bulky filling for the cross-rib effect.

GROS DE BERLIN. Woolen dress fabric made with alpaca or some other hair-fiber filling.

GROS DE CHINE. On the order of Gros d'Afrique but made with a finer silk warp.

GROS DE LONDRES. Lightweight silk or rayon dress goods with narrow and somewhat wider flat filling ribs alternating. The filling is the same size all over, only there are a larger number of picks in the wider ribs which are also covered with pairs of ends, while the narrow ribs are covered with the ends arranged alternately.

The cloth is piece-dyed or made in changeable or warp print effect. A glossy finish is applied to the goods which are used for dresses and the millinery trade.

GROS DE LYON. A filling-rib French fabric. The warp arrangement is one end of fine yarn, two ends of coarse yarn; two-ply cotton yarn gives the ribbed filling effect.

GROS DE MESSINE. French dress goods made of organzine warp and a rather bulky silk filling to obtain the rib effect.

GROS DE NAPLES. A strong, plain-woven silk cloth made of good quality organzine silk. Two-ply yarn is used each way with the warp texture higher than filling count.

GROS DES INDES. Silk cloth made with colored crossover stripes in filling direction. This plain-weave cloth is made entirely of grège silk; filling yarns vary in yarn count.

GROS DE SUISSE. Grège warp and filling are used in this French silk fabric which is made with a two-warp arrangement, a fine count of yarn is used for one warp while a coarse yarn is used for the second warp.

GROS DE SUEZ. Also known as turquoise silk, this dull-luster, silk cloth is made with fine ribs in an 18-inch width and used as bonnet and hat lining.

GROS D'ÉTÉ. 1. A crossrib silk or rayon cloth made with two sets of warp ends. 2. A two-warp dress-goods fabric, in which the warp tensions on the loom vary considerably so that the slack warp will produce a terry effect in the goods, is also called gros d'été.

GROS DE TOURS. Silk dress goods made from a two-ply or three-ply warp, organzine, and tram filling arranged two picks in the shed to produce a ribbed effect.

GROS D'ISPAHAN. French dress fabric made of greige silk warp in which three ends weave as one end; filling is of worsted.

GROS D'ORAN. A French silk brocade, rich in design with a rep-effect base weave construction. Used in expensive gowns for evening wear.

GROS D'ORLEANS. A French twilled-rib, greige warp and filling fabric. The warp and filling are dyed the same color. Some of the cloth is made with very smooth cotton filling of a color different than the warp; woven in pick-and-pick arrangement.

GROS FORTS. A strong, French upholstery fabric made of coarse but strong linen yarns in warp and filling.

GROS VELOUR. Plush woven with heavy cords or ribs in filling direction. If the ribs run in the warp direction the cloth is called long velour.

GROSGRAIN. A heavy, rather prominent ribbed fabric made from plain or rib weaves according to various combinations. The ribs will vary from a small number per inch to as high as 50 or 60 ribs to the inch. Made with silk or rayon warp and cotton filling, the fabric is rugged, durable, and of the formal type; it is dressy and in place at formal gatherings. It finds much use in ribbons, vestments, and ceremonial cloths.

In the so-called "Gros Family," there are numerous fabrics that are quite similar in many respects. Some fabrics in this family include gros des Indes, de Lyons, de Londres, de Naples, de Paris, and other type names for practically any city of note in the field of textiles that goes back to medieval days in the history of Europe. The cloth was very popular in the days of the cloth halls and guilds, from their first inception, in Europe. Many of these halls are still functioning. Grosgrain is often referred to as "bengaline cut to ribbon width." See BENGALINE.

GROSSE. Broad term for "second quality wool" raised along the Danube River area.

GROUND, GROUNDWORK. The base weave and fabric which surrounds the figures, fancy effects, and motifs in some materials. Simple weaves are used for groundwork.

GROUND COLOR. The background color against which the top colors in the manufacture of carpets create the pattern or motif in the design.

GROUND THREAD. The single or ply core, or heart yarn, used as the core or foundation about which other yarn or yarns, usually of the novelty or fancy type, are wound.

GROUND TOW. The various wastes picked up from hemp during its manipulation through to a finished rope.

GROUND WARP. 1. The warp yarn in the base or ground structure of a cloth. 2. The warp yarn that forms the foundation in the manufacture of pile cloths, and weaves with the ground filling to give firmness to the material.

GROUPED DRAWING-IN. A drawing-in draft in which two or more weaves have to be cared for. For example, a shirting fabric might have a plain-weave ground, a satin-weave stripe, and a twill stripe. All three weaves would have to be drawn-in so that they would weave on their own harnesses. The plain weave would need two harnesses, the satin might require five, while the twill might need four frames, a total of eleven harnesses in the drawing-in arrangement.

GROUP FLOAT. Where several warp or filling threads fail to interlace, and float over the yarns with which they should have interlaced. Caused by harness skips, poor timing, weak or snapped yarn, and other lapses.

GRU-GRU. A soft, fine West Indian fiber from plant of this name.

GUANA FIBER. A silken, yellowish seed hair of the Bombax tree, raised in Cuba.

GUANACO, GUANAQUITO, CHULENGO. With regard to habitation and species, the guanaco is a wild camel species which roams the high Andes Mountains from Ecuador to southern Patagonia in the Argentine. The term, guanaquito, means a young guanaco. Chulengo is merely another word for guanaquito.

As with vicuna, the supply of hair comes from the hunting and killing of the animals. There has been no domestication of the guanaco to date and therefore no supply of hair shorn from the animal, as in the case of alpaca. This race, like the vicuna, is being extinguished; severe government controls are in force to prevent any and all hunting. The chief difficulty concerning the hair of the animal is that after a month or so the fibers become very coarse and harsh, thereby making them unsuitable for spinning purposes. Thus, the animal must be killed when it is about fifteen days old; at this age, the fiber from the animal is highly desirable for spinning purposes. Skins of the older animals are used for fur rugs.

The mating season is such that the guanaco must be hunted during the months of November and December. The animals must be hunted in regions where they congregate; the chief hunting grounds, therefore, are in Patagonia, since other areas do not attract large numbers during this mating period.

Up to 1943 there was no restriction on the hunting of the guanaquito, since the animal was actually considered more or less of a pest which interfered with the breeding of sheep. More importance was placed on sheep than on the guanaquito. Both animals feed on the same grass and since this was rather scarce in some of the breeding areas at times, farmers would shoot the guanaquito simply to get rid of him.

By 1945 the catch rose to 200,000 skins, and the best estimates give a total population at present of about 300,000 heads. At this time, Argentina took very stringent steps to control the hunting of the animals. As a result, in 1946, only 57,000 were permitted to be killed. This number of killings was divided among 1,035 hunters, each of which had to own a government license.

Each hunter receives a specified number of "guanaquito tickets" and in order to dispose of the skins he must present a corresponding ticket to the buyer, who is strictly prohibited from purchasing skins without the corresponding tickets.

GUARD'S COATING. A long length overcoating with a half-belt in the back and an inverted center pleat; folds at the sides and back. Originated in England and used in officers' military coats.

GUAXIMA. See CADILLO.

GUAYABERA SHIRT. A shirt-like jacket used in sportswear; originated in the Caribbean Islands.

GUAYANILLA. A strong, white, lustrous cotton of the West Indies.

GUERNSEY. A close-fitting, knitted woolen shirt of the jersey-knit group.

GUIDE BAR. In warp knitting, it is the bar which carries the yarn and extends over the span or width of the knitting needles.

GUIDE LINES. Marks made by fugitive dyes on the front and back of a stocking as it is being knitted. These lines are used in the pre-boarding process to assure permanent coordination of knitted and molded shaping.

GUIDES. 1. A bladelike device with a hole at one end used in Raschel and tricot knitting machines to guide the feeding of the yarn to the needles. Guides on both warp machines are set in leads known as guide leads which in turn are bolted to the guide bar. 2. A bar, roller, porcelain eyelet, etc., which guides stock, sliver, slubbing, roving, yarn, etc., at the back, middle, or front of any textile frame or machine.

GUIMPE. A short blouse, with or without sleeves, often worn with a pinafore dress or to give fullness in the neck of a low-cut dress.

GUINEA CLOTHS. Heavily sized warp is used in these gray cotton fabrics made in England and shipped to the West African trade.

GUIOTE COTTON. A low-grade, short fiber cotton of the Philippines.

GUIPURE. Fancy threads of wire cord, whipped around with cotton, rayon or silk threads. The small patterns are stitched together.

GUIPURE D'ART. Linen net upon which raised intersecting patterns are worked.

GUIPURE DE FLANDERS. Pillow lace that is made separately with flowers that are connected by bars and brides.

GUISSAR SHEEP. This Bokharan-Russian sheep is the largest of the fat-tailed breeds. Raised first for mutton, and then for the wool, this animal weighs around 350 pounds, an exceedingly heavy weight for sheep.

GULF COTTON. Name for the bulk of cotton raised along the Gulf of Mexico, and the Mississippi River basin. Many seem to infer that the term implies cotton with a staple of 1 to 1½ inches. Others use a staple of ⅞ to 1 inch. Generally speaking, practically all of this cotton is Uplands, with the exception of Delta cotton, and the staple averages around 1 inch.

Gulf cotton, however, runs whiter than either Texas or Uplands cotton. The term, Gulf, is not used as much as formerly relative to buying and selling the staple. Gulf, as an over-all term, is now split into distinctive groups, some of which are known as Peeler, Bender, River, Canebrake, Red River.

GUM. 1. An amorphous, brittle, colloidal mass that comes from the drying of extruded sap of trees, shrubs, etc. True gums are complex hydrocarbons, usually soluble in water, but not in alcohol, ether, and the oils. The word "gum" is applied to true resins and to gum-resins. 2. Any of the various plant exudations to include gum, resin, resin gum, etc. 3. Gum, such as sericin, which cements the two filaments exuded from the silkworm when spinning its cocoon.

GUM ARABIC. Substance, also known as acacia, obtained by tapping a species of tree found in Asia, Africa and the East Indies. It is used in making

inks, and as an adhesive and as a filling material in textiles.

GUMMED TAPE. A narrow, thin strip of firm cotton material gummed on one side and used for mending purposes.

GUMMY FLEECE. One in which the yolk is coagulated deeper than the outer lock-tips; often caused by shearing when the fleece is damp.

GUMS. They are dense, sticky substances derived from certain shrubs or trees. Gums are chiefly acidic in reaction and find use in mixing colors for the printing of textiles and in treatment of animal fibers in textile manufacture.

GUM SILK. Undegummed silk or that which is in the raw state; also called hard silk. See SILK BOILOFF.

GUM TRAGACANTH. Many tropical plants produce the gum sap for this adhesive sizing ingredient. It comes in hard chip form, but will become gelatinous when mixed with water; a popular sizing agent.

GUM TWILL. Foulard is sometimes known by this name.

GUM WASTE. A silk waste which still has the gum in it, chiefly that obtained during the throwing of silk.

GUN-CLUB CHECKS. Men's and women's wear dress goods used for street and sportswear. Three colors of yarn are used in making the cloth. The warp and filling make a natty combination in the cloth. Men's wear cloth often has a smaller check than women's wear cloth. Men's wear cloth could be laid out in warp and filling, as 6 blue, 6 brown, 6 green in warp and filling arrangement. Women's wear cloth could be constructed as follows: 12 light brown, 12 dark brown, 12 green, in warp and filling.

GUNCOTTON. Raw cotton treated with a mixture of nitric acid and sulphuric acid produces this powerful explosive. When a flame is applied to the compound it merely burns rapidly. It will explode with the aid of an initial explosion as provided by a detonator. The cotton is cleansed, combed, dried, and, after treatment, is finally washed, pulped, and then pressed.

GUN FLAP. Noted on a trenchcoat, it is the extra layer of fabric which sets across the shoulder. Trenchcoats made their debut during World War I and were very popular for many years; still a staple type of coating. See Trench Coat.

GUNMETAL. The dull finish on leather, of the shade of a gun's metal. It is brighter than the so-called mat finish on leather.

GUNN COTTON. A variety of Rio Grande cotton, short in staple; grown in Mississippi.

GUNNY. A coarse, strong, jute sackcloth. See BURLAP.

GURRAH. A coarse, rugged muslin made in India.

GUSSET. A small triangular piece of material sewn into a garment for reinforcement.

GUT THREAD. Any type of base or core thread incorporated into woven, knitted, plaited, or braided fabric or yarn so as to limit extensibility.

GYPSUM. Hydrous sulphate of calcium used to weight or to dress cotton goods.

GYPSY CLOTH. A plain-weave, good-quality cotton flannelette, usually in cream color; used for boating, tennis, and sportswear in general.

GYRO-STRETCH. A stretch quilt fabric known for its good shape retention, a product of the West Coast Quilting Company, Inc., Los Angeles, California. Of sandwich-type construction, the outer shell is nylon taffeta to afford wind resistance; the backing is a layer of "Dacron" polyester fiberfill and a thin sheet of Scott apparel foam for warmth; base fabric is a scrim of cotton cheesecloth. In combining these four materials, the foam is held under tension during stitching. When released, the foam tends to relax. The resultant fabric has a very soft, puffy texture plus a virtually permanent stretch factor in one direction and on the bias. Outstanding for visual appeal, the product retains appearance and stretch qualities indefinitely without sagging, despite long wear and repeated launderings. Gyro-Stretch has excellent drape and exceptional "hanger appeal." It comes in plain and patterned shell fabrics with a choice of design in the stitching. It is used in many types of apparel.

H

HAARLEM CHECKS. First made in city of this name in Holland, it is a staple linen-curtain cloth in which blue and red checks are featured. Can also be made with other color checks and in cotton. Windowpane effects are also used in the patterns.

HABERDASHER. 1. One who deals in needles, pins, tapes, etc. Now implies a dealer in trimmings, accessories, linens, bindings, and other small articles of dress. 2. A men's furnishing store for hats, shirts, ties, underwear, gloves, etc.

HABERJECT. This fabric goes back to at least the time of the Magna Charta—1215. Little is known of the actual fabric except that it was composed of a mixed or mottled color, possibly comparable with present-day heather tweed. The French counterpart, hauberger, was also a coarse woolen cloth of heather effect, made in a coarse woolen construction.

HABILIMENTS. Attire, costume, dress, garb.

HABIT. The outer garment costume, dress or garb; often indicative of a particular rank, calling or pursuit. Examples are clerical garb; nun's veiling; riding habit; spectator clothes.

HABIT CLOTH. A fine quality English woolen or worsted fabric used for men's and women's wear.

HABUTAI. A fabric made of Japanese silk waste stock that can be twisted or thrown very little or not at all. (The term means soft or downy.) This plain-weave fabric is heavily sized and piece-dyed or printed. Many defects are seen in the cloth, which presents a typical "shot-about" effect. However, the defects do not injure the sale of the goods. Habutai is used for dresses, coats, shirting, office coats, etc.

HACKING POCKET. The slanted, flapped pocket noted on coats, jackets, suitings.

HACKLE. The device used to clean bast fibers such as flax, hemp, etc. Iron teeth are set in a board so that the stock may be combed for line fibers and tow fibers.

HACKLE COMB. The bristles of a flat-stripping brush are cleaned by this metal comblike device.

HACKLING. A process in flax manufacture which separates the fibers and combs out the short ones known as tow. Formerly done by hand, it is now done largely by machine. A handful of scutched fibers are thrown over iron combs, and the operator pulls the fibers through the teeth of the combs, each of which, in succession, has a progressively increasing number of teeth per unit. Several hacklings may be given the fibers, either by hand or by machine methods.

HACKLING MACHINE. See HACKLING.

HÆMOGLOBIN, HEMOGLOBIN. Blood pigment containing 0.4 per cent iron. It is a common source of staining.

HAINING WOOL. Popular Chinese wool used in carpet yarn.

HAIR. 1. Animal fiber lacking felting properties; it is usually straight, nonelastic, glossy, and stronger and straighter than wool fiber.

2. Machine-curled and fluffed hair from the manes and tails of horses and other animals; used in padding of furniture and mattresses.

HAIR, CURLED HAIR. Animal fibers which have been spun and curled, boiled or steamed, and then dried by heat. This stock has not been used before.

HAIR, HORSE AND COW. Obvious as to source, the fiber is used in millinery trade, and in suit lining to help the garment retain its shape.

HAIR AND WOOL FIBERS, COMPARISONS AND CONTRASTS BETWEEN. An animal fiber consists of a root situated in the depression of the skin (hair follicle), and a shaft or the hair proper. A typical hair has three defined tissues:

1. Epidermis or the outer layer.
2. Cortex or the cuticular layer.
3. Medulla or the pith.

Long, stiff, elastic hair of the hog is known as a bristle. Bristle hair is short, straight, and stiff, with a medulla such as the body hair of a horse.

Beard hair is long, straight, or slightly wavy, and the hair is regularly distributed, generally with a medulla, which gives the pelts of various animals their value. Human hair and hair from the manes and tails of horses also belong in this class.

Wool fibers are soft and flexible and the pronounced serrations peculiar to wool cause wool fibers to felt or mat easily, a decided advantage of wool fibers over other animal fibers.

'It is difficult to determine the point where an animal fiber ceases to be a hair, since the one by imperceptible gradations merges into the other, so that a continuous series may be formed, from the finest merino wool fiber to the rigid bristles of the wild boar. Thus, the fine, soft wool of the Australian Merino sheep merges into the crossbred sheep of New Zealand. This merges into the long English and Luster wool fibers, which in turn merge into alpaca and mohair materials with clearly marked but undeveloped scale structure. Again, such animals as the camel and the cashmere goat yield fibers which it would perhaps be difficult to classify rigidly as either wool or hair.

Wool fibers seem to make the most desirable fiber in the animal-fiber kingdom. Sufficient length, strength, and elasticity, together with certain surface cohesion to enable many fibers to be drawn and twisted in the spinning operation in order to form a coherent and continuous yarn or thread, prove to be valuable properties.

The power of absorbing coloring matters from solution and becoming dyed thereby, and the property of becoming bleached or decolorized when treated with suitable chemical agents, seem to give wool some advantage over the other animal fibers.

Wool fibers felt or mat easily, thereby causing them to have uses for which other animal fibers are unsuited.

The unmodified term Wool has special reference to the product obtained from the many varieties of sheep.

HAIRCLOTH. Used for covers for upholstery, as interlining and stiffener. Material is made from any of the major textile fibers in the warp, while the filling is made from single horsehair stock. The width of the cloth is as wide as the length of the horsehair used in the filling.

HAIRCORD. On the order of dimity, this plain-woven cotton cloth is recognized by ply-yarn cord stripes set about one quarter of an inch apart in the warp direction. An extra warp is used in the construction.

HAIRCORD. A floorcovering made by the use of tipless or unbladed wires. When made with other than hair surface yarns, the carpet is known as a cord carpet.

HAIR FIBERS. Specialty fibers obtained from animals other than sheep. Sometimes used alone but generally blended with wool, rayon staple, or cotton and made into apparel fabrics, novelties, etc. The main one is mohair; others are alpaca, camel, cashmere, rabbit, etc.

HAIRINESS IN RAW SILK. The condition of the thread when there are numerous loose ends of cocoon filament projecting from it.

HAIR-IN-FILLING. Often caused by poor winding and gives a flatness to the cloth since the yarn affected by hair will show a slight refraction of light.

HAIRLINE. Narrow striped coloreffect that resembles a hair. The use of stripings and fine, fancy lines sets off the wearer of the fabric by making him appear slightly taller than he or she actually is. Hairlines are staple cloths and often come forth in great demand from season to season.

HAIR NETS. Nets made of silk or from real hair. First made about 1850. China supplies a great portion of hair nets for the United States. This is because of the cheap labor conditions and access to raw material. The hair strands run from 20 to 26 inches. They dye readily. Used as covering for the head to keep in the wave, when retiring and when traveling.

HAIR SHIRT. Usually a shirt but can also mean a loincloth; made of horsehair and comparable fibers. Formerly worn next to the skin and served as a penitential garb, especially by monks, flagellants, and others to scourge themselves in discipline. Down through the ages hair shirts were worn by peasants throughout the world and they still prevail today in remote areas. These shirts, blouses, and garments scratch the person wearing the item and their use was accepted by the wearer.

HAIR STRIPE. Same as hairline stripe.

HAIRY. Cloth that has considerable fuzzy, protruding fiber surface on the face of the goods.

HALAR. This monofilament and multifilament fiber is made from a fluoropolymer which provides a greater strength-to-weight ratio than any other previously available. This product was developed by Allied Chemical Corporation, New York City, with Prodesco, Inc., Perkasie, Pennsylvania, aiding in the culmination of the project. Features include use of disperse colors to give lively, vivid shades which withstand 100-hour lightfastness in the fade-ometer. Woven and knit goods are said to have three times the abrasion resistance of comparable constructions of aromatic polyamides. It will not dissolve below 250° F. in any solvent and will not burn except in atmospheres with more than 60% oxygen. Halar is suited particularly for applications which require chemical/thermal resistance, nonflammability, and resistance to acids, strong oxidizing agents, and to bases and organic solvents. Uses include filters, mist eliminators, column packing, braided tubing, electrical lacing cord, etc.

HALF-AND-HALF-BOUND. The edge finish where the braid is applied evenly back and front covering the edge, and stitched only along the outer edges of the braid.

HALF BACK-STITCH. A stitch similar to a back stitch but having longer understitching, thus making a space between the top stitches.

HALF-BLEACHED. Linen yarn or fabric that has not been fully bleached.

HALF-BLEACHED FINISH. A finish cheaper to apply than a full-bleach. It is more satisfactory in many ways when compared with the latter. About one half of the natural coloring matter and pigment is removed in the treatment. Examples of this finish include unbleached muslin sheeting, toweling, Osnaburg-cretonne, duck, canvas, some moleskin cloth used for pocket lining, some crash toweling, cheesecloth, tobacco cloth, etc.

HALF-BLOOD. A theoretical American designation of wool compared in fineness with full-blooded merino wool as a standard; it is supposed to be between a 3/4 blood wool and a 3/8 blood wool in classification. Half-blood is inferior in all respects to 3/4 wool,

but is superior to 3/8 wool.

HALF-BLOOD WOOL YARN. This can be spun to about 25 or 35 cut and is drawn from one half to two thirds, depending on the weight of the yarn. A 30-cut yarn would be made from about a 12-cut slubbing and a 35-cut yarn from about 13-cut slubbing, on the finisher frame.

HALF-BRED SHEEP. Certain British breeds developed by crossing Mountain types with Luster, Demi-luster, and Down breeds. Examples are Cheviot, Masham, Swaledale.

HALF-BRED WOOLS. The crossing of Luster and Demi-luster sheep with the Mountain types produced a type of British wool classified as half-bred. It ranges from 40s to 50s in quality, about 6 inches in length, and has a characteristic crispness making it very useful in tweed trade. This wool is often called fine crossbred.

HALF-CARDIGAN STITCH. A slight variation of the full cardigan stitch. The reverse side of the fabric has the same series of wales as in the full length cardigan. However, on the face of the fabric the spacing between the wales, or lengthwise ribs, is closer.

HALF CHINTZ. One that is made with a ground of white or off-shade white. Any type of design is used, and there is no limit as to the color scheme.

HALF-COMBING WOOLS. Medium wools, such as produced by the British Down breeds, were at one time widely known as half-combing wools.

HALF-DAMASK. British term for damask made of silk or rayon warp and cotton or woolen filling.

HALF-HOSE. Short, ankle hose or socks.

HALF-LAP. The "half-hollow" shell of the cylinder on the cotton comber machine which performs the actual combing of the fibers. The surface of the shell is studded with seventeen brass bars clothed with steel pins. Pin sizes vary from bar to bar.

HALF-LINED. Garments which are partially lined or skeleton-lined.

HALF-ROUND RUCHE, CAULIFLOWER RUCHE. A flat ruche in which the filling forms a heavy uncut pile effect on the one side. The cross section of this type of ruche is practically semicircular. See RUCHE, RUCHING.

HALF-SILK. A silk fabric in which either the warp or the filling is made of some yarn other than silk.

HALF-THICK. An American fabric of the seventeenth century classed with Penistones, Linsey-woolseys, among others, for the purpose of taxation.

HALI. Turkish term for large size Oriental floor carpets and rugs.

HALTER. The strap-supporting front of a backless bodice.

HAMAMLIK. Turkish term for popular Oriental bath rugs which are made in squares.

HAMBURG. Independent beam lace made with cotton in which there is a solid groundwork to simulate fabric.

HAMBURG WOOL. A British embroidery wool finished with a gloss. Spun from fine worsted and dyed in brilliant colors. Usually of four-ply.

HAMBURG YARN. A British woolen embroidery yarn which has a glossy finish. Ply may vary.

HAMMERCLOTH. Originally used to cover seats in carriages, coaches, landaus, et al. Taken from the Dutch hemel, which means a covering, especially a bed covering of some sort. Apparently the fabric was of tough and strong construction since it was used to cover "the box-seat" in a coach into which were placed hammers and other tools to care for any breakdown of the vehicle en route to destination. And it might have been possible for a person to lie down on the covered seat in the vehicle.

HAMMOCK CLOTH. This lenowoven cloth is made from about 8/3s cotton yarn, both ways. The best grades of the cloth have from 16 to 20 ends per inch with filling texture of 12 to 16. Some lower textures average about 8 x 6. Fancy weaves and effects feature the material.

HAMPSHIRE SHEEP. This Down breed from Hampshire County in England is popular for crossbreeding in the western part of this country. The medium wool sorts to about 50s, and the fleece, which weighs from 9 to 10 pounds, sometimes has black fibers in it. Shrinkage is about 30 per cent.

HANADIANG FIBER. A strong Philippine bast fiber used for cordage.

HAND-BLOCKED. Fabrics printed by either wooden, linoleum, or metallic blocks, a slow tedious process.

HAND-DRAWN. See DRAWNWORK.

HAND-DRESSER'S FLAX. A twenty-pound bundle of hand-dressed or finished flax.

HAND-EMBROIDERED. Heavy point lace of Plauen which features fancy floral, or similar figures that are embroidered onto the motif.

HAND, HANDLE.

The reaction of the sense of touch, when fabrics are held in the hand. There are many factors which give "character or individuality" to a material observed through handling. A correct judgment may thus be made concerning its capabilities in content, working properties, drapability, feel, elasticity, fineness and softness, launderability, etc.

The term was originally applied to silk filaments, but the importance of a good handle to textiles has caused the term to take on more importance in other phases of this far-reaching industry.

A.S.T.M. gives the following evaluation on the hand (handle) of a fabric:

PHYSICAL PROPERTY:	EVALUATION RANGE:
Compressibility, ease of squeezing	Soft to hard, harsh
Density or weight per unit volume	Compact to open
Extensibility or ease of stretching	Stretch to nonstretch
Flexibility or ease of bending	Pliable to stiff
Resilience or ability to recover from deformation	Springiness to limpness
Surface contour or divergence of surface from plane	Rough to smooth
Surface friction or resistance to slipping	Harsh to slippery
Thermal character or temperature sensation to touch	Cool to warm.

HAND-FELLING. The sewing or hemming-down in a certain manner by hand. If done carefully, the stitches do not show on the right side of the fabric. Handwork is generally characterized by the use of a single thread. Machine work will reveal the interlocking of machine threads, where the stitches are placed regularly and the thread tension is usually even throughout. Some of the better-known handwork stitches include the hemming stitch, overcast, catch stitch or catstitch, and the slip stitch.

HAND-FINISHED. The final trim or finish applied to some article of apparel. Much hand-finishing is done on dresses, underwear, slips, and other ready-to-wear garments.

HAND HEMMING. The finishing of a hem by hand. This is done by making a fold in the cloth any desired width and then proceeding to finish the work by using a stitch appropriate for the material.

HANDKERCHIEF. A square article made from any of the major textile fibers. It serves as a necessity or an adornment. It varies in size and may be decorated by the use of lace, a border, design, or monogram. Often dyed or printed, the best grades are expensive and are usually made with a hand-rolled hem.

HANDKERCHIEF LAWN. Extremely lightweight soft lawn used for handkerchiefs and summer apparel.

HANDKERCHIEF LINEN. Material of cotton or linen, used for handkerchief cloth as well as for waists, collars, ruffles, and dress goods. The cloth is high in texture, light, medium or heavy in yarn size and weight. The goods have the tendency to wrinkle easily and soil readily, but absorption powers are good, and the linen washes well and can be brought back to a good finished condition after ironing.

Much of the material is printed. Textures range from 88 x 80 upwards to about 112 square. Often the fabric is woven with self-color or colored yarns, to give checks or satin stripes with two or three stripes to the width.

HAND KNITTING. Popular handcraft for sweaters, scarfs, mittens, suits, blankets, babies' things. Straight needles are usually used, or circular flexible ones.

HAND LOOM. The type of loom in universal usage prior to the inventions brought out on power looms by the great English inventors during the Industrial Revolution. It is worked solely by hand-and-foot power, and performs all the actions necessary to make woven goods—shedding, picking, and beating, plus the minor details. The looms are still in general use today in many sections of the world, particularly where modern industry and activity have not yet penetrated.

Hand-woven fabric is always in demand and desirable, since anything made by hand usually shows the result of good, individual workmanship. The cloth commands good prices. Much homespun and tweed from the British Isles are manufactured each year on the looms; Murray Bay, Canadian hand-loomed fabrics are seen in the best shops; Biltmore and Asheville cloths from the Carolina mountain area are well made and in demand despite the cost.

The power loom is made on the principles of the hand loom, with the addition of appliances and devices to increase production in this day and age of supply and demand, mass production, and uniform sizes, elaborate design, and intricate weaving.

See Illustrated Section.

HAND-LOOMED, HAND-WOVEN. Those materials, wide in scope and design, made on either a hand loom or a hand-foot power loom. Hand-woven fabrics express the imagination, individuality, and technique of the weaver.

HAND-ME-DOWN. 1. Ready-made clothes. 2. Secondhand clothes, given from one person, who has worn them, to another.

HAND PICK. A defect is observed in cloth when a pick is pulled out of line for a short distance, resulting in a small blemish or hole.

HAND-SEWN SEAMS. There are two types. French seam, which is hemmed down; and the Point Turc, which is a flat decorative seam finish with the appearance of a double hemstitch.

HAND SHIRRING. A gathering operation done by hand. The gathers are held in place by rows of stitches, one under the other. The rows of stitches are spaced according to effect desired.

HAND-SPUN. Yarn which has actually been spun by hand. Also, fabrics made from hand-spun yarn. Yarns and fabrics of this type are always interesting, intricate, and more unusual when compared with most machine-made fabrics on the market today.

HAND-WASHED WOOL. Wool washed before it is shorn from the sheep.

HANDWORK. Work done with the hands, as distinguished from work done by a machine.

HANGER. A wood or metal device from which garments are hung.

HANK. 1. A skein of reeled yarn. 2. The count, number or size of roving, such as a 1.5 or 2-hank roving. 3. Roving and yarn are spoken of in terms of definite yard lengths per pound for the standard. In cotton, for example, there are 840 yards in one pound of the #1 yarn; worsted is 560 yards; cut wool, 300 yards; run wool, 1,600 yards, etc.

HANK CLOCK. A clock used on roving frames to record the number of roving hanks that pass the delivery rollers. The dial is divided into 100 parts; the short hand of the clock records the full number of hanks, while the long hand shows the fraction of a hank delivered.

HANK-DYEING. Same as skein-dyeing.

HANK SIZING. Size applied to hanks or skeins, often for colored work, short warps, or experimental work.

HARATEEN. Little is known of this fabric except that it was made of combed woolen and/or worsted yarn in the seventeenth and eighteenth centuries. The outstanding English novelists of the era, such as Defoe, Fielding, Smollet, and Swift, mentioned the material in their writings, but there is no definite description of its construction and properties.

HARCHA-BENI GUIL. An open-fleece Morocco wool which has a staple length of 2.75 to 3.15 inches; fleece weight is 4.5 to 5 pounds.

HARDANGER LACE. Lace made by the women who live in Hardanger on the Hardanger Fiord in southwestern Norway, famous for their lacemaking. In its ancient original form it was worked with colored silks on a fine gauze netting in Persia and other Asiatic countries for many centuries. This lace, based on the principle of the square, is geometric in formation. The material necessary to make Hardanger includes scrim or loose-textured linen, a pair of very sharp, pointed scissors, a tapestry needle, and pearl cotton.

The stitches used include kloster stitch, Swedish weaving stitch, woven bars with picots, festoon stitch, lace stitch, Holbein technique, feather stitch, kloster blocks, diagonal kloster blocks, and fagoting stitch.

HARD COTTON. Brazilian and Peruvian cotton are hard, harsh, and wiry—giving a loose, spongy type of yarn which has a rather harsh appearance.

HARDEESY. A 13-ounce, twisted yarn tweed made in gun-club check motifs.

HARDEN, HURDEN. The poorest quality linen made from tow or hurds, the former name for present-day tow. Its only use seems to be for bagging, and low-run tablecloths, towels, and smocks.

HARDENING. Applied to man-made protein filaments, it is the treatment of filaments to render them completely insoluble in cold water and in cold dilute saline solutions.

HARD FIBERS. Bast fibers that are stiff, harsh, elongated, and yielded by the leaves or the stems of various plants. They are usually of the perennial type, and scraping and decorticating are used to obtain most of them. Examples include abaca, henequen, istle, and sisal.

HARD FINISH. Fabrics which have been finished without a nap of any kind. The term usually refers to worsteds.

HARDNESS. Soap-destroying minerals dissolved in water; of two kinds, temporary and permanent.

HARDNESS, PERMANENT. Water hardness derived from chlorides and sulphates of magnesium and calcium. Unchanged by heat.

HARDNESS, TEMPORARY. Bicarbonates of lime and magnesium, so named because under the influence of heat they are changed to carbonates and precipitated. They are unstable.

HARDS. Coarse, rejected fibers of flax cast out in the scutching operation.

HARD SCOURED WOOL. Scoured wool having a moisture regain of 13.6 per cent (equiv. to 12 per cent moisture content), a combined ether and alcohol extractable matter content of 1.5 per cent, and an ash content of 0.5 per cent.

HARD SILK. That which still contains the sericin or silk gum, undegummed.

HARD SIZING. This will give a sandpaper effect and feel to a cloth. Caused by the warp being allowed to remain immersed in sizing solution too long, or to dry too hard against a cylinder while out of action. Hard sizing may be prevented by keeping the slasher moving while the yarn is in process; reduce necessary stops to minimum.

HARD SOAP. Contains sodium compounds of fatty acids that harden on exposure to air.

HARD-SPUN, HARD-TWIST. Adjectives applied to yarn which has excessive twist. Such yarn is often not usable, since it may curl, become recessive, or may even loop.

HARD WASTES. A term including yarn and thread waste, and hard ends. The spinning, spooling, winding, dressing, and weaving departments of the mill supply this waste. Yarn wastes are kept separately in bags or bins according to color and quality. For example, a mill is spinning worsted yarn from 1/2, 3/8, and 1/4 blood stock; the yarn wastes from each type of wool would be kept apart from each other. A woolen mill would not put its white wastes in with merino white yarn waste, nor would it put solid color yarn waste with mixture waste.

The garnetting process is naturally severe on the fibers, and a large percentage of the stock is much shorter than that of wool yarn from which this waste material is secured.

Yarn wastes are made from recovered fibers. Worsted fibers that have been recovered make a superior raw material, since the fibers have good length, strength in spinning, and felting properties.

Garnetted worsted hard ends are better than the best grades of fibers reclaimed from rags.

Woolen yarn wastes are usually garnetted and consumed within the mill where they have originated.

Hard wastes are usually graded for fineness and color as Fine, Medium, and Low white or colored stock. Quality is often designated by the grade of the wool used, such as 1/2 blood white thread waste, 1/4 blood colored thread waste, and so on.

HARD WATER. Water which has a high magnesium or calcium content and requires a special soap to make suds. The degree of hardness of water depends on the lime and magnesium content present in the water. Ordinary soap causes the salts to curdle with the result that insoluble lime and magnesia soaps are produced.

HARE, HARL. Filaments of flax, ramie, jute, hemp, etc.

HARE OR JACK RABBIT. One of the well-known animals in the United States, this rodent exists everywhere in the world except on the island of Madagascar. Its hair texture is woolly and of interest not only to the textile trade, but also to hatters and furriers. The hare's clipped outer hairs, when blended with wool before the yarn is spun, give the finished goods an appearance of hairiness. When the fur fibers are used, the end fabric is soft in handle. The woolly texture of the hare's coat lends itself particularly well to felting. More than 50 per cent of all fur fibers used in woolen clothing are selected from the hare, the Angora goat, and the plain rabbit. The price range of the fiber is from four dollars to ten dollars per pound depending on the fiber length, fineness, and color.

HARGREAVES, JAMES. From 1754 to 1768, Hargreaves perfected methods of spinning yarn. His spinning jenny was the first machine to spin more than one thread of yarn at a time. Tradition has it that the frame was named in honor of his wife. He came from Standhill, near Blackburn, England, and is supposed to have received the idea "from seeing a one-thread wheel, overturned on the floor, when both the wheel and the spindle continued to revolve." The spindle had thus been thrown from a horizontal position to an upright one, and, if a number of spindles were placed upright, and side by side, several threads could be spun at once.

The spinning jenny was a forerunner of the spinning mule which was invented by Samuel Crompton in 1779, in England. For Mule Spinning: See Illustrated Section.

HARLEQUIN CHECK. Plaid in which three or more contrasting colors are used to give a contrasting or harmonious color effect. Found in cottons, rayons, and some silks, the effect is about the same as that known in woolens and worsted as gun-club.

HARN. British term for low-quality, coarse flax yarn.

HARNESS. The frame upon which the heddles used in weaving cloth are placed. Warp ends are drawn through the heddle eyes. Harnesses have an up-and-down movement in the loom which causes all the warp ends on the harnesses' frames that are raised to be up, and those that are lowered harnesses to be down. This action causes the formation of the shed of the loom to make the weaving of cloth possible. See Illustrated Section.

Harness frames are controlled in the loom so that, by their action, the designs in woven cloth are possible.

HARNESS CHAIN. An endless, wooden chain with each bar of the chain fitted with lags, according to the motif to be used in the weave in the fabric. The lags in each bar come under the jack-tip on the loom, causing the harnesses thus affected to rise and bring the warp ends drawn through the heddles on the particular harness to rise and form raisers in the cloth. Each bar represents one pick in the goods. The chain is located at the headstock side of the loom where the head motion, dobby, or otherwise is situated. The harness chain is made from the drawing-in draft used to draw-in the warp ends as prescribed by the designer of the material. Another, but serving the same purpose, is the chain built of all metal—the bars, rollers or balls, sinker disks, and cotter pins. See Illustrated Section.

HARNESS CHECK FABRICS. This spot-motif group of cloths is made on lappet looms, chiefly in Scotland. Made in check formation, textures are about 48-square with about 40s in the yarn count. The clipped-cluster effect made by the lappet warp uses a 14s or 16s yarn. The finish on these materials shows a very closely napped effect. There is no lappet weaving in the United States at present.

HARNESS CORDS. See JACQUARD HARNESS.

HARNESS DROP. One or more warp ends that float on the face or the back of a fabric as it is being woven in the loom. The effect may be noted for full or part width of the goods. Caused by one of the harness straps becoming broken, thereby not permitting the harness frame to function as it should.

HARNESS EYE. Same as the mail in Jacquard weaving. See JACQUARD HARNESS.

HARNESS FRAME. Two wooden laths upon which are suspended a series of cords or wires called heddles. Each heddle has a small eye through which a warp end passes. They are used to divide the warp threads in order to form the shed of the loom through which the shuttles pass in laying the picks in the shed.

HARNESS LEATHER. A term that includes collar and saddlery leathers. It is usually made of cattle hide that is oak or union-tanned, except for the considerable use of pigskins for saddle seats.

HARNESS LEVELING. Small filling dots or marks may be noted along a selvage edge when weaving fabric in a loom. Caused by a shuttle overshooting the warp ends in the raised portion of the warp shed of the loom. The harnesses must be checked in order to insure proper harness leveling at all times when the loom is in action.

HARNESS LEVER. Used on a dobby loom, it is a long, irregularly shaped, notched lever that takes care of the harness cords and rods to set the harness in proper alignment so that the shed will be able to open sufficiently wide to take care of all harnesses being used on the loom. The harness chain causes the jacks to rise when a riser lag comes under the jack-tip, and this, in turn, actuates the lever.

HARNESS MARK. Dark lines of roughed-up warp yarn which appears in woven fabric during weaving. Caused chiefly by the heddles on the harness frame not working smoothly, or by loose, tight, or badly worn heddles.

HARNESS SKIPS. Breaks in the weave or the failure of harnesses to work properly. Skips are often caused by harness straps that slip, snap, or break and work out of the plane and place provided for them. Skips form floats on either the face or the back of the goods.

HARNESS TIE. See JACQUARD HARNESS.

HARNESS TWINE. See JACQUARD HARNESS.

HARRISET. A wool shrinkage treatment perfected by the Harris Research Laboratories, Washington, D. C. Worsted top treated by the process requires no special preparation for spinning, and the treatment does not affect the hand. The rate of dye take-up is negligible, thereby necessitating only slight adjustments in the dye formula.

HARRIS TWEED. Sixty miles northwest of Scotland lie the Outer Hebrides, the home of Harris Tweed. Harris, Lewis, Barra, Benbecula, North Uist, and South Uist comprise the compact islands with the Harris and Lewis known locally as the Long Island. These islands are wide stretches of peat bogs and rocky moorland, unsuitable for cultivation and of little grazing value.

Except for the modern port city of Stornaway, the islands seem to have stood still; there are no towns, and the villages are called townships. The common grazing ground for the sheep is around the villages. The crofters' cottages stand out in bold isolation against the somber background of the hills and moors. Dwellings are very primitive, made of double dry walls of undressed stone, thatch-roofed, with the floors made of beaten earth with a stone hearth in the middle for the peat fire.

Furniture is very simple. The Harris Tweed industry has become the mainstay of the islanders who are kept busy with the ever-increasing demand for Harris Tweed all over the world.

Because of the paucity of grazing ground for sheep sufficient to provide for increasing demands for the fabrics, it has become necessary to import wool from the Scottish mainland. All wool used in making the fabrics must be virgin Scottish wool. After the fleeces are sorted for grade, the grease and other waste matters are washed out in the soft peaty water of the lochs or burns. Much vegetable matter is removed by hand. Drying follows washing or scouring which is done on stone walls or on lines under the influence of the sun and ocean breezes.

At the present time, only synthetic dyes are used for coloring. The old-time hand method of carding the fibers, tedious, time-consuming, and laborious, has been superseded by the use of machine carding frames. The womenfolk spin and ply the yarns, and it is now one of the few places in the Western world where this practice is still in vogue. Every piece of Harris Tweed is still hand-woven on looms in the home of the islanders. This is a laborious process but when a hand-woven tweed is compared with a power-loomed fabric, it will show at once that the results justify the labors expended.

Concerning finishing or waulking, the old-time hand methods have been pretty well superseded by mechanical means. This converts the loom fabric from a harsh hand to one that is appealing in touch and surface effect.

According to the Federal Trade Commission, Washington, D. C., "Harris Tweed" is limited to fabric made from virgin Scottish wool and woven on hand looms on the Islands of the Outer Hebrides. This eliminates the question of imitations, inasmuch as Harris Tweed is definitely a distinctive fabric. There are now two types—fabric made from hand-spun yarn and that made from machine-spun yarn.

HARRIS TWEED

The Harris Tweed Certification mark is owned and administered by The Harris Tweed Association, Ltd., London, England. Its exclusive trade-mark is the long familiar (since 1912) "orb mark," a ball-shaped figure surmounted by a cross. All of its wools are made into yarn in the spinning plants in the Outer Hebrides, and then the yarn is sent to the many crofters throughout the islands to be hand-woven into fabric and then returned to the spinning plants in Stornaway where the finishing departments of these mills finish the goods. The certification is then stamped onto the cloth, which is the guarantee that the tweed complies with the definition of Harris Tweed.

The fabric is finished at 28-29 inches wide, and the texture or pick count is 18 ends and 18 picks per inch in the finished cloth. Featherweight Harris Tweed weighs from 6 to 7½ ounces per lineal yard; Light Weight runs from 8 to 9 ounces while the Standard Weight ranges from 10 to 11 ounces per yard.

HARVARD CLOTH. Oxford shirting made with a twill rather than with the distinctive plain weave of true Oxford fabric.

HARVESTER DUCK. A particular type of number duck that comes in a variety of widths made to suit some special purpose. Used chiefly for conveyer belting on farm machinery.

HASLOCK. A lock of coarse beard hair grown over the pit of the throat of the Merino sheep. The name has been applied, somewhat indiscriminately, to harsh wools at large and to skin wool taken from Mountain sheep.

HASP. Jute or linen yarn in a 3600-yarn length.

HASTENING. Any of several compounds used to speed-up a chemical reaction as in the case of dyeing textile yarns or fabrics. Several types of salts are used for the purpose.

HASTINGS TAPESTRY. One of the major dates in world history is October 14, 1066, the day that the Norman King, William the Conqueror, defeated King Harold of England. This is the only successful invasion ever made on the British Isles. William actually entered England on September 27th and in three weeks had conquered England. This tapestry, to commorate the 900th anniversary of the Battle of Hastings, is actually an embroidery and was perfected by the Royal School of Needlework, London. Events depicted on it range from 1066 to the present time. In this span of nine centuries, the tapestry is set-up with nine events per century with a total of eighty-one in all.

Each panel is three feet high and the overall measurement is three feet high and forty-three feet in length. To choose the subjects it was necessary for Group Captain Ralph Ward, Organizer, to consult with historians to select and obtain copies and photography work from paintings and pictures. Subjects and topics were selected after research done in the Royal Palace, other palaces, the House of Parliment, The Royal Family, museums, books, and private homes. All pictures are symbolic representations of the events portrayed in the tapestry.

The panels are made by application-partly applied and worked with threads, cords, metallic threads and metals, mounted on stretchers backed with calico fabric. The tapestry is made in nine foot panels, each separately framed with an average of three pictures per panel. This beautiful piece of work takes its place alongside its counterpart in France, the Bayeux Tapestry. See Bayeux Tapestry.

HAT. Any covering for the head which consists of a crown and brim, or either one. It is usually made of felt by an interlocking of a mass of fibers.

HAT, PINCH-FRONT. A hat with the crown dented on either side near the front.

HAT BLOCK. A crown-shaped form over which hats are drawn to shape them during the hat-finishing operations.

HATCHELL. Same as hackle or comb used to comb some of the bast fibers.

HAT-FORMING MACHINE. A machine in which fur fibers are blown and sucked onto a whirling perforated cone by currents of air to form the cones from which hats are made.

HATRA. Product of Joseph Pernick Co., Inc., this English-developed yarn meter is used as a quality control device in knitting to read and interpret the speed at which the yarn is feeding into the needles of multi-fed circular knitting machines.

HAT SHAPE. A roughly blocked felt-fabric, cloth, or straw woman's hat before it has been reblocked, cut, and trimmed.

HAT STEAMER; A metal pan about twelve inches in diameter covered with heavy canvas; used to loosen the nap of felt hats. Steam is fed through the bottom as a hat is held, crown downward, in the pan.

HATTER'S FELT. Felt cloth used by manufacturers of headgear; in blocked condition it is known as the hat body.

HATTER'S PLUSH. Rabbit hair serves as the fiber for this fabric used for headgear. Silk plush is used for men's high hats, called hat-shag in Great Britain. Belgium, France, Australia, and the United States are the major sources for the coney or rabbit hair, although there are a great many other sources for these fibers.

HATTER'S SILK. Several types of silk fabric are used for lining and trimming the various types of headgear. Examples include satin, some crepe fabric, faille, some faconné, grosgrain, Jacquard silk fabrics, messaline, panne velvet, velvet, etc.

HAUBERGER. See HABERJECT.

HAUTE COUTURE OR HIGH-STYLE FASHION. A fashion which appeals especially to the smart, alert, style-conscious woman. It is often too new, extreme, or unbecoming for acceptance by the average woman, whose taste in fashion is fairly well standardized. This fashion is always well designed but is suitable for only certain functions and within limited social circles.

HAUTE-LISSE. French tapestry-weaving term for "high-leased." Haute-lissé is the opposite of basse-lissé "low-leased." It means that the warp threads hang perpendicularly from the warp beam.

HAUTE NOUVEAUTE. In French, haute means high or high class while nouveauté means novelty—hence, "novelties of good quality." Usually correlated with fine, appealing, rich-looking materials. There is always a host of novelty fabrics on the market and, very often, the fancy or novelty of today becomes the staple of tomorrow.

HAVELOCK. A cap cover, usually

of cotton, with a flap hanging over the back of the neck for sun protection in hot world areas. Originally worn by soldiers and travelers in these areas, the havelock is named for Sir Henry Havelock, 1795-1857, a noted British general who made his reputation in India at the time of the Sepoy Rebellion, 1857-59. This article is still an important item of garb in hot climates.

HAWICK. Scotch town noted for its tweeds.

HAWKINS' COTTON. An early-maturing American cotton from medium-sized, round bolls; staple is ¾ inch and lint yield is about 30 per cent.

HAWSER. Small cable twisted from three small ropes each of twenty strands.

HAWSER TWIST. Cord, rope, or twine in which the first and second twists go in the same direction while the third twist goes in the opposite direction—S-S-Z or Z-Z-S. See Illustrated Section.

HAZEL. The color of the hazelnut shell, reddish-yellow, it has medium brilliance and saturation.

HEAD. 1. An old English term to designate quality in the woolen sorting system.

2. A Scottish yarn measure of 1920 yards.

3. The skein or bundle into which flax or hemp yarn is made prior to packing for market.

4. That part of a hide which is cut off at the flare into the shoulder.

HEAD CHECK. A check with an advanced date to consummate payment without an immediate withdrawal of cash from the bank. Also a postdated check.

HEAD END. The beginning of a new piece of fabric in the loom, usually showing identification marks.

HEADING. Generally speaking, it means the beginning and the end of a piece of woven fabric, irrespective of the length. The British interpretation, however, describes a distinguishing mark woven into the fabric at the end of a pre-determined length. For example, some British mills will make goods to come off the loom in, say, a 110 or 120 yards or some similar yardage. When the loom has produced, say, 110 yards of fabric, the weaver arranges to insert at that point, some heavier and contrasting yarns in the filling direction in the cloth. Sometimes several picks of one color, then additional picks of another color are woven into the cloth.

Some manufacturers adopt a uniform combination of colors as standard for their goods; others arrange a different combination of colors and different size "headings" to meet the requirements of different customers. The heading in a cut, bolt, or run of cloth may or may not have the heading removed on delivery to the customer. When left in for the customer, the heading may serve as a sort of trademark that is often sought for by prospective buyers of the goods. The cloth is generally folded so that the headings show well on the face of the material. See Headend.

HEAD LEASE. During the dressing or slashing process, the section warps are leased, but the lease is removed when the warp yarn is slashed or dressed on the loom beam. The next lease is applied only when the warp is drawn-in through the heddles on the respective harnesses which are placed in the loom ready for weaving. The head lease prevents tangling after the warp is dressed; odd-numbered ends go over the first lease rod and under the second; even-numbered ends go under the first rod and over the second. See LEASE RODS.

HEADLINING. The material used to line the tops of automobiles. A soft-filled sheeting that is dyed, napped, and then given considerable felting is about the most popular type used.

HEAD MOTION. Various mechanisms used on looms to control the harness action. The average motion is heavy in weight and sturdier than the dobby-head type. Head motions are ideal when weaving wide fabrics and fancy weave constructions.

HEAD WOOL. Wool taken from the head and upper portion of the neck of sheep.

HEALD. English term for a heddle through which one or more warp yarns or threads are drawn according to some preconceived plan. These yarns are drawn through the heddle-eye of the heddle, either singly, in pairs, or with more than two ends per heddle eye. See HEDDLE.

HEALD SHAFT. British expression for the American term harness or harness frame which holds the heddles through which the warp yarns are drawn and controlled in setting up a loom to weave fabric. The top and bottom eyes or loops of the heddle are slipped onto the harness-frame bars and thereby kept under control and in proper place. A few heddles up to a great many may be set around the harness frame bars, dependent upon the number of ends in the warp, the number of harnesses to be used to make the pattern repeat, the size of the yarn, the drawing-in plan, the draft and chain, etc.

HEALD YARN. A smooth, even, and very uniform Egyptian cotton yarn which ranges from 40s to 60s in the carded type and from 70s and higher in the combed type. The yarn is plied four, five, or six times, and three or four of these plies are further folded or plied to give from twelve- to twenty-four-ply finished. Counts range from a low of 16/40s or 12/50s to a high of 12/100s or 16/90s.

HEART, HEART YARN. 1. Center of a core yarn. 2. The core strand in a rope.

HEART ROPE. The core or center rope used in making ropes of more than three strands. Usually a three-strand rope of soft construction, it is used to keep the outside strands equidistant from the center of the rope.

HEAT. Thermal energy, a mode of motion. When a change in the quantity of the heat in a body results in a change of temperature without a change of state, the heat is known as Sensible Heat. When a change in the quantity of heat in a substance results in a change of state, say from solid to liquid or liquid to vapor, without any temperature change, this type of heat is called Latent Heat.

HEATER BOX IN TEXTURED YARN PROCESSING. Sometimes called a Heater Tube, this is a basic part in a false-twist machine and sets the yarn in its twisted formation. These boxes come in varying sizes and the longer the box, the greater will be the processing speed in production. Some of the more recent types are equipped with solid state circuitry to provide heat control and even distribution.

HEATHCOAT, JOHN. He received patent rights for a bobbinet machine in 1808, a development of the Whittaker machine. The threads which crossed the warp were supplied from bobbins that worked with the threads from a semicircular frame. The strips were three inches wide, and they were joined together to make the finished product.

In 1809, Heathcoat brought out his second type of machine in Loughborough, Leicestershire, England. It could make machine-made strips of lace 18 inches wide. Within a year lacemakers produced the net and were tambouring and running in the patterns with the needle; 54-inch widths were soon available.

In 1813, he perfected his machine to the point where the bobbins traversed a specified width and would then return without going the full width of the machine. These narrow widths were known as quillings. Heathcoat's patents expired between 1823 and 1825, and from that time on there were many attempts to improve and simplify lacemaking methods. See LEAVERS, JOHN.

HEATHER. A popular flower in the British Isles; it is the basis of the yellow dye used in dyeing Harris tweeds.

HEATHER MIXTURE. Named for the Scotch heather, it is a blend yarn used in the knitting trade, and in homespun and tweed fabrics. Stock-dyed, basic-colored slivers, slubbings, and rovings are drawn, drafted, doubled, redoubled, and finally spun into a yarn which will show the shade of the color or colors which predominated in the original blending, oiling, and mixing of the stock. Used in suiting, topcoating, some overcoating, cap cloth, mufflers, golf hose, socks, stockings, knitting yarns.

Heathers, since they are stock-dyed and can vary considerably in quality and texture, admit the use of inferior, low-grade wool, wastes, and substitute fibers. These fibers, however, have to be supported by longer staple wool which serves as the carrier or base.

HEATHER YARN. Yarn spun from a mixture of black, brown, and gray natural wool, together with small amounts of red and green raw stock-dyed fibers.

HEAT MEASURE OF FIBERS. A device manufactured by the Minneapolis-Honeywell Regulator Company to measure the heat of fibers, especially nylon and other man-made fibers, during production to assure quality control and efficient processing. It is done by focusing radiated heat from the fabric through a lens into sensitive elements that indicate the temperature.

HEAT PRINTING. An adaptation of the decalcomania technique which uses heat and pressure to transfer designs or patterns from rolls of paper to fabric. Designs are limitless and at present six colors can be utilized. Dyes in the paper are made by CIBA, which has an interest in Societe des Procedes Sublistatic, the Swiss-based parent company of Sublistatic Corporation of America, sole supplier of the paper here. The heat printing process takes from only 15 to 30 seconds to complete and is a dry process that simultaneously thermosets the fabric at 375° F. The method is also known as thermoprinting, dry transfer, or, as the supplier calls it, the Sublistatic Process.

HEAT SET IN TEXTURED YARNS. The use of heat to fix or set crimp formation in textured yarns.

HEAT SETTING. Thermoplastic fibers such as vinyon, nylon, and saran can be set to any shape by heat treatment. They will then become stable dimensionally until heated to a tempera-

ture as high or higher than that at which they were set.

HEAVY CHEMICALS. The commonest acids and alkalis are known by this term—ammonia, caustic soda, muriatic acid, nitric acid, sulphuric acid, sulphur, et al.

HEAVY DUTY SYNTHETIC DETERGENT. Any of several cleansing agents fortified with a chemical builder which gives an improved cleansing action. See Detergent.

HEAVY GOODS. See INDUSTRIAL AND MECHANICAL FABRICS, THE APPLICATION OF.

HEAVY SHEER. See CREPE, TRIPLE SHEER.

HEAVY WOOL. Wool which has a high shrinkage in scouring; consequently, a low-yield fleece.

HEBERLEIN. Permanent finish designed for application to organdies and other fine fabrics. It gives a crispness which is retained through laundering and dry cleaning processes. Of Swiss origin, it is licensed to finishers here. Sometimes called Swiss finish. Registered trademark of Heberlein Patent Corporation, New York City, and High Point, North Carolina.

HECK. 1. A spinning wheel attachment that guides yarn onto the bobbin. 2. The expanding and contracting comb-like guide for warp threads as they are being leased and dressed for the warp beam. This comb is used in a saw-tooth arrangement with the sections riveted or joined so that they may be moved forward or backward, in or out at will. 3. A series of glass or steel rods located below the hooks on a Jacquard head motion. They serve as a grating to allow an even lift to all the harness eyes in the machine. See Illustrated Section.

HECTARE. A unit of measurement equal to 2.4711 acres of land.

HEDDLE. Also spelled heald, the English term. The warp ends are drawn through their respective heddle eyes according to the plan or motif in drawing in these ends. See Illustrated Section. Heddles keep the warp ends under control in a uniform manner. The top and the bottom loops of the heddles fit onto the respective bars of the harness frames. Heddles are made of fine, pressed steel wire, cord, or iron, dependent on the type of cloth to be woven.

HEDDLE, STANDARD. Pertains to the two flat steel heddles which support the leno or doup. Taken together they form the unit for making doup weaving possible. The standard heddles are mounted on separate harness frames, and lifting either of them will

cause the doup thread to rise. A skeleton harness arrangement takes care of the doup end in its loom action.

HEDDLE EYE. The hole or opening in the center of a heddle through which the warp end or ends may be drawn through by the drawer-in. See Illustrated Section.

HEDDLE GAUGE. An implement used to make string heddles.

HEDDLE HOOK, DRAWING-IN HOOK. A wire hook used to draw the warp threads through heddle eyes of the heddles. In the hand-weaving trade, the hooks may be made of wood, bone, or plastic.

HEDDLES.
1. WIRE HEDDLE: A round or flat wire which has an eyelet in the center, with a loop at the top and another at the bottom. The top and bottom loops fit onto the bars in the harness. The middle loop is the one through which the warp end is drawn. Ends may be drawn through singly, as they usually are, or they may be drawn through doubly or more, depending on the type of weave construction used. Pliable, pressed, or flat steel heddles are the best to use. Heddles aid in keeping the ends straight and under control at all times.

2. STEEL HEDDLE: A type of heddle which is cut with a die and can be obtained in any thickness desired suitable to the fabric to be woven. This type is closely related to the average wire heddle, previously noted.

3. DOUP HEDDLE: A special type used for leno or doup cloths and for various types of gauze weaving.

4. CORD HEDDLE: Often known as a String Heddle and used on looms which make the same material, year in and year out. These heddles are found mostly on cotton looms used for plain and small twill and satin cloths. Small weaves up to eight harnesses often use this type of heddle. The cord is specially prepared and treated to give good service. Cord heddles are cheap in price and can be ideal for continuous weaving on simple constructions.

HEDDLE STICKS. Flat piece of wood used to hold string heddles, one at the top and one at the bottom of each set of heddles. Also known as Harness Bars.

HEDGING. A standard business transaction, whereby a trader protects himself against possible price changes. A trader, for example, who owns 50,000 bales of cotton which he intends to use over a span of months may "hedge," by selling short 50,000 bales of cotton "futures." If, per chance, the price goes down, he may lose money on the cotton but would make it up on the sale of the futures. See FUTURES, FUTURES CON-TRACT.

HEEL TABS. The heel area of a full-fashioned stocking as it comes from the legger machine.

HEER. A unit of measure for jute and linen—600 yards or 1/24th of a spindle. A full spindle would have 14,400 yards.

HEILMANN COMB. This upright machine for combing worsted fibers as short as 1½ inches in length is the acme of perfection and does finer and cleaner work than the combers used on the English or Bradford system. The Noble or English comb rarely is able to comb fibers less than 2 inches in staple length.

In the Heilmann frame, the fibers are held tightly at one end and well combed prior to delivery to the front rollers of the machine. The layout of the machine is simpler than the English frame; the porcupines of the Heilmann comber do their work capably and neatly, and are based on the principle of combing one's hair with the fine mesh of the comb. Minute foreign matter is easily and effectively removed. Finally patented in 1845.

HELANCA. Registered trade-mark for a nylon or a polyester yarn made under license from the Heberlein Patent Corporation. Continuous filaments are specially engineered to create millions of microscopic curls, obtained through a torque (or tension) technique. The filament is first coiled like a spring and then is heat-set and twisted counter to the coil. The curls formed by this reverse twist open and close to give the stretch; the finer or lighter the denier, the greater will be the stretch.

Not all "stretch yarns" are Helanca. In order to bear the name of Helanca, the yarn must first be approved and then undergo continual tests in the Heberlein Testing Station, High Point, North Carolina. Thus, Helanca is the only torque yarn with universal quality standards because the specifications are kept uniform and constant among the licensees. Quality control is also exercised over fabrics and finished products bearing the trade-mark and made by the licensees.

HELANCA TEXTURED YARNS.

HELANCA: Conventional and false-twist nylon and "Dacron" textured yarns used in woven and knitted fabrics.

HELANCA HIGH TEST: Maximum stretch yarns of nylon and "Dacron" used in hosiery, swimwear, and leotards.

HELANCA NT: No torque nylon-textured yarn with considerable stretch and a soft, appealing hand; used in woven and knitted fabrics.

HELANCA SP: High elastic stretch yarn of nylon used in woven fabrics; popular in ski ensembles.

HELANCA SS: Highly bulked nylon yarn which has limited stretch and provides a smooth, even surface texture effect in woven and knitted cloths.

HELANCA SW: Textured nylon yarn with false-twist modified to give low stretch in effects such as bouclé or crepe in knitted fabrics.

HELD LOOP. Knitting term whereby a loop, which has been pulled through the loop of the previous course, is retained by the needle during the knitting of one or more additional courses.

HELIOTROPE. A reddish blue-red color that has medium saturation and low brilliance.

HELISTERES. A tree common to many South American countries which produces a strong bast fiber used in cordage by the natives.

HELIX. 1. A spiral motion or the result of spiralling. 2. A curve formed by a straight line drawn on a plane when that plane is wrapped around a cylindrical surface of any kind, as in a core yarn.

HELVETIAN VOILE. The registered trade-mark for a Swiss voile that has been given a chemical finish to make the cloth permanently crisp and, as in the case of Swiss organdy, able to be washed and dry cleaned, requiring only ironing, without starch, to restore the original finish. This fabric was originated in Switzerland.

HEM. A fold which may be used as a finish or as a decoration on a garment. A hem may be straight or curved. Curved hems must be narrow, whereas straight hems may be any width, the only requirement being good proportion for the placing. The first fold of a hem depends upon the width of the hem and the firmness of the fabric.

HEMMER. An attachment to a sewing machine, for turning under the edge of a piece of fabric, preparatory to stitching it down.

HEMMING. A slanting stitch through the cloth and the fold; stitch slants on the right side of the goods. Used to hold folded edges in place as hems and facings.

HEMP. This is found in the Philippines, Spain, Italy, Russia, Poland, and India. Russia produces more than all the other nations combined. The best quality comes from Italy. Hemp is grown in this country in the states of Kentucky, Illinois, Missouri, Indiana, and California. In recent years Wisconsin has begun raising the fiber, and excellent results have been obtained due to the mineral matter in the soil.

The fiber is difficult to bleach, a serious drawback to its progress. Like jute, the fiber comes from just inside the outer bark of the plant which grows from six to ten feet high. Hemp is stronger than jute and withstands water better than any other natural textile fiber. Uses of hemp are ropes, twines, cables, and rugs.

HEMP FLOOR COVERING. Low-grade and low-priced floor covering made of hemp or jute. See HESSIAN.

HEMP LINE AND TOW. The former implies the straight, parallel fibers that have been "prepared." Tow is the short fiber stock of varying lengths removed in breaking, scutching, hackling, or combing. It is often very gnarly, matted, and very irregular.

HEMPS. Vegetable matter removed from the sheets or packs used to hold wool.

HEMSTITCH. 1. To make a decorative finish by pulling out a number of parallel threads at the top of a hem, catching up an even number of the remaining threads, drawing the thread around them, and securing them by a stitch in the edge of the hem turn. The ornamental needlework is called hemstitching. 2. The stitch used to make this ornamental needlework. 3. To puncture the fabric with a large machine needle and to surround the perforation with stitches in imitation of hand hemstitching.

HEMSTITCHING. An ornamental stitch; when done by hand, a number of parallel threads are drawn and those remaining are fastened together in open sections in series. Hemstitching is also done by machine. It is used as an ornamental feature and is commonly found on handkerchiefs, hems, napkins, slips, tablecloths, etc.

HENEQUEN OR HENEQUIN, AND SISAL. These closely related plants are found in Mexico, chiefly in Yucatan. Fibers are obtained from the leaves, and henequin far outstrips sisal in the Mexican belt with regard to production and use. Sisal, however, is raised in British East Africa and in Indonesia; it comes from the same family group as the century plant and belongs to the agave species.

Henequin and sisal are rather easily obtained from the plant, and both are ideal in the manufacture of rope. Salt water, however, will quickly destroy the fiber, thereby limiting its use for maritime purposes. Binder twine, small diameter rope, and some hard-fiber twine are other uses of these two fibers. The binder twine is a favorite with workers in the grain fields, since it is ideal for bundling and tying.

HENNA. An Oriental shrub or small

tree with lance-shaped, entire leaves. The leaves produce a dyestuff, one of the world's oldest, which is orange-brown in color. Used to dye wool, leather, hair, etc.

HENRIETTA. Dress goods that vary somewhat in detail. Some of the material is like cashmere cloth, other cloth is of the salt-and-pepper type. One of the popular cloths of years ago and not much in use of recent years. Cloth comes in the white state or may be piece-dyed. Used in children's clothing. Weight ranges from seven to fourteen ounces.

HERALDRY. The art of practice of recording genealogies and blazoning arms or ensigns armorial; also for processions and other public ceremonies. The system of modification of a design by a change of color or the introduction of an overcheck gave rise to the expression "tartan heraldry."

HERCULON. Olefin fiber made on the melt spinning system which is resistant to acids, alkalies, bleaches, sunlight, and easy to clean. It has high tenacity and abrasion resistance, and dries quickly. It has circular shaped cross-sections, and comes in staple, continuous filament, and in bulk-continuous filament forms. These polypropylene yarns are dyed with certain acetate dyes, azoic, and polyester dyes. Herculon has excellent dimensional stability. Uses include indoor and outdoor carpeting, cordage, industrial fabrics, nonwoven fabrics, knitwear, and in blends for apparel pile cloths. Registered trademark of Herculese, Inc., Wilmington, Delaware.

HERDWICK. An extremely hardy, active British mountain sheep that produces a long carpet wool. Wool from Herdwick is coarse and kempy, 28s to 32s quality, and about 7 inches in length.

HEREKE. A coarse Turkish carpet wool.

HERIS RUGS. These are made of camel hair and have patterns of various types; the article is always one or more shades of brown.

HERLONG COTTON. A popular semicluster cotton raised in Alabama and Georgia. The medium-sized round bolls are late in maturing. The staple is about 15/16 inches, and the lint yield is about 30 per cent.

HERRINGBONE. Used for suitings, topcoatings, overcoatings, sport coats, dress goods in men's and women's wear. The cloth gives a weave-effect in fabric that resembles the vertebral structure of the herring. The clothes are staples always in demand. All herringbones are broken twill weaves, but all broken twill

weaves are not herringbones. The latter should balance perfectly to be called a herringbone and not a broken twill. Many types of stock, color and weaves are used in making the cloth. See WEAVE PATTERNS.

HERRINGBONE STITCH. The name for a catch stitch used in embroidery. It is used to form bands and to fill in motifs and borders. For heavy stems it is taken close together.

HERRINGBONE TWILL. A broken twill weave which gives a zigzag effect produced by alternating the direction of the twill. Also, at times, known as the chevron weave. See WEAVE; WEAVE CONSTRUCTIONS.

HESSIAN. Used for sacking purposes, it is a rough, coarse material made from the major bast fibers, alone or in combination.

HETEROTYPICAL FIBER. Carpet wool fibers that cannot really be classed as wool or hair. This kempy type of fiber denotes a form of meiosis (division) whereby the fiber structure will vary considerably along the entire length of itself.

HETEX. The registered trade-mark for an all-cotton fabric featured by burnt-out effects; often used for dress goods. The ground of the cloth often has a drawn-thread effect where some of the threads have been removed by chemical means so as to leave the motifs in bold relief.

H. G. COTTON. Hand-ginned cotton in India; sometimes called charkha or charka.

HIBRED COTTON. Popular cotton fiber with average to good fiber-length uniformity. Fineness varies from coarse to average with strength ranging from fair to very good. When used in counts of yarn around 22s the yarn strength is poor to fair; when used in counts around 36s the strength may be classed as poor. A feature of the fiber is that its neppiness is low.

HICKORY CLOTH. Resembles ticking somewhat, but of light weight and not so firm a weave. Much used as institution fabric and for work clothes.

HICKORY STRIPES. Cloth on the order of ticking but inferior in quality, lower in texture, and softer in feel. This rugged cloth is used in farm work, industry, and for cheap clothing. Twill weaves are used to make the goods.

HICOTT. Trademark of Mitsubishi Rayon Company, Ltd., for its novel morphological structured fiber which approximates cotton in properties. Formerly known as Fiber C-311, it is a monocomponent regenerated cellulosic fiber with a heterolateral structure

similar to a bicomponent fiber. Convolutions have a frequency of 60 to 120 tpi. Hicott has high wet modulus, good alkali resistance, and a cotton-like hand. It has a fibril structure and these fibrils are at an angle to the fiber axis because of the built-in convolutions.

Although Hicott does not have a flat cross-section, bulkiness is maintained by the three-dimensional structure imparted by the helical microcrimps which do provide better crease resistance in fabrics. Deniers are 1, 2, and 5 while fiber lengrhs range from 35 mm. to 102 mm. Hicott has good dyeability; tinctorial properties and color brilliancy are claimed to surpass those of cotton. Good moisture absorbency and pilling resistance are other properties of this fiber.

HIDE. Tanning term for pelt taken from one of the larger animals, such as cattle, in its entirety, containing the whole superficial area of the covering of the animal from which it was taken.

HIGH-BULK YARN. It is obtained by the use of varied length fibers in the same yarn which will have different shrinkages. One part, or ingredient, will have high shrinkage while the other will show little or no residual shrinkage. The end-use of the yarn determines the blend such as 60 per cent low shrinkage fibers and 40 per cent high shrinkage stock.

Actual bulking occurs when the yarn is allowed to relax in boiling water, either in the yarn or fabric state. It may be done in a boiling dyebath or by the heat of a steam press or calender frame. When subjected to the former treatment, the high-shrinkage fibers contract and cause the low-shrinkage fibers to curl or buckle and increase the yarn diameter and bulky appearance.

HIGH-BULK STAPLE YARN. Made on the cotton spinning system, the resultant yarn is a combination of high-shrink and normal-shrinkage staple stock. A sandwich blend of the two stocks is made before the picking operation, and the resultant lap is then processed the same as in the manufacture of cotton yarn.

Tow fiber is not involved in the making of this yarn. The staple stocks are manipulated by the spinner from the forms delivered by the manufacturer of the fibers. Heat stretching or steam relaxation is not done by the yarn spinner.

HIGH DENSITY BALE. One with a density of around 32 pounds per cubic foot and tightly compressed into a size of 60 x 24 x 18 inches.

HIGH DRAFT. See LONG DRAFT.

HIGH FASHION OR STYLE. Any

new creation, classic or fashion which is adopted by the leading fashion exponents; the "dernier mot" in the most exclusive current fashions.

HIGH HAT. A broad term used all through its rather interesting history in the field of headgear. High hats have been worn by many classes of persons in its history. Some artisans used to carry their equipment or tools in them, and the early rowing races between Cambridge and Oxford universities featured crews wearing high hats. At present this hat is worn by men on formal and social occasions while women wear them with riding clothes.

HIGHLANDERS. In ancient times a warlike race living in the northwestern Highlands, a mountainous and inaccessible country. The costume of the Highlanders was developed to a degree of splendor shown by few national costumes, and is rich in accessories, such as the sporran, the dirk, the bonnet, and the shoulder brooch, to name a few.

The Scottish Highlands lie north of a line running from the coast of Kincardineshire to the Firth of Clyde.

HIGHLAND SHEEP. A hardy breed of sheep found in the extreme north of Scotland and in the Orkney, Shetland, and Hebrides Islands. Largely of the Scotch Blackface type. Yields a coarse, rough, kempy wool, mostly used for homespun tweeds and as a carpet wool.

HIGHLAND WOOL. Long staple, coarse quality British wool used for carpets, rugs, and kindred materials.

HIGH LIGHT. A shiny or lustrous area observed on the surface of a starched fabric.

HIGH PILE. A pile in a fabric which is more than one eighth of an inch in height. When the pile is one eighth of an inch or less, the fabric is called a low-pile cloth. See Illustrated Section (Fabrics 80).

HIGH-PILE FABRIC, KNIT. Fur-like fabric used in the manufacture of coatings, collar trims, linings, and industrial materials such as paint rollers. The fabric is usually made by sliver and backing yarn technique or on the high loop-ground yarn principle on the weft knitting frame, or on the cut-pile and ground yarn principle on the Raschel knitting frame.

HIGH ROLL TAKE-UP. When the sand roll on a loom delivers the newly woven fabric on a loom directly to the cloth roll by means of frictional surface-contact.

HIGH SILK HAT. Rigid-brim, stiff-bodied hat used in formal wear only. The crown and upper brim are made of silk-finish beaver felt which has been ironed

to a high glossy finish or from black satin fabric which has been given high luster. The brim may be flat or curled, and binding is done with grosgrain nylon or silk. This headgear also comes in gray and brown as the occasion warrants.

HIGH SPEED WARPING. See WARPING.

HIGH-SPLICED HEEL. A reinforced sock, stocking or hose with the extra yarn above the regulation heel or shoe line.

HIGH TEMPERATURE DYEING. The dyeing of yarn on dye tubes at temperatures above the boil and at high pressure.

HIGH-TENACITY YARNS. These yarns have been developed for purposes where extra strength is necessary. They are used chiefly in tire fabric, but have been used to make tackle twill and similar specially durable fabrics required for military purposes. High-tenacity yarns are made on the viscose system.

HIGHTOWER COTTON. A large-boll Alabama cotton of medium staple.

HILDA. A lining fabric made with a filling-face twill weave, cotton warp, and alpaca filling.

HILLIARD COTTON. A variety of Uplands cotton similar to Peterkin with a staple of 3/4 inches to 15/16 inches and lint yield of about 35 per cent.

HILL SHEEP OR "OUT-BYES." Expressions used in Scotland implying sheep which are allowed to roam and graze freely over vast hirsels or rambling hill areas, as contrasted with "In-byes" or sheep which are confined within certain areas by means of a wall or some other type of barrier or enclosure. See HIRSEL, "IN-BYES."

HIMALAYA. A cotton cloth, plain-woven with very irregular filling yarn that has a long slub formation. This yarn alternates with a regulation pick and the fabric shows a rib-effect in the filling. It is a type of shantung.

HIMATION. In the days of Ancient History, it was a garment made from a rectangular piece of cloth thrown over the left shoulder and wrapped around the body. The word comes from the Greek, heimat, the stem of the word, hetma. It was really a heavyweight chiton and required more fabric; it was often made from a piece of goods that measured eight feet by six feet. For summer wear, this garment was made in silk for the more affluent families of the era. See Chiton, Peplos.

HINDU BLACK. A breed of sheep raised in Berar and Central India. The fleece weighs only 1½ to 2 pounds;

the very coarse staple, 2 to 4 inches long, is wiry and varies in color.

HIPRIDERS. A facetious name for jodphurs or riding breeches. These jodphurs, when worn by women, hug the hips not the waist.

HIRING HALL. See CENTRAL HIRING HALL.

HIRSEL. Term used in Scotland for all the sheep being tended under the direction of the "herd" or herder, the sheep of one shepherd. Implies a flock of sheep elsewhere in sheep-raising areas.

HITCH-BACKS. Caused by improper "loom start-up" after the weaver has had to attend to a cloth pick-out. Gives light or dark areas in the goods, loose filling pickage or under-tension warp blemish, etc.

HM 64. This modified viscose staple fiber of Courtaulds, Ltd., is like its Vincel polynosic fiber and comes from a modified viscose process and provides fiber of high strength, low extension, and high modulus. Round and smooth in cross-section, HM 64 is ideal in blends when high yarn counts are needed for use in blouses, dressgoods, and handkerchiefs; ideal stock for sewing thread, as well.

HMIDOU. House pants, originating in Morocco, which are short, puffy bloomers with embroidered metallic threads interspersed throughout for effect. The hmidou is usually worn over colored stockings, very often chartreuse or pink in color. Inspired by the garb of child servants in the Moroccan court life. Another type of hmidou is the straight, high-necked tunic worn over trousers or pants. A triangular pocket is observed just under the neckline. This type of hmidou is worn chiefly by acrobats, jesters, etc. Embroidery, simple or bizarre, is also a feature of the burnoose, caftan, djellaba, and the djiba. See Burnoose, Caftan, Djellaba, Djiba.

HOBBLE SKIRT. So called because of its narrow width, particularly at the bottom, which prevented the wearer from taking a normal step. It was in style around the end of World War I.

HODDEN GREY. A mixture of the natural black or gray wool with a larger bulk of white.

HOFFMAN, ADON J. In 1905, this American inventor perfected his famous Hoffman Press which revolutionized the garment industry throughout the entire world.

HOG, HOGGETT, TEG, TEGGETT. Sometimes called virgin wool, it is the first fleece shorn from a sheep when it is about one-year-old. It is longer, finer, and is of higher quality than wether wool.

HOGAN. A one-room house or cabin made of timber and earth used by nomadic sheepherders throughout the United States. The hogan is thought to have originated with the Navajo sheepherders in Arizona and New Mexico. This dwelling has prevailed for about two hundred years and can be found wherever sheep are herded in this country.

HOGSKIN. A grained leather used in the glove trade. The carpincho or peccary provides this product which is often buffed on the grain when it becomes what is known as buffed hogskin.

HOISTING ROPE. Heavy hemp rope is prepared with a widely spaced overlay of wire laid on a slant to the right. Similar rope is made with the slant to the left. Then numbers of these are combined, depending upon the thickness of the rope desired. The result is a very strong rope which will not spin when a heavy load is being hoisted. An example of this rope could be the use of six strands of seven wires each on a hemp core covered with a Z-twist or right-hand-twist layer of twelve strands of seven wires each. This construction will prevent any spinning by the rope.

HOLD-UP MOTION. Used in the weaving of borders in several fabrics, it will throw the take-up motion out of action for a time, so as to allow more picks to be run into the fabric for the desired effect. The harness chain controls this motion.

HOLE BOARD. See JACQUARD COMB-ERBOARD.

HOLES. Small perforations, openings, or actual holes of varying size caused by any number of things. Knots, broken places in the fabric, foreign matter, irregular loom action, shuttle splinters, faulty filling-control action, and finishing operations such as napping or shearing produce these areas. Shuttle smashes will often give large holes in the fabric. Usually fixed to perfection by finishing-department sewers.

HOLLAND. 1. Cotton cloth that is given a glazed or unglazed finish with some softener and filling material treatments to make it opaque. This plain-woven material is an imitation of the old-time linen that was given a beetled finish. Used for window and shade cloth. 2. An unbleached glazed or dull-finish linen, made chiefly in Holland for furniture covering. 3. General term for imported European linens.

HOLLANDA. Finely striped linen or cotton fabric used in Central American countries for children's dresses, dress goods, and summer slacks or trousers.

HOLLAND FINISH. A glazed or unglazed finish given to certain cotton materials to make them more or less opaque. An oil and a filling material are applied to the cloth which is then given a thorough calendering. Uses include curtain or shade fabric, tags, sign cloth.

HOLLOW-CUT VELVETEEN. A velveteen material much like corduroy. The pile is cut in graduated lengths so that it forms cameo-like ribs. Used for coats, suits, dresses, robes, etc.

HOLLYWOOD GAUZE. Nylon marquisette made in a fancy leno weave, used for experimental draping for costumes.

HOMBERG. A good quality felt hat in which the brim is rolled and the crown is dented lengthwise. A regulation or wide hatband and a narrow ribbon edging also feature this type of headgear. The hat was first worn in Homburg, Prussia, and has had popularity since the turn of the century with the well-dressed gentleman. Note that in this country the word is spelled Homburg.

HOME ECONOMICS. The art and science of home management with a college or high school curriculum, usually including studies in nutrition, the purchase, preparation, and service of food, interior decoration, textiles and clothing, child development, family relations, and household economics, as well as standards of living, budgeting of income, etc. Quite a number of outstanding colleges and universities have changed their names from Department or Division of Home Economics to new names that seem to be somewhat more inclusive so as to give an improved image of the term. A very fine publication in the field is *The Textile Handbook* published by The American Home Economics Association, 1600 Twentieth Street, North West, Washington, D. C. 20009.

HOMESPUN. Originally an undyed woolen cloth spun into yarn and woven in the home with the rather crude machinery used by the peasants and countryfolk the world over. The industry came to the fore in the British Isles and then spread to the Continent. Its popularity is owing to the substantial appearance and serviceable qualities. Homespun is woven to great extent on power looms today; genuine homespun cloth supply is very limited, and much power-loom cloth is sold as genuine homespun. The term is much abused, and the gullible buying public often is fooled when buying the cloth as to its possessing some particular quality. The cloth should always be made on a plain weave. Coarse, rugged yarn is used and quality varies much. The best material

is an ideal rough-and-ready type of cloth. All types and kinds of stock from the highest to the lowest go into the cloth in its wide range. See Illustrated Section (Fabrics 11).

HOMESPUNS AND TWEEDS. Tweed is the Scotch word for twill. Tweeds are closely allied to homespuns. They should be made from a 2-up and 2-down twill weave of 45 degrees. Homespuns and tweeds can be used to show readily the difference between the plain weave and the twill weave. In tweeds, several variations of twill weaves are often used—broken twills, straight twill weave, color effects, pointed twills, twilled baskets, fancy entwining twills, braided twills, diamond weaves, ice cream effects, and combinations of these weaves taken in a group. Much variation of design and color is noted in the cloth. Some of the more prominent tweeds that have won their place in the trade are: Scotch, English, Irish, Bannockburn, Donegal, Kenmare, Linton, and Harris.

There are certain cloths sold as homespuns which in reality are tweeds and vice versa. Consequently, in the trade, it can be seen that each cloth may be made with either weave, plain or some twill, and be accepted by the public under the name given to it. Homespun, when used as tweed, has the heaviest weight of the cloths in question. It has the average characteristics—yarn, feel, finish, twist, body. From this it may be gleaned that in the trade today the heavy homespun is classed as a tweed. Disregarding the trade and looking at the problem from the mill and manufacturing angles, the following may prove of interest: homespun must be made from plain weave, tweed from twill weave. After the cloth leaves the mill it may be called tweed or homespun to suit the whims of the public.

In many of the outlying districts of the world today both cloths are hand-loomed and the industry is on a firm footing. Many of our Southern States make quite a little of the cloth. Asheville homespuns from the Carolinas and other nearby sections are sold in the best stores in the large cities and bring high prices here and abroad. They have color backgrounds, tradition, sentiment, history, a psychological appeal and, best of all, are correctly advertised to catch the eye of the person who can afford to pay the rather high prices of these fabrics.

See Illustrated Section (Fabrics 11 and 21).

HOMEWORK. Production by employees or other individuals performed in a home outside the actual company premises.

HOMOGENIZER. A mixing apparatus which breaks down particle sizes of various substances in order to produce a better blend. Colors and starches, for example, can be homogenized.

HOMOPOLYMER. A manmade fiber which has a single chemical polymer in contradistinction with a copolymer.

HONAN. Silk pongee cloth made from wild silkworms raised in the Honan area in China. The fabric is noted for its uniformity of color since the worms are the only wild type that give even dyeing results. Also made with man-made fibers.

HONEYCOMB. A raised effect noted on cloth made of worsted yarn. Material is used as dress goods and suiting cloth. The appearance of the fabric resembles the cellular comb of the honey bee. The material is often called waffle cloth in the cotton trade. The high point on the one side of the cloth is the low point on the other side.

Cotton honeycomb or waffle cloth is used for draperies, jackets, skirts, women's and children's dresses and coats. Rather popular fabric. See Illustrated Section (Fabrics 55).

HONEYCOMB CANVAS. Used for embroidery ground, it is a bleached cotton canvas made in an almost square honeycomb weave effect.

HONEYCOMB QUILT. Honeycomb or waffle weaves are used to give the effect in this plain-texture, bleached cotton fabric made from low to medium counts of yarn.

HONEYCOMB RESEAU. Reseau, in French, means net or network. Thus, a diamond or hexagonal mesh network to form the ground in certain types of lace. Usually bleached and can come in light or pastel shades.

HONEYCOMB STITCH. A smocking stitch which gathers the fabric in a honeycomb cavity or diamond effect. Popular on blouses and peasant-type waists.

HONEYCOMB TOWELING. A rather rough feeling cotton or linen fabric made from the honeycomb or waffle weave. May be white or colored.

HONEYCOMB WEAVE. A fancy construction with the cloth having a pitted, cell-like appearance like a honeycomb. Usually, a rather loosely constructed fabric, the base of the fabric is plain weave. The high point of a honeycomb on the one side of the goods will be the low point on the reverse. Used for toweling, dress goods, bedspreads, etc.

HONITON. English bobbin lace that is noted for its distinctiveness and beauty of design. Honiton appliques show sprays, thistles, and other flower effects, all of which are worked separately and then manipulated onto a net.

Honiton has an interesting history. While known all over the world as Honiton, this lace originated in the seaside village of Beer, fifteen miles from Honiton, where it was made by "fish wives" as a cottage industry while the menfolk were at sea. The reason for the change of name to Honiton was that the stagecoaches between the major cities in England stopped there on the way from western England to Bristol and London. Small towns and villages did not warrant a stage stop, so the housewives took their wares to "staging towns" for transfer to the larger cities for sale. Lace made in Beer was no exception.

The name, Honiton Lace, was likely conferred as a sales gesture and to shed the name altogether. In the eighteenth and nineteenth century British Isles, "Beer Lace" would have had very little sales appeal in the temperance drawing rooms for which it was intended. Lace making, incidentally, has disappeared altogether from the village of Beer. Belgium and France are the centers where it is made today.

HONITON BRAID. Machine braid of ornamental oval figures connected by narrow bars. This narrow braiding is used for collars, handkerchiefs, and trimmings.

HOOD. A flexible covering for the head and the back of the neck, it is usually knitted or crocheted. A cowl worn by a monk or those used on academic gowns are known by this term.

HOOK AND EYE. A hook and an eye or loop for it to hook into, shaped in metal, used in place of button and buttonholes. Hooks and eyes are generally used on plackets to close the side, back, or front opening.

HOOKE, ROBERT. In 1664, he published his book *Micrographia,* in which he mentioned the possibility of making yarn of a synthetic nature, by mechanical means. This is the first recorded instance where the statement was made that it would be possible to make manmade yarns. It has taken almost three hundred years to produce these yarns— rayon, acetate, nylon, Dynel, Verel, Fiberglas, "Dacron," "Orlon," Acrilan, Arnel, etc.

HOOKE'S LAW. Within the elastic limit of any body, the ratio of the stress to the strain produced is constant.

HOOKED RUG. First made by pulling fine fabric strips through a foundation fabric such as burlap or canvas, with a wood or metal hook or needle. Much of this product is today power-loomed, but the old-time patterns are still in vogue. Most of these rugs have myriad coloring in them; some in good taste, others rather bizarre and shot-about in effect.

HOOKING MACHINE. A machine that tightens the twist of dyed yarn.

HOOKS. See HOOK AND EYE.

HOOP CUTTER. A large pair of hand pliers used to cut metal ties found on cotton bales.

HOOP-PETTICOAT. Popular in the eighteenth century and until about 1820, this petticoat was distended by the use of bone, cane, whalebone or wire. Popular in this country in the antebellum days prior to the War Between the States, 1861-1865. Forms of this garment included fan, bell, dome, oblong, et al.

HOP BAGGING OR POCKETING.
1. A jute bagging on the order of a tarpaulin, used for packing hops and similar products. 2. A four-leaf-twill-woven jute fabric which weighs from thirty-four to thirty-eight ounces in a 48-inch width. Made in England and shipped to all parts of the world.

HOPI ACALA. Cotton which is a cross between a modern Acala variety and a primitive Indian cotton known as "Hopi," named for the Hopi Indian tribe. It is a development of George Harrison of the U.S.D.A. Field Station. This fiber is noted for its great strength —90,000 to 100,000 pounds per square inch, about 10,000 pounds above any other cotton. Luster, smoothness, silk-like feel, circularity in fiber cross-section and ability to clean easily and well are other assets. Fiber staple is from $1\frac{1}{16}$ to $1\frac{3}{16}$ inches with well-developed cell walls.

HOPPER. A device into which material is deposited and from which it is automatically fed into a machine.

HOPPER FEEDER. See AUTOMATIC FEEDER.

HOPSACK, HOPSACKING. A term variously used, as follows:

1. A rough-surfaced fabric, bulky in nature and made from cotton, linen, and other vegetable fibers, alone or in combination. Somewhat simulating bagging or sacking, the cloth is popular for all types of sportswear for rugged, knock-about use. Comes in natural shades and colors.

2. Coarse bagging made of bast fibers, chiefly from hemp and jute.

3. A lightweight blanketing made with small repeat basket weaves. This article is known for its great warmth.

4. Woolen or worsted suiting fabric made from a 2-and-2 basket weave. This open type of material comes in a wide range of textures and weights. Often called hopsack serge, if made of worsted yarn.

5. A class of staple and fancy rough woolen cheviot apparel cloths in which a small basket weave is used, usually a 2-and-2 weave.

See Illustrated Section (Fabrics 49).

HOPSACK WEAVE. A small, plain basket weave such as the 2-and-2, 3-and-3, or the 4-and-4. These weaves may be written as 2-2, 3-3, and 4-4.

HORIZONTAL OPENER. A group of auxiliary machines in manipulating cotton in the free condition. Particular types of beaters act upon the stock in its passage from the feeding-in end of the machine to the delivery end of the frame. The purpose of the action is to loosen and open the cotton and thereby cause it to lose considerable portions of foreign matter.

HORIZONTAL WARPER. See WARP, WARPER.

HORNBLENDE. A common mineral, greenish-black or black, containing iron and silicate of magnesium, calcium and aluminum. This type of asbestos has only about 5 per cent water of crystallization.

HORROCKS. In 1803, he brought out the dressing frame to make warps for loom weaving.

HORSEHAIR. The body hair of the horse—more lustrous than cow hair. The length is from 1 cm. to 2cm., while mane and tail stock ranges from a few inches to several feet. It is used for stuffing in upholstery and summer horsehair hats, as a shape retainer in lapels of coats, and as "filler-in" stock. Russia sponsors the industry.

HORSE-HEAD ACTION. A device which rotates bobbins on a roving frame in their up-and-down motion. The mechanism has a swinging intermediate idler gear set between a fixed driving gear and the moving gear on the bobbin rail.

HORSES. Small levers on a hand loom that allow the harnesses to balance against each other. They are pieces of wood suspended from the top roller to which the harnesses are tied.

Rolls or pulleys are often used instead by many weavers since horses are sometimes difficult to keep in proper adjustment. Scandinavian type looms use horses, and 3, 5, 7, or 8 harnesses may be used on looms which have horse attachments.

HORSESHOE NECKLINE. May be a woven or knitted garment featured by a "horseshoe-shaped motif" at the neck instead of, for example, the basic "V" neckline. This "U" shaped neckline is rounded-out to give the effect to the wearer. Plenty of area is allowed to show

a blouse or waist. Used in medium to heavy bulky fabrics and garments.

HOSE. 1. A tube, more or less flexible (as contrasted to pipe), used for the purpose of carrying from one place to another any substance which will flow through under pressure. Three general methods are used to make hose: A. Braiding—fabric produced on a braiding machine and which is put between two layers of rubber and vulcanized. B. Wrapping—fabric and/or steel wire are wrapped around a rubber tube, covered with another layer of rubber and vulcanized. C. Weaving—a fabric in tube shape which may or may not be vulcanized to a rubber lining. Fibers used in unlined hose are plied, and they are cotton, rayon, linen, asbestos, etc., alone or in blends. 2. A leg covering for men, women, and children. See HOSIERY, etc.

HOSE CORD. Ply yarn, from 2 to 100, with a low-twist multiple, usually twisted through a compressor to obtain smoothness. It is possible to twist the low plies on a ring twister frame. Serves as the base in fire hose, hydraulic hose, some types of rubber hose.

HOSE DUCK. A soft and pliable open weave, wide number duck of about 40 inches, which runs from 10 to 24 ounces in weight. Used for hose, filter cloth, etc.

HOSIER. One who deals in hosier's wares—stockings, hose, etc.

HOSIERY. Knitted socks and stockings. The term in Great Britain has the added meaning of machine-made knitted articles of apparel, all of which would be sold by the hosier.

HOSIERY ABRASION MACHINE. An apparatus used to determine the relative resistance of hosiery to the frictional wear of shoes. It may be used on samples in the dry condition or in the moist state.

HOSIERY CLASSIFICATION. The more strands used in a hosiery thread, the greater will be its strength and its durability; the tighter the twist given, the greater will be the amount of yarn necessary—which, in turn, decreases the luster:

WEIGHT:	STRANDS:
Chiffon	2–4
Service chiffon	5
Semiservice	6–7
Medium service	7
Service	7–10
Heavy service	10

HOSIERY LENGTHS:

Women's short, 27 inches.
Women's medium, 30 inches.
Women's long, 33 inches.
Men's, 14–15 inches.

HOSIERY DENIER. The manner in which to calculate the weight or the

sheerness of hosiery made of silk, rayon, nylon, etc.: "2-thread" and "3-thread" are terms used to designate degrees of sheerness in silk hosiery only. This is because two or three threads of silk are twisted together to make the knitting yarn.

In nylon stockings, a single thread of selected size determines the sheerness of the stocking. The term used to denote the size of the nylon thread is "denier." A 50-denier thread is correspondingly finer than a 75-denier thread.

The size of the knitting stitch also contributes to the weight and sheerness of a stocking. This factor is defined as "gauge," which is simply the number of stitches per inch and a half. Thus, 39-gauge is a relatively coarse knit, 45-gauge is the standard general-purpose knit, 51-gauge is the fine knit, and 60-gauge is extremely fine.

COMPARISONS TO HELP YOU BUY:
50-denier is comparable with 3 to 4 thread.
75-denier is comparable with 5 to 6 thread.
100-denier is comparable with 7 thread.

HOSIERY KNITTING.

FULL-FASHIONED HOSIERY. This is knitted flat and it is shaped during the knitting by the inward transfer of the selvage stitches, usually two at a time, on each side, in order to provide the correct shape to properly fit the leg.

The narrowings are always located at the calf, heel and toe, and generally above the knee just below the shadow welt.

In stockings made by the single-unit method the fabric is also widened at the instep to form a heel pocket. This widening is usually over one needle at a time and may be made at the selvages where it is invisible, or some wales away from the selvage—in which case, a gore line is visible in the heel. The latter method provides a better-fitting stocking. The selvage edges are then joined by a seam.

CIRCULAR-KNIT HOSIERY. This type of fabric for hosiery is knit in a tubular or circular formation, and it is shaped by varying the tension at the various parts of the stocking. No seam is necessary, but a "Mock Seam" may be introduced to simulate full-fashioned hosiery. This type of seam can be recognized since it does not extend into the welt or sole areas of the article.

"Mock Fashioning Marks" are introduced sometimes to imitate full-fashioned hosiery, and they can be easily recognized since they appear as a small hole (tuck stitch) rather than as a raised mark as in the narrowing. Full-fashioned hosiery is the better fitting

HOSIERY MANUFACTURE, OUTLINE FOR USE IN.

Product Identification: Anklets or socks, knee, over-knee, stocking, leotards, tights.

Flow Sheet for Manufacturing Seamless and Full-Fashion Hosiery: Seamless, full fashion, knitting, dyeing, finishing-boarding, packaging.

Inventory Problems: 1. Style or design. 2. Color. 3. Length. 4. Size - infants, children, boys and girls, men's women's.

Processes Used in the Hosiery Industry:

Yarn Dyed:

Knitting
Inspection
Looping or Seaming
Inspection
Pre-boarding
Dyeing
Boarding
Matching and Pairing
Stamping or Labeling
Folding and Packaging

Pre-Dyed Yarn:

Knitting
Inspection
Looping or Seaming
Inspection
Boarding
Matching or Pairing
Stamping or Labeling
Folding and Packaging

HOSIERY PRODUCTS

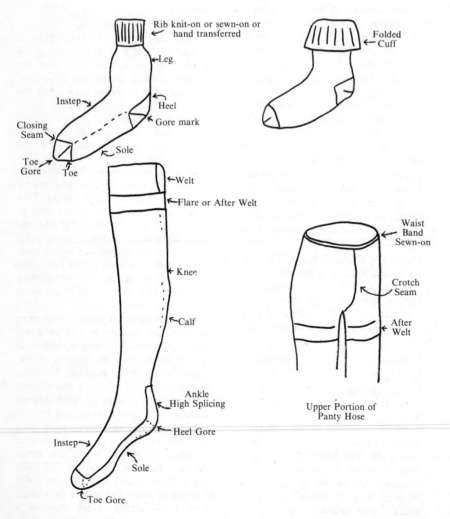

Rib knit-on or sewn-on or hand transferred
Leg
Instep
Heel
Gore mark
Closing Seam
Sole
Toe Gore
Toe

Folded Cuff

Welt
Flare or After Welt
Knee
Calf
Ankle High Splicing
Heel Gore
Instep
Sole
Toe Gore

Waist Band Sewn-on
Crotch Seam
After Welt
Upper Portion of Panty Hose

Courtesy: Knitting Dep't., Philadelphia College of Textiles and Science.

stocking, when compared with the circular or seamless type of stocking, because of the method of construction.

HOSIERY LENGTH, WOMEN'S. Short, 28 to 30 inches; medium, 30 to 32 inches; long, 32 to 35 inches.

HOSPITAL GAUZE. Cheesecloth which has been sterilized for hospital use.

HOT. Highly salable.

HOT-HEAD PRESS. A buck press which is heated by steam and/or electricity but which is not equipped to eject steam through the press surface of either buck. In some of these presses, the upper buck press surface (the ram or mobile buck) is a metal alloy with given surface texture while the lower buck (fixed buck) has a cloth covered surface. Some hot-head presses have both buck surfaces covered with cloth.

"HOT-HOUSE" LAMBS. Lambs which have been dropped in the fall and winter. Also called winter lambs.

HOT PRESS. Glazed boards and hot metal plates are used on this press to gloss or glaze cloth and paper.

HOTTENROTH NUMBER. This measure of the ripeness of viscose solution is expressed as the number of cubic centimeters of 10 per cent ammonium chloride solution needed to coagulate 20 grams of viscose, diluted with 30 cubic centimeters of water, under carefully controlled conditions of temperature and agitation.

HOT TEST. Name given to the shrinkage test for wool when the scoured stock is weighed immediately after drying and before the material has had a chance to condition.

HOUND'S TOOTH. A medium-sized broken-check effect, often used in checks, clear-finish worsteds, woolen dress goods, etc. The weave used is a four-end twill based on a herringbone weave with four ends to the right, followed by four ends to the left. The white is completely surrounded by colored yarn, and the check is a four-pointed star. This 2-up and 2-down basic construction fabric is a staple in the woolen trade. See Illustrated Section (Fabrics 39).

HOUPPELANDE. Pronounced hoopland, this fourteenth and fifteenth century full-length one-piece garment featured a full skirt and train, and the sleeves were loose or tight-fitting. This cloak or gown was made of silk and velvet, richly embroidered for lining and costume outer-effect with satin, velvet, or fur. Men and women wore the garment, which was, at times, made with a belted effect.

HOUSE FLANNEL. A broad term which covers the several types of flannel used in the home. Most of the material has a cotton warp and woolen or worsted filling.

HOUSEHOLD COTTONS, USES OF COTTON IN.

1. Accessories: Mops, oilcloth, towels.
2. Bed Cottons: Bedspreads, pillowcases, sheets.
3. Bedcovers: Blankets, quilts.
4. Bedding: Covers, mattresses, pillows.
5. Curtains: Shower, tapestry, window.
6. Floor Coverings: Carpets, mats, rugs, runners.
7. Furniture Covers: Ironing boards, slip covers.
8. Table Cottons: Napkins, pads, tablecloths.

HOUSEHOLD LINENS. These include art linen, bird's-eye, butcher, cambric, damask, fisheye, glass toweling, huck or huckaback, oatmeal cloth, sheet and pillowcase linen. The term, at present, includes those fabrics made with cotton as well as linen.

HOWE, ELIAS. In 1846, with his brother-in-law, General Nathaniel Banks of Civil War fame, he invented the sewing machine, one of the truly great inventions of all time. See Illustrated Section.

HOWELL COTTON. Similar to Peterkin and maturing earlier, this cotton has a 1-inch staple with a lint yield of about 35 per cent. An Upland variety raised in Louisiana.

HT-1 POLYAMIDE FIBER. Used as a base in the manufacture of high resistant manmade fiber paper ranging between 3 and 20 mils thick. End uses include high temperature transformer insulation, as well as applications which require prolonged exposure to high temperatures. A joint project of E.I. duPont de Nemours & Co., Inc., and Hollingsworth & Vose Co., East Walpole, Mass.

HUAHUA. Young animal of any species of llama.

HUALIQUIS. The clump of hair located under the throat of alpacas which serves as protection from exposure.

HUAMPO FIBER. A Peruvian bark fiber used in making coarse garments.

HUARIZO. The foal of llama sire and alpaca dam.

HUBBARD CLOTH. Registered trademark of Joseph D. Shakow Company, Inc., for a very strong, lightweight, water-repellent cotton cloth which finds much use in rainwear and in cold climates. The cloth in garments may be insulated to provide warmth to the wearer. Named for the late Father Bernard Hubbard, S.J., internationally known for his Artic

flying and exploring expeditions. Father Hubbard's base of operations was University of Santa Clara, Santa Clara, California.

HUCCATOON. A low-quality, low-price, English cotton of low texture used in the African trade.

HUCK, HUCKABACK. Soft, absorbent cotton fabric made to simulate linen cloth of same name. Made of soft yarns, the warp is about 14s while the filling is about single 10s. Construction ranges around 50 x 44. Comes in the white or in white with colored borders, either woven in or printed. Stripes may be a feature of the design. This rather strong fabric, used for toweling, has good absorption, is rough in surface finish so as to produce friction on vigorous application. Small squares stand out from the background of the fabric.

HUCKABACK WEAVES. Weaves that will give a pebbled or irregular surface effect on fabric. Plain weave is used to give foundation to the material, while the motif is developed from the huck effect which is rather loose, and has a series of floats, some of them rather long, adding to the looseness of the goods in certain areas. The floats, however, if well spaced by the designer, act as a good absorbing agency in toweling, glass toweling, etc.

HUDDERSFIELD. 1. City of Yorkshire, England; a center of the woolen and worsted manufacturers. 2. The name commonly given in this country to clay worsteds which originated in the mills of J. & B. Clay.

HUDDERSFIELD REED COUNTS. Dents per inch, times ends per dent —thus, 16s reed 4s means a sixteen reed times four ends per dent, or sixty-four ends to the inch in texture.

HUE. The tone that is imparted to one color by the partial addition of another, just enough to change the appearance of the original color. An example of this might be adding a small amount of blue to red, to give the red a bluish hue. A hue can be made by the actual color, or can be imparted to the first color, by the circumstances about it. A great number of hues are due to impurities in colors; absolutely pure colors do not exist.

HULL. The outer hard shell found on cotton seeds. Removed at the oil mill, they are hard, tough, dry and leathery, and make up about half of the weight of ginned seed.

Hull may be used as a base for explosives such as cordite, guncotton, and smokeless powder. It is used also in feed for cattle; in fertilizer and furfural; for packing and stuffing purposes; and in pressed paper.

HULLER GIN. Cotton which has been gathered with the bolls is ginned in this type of gin.

HULL FIBER. Implies the very short linter fibers taken from the second-time ginning in "the large cotton cities of the South," in the United States. Incidentally, some of these fibers are hardly long enough to show "two tips." If they are tipped, however, they will surely find some use in the cotton industry or in the by-products field.

HULL SEPARATOR. A device on a cotton gin which removes hulls, motes, shivers, burrs, etc., from the seed cotton. The mechanism is made up of a drum, fitted with many circular saws partially enclosed in a housing, and at one point a stripper roll revolving close to the saw cylinder. It is at the latter point that the undesirable matter is stripped from the cotton.

HUMERAL VEIL. The veil or scarf which matches the vestments worn by priests of the Roman Catholic Church when celebrating Mass. It serves at Solemn High Mass when, during the interval between the Offertory and the Pater Noster, the priest holds the paten; also when he raises the Blessed Sacrament at Benediction. The individual who carries the Blessed Sacrament in procession also uses this veil.

Worn around the shoulders, it is a development from the ancient hood known as the chaperon, superseded by the cowl which is allowed to hang around the shoulders of the celebrant.

HUMIDIFICATION. Spraying increased mist into the air to increase the humidity; done by the humidifiers in the mill room.

HUMIDIFIER. The device found in mill rooms which vaporizes water and sprays it into the atmosphere in order to increase the amount of moisture in the air.

HUMIDIFY. To increase by any method, the density of water vapor within a given area.

HUMIDISTAT. A regulatory device actuated by changes in humidity, used for automatic control of relative humidity.

HUMIDITY. The vaporous spray that is emitted in the several rooms of a textile plant. It is the percentage of water vapor in the air to the total amount possible at the same temperature. At 32 degrees F., a cubic foot of air contains two grams of water vapor; at 100 degrees F., the cubic foot of air will hold a maximum of 20 grams, or ten times as much as at 32 degrees.

HUMIDITY, ABSOLUTE. The weight of water vapor per unit volume, pounds per cubic foot, grains per cubic foot or grams per cubic centimeter.

HUMIDITY, RELATIVE. The ratio of the actual partial pressure of the water vapor in a space to the saturation pressure of pure water at the same temperature.

HUMIDITY RATIO. In a mixture of water vapor and air it is the actual weight of the water vapor per pound of dry air. Also known as Specific Humidity.

HUMMONS. An eighteenth century coarse plain-weave cotton cloth made in East India and used chiefly as a wrapper or bath towel.

HUMPS. Cotton term for the bulgy appearance in bales of cotton caused by the stitching-over of a patch after the "city crop" has been added.

HUNDREDS. The compactness of linen yarns or threads in a fabric. For example, a 12-hundred fabric has 1,200 pairs of warp yarns in a 37-inch width of goods, finished.

HUNGARIAN CARDING WOOL MERINO. This sheep breed was developed from crossing imported French Rambouillet with native sheep. Fleeces from rams approximate 20 to 25 pounds.

HUNGBACK. Some lightweight Scotch tweeds made in a 2-up and 2-down twill have checks, stripes, or windowpane effects made with yarns woven in a 3-up and 1-down twill weave, the so-called "hung" yarns.

HUNGERFINE. Very thin, weak, irregular wool caused by "starvation" of the animal from which the fibers were obtained.

HUNGRY WOOL. Inferior wool fibers which are the result of the sheep's being poorly or improperly fed.

HUNNICUTT COTTON. A round, medium-boll cotton raised in this country; 1-inch staple with about 32 per cent of lint.

HUNT, WALTER. In competition with Isaac Singer and Elias Howe, this Quaker inventor made a machine that he said would "sew, stitch, and seam fabric." His ideas embraced the eye-pointed needle and lockstitching. See Elias Howe, Isaac Singer, Singer Machine Operator.

HUNTER'S PINK. Brilliant scarlet velvet cloth worn by hunters. Also name for that color used on any fabric.

HUNTING AND DRESS TARTANS. The two chief types of tartans, or plaid cloth with distinguishing colors of a Scottish clan. Where a tartan was in its ordinary form too brilliant for safety in the field or use on the hill, a quieter type of color was used, sometimes quite a different design like the Hunting Stewart, which in no way resembles the Royal Stewart. In the dress tartans, scarlet or white would take the place of some darker color if the regular tartan seemed too somber for ceremonial occasions. No definite rule has ever been formulated for the changes, and all tartans do not show both varieties.

HUNTING SHIRT. 1. Any cotton, woolen, or linen shirt of subdued or inconspicuous color. 2. The deerskin, blouselike garment used by trappers and frontiersmen; it is often very ornamental.

HUNTING SUEDE. Made from calf skin, it is a suede upper leather that is finished on the suede side of the pelt or skin. The finish can also be obtained by the use of cattle hide or heavy goat skin.

HUSHALON. A registered trademark of American Felt Company, Glenville, Connecticut, for its acoustic felt fabric. Properties include colorfastness and resistance to flames, soil, and water. This decorative felt finds use in draperies, bedspreads, table cloths, upholstery, skirts, jumpers, dress table covers, handbags, throw rugs, etc.

HUSH CLOTH. Same as molleton or silence cloth.

HUSK. The inner portion of a cocoon; too fine to reel and known as silk waste.

HUSKING CLOTH. Cotton ticking used for work gloves and mittens.

HUSSONG DYE MACHINE. A skein dyeing machine whose features include a dye kettle and removable yarn carrier in which the skeins are suspended and remain stationary during the entire dyeing treatment. The dye liquor circulates around and through the skeins. Circulation of the bath is in two directions, and the direction of circulation can be automatically reversed.

Hussong is not a generic term, but means a machine made only by Hussong-Walker-Davis Company, Inc., Philadelphia, Pennsylvania, 19124.

HYCAR LATEX. A coating or impregnant for materials. The product has high resistance to oils, abrasion, flexing, and chemicals. Hycar-treated fabrics may be coated with any one of a number of other materials to impart additional properties. Vulcanization is not necessary in any processing. Normal drying periods apply, and no expensive solvents need be handled. Product of B. F. Goodrich Chemical Co.

HYDRATE. Compound formed by the union of molecules of water with other molecules or atoms.

HYDRATION. Combination of a substance with water; not necessarily in the form of a hydrate.

HYDRAULIC LEATHER. A collec-tive term often used for cattle-hide leathers, processed by oak, chrome, and combination tannages, and used for pump valves, piston packings, and so on.

HYDROCARBON. One of a large group of compounds that contain hydrogen and carbon only. There are several classes and types, including aliphatic, aromatic, saturated, and unsaturated.

HYDROCELLULOSE. A powdery product obtained from the union of cotton and hydrochloric or sulphuric acid.

HYDROCHLORIC ACID. Pertaining to or designating a colorless, corrosive, fuming compound, easily soluble in water, in which form it is often called muriatic acid.

HYDRO-EXTRACTING, WHIZZING. The removal of excess water and moisture from stock or material, thereby an aid to the manipulation of fibers, yarns, or fabrics. Whizzing takes only a few minutes to complete its work.

HYDROGEN. A colorless, invisible element; an odorless gas which burns with a pale blue flame whence its former name, Inflammable Air. It is the lightest substance known, has a specific gravity about one-fourteenth that of air, an atomic weight of 1, and has the chemical symbol, H.

It occures free in nature in small quantities in certain volcanic gases; an essential constituent of all animal and vegetable matter. Hydrogen forms two-thirds in volume and one-ninth in the weight of water (H_2O), which is the sole product of the combustion of hydrogen in ordinary air. It is a constituent of all acids, in which it can be replaced by bases to form salts.

HYDROGENATION. 1. To cause to combine with hydrogen. 2. To expose to hydrogen, or to effect chemical action of by the use of or by the exposure to hydrogen, as to hydrogenate oils. 3. To pass hydrogen through a fat or oil in the presence of a catalytic agent so as to raise the melting point of the substance. Cottonseed oil, for example, receives this treatment to make cooking fats.

HYDROGEN ION. See pH.

HYDROGEN PEROXIDE. A syrupy liquid whose aqueous solutions are important as bleaching agents and antiseptics. The usual solution is slightly acidic and contains about 3 per cent by weight of pure hydrogen peroxide. This compound is used in bleaching where the more drastic action of chlorine cannot be used.

HYDROLUX. A reducing and stabilizing agent for vat color dyeing and printing. The chemical has lubricating properties which give good running qualities to print pastes. In dyeing, it prevents premature oxidation of both sulphur and vat dyes thereby aiding for level dyeing. Trade-mark of Warwick Chemical Division, Sun Chemical Corporation, New York City.

HYDROMETER. An instrument that determines the density or specific gravity, especially of liquids and solutions. Also known as a densimeter. See BAUME, TWADDLE.

HYDROLYSIS. A chemical reaction through which a product is resolved into simpler substances in the presence of water.

HYDROPHILIC FIBER. The word, "hydrophilic," means water-favoring. Thus a hydrophilic fiber has a high water absorption and is moisture sensitive. Taken from the Greek, "hydor" meaning water and "philic" meaning to favor or to like. Examples of textile fibers in this category include acetate, 6.50%; cotton, 7.00%; flax, 10.00-12.00%; rayon, 13.00%; silk, 11.00% wool, 15.00-17.00%; worsted, 10.00%. These figures show the absorptive powers of these fibers given under normal conditions which are 65° F. relative humidity with a tolerance of two percent, plus or minus; standard atmosphere which is 70° F. with a tolerance to two percent, plus or minus. See Hydrophobic, Relative Humidity, Standard Condition, Standard Moisture Regain.

HYDROPHOBIC FIBER. The derivation of the word, "hydrophobic," is from the Greek, "hydor" meaning water and "phobos" meaning fear. Literally the interpretation means "water fearing" or "water hating." Thus, the dydrophobic fiber is one that is relatively non-water absorptive and moisture insensitive. The amount of water that any fiber in this category will absorb under normal conditions ranges from zero percent to 4.5 percent. Examples include acrylic, asbestos, glass, graphite, modacrylic, polyamide, such as nylon; olefin, polyester, polypropylene, vinylester. Incidentally, Teflon, is hydrophobic (water shedding), and oleophobic (oil shedding). See Hydrophilic, Oleo.

HYDROSCOPICITY. Often interchangeable with hygroscopicity, it implies that the moisture content of a fiber is a very important factor in fiber strength. In the case of the natural vegetable fibers, tensile strength will increase with increasing relative humidity up to certain limits. Some manmade fibers decrease in strength when wet (viscose rayon, cuprammonium rayon). The ability of a fiber to absorb

water can be measured by comparing weights at 1. Oven-dry weight, and 2. At relative humidity of 65 per cent and temperature of 70°.

HYDROSCOPIC OR MOISTURE-RETAINING PROPERTY. The ability of a fiber to retain moisture; possessed by all fibers but with varying degrees. Wool retains moisture content to a higher degree than other fibers because of its nature. This fact accounts for the added weight of untreated overcoats and felt hats worn in damp or rainy weather.

HYDROSTATIC TEST. Usually refers to testing, under pressure, of water-repellent properties.

HYDROSULPHITE. A reducing bleach or stripper liberating sulphur dioxide (SO_2) in solution. It is effective on some types of stains and used for stripping certain dyes.

HYDROVIZED. Cottons are Hydrovized by a product of Sea Island Mills, New York City. The process is applied to cottons for rainproofing, water repellency, windproofing, spot and stain resistance, and for protection against perspiration. The face of the fabric is given a Zelan treatment for water repellency, while the back of the goods is hydrovized.

HYDROXIDE. A strong base of an alkali metal. General composition, NaOH, KOH, etc. It should be noted that the hydroxide has no acid component in its make-up. It is entirely unneutralized.

HYDROXYL. A chemical term of the OH or active ion of a hydroxide.

HYGROMETER. Machine used for measuring the percentage of the moisture in the atmosphere.

HYGROSCOPIC. Property of absorbing moisture from the air; apparent in natural fibers, rayon, etc.

HYGROSCOPICITY. Hygroscopicity implies the ability of a textile fiber to take up a certain amount of moisture from the atmosphere without feeling damp or clammy. This moisture is held mechanically and is not combined chemically with the fiber.

HYGROSTAT. Same as humidistat.

HYMOLAL SALT. A term used to designate the sulphated fatty alcohols which are derived from the higher chin alcohols and possess soap properties.

HYPOCHLORITE BLEACHING. Bleaching of textiles, especially cotton, with sodium hypochlorite.

HYPOCHLORITE OF SODA. A solution of a chemical derived from hypochlorous acid and a sodium base,

commonly known as soda bleach, and prepared in various ways.

HYSTRON FIBERS, INC. The corporation was formed in 1966, a joint venture by Hercules, Inc., Wilmington, Delaware, and Farbwerke Hoechst, A.G. Frankfurt, Germany. At present the company makes a full line of polyester types of yarn sold under the registered trademark of TREVIRA. See Trevira.

"HYTEN" NYLON MONOFILAMENT. A sewing thread which has more limpness than any other nylon monofilament used for this purpose. Its excess stiffness overcomes the problem of poor sewability and makes it ideal for use in sewing shoes, carpets, mattresses, and upholstery. Melting point is 500° Fahrenheit. It is transparent and blends well with fabric, eliminating bobbin changes for each color used. "Hyten" is heat, weather, and sunlight resistant, 85 percent softer than soft cotton of identical denier. Does not support mildew or mold and is lint free. Product of E.I. duPont de Nemours & Co., Inc., Wilmington, Delaware.

I

IBYRIA, FIBER. A strong, silklike leaf fiber found in South America; ideal for cord and twine since it will not rot.

ICE COLORS. See AZO COLORS; INGRAIN COLORS.

ICELAND MOSS. A bast fiber raised chiefly in the Scandia countries which contains a pectinlike gum used as a stiffening or binding agent in sizing cotton goods.

ICE SILK. Loose term for slack twist, silk knitting, or embroidery yarn.

ICE WOOL. A variety of fine two-ply worsted yarn used chiefly for crocheting and hand knitting.

ICELAND WOOL. The wool from Icelandic sheep that have an outer covering of long coarse hair and a fine woolly undergrowth. This undergrowth is used for sweaters and shawls.

IDA CANVAS. An open-faced, unbleached linen canvas.

IDENTIFICATION OF STAINS. See STAINS (table).

IDENTIFICATION TEST. Any chemical, physical, microscopic or other test used to identify a fiber, yarn, fabric, finish, dyestuff, or other point about which knowledge is desired.

IFE HEMP. African Sansevieria yields fiber that is called ifé hemp; there are many types.

IGELIT. Developed during World War II, this chlorinated polyvinyl chloride fiber is better known as Pe-Ce fiber which comes in filament and staple form.

IGEPON. A synthetic detergent which eliminates hard-water problems, shortens production time, cuts costs, and assures highest quality in fabrics. Product of GAF Corporation, New York City.

IGG. Trademark name for manmade fibers produced by Internationale Galalith G.m.b.H., Hamburg-Harburg, West Germany. Fibers made by the company include Nylon Polyamide 6, polyethylene fiber, polypropylene, saran, and Vestan which is a polyvinylidene chloride (saran) fiber.

IIMAS, JIMAS. A four-harness Navajo Indian blanket in which the design shows diagonal and diamond effects.

ILE DE FRANCE. French breed of sheep of good quality which has a fleece weight of 9 to 11 pounds; staple length of the wool is 4 to 5 inches, entirely white, and of excellent quality.

ILICHA. Indian cotton and silk cloth used by women for shawls; handwoven.

ILLUMINATED MIXTURE. The color effect seen on some woolen and worsted fabrics when a small quantity of bright color is used on a dark background.

ILLUSION. A very fine, all-silk tulle which originated in France. Its cobweb appearance makes the cloth ideal for trimmings and veilings. Made in 54-inch and 72-inch widths.

ILOCANO CLOTH. Philippine fabric made of cotton in which bright-colored stripes or checks feature the design. Used for beachwear, play clothes, etc.

IMADONG. A Philippine bast fiber used for cordage.

IMAGO. The registered trade-mark for parchmented pattern effects that are referred to frequently as white pigmented-print organdies.

IMBABURA COTTON. A clean, white Peruvian cotton.

IMBE FIBER. A coarse Brazilian bast fiber is known as imbé; used for roping.

IMBERLINE STRIPE EFFECT. A cloth made with plain colored or pattern stripes that are about five inches or so in width. Narrow gold or yellow stripes separate the wide stripes. The fabric presents, at times, a rather bizarre effect because of the stripe combinations used.

IMBROCADO. Made chiefly in France, and to some degree in Italy, it is a trimming fabric accentuated by gold and silver threads.

IMITATION BACKED FABRICS. A class of fabrics largely used in the woolen industry for coatings and trouserings of medium weight. They are made from simple weaves, especially twills, rearranged to give an appearance similar to a true backed fabric. They may imitate either a warp or filling backed fabric and the constructions are similar to the cloths imitated.

IMITATION FUR. Textile fabrics made to simulate the genuine fur article. Some textile imitations are quite deceptive. Also called Fake Fur.

IMITATION FUR FABRIC. Material made to imitate genuine fur. The cloth is pile or plush in construction, and distinctive finishes are applied to make recognition an easy matter. Wool, silk, spun silk, rayon, and mohair are used to make these fabrics, which are dyed solid colors or spotted to make the effect realistic.

IMITATION HAIRCLOTH. A stiff interlining cloth not made with horsehair, but entirely or almost entirely of heavily sized vegetable fibers; some of the better grades have some horsehair inserted. Istle is much used in this cloth.

IMITATION LACE. Any machine-made lace as contrasted with handmade products.

IMITATION LEATHER. Drill, duck, sateen, sheeting, and kindred cotton fabrics coated with rubber, pyroxylin, or similar agents, to simulate leather. Embossing the goods gives them the appearance of alligator, pigskin, etc. This product is much used for lower-priced luggage and bags.

IMITATION LINEN FINISH. A term often used with or without discrimination for some finishes applied to cottons which cause them to simulate linen fabrics, noted for their rather kidlike feel. Beetling, a physical treatment, is often used in obtaining the finish.

IMITATION NATURAL WOOL. An imitation of natural wool produced by adding various dark-colored fibers to white wool in order to prevent the material from showing soiled effect too soon.

IMITATION REP, REPP. Low-grade simulation of genuine rep, characterized by a fine filling rib-effect in rather low texture; used for dress goods.

IMITATION WOOL. Man-made, or cotton and other bast fibers treated physically and/or chemically with a cold solution of caustic soda, sodium peroxide, equal parts of sodium perborate and ammonia, etc., to simulate wool fibers. Frowned upon by governmental and trade groups.

IMMATURE COTTON. Cotton which has been picked and baled before actual maturity; causes inferior staple.

IMMERSION TESTING. Testing by submerging the fabric in water or some other liquid.

IMMUNE COTTON. Treated cotton yarn which repels direct dyestuff; dyes like acetate yarn or fabric.

IMMUNIZED COTTON. A chemical treatment of some type to make cotton impervious to ordinary cotton dyes.

IMPARTIAL CHAIRMAN. A third party agreed upon by union and company to settle all disputes, or questions of differences between them.

IMPERFECT SELVAGE. Listing or selvage of fabric which has some defects such as ends-out, loose or tight areas, broken or open areas where the correct interlacing of the warp and the filling has not taken place.

IMPERFECTIONS IN SILK. Imperfections have a direct bearing on production, appearance, and quality of the cloth. Imperfections impede progress for good results. It pays to use a "little better raw stock" in the long run, as the difference will be noted in the cloth, when finished.

Poor Crossings occur from dilatory efforts on the part of the mill operatives, winders, and reelers. Much trouble is encountered in weaving the cloth, and it is often necessary to class the material as second.

Hairiness is noted in some silks more than in others. They are a series of projecting fibers that tend to give the cloth a dull and hairy appearance and feel.

Nibs are small white specks noted in silk thread.

Slugs are large, soft places in the thread apparently caused by small pieces of waste that become attached to the thread in reeling.

Loops are caused by the girl operative in reeling when she makes "a bad throw" in starting a fresh cocoon to supplant a spent one. This leaves a long thread that doubles or reverts back on itself forming a loop.

Lousy Silk shows small specks of detrimental nature on the face of the cloth. These may be caused at several places in manipulation of the raw stock to finished cloth.

IMPERIAL. 1. An Italian brocade of the better type characterized by the use of gold and silver threads worked into the motif. This silk fabric was mentioned by Marco Polo in the Thirteenth century. 2. An East Indian cotton cloth woven with fancy effects and used in apparel. 3. A high-quality Belgian gingham made with colored warp and filling stripe effects. 4. A rich-looking silk cloth in which various metallic threads are used to add beauty to the fabric. 5. Imperial Sateen is a heavy cotton cloth made on an 8-end, filling-effect, satin weave. Two adjacent ends are raised at each point of interlacing between the warp and the filling yarns —a "double-satin effect." Imperial is very compact in texture, since there are from two to four times as many filling picks as warp ends in the pick count. Finished with a short, thick nap, the material is used for work clothes. It is sometimes known as "lambskin" or "swansdown."

IMPERIAL COATING. A worsted fabric woven with 2-up, 2-down twill weave from fine Botany worsted yarns. The construction is about square and the threads are closely set, giving a firm, durable cloth but of a somewhat hard handle. Usually dyed navy blue and showerproofed.

IMPERIAL OTTOMAN. Heavy, ribbed Ottoman fabric is often known by this name. Used in evening wear and coating.

IMPERIAL SATEEN. 1. See IMPERIAL, 5. 2. Another name for "lambskin" and "swansdown."

IMPERIAL SERGE. Very similar to imperial coating, but contains fewer threads per inch and is a softer cloth, suitable for dress and costume cloths.

IMPERIAL SHIRTING. A well-bleached cotton shirting staple made and used in the British Isles; in the broadcloth-poplin shirting group.

IMPERIAL TAPE. British trademark for a strong, rather heavy cotton tape.

IMPERIAL VALLEY COTTON. High-grade staple raised in valley of this name in Southern California. Ranks with cotton raised in Durango and Yuma Valleys, in the same area.

IMPERMEABLE. Not permitting the passage of air or liquid.

IMPERVIOUS. Repellent or nonabsorbent toward a certain substance.

IMPID FIBER. Bast fiber raised in Philippines; used for cordage.

IMPORT DUTY ON RAW WOOL. The duty on imports of *raw wool* is a specific amount stated in terms of so many cents per clean pound. The duty on apparel wool of the type generally grown in this country is thirty-four cents per pound of "clean content," which means a pound of clean wool with normal moisture content after scouring. Wools of the type not grown in this country are imported free of duty when used for floor coverings, press cloth, knit or felt boots or heavy fulled lumbermen's socks.

IMPREGNATED FABRIC. One in which the interstices between the yarn are completely filled with an impregnating compound throughout the thickness of the material, as distinguished from sized or coated materials where the material is applied to the surface and these interstices are not completely filled. (Definition as decreed by A.S.-T.M., Philadelphia, Pennsylvania.)

IMPREGNATED YARN. A yarn in which the interstices are filled with an impregnating compound. (Definition as decreed by A.S.T.M., Philadelphia, Pennsylvania.)

IMPREGNATION. The dyeing of textiles by immersion in a bath liquor, or the saturation of material with a protective substance such as waterproofing, fireproofing, etc.

IMPREGNOLE. A family of products that impart water repellency and durable spot and stain resistance to various textile fibers. Impregnoles may be used alone or in conjunction with Permafresh resins and body-building agents such as polyvinyl acetates, starches, etc. When used with thermosetting resins a Permafresh-Impregnole finish is obtained which enhances the physical properties of the goods. Trademark name of Warwick Chemical Division, Sun Chemical Corporation, New York City.

IMPRIME. (Imprimé.) French for printed.

IMPROVED GERMAN FARM. This sheep breed was developed by crossing imported Merino sheep with native Bavarian sheep. The merino-type wool has a staple of 2¾ to 4 inches. These hardy sheep often travel as much as 250 miles when changing pasture. Fleece weight ranges from 8 to 15 pounds.

IMPROVED PROLIFIC COTTON. An Uplands cotton raised in North Carolina; has a 1-inch staple and lint yield of 30 per cent.

IMPROVED UPLANDS COTTON. "Improved" varieties of ordinary Uplands cotton are obtained by the selection of choice plants in the fields. The staples range from 1¼ inches to 1¾ inches; the cotton seems to be more lustrous than ordinary Uplands but does not compare with Egyptian fiber in this respect. Some cottons in this class include Allen's Long Staple, Bates' Big Boll Black Rattler, Bohemian, Commander, Cook's Long Staple, Culpeper, Excelsior, Moon, Peterkin, Richmond, Russell's Big Boll, Shine's Early Prolific, Sunflower.

IMULON. Nylon yarns of this name have found favor with the automobile industry since Imulon is used in Helanca yarns for upholstery purposes. This product of Hoffner Rayon Co., Philadelphia, Penna., may also be used to finish yarns that may be used in suitings, full-fashioned hosiery, men's suitings, tricot knitwear, and for identification purposes in cloth.

"IN-BYES." Sheep, in Scotland, which are kept within some sort of an enclosure such as a wall, a fence, or a barrier made of sods.

INCENTIVE WAGES. Plans for paying wages to employees in relation to their productivity.

INCH. One twelfth of a foot, or 2.54 centimeters. The inch is divided into halves, quarters, eighths, sixteenths, etc. Engineers often divide the inch into 10ths, 20ths, 30ths, etc.

INCLINED CLEANING BARS. See GRATE BARS.

INDANTHRENE AND INDIGO COLORS. They are "reduction" colors —that is, the color is reduced in the dye bath, and in this state is absorbed by the fiber. The goods are removed from the bath, exposed, and the oxidation develops the color in the air. Both of these vat colors are very fast to bleaching, washing, sunlight; much used today.

INDEPENDENT UNION. A labor organization not affiliated with the A. F. of L.–C. I. O.

INDIA CHINTZ. A rugged fabric made with large floral motifs, and used for upholstery, chiefly boudoir chairs and drapes.

INDIA HEMP. Another name for Sunn hemp.

INDIA LINON. High-grade, bleached lawn cloth which comes usually in a 30-inch width.

INDIA MUSLIN. 1. The high-quality muslins for which India has been noted for centuries. 2. Lancashire muslins made to simulate India muslin. Made of combed Egyptian cotton, the cloth is about 72 x 64, 120s warp, 90s filling.

INDIANA CLOTH. A combed-cotton lawn cloth that is given a water-repellent treatment so that it can be used in rubberized fabrics.

INDIAN BLANKET. All-wool or woolen filling blanket woven with characteristic Indian designs. The term should apply only to blankets actually handmade by the Indians, and such blankets should be so marked. The genuine Indian handmade blanket is more of a rug than a blanket. Today most Indian-design blankets are power-loom woven.

INDIAN CORDAGE. Cordage (ropes) made of coir or coconut fiber.

INDIAN COTTON. India, a major cotton-growing nation, uses a large proportion of its crop for home consumption; the remainder goes to China, Japan, and the Lancashire mills in England.

Hingunhat (Hinganghat) is the best

type, but its staple is only ⅞ inch; consequently, the counts spun are not very high. Dholera is the best known, and, with Dharwar, is in demand because of a 1-inch staple. Indian cloths are rather low in count of yarn, texture, and finish.

INDIAN COTTONS. The major cottons include Bengal-Sind, Broach, Burma, Cambodia, Cocanada, Comilla, Coompta-Dharwar, Dholera, Hingunhat (Hinganghat), Comra, Punjab-American, Salem, Sind-American, Tinnevelly (Tirunelveli), Westerns.

INDIAN DIMITY. A cross-rib dimity printed with floral warp stripes which may also appear on the ground texture between the ribs.

INDIAN HEAD. Registered trademark for a leading plain-weave, cotton fabric that has been a popular staple for more than 150 years; now owned by Indian Head, Inc. The original trademark with the well-known head of an Indian chief on it was brought out in 1806. This trademark was and still is known all over the world and has been imitated and counterfeited over 100 times, chiefly in some of the major Far Eastern countries. Nashua, New Hampshire, was the original home of Indian Head, and the fabric was first made in the Nashua Manufacturing Company, Inc. of that city.

INDIAN HEMP. 1. Fiber obtained from the *Apocynum cannabinum,* an American plant. It is light brown in color, very tenacious and long in fiber staple. American Indians use the fiber for making bags, cordage, matting, etc. 2. Hemp cultivated in India.

INDIAN LACE. Drawn work and bobbin lace made throughout India. Also implies edging and tape of India made with metallic threads or by the use of a core yarn about which silk thread is wound. Used much for turban decoration.

INDIAN LINEN. A fine, compact, combed cotton cloth or a fine, plain-weave linen material much used in women's and children's wear in India. The cotton fabric is given a smooth, lustrous finish to simulate its linen counterpart. Texture in each material is about 80-square.

INDIAN MADDER. Dye from East Indian plant. Known as munjeet.

INDIAN MALLOW. See ABUTILON.

INDIAN OKRA. A fairly strong, smooth, white, silken Indian bast fiber used in bagging and cordage as well as for adulterating jute.

INDIAN SILK. Hand-loomed plain-

weave fabric that is very thin in texture and soft in feel. Made chiefly in India.

INDIAN SHAWL. Same as a cashmere shawl. See CASHMERE SHAWL.

INDIA PRINT. Any cloth with a characteristic Indian design on it. Native patterns in brilliant colorings abound in this plain-weave cloth. Used in beachwear, hangings, and for general decorative purposes.

INDIA TANNED. Applies to hides and skins tanned in India. The leather is considered as a semitanned raw material and is usually retanned in this country before it is finished.

INDICATOR. A chemical which shows, by a change of color, the progress or termination of a certain reaction. It is also a physical phenomenon —such as that of suds which may be termed an indicator of the amount of soap in a solution.

INDIGO. 1. A dark blue pigment and dye obtained from indican, which is found in the sap of herbaceous shrubs such as indigofera and the woad plant. Because of the demand for indigo, it is made now synthetically from naphthalene and other bases. 2. A deep violet blue, not a primary color. 3. Indigo blue is the chief coloring matter of pure indigo, crystallizing in fine prisms of metallic luster. 4. A plain-woven cotton fabric in which white or colored dots are seen on a background of indigo blue.

INDIGO AUXILIARY. Another name for zinc dust which is used as a reducing agent in indigo dyeing.

INDIGO BLUE. This term is given to fabrics colored by indigo blue, a particularly fast color applied to textiles by the vat method of dyeing. Greensboro, North Carolina, is the center of indigo dyeing in this country.

Indigo blue is insoluble in water and most of the ordinary solvents. The method of dyeing is done by the temporary destruction of the blue, along with a change in the chemical composition. The use of de-oxidixing agents changes the indigo blue into indigo white, which dissolves at once in all alkaline solutions to form a colorless or light yellow solution. When exposed to the air, the white turns to blue.

Denim and some uniform fabrics that are given a kersey or beaver finish are dyed by this method.

INDIGO CARMINE. See INDIGO EXTRACT.

INDIGO DYEING. The blue vegetable dye extracted from indigo plant, largely replaced by synthetic dyes at

present. Highly resistant to acids, alkalies, light, washing, and even bleaching.

INDIGO EXTRACT, INDIGO CARMINE, SOLUBLE INDIGO, SAXONY BLUE. Dye obtained by treating indigo with concentrated sulphuric acid. Purity and composition will vary to marked degree in this extract which gives brighter shades than indigo but is not as fast in affinity.

INDIGOID. Pertains to a group of vat dyes characterized by the same chromophores or pigment-bearing sacs as in indigo.

INDIGO PLANT. A blue coloring substance, $C_{16}H_{10}N_2O_2$, is obtained from this plant by the decomposition of indican, a glucose contained in this plant. It is now synthetically produced from various aromatic hydrocarbons.

INDIGO PRINTS. Cotton cloth dyed on the indigo printing method which centers around Greensboro, N.C. The patterns are made by either the discharge or the resist method of printing, usually the former.

INDIGOTIN. Pure indigo which occurs as a dark blue powder with a copperlike luster, the blue coloring substance of crude indigo. This indigotin is about the same in properties as the synthetic indigo on the market today.

INDIGO VAT. A tank about four feet deep and ten feet long used to immerse cloth in indigo dye. The material is drawn in over a rack, around guide rollers, between squeeze rollers, and out over other guide rollers that allow proper exposure of dyed cloth to the air.

INDIVIDUALITY. The particular character or aggregate of qualities that distinguishes one person from another. It is also the state or quality of being individual; existence as a distinct individual. It has been said that the attire of a person individualizes the wearer to a marked degree whether it be on the positive or negative side.

INDUSTRIAL AND MECHANICAL FABRICS.

FOR THE LAUNDRY SUPPLY TRADE:

Laundry apron ducks	36″—3.50 Sheeting for Ironing Boards
Laundry nets and tubing	40″—3.15 Sheeting for Ironing Boards
Roll cover duck	
Roll cover sheeting	

FOR THE CONVERTING TRADE:

Army duck, waterproofed for various purposes	Sateens
	Sheeting
	Single and double
Drills	filling duck

FOR THE CONVERTING TRADE:

Enameling duck—	Twills
38″ to 100″ in-	Wagon cover duck
clusive	Wide duck, water-
Gabardine	proofed
Moleskin	Print cloths

FOR DRY GOODS JOBBERS AND CHAIN STORES:

Crash	Single filling duck
Denim	Turkish toweling
Double filling duck	Wide duck
Huck toweling	30″—2.50-2.85
Print cloth	.drill

INDUSTRIAL AND MECHANICAL FABRICS, THE APPLICATION OF.

1. FOR THE MECHANICAL RUBBER TRADE:

Army duck	Lawn cloths
Balloon fabrics	Leno or doup fab-
Belting duck	rics
Bootleg duck	Napped fabrics
Chafer fabric	Osnaburgs
Drills and twills,	Sateens
wide	Sheeting, narrow
Enameling ducks	and wide
Hose duck	Tire fabrics

2. FOR THE RUBBER, OILCLOTH, AND PYROXYLIN TRADE:

Wide drills and	Wide sateens and
twills	broken twills
Wide moleskins—	Wide sheeting
chafers	
Wide print cloths	

3. FOR THE SHOE TRADE:

37″ Army duck	Enameling duck
37″ drills	30″ Gem duck
37″ four-leaf twills	Leno or doup
	specialties

4. FOR THE USE OF FILTERING MEDIA—Chemical and Paint Manufacturers, Oil Refiners, Soap Manufacturers, Sugar Refiners, etc.:

Chain cloths	Drills
Duck	Twills

5. FOR THE LAUNDRY SUPPLY TRADE:

Laundry apron	36″—3.50 Sheeting
ducks	for Ironing
Laundry nets and	Boards
tubing	40″—3.15 Sheeting
Roll cover duck	for Ironing
Roll cover sheeting	Boards

6. FOR THE CONVERTING TRADE:

Army duck, water-	Print cloths
proofed for vari-	Sateens
ous purposes	Sheeting
Drills	Single and double
Enameling duck—	filling duck

6. FOR THE CONVERTING TRADE:

38″ to 100″ in-	Twills
clusive	Wagon cover duck
Gabardine	Wide duck, water-
Moleskin	proofed

7. FOR THE TENT AND AWNING TRADE:

Army duck	Numbered duck
Awning stripe	Single filling duck
Double filling duck	Tent twill
Mineral khaki	Waterproof duck
duck	

8. FOR SPECIALTY MANUFACTURERS:

Advertising spe-	Napped fabrics
cialties—duck,	Vat dyed fabrics
drill, print cloth,	Window shades—
sheeting	sheeting, print
Fireproof material	cloth, enameling
Golf bag duck	duck

9. FOR THE DRY GOODS, JOBBING, AND CHAIN-STORE TRADE:

Crash	Single filling duck
Denim	Turkish toweling
Double filling duck	Wide duck
Huck toweling	30″—2.50—2.85 drill
Print cloth	

Unbleached sheeting, 36″ to 40″ in standard constructions, as follows:

36″–3.50–64 x 68	36″–5.00–48 x 48
36″–3.75–64 x 64	36″–5.50–44 x 44
36″–4.00–56 x 60	36″–6.50–40 x 40
36″–4.25–56 x 56	40″–3.15–64 x 68
36″–4.50–56 x 52	40″–3.60–56 x 60
36″–4.70–48 x 52	

10. FOR FLAG MANUFACTURERS:

Bunting:	Single filling duck
Government	Print cloth
type—all wool	30″—2.50 and 2.85
Navy type	drill
—all wool	
Commercial	
—all cotton	
Sheeting	

11. FOR FABRICS USED FOR CLOTHING AND WORK-CLOTHING TRADE:

Army duck in	Gray drill, duck,
plain and water	twill
repellent finish	Indigo blue denim
Bedford cord, gab-	Khakis, drapery
ardine, jean,	fabrics, drill,
moleskin, sateen,	herringbone,
suede, suiting	jean, twill, up-
fabric	holstery fabric
Corduroys for	Single filling and
men's wear and	double filling
women's wear	duck
Express, hickory,	
and fancy stripes	

12. MISCELLANEOUS INDUSTRIES:

Abrasive industry: Drill, jean, double filling duck

Airplane and balloon: Balloon fabric, wing fabric

Army and Navy:

Boat covers—	Army duck, num-
	bered duck, pau-
	lins
Gun covers—	Army duck
Tents—	Army duck, shel-
	ter tent duck
Wagon and	
truck covers—	Numbered duck

Automobile industry: Headlinings: Broken twills, sateen, sheeting

Bakelite and synthetic resins: Duck

Buffing wheel manufacturers: Naught duck and sheeting

Railroads: Cab curtains and ceilings for refrigerator cars use Numbered duck

Shippings covers: Fabric to suit particular use

Spring covers: Double filling duck

Upholstery padding: Sheeting.

INDUSTRIAL FABRICS. A wide variety of fabrics, chiefly cotton, used in various mechanical processes or which, in turn, are processed or treated in order to become part of another product. Some fabrics of this type include print cloth, cheesecloth, tobacco cloth, duck of all types, sheeting, Osnaburg, filter twill, chain cloth, press cloth, jean, drill, twill, and broken twill cotton fabric, sateen, moleskin, multiple fabric, leno- or doup-woven fabric, terry, airplane cloth, balloon fabric, typewriter ribbon fabric.

INDUSTRIAL FABRICS, USES OF COTTON IN.

1. Airplanes, etc: Fuselage, gas cells, wings.

2. Athletic equipment: Covers, mats, nets, pads.

3. Automobiles, etc.: Body, seats, tires, top.

4. Bags: Feed, flour, salt, sugar.

5. Barber supplies: Hair aprons, pads, towels.

6. Belting, etc.: Belts, conveyors, hose.

7. Building supplies: Awnings, insulation, shades, wall covering.

8. Canvas shelters: Canopies, tarpaulins, tents.

9. Farm equipment: Aprons, binders, covers.

10. Filter cloths: Chemicals, foods, oil, sugar.

11. Flags and display: Bunting, signs, stage property.

12. Furniture: Chairs, cots, upholstery.

13. Insulation: Cords, tapes, wires.

14. Laundry supplies: Covers, net,

padding, twine.

15. Luggage: Bags, cases, trunks.

16. Marine equipment: Covers, lines, nets, sails.

17. Meat packaging: Casings, covers, twines.

18. Medical supplies: Absorbent cotton, gauze, tape.

19. Mortuary supplies: Caskets, shrouds, straps.

20. Office equipment: Machine covers, pads, ribbons.

21. Publishers' supplies: Bindings, book covers.

22. Railroad equipment: Car fittings and supplies.

23. Shoe materials: Canvas shoes, linings, rubbers.

INDUSTRIAL JURISPRUDENCE. The code of a company's employer-employee behavior as established through the precedent of decisions on day-to-day matters.

INDUSTRIAL UNION. A labor organization, the membership of which is composed of employees in particular industries, regardless of the type of work performed or the skill required.

INDUSTRIAL WIPING CLOTHS. Any of a host of absorbent cloths used in the commercial world and in industry to clean machines and their parts, etc. Examples include mops made of cheesecloth, drill, knit goods, tape, webbing; pots and other receptacles are often cleaned with some form of tinsel or other metallic products; polishing cloths of cheesecloth, drill, flannel, other napped fabrics, suedes, specially treated materials, etc.

INDUSTRY-WIDE BARGAINING. Collective bargaining by representatives of the companies in an industry, and of their employees with the view of arriving at one mutually acceptable agreement to cover all companies.

INEA. A dress-goods fabric made in France; cotton warp and alpaca filling.

INERT. Without chemical activity.

INFANTADO WOOL. A good quality merino wool of Spain.

INFRARED. That portion of the spectrum which comprises the rays from those that can just be seen by the eye to the longer rays which are invisible to the naked eye.

INGRAIN. 1. Name for Kidderminster carpets in this country. 2. Fabrics dyed in the fiber or yarn condition.

INGRAIN CARPET. Generally woven with a cotton or wool warp with wool filling; the width is usually one yard. The dyeing is in the thread or grain, which aids in distinguishing between ingrain and printed, piece-dyed or stamped carpets. The name is rather indiscriminately used, at times, to specify carpeting. Ingrain is the name for Kidderminster carpets in this country.

INGRAIN COLORS. Artificial dyestuffs, insoluble in water. Another name for azo colors. They are developed on cotton.

INGRAIN JUTE CARPETING. Merely an ingrain carpet made with cotton warp and jute filling yarns.

INGRAIN KNITTING YARN. Means that the yarns have been dyed prior to the knitting of fabric on the frame.

INHIBITOR. An agent which checks or prevents a chemical or a physical change.

INITIATION FEE. The sum of money charged to an individual who seeks admission to a union.

INKING. See SPECK-DYEING.

INKLE. Flemish weavers introduced this type of broad linen tape into England toward the end of the sixteenth century. The meaning has become modified to mean a group of people, such as refugees, who settle in a new area and then build up a very close association among themselves. The expression "as thick as inkle weavers" has the same connotation today as "close as two peas in a pod."

INKLE LOOM. See Indian-type Loom under LOOM AND WEAVING.

INORGANIC. Not having in its structure the carbon element as found in animal and vegetable matter. It should be observed, however, that carbolic acid, ether, and nylon, for example, are hardly animal or vegetable matter and they are not inorganic and they are not formed from living organisms or substances.

INORGANIC CHEMICALS IN TEXTILES, USES OF.

COTTON AND RAYON PROCESSING:

1. DESIZING: Caustic soda, sodium chloride, sulphuric acid.

2. SCOURING OR BOILING OUT: Caustic soda, soda ash, sodium bicarbonate, sodium phosphates, sodium silicate.

3. SCOURING: Muriatic acid, sulphuric acid.

4. MERCERIZING: Caustic soda, muriatic acid, sulphuric acid.

5. BLEACHING—COMPOUNDS: Calcium hypochlorite, hydrogen peroxide, sodium chlorite, sodium hypochlorite, sodium peroxide.

   Auxiliaries: Caustic soda, borax, sodium phosphates, sodium silicate, sodium sulphate.

   Antichlors: Hydrogen peroxide, sodium bisulphite.

6. DYEING AND PRINTING—EXHAUSTING AGENTS: Glauber's salts, sodium chloride.

   Aftertreatments: Copper sulphate

for lightfastness, potassium chromate for washfastness.

Scouring and/or pH Adjustments: Aqua ammonia, muriatic acid, potassium carbonate, sodium bicarbonate, sodium carbonate, sodium phosphates, sulphuric acid.

Mordants: Potassium bichromate, sodium bichromate.

Dyestuff Reduction: Caustic soda, soda ash, sodium hydrosulphite, sodium sulphide.

Diazotizing and Developing—Direct Dyestuffs: Caustic soda, muriatic acid, sodium nitrite, sulphuric acid.

Dyestuff Oxidation: Hydrogen peroxide, sodium chlorate, sodium perborate.

Dyestripping: Zinc hydrosulphite.

7. FINISHING—pH ADJUSTMENT: Aqua ammonia, soda ash, sodium bicarbonate.

   Resin Treatment Catalysts: Ammonium chloride, ammonium sulphate, diammonium phosphate, magnesium chloride, zinc nitrate.

   Fire Retardants: Borax, boric acid, ammonium sulfamate, antimony oxide, calcium carbonate.

WOOL PROCESSING:

1. PULLING: Lime, soda ash, sodium sulphide.

2. SCOURING: Caustic soda, soda ash, sodium bicarbonate, sodium phosphates.

3. CARBONIZING: Soda ash, sulphuric acid.

4. BLEACHING: Hydrogen peroxide, sodium silicate, aqua ammonia, sulphuric acid.

5. DYEING AND FINISHING—EXHAUSTING AGENTS: Acetic acid, ammonium sulphate, Glauber's salt, diammonium phosphate, sodium bisulphate, sulphuric acid.

MAN-MADE FIBER, YARN, AND FABRIC PROCESSING:

1. SCOURING: Glauber's salt, soda ash, sodium phosphates.

2. BLEACHING: Sodium chlorate.

3. DYEING AND PRINTING—EXHAUSTING AGENTS: Glauber's salt, sodium chloride.

   Aftertreatments: Copper sulphate for lightfastness, potassium chromate for washfastness.

   SCOURING AND/OR pH ADJUSTMENT: Aqua ammonia, muriatic acid, potassium carbonate, soda ash, sodium bicarbonate, sodium phosphates, sulphuric acid.

   Mordants: Potassium bichromate, sodium bichromate.

   Dyestuff Reduction: Caustic soda, soda ash, sodium hydrosulphite, sodium sulphide.

   Diazotizing and Developing—Direct Dyestuffs: Caustic soda, muratic acid, soda ash, sodium nitrite, sulphuric acid.

Dyestuff Oxidation: Hydrogen peroxide, sodium chlorate, sodium perborate.

Dyestripping: Zinc hydrosulphite.

4. FINISHING: Caustic soda, antimony oxide, sodium bicarbonate.

INORGANIC SOLVENT. Water, or a water-miscible, noncompound which possesses solvent properties. Common inorganic solvents include water, dilute hydrochloric acid used for rust stains, and hypo for iodine stains.

INSEAM. The inner seam of the leg of a pair of trousers, sometimes called the crotch seam; also the forearm seam of a sleeve.

INSERTION. Narrow lace that has a plain edge on wither side that will admit of insertion into a fabric.

INSET. A piece of cloth set or let into a garment.

INSIDE LINING. An extra lining given to afford additional body to a garment. It is usually made of unbleached muslin, comes in varying texture and quality, is sometimes known as tailor's canvas, and is used on the front of coats and jackets between the facing and the front.

INSOLUBILISING. In the manufacture of man-made filaments it is the process of rendering filaments resistant to, or insoluble in, hot acid dye baths. A typical test for the degree of insolubility is to heat the material for ninety minutes in a bath of 0.1 per cent of sulphuric acid and 0.25 per cent of sodium sulphate at 97-degrees, Centigrade. The loss in strength or weight than can be determined.

INSPISSATED. Dried up.

INSTEP. That part of a stocking which covers the arched forepart or instep of a human being.

INSULATING ABILITY. Wool possesses good insulating properties since air is trapped between tiny scales noted in wool yarns and there is only a slow passage of hot or cold air; thus, the body of the wearer is protected from extremes of heat and cold.

"INTAGLIO." Covers a group of lustrous, brocadelike patterns woven into nylon tricot knit fabric. Developed by Munsingwear, "Intaglio" is the first nylon tricot with a monotone woven motif.

INTAGLIO PRINTING. The engraving of the motif to be printed is cut or gouged-out below the surface of the printing cylinder. The "valley areas" carry the coloring matter for contact with the material to be printed. Fabrics colored by the use of the proc-

ess are referred to as Intaglio. See RELIEF PRINTING.

INTARSIA. Derived from the Italian, intarsiare, which means "inlay." Intarsia is a motif or decoration on a solid color knitted fabric made by using a different colored yarn in such a manner as to appear as though actually inlaid into the material. A flat single-bed latch needle machine is used for intarsia effects which are characterized by the following properties:

1. Clean, clearly defined color areas.
2. Absence of overlapping of the various colored yarns where the color areas abut each other and no reduction in the elasticity of the material because of overlapping.
3. Floats and bird's eye do not appear on the reverse side of the goods.
4. No change in fabric weight because of the extra dyed yarns used in the construction of the intarsia motif.

INTEGRATION. Implies the related functions and purposes of raw material, construction, color, finish, fabric, production, marketing, and merchandizing, all under the control of a single textile organization.

INTEGUMENT. Skin or outer covering of a body such as a silkworm; in textiles applied especially to sericulture.

INTENSITY. See COLOR, PROPERTIES OF.

INTERCEL. Name for an interlining for garments made with 100 per cent Celanese staple.

INTERFACIAL TENSION. The surface tension which exists between a solution and some other substance, such as a dirt particle, inside the solution. A low interfacial tension is necessary for emulsion stability.

INTERFACING. A woven or nonwoven fabric or material used to provide body and substance to a garment. Almost any type of fabric may be utilized. Selection of type of material to use depends upon fabric weight, flexibility, stiffness, and other specific properties pertinent to the task at hand. Some woven trademarks used include Armo, hair-canvas, Hymo, Lamicel, Siri, and Wigan. Nonwoven trademarks include Keybak, Pellon, Reemay, Textryl.

INTERGILLING. When gilling precedes combing in the manipulation of worsted fibers.

INTERLACE. To unite, insert, or interpose by lacing.

INTERLINING. A lining between ordinary lining and the outside fabric of a garment. In winter clothing, such as

coats and jackets, lamb's wool may be used for interlining as a resistance to cold.

INTERLINING FLANNEL. Cotton flannel that comes in a wide range of weights, usually mottled in color motif by color combination. The unbleached type of flannel is given heavy napping or gigging on the face and the back of the goods to provide bulk for interlinings used in jackets and coats.

INTERLOCK CLOTH. A double 1 x 1 rib fabric knitted on a latch needle machine using a cylinder and a dial. Long and short needles are arranged alternately in both the cylinder and the dial.

INTERLOCK KNITTING. A method of rib knitting on a circular frame with alternate long and short needles in cylinder and dial. The alternate needles knit and welt at alternate feeds. Consequently, each full course of the fabric necessitates the use of two consecutive feeds, each feed knitting a 1x1 rib course and one interlocked. There are two types of interlock machines:

1. Yard goods which produce continuous lengths of tubular fabric.
2. Garment-producing which knits interlock sweater bodies and sleeve sections with attached rib trim.

INTERMEDIATE CARD. The second card in a three-card woolen set. Usually has seven or eight pairs of workers and strippers. It is connected with the breaker card by an intermediate feed, and transfers the stock directly to the finisher card by an angle stripper. Also called second breaker.

INTERMEDIATE FEEDER. The method of keeping a controlled and even feed of cotton to the finisher beater section in the one-process picker machine. It is a hopper into which the cotton is placed, and by means of automatic attachments it is able to feed the beater section so that there will be an even flow of stock for manipulation.

INTERMEDIATE FRAME. Cotton, after leaving the drawing frame, is processed through a set of fly frames each of which drafts the stock to give attenuated slivers or slubbings which are progressively finer in counts. The machine set, in order, includes the slubbing, intermediate, roving, and jack frames. The intermediate frame is usually fed by two slubbing bobbins for each intermediate spindle.

INTERMEDIATE PICKER. A machine that converts four laps of loosely matted cotton fibers formed in the breaker picker into a single lap which is further processed on the finisher picker; it also cleans the fiber and produces an evener lap.

INTERMEDIATES. These are the starting chemical compounds which are used to build up the sequential steps in the formation and structure of a great many dyestuffs. Over 90 per cent of the dyes used in the United States today are of the synthetic type, and the base for these may come from benzene, naphthalene, anthracene, etc., classed as intermediates.

INTERMITTENT DRAW. Same as a skip draw. See SKIP DRAW.

INTERSECTING GILL BOX. A type of gill box having two sets of fallers, an upper one in addition to the conventional lower set.

INTERSEED FIBER DRAG. The resistance to the separation of the seeds in a lock of cotton caused by the intermeshing of the fibers in the lock among the seeds. Lint cotton will offer resistance to separation among the fibers.

INTERTWINE. To twine, twist, or tangle together; often happens in handling yarn.

INTERWEAVE. To interweave, as in the case of warp interlacing with filling.

IN-THE-DRAG. Tailoring term indicating that one is behind in his work and has to "pull out."

IN-THE-GRAY. Goods as they come from the loom in the unbleached condition. Also known as gray goods, the term is practically confined to cotton materials from the loom.

IN-THE-GREASE. Signifies wool in its natural state, as it comes from the sheep's back with all the grease and other impurities attached to it.

IN-THE-GUM. Natural raw silk prior to removal of sericin or silk gum.

IN-THE-ROUGH, IN-THE-CRUST, IN-THE-WHITE, IN-THE-BLUE. A group of terms that describe stock which has been tanned but not finished. In-the-rough or rough-tanned is commonly applied to vegetable-tanned cattle-hide leathers.

In-the-crust and in-the-white are used in reference to vegetable, alum, or formaldehyde-tanned sheep and lamb skins. In-the-blue refers to the chrome-tanned skins.

In-the-white also means in-the-pickle. These more or less equivalent meanings are used to describe stock which has undergone the process prior to tanning, but is not yet actually tanned.

INVERNESS. A long, loose, sleeveless cape, fitted at the neck and hanging on the shoulders. This woolen or worsted garment comes in plaid effects.

INVERTED PLEAT. A combination of two pleats with the edges turned to each other so as to meet or nearly meet.

INWEAVE. To weave in, to intertwine, to decorate by some type of weaving as in the case of lappet, doup, swivel, clipspot, and Jacquard weaving principles.

INWROUGHT. Worked in so as to be a component part of a fabric; a decoration or embellishment added to a particular cloth such as is observed in some brocade, brocatelle, tapestry, etc.

IODINE NUMBER. The number of centigrams of iodine absorbed by one gram of a substance being analyzed, such as oil, fat, grease, etc. It is a measure of the proportion of unsaturated compounds present in the substance being tested.

ION. An electrified component of an atom, molecule, or radical formed by the dissolution of an electrolyte and becoming a cation with a positive charge (plus) if electrons are lost, or an anion with a negative charge (minus) if electrons are gained. Thus, a molecule of sodium chloride, NaCl, in aqueous solution, dissociates with the sodium cation Na with a deficiency of one electron, and the chlorine anion, Cl-, with an excess of one electron. A short definition of ion is that it is any particle of less than colloidal size which has either a positive or a negative electric charge.

IONIZATION. Dissociation of molecules into charged particles.

IONIZATION CONSTANT. Expression in absolute units of the extent of the dissociation into ions of a chemical compound in solution.

IRAKI, IRAQI COTTON. A short-staple cotton grown extensively along the banks of the Tigris and Euphrates Rivers in Iraq; much used in making carpet yarn.

IRC DIVISION OF AMERICAN CYANAMID COMPANY, INC; FIBERS OF.

Dylok: A dyed-in-the-filament rayon yarn which comes in a variety of colors. Maximum fade-resistance is possible since the color is set into the fiber. Used in apparel, drapes, and upholstery.

Nurpon: A High-Module, High-Performance rayon staple which has cotton-like properties, is strong and tough, and has high dimensional stability. The yarn is devoid of nubs, slubs, and other undesirable matter. Used in fabric blends.

Tyweld: Very tough and durable fiber for industrial use. Much used in rubber housing, ties and welds yarn to rubber for the life of the item.

Villwyte: A heavy denier, continuous filament rayon yarn much used as a basic or raw material in manufacture of carbonized and graphitized yarns and materials. Originally developed for use in Space-Age applications and subsequently for other unique functions.

NOTE: The Industrial Fibers Division,

INTERNATIONAL YARN NUMBERING CONGRESS TABLES. The International Yarn Numbering Congress at its meeting in Vienna, Austria, in 1873 spent a great deal of time on the subject of denier. It was decreed finally that the denier should now be defined as the weight in grams of 10,000 meters of filament silk. The basis used today, however, in England and in the United States for the sizing of thrown silk filament is the weight in grams of 1,000 yards of the filament. To convert this weight into deniers it is necessary to multiply by the factor used, 33.36.

The Congress decreed the following denier table:

With the legal denier in use today of 0.05 grams for the length of 450 meters or 492.13 yards (often used in calculations as 492.2 yards) it is possible to convert to ounces by multiplying the grams by 0.0353.

Thus, if 1,000 yards of filament weigh three grams, it would be the equivalent of 33.36 times 3, or a 100.8-denier yarn.

TYPE	WEIGHT IN GRAMS	LENGTH IN METERS
1. Italian, legal	0.05	450 or 492.13 yards
2. Milan	0.051	476
3. Turin	0.0534	476
4. Lyons, Old Denier	0.531	476
5. Lyons, New Denier	0.531	500
6. International Denier	0.05	500

Painesville, Ohio, ceased the manufacture of its rayon filament fibers in December, 1972.

IRC NYLON. Nylon 6 staple fiber; registered trade-mark of Industrial Rayon Company, Division of American Cyanimid Co., Inc. New York City.

IRENE TWILL. An alpaca lining cloth made in Great Britain. A 2-up, 1-down twill is used in this cotton warp and alpaca filling material. Pick count is around 88 x 72.

IRIDESCENT. In silk weaving the term implies a color effect made by the use of warp ends and filling picks of varying tints or hues. Properly, iridescent effects will show alternating or intermingling colors, and refer to any glittering of colors which seem to change when rays of light fall onto the fabric without reference to what the colors are.

IRISH BEETLE FINISH. See BEETLED FINISH.

IRISH CAMBRIC. Made for centuries in Ireland, this plain-woven, all-linen cloth is constructed with high yarn counts. The fabric bleaches particularly well, and it is a favorite for handkerchiefs and underwear.

IRISH CROCHET. Hand-made lace, heavy in weight, noted for the distinctive beauty in pattern that is recognized by the whiteness of the linen yarn used. Substantial in feel and coarser than needle point.

IRISH DUCK. A plain-woven, very strong, all-linen fabric used for overalls, engineers' clothing, and other work clothes.

IRISHES. Plain-woven cotton cloth made in Northern Ireland. The texture is about 70 x 66; the cloth is given a starched and glazed finish.

IRISH EYE DIAPER. Diaper fabric made on a 2-up and 1-down twill weave.

IRISH FINISH. A very good imitation finish given to cottons to simulate linens.

IRISH FLAX. Flax obtained in Northern Ireland and Ireland, retted in bog areas to make the fiber tough and strong.

IRISH FRIEZE. Long staple, coarse wool is used to make this heavy, water-repellent overcoating used in Ireland. It is a stock-dyed fabric. Fabric weight is well over 24 ounces per yard with some of the heavier types over 30 ounces. Much of the cloth is now made with shoddy, mungo, reused fiber, re-manufactured fiber, extract wool, and other wastes in the content of the yarn and fabric. The material is one that will serve the wearer for many years.

IRISH LACE. General term used to designate lace made in the peasant areas of Ireland. The work is learned in the Irish convent schools and has been carried on for centuries. See IRISH CROCHET.

IRISH LAWN. A plain-woven, all-linen fabric made of high yarn counts. There are several qualities of Irish lawn on the market, and all of them have excellent surface because of the yarns used and care given in finishing.

IRISH LINEN. Used for handkerchiefs, collar and cuff sets, trimming and so on, the fabric is fine or very fine in texture, light in weight, grass-bleached, woven by hand, and receives very little dressing in manufacturing.

IRISH POINT. Combination of appliqué, cutwork, and embroidery on net with elaborate needle-stitching in the better qualities to enhance the pattern effect.

IRISH POPLIN. Fabric originally made in China; in time, Dublin made a comparable material. Organzine silk warp and Colonial wool filling were the yarns used.

One type of Irish poplin, made of linen, uses one fine end and one coarse end, and one fine pick and one coarse pick. The fine pick interlaces with the fine end, the latter serving as a raiser in the cloth; the coarse warp end interlaces with the coarse pick and is a raiser at the point of intersection. The chief use of the fabric is in nurses' uniforms and men's shirts.

IRISH POPLIN, HIGH GRADE. A characteristic Irish fabric made for many centuries in which silk warp and worsted filling are always used.

IRISH SEAL MASTERS. Inspectors of woven linens who, from 1721 to 1823, carefully examined the materials and affixed their seal if the quality was up to standard specifications. Woven linen could not be sold during this time unless given the approval seal.

IRISH TRIMMING. Simple woven lace that is used on white goods.

IRISH TWEED. White warp and dark shade filling of blue, gray, brown or black feature this popular, rugged men's-wear fabric. Used for suiting and coating.

IRISH WOOL. A rugged wool that sorts to around 46s when graded. See ROSCOMMON SHEEP, WOOL.

IRISH WORK. White embroidery that is worked onto a white background. The Irish are noted for this type of detailed work on handkerchiefs; hence, the name.

IRON. 1. A hand or electric device used to press out wrinkles and creases in materials on an ironing board. Electric irons can be regulated to correct heat temperature to be used on cloths made from the respective major textile fibers. 2. One iron equals 1/48th of one inch, to measure the thickness of sole leather. 3. A chemical element of the heavy metal class, commonly known in detergent processes in the oxidized form as iron oxide or rust.

IRON BUFF, NANKIN YELLOW. This buff to yellow dyestuff is formed by precipitating a hydrated ferric oxide within the fiber. Used on cotton fabric.

IRON FILTER. A device on the water system to remove iron from the water prior to use. There are two types—1. A mechanical ion exchange water softener attached to the water system which removes the iron in solution, actually ionized iron. 2. A fabric filter attached to faucets which lead to the washer and cause the removal of the iron in the form of rust.

IRONING. Smoothing of a fabric or garment by means of a heated iron manipulated by the ironer. Pressing is the smoothing of a fabric or a garment by using an iron under heavy pressure; a pressing machine does the work.

IRONING BOARD. A flat, cloth-covered, tapering board used to press clothes.

IRON LIQUOR. Used as a mordant in dyeing and printing, this dark-colored solution of crude acetate of iron is obtained by dissolving scrap iron in pyroligneous acid (crude acetic acid as derived from wood by heat, specifically by dry distillation).

IRON NITRATE. This basic sulphate of iron, made by the action of nitric acid on ferrous sulphate, is used in silk weighting. Known also as ferric sulphate, formula is $Fe_2(SO_4)3$.

IRONPROOFING. Some acetate fabric is given a treatment which makes it less susceptible to damage from high temperatures during ironing. The compound is usually derived from saponifying the surface of the material with caustic soda.

IRON YARN, IRON FABRIC. Cotton yarn or fabric which is given much stiffening or starching followed by glazing in order to make it satisfactory for use in belt banding, hat shapes, and lining.

IRREGULAR FILLING. See Illustrated Section (Fabrics 5).

IRREGULAR HOSE. That which is slightly imperfect and cannot be classed as a first.

IRREGULAR PICK. One that has not interlaced perfectly with the warp yarn; caused by broken picks, harness skips, irregular yarn, mispicks.

IRREGULAR SATIN WEAVE. See SATIN WEAVES.

IRRIGATED COTTON. Egyptian cotton is known by this name. The Cotton Exchange, New Orleans, Louisiana, uses this term which applies to that cotton raised in Arizona, California, and New Mexico, except for the fiber raised in Lea County, New Mexico, and the Pecos and El Paso Valleys in Texas. These three states are now in the group listed as major cotton growing states in the United States. The Indians of the Southwest are growers of much cotton raised there, and some of them have fairly good-sized areas of their own.

ISATIN. A yellowish or brownish-red crystalline compound used as a reagent and in the manufacture of vat dyes. Obtained by oxidizing indigo.

ISOMER. From the Greek, meaning part. In chemistry it is a compound which has the same molecular weight and formula as another but with a different structural formula, resulting in different properties.

ISOSTATIC POLYPROPYLENE, MONOFILAMENT. Produced by the polymerization of a solution of propylene in the presence of specific catalysts. It has no odor and no plasticizers. Burns slowly, melts in bead formation, around 340° F. Decomposes around 550° F. The filament is subject to ultraviolet degradation and therefore should be stabilized. It comes in cross-section, flat, and round shapes. Uses include auto seat covers, carpet backing, decorative fabrics, cordage, filter cloth, narrow fabrics, and outdoor furniture.

Multifilament Yarn and Staple. It is obtained by melt spinning, and has about the same reactions to chemicals and solvents as the monofilament stock. It, at present, does not absorb dyestuff. Uses include applications for filtration and insulation, carpet backing, sand bags, and comparable products.

ISOTROPIC STRENGTH. A term used in physics to mean having one or more properties that are the same in all directions.

ISPAHAN. A Persian woolen rug made with hand-tied knots.

ISTLE, IXTLE. Yellow fiber, hard, rugged, and exceptionally stiff; also called Tampico or Mexican fiber. Little attention has been given to raising it. Finds use in brushes and twine, and in low-grade sacks.

ITALIAN CLOTH. Twilled or smooth, glossy-faced fabric made of cotton and worsted yarns. Used as a garment lining. Italy contributed this fabric as a simulation of genuine silk lining-fabric. It is also called farmer's satin.

ITALIAN DESIGNERS. Italy has made tremendous strides in fashion and styles for the past several years. Below is a list of the major designers and their fields of specialization:

Women's High Fashion: These are all based in Rome - Antonelli, Balestra, Di Lazzaro, Fabiani, Faraoni, Fontana, Forquet, Franco e Manfredi, Galitzine, Garnett, Gsttinoni, Gregoriana, Lancetti, Andre Laug, Ognibene Zendman, Riva, Schuberth, Tita Rossi, Tiziani, Valentino, and Zanolli. Milan designers include Biki, Enzo, Livoli, Marucelli, Mial Schon, and Veneziani. Guidi of Florence, and Sarli of Naples complete this category.

Men's High Fashion: Those based in Rome include Brioni, Datti, Litrico, Rosati, Siviglia, and Valentini. Baratta and Wanver are located in Milan, Nativo in Florence, while Coccoli represents Turin.

Shirtmaking Creations are represented by Samo and Sir Bonser, both in Rome.

High Fashion Furs: Assunta and Fendi are based in Rome, while Milan boasts of Melloni, Parodi, Pellegrini, and Rossini & Porro. Viscardi is based in Turin.

ITALIAN FERRET. A binding braid or silk galloon.

ITALIAN HEMP. True hemp, *Cannabis sativa,* found in Italy. It is water-retted, creamy-white in cast, lustrous, soft, and pliable.

ITALIAN LINING. Made with cotton warp and alpaca filling on even-sided twill weave, this high-count cloth is bleached or dyed and is given an appealing lustrous finish. The cloth is a simulation of silk satin.

ITALIAN SILK. A very high-quality raw silk which has excellent cohesion and is suitable for single weaving. It has good strength and elasticity, is easily prepared, and is free from imperfections. It has the highest boil-off percentage of any filament brought to this country, 27 to 30 per cent. In addition to its use for dress goods, Italian silk is much used in the knitting trade for high-grade hosiery, underwear, and glove silk.

ITALIAN WOOL. The wool raised there now, along with that grown in Sardinia and Sicily, descended from Spanish merino and formerly was of high grade. Much of this breed has been crossbred thereby affecting the former full-blood merino fiber; it is, however, still classed as a fine wool and is used for much quality fabric in woolens and worsteds, and for blended fabrics. Carpet wool is also raised in Italy. Both types are used, for the most part, in Italy.

ITARSI FIBER. See SUNN.

IVORY. Creamy-white color of high brilliance and low saturation.

IXTLE. See ISTLE.

J

JABO. A rugged Philippine bast fiber used for cordage.

JABOT. An ornamentation used on ladies' waists and dresses. Jabots are made in various materials and are usually worn down the length of the waist front. They are sometimes made of lace and are very decorative.

J-BOX. A device used in many wet-finishing operations to make the cloth processing more or less continuous. The name comes from the fact that the box is made in the form of the letter J. The material is fed into the box at the top, and it plaits down to fill up the longer arm of the box before the cloth is pulled out of the shorter arm or opening. Timing is an important factor in operating the box.

JACCONETS, JACONAS, JACONETS. French term used in the broad sense to signify staple cottons of varying reed widths, textures, lengths, and finished widths. They are usually woven in the gray, may be finished as mull, cambric, lawn, nainsook, organdy, or voile.

JACK. 1. A tempered steel blade with either high or low butts, or both, whose primary function is to actuate the movement of the latch knitting needles. See Illustrated Section. 2. Part of a dobby head motion, it is a flat, upright metal device so fulcrumed that it will serve as a lever in the operation of the harnesses in the loom.

JACKET. A term best used to describe a ladies' short coatlike garment, with or without sleeves, which opens down the front and extends below the hips. Many jackets are made so that the finger tips will reach to the bottom of the pockets, the lower portion of the garment extending a few inches below the bottom of the pocket stitching.

A man's similar garment is correctly called a sack coat. However, different types are described best by their own terms. For example: a man's smoking jacket describes a type of coat worn by men indoors, at mealtime, or after meals. It is a comfortable type of lounging jacket.

JACKET, WOVEN OR FELT. Textile materials woven or pressed into tubular or sleeve form, ready for covering and shrinkage on a machine roll.

JACKET SWEATER. See WOMEN'S AND MISSES' SWEATERS.

JACK FRAME. A fine gauge roving frame used when spinning high yarn counts or when making soft-twist filling yarn to be used in certain cotton cloths which call for this type filling. It is the fourth frame in the roving frame series and, generally speaking, is not used to any considerable degree.

JACKING. Spinning term pertaining to the stretching of the yarn by the outward run of the mule frame carriage after the roving has been delivered to the feed rollers of the machine.

JACK SPOOL. The long, large wooden spool upon which the woolen roving is wound as it comes from the tape condenser on the last card of the set which performs the carding of the wool fibers. About 36 rovings are wound side by side on the spool which is set in the head stock of the mule-spinning frame ready to be fed into the machine for yarn-spinning. See Illustrated Section.

JACOBITE. An authentic tartan in which bright yellow predominated, worn as an emblem of adherence to the Stuart cause.

JACONET. 1. This East Indian cloth is much used in the bookbinding and shroud trades. Most of the material is now made in Great Britain. Jaconet is given a hard finish similar to lawn, and is smooth, lustrous, with considerable body. There is little call for the cloth in this country. 2. There is also a soft-finish cloth of this name found in the trade. It resembles heavy, soft finish English nainsook and is thinner than cambric.

Jaconet may be white, dyed, printed, or have woven stripes in pattern material.

JACQMAR. A very fine worsted fabric so light in weight and supple that it drapes like silk satin.

JACQUARD. An intricate method of weaving invented by Joseph Marie Jacquard of Lyons, France, at the beginning of the nineteenth century. See JACQUARD, JOSEPH MARIE, AND JACQUARD MACHINE; JACQUARD MACHINE AND WEAVING, HISTORICAL REVIEW OF.

Jacquard weaving produces elaborate weave effects in the loom by a set of perforated strips of cardboard, punched according to the motif, and substituted for the ordinary and restricted number of heddle frames and pattern chains. These card perforations, in connection with rods and cords, regulate the raising of the stationary warp thread mechanisms.

The Jacquard motion revolutionized the weaving industry. While of rather limited importance in the fabrication of

men's wear, it plays an important part in modern tapestry, brocade, brocatelle, damask, and figured dress-goods production.

The loom is a development of the old-time draw loom, and the designs are found in many fabrics made from the major textile fibers. Cotton and linen Jacquards are popular in the napery trade. See Illustrated Section (Fabrics 65, 67, 78).

JACQUARD, DOUBLE LIFT. DOUBLE CYLINDER MACHINE IN. A double machine in all particulars. The action of the knives is the same as the double lift single cylinder. The difference is that it has two sets of needles, and two cylinders, in addition to the two sets of hooks and knives.

In acting, one set of knives lifts while the other falls, just as in the double lift single cylinder, the chief point of difference being the two cylinders and their hooks and needles, which do away with the springing of the hooks that we find in the other machine.

Each cylinder acts the same as in the ordinary machine; consequently they work alternately, each one turning as its set of knives rises. By this method of acting it makes each cylinder turn half as many times as there are picks, and also makes it necessary that the cards be laced in two sets, the odd numbers in one set and the even numbers in the other, using the opposite positions for the No. 1 needle.

The shed formed is the same as in all the other double-lift machines.

The chief advantage is the speed that the machine can develop, and the disadvantage lies in the need for regulating the two sets of cards.

The difficulty in operation is in finding the pick, which takes more time and care than in other machines, consequently this machine is best used for single fabrics of not too high a grade.

Machines are made in all sizes—both French and Fine Index.

JACQUARD, DOUBLE LIFT, SINGLE CYLINDER MACHINE IN. This machine has two sets of hooks, two sets of knives, and one set of needles. Each set of knives has its own set of hooks, the needle controlling a hook in each set.

The knives are lifted alternately by two levers controlled by a double crank on the shaft of the loom. The cylinder is operated independently by a separate lever on the top shaft and moves back and forward at each pick of the loom while the griffe bars are lifted alternately.

The tails of the hooks that are controlled by a needle are tied to the same harness cord, so that either hook being lifted will lift the same cords and con-

sequently the same ends of the warp.

By this arrangement an end that is to be lifted for several successive picks is never fully dropped until the last pick, because when it is taken up on the first pick by one set of knives, it is caught halfway in its descent by the other set of knives that are ascending while the first set are descending, and so on, pick by pick, until the card no longer calls for a raiser in the cloth.

This method of handling warp thread is much easier on the warp than that of the ordinary single lift, where the ends are raised and dropped the full distance of the shed at each pick.

The alternating motion of the two sets of knives and levers gives an easy balancing motion to both warp and loom, making it possible to attain a greater speed than with the ordinary machines.

This type of machine is also built with a higher lift and longer hooks, making it suitable for rugs and carpets.

The regular double-lift single cylinder machine is largely used in the upholstery and silk trades, on account of the advantages spoken of above, and because of the accuracy and speed of the machine. Since, in the latter respect, it is limited only by the speed with which the cylinder can be turned, it is one of the most generally used machines in all classes of work. Machines can be obtained in all sizes and indexes, French and Fine Index.

JACQUARD, JOSEPH MARIE, AND JACQUARD MACHINE. Prior to the invention and exhibition of the final Jacquard loom in 1801 there were others who had worked on similar devices, but the warp ends had to be raised and lowered by a weaver's helper. Jacques de Vaucanson, among others, contributed to improvements of these earlier looms, with ideas given to Joseph Marie Jacquard, a repairer of earlier machines (see JACQUARD MACHINE AND WEAVING, HISTORICAL REVIEW OF). Jacquard began to experiment with the ideas around 1787 but was interrupted by the French Revolution, during which he saw action around Lyons.

In the early part of the nineteenth century Jacquard had actually completed his machine, which was exhibited in an Industrial Exposition in 1801. As a result he was presented to Napoleon, who complimented him and decreed that an annuity be granted to him. They became well acquainted. The machine was bought by the State in 1806.

The machine created a furor when it was introduced, and its rise was meteoric in other countries on the Continent. The loom, however, also actually caused many people to lose employment; it was estimated that one loom could do the work formerly done by one hundred persons. Disorder and rioting occurred in many textile centers in Europe as a result. As time wore on, in this transition to the factory system, the laboring classes began to see the value of the loom, and it was not too long before it was considered as a boon to the textile industry and the human race.

The Jacquard machine is a head motion for the loom that is placed above the loom and takes the place of the ordinary head motion that controls the harness frames. Major advantage of the machine is its ability to govern or control each single thread of warp, instead of a series of them as the ordinary harness loom does.

This controlling of each end in the warp gives the designer much more freedom and latitude to produce fancy, large, small and intricate motifs; in fact, there is no limit to the possibility of the design as far as the machine is concerned. The only limitation is in the texture of the yarn and the nature and the size of the yarns employed.

If it were possible to get yarn fine enough—and it is now being done to a high degree—a designer could put enough of these threads together in a small area and reproduce the most intricate design. As it is, some Jacquard effects are beautiful and interesting; 600 ends per inch in warp texture is not difficult to obtain—in triple fabric.

Within the last few years, Jacquard patterns have become rather elaborate and, at the same time, the minute detail has been exceptionally well done.

The reproduction of flowers, photographs, buildings, pastoral scenes, calendars, flags, coat labels, campaign ribbons, characters in fiction and real life, etc., is now an easy matter. The last half-century in Jacquard has shown marvelous advances and strides in the perfection of design and work. Production has been spurred on to a high degree. Distributive and consumer education have become aware of the possibilities for Jacquard fabrics in many uses for the home and in apparel.

See Illustrated Section (Also, same section, Fabrics 65, 67, 78).

JACQUARD A JOUR. Openwork (à jour, in daylight) gauze in elaborate figured effects.

JACQUARD BOTTOM BOARD. The board situated at the bottom of the machine. It is drilled with a great number of small holes.

JACQUARD CARD. A unit of the pattern chain used on a Jacquard loom. It is a cardboard strip, 3 x 10 inches, with holes similar to those in a player-piano roll punched in it. It is joined by wire eyes to other cardboard strips to form the Jacquard chain. See Illustrated Section.

JACQUARD CARD LACER. A machine which laces together, in a pattern chain form, the perforated Jacquard cards which control the operation of a Jacquard loom in weaving designs, motifs, or patterns into fabric.

JACQUARD CASTING-OUT. Process when some of the pattern-controlling hooks are thrown out of action, so they will not function when the motif to be woven does not require the use or action of all hooks in the tie.

JACQUARD CHINE. Brocades made with check motifs are called Jacquard Chiné.

JACQUARD COMBERBOARD. This very important part of a Jacquard loom is located about 14 inches above the warp threads, and is attached to the sides of the loom. It is ¾ to 1 inch thick, about 6 inches deep, and its length is equal to the width of the loom.

This board is drilled with a series of holes (hence it is sometimes called hole board) with one harness cord threaded through each hole, which produces the various effects and repeats. The holes are drilled in rows so that the holes in the second row are between those of the first and third rows, in a staggered order. In this way the holes are distributed evenly over the surface and do not weaken the board. Each row is drilled about 3 to 4½ inches in depth.

The purposes of the comberboard are as follows:

1. To retain the harness cords in a fixed position.
2. To distribute the cords evenly over the width of the cloth.
3. To allow only a vertical lift of the warp threads.
4. To regulate the texture in the reed. That is, the number of holes in one row multiplied by the number of rows per inch will equal the number of warp threads in 1 inch of the reed. This number cannot be increased but may be decreased.
5. A comberboard is made for each distinctive fabric.
6. The width of the drilled and threaded portion of the board must approximately equal the width of the fabric.
7. A threaded comberboard determines the maximum width of repeat.

JACQUARD CROSS-TIE. Commonly used in the United States, this tie-up is when the cards and the cylinder are to the right or to the left of the machine. Also called London Tye. See Illustrated Section.

JACQUARD CYLINDER. That part of a Jacquard loom which supports and holds the pattern cards in position, while the plungers which control the weaving of the pattern pass through the holes in the cards.

JACQUARD DRILL. A heavy drill material made with linen warp and cotton filling. Face-effect weaves are used to bring as much of the linen yarn on the face of the goods as possible.

JACQUARD GLACE. A Jacquard brocade made with strong color contrast in both warp and filling is known as glacé.

JACQUARD GRISAILLE. A gray effect is obtained from the use of a white warp and a black filling, or vice versa. Grisaillé is the French for "turned gray."

JACQUARD HARNESS. The complete harness of the Jacquard loom is spoken of as a tie-up, and it is of infinite variety. It is the connecting link between the machine and the loom that weaves the fabric. A great many effects are produced in cloth by the manner in which the tie-up is made and attached to the machine. See Illustrated Section.

The tie-up consists of the various parts of the Jacquard harness and the comberboard, through which are threaded the harness cords. The harness consists of a few parts, mostly linen cord or twine, and is arranged in the following manner, beginning at the machine:

1. HARNESS CORDS: Made of strong linen twine of the best quality, cable twisted. They are made into bundles according to the style of the tie-up, with a loop at the top, and are attached to the neck cords. When assembling the harness, it is necessary to have a bundle of cords for each hook used in the machine. Secondly, there must be a harness cord for each end in the warp.

2. TOP COUPLING: A loop of finer linen twine than that used for the harness cords, and without the cable twist. This coupling is attached to the lower end of the harness cord. Before the loop is formed by tying the two ends of the coupling together, a mail is slipped over one end.

3. MAIL: An oval-shaped piece of metal, usually brass or steel, pierced with three holes. The large one in the middle is for the warp thread. Through the small holes at each tip, the top and bottom couplings are threaded. Mail will vary in size according to the count of the yarn to be used in the warp.

4. BOTTOM COUPLINGS: Similar to the top coupling, about 6½ inches to 8 inches in diameter. They serve as a place of attachment for the lingoe. The

top coupling, mail, and bottom coupling correspond to the ordinary heddle in harness-loom work.

5. LINGOE: A thin metal weight varying in length and diameter. Its purpose is to keep the harness cords taut and, at the same time, to pull the hooks down after they have been lifted by the knives. The correct size of lingoe to use on a tie-up is determined by actual experience. A coarse warp yarn, for example, will require a heavier lingoe than a fine silk end. When lingoes used are too heavy, this condition can be offset by using a counter-balance-weight on the levers. This will result in an easier and quieter operation of the loom. The number of lingoes in one pound is used as the standard for size —12, 18, 24, etc.

The lingoes, top and bottom couplings, and mail are assembled into one complete unit away from the loom. Specially constructed steel heddles are now being used with a special type of lingoe, with the result that there is considerable saving of time when assembling the tie-up. See Illustrated Section.

JACQUARD HOOK. It is a long, slender, upright steel wire used on the machine. The upper part doubles back upon itself to form a hook which will rest over the lifting knife. The doubled-back lower end of the hook supports it when at rest. Each hook will control one or several harness cords so that each repeat of pattern will be identical in all respects. Hooks are sold in accordance with the number to be used in the machine, such as a 600-hook or a 1200-hook machine.

JACQUARD INDEX. The distance apart and the arrangement of the needles in the needle board in the head motion. The holes in the card and the cylinder must coincide with the index. Indexes include the French, Fine, American, Brussels and Wilton, and the Lace Curtain.

JACQUARD KNITTED FABRIC. Cloth which features an all-over or a sectional design in color and texture achieved by a Jacquard mechanism on a latch needle machine employing a cylinder and dial.

JACQUARD KNITTING. When designs in color are desired, a Jacquard frame is used in which the machine has a device that chooses or selects the needles and the color of the yarn to bring out the more or less elaborate pattern. Any design may be reproduced on fabric that has previously been drawn on the graph-design paper.

JACQUARD LACE MOTION. The principles of Jacquard taken from the Jacquard weaving motion were applied to lace in 1824, twenty-three years after patents were received for his loom action. It was not until 1837, however, that Ferguson conceived the idea of applying the Jacquard principles to the bobbins of the bobbinet machine. He used two guide bars in his machine to make it possible to produce a limitless number of motifs. Incidentally, Ferguson (who was from Nottingham, England) took out his patents in France since he was not guaranteed patent-law protection in his native country.

In 1841, Hooten Deverill, improving all the time on the work which had been done by Heathcoat, Leavers and Ferguson, improved the application of the basic Jacquard principles to the point where machine-made Jacquard motifs on Leavers machines were definitely assured. These principles and methods are still used today.

JACQUARD LEASH. Mill parlance for all the cords in a Jacquard harness which are attached to the one neck-cord.

JACQUARD LIFTING KNIVES. The triangular griff (griffe) blades on a Jacquard setup. The purpose of each knife is to lift the hooks that are to be "up" at the correct time. Controlled by the holes in the cards of the set on the loom.

JACQUARD LOOM HEAD MOTION. This motion is placed above the loom and takes the place of the ordinary motion that controls the harness frames. The chief advantage of the machine is in its ability to govern each single end in the warp, instead of only a series or group of threads as was the case prior to the Jacquard machine's becoming an actuality.

The control and governing of each end in the warp gives the designer much more freedom in producing all types and kinds of fancy figures. In fact, there is no limit to the possibility of the design as far as the machine itself is concerned. The only limitation is in the textures of the yarn in the fabric to be made and the nature and size of the yarns used.

Much has been done in the last quarter of a century to improve the industry, and production is now controlled to the point where the loom is considered as commonplace and one of the regular types of loom for the manufacture of textile fabrics.

JACQUARD MACHINE AND WEAVING, HISTORICAL REVIEW OF.

1. 1455—Silk spinning and throwing introduced into England.

2. 1480—Silk manufacturing introduced into France by Italian workers.

3. 1510—Tapestry weaving re-introduced into England by Thomas Sheldon.

4. 1662—Gobelin establishments in Paris, France, began to function.

5. 1725—Bouchon invented the perforated paper roll for working the draw loom.

6. 1728—Falcon used a chain of cards instead of the paper roll. The cards operated over a square prism. This plan of controlling the needles is still in vogue.

7. 1745—Vaucanson applied the griffe to the Falcon machine and placed the apparatus on top of the loom.

8. 1790—Joseph Marie Jacquard of Lyons, France (born July 7, 1752), made his first appearance as a repairer of previous machines.

9. 1801—Jacquard perfected his first machine and received a medal of award at the Paris Exposition.

10. 1820—Stephen Wilson, an English silk manufacturer, received his patent for a reading machine and a punching device for the cards of a Jacquard.

11. 1823—5000 Jacquard head motions were functioning in Coventry, England.

12. 1824—The William H. Horstmann Company introduced the first U.S.A. Jacquard in the Philadelphia area; it was used to make novelties and trimmings.

13. 1832—600 Jacquard head motions were in action in the Philadelphia area.

14. 1834—Jacquard died on August 7, in Oulins, near Lyons, France.

15. 1838—2200 of the head motions were now being used in the Philadelphia area.

16. 1842—A Jacquard machine with separate cylinder motion operated from a crankshaft was invented by J. Bellough.

17. 1849—Alfred Barlow invented the double Jacquard motion.

JACQUARD MECHANISM. A method of controlling the movement of needle jacks by means of paper or metal patterns on a knitting machine. The jacks in turn influence the functioning of the latch needles.

JACQUARD NECK-CORD. It is the connecting point of the Jacquard machine between the hook and the harness. The harness of a Jacquard consists of the neck or tail cords which are fastened to, or are suspended from, the hooks. The harness cords, the number of which depends upon the repeats of pattern per width of the cloth, are fastened to the neck cords and not the hook, itself. The neck or tail cord may be considered as the length or loop of thread connecting the hook with the harness.

JACQUARD NEEDLE-BOARD. A

board made of wood or brass with a number of small holes drilled in it. Each hole is of sufficient size to allow the free movement of the needle, which projects through it. The distance between these holes, and their diameter, is very important, and this is regulated by the index of the machine.

JACQUARD NEEDLE-BOX. Located at the opposite end of the needle board on the Jacquard loom, it contains the looped ends of the needles and the springs.

JACQUARD NEEDLES. These are made of wire and are the size of the hooks. By means of a loop that passes around the hook, the needle controls the backward and forward motion of the hook designating which ones are to be lifted by the knives and which are to rest on the grate.

One end of the needle passes through holes in the needle board, and the other end projects into the framework, called the needle box, and is looped at that place. Around this loop, there is a spring which keeps the needles in their correct positions, and at the same time helps the needles keep the hooks against the knives.

JACQUARD PATTERN CHAIN. The sequence of perforated Jacquard cards which have been laced together into endless formation. The rotation of the card-set governs the proper weaving of the cloth design, motif, or pattern.

JACQUARD POINT OR CENTER TIE. A tie made on both the English and the French systems, it is constructed by assigning two harness cords to each hook for each repeat of the motif. The comberboard is threaded so that one half of the repeat will be the reverse of the other. Thus, it is possible to obtain a width of the repeat twice that which would be possible with a straight tie, using the same number of hooks. This increased width of pattern is used in many cloths where elaborate effects are wanted.

JACQUARD PULLOVER. A piece of metal, shaped like a hook, which catches against a corner of the cylinder as it moves away from the needles and turns it until the hammer prevents further turning. In some machines there are two pullovers; one at the top, the other at the bottom. The extra pullover can be used to turn the cylinder in the opposite direction.

JACQUARD RAYE. Brocades which feature pronounced colored stripe effects are known as rayé (French for striped).

JACQUARD REPEATING MACHINE. A machine which automatically duplicates in blank cards the perforations of a sample Jacquard-loom pattern-chain.

JACQUARD STRAIGHT-THROUGH TIE. A tie in which one harness cord is provided for each hook for each repeat of the motif.

The first step in the construction of this tie is to indicate, with lines drawn on the comberboard, the exact location of each repeat. The number of holes in a repeat will equal the number of hooks used. Extra rows of holes in the board should be dropped on each side of the selvage.

The second step is to determine, exactly, the number of rows of hooks or needles used. It is customary to drop an equal number of rows from each side of the machine or to use the same number of rows on each side of the center of the machine.

JACQUARD SWEATER. It features allover figured designs—animals, foliage, trees, pastoral scenes, etc. The motif is knitted into the fabric. See JACQUARD KNITTING.

JACQUARD TIE. See JACQUARD HARNESS.

JACQUARD TIE; STRAIGHT OR NORWICH. The term is used when the Jacquard head motion is placed above the loom, with the cylinder and the cards over the warp of the fabric that is being woven.

JACQUARD, "UNITAPE." A revolutionary new Jacquard weaving model equipped with an indexing system that uses paper tape instead of the old-time cardboard pattern cards used since the inception of Jacquard looms. This is the first departure since that time in punching-out designs for Jacquard weaving. "Unitape" can be used on either rapier looms or on shuttle-type looms. Product of Thomas Halton Sons, Inc., Philadelphia, Pennsylvania. See Jacquard, Jacquard Card, Jacquard Card Lacer.

JACQUARD VELOUR. A velour coating fabric in which figured motifs are observed. It is made on a Jacquard loom, and this cloth is of good quality and rather costly since the raw material wool used is of good to excellent grade. The material is finished with the greatest of care. Another meaning of the term implies a lower grade cloth that is made on a pile fabric loom, finished with a rather high pile and then cut and sheared to simulate the true velour cloth.

"JACQUARD WEAVE." This does not actually exist. Jacquard designs, patterns, or motifs are made from the combination of two or more of the ordinary weave constructions: plain, twills, satins, ribs, baskets, etc. Examination of a Jacquard fabric under a pickglass will reveal that the design is made up of a combination of these simple weaves. Warp-effect and filling-effect weaves are used in combination or alternating arrangement to bring out the bright-and-dim effects observed on many Jacquards. See Illustrated Section (Fabrics 65, 67, 78).

JAC-SHIRT. A short, shirt-styled, straight-bottom jacket for outerwear. It is not lined and is made of durable fabric such as woolen plaid, corduroy, backed fabric, or Mackinac cloth.

JAFFER FABRICS. British term for plain-weave, yarn-dyed cottons made with multicolored warp and filling yarns. This "shot-about" cloth comes in some very pronounced color combinations and is often rather bizarre in appearance. Yarn combinations such as a pink, red, or orange warp and green, black, or yellow filling may be used to give the rather loud effect in the goods.

JAGANATH. This plain-woven cotton cloth is made from gray warp yarn and brown or white filling yarn. Known in the trade as Mock Grandrelle, the cloth is used for boot and shoe lining.

JAMAWAR. 1. A plain- or twill-woven fabric also called Chaporast—the most expensive of this woolen cloth—and Kaynamu, which is the least costly type. There are close to twenty qualities of this material made today. Much used in apparel. Shawls made with cashmere fiber in India are called JAMEWAR SHAWLS. They come in striped motifs, and the size is 1.5 yards by 3.75 yards.

JANAPAN. See SUNN.

JANUS CLOTH. A double-faced worsted fabric, each side different color.

JAPAN. A hard, brilliant, very lustrous lacquer or varnish that may be applied to fabrics, leather, wood, metal, etc. It may be used in belts, cap visors, play clothes, uniforms, etc. When applied to a fabric the term, JAPANNED, is also used.

JAPANESE CREPE. A fabric, much of which is imported from Japan, but some of it is now made here. It is quite rough, a trifle harsh in feel, and comes in white, prints, and plain colors. It is used for dress goods and is a good "knock-about" fabric.

JAPANESE HEMP. A high-quality hemp that appears in the trade in the form of very thin ribbons which are smooth and glossy, and light straw-color. Also raised in California.

JAPANESE NON-CELLULOSIC MAN-MADE FIBERS.
1. Nylon 6 under the names of NRC nylon and Amilan.
2. Vinylon is manufactured by dissolving polyvinyl alcohol in water

and then spinning into a coagulating bath insolubilized with aldehydes and then heat-stretched. Product of Kurashiki Rayon Company.

3. Kanabian is a vinyl alcohol staple fiber of Kanegafuchi Spinning Company, Ltd., in Osaka.

4. Kuralon is a polyvinyl alcohol fiber of Kurashiki Rayon Company, Ltd., in Osaka.

5. Exlan and Vonnel are acrylic fibers comparable with Courtelle, Acrilan, and "Orlon" acrylic fiber.

6. Tetoron is a polyester fiber comparable with "Dacron," Fortrel, Kodel, Terylene, and Vycron.

JAPANESE SILK. A yarn made from silk raised in Japan, the leading silk producing country of the world. From the cloth angle, it is a plain-weave material woven in Japanese mills, with the warp and filling identical in every detail. The cloth has good luster, soft feel, and is dyed in plain colors. The materials can be made in figured designs or may be printed in the same manner as calicoes. Habutai, nankeen, pongee, rajah, and shantung are types of the material. Used in coats, dresses, shirting, waists, underwear.

JAPAN MULBERRY BAST FIBER. A fiber used in the manufacture of ordinary paper.

JAPANNED LEATHER. See PATENT LEATHER.

JAPAN WAX. A textile softener which has a high melting-point and is ideal for fabrics which are to find use in hot, humid climates. It is yellowish in cast and comes in a hard, brittle form.

JAPERGONSI. A particular type of fine, high-textured muslin, embellished with gold thread listing, and made in Japan.

JAPONETTE. A printed cotton crepe fabric.

JARDINIERE. A design which features flowers, fruit, and leaves.

JARRE. The coarse hair taken from rabbit pelts prior to making hatter's plush, jarré is used for mattress stuffing.

JASPE. A durable cotton cloth, jaspé is made with a narrow woven stripe on a dobby loom with multicolored threads or with different shades of the same color. Has a shadow effect. Sometimes printed versions are shown in the market. Often small dots are woven into the fabric. Used for draperies and slipcovers.

JASPE, COTTON. The word, jaspé, implies fabrics with two or more colors that are usually narrow in width and cover the entire fabric in the warp direction. The effect may be achieved through yarn-dyed stock, by printing,

or by twisting two colors together with a low number of turns of twist per inch. The effect can also be obtained by arranging the ends in contrasting shades of the same color. Plain, basket, or small twill weaves are used to make the goods. Usually woven in 36-inch width, the cloth runs from two to five yards to the pound.

JASPER. A salt-and-pepper fabric made of wool with a black warp and a white filling, or vice versa.

JASPE SILK. Silk warps which have been printed in the hank state are called jaspé silk.

JAUMAVE ISTLE. A Mexican bast fiber obtained from the leaves of the plan *Jaumave Lechuguilla*. It grows in semi-arid areas, is stiff, almost white in color, resilient, and runs from one to more than two feet in length. Used in high-quality brushes.

JAVA, ADA, AIDA CANVAS. A foundation material used in embroidery. It comes in natural, brown, or bleached conditions.

JAVA COTTON. Another name for kapok. See KAPOK.

JAVA STRIPES. Striped cottons which have a red background; used for dress goods. Made in England and shipped to Africa and the Straits Settlements.

JAVA SUPERS. Plain-woven, rather heavily sized British cottons which find favor in the East Indian trade.

JAVELLE, JAVEL WATER. Sodium hypochlorite, NaOCl, comes under many names in the trade such as crystalline water, Oxydol, Rose-X, etc. This bleaching agent is very powerful in its action on vegetable fibers and never should be used at all on animal fibers.

JAWS. Clumpy, felted, or matted wool found underneath the jaws of the sheep.

JEAN. A warp-effect cotton cloth on the order of drill but made with higher counts of yarn, higher textures, and a finer diagonal twill line. A 2-up and 1-down left-hand twill weave is used to make jean. The British jean cloth is a 1-up and 2-down filling-face fabric that is bleached or dyed for use as lining fabric.

There is also another fabric of this name, a cotton or worsted material made in small twill weave. It is a rugged fabric that is used in low-priced clothing, blouses, and uniform fabric. The name comes from Genoa (Janua, Gênes). In the fourteenth and fifteenth centuries the Jàne was the English name for a coin of this city.

JEANNETTE. 1. A British woolen made on a 2-up and 1-down twill weave. 2. A lightweight jean cloth with a pre-

dominant warp effect on the face. 3. The name for a 1-up and 2-down twill weave.

JEANS VERSUS SLACKS. The continued use of one of the great staple fabrics, denim, has lead to much confusion between jeans and slacks. Both terms are now being used interchangeably in advertising, department stores, shops, etc. Both seem to serve the same purpose but, generally speaking, slacks seem to be considered on higher ground as to quality of fabric, tailoring, price, etc. Slacks are made with open seams, have waistbands, use findings, and pants or trousers in this category use this word. Jeans use closed seams, have a turned-over waist, use a yoke back, are devoid of findings, and seem to give the so-called Western Look. Types of pockets are not essential to either product. Jeans have horizontal patch pockets, bold, distinct stitching, metal buttons and snaps, rivets, and wide belt loops. They are also lower in price.

The customer today does not care whether the article is jeans or slacks as long as he is able to buy what meets with his approval. The terms, bells and flares, have also entered the picture to further add confusion, but without upsetting terminology. Names observed in advertising these wares reveal a host of names used by prospective purchasers - bells, casuals, casual jeans, casual slacks, denims, dress slacks, dress-up jeans, dungarees, flares, jeans, Levis, overalls, stove-pipes, workpants, wranglers. As long as these articles sell well, it makes little difference as to what the item is called. See Jean, Slacks.

JENAPPE. Genapping or gassing.

JENKINS COTTON. Also known as Poor Man's Friend, this early-maturing type of Rio Grande cotton has a 1-inch staple and a lint yield of about 35 per cent.

JENNETS. Rugged British cottons made with twill weaves; the cloths come in white or may be dyed or printed.

JENNY. See SPINNING JENNY.

JERGA. A contraction of the Spanish, exerga, and similar to the English word, serge, this Mexican plaid-effect woolen cloth is used in apparel.

JERK-BACKS. Filling yarn that is irregular along the selvage edge or which may have been pulled back into the cloth as it is being woven. Often caused by the filling catching onto the side fork or the front box plate of the loom as the cloth is being woven.

JERKIN. A close-fitting jacket or waistcoat; a short coat.

JERKIN LEATHER. See CLOTHING

LEATHER.

JERSEY. A plain-stitch knitted fabric, in contrast to rib-knit cloth. May be made by circular, flat, or warp knitting methods; the latter type jersey is now very popular as tricot-knit. Gives good service, launders very well, and is used in dress goods, sportswear, and underwear. Prints and solid colors are often very attractive and a good selling point for jersey.

Woven jersey cloth is a type of lightweight silk or rayon broadcloth in which some porosity in the weave prevails. Used in shirting and blouses in the white or in colors. Jersey is made from any of the major fibers.

JERSEY, ACETATE OR RAYON. A fine, rib-effect knitted fabric made of acetate or rayon yarn; comes in plain colors and prints. It drapes exceptionally well and gives excellent service in underwear and dress goods.

JERSEY FABRICS. A generic term applied to knitted piece goods.

JERSEY FLANNEL. Usually refers to wool jersey napped on the face of the goods. Used in children's wear, dress goods, sportswear, etc. Some fabrics, isolated, are called by this term, whether woven or knitted, when, in reality, they are not regulation jersey fabric.

JERSEY STITCH. Another name for the plain stitch found in medium and fine knit goods.

JERSEY TWEED. A soft-feeling woolen tweed that comes in plain colors; much used in women's wear ensembles which feature a tweed skirt of regulation or fancy twill effect and a jacket of plain jersey.

JERSEY WHEEL. See SPINNING WHEEL.

JERSEY WOOL. A fine, choice staple which is combed from the rest of the fleece.

JESUIT CLOTH. Suiting material of plain-weave construction worn by the members of the Society of Jesus, founded by Ignatius of Loyola, Spain, in 1534. The cloth is rather coarse, dyed black, and is made from hard twisted yarn. There is considerable call for this tropical worsted, worsted, or woolen cloth among religious orders throughout the world.

JESUIT LACE. The crochet guipure of Ireland.

JET. Another name for the spinneret used in the manufacture of acetate, rayon and other man-made textile fibers. See SPINNERET.

JET CRATERS. Deposits which often form around the orifices or holes on the face of the metal jets used in the extrusion of viscose.

JETEE. Used for cordage, twine, fish nets, etc., jetée is strong bast fiber coming from the East Indies.

JET RINGS. Annular deposits which form from time to time inside the orifices or holes of the metal jets or spinnerets when used in the extrusion of viscose. Coagulants which contain zinc sulphate often cause these deposits.

JETSPUN. Solution-dyed viscose rayon filament; registered trade-mark of American Enka Corporation, New York City.

JEW'S MALLOW FIBER. A member of the jute fiber group also known as pot herb. Obtained in India. This important fiber is secured by retting and washing carefully. Used for cordage and rope.

JHALAWAMI. The long-tailed Indian sheep known for its coarse black or gray wool.

JIG. This machine is used to dye piece goods. Full-width material is passed from a roller through the dye bath is an open vat, and then proceeds to another roller. The treatment is repeated until the desired shade is assured.

JIG-DYEING MACHINE. A machine in which cloth is dyed; the machine is composed of a large vat fitted with rollers to guide the cloth through a dye solution and subject it thoroughly to the action of the dye.

JIJIPAPA. Area in Ecuador is known for its manufacture of straw hats from prized straw fiber named for the area.

JIMPING. British term for pinking.

JOBBER. One who buys textiles in bulk from mills and then resells them to smaller dealers; really a "middleman." He is paid for his services, gives term payments, and makes his money from a "higher-price and less quantity" idea.

JOB EVALUATION. The system or technique of measuring jobs to determine their relative values.

JOCKEY CLOTH. An old-time and still popular staple high-quality cashmere fabric made in a 2-up, 1-down twill with silk warp. This British material also may have a merino woolen yarn in the filling such as the well-known botany type whose fibers come from Australian merino sheep. Two-ply warp and single filling yarn, with three times as many picks as warp ends, feature this material, used in apparel. Some of the goods may be made with a 1-up, 2-down twill thereby giving a filling face-effect on the fabric.

JODHPUR. 1. A low boot used for riding. 2. Trousers worn for horseback riding.

The trousers are tight-fitting around the calves to the ankle. Low shoes are worn with them instead of high riding boots.

JOINING. The joining of two or more sections to make a whole.

JOLOCIN. A coarse bast fiber of Central America used for cordage.

JOMAYU. Japanese term for good cocoons. There is an annual production of about 750 million pounds of cocoons; jomayu accounts for about 90 per cent of this yield.

JONES IMPROVED COTTON. A large, round boll cotton which matures late. Staple is 15/16 inch with a lint yield of about 31 per cent.

JONES LONG-STAPLE COTTON. A large boll, late-maturing cotton raised in the central and southern areas of the cotton belt. This Uplands variety has a staple of about 1-inch with a lint yield of about 30 per cent.

JONES NUMBER ONE COTTON. A variety of Rio Grande cotton with a staple of ¾ inch and lint yield of 33 per cent. Alabama is chief raising area.

JONOTE. A Central American bast fiber used for cordage.

JORIA. East Indian wool, finer in quality than the similar Vicanere wool; noted for its springy staple.

JOSEPH'S COAT. Facetious way of referring to a blanket range. See BLANKET RANGE.

JOSETTE. A strong, durable, well-woven, cotton-twill cloth that finds use in several types of sportswear, slacks, shirting, bags, jackets, etc.

JOUR DEUX PLACE. A translation of this term could be "two places for daylight." Hence, in its application it implies a leno or doup weave in a cloth with two rows of openwork made by the weave construction, either in full leno or half-leno weaves. When "deux" is replaced by the word, "trois," it means that there are three lines of openwork per repeat of pattern. The material is used for dress goods, shirting, etc.

JOURNEYMAN. An individual who has completed satisfactorily the apprenticeship period to learn a particular craft or skill.

JOURS. The openwork in cloth, embroidery, or lace. The designs in openwork (à jour—in daylight) on fabric are made by pressing the goods against a plate which has points arranged to form the motif and then pressing the material to hold the openings. The various stitches in bobbin and needlepoint laces fill out the designs, and these are known as fillings or lead-work.

JOUY DESIGNS. These derive from the toiles de Jouy which were originally made of cotton printed to simulate imported oriental masterpieces. First made in Rivière La Bièvre Valley, France. Jouy soon became the center of the industry. Oberkampf became the leader in this work, and by 1760 the influence of these designs was felt. Oberkampf introduced the printing of textiles by means of rollers; there could be as many colors as there were rollers in the machine setup. Jouy became most popular for dresses and interior decoration in the nineteenth century.

JOWERS COTTON. On the order of Peterkin cotton, Jowers has a 1-inch staple and lint yield of 34 per cent: a late-maturing cotton.

JUBBULPORE HEMP. A strong, high-quality Indian hemp.

JUDAS RED. This red color received its name from the idea that Judas Iscariot had red hair.

JUMBO COTTON. A prolific, early-maturing cotton of ¾-inch staple and 32 per cent lint yield.

JUMBO STITCH. A stitch used in heavy sweaters, made on a machine with two sets of needles to show the heavy, ribbed effect which is its main characteristic. A flat machine is used to do the work, generally speaking.

JUMEL COTTON. Another name for Maco cotton of Egypt. It has been a leading staple since 1820. Named for Jumel, the French engineer, who perfected the fiber so that it has commercial value.

JUMPER. 1. A loose jacket usually of the work-clothes type. 2. A dress that is sleeveless, usually worn with blouse underneath.

JUNGLE CLOTH. Trade name for the strong, heavy but compactly woven cotton cloths made for the U.S. Navy. Woven with about 300 picks to the inch, the fabric gives good results in windswept, frigid areas.

"JUNIOR PETITE." An apparel term used to describe the so-called "in-between" group which refers to the girl graduating from the "awkward stage and age" into the "sub-debutante" era. Refers to the classification of merchandise used in the lines to serve this group.

JUNK. Bits of cordage wastes of all types used to make mats, oakum, etc. Also used as a general descriptive term, at times, for other wastes and inferior articles.

JUPON, GIPON. A close-fitting, usually padded jacket, bearing heraldic arms and worn over armor. In time it became known as a doublet. From Old French word, jupe. See Doublet.

JURISDICTIONAL DISPUTE. The conflict between two or more unions to secure the membership of, and the representation for, employees in a plant or a unit of a plant, or the control of the specific work.

JUSI. A fabric, delicate in nature, made from a mixture of abaca, silk, and pina fiber. Manufactured in Manila, Philippine Islands.

JUTE. This bast fiber comes from the species known as *Corchorus capsularis*. Bengal and other parts of India, southern Asia, and tropical Africa are the centers where the fiber is raised. Bengal is the world market center. The plant grows from two to twelve feet in height, and the fiber layer is quite thick. The stalk produces two to five times as much fiber as the flax plant.

The leaves are light green in color and range from four to five inches long. They are about ½ inch in diameter at the base. The flowers of the plant are yellowish-white and grow in clusters opposite the leaves. Seed pods are quite irregular.

The plants are rippled and retted like flax. Stream-retting is the most popular treatment; it takes from three to four days to complete the work. Scutching and hackling are also given to the fiber. They free the stock from foreign matter to considerable degree. Raw jute fibers are from four to seven feet in length and are yellowish brown in color. Root ends, known as jute cutting, find use in making paper.

Jute spins well and is low in price. The greatest disadvantage of its fiber is that water and moisture cause it to disintegrate. When dry, jute is durable. It is not very strong, and much difficulty is encountered in bleaching it.

JUTE BAGGING. British heavy single-warp, single-filling, plain-weave fabric. Made with a warp, 8 to 12 pounds, per spyndle in a 4 to 7 reed or porter; there are 2 to 5 picks per inch of heavy rope yarn used as filling, 200 to 400 spyndle.

JUTE BUTTS. Waste ends of jute used as paper stock.

JUTE HEAD. A raw jute bale is made up of a number of bunches of jute called heads. Each of these is given a twist and folded over prior to being placed in the bale.

JUTE RUG BACKING. Made chiefly in England and this country, this single-construction jute material is made with plain weave and has stripes that are composed of two colors in a three-thread arrangement in each stripe. Used as rug backing.

JUTE SCRIM. An English material made with an open-mesh plain weave. It is used for baling or bagging vegetables for market and can be used in making tarred paper waterproof.

Jacquard label, front and back.

K

KABUL WOOL. A soft wool peculiar to Lahore, India, used in making high-grade shawls.

KACHOJI. Japanese for mosquito netting.

KADUNGAS. British term for plain-weave cottons printed with several colors on a dark background, usually indigo; similar to printed calico and percale in the United States. Much of the goods is exported all over the world.

KAFFIR HEMP. A strong South African white bast fiber used for coarse fabrics and roping.

KAGA. A general term for average-quality silk fabrics made in Japan.

KAHNAMI COTTON. A soft, silken staple cotton raised in Brazil and India.

KAIN KAPALA. A special type sarong embellished with an elaborate motif. At one end of the fabric, from selvage to selvage, there is a very fine, intricate design on the cloth which is known as the kapala.

KAIN PANDJANG. Originating in the Far East, this sarong has an allover motif and finds use as daily garb for Indonesian women.

KAINS. Colored woven cotton cloths made in England for the Straits Settlements.

KAIKI, KHAIKI. A plain-weave washable Japanese silk or cotton fabric of rather light weight.

KAKARALLY FIBER. Fine, thin layers of bast fiber obtained from the monkey-pot tree in South America; used for cordage, baskets, and warping bundles.

KAKEDA. A fine raw silk of Japan.

KAKI COTTON. A creamy-brown Egyptian cotton.

KALABATUN. Used for embroidering articles in India, it is a fine metallic thread, such as gold or silver, wound around a core thread. The thread is also used to embellish some cottons made in India.

KALASIRIS. The so-called New Kingdom in Ancient History began around 1,500 B.C. and lasted until about 330 B.C. Replacing the staple schenti of the Old rather long tunic with a fringe for adornment. Thin and somewhat transparent it showed the loin cloth worn next to the skin. A rectangular fabric was used, usually woven in a single piece, and worn by women who made it into a close-fitting garment with emphasis on the contour of the breasts. Shoulder straps kept it in place. Since the Egyptians held wool in contempt, cotton or linen was the fiber used. Other nations sometimes used wool

as well as these other fibers. See Schenti.

KALEMAUKION. The black, cylinder-shaped head-covering, with a flat brim at the top, worn commonly and for liturgical purposes by clerics of the Byzantine Rite of the Roman Catholic Church. Bishops and monks wear the Kalemaukion with a veil that covers it and falls down to the shoulders.

KALGAN. A Chinese carpet wool.

KALI. Iraq (Persian) floor covering which is a large felt matting embroidered with floral motifs with silk and metallic threads.

KALIAVA. A course, home-reeled silk used by Chinese natives.

KALMUCK. 1. A coarse woolen overcoating made from rough yarns and finished with a very shaggy face.

2. Term used in Europe for a type of cotton blanket cloth made with two colors of filling, one forming the face and the other the back.

KAMALA. Used in India as a bright orange dye, this orange-red powder comes from the fruit of the tree *Rottlera tinctoria*.

KANAKIN. The Japanese use this term to cover plain-weave cotton fabrics, white goods, prints of all types, shirtings, etc.

KANDAHAR. A good grade of East Indian carpet wool.

KANDAR. Trade name for resin treatment which produces a crisp, full-bodied, rich-textured finish on fabrics; durable to laundering and dry-cleaning. Product of U. S. Rubber Company, Naugatuck, Conn.

KANGAROO LEATHER. Produced exclusively in Australia, this kangaroo leather is tanned in the United States, usually vegetable or chrome-tanned, and often given a suede finish. One of the best of shoe upper leathers, it is close-grained, fine, and tough.

KANIKI. British cotton cloth made for the African export trade; merely a plain-weave, indigo or black-dyed material.

KANIKI MARDUF. A 2-up, 2-down twill is used to make this cotton fabric made with about 30s warp and filling yarn. The cloth is a staple in some parts of Africa.

KANO CHECKS. British export fabric shipped in the gray to Africa; cotton warp and filling and rather heavy in weight.

KANOKO. Crepe yarns feature this Japanese silk fabric that is light in weight, used as an ornament for the headdress, and usually dyed red, blue, or violet shades, casts, tones, and hues.

KAOLIN. A claylike compact, mealy in nature, which is a hydrous aluminum

silicate used in finishing some textile goods as a filler ingredient in the material; also used to make porcelain. See CHINA CLAY.

KAPA. See TAPA.

KAPAR. Broad term for Indian cottons used for dhooties, saris, and other loincloths, shawl fabrics, and veilings. May be hand-woven or made on power looms. See DHOOTIE, SARI.

KAPAS. Indian term for raw cotton with seed still in it.

KAPOK. Found in Borneo, Java, Sumatra, and Central America, it resembles cotton in some respects and seems to have the characteristics of silk in feel and smoothness. Kapok has been called the cotton-silk fiber despite the fact that, unlike cotton and silk, it is irregular, weak, transparent, and inconsistent. It is used for pillows, mattresses, and in upholstering furniture.

KAPOK OIL. These seeds of the Eriodendron and the Anfractuosum are obtained in the Dutch East Indies. They furnish a greenish-yellow oil used in the manufacture of margarine and soap.

KAPRON. The Soviet equivalent of nylon. First produced after World War II, stockings made from the fiber sold for about $7.50 in American currency. They now sell, in the cheapest range, for $2.50 a pair up to five or six dollars per pair in the better quality range. The Soviet ruble is now officially valued at twenty-five cents in American money, thus a pair of the lowest quality stocking would cost about ten rubles.

KARACHI. A leafy Indian and East Indian cotton, dull in cast but fairly long in staple and quite strong.

KARAKUL. Originally an Asiatic breed of sheep. The long carpet wool obtained from the fleece has made it a favorite in Texas. Skins plus wool from lambs of the breed, one to three days old, are called Astrakhan or Broadtail. Shrinkage is about 35 per cent. The name comes from the village of Kara Kul (Black Lake) in eastern Bokhara.

KARAKUL FABRIC. A heavyweight pile fabric of wool, used for coating. Made to simulate broadtail fur or Persian Lamb.

KARATAS. The wild pineapple of Central and South America yields a fine, white leaf fiber which is used in making hammocks, string, fishing line, etc.

KARAWAN. Turkish skin wool from native fat-tailed sheep.

KAREYA. Low-grade, plain-weave cotton fabric used in India. Made counts of yarns as low as 7s. This six-yard-cut length is used as waist fabric.

KARNAK, KARNOK. A high-type variety of good-yielding, long staple Egyptian cotton now grown in the Delta area. It is one of the most popular world cottons to be found in the market today.

KARPASI. Sanskrit term for cotton.

KARRELDOEK. A Dutch linen sail fabric.

KASHA CLOTH. 1. Fabric made from the hair fibers of the Tibet goat. Very soft in feel and napped with a slight crosswise streaked effect in the darker hairs used in the cloth. Rodier Frères, Paris, introduced the fabric several years ago. Ideal for dresses, jackets, etc. 2. A tan-colored cotton-lining flannel. 3. A cotton flannel with napped face and mottled color-effect, bordering on tan or ecru; an unbleached soft-filled sheeting.

Mixed yarns may be used with sized warp yarns that take the dye and filling yarns with natural wax that do not take the dye. When bale-dyed, the result is always mottled.

KASHGAR WEAVE EFFECT. Originated in India. It is a warp float effect made by "an all-figure warp" over heavy filling yarns and weaves plain weave with the binder picks. The binder warp is under all heavy picks and over-all binder picks. The construction is normally a two-warp and two-filling construction, but it can also be made with three or four figure warps. The effect is much used in various Jacquard weave effects.

KASHMIR. See CASHMERE.

KASHMIR WORSTED. Hand-spun worsted yarn is used in this hand-loom goods made with twice as many picks as ends—say, a 34 x 68. Pickage is "two picks per shed." Made in province of Kashmir, India, the cloth weighs around seven ounces per square yard.

KASSASBATCHI. A coarse Turkish wool used in Oriental carpets.

KATA AYA. Twill-weave cotton shirting made in Japan.

KATTUN. German term for cotton calico.

KAWAMATTA. Low-quality Japanese silk materials.

KECHE, KECHI. A type of Turkish carpeting made chiefly from goat's hair.

KECK, KECKLING. Maritime term to signify the use of old cabling or rope wound around usable cables to withstand chafing.

KEEL. 1. The Indian red, or Venetian red, ferruginous paint used to mark sheep. 2. This red ocher is also used to make either end of a warp or cut of cloth for identification purposes.

KEKCHI COTTON. A rapid-growing, early-maturing cotton of Guatemala. Used by U. S. Dept. of Agriculture to produce the popular Texas staple, Paymaster.

KELANTAN. A Malayan sheep, small in stature, that produces a short, coarse wool. These sheep weigh only 20 to 30 pounds.

KELAT. Baluchistan furnishes this good, short-fiber carpet wool.

KELIM. Made without a pile weave, this Persian or Turkish hand-woven rug is made of coarse wool. A needle is used in making the rug which reveals a motif with slits or open spaces between the warp threads where the colors of filling yarn are changed. Chinese silk tapestry made on this plan is known as Kossu.

KELLY COTTON. Also known as Marston, this late-maturing cotton has a staple of 1 inch to 1¼ inches with lint yield of about 30 per cent.

KELPIE PROCESS. Developed in Scotland in 1935, the process finds much favor in Canada and the British Isles. Wool can be treated in top, yarn, piece goods or in finished form of hosiery. There is no loss of yardage or weight results and no effect on handle or shade at any time. Features of the process include greater brilliance of color, permanent fiber softness, and resiliency, as well as retarded dirt penetration.

KELT. Sometimes spelled Celt, the fabric is similar to Irish tweed, and is noted for its white warp and black filling construction, or, black warp with white filling.

KEMBAN. Used in the Far East, it is a piece of fabric wound tightly around the chest. Arms and shoulders are not covered by the article.

KEM LOK. Tradename for a premium oil and water printing system which provides a far superior washfastness on all fabrics, particularly cotton/polyester blends which are to be treated for durable press finish. Certain curtain fabrics, for example, can withstand up to 50 home launderings if specified fabric instructions are carried out. Product of Sherwin Williams Chemicals Company, Inc., New York City.

KEMP. A very coarse, brittle fiber often found in poorly bred wools, especially carpet wools. Normally they are short, wavy, and tapering toward each end, strongly medullated and of a dead white or opaque color. They absorb dye poorly and consequently appear prominently in finished fabric unless further treated in some manner. At times kemp is mixed with wool for novelty effects, but it is used chiefly as a carpet wool.

KEMPY WOOL. Wool which contains considerable amounts of kemp and consequently is of low grade.

KENAF. A five-foot fiber is obtained from the bark of this bast fiber plant. Runs from light yellow to gray in cast and is used chiefly for cordage and twines. Sources are Africa and India. Other names used are Ambari, Da, Bimlipatam, Deccan hemp.

KENDAL GREEN. Name given to coarse woolen cloth originally made by the weavers of Kendal, England. This material is noted for its distinctive green shade and is a favorite color in high-quality homespuns.

KENDIR. A wild bast fiber grown in the area of the Adriatic Sea. Also known as Dog's Bane, the fiber may be used as a substitute for cotton in making coarse fabrics, as well as being used in bags, nets, and ropes.

KENTING. Plain-woven linen cloth used for lining; made in Ireland and on the Continent for several decades.

KENTUCKY ROUGH PRIME HEMP. According to the A.S.T.M., it is the best quality dew-retted hemp that has been broken but not hackled or combed.

KENTUCKY SINGLE-DRESSED. According to the A.S.T.M., it is hemp from this state prepared by being manipulated in drawing over a coarse hackle or comb.

KERATIN. The principal constituent of cuticle, feathers, hair, hoofs, and nails; rich in sulphur.

KERATINE. The combination of elements which form the wool fiber; approximations are: carbon, 50 per cent; oxygen, 22 per cent; nitrogen, 18 per cent; hydrogen, 6 per cent; sulphur, 2 per cent; traces of calcium, iron, and phosphorus.

KERCHIEF. Originally, a head covering. Now means a large decorative square or oblong piece of material such as cotton, acetate, rayon, silk. Usually comes in print effects or can be embroidered.

KERF. British term for the flocks gathered around shearing machines in the dry-finishing department of a mill.

KERMES. An ancient dyestuff obtained from the insects that infest the small oak tree, *Quercus coccifera.* Found in Asia Minor, the dye gives brilliant red or scarlet of fairly good fastness. Cochineal has replaced kermes to a marked degree.

KERRY HILL. A breed of British sheep popular in Wales because of its hardiness, ability to find pasturage and to endure excessive rainfall. The wool, noted for its whiteness, is firm and springy, and about 5 inches long. It is about 50s quality and for classing purposes is grouped with the Down wools.

KERSEY. Originated in Kersey, near Hadleigh, Suffolk County, England. Present-day kersey is heavily fulled or milled, and has a rather lustrous nap and a grain face. Luster is caused by the use of luster, crossbred wools such as Lincoln, Leicester, Cotswold, Romney Marsh, etc. Incidentally, in southern areas of this country there is a low-priced kersey that is a union fabric with much reused or remanufactured wool in it.

Face finish weaves are used to make the goods so that the ultimate finish will be acceptable to the trade. When compared with beaver, kersey is often fulled more, has a shorter nap, and much higher luster.

Kersey is finished like beaver, and the only difference in the two fabrics seems to be the quality of the raw stocks used, the latter ranging in grade from low through medium to a rather good grade of three-eighths or half-blood wool.

The material gives good wear and is of the dressy, conventional type of fabric. Blues, browns, and blacks are the colors used the most. Other colors are only seasonal. Fiber content must be declared. See BEAVER.

KERSEYMERE. A fancy woolen fabric on the order of cassimere. The name would tend to indicate that the cloth was a product of the mills along the waterways of Kersey, England, but since there are no meres (or lakes) in the vicinity of this town, it is more than likely that the name is a variation or corruption of "cassimere."

KERSEY, NARROW-LIST. The forerunner of present-day kersey fabric used for coatings of varying weights. Narrow-list was rather low in quality and identified by its narrow selvage edges. Kersey, incidentally, is one of the oldest fabrics made in England in some form or other. See SELVAGE.

KERSEYNET. On the order of kersey and kerseymere, this cloth is a lightweight men's wear fabric made of cotton warp and woolen filling.

KETONES. They are carbon compounds that have the general formula of R

C equals O. R stands for the

carbon-hydrogen group. Acetone is an important ketone.

Ketones result from the partial oxidation of alcohols, in which the hydroxyl (OH) group is linked to a carbon or atom, which is itself linked to other carbon atoms. valence of the connecting bond.

KETTSATIN. European term for the average warp-satin fabric of about 160 ends end 80 picks.

KEVERGIK. Turkish skin wool of the Merino sheep.

KEYBAK. A nonwoven, disposable towel marketed as Masslin Toweling and developed by Chicopee Mills, Inc., New York City. Geon, a vinyl latex of B. F. Goodrich Chemical Company, is used as the binder for the fabric whereby fibers such as cotton, rayon, and other natural or man-made fibers can be used to produce the fabric. The towel has the feel and appearance of regular toweling, along with durability and economy, and it has strength, high absorbency, and a clean appearance. Very popular in sports where this disposable article is used by bowlers, golfers, basketball players, etc.

KHADI. Made from about the poorest grade of cotton raised in India, this is a plain weave, coarse cloth made on hand looms. When spelled KHADIE, it is a fringed cotton made there which finds use as toweling.

KHAIKI. See KAIKI.

KHAKI, DERIVATION OF. A pure Persian (Iranian) word in which KHAKI is the genitive case and means literally "of dust," or KHAK-I, of which the I denotes the genitive case. Nadir Shah was responsible for Urdu, which means the language of the horde or the army and was mixed Persian-Indian dialect tongue that arose from the Persian Army invasion of India by Nadir Shah.

KHAKI COTTON. Some Chinese and Indian cottons are given this name when the staple is tan or reddish in cast.

KHANDESH COTTON. The poorest grade of Oomra, Indian cotton; Staple is very short, ½ inch to ⅝ inch. Lint yield is from 33 per cent to 38 per cent. Spins to 10s or 12s filling yarn.

KHANGA. Scarf fabric, printed or dyed, that is made in England for the East African trade.

KHOKLIBANGA COTTON. An East Indian cotton which has a strong staple but is yellowish in cast.

KHORASSAN. A fine diameter, long-staple Persian or Iranian wool which possesses good working properties.

KHORJI. Hand-woven, rich-looking silk brocade made for some of the reigning houses of the Far East. This Indian material is made with flowers and leaves in the motif enhanced by the use of gold threads on a colored relief. The border is done in gold on black and red silk ground for particular ornamentation.

KIBISSO, KIBIZZI. Name for several types of reeling wastes when manipulating silk filaments.

KICKBACK. Payment by an employee of part of his wages to the representative of a company, or of a union, as part of the private agreement between the two involved.

KICKLING. The use of old rope which is wound around cables to prevent too much friction or chafing.

KICK-OFF. To empty a washwheel of liquid after an operation.

KICK PLEAT. A variation of an inverted pleat to give breadth to a narrow skirt.

KID. 1. A young goat. 2. Commonly, this term now refers to shoe upper leather tanned from goat- or kidskins, and to glove leather tanned from goat- and lambskins. See FRENCH KID, GLOVE LEATHER. 3. The sleek fur of a young goat: white, gray, black, or spotted. Wearing qualities range from fair to poor. Judged by flatness of surface, softness, and pliability. Found in China.

KIDDER CARPET. Originated in Kidderminster, England. This cheap carpeting, made without pile construction, is rugged, rough, and is usually woven one yard in width.

KIDDERMINSTER CARPET. Carpeting that originated in place of that name in England. The first carpeting of this name was a coarse, double-faced floor covering made of worsted warp and woolen filling. Later, the carpet was made with triple construction and showed two faces, the figures alternating on both sides and without a pile construction. Other names are: Scotch carpet, Kilmarnock. In this country, the carpet is known as Ingrain.

KID-FINISHED CAMBRIC. A very smooth feeling cotton used as dress lining. Fabric is finished with exceptional care.

KID MOHAIR. Hair from the young Angora goat, comparable with lamb's wool.

KIDNEY COTTON. Trade name for Brazilian cotton, whose seeds of each lock are combined to resemble a kidney-shaped mass.

KIDUNGAS. British export cotton for the African trade; made of low quality, coarse yarn in which much foreign matter is seen. Used as headgear and apparel.

KIER. A container, vat, or some similar mechanical device in which stock, yarn, or cloth may be washed, scoured, boiled, rinsed, etc.

KIER-BOILING. Boiling-out cotton goods in an alkaline solution in the kier, before bleaching or dyeing. Many thousands of pounds of cloth can be processed at once; boiling may be continued for several hours under pressure.

KIERING. Process of scouring cotton, or washing or boiling it out, under pressure, in large tanks known as kiers.

KIETH COTTON. A medium boll, non-cluster, early-maturing Alabama cotton with a 1-inch staple and lint yield of about 33 per cent.

KIKAI. See KIBISSO.

KILIM. Name for a group of hand-woven flat-rugs that have been woven for centuries in the Middle East, mainly in Turkey. Compared with pile-woven oriental rugs in this same area, Kilim motifs are more schematic and pronounced in effect. Kilim rugs have been made for centuries by prospective brides to prove their domestic abilities. Today the Kilim is one type of a flat-woven rug, made in regulation tapestry weave so that the rug is reversible. Thus, the pattern is achieved in weaving the basic structure of the fabric. Other techniques used include adding the design to the basic material; it is either woven, added on the loom, or added by use of a needle. Other types are known by the techniques used and are either embroidered or brocaded rugs.

Turkish tribes, usually known for centuries for their geometric motifs, also used naturalistic patterns peculiar to Anatolian, Caucasian, and Persian motifs. The Turks borrowed these designs from neighboring Bulgarian and Serbian rug weavers. Obviously, these rugs are collector's items.

KILMARNOCK BONNET. The well-known, broad-topped woolen cap worn in Scotland and other countries. Plaid effects predominate in these caps.

KILO, KILOGRAM. Equals 2 pounds, 3.2 ounces, or 1,000 grains.

KILOWATT. Equals 1,000 watts, equivalent to approximately one and one-third horsepower.

KILT. The short, plaited skirt used in the dress of Scotch Highlanders; its origin is unknown, but it is supposed to have been first adopted somewhere between the eleventh and seventeenth centuries. It takes 7 yards of cloth 27 inches wide to make a kilt. The cloth is woven 54 or 56 inches and is split up the middle, the outer selvage always forming the lower edge of the kilt.

KILTED REGIMENTS. There are now five kilted Highland regiments in the British Army: the Black Watch, the Argyll and Sutherlands, the Gordons, the Seaforths, and the Camerons. In choosing the tartans for these regiments, the War Office followed the heraldic idea in using distinguishing overchecks on the same ground.

The Lowland regiments, although not kilted, have each their distinctive tartans, worn as trousers by the men and as trews and riding breeches by the officers. The pipers in all regiments wear kilts.

KIMONO. 1. A kind of loose robe or gown tied with a sash, worn as an outer garment by Japanese men and women. 2. A similar gown worn as a dressing robe by women of Western nations.

KIMONO FLANNEL. A soft-feeling, plain-weave cotton, woolen or blended cloth that can be dyed or printed; nap can be on one or both sides. Soft, cylindrical filling aids in making suitable nap. Also known as flannelette, it is used for blankets, nightwear, children's garments, robes, coverings, etc.

KIMONO SILK. Kimono and lining material; a soft, plain-woven, lightweight silk which is usually printed in elaborate designs.

KIN. Specifically a Japanese weight of 1.3251 pounds, commercially figured as 1.3277 pounds so that 756 kin weigh 1,000 pounds. Japanese raw-silk quotations are in Yen per Kin. See PICULE.

KINCOB. Outstanding hand-woven fabric made in India. Used in ceremonials, functions of state, etc. Made of silk, the material is richly embellished with gold and silver threads woven into the brocade background.

KINDERGARTEN CLOTH. Plain-weave cloth, rather hardy, and made with yarn-dyed warp stripes. Two ends are worked as one in the construction. The ratio of the warp and the filling is about three to one. Single-ply yarn is used. Uses include rompers, sun suits, doll cloth, and bunting.

KINETICS. The branch of dynamics which treats of the production or modification of the motion in bodies.

KINETIC SILHOUETTE. A silhouette which shows muscular or kinetic action to demonstrate the effects of draping, clinginess, pleating, and form.

KING COTTON. Senator James H. Hammond of South Carolina coined the expression "Cotton is King" in a speech in the Senate on March 4, 1858. Cotton was a potent factor in leading to the War Between the States, 1861–1865. Cotton is still King of Textile Fibers, the most versatile of all fibers. It has been said that cotton has over 10,000 uses.

KING IMPROVED COTTON. A small, round-boll, early-maturing cotton with $1\frac{1}{16}$-inch staple and lint yield of about 33 per cent. Also known as King Gold Dust and Tennessee Gold Dust, this variety of prolific Uplands cotton is considered as very desirable.

KINIK. A type of Turkish raw wool.

KINJI SHUSU. Japanese silk fabric made with satin weave; the face of the goods is often colored for some particular pattern. It is a kimono fabric.

KINKS. Yarn that recedes upon itself and causes loops which show as an extra loop in some goods. Kinks may be caused by poor shuttle-tensions or actions, irregular stop-motion actions, improper timing of the shed of the loom, faulty yarn twisting or winding, and one or more missing plies in the ply-yarn. Kink or kink-effects are often seen in pebble-finish rugs made on hand looms.

KINKY FILLING. Short, thin, or thick places running in the direction of the filling with an occasional small loop. Caused by improper conditioning, excess twist in spinning, or not enough shuttle tension. May be corrected by less twist, better conditioning, heavier shuttle fur, or more tension in the eye of the shuttle.

KIP, KIPSKIN. 1. Skin from an animal of the bovine species in size between a calf and a mature cow, weighing in the green-salted condition from 16 to 25 pounds. It also includes skins from calves which have grown larger than the size usually slaughtered for veal, and certain breeds of undersized cattle which may have reached maturity.

2. The term is also used for a pack of 30 finished chamois skins.

KIRK, TIMOTHY AND LESLIE, ROBERT. They were the first American inventors to receive patent rights for a power loom in this country. Patents obtained in 1792.

KIRKAGATCH COTTON. A cotton raised and used locally in Asia Minor.

KIRKCALDY STRIPE. A fabric made of cotton warp and linen filling featured by filling crossover stripes.

KIRMANI WOOL. Persian wool that is mixed with Pashmina wool—an adulterant fiber.

KIRSCHNER BEATER. See CARDING BEATER.

KIRTLE. Worn in the Middle Ages, it was a loose gown worn by women. The term also implied a man's coat or tunic, obsolete. The present term, girdle, is derived from this word.

KISSING STRINGS. Popular in the last half of the eighteenth century, they were bonnets made with side narrow fabric which was worn loose or tied under the chin; also called streamer or tie.

"KISS-OF-DEATH." John Kay invented his fly shuttle for power looms in England in 1733 at the beginning of the Industrial Revolution there. From that time on, "to thread the filling yarn" through the "eye of the shuttle," it was necessary "to suck the yarn through the eye" and draw it into the mouth, a very unsanitary thing to do. Mouth sores, canker, etc. resulted. This practice lasted for a great many years and it was not until the end of the War Between the States in America that the practice was supposed to end by law and the so-called "self-threading shuttle" came into being. However, it was a bit difficult to convince old-time weavers in New England mills to switch to the more sanitary method of threading filling yarn and, it was not until World War I that the practice actually ended in the United States.

KISSUTO. Broad term for cotton prints exported to or made in the several East African countries.

KLAUDER-WELDON DYE MACHINE. A rotary skein-dyeing machine whereby yarn skeins are mounted on wooden or stainless steel bars attached to a rotary dye wheel. The bars of sticks come in pairs; one is round, the other, square. Both bars are attached to the rotary wheel with the round stick on the outer periphery and the square stick between the axle and the periphery. As the rotary wheel turns it submerges and passes the suspended yarn into the dye liquor. The square stick, revolving at the same time, affords uniform and total immersion of each and every skein in the bath.

Each revolution of the rotary wheel causes a quarter turn of the square dye rods. Because one of the dye sticks on which the skeins are set revolves, uniform, level dyeing results after the run is completed. Product of Klauder-Weldon-Giles Machine Company, Inc., Frankford, Philadelphia, Pennsylvania, 10124.

KLEANKA, BRAN. A type of Russian buckram.

KNABS. Term for waste silk obtained in reeling from the cocoon.

KNAP. A heavy woolen British fabric, dyed blue and used in maritime circles for pea jackets, coatings, etc.

KNEE KICKER. A device which is studded with gripping teeth at one end and a padded cushion at the other, used to allow a little stretching of small carpet areas when the carpet is being laid. See Crab, Power Stretcher.

KNEIPP LINEN. A openwork, rough-faced twill fabric used for toweling in Germany, Austria, and Hungary. Made of all-linen, the fabric was formerly knitted.

KNIB. A term given to knotty and uneven places in the silk fiber.

KNICKERBOCKER YARN. Yarn with more or less brilliant spots of color in nub form. The sliver is printed before the stock is condensed into roving and yarn to obtain the effect.

KNICKERBOCKERS. These loose breeches made of wool, cotton, or linen, banded below the knee, are much used in sportswear and are commonly called knickers. They were greatly used by professional and amateur golfers up to a few years ago. They may be used now for almost any type of sport in the city or country, but slacks have rapidly taken the place of knickers since they are supposed to be more comfortable and can be made from a much larger variety of fabrics.

KNIFE. The two adjustable blades on the device used to catch knots, lumps, and knubs of yarn on a winder.

KNIFE-BLADE BEATER. See BLADE BEATER.

KNIFE PLEATS. Small pleats turned in the same direction to give a sawtooth knife effect.

KNIT-de-KNIT. Texturizing method whereby yarn is knitted into a circular sleeve. The resultant fabric is then heatset and the yarn is raveled, retaining its characteristic shape which was imparted to it in the knitting procedure.

KNIT, DOUBLE. Not considered a truly technical knitting term, it refers to any of several types of fine rib structures which have the look of a twice knitted jersey fabric. Because of its two-needle construction, the fabric provides a more dimensionally stable fabric than that noted in a single needle jersey material. Fabric weight is greater than that of the single-knit jersey fabric. See Illustrated Section.

KNIT, LAMINATED. A warp or weft knitted cloth bonded to urethane foam either by the use of an adhesive agent or flame lamination.

KNIT FABRIC, KNITTED FABRIC. A fabric composed or a series of interloopings from one or more yarns. In general, such fabrics may be classified as filling (weft) or warp knit. In the former, the yarns run generally crosswise and in the latter legnthwise. The cloth may be made on hand, flat, circular, warp-knitting frames, or by hand. See Illustrated Section (Fabrics 76, 77).

KNIT FABRIC CONSTRUCTION, BASIC PROPERTIES IN. Fabric properties are affected by the interaction of the fiber, yarn, fabric construction, dyeing, and finishing of the goods. The following considers the effect of construction only.

Flexibility and Drapeability: 1. Increase of courses per inch to afford stiffening. 2. Use of the English welt or Bourrelet. 3. Laid-in. 4. Intarsia. 5. Plating.

Compressibility: 1. Decrease of courses per inch to increase compressibility. 2. Use of the tuck stitch. 3. Use of rib, interlock, and purl fabric. 4. Pile. 5. Terry. 6. Blister.

Extensibility: 1. Decrease in courses per inch to increase extensibility. 2. Use of rib or purl fabrics. 3. Use of tuck stitch. 4. Needle set-out. 5. Elastic insertion.

Resilience: 1. Use of tuck stitch. 2. Use of rib, interlock or purl stitch. 3. Proper ratio of wales and courses.

Density: 1. Use of rib or interlock fabric. 2. Use of tuck stitch and miss-stitch. 3. Racking. 4. Terry. 5. Pile. 6. Laid-in.

Texture: 1. Tuck stitch for surface effect on face of jersey and rib fabrics. 2. Miss-stitch for surface interest on the face of rib stitch fabrics. 3. Miss-stitch for surface effect on back of jersey fabric. 4. Stitch transfer in pelerine, lace, and half-point.

Surface Friction: 1. As in *Texture*, above. 2. Plating. 3. Laid-in.

Thermal Character: 1. Stitch transfer. 2. Terry. 3. Pile. 4. Needle set-out. 5. Laid-in. 6. Drop-stitch. 7. Rib or interlock. 8. Blister.

KNIT FABRIC FINISHING, SOME TYPICAL PROCEDURES IN. These follow:

A. MANMADE YARN, HIGH BULK TREATMENT FOR USE IN FABRIC: *Natural or Greige Yarn:* 1. Knitting. 2. Dyeing and Finishing Applications. 3. Extracting. 4. Drying. 5. Calendering and Steaming. 6. Rolled Fabric.

Dyed Yarn: 1. Knitting. 2. Relaxation or Washing. 3. Calendering or Steaming. 4. Rolled Fabric.

B. MANMADE YARN, TEXTURED TREATMENT FOR USE IN FABRIC: *Natural or Greige Yarn:* 1. Knitting. 2. Relaxation. 3. Dyeing and Finishing Applications. 4. Extracting. 5. Drying. 6. Calendering or Steaming. 7. Heat Setting 8. Rolled Fabric.

Dyed Yarn: 1. Knitting. 2. Relaxation or Washing. 3. Calendering. 4. Heat Setting

KNIT FABRIC CONSTRUCTIONS, BASIC.

JERSEY OR PLAIN	1 x 1 RIB	1 x 1 PURL
Machine:		
1 set of needles	2 sets of needles	1 set of needles
1 needle bed	2 needle beds	2 needle beds
Needle Bed:	Needle Bed:	Needle Bed:
Straight or Circular	Straight or Circular	Straight or Circular
Fabric:		
Plain	Plain & Rib	Plain, Rib, Purl
	Offset needle tricks	Directly opposite tricks
Construction:		
All stitches are going in the same direction. Distinct face & back.	All stitches in one wale are in same direction & adjacent wale can go in the opposite direction.	All stitches in one course are in the same direction & alternate courses are different.
Unravel:		
Either end	Top down	Either edge
Dropstitch:		
Up or Down	Down	Up or Down
Elasticity:		
Good	Best	Best
Curl:		
Toward back Selvedge Front-top & bottom	None	None
Appearance:		
Face X Back O	Either side	Either side OOO
	X O X O X O	XXX

5. Rolled Fabric.

C. PILE KNIT FABRIC:

Natural or Greige Yarn: 1. Knitting. 2. Dyeing. 3. Extracting. 4. Drying. 5. Slitting and Gumming. 6. Latexing and Heatsetting. 7. Tigering. 8. Shearing. 9. Electrifying and Polishing. 10. Rolled Cloth.

Dyed Yarn: 1. Knitting. 2. Slitting and Gumming. 3. Latexing and Heat-Setting. 4. Tigering. 5. Shearing. 6. Electrifying 7. Rolled cloth.

D. WORSTED YARN KNIT FABRIC:

Natural or Greige Yarn: 1. Knitting. 2. Fulling - optional. 3. Shrinkproofing. 4. Dyeing and Finishing Applications. 5. Redmanizing - optional. 6. Extracting. 7. Drying. 8. Calendering or Steaming. 9. Decating. 10. Rolled fabric.

Dyed Yarn: 1. Knitting. 2. Calendering. 3. Decating. Rolled fabric.

E. COTTON KNIT FABRIC:

Natural or Greige Yarn: 1. Knitting. 2. Dyeing. 3. Redmanizing - optional. 4. Extracting. 5. Drying. 6. Finishing Applications or Printing and then finishing. 7. Drying. 8. Curing. 9. Calendering. 10. Laminating - optional. 11. Rolled fabric.

Dyed Yarn: 1. Knitting. 2. Finishing Applications. 3. Drying. 4. Curing. 5. Stripe mating. 6. Calendering. 7. Laminating - optional. 8. Rolled fabric.

Dyed Yarn: 1. Knitting. 2. Calendering. 3. Decating. Rolled fabric.

KNIT FABRICS AND APPAREL, DESIRABLE PROPERTIES IN. The tremendous advances achieved in knit fabrics since World War II have paid off for several years and its progress has been phenomenal. The following gives an insight into the properties of knitgoods and apparel in comfort, fit, packability, performance, support, etc.

Fabric weights are available for all seasons of the year, the structure of any type of knit apparel easily provides good form-fitness to the wearer; ironing is not necessary in laundering, smoothness is retained in the material, even in soft folds. A broad range of so-called standard sizes is not necessary in apparel because of the stretchability of the goods. Styling is very versatile despite the fact that fashion and style, especially in women's wear, changes very frequently. The host of textures on the market give the consumer a wide range from which to choose fabrics and apparel. Washing and comparable attention given to the articles are done easily and well. Knit articles of today are now made wrinkle-resistant and this has been a great boon to the industry.

Knitting is done at a much higher rate than woven fabric, and machines can be changed over from one item to another much quicker than in a weaving loom. In addition, short runs of goods and quick deliveries also are a feature in the knitgoods industry.

Knit garments are made with a minimum of buttons, lacings, zippers and other closures. Good body conformity is possible despite bodily changes and weight changes in the individual. Knit garments possess a satisfactory drape and provide support, usually with a minimum of tailoring.

Despite higher production in knitting over woven goods, the respective prices show that knitwear is about the same as woven articles and, up to twelve percent higher, at present. Knitgoods do not have the cover noted in woven cloths. Textured yarns or textured and spun yarn combinations have been one of the main reasons for the advance of knitwear, especially with regard to proper fit, comfort, and drape.

Cutting of knitgoods in the cuttingroom of the garment manufacturer has to be done with utmost care at all times. Slippage may occur between the upper and lower layers and this possibility is the bane of the manufacturer. Double-knits and tricot-knit fabrics may not always perform too well in the wale or vertical direction of the goods.

Packageability of knitwear has improved greatly. Ease of packing in various containers, wrinkles "hanging out," and the absence of that "out-of-the-container" look have given further impetus to the use of knitwear. Even rolled items usually "wrinkle-out" quickly after their hanging.

KNIT FABRIC SHRINKAGE GAUGE. A pneumatic means employed to measure restorability of knitted fabrics. The apparatus consists of an inflatable diaphragm in which there is set a circle of sample mounting pins. An air pressure and measuring system, and an automatic trigger gauge to release the air pressure when a predetermined sample dimension has been reached, are also features of the machine. The object of the instrument is to evaluate materials from the standpoint of restorability as normally encountered in end-uses.

KNIT FABRIC STANDARDS. In June, 1971, the Knitted Textile Association and the Textile Distributors Association in a cooperative effort established the number of imperfections allowable before a first quality goods becomes "seconds" as to rating. A four-point system assigns from one to four points chargeable for each fabric defect based on the size of the particular defect. The system provides a basis for arbitration proceedings. The Four-Point System for

Fabric Defects follows:

Size of Defect - Length in Inches

Three inches or less	One
Over three inches but not over six inches	Two
Over six inches but not over nine inches	Three
Over nine inches	Four

It should be noted that:

1. The table is not to be used for performance standards.

2. For example, if a 100 yard length has ten defects over nine inches long, and ten defects of three inches or smaller; this produces a rating of 50 points which is the maximum allowable for first-grade goods.

3. There is no direct relation to performance attributes such as pilling, snagging, and wearability.

4. The standards are not to be interpreted as to the suitability of the fabric for some particular terminal use.

5. The table covers all types of woven goods in fabric form; tricot and all other warp knits; all circular knits whether single or doubleknit, as well as some knit pile goods such as velours.

6. The table affords a common language for evaluating fabrics and does away with possible friction between fabric sources and customers.

7. The method is set-up for knitgoods 64 to 66 inches in width or less. Other special provisions are set-up for goods beyond this width.

8. Four points are the maximum number chargeable against one linear yard.

9. Quality is expressed in terms of a 100-yard length regardless of the length of the bolt, cut, or piece in question.

10. The Standards read: "Knitted fabrics having a width of 64-66 inches shall be classified as first quality if the number of points therein does not exceed 50 points on the assumed basis of 100 linear yards."

11. "Any hole other than a pin hole shall be considered a major defect and assigned a maximum number of points chargeable against a linear yard."

12. "Pin hole" indicates a minute space which may have been caused by a shifting of pattern where no break in the yarn has occurred.

13. The standards list a number of items that shall not be classed as defects and charged with penalty marks. These include barre marks, bowing, pinholes, etc., which "should not be given penalty marks" and must be judged by the extent and degree to which they occur, and their likely effect on the type of garment being cut."

14. There are some defects that occur within one inch of the fabric edge and are "irregularities" normal to the existing state of the art, beyond reasonable control of the manufacturer, inherent in any specified type of construction.

15. These standards are not intended to apply to "experimental, innovative, or specialty fabrics."

Courtesy of National Knitted Outerwear Association, Inc. and Textile Distributors Association, Inc.

KNIT FABRIC WEIGHT. The ounce weight per yard basis on which double knit fabrics are sold. Quotations, for example, are listed as 10, 12, 14 or 15 ounces per yard of fabric.

KNIT FABRIC YIELD. The number of yards per pound or the basis on which single knit fabric is sold. It is common, under the yield standard, to designate single knit fabric, for example, as being 1.5 or 2.0 yards, etc., of fabric.

KNITGOODS. The demand for knitwear for apparel and hosiery has shown a meteoric rise since the close of World War II. Knitting frames now seem capable of making any type of fabric that is produced on a loom, and can do the job more quickly. An example of this is the Morat knitting frame, made in Stuttgart, West Germany, which can produce practically any type of Jacquard fabric at great speed. Such fabrics are exceptionally clear both in details and in full-motif. It is possible that the weaving segment of the textile industry will follow the knitting segment, a complete turn-about from past experience. During the past ten years of so, fiber and yarn producers' research and development departments have been devoting increasingly more of their time and energy toward the field of knitting. It has been estimated that in this span of time more than 80 percent of research and development has been concerned with knitting problems and better knit products.

In 1960, the average woman bought 11.9 pairs of hosiery per year; in 1970 the figure rose to 17.5 pairs, a rise of about 68 percent. It will not be long until the figure will rise to twenty pairs. The miniskirt has been of tremendous value to the knitting industry and yarn manufacturers. Knitted pantyhose is a must for girls and women, and it has solved the major problems caused by the miniskirt. Pantyhose is also being worn by some men and reminds one of the old-time "Long-Johns" worn in cold weather. Pantyhose comes in either one piece, or in a combination of panty and hose. The types of pantyhose are now almost endless. Fancy hose for women covers a very wide range of gauge, texture, and motif. Around 1960, new techniques came in with which it was possible to knit "tubeless stockings" in nine minutes, a process that formerly took fifteen minutes. Because of the demand and increased production facilities, prices came down, and this made it possible for teenagers to switch from bobby-sox to full-length nylon stockings. Nylon yarns, such as Cantrece of duPont, along with many types of elastomeric yarns, have been of great impetus to the hosiery industry. Stretch sizes have been reduced from sixteen to eight, and efforts are being made to even further reduce this number. Fancy women's hose shows a myriad of textures, yarns and effects, and new effects are constantly coming onto the market.

KNIT MACHINES, DOUBLE. Yardgoods and sweater strips are made on circular and dial knitting frames in varying double knit constructions. There are two types of machines in this basic grouping, the Non-Jacquard and the Rib-Jacquard machines.

There are two sub-classes in the Non-Jacquard group — the restricted purpose type and the extended purpose type machines. The former has two categories. 1. The extended interlock frame which has two separate needle tracks in both the cylinder and the dial which work in conjunction with long and short or high and low butt needles. 2. Those machines equipped with two cam tracks in both the cylinder and the dial types and having separate cam controls for each track at each feed.

The extended purpose double knit frame category covers units which have individual needle selection but with a maximum pattern or design depth or not more than one revolution of the machine.

In contradistinction from the Non-Jacquard double knit machines, the Rib-Jacquard types are generally defined as frames which have a maximum pattern depth which exceeds one machine revolution and has some form of needle selection mechanism which can make a range of designs. Generally speaking, there are four types in the Rib-Jacquard machines. 1. Pattern wheel machine. 2. Pattern drum machines. 3. Punched roll machines. 4. Continuous machines. See Knit, Double.

KNIT PANEL. The term is applied

to knit fabrics which show vertical panel effects produced by the combination of knitting stitches. Thus, a 2 x 2 rib combined at intervals with the 1 x 1 rib stitch would produce such an effect; or the 1 x 1 rib stitch combined at intervals with the tuck stitch. Sometimes called panel rib knitting.

KNIT PAPER FABRIC. High strength, specially treated paper yarn used in some knit and mesh constructions. Finds use in some household and apparel articles, and may be dry-cleaned. Paper yarn (ersatz yarn) was first made by the Germans during World War I because of shortages in some textile fibers.

KNIT POSITION. The position in the knitting cycle where the knitting needle is extended to its furthermost point and catches new yarn in its hook and clears the old loop over the latch.

KNITTED ASTRAKHAN. As made today is in demand and much cheaper than the woven article. The cloth, as a substitute, is found in the fur trade for coatings and is popular in winter wear. People who cannot afford real Astrakhan buy the woven or knitted cloth of that name and become "the slaves of fashion," always noted in the textile trade.

KNITTED CLOTH FULLING. The process of treating woolen or worsted knit cloth to give it the appearance of a woven material. Some knitted fabric is difficult to distinguish from woven goods because the fulling, soaping, milling and shrinking have been so effective. These treatments give the goods a compact texture and appearance.

KNITTED FABRIC PRINTING. Utmost care and precaution have to be given knitgoods because of the nature of their construction. Four methods follow:

Direct Printing with Copper Rollers: This method is ideal for warp knitgoods. The fabric is gummed lightly to the back gray cloth to counteract possible slippage of the goods in processing. Printing is usually done on the reverse side of the material, since the back of the goods is smoother than the actual face of the cloth. (See page 218.)

Screen or Stencil Hand-Printing: Both warp and weft knit fabrics are colored by the method but compared with the other methods in use it is rather expensive since production is low and time-consuming.

Automatic Printing, Flat-Bed Screen: In one of the more recent developments in fabric printing of textiles, a heavy-guage neoprene belt is used, and the screens are set to a specially designed

set of lifting brackets, placed on each side of the belt. Cloth to be printed is is run onto the belt and the brackets automatically lift and lower the screens onto the material thereby printing the motif onto the goods. Production is low and time-consuming.

Rotary Screen Printing: The "Aljaba" machine is set up comparably with the direct or cylinder method of printing, which is done by means of copper rollers. Phosphor-bronze gauze screens on the rotary method are used instead of the rollers to produce the pattern. The printing color paste is fed into the inside of the frame where a small metal roller forces it through the open areas (or interstices) onto the fabric. Both warp and weft knitgoods may be colored by this method.

KNITTED FABRICS. Made by:

1. CROCHETING: The looping of a single yarn into fabric by means of one hooked needle. Crocheting is often used to finish-off the end of a knitted fabric.

2. NETTING: This is the knotting of threads into meshes that will not ravel. Knit fabric may ravel or disentangle.

3. KNOTTING: This is an intertwining of the parts of one or more threads so that they will not slip or loosen. Bows, laces, and similar types of mesh or porous work are examples of knotting.

4. TATTING: This is used to make edging that is lacelike in the final or finished form.

5. TYPES OF KNITTING NEEDLES USED: There are two types:

    I. Spring Needles: They are used to make fine, high-gauge materials for underwear and stockings.

    II. Latch Needles: They are used to make coarse, low-gauged knit fabrics. See Illustrated Section.

6. TYPES OF KNITTING AND KNITTED FABRICS:

SINGLE-KNITTED FABRIC: Fabric made from the one system of yarn. Several yarns may be combined, however, and passed into the machine as a single or individual yarn. The fabric which is made by an interlooping of yarn—a loop within a loop—is produced at a high rate of speed. Some single-knit fabric is made at the rate of about one yard per minute. Single cloth constructions that are popular in the trade are: Stockings, socks, mignonette, some tricolette, jersey, bathing suit fabric, scarves, cap cloth, dress goods, sportswear, etc. The fabric may run from the heavy, close, compact type of goods to the lightweight, sheer, diaphanous variety of material.

DOUBLE-KNITTED, PLAITED FABRIC: This is cloth that is made of two or more yarns of different source. The face of the fabric will show the one material on the face of the goods, while the back of the cloth will show the other type of yarn used. Heavy sweaters are often made in this manner. The weight of this type of fabric is from medium to heavy.

KNITTED PILE FABRIC: On a jersey machine, two ends of yarn, or as many as required, are fed into the same feed, one yarn forming a longer loop than the other. The loop side, actually the back of the fabric, becomes the face of the finished goods.

The material, either piece-dyed or yarn-dyed, may be used as it is, or it may be napped or sheared.

The fabric varies in weight from the fine-gauge sheer rayon, acetate, nylon, or silk for dress goods to the coarse-gauge, heavyweight cotton and wool blends suitable for coating.

CIRCULAR KNITTING: The fabric is made on a circular knitting machine to form a tubular fabric. Examples include jersey cloth, seamless hosiery, neckwear, stockinette, topcoating, and sleeving.

RIBBED FABRIC: This is made with two sets of needles which produce a ribbed or corrugated surface on the fabric. Jersey fabric is made with one set of needles which gives the cloth a smooth surface. Examples include ribbed fabric for use in bathing suits and underwear.

FLAT OUTERWEAR FABRIC: In the outerwear trade, a flat fabric is made on a machine which has the needles arranged in a straight line. The term is used to distinguish the fabric from that made on a circular frame, which produces a tubular material. Examples include sweaters, shirting, scarves, blouses, and ensembles.

FLAT UNDERWEAR FABRIC: A flat fabric that is made on a machine on one set of needles. It is so called to distinguish it from ribbed fabric, which is made with two sets of needles. Flat fabric has a smooth, flat surface; hence, the name. Jersey fabric is an example.

WARP-KNITTED FABRIC: This is fabric knitted from a flat, upright warp comparable with the warp used to make woven cloth where two systems of yarn, the warp and the filling, cross each other or interlace at right angles. In warp knitting there is one thread for each needle.

Examples include Milanese, tricolette, mignonette, jersey, etc.

FULL-FASHIONED HOSIERY: This fabric has a seam which runs down the back of the leg with a series of knots known as fashion marks. These marks are also observed under the instep. Full-fashioned is knitted on a flat machine into the proper shape for the stocking by the transferring of the loops.

SEAMLESS HOSIERY: This is recognized by the absence of the fashion marks and seam. Knitted circular or tubular.

See Illustrated Section.

KNITTED FLEECE. A soft, silklike pile fabric of considerable warmth. The name comes from its close resemblance to the raw wool of the sheep, which is known as a fleece.

KNITTED GARMENT MANUFACTURE OUTLINE.

Classification of the Product: Underwear, outerwear, hosiery, industrial.

Identification of Garment Features: Full-fashion products, hosiery, sweaters.

Inter-Relationship between Fabric and Garment: A. Fabric properties of drapeability, density, thermal character, stretch. B. Fabric construction such as jersey, purl, rib; Milanese, Raschel, simplex, tricot. B. Physical forms such as whether flat or tubular yard goods, unit pieces.

Effect of Product Line on Planning: A. Vertical Integrated Company - one product idea. B. Horizontal Integrated Company - many products.

Manufacture of Knitted Garment Versus Woven Garment: A. Shaping of fabric; cutting, full fashion. B. Fabrication pertinent to sewing equipment and knit-in features. C. The manufacturing flow.

Effect of Knitted Garment Finishing Procedures on Inventory and Warehousing: Consideration of garment dyeing, garment sizing, and packaging.

Underwear Products: A. Lingerie which includes camisoles, briefs, petti-pants, slips - full and half types. B. Foundations to include bra-lets, brassieres, corsets, garter belts, girdles. C. Sleepwear to include nightgowns and pajamas. D. Lounge wear to include housecoats, negligees, robes. E. Infants wear to include underpants and undershirts. F. Boys and girls underwear to include underpants and undershirts. G. Underwear for men to include briefs, undershirts, union suits.

Outerwear Products: These include blouses, coats, dresses, gloves, hats, skirts, suits, sweaters, swimwear.

Hosiery: Includes anklets, socks, over-knee, stockings, leotards, pantyhose, tights.

Industrial: Includes aerospace, automotive, bagging, cosmetic-wigs, electrical, fishing industry, housewear, medical uses, textile and comparable

processing.

FABRIC PROPERTIES. *Compressibility:* The compressible nature of a fabric which imparts a feel of luxury or pleasure, along with softness.

Density: The weight per unit volume and the interaction with drapeability.

Drapability: Ability of a fabric to hang in folds, bend, or have an appealing and pleasing, form-revealing appearance when used in apparel.

Stretch: Ability of a fabric to be elongated to a pre-determined point from which the fabric will recover to its original size and shape.

Surface Friction: The result of fiber, yarn type, fabric construction, and fabric finishing which will provide the "hand" or finish to the goods.

Thermal Character: Ability to transmit or retard the flow of heat through a fabric or garment.

KNITTED FABRIC CONSTRUCTION. 1. *Warp Knitting:* A fabric made by the use of parallel yarns set-up

so that each one operates with at least one needle to produce one stitch in the course or width of the goods. 2. *Filling or Weft Knitting:* Fabric made by the use of a yarn so that all needles receive the yarn and make loops in the course or width of the fabric.

PHYSICAL FORM. 1. *Machine Construction:* In Tubular Fabrics, the needles are arranged in the form of a circle or two parallel rows of needles. For Flat Knit Fabrics, the needles are arranged in a straight line to produce a cloth with two firm or perfect edges or selvages. 2. *Machine Control or Operation:* For Yard Goods continuous fabrics are cut into convenient lengths for handling. In handling Unit Pieces, continuous knitted lengths of fabric are used and these are separated into fabric pieces by the removal of a specially incorporated thread; or the knitting of individual pieces of fabric on an interrupted knitting basis. Pockets, belts, wristbands, etc, are knitted by this method.

KNITTED GARMENT FEATURES

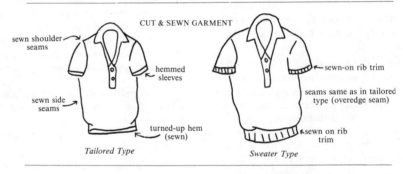

CUT & SEWN GARMENT

sewn shoulder seams — hemmed sleeves — sewn side seams — turned-up hem (sewn)

Tailored Type

sewn-on rib trim — seams same as in tailored type (overedge seam) — sewn on rib trim

Sweater Type

SWEATER OR SWEATER-SHIRT GARMENT

sewn seams — sewn seams — sewn seams — welt cuff — welt bottom (knit on)

Tailored Type

mock fashion marks — looped collar — knit-on rib trim — knit-on rib trim seams same as in tailored type (overedge seam)

Sweater type

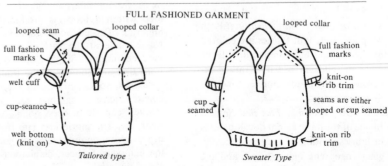

FULL FASHIONED GARMENT

looped seam — full fashion marks — welt cuff — cup-seamed — welt bottom (knit on)

looped collar

Tailored type

looped collar — full fashion marks — knit-on rib trim — seams are either looped or cup seamed — knit-on rib trim

cup seamed

Sweater Type

Reprinted with permission of *Knitting Times*. National Knitted Outerwear Association.

KNITTED GARMENTS AND WOVEN GARMENTS. MANUFACTURE OF.

Shaping by Conventional Methods: These include the action of hand shears, circular power knife, straight power knife, die cutting and power band saws.

Shaping by Full Fashion Methods: Done by hand, hand machine, power machine.

Fabrication of Cut and Sewn Shirt Sewing Equipment: Done on a Lockstitch Machine #301 Series or by an Eoveredging Machine of the #501 Series.

Fabrication of Full Fashion Items: Done by a looper, or cup-seamer.

Knitted-In Features: These include button holes, collars (plain or shaped), pleats, pockets, seamless, waist bands.

Manufacturing Flow Chart: See below.

Garment Finishing Processes: A. Full Fashion which are made from natural and manmade textile fibers in spun or filament form. B. Manmade fiber texturized yarns. C. Sweater-type garments made with natural fiber yarns or with manmade texturized yarns.

Garment Sizing: A. Done by use of manmade thermo-plastic fibers, such as nylon, or by the use of natural and manmade raw material.

There is such a great host of finishing operations in textiles that no effort is made here to cover any of these at all. All major methods and operations are covered in the book.

Packaging: This is accomplished by the use of bagging, boxing, hanging, etc.

KNITTED LOOP CLOTH.

Any type of pile or terry fabric which has a plated structure. Each loop in the fabric is made up of two distinct yarns, a ground yarn and a fancy or effect yarn. The loop is formed from the latter. The ground yarn is knitted-in, usually in a jersey stitch, while the latter is pulled out by a special device to make the looped or pile effect.

KNITTED PILE FABRIC.

Knit goods with one set of yarn forming longer loops than the other set of yarn. The loops may be uncut as in knitted terry cloth or sheared, napped, or brushed for some particular purpose.

KNITTED SHIRTS, MEN'S AND WOMEN'S.

There are seven basic types:

1. BASQUE: A crew neck pullover with short or long sleeves, depending on the season, with a horizontal stripe treatment in two or more colors.

2. GAUCHO: A short, widespread collar treatment on a knitted outerwear garment.

3. PLACKET: A two- or three-button effect underneath the collar on a pullover shirt. Very often the placket and collar contrast with the color of the body of the shirt.

4. POLO: A crew neck, short-sleeve garment usually of solid color with contrasting rib trimming around the neckline and at the sleeve end. The name comes from its resemblance to the garments worn by polo players.

5. T-BLOUSE: A smart, dressy type of T-shirt worn by women.

6. T-SHIRT: This is a plain, unadorned crew-neck garment designed for outerwear, and resembling the U.S. Navy skivie shirt.

7. MISCELLANEOUS: A wide variety of collar treatments is used to vary polo shirts, most of them coinciding with the currently popular styles used in men's dress shirts.

KNITTED STOCKING, THE PARTS OF A.

1. WELT: This is the hem or garter top and it is made of heavy or reinforced yarn to withstand garter strain. In women's hosiery this is generally made of double fabric.

2. RUN STOP: This consists of a narrow band, generally one course wide, of locked stitches to prevent runs from extending into the leg of the stocking and usually placed either at the end of the welt or shadow welt.

3. FASHION MARKS: These are visible as small dots or raised portions of the fabric wherever the stocking has been narrowed for fashioning purposes and are caused by the placing of the inwardly transferred stitch on a needle which already holds a stitch.

4. BOOT OR LEG: The area between the end of the welt or the shadow welt and the ankle.

5. SEAM: The row of small stitches that join the selvages of flat knit hosiery.

6. HIGH SPLICING: The reinforced portion of the stocking above the shoe line.

7. HEEL: The reinforced portion of the stocking of the lower heel below the shoe line.

8. SOLE: That part of the stocking generally reinforced and extending directly under the instep from the heel to the toe. Incidentally, in full fashioned hosiery made by the single-unit method, there is no definite line of demarcation between the heel and the sole.

9. TOE: The reinforced portion over the toe area.

KNITTED SUITS.

They are easy to care for and ideal in travel wardrobes. Knitted suits drape well, are resistant to mussing and wrinkling, and easily packable. Virtually all major natural and man-made fiber yarns find use on a 100 per cent basis or in blends. Novelty yarns are used often in the fabric, chiefly bouclé and chenille.

KNITTER, CIRCULAR MACHINE.

One who operates a circular machine and makes the adjustments, fixes "smash-ups," and takes off and replaces cylinders. In addition, he lengthens or shortens the chain, adjusts the consistency of the stitch according to the instructions, picks up drop-outs. He should be capable of performing all

MANUFACTURING FLOW CHART

GARMENT:	CUT & SEWN	SWEATER	FULL-FASHION
Dyed Yarn	knitting, dyeing, finishing, cutting, sewing, trimming, inspection, pressing, packaging.	knitting, dyeing, separating of strips, steaming, cutting, sewing, trimming, inspection, pressing, packaging.	knitting, trim, topping-on, knit body and parts, looping, cut seaming, rough mending, dyeing or washing, trim sewing, trimming, inspection, pressing, packaging.
Pre-Dyed Yarn	knitting, finishing, cutting, sewing, trimming, inspection, pressing, packaging.	knitting, washing, separating of strips, steaming, cutting, sewing, trimming, inspection, pressing, packaging.	knit, trim, topping-on, knit body and parts, looping, cup seaming, rough mending, dyeing or washing, trim sewing, trimming inspection, pressing, packaging.

operations pertinent to the smooth running of the machine.

KNITTER, FLAT HAND MACHINE. The person who operates a hand-knitting machine, and fashions and transfers the stitches with a hand decker to conform with the requirements; also sets and adjusts the machine.

KNITTER, PLAIN FLAT OR FLAT LINKS. One who operates plain flat or flat links machine; he makes adjustments and fixes smash-ups, makes necessary needle changes, lengthens or shortens the chain, adjusts consistency of the stitch being used, attends to drop-outs and should be able to perform all tasks in the running of the machine.

KNITTER, WARP MACHINE. One who operates a warp knitting machine of the flat type to produce warp knits, such as the Tricot (see Illustrated Section), the Milanese, and the Raschel. He mounts and ties up the cones for edging the fabric, starts the machine, tends to its operation; replaces empty cones of yarn, repairs broken threads, and remedies all defects which are bound to occur from time to time. The knitter checks on machine production to meet requirements.

KNITTER MECHANIC. One who sets up, adjusts, replaces and repairs the various types of knitting machines used in the knitting industry according to design, shape, and size of the desired product. He determines by examination of the product whether adjustments or repairs are necessary; makes adjustments; repairs or replaces broken or worn parts. He is very often the person who actually designs the fabric to be made.

KNITTING. Producing fabric on more than one needle by a method of interlooping yarn or yarns. The lengthwise rows of loops are known as wales; the crosswise, horizontal rows of loops as courses.

1. CIRCULAR KNITTING: The fabric comes from the knitting machine in the form of a tube. The threads run continuously in one direction in loops around the fabric.

2. FLAT KNITTING: Is similar in construction to circular knitting. The differences are: 1. The fabric comes from the knitting machine in a flat form just as woven fabrics do. 2. The threads run in loops, alternately back and forth across the fabric. 3. Flat knit fabrics are capable of being fashioned or shaped in the knitting.

3. WARP KNITTING: Here, the fabric usually comes from the knitting machine flat, just as woven and flat knit fabrics do. The threads run in loops in a lengthwise direction.

KNITTING, HELD LOOP IN. One which, having been pulled through the loop of the previous course, is kept by the needle during the knitting of one or more additional courses.

KNITTING, SEPARATING COURSE IN. A course of knitted loops which separate a garment or parts of a garment from one another. On removal of the course the parts become disjoined. The course may be cut, pulled out, or dissolved. Several courses may be made in consecutive order.

KNITTING, SLIVER. Plan of feeding individual ends of staple to knitting needles based on the principles of jersey knitting. The staple is locked into a high-pile position by means of a backing yarn set up in a jersey ground structure.

KNITTING, WEFT. A single yarn is fed to a number of needles in the filling, horizontal, or weft direction in the goods and the fabric is composed of loops formed into crosswise courses built-up on top of each other. Plain, purl, and rib stitches are made on this type frame and these three stitches are the foundation stitches for all other types of stitches from staple to fancy. Around fifty percent of all knitgoods are made on this method of knitting.

KNITTING ELEMENTS. There are two: 1. The sinker, which is a device on a circular machine used to hold down the fabric. 2. The jack, a tempered steel blade with either high or low butts whose primary function is to actuate the movement of latch knitting needles. See Illustrated Section.

KNITTING EYELET. An openwork mesh effect made by transferring sinker loops to two adjacent needles; usually two consecutive sinker loops are collected and transferred.

KNITTING GAUGE. This means the actual number of needles per 1½ inches on the machine:

1. 45-gauge has 45 needles per 1½ inches or 30 needles per inch.

2. 51-gauge has 51 needles per 1½ inches or 34 needles per inch.

3. 60-gauge has 60 needles per 1½ inches or 40 needles per inch.

4. 66-gauge has 66 needles per 1½ inches or 44 needles per inch.

5. 72-gauge has 72 needles per 1½ inches or 48 needles per inch.

Each needle knits one WALE, in the vertical row of stitches, while a COURSE is a row of horizontal stitches or loops that extend crosswise in the fabric. The higher the gauge, the finer will be

KNITTING
THE INTER-RELATIONSHIP OF FABRIC AND GARMENT
KNITTED FABRIC CONSTRUCTION CHART-Comparison of Warp and Weft Knit Fabrics

	Jersey	Weft 1 x 1 Rib	1 x 1 Purl	Tricot	Warp Raschel	Simplex	Milanese
Appearance	Face Back	Reversible	Reversible	Face Back	Face Back Reversible	Reversible	Face Back
Curl	Yes	None	None	Yes	Yes	None	Yes
Elasticity	Both	Width	Length	Width	Width	Width	Width
Ravel or Running	Both	Down	Both	Down	Down	Down	None

Drapeability	All well known for drapeability, modified through construction.	
Compressability	Thicker Fabrics	Thinner Fabrics
Density	Wide Range of Machinery	Finer Fabric and Machinery
Thermal Character	Warmth Due to Thickness	Thinner Fabrics

the texture of the stocking. In nylon hosiery knitting, the most commonly used gauge-denier setup is as follows:

1. 45-gauge will use a 40-denier and heavier sizes, if necessary.

2. 45- or 51-gauge will use a 30-denier size yarn.

3. 51- and 60-gauge will use a 20-denier or a 15-denier yarn.

4. 51- to 72-gauge will use a 15-denier or finer denier yarn size.

KNITTING LOCKS. A cam arrangement on the underside of the carriage in a knitting machine of the flat-bed type designed to actuate the movements of the jacks on the frame.

KNITTING MACHINE. A machine used to make knitted fabric. There are several types in use today: circular, flat, warp-type, latch and spring-needle types, plain, fancy, Jacquard, and others.

KNITTING MACHINE, GARMENT-LENGTH. One that makes the sweater body and the sleeve sections with attached rib trims on a continuous operation. A draw thread is used to separate the body and sleeve sections.

KNITTING NEEDLE. It is the loop-forming device in a knitting machine. There are two types of knitting needles in use in outerwear knitting. 1. The spring or spring-beard needle. 2. The latch needle.

The spring-beard needle has a flexible spring beard or hook, while the latch needle has a short hook which is closed off or opened by a swinging finger. See Illustrated Section.

KNITTING NEEDLE, COMPOUND. For the 1, the 2, or the 3-bar High Speed used in tricot knitting, a needle or set of needles used is capable of making 1,000 courses in the knitting operation per minute. Sketch of this type needle follows:

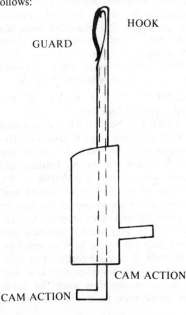

HOOK
GUARD
CAM ACTION
CAM ACTION

KNITTING GAUGE SYSTEMS.

Type Machine	Gauge Equals
1. German System proposed for all Knitting Machines, 1953:	Number of needles in 100 mm.
2. Straight Bar Plain Machines:	Number of needles in 1½ inches.
3. Straight Bar Rib Machines:	Number of needles in 1½ inches of either set of needles.
4. Bearded Needle Warp Machines:	English—number of needles in 1 inch. Saxon—number of needles in 1 Saxon inch which is 0.93 inches or 23.6 mm.

Type Machine	Gauge Equals
5. Simplex Machines:	Number of needles in one inch—English or Saxon, of one needle bar only.
6. Bearded Needle Circular Machines of the Challenger Type:	Number of needles in one inch of the circumference.
7. Loopwheel Machines:	Number of needles in 1½ inches of the circumference, theoretically.
8. Sinker Wheel Machines:	Gauge; German, fein—number of needles in one zoll. Gauge; German, grob—number of needles in 1½ zoll. The gauge is measured along the arc of the holes drilled in the needle ring to receive the cranked ends of the needles. A zoll is 1/36th of a meter (metre) or approximately 1.09 inches.
9. F.N.F. Warp Knitting Machines:	Number of needles in one inch.
10. Latch Needle Circular Machines:	Number of needles in one inch of circumference.
11. Circular Rib and Interlock Machines:	Number of tricks in one inch of the cylinder and/or dial. Thus, a machine with 10 tricks per inch in both cylinders and dial would be defined as a 10-gauge machine, or as a 10 x 10 gauge.
12. Circular Purl Machines:	Number of needles in one inch of circumference.
13. Flat Knitting Machines:	English—number of tricks in one inch of one needle bed. Swiss—needle spacing in mm. multiplied by 10.
14. Seamless Hose and Half-Hose Machines:	Number of needles in machine and the diameter of the needle cylinder in inches. Thus, 370 x 4½ means 370 needles in a cylinder of 4½ inches in diameter.
15. Latch Needle Warp Knitting Machines:	English—number of needles in two inches of one needle bed. Saxon—number of needles in two Saxon inches of one needle bed.
16. Linking and Point Seaming Machines:	English—points in an arc of 1½ inches. American—points in an arc of 1 inch. Gauge and point are used respectively to define the two systems. Thus, a 36-gauge linking machine would have 24 points per inch while a 24-point linking machine would have 24 points per inch.

With grateful appreciation for aid and permission given from the National Knitted Outerwear Association, 51 Madison Avenue, New York, N.Y. 10010.

KNITTING NEEDLE, DOUBLE HOOK. Latch needle used on links-and-links or purl knitting machine, either circular or flat-bed type.

KNITTING NEEDLE, FRICTION-LESS. One which moves easily and freely in the needle slot. Now popular in jersey knitting to overcome the problem of needle lines in production of "Orlon" and wool blend in jersey fabrics.

KNITTING NEEDLE, FRICTION-TYPE. One that is either slightly bent or is equipped with a spring tail. Because of frictional contact with the walls of the needle slot, the needle will not be relatively free in its movement in the slot.

KNITTING PROCESS, BASIC TERMINOLOGY USED IN.

Burr: A gear type device on a circular spring needle knitting machine which engages the needles in such a manner as to move the yarn feed into the frame to form loops. It makes the knit fabric, moves the loops along, and also casts off the loops from the needles.

Course: The row of loops which run crosswise in knitgoods. Corresponds to the filling or weft in woven goods. Knitgoods are made in course direction.

Courses per Inch and Wales per Inch: The former is measured in the "downward" direction in the goods; the latter is measured "across" the fabric.

Wales

Courses ⟶

Cylinder: A cylinder is a slotted cylindrical housing for needles in a circular knitting machine. The number of slots per circumferential inch of the cylinder determines the number of needles per inch.

Dial: The dial is a circular steel plate with slots cut into it in much the same fashion as the slots grooved into the cylinder. The slots are arranged radially and the needles operate in them. In the production of a rib fabric, needles in the dial always operate in conjunction with needles in the cylinder; the number of slots or grooves in the dial would generally conform to the number of such cuts in the cylinder.

Divider: A device similar to and working in conjunction with sinkers to form loops. Used primarily to equalize stitch size in full fashioned knitting machines of fine gauge.

Dog Drive: Mechanism on circular knitting machines for maintaining dial and cylinder in correct relation to each other.

Dogless Drive: A mechanical drive of either double ring gears or intermeshing and movable alignment pins to maintain correct relationship of cylinder and dial.

Feed: Area of machine where needle operates to receive yarn.

Jack or Slider: A tempered steel blade with either high, low butts or double butts, whose primary function is to actuate the movement of the Links type latch knitting needles.

Jersey Stitch: The jersey stitch is the basis or starting point of all knitted structures. The loops intermesh in one direction with the result that the fabric has one appearance on the face side and a wholly different on the reverse side.

Knock-Over Bit: A small thin steel blade set below the sinkers & dividers in a Cotton's Patent full-fashioned knitting machine. The function is to catch the loops as they drop from the sinkers & dividers and to hold the last knitted loop in place as the needles rises to its normal position.

Needle Bar: A bar to which needles are affixed and work collectively.

Needle Bed: This device is a flat slotted plate with grooves or slots cut into it. The knitting needles operate in these slots and the number of these determines the cut or guage of the knitting frame. A bed with eight slots per inch is known as an eight-cut machine.

Needle Loop: A loop in knitted fabric which has been drawn through a previous loop.

Needle Types, Comparison of:

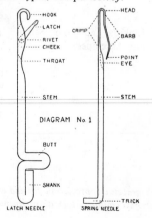

DIAGRAM No. 1

Presser: A device on a spring beard needle knitting machine designed to close the needle hook or beard in the formation of the knitted stitch.

Sinker: A thin blade device for creating loops. The loop forming sinker is always teamed on a knitting machine with the beard needle, while the holding-down sinker is only associated with the latch needle.

Sinker Loop: A loop connecting two adjacent needle loops.

Stitch: The basic unit of knitted fabric. The components of a stitch are a complete needle loop, a sinker loop and two connecting loop segments joining the needle loop to the one immediately preceding it.

Wale: It runs lengthwise in knitgoods and presents a rib line effect. Also known as the rib, it corresponds to the warp or vertical yarn in a woven fabric.

Yarn Carrier: A device on a knitting machine to feed yarn to needles or other loop-forming elements. The construction of the yarn carrier differs for each class of knitting machine.

KNITTING QUALITY. Actual measurement in inches of the greige length of tricot fabric made in knitting 480 courses or one rack in the knitting operation only. Thus, a 7½-inch quality fabric means that the actual measurement of 480 courses of fabric is 7½ inches, or 64 courses to the inch. Measured on the machine only.

KNITTING STITCH. The distance between the center of one loop to the center of the adjoining loop.

KNITTING YARN. Any yarn used to make knit goods, such as cotton yarns, spun and twisted particularly for knitting purposes. Knitting yarn is also made from wool, worsted, acetate, rayon, nylon, silk, and other materials. The yarn should, generally speaking, be uniform, flexible, and smooth. It is usually of low twist when compared with yarns used in the woven trade.

KNITTLES. The strands of two ropes twisted together.

KNIT TRANSFER TOP. Also called knit-of cuff, the term is used in reference to socks in which the cuff or top has been knit on the rib knitting machine and is then transferred to the needles of the footing or second machine for the production of the boot or leg and the foot. This topping or transferring is a very skilled operation and since each top has to be transferred individually, it is more costly when compared with the sewed-on-top. It is also a better construction since the yarns are continuous from the top of the sock through the toe. In the sewed-on top socks, the cuff and the body are knit separately and then joined by stitching. The seaming is apparent on examination.

KNIT TUBING. Tubular knitted fabric without seams; sweaters, skirts, and sleeves may be knitted in this manner.

KNOCKING OVER. A knitting action which causes a set of loops to slide off the ends of the needles onto the newly drawn yarn, thereby completing formation of the new loops.

KNOCK-OFF. Any device on any machine that will cause it to stop, knock-off, or throw certain gears out of mesh with other gears, thereby stopping the action.

"KNOCKOFF" or "BUMPOFF." Refers to almost any of the four thousand or so apparel houses on Seventh Avenue, New York City, who do not send representatives to the Paris, Rome, or New York City openings. A "knockoff" house doesn't have the considerable designer or stylist expenses and generally copies only those "numbers" that it is certain will become "best sellers" in the market; this does away with gambling on "slow movers."

The company owner or a representative usually goes to a department store, buys a recently arrived Paris, Rome, or New York original or creation that has been paid for or recently copied with permission of the creator, and then takes it to his own workroom for copying. It is practically impossible to curb these practices. Estimates reveal that there may be as many as a dozen or so "knock-offs" made annually by houses addicted to this practice, and that around ninety percent of the houses indulge in it. Of course, the practice does inestimable harm to the legitimate houses that bring out the originals, since the copies sell for a variable small fraction of the cost of the creation, classic, haute couture, gown, frock, or dress. For example, a creation may have been sold for $1,000 or more, and the copy may be available to the consumer for twenty-five dollars or slightly higher within a span of two month's time.

It may be said that in the apparel business that the house is either a creator or a pirate or a thief. The keystone of the practice is nothing more than chicanery, a lack of ethics, and outright stealing.

KNOCKOVER BIT. A small thin steel blade, set below the sinkers and the dividers in a full-fashioned knitting machine. Its function is to catch the loops as they drop from the sinkers and dividers and to hold the last knitted loop in place.

KNOP, KNOPPED, KNOPT YARN. A novelty yarn which shows vivid colored balls or lumps of fiber interspersed throughout the basic fibers in the yarn; a gray yarn might show knops of red, yellow, and blue to add color and tone to it. Used in men's suiting, sports coating, topcoating, etc.

KNOT. A joining by tying together (A.S.T.M.). See WEAVER'S KNOT, GHIORDES KNOT, SENNA KNOT.

KNOT-DYEING. See TIE-DYEING.

KNOTLESS YARN. A ply yarn that is devoid of knots. When it is necessary to piece the yarn, the individual strands are spliced together by hand or by machine, instead of knotting.

KNOTS, RUG. There are two types of knots used in the Oriental rug trade —Turkish or Ghiordes, and the Persian or Senna. The fineness of a rug determines the number of knots per square inch. See GHIORDES KNOT, PERSIAN KNOT.

KNOTTED LACE. Also known as knotting, it is a fancy interlacing of twisted and knotted threads that simulate, when completed, old handmade laces.

KNOTTED PILE. Hand-knotted short lengths of yarn made into pile formation for use in Oriental rugs.

KNOTTED YARN. See KNOP YARN.

KNOTTER. An automatic device used for tying knots in yarn; used at various stages in the manufacture of yarn.

KNOTTING. Lacelike fanciwork made by twisting and knotting threads. Knotwork may be decorative work consisting of or representing cords or the like, interlaced or knotted. It can also mean a type of fanciwork made by knotting fine silk over crochet cotton or cord.

KNOTWORK. Knotting, tatting, crocheting, and cordwork are resorted to in this wide range of embellishing materials and articles. Effects are obtained by interlacing and knotting for the final finish-off work.

KNUB. British term for the hard, compact, finer inner layer of the silk cocoon; used as waste silk.

KNUBS. Silk waste obtained in reeling cocoons.

KODAPAK. Eastman Chemical Products, Inc., cellulose acetate product coming in sheet, strip, or other forms. It is a thermoplastic cellulose ester sheet used for transparent containers, envelopes, window boxes, metalizing, advertising and display items, lamination, electrical insulation, and many other applications. Trade name.

KODEL. Registered trademark of

Eastman Chemical Products, Inc., New York City, for this lively, versatile polyester fiber engineered to meet the requirements of and the uses demanded by consumers. Its properties reveal outstanding resistance to pilling, high resistance to heat, high crease retention, wrinkle resistance, and excellent dimensional stability even without heat setting or other special processing. This naturally white fiber has a low specific gravity of 1.22.

Special Kodel fiber finds use in carpeting and knit applications such as hospital bedpads (poly 1-4 cyclohexylene-dimethylene terephthalate), is different from all other polyesters in its molecular structure, and is patented. Polyester gives the best results, as to color, with the use of disperse dyes.

Other modifications of Kodel include disperse dyed fiber, while another variation is used for sewing thread and fabrics where exceptional strength and abrasion resistance are factors. Kodel filament yarn has many uses in apparel and home furnishings, as well as in industrial uses. Kodel launders easily and well, and is ideally suited for wash-and-wear fabrics and garments. It has a host of other uses in outerwear for men, women, and children.

KODEL FIBERFILL. A special form of Eastman Kodel polyester used for bedspreads, mattresses, and upholstered furniture. Its light weight, warmth, and resilience are also important for its use in robes, outerwear, and sleeping bags.

KODEL POLYESTER 232. Unveiled in 1971, this polyester fiber filler has great resistance and softness for use in unbonded battings, in furniture, outerwear, and sleeping bags. Added loft and warmth, less weight, and increased ability to conform to body contour are features of the product.

KODEL POLYESTER FIBER, types of.

Type:	Description:
211	Lower tenacity fiber used in woolen and worsted blends, pile fabrics, and scatter rugs.
212	Special crimp for use in pile fabrics.
231	High, permanent crimp for fiberfill.
241	Regular carpet fiber.
411	Regular tenacity with optical brightener for woven and knit fabrics.
412	Low crimp for nonwoven applications.
414	Polishable fiber with optical brightener for use in pile fabrics.
421	High tenacity with optical bright-

ener for woven goods and sewing threads.

431 High, permanent crimp with optical brightener for fiberfill.

451 Regular tenacity with a blue-white cast for knit fabrics.

511 Basic dyeable fiber for use in woven and knit cloths.

541 Basic dyeable fiber for use in carpets.

641 Light dyeing fiber for use in carpets.

KOGALLA YARN. The best grade of coir yarn made in Ceylon, a leading locality for the fiber.

KOHEMP. The kudzu vine of China and Japan supply this bast fiber.

KOHORN STAPLE FIBER. A rayon fiber which combines some of the properties and advantages of wool with the low cost and the versatility of viscose rayon. This rough-surfaced fiber (which approximates wool in this respect) has a hollow space running throughout the fiber. The crimp is equal to that of wool and it is claimed to be stronger than wool in the dry state, and as strong as wool in the damp or wet condition. Fabrics may be 100 per cent staple or blended with wool according to demands of the trade.

KOLAH. Iranians (Persians) wear a tall, brimless hat that has been a tradition with Persian men for many centuries.

KOLINSKY. A type of heavy-furred China mink, dyed in sable or dark mink shades. Wearing qualities, excellent. Judged by lightness of pelt and depth of fur. Found in Siberia, China, and North Korea. Worn for informal and dress wear in jackets, scarves, and capes.

KOLORBON. A staple rayon fiber, solution-dyed fabric used in upholstery and in other home furnishings, Registered trademark of the American Enka Corporation, New York City.

KOPAN. A permanent cellulose finish that is a major development in modern fabric finishing. Suitable for many types of woven and knitted fabrics, particularly damasks, sheetings, and shirting. The finish imparts to each fiber a permanent coating which adds to durability, strength, and appearance. Outstanding properties of the finish are excellent shrinkage control, increase tensile strength, even penetration, elimination of slippage. Kopan serves as an excellent binder with fillers, pigments, and weighting compounds.

Kopan is a natural outgrowth of Permalon, used for military fabrics, chiefly head and mosquito netting. Kopan has all the advantages of Per-

malon plus a flexibility of formula which permits extensive variations for civilian usage and specific fabrics.

The best quality cellulose is used in making Kopan. Product of Harte & Co., New York City.

KORAKO. A New Zealand flax whose fine fibers are used in high-textured linen fabrics.

KOROSEAL. Trade-mark of the Goodrich Rubber Co., for a synthetic chemical produced from salt, limestone, and coal, which is used to coat fabrics and render them waterproof.

The chemical resistance of Koroseal is of primary importance in its use as an insulator on plating racks. It is also used as a coating for oil and gas pipelines in corrosive soil, as tubing for piping chemicals, transparent beer tubing, acid-resistant fabrics, gas-resistant fabrics, gas masks, food containers, bottle seals, and all types of protective coatings. Its flexibility and shock-absorbing properties are utilized in Koroseal sponge, gaskets, conveyer belting, and all types of molded articles, belts, suspenders, wallets, and luggage. The B. F. Goodrich Laboratories developed Koroseal (meaning a seal against corrosion).

KOSSU. See KELIM.

KRAEUSAL YARN. A German looped yarn made with two ground core threads which have the coarser or loop thread wound around them.

KRAFTCORD. A tightly twisted yarn made from cellulose fiber of a tiliaceous plant. Used as backing yarn in carpet weaves as an alternate for cotton or jute yarns.

KRENE. The trade-mark of the National Carbon Company to identify their products made of plastics, such as aprons, plastic fabric, rainwear material, shower curtaining, and window curtains.

KRIMMER. 1. A gray fur resembling Astrakhan or Persian lamb, made from the pelts of young lambs in the Crimean Peninsula region. 2. A pile fabric made in imitation of this fur.

KRISPGLO. A flat filament rayon yarn; a trademark of American Enka Corporation.

KRON. The best grade of Russian flax.

KROY PROCESS. Also known as the Lambda Process, the treatment prevents shrinkage "below the knitted size," and reduces the felting power of natural wool fibers to zero. This method for controlled shrinkage is a product of Kroy Wool Processors, a subsidiary of York Knitting Mills, Ltd., Toronto, Dominion of Canada.

KUBAN OR ROSTOFF WOOL. A

more or less white carpet grown in and around Rostov, U.S.S.R. See DONSKOI.

KULAH. The head covering worn by Moslem monks; made of cotton or linen.

KUMPTAS COTTON. A well-known cotton raised in India; staple is slightly below one inch and it spins to around 24s.

KUNSTSEIDE. Means artificial silk in German language, but it is now used as the word for rayon.

KURALON. Japanese trade name for a polyvinyl alcohol continuous filament and staple stock.

KURBELSTICKEREL. German for embroidery done by machine.

KURIWATA. Japanese for ginned cotton.

KURK. Fine soft wool, yielded by a species of white goat in Persia.

KURON. Registered trademark used by UniRoyal, Inc., for a one-way stretch elastic fabric, which contains no rubber threads, although rubber is used as the elastic element. Suitable for use in suspenders, garters, and elastic for underwear, pajamas, etc.

KURRACHEE COTTON. An East Indian cotton which is full of leaf, dull, and not too strong. Less than 1 inch in staple length, it spins to about single 24s.

KUSAK. A goodly length of vividly colored cloth wound around the waist by Turkish men.

KUZUMAYU. Japanese term for waste cocoons which constitute about 5 per cent of the annual cocoon poundage, which is about 750 million pounds in normal times.

KYNOL. Product of The Carborundum Company, Inc. Niagara Falls, New York, it has superior flame resistance when compared with any other comparable material. It is resistant to an oxyacetylene torch for many minutes and its long-term thermal stability in air is limited to 300° Fahrenheit. The cross-section is amorphous in structure. The strain behavior is typical of organic fibers such as wool and medium-tenacity viscose rayon. Average elongation values thirty percent while strength of 30,000 psi (1.8 grams per denier) is observed with a 14-micron-diameter fiber. Kynol is inert to practically all organic solvents and non-oxidizing acids. This is because of the relatively high cross-link density of the fibers. Hot caustic will degrade this fiber.

At present, Kynol is made in a 1½-inch staple length with a 14-micron diameter, circular cross-section. This product has good corrosion resistance against organic solvents and acids thereby making it a good potential for filtration of corrosive liquids and acids. It is used as insulation in aircraft and to fireproof fabrics and clothing.

L

L-22 AND L-24, MINIMUM STANDARDS OF AMERICAN STANDARDS ASSOCIATION. The standards of the American Standards Association, New York City, were approved for rayon and acetate fabrics on December 31, 1952, and revised in 1960. Minimum standards are provided on these materials with regard to terminal uses of the goods, the cutter and garment manufacturer, and the retailer and the consumer. Following World War II there was a maze of fabrics brought onto the market, which caused much chaos and confusion to all segments of the industry, let alone the public. The Association, keenly aware of the dilemma, undertook to do something about the bewildering conditions. It stated that "an American Standard is intended as a guide to aid the manufacturer, the consumer, and the general public. The existence of an American Standard does not in any respect preclude any party who has approved of the standard from manufacturing, selling, or using products, processes, or procedures not conforming to the standard."

Thus, it will be noted that acceptance of either or both standards is on a voluntary basis at all times. At the present time there are thirty-eight tests for women's and girls' apparel, twenty-three standards for men's and boys' apparel, and sixteen standards for the home-furnishings category.

In testing for setting the standards the use of the equipment in any well-establihsed or well-setup laboratory for chemical and physical testing will suffice. Other organizations that perform tests for standards include the American Society for Testing and Materials, the American Association of Textile Colorists and Chemists, and the International Standards Association. In addition, through research, development, experience, and experimental work the following groups have also contributed to the setting up of standards, working in conjunction for the most part, with the foregoing textile associations: groups and organizations that represent the government, various segments of industry, some academic institutions, services, and consumer units.

Textile-testing projects, both chemical and physical, undertaken and accepted, for example, by A.S.T.M. and A.A.T.C.C., are accepted by the American Standards Association with regard to essential performance requirements. All accepted tests provide a minimum level in serviceability and performance after a consideration of all angles presented in the particular project or test.

L-24 provides Institutional Standards sponsored by the American Hotel Association. The latest revision of standards occurred in 1957 and it is still used at the present time. This set of tests and requirements does what L-22 does for the home furnishing field. Some standards are used by both groups.

One of the outstanding facets of the A.S.A. is that if a fabric meets with its approval as to a minimum standard, "it does not imply that it is the best fabric in its class that a consumer can purchase, or the best value for the money expended; it does imply, however, that its minimum standard for performance and serviceability has been approved after all positive and negative aspects have been given full consideration."

LABEL. 1. A tag or ticket attached to any article. When attached to a garment it gives such information as size, fiber content, color, style, number, and price. 2. Woven labels are made on Jacquard looms, usually from 96 to 144 at a time on a double or triple batten loom. Although the labels are usually narrow, the loom is very wide since so many labels are made at the same time. Practically all major fibers may be used to make labels today. Labels of this type are used for identification of the manufacturer, point of origin of the fabric, name of the store where the article was purchased, name of the textile mill that made the goods, etc. The label business has grown by leaps and bounds and is now a very important one in American business. A label on a woman's coat, for example, is a mark of distinction—Anglo, Forstmann, Stroock, Worumbo, etc.

LABEL CLOTH. Heavily sized cotton fabric used for labels and tags.

LABELING ACT OF TEXTILE WEARING APPAREL OF JULY, 1972, FTC. The Federal Trade Commission, pursuant to the FTC Act, issued rules to govern the use of Care Labels for any article of wearing apparel or piece goods intended for and or terminal use. The Rules, effective July 3, 1972, require that all such articles shall bear permanent and prominent labels setting forth precise directions for refurbishment of the article after usage. The fabric,

domestic or foreign, must carry directions at all times, and they are to last for the life of the fabric. Penalty for non-compliance is $5,000.00.

There are certain exemptions which include headgear, footwear, and items such as "see-through" blouses which might be aesthetically injured by a label, as well as items which sell for less than $3.00. Outside the exemptions, the rule requires that "maximum" conditions of care be stated, as opposed to an escape such as labeling everything "Dry-clean Only."

It is estimated that labels will cost the manufacturer from $2.50 to as high as $35.00 per thousand. The cost of attaching them comes to around 2½ cents each, a considerable expense.

Under this ruling, the garment, or fabric intended for use in a garment, must exhibit satisfactory retention of appearance and shape after at least five launderings or three drycleanings by a method stated on the label affixed to the item. See Flammability Act, July, 1972.

LABIUM. The underlip of the silkworm. The two orifices or minute openings are located there, and it is through these that the worm emits the two fine filaments which are cemented together by the sericin or silk gum when it spins its cocoon. Sometimes known as the spinneret, this gave rise to the present-day spinnerets used in the manufacture of filaments in the man-made and synthetic fiber industries.

LABOR AGREEMENT. The written mutual understanding between the company and the union covering the various phases of their relationships.

LABOR DISPUTE. A conflict between a company and its employees, or a union, concerning some phases of their relationship.

LABOR UNION. An organization of workers formed for the purpose of dealing collectively with the employer on wages, hours, and working conditions, and for the mutual aid and protection in matters pertaining to their employment.

LABURNHAM. Continental and British fabric used for dress goods and made with silk, nylon, acetate, etc., warp and worsted filling in a 2-up, 1-down twill.

LAC. Strong thin cord.

LAC-DYE. Lac is a resinous substance exuded from an East Indian scale insect, *Tachardia lacca,* found on the twigs of trees. They increase so rapidly that in a very short time they cover the twigs with the encrustation. Extraction to obtain the dye is done with water.

Lac is the basis for lacquer, shellac, and varnish; its use, at present, in textiles is practically nil.

LACE. Derived from the Latin laqueus, meaning noose or snare. In Roman days it simply meant a cord which would hold by being tied or interwoven. In time, the term was applied to any openwork fabric of interwoven threads made from textile fibers.

Today, lace is an ornamental, openwork material made into some sort of design by intricate manipulation, either by hand or machine. Lacemaking was not developed until the halcyon days of Venice. Flanders, at this time, also became a great lace center because some of the Venetian workers settled there and brought the art of making lace with them. The Renaissance fully developed the industry in the Italian City-States.

Lace is used for collars, collar and cuff sets, coverings, curtaining, decoration, edging, fringe, pillows, runners, spreads, and trimming.

Some of the better known types of lace follow:

1. ALENÇON LACE: Delicate and durable lace with a solid design outlined with cord on sheer net ground. Best machine-made imitations have cord run by hand. Cannot be called "Alençon" unless actually made in Alençon, France.

2. ALOE LACE: Fragile lace made from aloe plant fibers in the Philippines and Italy.

3. ANTIQUE LACE: Handmade bobbin lace of heavy thread with large, often irregular, square knotted net on which designs are darned. Imitation antique lace used in draperies.

4. BATTENBERG LACE: A coarser form of Renaissance lace, made by hand or machine, of linen braid or tape and linen thread brought together to form various designs. Used for collars, cuffs. Machine-made for draperies, etc.

5. BINCHE LACE: Flemish bobbin lace having a scroll floral pattern and ground sprinkled with figures like snowflakes. Used for dresses, blouses, lingerie.

6. BRETON LACE: Net which has designs embroidered with heavy, often colored, thread.

7. CHANTILLY LACE: Bobbin lace with fine ground and designs outlined by cordonnet of thick, silky threads, used for trimmings on bridal veils.

8. DRESDEN POINT LACE: Type of drawnwork with ground of fine linen with some threads drawn and others embroidered and interlaced to form square mesh.

9. IRISH LACE: A variety of laces made in Ireland. The best known are crochet, net embroideries of Limerick, and Carrickmacross.

10. LILLE LACE: Fine bobbin lace with patterns outlined with flat cordonnet. Sometimes dotted.

11. MILAN LACE: Originally made in Milan. Tape lace with needle-point mesh and picot edging. Easily imitated by machine, but machine-made must be so described.

12. NEDDLE-POINT LACE: Lace made entirely with a sewing needle rather than with a bobbin. Worked with buttonhole and blanket stitches on paper pattern.

13. NOTTINGHAM LACE: Flat lace originally made in Nottingham, England. Now used as name for lace made anywhere on Nottingham-type machine.

14. RATINE LACE: Machine-made lace with groundwork of heavy loops similar to turkish toweling.

15. RENAISSANCE LACE: Woven tape motifs joined by a variety of flat stitches.

16. ROSE POINT LACE: Venetian needle-point lace which has a delicate and full design of flowers, foliage, and scrolls connected by string cordonnet.

17. SPANISH LACE: Any lace made in Spain. The most common is of silk with heavy flat floral designs held together with varying meshes.

18. TATTING LACE: Knotted lace worked with the fingers and a shuttle. Made in various designs, the most popular being the clover leaf and wheel.

19. VAL LACE: See Valenciennes lace below.

20. VALENCIENNES LACE: Flat bobbin lace worked in one piece with the same thread forming both the ground and the design. Real lace made of linen; the imitation of cotton. Commonly called Val. The imitation must be so described.

21. VENICE LACE: A needle-point lace decorated with floral motifs and designs connected with irregularly placed picot edges.

LACE, BUYING AND SELLING POINTS OF.

1. The product is delicate, fine, individualistic, and intricate in character.

2. Machine-made lace may have as much artistic value and motif as handmade lace.

3. Lace may be worn by maid or matron.

4. It adds daintiness, simplicity, dignity, poise, and does give an aristocratic look in dress.

5. Lace is feminine, and it adds charm to the attire in both day and evening wear.

6. As an accessory, lace finds much use in collar and cuff sets, handkerchiefs, dress trimmings.

7. It can raise a plain dress to the point of appeal and charm.

LACE, COTTON. Broad term for any lace made of cotton.

LACE, LAUNDERING OF. Lace will keep its shape better if it is pinned to a piece of muslin prior to washing. Old, delicate lace should be protected by putting it into a muslin or cotton pillow slip while washing it. Suds should be allowed to soak through the material and rubbing should be avoided. Lace should be rinsed in the bag and then removed for drying. Press lace on the wrong side. Machine-made lace will always have a flat, dull appearance.

LACE, SODIUM HYDROXIDE. By the use of a sodium hydroxide treatment, it is possible to give inexpensive lace a richer, more three-dimensional appearance. Soaking the lace in solution causes the fibers to swell and then crimp giving the fabric elasticity and a more appealing appearance.

LACE, STRAIGHT. A straight lace in which the mesh ground and the motif are made simultaneously.

LACE, WEFT-KNITTED. Openwork effect obtained by transferring needle loops on a plain stitch base.

LACE BARK. A fine, thin Jamaican bast fiber provides the thread for this lace, which is used for cordage, dress trimming, and headgear.

LACE CLOTH. Leno, mock leno, openwork fabric, knitted mesh fabric and wide lace are often known by this term. Lace cloth comes in white or pastel shades and is popular in summer attire.

LACE EFFECT. This refers to novelty goods of cotton, rayon, acetate, silk, or nylon which have been woven in leno or mock leno construction on a loom, or in a heavy machine embroidery effect on a relief of thin groundwork. See Illustrated Section (Fabrics 57, 58).

LACE FRAMES. The complex machines used to manufacture lace; also called bobbinette frames and warp net frames.

LACE INDUSTRY INVENTIONS. There were five basic inventions in the nineteenth century that greatly improved machine lace making with regard to the fabric produced, use of less labor, increased production, and lowering of the price of lace products. The inventions were:

1. 1835: Thomas Alcock perfected the Go-Through System of working the carriages on the frames.

2. 1841: Hooten Deverill, a great English inventor, applied to the Leavers machine the Jacquard motion acting on the warp threads in independent bars. This was fifteen years after the Jacquard application had been first made on a Leavers frame.

LACE INDUSTRY, SOME BASIC TERMS USED IN THE.

1. ALLOVER EMBROIDERY: This is thirty-six inches or more in width, and the motif is embroidered over the full width of the fabric. Cotton, linen, nylon, rayon, and silk serve as the yarns, while the fabric base may be organdy, plain dimity, cambric, longcloth, pique, etc. The product is without scallops on each side, and is made in white and pastel shades and colors suitable for everyday wear. This type of embroidery is used for blouses, dress fabrics, pillow covers.

2. ALLOVER LACE: A lace one yard or more wide, devoid of scallops, and with the design spread over the entire width. Many types of design motifs and color shades are used for the fabric, which is made into day and evening dresses.

3. BEADING EDGES: Refers to embroidery or lace in which the edges are perforated or open, so that ribbon may be drawn through and pulled up to give a ruffled effect.

4. BEADING GALLOON: A band used on some embroidery and lace, having both edges scalloped. It comes in varying widths, with openings in the center for ribbon to pass through, as shoulder straps in underwear, or to adorn dresses.

5. BEADING INSERTION: A straight edge applied to both sides of embroidery and lace, with openings in the center to permit ribbon to be pulled through and gathered or ruffled. Used on baby clothes, children's dresses, carriage covers, shoulder straps.

6. BOBBIN FINE: Machine-made lace, on the order of shadow lace, in which heavy threads outline the motif.

7. BOBBIN SPOOL: A spool with a head or flange on both ends. It holds the yarn or thread for spinning, weaving, or sewing.

8. BRIDE: A small strip or connection which links the details of ornamentation in lace. It may consist of threads overcast with buttonhole stitches, or of twisted or plaited threads. The English equivalent of this French term is "pearl-tie."

9. CORDONNET: The yarn, thread, or cord that outlines a lace motif.

10. HARDANGER LACE: This city on the Hardanger Fjord in southwestern Norway is famous for its lace, made by its women. The origin of this lace is very old: worked with colored silks on a fine gauze netting, it was made in Persia and other Asiatic countries for many centuries. Materials for making Hardanger include scrim or loose-textured linen, a pair of very sharp scissors, a tapestry needle, and pearl cotton.

    This lace is based on the principle of the square and is geometric in form. The stitches include kloster, Swedish weaving stitch, woven bars with picots, festoon stitch, lace stitch, Holbein technique, feather stitch, kloster blocks, diagonal kloster blocks, and fagoting stitch.

11. INSERTION: A section used on lace or embroidery for joining two pieces of fabric together; both sides are straight, and it is reinforced with extra threads to make sewing easier and to provide more strength.

12. LACE FABRIC: Sheer lightweight material with a doup or mock leno weave. Made in white and pastel shades, it finds use in summer dressgoods; this cloth gives good service, launders easily and well, and withstands rugged wear. It is not a true lace.

13. LACE FRAMES: The complex machines used to make lace—also known as bobbinette frames and warp net frames.

14. LACE SPRIG: A piece of lace fabric appliquéd to a net foundation.

15. LACE TIES: The connecting threads used in lace manufacture.

16. LACEWORK: Usually implies open-work hosiery which has been knitted.

17. LACE YARNS: Doubled yarns made from good to high-quality cotton yarns which range from 60's up to 240's in yarn size or count. Lace yarns are hard-twisted and usually gassed or singed to add smoothness and luster. Sheen and general appearance of lace yarns are very important since they add to the beauty of the material produced.

18. TOILE: The heavy filling or design of a lace motif in contradistinction to the background.

19. VEININGS: These are used to join the various parts of materials; they are useful as well as ornamental. Width is from ⅛ inch to ½ inch. In French called entredeux, which means "between two."

20. VRAIE: French word for "true"; used to designate lace that is real, true, or handmade.

3. 1849: James Olkknow, English inventor, perfected the perforated steel bar.

4. 1875: By this time Alcock's Go-Through System was in universal use, since some improvements had been effected.

5. 1891: W. H. Smith brought out his porcupine roller attachment, which was widely hailed in the trade.

LACE INSPECTION. There are two general types:

1. BROWN INSPECTION AND MENDING: A web of lace in the full width of the machine usually has many bands joined by lacer threads, and, while this web may be of any length, a 36-yard length seems to be the most desirable for inspection, mending, handling, and packaging. In the manufacture of lace there will be various damages or defects that must be remedied—broken threads, bars misgaiting or being too high or too low in the gait. When a flaw is observed the inspector ties a loose knot over the area so that they may be remedied by mending or by the use of a sewing machine. Mending is done quickly, and it is difficult to find the damaged area. Low-grade narrow lace is not mended. Brown inspection precedes finishing operations.

2. WHITE INSPECTION AND MENDING: Lace is brought to the "white" by washing, scouring, bleaching, extracting moisture, starching, and tentering. Any one of these operations may cause blemishes in the lace as it passes through the plant. Defects and flaws are fixed as in the case of the brown inspection and mending.

LACE LEATHER. A form of rawhide leather from cattle hides that is used for lacing together sections of driving belts. It is often prepared with an alum and oil and some other combination tannage.

LACELON. A gossamer, lacelike plastic which is rain- and stain-proof and flame-resistant, and may be washed and ironed as any ordinary fabric. Because of its fragile, fresh, summery appearance, it is used for women's headgear. In soft pastels, it is used for rollers, off-the-face and picture hats, most of which are trimmed with ribbon, silk flowers, and tulle.

Other uses for this product of Minnesota Mining and Manufacturing Company, Inc., include costume decoration, lampshade trimming, place mats, gift wrapping. Comes in 3- and 5-inch widths.

LACE PORCELAIN. Lace made of cotton or linen is impregnated with Kaolin, a pure white clay paste. After firing, the fibers have been consumed leaving the porcelain in the shape and appearance of lace.

LACES, FRENCH (There are three major types):

LINGERIE LACE

1. VALENCIENNES LACE: It is now made of long-staple cotton, nylon, or rayon. It comes in varying widths but is usually narrow for use in trimming lingerie, edging, insertion-work, or appliqué.

2. CHANTILLY-TYPE: Made in rayon or silk it comes in long bands or in flounces. Used for lingerie and smart, dressy garments.

3. ALENÇON-TYPE: Manufactured in and around Lyons, it is the finest of these three types and higher in price. Used for classic silk lingerie chiefly in appliqué motifs inserted into the fabric.

COUTURE LACE

1. RE-EMBROIDERED LACE: This presents an allover motif in which the patterns are enhanced by means of an embroidery outline thread either stitched on by machine after the lace has left the machine for the fine quality laces, or woven in while the lace is being made on the frame. Of late, this lace has been made with the re-embroidery outlined with other products than embroidery thread, such as ribbon, narrow braid, cellophane, metallic yarns, and threads.

2. FINE CHANTILLY-TYPE: These have been made since the time of the well-known Madame DuBarry (Jeanne Bécu, 1746–1793), a favorite of Louis XV who was guillotined during the French Revolution. The motif is outlined with a fine embroidery thread or, sometimes, worked right into the center of the pattern. This is the acme of perfection in fine fashion of today.

3. GUIPURE: This is the heaviest of the three laces, and its beauty and elegance of guipure comes from a judicious grouping of motifs. Used in couture fashions and for expensive blouses.

4. VEILING AND TULLE: 1. Although these items are not classed as lace, generally speaking, they still come under the commercial classification of lace. They are made on machines similar to those that manufacture lace, and this manufacture is governed by the same traditions that prevail throughout the entire lace industry in France today.

LACES, HANDMADE AND MACHINE-MADE. There are two distinct groups of laces—handmade and machine-made.

The handmade or real laces may be classed as follows:

1. Needle-point lace.

2. Pillow or bobbin lace.

3. Crocheted lace.

4. Darned lace.

NEEDLE-POINT LACE: The most expensive and most difficult type of lace to make. Made with a needle, the first step is to sketch the pattern on parchment which is then stitched down upon two pieces of linen. The thread is then laid on the leading lines drawn on the parchment, and fastened to the parchment here and there by stitches. The solid parts are filled in by the needle with buttonhole stitching. The meshes or ties are manipulated so as to link the different parts into the one fabric. A knife is then passed between the parchment and the linen thereby releasing the completed lace.

ALENÇON: The name comes from the city in France where it was first made. Alençon is still a leading world center for lacemaking. Birds, flowers, pastoral scenes and vases form the background of Alençon. The ground-patterns are made with animal and tree effects.

Machine-made laces may be summarized as follows:

The first machine lace was made in 1809 in England by John Heathcoat. By 1813, another Englishman, John Leavers, modified the arrangement of the bobbins and carriages used to make lace according to the principles of Heathcoat and the industry grew by leaps and bounds. It is said that Leavers added about fifteen million dollars of annual business to the industry. The machines were made in Nottingham, and in a short time some were exported to America. The cities of Bridgeport, Connecticut; New York; Paterson, New Jersey, and Philadelphia became the first lace centers in this country. Scranton and Wilkes-Barre, Pennsylvania, for many years, have been known for their laces. The center of the industry today, however, is Rhode Island, which produces close to 70 per cent of all Leavers lace made in this country.

Another way of making lace was perfected in Saint Gall, Switzerland, and in Plauen, Germany. This is the burnt-out method whereby, with the use of chemicals, animal fiber content used in the manufacture of the product is actually burned out, leaving the cotton embroidery work intact.

MACHINE-MADE LACES (There are three types):

ORIENTAL: This fine net is made with a heavily embroidered edge.

PRINCESS: Made of machine-braid on a machine-made net; put together by hand.

SHADOW: A fine mesh ground in which shadowlike patterns of finer mesh are seen.

COMPARISON OF MACHINE-MADE AND HANDMADE LACES:

1. There are irregularities in handmade lace, since the patterns do not repeat in exact, perfect order.

2. Handmade lace can be raveled without trouble.

3. Machine-made Cluny, Torchon, and other bobbin laces, when observed through a magnifying glass, show uneven threads and the use of two sizes of thread instead of one.

4. Cotton lace may be distinguished from linen lace by tipping the end of the respective threads. Cotton threads will become fuzzy and protrude; linen threads will taper to a point.

5. Insert a pin into threads of the pattern of machine-made lace and observe that it is possible to slide the threads back and forth; this is not possible in handmade lace.

6. Machine-made lace has a flat, dull appearance.

LACE SPRIG. A piece of lace fabric appliquéd to a net foundation.

LACE STICKS. Bobbins used to make lace are sometimes referred to by this expression.

LACE STITCHES. Open or raised effects produced on a knitting machine by a transfer of loops from the needles on which they are made to adjacent needles.

LACE STRIPES. Actually refers to leno or doup-woven fabric or one made on dobby loom with mock leno construction. Plain-weave background is used when made with the mock leno. Figure motif may be made of single or plied yarn. Texture is around 64 x 52. Used for blouses, waists, shirting, etc.

LACE TIES. The connecting threads used in lace manufacture.

LACET. 1. A registered trade-mark for a durable stiffener and shrinkage controller, owned by American Cyanamid Company. A resin product finish, based on melamine, for application to cotton or rayon Nottingham lace curtains. Also controls stretching. Its chemical nature is a melamine formaldehyde condensate in combination with other resin types and pigments. 2. Originally, a silk or cotton braid used to form patterned laces. In French it means a plaited string for clothes or a shoelace; in this country, braiding or cording used by the upholstery trade to cover seams.

LACETS BLEU. French for plaited string for clothes or a shoelace, braiding, or cording, colored blue. This interpretation implies a twill, coutil, drill, etc., that is dyed blue and used for pants, work clothes, slacks, shirting, etc. The same term is used for any narrow fabric, made of cotton, dyed blue.

LACEWORK. Usually implies openwork hosiery which has been knitted.

LACE YARNS. Doubled yarns made from good to high quality cotton yarns in counts which range from 60s to 240s. Lace yarns are hard-twisted and usually gassed or singed to add smoothness. Sheen and general appearance are potent factors in lace yarns.

LACHE. French word laché (loosened), meaning slack or crimped yarns in fabric caused by slippage or poor warp tension.

LACING. The combining of a series of Jacquard cards in order to form a pattern chain that controls the weaving in a Jacquard loom.

LACING NUMBER. This is a number found on rayon wrappings as the rayon is sent to the throwster. It indicates the batch of spinning solution from which the yarn was spun. Thus, yarns with the same lacing number should be identical.

LACIS. 1. Original meaning implied a type of darned net embroidery made in square formation. Present meaning is countable net, filet conté, which means "able to count the net construction." 2. Also implies embroidered or darned net, filet brodé or filet broderie, which means a filet or filagree type of embroidery.

LACQUER FINISH. A chemical treatment which produces a thin film on the surface of cloth; may be applied in a design. Not durable against drycleaning unless so stated.

LACTIC ACID. It is used as an assistant to mordant wool with bichrome, and to test dyes for fastness to perspiration. Formula is $C_3H_6O_3$, or $CH_3CH(OH)CO_2H$.

LACTOFIL. A Dutch fiber in which milk casein has been mixed with latex and glue.

LACTRON. Extruded rubber thread compounded from natural rubber latex in sizes suitable for textile applications.

LADAM COTTON. This Indian cotton is fine in diameter and reddish in cast. Also known as Nadam.

LADDER BRAID. An openwork, ladderlike braid used for lace and trimming.

LADDER EFFECT; LADDER WEAVE. A variation of twill constructions, usually in color-effect weaves in which a series of rising or lowering steps or effects are observed. Popular in some worsteds and woolens for both men's and women's wear apparel.

LADDER STITCH. An embroidery stitch which has the threads arranged to simulate the rungs of a ladder.

LADDER TAPE. The stout cotton tape or banding used on Venetian blinds.

LADY'S CLOTH. Popular in the Gay Nineties, it was a lightweight woolen broadcloth used for dress goods and coatings.

LAG. See DOBBY PATTERN CHAIN.

LAGOS COTTON. A rather strong, coarse African cotton which is brownish in cast and irregular in length. This dull cotton averages less than 1 inch in staple and spins to about 20s.

LA GUAYRAN COTTON. A silken West Indian cotton, irregular in length, with average staple of about 1¼ inches. Spins to about 40s.

LAHORE. The name of a province in India. The name is used to include certain fabrics such as a cashmere dress goods, a type of knotted cotton and wool floor covering, shawl fabric, a fine cashmere cloth made with figured patterns on a dobby loom, etc.

LAID FABRIC. Cloth which has no filling yarn in its construction. The warp ends are laid parallel and set into a binding material which holds the warp ends in place. Laid fabric yarn is treated and will rest on the cloth upon which it has been laid. Automobile tire fabric is an example.

LAID-IN FABRIC, KNITTED. A fabric made of two yarns, a ground yarn which is knitted in and a laid-in yarn which is tucked in. The ground yarn is usually finer in diameter and the superimposed yarn does not form a knitted loop.

The most popular laid-in structure is the 1x1 inlay, also known as hopsack. It is constructed by alternate needles tucking and missing at alternate feeds. There is also the rather popular 3x1 inlay in which the laid-in yarn floats over three needles at a time and is tucked-in on the fourth needle.

LAID WARP. Same as taped ends.

LAID WOOL. Wool clipped from sheep that have been greased or tarred as a protection against weather.

LAINE. French for wool; woolen or worsted cloth.

LAINE BRODIE, LAINE BRODEE. A coarse, rather bulky, two-ply woolen yarn used as filling in tapestry weaving.

LAINE DE CARMENIE. Persian goat's hair.

LAINE D'ETE. Laine means "wool" in French while d'été means "of summer." Hence, a summer woolen or one of light weight. This fabric was first made of all woolen yarn and was on the order of veiling fabric. At present, other lighter fibers and yarns are used in the cloth, although there is always some woolen or worsted fiber in the content. Acetate, rayon, and other fibers often have a greater content than the animal fibers as to content in the yarn and fabric.

LAINE TERNEAUX. French for merino wool.

LAISOT. A plain-weave linen cloth made with rather low count, coarse yarns. Textured at about 28-square, this white or pastel-colored fabric is used as dress goods and children's clothing. Laisot is in the crash family of linens.

LAIZES. French laces which have small dots or clusters over the ground work.

LAK. An Indian term which signifies the best reeled portion taken from tussah cocoons.

LAKE. 1. A deep red pigment made by combining some coloring matter—animal, as cochineal, or vegetable, as madder—with a metallic oxide, usually that of aluminum or tin, or the color of this pigment. 2. Any insoluble metallic compound which yields various colored pigments by the chemical interaction of a mordant and dye.

LAMA. Short for laminated and means that laminated threads are used to enhance some fabrics made in France. Gold, silver, aluminum, and even tinsel are used as the novelty threads. Also means a flannel made in France that is a lining cloth. Made in plain or small twills and either striped or dyed solid colors. Lama can also be interpreted to be llama. See LLAMA.

LAMB. 1. A young sheep. 2. There are many varieties of lamb fabric, from China, Persia, Russia, Siberia and South America; among these are the popular broadtail, caracul, and krimmer.

LAMB, SCOTCH. In Scotland, a lamb like any other lamb in any part of the world until it is a year old. The lamb then becomes known as a "hog" or "hogg," and may be a "tup-hogg" or a "yowe-hog." A castrated "tup-hogg" is known in Scotland as a "wedder." See HOG, HOGGETT, TEG, TEGGETT; WEATHER.

LAMBA. 1. A multicolored shawl or throw made from lamb's wool mixed with hair fibers. 2. Fabric made from leaves by the natives of Africa.

LAMBREQUIN. 1. Suspended or hung from a shelf or casing, this decorative fabric of any type conceals curtain fixtures, walls that need painting, etc. 2. Ornamental covering for a helmet.

LAMBS, WINTER. Lambs born in the fall or winter; also called hothouse lambs.

LAMBSDOWN. Plated knit cloth whose surface-effect shows a heavy, spongy fleece-effect made possible by the use of slack-twisted woolen yarn.

LAMBSKIN. 1. A lambskin dressed with the wool on the skin or pelt. Used for garments in severe winter areas. 2. Fabrics which are given finishes to resemble scoured lamb's wool. Fleecy fabrics in this group include molleton, silence cloth, flannel. 3. Lamb pelts taken before the animal is not more than two months old. 4. A satin weave, filling-effect cotton fabric made with compact texture. 5. The white leather apron used as a symbol in Freemasonry.

LAMB'S WOOL. Wool shorn from lambs up to seven months old. Soft and possessing superior spinning properties when compared with wool from older animals. Lamb's wool has a natural tip which is lost after the first or virgin clip has been taken from the sheep. The ends of sheep wool are very blunt.

LAMB WOOL AND SHEEP WOOL, DIFFERENCES IN. Hog or lamb wool is distinguished from wether or sheep wool in the following manner:

1. If the ends of the fibers are pointed, it may be assumed that they have been taken from a lamb; sheep wool fibers have blunt ends.
2. When staple is pulled from the fleece:
    I. If it is wether wool, the staple will come out cleanly without interfering with any of the surrounding fibers that have been pulled out.
    II. Hog wool is dirtier, greasier and oilier when compared with wether stock. Greater difficulty is encountered in pulling out fibers.

LAME. Any textile fabric in which metallic threads are used in the warp or in the filling for decorative purposes. Lamé fabrics are used chiefly in evening wear and slipper fabric. The word comes from the French for "worked with gold or silver wire."

LAMINATE. To beat, roll, or press into thin sheets or strips, such as metals or plastics.

LAMINATED FABRIC. Laminates have been known for many years in the metal, plastic, and rubber fields; the latter connection with the term, laminate, designates a combination of a plastic film or sheet with another material, plastic or other, the bonding of the two surfaces being done either by heat sealing or by the use of some ad-

hesive. The method of laminating is comparable with that used in the manufacture of plywood.

Laminated fabric is defined as a bonded combination of two or more sheeted layers, at least one being a textile material, and at least one of the other layers being a porous or nonporous plastic sheet. Woven, knitted, or nonwoven materials may be laminated. Heat sealing or the use of an adhesive or cement may be used. At present, the combining process on textile fabrics is achieved, in many instances, by actual gas heating of the foam used to a point where it becomes adhesive, sticky, or tacky, and then forcing the shell material to adhere to it so that when the cooling treatment is completed there is a firm bond to the fabric used. For example, "Laminated Jersey" has become a generic reference to jersey fabric that has been backed and bonded with a synthetic foam of the type known as "Curon" or "Scottfoam."

There are several methods under development at present, most of which have to do with the use of cold adhesive sprays and then combining the lining or backing fabric with the shell.

LAMINATION. The process of adhering one fabric to another by the use of an adhesive, a suitable compound, or by the application of heat. One side of the fabric is made of one material while the reverse is of another material.

LAMINATION, FABRIC-TO-FABRIC. Bonding or cementing two fabrics together without the use of any intermediate or carrier between them.

LAMINATION, FLAME. Warp or weft knitgoods which are bonded to a urethane foam backing. A continuous urethane foam sheet is passed over a butane gas flame, causing the exposed side of the foam to become tacky. At the same time, the fabric and foam make contact in a nip roller device which causes both items to become firmly bonded together.

LAMINATION, SANDWICH. As the term implies, it is the bonding of two fabrics to each of the two surfaces of a urethane foam sheet.

LAMPAS. A fabric made of two warps and one or more fillers. This type of fabric always works with the warp of the same color, so you can have a definite two-tone fabric or multicolored fabric where each flower has its own color combination with the same color in the warp.

LAMPASETTE. A single color warp is used in this material. Made on twill weave with the use of several colors in the filling to make the brocade effect possible. Usually made with silk or nylon warp and cotton or woolen filling. See LAMPAS.

LAMP WICKING. Wicks for lamps are made by using a flat or tubular fabric composed of coarse, soft-spun, loosely twisted cotton yarn.

LAMS, LAMMS. The horizontal bars or levers which extend between the harnesses and the treadles to which are attached the cords or chains. They allow the harnesses to be tied in combinations so that one foot may be used in treadling in hand-loom weaving. Two or more harnesses may be tied to one lam. Lams are necessary in multiple-harness hand-loom weaving.

The lams, in their action, allow the harness to be pulled directly down from the center, although the pedal to which they are attached may be far to the right or to the left of exact center. This action, incidentally, makes for a clear, clean shed. See Illustrated Section.

LANA. Latin word for wool, and either lana or contractions of it mean wool in Italy, Spain, Portugal, etc.

LANA DEL TAMBOR. A silky seed fiber used as stuffing, obtained from the bombax tree in Venezuela.

LANA FIBER. A "vegetable wool" fiber peculiar to Puerto Rico, and nearby areas. Taken from the lana tree, the fibers are similar to kapok and find use in stuffing, wadding, etc.

LANAPRESS. A 100 percent polyester nonwoven lining fabric used in durable press shirtings. Product of the Lantuck Division of Wellington Sears Company, New York City, a division of West Point-Pepperell Company, New York City and West Point, Georgia.

Lanapress can be used in pre-cured or post-cured processes in white and colored shirtings ranging from 100 percent cotton to 65/35 polyester/cotton. As a lining material, the fabric is said to equal a 150 or 250 denier polyester taffeta, at a cost comparable with regulation cotton interlinings.

LANATE. Woolly; specifically, in botany, provided or covered with long, fine wool-like hairs. From the Latin, lanatus or lana, meaning woolly, wool.

LANATIN. A method of modifying the physical properties of bast fibers, such as cotton, ramie, jute, hemp, etc.; rayon, acetate, and some other man-made filaments. Fibers thus treated are referred to, for example, as Lanatinized cotton, etc.

LANCASHIRE FLANNEL. English woolen flannel made with white listing. Usually made with yarn-dyed warp and filling in some shade of blue. Slight napping is given the goods.

LANCE JACQUARD. British term for fabrics made on lappet looms. The word, Jacquard, here is a misnomer. See LAPPET WEAVING.

LANCES. Cloths made when certain filling yarns cross over only selected warp ends and float over the others are called lancés in French.

LANELLA. Trade name for a well-known Swiss flannel made with cotton and wool in a 50-50 blend; high-grade stocks are used, and the cloth is used in many types of apparel for men, women, and children. See VIYELLA FLANNEL.

LANGLEY UNIT. The unit of energy that a swatch or sample receives when being tested for fastness to natural sunlight or in a Fade-Ometer. This method provides a common denominator for tests done anywhere in the world.

LANITAL. Trade name for the original protein fiber made from casein, produced in Belgium.

LANO DI VETRO. Glass fiber in Italian. The term goes back to the days of the early Renaissance, at which time glass filaments were first attempted and made. Present-day glass fibers are a development from these early efforts.

LANOLIN. This wool grease, often called yoke, is an oil secretion which comes from the sebaceous glands of sheep. Lanolin or yoke serves as a conditioner to keep wool fibers from becoming dry and possible brittle. Yolk is taken from the fiber in the scouring of the stock by a chemical sedimentation method.

Chiefly a mixture of cholesterol esters from the grease wool, this emollient in purified condition serves as the basis for the grease paints used in theatrical circles, ointments, salves, skin creams, and as a base in several other commercial products.

"LANO WOOL." Puerto Rican vegetable fiber resembling wool, fur; filler for cushions, pillows.

LANSDOWN, LANSDOWNE. An old-time fabric made on a three-leaf twill. Silk warp and worsted or cotton filling are used to make the cloth, which appears infrequently on the market.

LAOS. Crepe dressgoods made with grege silk warp and tussah silk filling with the latter sent into the fabric two picks of right-twist followed by two of left-twist.

LAP. Cotton wound in a lap form ready for further processing. Card lap is from 40 to 45 inches wide; sliver lap is ten inches wide; ribbon lap, 12 inches wide. Card lap will weigh around 40 pounds when ready for carding. Worsted top is often spoken of as lap in the mill. Fibers in lap form are easy to unwind and manipulate.

LAP ARBOR, LAP ROLL. Cotton lap is wound around this roll in the calender section of the picker machine. This steel bar is two to three inches in diameter, and there is a hole running through the center.

LAPBOARD. Used by seamstresses and tailors, it is a board for the lap, used instead of the regulation worktable.

LAPEL. The front part of a garment which is folded back. It is commonly called a revers. In jackets and coats the collar forms a continuation of the lapel.

LAPIN. Sheared rabbit; popular for trimmings on cloth coats.

LAPIS. Method of printing cotton fabric with indigo to obtain bright coloring effect.

LAPPET WEAVING. Form of weaving in which an extra warp is used in such a manner that it will produce designs over a portion of the background of a fabric.

The following is a brief description of the method: Long needles through which the figure threads are drawn are carried in a rack at the front of the reed. When the rack is lowered, the needles are pressed to the bottom of the loom shed and held in this position while the shuttle travels through, laying the loose pick. The rack is then raised and the pick is beaten into the cloth. After this fundamental action, the rack is shifted sideways to another point where the same operation takes place.

The sideways motion of the rack is controlled by a groove in the lappet wheel or by a pattern. It is this sideways motion that forms the pattern. Lappet weaving is done on cotton dress goods and upholstered materials.

LAPPING. A "cushion cloth" which serves the rollers of the printing machine. Virgin wool is used for the warp and filling of this cloth, which is about 80 yards long on the frame.

LAP ROD. The iron rod about which the cotton lap is wound. Extending beyond the limits of the actual lap, the rod is used to handle the stock conveniently so that it may be placed in sockets to be fed into the delivery end of the next machine, the cotton card.

LAP ROLL. A fluted surface, wooden roll upon which the cotton lap rests at the feeding-in end of the flat cotton card. The lap, when the machine is in action, unrolls by friction as the roll revolves.

LAP STICK. The small metal rod around which the wide sheet of cotton lap is wound as it comes from certain textile machines.

LAP WASTE. Soft wastes taken from cards, draw frames, roving frames, etc. Can be reprocessed since much of this waste is of good staple length.

LA RAZZA SARDA. Sheep originating in Africa and native to Sardinia for centuries. They produce a fleece ranging from two to eight pounds.

LARRIGAN LEATHER. The name for oil-tanned light hides used in moccasins.

LARVA. The immature, wingless, and often wormlike form in which certain insects hatch from the egg. Larva increase in size and development until they change into what is known as the pupa or chrysalis stage.

LASER. A maser that amplifies radiation of frequencies within or near the range of visible light; much used in industrial processes, and includes use in textiles. See Maser.

LASH. 1. To tie with cord, rope, etc. 2. First used on the old-time draw loom, it is a cord used to lift certain yarns to form the motif in weaving figured goods in a loom. See JACQUARD HARNESS; JACQUARD NECK-CORD.

LASHER. Cord or twine used for binding or tieing.

LASHY WOOL. Long staple fibers devoid of any curl.

LASSIS. Waste from silk and any fabrics made from this basic stock.

LASTEX. An elastic yarn, consisting of extruded rubber thread core covered with wrappings of cotton, silk, rayon or nylon. Made in a wide range of sizes, tensions, and elongations for application in elastic fabrics by knitting, weaving, embroidery, stitching, and shirring. Practical for all types of textile products where elasticity is desired. Used extensively in brassieres, corsets, underwear, millinery, gloves, surgical and garterless hose, slip covers, linings, footwear, bathing suits, belts, suspenders, garters, support garments, and notions. Product of UniRoyal, Inc., New York City.

LASTING. Made of cotton or wool, or of both fibers, this strong, closely textured material finds use in bags, boots, linings, trouserings, etc. Plain, twill, or small dobby effects may be used in construction.

LASTOCARB. A manufactured fiber in which the fiber-forming substance is a hydrocarbon such as natural rubber, polyisoprene, polybutadiene, copolymers of dienes and hydrocarbons, or copolymers of amorphous (non-crystalline) polyolefins.

LASTOCHLOR. A manufactured fiber in which the fiber-forming substance is a polychloroprene or a copolymer of chloroprene in which at least 35% by weight of the fiber-forming substance is composed of chloroprene units (-CH2-C=CH-CH2).

LASTRILE. A manufactured fiber in which the fiber-forming substance is (1) a hydrocarbon, such as natural rubber, polyisoprene, polybutadiene, copolymers of dienes and hydrocarbons of amorphous (crystalline) polyolefins; (2) a copolymer of acrylonitrile and a diene (such as butadiene) composed of not more than 50 per cent but at least 10 per cent by weight of acrylonitrile units; (3) a plychloroprene or a copolymer of chloroprene in which 35 per cent by weight of fiber-forming substances are composed of chloroprene units. The term "Lastrile" is the seventeenth generic term decreed by the Federal Trade Commission, Washington, D.C., March 1966. Lastrile falls into category (2), above. The first sixteen generic terms for Manufactured Fibers became effective March 3, 1960.

LAT. French for a filling pick used in weaving a fabric on a loom.

LATCH NEEDLE. A knitting-machine needle, the hook of which can be closed by a latch pinned or riveted to the shank of the needle; when the latch is closed, the needle which carries the yarn may be drawn through a loop to form a chain stitch. See Illustrated Section.

LATEX. The viscid, milky, complex emulsion of proteins, alkaloids, starches, resins, and other substances secreted by the cells of certain plants such as the milkweed, rubber tree, and poppy. The liquid extruded from the rubber tree, when the bark is cut, may be coagulated with lactic acid and compressed into sheets, or solidified into rubber.

LATHE. Occasionally a loom is known by this term.

LATICES. Plural of latex. See LATEX.

LATIGO LEATHER. An alum-tanned cattle-hide leather chiefly used for halters, cinches, etc.

LATON. A superfine elastic yarn consisting of low-twist, yarn-covered, fine-size, extruded rubber thread. Made in fine sizes and soft tensions, especially for slips, hosiery, underwear, linings, dresses, swim suits, and other articles of lightweight sheer fabrics.

LATTICE APRON. Used chiefly in the opening machines in the manipulation of cotton, it is an endless fabric or leather belting used to convey stock to the various machines. The wooden slats may or may not be clothed with pins or lags to aid the particular process. Slat sizes and their spacings vary with the several machines in which they are used.

LATTICE BRAID. Another name for ladder braid.

LATTICE OPENER AND CLEANER. Cotton that has already been opened up to some degree is given further cleasing by this mechanism. The Buckley Beater, which has about three-fourths of its perimeter studded with grid bars, furnishes the action. Air current and attenuation also enter into the action, thereby causing foreign matter to fall through the grid bars into a receptacle placed on the floor for this purpose. Latticed feed aprons present the cotton to the feed rollers; hence, the name.

LAUNDERING. Any and all steps resorted to so as to restore soiled articles to usable condition. Laundering embraces sorting, washing, rinsing, water extraction, and drying. Optional treatments may include pretreatment, spot and stain removal, starching, and ironing.

LAUNDER-OMETER. A standard laboratory machine used to test fabrics for colorfastness to washing.

LAUNDRY DUCK. Wide army duck used to cover rollers on mangles and other laundry equipment. Comes in widths of 72, 81, and 90 inches.

LAUNDRY GUIDE. Pertinent information provided to the user of a washing machine relative to controls setting. May come with the machine when purchased or in a booklet of instructions.

LAUNDRY NETTING. Ply or cable yarns are used to make this strong, plain, or doup-woven open-mesh cotton netting or bragging. Used in dye plants, laundries, etc.

LAUNDRY-PROOF. Laboratory-tested fabrics and garments which will withstand laundering without the loss of color or shrinking under ordinary washing conditions in a given length of time. The term can be applied only to materials so tested.

LAUNDRY-TESTED AND APPROVED SEAL. A seal awarded by the American Institute of Laundering to guide the buying public in the purchase of washable merchandise that has all the characteristics of launderability —color-fastness to gas, perspiration, sun and washing; tensile strength; dimensional stability; satisfactory construction.

LAUNDRY TRADE SHEETING. Sheeting in which coarse yarns, single 10s to 15s, are used. Sheeting is about 58-square in pick count or texture. Closely woven and rather heavy as to weight, it is used in hospitals, hotels, institutions, and schools.

LAVAL. General French term for linen fabrics.

LAVENDER. A light purple shade, a pale lilac color.

LAVENTINE. Thin silk sleeve-lining.

LAWN. This popular staple cotton cloth originated in the cloth halls of Laon, France during the Middle Ages. Lawn is light in weight, sheer, soft, washable, and is made with plain weave. It is crisper than voile but not as crisp as organdy. Fine, high counts of yarn, usually 60s or better, are used to make the cloth. Made with carded or combed yarns, this medium-starched finish material comes in widths of 36 inches, 40 inches and 45 inches. Lawn comes in the white or may be dyed or printed. The starched finish seems to prevail in the market today and this type of fabric is made from combed yarn.

Finishes Applied to Lawns: Batiste, chiffonette, dyed, calendered, friction-calendered, percaline, organdy, nainsook, lawn finish, printed, mercerized, schreinerized.

Uses of Lawn: Underwear, waists, dresses, pajamas, curtains, lingerie, collars, cuffs, infant's dresses, shirting, handkerchief material, scarfs, lamp shades.

Constructions of Lawn: See table.

LAWN FINISH. A medium, pure-starch finish that is not as firm and substantial when compared with organdy finish; used in cotton dress goods for summer wear.

LAY. 1. Name given to the collective parts of a loom which actually makes weaving possible. The lay comes forward when the loom is in action, and makes it possible for the movable parts to perform their functions. Parts of the lay of the loom include reed, reed-cap, raceplate, shuttles, shuttle boxes, picker sticks, lug straps, cams. 2. To make the disposition of paper patterns upon cloth before cutting, so arranged as to effect economy of fabric and to obtain exact matching of patterns. 3. A strand of rope (nautical).

LAY GEAR. The gear on roving and spinning frames that governs the lay of the roving or the yarn onto the bobbin.

LAYING. The doubling process used in making rope.

LAY-OFF. A company's action removing temporarily an employee from its payroll.

LAY RACE. Another name for the raceplate of the loom—it sets in front of the reed and the shuttles traverse the raceplate in going to the respective shuttle boxes on each side of the loom.

LAY SWORD. The support or legs for the lay of the loom. There are two swords, one on each side of a loom, properly bolted and accurately timed. The name for this support comes from the fact that the device resembles a sword in appearance. Attached to lay swords are the reed, reed cap, raceplate, shuttle boxes, and other active parts of the machine, directly or indirectly.

LEA. Wet spun-linen yarn in which the number of 300-yard lengths per pound determines the count of yarn. 12 lea make one hank; 200 lea or 16½ hanks make a bundle.

LEA CARPETING. Trade name for hair, wool, or jute pile floor covering in which the base of the cut pile loops are held firmly in place by an application of latex, rubber cement, or some other equally good adhesive. Also called patent-back carpeting.

LEADER. A piece of cloth, or some other suitable material, attached to one end of a bolt, length, or reel of cloth which serves to guide the material through a machine at the beginning of a process or treatment.

LEADER CLOTH. A strip of fabric left threaded through a textile machine to facilitate the "starting-up" of a new length of fabric through the machine; found on looms and printing machines.

LEADS. The "lead" used in knitting machines to serve as the bed for the knitting needles. Several needles are placed in sequence in the lead bed which is attached either to the needle bar or the guide bar.

LEAF. The same as harness, shaft, or end on a loom in referring to cloths made on a satin weave, such as an eight-end satin made with a base or counter of 3. This means that there are eight ends and eight picks in the single repeat. Leaf twills may be three, four, or more ends and picks per re-

peat. A four-leaf twill implies that there are four ends and four picks in one repeat of the weave.

LEAF OR HARD FIBERS. These are the rather stiff, elongated fibers from leaves or leaf stems, as in the case of abaca, henequen, sisal, istle, phormium.

LEAFY COTTON. Ginned cotton with considerable amounts of leaf matter. The minute objectionable matter is referred to as "pin" or "pepper" leaf.

LEAN WOOL. Harsh, kempy wool which is difficult to spin into yarn; especially deficient in waviness.

LEASE. 1. A system of crossing warp ends alternately at one end and in groups at the other end, to keep them in proper position and under control during beaming and weaving. 2. In weaving, the specific order of drawing-in the warp ends in the loom harnesses.

LEASE, SECTION. A lease inserted into a warp-section, or section of the warp yarn, during the warping.

LEASE, WARPING. The entire completed lease in a warp after all section leases have been made in the dressing or warping of the warp yarn.

LEASE, WEAVING. The lease in a warp in a loom which sets behind the heddles of the harnesses and is kept in place by two lease rods which govern and keep the entire warp yarns in place in the usual crisscross or alternating arrangement.

LEASE PEGS. The pegs on a warping frame between which the lease or cross is made.

LEASE RODS. The wooden or glass rods or bars used to hold the "cross of the threads" in place while the loom is being set up and threaded. The lease rods are set in the loom when the piece is to be woven and they are set between the whip roll and the harness frames. Also known as lease sticks.

LEASH. 1. Mill parlance for all the cords in a Jacquard tie-up that are attached to a single neck cord. 2. In a handloom the leashes are suspended between the top and bottom harness bars of the harness frame. In its simplest olden-time form, the leash is composed of two threads or cords looped together; in modern times, these thread loops have been replaced by metallic heddles on the harness frame. In the old-time draw loom the leash was suspended from the necking cord through the comberboard; it consisted of two loops of thread or wire between which was fastened a glass or metallic eye called the mail. The mail is still the name for the opening in the cord, top and bottom, and the warp thread is drawn through the middle eyelet or opening the same

LAWN

TYPE AND WIDTH:	TEXTURE:	YARN COUNTS:	
Combed: 36″, 40″, 45″	72 x 68 to 108 x 112	Warp: 60s-80s	Filling: 84-135s.
Indian: 30″	64 x 64 to 96 x 100	60s-80s	84-135s.
Carded: 36″, 40″	60 x 48 to 88 x 80	40s-50s	54-64s.

as an end is drawn through a heddle eye on an ordinary loom today. Called maillon in French.

LEATHER. The hide or skin of an animal, or any portion of such skin, when tanned, tawed, or otherwise dressed for use. In describing the classes of leather, the name of the animal from which the skin was taken is generally used. Thus, cowhide, goatskin, and other comparable names refer to the fact that the leather is actually made from the skins of those animals and should not be referred to otherwise without some explanation.

LEATHER, IMITATION OR SIMULATED. Knitted or woven base fabric is given a thermosetting-resin-coating to provide good feel or hand, appearance, flexibility, and the pliability of genuine leather. Uses are about the same as those of leather.

LEATHER CLOTH. Belongs in the melton family of fabrics; a low-quality simulation of melton, this plain-woven fabric is made with cotton warp and coarse, irregular wool filling. A thick, raised nap tends to cover the basic structure.

LEATHERETTE. Trade name for simulated leather. Cloth or paper serves as the base for this colored, embossed, and finished product. Used for bookbinding, novelties.

LEATHER FABRIC. Cottons or woolens treated to simulate leather. Varnishing, lacquering, graining, and finishing are parts of the work to be done to produce the article.

LEATHER FIBER. Inferior, low grade, and waste leather is often ground into a fibrous condition, and with the aid of a synthetic resin, manipulated into fabric formation which rather closely resembles "true" leather goods. Other names for this term include leather-fiber, ground leather-fiber, leather-fiber board, et al.

LEAVE OF ABSENCE. A period of time off requested by an employee for personal reasons, during which he is permitted to retain his employment rights.

LEAVERS, JOHN. Inventor of a lacemaking machine. Research on the work that had been done by Heathcoat and other predecessors, along with his own ideas, enabled Leavers to conceive the idea of setting all of the carriages in a lace machine in single-tier formation, with one fixed, constant motion in one gait instead of the traversing plan originated by Heathcoat.

Leavers completed his first machine in 1813 and the principles of present-day machines are practically the same as his original ideas. His first frame made an 18-inch width of lace, but within two years' time he had a machine that would make a 60-inch width. There were from 80 to 90 motions per minute when the machine was in operation. There are today over 700 Leavers machines in this country.

LEAVIN. Made in Italy, this polyvinyl chloride fiber has improved stability thereby retaining over 50 percent of its original tenacity in exposure to water at 90° Centigrade. Comes in white or solution-dyed staple form. With a carrier the fiber may be dyed at the boil, without a carrier it may be dyed under pressure of approximately 120° Centigrade.

LECHUGUILLA. Any of the Mexican agave plants that yield istle. See ISTLE.

LECITHIN. A protein material derived from various cereal and other vegetable by-products.

LEDA CLOTH. French wool velvet, velours de laine.

LEDGER BLADE. Set, straight-edge blade on cloth shearing machine.

LEE, WILLIAM. In 1586, the Reverend William Lee of Calverton, England, introduced his now famous stocking frame, a forerunner of present-day lace machines.

LEFT-HAND TWIST. Yarn twist which runs from right to left; also known as "Z" twist. See Illustrated Section.

LEFT-HAND TWILL. Any twill weave which runs to the left—that is, the twill or diagonal line on the face of the goods will run from the upper left-hand corner to the lower right-hand corner of the fabric. See Illustrated Section (Fabrics 33).

LEGHORN HAT. Hand-woven hat material made in Leghorn, Italy. A very fine bearded-wheat straw is used in making the braid strips which are woven into hats. The finer the straw and the smoother the weaving, the better is the grade of the hat.

LEG OF MUTTON, GIGOT SLEEVE. Popular in the second quarter of the nineteenth century, and still used somewhat at present, this sleeve is full at the shoulder, gradually decreases in size to the elbow, and is tight at the wristline. Lining, a pad, or a whalebone support kept the upper sleeve at a distended size.

LEHNER SILK. The nitrocellulose-method rayon, the first commercial type made in the United States. Production ceased here in 1934; no longer made anywhere in the world.

LEICESTER WOOLS. In this group are also Lincoln, Cotswold, Romney Marsh, and Cheviot wools, spoken of as Long British and Long Crossbreeds and now raised throughout the world. The rams weigh from 235 to 300 pounds, ewes from 175 to 250 pounds. See Illustrated Section. Fleece weight is from 7 to 16 pounds. The fiber length ranges from 4 to 16 inches, while the fiber diameter is from 1/700 inch to 1/950 inch; there are from 800 to 1000 serrations per inch in the fibers. Numbered at 40s to 44s.

These hardy Luster wools, which have the tendency to reflect light rays, are used in homespun, tweeds, Cheviot and Shetland fabrics for outerwear.

LEIGH. Inventor in 1772 of the apron feed for the card. This English invention caused increased production in carding so that it might cope with other machine operations in yarn manufacture.

LEISURE. Mill parlance for the selvage or listing of silks and velvets.

LEKTROSET PROCESS. A process of electronic twist-setting for tire cord and other textile products by which packages of the cord are passed through a high frequency electrical field. The cones which are used in the fillingless method of tire construction contain as much as eighteen or more pounds of rayon tire cord and still may be effectively treated. The process is completed in a very few minutes and results show a uniform reaction. Produced by I.R.C. Division of American Cyanamid Company, Inc., Wayne, New Jersey.

LENGTH OF BATH. A dyeing term to imply the ratio of liquid to the material. A short bath has a ratio of around 10 to 1, a long bath around 30 to 1.

LENGTH DISTRIBUTION. Chart, display or table to show the percentage proportions, by number or weight, of fibers of varying lengths, in a sample.

LENGTHWISE. This denotes the area covered by the warpwise thread; the opposite of crosswise.

LENGTHWISE FOLD. The fold or crease of a fabric formed by folding the material lengthwise. When folded, the selvages of the opposite sides meet each other.

LENO, DOUP, DOUPE. These names are applied to weaves used to make marquisette, mosquito netting, certain leno stripes in dress goods and shirting fabric, and in the manufacture of other porous materials.

Doup weaving requires two sets of harnesses—standard and skeleton. The doup warp ends, by means of the skeleton harnesses, can be made to weave on either side of the standard warp ends, and it is an easy matter to change the fancy ends from side to side over the basic or foundation warp ends. The harness chain, at the side of the loom, will govern the changing-over of the leno ends.

The standard or doup ends must both be drawn through the standard harness singly while the leno end is drawn through the skeleton harness. Both warp ends have to be drawn through the same reed split or dent.

The doup end has to be given a varying tension during weaving and this is provided for by means of the slackener motion that is attached to the loom. See Illustrated Section (Fabrics 57, 58, 60).

LENO CELLULAR. Woven material made on the order of pillow tubing by the use of a doup weave. Used for bags which hold vegetables, fruit, laundry, etc.

LENO COTTON. An Indian cotton print noted for its lacy weave construction.

LEONTINE. A silk dress goods with a three-color effect in the warp—black, purple, and white, arranged three ends to a set in alternate arrangement. White or off-white silk is used for the filling. Made in a 2-up and 2-down twill with a texture of around 200 x 120.

LEOPARD. A flat, short-haired fur, light colored with a bluish cast. Wearing qualities, fair. Found in Ceylon, India, China, and parts of Africa. Preferred skins come from Italian Somaliland. Worn for general use and sports. Leopard cat is the South American spotted cat, and not a leopard.

LEOTARD. A short, close-fitting garment, low in neck, fitted between the legs, and worn by dancers when practicing.

LEPIDOPTERA. The name of the order to which the silkworm belongs.

LET-OFF MARK. Thick and thin effects which occur at even or uneven intervals in weaving of fabric in a loom. Caused by the let-off motion of the loom needing attention for setting at proper tension.

LET-OFF MOTION. See LOOM, CHIEF MOTIONS OF.

LETONA. A bast fiber from the *Agave letonae*, found in San Salvador. Finer and softer than henequen, it is used for bagging and cordage. Also known as Salvador henequen, Salvador sisal.

LEUCO. The colorless or nearly colorless soluble compound obtained by the reduction of a dye. An example would be the compound formed by reducing a vat dye. See OXIDATION.

LEUCO DYE. A dye reduced from its original form and then regenerated by oxidation.

LEUR. The brushing pad used by a hatter.

LEVANT, THE. One of the oldest textile areas in the world, this area embraces the eastern Mediterranean Coast, from western Greece to western Egypt, including the coasts of Asia Minor and Syria. The word is also used to mean the Oriental area of the Middle East.

LEVANT COTTON. Turkish cotton noted for its long, harsh, strong, white staple.

LEVANT LEATHER. Leather from the goat, sheep, and seal that is drawn in tannage into a grain pattern. Like Morocco, the name has come to define a pattern as well as original leather. The term, unless followed by the word grained, should be confined to leather from drawn goatskin. Embossed goatskin should be termed "Levant-grained goatskin."

LEVANTINE. A stout twilled silk, each side of which is finished in the same way but in different colors.

LEVEL DYEING. Cloth which has been evenly or uniformly dyed and has no streaks or shaded areas.

LEVELING AGENT. A suitable chemical that will cause the dye to have even affinity on the yarn or cloth.

LEVERS. Bars on table looms which pull up the harnesses to make the shed of the loom—the opening between the "up" and the "down" warp threads or ends.

LEVIATHAN CANVAS. A coarse, open cotton canvas used in embroidery. High twist is given to the yarn in this rather wide open-spaced material. Woolen yarn is used in the embroidery, hence the large open spaces in the meshes.

LEVIATHAN STITCH. Three long stitches crossed by a fourth stitch. Also known as railway stitch, it is used on Leviathan canvas since the work can be quickly finished.

LEVIATHAN YARN. A soft, bulky woolen yarn composed of several ply yarns used for embroidery and knitting purposes.

LEXAN. A polycarbonate fiber spun from Lexan polycarbonate resin. Produced by General Electric Company, Inc., Schenectady, New York. See Lexel.

LEXEL. The base for this product is polycarbonate. It is derived from the reaction of bis-phenols, such as diphenyl propane, with carbonyl chloride also known as phosgene. Polymers of this group have been used in the plastics field for many years. The polymer may be processed by either the melt spun or the dry spun methods. Lexan, the base for Lexel, has elastic properties comparable with silk. Lexel is used at present chiefly in electrical and nuclear engineering, and in the rocket and space fields.

LEY, LYE. Any strong alkaline solution, particularly one used for the purpose of washing, such as soda lye, soap lye.

LEZARDE. French term for passementerie work or tape used to cover the area where the furniture cover joins the wood in upholstery.

LIAGE. French expression for the binding warp ends that bind the extra filling threads in brocade, brocatelle, etc.

LIBAU FLAX. A coarse Soviet flax known for its unclean fiber and unappealing appearance.

LIBBEY, EDWARD D. In 1893, at the time of the World's Fair in Chicago, he received a patent for drawing out the ends of heated glass rods with exceptionally fine filament and texture. This invention was the beginning of glass fibers as we know them today. Known as the Columbian Fair, the much publicized Glass Dress along with "Little Sheba," an Egyptian belly dancer, were greatly advertised and promoted. The crowds, however, were disappointed because the glass dress was not transparent and "Little Sheba," while bringing in crowds to the presentation, did not accomodate the crowds with her advertised sensational exotic dancing. The name, Libbey, still survives in two large companies today - Libbey, Owens-Ford Company, Inc., and Libbey Products Owens - Illinois, Inc.

LIBERATE. The liberating of oxygen from a solution so that it may perform its bleaching function. An example would be sodium hypochlorite, NaOCl, a bleaching agent from which oxygen would be freed for bleaching purposes, leaving sodium chloride, NaCl.

LIBERTY CLOTHS. The popular high-quality cloths controlled by Liberty, Limited, of London. The silk, rayon, and cotton fabrics produced by Liberty are often hand-blocked with an all-over floral print in inspiring, delicate patterns.

LIBERTY SATIN. A popular seven-, eight-, or ten-shaft satin weave fabric of raw silk warp and single, spun-silk filling. It was named for Liberty, Limited, London, England.

LIBFORM. A fabric made from specially engineered nylon that can be molded permanently, finds use in the foundation fabrics field, especially in brassieres. Produced as a result of research and development by Liberty Fabrics of New York, Inc., and Monsanto

Textiles Division, New York City.

LIBRARY BUCKRAM, BOOK BUCKRAM. Light duck, osnaburg, buckram, etc., that is coated with pyroxylin and given a smooth linenlike finish. Filling with starch compounds is done in work of this type, as well. The finishes are applied to books of many types.

LICHENS. A flowerless plant, commonly growing flat on a surface such as rock. Composed of loose, cellulose tissue, it is a slender white-celled fungus.

LICKER-IN. A roller covered with rather coarse card clothing—steel wire in leather fillet—that is located in the card in such a position that it will slowly and constantly draw in the cotton from the feed rollers of the card. The licker-in opens the stock to some degree and carries it to the carding drum.

LICKER-IN-COVER. Also called the bonnet, it is the metal hood or plate which sets over the upper surface of the licker-in roller on certain cotton machines.

LICKER-IN SCREEN. Extending from the mote knives to the cylinder, this casing encloses the underneath section of the licker-in roller on the cotton card. The triangular-shaped, barred area allows foreign matter to drop through, while the shell of the device is a curved metal plate.

LICKING. When fibers wrap themselves around a drawing roll on certain machines used in yarn manufacture.

LIENCILLO. South American term for cotton gray goods.

LIENZO. Unbleached cotton sheeting and shirting in the South American countries.

LIF. An African and Arabian leaf fiber taken from the date palm and used for coarse cloth and rope.

LIFT. The distance measured axially between the extremities of the body of the roving or yarn on a spindle, bobbin, or some comparable device to handle the stock.

LIFTER RODS. Found on ring-spinning frames, they are set in a vertical position in order to be free to slide up and down in their bushings. They support and give the traversing motion to the ring rail of the frame.

LIFTER ROLL. Found on a slubbing frame, this long, octagonal-shaped wooden roll, which extends across the back of the machine, aids in lifting the sliver from the coiler can so that it can be fed to the drawing rollers.

LIFTING APRON. Device on the initial cotton-opening machines. Its function is to take stock upwards, so that it can be fed to the feed apron. It is an endless canvas sheet, mounted on belts, to which are fastened the wooden slat arrangement fitted with steel spikes to carry the stock in this upward direction.

LIFTING PLAN. See CHAIN DRAFT.

LIGNE, LINE. French measurement used in textiles. It is one twelfth of a French inch; there are approximately eleven French lignes to the English inch.

LIGNIN. An organic substance which, with cellulose, forms the chief part of woody matter.

LIGNOCELLULOSE. The substance which makes up the woody and fibrous parts of plants, consisting of lignin combined with cellulose.

LILAC. A rose-purple color of high brilliance and low saturation.

LILION. Polyamide, nylon 6, filament and staple made by Societa Nazionale Industria Applicazoni Viscosa, Milan, Italy.

LILLE LACE. Lace from this famous textile city in France; the home of lisle cotton thread for hosiery. There is a close resemblance between Lille lace and that from Mechlin in Belgium. There is a clear, light ground on the construction that makes it one of the most beautiful of the simple thread laces.

LIMA COTTON. A coarse, harsh Peruvian cotton, used chiefly in home consumption.

LIMAWOOD. See BRAZIL, BRAZIL-WOOD.

LIMBRIC. A plain-woven cotton fabric on the order of poplin but differs with the latter cloth since it has fewer warp ends and more picks to the inch. Made of good quality yarn, the material is suitable for curtains and dress goods. Textures range from 68 x 96 to 72 x 108; warp counts are from 54s to 60s, while filling counts are from 30s to 32s.

LIME. Calcium oxide or hydroxide.

LIME, CHLORIDE OF. Ordinary chloride of lime bleach or calcium hypochlorite.

LIME OR GRAY SOUR. Refers to the first-time souring of cotton goods in finishing. The goods are passed through a weak solution of sulphuric or hydrochloric acid in a washing machine. The lime soaps decompose and the lime is converted into soluble salt.

LIME PROCESS. One of the methods used to obtain pulled wool. The hides of dead sheep are painted with lime on the flesh side so that the chemical action will loosen the fibers to the extent that they may be removed easily from the pelt. However, great care must be used in the treatment since it is an easy matter to injure the wool or pelt. If the wool is injured, uneven dyeing results.

LIMERICK. A form of embroidery, net, or muslin that originated in Ireland.

LIME SOAP. An insoluble soap produced when lime replaces the soda in a soap composition. A very troublesome form of by-product in detergent processes. A waterproof soap.

LIMOGES. 1. Common French bagging of strong hemp yarn. 2. A cotton, linen, or linen and cotton counterpane fabric made in colored stripe patterns.

LINCEUL. French for bed linen, sheeting, pillowcasing, etc.

LINCOLN GREEN. A substantial bright green color originally made in Lincoln, England. The color was supposed to match the green of the forest.

LINCOLN SHEEP. Possessing the longest staple of any wool grown, this popular long-wool breed originated in Lincoln County, England. Probably the world's largest rams are Lincolns; they weigh from 300 to 375 pounds. Rich, well-watered pastures are essential for these sheep, which are much used in crossbreeding. Fleece weighs from 12 to 16 pounds.

Lincoln belongs in the Luster wool group along with Leicester, Cotswold, Romney Marsh. See Illustrated Section.

LINCOLN VOLOSH. The result of crossbreeding British Lincoln and Russian Volosh sheep. A 15-pound fleece with staple fiber of about 6½ inches has resulted from the development of this sheep.

LINCOLN WOOL. A popular British wool with world-wide reputation. See LINCOLN SHEEP.

LINCORD. A style of buttonhole for collars and cuffs having a line of heavy cord or thread passed and worked around the opening.

LIND, JENNY. See Costume, Jenny Lind.

LINDBERGH JACKET. A sturdy, warm jacket comparable with the windbreaker, with deep pockets and fitted waistband and wrists. Named for the flying jacket used by General A. Lindbergh who made the first solo trans-Atlantic flight. The present day Eisenhower jacket is a modification of the Lindbergh jacket. See Eisenhower Jacket.

LINDEN CORD. Another name for Bedford Cord.

LIN DE PAYS. French for country linen; it is a dew-retted flax.

LINDLEY. Early experimenter who,

in 1799, invented the lace bobbin. In a short time, Irving and Skelton developed the spring which regulated the speed at which a thread is withdrawn in machine action. These inventions were instrumental in giving food for thought to subsequent inventors who became interested in the transition from the stocking frame to the highly elaborate lace machine. See HEATHCOAT, JOHN.

LINDLY DEFECT ANALYSER. A quality control device equipped with a photoelectric cell to check and to evaluate various yarn defects such as broken filaments, doubled ends, fly, slubs, stripbacks, etc. Product of Lindly & Co., Inc.

LINE. 1. In linen fibers, it is the opposite of tow. Line is the long, choice, desirable fiber, ten inches or more in length. Tow is the short fiber, less than ten inches long. Tow may be tangled, immature, of noil stock, and variable length. 2. A rather fine-diameter, strong cord or rope. 3. A colloquial term for linen.

LINEAR DENSITY. The weight per unit length expressed in grams per centimeter, pounds per foot, or the equivalent.

LINED. The inside part of any article; in garments the lining is usually made of contrasting material.

LINED CLOTH. Woven or knitted fabric which is made with a backing. Also includes woolen and worsted fabrics of distinctive coloring on the face or the back, blankets, coatings, robes, and rugs.

LINED WORK. Name applied to cloths made from diamond weaves.

LINE FLEECE. One which is between two distinct grades and standard qualities as to characteristics and possible working properties.

LINE MEASUREMENT. The twelfth part of a French inch, used in French measurement of textile fabrics. In stating the size of pearl and other buttons, the line is considered as the fortieth part of an inch; the buttons are measured for diameter to determine their numerical value. For comparison with English inch see LIGNE, LINE.

LINEN. Flax, the raw material used to make linen fabric, is a fine, soft bast fiber obtained from the stalks of the plant by the process of retting. The fibers are silver gray, bluish gray, brown, or creamy white in color and from 12 to 40 inches long. Flax has a soft, silky luster and is a good conductor of heat.

Flax line and tow refer to the lengths of the fibers used in industry. Line fibers are those ten inches or more in

length; tow fibers are shorter; naturally the line fibers are the more desirable.

There are several properties and characteristics of flax and linen that are important. Like cotton, linen is of vegetable origin and is classed as a dead fiber. The smoothness and lintlessness, however, of the fiber prevent the finished product from soiling as easily as many other fabrics. Flax is a coarse-pored fiber that takes up moisture rapidly, thereby making it very absorbent in linen materials. The property of absorbency and its ability to give off moisture rapidly by evaporation makes linen a *cool* fiber or fabric. See Illustrated Section (Fabrics 3).

LINEN, BANDLE. A narrow, coarse homespun linen made on hand looms in Ireland.

LINEN, OYSTER. An embroidery linen that is half-bleached or tinted to a cream or oyster color.

LINEN, RAYON, AND ACETATE; FEDERAL TRADE COMMISSION DECISION ON. In April 1960, The Federal Trade Commission rescinded its Practice Rules affecting Linen, Rayon, and Acetate. In RECISIONS OF TRADE PRACTICE RULES, are the following quotes—"Whereas, the Commission promulgated trade practice rules for the Linen Industry on February 1, 1941, the Rayon and Acetate Textile Industry on December 11, 1951; and

"Whereas, the Textile Fiber Products Identification Act (72 Stat. 1717; 15 U.S.C. 70) and the rules and regulations issued thereunder, effective as of March 3, 1960, so limit the application of the above-mentioned trade practice rules as to obviate their revision; and

"Whereas, the recisions of the trade practice rules for the Linen Industry and the Rayon and Acetate Textile Industry will not affect the Commission's jurisdiction under the statutes upon which such trade practice rules were based:

"It is ordered, That the trade practice rules for the Linen Industry and the Rayon and Acetate Textile Industry be and the same are hereby rescinded,

By the Commission,
Robert M. Parrish,
Secretary (April 5, 1960)."

LINEN, STAMPED. Usually small linen products that have been embroidered, or screen-printed to enhance the fabric.

LINEN CAMBRIC. Cloth may be sheer or coarse; of plain weave. Known also as handkerchief linen. Used also for dress goods.

If fairly good quality is used, fabric will give excellent wear and service. Material is sized and gives neat appearance after laundering.

Cotton cambric is made from print-

cloth of lightweight sheeting construction. It is given special sizing treatment and a calender finish.

LINEN CANVAS. There are several fabrics in this category: 1. Open-mesh canvas is used for embroidery; made of hard-twisted yarn, the cloth is very durable and the most popular cloth in this group is known as Java canvas. 2. Close-woven canvas is made from hard-twisted yarn in plain-weave construction; comes in various weights, and finishes range from the heavily sized varieties to soft effects.

LINEN CHECK. The ordinary plain colored checks used for linen dress goods and aprons; usually 8 x 8, 12 x 12, or 16 x 16.

LINEN CRASH. See CRASH.

LINEN DAMASK. A single damask is made on a five-shaft satin weave; double damask is made on an eight-end satin construction. All damask is made on Jacquard looms.

This reversible fabric is very durable, the higher the texture the better will be the quality. Damask will launder well, retain luster and may be all linen, all cotton, or a union material —say cotton warp and linen filling. The smaller motifs give the greater strength to the goods because of shorter float yarns. More luster is possible on the double type because of longer yarn floats, but the single type damask usually gives longer wear. Used for coverings, doilies, curtains, guest towels, napkins, runners, and tablecloths. See Illustrated Section (Fabrics 68).

LINEN FINISH, SIMULATED. Applied to cotton fabric, it is obtained by beetling to give a soft, full, kidskin type of hand. Mercerizing is also given the cloth which requires special sizings and pressings so as to flatten out the fabric to produce the effect. Rays of light are reflected by the finish, which is not permanent.

LINEN FINISHES, MAJOR. They are beetled, calendered, chased, filled, friction-calendered, mercerized, sized.

LINEN FROM COTTON, TESTS TO DISTINGUISH—
1. OLIVE OIL TEST: Place a drop of olive oil on the sample. Blot in and place over a dark background. If the sample appears translucent, the material is linen; if opaque, the cloth is cotton.
2. MAGENTA TEST: If the sample has been dyed, the color must be removed. Place the sample in a 1 per cent alcoholic solution of Magenta, a red dye. Remove the sample and rinse with water. If the color washes out the cloth is cotton; if the color remains pink or red, the cloth is linen. It is the

pectin in the linen that acts as a mordant for the dyestuff.

3. ANILINE RED TEST: A sample of cotton and one of linen are immersed in a light alcoholic solution of aniline red, for a short time. The samples are thoroughly washed and then soaked in a caustic ammonia bath for two hours. Linen will become dark red; the cotton will not be affected.

LINEN MESH. Open-mesh fabric. Extremely strong and washes very easily. Used for children's clothes, men's shirts.

LINEN POT. A length, usually 10,000 yards of linen, sewed into a continuous form ready for bleaching operation.

LINEN ROUGHS. Lightweight linen canvas used as suit lining in the cutting-up trade; sold in brown or natural shades.

LINEN RUG, FLAX RUG. Reversible, plain-woven, all-flax covering used for narrow areas such as hallways.

LINENS, HOUSEHOLD SIZES OF.
1. Breakfast cloth is from 45″ x 45″ to 63″ x 80″; napkins, 13″ x 13″.
2. Luncheon cloth is 54″ x 54″; runners, 18″ x 72″; doilies, 12″ x 18″; napkins, 20″ x 20″.
3. Bridge cloth is 36″ x 36″; napkins, 14″ x 14″.
4. Dinner cloth is from 72″ x 90″ to 72″ x 126″; napkins, from 16″ x 16″ to 26″ x 26″.
5. Buffet runner is 18″ x 72″; center cloth, 16″ x 24‡; sides, 12″ x 18″; side cloth, 12″ x 18″.
6. Tea wagon cloth is from 14″ x 20″ to 16″ x 24″.
7. Standard double linen with box mattress is 90″ wide x 108″ long.
8. Standard double bed linen is 81″ wide x 108″ long.
9. Three quarter bed linen is 72″ wide x 108″ long.
10. Single bed linen is 63″ wide x 108″ long.
11. Cot linen is 52″ wide x 108″ long.
12. NOTE: Sizes other than these are made, and depend on local conditions and needs.

LINEN SETT. The number of reed splits or dents in a 40-inch reed width. Thus, 800 dents, two-ends per dent or split, on a 40-inch reed width would give 40 ends to the inch:

$$800 \times 2 = 1600. \frac{1600}{40} = 40,$$ number of ends per inch.

LINEN STRAW. Any closely braided or woven straw, fine in texture, which is given a finish to simulate finished line fabric.

LINEN TESTER. A pickglass.

LINEN-TEXTURED RAYON. A large and important category of rayon fabrics having the distinctive textures of linens. These range from sheer handkerchief-linen texture to heavier, rougher "butcher-linen" texture. Usually plain-weave. Used in lighter weight for handkerchiefs, women's and children's dresses, tablecloths, towels, sheets, pillowcases; heavier weights for summer coats, suits, sportswear.

LINEN WEAVE. The plain or tabby weave.

LINEN YARN, BOILED. Yarn that has been boiled once or twice in soda lye. There is a loss in weight of 5 to 10 per cent.

LINEN YARN, CREAMED. Yarn which has been boiled and partly bleached by bleaching powder. The loss in weight is about 12 per cent.

LINEN YARN, NUMBERING OR THE COUNTS OF YARN IN. A cut is 300 yards, a spindle is 14,400 yards. To find the linen counts, the following example is given:

An 8-pound linen yarn means that a spindle of linen weighs 8 pounds, or that the yarn is a 6 lea or cut.

To obtain these figures:

$$\frac{14,400}{8} = 1800.$$

$$\frac{1800}{300} = 6,$$ the lea count of the linen yarn. This explanation is on the English method. Other major standards follow:

1. AUSTRIA: The count equals the number of hanks that are equal to ten English pounds. Each hank contains 3600 ell; one ell is equivalent to 30.68 inches.

One schock is composed of 12 bundles, 60 pieces, 240 hanks, 4800 cuts, or 288,000 threads.

2. BELGIUM: A pacquet contains 180,000 threads.

3. DORSET AND SOMERSET, ENGLAND: This method takes the weight of 21,600 yards, called dozen or 12 half-hanks.

4. ENGLAND: The count equals the number of hanks or lea per pound. The lea or cut is 300 yards long.

5. ENGLAND AND IRELAND: One bundle contains 16⅔ hanks, or 200 cuts or lea, 24,000 threads or 60,000 yards.

6. FRANCE: The count is number of hanks each 1000 meters long contained in 500 grams. A pacquet contains 360,000 yards.

7. SCOTLAND: A spindle or spangle has 2 hasps, 4 hanks, 24 beers, 48 cuts, 5760 threads of 14,400 yards. See LEA.

LINET. French lining cloth made of unbleached linen.

LING. A fine, silklike, leaf fiber of the Philippines used for clothing and cordage.

LINGE. French for linen.

LINGERIE. First manufactured in this country in the Centennial Year, 1876, silk lingerie came into general acceptance about 1915. Rayon and nylon, however, have replaced silk at the present time in popularity.

Lingerie may be defined as women's intimate apparel such as panties, slips, etc.

Features of the quality of lingerie include cutting by hand machine, accurately proportioned patterns, reinforced seams, sufficient yardage and true bias. The latter is cut at the 45-degree angle and prevents riding-up, sagging, twisting, and makes for better wear. The fit in lingerie is important since it brings comfort to the wearer.

LINGO, LINGOE. A weight, part of the shedding mechanism of a loom, used for depressing one end of warp in a Jacquard loom.

LINING. The inside portion of a garment. Lining used in coats and jackets is usually made of crepe, satin, rayon acetate, Skinner's Satin, etc.

LINING FABRICS, MAJOR. 1. Clothing and Apparel: Alpaca, brilliantine, brocade, calico, cambric, chambray, charmeuse, cottonade, crepes of many types, crepe de Chine, crinoline, domet, duvetyne, flat crepe, foulard, Indian linen, Jacquard silks, lawn, madras, moleskin, net, organdy, percale, piqué, pongee, rayon alpaca, sateen, satin, serge, silesia, soisette, suède cloth, swiss, tarlatan, Venetian, voile.

2. Casket and Box Lining: Chintz, flannel, plush, printcloth, sateen, satin, sheeting, velvet, velveteen.

3. Dressbanding: Buckram, grosgrain ribbon, self-fabric, tarlatan.

4. Fur Coats: Brocade, casha cloth, crepes, plaid flannel, velour.

5. Glove Lining: Eiderdown, flannel, suède, wool-knit.

6. Hats: Buckram, crinoline, mull, printcloth, sateen, satin, suède, tarlatan, Venetian.

7. Interlining: Baize, cheesecloth, drill, jean cloth, wigan, wigwam, wool or cotton wadding.

8. Luggage: Brocade, cretonne, moire, sateen, satin, silesia, suède, Venetian.

9. Neckwear: Beachcloth of several types and textures.

10. Pocket Lining: Drill, duvetyne, eiderdown, flannel, moleskin, sateen, satin, silesia, suède, rayon fabric lining, Venetian velveteen.

11. Pocketbooks: Buckram, moire, suède, tarlatan.

12. Shoe Lining: Beaver cloth, cotton twill, drill, duck, eiderdown, flannel, gabardine, jean, Osnaburg, slipper satin, suède.

LINING FELT. Made of a composition of hair and asbestos, and often mixed with plaster of Paris, this product finds use in boiler and pipe insulation.

LINING TYPES. A lining is a fabric which partially or entirely covers the inside surface of a garment thereby forming an inside finish. The coats of men's suits may have one of several linings, the yoke and the sleeves always being lined, with the exception of men's washable summer suits. The types follow:

1. FULL LINING: The front quarters and the back are full lined. This is often found in the lower-priced men's wear.

2. HALF LINING: The front quarters are full lined, the back is not lined.

3. QUARTER LINING: The front quarters are lined full depth, but only partial width is used at the lower edge. The lining tapers from under the arm to a few inches width at the bottom of the coat. The back is not lined.

4. SKELETON LINING: The front quarters are not lined full width or depth, the lining slopes from slightly below the armpit to the front facing with only sufficient depth to cover the inside pocket. The back is not lined.

5. THREE-QUARTER LINING: The front quarters are lined as in the quarter lining, while the back lining reaches from the shoulder to half the length of the coat.

LINKING. Knitting term for the joining together of the knitted loops in a part of a garment. Linking may join together two courses of knitting or one course with the edge loops.

LINKS-AND-LINKS MACHINE. A circular or flat type of machine which produces fancy and purl stitches in the goods. Links-and-links is the principle of knitting by means of which any needle can be transferred from the one needle bed to the opposite one in order to produce the novelty effect.

LINO. English term for leno.

LINOLEUM. This floor covering is made from a burlap base. Oxidized linseed is mixed with ground cork and other pigments to give the composition which is rolled over the base. Linoleum comes in plain, printed, or inlaid patterns. Plain linoleum has a single color face; the printed type has colored designs; inlaid has colored motifs which penetrate through to the burlap base.

LINON. A fine, closely woven plain fabric known for its excellent wearing and washing qualities. Made from combed cotton yarn of long-staple stock, it resembles as much as possible fine linen fabric. Woven with about 90s warp and 110s filling, with a pick count approximating 108 x 110, this firm fabric is bleached, gassed, or singed, lightly starched, and well pressed. Linon is French for a lawn fabric.

LINON A JOUR. French for gauzelike linen fabric.

LINSEED. See LINSEED OIL.

LINSEED FLAX. Various types of flax raised only for the seed yield.

LINSEED OIL. Oil obtained from seeds of the flax plant; raised in Argentina, India, Canada, Russia, Uruguay, and the United States. Characteristics of the oil are acrid taste and odor, yellow to brown in color, and darkening and thickening when exposed to air.

Adulterants used are cottonseed oil, semi-drying oils, rosin oils, mineral oils, and menhaden oils. Among uses are food, light-colored paints, printers' ink, and linoleum.

LINSEL. French dress goods made of linen warp and woolen filling; plain or twills are used in construction.

LINSEY. 1. British cloth made of linen warp and worsted filling. It is coarse, durable, and strong and gives good wear.

2. Rag-sorting term which implies wool fabrics with vegetable matter in them, such as carpets, dress goods, flannels, other union fabrics.

LINSEY-WOOLSEY. Cloth made of linen and woolen yarn. Cotton may be used instead of linen. Either stock is always the warp. Animal fibers always are the filling. Cloth is of loose structure, coarse, and often highly colored. It originated in England and was much in use in the Colonies at one time. It is more or less obsolete now. A little of the cloth finds use by rural folk in outlying districts.

LINT. 1. Good, workable fiber used to make yarn. In this sense, it is the staple cotton fiber which will withstand machine treatment. 2. Fly that floats around mill rooms during the manipulation of stock. 3. The minute fibers that cling to clothing, especially blue garments. 4. The waste from the cotton ginning process. This will amount roughly to about one third. The second third will be the choice fiber stock; the last third is made up of foreign matter such as leaf, burr, sand, etc.

Lint should not be confused with linters, the short brown fibers taken from the seeds in ginning, usually from second-time ginning. The meaning of lint depends, to a great degree, on local usage, since the above meanings are not closely allied. See Linters.

LINT BLADE. A heavy, soft brass blade that removes dirt, lint, fuzziness, and protruding fiber left on the print rollers of the priming machine after contact has been made with the printed goods. This blade, which extends the width of the roller, helps to prevent smudgy effects on the cloth as it is printed.

LINT COTTON. The good, workable fiber used to make yarn, the staple cotton fiber that can be processed on textile machinery. Lint cotton also implies the amount of usable fiber obtained from the cotton boll; one third of the weight is the actual usable fiber while the other two thirds is made up of seed, burr, sand, motes, linters.

LINTERS. The short, fuzzy cotton fibers which cover the seeds of certain types of cotton after the lint cotton or fiber has been removed at the cotton gin. Linters are very short, usually less than 1/8 inch, and they may be gray, greenish, or brown in color. One ton of cottonseed will yield over 200 pounds of linters. The production of linters is governed by the staple length of the fiber, the efficiency of the cotton gins and the types of other equipment used in the processing. About 30 per cent of the total production taken from the seed is first-cut or first-time linters, while second-cut linters provide the remaining 70 per cent. First-cut linters, under normal conditions, sell for around 15 to 18 cents per pound; second-cut linters are about 4 cents per pound less in price. Linters are used in the manufacture of guncotton, the stuffing in upholstery, absorbent cotton, mattresses, and the manufacture of pure cellulose sheets in the making of rayon and acetate.

LINTEUM, LINTHEUM. An ancient veil used to cover the chalice and paten in the early days of the Christian Church. It is replaced today by the chalice veil.

LINTON TWEED. A distinctive range of tweed fabrics used in summer and winter coatings and ensembles for women's wear. Fabric weight runs from 8–18 ounces with most of the material averaging 12–14 ounces per yard. Australian merino wool, 66s to 72s (medium to fine in quality) is used to make the materials, well known for their extreme softness, wide variance in motif and design, and appealing hand.

The yarn used is figured on the Galashiels system of 300 yards, where the number of cuts in 24 ounces is the count of the yarn. All Linton tweed is woven on power looms in 60-yard cut lengths, and the finished width is 54 inches. Product of Linton Tweeds, Ltd., Carlisle, England.

LINT PERCENTAGE, COTTON. The amount of lint obtained from seed cotton with regard to the total weight of seed and lint; seed averages about two thirds of total weight; lint, about one third.

LIQUOR. A chemical term used to reduce wood chips to pulp and to remove chemical impurities. Wood chips immersed in the liquor are cooked to a pulpy state.

LIQUOR RATIO. The ratio between the weight of a liquor used in any process and the weight of the fibrous material used.

LIRELLE. A modified rayon fiber noted for its strength when both wet and dry. Blended with cotton it provides greater strength, increased stability, and a more pleasing hand; in blends with polyester and comparable manmade fibers it affords greater comfort, deeper clarity of color and increased luster on fabrics. Major properties of this product of Courtaulds North America, Inc., include outstanding stability in laundering, drycelanability, excellent . flexibility, versatility, drapeability, and colorfastness. Lirelle is moth resistent.

LISERE. Liséré has several meanings. 1. A straw braid. 2. Narrow ribbon used as binding or piping for a seam. 3. A French silk cord made with filling of brocaded flowers and Jacquard figures in the warp. 4. The edge of a handkerchief, ribbon, or napkin made in a color different from the body of the cloth.

LISIERE. A French word for selvage is lisière.

LISLE FABRIC. Knit cloth made from high-grade cotton yarn that has been combed and is used in the two-ply state. The projecting ends of the goods are singed off to give the material a smooth surface that is silklike in appearance. The yarn is mercerized to enhance the appearance.

Lisle is a contraction of Lille, a noted textile center in France. The yarn is used in hosiery, underwear, and gloves. Egyptian cotton is ideal to use in the manufacture of lisle yarn.

LISLE THREAD. A fine, hard-twisted thread now spun almost exclusively from long-stapled Egyptian cotton. To obtain compactness and solidity in the yarn, it is usually spun and twisted in a moist atmosphere, and it is often passed over a hot plate or series of jets (gassing) to remove the ooze and fuzz in order to produce a

smooth surface. The brilliant finish on lisle thread is obtained by the calendering process and sometimes by a treatment with tallow after dyeing.

Knitted lisle garments have a dry, cool feel, since the material has elasticity and porosity. Each fiber of the thread retains its separateness, and the smooth threads can adapt themselves easily to the shape of the body and to any motion. Lisle is unexcelled for hose, gloves, and underwear when these requirements are specified.

LISLE YARN. Used for hosiery, it is a highly lustrous, soft-twisted ply yarn usually combed, mercerized, and gassed.

LISSE. Lissé is used in two senses: 1. French term for warp. 2. A dress silk gauze fabric.

LISTADOES. Colored cotton goods made in England for the Central American trade.

LISTED CLOTH. That which has faulty selvage caused by poor tension, breakages, curling selvage, gnarly ends, tears, strains, etc.

LISTING OR SELVAGE, SELVEDGE. Taken from the words "list" (or border), and "self-edge." The series of ends found on the edges of woven cloth. These ends are part of the warp and run in the vertical direction in the goods.

The primary function of the selvage is to hold out the warp so that the shuttle with the filling does not pull in the warp in width, thereby causing poor loom action. Another function is to allow the dyer of the cloth a hold on the edges for clips and pins, so that they do not tear the body of the goods. The selvage keeps the edges of the cloth parallel and straight. It is distinguished from body of the cloth in the following ways:

1. By the use of a weave that is different from the body of the warp.

2. By the use of colored ends different from those of the warp.

3. By increased twist in the selvage ends.

4. By the doubling up of the ends that constitute the selvage. This is done by placing two ends through each heddle eye instead of the customary single end. This will give the selvage sufficient strength to withstand and offset the friction that the filling might give as it comes off the nose of the bobbin. The doubled ends give a firmer feel and substance to the edges of the cloth.

Listing may or may not be cut from the cloth in the cutting-up house. Cottons often have the listing cut off prior to manipulation of the cloth into a garment. Woolens, worsteds and rayons retain the selvage, which is placed underneath and covered up in the cut, fit and trim of the garment. It is found along the seams on the under side of the finished garment.

LISTONES. Latin American term for silk and velvet ribbons.

LITEAU. French term for some kinds of napery made with red and blue filling stripes or checks.

LITHOGRAPHIC PRINTING. Printing of fabric from the lithographer's stone the same as is done on paper.

LITMUS. A blue dyestuff made by fermenting certain coarsely powdered lichens. It is turned red by acids, blue by bases or alkalies. Also known as lacmus, the word means color moss. It is also an unsized paper dipped into a litmus solution used to test solutions for acidity and alkalinity.

LITRE. Nearly 1¾ pints.

LITTLE, ARTHUR D. American chemical engineer. From 1890 to 1894, Cross and Bevan made some valuable contributions to what was later to be known as the cellulose acetate method of making man-made fibers. While this method did not come into its own until after the World War, Arthur Little, in this country in 1895, improved upon the findings of the two English scientists. Arthur D. Little Company is located in Cambridge, Massachusetts, a leading engineering and research company for many years.

LITURGICAL COLORS. The use of color as a symbol in church liturgy is of early origin. Color as such became a mark of distinction in dress with white being the predominant color during the days of the Roman Empire and the Middle Ages adding a sequence of colors.

The modern sequence of colors is: white, red, green, violet or purple, and black. Any shade of these colors is permitted, while Cloth of Gold (never yellow) may be used in place of white, red, or green on major feast days. Cloth of Silver may replace white. In the Roman Catholic Church rose vestments may be worn on the fourth Sunday of Lent and the third Sunday of Advent.

LIVER ROT. Infestation of sheep by the liver fluke of this so-called rot is a bane to sheep farmers. Veterinarians are constantly on the alert for this dreaded sheep disease.

LIVERY. 1. Coarse, matted, skirting-wool obtained from English cross-bred fleeces. 2. Uniform, especially of a servant.

LIVERY TWEED. A British whipcord made with woolen yarn in such compact texture that it resembles a high-texture tweed. Used in regal, uniform, and livery garments.

LIVE SPINDLE. One that is power-driven and rotates a bobbin upon which yarn is wound.

LIVE WOOL. Lofty, springy, resilient wool taken from live sheep.

LIXIVITATION. The process of separating a soluble substance from an insoluble substance by the percolation of water.

LIXIVIUM. This term is used in old dye books and implies water impregnated with alkaline salts extracted by lixivitation from wood ashes. Also called lye.

LIZARD. A rope with several rings spliced into it.

LLAMA. The members of the llama family include four distinct types and two hybrid types. The distinct types are llama, alpaca, guanaco or huanaco, and vicuna; the hybrids are huarizo, the offspring from a llama father and an alpaca mother, and paco-llama or misti, the offspring from an alpaca father and a llama mother.

Llama are raised in Bolivia, Peru, southern Ecuador and northwestern Argentina. Lake Titicaca, 125 miles long and 75 miles wide, which forms a part of the boundary between Bolivia and Peru, is the center of Llamaland.

The animal, which weighs about 250 pounds and is about one third the size of a camel, has a natural habitat around 12,000 feet; hence, llama are found in the Andes Mountains of the aforementioned countries. The life span of the animal is 10 to 14 years. The animal is not found north of the equator.

Full fleece-bearing capacity of the llama is not obtained until the animal is more than four years old. The fleece, obtained every two years, weighs about five pounds; the staple length ranges from 6 to 12 inches.

The outer coat of the animal is thick and coarse; the hair next to the body is very fine and closely resembles the hair of the alpaca. In the preliminary color grading the seven basic colors obtained are white, gray, light brown, dark brown, black, and piebald. Underbelly is usually white.

LLAMA SHIRTING. High quality shirting or blouse fabric made from yarn which has a content of 50 to 80 per cent wool with the remaining percentage of cotton. Textures run from 44-square to 50-square. The yarn for this material is figured in terms of the worsted standard, 560 yarns in one pound of the Number One yarn. Warp varies from 16s to 20s, while the filling ranges from 12s to 18s. Plain or twill weaves are used and stripe effects are

a feature of the material. The yarn used in this material is always referred to as llama yarn. It is now used in pajama fabric in Great Britain and on the Continent.

LLAMA YARN. A cotton and wool mixture which has no llama fiber in it.

LOAD. A laundry term broken down as follows: 1. A load of fabrics or clothes placed in the home washing machine for a single cycle of washing and/or drying. 2. A load of fabrics or garments which are able to flex or circulate easily and freely in the solution in the machine. 3. A load of garments which will freely tumble in the machine dryer for good results without unnecessary wrinkling. Loading weights may vary because of the type of washer, dryer, and the items being treated.

LOADED. Dyer's term for cloth overcharged with gums, salts, or other dressings for extra weight.

LOADING. Otherwise known in the leather trade as filling or stuffing, the use of the term really means that the filling or stuffing has been carried to excess, to increase the weight of leather.

LOAGHTAN SHEEP. An original sheep breed which lives in a semi-wild state in Iceland. These sheep develop extra horns and some rams may have as many as six of these horns.

LOCAL. A subdivision of a national or an international union confined to a limited area, or a definite company.

LOCHREA. A bleached Irish linen made with coarse yarns and rather low in pick count. In unbleached state it finds use as aprons.

LOCK. A wool tuft about the size of a man's finger or thumb which tends to stay or stick together when shorn from the sheep.

LOCK, COTTON. Seed cotton from a section of a cotton boll. There may be three, four, or five locks in a cotton boll.

LOCKING COURSE IN KNITTING. It is given to goods knitted on rib or purl machines before the stitches are cast from one bank of needles at the end of a garment or part of a garment. Its purpose is to prevent dropped stitches from running back through the previous garment or piece.

LOCK-LINED FABRICS. This product of Lock-Lined, Inc., New York City, is a fabric innovation that permanently "locks" lining to its outer fabric "together as one." Fabrics of this name cover the patents in which the fusing of any type lining to any type of outer fabric is done, in rigid or stretch constructions. Acetate or nlyon are used as the lining in tricot knit construction because of their inherent properties, such as absorption of body moisture in the case of

acetate, fastness to color, and fabric porosity to allow the fabric "to breathe." These properties also include elasticity that stretches and returns to normal shape on release of tension, and abrasion resistance.

In the manufacture of a blouse, dress, skirt slack or practically any type garment, the quality of acetate tricot lining holds and controls the original fit of the garment. Crease is retained in the garment which shrugs off wrinkles and maintains shape. Other qualities of Lock-Lined Fabrics include added body and strength, fine tailoring and drapeability, improved finished garment, greater economy of production, ease of alteration, increased strength at points of stress and strain, and an appealing smoothness when worn next to the human body. Garments of this type are guaranteed washable if the face fabric is washable, dry-cleanable to the extent that they can withstand fifteen cleanings, the same number of times that a woman would dry-clean a woolen garment during a five year span of time. Ease in pressing is another positibe advantage. The processing method is licensed by the company to its licensees.

LOCK STITCH. A sewing machine stitch by which the lower thread is interlaced with the upper thread and held fast.

LOCK YARN. See BOUCLE.

LOCKOUT. 1. Thick, straggly wool stock which shows a waste tip which extends the length of the staple, difficult to manipulate in manufacture of yarn. 2. In labor circles, it is a voluntary closing-down by a company to prevent employees from working.

LOCKS. Odds-and-ends of waste gathered in sorting of sheep fleeces.

LOCRENAN. A French sailcloth made from unbleached hemp; coarse and heavy.

LOCUST BEAN GUM. This North American tree of the bean family provides a pectin gum obtained from the bean; used in sizing.

LODEN CLOTH. This fabric originated in the province of Tyrol in western Austria in the eleventh century. The peasants who first made the cloth in this mountainous district, called Loderers, loomed the material from the rough and oily wool of the mountain sheep of the area. Some camel hair, at times, is blended with the better quality fabric of this name. The fabric is a thick, fulled, soft material and is quite waterproof without being treated chemically. It is an ideal cloth for use in winter wear garments such as sports clothes, finger-tip or full-length coatings throughout the world. A feature of the garment is that it is usually made in double-breasted coating to allow for free and easy movement despite the bulk of the goods used to make the garment.

LODGE. A subdivision of certain national or international unions. Similar to a local.

LOFTSPUN SYSTEMS. Trade name of the Roberts Company, Sanford, North Carolina, which applies to machinery included in the LoftSpun System and the yarn produced on that equipment. The Systems offer an economical way to produce quality loft yarns at high speeds. The Systems were arrived at to help reduce initial machinery investment, operating costs, and floor space requirements. Yarns made on the System may be produced from all manmade fibers such as acrylics, nylons, polyesters, polypropylenes, and rayons with all their variations and blends of these fibers, as well as from natural fibers and blends.

The LoftSpun Systems bring out the fullness qualities of the fibers using a parallel fiber system. Drawn and undrawn stock, produced as waste and thread waste, may be regenerated with modern equipment for use in the LoftSpun blends.

The Systems are applied in two processing methods—Classic or Can-Back, and each system is available in coarse count and fine count of yarn variations. A full range of yarn counts is covered, from .65s to 8s and higher cotton count, single or plied, in very few and simplified production steps. The selection of system and variation depends upon yarn size or count, and end or terminal use.

All LoftSpun Systems are similar in the initial process stages, beginning with intimate pre-blending of fibers and proceeding through the DynaCard and ParaDrafter operations. A total of 72 doublings is achieved in the ParaDrafter spinning operation alone in addition to earlier blending. Differences in Systems occur in spinning frame and in method employed. After spinning, yarn can then proceed through doubling, twisting, and winding, as required. A balanced unit produces 300 to 400 pounds an hour, or from 35,000 to 50,000 pounds in a 120 hour week.

LOFTY. High-grade wool, opposite of frowsy wool. It is full of life, elastic, springy, and gives a low yield because of the high yolk content in the fleece.

LOGWOOD. This vegetable dye must be used with a mordant since without the latter, no coloring action is possible. It is found in Campeche, Yucatan, and other Mexican states, and in Central America. Logwood and other roots, shrubs, herbs, and barks contain, in some form or other, the coloring matter that can be extracted and used in dyeing of textiles. Blacks on silk are dyed with

logwood. It is also much used in fur dyeing.

LOINCLOTH. The same as waistcloth, it partially covers the waist, passing over the hips and between the thighs.

LOKAO. The bark of the Chinese species of Rhamnus furnishes this green vegetable dye. Known also as Chinese green.

LONA. Used in Central and South Americas, it is a canvas or duck fabric textured about 14 x 16. Warp counts of yarn are about 6s while filling is around 8s; ply yarns are used in each instance, and there may be a variance in the ply such as 2, 3, 4, or 6 ply, dependent on fabric weight desired. Used chiefly for sailcloth.

LONDON BINDING. A two-ply warp is used in this binding or tape which is made in widths of one inch or wider. Better grades use a two-ply filling yarn.

LONDON CORD. British term for a particular type of Bedford cord. The cords are made with a satin weave, thereby adding better luster to the material. Repeats of pattern are always small and it can be woven in a repeat as small as 8 ends and 6 picks.

LONDON SHRUNK. This trademark is held by Perrott & Perrott (Holdings) Ltd., and is over 250 years old. It is a hot-and-cold water treatment given to worsted fabrics especially so as to obtain definite shrinkage percentages; all worsteds should be afforded this treatment. London Shrunk relaxes stresses and strains left in the fabric after manufacture. It provides a supple and mellow hand and gives a smart appearance to the goods. The shrunken cloth is refinished after the treatment in accordance with the wishes of the purchaser of the goods.

LONDON TYE. Jacquard harness tie-up, planned so that the cards on the loom head-motion pass from the cylinders over the side of the loom instead of over the back of the head motion as would otherwise be the case. The latter method of mounting the cards is called French tie.

LONG BATH. A great volume of liquid for the weight of the material being dyed or treated. The ratio is around 30 to 1.

LONG CHAIN DYEING. A chain process used to color thread. See CHAIN DYEING.

LONGCLOTH. A fine, plain-weave fabric of superior quality made from high-grade cotton. The cloth has high texture and genuine whiteness in finished appearance; medium twisted yarn

is used.

In recent years, longcloth seems to have lost some of its popularity because it has been imitated and cheapened to the extent that less expensive material fits the needs formerly cared for by it.

The fabric differs from batiste in that texture is higher, yarn is softer, and the cloth has purer whiteness. Textures are about 88 x 80 in the goods which may be printed or dyed, and are used for lingerie, dress goods, children's wear, and underwear.

LONGCLOTH, SILK. Dyed in all colors, this plain-weave silk cloth is made with two-ply warp and singles filling; used chiefly for dress goods, and in pastel and flesh shades for underwear. This longcloth can also be made from several of the man-made fibers today.

LONG DRAFT. A popular, much discussed term for the system of roving or spinning which admits of the use of higher drafts than would ordinarily be expected from the stock at hand. Obtained in several ways, the general principle embraces drafting by rollers in addition to the use of various devices to better control the fibers as they are being manipulated in actual drawing operation. (Sometimes called high draft.)

LONG-LIFE CRAVENETTE. A very durable water-repellent finish to resist perspiration, spots, stains, and water. Several dry cleanings or washings may be given before it outlives its usefulness.

LONG NOIL. Refers to the best grade of silk noil in Great Britain.

LONG POLL. Plush cloths made in the British Isles, characterized by a shaggy, irregular face effect. It is not a staple cloth at present.

LONG-STAPLE COTTON. That cotton whose length is 1⅛ inches or over in actual staple length.

LONG-STAPLE UPLANDS. The high-grade cotton raised chiefly in the Valley Area in this country. Staple is from one inch to 1³²⁄₃₂ inches; it is the most important cotton, generally speaking, raised in America. Also known as Peeler and Delta cotton.

LONGOTTE. A coarse, stout, heavy, plain-woven calico.

LONGS. This implies that cotton spinners have more cotton than they can use on hand.

LONG WOOL. Lustrous, straight, strong wool with staple length of seven inches or more; the latter staple length is variable; some fibers will run up to 20 inches in length. Long wool is about the same as Luster wool, and it grades from 36s to 40s in quality.

LONGWOOL SHEEP. They include Lincoln, Leicester, Cotswold, Romney Marsh, Cheviot, and Oxford Down. See Illustrated Section.

LONK SHEEP. A large, hardy mutton type raised on the moors of Lancashire and Yorkshire. It gives a good, close-grained mutton. The wool is soft, has a staple of about 6 inches, and averages 40s in quality.

LOOK-OVER. English term for one who performs the duties of the percher, inspector, and final inspector of cloth.

LOOM, BACK-STRAP. In this popular type of hand loom, the warp is held taut between the end bars of the loom; the upper-end-bar is fastened to a tree, post, or some other sturdy support while the lower end-bar is held in place by being wound around the hips of the weaver. This loom permits the weaver to control tensions, an important item. Also, finished woven fabric can be taken straight from the loom. The loom may be rolled up and set in a small area, or it can be taken anywhere for use such as on a picnic, vacation, a meeting of some sort, etc.

This type of loom is thought of as a two-shed loom but this is not always true. Peruvians, Mexicans, and American Indians have been known to use a multiple-heddle loom on which to make fancy twills or baskets, double, and even triple woven goods.

Weaving width on a back-strap loom depends on the length of the arms of the weaver, up to 30 inches or less. Length of fabric woven depends on the amount of woven cloth that can be easily rolled onto the lower bar.

Most end-bars are less than 40 inches long but their length must be in proportion to the piece of fabric being woven. A few extra inches on each end provides sufficient space for tie-ups and to allow a small amount of safety in handling. If the ends are too long, in proportion to the weaving, there will likely be difficulty in balancing the loom. The loom is usually fastened on a slant or angle with the upper-bar higher than the lower one. Loom bars are notched about an inch or so from the end, thereby providing a place for the ropes and the back-strap cords. These end-bars are smooth and never polished. Only the batten has a luster or polish and this comes from contact in usage.

LOOM, HARNESSES AND HEDDLES ON.

1. REGULAR HARNESSES: Those of a type which controls a definite system of threads and is limited in scope.

2. JACQUARD HARNESSES: Those having a combination of thread control which is not limited in scope.

The regular type of harness is as

follows: A frame usually made of wood, consisting of two small, flat pressed-steel bars that extend the width of the harness frame. Harness frames, upright in the loom, are kept in place at the top and bottom by means of straps attached to the jack in the head motion of the loom.

Heddles are added to, or taken from, the harness frame by taking out the cotter pins on the one end of the frame and loosening the nuts on the other end. This allows the bars to slide back and forth, and the matter of adding or taking away heddles is simple. The heddles easily fit onto the bars in the frame by means of the top and bottom hook loops.

All ends that weave alike usually go on the same harness. An end, with the exception of intricate doup weaving, usually goes through one heddle eye only.

LOOM, JET. In the early 1960's, the Swedish Maxbo was the first important type brought out in this manner of weaving fabric. Other looms in this category include the Elitex and the Kovo in Czechoslovakia, and the Japanese Prince Loom. The use of a water jet has proved to be ideal for the use of filament yarns used as filling in fabric, but there may be some difficulty when the hydrophobic fibers, such as nylon and polyester, are used. Production is high; for example, many water-jet looms provide a filament pickage of around 400 ppm.

LOOM, MAJOR PARTS OF A.

1. WARP BEAM OR WARP ROLL: The roll upon which all warp ends are uniformly, snugly, and evenly wound. For certain types of weaving—double cloth, terry toweling, pile fabric weaving, etc.—two or more warp beans are used on the loom.

2. WHIP ROLL: It sets above the warp beam and guides the warp ends as they come up from the warp beam on their way to the lease rods and heddles. This guide roller is in the same flat plane with the breast beam and selvage edges. The arrangement makes weaving possible.

3. WARP: The total number of threads or ends which make up the entire warp in the loom. The warp is always under tension.

4. ENDS: The individual yarns which, when taken collectively, make up the warp.

5. LEASE RODS: Two wooden or glass rods set between the whip roll and the harness frames. These rods help to keep the lease in the warp threads. For example, all even-numbered warp ends may pass over the back lease rod and under the front lease rod; all odd-numbered warp ends

may pass under the back lease rod and over the front lease rod. By this arrangement of warp threads, the lease rods aid considerably in finding broken warp ends, keeping the ends under control, and preventing possible gnarling, tangling and rolling of the warp ends. In addition the rods cause the ends to enter the heddle eyes on the harness frames in an even, uniform manner.

6. HEDDLES: Usually made of fine pressed-steel wire, they have a hole or eye in the center through which the respective warp ends are drawn.

7. HARNESSES: The wooden frames upon which the heddles are placed by means of a top-heddle loop and a bottom-heddle loop. The harnesses form the shed in the loom when some of them are raised while others are lowered.

8. SHUTTLE AND BOBBIN: The shuttle passes through the warp shed formed by the raising and lowering of the ends in the warp.

The filling yarn is wound on a bobbin which sets in the shuttle. This yarn is unwound and left in the shed as the shuttle passes through in going from the shuttle box on the one side of the loom to the shuttle box on the other side.

The reed then beats the loose pick in the shed into the cloth.

9. BREAST BEAM: The bar, wooden or otherwise, at the front of the loom over which the cloth passes on its way to the cloth roller. This beam runs parallel with the reed, lease rods, and whip roll; these four parts of the loom must be parallel to produce cloth because of the fact that the warp must interlace at right angles with the filling to make woven fabric.

10. CLOTH ROLLER: A roller across the front of the loom, below the breast beam, onto which the newly woven material is wound.

Each piece, bolt or cut of cloth is taken from the cloth roller when the correct cloth yardage has been woven.

Cut lengths of cloth will vary considerably dependent upon local conditions. Sixty to eighty yards seems to be the length desired for woolen and worsted goods; forty to fifty yards for rayon and cotton goods. There is no cut-and-dried rule as to what a cut-length should be in actual yardage.

11. LET-OFF MOTION: The slow unwinding of the yarn from the warp beam to supply an even flow of warp yarn to replace this yarn as it is fed into the loom and woven into fabric. The motion is usually governed by the action of the warp beam and the whip roll, working in conjunction with one another.

12. TAKE-UP MOTION: The winding of the newly woven cloth onto the cloth roller at the front of the loom. The speed at which this roller turns is governed by a take-up pawl and a set of gears usually located at the lower right-hand side near the front of the loom. The pick-wheel governs the compactness of the goods and the pickage of the filling in the fabric being woven.

13. REED: The comblike device through which the warp ends are drawn after leaving the heddles and the harnesses. Reeds are usually made of fine, pressed-steel wire, and the spaces between these wires are known as reed-splits or reed-dents.

The reed prevents the warp ends from gnarling or tangling with one another; it keeps the warp ends level, straight, and true and serves as a control for the ends being fed in evenly to the newly woven cloth. The reed by its to-and-fro action beats the loose filling pick, lying in the shed of the loom, into its proper place in the woven goods. The reed is parallel with the whip roll and lease rods, and is at right angles to the selvages.

14. TEMPLES: Devices at each edge of the cloth to keep woven fabric at the proper width in the loom during weaving. Another purpose is to keep the warp ends at the correct width and angle so that they will weave at right angles with the filling yarn; acts as an auxiliary to the reed in this respect.

LOOM, MOCK SPACE. A loom fitted with a batten which has two rows of shuttles or battens in a staggered formation so that the top set fits over the spaces in the bottom tier of shuttles. May be the fly-shot type or the rack-and-pinion type.

LOOM, RAPIER. Several manufacturers make this type of loom including Draper Division (Hopedale, Massachusetts) of North American Rockwell Corporation, Dornier, Iwer, and Roscher. Comparable with the Sulzer loom, it generally finds much usage with spun, rather than filament, filling yarns. Filament yarn, if used, may give trouble when gripping the yarn, but this problem is gradually being alleviated. Pickage ranges from 190 to 240 picks per minute.

LOOM, SHUTTLELESS. Its first appearance was around 1945 and was caused by the intensity and competition in woven fabrics. It was around this time, following World War II, that knitting began its meteoric rise and much attention was now given to this type of loom to enhance the efforts of woven fabric mills. In addition, around this time centering in Dalton, Georgia, large size bedspreads became the rage and wider looms were needed to take care of the reed space in the loom necessary to make these wide goods. Reed space up to 140 inches in width was needed.

This type of loom is operated by an air-jet or a water-jet. The latter operates at a faster speed than the former and can produce goods two or more times faster than the conventional type of loom. As to loom pickage, about 260 picks per minute seem to give the best results. Though picks up to around 500 per minute have been attained, this speed does cause trouble when the loom is in operation. Breakage, slippage, tautness, and other problems present themselves above the 260 picks-per-minute speed.

The water-jet-loom finds great use in weaving filament yarns of manmade fibers but these must be the type that will neither absorb nor deteriorate in water. Rayon, incidentally, because of its water absorption property, is not ideal for this type of loom.

On the other hand, the old-time conventional loom has not lost all to the shuttleless loom. They still have many of the advantages which led to their widespread use in the past and prior to the coming of the shuttleless loom; dependency, versatility, volume production, and especially the fact that one weaver can operate and control many looms at one time. Some sheeting mill, for example, may have 24, 36, or more looms assigned to a single weaver. Automation has aided conventional weaving, as well. Wider and speedier looms have come over the horizon from the loom manufacturers for the last twenty years and the old-time loom is still with us and will be for many years to come.

LOOM, SULZER PROJECTILE. This Swiss loom uses a small bullet-like projectile to grasp the filling yarn and carry it across the raceplate of the loom from side to side, and at high number of picks per minute, up to about 300 ppm. Ideal in weaving woolen and worsted goods, sheeting, shirting and printcloth.

LOOM AND WEAVING. A loom is a machine, hand or power driven, necessary to weave cloth. It consists essentially of parts that make it possible to have two systems of thread or yarn, called warp and filling, weave or interlace at right angles to each other. The earliest looms of which we have knowledge provided a means of hanging one set of threads in a vertical position through which the crossing threads were interlaced. Apparently, the first improvement consisted of a means to tighten these threads, either by hanging weights at the bottom end or by joining their two ends in such a way so as to form a loop over horizontal, parallel bars.

The following terms used in weaving parlance are synonymous: 1. Warp and end—the vertical or lengthwise yarns in woven cloth. 2. Filling and pick—the crosswise yarns in woven cloth.

Horizontal looms were used by the early Egyptians and other civilizations in early world history. In the simplest form, this type of loom provided for the tethering of a bar that carried the lengthwise warp ends to a stake in the ground. A bar at the farther end was secured to the person of the weaver, who had a straight set of warp threads through which it was possible to cross or interlace the filling yarns.

Primitive weavers improvised from simple materials a plain device or arrangement called a heddle or heald. This device enabled the alternate warp threads to be raised. Thus a shed was formed—an opening between the raised and unraised or lowered threads or groups, through which the filling picks could be more easily passed.

At an uncertain date prior to the Middle Ages, some tribes, in what is now Great Britain, improved the apparatus by adding a frame—a warp beam. This beam was used to hold the warp ends and another beam was installed to take care of the woven cloth as it came from the loom, the cloth beam or roller.

The power loom of today is substantially the hand loom adapted to rotary driving. The frame is iron instead of wood; the sley or oscillating frame is pivoted below and driven by a crank; and the picking arm is actuated by a cone that turns on a vertical rod. The lift of the heddle shafts is controlled by tappets or cams. The motions are timed accurately in order to give a high rate of speed and production. The weaver, free from supplying power, has merely to apply the filling threads to the shuttle.

Major types of looms in use today:

1. AUTOMATIC LOOM: Built for simple or plain weaving of cloth with the addition of an automatic shuttle device to change the filling as it runs out. This type of loom makes for production. The machine does not stop while the new filling bobbin is set in to replace the one that has just run out. With suitable organization of labor, one weaver may take care of several of these looms. He may care for forty-eight or more looms at one time.

2. LOOMS FOR FANCY WEAVING: Have parts that are additional to those found on plain looms. Stripes of color are arranged for in the warping, but the crossing stripes to form checks and plaids are put into the cloth by the fill-

ing bobbin in the shuttle. There must be as many shuttles as there are colors of filling to be used in the cloth design. The shuttles are placed in boxes at the end of the sley or warp, and the mechanism provides that the particular box shall be in position at the instant or exact time required.

3. DOBBY LOOM: Weaves fancy materials. The dobby loom is built so that it can take care of many harnesses. Some looms have from sixteen to thirty frames in them. The sixteen-harness motions are used the most, whereas twenty- and thirty-harness motions are used for the more complicated weaves are novelty effects. The particular heddles on some one harness can be lifted at a given moment by means of metal projections that engage the holes in strips or bars of metal plates that are successively present in endless chain form. This is called the draft chain or pattern chain.

4. DOUBLE-CYLINDER DOBBY LOOM: If it is desired to weave a pattern that contains a great many picks in the repeat, a large number of bars must be built for the pattern picks since, even on the double index dobby, one bar represents only two picks. When patterns of several hundred picks are woven, this becomes a matter of considerable importance as a long chain always requires much time in building.

To overcome the difficulty of building long pattern chains, the double-cylinder dobby is largely used. The pattern chain for one weave is placed on one of the cylinders while the pattern chain for the other weave is placed on the second cylinder. Since it is possible to send either cylinder around as many times as there are repeats of the weave before changing onto the other cylinder, it is possible to build only one repeat for each weave, providing that the number of bars in one repeat is sufficient to go around the cylinder; if the repeat has fewer bars a sufficient number of repeats must be built to encircle the cylinder.

5. JACQUARD LOOM: Provides for the lifting or raising of individual warp ends without reference to adjacent warp threads. The loom is a development of the power loom. In the Jacquard head motion there are perforated cards and the needles of the cylinder in this head stock select the required warp end or group of ends. They raise these ends, which are lifted by means of hooks and form the top part of the shed of the warp in order to admit the passage of the filling pick through the opening formed.

6. OTHER TYPES OF LOOMS FOR SPECIAL WORK: Outstanding types are: LENO OR DOUP LOOM: Weaves cloth

in such a way that certain warp threads twist or cross halfway around or over other warp ends. There are two sets of harnesses used, standard and skeleton. This loom is used for marquisette, curtains, draperies, novelty, and fancy perforated effects in cloth.

LAPPET LOOM: Uses an extra warp to produce small fancy effects in cloth. There is a base warp, and a lappet warp takes care of placing the figured design in the material. Few of these looms are now in use here.

SWIVEL OR CLIP-SPOT LOOM: Makes small designs or effects on cloth by means of an extra filling or swivel. The results are the same as those noted on a lappet loom. Few of these looms are now in use.

PILE FABRIC LOOM: Material from this type of loom is made with an extra set or sets of yarns that are looped on the face of the cloth. The fabric may be cut or uncut to give the pile effect. Cutting or looping is done by means of rods which, if they are tipped at the one end with a blade, will give a cut-pile effect; if there is no blade at the one end of the wire, the material will become an uncut-pile fabric. Plushes of all types are made on these looms.

INDIAN-TYPE LOOM: Also called the inkle or belt loom, provided with frames for loopers, tapestry, or upright looms in hand weaving.

LOOM BEAM. A beam to hold warp yarn. In weaving, it is located at the back of the loom, and from it the ends slowly unwind. Usually there is one beam to a loom, but sometimes there may be two, three, or more.

LOOM-FIGURED. Fabrics which have the designs woven in during weaving in contradistinction to printed, embroidered or appliquéd patterns on textile materials.

LOOM-FINISHED. Material sold in the same condition in which the goods came from the loom—duck, webbing, canvas, burlap, etc.

LOOM FIXER. One who is responsible for replacing broken parts and worn parts and for making necessary adjustments to the various loom motions; sees that the loom produces good fabric; responsible for the upkeep and repair of all equipment. The fixer should be able to give instruction in weaving.

LOOM GOODS, LOOM STATE. Woven goods, especially woolens and worsteds and those blended fabrics in which these two fibers serve as the major or base fiber, as they come from the loom and are made ready for perching. Rather synonymous with greige or gray goods.

LOOMING. 1. Same as weaving. 2. British term for drawing-in and reeding-in of warp ends according to the drawing-in plan for the weave construction.

LOOM MOTIONS, MECHANICAL. The six basic motions for a hand loom include shedding, picking, beating-up, take-up, let-off, and pattern. In power weaving there are six common types of motions used to raise or lower harnesses in conformity with a given weaving plan. These are:

1. CONE MOTION: This motion is practically obsolete at present since it permits the weaving of only plain patterns.

2. UNDER-CAM MOTION: In most instances this motion is positive in action and its capacity is limited to six harnesses. This seems to be flexible enough for most of the basic weaves on cotton or woolen looms.

3. SIDE-CAM MOTION: This is the most positive as far as shedding is concerned. It has the disadvantage, however, of being expensive to change over and usually requires additional floor space. The loom capacity is ordinarily eight shafts or harnesses.

4. DOBBY LOOM MOTION: The most common is the single index, double lift single cylinder. At present, however, this motion is practically obsolete since it does not have the capacity of the double index or double cylinder. This latter motion is popular today; it has a chain cylinder, is driven by a sprocket and chain from the crank shaft. The pattern chain has a maximum of thirty bars and 300 pegs per loom. The dobby is driven by means of a crank on the end of the bottom shaft.

5. HEAD OR GEM HEAD MOTIONS: These motions are built with capacity of 8 to 32 harnesses. These seem to be the most nearly ideal type of harness motions and they are positive in action. The motions are not built for high speed but rather for heavier types of work and box looms where speed is not too important.

6. JACQUARD HEAD MOTION: See LOOM AND WEAVING; JACQUARD LOOM.

LOOMS, CHIEF MOTIONS OF. There are six chief motions on a power loom. The principal motions are shedding, picking, beating-up; the auxiliary motions are take-up, let-off, pattern. The first three motions are linked together as follows:

1. SHEDDING MOTION: The separating of the warp ends into an upper and lower system of threads to permit the shuttle to pass through the space that has been formed. The warp ends are drawn through heddle eyes in the correct manner, and in the turning-over of the crank shaft of the loom a shed is

formed with each turn.

2. PICKING MOTION: The actual passing of the shuttle through the shed of the loom. The shuttle passes over the lowered ends of the shed and under its raised ends. The shed allows the shuttle to pass through it and thereby makes it possible for the shuttle to deposit the pick or filling yarn.

3. BEATING-UP: The actual beating into place of the loose pick that was placed in the shed of the loom in the picking motion. Beating-up makes each and every deposited yarn a component part of the woven cloth. The reed beats this pick into place with each consecutive turn of the crankshaft.

The auxiliary motions are as follows:

1. TAKE-UP MOTION: The motion is positive when the sand roller moves a fractional part of an inch in direct ratio to the take-up wheel. The motion is semi-positive when the sand roller is not definitely controlled.

2. LET-OFF MOTION: The motion is frictional when there is a definite amount of warp allowed to leave the warp beam according to the beating-up of the lay of the loom. It is positive when the lay and the let-off work in two ratios, taking up just as much as is let off.

3. PATTERN MOTION: Not found on all looms, but generally used on machines where more than one color is desired. It is found in the following ratios:

From a 2 x 1 box loom to a 6 x 1 gingham loom.

From a 2 x 2 box loom controlling three colors.

From a 4 x 4 box loom controlling seven colors, pick and pick type.

LOOM SMASH. This occurs when a large number of warp ends become broken in the weaving of fabric; may be caused by loops, knots, poor tensions, unpolished shuttles, when two shuttles come together in the shed, and other mishaps.

LOOM STATE. Fabric from the loom and before any wet or dry treatment is given to the cloth.

LOONGEE. English term for a variety of colored woven or printed cotton goods popular for the export trade, chiefly India.

LOOP. A doubling or folding of yarn, thread, or braid in order to make a ring or eye through which another cord or the like may be run through.

Blind loops are used on garments fastened with hooks and eyes to take the place of metal eyes. They are used when there is only one loop to be made, as at the neckline, on a slashed opening; also used in place of fabric loops, on the opening at the wrist.

Fabric loops are often suitable for buttonholes on openings where a buttonhole could not be used. They are decorative and easy to apply, and are especially appropriate for use on bound or faced slashes. Loops may be used from the dress fabric, of rayon, cotton, or other fabrics for decoration.

LOOP BAND. A spinning band in which there is a loop in one end. Four strands of roving are twisted together and then two of these are combined for final twisting.

LOOP DRYER. A dryer that does its work without tension; the roller type that is equipped with rollers over which the cloth passes as warm air circulates throughout the chamber.

LOOPED FILLING PILE FABRIC. See PILE FABRIC, LOOPED FILLING.

LOOPED SURFACE EFFECT. Fabrics which use looped yarns that show to advantage on the face of the goods. The effects may be made from yarns such as looped, bug, nub, Knickerbocker, novelty, etc. When the fabric is woven, these effects or loops create a dimensional surface-effect which adds to the appearance of the goods. Ideal for women's winter coatings of various types.

LOOPER. The machine used for looping purposes. It has a horizontal disc with the rim closely set with grooved points and set-up to rotate at a slow speed. The operator pushes the stitches of the fabric onto the points and the machine then unites the edges and cuts off the excess material.

LOOPER CLIP. The circular end of knit material that is cut from the toe of a sock in the looping operation. This cutting is also resorted to in making hand-woven rugs and other articles of similar nature.

LOOPER POINTS. Small needle-like pieces of steel, mounted on a looping machine on which the end stitches of a stocking or garment are hung.

LOOPERS. Refers to the thin flat steel components which move alongside the inserted needles and hook the tufting yarns into place.

LOOP FABRIC. See KNOP.

LOOPING. A semi-knitting process in which different parts of a sweater, previously knitted or cut to shape, are joined together to achieve the effect of uninterrupted knitting. Looping is used in cut-and-sewn and full-fashioned sweaters. The first method is used mainly to join collars to sweaters, the second method for the same purpose, and also to join sweater parts in the shoulder and at the crown of the sleeves.

LOOPING ELEMENT. The parts of a knitting machine actually in contact with the yarn—needle, sinker, and the point or transfer.

LOOPING FRAME. A flat piece of metal with four upright posts or pins used to hold several skeins of yarn to be tied into a bundle.

LOOPING MACHINE. A machine that knits two parts of a knitted garment or stocking together.

LOOP-KNOT. A snarl or curl produced by filling yarn receding upon itself.

LOOPLESS TOE. The toe area in a full-fashioned hose which has been narrowed to the point where it can be closed only by seaming.

LOOP, LOOPED PILE. See PILE FABRIC, LOOPED FILLING.

LOOP OR LOOPED PILE FABRIC. Any of the pile fabrics made on the principle of weaving Turkish toweling or Terry cloth. The pile is always of the uncut type, and blades, tipped or tipless, are not needed to obtain the uncut pile effect. A "trick" or recessive reed is used in the weaving of the goods on the loom to achieve the effect. See PILE FABRIC, LOOPED FILLING PILE, etc.

LOOP RUCHE, TAPE RUCHE. A ruche in which the skirt is in the form of an uncut pile. See FRINGE.

LOOPS. They form a bend, curve, noose, or ring and may be used with buttons in place of snaps, hooks and eyes, and zippers. In lightweight fabrics loops can be used as fasteners where buttonholes are not essential.

LOOP SELVAGE. See SELVAGE, LOOP.

LOOP STITCH. A stitch used in embroidery; it is fastened at the loop end by a short stitch.

"LOOP THE LOOP." A type of hosiery brought about by the great use of the mini skirt which made pantyhose a necessity; also know as "LTL." Introduced in October, 1968, LTL eliminates problems of garter-bulge and stockings that are too short. Registered trademark of Burlington Industries, New York City.

LOOP TRANSFER, KNITTING. The method of moving loops, partially or totally, from the position in which they were made to other needles for the purpose of styling.

LOOP-WHEEL MACHINE. A circular spring-beard needle knitting machine, equipped with a loop wheel or burrs (steel blades set in at an angle to the loopwheel hub) for feeding yarn to the needles, moving the fabric up and down, cast-off, etc.

In making jersey fabric, for example, a sinker burr, a lander burr, and a cast-off burr are necessary. A wide range of fabrics can be made on loop-wheel machines, including plain and fancy jersey, terry fabric, plaited fabrics, pile cloths, eyelet structures, and elasticized materials. Most loop-wheel machines consist of a table upon which two cylinders are supported. The cylinders are rotated by a shaft which runs underneath the table. The take-up mechanism is supported above the cylinders.

LOOPY, LOOPED SELVAGE. That which has a run of loops in the selvage caused by uneven shuttle tension, improperly set loom beam heads, improper harness timing, or an accumulation of waste behind the warp drop-wires.

LOOP YARN. A "circular-effect yarn," as the name implies. Complete loops are seen in these yarns which appear in mohair, woolen, and some synthetic yarns.

LOOSE-BACK. Quilting upon which the binding warp floats are on the back of the material. Also implies the welts observed when wadding fillings are not interlaced with the warp.

LOOSE COTTON. That obtained from a bale or prior to its being made into lap form.

LOOSE COURSE. Knit goods in which a row of loops is larger, looser, or longer than the body of the material. Intentionally made, it is employed where necessary to facilitate the topping-on operation as in the case of a ribbed top for men's socks.

LOOSE ENDS. Looped or curled warp ends observed on the face of a fabric. Often found in the first cut of cloth from the entire warp length on the loom. At this time it is apparent that warp tensions have not been made perfect. Loose ends may also occur between the warp beam and the back of the warp motion drop-wires. In fact, broken ends may be looked for in this same area.

LOOSE-KNITTING COURSE. One complete course of loops longer than the regular stitch; made by pressing the cylinder stitch cam downward while the cams are making one complete revolution. Facilitates the topping operation.

LOOSE PICKS. Actual loose picks that have not woven into the goods in the proper manner. Caused by irregular filling motion or shuttle action or by poor or faulty winding of the yarn prior to weaving. Uneven diameter yarn is also a cause for loose picks.

LOOSE REED. One whose top is riveted and pivoted so that the bottom can move in arc direction. Used, for example, in weaving terry cloth or Turkish toweling where the reed does not come into the fell of the cloth on the two loose filling picks, and then does beat all the way into the fell on the third pick. The third, or fast pick, because of the reed beating in tightly, brings the two loose picks into the fabric and causes the pile or accordion effect to be created in the goods.

LOOSE SELVAGES. Listing that works loose because of uneven filling tension and action against the yarns in the material that make up the selvage. The term also includes selvage ends that have become broken and have not been repaired; this may cause other ends to break in a short time. Loose selvages impair the appearance of the finished goods; they may give trouble in manipulation of the fabric into a garment.

LORETTE. A blended fabric of 55 per cent Orlon and 45 per cent wool used for sportswear, dress goods, suitings, robes and children's wear. The fabric comes in two weights, 7½ ounce and 9 ounce, and is finished at 58 inches. Washability, resilience, and wrinkle-resistance are of the best and the pleat retention of Lorette will save many ironings. The fabric has the appearance and the feel of worsted plus the dimensional stability feature of Orlon which permits home machine washing as well as commercial laundering.

The material is nonshrinkable because of the manner of blending the fibers. A product of Deering, Milliken & Co., Inc.

LOT CARD. A card on which identifying information such as size, color, and lot number is recorded. The card is attached to bundles of material in process.

LOTS "STAR H. I." Small lots of wool, three bales or less, which are usually sold at the end of the London Colonial Wool Sales.

LOUISIANA COTTON. General name given to Uplands cotton of short staple raised in Louisiana and adjacent areas.

LOUISINE. The weave is plain or taffeta, but, while taffeta has more ends than picks, this cloth has more picks than ends. A typical taffeta could have one hundred and forty-four ends, and would be set, say, 72 inches in the reed. Ninety-six picks would be used. In the Louisine there are groups of ends which weave alike, spaced and placed in the same heddles and harnesses. Picks that weave alike would also be spaced and

weave alike in the same shed. The plan causes two picks to cross a single warp end and thus produce a small rib effect. Texture may be 90 x 120. The fabric shows a minute rib or basket effect. This sofe, spongy material is made with silk.

LOUIS PHILIPPE COSTUME. See Costume, Louis Philippe Era.

LOUIS QUINZE LACE. This "Louis the Fifteenth Lace" is a simulated tape lace in which the motifs are done in narrow braid formation connected by bars. Made of linen or cotton, it comes in varying widths with parallel edges.

LOUIS TREIZE BRAID. This "Louis the Thirteenth Braid" is an English term for narrow linen braid made to simulate genuine tape lace.

LOUSY SILK. Small specks of a detrimental nature on the face of the goods. They may be caused at several places in the manipulation of the silk from the raw state to the finished fabric.

LOVAT. A cheviot woolen fabric which originated in Scotland and was named for the Scottish sportsman, Lord Lovat. The colorings in fabrics under this name are noted for their brilliant, sparkling mixture effect. The mixes are prepared so that the resultant color will not be dull or somber, and so that one color will not cancel out the others used in the blend.

The Lovat Mixture is still popular and found only in higher quality fabrics and suitings. The idea of Lovat Mixture has spread to the armed forces of the world—British Khaki, German Field Grey, Horizon Blue of the French, Air Force Blue of the United States Air Force. Murat or Moorit, a warm, middle-toned brown, is also derived from Lovat. See MURAT, MOORIT.

LOVE. A thin, black silk mourning fabric. Now superseded by the term silk crepe.

LOWE, HORACE. An outstanding chemist of his time and a native of the Lancashire District in England who in 1844 accidently discovered what is now known as mercerizing cotton. In 1890, Lowe applied tension to yarn during the process of mercerizing and noted that it not only controlled the shrinkage but added strength and provided a soft, appealing, permanent luster. Lowe did much work on both yarn and fabric before announcing his findings. Thus, Lowe made commercially valuable what is now known as Mercerization, a truly great asset and improvement for one of the world's oldest textile fibers, cotton. See Mercer, John; Mercerized Cotton, Tests for; Mercerized Finish, Mercerizer.

LOW-END. General term for fabric of inferior or low quality or a mill that makes low-grade textiles.

LOW-END WOOLENS. Those made of reused, remanufactured, and other comparable fibers. Quality and price are rather low.

LOW PILE. See HIGH PILE.

LOW ROLL TAKE-UP MOTION. Found chiefly on woolen and rayon looms, it is a series of gears, usually six, that in their action wind the cloth onto the cloth roller. This low roll is near the floor at the front of the loom, and it is situated under the breast beam, guide roller, and sand roller.

LOWRY BALE. A cylindrical cotton bale from a continuous layer of cotton, wrapped in bagging held in place by wire ties; the bale averages 250 pounds.

LOW-SLOPE COLLAR. Shirt collar featured by a deep slope toward the front of the shirt. May be made as a button-down collar or without this effect.

LOW WOOL. Another name for coarse wool.

LOYNES. A particularly fine, smooth surface-finish woolen, printed in pastel shades.

LOZENGE EFFECT. 1. A rhombus with all sides equal, having two acute and two obtuse angles. 2. A group of small repeat weaves, usually derived from some basic twill weave, in which the direction of the diagonals changes from time to time to give a rhombus or lozenge formation.

LUANA. Similar to fuji but made with a slightly larger cross-rib effect, the texture is about 108 x 48 with the warp made of acetate and the filling of acetate and rayon. The structure provides good body, strength, and wearing qualities. Used in blouses, dress goods, ensembles, men's shirts, slacks, two-piece dresses, and women's slacks.

LUBRICANT. Anything that lubricates, such as graphite, grease, oil. Used to make surfaces smooth and slippery, and to minimize friction and prevent cohesion. Much used in various phases of the textile industry.

LUBRICATED YARN. A term which usually refers to any of the man-made yarns which have been soaked or treated with some desirable lubricant to insure smoother work in the knitting frame. Natural fiber yarns may or may not be lubricated.

LUCITE; PLEXIGLASS. Lucite is a trademark for any of a class of methyl methacrylate ester polymers used chiefly as a substitute for glass. Plexiglass or Plexiglas is a lightweight thermoplastic polymer of methyl methacrylate, resistant to weathering, and used chiefly for signs and windows. They are nontoxic,

odorless, and tasteless. Burning rate is low.

These acrylics of the plastic family are delicate and light in weight but can withstand temperature changes and sharp blows; they may be tinted in a full range of transparent, translucent, and opaque colors. Main uses are in hair brushes, lamps, tables, decorative shelves, etc. See Plastics, Ester, Polymer.

LUGGAGE CLOTH. Sometimes also called transportation fabric, this rather loosely applied term may imply cotton cloth which has been coated or treated on the one side with transparent pyroxylin finish. Any of the very simple weaves are used to give the effects which are often striped for identification purposes. Used for all types of luggage and casings, etc.

LUG STRAP. The strong strap at the middle of the picker stick on a loom which receives motion from the picking shaft and transmits it to the shuttle by helping to throw it through the shed of the loom when weaving. It is set above the shoe and beneath the shuttle-box attachment.

LUMARITH. This plastic is a transparent sheeting pliable enough to warp a powder puff but rigid enough for shaping into a lunchbox. It will not stretch or shrink, and is dust-proof and resistant to moisture. A cellulose acetate product of the Celanese Corporation of America.

LUMBERJACK. It is made of overcoating fabric, leather, or a combination of cloth and leather. The bottom and the opening are often made of knitted fabric. The jacket is short, is made in straight lines, and may be buttoned or closed by a slide fastener. Reprocessed, reused, and coarse wools are used to make this popular apparel article, ideal for cold-weather wear. The designs come in plaids, solid colors, and vivid or subdued patterns.

LUMBERMAN SOCKS. The very heavy, low-gauge, woolen socks with a stout ribbed top used for outdoor work in cold areas. Often made in red and white although any color combination can be used.

LUMEN. The inner cavity of a cell or tubular organ. This canal runs in a longitudinal direction in a fiber, and it may be large and continuous or small and discontinuous.

LUMP. 1. Cloths woven 130 yards long and 90 inches wide which are to be split and cut into half lengths. This procedure is followed in the British Isles. 2. A length of unfinished goods that is longer than the regulation cut length. 3. The cut of batched or lumped cloth as it is being removed from the

loom.

LUMPS. 1. Fabric woven in a double or triple tier that is to be cut or split after being taken from the loom; often done in weaving velvet. From this plan it is possible to weave, say, three tiers of velvet, each 29-inches wide, one on top of the other and with the necessary selvages provided. Finished goods make three individual fabrics with selvage edges intact. 2. Gray goods from the loom and prior to finishing operations. 3. A British term comparable with the American term, "double-cut," and implies a long piece or cut of goods. Most British lumps run from 100 to 120 yards in length, as against the American cut-length of 40 to 100 yards. The British often refer to American fabric lengths as "half-lumps," comparable with the term, "single cut," used in this country.

LUNGEE, LUNGI. Fabric made in India. Comes in loom-finish, bleached or colored condition. Used for loincloth, scarf, or turban fabric, varying grades of cotton and different textures are features of the fabric. Considerable variance in price because of the wide range of fabric under this name is noted.

LUPIS. High-grade Manila hemp of the Philippines used in high-textured dress goods.

LUREX. A metallic yarn of plastic-coated aluminum made for use in lamé fabrics. The yarn is composed of an aluminum-base fiber sandwiched between two plies of specially formulated plastic film. Special processing and adhesives make the yarn impervious to tarnish, and also much lighter than ordinary metallic yarns. Lurex is used in evening-wear fabrics, curtains, and millinery fabrics. Product of the Dobeckmun Company, a Division of The Dow Chemical Company, Inc.

LUREX C-50. A non-laminated metallic filament made of a metallized polyester base protected on both sides by a plastic coating. Made by The Dow Chemical Company, Inc., Midland, Michigan, it comes in standard gold, silver, and a range of colors, multi-colors, and ombre's. The yarn is only 1/64-inches wide and there are 58,000 yards to the pound. Used in fabrics and garments to enhance the motif or design. It can be pressed and drycleaned easily.

LUSETTES. Silkworms which die because they cannot molt or shed their covering are called lusettes.

LUSTER. 1. The gloss, shine, or luster imparted on the face of any fabric in the finishing process. 2. The power that a cloth has of reflecting light; for example, silk is very lustrous, whereas cotton and woolen materials do not reflect much light. Rayons may be lustrous or nonlustrous. 3. The natural gloss of alpaca, mohair, Lincoln, Leicester, and other rugged wools.

LUSTER CLOTHS. Broad name given to lining material of union construction-cotton warp and mohair filling, rayon or acetate warp and mohair or some other hair fiber used as filling. Luster wool is sometimes used in making luster cloth.

LUSTERING. Cottons, particularly broadcloths, are given sales appeal by mercerizing, frictioning, and filling. Mercerizing is a treatment with caustic soda and is permanent. Frictioning is the application of sliding heavy pressure by the use of a calender; often referred to as friction-calendering. The fabric is generally "filled" with starch, gelatin, resins, or other materials before the pressing process.

Mercerized finishes are not impaired by water, whereas filled or pressed finishes lose their lusters partially or totally. Spattering with water would constitute a test.

LUSTER LINING. A 1-up and 4-down, filling-effect twill made with cotton warp and luster worsted or mohair filling. This British fabric may be made in plain or other small-repeat constructions.

LUSTER PILE FABRIC. Any cut pile fabric woven with surface yarns spun from soft types of staple and chemically washed, like hand-woven Oriental fabrics, to give a bright sheen.

LUSTER RAYE. English term for lustrous silk Jacquard fabrics of several types. Raye or rayé means "light's rays" in one meaning of the word. The term is usually given to piece-dyed materials with a natural or effected luster finish.

LUSTER WOOLS. A group of five major wools which originated in Great Britain but now are grown all over the world. There are many subtypes because of crossbreeding. These wools are: Lincoln, from county of that name in England; Leicester, from Leicester County; Romney Marsh, from Kent County; Cotswold, from Gloucester County; Cheviot, from the ranges of Scotland. The wool fibers reflect the rays of light, are rugged, harsh, hardy, and make ideal yarn for homespun, tweed, Cheviot, and Shetland fabrics, coating, sports togs, and cap cloth of the English type.

Luster wool fibers range from 4 to 6 inches to 14 or more inches in length. Fiber diameter ranges from 1/700th to 1/950th inches; serrations from 800 to 1000 per inch, and the fleece weight from 9 to 16 pounds. Luster rams

weigh 225 pounds to about 300 pounds; ewes from 175 pounds to about 240 pounds.

LUSTRENE. A thin, twill fabric used as lining cloth; may be made of cotton, rayon, or acetate.

LUSTER YARN. 1. English term for dyed silk yarn with a natural or effected luster finish. 2. A well-twisted woolen yarn made from luster wool such as Lincoln, Leicester, Cotswold, or Romney Marsh wools. See LUSTER CLOTHS, LUSTER WOOLS.

LUSTREUX. A piece-dyed, all-silk fabric made with faille-effect face.

LUSTRING. Often known as "lutestring," this seventeenth-century fabric was made of silk and given a high luster finish for use in ladies' dress goods.

LUSTRON. A polystyrene which is made by a series of reactions, from organic chemicals, benzene, and ethylene, which are produced from coal and petroleum respectively. Lustron is the lightest of all plastics. It possesses excellent electrical properties and exceptional resistance to acids, alkalis, and alcohols. Lustron has surface hardness and a limitless range of colors are used in the finished product. It has the ability to pipe light around corners. Lustron has dimensional stability, high heat-distortion temperature, and unusual strength at low temperatures.

This is a product of Monsanto Chemical Co.

LUTESTRING. An old-time women's-wear silk goods noted for its high sheen finish. 2. A highly polished, narrow ribbon without a selvage.

LUXEUIL. General term for handmade lace of Luxeuil, France. More specifically, it is those laces of stout, rugged, heavy type used for curtains, doilies, runners, drapery material, bibs, and tidies.

"LYCRA." Created by Du Pont, this spandex textile fiber has unique elastic qualities in that it can be used in very lightweight, durable fabrics of long-lasting elasticity. It has excellent tensile strength, a long flex life, and high resistance to abrasion and heat degradation. Its restraining power is claimed to be two or three times greater than that of comparable fibers. Fabrics in which the fiber is used withstand washing and drying in automatic washers, and the fiber is resistant to perspiration, and cosmetic oils, and lotions. "Lycra" is used in bras, foundations, surgical hosiery, narrow elastic fabrics, swim suits, industrial and military uses.

LYCRA TYPE 124. Designation of the first or original Lycra produced by E. I. duPont de Nemours & Company, Inc., Wilmington, Delaware. This elas-

tomeric fiber is made from a segmented polyurethane. See Lycra.

LYCRA TYPE 126. A product of E. I. duPont de Nemours & Company, Inc., Wilmington, Delaware, especially engineered to be non-yellowing in washers and dryers and even when exposed to bleaching agents. Atmospheric resistance is superior to other types of Lycra, but it does not seem to have the strength of Type 124 which has the greatest holding power of all types of the product and which is the most widely used type of Lycra at the present time.

LYE. A caustic soda or caustic potash solution. Also used in connection with solid caustic soda sold in cans.

LYONS SATIN. Named for Lyons, France, it is a rich, very lustrous satin-faced cloth made with a twill back which is slightly discernible on the face of the goods. Usually made of all silk, but some English versions use silk and fine cotton yarns. Some of the all-silk fabric is made with a dull luster face effect. Used chiefly for lining, trimming and has been used for dress goods. See LYONS VELVET, SATIN, SATIN WEAVES.

LYONS VELVET. The best quality of millinery velvet comes from Lyons, France. The fabric is soft and thick in texture, featured by a deep silk-pile effect. It is used for fitted and draped hats both large and small, and for handmade flowers and appliqué embroidery.

LYOTROPIC. An element dependent on the forces existing between constituents in a solution and not on their properties as units.

M

MAARAD. This cotton raised in Egypt has been developed from American Pima cotton seeds. The staple is long and the cast is brownish; a very desirable cotton in the trade.

MABEL. The 5-up, 1-down twill weave in Great Britain; used to make a type of alpaca lining there.

MACAMBIRA. Used as substitute for jute in Brazil. The fiber makes bags, canvas, floor coverings.

MacALLISTER COTTON. See PEERLESS COTTON.

MACANA. English export cotton fabric made of plain weave; small colored checks feature this soft-finish fabric.

MACARON, MACAROON. Coiled, looped, round, or spiral ornaments used for trimming on hats, dresses, and upholstery. It is made of self-material which is processed into a thin tube which is then fastened to the foundation. The French macaron probably derived from the Italian maccherone, (macaroni)—it is referred to in "Yankee Doodle"; was also used to mean a dandy.

MACARTHUR, CAPTAIN JOHN. See Australian Merino, Merino Sheep.

MACCLESFIELD REED COUNT. Used for silk and rayon fabrics the count is based on the number of reed splits in 36 inches, and the number of ends per dent. A 1200-4s would mean a reed of 1200 dents with four ends per dent in a 36-inch reed width.

MACCLESFIELD TIE SILK. A high-texture, hand-woven tie silk characterized by a small all-over texture. Ties made of this fabric give splendid wear and may be purchased only in the more exclusive shops.

MACEIO COTTON. A harsh, wiry Peruvian staple of about 1⅛-inch staple. Used for warp yarn up to about 40s.

MacFARLANE. An overcoat with cape attached. It is made from any of several types of heavy woolen fabrics, and large plaid effects are often used.

MACHINE. Any device for performing work; any apparatus for applying mechanical power.

MACHINE BUFF. See UPHOLSTERY LEATHER.

MACHINE BUTTONHOLE. Buttonhole made by machine instead of by hand; used on cheaper types of merchandise; while it is more uniform and neater than handwork, it is considered cheaper because it does not usually give as good service as the hand effort.

MACHINE COTTON. British term for sewing-machine cotton thread.

MACHINE KNITTING. Knitting fabric on a hand knitting frame or on a power machine. Flat knitting will make flat fabrics while circular knitting will produce tubular material. Warp or weft knitting is done on machines; other types include latch or springbeard knitting, fancy, Jacquard.

MACHINE LAWS. Pertinent to all types of machines, the laws here pertain to the drafting of cotton fibers as well as to the drafting of any textile fibers being processed into yarn. The following information covers the functions of these laws:

(*a*) The work done on a machine is the *input* and equals the product of the effort force and the effort distance.

(*b*) The work done by a machine is the *output* and equals the product of the resistance and the resistance distance. Thus:

Input-E (Effort) times DE (Effort Distance).

Output-R (Resistance) times DR (Resistance Distance).

(*c*) Theoretically, *input* should equal *output* because some of the *input* is used to overcome the friction on the machine. The energy lost turns into heat so that there is no violation of the law of the conservation of energy.

(*d*) Therefore, the laws of machine are: *Input* equals the useful work *Output* plus the losses caused by friction.

MACHINE OF GOODS. This embroidery term signifies two cuts or coupes of fabric; one width of the goods runs ten or fifteen yards long for the top and the bottom of the frame. Total yardage runs from twenty to thirty yards.

MACHINE PINKING OF CLOTH. This is done by a pinking machine which cuts swatches of cloth for the trade. The feature of the machine is that it gives a scalloped edge to the goods to prevent raveling of the edges. Pinking may also be done by hand pinking shears.

MACHINE TWIST. 1. A three-ply silk thread spun with left-hand twist. 2. Sewing thread for use in sewing machines; made from any of the major fibers.

MACHINE WOOL. Shoddy and mungo are sometimes known by this name.

MacINTOSH. An old-time, popular waterproof coating named for Charles MacIntosh, who in 1823 developed the method which still carries his name. He applied a mixture of crude rubber and coal-tar naphtha between two pieces of cloth and joined them by pressure. Warm weather causes this fabric to become soft, soggy, and sticky; cold weather makes the cloth hard and stiff.

MACKINAC OR MACKINAW CLOTH. An extra heavy cloth used in cold climates. Used as blankets, shirts, Mackinaws, reefer cloth, underwear, and lumberjackets. An ordinary grade of wool is used, and varying amounts of shoddy and wastes find their way to this cloth. Much of the cloth is in plaid design. The material is given a severe treatment in wet finishing and it is napped on both sides, the weave being covered up because of the rigid treatment. Cotton warp is often used. Filling is softly spun yarn so as to insure results wanted in finishing operations. The weight of the material ranges from 14 to 28 ounces or so per yard. Miners, lumbermen, hunters, fishermen, trappers and cowpunchers use much of the fabric. Named for Mackinac Island, Michigan. Sometimes called ski cloth, snow cloth, windbreaker fabric.

MacNAB HARRIS. A hand-loomed tweed made of mill-spun yarn which shows a uniformity of color not possible with homespun yarn.

MACO COTTON. This interesting Egyptian tree cotton has been a favorite staple since 1820. Around that time by hybridization, chiefly with American Sea Island cotton, Maco laid the foundation for the rise of brown and white Egyptian cottons, leaders in the cotton marts of the world even at the present time. For many years Brazil has been a great producer of this staple, and it is now a major cotton raised there. The tree will bear from about seven years up to fifteen or more years. The tree branches often bend low because of the weight of the bolls. Since the bolls ripen simultaneously the first picking is completed in July. New leaves and bolls will form readily if the ground has sufficient moisture, and a second crop is picked in late September or early October.

This long staple, smooth, strong, glossy cotton has a length of 1⅛ to 1¼ inches and sometimes a bit longer. The yarns counts obtainable may be as high as 120s. Much used in the manufacture of hosiery and underwear fabrics and in certain woven goods. Maco takes dyes easily and well. Maco, in a boiling solution of diluted nitric acid, is not affected; so-called Maco will change color. In some areas Maco has been known as Moco cotton. See BRAZILIAN COTTON, EGYPTIAN COTTON, JUMEL COTTON, MACO MF-1.

MACO-FOOT. Black wool hosiery with natural-color cotton foot made of Maco cotton.

MACO MF-1. Maco cotton, indigenous to the dry soil in northeast Brazil, is a tree cotton, a perennial which grows and produces from seven to eight up to fifteen to twenty years. It survives long periods without rainfall. Maco, of late, has been given much attention, and several new strains have been developed. Raised in the state of Rio Grande de Norte, one of the new strains is MF-1. This long staple, silky, strong, creamish-in-cast cotton compares favorably with the superior varieties now available in the world cotton market. Maco is also called Serido, and occasionally has been known as Moco cotton. See BRAZILIAN COTTON.

MACO PERCALE. A lightweight cambric very popular in the South American trade and made from Maco-Egyptian cotton. Yarns are about 64s and texture is about 120 square.

MACO YARN. A popular yarn made of natural-shade Egyptian cotton, usually ecru in cast.

MACRAME. Knotting, a treatment of the fringed ends of fabric, may be considered as a forerunner of bobbin lace, which is made, when constructed separately as a fringe, on a pillow by knotting and not by plaiting. Macramé is of Arabic origin and means a trimming or a fringe.

In the sixteenth century, Genoa became the center for this lace. Italy produces this material today and uses a very heavy cord which is shown chiefly in geometrical and symmetrical motifs. The lace is popular in white, ecru, and light tan shades and metallic yarn is sometimes used to enhance the appearance.

MADAPOLAM. A cotton cloth simulating nainsook in which the finishing must be carefully done to obtain softness. Made of 44s to 68s warp and filling; the textures range from 68 to 84 by 62 to 112.

MADDER. The plant, *Rubia tinctorium,* found in Asia; the plant root produces a rich, fast scarlet dyestuff. Madder, also known as alizarine, is used much in making artificial dyestuffs.

MADDER BLEACH. Denotes the most exhaustive method used to obtain a white background for calico printing. The operations through which the cotton goods may pass are singeing, shearing, washing, boiling in lime solution, acid treatment, lye boil and bleaching powder treatment, followed by thorough rinsing and drying.

MADDER STYLE PRINTING. Bleached fabric is printed with a mordant which is then fixed on the goods. The cloth is then piece-dyed with alizarine and the mordanted areas will show the colored effect. By the use of several mordants, various colors are obtainable from one dyeing. Alizarine, incidentally, is the successor to madder, but the old name still persists when this method is used.

MADEIRA EMBROIDERY. This fine white embroidery originated with the various orders of nuns on the island of this name. It is punctured with eyelets upon the solid foundation. The best of fine linen, cambric, or longcloth is used in the work.

MADRAPA. A coarse East Indian muslin.

MADRAS. Originated in Madras, India, and is one of the oldest staples in the cotton trade. The fabric is made on a plain background which may be colored or white, with stripes, cords or small checks to form the pattern. Made on a plain loom.

Plain dobby or a Jacquard loom is used to make some of the shirting, while madras curtain cloth is made on a leno loom from a gauze or doup weave. The large floral effects are formed by filling floats which are sheared in the finishing. Rayon and silk are used to make some madras cloth. When cotton is used it is usually Arizona or Egyptian, carded or combed, dependent on the quality fabric desired; 2/80s or 1/40s are popular counts of yarn used. Textures run from 68 to 76 in both directions.

MADRAS COTTON. A low-grade Indian cotton of about ⅞-inch staple. Spun to about 10s.

MADRAS GAUZE. Gauze-weave fabric in which the extra-filling yarn is used to give the effect. The floats in the design are clipped so that the spot-effects will result.

MADRAS GINGHAM. High-quality shirting, lighter in weight than the average madras; also lighter than zephyr gingham, which is allied with it.

MADRAS GOODS. Indian export cottons made of white warp and dark-colored filling yarn; the yarn counts are about 12s.

MADRAS HANDKERCHIEF. 1. The true fabric is hand woven in the Madras Presidency of India and used as an article of dress by native women. Dyed in various colors. Much of the cloth is now woven on power looms throughout the world. 2. Simulated English cloth characterized by gray filling in lieu of the white filling used in the genuine material.

MADRAS HEMP. Another name for Sunn hemp.

MADRAS LACE. A black and white silk, cotton, or nylon bobbin lace made in Maltese motifs.

MADRAS MUSLIN. Sheer cotton made of doup weave in which the extra filling, lower in count than the ground filling, is used to make the figures.

MADRAS SHEEP. A breed of sheep developed in India by crossing imported sheep with native stock. The breed is now peculiar to the Malay States.

MAGAZINE LOOM. There are two types:
1. BATTERY TYPE: This loom takes the empty bobbin from the shuttle and automatically places a new, full one into the same shuttle without stoppage of the loom. This type of magazine on the loom restricts the machine to one box on each end of the raceplate, one shuttle and one-color filling.
2. CROMPTON AND KNOWLES FOUR-CELL TYPE: This type of magazine admits the use of four colors in the filling. There are four boxes for the shuttle on one end of the raceplate. The cell is divided into four slots. Each slot will take care of a number of bobbins of filling yarn. In this type of loom, the empty bobbin is removed from the shuttle and a new, full one automatically replaces it.

There is another type of loom which automatically removes both shuttle and empty bobbin and replaces them with a new shuttle and a full bobbin of filling yarn. The loom does not stop to make the change.

All of these looms are made with the idea of increased production and a weaver should be able to take care of as many as twenty-four looms. Some expert weavers can handle as many as forty-eight looms that are fully automatic.

Whenever possible, simple and plain constructions are made on these looms, which are one of the wonders of this modern, scientific age. Much of the work formerly done on the so-called plain loom is now cared for by automatic looms.

MAGENTA. A purplish shade of red. Named for the Magenta River in Italy which, following one of the battles during the Napoleonic Era, was said by Napoleon "to run red with blood."

MAGNANERIE. A cocoonery, which is a room or building where silkworms are raised.

MAGNESIUM. An alkaline earth metal like calcium and barium; very similar to calcium in chemical reactions.

MAGRUDER COTTON. There are two types, Magruder Marvel and Magruder XL. Both types are early-maturing, have a staple of about 1⅛ inches with a lint yield of about 33 per cent.

MAGUEY. See CANTALA.

MAHLO TEXTOMETER. Controls automatically the moisture content of fabrics as they emerge from dryers through contact electrodes which transfer conductivity readings in moisture values, in turn, activating a speed-regulating pilot motor. Product of Cosa Corporation.

MAH, MAK. Egyptian term for flax or linen.

MAHOE, MAHAUT, MAHANT. A soft, white fiber from the hibiscus plant in Central America and the West Indies, it serves as a hemp substitute.

MAHOLTINE FIBER. A bast fiber obtained from a species of the abutilon plant in Central America, India, and Africa. Although the fiber is related to the cotton plant, the properties and characteristics are such that commercially it is classed as a jute and is used as a substitute for it.

MAHOT PINCET. A strong South

American bast fiber used for cordage.

MAHUVA COTTON. A good quality Indian cotton raised in the Bombay area—classed from good to fine.

MAIL. See JACQUARD HARNESS.

MAILBAG DUCK. Several numbers of duck are used for mailbags and other carriers; usually made with some sort of colored striping for identification purposes.

MAIL CLOTH. Rather heavy lustrous silk foundation material used in embroidery work.

MAILLE. Maillé is the French term for mesh in lace, veiling, knit goods, etc.

MAILLOT. From the French meaning tights; merely a plain, close-fitting, one-piece bathing suit.

MAIL NET. A leno weave is used to make this net fabric which has a sort of triangular mesh effect.

MAIMAL. High-quality Indian cotton muslin usually embroidered with metallic yarns. Also, the East African term for bleached cotton muslin.

MAINLINER. A rayon moss-crepe fabric with heavy handle and the appearance of wool.

MAINTENANCE OF MEMBERSHIP. The union status agreed to by a company in which, for the duration of the agreement, all existing and future union members are required to remain in good standing in the union, as a condition of continued employment, but no employee is required to join the union. The term also covers the maintenance of certain jobs as union jobs, or a fixed minimum number of percentage of union members.

MAISON DE COUTURE. French for a dressmaking establishment. See COUTURE.

MAIZE FLOUR. This sizing ingredient made from maize has to undergo considerable boiling to break up the granular formation. In its changed condition, as cornstarch, it is much used for sizing yarn prior to the weaving of the fabric.

MAJAGUA FIBER. A long, Central American bast fiber which does not deteriorate in water.

MAKAT. A French twilled woolen fabric, light in weight and in color, which is exported to the Levant.

MAK FLAX. Ancient Egyptian term for flax and linen.

MAKHTUL. Indian name for a coarse grade of reeled silk. Reeling is done by the natives.

MAKING THE LAY. Laying of paper patterns on cloth so that cutting may be done in the most advantageous way.

MAKING-UP. 1. The feeding of fiber stock into the back rollers of a preparing box or machine, and also the transferring of the prepared laps or slivers from one machine to another. 2. Finished cloth for market is "made-up" by measuring, rolling, ticketing, wrapping, and labeling.

MAKKO JUMEL. The first cotton to be cultivated in Egypt. Makko Bey, Egyptian ruler, raised the plants from East Indian seeds but did not believe the cotton was of value until his attention was directed to its possibilities by Jumel, the noted French cotton expert; he had been more interested in the raising of the flower on the plant than in the actual staple. Incidentally, the cotton is now extinct; Ashmouni cotton seems to have replaced Makko. See MACO COTTON; EGYPTIAN COTTON.

MALABAR. An East Indian handkerchief cloth, made in brilliant, contrasting colors. England and India make most of this vivid, cheap material which is used in the African trade. Malabar gave rise to the use of color in women's handkerchiefs in America.

MALABAR CARPET. Coarse Indian wool is used in this knotted wool carpeting featured by rather large, highly colored motifs of Hindu origin.

MALACHRA FIBER. A long, fine silken bast fiber raised in the West Indies, it resembles jute and is used for roping.

MALAPAO FIBER. A Philippine bast fiber used for rope.

MALASIAG FIBER. Bast fiber obtained from a species of the Ardista in the Philippines; used for ropes.

MALEECH KARAKUL. A sheep breed developed from native Russian Maleech sheep crossed with Karakul stock.

MALINES, MECHLIN LACE. Lace that originated in the city of Malines or Mechlin, Belgium. The product is a very fine net silk that is not very durable. The stiffness of the lace is caused by the sizing which is affected by moisture or dampness. Malines, whose origin goes back to the Middle Ages, is used for coverings, dresses, hats, scarfs, veilings.

Mechlin pillow lace shows a pattern outlined by a fine but distinct thread or cord. Genuine Mechlin usually has the ground pattern constructed in flower designs, birds, and novelty effects. Brussels lace does not have longer hexagonal meshes than Mechlin.

MALINO. Hawaiian aloe leaf fiber used for cordage.

MALMAL, MAMMAL. General term for fine cotton muslin embroidered with silk and metallic thread such as gold or silver; used in India and other Eastern and Far Eastern countries.

MALO. Netted cloth made from the olona fiber found in Hawaii. Used for apparel by the natives.

MALTESE. Coarse machine-made cotton lace which resembles torchon. It has no regular ground, and the patterns are usually connected with heavy stitchwork. Maltese crosses are a feature of the design.

MALTESE LACE. The feature of true Maltese lace is the wheat-grain ornament. In 1833 Lady Hamilton Chichester introduced lacemaking in Malta, and by adopting Genoese designs gave rise to what is known as Maltese lace by means of workers imported from Genoa.

Another type of lace known by this name, but in reality not true Maltese, is the heavy pillow guipure lace made with plaited Vandyke points and wheat-grain ornamentation. Much of this is produced in England, as well as in Italy.

MALTING. Implies desizing of textile materials by the use of various types of malts.

MALVA BLANCA. Cuban cadillo fiber.

MANAGEMENT PREROGATIVES. The rights of a company to take certain actions without prior consultations with a union. It claims these rights because of its plant ownership.

MANCHEGA. A Spanish breed of sheep producing a medium wool similar to that of Down sheep.

MANCHESTER VELVET. An English all-cotton velvet made with a plain-weave back; originated in Manchester, England.

MANDARIN COAT. A loose, full-length coat, originating in China and worn by mandarins or officials. It is richly embroidered silk coating with wide sleeves and small round stand-up collar. The style has been adopted by women for evening wraps. It is made of silk, rayon, and mixed fabric, and may or may not be trimmed with fur.

MANDEVILLE, MANDIVILLE. Originally a military coat, this jacket is on the order of the present day suit coating but made with a stand-up collar. Linked with the cassock, side seams or vents were noted on this jacket; it was buttoned for closure but the lowest button ended at the abdomen. It was put on the same way as a turtleneck sweater and like the Sad Sack dress of the mid-20th century, could be worn with the face at the back, and vice versa. Panels were made in either the same or different designs. Like the Sad Sack, it was considered to be a real, "dizzy" type of garb. See Cassock.

MANDREL. A bar of steel, centered at both ends, forced into a piece which is to be turned on centers. It is used to support work that may have a hole in it, that could not be supported in any other way. It is used on a printing machine to set the shaft in the copper print roller.

MANGLE. A machine for smoothing fabrics following washing, as household materials. It is also used in the mill, chiefly on cottons, for starching, back filling, etc. The machine comes in various makes, but the principle consists of rollers and a vat or kier to hold the solution.

MANIKIN, MANNEQUIN. A human model or dummy form used by garment manufacturers and dressmakers to fit and adjust garments. A young woman model.

MANILA HEMP. Hemp also called abaca, grown chiefly in the Philippine Islands. It belongs to the banana family, and grows to the size of a small tree. The fiber is obtained from the leaf stalks which form on the trunk of the tree. Compared with sisal, the fiber has greater diameter, is not as stiff, and is stronger. (Russian hemp is strongest of all; Italian is the finest in diameter.) See ABACA; HENEQUEN.

MANILA MAGUEY. See CANTALA.

MANILA ROPE. General term for rope made from abaca fiber.

MANIPLE. A band of silk, acetate, or rayon, the same color as the chasuble, worn over the left forearm of a priest. It is about two feet long and four inches wide and is symbolic of the fruit of good works.

The chasuble, dalmatic, maniple, and tunic are in the five liturgical colors to be worn according to the liturgy of the day or season as celebrated by some of the Christian churches.

MANIPULATED CLOTH. Manipulation of woolen and worsted cloths is not literally a hand process of preparing and combining, as the term "manipulated" implies; manipulated cloths are cloths in which the yarns are part wool and part cotton. The yarn is usually made from homogeneous combinations of fibers in the carding and spinning operations. Cloths that have a small percentage of cotton in them are often spoken of, in the trade, as "commercial all-wool fabrics."

MANMADE FIBER FORMS. These follow:

Monofilament: A single filament or strand of continuous length; may be a mile long. *Filament:* Two or more continuous monofilaments held together by twist of some other means; may be miles long. *Tow:* Large assemblages or bundles of continuous monofilaments devoid of any twist. *Staple:* Discontinuous lengths of fibers which have been broken or cut into desired lengths from the tow, composed of good sized bundles of tow.

Contemporary Adaptation of an Authentic West African Design

from *Creative West African Fashion*

MANMADE FIBER PRODUCERS IN THE UNITED STATES. Information on all manmade fiber producers, plant locations, fibers produced, fiber trademarks by generic names, and trademarks not classified as "fiber trademarks" will be found in the exceptionally important book - *The Manmade Fiber Fact Book,* published by the Man-Made Fiber Producers Association, Inc., 1150 Seventeenth Street Northwest, Washington, D.C. 20036.

MANMADE FIBERS, CHEMICAL CRIMPING OF. By spinning and hardening a cross-section and fiber size can be altered. Because the outer shell or surface hardens more quickly than the inner core, a thicker shell develops on one side, providing the possibility of crimping. Better loftiness in either bulky or open effects is obtained since the filaments are not suppressed or packed down during the treatment.

MANMADE FIBERS, CLASSIFICATION OF.
Cellulosic Fibers: Acetate, Rayon, and Triacetate.
Noncellulosic Fibers: Acrylic, Anidex, *Azlon, Glass, *Lastrile, Metallic, Modacrylic, Nylon, *Nytril, Olefin, Polyester, Rubber, Saran, Spandex, *Vinal, Vinyon. *These fibers are not made in United States at present time.

MANMADE FIBERS, DEBUT DATES OF. These follow:

1910 - *Rayon* by American Viscose Company, Inc., Marcus Hook, Pennsylvania. Now a Division of FMC Corporation.

1924 - *Acetate* by Celanese Corporation, Amcella-Cumberland, Maryland.

1930 - *Rubber* by UniRoyal, Inc., New York City, and Winnsboro, South Carolina.

1936 - *Glass Fiber* by Owens-Illinois Glass Company, Inc., Alton, Illinois, and Corning Glass Works, Corning, New York. Is now Owens-Corning-Fiberglas Corporation, New York City.

1939 - *Nylon* (polyamide fiber) by E. I. duPont de Nemours & Company, Inc., Wilmington, Delaware.

1939 - *Vinyon* by American Viscose Company, Inc., FMC Corporation.

1941 - *Saran* by Firestone Plastics Company, Inc., predecessor of Firestone Synthetic Fibers and Textiles Company, Inc. Produced at present by Enjay Fibers and Laminates Company, Division of Enjay Chemical Company, Inc., Odenton, Maryland.

1946 - *Metallic* by the Dobackmun Company, Inc., now a Division of Dow Badische Company, Inc., Williamsburg, Virginia.

1949 - *Modacrylic Dynel* by Union Carbide Corporation, New York City.

1949 - *Olefin Monofilaments* by Hercules, Inc., Wilmington, Delaware.

1950 - *Acrylic* ("Orlon") by E. I. duPont de Nemours & Co., Inc., Wilmington, Delaware.

1954 - *Triacetate* (Arnel) by Celanese Corporation, New York City.

1959 - *Spandex* by E. I. dePont de Nemours & Company, Inc., Wilmington, Delaware.

1961 - *Olefin Multifilament Propylene* by Hercules, Inc., Wilmington, Delaware.

NOTE: On October 29, 1969, The Federal Trade Commission decreed that Rule 7 of the *Textile Fiber Products Identification Act* (effective March 3, 1960) be amended and to add a new term, Anidex, which is a derivation or modified type of Modacrylic Fibers. See Anidex, Modacrylic.

NOTE: The following fibers which appear in the T.F.P.I. ACT are not at present made in the United States - *Azlon, Lastrille, Nytril,* and *Vinal.*
NOTE: Qiana, a modified type of Nylong was introduced to the textile industry on November 5th, 1969 at the American Association for Textile Technology, Inc., Hotel McAlpin, New York City.

MANMADE FIBERS, MODIFICATIONS USED ON. There are several ways to modify these fibers to provide a goodly number of fiber changes. These follow:
Dyeability: 1. Graft polymerization of other fiber types. 2. Use of chemical additives. *Filaments to Provide Spun-*

MANMADE FIBERS, DEFINITIONS AND TERMS USED IN MANUFACTURE OF. The rise of new textile fibers in this synthetic age has produced a new vocabulary of terms that are met with daily in the industry. These reference terms should be of value to the reader, since all, at some time or other, have played their part in the study and development of manmade fibers. It is realized that most of the terms are technical in nature; but they may be of some aid to the student of textiles, particularly to one having a textile or scientific background. The definitions follow:

Acrylic: Designating an acid-$C^3H^4O^2$-which has a sharp, acrid odor; prepared from acrolein or from certain derivatives of propionic acid. Used in organic synthesis in the manufacture of plastics. Also known as propenoic acid.

"Orlon" fiber, for example, is a true manmade filament or fiber made with an acrylic base and is polyacrylonitrile fiber. Acrilan and Dynel, as well as some of the newer fibers, are partly acrylic in composition.

Atom: The smallest part of an element that can enter into the composition of a molecule. It is not a particle of a chemical compound; a compound must have at least two atoms.

Catalyst: A substance which hastens a chemical change in other chemicals when mixed together with them. The catalyst itself undergoes no permanent change, and may be recovered when the action terminates. In the manufacture of plastics, for example, catalytic agents include acetone, alcohol, caustic soda, distilled water, and sulfuric acid.

Consensation: Water is separated from milk by the evaporation of one constituent from a mixture of materials—really the opposite of condensation. For example, water is evaporated from a wet towel, but water is condensed from hot air as moisture on a cold towel or cold wall. Many types of plastic are made by condensation. This action is not a separation as in taking water from milk, but is the actual splitting off of the hydrogen from one compound and the OH from another compound. The H and the OH unite to form water. Water does not become present until actual condensation takes place. After one chemical has lost its H, and the other its OH, the two molecules can then unite by combining their terminals that are now left "hungry" for a partner.

Dimensional Stability: The quality which enables a fabric or a garment to withstand any type of change in measurement through repeated launderings. The generally accepted standard is that the garment should not shrink out of fit (that is, shrinkage should be less than 3 per cent) or become distorted after five launderings by the appropriate methods. Note, however, that worsted trousers that shorten or lengthen with changes in relative humidity, or carpets that ripple or tear with changes in humidity, would have poor dimensional stability regardless of laundering.

Ethyl: The hypothetical radical of the carbon series (C^2H^5), the base for common alcohol, ether, acetic acid, and a rather large number of compounds—hydride, chloride, iodide, alcohol.

Ethylene: The diatomic hydrocarbon or olefin of the ethyl series, C^2H^4.

Formaldehyde: A colorless gas obtained from wood alcohol (methanol). Finds much use as a preservative and disinfectant. This formic aldehyde is an important reagent in some phases of textile chemistry.

Furfural: Obtained from cottonseed hulls, it is used with phenol to form thermosetting plastics comparable with the phenol formaldehyde group of plastics.

Hydrocarbon: One of a large group of compounds that contain hydrogen and carbon only. There are several classes and types, including the aliphatic, aromatic, saturated, and unsaturated.

Inhibitor: An agent which slows down, checks, diminishes, or prevents a physical or chemical change.

Inorganic: Not having in its structure the carbon element as found in animal and vegetable matter. It should be observed, however, that carbolic acid, ether, and nylon, for example, are not exactly animal or vegetable matter, nor are they inorganic or formed from living organisms or substances.

Inorganic Solvent: A solvent which lacks the carbon element: for example, water, or a water-miscible noncompound which possesses solvent properties; other examples include dilute hydrochloric acid used on rust stains, and hypo used on iodine stains.

Ketone: From the German, a modification of acetone: the name given to a class of chemical compounds formed by the oxidation of the secondary alcohols or carbinols, to which they stand in some respects in the same relation as aldehydes. The lowest of the series, dimethyl-ketone, is common acetone.

Molecules: The smallest unit of an element or a compound that retains chemical identity with the same element or compound in the mass. In modern chemistry, the mole-

Life Aesthetics: Done by physical modifications or treatments. *Flame Retardancy:* Use of chemical modifications and/or by additives. *Fiber Loftiness to Provide Crimp-Like Effect:* 1. Use of bi-component fibers. 2. Blending of fibers. 3. Chemical treatments or additives. 4. Use of mixed-polymer fibers. 5. Physical treatments to achieve desired effects. *Luster or Sheen Improvement:* 1. Modifying cross-section of fibers. 2. "Roughing" of fibers; done by moire treatment, cire finish (to bring out luster or sheen) and by calendering with one roller going at slightly higher speed than the other calender roller. *Moldable Fibers to Lower Garment's Manufacturing Costs:* Chemical modifications are used. *Pilling Elimination:* Chemical or physical treatments are used. *Static Electricity Build-Up and Moisture Absorbency:* 1. Done by use of graft polymerization of other fibers as to type. 2. Use of chemical treatments or additives. *Sense of Touch and Scroop:* 1. Bulking or permanently crimping fibers. 2. Changing fiber surfaces chemically or physically. 3. Modifying fiber cross-section. 4. Roughening or altering fiber surface. *Temperature Control by Way of Conductive Polymers:* Use of additives, chemical modifications or by treatments. *Fiber Fullness or Bulkiness for Eye and Touch Appeal:* Done by chemical or physical modifications or treatments. *Washing and Cleaning Performance:* Chemical modifications such as those used for crease retention or crease resistance. *Whiteness Retention:* Use of chemical treatments or additives.

MAN-MADE FIBERS AND FILAMENTS. These fibers were first recognized in 1925, when the Federal Trade Commission permitted the use of the name rayon for man-made yarns obtained from cellulose or its derivative. As there were several ways to make these yarns and materials, and as the production and types of rayon increased and had been given various trade names, the Commission ruled again in 1937 that any fiber or yarn produced chemically from cellulose must be designated as rayon. This, at the time, applied to both rayon and acetate fibers. In 1952, the Commission divorced acetate from rayon, that is, acetate was no longer referred to as acetate rayon; it is actually a cellulose derivative and not a regenerated type of textile fiber.

Since 1939, when nylon made its debut, there has been a host of new fibers developed which are not made from cellulose base. During this span of time to the present various names

cules of each element or compound are assumed to be of uniform size and mass, representing the smallest portion into which the substance can be divided without losing its chemical identity.

Natural Resin: A family of solid or semi-solid organic substances of vegetable origin. Found, for example, in resin; and used in soaps, varnishes, and drying agents. Another example, lac, is obtained from the lac bug of India, and is much used in the manufacture of shellac and similar products. The resins, which are brittle and have a waxlike luster, are insoluble in water.

Olefin: The name for a series of hydrocarbons homologous with olefiant gas or ethylene; general formula is C H

Organic: A broad term, applied to substances obtained from living organisms, or any substances which consist largely of hydrogen, oxygen, and carbon. The other general class of substances is the inorganic or mineral group.

Organic Acid: One which contains carbon, such as acetic, formic, oxalic acids. All organic acids contain carbon; all inorganic acids are devoid of carbon.

Organic Solvent: Contains the element carbon, the only known chemical element for which there is no known solvent. The symbol for carbon, C, will appear in the formula. This type of solvent is used in the removal of stains greasy in nature. Since the vapors are injurious when inhaled in large quantities, all organic solvents should be used in well-ventilated quarters. Some organic solvents are wood alcohol, ether, benzene, gasoline, carbon tetrachloride, benzol, acetic acid, chloroform.

pH: A term used to express acidity or alkalinity of solutions. For solutions which are on the acid side, the pH is less than 7; on the alkaline side, it is more than 7.

Plasticizer: A chemical added to plastics to soften, increase malleability, or to make more readily deformable. There are several plasticizers on the market, and they are ideal when used with thermoplastic plastics such as camphor, high-boiling esters, and polynaphthalenes.

Polymer: A comparatively large molecule produced by linking together many molecules of a nomomeric substance. Such a reaction is known as polymerization. If two or more different monomeric substances are mixed prior to polymerization, the product of the reaction is known as a copolymer. Nylon is an example of a copolymer.

Radical: Taken from the Latin, and means "root." It is an element or an atom, or a group of these, forming the base of a compound, and remaining unaltered during the ordinary chemical reactions to which it is subject.

Resin: An amorphous organic substance exuded by plants, and soluble in alcohol and ether. Any of various substances which have properties similar to true resin and which are made by chemical synthesis—especially those substances used in the manufacture of plastics.

Resinoid: Implies that the product is a synthetic resin.

Solvent: A liquid in which substances will easily dissolve. Water is often referred to as the universal solvent, since it will dissolve almost anything to some degree. The textile industry uses a very large range of solvents depending upon the specific operation involved.

Staple Fiber: Filaments which have been cut to a predetermined length. This stock may be spun on the cotton, woolen, worsted, flax, or spun-silk systems, and finds much use in dressgoods and suiting fabrics.

Staple fiber is often mixed with other major textile fibers in varying amounts to bring about a new yarn and a new fabric effect. Practically all the manmade filaments are cut into staple length for use alone or for mixing with other fibers.

Tar: It is found in cigarettes, oil, wood, cotton, bituminous coal, etc. The distillation of bituminous coal produces a dark-brown liquid of very heavy viscosity; it is used to make coal tar used in certain plastics, dyes, and explosive materials.

Thermoplastic Plastic: One that will soften when exposed to heat and will harden again when the source of heat is removed. Plastic material which is permanently fusible is known as thermoplastic.

Thermoset Plastic: Plastic set permanently into shape or form by the use of heat; heat applied later may produce a charred formation without causing the plastic to melt or lose shape.

Tow: A large group of continuous filaments, such as acetate or rayon, Kodel, nylon, etc., without any definite twist. The tow stock is cut into definite set lengths and is known as staple fiber. It is used to make blended or mixture-type yarns in which two or more different fibers (natural and/or manmade) are used. Staple fiber also may be used alone in making a spun yarn such as spun acetate, spun rayon, or spun nylon.

Vinyl: The compound univalent radical, CH^2CH, isomeric with many derivatives of ethylene—the hydride of vinyl.

were applied as to the types of fibers they represented. Names given to these fibers included Synthetic Fibers, Specially Man-made Fibers, Test Tube Fibers, Chemical Fibers, etc. Today all these fibers are placed in specific categories as per The Textile Fiber Products Identification Act, effective on March 3, 1960. See FIBER KINGDOMS, TEXTILE; ACETATE; RAYON; THE TEXTILE FIBER PRODUCTS IDENTIFICATION ACT; Illustrated Section.

MANMADE FIBERS FEDERATION, THE BRITISH. One of the truly great Textile Fiber Associations at the present time, this association is comprised of the following groups:

British Spinners' and Doublers' Association.

Manmade Fibres Producers' Committee.

National Hosiery Manufacturers' Federation.

Silk and Manmade Fibre Users' Association.

Textile Converters Association.

Textile Finishing Traded Association.

United Kingdom Textile Manufacturers' Association.

Major Manmade Fibre Producers in Great Britain include:

British Celanese, Ltd., 22 Hanover Square, London, W.I.

British Enkalon, Ltd., Enkalon House, Regent Road, Leicester.

Courtaulds, Ltd., 22 Hanover Square, London, W.I.

ICI Fibres, Ltd., Hookstone Road, Harrogate.

Lansil, Ltd., Lancaster.

Monsanto Textiles, Ltd., 10-18 Victoria Street, London, S.W.I.

MANMADE FIBER SPINNING METHODS. These follow:

Wet Spinning: Used in manufacture of rayon, and these three acrylic fibers - Acrilan of Monsanto, Creslan of American Cyanamid Company, and Zefran of Dow Badische Company. This method was the first one used in the manufacture of manmade fibers and is the most complex of the three methods in use at present. The fibers are hardened by extruding the filaments with chemical baths which convert or regenerate the soluble compound into an insoluble one. Washing, bleaching, and comparable treatments are necessary prior to further manipulation.

1. Raw material is dissolved by chemicals. (solid)

2. The fiber is created in an acidic bath. (liquid)

3. The fiber solidifies when coagulated by acid treatment. (solid)

Dry or Solvent Spinning: Used in manufacture of acetate, modacrylics, "Orlon" Acrylic, and Vinyon. Known as the direct method, this process requires a solvent which evaporates, thereby permitting the filament to be recovered later on in manipulation. Washing and comparable treatments are not necessary.

1. Resin solids are dissolved by use of solvent.
2. Fiber is created in warm atmospheric condition.
3. Solidifying is done by evaporation of the solvent which is recovered.

Melt Spinning: Used in manufacture of nylon, olefins, polyester, and Saran. This plan, the least expensive of the three processes, is a direct spinning process with very high spinning speeds. Use of solvents is not necessary, nor is washing and comparable treatments. The fibers take on the shape of the orifices in the spinneret used in the fiber manufacture.

1. Resin solids are melted in an autoclave, an apparatus, machine, or device which uses steam under pressure.
2. The fiber is spun in room temperature conditions.
3. Solidification of the fiber is brought about by cooling.

MAN-MADE TEXTILE FIBERS AND THE TEXTILE FIBER PRODUCTS IDENTIFICATION ACT OF JUNE 3, 1959. Formerly, the Manmade Fibers were more or less divided into two categories. The term, Manmade Fibers, was used to indicate the cellulosic fibers, Acetate and Rayon (Viscose and Cuprammonium/Bemberg). The Non-Cellulosic Fibers have been known by various names since their inception, such as Synthetic, New Synthetic, Miracle, Test Tube, Chemical, Specially Man-made, etc. With the advent of The Textile Fiber Products Identification Act, both the cellulosic and the non-cellulosic fibers are now under the one caption, THE MAN-MADE FIBERS. The Federal Trade Commission, Washington, District of Columbia, has established a set of categories and terms which take care of all the fibers, cellulosic or non-cellulosic, in the man-made group of textile fibers.

Under this Act, there is now a clear cut line of demarcation with regard to all these fibers. The Act was decreed by the Commission on June 3, 1959, approved by Congress on September 2, 1959, and became effective on March 3, 1960.

Incidentally, in this maze of fibers, there are about 125 brand names and

Contemporary designer's interpretation of the "Agbada", a Nigerian costume.

From *Creative West African Fashion.*

trade names alone for acetate and rayon in the United States. There are about 575 for the rest of the fibers classed as Man-Made Fibers, a total of 700. There are about 350 brand names and trade names for acetate and rayon throughout the rest of the world, and about 650 for the rest of the fibers, a total of about 1,700 names. Thus, The Textile Fiber Products Identification Act is timely and will standardize all these fibers into proper categories. These non-cellulosic fibers include polyamide, polyvinyl, polyacrylic, styrol, propolyene, butadiene, special cellulosics, protein, glass, etc.

Generic Names and Definitions of Manufactured Fibers Under Rule 7 of the Rules and Regulations under The Textile Fiber Products Identification Act lists the generic names and definitions as set forth by the decrees of the Federal Trade Commission.

The purpose of the Act is "to protect producers and consumers against misbranding and false advertising of the fiber content of textile fiber products, and other purposes." In addition to the definitions herewith listed, some representative trade names have been added in the respective categories, eighteen altogether. Under the Rules the generic term is required to be used in conjunction with the fiber name in labeling and advertising textile products.

The following is the listing of the new captions along with characteristic examples for each category.

1. *Rayon:* A manufactured fiber composed of regenerated cellulose, as well as manufactured fibers composed of regenerated cellulose in which substituents have replaced not more than 15 per cent of the hydrogene of the hydroxyl groups. Thus, rayon is a man-made cellulosic fiber, a regenerated type of fiber-solid to liquid and back to solid in forms.

Examples include:

   Avicolor, Avril, Avisco, Purilon, Rayflex — Avisco, FMC.

   Bemberg, Bembella, Cupioni, Cupracolor, Cuprel, Cuprassah, Dream Slub, Flaikona, Multi-Cupioni, Nublite, Parfe, Strata, Stratella, Tusson — Bemberg Industries, Inc. (Bemberg Industries is sole manufacturer of Bemberg or Cuprammonium Rayon in the United States.)

   Coloray, Fibro, Lirelle — Courtaulds North America.

   Jetspun, Kolorbon, Skybloom, Skyloft, Zantrel 700 — American Enka..

   Narcon, Ni-Narco, Super Narco; Ondelette Viscose Rayon (All registered

trademarks) — Beaunit Corporation. Strawn, Tyron, Tyweld, Villwyte — IRC Fibers; American Cyanamid Co. (Ceased production of filament rayon, December, 1972).

2. *Acetate and Triacetate:* A manufactured fiber in which the fiber-forming substance is cellulose acetate. Where not less than 92 per cent of the hydroxyl groups are acetylated, the term, Triacetate, may be used as a generic description of the fiber. A man-made cellulosic fiber, a cellulose derivative fiber, and not of the regenerated type as viscose rayon and cuprammonium rayon.

Examples include:

   Acele - Du Pont. Avicolor - Avisco, FMC. Celacrimp, Celaloft, Celanese, Celara (all acetate); Arnel (triacetate) - Celanese Corporation. Chromspun, Estron, Loftura - Tennessee Eastman.

3. *Acrylic:* A manufactured fiber in which the fiber-forming substance is any long chain synthetic polymer composed of at least 85 percent by weight of acrylonitrile units.

$$(CH^2-CH-)$$
$$|$$
$$CN$$

Examples include:

   Acrilan - copolymer of acrylonitrile with vinyl derivatives; A-Acrilan to include Types B-98, 16, 57, 71, etc. — Monsanto Textiles, Inc.

   Creslan, true acrylic because 85% or more is acrylonitrile — American Cyanamid Company.

   "Orlon," based on a polymer of acrylonitrile — Du Pont de Nemours & Co., Inc.

   Zefran Acrylic-Dow Badische, Co., Inc.

4. *Modacrylic:* A modified fiber in which the fiber-forming substance is any long chain synthetic polymer composed of less than 85 per cent but at least 35 per cent by weight of acrylonitrile units $(-CH^2-CH-)$. The term is a combina-

$$|$$
$$CN$$

tion of the words, modified and acrylonitrile.

This definition of *Modacrylic* was adopted on June 3, 1959, and became effective with the promulgation of the T.F. P.I. Act which actually became law on March 3, 1960. On October 31, 1969, the eighteenth term and category of man-made fibers became effective. The term is *Anidex.* Examples include:

   Dynel, copolymer of acrylonitrile and vinyl chloride (Vinyon N) Textile Fibers Division, Union Carbide Chemicals Company, Division of

Union Carbide Corporation. Verel, modified acrylic fiber - Tennessee Eastman Company, a Unit of Eastman Chemical Products, Inc.

5. *Anidex:* A manufactured fiber in which the fiber-forming substance is any long chain synthetic polymer composed of at least 50% by weight of one or more esters of monohydric alcohol and acrylic acid. *Modacrylic* is redefined as formerly, with the added provision that it does not include those fibers which qualify under the Anidex category. Product is known as Anim/8™.

6. *Nylon:* A manufactured fiber in which the fiber-forming substance is any long chain synthetic polyamide having recurring amide groups, $(-C-NH-)$, as

$$|$$
$$O$$

an integral part of the polymer chain.

Examples include:

   Caprolan, Golden Caprolan — Allied Chemical Corporation.

   Antron, Cantrece, Cordura, Nomex, Nylon Elastic, Qiana — DuPont.

   Blue "C," Cadon, C-Chemstrand Nylon, Cumuloft, Speckelon — Monsanto Textiles, Inc.; Known as Perlon L, in Germany — Bayer Farbenfabriken, AK., Leverkusen. The fiber base is a polyamide polymer of caprolactam.

   Celanese Nylon — Celanese and Fiber Industries.

   Courtaulds Nylon — Courtaulds North America.

   Enka Nylon, Enkaloft, Enkalure, Spectrodye — American Enka.

   Nyloft Nylon — IRC Fibers, Division of American Cyanamid Co., Inc.

   Phillips 66 Nylon — Phillips Fibers Corporation.

   Qulon — Beaunit Fibers.

   Zefran Nylon - Dow Badische Co., Inc.

7. *Nytril:* A manufactured fiber containing at least 85 per cent of a long chain polymer of vinylidene dinitrile $(-CH^2-C(CN)^2-)$, where the vinylidene dinitrile content is not less than every other unit in the polymer chain. There is not any nitrile fiber made in the United States at present.

8. *Olefin:* A manufactured fiber in which the fiber-forming substance is any long chain synthetic polymer composed of at least 85 per cent by weight of ethylene, propylene, or other olefin units.

Examples include:

   Dural -- Celanese.

   Cournova — Courtaulds.

   Velon LP, Velon NF, Velon PS — Firestone.

Herculon — Hercules.
Marvess — Phillips Fibers.
DLP Group, Tufton — Thiokol.
Polycrest, Royalene — UniRoyal.
Vogt, Voples — Vogt Mfg. Co., Inc.

9. *Polyester:* A manufactured fiber in which the fiber-forming substance is any long chain polymer composed of at least 85 per cent by weight of an ester of di-hydric alcohol and terephthalic acid (p—HOOC—C⁶H⁴—COOH—).

Examples include:

Source — Allied Chemical.
Enka, Encron — American Enka.
Puff Stuff, Super Stuff, Tough Stuff, Vycron — Beaunit.
Fortrel, Fortrel 7 — Celanese and Fiber Industries, Inc.
Lirelle — Courtaulds.
"Dacron," Mylar — Du Pont.
Kodel — Eastman.
Goodyear Polyester — Goodyear.
Trevira, Trevira Star — Hoechst.
Polyester — IRC of American Cyanamid.
Blue "C" — Monsanto.
Quintess — Phillips Fibers.
Wellene, Wellman — Wellman.

10. *Rubber:* A manufactured fiber in which the fiber-forming substance is either natural or synthetic rubber.

Examples include:

Buthane, Hi-Flex - B.F. Goodrich Co., Inc. Contro or Rolled Latex - Firestone Tire & Rubber Co., Inc. Darleen, cut rubber yarn - Darlington Fabrics Corporation. Lactron, extruded rubber thread; Lastex, elastic yarn; Laton, elastic yarn; Revere, a cut-rubber thread, and a rubber tension tape; Filatex, elastic yarn whose core is round; of estruded latex - Uni-Royal Fibers and Textile Division, UniRoyal Inc.

11. *Saran:* A manufactured fiber in which the fiber-forming substance is any long chain synthetic polymer composed of at least 80 per cent by weight of vinylidene chloride units (—CH²—CCl²—).

Examples include:

Saran Monofilament — Amtech, Inc.
Saran Monofilament — S.E. Polymers, Inc.

12. *Spandex:* A manufactured fiber in which the fiber-forming substance is composed of a long chain polymer of at least 85 percent of a segmented polyurethane.

Examples include:

Clearspan, Glospan — Globe.
Lycra — DuPont.
Unel — Union Carbide Corporation.

13. *Vinal:* A manufactured fiber in which the fiber-forming substance is any long chain synthetic polymer composed of at least 50 per cent of the weight of the vinyl alcohol units and any one or more of the various acetal units is at least 85 per cent by weight of the fiber. At present, Vinal is made in Japan, but none is produced in the United States.

14. *Vinyon:* A manufactured fiber in which the fiber-forming substance is any long chain synthetic polymer composed of at least 85 per cent by weight of vinyl chloride units (—CH²—CHOH—).

Example:

Avisco Vinyon (Vinyon HH) acetone-soluble copolymer of vinyl chloride and vinyl acetate, American Viscose Corporation.

15. *Azlon:* A manufactured fiber in which the fiber-forming substance is composed of any regenerated naturally occuring proteins. Not manufactured in the United States at present. Formerly known as "semi-synthetic" fiber.

Examples:

Alginate, from seaweed, England. Casein fiber, from casein, Belgium. Enkasa, from casein, Holland. Lanital, from casein, Belgium. Merinova, from skim milk, Italy.

16. *Glass:* A product in which the fiber-forming substance is glass. Examples include:

Aercor, Fiberglas - Ownes-Corning Fiberglas Corporation. Garan, Vitron, LOF - Johns Manville Fiber Glass, Inc. Modiglass - Modiglass Fibers, Inc. PPG - PPG Industries, Inc. Unifab, Uniformat, Unirove - Ferro Corporation. Uniglass - United Merchants Industrial Fabrics, Inc.

NOTE: In this Glass Fiber Group, specially prepared glass marbles are melted in an electric furnace. Melted glass is then extruded through orifices to form continuous filaments and drawn to the desired size.

17. *Metallic:* A manufactured fiber composed of metal, plastic-coated metal, metal-coated plastic, or a core completely covered by metal.

Examples include:

Alistran, Bu-Tex, Dura-Stran - Multi-Tex Products, Inc. *Chromeflex - Types MF, MM, NL - Metal Film Co., Inc. Diamond, *Metlon Types F, LMP, Mark II Staple, Ultrathin - Metlon Corporation. *Fairfax Types 260, 150F, 150F-CR, 50V, 100V, 150V 50 V-NL - Fairtex Sales, Riegel Paper Corporation. Lame, **Lame with Mylar in three types; foil type, metallized, and non-laminated - Standard Yarn Mills, Inc. *Lurex Metallic yarn; *Lurex MF; *Lurex MM; *Lurex C-50;

*Lurex D - Dow BadischeCo., Inc.
*Malora, **Malora with Mylar, Malora with Mylar - M.L. Metallic Cellophane - Malina Corporation.
*Registered in United States Patent Office.
**DuPont registered trade mark for its polyester film.

NOTE: Metallic yarns are now made with Mylar ("Dacron") film as well as with acetate film. Mylar metallic yarns withstand higher temperatures and more rugged finishing and laundering than the acetate-type yarns.

18. *Lastrile:* A manufactured fiber in which the fiber-forming substance is (1.) a hydrocarbon, such as natural rubber, polyisoprene, polybutadiene, copolymers of dienes and hydrocarbons of amorphous (crystalline) polyolefins; (2) a copolymer of acrylonitrile and a diene (such as butadiene) composed of not more than 50 per cent but at least 10 per cent by weight of acrylonitrile units; (3) a polychloroprene or a copolymer of chloroprene in which 35 per cent by weight of fiber-forming substances are composed of chloroprene units. The term "Lastrile" is the seventeenth generic term decreed by the Federal Trade Commission, Washington, D.C., March, 1966. Lastrile falls into category (2), above. The first sixteen generic terms for Manufactured Fibers became effective March 3, 1960.

NOTE: The following fibers are not listed in any of the foregoing categories:

Algil: A polyacrylonitrile-Styrene of Polymers, Inc.

Avceram: A ceramic-rayon of FMC Corporation, American Viscose.

Basic: A carbon fiber of Basic-Carbon Corporation.

Bristrand: A polyvinyl Chloride-Acetate fiber of Polymers, Inc.

Fiberfrax: An alumina-Silica Ceramic of The Carborundum Company, Inc.

National: A carbon fiber of Union Carbide Corporation.

Orofil: An acrylic-Content Elastomer of Rohm and Haas.

Polyfiber: A polystyrene fiber of Dow Chemical Co., Inc.

Shalon: A polystyrene fiber of Polymers, Inc.

Teflon: A polytetrafluroethylene product of DuPont.

Thornel: A graphite fiber of Union Carbide Corporation.

Tipersul: A fibrous Potassium Titanite of DuPont.

MANMADE YARNS, COMPARISON OF FILAMENT AND SPUN YARNS IN. These follow:

Filament Yarns:

1. Fiber strength fully used
2. Long, continuous length; may be miles in length and rather closely set
3. Lustrous and smooth with no fuzziness
4. Devoid of lint
5. Does not pill easily
6. Rather devoid of soil, stains
7. Cool to touch
8. Provides little bulk or loft to materials

9. Fiber content determines absorbency; variable, ideal for skin contact from cloths.

Spun Yarns:

Fiber strength not used in totality
Made of short fibers that are well twisted and may have fuzzy or protruding strands
Usually dull or semi-dull with a fuzzy surface
Shows some lint surface
May have tendency to pill or bunch
Soils rather handily
Warm in touch or hand
Bulkiness and loftiness easily achieved and usually dependent on yarn itself, count of yarn and turns of twist per inch.
Varying degrees in absorbency dependent on local conditions. Acetate, rayon and silk absorbent; thermoplastic yarns low in absorbency.

MANNEQUIN. See MANIKIN.

MANTA. A type of multi-colored blanket, about a square yard in size, tied around the shoulders and neck, and worn by women in South America. This useful article is used for carrying purposes, and its constant use gives the peasantry their typically stooped appearance.

MANTEAU. A cloak or mantle; usually a woman's outer garment, chiefly one that is open in front and displays the skirt.

MANTELLETTA. A short robe of silk or wool, without sleeves. Worn by clergy of the Roman Catholic Church.

MANTILLA. The well-known head covering worn by women in Latin countries. It is made of heavy black, white, or colored lace, arranged over the comb, worn off the face or as a veil. The term also refers to a lightweight cape or cloak.

MANTLE. A sleeveless cloak which may be worn over other garments; made of wool, worsted, or silk, it is intended to be folded about the person.

MANTLE CLOTHS. British term which includes every description of material suitable for making mantles, capes, cloaks, etc., for both men and women.

MANUFACTURER'S TWIST. Implies a very few turns of twist in a fiber, filament, yarn, or cord set in during the manufacturing process. Usually runs from two, four, or five turns of twist per inch; often used to hold fibers or filaments together in a rather loose but cohesive form.

MANX TWEED. Made on the Isle of Man, the fabric ranges between fifteen and sixteen ounces per yard. The warp is dove-gray in color while the

filling is one pick of solid brown and one of brown and bright green twisted together. Popular in men's wear coating and suiting.

MARABOUT, MARABOU. 1. A single-warp, five- or eight-shaft satin-weave, silk satin fabric used in the millinery trade. 2. A white silk thread used in crepe weaving. It is made of three strands which are given high twist and dyed in the gum condition. 3. A light silk dress goods or ribbon made of marabout yarn in plain-weave construction. 4. A thrown or twisted raw-silk thread. 5. Soft feather edging (from marabou or adjutant bird).

MARANA. A fine wool dress crepe with outstanding draping qualities.

MARBLE SILK. Silk fabric which has a mottled appearance caused by the use of multi-colored filling yarn or by warp printing prior to cloth weaving. A lightweight fabric, it has occasional popularity.

MARCASITE. Highly polished steel or some other metal ornament that is cut very fine for the motif effect. Popular in jewelry decoration.

MARCELINE. 1. A thin, light, closely woven, diaphanous silk fabric made in plain weave. Named for Marcelin, France. 2. A plain-woven, luster-silk fabric made of two-ply warp and single-filling yarns. 3. A plain silk cloth made of single warp and with one, two, or three picks placed in the same shed of the loom to produce a ribbed or corded effect in the horizontal direction. 4. A thin lining material made of rayon or silk, or of silk and rayon combined.

MARCELLA. A cotton or linen fabric made on a small twill repeat; used for waistcoating and vesting.

MARCO POLO SHEEP. Wild sheep, *Ovis poli.* Comes from the Pamir Pla-

teau and other Central Asia sheep-raising areas. The animal is large in stature and has considerable horn spread.

MARDUFF. East African term for dress goods made of twill weave in a rather heavy cotton cloth. Heavier grades find use for sailcloth, tentcloth, covering, etc.

MARGHERITA. An Italian machine-made net. See NET, NETTING.

MARIAGES. Raw silk imperfection, in that double threads run together on the winding reel as the filaments from the cocoon are unwound; separation of the mariages is done by the throwster.

MARINE STRIPES. Plain-weave, British cottons identified by stripes of equal width in blue and white, off-white, or ecru. Textured around 64-square, 64 x 60, etc. Counts of yarn as about 28s to 32s.

MARK-DOWN. To lower the price of an item.

MARKER. One who can outline the various garment parts on the top layer of the multiple set-up of material in layer form. The cloth will be used by the machine cutter as a top lay and guide to cutting.

MARKET BLEACH. The particular bleach desired for a specific fabric use in the trade.

MARKETING. The manufacture of an article suitable for sale either by demand or by creation of a commercial outlet. In textiles, the steps that must be followed from raw stock to consumer goods are: raw material, carding and spinning into yarn, weaving or knitting (of the gray or loom goods), converting and finishing.

The following points are also of importance in the marketing of textiles and garments into merchantable goods: men, material, machinery, money, factory management and engineering, methods, job specialization and assembly line, mass production, and uniform sizes for proper merchandising to cope with supply and demand.

MARKETING QUOTAS. Related to Acreage Allotments, it means that only that portion of a farmer's output that is under acreage allotments may be marketed. If, perchance, he does sell over his quota, he loses price supports.

MARKETING UNITS. The following show the units that may be employed in presenting textiles to the public: the broker, commission merchant, converter, department store, jobber, mill selling force for direct selling from producer to the consumer, resident buyer who may take care of group buying, retail salesman, wholesaler, selling agent, traveling salesman.

MARKING. 1. The stenciling, labeling, or marking of wool bales which are to be sold at auction sales in the wool-buying centers. The bales thus marked show the name of the grower, the station from whence came the wool, weights, etc. 2. In the mill, it is the actual marking of cloth with the lot number and other essential data so that the material may be traced at any time. Marking is usually done by use of a stamp pad and indelible ink. 3. The arrangement of the pattern pieces on paper or material. It is sometimes called a layout. All marking is done as economically as possible so as to save yardage in cloth.

MARKING GRAPHITE. A flat piece of graphite or chalk used to mark on either cloth or paper.

MARKING-OFF. The staining of white areas of a material by surrounding color motifs, usually caused by the fugitivity of one or more colors.

MARKS. 1. Letters and numbers on the tare or label of a cotton bale to enable one lot of cotton to be distinguished from another. 2. Raised dots on either side of a seam in full-fashioned hosiery.

MARK-UP. To increase the price of an item. Also the term for a legitimate profit.

MARLI, MARLY. Named for a French village not far from Paris, it was originally a light hexagonal mesh net into which small figures such as rosettes were manipulated. After the Napoleonic Era it passed into oblivion, but it was the article that gave rise to present-day tulle used for dresses, trimmings, and costumes in the performing arts.

MARLING. Small tarred rope used to tie ropes and cables.

MARL YARN. The mottling of two contrasting colors which are run through the roving frame and then spun in the usual manner.

MARMOT. A medium-long, straight-haired fur, ranging from bluish-gray to yellow, but usually dyed to look like mink. Wearing qualities, fair. Judged by silkiness and heaviness of fur. Found in Mongolia, Manchuria, and parts of Russia. There are also European and American species. For general and dress wear.

MAR-MOUCHA. Moroccan sheep which yields a coarse, straight fleece that weighs only three or four pounds. The fiber is very long and straggly and may even reach to the ground. Staple length is at least 10 inches. The two types of this sheep are called Northern and Southern.

MAROCAIN. A crepe fabric featured by a ribbed effect. It is made of wool, rayon, or silk, or of a combination of these fibers. A heavy, exaggerated Canton crepe in texture. Used in suits of the dressmaker type.

MAROON. A color, yellowish-red in hue, of medium saturation and low brilliance. By extension, any color of low brilliance, a hue which varies from reddish-blue to reddish-yellow, and of low or medium saturation.

MARQUISE. A Jacquard fabric made of organzine or schappe silk warp and cotton filling. Used in the upholstery trade.

MARQUISETTE. Fine mesh-construction fabric. See Illustrated Section (Fabrics 59). Generally speaking it is not necessarily made of a specific type of weave. Usually made full leno, with two ends working in leno motions. Marquisette may be made on a one-, two-, or three-pick construction; it is classed as a full leno or doup construction because both ends work in leno heddles.

This lightweight material comes in white, in solid colors, and in novelty effects. Made with cotton, rayon, or silk, it gives good service and launders very well. The better grades of cotton are used to make the cloth when cotton is the fiber used. Uses include window curtains and dresswear. Incidentally, the term gauze is often confused with marquisette. A French term, gauze (see GAUZE) is sometimes made with a leno weave; it can be made plain, as in the case of cheesecloth. Gauze bandages, for example, are not made with leno weaves.

MARSEILLES. A cotton double-cloth made of two plain-woven fabrics; one warp is used for the stitching arrangement and one filling is loosely spun so that the effect may be obtained. The figures are embossed, and they are formed by the interweaving of all threads with each other according to the plan of the designer. The two fabrics are united in the ground areas of the goods. Used chiefly for bedspreads, counterpanes, quilts.

MARSELLA. Made with twill weave, this bleached linen fabric is given a soft finish; comparable with Marcella.

MARTEN. Baum (European), Japanese, stone (European). A long straight-haired fur in light yellow, or slate-color, usually dyed. Wearing qualities, fair. Judged by fullness, silkiness, and softness. Found in North America, Europe, Russia, and Japan. Worn generally and for dress.

MARTIN COTTON. Same as Kelly cotton.

MARTINGALE. A half belt, often worn low or at the underarm level to restrain the fullness of a garment.

MARVELLA OR MARVELLO. Women's wear coating cloth of high quality. It is a high-luster, pile fabric that weighs from twenty to thirty ounces per yard. Warp is usually worsted and filling mohair and silk, although other combinations are used, dependent on the quality of cloth wanted. The material is made in the finishing; piece-dyed cloth.

"MARVEL METER." A quality control device used in knitting plants as a course counter which indicates electrically on its dial the number of courses in the fabric inserted in the machine under a uniform tension factor. The dial has secondary pointers for minimum and maximum course readings for definite constructions and standards. Can be used for counting on fine-denier nylon stockings, and model is adapted for full-fashioned outerwear fabric as well. Product of Marvel Specialty Co., Inc.

MARVESS. A melt spun polypropylene olefin fiber made by Phillips Fibers Corporation, a subsidiary of Phillips Petroleum Company, Inc. Available in natural and solution-dyed colors, this product is high in tenacity and abrasion resistance; it has a circular cross-section, rapidly, and is chemically resistant to acids and alkalies at room temperatures and does not give trouble in dyeing. Uses include filtration and insulation items, cordage, nonwoven goods, pile cloths, floorcoverings, and in some woven and knitted cloths for apparel.

MARY STUART CAP. The characteristic, small cap, usually of delicate fabric and lace-trimmed, with a peak point at the center of the forehead. This 16th century cap was in favor for many years and has periodic waves of popularity. It was the forerunner of the chick headgear introduced by Empress Eugenie, wife of Napoleon III, King of France. Named after Mary, Queen of Scots, 1542-1587, cousin of Elizabeth I of England. See Costume, Elizabethan; Second Empire Period, 1853-1870, under Costume, History of.

MASALIA. Dress goods of the nainsook type which have a smooth, appealing finish. Much of the fabric is watermarked, and this depends on the weave used and the finish applied to the cloth, noted for its silken appearance.

MASCADES. A plain-weave silk fabric that comes in solid colors, usually pastel, black, or white, or in prints, and used for mantillas in Latin American countries; also used in the Mediterranean countries.

MASER. A device for amplifying electrical impulses by stimulated emission of radiation. Obtained by microwave amplification, stimulation, emission of radiation. See Laser.

MASHAM. A British half-bred sheep obtained by crossing Wensleydale rams and Greyface ewes. It is an ideal mutton sheep and produces an open wool of about 46s quality, 5 to 6 inches long, and having good handling properties.

MASI CLOTH. Fabric made from fiber obtained from the bark of the Masi tree. This Fiji Island material is used locally.

MASKS. A face covering with openings for the eyes and the mouth. Originally used in classical antiquity, in time they were used to hide one's identity from enemies and for protection from the cold, wintry weather, and from the sun in warmer weather. In the 18th century, masks were much used in the American colonies. Often made of dark blue or black velvet, they were held on by a silver mouthpiece. Silk and linen were also much used in masks, with an attached cord making it possible to tie them under the chin. At the turn of the century, goggles were added for use when motoring. They are still popular in society for fancy dressed balls, parties, masquerades, etc.

MASSLINN. A nonwoven fabric made from a blend of cotton and rayon fibers by a method that completely eliminates spinning and weaving. Several continuous webs of fibers are set down in layer form and then run through a machine, which deposits adhesive on the face of the material to bind each fiber into place. A sheer, feltlike substance on the order of paper in appearance will result. This soft, silklike product, if pulled in the direction of the fibers, will show considerable toughness and strength. A hard pull in the other direction will cause the fibers to separate; the material, however, will not tear or crumble as easily as paper. Trade name of the Chicopee Sales Corporation and used for napkins, guest towels. Since the price of the article is very low the napkins or towels may be discarded after using.

MASS STRESS. The force per unit mass per unit length, e.g., the grams per denier, referred to the dimensions of the unstrained material. This measure of stress is used in the same manner as the force per unit area.

MAT. 1. A rug made of old ropes, interwoven and then beaten flat. 2. A coarse material made by weaving or intertwining any of several of the bast or vegetable fibers, used for floor covering, called also matting. 3. A material placed under dishes when serving; does away with noise and protects the table. 4. A small floor covering. 5. The closed or solid area in a piece of lace. 6. Verb meaning to entangle or to felt together.

MAT, MATTE, MATT FINISH. The smooth, dull finish found on upper leather. Not necessarily smooth finish on other types of leather.

MAT, MATT WEAVE. Another name for basket or hopsack weave, usually the 2-and-2 or the 3-and-3 basket weaves.

MATAMOROS HEMP. See ISTLE.

MATCHING. Made by sorting fleeces and putting together those portions of different fleeces which correspond in quality.

MATELASSE, MATELLASSE. Figured fabric made on dobby or Jacquard looms. The patterns stand out and give a "pouch" or "quilted" effect to the goods. Comes in colors and in novelty effects. Made in cotton, rayon, silk, or wool, the cloth will give good wear, drape well, but must be laundered with utmost care. Matelassé garments are very attractive and, when in vogue, are much in demand. Some cotton fabric is used for bedspreads.

Matelas means mattress in French (from Arabian matrah, meaning bed). As used in textile weaves, matelasse or matelassé means a raised effect by interlacings of the yarn which show a quilted surface on the fabric. Some of the fabric may have tinsel threads worked into the pattern. See Illustrated Section (Fabrics 51).

MATELASSE ORGANDY. A term that describes crinkle-surfaced (matelassé) or crepe organdy, and expressly those materials which have a slight blistered or raised effect.

MATERIAL. 1. The units, parts, portions, or substances of which an article is made or can be made. 2. Synonymous with goods, fabric, cloth, stuff, etc.

MATOW. Raw silk obtained from douppioni silk in Canton, China. Most of the product is sent to India for manipulation.

MATTER. Any substance that one can see and feel, that has weight and occupies space. Every space in the universe is occupied by matter of some kind. Different forms of matter can be distinguished by the senses. That matter can neither be created nor destroyed is called the Law of Conservation of Matter. Matter undergoes changes in appearance and may be changed from one state to another. Two or more substances may dissolve in a liquid in any proportion to form a mixture, i.e., ice to water.

Matter is inert when at rest it tends to stay at rest; when in motion it tends to stay in motion. For example, scissors lie still on a table until some force makes them move. A sewing machine tends to continue to run even after the power has been shut off.

No two bodies of matter can occupy the same space at the same time, such as pieces of fabric on a shelf or cleaning fluid poured into a dish formerly filled with air.

Matter has weight, one of its most distinguishing characteristics, such as the weight of known gases or liquids. Matter is subject to constant change.

MATT FIBRO. The dull type of viscose rayon staple fiber produced by Courtaulds, Limited, England. Trade name.

MATTING. General term for floor covering, foot mats, entryway mats, etc.

MATTING OXFORD. Oxford shirting which is made with small basket weaves, sometimes called matt weaves.

MATTRESS. A large container, for a bed, that is stuffed with cotton batting, hair, wool, flocks, straw, or similar materials; it is tufted or quilted.

MATTRESS DUCK. Implies single-filling flat duck.

MATTRESS FLAMMABILITY STANDARD. On May 31, 1972, FTC effected the adoption of DOC FF H-72 which provides for a whole mattress test which covers performance of mattresses and mattress pads in resisting ignition by means of burning cigarettes. Lighted cigarettes of a certain description are lodged in critical areas of the mattress structure such as tufting, flat surfaces, and taped edges and allowed to burn to extinction. Water soaking has been eliminated.

The mattress or pad is then examined for combustion. The test criterion is the char length which is specified as not more than 5.0 cm. (two inches) in any direction from the nearest point of contact with the cigarette. Provisions are made for the bare mattress, sheet covered mattresses, and the mattress after prescribed leeching treatment. Becomes fully effective on June 1, 1973, at which time all manufacturers will have to comply with the ruling.

MATT SHIRTING. Same as Oxford shirting. See Illustrated Section (Fabrics 6).

MATT WEAVE. A 2-2 or 3-3 basket or hopsack weave.

MATT YARN. Another name for dull-luster acetate or rayon yarn.

MATURATION. A term used in

rayon manufacture to denote the ripening of the stored cellulose solution prior to the spinning procedure. Ripening requires from about 40 to about 60 hours.

MATURING. Same as ripening when speaking of cotton.

MATURITY. Pertains to the thickness of the fiber wall in speaking of cotton. Maturity depends upon the degree to which the lumen (stalk tube) has been obliterated by the cellulose which constitutes the walls.

MAUD. A double-cloth fabric made of coarse two-ply cotton warp and heavy wool filling with more picks per inch than ends. Both face and back weaves are filling face, giving a wool surface on both sides. Gray and black fillings are usual and the design is made by interchanging the two. Used for shawls, steamer blankets, throws, etc.

MAURITIUS HEMP. Strong leaf fiber found in Mauritius. It resembles sisal to a considerable degree, and is used for cordage and gunny bags.

MAURITIUS WEED. A kind of lichen used as a source for archil.

MAUSARI, MAUSOORI, OR KAPAR. An Indian netting made in India for protection against insects; comes plain or in checked designs.

MAUVE. 1. A purple pigment and dye obtained from mauvein. 2. A rosy-purple color. 3. The first commercial coal-tar color, discovered by the English scientist, H. W. Perkins, in 1856. Also known as Perkins' Violet.

MAWATA. Japanese term for the waste from pierced or damaged cocoons, and double cocoons or douppioni. After being boiled-off, this type of waste serves as wadding or batting in winter clothing.

MAXBO SHUTTLELESS LOOM. This Swedish loom has the shuttle replaced by an air nozzle, from which a concentrated jet of air is ejected to blow the filling yarn through the shed of the loom. The action reduces stress on the warp ends; pickage is from 320 to 400 per minute depending on width and type of fabric.

Two large-capacity bobbins more than a foot high feed the filling yarn into the loom, a time saver and step reducer. There is no shuttle stroke on the loom, and a stable vibration absorbs the box frames. The reed is balanced by counter weights, and the loom thus dispenses with the need for anchoring.

There is no shuttle against the reed, thereby allowing for thinner dents than usual and with increased lateral resilience. Knots pass freely without entangling through the reed splits. The

warp yarn regulator is entirely automatic and does not require setting. It is actuated by the tension beam and retains a constant warp tension from the loaded to the empty bobbin. Warp tension is governed by tension springs.

All movements to yarn feeding devices, heddles, reed, and roller and warp regulator are incorporated in the box frames; lubrication is necessary only once a year. All other lubricating points are fed from an oil pump built in the left-hand frame. Transmissions, connecting linkage, and most of the other moving parts are completely enclosed in the box frames. Thus, the reduction of accidents is possible.

Permanent magnets operate the contacts in the filling detector and minimize wear and tear on the loom. There is an electrically or mechanically operated warp detector that comes with the loom.

MAXEY COTTON. See MEYER'S TEXAS COTTON.

MAXI COAT. Making its debut in early fall of 1969, this coat with its longer length aroused the usual furor, as did many of its antecedents in the last five or so years. Coming down to the ankles, this garment may be a hindrance to the wearer and a real safety hazard. The maxi wearer has to watch not to trip on curbs, escalators, stairs, when trying to get into a cab, bus, elevator, or revolving door. However, they do provide warmth which is especially needed for the wearers of miniskirts.

MAYO TWILL. See CAMPBELL TWILL.

MAZAMET. Name given to a type of French melton. Named for the city of this name in France. See "Mazamet" Wool.

"MAZAMET" WOOL. A slipe wool taken from the pelts of dead sheep by treating the pelts with lime and sodium sulphide or some other depilatory agent. Dependent on local conditions the treatment takes from about 24 hours to as high as 72 hours in order to take off the fibers easily and quickly. The hide is not at all injured in the treatment. Also known as fellmongered wool, the stock usually goes into lower grade fabrics, is inferior in working properties, and can be blended with satisfactory results with ordinary fleece wool. Named for the largest "wool pullery town" in the world, Mazamet, France. See Fell, Fellmongering, Pulled Wool; Pulled Wool, Methods to Obtain, Slipe Wool.

MAZET. A 100 per cent "Orlon" acrylic yarn produced by the Turbo Stapler Method for use in sweaters and comparable knitted fabrics; owned

by Deering, Milliken Company, Inc. See TURBO CONVERTER, TURBO STAPLER.

McKAY STITCHING. This is a sole-stitching method for shoes invented by Lyman Blake. It is comparable with shoe welt construction, except that the outsole, insole, and upper are all stitched together at one time. Patent rights to the invention were acquired by Gordon McKay and the stitch was then given his name.

MEAL, COTTONSEED. The greenish yellow powder obtained from grinding the cake after the oil has been extracted from the seed. Rich in nitrogen, it is used for cattle food, dyestuffs, fertilizer.

MEASURING CHECK. Any device used on machines to measure the lengths of yarn or fabric as it passes through.

MEATY COTTON. Low-waste cotton that will take the twist well when spun into yarn.

MECHANICAL ACTION. The combined flexing, abrasive, and compressive detergent effect produced by a running washwheel.

MECHANICAL FABRICS. A large group of heavy, rugged fabrics used in many industries—duck, canvas, filter fabric, sheeting for the laundry trades, drill for chemical and oil filters, awning cloth, and many others.

MECHANICAL FINISHES ON FABRICS, MAJOR.

1. SINGEING: This treatment will produce smoothness on the material. Protruding fibers, lint, and fuzz are removed by singeing without injury to the goods, by passing the cloth rapidly over gas jets or electric plates.

2. SHRINKAGE CONTROL: During weaving and certain procedures in finishing, the cloth is held under tensions which, when released, will allow the goods to contract or shrink. The production of serviceable goods necessitates the dimensional stabilization of the material to prevent this shrinkage from occurring during consumer use. The potential shrinkage is determined and then actually duplicated in the finishing process. Cotton fabrics identified by trade names Rigmel-Shrunk (Bradford Dyeing Association) or Sanforized (Cluett, Peabody & Co.) are mechanically manipulated to achieve planned dimensions that allow anticipation of residual shrinkage of less than 1 per cent.

3. NAPPING AND SHEARING: A third dimension can be added to fabric constructions by pulling the top protruding fibers out above the surface of the fabric. Card-clothing wire brushes, usu-

ally with fine pressed-steel wire from one-half inch to more than an inch in length, lift the loose fibers to the surface and these form a sort of fleece-effect on the cloth. The nap may be left on or it can be sheared to give a smooth, appealing surface-effect to the material.

4. EMBOSSING: Embossed or etched motifs, formerly set into fabric in the weaving of the cloth, are now often applied in the finishing. A heated engraved roller is used for the effect and it is set over a larger fabric roller. As the goods pass between the two rollers, the motif or design registers on the cloth.

5. TENTERING: In the early finishing processes, the cloth often becomes irregular in width. Tentering will bring the cloth to the correct width. This machine, by means of a series of tenters or hooks formed in a long, endless chain on each side of the selvages of the goods, grips the selvage edges and gently but firmly pulls the fabric into proper shape and width as steam and heat are applied in the operation.

6. CALENDERING: In reality this is a machine-pressing operation. The cloth passes around a series of heavy, highly polished steam-heated rollers which flatten the fibers and yarn and smooth the surface of the goods. Calendering may or may not be permanent, and this depends upon the cost of the goods, the type of calendering desired, and the end-use of the material.

MECHANICAL PICKING. Picking of cotton by machine. Hundreds of attempts have been made in this country to perfect the mechanical picker, but only since about 1936 has definite progress been made, particularly by the Rust Brothers of Memphis, Tennessee. A basic objection to this type of picking, by some people, is that the grade of cotton is lowered because some varying amounts of leaf and other foreign matter are picked along with the cotton.

MEDALLION. A single, detached pattern.

MEDIATION. Third-party attempt to reconcile the differences existing between a company and its employees, and their union. Similar to conciliation.

MEDICI. A particular type of torchon edging with a scalloped effect on one edge. Named for the Medici family, well known in world history.

MEDIUM SPREAD COLLAR. Shirt collar with the points at medium or average spread at the front; may vary as to length.

MEDIUM STRIPES. A very broad term. There are several provincial in-terpretations of this term dependent on the fabric and the method of striping, along with the width of the stripes. Some stripings, in shirting and dress goods, for example, could be a suitable width and made from a twill or satin formation. Another medium stripe effect could be a stripe of ten threads broken into two five-shaft satin weaves, one of warp-effect, the other of filling effect, a sort of reversible satin weave effect, in the vertical direction in the goods. Effects like these appear in madras shirting, some cotton dress goods, etc.

MEDIUM WOOLS. 1. Those wools which average in length between long and short wools. Short wool ranges from 1 to 6 inches; long wool is from 6 to 12 or more inches in staple length.

2. Sometimes refers to the general quality of wool and includes wool that is high quarter-blood, three-eighths-blood, and low half-blood wool. Medium wools grade between 50s and 58s in quality.

MEDULLA. The central portion of an organ or tissue; e.g., the central part of a wool fiber.

MEEN POW. Chinese term used in the great Canton area for cotton goods, chiefly shirting fabrics.

MEGILA. Indian term for jute fabric.

MEHERJUN. The coarse Persian wool suitable for carpet yarn.

MEISEN. Japan makes this plain-woven silk fabric which has various colored or white motifs applied by hand coloring of the warp and the filling. Crosses feature the pattern effect.

MELAMINE. Made by combining various fillers with thermosetting mela-mine-formaldehyde resins. These compounds combine more effectively than any other plastic materials the appearance values of thermoplastics with the heat resistance, and other physical qualities, of thermosetting types.

Outstanding properties include high heat resistance, high arc resistance, low water absorption, resistance to acids, alkalis, boiling water, and the effects of water and age. A wide range of colors with excellent fastness may be used in the product.

Melamine may be used for textile finishes to give shrinkage control, wrinkle resistance, crispness, water repellency, soil resistance, etc.

MELAMINE RESINS. Made by reacting melamine with formaldehyde; the resulting product and some of its derivatives may be used for textile finishes to provide shrinkage control, wrinkle-resistance, crispness, soil-resistance, etc.

MELANGE. 1. Handmade pillow lace of silk which shows a combination (mélange) of conventional Chantilly lace with Spanish effects in the design. 2. French term (mélange) for mixture effects in fabrics. It is found in yarn spun from mixed stock, printed top, cloth woven from Vigoreux-printed slubbing after it has been made into yarn, and in fabrics sold as mixed or mixture goods.

MELANGE LUSTRE. A Bradford Luster fabric in which the stock that is to be used ultimately for filling is printed in sliver, slub, or top form. This type of coloring is now referred to as Vigoreux Printing as done or applied on worsted stock for Vigoreux printed fabrics.

MELANGE PRINTING. Another name for Vigoreux Printing used in worsted printing of tops. The slubbing or sliver top is printed with bands of thickened dye paste, with intervening blank bands to produce a color-and-no-color formation. The stock is steamed subsequently, washed, back-washed, gilled, and combed to give a very even mixture of dyed and undyed lengths of fibers. The doublings, redoublings, drawings, draftings, and attenuating of the fibers produce this very even color melange. See VIGOREUX PRINTING.

MELANGE YARN. Yarn made from colored slivers or tops as apart from a so-called mixture yarn in that the fibers in melange show a great many shades, casts, tones, and hues to produce a rather distinct color effect in the finished spun yarn.

MELROSE. Double twill cloth of silk and wool, named for Melrose on the Tweed River in Scotland.

MELTON. Cloth that originated in Melton Mowbray, the long popular fox-hunting resort in England, known the world over. Originally a hunting cloth, melton is now classed with kersey, beaver, and broadcloth. Melton does not have a so-called "laid-nap." It is dull and nonlustrous and comes in many qualities, depending on the grade of stock used.

Melton may be finished in the following manner: soaping with good quality soap; fulling for three to four hours; scouring with a medium-consistency good grade of soap and alkali until well cleansed; hot and cold rinses applied, followed by carbonizing, neutralizing, washing, steaming, drying; then shearing with three runs on the face of the goods. Steam-brushing is an optional operation. There is no raising in a true melton.

The fabric is used for overcoating, uniform cloth, pea jackets, regal livery,

MELTING POINT OF SOME CELLULOSIC AND NON-CELLUSOSIC FIBERS. The heat sensitivity of textile fibers of thermoplastic base, for example, shows that they will soften on heat application. The degree of sensitivity varies with the various fibers. Melting is actually a separating of the molecules in a fiber, causing them to vibrate with such force that they become separated or melt. Cellulosic and protein fibers will not melt because of the strong attractive forces in the hydroxyl groups in them. The melting points follow:

FIBER	MELTING POINT, FAHRENHEIT	FIBER	MELTING POINT, FAHRENHEIT
Acetate-cellulosic	500	Nylon 66	482
Acrilan	Sticks at 470, no melting point	Olefin	230 to 345, depending on the type of fiber
Arnel-cellulosic base	572	"Orlon"	No practical melting point, sticks at 445
Creslan	Sticks at 468, no melting point	Rayon-cellulosic	300
"Dacron"	480	Saran	340
Dynel	Does not melt or drip	Verel	About 300
Kodel	480	Vinyon HH	275-330
Nylon 6	420	Zefran	Sticking point at 490

and Metropolitan cloth for the police and fire departments. The rigid construction of the fabric affords excellent wear, since the finishing treatments cover up all interlacings of the warp and filling, thereby making a genuinely "solid" cloth.

MELTONETTE. Women's wear cloth of very lightweight melton.

MELT SPINNING. The process whereby man-made or manufactured fibers are formed by the extrusion of a melted polymer into a cooling or chilling area or zone. Cold gas or an air stream does the cooling. See DRY SPINNING, WET SPINNING.

MEMPHIS COTTON. A popular cotton raised in the Memphis area; it is bluish in cast and has a staple of slightly more than 1 inch. It is ideal for extra-hard twist yarn ranging from 40s to 50s in yarn count.

MEN, JAPANESE. In Japanese, *men chijimi* means cotton crepe, while *men shusu* implies a cotton sateen cloth. *Menhofu* is cotton duck; *menneru* is flannelette.

MENDER. A worker able to repair all types and kinds of defects in fabric or apparel, such as holes, dropstitches, runs, pulled threads, mispicks, threads out, bad start-up marks, etc. The work is done with a needle and all blemishes, large or small, must be remedied by the mender. The operator, at times, may be called upon actually to weave-in the construction in the material according to the weave used in the fabric. The mender is usually an experienced examiner.

MENDING. 1. To remedy or fix damaged, defaced, or torn fabric. 2. Woolens and worsteds, following perching, are burled, specked, mended, and given final sewing treatment before they are sent to the wet-finishing operations in the mill. The necessity of mending may be caused by the following blemishes or flaws in fabrics, among others: ends out, mispicks, harness skips, small holes, shuttle smashes, loose warp ends, or filling picks.

MENDING BAGGING. Similar to plain cotton bagging, this jute cloth made in England is used to mend bales of cotton and wool from which samples may have been taken by prospective buyers, who may cut a bale at any place to obtain samples of the raw stock.

MENDING COTTON. Same as darning cotton.

MENHOFU. Japanese term for cotton duck.

MENIN LACE. Valenciennes lace of good quality.

MENKWA COTTON. Japanese for raw cotton.

MEN'S TAILORING, MANUFACTURING FEATURES IN.

OUTSIDE STORY:

1. COAT: Good styling, accurate full cut.

2. Front: Well-matched fabric pattern, good drape, proportional shoulders.

3. Collar: Hand felled, smooth fitting. Well-shaped collar and lapels.

4. Pockets: Well-matched stripes, checks, or plaids, corners reinforced.

5. Sleeve: Good drape, smooth easy fit, ample armhole, elbow width.

6. Buttonholes: Hand sewn with silk, reinforced with gimp.

7. Buttons: Good quality composition, sewn with linen thread.

8. TROUSERS: Cut full seated, good drape to avoid bagging.

9. Belt-loops: Well-placed, securely sewn.

10. Closing: Approved zippers with tape to match cloth.

QUALITY FEATURES, OUTSIDE STORY:

1. COAT: Front shaped with preshrunk Hymo cloth, hand basted.

2. Collar-lapels: Linen interlining, hand basting.

3. Body and Sleeve lining: Good quality rayon twill, perspiration proof.

4. Pockets: Strong cotton twill linings, reinforcements at top and corners.

5. Front Edges: Reinforced with linen tape from lapel notch to bottom.

6. Armholes: Reinforced with strong tape, shields inserted.

7. Shoulders: Hand basted for smooth lines.

8. Seams: Wide, well sewn with closely spaced stitches.

9. Back: Skeleton lining, bound seams.

10. VEST: Well designed to fit smoothly.

QUALITY FEATURES, BASIC MATERIAL:

1. GOOD QUALITY: Wool, silk, cotton, linen, rayon, nylon.

2. DURABILITY: Fast color, shrinkage, elasticity and strength.

3. SPECIAL FINISHES: Naphthalated, Sanforized-shrunk, Sanitized, Amuno Moth-proofed, Tebelized, Cravenette treated, Zelan finished, London-shrunk.

4. CLEANABILITY: Laundering or dry cleaning.

5. LININGS: Silk, rayon, cotton—serviceable, practical, attractive.

6. INTERLININGS: Linen, cotton, hair

cloth—serviceable, practical for use.

7. GOOD QUALITY: Buttons, snap fasteners, zippers, or other closures.

8. GOOD QUALITY: Silk, cotton, nylon, or linen sewing thread.

WORKMANSHIP:

1. SEAMS: Secure, straight, neat.
2. MACHINE STITCHES: Well spaced.
3. EDGES: Well finished.
4. CLOSURES: Smooth and firm.
5. BUTTONS: Securely fastened. Buttonholes serviceable and neat.
6. HAND SEWING: Secure and inconspicuous.

STYLE AND SUITABILITY:

1. FABRIC WEAVE: Pattern, color becoming to wearer.
2. PRACTICAL: For purpose.
3. NEW, APPROPRIATE CUT OR STYLING.

COMFORT AND FIT:

1. GARMENT: Accurately sized.
2. EFFECT OF CLEANSING: On size.
3. CORRECT FIT: In all positions.
4. COMFORTABLE WEIGHT: For events or weather.

IDENTIFICATION:

LABEL OR TAG ON GARMENT GIVING:

1. NATIONALLY KNOWN, DEPENDABLE BRAND NAME.
2. NAME OF MANUFACTURER.
3. BASIC MATERIAL.
4. CONSTRUCTION, UNSEEN QUALITIES AND CHARACTERISTICS.

BASIC FASHION MODELS, MEN'S SUITS:

DRAPE: Created to achieve the heavy, strong masculine features. The shoulders are wide, built up high and squared with large shoulder pads. Sleeves are full at the top and reduced at the bottom to a natural width. The back is full across the blades with smooth, straight hanging side seams. The length in proportion to the width across shoulders and chest. The fronts are full with decided breaks at the chest, looseness at the waist and close fitting at the seat. Lapels are long and wide with a low collar notch. Buttons and pockets are set low in proportion to the length of lapel and coat.

SEMI-CONSERVATIVE (American Lounge): Gives an impression of tall, trim smartness. The shoulders are slightly squared and of moderate width. The chest is cut easy but not full. The back is comfortably easy over the blades, rather straight down over the waist and trim at the hipline and bottom. Lapels are long and narrow. Buttons and pockets are placed low in order to carry out the illusion.

CONSERVATIVE (Natural Look): Created to attain the appearance of height and casual smartness. It is cut with rather narrow shoulders and lightly padded. Body lines are straight, easy and comfortable but not loose. There is no exaggeration of fullness at the chest or blades. The back is cut with gentle easy lines with sufficient room over seat and bottom to allow for center vent. Lapels are shorter, narrower and with a higher lapel notch and roll. Buttons and pockets are placed higher than on the "Semi-Conservative, American Lounge Model."

CARE AND MAINTENANCE OF SUITS:

1. Wear two or more suits in rotation for maximum service. Brush and place on hangers in current of air after wearing. Cover shoulders and collar from dust when suit hangs in closet.

2. To remove grease, place spot face-down on blotter. Wet absorbent cloth with cleansing fluid and stroke wrong side of fabric toward center of spot until it disappears. Brush along the grain of the fabric. Remove sugar spot with water.

3. Dry-cleaning, steaming, and pressing restore original freshness of the suit.

4. Snags, tears, moth holes and burns may be rewoven by professional weaver or mended neatly. Buttons pulled off should be replaced at once.

MERAKLON. A polypropylene filament and staple in the Olefin Group made in Italy by Montecatini Societa Generale per l'Industria Mineraria e

Chimica Anonima, with the plant location in Terni, Italy. Derived from petroleum, it competes with regenerated cellulosic fibers such as Viscose Rayon and Cuprammonium Rayon. Used in knitwear and dress goods, carpets, blankets, and upholstery.

MERCER. Old-time British term for a fabric dealer.

MERCER, JOHN. A noted scientist who had some interest in dyeing cotton yarn and fabric made a phenomenal, accidental discovery in 1844. Leaving a piece of cotton cloth in a room-temperature caustic soda solution overnight, he found a much changed fabric the next morning. It had become thickened, fuller in appearance, shrunken in both warp and filling directions, and was semi-transparent. Further study revealed that the yarn and fabric had increased affinity for dyestuff. For fifty-six years the process made little headway in textile dyeing circles since the saving in dyestuffs did not offset the cost of the excessive shrinkage. Mercer did not follow-up his findings since he was interested in other scientific fields. It was not until 1890, because of the efforts of Horace Lowe, that mercerization came into its own in the cotton textile industry. See Lowe, Horace; Mercerized Cotton; Mercerized Finish.

MERCERIZED COTTON. Cotton yarn or fabric which has been mercerized; applied chiefly to combed yarns and fabrics. See MERCERIZED FINISHER; MERCERIZER; MERCERIZING.

MERCERIZED COTTON, TESTS FOR.

1. MICROSCOPIC TEST: Fibers are cut 0.2 mm. long and are then mounted in mineral oil. The number of fibers with no twist, for a definite number of fibers taken, is counted. The twist must be greater than 90 degrees to be counted. Unmercerized material will have less than 15 per cent of the fibers with no twist in them.

2. BARIUM ACTIVITY NUMBER: A sample of unmercerized cotton is run at the same time. Exactly two grams of the scoured sample to be tested is weighed without consideration of regain.

The weighed material is placed in a small conical flask. A 10 c.c. pipette is used to pipette 30 c.c. of approximately .25N barium hydroxide solution into the conical flask. The number of flasks used in the test for comparative purposes are stoppered and kept at room temperature for two hours with frequent shaking.

10 c.c. of the solution from each flask is drawn out and run into separate flasks. Titration is done with $\frac{N}{10}$

hydrochloric acid using phenolphthalein as the indicator. A titration is also made on 10 c.c. of the unused barium hydroxide.

The Barium Activity Number equals:

$$\frac{A - B}{A - C} \times 100.$$

A equals the c.c. of acid for unused barium hydroxide titration.

B equals the c.c. of acid for the mercerized sample.

C equals the c.c. of acid for unmercerized samples.

Unmercerized gives a number of about 100. Mercerized gives a number above 115.

MERCERIZED FINISH. Finish achieved by running goods through a tentering frame at high speed velocity, the cloth being submerged in a solution in the frame vat so that it will take on the silken finish. Some mercerized cloths are dress goods, cotton, poplin, sateen, shirting, soisette finish. See MERCERIZER; MERCERIZING.

MERCERIZED FINISH, FULL OR DOUBLE. Cotton cloth which has received full-strength mercerization treatment—55 degrees Twaddell hydrometer (Twaddle)—in cold caustic-soda bath. Mercerization is not increased at temperature above this mark. Mercerization begins at about 15 degrees Twaddell (Twaddle).

MERCERIZED SEWING THREAD. The trade-mark for J. & P. Coats Co. and Clark's O.N.T. Boilfast mercerized cotton thread, a three-cord thread made in a wide range of colors. (In 1953, these two companies merged.)

MERCERIZED WOOL. Wool is treated for a brief period at a low temperature in an 80-degree Twaddell (Twaddle) solution of caustic soda. The effect is a high luster to the wool at the expense of possible felting treatment.

MERCERIZER. 1. A group of machines including mangles and tentering frame through which cloth is run to acquire a lustrous finish simulating silk. One of the mangles contains caustic solution, one a dilute sulphuric acid solution, and another pure rinse water. 2. A machine for mercerizing yarn consisting of several rollers over which skeins of yarn are slipped and lowered into vats of caustic solution.

MERCERIZING. Process by which cottons take on a permanent silken luster when treated in a cold caustic-soda bath at room temperature. The yarn or fabric will also become stronger, more absorbent, and more susceptible to dyestuffs. Discovered by accident in 1844 by John Mercer, the well-known and revered calico printer of England.

MERCERIZING PLANT, SECTION MAN. One who understands the instruments used for bath controls, including the thermometer and the hydrometer; must have an over-all comprehension of the complete job in the mercerizing plant.

MERCERIZING VISCOSE PULP. In the manufacture of viscose rayon the pulp sheets are steeped in a solution of sodium hydroxide for conversion into alkali-cellulose.

MERCHANDISING. The total planning, advertising, promotion, and all other activities involved in promoting the sales of products. Timing is an important factor.

MERCHANT TAILOR. A tailor who keeps and sells materials for the garments which he makes.

MERCILINE. A closely woven, thin, diaphanous silk fabric. See MARCELINE.

MERCURY. Also know as quicksilver, its symbol is Hg. It is a heavy, white, metallic element, noted for its fluidity at ordinary temperatures. It is toxic or poisonous and is the only common metal which is liquid at ordinary temperatures. Based on one part per million, as used to measure mercury contamination, this element has been compared with one ounce of vermouth in 7,530 gallons of gin.

MERGE NUMBER. The number which identifies all nylon which has come from the same spinning solution. Similar to lacing number used to identify rayon as it comes from the spinning solution.

MERINO. (The Spanish word "merino" signified roving from pasture to pasture, said of sheep; probably from the Latin, "major," greater.) 1. (Capitalized) A famous breed of sheep, of Spanish origin. 2. (Not capitalized) The very fine quality of wool of the Merino breed of sheep. Hence a cloth of such material. The term "merino" is now applied also to knitted woolen fabrics, notably undergarments constructed of yarns with an admixture of cotton to prevent shrinkage in laundering. See MERINO SHEEP; MERINO WOOLS.

MERINO, WORSTED. This is a misnomer and was born during World War I. The term referred to the sock made for the United States Navy. The content was either French-spun worsted yarn or woolen yarn mixed with an equal percentage of cotton. The worsted-cotton combination was the better type. The woolen type often contained reworked wool fibers, and the sock was rather bulky and unwieldy.

MERINO SHEEP. A sheep of the Merino breed. See Illustrated Section. They produce the highest, finest, and

best wool in the world. The aristocrat of sheep and wool. There has been much conjecture and discussion about the origin of Merino sheep. It is likely that they originated in what is now Italy and Spain. Some claim that, as a class, Merino did not exist until the fifteenth century. Others place this time in the early days of the Renaissance in the twelfth and thirteenth centuries.

The Saracens, who fought the Spaniards for seven centuries, and were finally overthrown and driven from Europe at the conquest of Granada in 1492, were great breeders of sheep. They did much in crossbreeding to improve their flocks. They, no doubt, introduced this type of sheep into Europe and it may have been before the twelfth century. The intellectual and clever Saracens developed their flocks to the utmost; their fleeces excelled all others. Flocks of sheep raised by them compared very well with the best Merino flocks of Italy and Spain.

The staple ranges from 1 to 5 inches and all working properties are of the best. Wools classed as Merino are: Ohio Merino, Saxony Merino of Germany, Silesia of Austria, Rambouillet of France, Port Philip and Botany Bay of Australia, South American Merino, South African Merino, New Zealand and Tasmanian Merino. Small flocks of Merino are found in Italy, Sweden, Denmark, and Germany.

The diameter of the merino fiber is from 1/500 to 1/1750 inches and fiber length is from 1 to 5 inches. Serrations range from 2400 to 3000 per inch. The ram weight is between 150 and 235 pounds; ewes weigh from 105 pounds to 155 pounds.

The grease fleece obtained from Merino sheep weighs from 17 pounds to 22 pounds. Yolk and suint are heavy in the fleeces, so that the yield is lowest when compared with all other classified wools. After scouring, approximately one third of the original weight is wool fiber.

MERINO TULLE. A lightweight French woolen or worsted dress-goods fabric of high quality; actually a "woolen tulle."

MERINOVA. A casein fiber produced by Snia Viscosa Company of Italy, which has replaced the old-time—and the first—casein fiber to be marketed, Lanital. This fiber was made in Italy up to the end of World War II. It is now produced in Belgium and Italy.

MERINO VOLOSH. Hybrid sheep breed of the Soviet Union, produced by crossing imported Merino rams with Volosh ewes; the quality of the wool obtained has increased constantly because of the fine-wool rams used in the breeding.

MERINO WOOL. The best grades of this wool in the world come from Botany Bay and Port Philip areas of Australia. This Merino stock is used for worsted cloths of the better grade. Merino wool is listed as a Class One Wool, and 85 per cent of all Australian wool is merino. Other world centers for the fleeces are Ohio, Silesia in Austria, Saxony in Germany, France, Argentina, Spain, and the Union of South Africa.

Merino wools have the best working properties and have been spun, for commercial purposes, to 80s worsted counts.

MERINO YARN. 1. The best grade of worsted yarn in the woven trade. 2. In the knitted trade, the term implies the best grade used for woolen and worsteds knitting. However, there is the understanding that it may contain re-used, remanufactured, shoddy or mungo wool stock in the yarn. The yarn is generally comparable with a three-eighths blood wool. Knitted fabric, generally speaking, does not require yarn any better than this quality when its uses are considered. 3. A knit goods yarn made of a blend of cotton and wool fibers.

MERLETTO. The Italian term for bobbin lace.

MERLETTO LACES. Some of these follow:
1. BIONDO: The original blond lace made in Venice.
2. GRECO: Italian expression for Greek bobbin lace; where it was made.
3. MAGLIE: Means net ground lace in Italian.
4. MAGLIE QUADRATA: Italian for knotted mesh lace.
5. PIOMBINI: Bobbin lace in Italian.
6. POLYCHROMO: Italian for the now obsolete bobbin lace with motifs in multicolored silk thread arrangement.
7. RETINE RICAMATE: Italian for embroidery work on a net groundwork.
8. TOMBOLA: Italian for bobbin lace. See MERLETTO.

MERRIN WOOL. Wool removed from dead sheep, especially from partly decomposed range animals. Has a yellowish tint very difficult to remove.

MERROW OPERATOR. One who uses the Merrow sewing machine, or some comparable type, to perform one or more joining and hemming operations on garments or the complete sewing of the garment. A junior operator performs the minor sewing operations.

"MERVE." Originally a silk material made with a satin weave on the face of the goods with a backing made of twill-weave construction. Often referred to as a cotton-back satin in the trade.

Of late years the term is given its full spelling of Merveilleux, a cloth made with silk, rayon, or acetate face and cotton back. See MERVEILLEUX.

MERVEILLEUX. An all-silk or rayon, or silk and cotton mixture cloth made on a twill weave. Used as lining in men's outer apparel.

MERV WOOL. A carpet wool raised in many areas of Central Asia. More than half the fleece is white while the rest of it is mottled with gray to black fibers.

MESCAL MAGUEY. Fiber used for twine and cordage, and found in western Mexico. Compared with sisal, it is finer and softer. It is harsh, and light yellowish or straw color. The name is taken from the plant from which it is obtained.

MESH. An open, porous network material which is held together by the interlacing of the thread to form the fabric. The system of knotting used employs a thread or cord which is usually arranged to form some sort of decorative effect. The fiber content in mesh fabrics must be declared. Examples of mesh include fishnet, gores, hats, stockings, and veilings.

MESHI. Biblical term for silk.

MESSALINE. A five-end satin weave fabric made in rayon or silk and noted for its softness and pliability. Messaline should be manipulated with care; it launders well, is lustrous, and is a very dressy women's wear cloth.

MESS JACKET. The white, short, fitted jacket without a tail effect worn on formal occasions by officers in the armed services. Facetiously referred to as a "straight jacket."

MESTIZA, METIS, METZ. General term usually signifying South American merino wool. The term means mixed and can be applied to crossbred wool, which results from breeding pure Merino sheep with the native Creola or Criolla sheep of South America.

MESTIZA BURRS. Burrs, thistles, etc., found in wool fleeces, chiefly those from South America.

META-CHROME, MONO-CHROME DYEING. The dyeing of mordant colors with the mordant and the dye-stuff in the one bath at the same time.

METAL FABRIC; METALLIC FABRIC. Decorative or apparel fabric made of silk, rayon, or cotton warp, and metallic filling such as gold, silver, copper, tinsel, aluminum, etc. A favorite in the millinery trade, it is also used for draperies, dresses, evening gowns, slippers, lampshades, tunics, upholstery. The thread used is often referred to as lame, or laminated thread.

METALIZED, METALLIZED DYES. The term is applied to the group of dyes which have metals in their molecules. These dyes are applied to the fiber in an acid dye bath. They are generally superior, as far as wash fastness is concerned, to acid dyes.

METALIZING. A method of plating plastic film with a continuous film of metal to obtain a brilliant reflecting surface. Often used in textiles on Mylar to produce metallic yarns.

METAL LACE. Formerly made by hand and practically extinct. Extant pieces are found in museums, etc. It is now made by machine in net foundation with the metallic threads interspersed throughout the material to form the motif.

METALLIC CLOTH. Any fabric, usually silk, that has gold, silver, tinsel, or other metal threads interspersed throughout the design in the cloth. Lamé is a metallic fabric. Cloths of this type have a cross-rib or rep effect, are rather stiff, harsh, stately, formal, prone to tarnish, and quite durable. Ideal for evening wear, these fabrics come in many grades and qualities.

METALLIC THREADS. Lustrous threads made of metal strands, popular since the Middle Ages. These threads have brilliancy when placed on a plain background material. They are used in decorative fabrics, brocade, brocatelle, damask, and in evening apparel. Woven screen wire for doors and windows, Pullman screening, fencing, chicken wire, ranch fencing, and garden wire may also be considered as made of metallic threads.

METALLIC YARN, TYPES OF. 1. *Foil Type:* There is an inside layer, usually aluminum foil, sandwiched between two layers of plastic film. When a silver shade is desired, the adhesive is clear in color; when other colors are wanted, pigment is added to the adhesive or printed onto the film prior to laminating. 2. *Metallized Type:* While a sandwich of clear plastic film is used, the inside layer consists of a clear plastic film that has been vacuum-plated with a vaporized metal, usually aluminum. Color is brought about in the same manner as in the Foil Type.

METALLIC YARNS AND FABRICS. Metallic yarns have had considerable rise in recent years, and they are now made with an acetate film or a mylar ("Dacron") film to enhance the finished yarn. Use of these yarns is now widespread in many fields of the textile and apparel industries.

Some leading manufacturers of metallic yarns include: Metal Film Co., Inc.,

New York City - the Chromeflex products; Fairtex Corp., Charlotte, North Carolina - the Fairtex products; Standard Yarn Mills, Inc., Glendale, Long Island, New York - the Lame' products; The Dobeckmun Co., a Division of Dow Chemical Co., Lurex Yarn Division - the Lurex products; Malina Co., New York City - the Malora products; Metlon Corp., Subsidiary of Acme Backing Corp., New York City - the Metlon products; E. I. du Pont de Nemours & Co., Inc., Wilmington, Delaware - Their product, Mylar, polyester film is much used in conjunction with the above metallic yarns such as Lame' with Mylar (metalized), Metlon with Mylar, Fairtex with Mylar, etc.

METALLIC YARNS AND FABRICS. SOME MAJOR

Metallic Yarns or Threads: These are lustrous yarns or threads of metal strands, and they have been popular since the Middle Ages. These strands have brilliancy, particularly when placed on a plain background material. They are used in brocade, brocatelle, damask, and other decorative fabrics, and in evening apparel. They have also found favor in daytime wear in the women's wear field.

Woven screening of many types for doors and windows, Pullman screening, fencing, chicken wire, ranch fencing, and garden wire are also made with metallic threads or yarns.

Metallic Cloth: Any fabric, usually silk, that has gold, silver, tinsel or other metal threads interspersed throughout the motif in a fabric, hanging, cloth, or tapestry. Lame' is a metallic fabric. Cloths of this type usually have a cross-rib or repp effect, are rather stiff, harsh, stately, formal, prone to tarnish, and quite durable. Ideal for evening wear, these fabrics come in many varying grades and qualities.

Metlon: This is a non-tarnishing metallic yarn made by laminating an extremely bright aluminum foil between two plies of specially formulated plastic film. Registered trademark of Metlon Corporation, New York City.

Metallic Yarns Made with Acetate and Mylar Compared: Acetate and Mylar film (Dacron) are used in the manufacture of the present-day yarns. Mylar base yarn will withstand higher temperatures and more rugged fabric-finishing and laundering than the acetate type.

Some metallic yarn is made of thin aluminum foil sandwiched between layers of film; another type uses metalized aluminum (vaporized in vacuum) sprayed on the binder between the layers of film.

Mylar film is stronger and thinner and will give a larger yield than the acetate-film yarn. Its cost per thousand yards is not much higher when compared with the acetate type. There is, however, at present a rather substantial price difference between the two on the pound basis, acetate being the less expensive. Width of the film and its thickness vary as does the price per pound.

A large variety of colors and combinations of two or more colors are available. These narrow ribbons of glittering metallic yarns are finding increasing use in many types of apparel and household furnishings, and in some industrial fabrics.

METALLIC YARNS INSTITUTE DEFINITIONS. The Institute defines a metallic yarn as continuous filament produced by a combination of plastic film and metallic component so that the metallic component is protected.

ACETATE BUTYRATE, ALUMINUM FOIL: A continuous flat monofilament composed of aluminum foil laminated on both reflective surfaces with cellulose butyrate film.

CELLOPHANE, ALUMINUM FOIL: A continuous flat monofilament composed of aluminum foil laminated on both reflective surfaces with cellophane film.

POLYESTER, ALUMINUM FOIL: A continuous flat monofilament composed of aluminum foil laminated on both reflective surfaces with polyester film.

POLYESTER, ALUMINUM METALLIZED POLYESTER: A continuous flat monofilament composed of aluminum metallized polyester laminated on its metallized surface or surfaces with polyester film.

POLYESTER, ALUMINUM METALLIZED, NON-LAMINATED: A continuous flat monofilament composed of a single layer of aluminum metallized polyester protected on its metallized surface.

MYLAR: Du Pont's trade-mark for its polyester film which is supplied in continuous sheet form for laminating the foil used in metallic yarns. Du Pont does not laminate the foil or slit the film to filament widths. These operations are done by the converters in this industry. See MYLAR.

METALLINE CLOTH. Material of bright, metallic colors and brilliant luster. Made with silk or cotton warp and rayon or silk filling. An imitation of metallic fabric and used for the same purposes.

METAL PEGS. Refers to the small metal lugs or pins, an inch or so in length, arranged in the pattern chain on a dobby loom to control weaving of the motif or design in the fabric.

METAL PRINTING. When gold, silver, or alloys are used to give a dot effect on material, the method is spoken of as metal or metallic printing.

METERING PUMP. A device which pumps and measures the viscous viscose solution as it is sent to the spinnerets.

METER LEATHER. A specialty leather prepared from selected sheepskins of non-porous nature. Used for measuring bags of gas meters.

METHYLS. Hypothetically, radical—a compound of hydrogen and carbon which exists only in combination. Present in wood alcohol and other compounds.

METIER. Used to describe the bank of cells or compartments used in the dry-spinning method in the manufacture of cellulose acetate.

METLON. A non-tarnishing metallic yarn produced by laminating an extremely bright aluminum foil between two plies of specially formulated plastic film. A registered trade-mark of the Metlon Corporation.

METLON CORPORATION. A subsidiary of Acme Backing Corporation, New York City, its products follow:

Diamond is a ribbon-shaped yarn made from clear plastic film. Made in a 1/64-inch width it is much used for decorative purposes.

Metlon F, Metlon LMP, Metlon Staple, and Metlon Ultrathin are all registered trademark names of the company. All these products have excellent resistance to heat and light, and rate fair to excellent in reactions to acids, alkalis, and the usual conventional chemicals used in the industry. Uses of all these products for decorative purposes include woven and knitted outerwear, decorative fabrics, napery, sportswear, automobile fabrics, bags, headgear, braiding, and narrow woven webbings and tapes.

METLON MARK II. A laminated metallic yarn composed of aluminum foil protected on each side by a layer of specifically engineered olefin film; it has considerable brightness and clarity. Of great strength, Mark II is ideal for manipulating in embroidery, lace, quilting, etc. A 1/64-inch width provides 16,500 yards to the pound. Product of Metlon Corporation, New York City.

METRE OR METER. The standard lineal length of the metric system—39.37 inches.

METZ CORD. A fine worsted dress goods made with a 2-up, 2-down broken twill, going to the left because of the broken effect made in the weave. This provides a fine cord line on the face of the goods. This union fabric made of fine cotton warp and worsted filling of about 60s count is textured at about twice as many picks as ends—70 to 80 ends and 120 to 140 picks.

MEWLON. Registered trademark of Unitika, Ltd., Osaka, Japan, for its Vinylon (polyvinyl chloride) manmade textile fiber. Having properties closely resembling those of cotton, it has a high rating in certain industrial uses and ranks very well with nylon and polyester in its performance. It is also an economical fiber to use. Outstanding properties include adhesiveness, strength, elongation, impact resistance, elastic recovery to elongation.

Mewlon in apparel is used for knit-goods, linings, overalls, pajamas, and underwear. Industrial uses include baggings, backing for polyvinyl chloride (PVC) coatings and as a binder product for use in making paper; chafer fabric for tires, conveyor belting, filter fabrics, fishnets and twine, gloves, hose, roping, sewing thread, sheets for ships and vehicles, tire cord, protective a-prons, etc.

Incidentally, Japan is the only country in the world that produces Vinylon and the products made from it. In addition to Unitika, the only other company which makes the fiber is Kurashiki Rayon Co., Ltd., Osaka, Japan and its tradename for the fiber is Kuralon. See Polyvinyl Alcohol, Unitika, Ltd.; Vinal, Vinal Acetate, Vinylidene Chloride, Vinylon.

MEXICAINE. A variant of the well-known ancient Pekins, fabrics noted for their horizontal band effects made with different weave constructions. See PEKIN, POIL TRAINANT.

MEXICAN. An English cotton fabric, white or colored, and made with five bars of red in the heading. It is exported to Central America as dress goods.

MEXICAN BURR. A long-standing term used for clustered cotton bolls found in Mexican cottons; likely the forerunner of present day cottons known for the clusters.

MEXICAN COTTON. One of the oldest varieties of cotton known. Most American short- and medium-staple cottons have been developed from Mexican cotton. The well-known Mexican Burr cotton has clustered bolls and is the original source for most of the cluster types of cotton developed.

MEXICAN DRAWNWORK. Small,

round medallions, either single or in strips, with threads drawn to form wheel-effects. Mexican and Teneriffe drawnwork of Wales are about the same. Machine-made imitations are made in Nottingham, Calais, and St. Gall to supply the demand.

MEXICAN COSTUME. See Costume Mexican.

MEXICAN FIBER. Another term for istle, ixtle.

MEXICAN GRASS. See SISAL.

MEXICANS. British term for several types of cottons used in the export trade. They are plain or twill cloths, dyed various colors.

MEXICAN SHEEP. An old-time and still used term to signify the wools obtained from sheep in the southwestern states of the United States, as well as a broad term for Mexican sheep. This term is a very loose one and does not actually refer to the particular grades raised in our southwestern states.

MEXICAN SISAL. Term often given to henequen.

MEYER'S TEXAS COTTON. An Uplands variety of 1⅛-inch staple and about 31 per cent in lint yield. Also known as Maxey Cotton.

MEZCAL, MESCAL. A hard bast fiber obtained from the leaves of the mezcal plant found in Mexico and Central America. Yellow in cast, from 2 to 5 feet in length, the fiber is somewhat finer and softer than henequen. Used with other fibers to make cordage and twine.

MEZZETTA. A Sicilian raw silk.

MEZZO PUNTO. Another name for Beggar's Lace.

MICA. Any of a class of silicates, crystallizing in the monoclinic system and which can be separated into very thin, tough scales, colorless to jet-black. Used as a filler material in some plastic products. The transparent variety is known as isinglass.

MICROGRAPH. A microscopic picture.

MICRON. One-thousandth part of a millimeter, or one-millionth part of a meter.

MICROSCOPE. Pertaining to a microscope or microscopy; a view of an object made visible only by the use of the microscope.

MICROSCOPICAL DETERMINATION. By the use of the microscope many determinations may be made in connection with fibers, fabrics, and finishes; for example, the grades and the qualities of fibers, amount of fiber content in a mixed fabric, degree of mercerization in cotton goods, construction of fibers, etc.

MICRO-STRETCHING. Also known as M-S, it is a patented technology licensed on a worldwide basis by Cluett, Peabody & Company, Inc., New York City. The term implies a "uniform increment stretching" of a fabric in the filling or widthwise direction. Because of the method used, fabrics which were micro-stretched during processing can be finished wider than normal and compressively shrunk within the "Sanforized" label requirements. In addition, the fabrics have a better tensile and tear strength in the filling or crosswise direction.

Generally speaking, micro-stretched fabrics which have been resin-treated or cross-linked will be finished as wide or slightly wider than their gray goods or loom width. The fabric width is usually handled in this manner so as to retain greater strength after curing. Substantial width increases may also be obtained on fabrics which are not resin or cross-link finished, though there is not any substantial increase in the strength of these materials.

Micro-stretch reduces loss in strength because of resin finishing or cross-linking but does not materially improve the strength of fabrics not subjected to this type of finishing. Micro-stretch can be used to achieve different effects on different fabrics. These follow:

1. It may be used to soften stiff materials in all fiber constructions.

2. Increased width may be obtained prior to mercerizing, especially on chainless mercerizing machines; pertains to cotton and cotton blended fabrics.

3. Increased width is possible before the thermosetting treatment, as in the case of manmade and blended materials.

4. Improved hand and luster may be enhanced, especially on cottons.

5. Reduced extensibility is possible in manmade fiber cloths, as in the case of sailcloth.

6. Micro-stretching makes possible the achieving of a uniform and predeterminable extensibility over the entire width of fabrics in the filling direction. This is often important for coatings, laminations, etc., in practically all major fiber constructions.

7. It also aids in the rearrangement on the fibers in the filling yarn. This includes the transfer of crimp, the removal of crimp, the desegregation of fiber-blends in filling yarns in the goods, within certain limits applicable to all fibers and fiber-blends.

8. Improved uniformity and evenness of fabric weave constructions from the edges to the middle of the goods, are also pos-

sible. Results of this action can be observed in the instance of rectangular or square printing or woven patterns or designs that have become distorted because of being stretched differently at and near the listing or selvage edges. Applicable to all fiber and fiber blends. 9. Gaining width before or after treatments, during which the fabric cannot be held or gripped at the edges which often happens in cylinder drying, thermosetting on the drum-type heat-setting machines, or on chainless mercerizing widths, etc. Applicable to all fibers and fiber blends.

MI-CUIT SILK. Silk which has from 4 per cent to 8 per cent of the silk gum still in it. Cuit silk has all gum removed—from 10 per cent to about 25 per cent, the total amount of sericin found in raw silk fibers dependent on the grade of filament.

MIDANI. Made in the Levant area, it is a hand-woven cloth of silk warp and cotton filling in a 2-up, 1-down twill. This striped fabric has its stripings set off by thin white lines to separate them at set intervals.

MIDDLING. Cotton is officially graded into nine full grades. The middle or Number Five grade is middling, the standard by which all cottons are classed and compared. Thus, there are four grades above middling and four types below this type.

Middling cotton is white, relatively free of gin cuts and neps, and has an average amount of rather large leaf pieces.

The term is used in conjunction with six other qualities, such as good middling, middling fair, etc. See COTTON, grading table (United States).

MIDDY BLOUSE. A slip-on blouse with a sailor collar, made of jean, twill, or drill cotton cloth, and used in maritime and school circles. This high-texture, well-sized material gives excellent service since it will wash and launder very well.

MIDDY TWILL. Twilled jean fabric that may or may not be mercerized; is of good texture and made from strong yarn. It is used for uniform cloth, middy fabric, sportswear, and children's wear. Excellent wear and easy launderability are features of the cloth.

MIDRIFF. That portion of the body between the chest and the abdomen. Usually refers to a garment that accents this portion.

MID-VICTORIAN. Referring to the style of garment worn during the reign of Queen Victoria, 1837–1901.

MI-FILS. Very fine, high textured French cambric.

MIGNARDISE. A type of crochet work made by the insertion of fine, narrow ribbon into the motif as the heavier part of the design effect that would otherwise be made by crocheting.

MIGNONETTE, TRICOLETTE. Knitted rayon or silk materials made on circular machines. Very elastic, has some porosity, comes in white, flesh, pink and other colors. Underwear and dress cloth. Mignonette is of finer mesh and gauge.

Tendency to slip, run, and creep. Very lustrous and will last if cared for well. Difficult to cut and sew. Tricolette was the first knitted dress goods fabric to appear in the trade, 1924.

MIGNONETTE NET. 1. A cotton gauze-type of machine net used for curtaining. 2. Lightweight bobbin lace made in narrow strips; simulates tulle.

MIGRATION. The movement of a dye from one area of a dyed material to another area. Also includes the moving of color from a dyed area to an undyed section of the goods.

MIGRATION INHIBITOR. Substances used in the textile industry to prevent the migration or shifting of coloring matter on fabrics.

MIKADO. A lightweight, all-silk taffeta much used in England.

MIL. A unit of measurement used to obtain diameter of textile filaments and wire. It measures 1/1000th of an inch.

MI-LAINE. French for "half wool" and refers to some fabrics of the union type in which cotton warp and wool or worsted filling are used.

MILANAISE. 1. French term for a silk or rayon yarn with a cotton core. 2. A narrow braiding formed by one cord being twisted spirally around another. Called "Napolitaine," this braiding is used in upholstery work. 3. A corded material made on the principle of doup weaving so that the threads which form the cord are totally hidden from view.

MILAN BRAID. A flat mohair braid used for trimming and binding.

MILANESE. A variety of warp knit fabric in which the threads go in a diagonal direction and are interknitted at every course. These fabrics are characterized by a fine rib on the face and a faint diagonal or diamond effect on the back, and, if well made, are run resistant. Milanese fabrics do not have the variety of pattern found in tricot fabrics, but they are extensively made today of acetate, rayon, nylon, Dacron, etc. Of the lightweight, sheer type of goods, the fabric is popular in underwear and gloves. In some European

centers where the cloth is made, it is known, when made of silk, as Milanese Silk.

MILANESE CORDS. Named for the city of Milan, Italy, the fabrics present warp rib-effects which are made of cotton cord yarn covered by means of a silk warp which works on the principle of leno or doup weaving. The cord threads of cotton are completely covered and do not show on the face or back of the cloth.

MILANESE LACE. The fabric is made in the Philippines from the bast fiber, abaca. This drawn work, open embroidery effect product is not popular at present and seems to be dying out.

MILANO RIB. A three-course structure made of one course of the 1 x 1 rib, knitted on cylinder and dial. One course is knitted on dial needles, and the other course is knitted on cylinder needles only. See Milano Rib, Modified.

MILANO RIB, MODIFIED. A four-feed repeat structure comparable with Milano Rib except that two interlocking courses replace the single rib course in the knitting cycle. See Milano Rib.

MILAN POINT. Originally applied to plaited gold and silver lace, and reticella, the term now implies pillow lace. The word "point" is actually incorrect, but it is commonly used in the trade to signify this particular product. The machine-made lace of today, called by this name, has the design outlined in silk or nylon. See RETICELLA.

MILAN STRAW. Made from fine wheat-straw and named for Milan, Italy, it is used in the same manner as liséré and hemp braiding in the millinery trade.

MILDEW. A spore-forming fungi which appears on fabrics in various colors, the most common of which is black. Its growth is formed by a warm, moist but not too wet, confined atmosphere. Soaps and sizings are conducive to its growth which is manifest by black spotted areas on the goods.

Its removal is difficult because of several factors. First, as it grows, its roots spread through the fibers in the cloth forming protective sacs in a pigmentlike mass. Second, in growing, the fungi manufactures crystalline and resinous substances which only very strong bleaches such as hypochlorites or peroxides will remove. Excessive bleaching is not always advisable.

Mildew can be discouraged through the use of Fluoride (Sour). This ingredient can be added to the starch when it is being cooked. Formaldehyde should be added when cooked starch is used.

On dyed cloth, mildew discolorization and possible destruction is caused by a chemical reaction between the dye and the mold. On wool, the fungi will grow faster if alkali is present. If suds are left in blankets to insure softness, and they are then stored in a warm place, the growth of mildew will be encouraged. Acidification of the last rinse water is a good precaution against this. Fungi will cause more destruction on wool than on cotton. The various other methods used for the prevention of mildew are impractical for laundry use.

MILDEW-RESISTANT. The treatment of textiles to cause them to be impervious to mildew and mold. There are several factors to be considered in laboratory testing prior to the use of the term. For example, a textile plant survey conducted by Givaudan-Delawanna Company revealed these factors concerning mildew-resistant finishes: durability, flexibility, heat and light resistance, noncorrosiveness, nontoxic properties, permanency, water-resistance, weather resistance. A majority of mills reporting in the survey preferred chlorinated phenols, followed by mercurials and metallic soaps in treating textiles for this purpose.

MILENAISE. Not to be confused with Milanaise, this British cloth is a plain-weave cotton textured around 68-square to 72-square.

MILITARY BRAID. 1. The flat, coarse, ribbed worsted braid used to decorate a fez or tunic, and as a trimming on some women's apparel such as coatings. 2. Any of a host of braidings used on uniforms and for decorative purposes.

MILITARY CORD. Another name for Bedford Cord.

MILIUM. Trade-mark of Deering, Milliken & Co., Inc., for metal-insulated fabrics. Practically any fabric of natural or man-made fibers, or blends of these, can be metal-insulated, using as a barrier of radiant heat aluminum or other metal flakes in a resin base. These porous, metal-insulated fabrics allow the body to breathe freely, provide insulation against cold, and prevent the loss of body heat. In summer, they reflect the rays of the sun, thus keeping the wearer cooler.

MILIUM PLUS LINING. This lining-plus-insulation fabric, used for women's and childrens' wear, features a thin layer of laminated foam coated with insulative particles. The resultant fabric affords better insulation, in addition to improved resiliency and increased wrinkle resistance while retaining porosity. Product of Deering Mil-

liken, Inc., New York City.

MILKWEED. One of a genus Asclepias, common in the United States. The pod produces lustrous, downy fiber sometimes known as vegetable silk. Used as stuffing for mattresses and pillows. Mistakenly called kapok, at times.

MILL. 1. The building or buildings that are used to manufacture products, as in the case of a cotton mill, a woolen plant, etc. 2. Mill or milling, in finishing goods, is synonymous with fulling. 3. As a verb, to mill means to throw, as in silk, rayon, or acetate manufacture.

MILLBOARD. The thick cardboard placed between the folds of cloth during the process of pressing.

MILLED. Synonym for fulled or felted woven fabrics.

MILL ENDS. Mill remnants or short lengths of fabrics.

MILL-FINISH FABRICS. Cloths which need no converting. After being woven, they may be sized to give strength and support, often Sanforized, and then are ready for market. Examples include denim, cottonade, express stripes, constitution cloth, some specified canvas, and duck. The term also means fabric as it is ready to leave the plain in finished state. This finish is removed in the cut-fit-trim centers prior to manipulation into garments.

MILLE FLEURS. French for "a thousand flowers," such as found on some of the European tapestries used for background. This effect has been a feature in some tapestries since the sixteenth century.

MILLE POINTS. French for "a thousand points," and refers to woolen or worsted cloths made with small dobby-loom effects or suiting fabric such as bird's-eye, tack effect, etc. The fabrics are given a clear finish.

MILLERAIN. British trade name for a finishing process which uses a method of hot pressing or calendering to make certain cloths water repellent. Fabrics treated with the method will not shrink nor cockle, and dirt particles, etc., are easily removed.

MILLE RAYE. 1. Certain fabrics will show light reflection very well because of the type or types of yarn used, the construction, the method used to color the fabric, and the finish on the goods. Noted in some cross-dyed cloths, taffetas, some silk cloths, etc. Mille rayé, in French, means "a thousand rays," and the effect of these rays may cause a striped effect or one that is melange or mottled. Rayé, the French word, is used along with the basic name of the fabric to imply the effect. 2. The name for certain cloths made from the

major fibers characterized by distinct lines in the warp direction of black, white, or of strong colors. 3. Signifies a fine, warp rib cloth usually made of silk and which will reflect the rays of light at times.

MILLER'S GAUZE. The British use this name for silk or nylon bolting cloth such as used on the frames for screen or stencil printing.

MILLINERY. Hats, bonnets, head-dresses, or headgear of any type worn by women.

MILLINERY BLOCKER. One who can block felts, straw or fabric hats either by hand or by machine. The blocker should be able to size hats either before or after blocking; he must know the working properties of wool, fur, felt, straw, and fabrics. He should be able to determine the amount of sizing necessary for each type of material; he must know the differences in working straws—pressing, welting, steaming, sizing. The technique used in blocking fabrics is essential.

MILLINERY FELT. Felt made of wool, wool and cotton composition, or fur; beating, heating, and pressing make it possible to roll the composition into sheets. Body felts are blocked from sheets by specially made steel machines. Beaver and velours are the leading fur felts. Fur for this type of felt is drawn through the material by an electric process; the best grades come from Austria, France, and Switzerland.

MILLINERY HAIR. This transparent braid is made from composition yarns. Switzerland makes the best quality braid; Germany makes the medium grade and domestic localities make the inferior type. The best grades have a fine luster and body which makes them ideal for transparent hats in summer and for use with silk and taffeta on early spring hats.

MILLING. The operation of fulling textile fabrics.

MILLING FLOCKS. English term for short waste fibers of all types, such as picked up in the various departments of a mill; the blizzard of short fibers taken from certain floor coverings in the mill as they are being processed, reworked fibers, etc. Too short to be spun alone, these wastes, legion in number, are mixed with other, longer staple stocks and go into spun yarns. The range in these yarns is very wide, and the flocks are usually manipulated with the carrying fibers into low or very low-quality yarns and fabrics.

MILLON'S REAGENT. Soluble mercury in excess of nitric acid will give a red color on silk or wool but not on cotton. Formula is $Hg(NO_3)_2$—mercuric nitrate.

MILL RUN. Ungraded yarn or fabric yardage.

MILL WASTES. A very broad term to include any and all wastes from the machines used to card fibers, spin yarn and weave cloth. Includes:

1. SWEEPING WASTE: Lint and sweepings from any of the rooms in the textile plant. These short, fluffy fibers are used for flocks in finishing woolen coatings of low and medium grade.

2. BURR WASTE: Waste stock from which burrs, seeds, etc., have been removed by carbonization. It varies in accordance with the stocks from which these wastes were obtained. This waste comes only from wool, and to some degree, from the other animal fibers.

3. LAP WASTE: Fibers that vary in length and are obtained in any of the combing, drawing, or spinning operations. Much of this stock is returned to the initial machines for reworking into lower quality and shorter staple blends and mixes.

4. CARD WASTE: Short, immature, dead or fluffy fibers picked up in any carding operation. Card waste is used for blending purposes in low-grade woolens, flocks in overcoating, flocking in wall paper, candlewicks, and all kinds of low-grade yarn.

5. YARN OR THREAD WASTE: It is obtained from the jack spools, dressing frame, warp beam, filling bobbins, woven-out warps, etc. If the waste is made of animal fiber it is necessary to garnet the stock since there would be considerable twist in the yarn; mixture yarns must be carbonized to salvage the animal fibers if the stock is to be manipulated into lower quality fabric.

MILL WRINKLES. Creases which have been caused by passing cloth while twisted through rollers after washing, scouring, etc. They are very difficult to remove and are the bane of finishers in the mill.

MILTON. Very likely a contraction of the word, melton. See MELTON.

MINERAL. Any substance that is neither animal nor vegetable; any chemical substance which results naturally from inorganic processes. The mineral asbestos, for example, is used in laundries. Asbestos woven covers are made to the full width of the flat work ironer chest so that the cotton duck will not become damaged because of excessive heat or burning when the apron is not in action.

MINERAL ACID. One without carbon, such as sulphuric, hydrochloric, nitric acids.

MINERAL DYES. A group of natural dyes that include iron black, iron buff, manganese bistre, chrome yellow, Prussian blue, et al. The compounds are precipitated in the form of salt on the fibers. They are used chiefly on industrial fabrics, since they possess very good fastness properties.

MINERAL FIBERS. Asbestos is the most important mineral fiber; spun glass, slag wool, tinsel threads, and those manipulated from gold, copper, silver, and alloy threads which are made from a combination of minerals complete the group.

MINERAL KHAKI. A combination of hydrated ferric hydroxide and chrome hydroxide serves as the base for this color. A solution of the soluble acetate of each of these metals is padded on the goods, and the hydroxide formed by alkali treatment, plus drying, will give the final shade.

MINERAL OIL. Any of various oils derived from inorganic matter, especially petroleum and its products.

MINERAL TANNAGE. Leather produced by the use of chromium salts, alum, and comparable agents other than "the vegetable tannages."

MINERAL WOOL. A fibrous wool-like material made by blowing a powerful jet of air or steam through melted slag. Used as an insulating and packing material.

MINIFIL, MINIFILAMENT. A general, and at times misunderstood, term, which refers to man-made filaments such as denier counts of 100 to 200 with filaments numbering 10 to 24 or so. Product of American Viscose Corporation.

MINK. North American, Ranch, Eastern, Japanese, China. A member of the weasel family with short, glossy hair ranging in color from orange-yellow to dark brown. Wearing qualities, for most, excellent; for Japanese, fair. Judged by dense underfur, natural color, silkiness, and lightness of weight. Found in North America, Russia, China, Japan. For general, as well as formal, wear.

North American mink is the most valuable. Eastern mink is the trade name applied to better grades from New England States. American mink is either ranch-raised or wild. Ranch mink is generally better in color and lighter in weight, and tends to run more uniform than wild mink. All mutation mink is ranch-raised. Of the three strains—Yukon, Labrador, and Eastern —Yukon is considered best.

The best wild mink comes from the Labrador Peninsula, in Newfoundland, or the Province of Quebec, Canada. Wild mink reputedly keeps its color longer than ranch mink.

MIORO SHEEP. A Sardinian sheep which produces a coarse wool used for clothing of low quality, and for carpet yarns. Sometimes called Arbaccio.

MIRECOURT. Belgian town which made the first Leavers machine-made cotton lace on a bobbin-fining set-out. It is recognized by its finely woven net, known as half-fining.

MIRESHKA. Fancy work done in Russia which uses the embroidery of colored yarns into canvas foundation; drawn thread effects are seen in the completed article.

MIROIR. French for polished or mirror surface; used for the gloss or luster given to many fabrics during the finishing operations.

MIRROR VELVET. See CUT VELVET.

MISCIBILITY. That which can be mixed, as in the case of the various ingredients used in a typical dye bath to color textiles.

MISPICKS. Missing filling picks in the material which have not been cast all the way through the shed of the loom or have become broken in the loom shed; failing to interlace in the proper manner with warp because of some mechanical defect in weaving. One of the commonest defects encountered in weaving.

MISSED LOOP IN KNITTING. A length or lengths of yarn not received by a needle and connecting two loops of the same course that are not in adjacent wales.

MISSION CLOTH. Low-grade type of monk's cloth used for drapes and hangings. It is seen often with a printed border, and may or may not be stencil-printed if a design is desired.

MISSION NET. Also known as fish net, it is made in the same way as Boston net, but it is much larger and coarser in appearance.

MIS-STITCH. A knitting term also called Float-Stitch or Welt-Stitch. It is made when the knitting needle holds the old loop and does not receive a new yarn; that is, a needle is held in a non-working position as the yarn is guided to the needles in the working position. A Mis-stitch is not a Mis-loop.

The Mis-stitch is done on purpose in order to obtain some special or particular effect. It is used to "hide colors" or to float threads so that brushing or napping will be effective on the finished goods. It is lighter and narrower than the tuck stitch type of fabric.

MISTI. The foal of an alpaca sire and llama dam. From the Quichua language, the aboriginal Peruvian tongue.

MISTRAL. Worsted dress-goods fabric which has a nub effect caused by the mixture of stock colors and the twist given to the yarn prior to weaving of the cloth.

MITAFIFFI COTTON. A popular Egyptian cotton, light brown in cast, but darker than Sakellaridis which runs to the white. It ranges from 1¼ inches to 1½ inches in staple, and the counts of yarn made usually range from 70s to 100s and upwards.

MITCHELINE. Bed covering made of two warps and two fillings. In order to increase design possibilities, the double plain weave is used, and squares, stripings, and oblongs are seen on the face of the material. The counts of yarn may or may not be the same.

MITIN. Mothproofing process for wool and wool mixtures. Acting like a fast wool dye, it provides a permanent proof that resists washing, dry cleaning, and all conditions of wear. It does not affect the hand of cloth, the color, or other properties found in materials of this type. Mitin gives no odor, is non-toxic, and does not irritate the skin. Trade-mark of Ciba-Geigy Corporation.

MITRE. 1. The liturgical high, peaked headdress proper to the bishops of the Latin rite in the Roman Catholic Church. It is symbolic in the consecration of a bishop as "the helmet of salvation," and in general as a symbol of the teaching authority of the Church. There are three kinds of mitres - white cloth, gold cloth, and the precious mitre of costly gold fabric, embellished and studded with jewels. 2. The point of contact where two pieces of carpet, or other materials, join at an angle, usually of 45 degrees to form a right angle. Mitre may be made of any combination of angles and the point of contact may be of various lengths.

MITTEN. Knitted material used as covering for the hand. There are sheaths for the four fingers and thumb. The difference between a glove and a mitten is that the former has a sheath for each of the four fingers, while the mitten has one sheath for the entire four fingers. Mittens and gloves are either seamless, full-fashioned, or cut. Mittens are seamless, but gloves may be made on any of the three types used in the trade.

MITTEN FLANNEL. See GLOVE FLANNEL.

MIWATA COTTON. Japanese term for unginned cotton.

MIXED CHECKS. Applied to cloths whose check effects are mottled or more or less "shot-about" in the pattern. Also includes a type of union fabric where the white stripes are made with linen and the colored checking effect is made with cotton. Other warp and filling combinations may be used to provide mixed checks in textile fabrics.

MIXED FABRICS. Another name for a union material, cloth that has two or more types of fibers in it.

MIXED FILLING. When a bobbin of the wrong size or color has been woven into the material by mistake. This error may be laid to sheer carelessness or oversight by the weavers. Picking-out of the spoiled area causes the weaver to lose much time and production.

MIXED FILLING ARRANGEMENT. The filling in silk, rayon, and other sheer fabrics is usually woven from two or more shuttles on box looms. The action keeps shady effects in the filling direction in the cloth at a minimum.

MIXED-PACKED COTTON. Samples from a bale which show a difference or more than two grades or color gradations, or a difference in staple length of more than ³⁄₃₂ inches.

MIXING. Taking cotton from a series of bales and mixing it so as to obtain the desired, uniform mix. Cotton is mixed on the "layer plan."

MIXING PICKER. Any of various machines used in the preparatory processes in woolen manufacture. Their function is principally to mix the stock, open it still further and deliver it in the most suitable condition to the card. Different types are called teaser, fearnaught, willow, etc.

MIXTURE. Stock, yarn, or fabric composed of two or more different textile fibers. Also implies the use of two or more colors in fiber condition of a blend or mix, in the yarn or in the finished material.

MIXTURE CREPE. Any crepe material which has a warp different from the filling, with regard to the raw material used.

MIXTURE FABRIC. One made with a warp yarn wholly of one fiber, and a filling yarn wholly of another fiber, including fabrics in which either the warp or the filling yarn may be a plied yarn.

MIXTURE YARN. A yarn spun from fibers of different properties, characteristics, color, luster, etc. Blending is done usually in raw stock condition, although blending of certain sorts occurs in the drawing operations.

"mm²/mm³." This term refers to the number of square millimeters of exterior surface of cotton fibers per cubic millimeter of fibrous material. As the fiber becomes smaller, the amount of surface-per-unit volume of fibrous material becomes greater.

A coarse cotton is likely to have an area of 300 or more mm²/mm³ of fibrous material, whereas the average cotton would run 400 mm²/mm³, and fine cottons would be around 500 mm²/mm³.

MMF-45. A crimped rayon yarn which possesses wool-like properties. Ideal for blends, it is composed of several varied cross-sections of both light and heavy denier sizes. Cross-sections may be round, circular, square, oblong, or irregular. This heterogenously formed fiber is a product of Sateri Corporation, Valkeakoski, about seventy-five miles north of Helsinki, Finland.

MOBILE COTTON. 1. Short staple Upland cotton, mostly ⅞ inch in length, shipped under Mobile, Alabama, bill of lading. 2. A rather soft, soiled staple raised in the Mobile area. Used with other staples for yarn to be used in carpets and rugs, lamp wicks, and sponge cloths.

MOCCA. In embroidery, the spider-like stitching stitched over an open eyelet. The entire hole is called by this term.

MOCCASIN. Derived from the footwear of the American Indian, it is now modified into a type of shoe which features a strap over the instep. This slip-on sport shoe is often known as a loafer. The strap may be stitched to the body of the shoe or, if free, slipped through a buckle for fastening.

MOCH. French expression for fully sealed, unbroken bundles or packages of spun silk. The English use the term to signify silk of this type sent to Great Britain from the Continent, etc.

MOCHA LEATHER. See GLOVE LEATHERS.

MOCKADO. A simulated velvet popular in the swashbuckling days of the sixteenth and seventeenth centuries; a long-napped woolen fabric of varying weights.

MOCK CAKE. A package of yarn obtained by winding on a collapsible reel, swift, mandril, or former. The package, after being formed, is removed from the device and has about the same dimensions as a rayon cake. It is, however, usually built up from the inside to the outside in contradistinction to the rayon cake.

MOCK CHENILLE YARN. It is made by doubling two or more unbalanced corkscrew yarns in reverse direction to form a balanced structure. See MOCK TWIST.

MOCK CREPE. See MOCK ROMAINE CREPE, ROMAINE CREPE, MOCK TWIST.

MOCK EGYPTIAN COTTON. Cotton yarn or cloth that has been given a buff or ecru coloring to simulate certain Egyptian cottons whose natural tint is buff or ecru.

MOCK FASHIONING. See HOSIERY KNITTING.

MOCK GRANDRELLE. A single spun yarn made from double roving; a colored and a white roving combination, or one from two different colored rovings.

MOCK LENO. Lightweight cloths made with plain or colored stripes. There are regular open-warp stripes formed in the weave by the interlacing of groups of closely placed warp and filling threads, without being deflected from their relative parallel position. The groups are separated from each other on the order of leno or doup construction.

MOCK QUILTING. Mock means to mimic or to simulate. Applied to quilting, it is a British term for a material made of some piqué or honeycomb construction to simulate a quilted spread, dress goods, counterpane, etc. This cotton product does not have the full texture of regulation quilting.

MOCK ROMAINE CREPE. Similar to a true Romaine as to warp make-up with the filling of single pickage of 200-denier acetate or rayon yarn twisted with 24 turns; the filling in true Romaine generally illustrates a combination yarn. See ROMAINE CREPE.

MOCK SEAM. English hosiery, the leg of which is cut and the foot fashioned. Also implies knitted hosiery with a seam which runs down the back of the stocking by means of twin-needle stitching in the one operation without cutting the article.

MOCK TWIST. A single yarn which gives the appearance of a twisted yarn of two colors. The interspersing of color is brought about by feeding a white and a colored slubbing into the frame, or by feeding in two contrasting colored slubbings. The mottled effect produced is popular, at times, in sports hosiery and children's stockings.

MODACRYLIC, REDEFINED DEFINITION OF. Effective October 31st, 1969, a redefinition of Modacrylic is "to exclude those fibers which qualify under the term, ANIDEX;" the eighteenth term in the list of Manmade Fiber definitions as decreed by the Federal Trade Commission relative to the Textile Fiber Products Identification Act of 1960. See Anidex.

MODACRYLIC FIBER. A manufactured fiber in which the fiber-forming substance is any long chain synthetic polymer composed of less than 85 per cent but at least 35 per cent by weight of acrylonitrile units. Dynel and Verel are examples.

MODE. Any type of a filling-in stitch used in lacemaking; also called filling, jours, lead works, etc., See ALAMODE.

MODEL. Any person or manikin whose profession is posing with, demonstrating, using, or wearing a product for advertising or display. Today modeling has become big business and taken on great proportions. It should be noted that there are models, and "there are models," from the true professional to the amateur. It is rather infrequent that female models appear in a natural pose in modeling clothes; this artificial pose is an asset in drawing attention to the model in advertising the item being shown. Though many are called but few are chosen, professional models, men, women, and children do make a very good living.

MODERN FASHIONS AND STYLES, INFLUENCES ON. Many nations have contributed to the present-day fashions and styles, in short from Afghanistan to Zululand. Some few, however, of the major contributions are as follows:

1. BOHEMIAN: The large embroidered cap; embroidered sleeves; colored ribbons; the use of red as a color; elaborately decorated aprons; the use of the flower wreath once used to denote an unmarried girl.

2. BYZANTINE: Costumes of straight-hanging effect in rich silks embroidered with precious stones, gold, or silver.

3. CHINESE: The use of the plain or embroidered robe and trousers. Wide coat sleeves originated with the Chinese; mandarin collars.

4. JAPANESE: The long kimono and the use of a sash with a bow in the back.

5. MODERN GREEK: Coats decorated with gold embroidery on velvet, and trouser effects caused by the Ottoman influence.

6. RUSSIAN: The use of the short, flare jacket with yoke of different fabric, the skirt noted for its fullness and the peasant-costume beauty, richness, and variety. Jackets may or may not be sleeveless.

7. SPANISH: The use of the mantilla held in place by a comb in the back of the hair, the colorful, richly trimmed skirt and the use of lace.

MODE SHADES. Those in demand as the whims of fashion and style change constantly; has particular reference to hosiery and custom-tailored women's wear apparel.

MODICA. Sicilian raw silk.

MODIFIED. Limited or slightly altered to some particular form for some definite purpose or result.

MODIFIED CELLULOSE FIBER. A fiber made by incorporating a synthetic resin, casein, etc., in a viscose spinning solution, produced as staple with a soft handle and dyeing properties like wool. It is also referred to as basified wool.

MODIFIED CONTINUOUS FILAMENT. General broad term to imply man-made fibers or filaments which have been modified along certain lines such as bulk, stretch, textured yarns, etc.

MODIFIED STAPLE FIBER. Acetate or rayon staple fiber or spun yarn treated to produce wool-like properties in the product.

MODIFIED VISCOSE STAPLE. Viscose process staple which contains a small percentage of casein to give wool dyeing characteristics. Rayolanda is the British trade name for modified viscose staple fiber; Cisalfa the Italian name for the product.

MODOC, MODOCK WOOL. 1. Pulled wool from the sandy, short, fine-territory skins obtained from certain sheep grown west of the Mississippi-Missouri River. 2. Reclaimed wool fiber from hard-woven and pulled fabrics.

MODULUS, SECANT. The ratio of change in stress to change in strain between two points on a stress-strain diagram, especially the points of zero stress and breaking stress.

MODULUS, TANGENT. The ratio of change in stress to change in strain derived from the tangent to any point on a stress-strain curve.

MODULUS, YOUNG'S. For perfectly elastic materials, it is the ratio of change in stress to change in strain within the elastic limits of the material. The ratio is calculated from the stress expressed in the force per unit cross-sectional area, and the strain expressed as a fraction of the original length. It should be noted that modulus calculated in the foregoing explanation is equivalent to the force required to strain the sample 100 per cent of its original length, at the rate prevailing below the elastic limit.

MODULUS OF ELASTICITY. Modulus means a number, coefficient, or quantity that measures a force, function, or effect. Applied to elasticity it is the load necessary to stretch a specimen of unit cross-sectional area a unit amount. It is expressed in terms of pounds per square inch, dynes per square centimeter, or kilograms per square millimeter. It also implies the ratio of unit stress to unit strain. In the case of most textile fibers, the term implies only the initial portion of the stress-strain curve in which the stress is proportional to the strain, and the term itself refers only to this part of the curve.

MOGADOR. A corded, plain-weave material of a silk or rayon warp and cotton or linen filling to give it firmness or stiffness. This neckwear material comes in regimental, college, blazer, Algerian and Moroccan stripes, in a wide range of quality. Some Mogador is moiréd.

MOGADOR WOOL. A Moroccan wool brown in cast, irregular, kempy, and dull in appearance; named for this city in Morocco.

MOHAIR. The Angora goat, which furnishes mohair, is one of the oldest animals known to man. Mohair is 2½ times as strong as wool and will outwear it. The goats are raised in South Africa, Western Asia, Turkey, and neighboring countries, and in Texas, California and Oregon. Kerrville is the great center of the mohair industry in Texas.

Foreign mohair, 9 to 12 inches in staple length, is allowed a full year's growth prior to shearing; domestic fleeces are obtained bi-annually in California and Texas, annually in Oregon. The hair of the animals found in Texas and California will fall out if allowed a full year's growth. Texas fleeces weigh about 2½ pounds; Oregon fleeces about four pounds.

Angora goat fleeces show fibers which average about 9 inches. The fibers, which are very strong, high in luster, whitish in shade, fairly soft in handle, and straight in staple appearance, possess good uniformity. The diameter is about 1/700 inch. The length and luster of mohair fiber is more desirable than staple fineness. Mohair is used for braid, fancy dress materials, felt hats, linings, and plushes.

MOHAIR BRAID. A black or colored braid made possible by the use of two mohair cords in the construction; also known as Russian Braid.

MOHAIR CLOTH. Cloth made from the hair of the Angora goat. Used for lining, is lustrous, made in plain and twill weaves, dyed in natural shade or in other colors. Mohair cloth is made with the straight fiber, or of adulterated stock. Wide range of cloth is in this type of material.

MOIRE IMPERIALE. An indistinct, allover moiré or watermarked effect found on some faille, taffeta, certain cotton fabrics, etc. There is no set pattern in this type of finish applied to the fabrics.

MOHAIR LUSTERS. Broad term to cover lining fabrics made of cotton warp and mohair filling; usually dyed black or gray. Some of the fabric may be used for low-priced dress goods.

MOHAIR RUG. A rug made of mohair warp and cotton filling and backing. A warp pile made of cotton accompanies this lustrous rug.

MOHAVE YUCCA. Fiber raised in Arizona, California, and New Mexico. It is compared with banana yucca since it grows in the same regions as the latter, but at lower altitudes. It is finer, softer, and weaker than the banana fiber.

MOIRÉ. A textile fabric with a moiré (watermarked) finish, especially a corded silk, acetate, or rayon. Produced by passing the fabric between engraved cylinders which press the design into the material, causing the crushed and uncrushed parts to reflect the light differently. The pattern is not permanent except on acetate. Makes appealing formal dresses for women.

MOIRÉ, ACETATE. A permanent-finish, watermarked taffeta that drapes well; gives good service, and is popular for evening wear. Comes in white, solid colors, or wide stripe effects.

MOIRÉ, WATERMARKING. A watered, or a bright-and-dim effect, given to acetate, rayon, silk, and cotton fabrics. Produced by means of engraved rollers which exert very heavy pressure on the goods in order to enhance its beauty. Much taffeta, voile, and organdy receives the finish. Acetate fabrics will retain the finish permanently, rayons will not. See MOIRE PROCESS; Illustrated Section (Fabrics 17).

MOIRÉ À POIS. The moiré effect of small spots or peas (pois) on the face of silk or rayon fabric; spots are usually applied in a satin-weave order.

MOIRÉ À RETOURS. Moiré effects on fabric which show that each half of the cloth has the same effect but in reverse; the cloth is folded selvage-to-selvage to obtain the results.

MOIRÉ LISSE. Fabric which has a glossy, all-over surface finish but one devoid of watermarking effects.

MOIRÉ MILLE FLEURS. Printed cloth with small floral effects; the term, when narrowly applied, refers to cloth made from silk warp and worsted filling in poplin or rep effect.

MOIRÉ NACRE. Silk or rayon fabric dyed to imitate the mother-of-pearl inside of sea shells (nacre). The cloth is used chiefly in evening wear and for bridal raiment.

MOIRÉ OCEAN. Moiré or watermarked effect which is undulating in effect to simulate the waves of the ocean.

MOIRÉ POPLIN. A silk-warp, wool-filling fabric which has been moiréd.

Rep- or poplin-effect weaves are used.

MOIRÉ PROCESS. There are a number of different methods used to produce a moiré, and each of these produces its own peculiar style of patterns. There is the Pekin, Antique Velour, Pick-on-Pick, and the two discussed below:

1. FRANÇAIS OR BAR MOIRÉ: The goods are run up on a beam, doubled, while retarding certain sections of the filling, as they pass a fixed point. This operation is called "tracing," and produces a motif in which all the lines run warp-wise. This style of moiré is called Français and the shiny areas between are called bars. If it is desired to trace twenty bars on a given fabric, the material is then called a "Twenty-Bar Français."

2. SCRATCH METHOD OF MOIRÉ. This popular method is known as Scratch, and it permits production of figured motifs such as teardrops, flowers, tropical palms, stars, etc. In this method, the fabric is doubled, then run through a so-called scratching machine which somewhat resembles a roller printing machine, having an engraved roller made of rubber. Bearing against this engraved roller, and revolving at a higher speed, are a series of scratch blades, set into a scratch roller along the lines of a lawn mower. The double cloth is run between the scratch blades and the engraved rubber roller, and the filling yarn in the fabric is shifted in those places where the blades find resistance in the raised places of the engraved rubber roller. Although only a limited number of cloths are suitable for this method, chiefly 200- and 300-denier taffetas, and selected tie-silk failles, it has been very popular since its adaptation to acetate taffetas a few years ago. Pattern styles other than Français and Scratch, such as Pekin, Antique, Miroire, and Velour are achieved by the use of special equipment, such as mangles, plate presses, etc., and are still in occasional demand, but require, as a rule, cloth especially woven for the purpose, usually yarn- or skein-dyed materials.

MOIRÉ RENAISSANCE. Silk or rayon warp and cotton filling are used in this coarse rib-effect cloth. The material is folded, calendered, or friction-calendered, and then pressed to develop the permanent striped moiré pattern.

MOIRÉ RONDE. Rounded (rondé) moiré (watermarked) effects on some silks and rayons; the cloth is also known as moiré française.

MOIRÉ SCINTILLANT. Cloth with a lustrous or brilliant moiré (watermarked) effect in which the tram or filling threads are woven to enhance the scintillating beauty of the material.

MOIRÉ SOLEIL. A lustrous silk or rayon with an indistinct or mottled watermarked effect.

MOIRÉ SUPREME. Silk or rayon in which a warp-effect satin weave enhances the brilliant moiré effect.

MOIRÉ TABISÉE. Cloth with moiré effects obtained by calendering or friction-calendering. (Tabisée means made wavy.)

MOIRÉ TAFFETA. See MOIRÉ PROCESS.

MOIRÉ VELOUR. Decorative fabric made of silk or rayon warp and cotton filling. The material is cheap, rather open, and loosely woven.

MOIRETTE. Comparable with cotton moreen except for finer-warp yarn in the construction.

MOISTURE CONTENT. The moisture calculated as a percentage of weight of the specimen.

$$\frac{A-B \times 100}{A} \quad \frac{100-94 \times 100}{100} = 6\%$$

A is weight of specimen before drying. B is dry weight of specimen. See Moisture Regain.

MOISTURE COTTON, MANCHESTER METHOD. The standard is fixed at 7.834 pounds. On exposure to air, 100 pounds of bone-dry cotton will take on 8½ pounds of moisture, a total of 108½ pounds; thus, 108½ pounds will contain 8½ pounds of moisture; 100 pounds of cotton will contain 7.834 pounds of moisture.

MOISTURE EQUILIBRIUM. The conditions reached by a sample of textile material when it no longer will absorb or take up moisture from or give up moisture to the surrounding atmosphere.

MOISTURE-FREE WEIGHT. Fabric weight after it has been dried to a constant weight by an approved procedure. Can also imply the bone-dry weight.

MOISTURE PERCENTAGE. This is found by definite prescribed methods and is stated as a percentage of the weight of the sample, either in the original, or in the oven-dry weight as found in a conditioning oven used for the purpose.

MOISTURE REGAIN. The moisture calculated as a percentage when a specimen is brought into equilibrium at standard atmosphere from a lower moisture regain.

$$\frac{A-B \times 100}{A} \quad \frac{100-94}{94} = \frac{6 \times 100}{94} = 6\%$$

A is the specimen before drying. B is the dry weight of specimen. See Moisture Content.

MOISTURE REGAIN OF SOME MAJOR TEXTILE FIBERS. Moisture is water or some other liquid which renders anything moist. Absorbency means to take up or receive in by chemical or molecular action. Moisture regain is the percentage which the weight of moisture in a textile material represents of its bone dry weight. Sometimes referred to as content. Percentages of moisture regain in fibers follows (standard conditions:

FIBER:	PERCENT OF MOISTURE REGAIN:
Acetate	6.00
Acrilan	1.50
Arnel	3.00
Cotton	6.00-8.00
Creslan	1.50
"Dacron"	0.50
Dynel	0.40
Flax	10.0-12.00
Fortisan	10.70
Fortrel	0.40
Kodel	0.40
Lycra	0.30
Mercerized cotton	10.00-11.00
Nylon 6	4.50
Nylon 66	8.00
Nytril	2.60
Olefins	0.00
"Orlon"	1.50-2.50
Rayon, regular	12.00-13.00
Rayon, high wet modulus	12.20
Silk	10.00
Verel	3.00-4.00
Vycron	0.40
Wool	15.00-25.00
Worsted	10.00-15.00
Zefran	2.50

MOISTURE TRANSPORT. Property of a fabric to absorb moistures, including perspiration, and wick them to the surface of the goods where evaporation occurs. Moisture transport is determined in wear testing methods by laboratory use of the AATCC Test Method 79-1954-"Absorbency of Bleached, Woven Cloth." See Nylon 22N, Monsanto.

MOITING. The removing of small particles of foreign matter from wool fleeces during sorting.

MOITS, MOTES. Refers to all foreign matter found in wool, such as burrs, hay, leaves, seeds, thorns, twigs, etc.

MOITY. Wool fleece with considerable vegetable matter in it.

MOJO FIBER. The mojo tree in Honduras produces this tough, durable bast fiber of good elasticity; used for rope.

MOLAINE. Made to simulate delaine fabric, this British material is a plain-weave, union cloth of cotton warp and wool filling. The term also implies that mohair might be used instead of the wool for filling.

MOLD. A fungus growth peculiar to food, clothing, walls, etc. It will attack wool and fur and will cause vegetable matter to decay. This fungus is called a saprophyte, or an organism that lives on dead or decaying matter.

MOLDABLE FABRIC OR TEXTILE. One which can be shaped or formed by a system of molding, whereby the fibers of yarns in the fabric are drawn, attenuated, or stretched; the molded area of the fabric has significantly greater area than its original plane, from which it was drawn.

MOLDED-FABRIC PRODUCTS. Since all man-made fibers, rayon excepted, are thermoplastic in structure, this property permits the necessary molecular change to occur when heat and pressure are applied. Thus, molding may be applied to fluffy pile textures as well as to leather-like flat fabrics. Molded fabrics retain their original shape permanently, unaffected by washing, wear, heat, or moisture; the "newness" of a product is literally molded into it. This revolutionary phase in textiles is ideal for brassières, swimwear, stuffed animals, shoes, gloves, transportation fabric, slipcovers, upholstery, etc. Product of International Fabric Molders, Inc., New York City.

MOLE. A soft, fine-textured fur, slate-colored, often dyed brown, black, and occasionally green, red, and blue. Wearing qualities, poor. Judged by softness and luster. Found in Belgium, Scotland, France, and Holland. Worn for dress.

MOLECULE. The smallest quantity of any substance which can exist separately and still retain the characteristics of the substance; a group of atoms acting as a physical unit. A molecule of water, for example, is made up of two hydrogen atoms and one oxygen—H_2O.

MOLESKIN CLOTH. A one-warp, two-filling rugged cotton fabric in which there is a two-and-one face-filling arrangement—two picks of face filling to one pick of back filling. Made in satin construction, the cloth is given a thick, soft nap on the back to simulate mole fur. Used for coat linings, semidress trousers, and work clothes.

MOLINE. It is made with spun silk warp and ordinary silk tram filling; in the taffeta family of fabrics.

MOLLETON. (From French for melton.) Name given to silence cloth in cotton goods trade. The fabric is

MOLDED FABRICS

Acrylics, modacrylics, polyesters, nylons, and polyolefins are classed as thermoformable (heat-formable) fibers. They can, by themselves or in certain types of blends with other fibers, by the application of heat and force or energy, be deformed into shapes which have dimensional stability in use. Woven, knitted, nonwoven fabrics and felt made of these thermoformable fibers may be molded. A molded fabric may be defined as one which can be shaped or formed by a system of molding, whereby the fibers of the yarn in the fabric are drawn, attenuated, or stretched; the molded area of the fabric has significantly greater area than its original plane from which it was drawn.

Molded fabrics have had continued success in the textile and apparel industries. With the exception of rayon (viscose and cuprammonium), all other man-made fibers are thermoplastic in nature, and it is this property which permits the necessary molecular change when heat and pressure are applied. Thus, molding may be applied to a fluffy pile fabric or to leatherlike flat fabrics.

Three methods are used in heat-shaping or forming of the fibers. They are:

1. Compression-Forming Method

Two molds, or a male and a female die, may be used to produce more complex and intricate designs and shapes. The process is comparable with plug molding. Because of the pressure developed, the shaped article is usually stiffer and glossier than those formed by the plug method or the modified vacuum method.

2. Modified Vacuum-Forming Method

The fabric is preheated to a pliable or formable temperature and is deformed into the desired shape. A plug assist may be used to cause the fabric to conform to the molded shape. An elastic impermeable membrane is placed on one side of the fabric with a vacuum on the other side in order to achieve the closest conformation to the shape of the mold. Either male or female molds may be used.

3. Plug-Molding Method

A cooled or heated mold of any shape, reasonable size or design is forced into a fabric which has been preheated.

Molded fabrics will retain their shape permanently, are unaffected by washing, wear, heat or moisture within normal, reasonable limits. The "newness" of a product is literally molded into it. This revolutionary phase in fabric development and engineering in apparel makes molded fabrics ideal for brassieres, swimwear, stuffed animals, gloves, shoes, transportation fabric, slip covers, upholstery, headgear, etc.

---

heavily felted and napped on both sides; used as a protecting cloth under the tablecloth to absorb the rattling of dishes and to protect the finish on the table.

MOLTEN-METAL DYEING PROCESS. Dyeing of fabric which has been impregnated with an aqueous dye solution and then passed through a bath of molten metal at a temperature usually not above 100 degrees Centigrade.

MOMIE CLOTH. A crinkled, lusterless black fabric made with cotton warp and wool filling. Used chiefly as mourning fabric.

MOMIE CREPE. Lightweight cotton fabric in a crepe or granite weave. Ordinary twist yarn is used. The term, at times, may be a misnomer in its application.

MOMIE TOWELING. A soft-textured crash toweling in which the warp and filling yarns have spiral twist caused by the use of a fine yarn combined with a coarse yarn. The fabric is very irregular in appearance and has very good absorption.

MOMIE WEAVE. An irregular weave of small repeat such as a double satin, granite or quarter-turn. The weave is used in the manufacture of heavy, soft-textured, crash toweling. The yarns used in both systems are spiral-twisted, the twisting of a fine yarn with a coarse one. The irregular weave and irregular filling floats will produce a rough, granitelike surface effect.

MOMMIE, MOMME. A Japanese weight which equals .13228 English ounce, or 3.75 metric grams, and used for measuring and stating the weight of

silk cloths. The weight equals 37.874 grains. There are 120.96 mommie to the pound.

MOMMIE CLOTH. Fabric made to imitate silk cloth of this name. When made of cotton, a crepe weave is used; there also is a cloth of this name on the market made of cotton warp and wool filling.

MOMMY OR MUMMY CLOTH. When this term is applied to a cloth it usually means that the fabric is not made for the export trade; consequently, little of the goods finds its way to this country. None of the cloth is made here. For want of a better name, the term mummy is given the cloth.

MON-CHIRIMEN. A fine silk crepe cloth with high luster used in Japan for embroidery purposes.

MONDRIAAN, PETER CORNELIS. 1964 saw the birth and demise of Mondrian motifs in women's dresses. These were named in honor of Mondriaan (1872-1944), the noted Dutch abstract painter and founder of the Neoplastic Movement, which featured geometrical patterns and motifs - coin dots, circles, oblongs, lines, and other geometrical effects. Though they took the fashion world by storm, these items of dress failed to last more than a year and merely faded away.

MONEY-BUSH COTTON. A variety of Uplands raised in the Mississippi area. Not as important as formerly.

MONFLOW, MOUFFLON WOOL. Wild sheep from the Mediterranean area—Corsica, Greece, Crete, Sicily, etc.

MONK'S CLOTH. A 4-and-4 basket weave is used to make this heavy fabric that is used for couch covers, hangings, and furniture fabric. It is not easy to sew or manipulate and the yarns may have a tendency to slide. The material may sag in time, depending on the compactness of the texture. This rough, substantial cloth can also be made from other small basket-weaves.

MONK'S CLOTH, FANCY. Made with honeycomb or spot-weave effects, this fabric is tinted to simulate unbleached material. This cotton cloth finds use in hangings, some coating, and in garb for beach wear.

MONK-STRAP SHOE. A type of shoe with a strap across the instep and embellished by a buckle on the side; comes in many variations and styles.

MONO-CHROME DYEING. See META-CHROME DYEING.

MONOFIL, MONOFILAMENT. A single large filament from man-made fibers such as acetate, rayon, nylon, "Orlon," "Dacron," Fiberglas, etc.

MONOFLEX. A flexible fabric used in the waistband of skirts and trousers to prevent "roll-out," it keeps the waistband smooth and snug when relaxed or in action. When used "under the coat," it gives the chest and shoulder areas shape retention and support.

The fabric is made with cotton warp while the filling is DuPont monofilament yarn. It comes in a wide selection of thicknesses to permit a wide degree of resiliency. It is limp in the warp direction and stiff in the direction of the monofilament filling. Monoflex can be bleached or dyed and is impervious to drycleaning and repeated washings. Highly desirable fabric wherever support is needed. Registered trademark of Michie Textiles, Inc., Philadelphia, Pennsylvania, 19122.

MONOGENETIC DYE. A dyestuff which gives only one color to textile yarn or fabric when applied.

MONOPLEX 11. Plasticizer for polyvinyl and copolymers for use in coated fabrics, luggage, rainwear, shower curtains, and upholstery. The product is a dialkyl ester of a synthetic long-chain dibasic acid which shows high plasticizing efficiency in polyvinyl-chloride stocks, with temperature and ultraviolet resistant properties at much lower volatility than is usually found combined with such solvating action. Treated products drape well.

MONOPLEX 16 FINISH. A high molecular weight nitrile plasticizer which yields polyvinyl-chloride stocks of superior heat and ultraviolet stability, excellent permanence, good low-temperature flexibility, and very low water-sensitivity. The relation of temperature to the solvating action of Monoplex 16 is ideal for dispersion compounding. Product of Resinous Products & Chemical Co.

MONOPOLYMER, MONO-POLY-MER. A single chemical polymer, as distinguished from a copolymer which is made from two or more monomeric substances. Nylon is an example of a copolymer.

MONOTONE TWEED. Tweed of mixed effect made by weaving together yarns of different shades of the same color. Must be made of all wool.

MONSANTO A07 TIRE YARN. Made of 6.6 nylon tire yarn, this registered trademark of Monsanto Textiles Division, Monsanto Company, Inc., has superior strength and bruise resistance to impact. It surpasses other types of yarn in strength retention and tenacity and is 9 percent more tenacious than A06. Stability is noted in a wide range of temperatures. After stringent vulcanization testing, a strong bond develops between the yarn and rubber, thereby giving potential advantages in recappability of tires. A07 is ideal for heavy duty equipment and vehicles which require high-speed performance.

MONSANTO MODACRYLIC FIBER. In 1970, Monsanto Company, Textiles Division, entered the modacrylic fiber field with its Elura which comes in staple and tow forms.

MONSANTO MODACRYLIC "SELF-EXTINGUISHING" FIBER. Known as SEF, this fiber which possesses excellent flame-retardant properties was unveiled in 1972 and is spun on the cotton or the woolen systems. Its features are not impaired by the application of most softeners, hand builders, and water repellents, or even after repeated launderings in hard water using conventional soaps. Properly constructed garments of SEF will extinguish flames when the source is removed. It passes the U.S. Department of Commerce Test Standard of DOC FF 3-71 for children's sleepwear.

MONSANTO NYLON TRADEMARK. Used as registered trademark by Monsanto, Inc., New York City, for its nylon filaments and yarns with the following trademark; C-Chemstrand nylon (Capital "C" with "Chemstrand nylon" printed in open space in the middle of the capital and in the break at the margin).

MONSANTO TYPE L80 YARN. This yarn replaced Type L60 in Actionwear textured hosiery yarn in 1971. This multifilament nylon yarn has super-stretch, excellent recovery, and outstanding knitability. It can be used on all types of hosiery frames, 2, 4, and 8 feed; provides high yield with splendid yarn uniformity. Registered trademark of Monsanto Company, Inc., Textiles Division, 1114 Sixth Avenue, New York City, 10036.

MONTAGNAC. The registered trademark of E. de Montagnac et Fils, Sedan, France. The fabric is classed as a soft material and the warp is entirely hidden by the filling. Montagnac is heavily fulled and given great care in further finishing in order to produce the characteristic hand-beaten tufts for the curled effect on the surface of the material.

The material has a fabric weight of thirty-six ounces per yard. Twill weaves are used in the cloth construction. Montagnac is made with wool and cashmere stock. The cashmere adds much to the appearance, feel, and beauty of the fabric. This silky feel is one of the main assets of the cloth, which is made into smart, dressy overcoating.

MONTBELIARD. A blue and white striped or crossed-effect, rugged, and compactly woven French cotton ticking.

MONTEITH. Cotton handkerchief fabric made in Britain, characterized by white coin-dot effect on dyed ground. Named for the Scotch manufacturer who brought this cloth onto the market.

MONTEVIDEO WOOL. See URUGUAY WOOL.

MONTURE. The harness in a drawloom. It is the total of the leashes and the cords which control them, i.e., the pulley cords and the necking cords.

MOODY, PAUL. A mechanic from Amesbury, Massachusetts, he found work with the famous Lowell Manufacturing Company, Inc., in Lowell and there perfected his ideas for the use of belting in transmitting energy from an engine to various floor shafts in textile mills. A true genius of the times, he made models for the company on improved cotton-spinning frames and a power loom. His belting idea received its first patent in 1826.

MOON COTTON. A strong, lustrous type of Uplands cotton of about 1¼ inch staple with a lint yield of about 32 per cent; a large boll cotton.

MOORE'S 33. Developed in 1957, this new variety of cotton in North Carolina is capable of producing high yields in the cotton belt. A product of the North Carolina Improvements Association, it has large bolls, is easy to pick, storm resistant, and shows a high lint percentage. Staple length is from 1¹⁄₁₆ inches to 1⅛ inches.

MOORISH LACE OR DENTELLE DE MORESSE. It has been made for many centuries in Morocco, is still made there and elsewhere, and is used for edging on dresses and fine toweling.

MOORVA. The *Sansevieria Roxburghiana* bast fibers, raised in India.

MOP. An instrument or product for cleaning. The most frequent use is for cleaning floors. There are two types: 1. Wet mop used for washing. 2. Dry mop or dust mop used for dusting or wiping.

DRY OR DUST MOP: It is made with a few ounces (three to eight) of soft-twist yarn, usually colored yarn, and a wide variety of color is found in this product today. The yarn size is a single 1s or 2s cotton in a two, 3- or 4-ply construction. Rayon or nylon fiber is also used. Nylon is used in natural color as well as in a variety of colors. There are types of dust mop. One of them consists of strands of yarn six to eight inches long, in a 2-ply or a 4-ply soft twist yarn, inserted between two strands of No. 11 or No. 12 wire, after which the two strands of wire are twisted together, resulting in the yarn being firmly held by the wire.

The wire with the yarn is then shaped into the form the mop is to be given. The other type is called Mitt Mop. It consists of a pocket made of some fabric, to one side of which strands of yarn have been sewed. When this type is being used, a wire frame on the handle is inserted into the cloth pocket. Without the handle, it can be used as a hand duster. It also has the feature of easy removal from the frame for washing.

WET MOP: There are two types, mopheads for attachment to separate handles, and complete mops which are attached permanently to handles when being manufactured. Both are made from yarns either medium-twist or hard-twist, generally in a construction of either 4-ply or 8-ply, although at times a higher ply is used if the singles yarn is of a finer size or count. The usual range of size of the single yarn in wet mop yarns is from 50-hank to a 4s cotton yarn count. The yarns are generally spun either from cotton waste or rayon staple stock. There is also a special type which consists of a cellulose sponge covering around the cotton yarn.

Mopheads are made by sewing a tape or narrow fabric in the center of a cut length of a grouping of plied yarns. Often for large size industrial uses, mopheads, instead of the tape, use a center cloth, four to six inches wide, with extra rows of stitching used. There are from 100 to 300 ends of the yarn used, and they run from 20 to 30 inches in length, depending on the weight of the mophead desired. After the mophead has been sewed, it is folded in half so that the center tape is at the top, and the mophead is half the length of the above figures which represented the opened-out dimension.

Following folding over, all the strands then hang in a mass grouping. When put to use, the mophead is inserted in a handle with a clamp arrangement to hold the mophead in place.

Mops, complete with handles, variously known as handle mops, stick mops, and yacht mops, are made with the yarn attached to the handle by a winding and tying process which uses either wire or cord. They are generally made with the yarn attached in a permanent manner, but there are some special types which permit the removal and replacement of the head, a feature of the sewed mophead.

MOPLEN. Italian trade name for a polypropylene filament and fiber.

MOQUETTE CARPET. A carpet of American origin despite its French name. In French, moquette means "tufts of wool." The old imported Axminster had long been beyond the reach of the average housewife's purse; consequently Moquette was introduced in 1875 to simulate Axminster so that it would compete with the latter and at a lower price. Moquette immediately sprang into popularity here although it has failed to have much influence in Continental markets.

At present the name Axminster is used to designate a carpeting which is more or less synonymous with Moquette, differing chiefly in the number of tufts of wool to the inch or in the manner of fastening the tufts more or less firmly in the fabric.

Moquette, while woven somewhat after the manner of Brussels, should strictly speaking be classed among Axminsters. It is ribbed-back with a deep, tufted pile capable of attractive color treatment.

MOQUI. A short-fibered, greenish-white cast cotton of short staple raised chiefly by the Moqui or Hopi Indians of Arizona. Blankets of this name are also made by these Indians, and black, blue, and brown stripes usually feature the article.

MORAVIAN. An eight-thread or eight-strand English sewing cotton.

MORDANT. Any substance which, by combining with a dyestuff to form an insoluble compound or lake, serves to produce a fixed color in a textile fiber, leather, etc. Most mordants are metallic salts, although some are acidic in nature, such as tannic acid.

The formation of a mordant, for example, could be as follows: Tannic acid is soluble in water. Tartar emetic is also soluble in water. However, they combine to form an insoluble mordant.

MORDANT DYES. Dyes which have no direct affinity for un-mordanted material but will dye on goods upon which a metallic mordant has been applied. Because cellulosic fibers and filaments have comparatively poor affinity for metallic mordants, as compared with animal fibers such as wool, worsted, and silk, these dyes are not used for acetate and rayon materials. Gradually being replaced by azoic and vat dyes and their derivatives.

MORDANTING. Application of a mordant to a textile fiber, yarn, or fabric.

MOREA. A cotton raised in Greece. Also, a fancy striped satin fabric in which cotton warp and silk filling are used; given high luster in finishing.

MOREEN. The original moreen was a plain-weave, high-yarn count worsted which was given a moiré or water-marked finish. The fabric closely resembled present-day poplin.

Moreen is now made with a rib effect in the warp direction—the opposite of poplin, which is made with cylindrical filling. Medium-weight fabric is embossed or watermarked; the heavier type may be used for men's summer suiting.

MORENOS. Portuguese and Spanish term for various grades of unbleached linens imported by the South American countries, especially from France and Belgium.

MORESQUE. Effect of unusual texture given by two shades of the same color (usually one light and one dark) twisted together.

MORETTI. A variety of the white mulberry tree brought out in 1815 by Professor Moretti of Pavia, Italy, a leading sericulturist of his era.

MORI. The specific scientific name for a silkworm.

MORICHE FIBER. Venezuelan bast fiber obtained from the Ita palm. Of strength and durability; used for cordage.

MORINDONE. The root bark of various species of the morinda provide this orange-red, crystalline dye extract. See AAL.

MOROCCO LEATHER. The distinctive, natural grain, vegetable-tanned fancy goatskin, to which the name is properly restricted. Originally implying this type of leather from Morocco only, the term now includes all goatskin leather. Its application to anything but fancy leather is incorrect, but the term has become so prevalent that it has now become necessary to use the word, "genuine" to designate the true leather. Morocco grain is applied to embossed imitations of the natural goat grain or other kinds of leather.

MORRIS CARPET. Name for the originator, William Morris of England, this floor covering has been made for well over 100 years. Coloring is done with vegetable dyes in floral motifs in which the acanthus is the main theme. Acanthus is a large-sized leaf in which the spinal lines are easily seen.

MORTLING. Name in England for wool taken from dead sheep.

MORUS. The botanical generic name of the mulberry.

MOSAIC CANVAS. A fine textured canvas used for embroidery work; made from silk, linen, or cotton threads.

MOSAIC DISEASE. See RUST.

MOSCHATUS HEMP. See OKRA.

MOSCOW. Overcoating of the shaggy, napped type, heavy in weight. Cloth gives warmth and somewhat resembles Shetland cloth. Name is given because of the fact that the cloth is in favor in Soviet Russia as well as in other cold sections of the world, where it is used for winter wear. There are many types and grades of the cloth, ranging from very low quality to high, expensive materials.

MOSCOW CANVAS. A canvas of long standing in which novelty effects are embroidered with metallic threads or brightly colored yarns; the effect is that of straw that has been plaited.

MOSQUETAIRE. A genuine or fancied resemblance to costumes worn by the French Musketeers from 1622 until about 1815. Articles of dress include a cloth coat with buttons; the turnover collar, the deep, flared cuff; gloves with the long, loose wrist effect; the large types of headgear with plumes and other embellishments; the long, tight shirred sleeve. Variations of all these are more or less rampent in today's styles.

MOSQUITO NETTING. Used for screening and netting, it is a heavily sized, plain or barred cloth which is referred to in terms of meshes-to-the-inch, such as 12, 18, 36, etc. The more meshes, the better the fabric. It can be bleached, or dyed in solid colors.

MOSS BEGE. See CHENILLE FABRIC.

MOSS CREPE, MOSSY CREPE, SAND CREPE. Spun-rayon warp and filament rayon filling are used in this fabric, in which the two-ply warp yarn is very coarse and bulkier than the filling. Ends and picks are about square. Rather soft in texture, it is used for dress goods and evening wear.

MOSSES. Large hanks of reeled silk, about one pound in weight, produced by the Chinese in home industries.

MOSS OR MOSSING FINISH. English term for woolen cloths which have been napped or gigged in finishing; the weave construction, however, can be observed in the finished goods.

MOSS YARN. Coarse woolen yarn with a fuzzy surface used in embroidery.

MOSSY COTTON. That which has considerable amounts of short and immature fiber content.

MOTCHENETZ. Water-retted Russian flax.

MOTE. Small black specks seen in cotton yarn or cloth. They were not removed by the cotton gin or the successive machines through which the cotton passed from raw stock to spun yarn or woven cloth.

MOTE KNIVES. Set close to the teeth of the licker-in roller, these two long, sharp-edged metal blades or bars remove hulls, husks, motes, and other undesirable matter from the cotton. The knives, in performing their work, have to be set very close to each other.

MOTHPROOFING. Treating woolen goods so as to render them less susceptible to attacks by clothes moths. Done by use of a repellent.

MOTH REPELLENCY. Chemical treatment of wool to make it impervious to moth attack. The several processes differ in their resistance to dry cleaning and laundering.

MOTHS. Pests which infest wool in all stages, whether in grease or scoured state. Moths lay their eggs on the fibers; thus nutriment is furnished for the larvae, with the result that holes often appear in wool stock or cloth.

MOTIF. A design, repeat, pattern, figure or plan used to give some particular effect on a fabric. There is a motif in a cheap cotton print handkerchief as well as in an expensive Jacquard brocatelle or a carpet. See Illustrated Section (Fabrics 69).

MOTLEY. The use of a series of different colors in the warp or filling, or the use of warp printing methods to give a mottled or hazy effect to the design. Used in bedspreads, dress goods, and novelty squares for the neck or head.

MOTRIL. A Spanish cotton that is strong, lustrous, and has a white to reddish-yellow color cast.

MOTTLED. An appearance similar to that of a surface with colored spots. Batik-dyed and tie-dyed designs show this effect. Camouflage cloth is also mottled.

MOTTLED YARN. The result of twisting together two contrasting colored yarns.

MOUFLON, MOUFFLON. A wild sheep (*Ovis musimon*) inhabiting the mountains of Sardinia and Corsica. It has large horns curved into a semicircle. Thought to have played a considerable part in the development of the modern domestic sheep. Name sometimes extended, with certain qualifications, to other wild sheep with similar horns.

MOULINAGE. The last operation in raw-silk spinning, prior to weaving and dyeing.

MOULINE TWIST. A fancy yarn made of four threads doubled together is called Mouliné twist. A hard-twist, two-ply yarn is plied, with three other single threads, in a reverse direction and with fewer turns per inch. The yarn may also be made of three threads plied together, in which case the hard-twist yarn is bulkier than the others.

MOUNTAIN CORK. A type of asbestos known for its texture and lightness.

MOUNTAIN FLAX. Local name for asbestos in Canada and the British Isles.

MOUNTAIN LEATHER. A type of asbestos that comes in thin, flexible sheets and has the toughness of leather.

MOUNTAIN SHEEP. 1. Wild sheep in various mountain areas throughout the world. 2. The Bighorn or Rocky Mountain wild sheep in this country. 3. The active, small, rugged sheep raised in the hills and mountain areas in the British Isles. Kerry, Lonk, and Scotch Blackface may be included in this group.

MOURAT WOOL. Fine, brownish-colored wool from the Shetland and neighboring islands.

MOURNING CREPE. 1. Any material used for mourning purposes provided the fabric is made of a crepe weave or is given a crepe finish. Made from any of the major fibers, it is used in millinery, dress goods, trimming. 2. A lightweight silk or rayon mourning crepe.

MOUSE SKIN. Facetious term sometimes given duvetyne and suède fabrics. See DUVETYNE, SUÈDE FABRIC, SUÈDE FINISH.

MOUSSELINE. Word taken from French mousseline de soie, silk muslin. Originally made in silk and now made in rayon. Firmer than chiffon, stiffer than rayon voile. A sheer, crisp, formal fabric. Plain weave. Used for evening wear, collars, cuffs, trimmings.

MOUSSELINE DE LAINE. French for wool muslin. This lightweight, plain-weave dress goods is made of worsted. The cloth is often printed and quality varies according to the content used in the goods. Cloth of this name is made from fiber content other than worsted, hence the wide range in price and texture.

MOUSSELINE DE SOIE. Silk muslin on the order of chiffon with a crisp, firm finish. While cool to the wearer and popular in evening wear, the material does not launder satisfactorily. Its service to the wearer is comparatively short.

MOUSSELINE MATTE. In the mousseline family of fabrics, it is an all-silk material, devoid of luster. The matté effect shows a slight nap effect on the face of the cloth; used chiefly for evening wear and cocktail dresses.

MOUSSELINE SATIN. An eight-shaft satin-weave, all-silk fabric made of fine silk or rayon yarn: 50-denier warp and 100-denier filling are used in this high-reed, low-pickage material which has a nonlustrous finish.

MOUTAN MUSLIN. British term for lightweight cotton dress goods made on lappet looms which provide sprigs, clusters, and similar novelty effects on the face. It is made with two warps and one filling, with the lappet warp either a two-ply or three-ply yarn. Made in both carded or combed yarn goods.

MOUTON. A short-to-medium-length "fur" with a dense pile; the trade name for a processed sheep pelt. Usually dyed beaver-color, or darker brown, beige, gray, and, occasionally, red, green, and blue. Wearing qualities, good. Judged by density of pile, softness and pliability of pelt. Found in Australia, Argentina, South Africa, and parts of America. For sports, business, and school wear.

MOVA SILK. British expression to imply schappe silk, a waste silk, See SCHAPPE SILK.

MOVIL. A polyvinyl fiber made from acetylene and hydrochloric acid. Manufactured by Polymer de Terni, Milan, Italy.

MOZAMBIQUE. An open-mesh, fine, lightweight fabric made of combed cotton warp and mohair filling. Checks, plaids, overplaids, or openwork effects feature the material.

MOZZETTA. A non-liturgical vestment. It is a short cape of silk, wool, or some manmade fiber fabric. Reaching to the elbows, open in front, and only fastened at the throat, it has a row of buttons for fastening. The collar in the back is affixed to a small hood which is not used, but is rather a vestige of a vestment of earlier times. The mozzetta is worn over the rochet, is a mark of jurisdiction, and is permitted to be worn by cardinals, archbishops, and bishops of the Roman Catholic Church in their own dioceses and by abbots in their abbeys.

MUCUNA FIBER. Leaf fiber obtained from the *Mucuna urens* in Brazil. Strong; used for rope.

MUFF. Separate, pillow-like or tubular covering for the hands, worn for warmth in fashion since the end of the sixteenth century. Made of woolen fabric, feathers, or fur. Now worn chiefly by women and children, but carried by men in U.S. as late as the eighteenth century.

MUFF DYEING. A muff is a colorless package that gets its name from its similarity with the soft, thick, usually fur covering of the same name which protects the hands from cold weather. Muff dyeing had its beginning in the winding and dyeing of "false cakes" of rayon filament yarn. With the development of nylon stretch yarns, skeins were wound on reels and steam-bulked to form packages known as muffs; ideal method to dye high bulked yarns since there is adequate space to allow high shrinkages.

MUFFLER. Originally a sort of kerchief worn by women to cover the lower part of the face either for protection against wind or sun, or for concealment. Now, an ornamental scarf or wrapper of wool, rayon, silk, etc., used in winter as a protection for the throat. Made in two styles, long and narrow or a large square.

MUFTI. Civilian clothes as distinguished from military.

MUGA, MOONGA SILK. Silk produced from the cocoons of the muga moth, native to India.

MUKA. New Zealand hemp.

MULBERRY. Reddish-blue in hue, this color has very low saturation and brilliance.

MULBERRY SILK. The product from those worms which have fed upon the leaves of cultivated mulberry trees, to distinguish the silk from wild or Tussah silk which has been raised on the leaves of the oak, cherry tree, castor oil plant, and various bushes.

MULE. A type of spinning frame which has an intermittent action. It draws out and twists a length of yarn, then winds it in the form of a cop, repeating the cycle several times each minute. Used to a considerable extent for spinning wool but only to a limited extent, in this country, for cotton and then for fine counts or waste yarns. See Illustrated Section.

MULE CARRIAGE. The front, movable section of the mule-spinning frame which moves to and from the head stock of the machine. The carriage supports the spindles, faller wires, spindle drums, friction bands and other appliances.

MULEFRAME. The stationary part of the mule-spinning machine, which contains the drawing mechanism, the roving jack spools or rollers set on supports which help to feed the roving of the feeding-in rollers of the machine.

MULE-FRAME COPPING ACTION. The parts on the mule-spinning frame that control the copping or bobbin action—copping rail, plates, shaper wheel, shaper catch, worm, and the trail lever which connects the locking lever to the copping rail. The latter on the mule is connected to the faller wires to determine the build or chase of the cop as the spun yarn winds onto it.

MULE-FRAME WINDING. Winding and spinning are intermittent actions and after each length or stretch of yarn has received its proper amount of twist, the spindle rotates to wind the newly spun yarn onto the cop or bobbin. The winding motion swings into action to wind the yarn onto the bobbins in an even and uniform manner on the inward run of the mule carriage.

MULE QUADRANT. This important part of the mule spinning frame takes its name from the fact that this gear is made with a 90-degree angle, one quarter of a circle, which has 360 degrees in it. The circular frame of the quadrant is toothed. These teeth mesh with the strong, deep teeth of the star wheel, as the quadrant goes up or down when the mule is in action, on the inward or outward run. The meshing of these teeth do much to cause the even working and regular motion of the mule carriage. No jerky, irregular motion is possible, and the carriage action will be smooth, even and uniform.

MULE SPINNER. A type of spinning frame sometimes used for spinning high-quality yarn. The cheaper production costs of the ring spinning frame have curtailed mule spinning to a considerable degree here. See Illustrated Section.

MULE SPINNING. A system of spinning which produces an extremely fine cotton yarn, but at a slower process when compared with the ring spinning method. Widely used in the British Isles, but overshadowed by the ring method in the United States. See Illustrated section.

MULE SPINNING, DIFFERENCES IN WOOL, WORSTED, AND COTTON. In the mule spinning of cotton and worsted there is a continuous feeding-in of the roving to the machine on the outward run of the carriage. However, in spinning woolen yarn there is a different way resorted to in order to feed the stock to the frame, because of the very nature of the fibers that go to make up wool yarn.

On the woolen mule, for example, say 24 inches of roving are fed into the frame while the carriage is going out from the head stock an equal number of inches. When the desired number of inches have been fed in, the machine stops for a few seconds; gears shift, some come into play, others go out of play, while some continue to do their work.

Then, as the carriage continues to go out on its run, the original 24 inches are drawn out, say, an additional 48 inches. This will give a total drawing of 72 inches. Thus, a draft of three has been applied to the fibers.

The reason for this arrangement is that the fibers which make up woolen yarn are more or less of a conglomerate mass, irregular, uneven, not as uniform as worsted or cotton stock, and may vary from 1 to 12 or more inches in length. There may also be other fibers of a mix or waste nature being manipulated with the woolen fibers. These must be taken into account when actual spinning is to be done.

MULE TWIST. General term for cotton warp yarn spun on the mule.

MULL, INDIAN. A plain-weave, unsized, lightweight cotton fabric originally made in India; now made in many textile centers in many qualities. Pick count average is around 80 x 72 with yarn counts ranging from 90s to 100s. Used chiefly as dress goods.

MULL, MULLE. 1. A plain-woven, soft, sheer cotton, rayon, or silk dress

goods. Comes in white, printed, or dyed effects. 2. A starched cotton, coarse in feel, which is given sizing to make it suitable for underlining material in the millinery trade.

MULL-CHIFFON. A very fine Swiss lawn cloth.

MULL MUSLIN. A muslin devoid of any sizing or filling compounds; a very light dress goods in the zephyr class. See MULL, ZEPHYR.

MULMUL. Archaic term for muslin, contraction of Mosul, in Mesopotamia.

MULTICAULIS. A species of Morus often known as the Chinese mulberry.

MULTIFILAMENT. A term applied to rayon yarns having many fine filaments. For example, 150-denier yarn with 40 filaments would be considered a standard filament count yarn in that denier size, but 150-denier yarn, with say 90 filaments, would be considered a multifilament yarn.

MULTIFILAMENT YARN. This is a yarn which has two or more filaments; the normal multifilament range used by throwsters is from 7 to 75, depending upon the type of yarn in question.

MULTIFLORA COTTON. An early-ripening Alabama cotton of medium-long staple and good cluster bolls.

MULTI-KROME. A development of the Wool Bureau, New York City, to give fiber-mixed dyed textiles the economic advantages of 100% wool. Degreased raw wool is chemically treated so that it will respond to dyestuffs in a different manner than regular wool which is colored by acid dyes. When treated and untreated wool are blended in the same fabric, they can now provide two-color effects in a single dye bath. Especially used in dyeing floorcovering, knitgoods and woven goods.

MULTI-PIECE LOOM. A loom that can weave two or more pieces of narrow fabric at the same time. Also called Multi-space or Multi-shuttle. See NARROW FABRICS.

MULTIPLE FABRIC. Any cloth made of two or more distinct cloths bound or stitched together in the weaving—double, triple, quadruple, etc.

MULTIPLE-PROCESS PICKING. Now largely replaced by the "one-process system" in preparing cotton for carding, the method of picking uses a breaker and finisher or a breaker, intermediate, and finisher set.

MULTIPLE WINDING. Winding of two or more ends to a package, such as a cone, bobbin, cheese, or tube, in parallel arrangement.

MULTIPLIER MOTION. Action found on box looms. Its purpose is to

shorten the length of the box chain, especially when the pattern has a great many picks of the same kind in the repeat. Because of this action, the box chain can be stopped and an auxiliary multiplier chain operates for the desired number of picks.

MULTI-PRODUCTS CORPORATION. This company, located in Kearney, New Jersey, manufactures the following yarns:

Alistran: An extremely bright aluminum foil sandwiched between layers of cellophane film. Comes in widths from 1/16 inch to 1/100 inch. Used with or without support. Used for trimming.

Bu-Tex: Sandwiched between layers of cellulose acetate butyrate film and comes in widths from 1/16 to 1/64 inch. Can be used without support but may be supported with rayon or nylon.

Chromeflex MF: A foil which is laminated to polyester and may be supported or twisted with various combinations of textile yarns.

Chromeflex MM: A metalized polyester laminated to clear polyester. May or may not be supported. Used in many types of decoration.

Chromeflex NL: A registered trademark product of the company, this is a coated metalized polyester which may or may not be supported. It is the softest and thinnest metallic yarn made, is non-tarnishable, and may be hand-washed, drycleaned, and dry ironed under 180° F. Decorative product used where softness, high flexibility, and high styling are desired.

Dura-Stran: A very lustrous aluminum foil sandwiched between layers of Mylar film. Has high yield. Is non-tarnishable and mothproof and may be drycleaned or home laundered. Has many uses in decoration in better quality products.

MULTI-ROLL MACHINE. A machine for shrinking and strengthening the felt cones from which hats are made. The machine consists of a train of rubber-covered rolls similar to those of a household wringer. Streams of hot water play over the rolls so that the hat bodies are alternately wetted and squeezed as they pass through the machine.

MULTI-UNION BARGAINING. Collective bargaining in which the employees are represented by two or more unions, who combine to negotiate a labor agreement, with a company or group of companies.

MUMMY CANVAS. A compact, rather heavy canvas made of unbleached linen which presents an ecru, buff, or brownish color cast.

MUMMY CLOTH. One which resembles crepe; made of silk warp and woolen filling in the better qualities, and with cotton warp and wool filling in the lower qualities. Used chiefly as a mourning fabric because of its lusterless face effect.

Another meaning of the term is a fine, closely woven linen material used in ancient Egypt for wrapping mummies. The best examples have a two-ply warp and single filling with the warp count in texture showing two or three times that of the filling picks. One staple type has 140 ends and 64 picks in one square inch of fabric, made of 100s linen both ways. Some of the very fine cloth has been made with as many as 540 ends per inch.

A third meaning of the term is an unbleached, plain-woven, heavy linen or cotton fabric, used as a ground cloth for embroidery.

MUNGO. Wool fibers obtained from felted rags which have been passed through the garnetting machine. Fiber length is ¼ to about ¾ inches long. Shoddy is secured from unfelted rags.

MUNJ FIBER. Strong, elastic fiber which resists the action of water. Used for baskets, mats, and ropes. Comes from a species of sugar cane in India.

MURAT, MOORIT. Etymology is not known but the terms imply a middle-toned, warm brownish color cast or shade. The so-called black is in reality an attractive dark brown shade which has considerable appeal, a shade that will cause one to look at it again and again. Murat colors are much used in knit goods where they have a very soft, appealing hand not obtained by dyed shades of the same colors. The colors, however, are not considered as very fast to light. See LOVAT.

MURAT LACE. A bobbin lace, very similar to Malines lace of Belgium, made in Auvergne, France. See MALINES LACE.

MURGA FIBER. Native name for Indian bow-string hemp.

MURGALA. Indian word for "peacock's neck" and implies the brilliant, iridescent effect seen on the neck of the peacock. Fabric of this name which originated in India is a medley of color made possible by the use of brilliantly colored silk and metallic yarns.

MUREXIDE. A rich purple color obtained by the action of nitric acid upon uric acid.

MURIATIC ACID. See HYDRO-CHLORIC ACID.

MURRAIN. Wool obtained from dead sheep; dead wool.

MURURUNI FIBER. Used for baskets and hats, this leaf fiber is obtained from a palm tree in Brazil.

MUSA TEXTILES. See ABACA.

MUSCARDINE. A fungus-type disease that is very injurious to silkworms.

MUSETTE BAG. Suspended by a strap and worn over the shoulder, it is made of leather, imitation leather, plastic, or fabric. Serves as a bag, container, or sack.

MUSHKA. An Indian silk material which may be plain or in colored stripe effects. Made from waste silks of several types, there is much variation in the quality of the fabric, as well as in pick count.

MUSHROO, MUSHRU. An East Indian cotton-back, its silk satin-face fabric identified by brightly colored figures in motif.

MUSHY WOOL. Irregular staple wool which is dry, loose, and open. Considerable noil and waste are produced in manipulation. Mushy wool may be caused by climatic conditions, diseased or sick sheep, poor forage, poor mineral matter in the soil.

MUSKRAT. Southern, black, or brown (Northern), short-haired fur ranging from light brown to dark bluish-brown and silvery-gray, usually dyed to simulate mink, sable, or seal. Wearing qualities, good. Judged by depth of underfur and thickness of hair. Found in North America. For dressy and general wear.

Southern muskrat comes from Texas and Louisiana; black muskrat (used naturally) comes from New Jersey, brown muskrat comes from New York State. Hudson Seal is the trade term for a muskrat that has been plucked, sheared, and dyed to resemble black-dyed Alaska sealskin. Silver muskrat is the silver-toned belly of a Southern muskrat.

MUSLIN. One of the oldest staples known, it originated in Mosul in Mesopotamia. Muslin is made from a print-cloth sheeting and is used for aprons, blouses, bedspreds, curtains, handkerchiefs, house dresses, interlinings, linings, pattern making, pajamas, pillowcases, sheets, rompers, underwear, window shades and a host of other articles.

Muslin narrow print cloths are from 24 inches to 36 inches wide, have a construction of 56 to 72 by 44 to 76; the warp yarns average 30s, and the filling yarns range from 38s to 44s.

Wide print cloths are from 36 inches to 86 inches wide, have a construction of 56 to 80 by 44 to 80; the warp and filling yarns are about the same as for

narrow print cloths. In some cases, however, the yarns used may be as low as 12s and as high as 100s in certain muslins.

Muslin implies cotton cloth of good quality in the finished state. Lightweight sheeting printcloth is called unbleached muslin in the stores.

Swiss muslin is slightly heavier than organdy and runs from sixteen to twenty yards to the pound. There is less gloss on the finish of muslin when compared with organdy.

Dotted swiss, in Switzerland and the British Isles, is often woven with minute dots called Swiss dots or sprigs. Genuine Swiss muslin is made on hand looms; from four to twenty interlacings are used to make the sprigs.

In the United States, and in Scotland, the dots are worked into the cloth woven on the lappet method of weaving. The loom has a special attachment that takes care of the fancy warp ends that will make the dots. The tamber (tambour) dot is an outstanding pattern design seen in the so-called lappet muslin. Some of the cloth is made on a swivel loom by the use of an extra filling to give the clipped-spot effect seen in some of the goods.

MUSLIN, THREAD HARNESS. An English term for a fabric made on a Jacquard loom comparable with book harness muslin, but of better and finer quality. The design is accomplished by having the coarse filling pick that provides the effect weave on a pick-and-pick arrangement with the ground filling pick. The floats in the figured filling are cut off to provide the final pattern. Textured around 60-square, yarn counts of about 60s are used with the filling figuring pick about a 1/10s in yarn count.

MUSLIN DE LAINE. Plain-woven, lightweight worsted fabric used as dress goods. Yarns range from 2/50s, upward.

MUSLINETTE. 1. Domestic lightweight muslin which has the same uses as the regular muslin. 2. A rather thick or heavy British muslin used as dress goods.

MUSLIN SHEETING. A carded yarn, plain-weave sheeting made with strong, compact tape selvages. It comes in a variety of constructions from 56 x 44 to 72 x 76. 18s to 30s yarns are used to make the cloth, which is finished anywhere from 48 inches up to 120 inches. Usually bleached and finished with little sizing, used for sheets and pillowcases.

MUSQUASH. A rodent from Europe, North America, and Russia. The best quality is found in North America. It may be dyed and striped to simulate various shades of mink or can be used in natural condition. Not found as often as previously the better skins are unhaired in the same manner as beaver or nutria. When dyed black, the product is known as "Seal Musquash."

MUTATION. A fur, for example, in which the natural color has been altered by selective breeding. Biologically, it is a sudden departure from the parent type as when an individual differs from his parents in one or more heritable characteristics brought about by a change in a gene or chromosome.

MUTKA. A hand-woven, silk material made on hand looms in India. Native silk is used and the fabric is coarse and irregular; used in home consumption for garments.

MYKON. A family of textile softeners and fiber lubricants which include Anionic, Cationic, and Nonionic products. These chemicals are usually added to thermosetting resin formulations so as to improve feel or hand of various types of fabrics, in addition to upgrading tear strength and sewing properties. Mykons are used alone or with starch finishes. Most Mykons are readily soluble in water, will not turn yellow or scorch, and do not retain chlorine. Trade-mark of Warwick Chemical Division, Sun Chemical Corporation, New York City.

MYLAR. This product is a polyester film made from polyethylene terephthalate, the polymer formed by the condensation reaction between ethylene glycol and terephthalic acid. It has a combination of physical, electrical, and chemical properties which made it suitable for a series of new industrial uses. Strong, tough, and durable, it has excellent insulating properties. It retains its flexibility at very low temperatures. Mylar retains its physical and electrical properties under a wide range of heat and humidity changes. Possesses excellent resistance to attack by chemicals.

It may be transparent or metalized and comes in extremely thin sections; the maximum width of a sheet or roll is 50-55 inches. Tensile strength is 17,000-25,000 pounds per square inch. Its elongation break ranges from 70-130 per cent.

Mylar is used in electrical and industrial tapes, electrical insulation, fabric backing, packaging, and for decorative purposes. In the textile field, it finds much use with metallic yarns, such as lame', using Mylar in foil or in metalized structure. Some of the metallic yarns it is used with include Fairtex of Metal Film Company, Inc.; Lame', produced by Standard Yarn Mills, Inc; Lurex-MM, made by The Dobeckman

Company; and with Malora of the Malina Company. The versatile product is manufactured by E. I. duPont de Nemours & Co., Inc.

MYLAST. A modified filament yarn produced by Clarence L. Meyer & Co., Philadelphia, Penna.

MYROBALANS. The fruit of several species of trees which grow in China and the East Indies, known for their tannin content used in manufacture of tannic acid.

The tannin content ranges from 25 per cent to 40 per cent.

MYSORE SHEEP. Indian sheep which have a staple fiber 3 to 4 inches long. The wool varies from light gray to black in color. Fleeces weigh only four pounds. Most of the wool is used for local consumption.

MYSORE SILK. Broad term for an East Indian silk dress goods. It is soft in hand, comes in plain weave, and may be dyed or printed in floral motifs.

N

NAC, NACHIZ, NAK, NAKH, NASSIS, NASSIT, NECIDJ, NEKH. This group of names can be traced to the days of Marco Polo and his travels in the middle of the thirteenth century, the greatest century, excepting the present one, for the progress of man. These terms applied to some of the rich silk brocades and similar fabrics mentioned by Polo in his writings. This pathfinder made it possible, after his return to Italy with the materials for the Italian City States under sponsorship of the noted Italian families, to begin the manufacture of these fabrics in this and the subsequent centuries. Many of the original fabrics are still extant and may be found in the Vatican, museums, and in the homes of affluent families throughout the world. The fabrics Marco Polo brought back to Italy on his return were made chiefly in Bagdad, Damascus, Nirsabur, and other cities farther to the East than these centers.

NACRE. The iridescent, changeable effect observed on some silk or rayon fabrics. (Nacré, from French nacre, for mother-of-pearl.) The effect is obtained by the use of contrasting colors in the warp and in the filling.

NACRE VELVET. See VELVET.

NADAM. A short staple Indian cotton of ⅜ to ⅞ inches long.

NAE. A netting with fine, close mesh made in the Hawaiian Islands; used for garments.

NAGO NODZI. Hand-woven Navajo Indian blankets with black and white filling stripes interspersed with small

red areas to brighten the cloth.

NAIL. Old English measurement of 2¼ inches or 1/16th of a yard.

NAILHEAD. A rather loose term associated with clear-finish worsteds of the sharkskin type. Small patterns appear in worsted goods of this type usually made on color-effect weaves of small repeat. This and comparable effects usually appear on good color contrast materials. Included in the group are dot, birdseye, barleycorn, small houndstooth, and hopsack which is shown in a very small basket weave effect.

NAILON. Polyamide, nylon 66 staple and yarn manufactured by Societa Rhodiatoce S. p. A., Milan Italy.

NAINSOOK. A fine, soft cotton material made in plain weave. The better qualities have a polished surface effect, while the lower grades do not achieve this effect. Several cloths such as cambric, longcloth, handkerchief linen, etc., are finished from the same gray goods that could be used for a subsequent nainsook finished fabric, showing that fabrics are "made in the finishing." Nainsook, usually not quite as fine in texture as batiste, comes in white, pastel colors, and prints, and is used mainly in infants' wear, lingerie, blouses, and some dress goods. Textures range about 108 x 96 with counts of yarn about 44s to 50s or higher. English nainsook has a definite soft finish while the French type has a crisper finish done by calendering.

NAINSOOK CHECKS. Nainsook and closely related cloths, in the white or dyed, set-off by stripes of twill or satin weave, or small check or windowpane effects of the same type of stripes as aforementioned.

NAKHAI BICLIIDI. Mexican and Navajo blanketing made with stripe effects in black, blue, red, and white; either made on hand loom or power looms. The stripes are in the crosswise direction.

NAMAZLIK. An unusually wellmade and well-textured prayer rug made in Turkey; features a mosque motif.

NAMGALI. Hand-loomed silk fabric made in India and featured by religious figures and names. Used in provincial apparel.

NAMDAS. Plain-weave, hand-loom woolen fabric made chiefly in Tibet. Usually finished with embroidery, it is used, after being highly felted, for floor covering.

NANCY. First made in city of that name in France, it is drawn work, often embroidered with colored yarns or threads, and comparable with Dresden Point and Hamburg Point.

NANDEL. DuPont certification mark for fabrics of "Orlon" acrylic Rotofil yarn. The fabric may be piece or yarn dyed, as well as printed, with clarity, brilliance, and depth characteristics of "Orlon" acrylic fiber. It has exceptional fuzz and pill resistance, better than most spun yarns during washing and drycleaning; it resists shrinkage and color change, and garments made from it retain original shape after repeated washing and wear. From soft and supple to crisp and firm, Nandel fabrics resist wrinkling during wear, may be machine washed, machine dried, and require little or no ironing. Uses include high quality and fine count constructions for blouses, dress shirts, dresses, slacks, sleepwear, and sport shirts. See Rotofil.

NANKEEN TWILL. One of the names for the simple 2-up, 1-down twill weave.

NANKIN. 1. Name of the city in China where in the eighteenth century fabric of that name was made, a plain silk cloth that was similar to present day shantung made with silk. The name today implies colored silk threads used to make some cream colored laces in France. 2. High-texture, plain-woven cotton made with white warp and colored filling; used for ticking. 3. A similar term, NANKEEN, has become obsolete except for a British material made in a 3-shaft twill weave, dyed buff or ecru and used as a lining fabric. Formerly, several fabrics had this name given them but they are no longer made.

NANKIN BUTTONS. Tough, matted, silk wastes that are most difficult to manipulate. The clumps of matted fibers can be broken into fiber form and then spun on the spun-silk system of spinning.

NANKIN YELLOW. Iron buff.

NANKO, NANAKO. Made with native silk yarn, it is a plain Japanese silk cloth used in apparel.

NAP. 1. The fuzzy or protruding fibers noted on the surface of a finished material. Nap covers up to a great degree the interlacings between the warp and the filling threads. It gives added warmth to the wearer. The length of the nap will vary somewhat in the several cloths given this type of finish. Nap is applied to flannel of all kinds, cricket cloth, blanketing, baby clothes, silence cloth, molleton, some lining fabrics, overcoatings, knitted fabrics, etc.

2. The Oxford Dictionary gives the following information anent the term: "Nap" or "Naep," from the Middle English (ante Middle Dutch or Middle Low German "Noppe," related to "Noppen; Nap"). Originally the raised layer of projecting fibers on the sur-

face of the textile fabric requiring to be smoothed by shearing treatment; in later use the surface given to cloth by artificial raising of the short fibers, with subsequent cutting and smoothing of the pile.

3. A cloth having a "nap" on it.
4. Surface resembling the nap of cloth.
5. The smooth and glossy surface of a beaver, felt, or silk hat.

NAPALEATHER. See GLOVE LEATHER.

NAPERY. Household linen, chiefly table linen.

NAPHTHALATING. A process by which virgin wool is gently cleansed in three baths of naphtha and then rinsed in clean flowing water. No soap or alkaline solutions are used; raking, forking, and excessive handling are eliminated. The wool retains its original life, strength, and resiliency.

The first bath removes large amounts of the grease; most of the remaining grease is removed by the second bath. The third bath removes all of the remaining grease but leaves the natural potash for further cleansing of the wool, which follows in a clear rinsing bath.

NAPHTHOL DYES. Also called azoic, ingrain, and ice, these dyes are made from a chemical naphtha base. A developer is set on the yarn or fabric, followed by a second component, which is diazotized and then coupled with the material in the fiber in the developing bath to give the color. Much used on cotton for reddish shades; these dyes have good properties except in fastness to light. Color-matching is a difficult problem when these dyes are used.

NAPHTHOL PREPARE-CANS MACHINE. This machine treats material with a chemical to make it more receptive to printing colors; it consists of a mangle with a trough for the chemical, drying cans, and a swing folding attachment.

NAPHTHOL SOAPING MACHINE. A machine used to dissolve the printing base from printed cloth, consisting of two wooden tanks which contain, respectively, heated water and caustic solution. Cloth is drawn through a series of idler rollers by powered rubber squeeze rollers and passes through the liquids.

NAPIER. 1. A substantial floor covering made of hemp and jute. 2. A double-faced overcoating which has a wool and good-quality hairfiber face, and a backing composed mainly of hair fibers, such as camel hair, vicuna, cashmere.

NAPKIN. A fabric which ranges from 10 inches square to about 30 inches square, used to protect the clothing while dining. The best is linen damask; other types are made from crash, cotton print cloth, or novelty woven fabrics with Jacquard motifs in them.

NAPOLEON. In 1806, this French emperor blockaded Great Britain thereby cutting off importation of silk thread for use in the Isles. This blockade had a great effect on the entire textile industry. Patrick Clark of the Paisley shawl plant in Scotland began the manufacture of cotton yarn there and in a short time had produced a very satisfactory thread. James Coats, in the same town, followed suit (now the famous Coats & Clark Company, Inc.) and cotton yarn was on its way.

In 1808, Spain, under the duress of Napoleon and to raise money for war purposes, sold some prize merino sheep to England and a few other favored nations, rather than risk the possibility of the French taking them for their own herds. Thus, Spain's hold on the Golden Fleece of Spain was broken. In 1810, Spain sent 4,000 merino sheep to Vermont and laid the foundation for the great merino industry here.

Napoleon did provide money and protection for Joseph Marie Jacquard and his fabulous loom which was unveiled in 1801 in Ouellens, near Paris, for at that time, it was thought that the loom, which now can do the work formerly done by 150 operators, would cause a real panic and rioting among textile workers. See Jacquard, Joseph Marie; Jacquard Machine and Weaving, Historical Review of; Merino Sheep, Merino Wool under caption Wool.

NAPOLEONIC COSTUME. See Costume, Napoleon.

NAPOLITAINE. A French flannel made with woolen yarn, piece-dyed and occasionally printed for use in dress goods, shawls, scarves, etc.

NAPPA. A soft feeling, full grain, gloving leather made from unsplit kid skin, lamb skin, or sheep skin.

NAPPE. French for tablecloth; hence, napery.

NAPPED AND PILE CLOTHS, DIFFERENCE BETWEEN. In a napped cloth the fibers are raised by teasels or a card clothing roller.

In a pile fabric extra threads are used in the weave. These threads, when they are cut in the loom by means of knife-blade action, show a nap or raised surface of projecting ends on the face. The pile ends are held in place by a basic weave that forms the body of the material. The pile ends may readily be pulled out with the fingers.

Uncut pile fabrics are made by the ends going over the blade and remaining in this uncut looped form in the material. Since there is no sharp blade at the end of the pile wire, the ends that form the pile effect will not be cut.

In napping cloth it is not out of the ordinary to run it several times through the napper machine. Napping is often done in the gray goods state. Too vigorous a treatment will injure and fray the material. Some cloths are napped only once, depending on the type of nap desired.

NAPPED FABRICS. Broad term applied to cotton fabrics identified by the nap on the surface of the goods. Softspun filling makes possible the characteristic finish in cloths such as Canton flannel, domett, flannel, moleskin, molleton, and some linings.

NAPPED-FINISH GOODS. These may be of a single or double finish, slight or heavy. Single finish occurs when one side of the goods is napped; double finish fabric has both sides of the material napped.

A slight finish occurs when the napped cloth is not as high in protruding fibers nor as thick when compared with heavy nap. The finish is given to fabrics known for their napped characteristics and for those that can withstand the rigors of the treatment. Certain woolen and cotton cloths receive this type of treatment—baby clothes, blankets, domett, flannel, lining, molleton, silence cloth, etc.

The finish is applied by rollers covered with 1-inch card clothing similar to that used on the fancy roller of the woolen card, or by a roller clothed with teasels.

Some fabrics are given from three to four up to ten or twelve roller treatments to obtain the desired napped effect for the surface finish. The napping may be done in the gray goods state as well as in the regular finishing operations. Many woolen fabrics may be given this treatment—beaver, broadcloth, chinchilla, fleece, kersey, melton, Montagnac, Saxony, zibeline, etc.

NAPPER. The person or machine that performs napping. See NAPPING.

NAPPER FLOCK. Waste removed from cloth in the napping process. See NAPPING.

NAPPER SET. Six cut-lengths of cloth of the same weave sewn together end to end for treatment by the napping machine.

NAPPING. Process raising face of cloth nap. Cloth, before napping, is unattractive and irregular in appearance.

The surface is uneven and shaggy because of protruding fibers.

Nap on the face of cloth may be raised for several reasons: to make the cloth give more warmth to the wearer, to give it more body and make the material more compact, to make the fabric softer or smoother in feel, for durability, to help cover up the spaces between the interlacings of the yarns, and to add to the selling points of the garment.

Minor defects and blemishes are covered up by napping. It is an easy matter to bring coarse, inferior cloth to the point where it will be appealing to the eye of the prospective purchaser. It may also have the tendency to make the layman believe that the cloth is better than it really is. Looks and appearance are influences in material selection, and the wearing quality is often overlooked. Napping will sometimes "make" a fabric.

Napping, gigging, or raising is accomplished by passing the cloth in a tightly stretched condition, over a revolving cylinder or roller, inlaid with teasels. The roller may be clothed with card clothing instead of teasels. If wire is used, the length of it is from ⅞ to 1⅛ inches, set in leather fillet.

NAPPING COTTON. Broad name given to cottons that are soft-spun and easy to manipulate in napping for use in blankets and other fabrics where a good, rather dense nap is wanted. Examples could include molleton, silence cloth, certain cleaning cloths, polishing fabrics, etc. Used exclusively for filling yarn.

NAPPY COTTON. Matted mass formation of cotton fibers in the bale.

NAPS. British term for heavy woolen overcoatings usually dyed in plain colors. Fabrics of this type are well finished by fulling, milling, soaping, felting, etc. The word, in one sense, implies face-finished fabrics with a smooth, clean nap such as kersey, beaver, melton, some broadcloth, etc. In another sense, it identifies those coatings with a definite face finish such as Witney, Whitney, Waverley, etc. A UNION NAP FABRIC is one in which the warp is cotton yarn instead of the woolen or worsted yarn used in the higher value fabrics.

NARCO. Registered trademark of Beaunit Corporation under which viscose rayon yarn and fabrics are marketed and promoted.

NARDURA. A high-tenacity viscose rayon sold under the registered trademark owned by Beaunit Corporation, New York City.

NARRAINGUNJ FIBER. A high-grade jute fiber raised along the Bram-haputra River. Most of the fiber is cream color but it is red-tinged at the tips; the roots of the plant are red. The fiber is ideal for jute warp because of its strength, softness, and length.

NARROW CARPET. Fabric woven 27 inches (3/4) and 36 inches (4/4) in width to distinguish from broadloom widths used in carpeting.

NARROW CLOTH. In the woolen and worsted trade, fabrics less than 52 inches wide. See NARROW FABRICS; NARROW GOODS.

NARROW DUCK. Used for conveyer belting, small sails, etc., the term implies Number duck which varies in width from 6 to 20 inches. Weight is similar to that of sail duck.

NARROW FABRICS. 1. Ribbon, tape, and webbing will run from ½ inch to 3 inches in width, in the narrow sense. These fabrics are woven on narrow looms where it is possible to weave from 96 to 144 pieces at the one time. 2. Some fabrics under 18 inches in width. 3. In the broadest sense, any fabric under 27 inches wide; when wider than 27 inches, the material is called broadgoods.

NARROW FABRIC SKIRT. A fringe.

NARROW GOODS. Cloths 27 inches or less in width are called narrow. Nine inches equals one quarter; hence, fabric known as narrow is a three-quarter goods. Fabrics in this field include webbings and ribbons woven on narrow fabric looms, where it is possible to weave from 96 to 144 pieces of fabric at one time on either straight or circular battens, swivels, or shuttles. The term in the cotton trade signifies any fabric under 40 inches wide.

NARROWING. The reduction of the number of stitches in knitting so as to obtain the desired shape of the article.

NARROWING POINT. A pointed metal device which transfers loops to adjacent needles in the narrowing operation in a knitting machine.

NARROW SHEETING. Cloth to be used for converting and industrial purposes is generally 40 inches or less in width. Made in many constructions, there are three general groups of sheeting which are based on the counts of yarn:

1. Coarse yarns from 1/10 to 1/15.
2. Medium yarns from 1/16 to 1/21.
3. Lightweight yarns from 1/22 to 1/29.

NARROW WALE. Narrow diagonal lines seen in some woolens and worsteds.

NARROW WARES. Braid, cord, ribbon, and comparable notions.

NARROW WIDTH. Cloth of incorrect width. Very often the cause of this defect is a too rigid treatment in fabric finishing. Narrow width may be traced to a great many causes. Tentering of the cloth will often bring the cloth back to its original contract width.

NATAL HEMP. Another name for piteira.

NATIONAL COTTON COUNCIL, THE. Based in Memphis, Tennessee, this is the only central organization that represents the more than 12 million people who comprise the American cotton industry. This representative body has 244 delegates chosen by the nation's cotton farmers, ginners, warehousemen, merchants, spinners, and cottonseed crushers through their own state organizations. Each branch of the cotton industry has equal representation on the Council. Each of the six branches, voting separately, must approve every recommendation by a two-thirds majority, thus assuring complete unity of action and purpose. The one goal of the Council is to increase the consumption of American cotton, cottonseed, and their products, both at home and abroad. It seeks that goal through comprehensive programs of promotion, research, and production efficiency.

NATIONAL FEDERATION OF TEXTILES, INC. Located in New York City, the Federation had in its membership nearly 80 per cent of the looms customarily engaged in the weaving of acetate, rayon, other man-made fibers, and silk, alone or blended. It was successor to the Silk Association of America, organized in 1872, and the National Association of Rayon Weavers, organized in 1933. The services to industry which it featured were commercial arbitration of contract disputes, clearance and registration of first-submitted fabric designs, clearance and recording of trade names, impartial examination of fabrics, and a wide variety of general information services concerning industry practices, government regulations, and the like. The Federation became a part of The American Cotton Manufacturers Institute, Inc., on May 1, 1958.

NATIONAL RETAIL MERCHANTS ASSOCIATION GUIDE FOR IMPROVED AND PERMANENT CARE, LABELING OF CONSUMER TEXTILE PRODUCTS. Adopted in March, 1967, the following tabulations are important to the consumer:

WASHING MACHINE METHODS
Cold Rinse - Temperature of rinse water from cold water tap up to 75° F.

Cold Wash - Initial water temperature setting from cold water tap up to 75° F.

Delicate Cycle - Reduced agitation and time.

Durable or Permanent Press Cycle - Cold rinse before reduced spinning.

Gentle Cycle - Reduced agitation and time.

Hot Wash - Initial water temperature directly from hot water tap from 130° F., to 150° F., or slightly higher.

Lukewarm Wash - Initial water temperature of 90° F. to 110° F. "Hand comfortable."

Medium Wash - Initial water temperature of setting of 110° F. to 130° F.

Washable or Machine Washable - Products can be washed, bleached, dried, and pressed by any customary method including an acid sour rinse commonly used in commerical laundering.

Rinse Thoroughly - Implies complete detergent or soap removal by multiple rinses.

Separate Wash - Wash alone or with like or comparable colors.

Synthetic or Manmade Cycle - Cold rinse before reduced spinning.

Warm Rinse - Initial water temperature of 110° F. up to 130° F.

Warm Wash - Initial water temperature of 90° F. to 110° F. "Hand comfortable."

Wash-and-Wear Cycle - Cold rinse before reduced spinning.

WASHING, NON-MACHINE METHODS
Hand Wash, Hand Washable or Wash by Hand - Products must be laundered by hand in lukewarm water from 90° F. to 110° F., with special care and may be bleached.
Does not exclude drycleaning on outerwear and decorative household items.

Hand Wash only - Same as above except for drycleaning.

No Wring or Twist - Implies importance of preventing distortion and wrinkles. Usually drip dry method required.

Rinse Thoroughly - Implies complete detergent or soap removal by multiple rinsing.

DRYING TO INCLUDE ALL METHODS
Drip Dry - Hang wet with or without hand shaping and smoothing.

Hang Dry - Hang damp from bar or line in or out of doors.

Tumble Dry, High - High heat.

Tumble Dry, Low - Low heat.

Tumble Dry, Medium - Medium heat.

Tumble Dry, Prompt Removal - Items should be removed at once to prevent wrinkling.

Tumble Dry; Durable Press, Permanent Press, or Wash-and-Wear - Medium to high.

IRONING AND PRESSING
Cool Iron - Lowest temperature setting.

Hot Iron - Highest temperature setting.

No Iron or No Press - Item should not be smoothed or finished by anything hot in nature.

Warm Iron - Medium temperature setting.

DRYCLEANING, ALL PROCEDURES
Dryclean or Dryclean Only - Item may be drycleaned commercially or in self-service stores in a machine with any of the conventional organic solvents used - flurocarbon, perchlorethylene, Stoddard Solvent - including hot tumble drying up to 160° F. and restoration by the steam press or steam-air finishing.

Dryclean with No Steam Used - No steam is used which is normally necessary to pressing where shrinkage or damage may occur.

Dryclean with Stoddard Solvent - This procedure restricts drycleaning to use of petroleum or flurocarbon solvent.

Professional or Commerical Drycleaning - This excludes any use of self-service facilities.

FUR AND LEATHER CLEANING

Professional Cleaning Only - For use on suede, leather, and plastic garments when professional care only is indicated.

Professional Cleaning Without Use of Any Chlorinated Solvent - Same as foregoing except that the method is limited to the use of a petroleum or flurocarbon solvent.

MISCELLANEOUS INSTRUCTIONS

Fluff Dry - Tumble dry, no heat to be applied.

No Starch - (Obvious)

Use of Fabric Softener - Use of any product made for this purpose.

Courtesy of: National Retail Merchants Association, 100 West 31st Street, New York City

NATIVE CLOTH. English cotton cloth made in warp effect weaves into which elaborate patterns are woven. There is a series of cords woven into the goods every four inches or six inches. The cloth is popular in the African trade.

NATIVE SILK. Used in Great Britain to signify raw silk from the Asian areas in the original skein forms and not in a re-reeled condition. A very irregular, unclean type of fiber.

NATIVE WOOLS. Those raised east of the Mississippi-Missouri rivers. Also implies unimproved wool from sheep raised in various world centers where modern animal husbandry has not penetrated.

NATTÉ. A basket-weave silk dress-goods material, natté has the warp and filling of contrasting colors.

NATURAL. 1. Flesh-color. 2. Yarn spun from a mixture of naturally colored wool—black, brown, gray, etc.

NATURAL DYESTUFF. Any dye obtained from various plants such as cochineal, indigo, logwood, quercitron, etc. In general, any dyestuff not classed as a coal-tar color.

NATURAL FIBERS, CHEMICAL FORMULAE OF MAJOR. Consideration of the natural textile fibers—cotton, linen, silk and wool—reveals the following set-up of the molecules:

COTTON-CELLULOSE:	WOOL-KERATIN:
$(C_6H_{10}O_5)n$	$(C_{42}H_{157}O_{15}H_5S)n$
LINEN-CELLULOSE:	SILK-FIBROIN:
$(C_6H_{10}O_5)n$	$(C_{24}H_{38}O_8N_8)n$

Here "n" represents a high number, and Carbon, Hydrogen, Oxygen, Nitrogen, and sulphur represent the symbols C, H, O, N, and S, respectively. These atoms are in groups, as indicated by the formulae, and each long molecule is made up of a chain of these groups joined end-to-end. Thus, the molecular chains for these typical fibers are seen from the illustrations above to be quite complicated and rather long.

In some fibers, notably wool, these molecular chains are kept together by definite lateral linkages, but in other fibers the evidence of such linkage is smaller. It should be noted that wool contains an element of sulphur, silk does not.

NATURAL GRAY YARN. Yarn spun from a blend of black, brown, or gray wools, unbleached and undyed.

NATURALIA. Plain-weave tropical-worsted fabric made with natural colored yarns; about a 10-ounce cloth finished around 56 inches wide.

NATURALISTIC DESIGN. The opposite of conventional design. A design taken from nature may be termed a naturalistic design.

NATURAL RESIN. A family of solid or semi-solid organic substances or vegetable origin. Found, for example, in rosin and used in soaps, varnishes, and drying agents. Another example, lac, is obtained from the mica bug of India, and is much used in the manufacture of shellac and similar products. The resins, which are brittle and have a waxlike luster, are insoluble in water.

NATURAL WOOL. Broad term applied to undyed or unbleached wool, which is often imitated by adding dark-colored fibers to the white wool so as to prevent the material from showing soiled effects too quickly.

NATURELL. A plain-weave, light-weight cotton given a soft finish; used for undergarments in the Teutonic nations. Usually dyed in light colors, and also comes in the white.

NAUDIN AND SCHUTZENBURGER. In 1869, these two chemists performed the first successful experiments which, in time, were to lay the foundation for commercial acetate yarn.

NAUGAHYDE. Trade name for vinyl-resin-coated upholstery fabric controlled by UniRoyal Fiber and Textile Division, UniRoyal, Inc., Winnsboro, South Carolina.

NAUGHT DUCK. Ducks which are heavier than Number One duck and designated as 1/0, 2/0, etc. A 6/0 duck, for example, weighs 24 ounces per yard based on the 22-inch standard width. The range runs from Number 1/0 up to and including Number 15/0, with widths ranging from 6 to 56 inches. Naught duck is the heaviest single woven or construction fabric and is durable, strong, and has very high tensile strength. The high texture and many yarns used in the ply-count cause the fabric to be stiff, harsh, boardy, and highly resistant to water penetration.

NAVAJO RUG. Distinctive type of hand-woven rug or covering made by the Navajo Indians of the Southwest. The strong cotton warp is very well covered by the bulky woolen filling used. The rug is a reversible, and the designs used are very attractive and have considerable merit. The art of making the rug seems to have degenerated, and some Navajo rugs are now made on power looms to keep abreast of the demand. Also called blanket.

NAVAJO SHEEP, IMPROVED. Developed by the United States Department of Agriculture, two new strains of this stock are now used. One is an improved fleece which produces a wool ideal for yarns used by the Indians in weaving the well-known hand-woven Navajo blankets and rugs. The other type is used to make commercial wool yarn, woven into various types of fabrics on power looms. Navajo ewes were crossbred with high grade, improved rams of some of the better grades of Western sheep. The sheep are now able to withstand the very hot, dry, rugged ranges of the Southwest. Fleece weight has been doubled, and the fibers are now free of the former hollow, brittle properties which often accounted for as much as seventy per cent of the fleece from the original sheep.

NAVAJO WOOL. Coarse, ideal carpet wool raised in the New Mexico area and used mainly for blankets and floor covering.

NAVAL LACE. Term that covers any type of gold braid used in naval circles.

NAVSARI COTTON. An Indian cotton of $7/8$-inch staple with lint yield of about 31 per cent. Used to make 30s warp and 40s filling yarns.

NAVY, NAVY BLUE. Any of the various shades of dark blue, below indigo in saturation and brilliance.

NEAR-SILK. Term sometimes used in cotton trade to signify a mercerized cotton lining material.

NEATNESS. An expression used to denote quality of raw silk that is devoid of hairiness, loops, nibs, etc.

NEAT WOOL. The sides of the average Luster sheep furnish this combing wool stock, which is used for 32s to 36s worsted yarn.

NECKBAND. A band which goes around the neck, often part of a garment; chiefly, the band of a shirt to which a collar is attached.

NECKCLOTH. A piece of any fabric worn around the neck.

NECK CORDS. See JACQUARD NECK CORD.

NECKERCHIEF. A kerchief for the neck.

NECKING. A term used in the manufacture of man-made filaments which refers to the sudden reduction in the diameter when stretching undrawn filaments.

NECKING CORD. In a drawloom it is the cord which makes the neck between the leashes and the pulley cord.

NECKTIE. A scarf, band, or tie, commonly of silk or rayon, passing around the collar or neck and tied in front. Made in various styles: four-in-hand, bow, Windsor.

NECKWEAR. A general term covering the numerous varieties and styles of neckties, cravats, bows, ribbons, etc., worn around the neck.

NECKWEAR FABRICS.

1. ARMURE WEAVES: Pebbled surface effect in small twill-weave constructions.

2. BANDANNA: From the Hindu, bandhnu, and implies blotch-printed cotton, the print effect on a colored background.

3. BARATHEA: A close mesh effect that originated in England.

4. BATIK: Javanese method of dyeing done with the aid of wax to obtain the actual design. Fabric is dyed where the wax does not appear on the material. To secure various colors several dyeings may be made. A variegated effect appears on completion of this hand process of coloring.

5. BIRD'S-EYE: Diamond twill effect with small dots in the center of each figure.

6. CANNELE: Taffeta-type fabric on the order of rep.

7. CHALLIS: Lightweight wool, worsted, or "mixed fabric" originally made in Norwich, England.

8. CHINESE DAMASK: Satin figures on a so-called satin-twill effect in the material. Named for Damascus, the famous Middle Ages silk center.

9. DOBBY PATTERNS: Small diamond, oval, or rectangular figures or stripes to simulate real Jacquard effects. Can be made on plain or "dobby attachment" looms.

10. FAILLE: Flat filling-rib fabric made in soft-effect weaves; often made with a "Jacquard effect."

11. FOULARD: Originally a twill-woven cloth but now made in plain construction as well, the fabric has small colored or white effects on a colored background. Thought to have originated in India. The cloth became popular in Great Britain in the 90s, when it was known as Surah.

12. GROSGRAIN: Of Italian origin, this ribbed-effect received its name from gros (large) and grain (kernel).

13. HERRINGBONE: Chevron-effect striped motifs.

14. HOUND'S TOOTH: A small, neat, all-over check effect.

15. JACQUARD DESIGNS: Patterns which may be small, medium-size or large—and conservative or "wild" in effect. Made on a Jacquard loom whereby every warp end may be raised or lowered at will to obtain the design. Any scene, picture, or effect may be reproduced on the loom.

16. LOUISINE: A fine basket texture hardly visible to the naked eye. Small checks and plaids feature the design.

17. MACCLESFIELD: Rayon or silk fabric on the order of Spitalsfield, the name of a neighboring town in England.

18. MATTE: A dull greenish-gray color or shade named for "Mate Tea," a self-evident English naval term.

19. MOGADOR: Named for this old fortified city in Morocco, cloth of this name was made with white warp and white filling effect on the surface; the cloth may be made in double cloth construction. In this country the term implies a neckwear fabric made of rayon or silk warp and cotton filling, the latter being entirely covered up by the warp structure. The cord or ribline runs in the filling direction because heavy, cylindrical filling is used. Appears in bright, clean-cut regimental, college, blazer, or sundry stripes. May be moiréd.

20. MOIRÉ: Moiré is any moiréd fabric, watermarked, as faille and taffeta, as well as other fabrics where the effect adds to the appearance of the goods moiréd. Done by a "yard-stick-tool" or by engraved rollers.

21. NATTE: Means braided in French, and the natté fabric gives a sort of hopsack or basket-weave effect.

22. OMBRE: Shade (ombre); a shaded (ombré) effect in cravat fabric usually running from light to dark shades of the same basic color.

23. OTTOMAN: A member of the faille family group of fabrics, the material gives a type of corduroy effect. Compared with faille the rib effect is wider and coarser and runs in the warp direction, the opposite of the rib in faille.

24. OVERCHECK: A check or plaid designed "over" a subdued ground check-effect.

25. PERSIANS: Oriental designs and color motifs taken from the designs seen in genuine Cashmere shawls.

26. PIECE-DYES: In this sense, implies tie fabric made of some sort of crepe-weave construction. Single-color fabrics.

27. POPLIN: Fine cord which runs in the filling direction characterizes this material. Made of rayon or silk warp and wool, worsted or cotton filling. Named for one of the popes of the Middle Ages period. Material may be solid color or printed. See Illustrated Section (Fabrics 7).

28. REGENCE: Also known as Charvet. A rich, luxurious material with a soft, flat corded texture.

29. RHADZIMIR: A small check-effect made on twill weaves.

30. REP, REPP: Originally a silk ribbed-effect fabric that originated in England. The stripe or figure effects add to the cord effect which runs in the filling direction.

31. SATIN: Mentioned by Chaucer in his "Cloths of gold and satins rich of hue," this well-known material presents a luster surface-effect. Usually made with warp-effect satin construction. Comes in solid colors, stripes, and prints.

32. SATIN FACONNE: Fancy Jacquard effects on a satin background.

33. SHAFT PATTERNS: Implies any pattern made on a plain loom.

34. SHANTUNG: Made from silk or rayon. When made of silk the thread is taken by reeling directly from the Tussah or wild-silk cocoons. The original silk gum or sericin remains in the cloth and aids in obtaining the rough surface-effect. Of Chinese origin.

35. SHEPHERD PLAIDS: Checks or plaids usually taken from the Scotch tartan or official clan plaids which originated with the Scottish shepherds many centuries ago. Always a popular staple tie fabric.

36. SPITALSFIELD: This fabric was originally hand-loomed in this ancient textile area now a part of the City of London. First made from silk, these small, all-over designs are also produced in rayon constructions.

37. TARTAN: The general name for plaids. Originally made with wool or worsted yarn, the fabric is now made from practically all of the major textile fibers and filaments. The color and design comes from the official Highland Clan plaids of Scotland such as MacPhee, Campbell, Cameron-Carnegie, MacGregor, etc.

38. TWILL: Smooth fabric made from any of the small twill constructions. The diagonal effect should run from the lower left-hand corner of the goods to the upper right-hand corner

of the material—usually at a 45-degree angle. The quality varies considerably in this tie cloth.

39. WARP-PRINT: Pattern obtained by printing the warp prior to weaving of the fabric. Gives a subdued effect to the goods.

40. WARP-PRINT SATIN STRIPE: Satin-weave stripes feature this material which may combine several more or less elaborate types of weaves and textures.

41. YARN DYES: Also known as skein dyes. The term implies fabrics which are made with stripe, check, block, or plaid effects. The yarn is dyed prior to weaving of the fabric.

NEEDLE. 1. A small device used in sewing, made of steel, sharply pointed at one end with an eyelet at the other end for the thread. 2. A fine rod or wire used in knitting or a hooked instrument used in crocheting or netting. 3. A horizontal wire used in a Jacquard head-motion to control the to-and-fro motion of the hooks of the machine and thereby control and designate which hooks are to be raised by the lifting knives in the head-motion. One end of this needle passes through a hole in the needle board while the other end rests in the needle box.

NEEDLE BED. A flat slotted plate in which knitting needles operate under the influence of jacks or cams.

NEEDLE BOARD. See JACQUARD NEEDLE-BOARD.

NEEDLE BOX. See JACQUARD NEEDLE-BOX.

NEEDLE COMPOUND. Also called a two-piece needle, it is a knitting needle which has two separately controlled parts—a hook member and a hook-closing member.

NEEDLE HOUSING IN KNITTING. There are three elements concerned:

1. CYLINDER: A slotted cylindrical housing for the needles in a circular machine. The cut of a cylinder is the number of needles in one inch of the circumference of the cylinder.

2. NEEDLE BED: A flat slotted plate in which knitting needles slide.

3. DIAL: The horizontal needle housing in circular machines of the rib and interlock types.

NEEDLEIZING. The name which covers the processes used in the finishing of Quadriga Cloth, a trade-mark name used on a brand of 80-square percale produced by Ely and Walker, St. Louis, Missouri. Needleizing has to do primarily with the method used to remove all properties of both cloth and finish which would make sewing considerably easier because of less resist-

ance to the needle. See QUADRIGA CLOTH.

NEEDLE LACE. Made with a single needle and thread; each opening is called a mesh and is completed as the work progresses. It is the opposite of bobbin or pillow lace in which many threads are used, each one being twisted about another and then carried on to the next mesh before the completion of the first mesh. Lace made by hand is called real or point lace; machine-made lace is a simulation or imitation of handmade lace. Lace is made of the ground and motif or pattern sections or areas.

NEEDLE LEADS. A group of latch needles cast in lead and used in Raschel knitting. On German model Raschel machines, the leads measure approximately 1⅞ inches and on the American model Raschel the lead measures 2 inches.

NEEDLE LINES. Lengthwise streaks in knit goods made by a needle not properly aligned or poorly spaced.

NEEDLE LOOM. One in which the filling is carried through the shed by a long pointed needle.

NEEDLELOOM SELVAGE, SHUTTLELESS LOOM EDGE. There are several types of shuttleless looms used in narrow fabric weaving. In the case of one, or sometimes two, the edges are different when compared with ordinary selvage edges. In needleloom edge the filling is held in position at the turn of the threads other than the warp threads; an independent thread is used to lock the filling into position at the end of the goods. Thus, this is not a true woven selvage edge.

NEEDLE LOOPS. The form which the yarn takes in knitting as it is drawn around the knitting needle when it performs its action of knitting. The needle loop is aided in completing a full stitch by the sinker loop.

NEEDLE LOOP TRANSFER, KNITTING. A needle loop moved partially or totally from the position in which it was made to one or more other needles for styling purposes.

NEEDLE POINT, NEEDLE-POINT LACE. Any lace made with a needle irrespective of design, motif, pattern, or style.

NEEDLE-POINT FABRIC. A staple or novelty women's wear coating usually of good quality and made by the better mills. The rather compact texture presents a surface effect that resembles "pin-point" because the fancy yarns used have the tendency to curl into minute points. Yarns on the order of bouclé or ratine used for effect.

NEEDLE-POINT OR POINT

LACE; HANDMADE. Lace made with a needle or single thread, using variations of the buttonhole stitch.

NEEDLE PROTECTOR. An electrical device in a knitting frame designed to prevent needle breakage caused by lumps, slubs, or bunched yarn at the needle.

NEEDLE-PUNCHING. Batts, layers, or webs of very short loose fibers needled into a base, core, or woven scrim fabric to provide a felted or flat-textured material. Needle-punched fabric may be embossed, decorated, laminated into a cushion form, or otherwise finished.

NEEDLE-RUN LACE. The net or the net ground is machine-made and has a motif in it while the outline of the design is effected by hand with a needle.

NEEDLES, COMPOUND. Knitting needles that can perform the functions of both latch and spring needles.

NEEDLE TAPESTRY. Fabric in which the motif is embroidered to simulate a tapestry. See TAPESTRY.

NEEDLEWORK. Handmade embroidery of all types when produced by means of a needle.

NEGLIGEE. A decorative dressing gown made with flowing lines. Worn indoors, it may be held at the waistline by a ribbon, sash, or belt. It is often called a kimono but has distinctive style features of its own. Silk and rayon are the materials generally used to make the garments which come in many colors, patterns, and styles.

NEGOTIATING RANGES. The minimum and the maximum a negotiator expects to concede and demand on any clause during the collective bargaining sessions.

NEGOTIATOR. Representative of a company, or of employees, who is responsible for handling collective bargaining.

NEGREPELLISE, NEGREPILISSE. The "nègre" in French means black. The term implies a black-dyed cloth, one that is fulled heavily, and has a long, dense nap on the face of the goods. Made from small twill weaves. Used in apparel.

NEGRETTI SHEEP. Sheep, native to Spain, which are now raised in several world centers. The wool is fine, soft, and has the best of working properties. Negretti are extensively raised in Germany and form the basis for much of the best-grade materials made there. South American wool countries now specialize in raising the sheep.

NEIGE. This word means snow, in French. A broad term signifying white effect noted in some materials, chiefly in laces.

NEIGELLI, NEGELLI. An Indian fabric made from the sunn fiber. It is a plain-weave cloth, made on hand looms, and is very coarse in nature.

NEOPRENE. Trade name for a type of synthetic rubber produced by E. I. du Pont de Nemours & Co., Inc.

NEP, NEPS, NEPPY. 1. Small, knotted, or tangled clumps of cotton fibers. 2. In the carding of fibers the term is given to lumps or tufts of cotton, rayon, spun silk, or wool which accrue in the card clothing of the rollers during the action. 3. Small tangled masses of fibers which show as white specks in yarns and fabrics; comparable with off-shade specks. 4. Cotton obtained when the gin is overcrowded or the saws have been set too close together. This stock is not desirable for spinning.

NEQUEN CLOTH. Fabric made from the fibers of the agave plant found in Central America.

NERI. Italian term for a grade of waste silk, obtained from the inner smooth skin of cocoons; left over in the residuum in the reeling process.

NET, NETTING. 1. An openwork material usually made on a lace machine. It forms the foundation for a great variety of laces. Uses include curtaining, hangings, millinery, pillows, and runners. 2. A material made of thread or twine which is knotted into meshes or designs. It is commonly used for dresses and evening wear. 3. A network made of cord. 4. A lightweight cotton material used as mosquito netting and screening. Leno weaves are used to make the material, which is reinforced at intervals by the closely beaten-up filling which forms a type of tape effect.

NET CANVAS. Linen or cotton canvas that has been treated with sizing to afford stiffness to make it suitable for use as a foundation material in needle and lace work. Bleached for whiteness, dyed black, or can be used in the natural shades.

NET LENO. Fabric in which the leno or doup ends float on the face of the cloth to produce a sort of zigzag or rickrack effect.

NETS, GO-BACK. Used in the laundry trades, they are woven with colored filling, usually in a cable cord construction. They are used for re-runs and wash-overs and are easily identified. Red and blue are the most popular colors used, and every laundry should have them on hand.

NETS, KNITTED. These laundry nets must be given utmost care to prevent yarn raveling since a small break will cause the article to need repair.

They are difficult to repair and, as yet, are not too satisfactory for use in laundries. The Government issues specifications for these nets.

NETS, KNOTTED. These are on the order of tennis netting, fish seines, or Pullman hammocks. They are not woven or knitted but are actually knotted either by hand or on bobbinette machines, which are slow in production and rather expensive of operation. Knotted nets have a large mesh that will not slip nor spread, but the hard knots are rather severe on the linen contained in the nets. High cost of these nets has impeded its popularity.

NETS, LAUNDRY. The two most popular methods of making these nets are by the use of a plain weave or by the leno or doup construction. A third method is used, and it employs the cabled cord system of yarn, warp, and filling, in a leno construction. Nets are now woven tubular and in a continuous length without any seams on the sides. This arrangement is made possible in that when the shuttle is thrown to the left in weaving, it weaves a pick of filling on the underside of the fabric. The material on the loom assumes almost the flat position of a net lying on a table. The tubular construction can hardly be noticed until the bag is opened for inspection. The filling in the weaving goes from the front to the back, on and on up the net in spiral formation.

NET SILK. English term for thrown silk.

NETTING. Any fabric which is made up of crossing threads, yarns, ropes, wires, etc. Netting is an open-mesh type of article whether it is made of thread or wire.

NETTLE. The short, fine stem-fiber of the nettle plant which is used in Teutonic countries for twine and cloth. This fiber is much resorted to when more desirable raw materials cannot be obtained.

NETTLE CLOTH. When leather became scarce in Germany during World War I, this rugged cotton cloth was made to care for the shortage.

NETWORK. Open fabric, woven or tied with meshes or knots at the crossings of the yarns, which leaves open spaces or meshes in the article.

NEUILLY. Power loom tapestry is made in this French city to simulate genuine Gobelin and Beauvais tapestries.

NEUTRAL. Neither alkaline nor acidic.

NEUTRALIZE. To change from either acid or alkaline condition to a neutral condition.

NEUTRAL ROPE. A thoroughly set rope that will not twist or untwist.

NEUTRAL SOAP. Soap that should be free from fatty acid and free alkali; it should dissolve in both hard or soft water. For laundry and textile purposes, a soap should be used that does not contain free alkali in excess of .5 per cent. The natural fats that may be found are glyceroles of fatty acid: palmitic acid, $C_{15}H_{31}COOH$; stearic acid, $C_{17}H_{35}COOH$; oleic acid, $C_{17}H_{33}COOH$.

NEVER-PRESS. The durable press process developed by Wamsutta Mills, Lyman, South Carolina.

NEW, NEW CLIPS. Cuttings, clippings, and other odds-and-ends of woolen and worsted fabrics collected in the cut-fit-and-trim garment factory. These clips, and those from other sources, are sent to garnetting machines in plants, which reclaim the fibers from the fabrics so that they may be used in future cloth manufacture.

NEW ORLEANS, ORLEANS COTTON. A term used in connection with Upland cotton, the staple of which is mostly ⅞ of an inch, shipped under New Orleans bill of lading.

NEW ZEALAND COTTON. This is not a cotton but the name for fine, strong bast fibers obtained from the ribbon tree in New Zealand. Used for fishing lines.

NEW ZEALAND FLAX. This comes from a plant of the lily family. It is an ideal fiber in the making of rope. The fiber is classed with Mauritius hemp, aloe, bowstring hemp, pandanus, and yucca.

NEW ZEALAND HEMP. Phormium is known by this name.

NEW ZEALAND TWILL. Name for the 2-up, 2-down twill used in making a coarse jute bagging.

NEW ZEALAND WOOL. A crossbred wool obtained from merino ewes and "luster-wool" rams such as Lincoln, Leicester, Cotswold, and Romney Marsh, leading Class Three World Wools. The staple works well when mixed with wool wastes such as shoddy, mungo, extract wool, reused wool, remanufactured wool, etc. See LUSTER WOOLS; WOOL CLASSIFICATIONS, WORLD.

NEYANDA. See SAN SANSEVIERIA.

NIANTIC FOOT. A full fashioned hosiery foot made in two sections with the seams on either side of the foot and with seamless heel and toe pouches. The completed Niantic foot hose is made on two machines, the legger and the footer.

NIBS, RAW SILK. 1. Small white specks found in silk thread. 2. Small slubby areas less than 3 mm. or ⅛ inch long.

NICOLON. An asbestos yarn which virtually eliminates dust problems encountered in braiding, knitting, or weaving asbestos products. The patented process is one in which the asbestos fibers are opened chemically and formed into yarn by chemical and mechanical treatments. Carrier fibers are not needed in the processing. Compared with conventional asbestos yarn, Nicolon has increased breaking strength, better elongation, lower density, superior smoothness, and better heat and moisture resistance. Terminal uses include braided and woven tubing, brake linings, filter fabrics, fire resistant clothing, pressing pads, insulating tapes, etc. Product of Nicotex, Inc., a subsidiary of Nicolet Industries, Inc., in the plant of the former company in Ambler, Pennsylvania.

NID D'ABEILLE. This is the French word for bee's nest, and the term means a motif or design of honeycomb structure, a variation of the piqué weave.

NIGHT SHIFT. A schedule of working hours that requires employees to work during the night.

NINETY-DAY COTTON. An early-maturing, medium-sized cotton boll which produces a fiber of about ¾-inch staple. An American type.

NIMES. A piece-dyed woolen fabric which originated in this town in France. Texture about 44-square and made of about 36s worsted yarn, the cloth is made with plain weave. Incidentally, the term "de Nimes" gave rise to present day denim, a contraction of "de Nimes." See DENIM.

NINON. Sheer rayon or nylon fabric made of plain weave. Several varieties on the market. Washable, comes in a variety of constructions and is used much for curtains and portières.

NIP. 1. A very thin or weak place in yarn. 2. The point of contact between the bottom and top rollers on any textile machine.

NIPPERS. On the Heilman comb there are two sets of jaws which alternately grip and release the fibers being combed. There are two parts to the mechanism which hold the stock in place; the upper part is the nipper knife while the lower part is the nipper plate or the cushion late.

NISHIJIN. A Japanese silk brocade made on a Jacquard loom. This cloth has a great number of different colored fillings in it, anywhere from 20 to as many as 40. Thus, the weaving of this material is very slow while the price is high.

NISTRI. See DESI.

NITRIC ACID. A colorless, highly corrosive liquid, HNO_3, found in nature in small quantities, but usually made by decomposing sodium or potassium nitrate with sulphuric acid. This strong oxidizing agent is also called Aqua Fortis. Animal fibers are stained yellow by this acid.

NITRIC ACID ON COTTON. Cotton, when treated with this acid and then heated, will dissolve rapidly and form nitrocellulose, a powerful explosive.

NITROCELLULOSE RAYON. Filament made of regenerated cellulose (denitrated nitrocellulose) that has been coagulated and solidified from a solution of nitrated cellulose. Originally known as de Chardonnet Rayon, it was the first rayon to be marketed; it is now extinct.

NITRON. Cellulose nitrate. Sheets, rods, and tubes of Nitron are characterized by a broad range of color, high luster, good dimensional stability, toughness, and strength. They may be cemented, laminated, and otherwise fabricated with exceptional ease. Nitron is used for aircraft windshields, blown toys, calendars, cutlery handles, detonation caps, fountain pens, golf-club sheathing, grommets, optical frames, piano keys, printed badges, shell parts, toothbrush handles, tool handles, etc. Product of Monsanto Chemical Co.

NOBLE COMBER. Machine for combing worsted, also known as the circular comb. It is used on the English or Bradford system in making worsted yarn. Made of three circles that are filled with sharp, upright pins; the large circle is about 44 inches in diameter, the two smaller ones, from 18 to 20 inches in diameter. The two small circles revolve, inside of the large circle, on the principle of a differential.

Feeding of stock to the comber is done by passing the sliver through a series of drums set in the frame. There are 18 drums, each of which has four compartments or spaces to care for four individual slivers from the top to the balling head. Thus, 72 ends may be manipulated by the comber at the one time.

As the circles draw away from each other, there is a fringe of stock ready to be combed. This fringe is treated by the large circle which takes out the long, choice fibers of the same length. The two inner circles gather up the noil or fibers under the required or set length. The top is passed out of the machine, while the noil goes through a funnel or trumpet into a can or receptacle that is placed at the side of the frame. Combing may be compared to the combing of the hair on the head of

the human being. The more rigid the combing, the greater is the foreign matter removed; the greater the number of teeth in the circles, the finer will be the results, the better will be the combing.

The top fibers are processed into worsted yarn by the ensuing machines. See Illustrated Section.

NOBLE WOOL. Any wool that can be manipulated on a Noble comber. See NOBLE COMBER.

NODE CLOTH. Dress fabric of the bourette-bouclé type. The distinguishing feature in fabric of this type is the group or bunch of yarns, twisted and manipulated together to set off the appearance of the material. Any of the major fibers can be used in this cloth.

NOGG. The space between a staple in one twill or rib line and the corresponding staple in the next line in spacing staples in card clothing on the rollers. Measured in lengthwise direction.

NOIL. 1. The short fibers taken from any machine operation in the processing of textile fibers. They are obtained mostly in carding and combing operations. The stock may be high in quality but very short in length, too short to admit its being manipulated into yarn by itself. Noil is worked in with longer staple fibers to make yarn. Some noil may be of medium or inferior quality.

2. Short fibers that may be mixed in with longer staple woolen or worsted fibers in yarn manufacture; obtained from various frames.

3. Woolen or worsted fibers taken from the carding and combing operations which find extensive use in blends and fulled woolen goods.

4. Stock that has been over-carded or garnetted to produce tiny balls, pills, or slubs which are introduced into normal stock to produce uneven drawing which will give nubby or tweedy yarn. The yarn is popular for certain types of suiting and dress goods in men's wear and women's wear.

5. Silk noil is a by-product of the spun-silk industry. It consists of the short fibers which are combed out of the silk waste and are not suitable for clean, even yarns. Silk noil, nevertheless, is spun into noil yarns, which are very uneven and lumpy; it is also used in blends for novelty effects.

NOIL, RECOMBER'S. The shorter staple fibers obtained in a recombing treatment; as many as five recombings may be used and each successive combing will produce some fibers which are not of the desired staple length needed for manipulation into finished, spun yarn.

NOIL SILK. See Silk Noil.

NO-IRON COTTON. See "WASH AND WEAR."

NOMAD CARPET. Named for the nomadic tribes that ranged central Asia centuries ago, this article is the general name given to Persian (Iraq) carpets and rugs known for their simple, plain patterns. This rug is still a staple floor covering in many countries in this area.

NO-MARK COTTON. When cotton is baled the compressors paint some distinguishing mark, a series of letters, on every bale no matter the size of the bale. Often the letters are missing when the cotton arrives at destination—usually because the tares or covers have been torn off by country damage.

NOMELLE. A new certification mark for yarns which contain an acrylic fiber of E.I. duPont de Nemours & Co., Inc., Wilmington, Delaware. The mark is used only on yarns which meet the duPont fiber content specifications. It is a bright, smooth, and soft fiber made in tow form at present. Designated as TYPE 43, it is handled like TYPE 42 acrylic in spinning, knitting, and piece-, skein-, and package-dyeing, and can be processed on the Turbo Stapler. It is manufactured in Camden, South Carolina.

NOMEX. A protective clothing of 100 percent Nomex nylon which will never lose its flame retardancy. Nomex will last six to twelve times longer than treated cotton garments. Flame retardancy of Nomex is an inherent property of the fiber; it will neither wash nor wear out. It resists stains and soiling and has good acid and chemical resistance, cleans readily by any method, and does not shrink out of shape. Registered trademark of E.I. duPont de Nemours & Co., Inc., Wilmington, Delaware.

NOMEX M. Also a registered trademark of duPont, for its fiber-for-paper product which is made by combining

"NOMEX" NYLON. Originally known as HT-1, this trademarked product of duPont is designed for high temperatures which cannot be withstood by any other organic fibers now in commercial use. Produced in filament, staple and various weight paper-structures, it can withstand prolonged exposure up to 500° F. It will not melt, will burn only on exposure to flame, and may be used at higher temperatures for short periods. Highly resistant to stretch and to degradation from common solvents and radiation, "Nomex" papers and yarns have excellent electrical properties. Uses include electrical insulation components which are made from the paper-like material, filter bags for high temperature gas filtration, laundry pads, for both home and commercial usage,

and for protective clothing for industrial and military uses.

NOMUD CARPET. A felted Persian (Iraq) carpet that does not use the usual knotted pile construction found in most Persian rugs. See GHIORDES KNOT, GHIORDES RUG; FLOOR COVERINGS, CLASSIFICATION OF.

NON-CELLULOSIC FIBERS. These are manmade, "synthetic," or manufactured textile fibers made from chemical polymers. Some examples follow:

1. *Acrylic:* Acrilan, A-Acrilan, Acrilan-Spectran, Anywear, Chemstrand-Acrylic (Monsanto); Courtelle (Courtaulds); Creslan, (American Cyanamid); Dralon (Bayer); "Orlon," (DuPont); Zefran II, Zefkrome (Dow Badische).
2. *Anidex:* Anim/8™, (Rohm and Haas).
3. *Azlon:* Not made in the United States at present.
4. *Glass:* Beta and Fiberglas (Owens-Corning); Garan and Vitron (Johns-Manville) PPG (PPG Industries); Ultrastrand (Gustin-Bacon); Unistrand (Ferro).
5. *Lastrile:* Not made in United States commercially, as yet. (Rohm and Haas).
6. *Metallic:* Alistran, BU-tex, and Durastran (Multi-Tex Products); Chromeflex range (Metal Film), Fairtex range (Fairtex-Riegel Paper); Lame' range (Standard Yarn Mills); Lurex range (Dow Badische); Malora range (Malina Company); Metlon range (Metlon-Acme Backing Co.).
7. *Modacrylic:* Dynel (Union Carbide); Teklan (Courtaulds), Verel (Eastman).
8. *Nylon:* Nylon 6 - Ayrlyn (Rohm and Hass); Beaunit nylon (Beaunit); Caprolan (Allied Chemical); Celon (Courtaulds); Dorlon (Bayer); Enkaloft (American Enka); IRC nylon (American Cyanamid); Lilion (Snia Viscosa); Enjay nylon (Enjay Chemical); Nytelle (Firestone); Nylon 6,6: Antron, Cantrece, Qiana (DuPont); Blue "O", Cadon, C-Chemstrand, Cumuloft (Monsanto); Phillips 66 (Phillips); Qulon (Beaunit); Wellon (Wellman).
9. *Nytril:* Not made in the United States at present.
10. *Olefin:* Amco, and American (American Manufacturing Co.); DLP Group (Thiokol); Herculon (Hercules); Marvess (Phillips); Polycrest (UniRoyal).
11. *Polyester:* Avlin (Avisco); Blue "C" (Monsanto); "Dacron" (DuPont); Encron (American Enka); Fortrel (Fiber Industries and Celanese); Kodel (Eastman); Quintess (Phillips); Tergal and Terital (Soc. Rhodiaceta); Terlenka (AKU); Terylene (I.C.I.); Trevira Hoechst (Hystron Fibers); Vycron (Beaunit); Wellene (Well-

man).
12. *Rubber:* Contro or Rolled Latex (Firestone); Darleen (Darlington Fabrics); Filatex (Filatex); Lactron, Lastex, Laton, Revere (UniRoyal).
13. *Saran:* Saran (Amtech, Inc.).
14. *Spandex:* Glospan (Globe); Lycra (DuPont); Vyrene (UniRoyal). (UniRoyal).
15. *Vinal:* Not made in this country at present time.
16. *Vinyon:* Avisco Vinyon (Avisco); Voplex Vinyon (Voplex).

NOTES:

1. *Glass Fiber Group:* Specially prepared glass marbles are melted in an electric furnace. Melted glass is then extruded through orifices to form continuous filaments, and then drawn to desired size.

2. *Metallic Fiber Group:* Metallic yarns are now made with Mylar ("Dacron") film as well as with acetate film. Mylar metallic yarns withstand higher temperatures and more rugged finishing and laundering than the acetate-type yarns.

3. On October 29, 1969, The Federal Trade Commission decreed that Rule 7 of *The Textile Fiber Products Identification Act* (effective March 3, 1960) be amended and to add a new term Anidex which is a derivation or modified type of Modacrylic Fiber. See Anidex, Modacrylic.

4. The following fibers in T.F.P.I. Act are not made at the present time in the United States - *Azlon, Lastrile, Nytril,* and *Vinal.*

5. *Qiana* (duPont) is a modified type of Nylon introduced before the American Association for Textile Technology, Inc., in the Hotel McAlpin, New York City, on November 5th, 1969.

NONCRUSHABLE LINEN. Plain-weave cloth with highly twisted filling yarn or finished with resin, to enhance elasticity. Has about the same uses as dress linen. Serviceable, durable, does not wrinkle, launders well.

NON-FRICTION TYPE KNITTING NEEDLE. A latch needle that is made perfectly straight so that it fits loosely in the tricks and exerts no pressure on the trick walls.

NON-IONIC. Detergent action devoid of positive or negative charges. The action is compatible with both anionic and cationic actions and reactions. Non-ionic does not conduct electrical charge or current; it increases penetration wetting action, and detergent action. Other features include the facts that it will not ionize and consequently works in both hard and soft waters; it is not precipitated by calcium or magnesium salts.

NON-IONIC DYES. Water-soluble dyes which do not dissociate electrolitically in a water or aqueous solution.

NONRAVEL. The place in a stocking where a lock stitch has been run in at the bottom of the welt. Also implies the whole welt being made of lock-stitch mesh so that any run originating in the welt (from garter pull usually) will not proceed down the leg of the stocking.

NONRUN. Term applied to hose made in knitted lock-stitch mesh, so that, if a yarn breaks, a run cannot proceed farther than the nearest lock stitch.

NON-SHAATNESS. See Shaatness, Non.

NONSHATTERABLE GLASS. Glass made shatter-proof by the use of an acetate filler between layers. Serves several purposes but is an especial boon to the automobile industry.

NONSHRINK. See SHRINKAGE; SHRUNK FINISH.

NONSLIP FINISH. Finish applied to a thread to resist sliding when in contact with another thread.

NONTEXTILE. A broad merchandise term used in home furnishings and clothing implying that they are not made from fibers of some sort.

NONWOVEN FABRIC. At present this term has several interpretations and implications, none of which is accepted widely. Generally speaking, the fabric is one made without the benefit of a loom, a literal meaning that encompasses felt, knitted, and tufted goods as well as a long list of non-textile products. The best definition to date seems to be the one furnished by the Joint Nonwoven Fabrics Committee of the American Society of Testing and Materials, Inc., (ASTM), and the American Association of Textile Chemists and Colorists (AATCC). This group defines the term as "a structure produced by bonding or the interlocking of fibers, or both, done by mechanical, chemical, thermal, or solvent means, and the combinations thereof. The term does not include fabrics which are woven, knitted, tufted, or constructed by wool felting processes."

There are, at present, four types of nonwoven materials: 1. Needled or punched felts. 2. Bonded fiber fabrics. 3. Reinforced paper fabrics. 4. The so-called second generation nonwoven fabrics such as spunbonded materials and the needle-punched fabrics. Excluded at the present time - stitch-bonded materials, flocked and tufted products,

woven felts, paddings and kindred types of fabrics.

Another definition is that a nonwoven fabric is a web or continuous sheet of staple length fibers, laid down mechanically or depoisited by air. These fibers may be preferentially oriented in one direction or may be deposited in a random manner. The web or sheet of fibers is then bonded together by the use of an adhesive.

NONWOVEN FABRICS, LATICES USED IN THE MANUFACTURE OF. These follow:

Acrylic Resins - Interlinings, luggage fabrics, backings for reinforced plastics and outerwear.

Butadiene Acrylonitrile and *Butadiene Styrene* - Interlinings, wiping cloths, mops, innersoles, belt inserts, book bindings, luggage.

Low Melt Thermoplastic Fibers (Vinyon and "Dacron" polyester fiber) - Tea bags, ribbons, cable wrappings, and electrical insulation.

Melamine Resins - Cross linking agents for other bonding agents and air gas filtration.

Modified Urea Resins - Most commonly used in combination with other resins (acrylonitrile and acrylics) to improve washing and drycleaning properties and to modify the hand.

Natural Rubber - Leather substitutes, snowlinings and gasket materials.

Phenol Formaldehyde - Industrial batting; insulation, packaging, and acoustical material.

Phenolic Resins - Insulation, sound-proofing, lamp shades, filter binders.

Polyvinyl Alcohol - Decorative ribbons and wrappings.

Starches - Liquid filters, nonwovens for electrical insulation.

Vinyl and Polyvinyl Acetates - Liquid filters, sanitary products, diapers, ribbons, quilted battings, rug backing, coated fabrics.

Vinyl and *Polyvinyl Chlorides* - Automotive side door paneling, backing for vinyl upholstery, heat-sealable battings, quilted battings.

NONWOVEN FABRICS, SOME These follow:

1. WET-WEB NONWOVEN FABRICS MADE ON PAPER MACHINERY:
Hovolon: 75 percent cellulose and 25 percent synthetic nonwoven. Synthetic used can be nylon, "Dacron," "Orlon," et al. An acrylic binder is used in processing. Registered trademark of Hollingsworth & Vose Company, Inc., East Walpole, Massachusetts. The manufacturing is

done in Greenwich, New York.

2. REINFORCED PAPER NONWOVEN FABRICS MADE AS A SANDWICH:
Dura-Weve Nonwoven Fabric: It is a 100 percent bleached pulp stock that is treated with wet-strength chemicals and made fire retardant. It is made of plies of this paper reinforced with scrim made of man-made fibers. Product of the Scott Paper Company, Inc., Chester, Pennsylvania.

Scrim Reinforced Material: Manufactured by Kimberly-Clark Company, it is now made in about one hundred constructions, with eighteen post-finishing treatments for water absorption or resistance, fire resistance, abrasion stamina, embossibility, plasticizing, etc. It is made in Appleton, Wisconsin. A registered trademark.

Kaycel: Trade name of Kimberly-Stevens Company, Inc., it is a scrim-re-inforced fabric with scrim cross-laid in a waffle or honeycomb pattern. The scrim may be cotton, nylon, rayon, polyester, glass, or in combinations of several types. Single or double-ply cellulose fabric is used.

3. DRY-PROCESS NONWOVEN FABRICS MADE ON TEXTILE PROCESSING EQUIPMENT:
Bondaire: Rando web, low density, high-loft material made from staple fibers which impart a machine and cross-machine strength. Fibers used include rayon, nylon, polyester, modacrylic. Registered trademark of Kimberly-Stevens, New Milford, Connecticut.

Chixel Brand Nonwoven Fabric: Cellulose nonwoven fabric made with cotton and paper. Made by Chicopee Mills, New York City, in Milltown, New Jersey and North Little Rock, Arkansas. It is a registered trademark.

Keybak Brand Nonwoven Fabric: Rayon staple used in lengths which vary from one-inch to 2½-inches, bonded with resinous materials. Product of Chicopee Mills, Inc., New York City, with plants in Milltown, New Jersey, and North Little Rock, Arkansas.

Kyron Nonwoven Fabric: Registered trademark of Kimberly-Stevens Company, New York City and the plant is in New Milford, Connecticut. The product is Rando-web produced from staple fibers which impart a machine and cross machine strength.

NONWOVEN FABRICS, PROPERTIES AND CHARACTERISTICS OF.

1. Fibers in a nonwoven fabric may be oriented preferentially in one direction or they may be laid or set in a random manner.
2. All fabrics must rely on the base fiber or fibers used in the web, and in the bonding agent applied to the fibers.
3. Random orientation of the fibers is obtained by the use of a multiple lap arrangement.
4. High production in trimming and slitting nonwoven fabric has now reached 750 yards per minute.
5. There is no system of yarn or thread used to make nonwoven fabrics; they have no warp and no filling as in woven fabrics, or loops as in knitted materials.
6. Physical and aesthetic properties of the fabrics cover a wide range, depending on the fiber or fibers used, and, to considerable degree, on the resin or fiber used as a binder.
7. An important functional property is bulk. A nonwoven fabric has at least twice the bulk and covering power of a woven cloth of equivalent weight—often a distinct advantage.
8. In appearance, the fabrics may be paper-like, felt-like, or woven-like. Strength may vary from that of paper to a woven fabric. And a fabric having equal strength in all directions can be obtained through a random orientation of the base fibers used.
9. Porosity comes in a wide range.
10. Hand may run from hard to soft.
11. Nonwoven fabrics will not ravel or fray.
12. In fabrication the fabrics may be sewn, glued, or heat-bonded.
13. Some major uses include skirting, backing for vinyl coating, electrical insulation, apparel interlining, and containers.

Rayon, nylon, polyester, and acrylic fibers are used in manufacture.

Leno-Web: Registered trademark of The Kendall Company, Inc., Boston, Masschusetts, it comes in apertured or textured surface. The fabric is made with or without polymeric binder system. Made in Walpole, Massachusetts.

Lexon Nonwoven Fabric: Registered trademark of The Kendall Company, Inc., Boston, Massachusetts. It has a random fiber distribution for balanced strength. Made in Walpole, Massachusetts. See Leno-Web.

Masslinn Brand Nonwoven Fabric: A solid sheet of nonwoven fabric in which the process eliminates spinning and uses resins as the bonding agent for the fibers. Made in Milltown, New Jersey and North Little Rock, Arkansas by Chicopee Mills, Inc. A registered trademark.

Lowndex: A nonwoven material which contains 100 percent rayon stock in unidirectional lengths of 1½ to 3-inch lengths. A binding agent is used in the fabric which comes in varying constructions and weights. Registered trademark of Lowndes Products, Inc., Easley, South Carolina.

Novonette: Nonwoven fabric with textured or apertured surface. It is made with or without chemical binder to provide a wide range as to properties. Registered trademark of The Kendall Company, Inc., Walpole, Massachusetts, where the product is made.

Sofnet Brand Nonwoven Fabric: Registered trademark of Chicopee Mills, Inc., New York City. The Hospital Division of Johnson & Johnson uses this trademark for Keybak Brand nonwoven fabric. Made in Milltown, New Jersey and North Little Rock, Arkansas.

Viskon Brand Nonwoven Fabric: Also made by Chicopee Mills, Inc., and a registered brand name, it is comparable with Masslinn Brand nonwoven fabric. Made in North Little Rock, Arkansas.

Webline Nonwoven Fabric: Registered trademark of The Kendall Company, Inc., Walpole, Massachusetts, it is a print-bonded, oriented nonwoven fabric in which the fiber and the binder may vary. Made in Walpole, Massachusetts.

Weblox Nonwoven Fabric: It utilizes a mechanical entanglement of the fibers in lieu of a chemical binder. Registered trademark of The Kendall Company, Inc., Walpole, Massachusetts, and made there.

Webloy Nonwoven Fabric: Nonwoven fabric which employs thermoplastic or thermosetting plastic to bind oriented or random webs. Unification is obtained by a hot calendering method. Registered trademark of The Kendall Company, Inc., Walpole, Massachusetts, where it is manufactured.

Webril Nonwoven Fabric: There are three types of ths product which is a registered trademark of The Kendall Company, Inc., Walpole, Massachusetts, where they are manufactured:

M Series: Uses a thermoplastic fiber for the binder. The webs formed by these fibers are bonded together by a hot calendering process.

R Series: Composed of 100 percent cotton fibers in bleached state. The fabric is formed by an elaborate entangling process which does not use any type of binding agent.

T Series: A web bonded, oriented nonwoven fabric in which fiber and binder may be varied.

4. PLASTIC NONWOVEN FABRICS:
Reemay: A spunbonded polyester; in the spunbonding process the fibers are spun in a conventional manner and then formed into a sheet or web and bonded into position. The result produces a sheet of continuous filaments which contain no paper at all, as well as no binders or fillers. Registered trademark of E.I. duPont de Nemours & Co., Inc., Wilmington, Delaware.

Tyvek: This is a spunbonded olefin product formed by the random distribution of very fine continuous polyethylene fibers which are self-bonded by heat and pressure. Registered trademark of E.I. duPont de Nemours & Co., Inc., Wilmington, Delaware.

OTHER NONWOVEN FABRICS:

Tissue-Fiber Laminate: Registered trademark of Kimberly-Clark Corporation, Neenah, Wisconsin, it is a smoother and denser base material than Kaycel. Kimlon brand products, made from TFL, are reinforced with oriented textile fibers rather than from cross-laid rayon scrim.

NONWOVENS, USES OF. These follow:

Consumer Products: Aprons, bibs, blankets, book coverings, dishcloths, disposable diapers, draperies, dust cloths, interlinings and interfacings for apparel and handbags, napkins, nonwoven apparel of several types, nonwoven carpet and rug face and backing, pennants, poromeric shoe uppers, punched or needle felts, broadloom linings, cushions, sanitary napkin covers and tampon materials, quilting, oilcloth, shoulder pads, tea bags, towels, tapes and ribbons, polishing and wiping cloths, wall coverings, window shades, vacuum cleaner bags.

Industrial and Commercial Products: Bagging and wrapping fabrics, filters for air, dairy, chemical, high pressure laminates, and oil; bags and containers for certain materials such as desicants; electrical insulators of many types such as for cables, etc., nonwoven carpet and rug face and backing, casket lining, maps, plastic film backing, polishing and wiping cloths, tapes and ribbons, uniforms and other service materials.

Hospital Products: Bandages, garments and uniforms for doctors, nurses, and other personnel, operating caps and masks, patient gowns, sheets and pillowcases, surgical drapes and dressings, etc.

Military Products: Cargo parachutes, decontamination clothing, disposable cups, plates and other utensils used when eating, gas masks, sleeping bags, some uniform fabrics, surgical garments, tents, towels and washcloths, curtains, etc.

NORANE. A group of chemicals which impart durable water repellency and spot and stain resistance to all fibers. There are specific Noranes for various end-uses and fibers. Water repellency is durable to repeated launderings and dry cleanings. Norane may be used alone or in conjunction with Permafresh resins. In this manner, a synergistic Permafresh-Norane effect is obtained whereby water-repellent, quick-drying wash-and-wear fabrics are obtained. Noranes may be applied by padding or exhaustive techniques. Some

require curing, others may be simply dried onto the material. Trade-mark of Warwick Chemical Division, Sun Chemical Corporation, New York City.

NORFOLK JACKET. Named for one of the Dukes of Norfolk (the Howard Family of England) around the turn of the present century. Made popular by Edward VII of Great Britain, it is hip-length, single-breasted, box-front, with the back set off by the use of a belt. A yoke may also be used on the front and back of the garment. This comfortable type of jacket is not as popular as formerly, but the coat does have some call in boys' wear today.

NORFOLK SHEEP. Formerly an important British breed of sheep; it was used to develop the present-day Suffolk breed.

NORFOLK SUITING. Named for that county in England. This type of belted and pleated suiting has waves of popularity, mostly in boys' clothing and in summer and golf toggery clothes.

NORMAL MIXTURE. In knitting parlance it implies a yarn made of cotton and wool in a black-and-white combination to give some varying shade of gray. The amount of black used determines the depth of the gray shade.

NORMANDIE. A Leavers cotton lace made on a bobbin-fining set-out that is plain or outlined with coarse threads. Made as wide as eight inches, the lace is identified by diamond, filet, Point de Paris or round-hole meshes. Originally called Platt Valenciennes, the lace is now made with a warp as well as back and front gimps.

NORTHAMPTONSHIRE LACE. British bobbin lace with a fine mesh that compares with Brussels, Lille, Valenciennes laces. Sometimes referred to as baby lace. See LACE.

NORTHERN MAR-MOUCHA. Native to Morocco, a type of sheep known for its coarse, straight fleece of about three pounds. The white but uneven fleece shows a staple of about 10 inches, which seems to practically cover the animal in entirety. Some fibers will touch the ground.

NORTHERNS COTTON. An Indian cotton of two types—reddish-tinge and white. The staple is about ⅞ inch, lint yield is about 27 per cent, and the cotton spins to about 20s, suitable for warp yarn.

NORWICH TYE. A system in Jacquard work in which the head motion is set at right angles to the lower comberboard. This tye (tie) enables the weaver to scan the cards as they pass over the cylinder.

NOSHI ITO. A Japanese reeling silk

waste which contains other foreign matters that have an effect on the cast of the silk which runs from gray to off-white in color.

NO-TAIL SHEEP. Originating with six fat-rumped sheep brought from Siberia to this country in 1913, this breed was developed by crossing the sheep with Cheviot, Hampshire, Shropshire, and later on with Rambouillet and Southdown. The tails were not eliminated in the first crossing, but in the second crossing it was necessary to dock only a small percentage. Fleeces run from about 7.5 to 9.5 pounds; the wool sorts chiefly to ½ blood and ⅜ blood.

NOTCHED LAPEL. One on which the top line slants downward in line with the collar seam.

NOTCHES. A small U or V shape cut in a pattern. They are used as a guide to join the section parts of the garment together.

NO-THROW. A silk filament which has just enough twist or cohesion to hold the respective strands together.

NOTION AND TRIMMINGS, MANUFACTURERS. Bailey, Green & Elder Company, and Franken Trim, Inc.; (both companies in the Lyntex Corporation), Blumenthal & Co., Inc.; Sol Kahaner & Brother, Inc.; (Unit of Willcox & Gibbs Co., Inc.;) Streamline Buttons, Inc.

NOTTINGHAM LACE. A lace which originated in this English city, long known for its machine-made lace. Strictly speaking, it is a curtain lace, but the name now implies all laces made in Nottingham.

NOUE. French for knotted: noué.

NOUKA. Georgian wool of good quality.

NOUVEAUTÉ. 1. Nouveauté-novelty (French). 2. Braiding, edging and other trimming used to improve apparel garments. 3. Fabrics not considered as real staples in the trade—novelty fabrics.

NOVEL TEXTILE DESIGN. One that has never before, anywhere in the world, been represented pictorially as a textile design or been applied to or incorporated in any textile.

NOVELTY-WEAVE. Any small weave made from a combination of the staple basic weaves such as plain, twill, satin, basket, and rib. Novelty-weave effects are used in counterpanes, dress goods, shirtings, linens, and stripe effects. See Illustrated Section (Fabrics 23, 42, 54).

NOVELTY YARN. A single or ply yarn which differs in construction from an ordinary single or ply yarn. The structure is such that irregular effects or patterns are produced in the yarn. Examples are flake, bouclé, bead, Knickerbocker, slub, bug.

N.P.I. The number of needles-per-inch in the cylinder or needle bed in a knitting machine. Sometimes referred to as the "cut" and often mistakenly called the "gauge."

NOZZLE. The jet or spineret used in making rayon. See Illustrated Section.

NUAGE. From French. Clouded, mottled, shaded, or hazy effects observed in some textile fabrics.

NUANCE. A shade of difference or tone in a color made by folding or draping a transparent fabric over the base material.

NUB. 1. Small specks, neps, lumps, knots, etc. 2. A small mass or ball of fibers usually made on the card and, at first, considered as waste. They are now dyed brilliant colors and are interspersed in yarn to give it brightness. Some novelty yarns of this type are Knickerbocker, bug, slub, etc.

NUBROOT. Abnormally short or missing taproots in mature cotton plants caused by deterioration of the embryo root within the cotton seeds. This condition can lower yields by as much as 25 per cent. Nubroot is also caused by strangulation of the roots by soil compaction or hardpan, or damage to the seedlings by soil fungi. Cotton plants afflicted with nubroot are weaker than ordinary plants and set fewer bolls which have the tendency to wilt readily and may topple over during periods of moisture stress.

NUBUCK. A rugged suede shoe upper leather which as a fine nap, often white, and finished on the grain side. Cattle hide is used for this purpose.

NUB YARN. Yarn is made on double roller machines where one roller stops at certain intervals, regularly or irregularly, while the second roller sets up or builds a nub effect or a base thread. In some cases, nub yarns are bound by a binder or third thread, while other effects can be created without this binder yarn.

NUBIA. A type of ornamental scarf knitted or crocheted of soft fleecy woolen yarns, worn by women about the head and neck.

NUDNICK. A bothersome customer.

NUFIL. Registered trademark for the polypropylene film tape produced by ICI Fibers, Ltd., Great Britain. Created in 1965, it is ideal for use in fishing nets and other marine purposes.

NUMBER. 1. The number or units of standard lengths per standard weight, as in cotton, wool, worsted yarns. 2. The number of standard weights per standard length, as in rayon, acetate,

silk, nylon, et al. See YARN NUMBERING.

NUMBER DUCK, NUMBERED DUCK. See DUCK.

NUMBERING SYSTEM, COTTON. This is based on the number of hanks of yarn, each 840 yards long, necessary to weigh one pound.

NUMBER; NUMBER, YARN. See YARN NUMBER.

NUMDAH RUG. A rug imported from India that is made of wool, felted instead of being woven. This washable, practical bedroom rug is embroidered with wool threads to add to the effect.

NUN'S COTTON. Fine, high-quality white cotton embroidery yarn is often known by this term.

NUN'S VEILING. Religious garb with some call in the dress-goods trade. Cloth is all worsted, all silk, worsted and silk, or other combinations. The fine, sheer types made are dyed black or brown in the piece, but other colors are given when there is a call for the material in the dress-goods trade. Fabric shines with wear. This cloth, when used by laymen, is made into dresses, cloaks, kimonos, and babies' coatings.

NUN'S WORK. The early name for needlework, lace, embroidery, knitting, edging, etc., because these arts were first cultivated and sponsored in the convents of Europe. Many Orders are still very adept in such work, which is still taught in parochial schools all over the world.

NURMA COTTON. An exceptionally white cotton raised in the Dharwar area of India. Yarn made from the staple is used by the Hindus for spiritual purposes.

NURSES' CLOTH. Stiff, firm, white cotton cloth made with a left-hand twill weave of small repeat. Given a linen-like finish, it serves as nurses' uniform fabric. The name is also applied in England to white woven cotton material made with white stripes on blue ground. Nylon is much used at present for nurses' uniform fabric.

NUT. Overhead. "We have a large 'nut.'"

NUTGALL. 1. The extrusion from a disease on twigs of various types of oak trees. 2. Chinese nutgall comes from the leaf stalk of a type of sumac. A puncture of the swelling gives the gall, which is rolled into a half-inch ball. The product contains an excellent tannin for use in dyeing and tanning.

NUTRIA. A native of South America, this aquatic rodent has a beautiful silky fine belly undergrowth which is unlike other similar animals because the nutria dwells in streams that are colder than the atmosphere. Remaining in shallow portions, its back is exposed

to the air and does not require the fur protection demanded by the stomach. The bellies, after the guard hairs are removed, are used by furriers. The textile industry also uses nutria fur fibers in blends emphasizing softness. Nutria sells at around five dollars per pound for the textile industry.

NYGUARD. This nylon zipper features individual teeth that interlock rather than teeth that intermesh. Nyguard runs more smoothly, does away with popping, is stronger and generally appears to be much more acceptable to men than the old coil zipper used on trousers. Product of Scovill Manufacturing Company, Inc., Waterbury, Connecticut.

"NYLEX." A durable, strong nylon thread of the Nylex Company, a division of Advance Silk Thread Company, Hackensack, New Jersey. It is the most resistant thread in use today to breaking, shrinking, snagging, and fraying and is used for hand and machine sewing. Far stronger than any six-cord cotton thread, it may be used for practically any type of sewing. Because of its great strength the thread should be cut at an angle with scissors rather than attempting to break it.

NYLOFT. Continuous filament, textured nylon yarn for use in floorcovering. Trademark is owned by Firestone Synthetic Fibers Company, a Division of Firestone Tire & Rubber Company.

NYLON. The generic name chosen by the E. I. du Pont de Nemours & Co., Inc., for a group of proteinlike chemical products classed as synthetic linear polymers. The term nylon includes a vast group of chemically related products, the physical properties of which differ considerably.

Of especial interest to the textile industry is nylon in filament-yarn form; made from a polymer in flake form, it is melted and forced through a spinneret. It is produced in deniers ranging from 10 to 210, with an individual filament size of about 3 denier. There are two main types—Nylon 6 and Nylon 66, both in filament and staple.

Uses include combination fabrics such as those of rayon, synthetic, and natural fibers; hosiery, knitted lingerie, underwear; woven underwear, dress goods, shirting. Industrial uses include tire fabric, filter fabric, laundry netting, pressing fabrics, belting, and fuel cells.

Nylon staple fiber is used in men's hose, tricot knitted garments, rugs and upholstery, and for blending in durable suiting fabrics such as play clothes, sportswear, uniform fabrics and work clothes. See Illustrated Section.

NYLON, CRIMP-SET. A heat-setting process gives nylon yarn crimpiness which resembles that found in hairy fibers such as wool and worsted. Crimpset nylon differs from crimped nylon in that the latter achieves its crimp by mechanical methods and not by thermosetting, as is the case in crimp-set nylon yarn.

NYLON, N-44. This product of DuPont effectively reduces "flat spotting" in nylon tire yarn. It is used in original equipment and for replacement passenger tires. N-44 retains all the attributes of the conventional nylon tire yarn plus its new property of "spot reduction."

NYLON, NORMAL OR REGULATION. Nylon Type 6.6, invented in the U.S., is often referred to as normal or regulation nylon. This is the type in which the polymer is obtained from adipic acid and hexamethylenediamine. Type 6, incidentally, is obtained from the polymerization of caprolactam and was developed in Germany by Dr. Paul Schlack in 1938.

NYLON, SPARKLING. Du Pont trade-mark for its nylon fiber that has permanent glitter because of light refraction.

NYLON, TYPES OF. These follow:

TYPE 91: Super white, normal tenacity yarns for intimate apparel only.

TYPE 100: Bright, normal tenacity, continuous filament, staple and tow for general use.

TYPE 101: Bright, normal tenacity, heat set staple and tow.

TYPE 109: Bright, normal tenacity, heat set, heat resistant; comes in staple only and for industrial use.

TYPE 140: Color-sealed black, normal tenacity, continuous filament for style diversification in knit and woven fabrics.

TYPE 200: Semidull, normal tenacity, continuous filament, staple and tow for general textile uses.

TYPE 201: Semidull, heat set, normal tenacity, staple and tow for general textile uses.

TYPE 209: Semidull, normal tenacity, industrial yarn for electrical industry; continuous filament and has good dielectric properties.

TYPE 280: Semidull, normal tenacity, improved light durability and dye lightfastness; continuous filament for general textile uses.

TYPE 288: Semidull, normal tenacity, light-resistant yarns designed specifically for trade texturing; continuous filament.

TYPE 300: Bright, high tenacity; continuous filament for industrial and upholstery fabrics.

TYPE 330: Bright, high tenacity, improved light and heat durability; continuous filament and used for industrial purposes.

TYPE 400: Semidull, high tenacity, continuous filament for industrial uses.

TYPE 420: Semidull, high tenacity, high modulus, no crimp, not heat set. Comes in staple only and used as reinforcing fiber for cellulosic blends.

TYPE 501: Crimp-textured trilobal cross-section yarn; continuous filament and used in manufacture of carpets.

TYPE 520: Deep dyeing, normal tenacity, multifilament yarn for cross-dye styling effect with regular yarn in woven and knit fabrics.

TYPE 560: Trilobal cross-section, normal tenacity, multifilament yarn for improved aesthetics, including hand and luster.

TYPE 600: Dull, normal tenacity, staple and tow for carpets and rugs.

TYPE 601: Dull, heat set, normal tenacity; staple and tow for carpets and rugs.

TYPE 680: Dull, normal tenacity, light resistant, continuous filament; primarily of fine denier sizes for lingerie.

TYPE 700: Bright, high tenacity, heat and light resistant; comes in

heavy denier, and this continuous filament is used in industrial applications.

TYPE 707: Bright, high tenacity, heat and light resistant; continuous filament of heavy denier for use in cordage yarns.

Courtesy of:
E. I. du Pont de
Nemours & Co., Inc.

NYLON 11. See RILSAN.

NYLON 22N, MONSANTO. Trademark of Monsanto, Inc., New York City, for use in tricot knitting. This antistatic nylon has its ingredients built into the fiber which, at present, is Nylon 6.6. Its nature is such that they cannot be washed, ironed, or worn-out. Its use improves lack of clingability, moisture transport, opacity, soil release, and whiteness retention. Products made of this yarn can be dyed in full ranges of color, and colorfastness is entirely satisfactory though darker shades do need more colorants. Ideal for printing, textured yarns may be used in construction. Beam or beck methods are used in the dyeing process. Suggested temperatures are from 75° F. to 80° F., with relative humidity from 60° F. to 65° F. See Moisture Transport.

NYLON BRISTLE FILAMENTS. One form in which nylon is manufactured is called the monofilament form— that is, one single solid strand. This covers all nylon filaments .050 inch in diameter or over. One of the main uses for these monofilaments, after cutting into required lengths, is for bristles in toothbrushes, hairbrushes, and industrial brushes of many kinds.

NYLON CHIFFON. Material used in needlework and embroidery; has great strength in addition to sheerness.

NYLON CORDED VELVET. Fabric on which the effect is made by cutting into the pile instead of weaving, as on the order of corduroy.

NYLON CRUSHED VELVET. Permanent-set finish fabric given pressure and heat treatments to be used in housecoats and robes where washability is a factor.

NYLON FOUR. Invented by Dr. Carl E. Barns, president of Alrac Corporation, Stamford, Connecticut, it is made in filament and staple forms. Thirteen years of research and development were spent on its creation. Its absorption compares with that of cotton; moisture content of approximately 6% is the same as cotton. The basic monomer for Nylon 4 is 2-pyrrolidone making it possible to have a good competitive price among comparable products.

Strength and abrasion resistance are

NYLON, RUBBER, AND SPANDEX, SOME COMPARISONS AMONG.

PROPERTY	NYLON	SPANDEX	RUBBER
Elongation	25 percent	625 percent	540 percent
Durability	Excellent	Excellent	Fair-good
Dyeability	Good-very good	Good	Poor
Minimum denier	7.5 to 10.00	20	100
Tenacity in grams per denier	4.2	1.2	.34

two of the outstanding factors of this nylon. It easily takes resin finishes and can be used in blends in durable press fabrics. Dyeing and finishing is done on conventional machines, the same as those used on other manmade fibers. Melting point is 265° Centigrade; ironing point is the same as that for cotton.

NYLON FROM "DACRON," TEST TO DISTINGUISH. Nylon can be stained or dyed with an alcohol solution of certain acid colors at room temperature. "Dacron" is not dyed or deeply stained by such a solution. Individual ends may be identified as follows:
1. Dissolve 2 to 5 grams of DuPont Anthraquinone Blue SWF in one liter of denatured alcohol at room temperature.
2. Pain or swab the solution across the fabric or dip the ends into the dye solution for ten to fifteen minutes.
3. Allow a few minutes for the alcohol to evaporate from fabric or yarn. Then wash with clear water to remove excess dye.
4. Inspect the ends. Nylon will stain a medium blue; "Dacron" will not stain. A white background placed beneath dark warp ends provides contrast to aid in the identification.

NYLONIZING. Trade-mark of Hans C. Bick, Inc., for a process of bonding Type 6 nylon fabric to give it faster moisture absorbency, a softer hand, and greater wearing comfort. Developed for nylon fabrics, it is now used for rayon, acetate, cotton, and blends.

NYLON-L. Product of Toyo Rayon Company, Japan, in which the method of manufacture sets anti-static properties into the yarn during processing, not in the finishing process as is done in conventional nylon products. Trade name for this nylon is *Toray Nylon Parel*. Because of the anti-static properties, the company claims that dust and other minute particles are kept at a minimum thereby affording better cleanliness and brightness over a longer period of time.

NYLON PUCKERED FABRIC. The original nylon pucker fabric was made of preshrunk and nonshrunk nylon yarns. For example, if the designer wanted a one-quarter-inch pucker stripe on a 180 end taffeta, he would preshrink half of his warp yarn, and then arrange his layout as follows: 45 ends of preshrunk nylon, 45 ends of nonshrunk nylon, repeated across entire width of the goods. All yarn would be on a single beam. After the fabric is woven, and when the goods have been boiled-off in finishing, the nylon yarn that had not been preshrunk would shrink, while the other yarn, really having no place to go, would pucker in the material.

A second method to obtain the effect is by printing with phenol. A plain taffeta which has not been heat set, when printed in floral motifs, checks, stripes, etc., with phenol paste, will pucker at the areas where the design has been printed.

A third method may be obtained through the use of different denier yarn and various weaves. For example, an arrangement of a 15 monofil nylon yarn with a 70-denier nylon yarn, using a Louisine weave (2-1 or 1-2 basket weave), will give the effect, usually in the plan of two warp ends of the 15-denier monofil yarn over one pick of the 70-denier nylon yarn. This plan allows the goods to pucker because of the difference in the takeup in weaving the cloth. The same principle may be applied for pucker effects in the filling direction of the fabric. Various small weaves are used to obtain various effects in either warp or filling direction.

Thus, in this third method, any reasonable number of ends of warp may be used of both 15-denier and 70-denier yarns. The number of ends should depend upon the width of the stripe desired. The 70-denier yarn could weave on the 2-1 basket effect while the 15-denier yarn would be drawn-in to weave in plain-weave order so that different shrinkages and take-ups would be realized in the finishing of the goods. For this effect one or two warp beams may be used.

NYLONS, BRITISH. The major nylons produced in Great Britain are - Enkalon of British Enkalon, Ltd.; Bri-Nylon of ICI Fibres, Ltd.; and Blue "C" Nylon of Monsanto Textiles, Ltd.

NYLON SEERSUCKER TAFFETA. Taffeta-type fabric construction made in plain-weave or in plain-weave variations; comes in stripes or checks formed by contrasting "hill-and-dale" areas. The fabric is wrinkle-resistant, quick-drying, and does not have to be ironed.

NYLON STRAW. Sold under the name of Yuva, it is produced by Viscose Suisse, Emmenbruecke, Seitzerland. A monofilament straw used in knit and woven shoes, automobile and curtain fabrics, belts, hats, handbags, and lampshades.

NYLON TULLE. Fabric which is knitted on a tricot machine and may be made with a soft finish ideal for dress goods or in a crisp finish for use in millinery.

NYLON TYPE 472. This nylon is the original fiber for *Qiana* which is labeled only to accepted textiles by E.I. duPont de Nemours & Company, Inc., Wilmington, Delaware. Basically Qiana is a concept and not a single chemical.

Nylons, of which there are many variations, have different building blocks and variable properties engineered for specific uses. Presently based in Chattanooga, Tennessee, the physical properties follow:

Density	1.03
Elongation	30 percent
Ironing Temperature	365° F.
Modulus	30
Moisture Regain	2.5 percent
Shrinkage (heat)	10 percent
Tenacity	3.3 gpd.
Ultra Violet	Resistant

Dimensionally stable to heat and to humidity.

NYLON TYPE 714. An improved nylon tire yarn of Du Pont which has improved adhesion and up to 25 per cent better fatigue resistance to other yarns. The type has improved flexibility, decided asset for it. The first use of nylon as a tire reinforcing material was in 1940 when it was used to solve difficult tire problems for the armed forces. The first nylon tires had a strength of about six grams per denier, double the strength of the rayon yarns then in use, and much stronger than even the best of the improved high tenacity rayons used today. Type 714 has a strength of more than nine grams per denier.

NYLON VELVET. Material given a Zelan finish for water repellency for use in bathing suits and in rainwear.

NYMCRYLON. An acrylic fiber made in Holland comparable with Orlon acrylic fiber made by Du Pont.

NYTELLE. Nylon produced by Firestone Fibers Company, Hopewell, Virginia, and used mainly in the hosiery and tricot-fabric trades.

NYTRIL ALLOY. Term used by some fiber manufacturers to apply to their Nytril fibers.

NYTRIL FIBER. This manufactured fiber contains at least 85 per cent of a long chain polymer of vinylidene dinitrile where this content is not less than every other unit in the polymer chain. The defunct fiber, Darvan, was a nytril fiber. This type fiber is no longer produced in the United States and has almost passed into oblivion.

O

OAKUM. When mixed with tar, these coarse flax and hemp fibers, obtained in the scutching operation, are used in caulking ships. Old ropes, after being broken down, are tarred and used for the same purpose.

OATCAKE LINEN. Same as oatmeal cloth.

OATMEAL CLOTH. A soft, heavy linen cloth with a crepe, pebble, granite, or ratiné effect to make it resemble oatmeal paper. This towel fabric, also known as mummie cloth, is strong, durable, and launders well.

Varying qualities of filling, including waste filling, are used in oatmeal cloth which comes in the natural or unbleached state. It may be used for draping, dress goods, and upholstery.

OATMEAL WEAVES. Name for certain crepe, granite, quarter-turn and double satin weaves of small repeat—because they afford a mottled or speckled effect on fabric.

OATS COTTON. A vigorous, prolific plant produces this early-maturing cotton which has a 1-inch staple and a 32 per cent lint yield.

OBI. The broad sash worn by women in the Far East—as on the kimono; made of silk moire taffeta, plain taffeta, brocaded silk, or plain-woven silk.

OBIJI. A Japanese sash material; name comes from "obi" which means sash and "ji" which is the Japanese word for fabric.

OCEAN PEARL BUTTONS. The best grade of pearl buttons is made of imported ocean shells. As compared with fresh-water pearl buttons made from shells obtained from inland waterways in the United States, the ocean pearl buttons are more iridescent, more translucent, have greater luster and a brighter finish. Fresh-water pearls have a chalky or milky appearance and are on the dull side in luster. There is, at times, considerable discoloration and spotted areas, as well. Fresh-water pearl buttons cost about two-thirds the price of ocean pearl buttons; plastic buttons cost about one-tenth the cost of ocean pearl buttons.

ODOR. A smell; an unusual, usually offensive odor may be noted in some goods in finishing or after laundering. This may be caused by mold growth, mildew, decomposed soap, certain sours, etc.

OEILLET, OILLET. French for eyelet and means a hole, opening or space worked into a fabric for the passage of a cord or lace.

OFFAL. The less valuable parts of hides and skins—head, shoulders, belly—are known by this collective term. In this sense, however, offal does not mean waste since, in the heavy leather field, these parts are separated and diverted into special uses.

OFFSET TWILLS. Another name for braided twill weaves.

OFF-SHADE. Color in fabric that matches only in spots or places and is irregular throughout the piece. A peculiar or poor cast will result from off-shades in goods. This effect is noted and sought for in cloth from side-to-side, side-to-center, and from end-to-end.

OFF-SIDE. Where the shuttles in a loom enter shuttle boxes eye-first, at the one side of the loom.

OFF-SORTS. Products obtained in wool sorting, from fine to coarse stock. They are certain quantities of short, kempy, frowsy, dungy, be-colored locks of wool and are not of the regular sort in grading.

OFF-SQUARE. In fabric it is the percentage of warp crimp minus the percentage of filling crimp. It means also a fabric that is supposed to be square (the same number of ends and picks per inch) but which does not show a true, square pick count.

OHIO MERINO. See MERINO SHEEP, MERINO WOOL.

OHM. The unit in which the resistance of a conductor to the passing of electric energy is expressed.

OIL. A vegetable or animal oil is a liquid fat or glyceride. A mineral oil is a hydrocarbon material that contains no glyceride and is not saponifiable; it is only emulsifiable.

OIL, COTTONSEED. The pale yellow, practically odorless and tasteless, oily liquid extracted from cotton seeds. It is used as fatty acid in making soap, soap powder, washing powders; in making cosmetics, explosives, dressings, lotions, etc. Other uses for this most valuable by-product include packing oil for sardines and certain fruits, pitch, refined oil, shortening and frying, and in vegetable stearin with refined oils, butter substitutes, candles, waxes.

OIL BELT DUCK. Compactly woven fabric made of ply yarn that is not higher than 8s in yarn count. It comes in various widths, but is usually a 32-ounce fabric with the weight figured on the square-yard basis.

OILCLOTH. Fabric which is treated with linseed-oil varnish to give a patent-leather effect. When used for table covers or shelf covering, it may be given a satiny sheen and finish. It comes in plain colors or printed designs. Other uses include waterproof garments for outerwear, book bags, covers, belts, bibs, pencil cases, and other containers, surgical supplies, bags, and luggage.

OIL-COMBED WORSTED TOPS. Those which contain added oil for the smoother working of the fibers during manipulation.

OIL COMBING. Combing in oil. See COMBING-IN-OIL.

OILED WOOL. Unscoured or undyed wool fibers, before spinning, which contain oil that is not to be ultimately removed from the stock in the manufacturing processes.

OILING. Spraying of oil on the various layers of stock in wool manufacturing to insure evenness and smoothness in running the wool through the various operations. It is done usually by means of an automatic sprinkler machine. The principle involved is the same as that in using a watering can to water a garden, or that of a street sprinkler. The various emulsions used are made from palm, lard, oleic, olive, and other oils.

OILLESS HESSIAN. An English jute fabric guaranteed to have less than a fixed percentage of oil. Soap and soluble oil are used as the softener, while the dressing mixture contains only flour and farina. It is used for filter fabric.

OIL OF VITRIOL. Sulphuric acid, H_2SO_4.

OIL-PRESS DUCK. One of the heavier Naught ducks.

OILED SILK. Silk sheer fabrics in the gum state may be treated with linseed oil, at high temperature, then dried and made waterproof. The linseed oil oxidizes to a hard, smooth, translucent surface. This pliable cloth is used for medical supplies and raincoats, also shower curtains.

OILSKIN. Cotton, linen, silk, manmade, or synthetic yarn material which has been treated with linseed oil, varnish, or pigment in varnish. In plain colors, the fabric is used for rainwear and sailors' or fishermen's clothing; in printed effects it has several household uses.

OIL STAINS. Stains and marks detrimental to goods. They are acquired in a great number of ways and must be removed in cloth scouring. Many oil spots are the result of carelessness as the cloth is moved from room to room in the cloth-finishing procedure. See STAIN REMOVAL.

OILSTREAKS. Black or stained areas running in the warp or the filling direction. They may be caused by careless oiling of roll stands and saddles in carding or spinning room, or careless oiling in almost any department; dropping of bobbins on floor during handling, oil dropping into the warp from overhead shafting, unclean hands on the part of the operatives, etc. Utmost care in oiling and clean handling of bobbins, yarn, and goods is essential.

OIL TANNAGE. Tanning with animal oils, such as used in the manufacture of some soft leathers, particularly chamois and certain types of buckskin.

Fish oils are much used in the treatment.

OIL-TREATED FABRICS. These cloths are given a linseed-oil processing to make them waterproof. Several cotton cloths serve as the base fabric—sheeting, muslin, print cloth, lawn, and kindred cloths. Silk and a few of the man-made fiber materials can be oil-treated. The main uses are for slickers, ponchos, and other waterproof garments.

OILED YARN. Same as lubricated yarn.

OISUPON. The Greek word for lanolin (purified sheep grease). Around 500 B.C., Dioscorides, physician to Emperor Nero, wrote a treatise on purified sheep grease, commonly known as yolk today. The yolk is separated from the suint and other foreign matter when the fleece is scoured to obtain the cleansed fibers.

OKRA. A tall annual herb of the okra plant, *Abelmoschus esculentus*. Raised and used in India for cordage and bagging, and as a jute adulterant.

OKRA COTTON. An old-time cotton of 1-inch staple and about 32 per cent lint yield. The bolls are well clustered, small, round, and early maturing. Also known as Farrar forked leaf, okra leaf.

OLANE. Polyolefin fiber produced by AviSun Corporation, New Castle, Delaware; company jointly owned by American Viscose Corporation and Sun Oil Company, Inc.

OLATE. A pure, neutral, low-titer flake soap used as a scouring and fulling agent. It is fast-dissolving and fast-rinsing and has a gentle cleansing action. Affords good protection against uneven shrinkage and non-uniform fulling. Efficiency is retained at lower-than-average temperatures.

OLD FUSTIC. Same as fustic.

OLEFIN. Generic term for a fiber in which the fiber-forming substance is any long chain syntheitc polymer of at least 85%, by weight, of ethylene, propylene, or other olefin units. Examples include Celanese Fibers Marketing Company, Inc.; Enjay Fibers and Laminates Company, Inc.; Hercules, Inc.; Phillips Fibers Corporation; UniRoyal Fiber and Textile Division of UniRoyal.

OLEFINE. The name for a series of hydrocarbons homologous with olefiant gas or ethylene; general formula is C_nH_{2n}.

OLEIC. An unsaturated fatty acid obtained from vegetable oils and fats. It is the basis of low-titer soaps.

OLEIC ACID. An oily compound contained as an ester in most mixed oils and fats, and obtained by saponification with an alkali. Used as a water softener, in waterproofing textiles, and in the manufacture of Turkey red oil.

OLEIN. The solid precipitate which settles out of vegetable and animal oils upon cooling. The term is applied to Oleic acid or red oil.

OLEO. A prefix borrowed from the Latin, meaning "oil;" used in the formation of compound words such as oleophilic (oil attracting) and oleophobic (oil repelling) with regard to absorption by a textile fiber. See Hydrophilic, Hydrophobic, Relative Humidity, Standard Condition, Standard Moisture Regain.

OLEORESINOUS. A material produced by the combination of an oil and a resin.

OLIVE. A dull, medium, yellowish green color, like that of an unripe olive.

OLIVE-DRAB FLANNEL. Flannel of the olive shade made to exact specifications by the United States Government, for uniform material.

OLIVE OIL. The oil from olives, like other oils used in the woolen and worsted industry, serves as a lubricant, in making sulphonated oil, and is used in between the blending and mixing operations in preparation of the fibers for carding.

OLONA FIBER. Hawaii produces this strong, durable bast fiber which is used for cords, fishing nets, lines, and Malo fabric.

OMBRE. Shaded (French, ombre, or shade) effects in finished cloth produced by using dyed yarn in weaving the material. Colors range from light to dark shades of some particular color; ombré cloth is popular, at times, in dress goods and suiting.

OMBRE, FONDU OR "RAINBOW" PRINTING. The French word, ombré, means a shaded stripe effect, running from light to dark in cast. This variation of block printing employs a frame faced with silk or nylon bolting cloth of very fine mesh. The colored liquors are set into the frame in a crosswise direction. The squeegee roller then works on the colors in a vertical direction to produce the effect called "rainbow," with the aid of blocks to apply the color to the fabric. OMBRÉ RAYÉ is the effect made by alternating stripes with stripes of the foundation color.

OMBRELLINO. From the Italian, literally, "little umbrella." It has a flat top made of white silk or nylon and ornamented with gold fringe, and is supported by a longer staff than the ordinary umbrella. It is used as a canopy in Roman Catholic services when the Blessed Sacrament is carried from one place to another in other than a solemn procession. See Baldachin.

OMBRE REED. An American expression, ombré reed means reed marks in cloth caused by irregular reeding, incorrect spacing or weak-pressed steel wires in the reed.

OMOPHORION. A vestment worn by Bishops of the Byzantine Rite of the Roman Catholic Church. It consists of a ten-inch wide band of silk or silk velvet which is wrapped loosely around the neck so that one end hangs over the left shoulder in front, and the other over the left shoulder to the back, the ends reaching almost to the ground. It corresponds to the pallium of the Roman Rite. See Pallium.

ON-CALL COTTON. Cotton which has been selected for use and sold at a price agreeable to seller and spinner when it is needed or "called" by the latter.

ONDE. French dress goods of cotton warp and bright-colored wool filling. Supposed to have originated in Orléans, France, ondé is cross-dyed—thereby causing the warp and the filling to show different color-effects in the finished goods. The term also implies cotton, woolen, silk, acetate and rayon fabrics which have been moiréd or watermarked in the finishing of the material.

"ONDELETTE." A continuous filament rayon yarn which contains randomly spaced, entangled slubs, and resembles textures such as those observed in Douppioni silk fabrics. This Du Pont product is used in dresswear, neckwear, men's sport shirts, suitings, casement cloth, curtains, and draperies.

ONDINE. A heavy-corded bengaline in which every third filling cord has a wavy or crinkled (ondiné) effect.

ONDULE. See ONDULE REED.

ONDULE REED. Reed known as ondulé is used in weaving fabric in which groups of reed wires alternately converge toward the top and the bottom. In weaving, the reed is raised and lowered in the loom lay to force the warp ends to come close together at times, and apart at other times. The effect caused by the use of this reed is an undulating or wavy motif in the fabric, to the right and to the left in direction. See PAQUET REED.

ONE - HUNDRED - PER - CENT THROWN METHOD. A manner of dealing with waste made in silk-throwing operations; the throwster pays for all of the waste made and is then reimbursed by a proper addition to his price for the throwing of the silk. See THROWING.

ONE-PROCESS PICKER. A machine that does the work of several individual machines in the cotton-picking system in the mill. Used chiefly in mills that run large lots of stock and comparatively few types of cotton in the mixes.

ONE-SIDED TERRY FABRIC. That which has the uncut pile threads on only one side of the goods.

ONE-THROW YARN. Silk yarn composed of several single threads twisted together at one doubling; fourteen to sixteen ends may be doubled on this plan.

ONION BAGGING. A strong container fabric made with leno or doup weave to hold onions, other vegetables, and citrus fruits. With this type of fabric area air can reach the products contained in them very readily thereby prolonging freshness. The advantages for display and selling purposes are aided with this type of openwork fabric. See MESH.

ONIUM DYE. A water-soluble cationic dye in which the ionisable group is an ammonium, sulphonium, phosphonium, or oxonium radical. See RADICAL.

"O.N.T." A cotton thread developed by George Clark of the Clark family around 1861 and called "Our New Thread." In 1865, "O.N.T." was created from the expression "Our New Thread" and also acquired the name "O.N.T. Beats All Others." Since 1865 "O.N.T." has been used on millions of spools of thread to the present day. The Clark Thread Company made its first application for formal registration of the trdemark in 1872, and recited in the papers that the letters had been in use for more than six years, replacing the words "Our New Thread" which had been used for about four years prior to the changeover to the letters.

OOMRAWUTTEE COTTON. A popular Indian cotton of about ⅞-inch staple. It has a good cream color, is strong and uniform throughout, and is cleaner than most Indian cottons. Used to spin 16s warp and 22s filling yarns. Much sought for in the English market.

OOZE. 1. Suède calfskin used for glove material that is finished on the grain side. 2. Broad term used to imply loose, straggly, protruding fibers on the surface of yarns.

OOZE LEATHER. See SUEDE FINISH.

OPAL. The registered trade-mark for muslin which has a wool-like finish that appears on sheer cottons and particularly on handkerchiefs. Opal transparent is a transparent-pattern effect on an opaque background.

OPALINE. High-quality, white lawn cloth with a soft, appealing finish.

Comes in 36-inch width.

OPAQUE. Not allowing light to pass through; not transparent.

OPEN-BAND. British term for Z-twist.

OPEN BOIL. Scouring of cellulose textiles with alkaline liquors in open-topped vats or kiers at or near the boiling point. Scourings below the boil are usually referred to as steeps or steepings.

OPEN DRAWING. The first method used in drawing worsted top and based on the principle of flyer spinning. Used on crossbred or Luster wools, coarse, long mohair, etc., the top or sliver is flat and level. One of the features of open drawing is that when a flyer is used for twisting and winding, the bobbin on the spindle is loose and rather free so that it may be carried around easily by the slubbing.

OPENER, COTTON. In the opener, the stock is taken care of by a series of cylinder-bar spur-teeth set in the rapidly revolving cylinder. The cotton is flung, by means of centrifugal force, against an iron grid many times. This loosens up the stock. There is a strong current of air blown through which aids in the opening of the cotton. Much foreign matter is removed in this treatment. The dirt is thrown out through grid spaces and is carried off. The lint gradually works its way along a channel and finally passes between two large rollers, which compress it into a sheet of cotton batting.

This sheet or lap is rolled into a large roll about two feet in diameter and about 40 inches in width. When the cotton has arrived at the lap stage, it is ready for doubling and blending.

Plants making the higher types and grades of yarn find it vitally important to have the strength and evenness accurate. To insure this in the finisher picker, four laps are fed into the machine, one on top the other, in layer form. Thus, the four laps come out of the picker as a well-blended whole, and the final lap is made up of the component fibers of the four laps that were fed in. This picker is also known as a scutcher, and the treatment the stock receives in going through, in addition to the blending of the cotton, gets out additional particles of foreign matter. As evener laps result from this treatment, the cotton is more attractive, cleaner, and better to handle.

The lap then is fed from the Opener Room into the Card Room by means of a mono-rail conveyer. The fibers, of course, are not parallel at all and are in the same condition as they came from the grids of the opener machine.

OPENER PICKER. An auxiliary cleaning machine used when high-quality cotton yarn is desired. The machine precedes the breaker picker and follows the bale breaker.

OPENING. Covers the initial treatments given to raw cotton; the separation and opening up of the cotton to remove compression because of baling and shipping. Heavier impurities are also removed from the stock. The bale breaker and various picker machines perform the work. The action of opening machines may be revolving and tumbling, beating, air draft, and suction. Opening is concluded when the cotton lap is made ready for actual carding.

OPENING MACHINES. The auxiliary machines used in cotton yarn manufacture; the machines that precede the cotton card—bale breaker, automatic feeder, vertical opener, lattice opener.

OPENING ROOM. The section of a cotton plant where the opening machines are located—breakers, feeders, openers, conducting trunks, and all other necessary equipment. It is usually located near the sources for raw cotton.

OPEN SHED. One in which the warp is divided into a top line and a bottom line as the loom is in motion. The threads never come together in one line at any time. See CLOSE SHED.

OPEN SHOP. Company in which union membership is not a condition for employment, or continued employment. Usually one in which there is no union present.

OPEN WOOL. The opposite of dense wool; sheep which raise this type often show a sparse or open area down the spine. Merino fleeces are an example of dense wool; many long wools and crossbreds typify open wool.

OPENWORK. Material which has openings or spaces that are observed in groundwork of close-textured fabric to improve the motif or effect. It is found in crochet work, embroidery, knitted material, knot work, netting, tatting, leno, or doup-woven fabrics.

OPENWORK KNITTING STITCH. A plan used chiefly in hand knitting whereby the open space or hole is made as the yarn is thrown over the needle and the next two stitches are knitted as one.

OPERA HAT. On the order of the high silk hat, it is usually made of nylon or silk grosgrain fabric set over a collapsable metallic crown frame. Now used in formal or semi-formal evening wear.

OPERA HOSE. Hosiery made of an extra length, for use chiefly in the theatrical world.

OPERATOR. A merchant who does

things in a "big" way.

OPORTO. Coarse Portuguese wool; used for carpets.

OPOSSUM. The only marsupial outside of Australia, this beast thrives in Australia, and the southern U.S. and is found as far south as Argentina. It is about cat size, has a white face and fur that is loose, grayish, and white tipped. The pelting is used chiefly as trimming for cloth coats. In textile fabrics, the hair is separated from the undergrowth and only the latter used. The price of the fur for textile blends varies from two to ten dollars per pound. Australia and New Zealand are by far the biggest producers of opossum.

OPTICAL BLEACH. Colorless dyes applied to white fabrics so as to make them appear an intense white by fluorescing strongly in ultraviolet light.

OPTICAL DYE. See FLUORESCENT DYE.

OPTIMO STRAW HAT. Usually of the panama variety, it has an undented crown with a distinctive ridge which runs through the crown center from front to back.

OPUHE FIBER. A very strong Hawaiian bast fiber used for fishing nets.

OPUS. A Latin term, the English equivalent of which is "work," used in textiles with particular reference to lace work, embroidery work, etc. Opus filatorium, for example, means darning embroidery on a square mesh foundation.

ORANGE. A reddish yellow color, also, a pigment of this color. It is high in saturation and medium to high in brilliance.

ORARION. The stole worn by the deacon in the Byzantine Rite of the Roman Catholic Church. Made of a narrow band of silk or nylon, four yards in lingth. Embroidered three times in Greek is the word, "Holy."

ORCEIN. Reddish brown coloring matter obtained from orcein by the action of aqueous ammonia and air; a tinctorial principle of archil.

ORCHID. Any of the various delicate, rosy purple tints, medium in brilliance and saturation.

ORCHIL. See ARCHIL.

ORCIN, ORCINOL. A colorless, crystalline compound obtained from certain lichens, as archil, and from aloes. It is now made synthetically from toluene derivatives and readily changes into orcein.

ORDINARY. 1. This term is used to distinguish certain wool from "staple wool," in describing the territory clothing and carding wools. 2. In the cotton trade it means the lowest two of the nine standard grades of cotton, used in grading or classing the staple— "good ordinary" and "strict good ordinary."

ORDINARY TWILLS. The same as the common twills—right-hand, left-hand, broken, herringbone, etc. Includes the 2-up, 1-down; 1-up, 2-down; 2-up, 2-down; 3-up, 3-down, etc.

ORENBURG SHAWL. A framework knitted material, made by shifting certain loops sideways the distance of several needles to form the pattern.

ORGANDY. A light, transparent silk fabric on the order of cotton organdy. Cotton organdy is stiff, has a hard finish, a watermarked or moiré effect, and is transparent. It is made of Arizona or Egyptian cotton, single 140s warp and 100s filling, gassed, and neatly finished. Texture runs from eighty to ninety ends and picks for inch. It comes in white or solid colors, and can be printed. Pastel shades are very popular.

Brilliant spots of color are seen in some of the goods. These are woven in by lappet, swivel, or clipspot methods of weaving. Much organdy is given "permanent swiss finish." Finished from 40- to 45-inches wide, there are from ten to as many as twenty yards of the fabric to the pound.

Uses for silk and cotton organdy include collar and cuff sets, bedspreads, curtains, blouses and waists, baby bonnets, artificial flowers, doll clothes, millinery, neckwear, summer dresses.

ORGANDY FINISH. A thin, transparent finish given to muslin made of fine cotton yarns which have more than the usual amount of twist in them. The crisp, sheer finish is obtained by the use of acid or resin. The fabric has permanent finish, as in the case of swiss organdy.

ORGANIC. A broad term, applied to substances obtained from living organisms, or any substances which consist largely of hydrogen, oxygen, and carbon. The other general class of substance is the mineral or inorganic group.

ORGANIC ACID. One which contains carbon, such as acetic, formic, oxalic acids. All organic acids contain carbon; all inorganic acids are devoid of carbon.

ORGANIC SOLVENT. Contains the element, carbon, the only known chemical element for which there is no known solvent. The symbol for carbon, "C," will appear in the formula. This type of solvent is used in the removal of stains, greasy in nature. Since the vapors of all organic solvents are injurious when inhaled in large quantities, they should be used in well ventilated quarters. Some organic solvents are wood alcohol, ether, benzene, gasoline, carbon tetrachloride, benzol, acetic acid, chloroform.

ORGANZA. Thin, transparent, stiff, wiry rayon or silk fabric which crushes or musses easily but is readily pressed. Plain-weave fabric. Used for evening dresses, trimmings, neckwear, and as foundation material over which delicate sheer materials are worn.

ORGANZARI. An adaption of Indian Sari fabric made with silk yarn and given a crisp, stiff finish. Tissue-weave constructions are used in this piece-dyed or yarn-dyed material, often made with brighter-than-pastel shades. Striped motifs are also used. The designs range from small effects to rather large patterns. Trade name of Rémond-Holland Co.

ORGANZINE. It is a "warp yarn in the silk trade." Tram is the name for filling yarn and obviously will not require as much twist as organzine.

In tram, the three original filatures are doubled together with little or no twist to make what is known as singles.

In organzine, the thread is made from a series of continuous filaments taken from three to eleven cocoons. The threads are given sixteen turns of twist per inch in the first-time spinning, and then two threads from the first spinning operation are taken and given fourteen turns of twist in the opposite direction. This is called second-time spinning, and it will give a thread that is strong and durable. There is no chance of raveling of the threads because of the manner in which the yarn was spun and twisted.

ORIENTAL LACES. Refers, in one sense, to the ancient lace work done in Arabia, Egypt, Greece, Rome, China, Japan, India, Turkey, and Persia (Iran). In another interpretation, the term refers to these laces made throughout the world, either by hand or by machine, made to simulate more or less the ancient laces now usually found in museums, private collections, etc.

ORIENTAL REPRODUCTIONS. Machine-made rugs made in this country to simulate Oriental designs and given luster finish to enhance the surface effect. Often referred to as American Orientals, naturally a misnomer.

ORIENTAL RUG KNOTS. The fineness of an oriental rug is determined by the number of knots used per inch. Two types of knots are used; Turkish or Ghiordes and Persian or Senna.

ORIENTAL RUGS.

1. DEVELOPMENT: Oriental rugs are an ancient handicraft believed to have originated in Egypt. Persia has always

led the world in products of the loom. Greeks, Arabs, and Spaniards also practiced the art at an early date; Crusaders took back to Europe knowledge and desire for these rugs, through Italy to England. They are now popular in America.

2. USES: In the Orient as carpets, divans, pillows, cushion covers, portières or wall hangings, beds, prayer rugs, saddle bags, royal palace furnishings.

Prayer rugs: originated with Mohammedans; at an appointed hour, the follower prostrates himself on his rug, head resting on the niche pointing toward Mecca. Some prayer rugs have three or more niches as though intended for a family.

3. WORKERS: Most rug weaving in the Orient is done by women, who toil from early morning to night, beginning industry at the age of six years. In parts of India and Kirman, men and boys are weavers under the government and commercialized workers. A worker receives ten to fifteen cents per day. A rug that takes four years to make may be bought for eighty dollars on the spot.

4. WEAVING: The same method of weaving is used today as was used 2,000 years ago. The loom has two horizontal poles according to the width of the proposed carpet. One is placed about a foot above the floor, the other 6 or 7 feet higher and parallel with it. Between these beams stretch the warp which forms the foundation. Small bobbins of dyed material are passed over and under the warp threads twice. The two ends are brought to the front and the end is cut to form a pile. This is repeated according to the design. Each row is hammered down with a comb. Between each row the warps are crossed, a shot of hemp or cotton is introduced between them. Every few rows the pile is trimmed.

5. KNOTS TO THE SQUARE INCH: Kirmans or Sennas have from four to six hundred knots to the square inch.

Some Turkish have as few as thirty.

One pair of Senna rugs six feet four inches by four feet four inches is said to have nine hundred and twenty-four knots to the square inch, and to have taken fifteen years to make.

A skillful weaver can tie three knots per minute. A Kirman rug five feet by eight feet containing four hundred knots per square inch can be made in four years if worked at eight hours daily. A rug of the same quality ten feet by twelve feet would take about ten years to make, while a coarse modern Turkish rug, with forty knots to the square inch, will take less than two years.

6. MATERIALS: The wool is washed, sorted, cleaned, carded, and spun all by hand. Oriental rugs consists of wool from sheep and goats, silk, camel hair, cotton, linen, and hemp. Silk and wool are often used as the warp and woof.

7. COLOR: A natural untutored instinct is used by designer or weaver to procure the colors. Permanence is due to use of animal and vegetable dyes.

Brown: green husks of walnuts or valonia.
Crimson: sea mollusk.
Scarlet: sheep's blood.
Red: insect of Egypt.
Blue: indigo plants.
Red: madder plants.
Yellow: Persian berry or fungus.
Reddish Orange: Henna plant.
Red has preserving qualities. Black often destroys fibers of fabrics.

Dyeing is a fine art. Plants and animals are raised by the dyers.

Color depends upon water, temperature, atmospheric condition, exposure and dippings. The color secrets are held through generations.

The introduction of anilin or coal-tar dyes is destroying dyeing as an art; more crude, cheap, used commercially, not always permanent.

8. DESIGN: Attraction depends on predominating color; general scheme of design; pattern detail.

Origin of design believed to be geometrical.

Persian carpet design may imitate walled-in garden—flowers, trees, birds and animals.

Aryan or floral type:
  Persian.
  East Indian.

Geometric:
  Turkonian.
  Caucasian.

Combination:
  Turkish.
  Kurdish.

ORIFICE. A single minute hole or opening in the face of a spinneret. The number of orifices in the spinneret will vary; the greater the number of holes, the finer will be the resultant filaments delivered into the hardening liquor or bath.

ORLEANS. A plain-weave or a plain-woven dress goods of cotton warp and bright-colored wool or worsted filling. Closely woven, it has about twice as many picks as ends; also known as Luster Orleans, the cloth may be cross-dyed to show different color-effects in the warp and the filling.

ORLEANS COTTON. An American cotton of uniformity, good staple, and even color; spins from 60s to 100s. See NEW ORLEANS COTTON.

ORLEANTINE. 1. A French variant of serge made with 2-ply worsted yarns in both directions. Novelty twill weaves in repeats ranging from 8 to 16 threads are used in the materials which texture around 72 x 68. Warp counts are around 2/30s and the filling yarns about 2/36s. 2. Also the name for comparable material made in repeats of 8 ends and 6 picks, etc.

"ORLON." Trade-mark for a continuous filament or staple fiber produced by E. I. du Pont de Nemours & Co., Inc., The raw materials which may be used for Orlon include coal, air, limestone, natural gases, petroleum, water. The product is a fiber based on a polymer of acrylonitrile and therefore is classed as an acrylic fiber.

Features of Orlon include resistance to sunlight and atmospheric gases which makes it ideal for awnings, curtains and other outdoor uses; stability, little or no shrinkage in fabrics, a soft, warm hand, and good drapability. The same washing techniques and ironing temperatures as used for acetate and nylon apply to Orlon.

The filaments have a tensile strength which corresponds to from 60,000 to 75,000 pounds per square inch when dry, and the strength is almost as good when wet. The fibers have good elasticity and low moisture absorption. Orlon is resistant to chemicals, chiefly acids, and it has the ability to withstand high temperatures, thereby providing suitability for various industrial uses.

Other uses for the filament yarn are evening wear, sports fabrics, rainwear fabric, and in combination materials, such as acetate-viscose-Orlon, for various uses.

Orlon staple fiber can be used in bulky suiting fabric, overcoatings and topcoatings, dress fabrics, woolen-type fabrics, knitted wear, and washable woven sportswear. See Illustrated Section.

"ORLON" ACRYLIC FIBER, TYPES OF. These follow:

Type 33: The first bi-component acrylic fiber of duPont for use in carpets. Used with conventional homofiber, it produces a high-bulk carpet staple stock. Inherent crimping comes from the unusual physical make-up wherein each fiber is composed of two longitudinal parts, much the same as if two threads were fused side by side. Each of these parts reacts differently to moisture. One segment shrinks more than the other when dried, pulling the other segment with it into a spiral contour, thereby providing the natural crimp after the fiber is formed. Other features include ease of processing in carpet manufacture, piece dyeing, more luxurious textures, excellent resilience, cleanability, and freedom from static electricity.

Type 36: Unveiled in the plant of du-Pont in Dordrecht, Holland, this type is much used in the European carpet trade. Features include ease of processing, high bulking quality and good dyeability.

TYPE 38: A regular shrinkage staple, containing a mixture of deniers (approximately average of 3.0 denier) and designed for the pile fabric trade.

TYPE 42. This type broadly designates a great number of items, produced in semidull and bright lusters; staple and tow forms, generally in the regular and high shrinkage categories. Staple lengths range from 1¼ inches to 4½ inches. Comes in wide denier range.

TYPE 72: A staple engineered for use in 100 per cent form or in blends with cotton for skin-contact apparel types of fabrics.

TYPE 75: A regular shrinkage staple used primarily in blends of rayon and cotton for outerwear fabrics made on the cotton-rayon system of spinning. See "ORLON SAYELLE" BI-COMPONENT ACRYLIC FIBER.

Courtesy of E. I. du Pont de Nemours & Co., Inc.

"ORLON" FROM "ACRILAN"; TEST TO DISTINGUISH. A rapid dye test is used to distinguish "Orlon" Type 42 acrylic fiber, a product of the duPont Company, and "Acrilan" acrylic fiber, a produce of Monsanto Textiles Division. Samples of staple, spun yarn or fabric, of any convenient size, are boiled for five minutes in a water solution containing (based on the weight of the water):

0.2 per cent Du Pont Anthraquinone Blue SWF Conc. 150 per cent 0.5 acetic acid.

"Orlon" is not stained by the treatment, while "Acrilan" is dyed to a medium blue shade. If the sample has been dyed previously, the shade of "Orlon" is essentially unaffected, while that of "Acrilan" is altered. The "Acrilan" shade becomes much bluer or if the original shade was blue, heavier.

"ORLON SAYELLE" BI-COMPONENT ACRYLIC FIBER, TYPES OF. These follow:

TYPE 21: Comes in six-denier staple and tow and three-denied staple. Products are designed for bulky and/or novelty stitch-type garments.

TYPE 24: Available in three-denier staple, with improved performance to enable the manufacture of fine gauge, full-fashion knitwear.

TYPE 37: A carpet staple engineered for use in blends with wool and the modacrylic fibers.

TYPE 82: A product designed for blending with "Orlon Sayelle" or other "Orlon" products to produce new aesthetics in knit and woven fabrics. See "ORLON" ACRYLIC FIBER, TYPES OF.

Courtesy of E. I. du Pont de Nemours & Co., Inc.

"ORLON" TYPE 44. This acrylic fiber is used in combination with "Orlon" Type 42 for multi-color styling effects in a single bath piece dyeing method. The fiber is acid-dyeable and is engineered to complement the basic-dyeable "Orlon" Type 42. Five variations of the two colors obtained in dyeing can be obtained in the single dye dye bath to produce argyles, bars, heathers, stripes, and other fancy motifs. Product of E. I. du Pont de Nemours & Co., Inc.

OROFIL. An elastomeric fiber made by Rhee Industries Division of Rohm & Haas Co., Philadelphia, Pennsylvania. It is not a spandex fiber, but an elastomeric material of different chemical structure. Garments made from the fiber are resistant to discoloration from bleaches and detergents, can be washed in conventional laundry equipment without becoming dingy or yellow. It is possible to machine-dry garments which contain Orofil at the usual settings for manmades without discoloration.

OPTICAL BLEACH. A colorless flourescent dye used to provide increased whiteness to a textile fiber, yarn, or fabric. This bleach provides poor lightfastness. See BRIGHTNER.

ORSA LACE. A coarse Swedish lace made by the peasants from unbleached linen yarn.

ORSEILLE. See ARCHIL.

ORSEY. Another name for organzine silk.

ORTICA. Nettle fibers are sometimes known by this name. See NETTLE.

OSAGE ORANGE. A spreading tree, native to Arkansas, furnishing a natural dyestuff obtained by extraction.

OSCILLATE. To vibrate back and forth—characteristic of colloids in certain soaps and detergents.

OSMAN. A firm, rugged terry toweling in which the ground and pile picks are beaten into place by the reed on every fourth pick. The filling repeat is actually on six picks; for the first two

picks the reed is "loose." It then becomes "fast" on the next four picks, thereby causing the texture to become firm. Ordinary Osman or Terry structure reveals that the reed "recedes" on the first two picks and "closes-up" on the third pick to make all three secure in the fabric.

OSMOMETER. A scientific instrument to determine the strength of odors in numerical values. Measurements are based on the air-dilution principle by diluting and mixing quantities of odor-free air and odorous air in various concentrations with the dilution being performed under pressure.

OSNABURG. A coarse cotton cloth, often made with part waste, of plain weave, medium to heavy in weight, and resembling crash. It is named for the city of Osnabrück, Germany, where it was first made. When it is sold, either the term P.W. (part-waste) or the term CLEAN should be used to describe it. Some of the fabric, because of the dirtiness of the waste used, is sold as Grade B Osnaburg. P.W. cloths are made with red-tinged cotton. Motes, dirt, and card wastes are found in the dingy, off-color cloths. In bleaching, however, most impurities may be bleached out and the fabric will resemble a coarse-yarn linen.

Widths vary from 28 inches to 60 inches; textures range from 20-square to 40-square; warp yarn counts run from 5s to 14s, while filling yarn counts may be as low as 4s and as high as 12s.

In the gray state, some of the uses of the cloth include bags, box-spring covers, mattress coverings, shoe linings, pipe coverings, tire linings, and base for linoleums and imitation leathers.

Finishes applied to Osnaburg include chased or beetled in pocketing and simulated linen fabric, elastic duck, mercerized, napped, canvas, printing-crash finish, and cretonne.

Some of the uses of the fabric in the finished condition include draperies, upholstery covers, play suits, beach wear, suits, work shirts, linings, and sportswear.

The cloth seems to have greatest call for use as cretonne, and in the South for plantation purposes. The average fabric is coarse and rough depending on the amount of foreign matter contained in the yarns. The cloth is sold in the gray state or finished, can be obtained in checks or stripes, and may be bleached, dyed, or printed.

The best types may be classed as coarse sheeting. The heavier qualities are sold on the ounce-per-yard weight while the lighter cloths are sold on the yard-per-ounce weight. Narrow widths, with colored selvages, are used for toweling.

OSSAN. The stockings worn by the Scottish Highlanders; made of high-grade, well-scoured wool yarn.

OTTER. A medium-long straight-haired fur, yellow-brown to dark brown in color, the largest member of the weasel family. Wearing qualities, good. Judged by dark brown natural color and fullness and silkiness of fur. Found in all coastal regions with the exception of Australia. For sports and general wear.

OTTOMAN. A heavy, plain type of silk or rayon fabric that has wide, rather flat ribs made by cotton, worsted, silk, or rayon filling, which does not show on the face or the back of the goods. The warp covers the filling in entirety. The original Ottoman weave was a diagonal-rib effect, made from a steep twill-weave, such as the $\frac{4\ 1\ 1}{1\ 1\ 4}$, 75-degree twill, right-hand or left-hand in direction.

The method of construction caused a flatter rib than that noted in Faille Française. The idea carried out in the manufacture of Ottoman is to eliminate the extra binder warp by having the ends act, at certain interlacings, as binder and rib combined.

Both faille and Faille Française have their cords in the filling direction as in Ottoman. Two, three, or more picks are used to make this rib effect. Because of the tightness in texture, it is possible to have the rib in the filling direction, despite the fact that a diagonal or steep twill-weave is used in the construction.

OUATE. The French word, ouaté, implies wadded, wadding, batted, batting. Implies wadding or batting used in the manufacture of apparel.

OUATE VEGETABLE. "Tree cotton" used for stuffing and wadding. Includes fibers such as kapok used for this purpose.

OUDENARDE. A Belgian tapestry noted for its foilage and landscape motifs.

OUNCE. In the leather industry, a weight term that indicates the substance of certain kinds of leather, such as bag or case leather. In theory, it is based upon the assumption that one square foot of leather will weigh a certain number of ounces and will uniformly be of a certain thickness; hence, a three-ounce leather theoretically would be one square foot of leather that weighs three ounces. In practice, this varies because of specific gravity of various tanning materials used, and for this reason a splitter's gauge has been adopted which controls the commercial thickness of leather when sold by the square foot.

OUNCE DUCK. See DUCKS, OUNCE.

OUNCE THREAD. Also known as nun's thread, it is fine linen yarn, made in the British Isles, and used in making lace and embroidery.

OUTING CLOTH. Cloth used for tennis, cricket, light field sports, and general outdoor recreations. The material is made of plain weave, has wide range of plain colors or may be striped in pattern. The name is also applied, at times, to fancy flannels, white and cream-colored serges and straight flannel cloth. Fiber content must be declared in this cloth which is also known as Domett.

OUTING FLANNEL. Fleecy, soft-napped fabric that will not irritate the skin. Chief use is in infants' garments. Although a sized or starched material, these products must be carefully removed prior to usage for protection of the wearer and to prevent interference with the napping treatment given to the goods. Plain-weave fabric.

Woven in stripes, plaids or checks in addition to the white goods. May be piece-dyed and occasionally printed. Also classed as a spun rayon material, as well as cotton. Fiber content must be declared in outing flannel.

OUTRIGHT SALE. A sale by which the wool grower sells shorn wool to the wool manufacturer or, as is more generally the case, the wool dealer.

OUTSIZE. This is a stocking that has a regular size foot; the leg, however, is knitted larger than the leg of the ordinary stocking and it is used by stouter women, who require them.

OUVRÉ. The French term ouvré is used for checks and small patterns produced on a plain or a dobby loom. The term is in contradistinction to damassé, which refers to small, medium, or large designs made on a Jacquard loom.

OUVRÉES. All silk yarns of the thrown variety used for weaving purposes are ouvrées.

OVAL DENT REED. One in which the reed wires are oval in cross-section formation instead of the conventional flat type. Its purpose is to reduce yarn chafing. Used in weaving very fine fabrics.

OVEN. A chamber used by garment manufacturers to apply heat to the garment in order to set, or cure, a durable press finish on the article.

OVEN-DRY WEIGHT. See CONDITIONING, FIBER WEIGHT IN.

OVERALL, HIGH-BACK. A bib overall is made with the back portion extending above the waist and partially covering the back of the wearer. High-back overall is made usually without a waistband in the back. This contrasts with the suspender-type overall in which a waistband is usually used and the suspender straps extend to the waist in the back.

OVERALLS. A loose fitting trouser constructed with bib, pockets, and top straps. Denim, hickory stripes, express stripes, and cottonade are used for this long-wearing, rugged work garment.

OVERCASTING STITCH. One of the basic stitches, third in importance in the art of sewing. A slanting stitch is used mainly to protect raw edges from raveling or to hold edges together.

OVERCHECK. The use of a check design over a ground check effect; the overcheck is of a color combination different from the ground pattern.

OVERCOAT. A coat, commonly reaching to the knees or lower, worn over a suit, particularly in cold weather.

OVERCOATING. Material of any description suitable for overcoats. Usually implies a rather thick, heavyweight fabric weighing eighteen ounces or more per yard. Examples include melton, kersey, beaver, Montagnac, Whitney, Worumbo, fleece.

OVERDRYING. Five percent of the actual dry weight of the load of items is the figure used as the medium for the use of this term. All fibers, mainly the natural fibers, do possess residual moisture which is an asset to the load and this should not be removed from the particular lot being treated.

OVER-END CREEL. The device used to draw off yarn over the end of the package, as from a cone or bobbin.

OVERFINE WOOL. Wool that is too dry, lifeless, and tender for its regular quality rating.

OVERGARMENT. Any type of topcoating, overcoating, jacket, etc., worn over other garments.

OVERGROWN WOOL. Wool with an overlength staple for its particular classification.

OVERHANDING. Sewing with a short overhand stitch. It is made by short over-and-over stitches done close together. The needle is always inserted vertically. It is used to join selvages, eyelets, and finished edges.

OVERLOAD. A load, in excess of the maximum rated capacity of a washwheel or similar device for the most efficient action by the liquid.

OVERLOOKER. British term for the mill overseer.

OVERPICK. A method of picking in weaving when the picker stick moves through the arc of a circle over the top of the shuttle box.

OVERPLAID. In reality a double plaid. This is a cloth in which the weave or, more often, the color effect is arranged in blocks of the same or different sizes, one over the other. Again, the cloth may show a plaid design on a checked ground construction. This effect is noted in English mufti and in golf togs, neat business woolens and worsteds in morning, lounge and semi-formal wear. This cloth goes under the name, sometimes, of Glen Urquhart, the name of the Scottish clan that is given credit for bringing this cloth to the fore. Urquharts are usually light or medium in weight, running from nine to thirteen ounces. Two, three, or more colors are used in designing the patterns. Overplaids are ideal for travel as they do not show the dirt as readily as other cloths, generally speaking. Uses of the cloth as overcoating and topcoating is considerable. Overplaids are "cycle cloths" that come in vogue about every seven or eleven years; when in demand, they seem to overshadow other fabrics. There are many grades and qualities found on the market as staples.

Incidentally, the true Glen Urquhart plaid of the Scottish District Checks will show a left-hand twill line on the face of the goods; particularly will this effect be noted at the "four-by-four areas" where the same and the contrasting colored yarns interlace to form the larger blocks or checks in the pattern.

It is the only plaid made in this manner; all others should be made with the easily observed right-hand twill diagonal lines. Most Urquhart plaid, however, is also made, today, with the conventional "right-hand twill-effect" running from the lower left to the upper right on the face of the cloth in the color-effect construction used.

See Illustrated Section (Fabrics 38).

OVERPRINT. Colors or designs printed over other colors or motifs. It is resorted to when it is desired to alter shades and to tone down certain vivid colors or effects. Often used in floral effects in cloth.

OVERSEER. The head or supervisor of a mill or a mill department.

OVERSHOT, UNDERSHOT FLOATS. These are warp ends and filling picks which do not interlace in correct order. These floats are caused by ends breaking and catching in the shed of the loom, lint or waste falling into the shed, harnesses improperly set, poor tensions, etc. A suggested remedy is to set the harnesses and the reed so as to quickly jerk the broken ends out of the harnesses and reed in order to prevent gnarling or tangling.

OVERSPUN YARN. Yarn which has received too much twist in places, thereby causes thin lengths in it. It is usually caused by spinning to counts too high for the quality of the raw material. Sometimes called twitty yarn.

OVERTIME. Time worked by an employee outside of, or in addition to, his regular working time.

OVER-WIDTH. Fabric that is too wide for easy manipulation. Extra washing and shrinking may bring cloth to the proper width.

OWLING. Term used in the olden days in England, when it was forbidden to export sheep or wool without paying the export taxes. Much smuggling occurred because of the rigid laws England had invoked on sheep raising and wool manufacture, to keep the industry within the confines of England.

OXALATE. A chemical salt formed by chemical reaction of oxalic acid and some suitable base such as alkali. Sodium oxalate is a by-product in souring and washing processes.

OXALIC ACID. A solid, crystalline, organic acid which has good iron solvent properties. It is a good reducing agent or bleach neutralizer, but is a hard rinser and destructive to textile goods if allowed to remain in the fibers, even in traces. It can be made synthetically in various ways; for example, decomposing sugar with nitric acid.

OXFORD. A rather soft, porous cotton fabric made from fine count of warp and a coarse, soft-spun filling yarn; warp and filling are usually combed but lower qualities may be made of carded yarn. In the warp two ends are made to weave as one and they alternate in plain-weave formation with each pick. Fabric usually has twice as many ends as picks, and it is all-white, although striped warp-effect is not uncommon. This material will soil easily.

OXFORD CHAMBRAY. Oxford fabric made with colored warp yarn and white filling. Same as chambray except for the bulky, loosely twisted filling yarn which characterizes all cotton Oxford material.

OXFORD CLOTH. Plain, basket or twill weaves are used in this cotton or rayon cloth. There are two yarns which travel as one in the warp, and one filling yarn equal in size to the two warp yarns. Better grades of cloth are mercerized if made of cotton yarn. Filling is bulky and loosely twisted.

Rather heavy cloth which launders well. This shirting fabric has a tendency to soil easily; used also for jackets, shirts, skirts, and summer suiting. See Illustrated Section (Fabrics 6).

OXFORD GRAY. A term used chiefly in the woolen and worsted trade to denote any cloth that is gray in shade, depending on the varying percentages of black and white stocks used. It comes in light, medium, and dark shades; very popular color for men's wear since it "sheds dirt and soil marks."

OXFORD MIXTURE. Usually a color effect in dark gray, noted in woolens and worsteds. The degree of shade is governed by the mixed percentages of black and white stocks used. Mixing takes place prior to the carding and spinning of the yarn. Its reference to Oxford, England, has suggested calling the lighter weight mixture cloths by the name of Cambridge, the rival university of Oxford. Oxford and Cambridge are the two oldest universities in England and are known all over the world. Their colors are dark blue and light blue respectively. Hence, the use of dark and light oxfords or grays under those two names. In this country much gray cloth is given the name of Oxford.

OXFORD SHEEP. The largest of English Down breeds of sheep. Oxford gives a staple fleece length of 3 to 4 inches with some extra-length fibers. Shearing from 10 to 12 pounds of wool, the shrinkage is about 30 per cent. The breed is popular in the Middle West. See Illustrated Section.

OXIDATION. A chemical union of oxygen with some other element or group of elements where the oxygen will gain electrons as the result of the combination. The rusting of iron involves the combination of iron with oxygen. In this case, the iron will give up 2 electrons to the oxygen which therefore gains 2 electrons.

The iron is said to have a valence of plus 2 whereas the oxygen has a valence of minus 2.

Heat is released during an oxidation reaction. Burning is a form of rapid oxidation where the heat released is observed readily.

In the case where oxygen is removed from a compound, the compound is said to have been reduced. If a compound of mercury and oxygen is heated, the oxygen is driven off, leaving the mercury in its elemental form. The compound has been reduced.

Vat dyes are oxygen compounds which are insoluble in water. By reduction they are changed to a soluble, leuco (colorless) form, and in that condition are taken up by the fibers, and then by oxidation are reconverted into the colored, insoluble state.

OXIDE. A compound of oxygen with other elements. Iron rust, for example, is iron oxide.

OXIDIZE. To add oxygen to any material by chemical combination. Chlorine bleaching is an oxidizing action.

OXIDIZED COLOR. A dyestuff that is developed to its full strength by the application of chemicals which oxidize it.

OXIDIZED DYE. See ANILINE BLACK.

OXIDIZER. Creates oxygen. "Rinso," for example, has sodium perborate in it, and the oxygen acts as a bleach.

OXIDIZING AGENT. Any substance which can furnish oxygen to which another substance may unite. Hydrogen peroxide, for example, will bleach silk and wool because it liberates oxygen which will combine with the dye to form a colorless product.

OXO WOOL. A flax substitute for wool.

OXYCELLULOSE. A structureless cellulose derivative obtained when cellulose is treated with strong oxidizing agents, such as chlorine bleach or harsh alkalies. It is soluble in an alkaline solution and turns yellow in the presence of alkali. Yellow goods are often caused by oxycellulose discoloration. When cotton is overbleached, the cellulose is oxidized into oxycellulose. Bleached cotton, for example, when treated with Neocarmin W, will cause cellulose to turn blue while the oxycellulose becomes red.

OXYGEN. A non-metallic element that is a colorless, invisible gas without taste or smell. It is the most abundant of all existing chemical elements. Found free in the atmosphere, it will combine with many other elements to form compounds, such as water, carbon dioxide, etc. Ordinary water is about 89 per cent oxygen. The active bleaching type of oxygen is the atomic oxygen derived chemically and from ozone.

OYAH LACE. A Turkish crochet lace, coarse in looks and hand, made usually with waste silk yarns in floral motifs.

OZONE. A saturated oxygen molecule of composition O_3. It is a gas of blue color with a pungent odor something like chlorine. It breaks down easily into the ordinary oxygen molecule O_2 and one atom of oxygen, O. The odor of ozone is observed frequently after an electrical storm during the summer months.

OZONE FADING. Occurs on dyed acetate and polyester materials. This "fading due to atmospheric conditions" is different from the color changes or migrations caused by nitrogen oxides and referred to as gas fading. See GAS FADING.

P

PACIFIC CONVERTER. Invented by Robert Wilkie, this great machine made its debut in 1941, and it is produced by Warner & Swasey Company, Cleveland, Ohio. The machine is the diagonal-cut type, and several tows of total denier of between 1.5-million and 2.0-million are fed into the converter through a creel with many nubbing bars to level the tow and to prevent crossed filaments from entering the cutting roll. The cutting device is a helical roll which operates against a solid roll or anvil. The tow, in passing through the cutting rolls is cut at a sharp diagonal to the line of the filaments. Following this, the fibers are then debonded by intermeshing rolls so as to break open any section or area of fibers that may have fused together. Shuffling and drafting—the next operation—causes the fibers to spread apart to improve fiber drafting. Then the fiber web, about 14 inches in width is rolled together by the diagonal roll and collected by the crimper. Lastly, the crimper condenses the sliver to hold it together and gives a slight waved or crimped effect to the stock. The sliver is then collected in the conventional can arrangement. This tow-to-top method of treating fibers has increased considerably in the last few years. See TOW CONVERSION; TURBO CONVERTER; BULK OR BULKED YARN.

PACIFIXED. In 1946, this trademark was registered by Pacific Mills, Inc., now a division of Burlington Industries, Inc., New York City. It covers a shrinkproof process applied to woolen goods in which moisture absorbency and porosity are not affected; colors are fast to sunlight and washing.

PACK. 1. A 240-pound measure (British) for worsted top and flax. 2. A 60,000-yard measure for linen yarn.

PACKAGE. General term implying any wound arrangement of yarn such as found on a cheese or cone.

PACKAGE DYEING. A method of dyeing yarns on cones, cops, and other put-ups, or packages. The dye solution passes from the center of the package outward and then from the outside through to the center. Beamed warp yarn may be handled in this way. Most carded and combed cotton yarn used in the knitted outerwear industry is dyed in this manner.

PACK-AND-SACK. The tare weight of wrappings for an Australian wool bale; the pack weighs eleven pounds, the sack, two pounds.

PACKCLOTH. A general term that signifies burlap, canvas, duck, or mail bagging made to be used as some sort of bag or container in which articles may be carried or shipped.

PACK MOTH. The *Anacampsis sarcitello,* whose larva is very destructive to wool fibers.

PACK THREAD. A 2- or 3-ply hemp or flax twine—used for tying bundles.

PACO. Another name for alpaca.

PACO-LLAMA. Foal of alpaca sire and llama dam.

PACO-PACO. Also known as Malva Pendao, banner mallow. The fiber is found in northern Brazil and has many properties that compare with jute.

PA COTTON. Partially acetylated cotton which is known for its resistance to damage from heat, mildew, and rot. Compared with fully acetylated cotton this cotton is inferior in a strip breaking test for fabric, in flat abrasion testing, in flex abrasion and in most tear testing for strength. See ACETYLATION.

PACO-VICUNA. Foal of alpaca sire and vicuna dam.

PACPUTAN. Coarse type of wool. The northwestern frontier of India is the area where it is produced.

PAD. 1. A cushion, mass, or stuffing of some type. 2. To impregnate fabric with dyestuff, mordant, etc.

PADDED BACK LINING. Fancy waist and skirting material that finds use as lining. The cloth is often printed black on one side to prevent the printed pattern on the face of the goods from showing through. A natural back lining is solid-colored, printed on one side.

PADDER. A machine used to dye piece goods in a mangle by a continuous passage of the material through the dye liquor and squeeze rollers. See PADDING.

PADDING, PADDING MACHINE. The application of dyestuff to fabric by a padding machine. It is equipped with a set of wringers that actually force the dyestuff through the material, and the padded cloth is then developed in an open washer machine. The steam box will develop the final color.

This method of coloring is economical and only one application is necessary. Production is very good. Fast colors, the vat colors, are used to a great degree in pad or vat dyeing when large volume is wanted and production is an incentive. Some goods dyed this way include summer-wear fabric, solid-color sheeting, some curtain and upholstery cloth, and pastel color material.

PADDING STITCH. It resembles a zigzag or herringbone basting stitch in which the needle may or may not go entirely through one of the pieces of goods, according to the work at hand. The stitch may be held together in close rows or loosely spaced; it aids much in shaping a garment.

PADDLE DYEING MACHINE. Much used in the outerwear industry to dye continuous lengths of sweater strips or fully assembled sweaters. In the machine, wide, short blades are attached to a circular drive. The blades dip into the dye bath a few inches thereby rotating and circulating the liquor.

The paddles or blades in the overhead type machine extend the width of the machine. In the side-paddle-type machine, the paddles function from an island position. Longer blades are used in this machine than in the overhead type machine and give more vigorous agitation to the dye liquor.

PADDOCK. British worsted fabric made with a 2-up and 1-down twill and used for light overcoating and topcoats; is somewhat on the order of gabardine and has about the same uses, particularly used for raincoating when made water-repellent.

PADS OR PADDING. Specially made devices used to pad sleeves in order to make them extend and give a broad-shouldered effect.

Padding is also used under the shoulder seams of men's jackets in order to build up and make the shoulders appear broader and less sloped.

PAD STEAM CONTINUOUS DYEING. A method of applying vat and other fast colors in which high temperature and consecutive arrangement of equipment result in marked savings in the time and cost.

PADUSOY. Contraction of Soie de Padua. The rich, cord-effect silk fabrics made for centuries in Padua and other silk centers in Italy. Since the days of the Renaissance, these heavy silks (such as bengaline, grosgrain, poplin and rep) have served as vestments, hangings, and for use in regal livery.

PAESANO. The name for the two leading hemp fibers raised in the Naples district of Italy. Cordaggio is the name for the two poorer qualities.

PAHANG. Malay States breed of sheep known for its harsh, coarse, short staple fiber. The animals weigh about twenty-five pounds but are sturdy in build.

PAILLETTE. One of the many small, glittering disks often sewn on fabric for embellishment.

PAIMA. Fiber found in Mexico and used for paper twine. It is a hard fiber that runs from white to brownish yellow in color. It is obtained from the leaves of the yucca tree.

PAINA. A wild, lustrous seed fiber found in Brazil. It is used for pillow stuffing.

PAINTERS' CANVAS. A fine, corded woven fabric made of cotton or linen with one side ribbed and the other side simulating knit fabric.

PAISLEY. A distinctive worsted material which originated in the Scottish city of this name. Scroll designs cover the surface of the goods; colors range from red, brown, and orange to black. Small spots of other colors are interspersed to bring about a more brilliant motif. The material is popular for coverings, shawls, and throws. The mixture of colors makes this Jacquard-woven cloth truly distinctive. In addition to being made from worsted yarn, much of the original fabric was made with cashmere hair fiber and motifs said to have originated in India, making it a very expensive material.

Silk or rayon fabric of this name is a simulation of the originals which are still extant. Used for blouses, dress goods, kerchiefs, trimming, and covering.

PAISLEY SHAWL. A fine quality worsted shawl made in Paisley, Scotland, in designs and colors similar to those of the genuine Cashmere shawls of India. At one time the shawl industry in Paisley was of considerable importance, but changing fashions have affected it adversely.

PAJAMA CHECK. Barred dimity or nainsook, used as B. V. D.* cloth and underwear for athletic purposes.

*B.V.D. is the registered trademark of the B.V.D. Company, Inc.

PAJAMAS, PYJAMAS. Coat or blouse and trousers. This native garb of the Oriental nations is used for sleeping, lounging, beachwear; also used for afternoon and evening wear in the home. Made from cotton, silk, rayon. Pajamas come in many styles.

PAJAM, PUNJAM, PAMJUM. Cotton cloth made in India, the forerunner of pajama fabric in Great Britain and the United States.

PAKAMA. Colored cotton cloth of varying quality used as loincloth in the Far East. Texture ranges from 58 to 80 by 36 to 44. Warp yarn counts are 32s; filling, 20s. The warp pattern in the cloth is of various colors. In the checking, about 8 inches of one color is woven; this is followed by a fancy effect of 1 inch to 1½ inches. The center is then woven in the checking effect which is followed by another fancy heading, and then the one-color effect is woven for another 8 inches to complete the woven pattern.

PALAMPOOR, PALAMPORE. 1. Indian print cottons used for clothing, prayer rugs, canopies, and bedcovers. Comparable with chintz in this country. 2. Rich Chinese and Indian prints used for cotton counterpanes.

PALL. 1. Fine woolen or worsted fabric used for robes, academic gowns, etc. 2. A mourning cloth placed over a bier, coffin, or tomb.

PALLAS. These English colored-woven cotton scarves of plain weave, with ends in the borders taped, are used for native dress in Africa.

PALLIUM. A yokelike band of white wool with pendants on the breast and back, adorned with black crosses. It is worn as a sign of jurisdiction by metropolitan archbishops, some bishops, and the Pope. The cloth is of high texture and rather heavy in weight. The very best merino wool is used to make the goods. Pallium also means a garment similar to the himation, and the Greeks wore it over the chiton.

PALMA, PALMA BARRETA, PALMA ISTLE. A hard Mexican fiber which runs from white to brownish yellow in color. Obtained from the leaves of the yucca tree, and when processed is used in paper twine.

PALM BEACH. Registered trademark of Palm Beach Company, Inc., Cincinnati, Ohio, used by the company and its licensees on textiles made by various combinations of animal fibers, such as mohair, silk, and wool; vegetable fibers, such as cotton and linen; and man-made fibers, such as acetate, rayon, nylon, Dacron, etc., as well as garments made there-from for summer apparel.

PALMERING. A finishing treatment afforded satins, taffetas, and twills. Its purpose is to give mellowness to the hand of the goods and the equipment consists of a large steam-heated cylinder covered with an endless papermaker's felt apron. The material is led between two continuous aprons, and the heat, aided by the smoothness of the aprons, will give the goods a smooth, calendered effect which is more appealing than an ordinary calender finish. A very popular method used in finishing-plants of the United States.

PALMET. A black leaf fiber found in South Africa and used as substitute for horsehair.

PALMETTO. The name for the leaf fiber yielded by the palmetto tree. It is used for hats, mats, baskets, and other purposes.

PALMILLA. A type of yucca tree, three to fifteen feet in height, furnishes this bast fiber. Obtained from the leaves of the tree, the fibers are fine and soft, but of little commercial value. Found in southern United States and in northern Mexico.

PALMITIC. A higher saturated fatty acid rather similar to stearic acid. It is solid and is always found in admixture with stearic acid in the higher titre soaps.

PALO BORRACHO. Argentina, Ecuador, and Peru are the sources for this tree whose pods give a fiber that resembles kapok, and is sometimes used for the latter fiber.

PALUNGOA FIBER. A soft, white, durable, Indian bast fiber which serves as a substitute for hemp.

PAM. Short name for pashim, pashmina.

PAMPA. Hardy sheep raised throughout South America which gives a long, straight, harsh, bright wool.

PAMPAKOPETRA FIBER. The name means "stone cotton" and refers to asbestos found in Cyprus and Euboea, a high-quality fiber.

PANACHE. French for bizarre, startling, or variegated motifs, in textile fabrics.

PANAMA. Summer suiting that ranges from ten to fifteen ounces in weight. Piece, yarn, or skein-dyed and usually made of cotton warp and worsted filling, although other combinations are resorted to from time to time. Plain-weave material. Cloth appears in solid shades and mixtures.

PANAMA CANVAS. A substantial, ecru-colored, basket-weave canvas which is given a beetled finish and used for embroidery purposes.

PANAMA SHEEP. Rapidly gaining in popularity in this country, this breed of sheep was developed in Idaho by crossing pure-bred Rambouillet with selected Lincoln ewes. The wool grades 56s to 60s in quality, and is of combing length. Panama shows an improved quality wool and mutton conformation.

PANAMA SUITING. Of the same family group as Palm Beach cloth. Usually made in solid shades and piece-dyed. It does not wrinkle easily, nor does it show dirt readily. This cloth, used in skirts, dresses, and suitings for summer wear, is made of plain weave, and is smooth to the touch but a bit wiry in feel. See PALM BEACH.

PANAMA WEAVE. A basket or matt weave made on any of the following plans: 2–2, 3–3, 4–4.

PANDANUS FIBER. The leaves of a palm found in East Africa, India, and Polynesia; used for baskets, hats, matting.

P & L. A charge account charged off as uncollectible. (Profit and loss.)

PANGOLO COTTON. A strong, brownish Egyptian cotton noted for its silken luster.

PANHISTOPHYTON. Name given by Lebert to the floating corpuscles in the bodies of silkworms afflicted with pébrine. See PÉBRINE.

PANNE. A satin-faced, velvet or silk material named from the French for "plush," which has a high luster made possible by the tremendous roller-pressure treatment given the material in finishing. Panne velvet is often referred to as panne and is a staple silk fabric.

The term was originally spelled "penne," and implied a pile cloth which had a longer or higher pile-effect than velvet but a shorter one than plush.

PANNE SATIN. Silk or rayon satin with an unusually high luster because of a special finish. If made of rayon or acetate, fiber content must be declared.

PANNE VELVET. Silk or rayon velvet with a finish in which the pile is flattened and laid in one direction. Lustrous and lightweight. If made of rayon, fiber content must be declared. From the French word for plush.

PANNIER. Means saddle bags and implies the type of drape at the sides of a skirt to give the effect of oval-shaped side hoops.

PANTOGRAPH. An apparatus for copying designs to any scale within the capacity of the device. A dummy point traced over the original drawing moves a series of arms to a stylus that reproduces the traced line in larger or smaller scale. The machine is used in the printing industry for transferring the artist's design to the copper printing roller.

PANTS. Panteleone, one of the comedians in a 13th century Italian comedy, wore what today are called pants - baggy leg garments similar to knickerbockers.

PANTYHOSE. A one-piece body garment that fits over the hips and serves as a stocking; the panty and hose are not detachable. There are garments on the market in which the top part serves as a panty and is separate from the rest of the hose and may be attached. However, through these articles serve the same purpose as pantyhose, they are not the same garments.

PANUNG. There are three types of this material which is used in the Far East in countries like Thailand, Viet Nam, Cambodia, etc. 1. A cotton cloth printed with checks or stripes with stripes at both ends of the piece which measures 10 feet by 3 feet. This is known as PATA. 2. The PAPOON which is woven with narrow striped effects with the selvage the identical color of that seen in the body of the goods. Fast colors are used in the goods. 3. The poorest quality is known as PALAI and uses a low-grade cotton, thereby making it necessary to size or starch the goods to give it some body. See PAPOON.

PAON VELVET. Fabric with a laid finish not so heavily pressed as panne or mirror velvet. Used entirely for millinery and trimming purposes. See PANNE VELVET.

PAPAIN. A dried juice of the papaya tree formerly used for degumming silk but now used on wool fibers to obtain uniform penetration of the enzyme solution in the material being treated.

PAPER. A thin material made from wood pulp which has a host of uses; an important item in the textile industry.

Paper has not alwasy been in use. In fact, it was not until 2300 B.C. that papyrus replaced clay paintings and tablets which had been used as a means of communication among ancient peoples. For the next 20 centuries, papyrus was used for the written word and not until 105 A.D. did the Chinese invent paper. Around 751 A.D. paper was substituted for papyrus and in 900 A.D. paper began to be used in Egypt. The Moors introduced paper in Spain around 1150 A.D.; paper mills were set-up in Italy - 1276, France - 1348, Germany - 1390, and England - 1495.

Originally developed at Pergamum, an ancient kingdom on the coast of Asia Minor, parchment paper was first made from untanned skins of the calf, goat, and sheep. The skins were soaked in water, treated with lime to loosen the hair, then scraped, washed, stretched, and dried. Finally they were rubbed with chalk and pumic stone. This parchment was foldable and could be assembled into book form.

In due time, Vellum, a superior type of parchment, was made from the hide of a calf or kid and was used for important manuscripts through-out the Middle Ages. From Vellum, paper, as we know it today, was developed. Made from vegetable fiber and water, the fiber used is wood pulp ground from the chips. Water is forced into the pulp with the fibers being crossed; then wet paper is sent through a drying operation and finally wound onto rollers.

PAPER, WET STRENGTH OF. Refers to the resistance of paper products to tearing when moist. It is accomplished by adding various resins to the pulp used in making paper. One resin for example, melamine, increases the dry strength and more than triples the wet strength of paper and paperboard. Wet-strength papers are used for towels, napkins, frozen-food packaging, industrial wipers, shipping sacks, etc.

PAPER CAMBRIC. Thin, narrow cambric or muslin, glazed and stiffened to be used for lining or as a fine foundation.

PAPER CLOTH. The use of paper as a textile yarn came into being during World War I when the Austrians and the Germans began to use it for clothing and shoes. Thin sheets of paper pulp were cut into narrow widths and then twisted into a yarn. As yet, the use of paper is not practical although some cheap mats and rugs are made with paper filling. Developments are being made in the use of paper and long, individual fibers of cellulose extracted from wood. These fibers resemble cotton and may be manipulated in somewhat the same manner as cotton.

One of the drawbacks to the use of paper is the fact that it cannot be laundered. However, possible uses of the fiber include cord, curtain material, clothing, shoes, matting, bagging.

PAPER FELT DUCK. See DUCK.

PAPER FIBER. Any textile fiber which is too short to combine with others by twisting into yarn but which can be used in paper making to add strength.

PAPERMAKER'S FELT. A woven fabric which resembles a large endless belt, generally made from choice wool and sometimes from special man-made fibers, which operates on a paper machine to carry the sheet of paper, to drain excess water from the material being manufactured, and in many cases to even drive certain rolls on the machine.

The material received its name of "felt" because it replaced the ancient method of making paper by squeezing it between pieces of pressed felt which, of course, is still made from a mass of interlocked fibers and contains no yarn of any kind in it. Finished "felts" do have a good reason for being so named since in the final shrinking or finishing operation, the wool fibers actually felt or mat together because of heat, pressure, and moisture exerted on the mass of fibers contained in the yarns used to weave the fabric.

PAPER MULBERRY FIBER. Bast fiber from the inner bark of the tree, *Broussonetia papyrifera.* Used a great deal in the Pacific Islands. See TAPA CLOTH.

PAPER MUSLIN. Ordinary muslin which has a stiff, glazed finish; used for lining.

PAPERY. Excessive smoothness given to cotton cloths by the use of sizes in the finishing of the goods.

PAPIER MACHE. Strong, lightweight paper mixture. Papier maché can be shaped or molded into many forms and objects requiring strength with lightness, as dress forms.

PAPOON. A cotton cloth usually made with a 2-and-2 stripe of different colors in warp and filling. Papoon has a very wide selvage of the same color as the warp. The checked pattern is as follows: about 6 inches of the ground color is woven, followed by a heading of four picks of some contrasting color; next, four picks of ground color, one half inch of contrasting color, four picks of ground color, and four picks of contrasting color. Then the center is woven of the ground color for the length desired; after which, another heading followed by 6 inches of ground color is made.

PAPOULA DE SAN FRANCISCO, SAN FRANCISCO POPPY. Fiber found along riverbanks in Brazil. Used for bagging, cord, rope, and in ship calking. A siccative oil obtained from the seeds is used in lacquers, paints, and varnishes. The decorticated stalks find use in the manufacture of cellulose.

PAPPING. Old-time name for starch or size in the Great Britain.

PAPUSHES. Bright-colored slippers with pointed toes worn chiefly by the Algerians. Ideal for comfort around the house they now come in many varieties and styles.

PAPYRUS. Raised along the Nile River in Egypt, it is a dedge or tufted marsh plant which differs from comparable grasses in that it has a solid stem and a small, one-seeded fruit, developing from a simple ovary with a thin wall attached to the seed at only one point. Roots of this plant find use as fuel while the pith may be eaten. The stem of the plant is used in sandals, boats, boxes, cloth, sailcloth, and twine. At present it is a great source for writing material.

The words paper and papyrus are practically synonomous, and in olden times writing paper was made by laying slices or strips of the sedge side-by-side in two layers, set at right angles. These layers were then pressed together aided by the use of an adhesive usually made of the juice of the plant. The sheets were then glued end-to-end and then wound onto a wooden rod so as to form manuscripts. The glue used came from bones, hides, and the hooves of animals. See Paper.

PAQUET REED. Compared with the ondulé reed which has a swinging bilateral action of the reed in making, for example, lappet fabrics, this reed is of the "rise-and-fall" type necessary to make fancy, wavy, openwork effects in cloth. The reed, in its action, becomes free from warp ends and causes the fabric to become more open by the use of a fine or a loosely picked filling. Ondulé reeds originated in Spain; paquet in France.

PARA, PARANITRANILINE RED. Along with Malachite green, Pará red was the first of the naphthol colors to be developed. A brilliant red, very fast to chlorine and light, is obtained by running the goods in a solution of betanaphthol, then diazotizing and developing with a solution of paranitraniline red at ice-cold temperatures. See NAPHTHOL DYES; DIAZOTIZING.

PARA COTTON. A Brazilian cotton with varying staple length; Pará cotton has good strength but much foreign matter. Bales range from 220 pounds to 330 pounds.

PARACHUTE FABRIC. A compactly woven, lightweight fabric comparable with airplane cloth. It is made of silk, nylon, rayon, or cotton. If the cloth is to be used for personnel, it is made of silk or nylon; rayon or cotton is the fabric used as a carrier for bombs, cargoes, etc.

PARAFFIN. A translucent, solid, waxy mixture that is a mixture of hydrocarbons, indifferent to most chemical reagents. It is derived chiefly, at present, from distillation of petroleum. Used in glazing, size mixtures, waterproofing, etc.

PARAFFIN DUCK. Canvas or duck that has been treated with a paraffin preparation. It is stiff, heavy, and waterproof. It is used for coats and trousers by loggers, lumbermen, hunters, and fishermen. Some of the fabric is used as tent material.

PARAGUAY. Cotton lace made on a Leavers machine in which the independent beams have wheeled patterns comparable with Teneriffe lace, with fine drawnwork motifs of spider-web texture.

PARAIBA COTTON. A Brazilian cotton of medium grade. The harsh, wiry staple of cream-color is about 1¼ inches long. May be spun to 60s yarn.

PARALLELING. To cause strands or fibers to lie even and straight after some machine operation, such as combing or drawing.

PARALLEL MOTION. The rocker arm that rests on the shoe in the picker stick arrangement on a loom. Its function is to cause the picker stick, in its throwing action, to become parallel with the race plate over which the pick travels.

PARALLEL SPINNING. A method by which rayon thread is formed at the nozzles and cross-wound upon flanged bobbins, the thread being a bundle of parallel untwisted filaments. These are afterwards washed, twisted, and reeled into hanks.

PARAMATTA. Material for dress goods, somewhat on the order of Coburg fabric. Made of cotton warp and fine wool yarn filling. A 1-up and 2-down weave is used; there are about twice as many ends as filling per inch in the texture.

PARAMETER. Used in some phases of textile texting procedures, it is a constant or variable term in a function that determines the specific form of the function but not its general nature, as **a** in **f (x)** equals **ax,** where **a** determines only the slope of the line described by **f (x).** The term also finds use in research and development circles.

PARA PIASSAVA. Palm fiber found in the sandy soil along the rivers of Brazil and Venezuela. Fine and soft but affected by dampness. Pará piassava is also known as Monkey bass; it is used for brooms, brushes, and cordage.

PARATURA. See Apparel.

PARCELING. Wrapping of old canvas around ropes for protective purposes.

PARCHMENT. A tawing process applied to sheepskins. Vellum is about the same as parchment except that it is made from calfskin. In addition to its uses as parchment for records, it is also used for banjos and drumheads, lampshades, etc.

PARCHMENT COTTON. A plain-weave cotton fabric of fine structure which is treated in finishing to simulate true skin parchment.

PARCHMENTIZING. A finishing process which makes a short contact with sulphuric acid of high concentration in order to produce a variety of effects dependent on the type of fabric and the local conditions used. Effects range from a transparent organdy effect to a linen-like hand and surface texture on cottons. Reagents other than sulphuric acid may be used in parchmentizing.

PARDESSUS. Another name for a redingote-shaped mantle or long coat.

PARE. The so-called desirable look to obtain in appearance; garb that is tailored but not tailored along mannish lines. Also implies an appearance that is pared to essentials and is functional.

PAREMENTS. Expensive fabrics on the type of brocades and figured damasks which are heavy in weight and beautifully figured. Gold and silver threads are interspersed throughout the material, which is used for altar cloths, ecclesiastical robes, ceremonials, and coronations.

PARESSEUSE. French term ("lazy") used for mispick.

PARFE. Registered trademark of Beaunit Corporation, New York City. Parfe is a rayon yarn which has color applied in a random order along its length.

PARING-OFF. Cutting or snipping off excess edging on a garment when the edges are to be given a raw finish.

PARIS BINDING. It is made of a warp twill or small herringbone weave and has a stiff hand without being given any finishing treatment. Made of cotton, mercerized cotton, rayon, acetate, etc. May be given a polishing for some particular use as a binding.

PARISIENNE. 1. A French silk fabric featured by small motifs; this broad term may have the pattern made in a number of ways—printed, dobby design, warp floats, lappet weaving, etc. 2. Name for dress goods made from union fabric such as a silk warp and woolen or worsted filling. 3. A black or dark blue dress fabric made of good quality merino wool.

PARIS POINT. The round seam, edged at each side with a row of straight stitches; seen on back of gloves.

PARITANEWHA FIBER. New Zealand hemp which is not raised near the swamp lands.

PARITY. A price calculated to give the farmer a fair return in relation to his costs as in the case of raising sheep or cotton.

PARKA. An overshirt with an attached hood or cowl. The original was made of animal skins and used by the Eskimos. Popular in winter sports—skating, skiing, etc.

PARKAL. Percale in India; usually an imported fabric.

PARM-NARM. Expensive fabric from Ibex wool, a type of pashmina. Fine, soft shawl and dress-goods fabric.

PARNA. Indian cloth woven on hand looms. Made with plain weave in check effects; usually made of cotton. The fabric serves as toweling.

PARRAGAN. A type of double camlet used for dress goods and upholstery,

chiefly in the seventeenth century. See CAMLET.

PARTRIDGE CLOTH. A mottled corduroy.

PARTS. Means the actual parts, devices, or mechanisms found on any textile machine.

PASAC FIBER. A Philippine fiber used for bags, cordage, mats.

PASHIM, PASHMINA, PASHM, PUSHMINA. The fine downy hair of the goats raised in Kashmir and other northern India provinces. The hair is cut from the animal once a year, and the soft pashim or remaining down fibers are combed out, separated, and graded by hand.

The wild goats give a black or gray hair known as shabri. If the hair is taken from the older animals, it is white or silver gray and is called shah-tush.

Domesticated goats yield the best quality hair which is known as turfani pashim or phum. The best shawls are made from these fibers.

PASMO. A parasite that attacks a more or less mature flax plant. Particularly devastating to flax plants raised for their oil since these are harvested about one month later than fiber flax plants. Botanic name is septoria lini sporophores.

PASS. The total of all the fillings working in conjunction with one another in the manufacture of a textile fabric. An individual pick is also called lat, in French, See LAT.

PASSEE. French (passée) for pick or filling in woven goods.

PASSEMENT. The pricked parchment pattern upon which both needlepoint and bobbin laces are wrought.

PASSEMENT AU FUSEAU. Lace made on the pillow.

PASSEMENT A L'AIGUILLE. Lace made with the needle by hand.

PASSEMENTERIE. General term applied to heavy edgings and trimmings, made of gimp, cord, beads, and so on. Used a great deal to decorate many materials. European countries specialize in this work.

The design for the work is drawn on a thick strip of paper, and is then given to the worker, who places the pattern on the cloth. The operative then sews the design on the goods to enrich them, after removing the basting threads to complete the ornamentation.

PASTEUR, LOUIS. The Father of Modern Sericulture. In the 1860s he saved the silk-industry for the world. Sericulture, because of diseased worms, all but passed out of existence. By his scientific methods, Pasteur established a selective method of choosing eggs.

The female moth produces about 350 eggs, and dies within 48 hours. Pasteur examined every dead moth, and if it was found to have been diseased, all eggs from the moth were burned. He was given full control of the raising of silkworms by all interested nations. All worms were classified for microscopic testing. Healthy eggs were the only ones permitted to develop, and in this way, the industry was saved by the Father of Modern Sericulture.

PASTILLE. 1. Round raised dots or small figures which appear on chiffon net, veiling and other diaphanous fabrics. These small fancy effects are either woven in or appliquéd to the material. 2. A pattern which is composed of dots only: foulard, bandanna, and some tie silks.

PASTING. During finishing processes, cloth is subjected to heavy pressure between calender and other rollers. Thick seams in the cloth may injure the rollers. To permit the cloth to pass readily between the rollers, pasting takes the places of stitching. The ends of the pieces of cloth are pasted together to form a continuous run through the calendering machine.

PAT, PATTI. Outer hair of goats found in the Far East; the under-hair is called pashm. Patti also means the woolen fabric, hand woven in a width of from 9 inches to 18 inches and used chiefly in India. The hand-spun yarn is very coarse, and is made from the pat hair of goats.

PATADIONG CLOTH. Cotton fabric made in the Visayan Islands. The peasant women use this brilliantly colored, plaid-effect fabric for apparel and in sarong fashion when bathing.

PATAGONIAN. Wool from the southern part of Argentine known as Patagonia. The wool may be merino or high-type crossbred; fibers are quite dirty when shorn but a good white results when scoured. Chubut, Rio Negro, and Santa Cruz are the three leading types of this staple, which grades to about 60s.

PATCH. 1. A small swatch of material, usually cloth, used to repair a garment. 2. A patch, such as court plaster, applied to the skin, or to set off the complexion, a mark of beauty in the Colonial days. 3. An insignia for identification such as the symbol for the First Army of the United States, the "A."

PATCH POCKET. A flapless pocket made by sewing a piece of self fabric to the exterior of a coat or jacket; is usually a double-stitch pocketing.

PATCHWORK. An article, such as a patchwork quilt, made from small pieces of fabrics sewed together in some form of design. The finished product is usually padded and quilt-stitched.

PATENT. Covers the inventions on machines or processes, textile or otherwise. The Patent Act of 1952, Patent Office, Washington, D.C., defines a patentable invention as one pertaining to a machine, an article of manufacture, a process, a composition of matter, or improvements in any of the foregoing. There are also special patents a concern may obtain to cover its own special processes, as well. A patent has a life span of seventeen years, beginning with the date of the grant. After that time the patent becomes public property and may be used by anyone. The only way to have your patent extended is to win a special act of Congress, a very rare occurrence.

PATENT AXMINSTER. A power-loomed, cut-pile carpet made with double filling.

PATENT BARK. Ground quercitron is boiled with dilute sulphuric acid to produce this dyeing product which must be well washed and dried following the boiling.

PATENT CORDAGE. Cord or rope spun by natives.

PATENT LEATHER. A common term which implies the finish produced by covering the surface of leather with successive treatments of daub and varnish, each of which must be carefully dried. The term is often loosely applied to any leather that has been given a varnish finish, but the best usage of the trade restricts it chiefly to shoe and bag leather. This leaves the terms "enameled" and "japanned" to describe the fancy and upholstery leathers made by the same or kindred processes. In the shoe trade most of the patent leather used comes from cattle hides, known as patent sides, or kips. At present horsehides, coltskins (known as patent colt), kidskins, and calfskins are used.

PATENT SATIN QUILT. See MITCH-ELINE.

PATENT-SELVAGE HESSIAN. This English jute material weighs from 9 to 14 ounces per yard in a 40-inch width. There are two or more narrow widths in the loom which are separated by inside or center selvages. There may be as many as eight selvages in the goods, depending upon the service the goods are to give. Wider fabrics are used to make bags; narrow goods are used for tubing and wrapping of trees, shrubs, bicycles, and other commodities for protection.

PATHAS. English papoons featured by check effects, and popular in India.

See PAPOON.

PATOLA. An East Indian silk material of varying qualities used as wedding gown fabric.

PATOLA WORK. This is a multicolored, fine silk textured wedding gown or sari worn by the people of Gujerat. The construction is plain weave in which pattern-dyed warp and filling yarns are interlaced very carefully by the weavers. *Patola* is the term used for the goods when made in southern Asia while, in adjacent areas of the Far East, the work is called *Double Ikat*. Before weaving, the yarns are dyed according to a plan which has been worked out on paper. The operatives, following the motif, take small bundles of the warp yarns and tightly wrap cotton twine around certain areas of them. The entire warp is then immersed in the dye bath for the initial dyeing. The entire warp is then wrapped at other points and dyed again. The procedure is repeated, usually up to five dippings, beginning with the lighter shades and working up to the darker colors. The cotton twine serves as a resistance toward the dye coloring, in that it does not permit coloring matter to work through the silk threads it tightly binds. Filling yarns are treated in the same manner. When wrapping and dyeing of the entire warp and filling is completed, the weavers then set the warp yarns onto a simple loom. When the loom is in action, filling yarns cross exactly at the predetermined areas of the warp yarns - red on red, blue on blue, green on hreen, etc. - to produce the interesting, intriguing patterns depicting animal, plant, and geometric designs. See Screen Printing, Tjap Printing, Tie Dyeing.

PATOLE. Silk fabric which has much decoration along with a border effect of tie-dyed or hand-blocked motifs. Worn by women of the East as a sari. Also called Patalo.

PATTERN. 1. An outline of a garment on paper. It embodies usually all the pieces necessary to cut a complete garment from material. 2. A single repeat of a weave formation.

PATTERN CARD. The perforated card used in Jacquard weaving.

PATTERN CHAIN. 1. The same as the harness chain used on a loom to make the design in the woven goods. 2. Another name for the box chain on a loom. 3. In knitting, it is the chain used on ribbers and other machines. It is made up of small, interchangeable iron links or lags arranged so that a set length of fabric is knitted for each link.

PATTERNED. Applied to silks and

rayons the term implies a more or less all-over-design fabric.

PATTERN FILLING. Filling yarn which goes from selvage to selvage in order to take part exclusively in the formation of pattern effects in textiles which have a ground filling for the background of the material.

PATTERN WARP. Synonymous with blanket range.

PATTERN WEAVER. A weaver of much skill used to weave blanket ranges.

PATTERN WHEEL. A mechanism in circular knitting which controls needle movements. Its function on jersey machines is to allow some needles to tuck and/or welt while others knit. The wheel is also used on rib machines to select the cylinder needles.

PATU, PATTU. Homespun or tweed of East Indian origin which is used as a shawl or throw.

PATWA FIBER. A strong bast fiber used for cordage. It is raised in India.

PAUKPAN FIBER. Fiber obtained from a bush in Burma. Used to make cords and sun hats.

PAULIN, 'PAULIN. Short for tarpaulin or comparable type of covering.

PAUNCH MAT. Mats that have been made from rope used on ships.

PAWL. A hinged or pivoted piece of metal that is shaped so that it will engage with the teeth of a ratchet.

PAYTA COTTON. A Peruvian cotton of grayish cast, little luster but rather strong. Named for city of that name in Peru.

PBI. This polybenzimidazole fiber is capable of withstanding temperatures up to 350′ Fahrenheit for extended periods of time and can retain its strength during a short exposure to 1000-degree temperatures.

PBI is used for space age purposes such as braking parachutes for high speed jet planes, re-entry drogue chutes, and moon suits. Product of the Celanese Corporation of America, New York City.

P/C, P-C. Contractions used to mean a blend fabric composed of polyester and cotton ingredients. See Polyester.

PEACH. A reddish red-yellow hue, of low saturation and high brilliance.

PEACHWOOD. See BRAZILWOOD.

PEA JACKET. The early 19th Century produced the famous court dandy Count D'Orsay, a younger contemporary of Beau Brummell. Caught in a severe rain storm, the coatless D'Orsay bought a jacket from a Dutch sailor, turned the deep collar up for protection, and immediately set the style for the pea jacket.

The name comes from the Dutch word, pia, which describes a coat of short length, made with harsh, strong wool, and sturdy in structure. It has for centuries been an important item in maritime circles. Our navy issues the pea jacket or reefer length coat which provides much warmth and can withstand very rugged wear. Usually dyed dark blue, the fabric used may be melton, kersey, beaver, mackinac fabric, et al.

PEAKED LAPEL. This type lapel shows the top line slanting up from the horizontal.

PEANIT STRAW. An inexpensive straw of the "exotic type" imported from Java. The word, exotic, in the straw industry implies any fine, smooth, closely woven straw whether natural or synthetic.

PEANUT. A merchant operating in a small way.

PEANUT FIBER. See SARELON.

PEARCE COTTON. An early-maturing Uplands cotton of medium long fiber and about 32 per cent lint yield.

PEARL ASH. Potassium carbonate, a very hygroscopic and rather destructive material. It is the equivalent of soda ash, which is sodium carbonate.

PEARL BRAID. Braid made of three or more ondé yarns.

PEARL COTTON. A two-ply mercerized cotton thread made with loose twist in order to give a cord or rope effect. Comes in all colors. Used in embroidery and hand weaving.

PEARL EDGE. An edging of small loops observed on lace or ribbon.

PEARL GRAY. A neutral gray color of high brilliance.

PEARL KNITTING. Same as purl knitting.

PEAR OR CONE DESIGN. The commonest of all field designs used in weaving Persian carpets and rugs. The design is used in Herat, Khorassan, Sarabend, Senna and Shiraz rugs. Used in borders as well as in the base designs.

PEASANT COSTUME. The costume, garb, raiment or dress worn by the peasants or country folks in various parts of the world, chiefly on dress occasions in Europe, Asia, and Africa. European costumes, particularly, are vivid, in most instances attractive, and express the native skills, traditions, and customs and climate of the particular area of country.

PEASANT LACE. This broad term implies any plain or simple lace, usually coarse in nature, made by peasants. It is usually of the bobbin type such as Dalmatian or Torchon.

PEASANT SLEEVE. The long, rectangular shaped sleeve that is set in a drop-shoulder waist and gathered at the belt line.

PEAU. French word for skin. Often used in naming certain French-made woolens, rayons or silks; as peau de cygne (swan), peau de pêche (peach), peau de soie (silk).

PEAU D'ANGE, ANGEL SKIN. A smooth, high-textured finish given to some silk fabrics of crepe or satin which resemble, supposedly, the skin of an angel. The fabric is used for evening wear and wedding gowns. Always made on a twelve-shaft satin weave.

PEAU DE CYGNE. A silk or rayon cloth made on an eight-shaft satin weave; high-texture, fine yarn counts, lustrous finish, and good handle or feel are features of the material. This crepe-effect fabric when made on a five-shaft satin is known as Messaline. Used for dress goods and suitings.

PEAU DE DIABLE. This "devilskin" French-made cloth is a printed cotton trousering used the same as denim in this country.

PEAU DE GANT. A white or cream-finished brocaded cloth made on a twill background. Peau de gant means glove skin, because of the close, strong, compact texture of the material.

PEAU DE MOUTON. An imitation sheepskin cloth made of worsted or high-grade woolen yarn on twill weaves. The curled-pile finish makes the fabric desirable for ladies' coatings.

PEAU DE PECHE. The cloth has a slightly roughened finish simulating the skin of a peach; made of cotton warp and silk or rayon filling.

PEAU DE POULE. An eight-harness French serge made from high quality woolen yarn and dyed in the piece. Used for formal suiting.

PEAU DE SINGE. Supposed to resemble monkey skin (or fur), this shaggy fabric, plain or figure, is made with schappe silk warp and cotton filling. The surface finish is roughened to give the effect.

PEAU DE SOIE. Soft, satin-face, good-quality cloth which has dull luster and is made of silk or rayon. A grainy appearance is a characteristic in the cloth, which may have a single or a double face construction. Fine, close ribs are seen in filling direction. The eight-shaft satin weave is used to make the cloth and an additional raiser is added to each basic raiser on the right or the left side to enhance the pebble effect. Best grades present about the same appearance and permit the use of the material as a reversible. Lower qualities are finished on only one side. Peau de soie means "silk skin." Uses include evening gowns, and facing for dress coats, coatings, dresses and trimmings.

PEAU DE SOURIS. This soft-finished silk cloth ("mouseskin") resembles duvetyne.

PEAU DE SUEDE. Check-plaid designs feature this woolen dress fabric which has a napped finish on the order of suède.

PEAU D'OURS. A French overcoating cloth with a long, shaggy face finish to simulate the hair of a bear.

PEBBLE. The irregular, rough or granitelike surface-effect observed on certain fabrics such as crepes and on those made with combination yarns from thrown yarns. The effect is also possible on fabrics made from some of the natural-fiber yarns. Pebble effect is caused by the amount and type of twist given to the yarn in the correct fabric construction.

PEBBLE CHEVIOT. Overcoating material that runs from sixteen to twenty-five ounces per yard. Made of twill weaves, piece-dyed, cloth has a shaggy, nubby, curly appearance in finished state. Wool or worsted, alone or in combination, used in making the material, which is a staple cloth with special waves of popularity from time to time.

PEBBLE-EFFECT FABRIC. A plain weave in which certain raisers are left out in the construction according to the plan of the designer of the goods, thereby increasing the granite, pebble, or crimp effect noted in the material. This effect is particularly noticeable on crepe and comparable cloths which come in high or excessible twist, warp, and filling, and with crepe weave. Ideal for certain woolens, cottons, and some manmade fiber goods for use in apparel.

PEBBLE WEAVE. A cloth with a pebble effect, formed by either a special weave or highly twisted yarns which shrink when wet.

PEBRINE. Silkworms and other caterpillars are often afflicted with pébrine, a contagious disease caused by a species of protozoa, *Nosema bombycis.*

PECCARY. See GLOVE LEATHERS.

PE CE. A copolymer from chlorinated polyvinyl chloride which made its debut in 1936 and which German chemists claimed to have been the first truly synthetic textile fiber. It never approached prominence but it did provide the basis from which Dr. Wallace H. Carothers of

E. I. duPont de Nemours & Co., Inc., Wilmington, Delaware, and his group of scientists finally brought out the great fiber, nylon. Pe Ce was the basis and source for the development of polymer chemistry.

PECORA DELLE LANGHE. An Italian sheep breed known for its poor wool staple; the sheep, however, are excellent milkers.

PECTIC ACID. The gelatinous acid formed by the decomposition of pectin, which is found in nearly all vegetable substances.

PECTIN. Any of a class of water-soluble compounds of high molecular weight found in various fruits and vegetables, of aid to jelly making.

PECTOCELLULOSE. Any of closely related pectic compounds allied with ordinary cellulosic substances.

PECTOSE. See CUTOSE.

PEDAL FEED. Sometimes used on cotton picker machines to feed short staple cotton to the beater. A number of narrow curved plates are set under the feed roller so that the cotton can be gripped much closer to the action of the beater. A similar action may be used as an evener motion in handling loose cotton.

PEDDLE. The forced sale of an item.

PEDDLER'S WOOL. See CLIPPINGS.

PEEK-A-BOO WAIST. Shirtwaist made or partly made of eyelet embroidery or sheer fabric. Especially fashionable in the late 1900's and turn of the present century; it has waves of popularity in present day fashion and style, as well.

PEELER COTTON. Also known as Delta, it has a staple of about 1¼ inch and is grown along the Gulf of Mexico and in the bottomlands of the Mississippi. Peeler was originally a distinct Southern cotton but it appears to be somewhat overshadowed by cottons that have had more success in recent years. The only cottons superior to Peeler are Sea Island, the best grown anywhere in the world but small in production, Sakellaridis-Egyptian, and Pima-Arizona.

PEERLESS COTTON. A small-boll, early-maturing Uplands cotton which has a staple of slightly more than one inch and a lint yield of about 33 per cent. Considered as one of the best Uplands cottons; other names for it include Crawford Premium, Crawford Peerless, Sutton Peerless, and The Premium.

PEGGING. Velveteens may be finished by applying friction to the pile effect with wooden blocks or soap-

stone to give increased luster.

PEGGING PLAN. The placing of the wooden pegs in the dobby lags, for weaving the pattern or design on a dobby loom. Also called lifting plan or weaving plan.

PEG-TOP. Trousers or skirt full at the top and narrow at the ankles.

PEG YARN. The yarn which is processed to form the leg or the boot in full-fashioned or circular hosiery. This yarn usually has from 20 to 40 turns of Z-twist per inch.

PEIGNOIR. 1. The covering worn over the shoulders while the hair is being dressed. Hence, loose robe for boudoir. 2. A cloak worn by bathers while walking on the beach, often made of terry cloth to take the place of a towel after bathing.

PEKIN. 1. A motif in which the white and the colored stripes are of equal width. 2. A broad-striped silk dress goods, in which broad satin stripes alternate with white rep stripes of equal width. 3. Term used in the French silk industry for fabrics made with longitudinal stripes made from a variety of suitable weave constructions. See MEXICAINE.

PEKIN CREPE. A silk or rayon striped fabric made with a crepe effect which is made possible by the use of regular right-hand and left-hand twisted crepe filling yarn in a two-and-two plan.

PEKIN GAUZE. Gauze or velvet fabrics made in alternate stripe design.

PEKIN STRIPES. General term given to fabrics whose design shows stripes of equal width; found in all types of dress goods made from any of the major textile fibers or filaments.

PELADE. French term for wool pulled (peladé) from slaughtered sheep in Egypt, Syria, and adjacent areas.

PELAGE. French for the coat or covering of an animal of the mammal variety such as sheep, fur-bearing animals, alpaca, llama, etc.

PELERINE. A cape or tippet, popular in England and the American Colonies in the seventeenth and eighteenth centuries. It was waist-length in the back and was finished off in the front with long, pointed ends or tips.

PELERINE WORK. Framework knitting in which the shifting of the sinker loops form the design; much used in making shawl fabric.

PELISSE, PELISSON. The former term is used the most, and there are two meanings for the term. 1. A woven or knitted fabric made in France and used as a long dress, gown, or cassock. Usually made of silk, wool, worsted and some of the man-made fibers, the material is soft in hand, variable in weight, and with some variance in quality. The goods are finished at sixty or more inches in width. 2. Originally, pelisse was made in the twelfth century and was a staple article of dress for many centuries. It was a long, outer coating or mantle that was sometimes lined with fur for use in cold climates. Present-day fabric of this name is a modification of the original fabric.

PELLA. A loose-fitting outdoor cloaking on the order of a tunic but rectangular in shape. See Tunic, Tunics, Roman Double.

PELLETON HAIR. Goat's hair used in making hats; most of the hair comes from Asia Minor and is shipped to France for the hat industry.

PELLON. The trade-name for nonwoven textiles produced by the Pellon Corporation, New York City. Used for inner construction, Pellon is made from natural and/or man-made fibers placed at random, and then bonded together by chemicals and heat.

Pellon can be smooth, soft, firm, supple, thick, or thin, depending upon the end use for which it is engineered. The prime function of Pellon is to give and hold the shape, and it is used in women's dresses, suits, coatings, sportswear, fur coatings, separates, swimwear, bras, lingerie, children's clothes, men's wear, shirtings, neckwear, rainwear, headgear, belts, luggage, shoes, women's handbags, and backing for vinyl fabrics and numerous industrial uses. In addition to its shaping properties, it is resilient, crease resistant, porous, light in weight, washable, drycleanable, and quick drying. It has equal flexibility in all directions and will not ravel nor fray. Its All-Bias Pellon is the only interfacing with "give" in all directions.

PELOMITE. A nonwoven stabilizer that can produce a fabric with the touch of a hot iron. A nonwoven construction with tiny fusing granules on one side, Pelomite has the quality of fusing with any outer fabric when the two are pressed together with a hot iron. Much used by home sewers as well as by the apparel industries. Product of Pellon Corporation, New York City.

PELOTAGE HAIR. The lowest grade of hair obtained from the vicuna.

PELT. 1. Skin, especially one with hair on it. 2. The skin of hair or wool-bearing animals prior to removal by shearing or other methods.

PELTERIE. The fur market in Flanders during the Renaissance particularly in the sixteenth century. Known as the Pellicerie in Italy, the Pelleterie in France, and the Pelt, Skin, or Fur Market in England.

PELT WOOL. 1. Short wool taken from the pelts of sheep which have been killed within three months of shearing. 2. Wool from the pelts of slaughtered sheep. It is obtained in the slaughterhouses where the carcass of the sheep is more important than the wool; the fleece is a by-product. See PULLED WOOL.

PELUCHE. French for plush. See PLUSH.

PELUCHE ARGENT. This "silver-plush" fabric is a French velvet made with silk or rayon warp, with two picks of silk or rayon to one of silver-colored thread or yarn. A silver chenille pick is inserted into the cloth every ten picks to give the pile effect.

PELUCHE DOUBLE. A double plush (peluche doublé) made with two superimposed fabrics.

PELUCHE DUVET. Silk or rayon warp and cotton filling form the ground construction; the pile effect is of the swansdown type; heavy pickage in the pile construction.

PELUCHE GAUFREE. Plush which has embossed designs (gaufrée).

PELUCHE LEGERE. A plush (legère = light), in the second-grade group since only one quarter of the warp is used to give the pile effect. (A first-grade plush would have one third of the warp used for the pile effect.)

PELUCHE LONG POIL. A French plush made from silk or rayon warp and schappe silk filling; has an extra-long pile-effect that is very shaggy in surface.

PELUCHE OMBRE. Plush made so that the coloring tapers off from a rather deep, full color into very light shades of the color (ombré = shaded).

PENANG. A heavyweight percale which has the same uses as the ordinary type.

PENCIL STRIPES. Suiting and dress-goods fabric which has fine, light, white or tinted stripes which run in the warp direction. The body of the goods is usually dull or dark so as to aid the contrast effect.

PENETRANT. A substance used to force or enter into the interior parts of something, to permeate. In textiles, it is used, for example, to make ingredients that are not soluble penetrate yarn or fabric to complete an action. Examples include soaps and sulphonated oils.

PENETRATE. In the detergent process, it means completely wet-out fiber and the displacing of protecting air pockets, etc.

PENETRABILITY. The measure of a fabric to resist penetration by rain by means of the Drop Penetration Test or the Hydroscopic Pressure Test (ASTM). The term is also used to determine the ability of dye or coloring matter to penetrate into a fabric. Some dyes because of their nature and properties and the type of goods to which they are applied, show excellent penetrability into the goods. Others will show only partial penetrability into the material and the rating is good, fair, poor.

PENELOPE CANVAS. Usually made of mock-leno weave, this cloth is not as popular as it was in former days. Only serviceable for embroidery or beadwork foundation, it is usually woven or rather coarse two-ply yarn, often in a 23-inch width. The weave is very open, but the cloth is given a stiff, starched finish. Importers insist on accuracy concerning the mesh as to size—⅛ inch, 3⁄16 inch, ¼ inch, etc. Even yarns are checked and, in sizing, care must be taken that proper stiffness has been applied so that the individual threads can be easily pulled out.

PENNISTONE SHEEP. An unimproved type which gives a coarse, harsh wool of average length. Known as a Mountain sheep, it is raised chiefly in Cheshire, Derbyshire, Lancashire, and Yorkshire, England.

PENSION. The amount of money paid at regular intervals, usually weekly or monthly, to an employee who has retired from a company's employ after reaching a specified age or working beyond a specified period of time.

PENTA-LOBAL. A manmade fiber whose cross-section has been modified from a circular shape into one that is five-sided; seems to improve yarn luster.

PEPITA. Named for a noted Spanish actress, this fabric is a two-color shepherd's plaid; it may be a design in which one or two colors and white are used, or for example, a check, say, with a brown and blue arrangement in a 4-and-4, 6-and-6, or 8-and-8 warp and filling arrangement. See CHECK.

PEPLOS. The very expensive shawl-like upper garment worn by the upperclass women in ancient Greece.

PEPLUM. A garment section, straight or flared, below the waist line. It is commonly hip-length; used with jackets, blouses, and dresses.

PEPPER-AND-SALT. Apparel material of fine, speckled effect. The appearance of the cloth suggests a mixture of salt and peper. Cloth is made in shades of gray, brown, green and blue. The effect is obtained by the use of two-colored twisted yarns, ordinarily in black and white, or by the intricacy of the weave with two or more solid-color yarns.

PEPPER TRASH. Slightly larger foreign particles than pin trash, found in cotton; gives a peppered look to stock.

PEPSIN. An enzyme of the body. The digestive action of pepsin may be used for removal of spots made by protein substances. Bought in powdered form and applied to fabrics, it will soften many types of stains so that they will easily be washed out by water. Some stains affected by pepsin include argyrol, blood, egg, gelatin, glue, ice cream, meat juice, milk, perspiration. Stains set by alcohol or heat will soften because of the action of this enzyme.

The procedure follows: the stained area should contain no soap or other alkali which might destroy the action. Lukewarm water should be used to dampen the stain, and then the pepsin powder should be sprinkled over the stained area. Allow to stand for one-half hour and keep the spot in dampened condition. Sponging and rinsing with water follow.

PEPTIZING. The breaking down of large aggregates of solid soil and suspending them firmly to prevent redisposition. This action is highly developed in some detergents.

PEPYS, SAMUEL. Pronounced "peeps," he was the great English diarist of the seventeenth century (1633–1703). He wrote on all topics, discreet and indiscreet, and has given to posterity much about fashion, style, vogue, dress, manners, and deportment of all classes of people as he observed them in Great Britain and on the Continent. Following the end of the Cromwell regime in Britain, Pepys was the administrator of the Royal Navy. Pepys is still read and quoted up to the present time.

PERALTA ROLLER. This burr crusher consists of two highly polished chilled steel rolls, with a spring attachment at either end, and place in front of the first breaker doffer on the woolen card. It is driven from the main cylinder shaft by a leather belt so that the speed of the rolls coincides with the speed of the doffer rolls and the stock is taken away from the burr crusher at the same speed as it is delivered to it.

Each roll has a diameter of twelve inches, and the length varies with the width of the card. The rolls each weigh 2,000 pounds, but pressure is applied by the springs at either end so that about 10,000 pounds pressure can be applied to the web of stock. In this way the burrs are crushed without damaging the stock in any way, be-

cause of the inherent elasticity of the wool fiber, and since the weak places on the yarn are generally adjacent to the burrs or shives in the stock, stronger yarn results from the elimination of the burrs and shives. The pressure is so great that a small piece of cotton string placed between the burr-crushing rolls emerges in the form of a fine dust.

PERBORATE. A higher oxidized borate which is capable of splitting off oxygen and forming hydrogen peroxide when dissolved in water. Used occasionally for bleaching wool, silk, etc., but is a rather expensive item to use.

PERCALE. A staple cotton cloth of good, fine texture in the cambric group made from cylindrical yarn. The fabric has more dressing than ordinary muslin but does not have the gloss or sheen of dress or linen cambric. This compact plain-weave cloth comes in the white or is printed. It withstands rugged wear and finds use in dresses, beachcloth, aprons, dressmaking. Percale has higher texture than calico.

PERCALE SHEETING. The finest cotton sheeting available, made of combed yarn. Has a soft, silklike feel. Made of single 40s or better, the pick count ranges from 180 to 200 for total number of ends and picks combined, per inch. This smooth, luxuriant sheeting was first made by Wamsutta Mills, New Bedford, Mass.

PERCALINE. Used for dress goods, lining, petticoating, shirting—a fine, sheer linen or cotton cloth of the cambric variety, made with a plain weave. The high glossy finish is a feature of the goods which are starched with varying degrees of stiffness. The cloth is lighter in weight than percale and much of it is dyed in the darker shades. Given beetled or chased finish and sometimes called cotton taffeta or Silesia.

PERCHES. Medium-grade French linens are called perchés.

PERCHING. Cloth, after it is taken from the loom, goes to the percher, who is usually an experienced weaver. He can detect at once all kinds of blemishes. He gets slightly more in wages than the regular weavers. The perch itself is made of three parts—two upright posts with a roller crossbar that revolves. This arrangement is similar to the uprights and crossbar on a football gridiron.

The percher stands so that the north light will be accessible. The cut of cloth to be perched is thrown over the roller bar and has been led from a roller wagon that is in back of the

percher. The cloth, after leaving the roller and having been marked off as to defects, goes into an empty wagon that is in front of the percher. Thus, the position of the percher is such that he can readily look through the cloth with the aid of the north light, and in that way, all the defects are readily noted and marked by him with chalk.

These chalk marks will attract the attention, in the Dry-finishing Room, of the speckers, menders, and burlers. They will fix as many of the blemishes as they can. What they cannot remedy is taken care of by the experienced sewers. When the cloth leaves the sewers, it is ready for the wet-finishing operations, and the material is as perfect in construction as is possible.

Defects caught in perching include wrong filling bobbin, ends or picks out, rolling or cut selvage, selvage ends out, dead colors, harness skips, swollen or skipped dents that cause reed marks, wrong draws, specky goods, uneven double and twist.

PERFORATED TUBE. A stainless steel or a paper yarn put-up used in package dyeing. There are two sizes, ⅝ of an inch and 1⅝ inches, as to diameter dimension.

PERIOD DRESS. A dress that shows the influence of raiment from some particular period in the history of costume that still has an effect on present-day dress. Examples include Oriental, Greek, Roman, Renaissance, Directoire, Gay Nineties, etc.

PERISHED STAPLE. Cotton which has been destroyed by the elements or other causes.

PERKIN, SIR WILLIAM HENRY. The English chemist who produced the first synthetic dye in 1856.

PERKINS, JACOB. In the early 1800's, this American invented a small cylinder to press designs onto copper rollers, thereby creating an economical way to cover rollers and increase their use in the printing of textile goods. This was a forerunner of what is today called mass production. Perkins's ideas were introduced to several printing mills here by another inventor named Lockett, in 1808. The method is still used in printing fine fabrics.

PERLE. A finishing operation resorted to when it is desired to roll long-nap, pile threads into compact balls or nubs (perlé = pearled).

PERLIN. Scotch for lace.

PERLOK. A process by means of which any continuous filament tow is broken or cut, resulting in a top or sliver. This heavy tow process may be defined as a modified system of stretch-breaking a tow, 200,000 total denier and up. The product resembles a combed sliver and is handled in the same manner as the sliver. Perlock staplers have been built under the Lohrke patent by R. H. Hood Company, Philadelphia, Pennsylvania, and Turbo Machine Company, Lansdale, Pennsylvania. See SLIVER, TOW, DENIER.

PERLON. The trade-mark of the PERLON-Warenzeichenverband e. V., Frankfurt am Main (PERLON—Trademark Association) registered in all important countries of the world, and related to polyamide threads, fibers, filaments, and bristles manufactured by the following licensed users:

Badische Anilin- & Soda-Fabrik AG., Ludwigshafen am Rhein, Farbenfabriken Bayer Aktiengesellschaft, Leverkusen-Bayerwerk, Farbwerke Hoechst AG., vormals Meister Lucius & Bruening, Frankfurt/Main-Hoechst, Phrix-Werke Aktiengesellschaft, Hamburg, Spinnstofffabrik Zehlendorf Aktiengesellschaft, Berlin-Zehlendorf, and Vereinigte Glanzstoff-Fabriken AG., Wuppertal-Elberfeld.

In 1938, Dr. Paul Schlack realized for the first time, the polymerisation of Caprolactam. The result was the Poly-ε-Amino-Caprolactam which, by further processing in the melting and spinning procedures, could finally be turned into PERLON. Raw materials for PERLON are carbon, hydrogen, oxygen, and nitrogen. After complicated chemical reactions and then mixed in the exact proportions these elements will form the snow-white crystalline substance Caprolactam. This consists of 6 carbon atoms, 11 hydrogen atoms, 1 oxygen atom, and 1 nitrogen atom.

When exposed to heat, this polyamide becomes liquid, in which form it is forced through close spinning nozzles; the fine filaments leaving the orifices in the spinneret become solid as soon as exposed to the air. The polyamide filament still possesses high dilatability so that in the subsequent elongation process it is stretched to four times the length it had before. By the process the filament acquires extraordinary resistance to tearing or rupturing.

PERLON filament or the staple fiber may have wool-like or cotton-like properties dependent on the end-requirements.

It should be borne in mind that nylon and PERLON are classed as polyamide fibers, and that they are similar to each other in chemical properties, and that nylon is a generic term while PERLON is a trade-mark which belongs to PERLON-Warenzeichenverband e. V., Frankfurt/Main, Germany, and that this word is their exclusive property.

PERLON U. It originated in Germany during World War II and is spun from polyurethane resulting from the reaction of 1,4-butanediol with hexamethylene diisocyanate. Perlon U does not compare well with nylon but in the past few years urethanes have become the basis of the well-known and important spandex fibers which are very elastic and have the same uses as rubber filaments. See Perlon.

"PERMA-BOND." A specialized process for fusing urethane, of proper formation, to fabrics, textiles in general, or nonwoven materials. No foreign or hostile chemicals or compounds are used to achieve this bond effect. "PERMA-BOND" FOAM is the adoption of urethane foams by the textile and apparel industries to improve tear strength, drapeability, tensile strength, compressibility (good seams), and resistance to cleaning fluids and soap alkalies. One type is 1/16-inches thick and weighs about 1½ ounces per square yard. Uses include quilted combinations where it provides about as much insulation as 6 ounces of reprocessed wool batting. Thus, considerably less thickness and weight permits better styling and a permanent insulation that does not bunch, lump, or separate. The second type is 3/32-inches thick, and the Foam weighs about 2¼ ounces per square yard. It is approximately equivalent to 8 or 10 ounces of reprocessed wool batting. Manufactured by A. D. Gosman Corporation, Carteret, New Jersey.

PERMAFRESH. A group of thermosetting formaldehydes containing resins. Permafresh imparts a variety of desirable physical qualities to fabrics such as minimum-care wash-and-wear characteristics, durable chlorine resistance, improved lightfastness, shrinkage control, crease resistance, and a variety of hands, ranging from soft and draping to resilient firmness caused by selective use of these resins. Cottons, rayons, and blends are the primary textiles upgraded by the resins, some of which are applicable to the major man-made fibers. Trade-mark product of Warwick Chemical Division, Sun Chemical Corporation, New York City.

PERMALON. This derivative of vinylidene chloride is used to make coarse yarns or cords. Has a tensile strength of about 35,000 pounds per square inch and an elongation of about 15 per cent at the breaking point. It is nonflammable, not affected by water and is insoluble in benzene, carbon tetrachloride, gasoline, hydrochloric acid, sulphuric acid, and caustic soda. Used in fishing leaders, fly screens, tennis racquets, and trolling lines.

PERMANENT FINISH. A much-used term given to a host of materials for which some particular claim is made. Examples may include moiré or watermarked finish on taffeta, crispness noted on organdy or dimity, smoothness on broadcloth, embossed fabrics, crepe effects, glazed materials. The term also implies fabrics which are crease-resistant, shrinkage-resistant and wear-resistant. In reality, the better and safer term to use is "Durable Finish." Actually, very few finishes are permanent for the life of a fabric or garment.

PERMANENT-FIRE-RETARDANT RAYON. Also known as PFR RAYON, this trademark of the American Viscose Division of FMC Corporation, Philadelphia, Pennsylvania, was unveiled in 1967. Its manufacture involves the introduction of a water-insolululble organophosphorous compound into the viscose spinning solution prior to spinning. An ideal treatment for sleepwear and comparable fabrics which, without its use, might become readily flammable, especially with children. No loss of aesthetics results from its use and the loss in wear life is limited.

PERMANENT HARDNESS. This is caused in water by sulphate remaining after boiling at the boiling point.

PERMANENT PRESS. A fabric finish which enables a garment to hold its shape after alundering and tumble drying; requires no ironing. The term is linked with DURABLE PRESS and both terms are used interchangeably.

PERMANGANATE. There are several permanganates, but the one most frequently met is potassium permanganate, a strong oxidizing agent. Used much in stain removal.

PERMANIS COTTON. An ordinary type of Pernambuco cotton of average staple, harsh in feel, and usually mixed with other raw stocks since the staple is wiry if used alone.

PERMEABILITY. A condition or state of being penetrated by air, gas, liquid, etc. For example, the term "air permeability" would imply that air was able to penetrate or pass through a fabric. If air could not pass through a fabric it is said that the cloth is impervious to air.

PERMEL PLUS. Trade-mark of American Cyanamid Co. for a washable, water-repellent finishing process which also gives crease- and soil-resistance to the fabric. The finish increases the durability and strength of the goods to which it is applied.

PERNAMBUCO COTTON. A rather good quality Brazilian cotton of about 1¼ inch staple. Also known as Pernama, the cotton can be spun to about 60s.

PERNYI SILKWORM. The wild silkworm of China, *Antherea pernyi*. Feeds on oak leaves. The cocoon is rather large and is brown to yellow in cast.

PEROXIDASE. A particularly developed enzyme whose function is to decompose organic peroxides.

PEROXIDE. A chemical substance which will evolve atomic oxygen for bleaching. Hydrogen peroxide commonly is used for stain removing and small bleaching jobs. Sodium peroxide is used in industrial bleaching.

PEROXIDE BLEACHING. Bleaching of textiles in solutions of hydrogen peroxide. Among skein dyers the yarn is steeped overnight in a bath of dilute hydrogen peroxide. Rinsing, an acetic acid sour, and a final rinse are given the yarn to complete the bleaching action.

PERPETUANA. An old-time woolen fabric, identified by the glossy finish, which is still used in rural sections of the world for coating fabric and men's and women's suiting. The cloth is made in single colors. Usually drab in effect despite the finish.

PERROQUETS. French sail fabrics made of hemp.

PERROTINE PRINTING. Group block printing by a simple machine, instead of by hand with single blocks. A number of blocks, usually twelve, are fastened into a frame, the color is applied, and then the blocks are pressed onto the fabric. The resulting group can then be cut into sections, for example, into a size suitable for handkerchiefs. Invented by Perrot, a noted printer of France, about 1830, the method is outmoded at present.

PERSE, PERSENING. Waterproofed jute and linen cloths.

PERSIAN. See E.I.; Kip, Kipskin.

PERSIAN BERRIES. The dried unripe fruit of various species of Rhamnus; also known as French berries and grains of Avignon; extract used as yellow dyestuff.

PERSIAN CORD. Made of fine cotton warp and high-count worsted filling, this plain-weave fabric presents a ribbed or corded effect because two warp ends are made to weave as a single end. The drawing-in, reeding, and loom set-up takes care of the effect in the fabric. Also called Russel cord.

PERSIAN KNOT. Sometimes known as the Senna knot, it is one of the two knots used to tie-in the pile effects in Oriental rugs. A loop is formed around the warp end and is made fast by being pulled into place so that the pile will be spaces between all warp threads. See GHIORDES KNOT.

PERSIAN LAMB. The best grades of Karakul lambskins; they have very pronounced, uniform, tight curls. The term Persian was given to these lambs for the reason that at one time all skins found their way to the European markets from Persia. The impression prevailed that all the skins were produced there.

Black, gray, or brown are the predominating colors when the skins appear in fur garments. Wearing quality is superb. The skin or the garment is judged by the tightness of the curl and the luster of the hair. Found in Afghanistan, Africa, Russia, Siberia.

Cross Persian lamb is a term applied loosely to lamb not of the Persian group but having some of its characteristics.

PERSIAN LAWN. The best lawn cloth made. It is thin, sheer, and has high luster. It is softer and has more luster than batiste, but it is not so sheer as organdy. Little of the cloth is seen here; however, it is in demand in the European trade, chiefly in the British Isles.

PERSIAN MOROCCO. Hair sheepskins with Morocco grain, natural or embossed. It is a misnomer in the bag trade when applied to other sheepskins, and in the book trade when applied to goatskins as distinguished from "Turkey Morocco." The term should be confined solely to hair sheepskins. See TURKEY MOROCCO.

PERSIAN PRINT. Shipped from England to the East, a low-quality, plain-weave cotton cloth known for its brilliant coloring in large-pattern effect.

PERSIAN RUGS. These rugs, which should be made in Iran, are the nearest to perfection from the angle of loom technique, actual weaving, and work. Floral patterns, mosaic designs, and splendid backgrounds are characteristics of these highly sought rugs. Persians have a fine, even texture, clever, intricate designs, and excellent color harmony effects. Leading Persians include Bijar, Djushaghen, Feraghan, Gorevan, Harmadam, Herat, Herez, Ispaham, Kara-Dagh, Kermanshah, Khorassan, Kirman, Kurdistan, Mahal, Meshed, Mosul, Muskabad, Sarabend, Sarak, Sarouk, Savalan, Sehna, Serapi, Shiraz, Suj-Boulak, Tabriz.

PERSIANS. India-tanned, hair-sheepskin leathers. Strictly speaking, the term should apply only to India-tanned sheepskins, although it used to include goatskins, as well. Leathers from the issue of crossbreeding goats with sheep are sometimes called Persians.

PERSIS. Archil.

PERSONNEL TRAINING MAN. One who can train workers in every manufacturing phase. It is obvious that the fate of a fabric or garment may well rest in his hands.

PERSPIRATION. A body excretion which contains salt, albumin, fatty acid, and which may be either acidic or alkaline, depending upon the individual. Its composition, strange to relate, is not accurately known.

PERSPIRATION-RESISTANT. Said of fabrics or garments that resist acid or alkaline perspiration. Laboratory test results should be consulted prior to selling any fabric as prespiration-resistant.

PERUVIAN COTTON. Sometimes known as "Tree Cotton." The name is given because the cotton grows on trees 10 to 12 feet high. The fibers work well with wool on the woolen system, and it is much sought for by manufacturers. The fibers are long, wiry, and clean. There are four types of Peruvian cotton:

1. Rough Peruvian works best with wool. Its staple is 1¼ inches, has good luster and appearance.

2. Smooth Peruvian is a regular cotton similar to American cottons.

3. Sea Island Peruvian is the best of the three and is used for finer cotton yarns and in blankets, dress goods, and coating fabric.

4. Tanguis, a cross between rough and smooth types, is now the favorite staple and makes up the major portion of the Peruvian crop. It is a very white cotton, and has a natural crinkle which adds to its value. Staple runs from 1 inch to 1½ inches.

All Peruvian cottons are ideal for blending with wool.

PERUVIAN EMBROIDERY. An important and beautiful embroidery and darned work, done on linen or silk foundation fabrics with floral, pastoral, and nature scenes predominating. Used for borders and edgings for articles that can withstand constant washing.

PERVAL. Trade name for wool pulp product simulating cotton muslin. Used for sheeting, pillowcases, aprons.

PETATE FIBER. Strong bast fiber used in mats. The buri palm leaves of the Philippines are its source.

PETERKIN COTTON. An interesting Uplands cotton that comes from a medium-size plant which produces oval balls, nonclustrous in nature. This average-maturing cotton has about 1-inch staple with a lint yield of approximately 35 per cent. It is one of the best Rio

Grande-type cottons, and is a large lint producer. Also known as Audrey Peterkin, Brazier Peterkin, Crossland, Texas Wood, Wise.

PETERKIN LIMB CLUSTER COTTON. Cluster-type Peterkin cotton; also called Peterkin New Cluster.

PETER PAN COLLAR. A youthful, turned-down collar, from two to three inches in width with rounded ends in the front, often stiffly starched. Named for Peter Pan, the classical character created by Sir James Matthew Barrie, 1860-1937, Scottish novelist and playwright and a master of whimsey. Maude Adams, one of the most beloved actresses of all time, made the Peter Pan costume famous. Her costume had a short belted tunic covered with leaves, tight knee breeches, pointed shoes, the typical Peter Pan collar, and the small perky hat with its feather.

PETERSBURG FLAX. Natural brownish Russian flax that is of high quality and gives excellent wear.

PETERSHAM. 1. A rough-napped, rather bulky woolen cloth used in maritime circles and in men's heavy overcoating. It has the same uses as reefers, ulsters, and sailors' pea jackets. 2. A ribbon material with cord or bengaline stripes which is used for inner belts, hatbands, and trimming. 3. A narrow braid or belting used for skirt-tops.

PETIT. A French term (meaning small, lesser) which suggests a fabric of lighter weight or inferior quality than the standard or customary make of that particular fabric.

PETITE BRIDES. French term for the small, hexagonal mesh ground in needle-point lace wherein each side is made of two highly twisted threads to give proper support.

PETIT GULF COTTON. An Uplands-type cotton of 1-inch staple and about 30 per cent lint yield. The plant is large, not prolific, has medium-sized bolls, and does not mature early.

PETITS CARREAUX. An 8-end, 4-pick repeat is used to give the small check motif to this French serge of low to medium quality. Worsted or worsted and waste stocks are used to make the material. Petits carreaux means "little squares." See SERGETTE.

PETIT TOILE. A plain-woven, fine, strong French linen made with red and white, or blue and white, checks or stripes. Used chiefly for napery and curtains, it may be used for dress goods. The check effects may or may not have small dobby motifs of white on the colored squares; in that event the fabric would be made on a dobby loom.

PETIT VELOURS. French for a lightweight cotton velvet.

PFLEIDERING. The process of chopping or shredding into a flake form the pressed alkali cellulose block sheets in a machine named for its inventor, the German scientist, Pfleiderer.

PHASE. Technical term used to describe certain parts of complex mixtures, etc. In the ordinary emulsion, oil is the dispersed phase, and the detergent solution is the dispersing phase. Smoke in the atmosphere is the dispersed phase, with the atmosphere the dispersing phase.

PHENOL. A white, crystalline organic compound obtained from coal tar. Also the name for a series of derivatives from benzol in which hydrogen of the benzol ring has been replaced by hydroxyl. Also, in chemistry, a carbonic acid; a hydroxyl derivate of benzene; in addition, any analogous hydroxyl derivative of benzene.

PHENOLPHTHALEIN. A chemical that indicates the chemical condition of textile goods by turning pink or purple if applied to goods having a basic reaction, and remaining colorless on goods having an acid reaction.

PHENOMENA. Certain characteristics and definite actions, both physical and chemical, exhibited by different substances.

PHILIPPINE MAGUEY. Another name for Cantala.

PHILLIPS FIBERS CORPORATION. This corporation is a subsidiary of Phillips Petroleum, Bartlesville, Oklahoma. Phillips 66 Fibers Marketing Offices are located in New York City and Company Headquarters are in Greenville, South Carolina. *Marvess* is the olefin fiber produced in Spartanburg, South Carolina; *Phillips 66 Nylon* is manufactured in Puerto Rico while *Quintess Filament Polyester Fiber* for apparel is made in Rock Mount, North Carolina.

PHILLIPS FIRE RETARDANT FIBER RESIN. A flame retardant polypropylene resin for fiber production to sustain the integrity of the physical properties of the original plastic. It contains a patented additive which is a high melt flow homopolymer called Marlex HRV-120-01. Product of Phillips Petroleum Company, Greenville, South Carolina.

PHORMIUM. This hardy, strong New Zealand hemp runs from brown to white in cast. Used for binder twine.

PHOSPHATE. Chemically and loosely, it is a salt or ester of phosphoric acid; a tertiary salt of orthophosphoric acid, such as sodium phosphate. Agriculturally, it is a fertilizing material

which contains compounds of phosphorus. It is also used as a carbonated drink of water and fruit syrup containing a very small amount of phosphoric acid. See Detergent, Detergents, Food and Drug Administration Assessment of, Ester.

PHOSPHORESCENCE. Its phenomenon is the re-emission of light by certain bodies which have the property of absorbing ultraviolet and other rays to which they are exposed and storing a portion of this energy, later to be given off again as visible light. Examples of these are metallic phosphors such as zinc sulfide; natural minerals such as willemite, sphalerite, aragonite; or synthetic phosphors.

PHOSPHOROUS. Chemically a solid, nonmetallic element which exists in at least two allotropic (one of two or more existing forms of an element) forms, one that is yellow, flammable, poisonous, and luminous in the dark; and another that is red, less flammable, and less poisonous. See Phosphate, Detergents and all variances of this term; Detergents, Food and Drug Administration Assessment of, Ester.

PHOTEE COTTON. High-quality cotton, raised along the banks of the Brahmaputra River in India and used in making the best quality Dacca muslin.

PHOTOGRAPHIC PRINTING. This method of printing makes it possible to do very fine work on textiles which otherwise would be most difficult to do by the roller method. Dark ground and solid effects, as well as fine detail work, can be executed on cloth colored in this manner in one continuous etching operation.

The design is photographed, and the negative is then covered with a screen plate. In this way it is possible to break up the solid areas of the design so that the dark portions of the negative will then be shown by fine lines.

A contact print is made by projecting a light through the screen plate onto another film. As many exposures are made as are necessary to produce a complete film covering the entire copper roller.

The film is then placed around a roller which has been previously treated with a sensitizing solution. A powerful arc light is then focused upon it. Wherever the light passes through the film it affects the sensitized roller, baking the chemical coating and causing it to harden.

Warm water is then used to wash the roller to take away the sensitizing solution areas which were not exposed to light. The copper roller is then placed in a bath of iron perchloride for several minutes. The solution etches the bare portions of the roller. These gougings form the engraved pattern that is to be printed. Afterwards the roller is washed to rid it of the portions covered with the baked sensitized solution which have resisted the action of the cutting or etching bath. Dress goods of many types are printed in this novel, popular manner.

PHOTOMETER. An optical instrument for measuring the light reflectancy of surfaces. Used in whiteness, soil removal, and color-fading determinations for laboratory check-ups on formula improvement and control.

PHOTOMICROGRAPH. Attaching a camera to a microscope enlarges the specimen or photograph so that it may be more easily seen by the observer.

PHRYGIAN. Name for the soft cap worn by the Greeks in ancient times. It was the forerunner of the so-called "Red Cap of Liberty" worn by the French revolutionaries in the last quarter of the 18th century.

PHULKARI. A type of embroidered fabric made in the Punjab areas of India and West Pakistan; used mainly for the *Chaddar,* a headgear traditionally worn by women for nuptial festivities. The so-called "true Phulkari," originally made by the Jat tribes in the Rohtak region, was embellished by a motif which was "diapered at intervals all over the fabric."

Some of this work is a pictorial representation of village life and bucolic scenes, for adornment's sake, and some of the designs veer toward marriage symbols. Floral motifs are often made in geometrical forms, and the stitches are usually rather long and may completely cover the fabric being used. The basic stitch used is the "false satin stitch," although double running, flat running, and even looped stitch formation may be utilized. The finer, costlier types of fabric are known as Bagh Work and are made for affluent customers.

In most cases, coloring of this work is now done by commercial dyes. Formerly all coloring was done by the use of plant dyes and some of the more intricate and higher priced items are still colored in this manner.

PHULSHUTA COTTON. A short, soft, pure white cotton raised in Bengal, India, and used locally.

PHYSICAL TESTING. Those tests made on stock, yarn, and fabric performed physically in contradistinction to chemical testing of textiles—yarn breakage, fabric breakage, abrasion testing, Mullen's tester for knit fabric, etc. See Illustrated Section.

PIANO LEATHERS. A blanket term for the many types of highly specialized leathers used for various purposes in the manufacture of pianos. These leathers are made of selected skivers, full-grain sheepskins, or deerskins.

PIASSAVA. A fiber obtained from the Piassava palm grown in Brazil and Africa. It is thick, brown to black in color, and used in brooms.

PICK. A filling thread or yarn that runs crosswise or horizontally in the woven goods. See WEFT.

PICKADIL, PICCADILLY. In the seventeenth century a picdadil was defined as "that round hem or several divisions set together about the skirt of a garment or other thing; also a kind of stiff collar, made in the fashion of a band." In 1620 a tailor who had done well out of pickadils, built himself a home which became known as Pickadilly Hall and which lent its name to the London area now known as Piccadilly and Piccadilly Circus.

PICK-AND-PICK. The throwing of single picks of different colors through the shed of the loom in weaving.

PICK-AT-WILL. Box-loom weaving, which means that the loom is so constructed that the picking arrangement of colors can be manipulated at will to give fancy effects in the fabric.

PICK CLOCK. An automatic counting device attached to a loom that registers the number of filling picks woven into a fabric. Weavers may be paid at the rate of "so many mills per pick."

PICK COUNTER. Same as pick glass. See Illustrated Section.

PICKELHAUBE. The spiked helmet worn by the Imperial Army officers of Germany for many decades; World War I brought about their demise along with the defeat of Germany in 1918.

PICKER. 1. A machine that tears apart matted fiber, such as cotton, with a rapidly revolving, sharp-toothed drum, and cleans the undesirable matter from the loosened fiber by air currents. 2. The mechanical part of a loom which causes the shuttle in the loom to pass through the warp shed as the harnesses are raised and lowered in the loom action. 3. A picker of cotton in field; also the automatic cotton picker. See Illustrated Section.

PICKER LAP. The lap or web obtained as the cotton comes from the finisher picker machine in cotton yarn manufacture. The object of the machine is to produce an even sheet or webbing that is comparatively free from the

heavier impurities. The lap is about forty-five inches wide, and weighs about forty-five pounds, as it goes into the card. There is a rod that goes through the middle of the rolled lap form. The two ends of this rod are set in a stanchion so that the cotton may be fed into the card in an easy, smooth, uniform manner, as it unwinds.

PICKER LEATHER. There are various types of leather for pickers used in textile plants. They may be very soft and mellow, or tough, heavily stuffed steer hides, like comber and gill box apron leather. Picker or check straps are often made from a glycerine tanned rawhide which is a strong and pliable leather. For loop pickers, a belting leather is often used, and for heavy-duty pickers a hard rawhide, usually made from buffalo hides, is used.

PICKER OR SCUTCHER. Often referred to as the opening picker machine. The cotton is fed from the mixing room to the opener by means of a chute, which is even with the floor of the mixing room to expedite the work.

The cotton comes down the chute to the hopper feed, which helps to break up the clumps by means of a revolving, spiked cylinder over a traveling, spiked lattice arrangement. From the hopper feed, the stock is delivered to the porcupine, a spiked cylinder about 40 inches in diameter, traveling at a speed of about 500 rpm. This cylinder breaks up the cotton with the help of bars that are set underneath it. Through the openings between the bars, all kinds of loose, foreign matter drop into a receptacle, which, when filled, can be taken out. If too much cotton falls through the bars, they may be closed or the spaces may be made smaller.

The cotton is then drawn to the cages by means of a fan placed under the machine. If there is not sufficient draft, this may be regulated by means of dampers on the opener side.

The cotton passes between the cages to the calender rollers, where it is condensed by its passage between these rollers. The last roller on the machine, the lap roller, winds the cotton into a sheet-lap form.

PICKER STICKS. The two sticks which aid and govern the throwing of the shuttles from box to box at each end of the raceplate of the loom. The entire action is comparable with a person throwing a baseball. The picker stick is aided by the lug strap, the rocker arm, the raiser cam, and the pick ball which travels on the cam.

PICKER STRAP. The strap or cord

fastened to the picker.

PICKERED. Clumpy or matted fleeces which have to be opened up by the wool picker machine.

PICKETING. The union's method of posting individuals in front of a company's premises to notify all passers-by of the existence of a labor dispute.

PICK FINDING. The process of letting-up or turning-back the warp in the loom and picking out the few picks that have been woven after a mispick or some other blemish has occurred. After the mispick has been remedied, the warp is made taut and the loom is ready for setting and continued weaving.

PICK GEAR. A gear in the chain of gears at the front of a loom, which governs the number of picks per inch going into the fabric as it is being woven. It is necessary to change this gear if the number of picks is to be changed. This can be done easily since it is held in place by a cotter pin and can be conveniently removed for the new gear.

PICK GLASS. A single or double lens glass used in analyzing and dissecting cloth. Comes in ¼ inch, ½ inch and 1 and 2 inch sizes. For good results, a one-inch glass should be used. The device is hinged so that it may be readily folded up. Also known as a counting-glass, linen-tester, or pick counter.

PICKING. 1. Gathering cotton bolls from the plant.

2. Also called specking or burling: the removing of extraneous vegetable matter from the face of woolen goods—kemp, chaff, straw, shives, etc.

3. In cotton yarn manufacture, one of the first operations, the object of which is to continue the opening process and to cast out the heavier wastes in cleaning the stock. Picking forms the cotton into layer condition and winds it into a cylindrical roll that will be about 45 inches wide. The lap has a weight of about 45 pounds.

4. The second of the three essential motions in weaving cloth—shedding, picking, beating-up. It is the action which occurs when the shuttle passes through the shed of the loom from the shuttle box on the one side of the raceplate of the loom to the correct box on the opposite side of the machine.

PICKING, COTTON. Some cotton picking is still done by hand. The picker has a long sack of cotton duck, thrown over his shoulder, which he drags along the ground while working. The sack will hold about 60 pounds of cotton. Expert pickers will gather about 200 pounds a day, at least. Machine cotton

picking is making heavy inroads on hand-picking personnel.

PICKING OUT. 1. Taking threads from a fabric—warp, or filling, or both—to determine the weave or to complete a full analysis of a one-inch square sample, or some other size. 2. Actual picking out of filling picks that must be removed from the cloth, as it is being woven, because of some flaw or blemish such as shuttle smash, skipping, holes.

PICKING TONGS. See BURLING; BURLING IRONS.

PICKINGS. 1. Undesirable cotton staple from country-damaged bales or parts thereof. 2. Merino wool which contains dry vegetable matter which has to be removed before or during manipulation.

PICKLOCK. A term in grading wool that signifies the stock as XX or even better. Also implies the "pick-of-the-lock or fleece." There is, in reality, no picklock today, except in some of the more or less isolated sections in the back country of some of the mountainous states. West Virginia, Tennessee, Kentucky, and a few other states grow some of this wool, which is used in home consumption.

PICKOVER. Old-time term for a yarn float.

PICKWHEEL. A toothed gear or wheel on a loom which governs the number of picks per inch to be placed into the cloth.

PICOT. A small loop that projects from the edge of lace, a garment, or a ribbon. The picot loop is made by placing a wire which runs parallel to the selvage or edge of the fabric; the wire will catch certain picks in the weave to form the effect. After the wire is removed from the goods, the loop effect remains. In the lace trade, the term implies the small loops used for decoration. Picot may appear on one or both sides of the fabric.

PICOT POINT. One of a number of needles that are inserted in a holder—picot bar, in a knitting machine. The points produce a row of large, wide stitches, picot stripe, at the top of the stocking.

PICOT YARN. Another name for loop yarn.

PICROLITE. Masses of fibers taken from "serpentine rock." Belonging to the asbestos family of fibers, these non-flexible crystals can have a length of about one foot. Low in quality, it is also known as bastard asbestos.

PICULE, PICUL, PECUL. A Chinese weight 133⅓ pounds used in the silk trade. Chinese, Japanese, and Tussah silk bales average from 130 to 135 pounds per bale.

Chinese bales are quoted in Taels per Picule. Japanese bales are listed in Yen per 100 Kin, which is 132.77 pounds in weight; Canton bales weigh 80 Catties, 106⅔ pounds. A Cattie is 1⅓ pounds. See KIN, TAEL.

PIECE. A standard length of a woven cloth as 40, 60, or 80 yards.

PIECE-DYED CLOTH. Any material that has been dyed some solid color or shade. One of the group of the three greatest methods of dyeing—piece-, stock-, and yarn- or skein-dyeing.

PIECE-DYED SATIN. A staple fabric woven with a 50 reed, six ends per dent, or a 70 reed with five ends per dent, double. 20/22 denier, raw silk is used in the warp, and a 60/1 spun silk is used in the filling. There are 90 picks in this five-shaft or eight-shaft satin weave cloth. In silk, the material is often known as charmeuse. Much rayon fabric of this construction is also made. It is popular in evening wear.

PIECE-DYEING. The dyeing of cloth rather than raw stock or yarn. It is a continuous or semicontinuous process which takes place in a dye-beck, box, jig, or some other form of continuous machine.

The greige cloth is scoured usually in a separate machine and is then loaded on one of the above types of dyeing machines. On jigs and continuous machines the cloth is handled in the open width while on the dye-beck it is in rope form.

Piece-dyeing is very popular because of the inherent flexibility of this method from an economic standpoint. It is far more economical to weave fabric with undyed yarns and subsequently to dye the fabric into popular shades than to yarn-dye with the hazard that the colors may not be popular when marketed.

There is also considerable manufacturing waste between yarn-dyeing and the production of the finished goods. Recent techniques have made it possible to piece-dye with the finished result equal in fastness to yarn-dyed or the so-called ingrain dyeing.

PIECE GOODS. Cloth sold by the yard or some definite cut length. When a bolt of cloth is classed as piece goods, the respective length of the material will vary but keep within a certain definite length range with regard to yardage.

PIECE GOODS BUYER, APPAREL. One who supervises purchases of all materials. The buyer works with the designers in planning the line, analyzes textile costs and the working qualities of textiles, works closely with designers, distributes materials, must know the markets and the availability of cloth. The buyer must understand restrictions and be ready to furnish substitute material if some of his sources run dry or cannot deliver on time. A thorough knowledge of raw material, construction, color, and finish of materials is a vital essential.

The Assistant Piece Goods Buyer keeps records and helps to locate new sources of materials by constantly analyzing market records. The buyer must know how to calculate yardages, measure and distribute materials.

PIECER. The spinner's helper whose work it is to join, twist, or splice broken ends which occur in the process of spinning the roving into yarn.

PIECES. Odds-and-ends and small batches of wool picked up from the sorting room in the mill. Sold in varying size batches.

PIECEWORK. Work performed by an employee for a specific wage per piece produced.

PIECING. Joining or splicing two ends of sliver, slubbing, roving, or yarn into a single strand.

PIECING-OUT. Flax parlance for the separation of fingers and stricks into bundles of suitable size for hand dressing, roughing and machine hackling or combing. Four to seven pieces per pound is average for manipulation.

PIECING-UP. The tying together or splicing of broken sliver, slubbing, roving, or yarn; may be done by twisting or tying knots, such as the weaver's knot in the case of broken yarn.

PIED. French word for step or foot and implies two or more colors in a "step formation" of intensity and effect, and may be a two-tone or a three-tone of one color or combination of harmonious colors.

PIERCED COCOON. One that has been pierced by the moth coming through the cocoon wall. The short, resultant silk fibers are spun into yarn on the spun-silk system of spinning.

PIERRE VELUE COTTON. This cotton of high boll-yield is raised in the Antilles. The staple is fine and of good quality.

PIE WOOL. Fibers obtained from skin pieces which have been sweated in lot form; usually obtained from shankings and skin trimmings.

PIG. See GLOVE LEATHERS.

PIGMENT. 1. A chemical substance giving color; especially, one used in the manufacture of dull-luster rayon yarn. Titanium dioxide or barium sulphate may be used for this purpose. 2. Color material used in the dope dyeing or spun-dyeing process of man-made fibers.

PIGMENT DYES. Dyes applied to cotton and rayon, which are insoluble and so applied from a colloidal dispersion. Fastness to light of the group is an outstanding feature, but fastness to washing may vary. Pigment dyes are much used for military purposes where extreme fastness to light is essential.

PIGMENTED RESIN EMULSION COLORS. Pigment added to synthetic resins in emulsion form enable color to be mechanically bonded to fabric in prints or in plain shades.

PIGMENTED YARN. A dull or colored yarn spun from a solution to which a pigment has been added.

PIGMENT FINISH. This denotes leather whose surface is coated with a material that contains pigment or other opaque material.

PIGMENT PADDING. Application of dyes to fabric by the padding process through an aqueous dispersion of the dye being used. Often used in vat dyeing. See PADDING.

PIGMENT PRINTING. Insoluble pigments are mixed with an albumen thickener and then applied to the cotton goods. The thickener fixes the color on the cloth after color has been set by steam in the steam chamber.

PIGMENT RAYON. This dull material has been made so by the addition of a finely divided pigment added to the rayon mixture prior to yarn spinning. The pigment becomes actually a part of the yarn when it is spun.

PIGMENT STYLE, PIGMENT METHOD. In the printing of cotton textiles, pigments are mixed with a thickener and applied to the goods. The thickener fixes the color on the goods after it has been set by steam in the chamber.

PIGMENT TAFFETA. See TAFFETA.

PIGSKIN. Merely the skin or hide from a domesticated pig. The term cannot be given to leather made from the flesh split of a pig skin.

PIK. A variable unit of measurement which ranges from 18 to 30 inches, and is used in the Far East and Africa for provincial measurements to suit some purpose.

PIKER. A trader in raw cotton who makes a quick transaction on small capital or on "a shoestring."

PILE. The raised loops or tufts that form all or a portion of the surface of fabric. Pile fabrics may be warp pile, filling pile, or knotted pile. Not to be confused with nap, the pile effect may be cut, uncut, looped or curled. Plush is pile fabric with a pile

of $\frac{1}{8}$ inch or more, while velvet has a pile less than $\frac{1}{8}$ inch. See Illustrated Section (Fabrics 74, 79, 80).

PILE, LASHED. The pile picks interlace with three warp ends between the floats in a "W" formation plan in this filling pile fabric. See PILE FABRIC WEAVING.

PILE CARPET. A carpet having a surface of cut or uncut pile, or a combination of the two.

PILE CRUSH. Depression of the pile effect in a floorcovering, caused by excessive walking or traffic on the face of the article. Is also noted on velvet, velveteen, and comparable pile fabrics, caused by abrasion and friction. Much used in testing pile fabrics for performance results. See Velvet, Velveteen.

PILE FABRIC. A material that, to some degree, resembles fur. The cloth may be cut or uncut. It has a nap on the face of the goods, or it can be made so that there will be long loops in the uncut type of material. Pile cloth may be soft or harsh in feel, have considerable body, and an appealing appearance.

Some common pile cloths include terry toweling, furniture covering, velvet, velveteen, panne velvet, corduroy, runners, rugs and carpets, mohair plush, car seat plush, straight plush and that used in automobile upholstery, imitation fur fabric, powder puff cloth, etc.

PILE FABRIC, CUT. A fabric made on the principles of pile weaving where the warp or the filling system of threads has been cut. There are two kinds of cut-pile fabrics, warp cut and filling cut. The cutting of a system of threads in the construction of the goods does away with a looped-pile fabric, where the pile threads are raised but not cut in order to give a fuzzy or bushy appearance on the face of the goods.

In the cutting of the pile in pile fabric, the threads in the cloth to be cut, so as to give the desired effect, are taken care of by the sharp, razorlike blade(s) located at one end of the reed in the loom. This tip or knife does not cut the warp immediately after the latter has been made to interlace with the filling, but cuts it some little distance from where the last pick has just been beaten into place.

The action follows:

1. A pick is placed into the fabric. Then the action of the wire or rod begins. This blade goes into the cloth but does not cut the warp at this point, for the shed in the weaving is open far enough to allow the blade to pass from one side of the loom to the other without any cutting action. As the loom continues to work, this blade

goes farther and farther away from the race plate of the loom and from the reed, as well. It remains part of the goods being woven.

2. When the blade has worked out its course and reached the limit of its weaving action, it is then ready to be automatically pulled back to the other side of the loom. This action is such that the knife edge, as it is pulled back through the fabric, actually cuts the warp threads that were looped over it. As these threads of pile warp are cut, the fibers in the yarns spring into a brush-life formation on the face of the goods.

3. The blade, in the continuance of its course, then goes into the shed of the loom again, and in time, it will cut the next set of warp ends that are looped over it when the blade is ready to be pulled back to the other side of the loom.

4. Thus, the warp threads are cut and the material is a cut-pile material with the pile running in the filling direction. The ends that are over the blade, obviously, are the ones that are cut and not those ends that are under the blade.

5. It should be realized that in obtaining this action, there must be two sheds in the loom movement—one for the wire and one for the ground weave, in consecutive order.

The three inches or so on the loom of uncut pile that lies in front of the reed, is necessary because there must be a sufficient length of fabric woven so that the interlooping of the warp and the filling threads will keep the material tightly interlaced. By this action, the warp, when it is cut, will be able to withstand the action without weakening any part of the material that is being woven in the loom.

Filling-pile fabrics are, if they are to be cut in the loom, cut by stationary knives set into the loom above the breast beam and attached to the harnesses. As the pick gradually works toward the breast beam away from the reed, it must pass over the sharp edges of the cutting knife or blade. Thus, the pile fabric is formed as the loops are cut. Corduroy, however, is cut after the goods have been woven and taken from the loom—a separate operation given to this filling-pile fabric. See Illustrated Section (Fabrics 70).

PILE FABRIC, LOOPED FILLING. The production of pile fabrics, in which the face is made up of loops of filling pile, depends on the construction of the weave, material used, and the difference between the reed width and finish width.

The weave is planned for one warp and two fillings, a pile and a ground

filling. The ground filling will interlace comparatively tight while the pile filling will interlace tightly where it is to be hidden and forms long floats on the face of the cloth, where the loops are to be produced.

Best results are obtained by using wool for the ground filling. This is because of the shrinking qualities of that fiber. The pile filling should be of loosely twisted mohair, wool of the Luster type, or other hair fibers. All of these may be steamed while on the bobbin, in order to "set" the filling and give it the tendency to curl when unwound.

The material is set wide in the reed, and when shrunken in, the ground filling shortens by shrinking, while the mohair or Luster wool does not shorten. Instead they will form into curls, nubs, or loops, where they floated on the face of the construction.

The following lay-out would show the construction data of a cloth in this class.

Warp: 11 ends of 4/8s black cotton, then 3126 ends of 2/20s black cotton, then 11 ends of 4/8s black cotton, for the listing. This would make 22 ends of selvage altogether. The warp would be reeded two ends per dent in an 18.5 reed, making 84.5 inches inside of the selvage. Material would be finished at 56 inches.

Filling: 15 picks of No. 2 mohair for the pile, and 15 picks of 12 cut wool for the ground weave.

PILE FABRIC LOOM. See LOOM AND WEAVING.

PILE FABRIC WEAVING. Double-plush weaving is the manufacture of two distinct fabrics at the same time. The number of ground-ends in both the top and the bottom pieces must be evenly divided so that, in warping or beaming, sufficient ends are arranged on the beam to form two distinct sheds —top and bottom. The same is true of the pile ends when there is more than one pile end in one dent or reed split.

One pile end is used in one dent, first weaving over one pick in the top piece and then weaving under one pick in the bottom piece, thereby forming a top shed for the top shuttle, and the bottom shuttle being in the ground warp shed.

The pile harness is down on the second pick, thereby forming a bottom shed for the bottom shuttle, while the top shuttle is in the ground warp shed. This action is exactly the same in the second dent with the pile warp end offset by one pick.

The fabric is woven double until it reaches the breast beam; then it is cut by a knife, and both the top and the bottom cloths are of the same construc-

tion. Before it is woven in fabric, the pile yarn passes over or through various loom parts such as the plush roll, tension bars, stop motions, lease rods, through the harness and reed, over the breast beam, and then is cut by means of a knife which travels across the loom from side to side cutting the pile exactly in the center between the top and the bottom piece. Each piece is then taken up on pin rolls and it then

1. THE "V" WEAVE

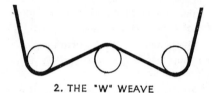

2. THE "W" WEAVE

3. THE FOUR-PICK TUFT CONSTRUCTION

continues on to the take-up rolls. See Illustrated Section.

Figure #1 is a cross-section view of a two-pick or "V" weave, the pile end going over two picks to form a repeat. In a two-pick or "V" weave, the tuft or pile end is held in or kept from pushing through the back by means of a very thin application of rubber coating. When a coating is not used, a cover warp (that is, two cotton ground ends binding exactly the same as the pile end) is used plus the two regular ground ends already shown in Figure #1.

These two ends cover the pile end on the back of the fabric and keep the tuft from pushing out. A very thin rubber coating on the back is most commonly used as a means for anchorage. Fabrics of these types of weaves are used in automobile and furniture upholstery, velvets, and draperies.

Another common plush weave is the "W" weave that repeats on three picks and is woven one or two ends per reed dent. There is also a lister weave which is woven two pile ends per dent and repeats on 8 picks to form a four-pick tuft. Fabrics which use this type of construction are plushes on high-pile fabrics to be used in toys, slippers, imitation fur fabrics, etc. See Illustrated Section.

← Warp
← Filling

Uncut pile fabric

← Warp
← Filling

Cut pile fabric

← Warp
← Filling

Pile fabric weaving to show the "V" interlacing to hold pile yarn in place

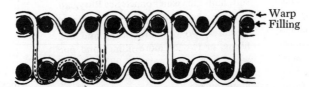

← Warp
← Filling

Pile fabric weaving to show the "W" interlacing to hold pile yarn in place. This formation is firmer than the "V" formation.

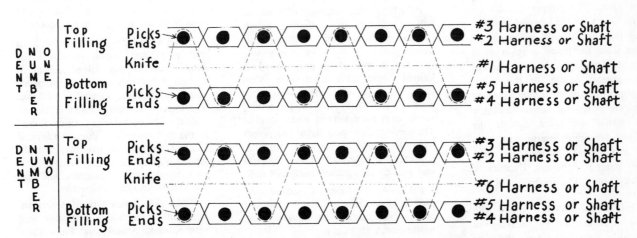

SIDE VIEW OF PILE FABRIC WEAVING

PILE HEIGHT. The length of the pile yarn or tuft as it rises from the base of backing of a carpet.

PILE LINER. When yarn is tufted there is usually a loop left at the top of the yarn. In making pile liner, these loops are sheared off to present upright, straight yarn. The fibers in the yarn are then manipulated into a dense mass surface resembling fur. Dynel and Verel, modacrylic fibers, are used since they give the best effects and results. Printing of the fabric provides the simulation of animal fur. In final finishing, the surface of the goods may be made smooth and even or given a sculptured effect.

"PILE - MATIC" SHUTTLELESS LOOM. This loom is especially engineered to make high-pile plush fabrics, upholstery, and other fabrics such as velour, chenille, mohair, velvet, and simulated fur. The loom is made from a combination of designs by Van de Wiele and Dornier, West Germany. Fabric width can be as much as 62 inches and multi-colored effects are obtained by use of both right and left color selectors. The rapiers go through the full length of the shed and catch the filling or weft yarn at the opposite side and then pull the yarn through the bottom shed from right to left and for the top shed from left to right. Yarns of different counts and irregular twists can be used in original effects.

Because there is not any center shed transfer of the wefts, the rubbing or friction which occurs in weaving looms with a center shed transfer is eliminated in this loom, thereby doing away with any possible chance of yarn damage or broken ends.

There is no crankshaft on this loom. When the machine is reversed, the gripper needles are held automatically outside the sheds for easier location of broken yarn. The gripper needles remain in time with the weaving machine so that they are always in the correct position when the frame is again set in motion. This prevents warp end damage by the gripper needles or the heads. Each gripper needle has its own guiding system composed of seven eccentric rollers which are fitted outside the sheds and are adjustable in both horizontal and vertical planes. The agent for this loom is Atkinson, Haserick & Company, Inc., Framingham, Massachusetts.

PILE-ON-PILE. Velvets made with varying pile heights by weaving or shearing. In warp pile fabrics the wires used have varying thicknesses along their length, thereby producing long pile in the thick places and short pile in the thin places.

In filling pile cloths, the floats will vary in length. Short floats will give a short pile effect; long floats will produce a longer pile.

To obtain a pattern of this type through finishing, part of the pile is pressed down by embossed rollers or blocks. That portion of the pile re-remaining upright is then sheared to an even nap. The pressed areas are then brushed upwards to form the design or motif.

PILEUM. A tight-fitting felt cap worn by the Greeks and Romans at meal time, theatrical performances, and festivals. Comes from the Greek, pilos, which signifies a covering or cap and is considered a symbol of liberty.

PILEUS. A felt, rimless type of headgear, this article was originally worn by the Romans and was a forerunner of the present day beret. It was a cross between the wide brim hat of the Greeks and the soft, limp Phrygian bonnet. See Phrygian.

PILE WEAVE CONSTRUCTION. Requires two or more warps and one filling, or two or more fillings and one warp. The extra warp or filling, called the "pile" warp or filling, forms the loops on the face of the fabric. These loops may be cut or uncut as desired. If the loops are cut, it has been done by knife blades which are attached to the loom, except in fine velvets, in which this is a separate process.

PILE YARN. See PILE WEAVE CONSTRUCTION.

PILE YARN, DEAD. Refers to a Wilton carpet, usually having a figured motif, in which the yarns are hidden in the backing structure when not forming a pile tuft effect on the face of the rug. Because of the use of these hidden layers of yarn, Wilton is referred to as "the rug of hidden value."

PILLING. The tendency of fibers to ball or roll up. It is common in all fabrics which are knitted from yarns which possess a hairy or wooly surface but is particularly pronounced in knitted fabric made from spun nylon yarn. Pilling results when loose fiber ends escape from low-twist knitting yarns spun on relatively short staples. The loose ends, especially at the points where the fabric is exposed to rubbing, collect on the surface of the material and ball up into rather unsightly fluff.

PILLOW. Cushion or stuffed pad used in lacemaking to hold designs and bobbin. See PILLOW OR BOBBIN LACE, HANDMADE.

PILLOW BAR. The groundwork in lace in which the bars may be plain or of a small pearl edging; consists of irregular groups of threads drawn from one part of the motif to another area.

PILLOWCASE LINEN. Plain-weave, high-count, good texture, bleached linen. Yarn is very smooth and has high count of turns of twist per inch.

Launders easily and well, sheds dirt, has cool feel and appearance, is strong and durable. Very desirable cloth. Cotton fabric is made to simulate the linen fabric.

PILLOW CORD. Used to bind the edges of fancy pillows, certain laces, and some novelty work, it is done with brightly colored thread of cotton, acetate, nylon, silk, etc.

PILLOW LACE. See PILLOW OR BOBBIN LACE.

PILLOW OR BOBBIN LACE, HANDMADE. Lace made on a pillow from bobbin threads interwoven and held to the pattern on the pillow by pins. The number of bobbins in a single pattern may be a few, or several hundred.

PILLOW SHAM. An ornamental covering of any sort laid over a pillow when not in use.

PILLOW TUBING. Woven on a cam loom, this cotton double-cloth is stitched while weaving on both sides, forming a tube. The cloth is bleached, cut into required lengths, and sewed at one end while the other is open and hemmed. Widths are from 18 to 24 inches, and circumference runs from 42 to 45 inches. Carded yarn is used chiefly. The texture is good, and compact.

PILOT CLOTH. Uniform cloth that is heavy, bulky, and strongly made. Wool is the fiber used, and the cloth is on the order of the average kersey. It is not as lustrous as the latter cloth. The material is drab in finish and is dyed navy blue or some dark color. An ideal cloth for seafaring men. The weight runs from 20 to 30 or more ounces.

PIMA COTTON. One of the cottons that years ago helped to sound the death knell for Sea Island cotton. It is named for this county in Arizona, and is raised there, as well as in Texas and lower California. Pima is classed with the best of Arizona cottons. Raised in the Salt River and Yuma Valleys, it is ideal for use in tire fabric, high-grade shirting. Of average staple, it is very tough, strong, smooth, and has the best of working properties.

PIMA S-1. A new type of American-Egyptian cotton which compares well with Karnak, Amsak, and Pima 32.

PIMA 32. An American cotton developed by crossing "S x P," "Pima," and "Giza 7," an Egyptian variety. This cotton is gradually replacing Amsak, a former favorite among cotton growers.

PINA CLOTH. A transparent, hand-woven cloth made in the Philippines. Made from the fibers of the pineapple plant, it is mixed with silk, at times, and simulates mousseline de soie.

Embroidered pina is highly prized as an heirloom.

Pina lace compares well with genuine European laces.

The fiber itself is obtained from pulp that is dried and joined end-to-end; then the yarn is woven in plain effect to make fabric. Hand-pounding of the fabric aids to give the final, appealing appearance.

PINAFORE. A sleeveless garment that can be worn by itself in warm weather, but is often used as an apron to protect wearing apparel from becoming soiled. Originally intended for children's wear, the attractive modern designs have caused it to become popular in women's wear.

PIN APRON. See LIFTING APRON.

PIN APRON STRIPPER. See DOFFER BEATER.

PINARA COTTON. A type of Peruvian cotton.

PIN BONE LACE. A bone or thorn pin, or the regulation pin used today, is used to effect the bobbin work on this type of pillow lace.

PINCHBACK COAT. Jacket or coat —for men's or women's wear—which is pleated but otherwise fits snugly to the back.

PIN CHECK. 1. A minute check-effect caused by a combination of weave and color. Popular in certain clear-finish worsteds for men's suiting and women's wear mannish-type worsted suiting.

2. Cotton cloth used as work clothes in which the effect shows white dots in straight rows, vertically and horizontally on blue background.

3. A fine rayon or acetate fabric made with different colored yarns. The checks are very small, and the fabric gives good service.

PINCH FRONT. Any type of headgear in which the crown is pinched at the front. Sometimes called a centerdent.

PIN COP. The regulation size cop ready for the shuttle.

PIN COPS. Small-size cops used for winding cotton filling yarn.

PIN CUSHION. A stuffed piece of material, usually about two inches square, into which pins are placed for use and convenience.

PIN CYLINDER. A small steel cylinder which has four or more rows

of heavy steel lags or spikes situated close to the top of a lifting apron. The function of the cylinder is to knock back into the hopper feed unruly clumps of stock that might cause trouble in manipulation. The use of a cylinder of this sort assures an even-feeding of cotton stock to the feed apron of the machine in question. Other names include combing roll, evener roll, spike roll, stripper comb, stripper roll, etc.

PIN DOT. The smallest dot used on textile fabrics. See POLKA DOT.

PIN DRAFTING. It extends the field of pin control over lightweight sliver to the reducer stage in the Bradford system of making worsted yarn, the fore-finisher of the French system, and the long-draft roving frame of the abbreviated or the American system of spinning yarn. The pin drafter represents an advanced design of screw gill, incorporating functions of the open-type drawing machine as well. The main points of difference between the pin drafter and a gill box are the extra long faller bed, high speed faller action, and the flat pins of the pin drafter. It has no back-draft rollers, consequently there are no ratch lengths to be set.

The pin drafter handles all-wool stock, blends of wool with man-made cut staple, and those types of 100 per cent man-made cut staple possessing induced or inherent crimp.

PINEAPPLE CLOTH. See PINA CLOTH.

PINEAPPLE FIBER. Found in China, Mexico, and Central American countries, it is long, white, and silken. It comes from the leaves of the plant and serves as a substitute for silk and cotton, and may be used in mixes of cotton and wool. The fiber is used in the manufacture of the well-known, expensive pina cloth of the Philippine Islands, a fabric high in texture and very durable. Labor costs prohibit the raising of the fiber in the United States.

PINEAPPLE STITCH. A stitch which creates an oval design on knitted fabric which simulates the shape of the pineapple.

PINE OIL. A steam distillation by-product obtained in the manufacture of turpentine and rosin from pine stumps.

PINE TREE FABRIC. A heavy, strong, well-wearing, fulled woolen fabric used in cold climates for clothing such as Mackinacs, ulsters, coatings, parkas, etc. Much of this fabric is used along the Canadian-American border into the "wilds of Canada." The material may be in plain colors, or in checks, plaids, etc.

PINK. A very light pale red color, on the blue or purple side, of high brilliance and low saturation.

PINK BOLL ROT. See ANTHRACNOSE.

PINK BOLLWORM. This destructive pest bores into the flowers or bolls of cotton. The name comes from the pinkish larva of a dark brown moth.

PINKED SEAM. A seam, the waste edge of which has been cut with a serrated edge to reduce the tendency of the material to ravel.

PINKING. The process of finishing a seam to prevent raveling. It is done by a pinking scissors or machine. The result is a saw-like edge which runs the length of the seam.

PINKING MACHINE. An apparatus that cuts fabric with a blade or cutter to produce a serrated or pinked edge.

PINKING SHEARS. A special type of shears that give the edges of material a zigzag effect as it cuts. This prevents raveling of the edges and gives it a finish at the same time.

PINNA, PINNA SILK. See BYSSUS SILK.

PINNI. A native reddish-brown cotton grown in Burma serves as the raw material for this coarse Indian fabric made on the hand looms in the cottage industries of India.

PINOKPOK. Made in the Philippines from abaca, this woven cloth undergoes much hand-pounding until it takes on the appearance of linen. May be used for high-quality sportswear.

PIN RIB. Fabric in which fine cords appear in the warp or filling. Observed in madras shirting, some dress goods. Narrow corduroy is spoken of as pin wale because these cord or pile effects are fine in structure and there are many of them in one inch of the goods.

PIN SEAL, PIN GRAIN. Either term is applied to natural grain or high-grade sealskin tanned for fancy leather. The effect is simulated on sheepskin, goatskin, calfskin, and cowhide, but they should be described as "pin-grain sheepskin," etc.

PIN STRIPE. 1. Cotton work-clothes fabric which has closely spaced white stripes on a dark background, usually blue or brown. 2. Narrow, single end stripe used to ornament worsted fabric; may be of mercerized cotton, rayon, spun silk or "treated" yarn.

PIN STRIPES. The narrowest of all stripes noted in textile fabrics; they are about the size of a pin scratch. Spun silk, silk, or rayon yarns are usually found in pin-stripe fabrics in the woolen and worsted suiting trade, chiefly in the case of worsteds.

PIN TRASH. Minute particles of trash found in lint cotton.

PIN WALE. Corduroy made with very narrow ribs or wales. See PIN RIB.

PINWORK. Done in needle-point lace, it is the raising of fine stitches from the surface of the motif to add beauty to the product.

PIPING. 1. A narrow bias fold or a cord used in finishing edges; any edge extending from another. Much used in dressmaking. 2. Narrow piece of leather or fabric sewed into seam form or an edge of a shoe for finish.

PIQUÉ. From the French. A cloth simulating an older cloth of pleated weave appearance. A true piqué is characterized by heavy corded, ribbed, or ridged wales in the filling direction.

In its best and original form, two warps (face and back) and three fillings (face, back, and stuffer) are employed. As is usual with double cloths, the face-warp and the face-filling interweave for the face effect, bound down at spaced points by the back warp and the back filling, which also serve to restrict displacement of the heavy stuffer picks when they are used. Stuffers will create a full, rounded rib effect by pressure under the face system of threads; they never appear on the face of the goods but occupy a position between the face and back systems of yarn. Another desirable function of the stuffer threads is the addition of substance and weight to the fabric.

The piqué fabric, medium to heavy in weight, is generally made of combed face yarn and carded back and stuffer yarns. It is very durable, launders well, and is rather expensive for a cotton material since it requires relatively high pickage and the use of the Jacquard or dobby box loom with slower than regular loom speed. The type of loom has no effect on the characteristic appearance of the cloth.

The so-called Bedford Cord, which is strictly a piqué effect in a warp-wise direction, is many times loosely referred to as "piqué"; this is a misnomer, and both terms should be used correctly to avoid confusion.

In recent years, a twill weave with a few ends face-up, alternating with a few ends face-down, has appeared in rayon fabrics called piqué. However, this is a misnomer.

Piqué is used for collar and cuff sets, infants' coats and bonnets, neckwear, shirts, vests, and women's and children's wear. See BEDFORD CORD.

See Illustrated Section (Fabrics 53).

PIQUET. French term for imitation gauze, made by omitting one warp end in every three or four ends.

PIQUÉ, WARP KNITTED. It is made with two guide bars in order to show pronounced cord effects in the vertical direction. The areas between the cords are obtained by omitting one or more yarns from the guide bar which is making the smaller underlap.

PIQUÉ VOILE. A piqué motif or effect that is noted in some voile fabric.

PIQUÉ WEAVE, WARP. Also known, very often, as Bedford Cord, the appearance of this weave is the corded, ribbed, or ridged wales running in the warp direction. There are two. wales in each repeat of the weave. The weave can be broken down into its essential parts which are a combination of plain weave and a 3-up and 1-down twill. Any reasonable number of twill ends may be used, but generally each wale is separated by only two plain ends to define the sides of the cord or wale.

There are two accepted ways of combining. Weave Number 1 begins at the left with one end of plain weave followed by the first and second movements of a 3-up and 1-down twill, repeated. Two ends of plain weave are next in order followed by the third and fourth movements of the twill effect, repeated. One end of plain weave completes the action. In this weave, attention is called to the alternate binding of the plain weave opposing the twill.

Weave Number 2 is not only easier to weave but it also gives a better appearance to the woven fabric. This weave begins at the left with one plain end followed by the first and third movements of the 3-up and 1-down twill, repeated; two ends of plain are followed by the second and fourth movements of the twill, repeated; finally, one end of plain completes the weave. As previously stated, attention should be given to the alternate binding of the plain weave opposing the twill.

Stuffer ends, which are usually heavier than the face ends, are often used, as in the case of piqué, to give round-

ness to the cord and to add weight to the fabric. In weaving, they follow, to some extent, the twill movements in the respective wales; they must be "down" for all face picks and "up" over all back picks when being woven. See BEDFORD CORD.

PIRL THREAD. A metallic thread made spiral.

PIRN. 1. Scotch term for a small spindle used in weaving tweed and kindred fabrics.

2. A wooden bobbin which sets into the shuttle. It has a chase, nose or tapering tip, like a cop, which enables the yarn to come off or unwind easily.

3. The bobbin on a spinning wheel.

4. A British term rarely used here meaning a paper tube used on a shuttle spindle.

PISHTEH. Biblical term for flax and linen.

PITA, PITA FLOJA. Plant raised in Central and South America, and Mexico. A pineapple, but larger than the common species. The creamy white fiber ranges from 5 to 8 feet in length, is strong and resistant to deterioration by sea water. Other names for this agave-aloe fiber, obtained from the plant leaves, are silk grass, wild pineapple, pita de corojo.

PITAMBAR. Silk warp and woolen filling are used in this Indian cloth made with a plain or ordinary ground construction enhanced by rather large floral motifs. Bizarre colorings feature the fabric, which serves as ceremonial fabric at festivals and religious ceremonies. It is used by the Brahmins and the Hindus. Imitation cotton prints of the woven fabrics are also known by this term. See DHOOTIES.

PITCH. Means the number of warp yarns per inch crosswise of the loom. It is usually stated in relation to 27 inch or 3/4 width. Standard pitch for Wilton is 256, Axminster 189.

PITCH, MACHINE. The size of the threads on a screw, and the size of the teeth on a gear wheel. In measuring the pitch of screws, the distance from the center of one thread to the center of the next thread is taken. In measuring the pitch of gear wheels, the distance from the center of one tooth to the center of the next tooth is taken at a point a little less than halfway down the tooth.

PITCHY WOOL. Grease wool.

PITEIRA. Used in connection with other fibers to improve the color of rope. This nearly white fiber, also known as Mauritius hemp, is raised in Brazil, India, Mauritius, and Natal.

PITRE. A hard bast fiber obtained from the leaves of the plant of this name found in the Caribbean area. Similar to henequen, the fiber is softer and finer, and is prepared by hand. Used for cordage, bagging, sacks, etc. See CABULLA; CAJUN; CANTALA; MAGUEY; PITA.

PITTMAN COTTON. An early-maturing Louisiana cotton of one-inch staple and lint-yield of about 31 per cent. This cluster-boll cotton is also called Pittman Extra Prolific, Pittmann Improved.

PIZZO. A name for blond lace made in and around Genoa, Italy.

pK. Expression of the extent of the dissociation of an electrolyte; the negative logarithm of the ionization constant of a compound.

PLACARDER. French word meaning "to resist or to repel." It refers here to resist dyeing in which the motif does not take on the color because of the resist paste or agent used while the ground of the fabric takes on the color in this dyeing operation in a full resist printing process or method.

PLACKET. A strip of material about ten inches long and about 2½ inches wide. It is used to finish openings which enable the wearer to put on a garment with some degree of ease. It is usually cut on the straight grain. A zipper is sometimes used in place of the placket.

PLACKET SHIRT. See KNITTED SHIRTS; MEN'S AND WOMEN'S.

PLAID. A yarn or skein-dyed fabric consisting of colored bars crossing each other to form varied squares or oblongs; a plaid makes a one-way or an all-over design. Beautiful color combinations may be derived from proper matching of the squares at the seams. Plaids are used in gingham, dress goods, coating, shirting, plaid back overcoating, ribbon, suiting, blankets, and robes. Other meanings include a traveling rug or shawl, so-called because the designs are usually in plaid effect, and a Scotch kilt.

PLAID BACK. A light, medium, or heavy overcoating made on the double-cloth principle—two systems of warp and filling, with a binder warp or filling arrangement. The underside of the cloth is a plaid—a series of cross stripes that form a dull or vivid effect. Weight, warmth, and the covering up of the interlacings are features of the material. Plaid backs take the place of linings in some of the cloths used for coating material.

PLAID FLANNEL. Plain or twill flannel, made of cotton, wool, or man-made fiber and natural fiber combinations, which shows plaid effect. Most of the fabric today is given a soft nap and

is used for shirting. Popular in collegiate circles.

PLAIDS. Popular method in textile design used to obtain patterns by means of several colors, according to some plan or motif. A true plaid is one which has the same arrangement of colors in warp and filling, and produces a series of checks, made by crossing each other in the warp with different colors of filling.

The general action of colors in a plaid is to decrease the contrast among the colors. With tones of a color, it is necessary to have more tone contrast, because when the light and dark tones cross each other, a new tone is seen. Consequently, there must be sufficient contrast to preserve the check appearance of the pattern.

The best combinations are formed with analogous colors because where different colors cross each other, new ones are obtained. These are formed by the mixture of original colors used.

It is necessary, also, that a good contrast of tone be present in order to keep the plaid from having a smeary appearance.

The average plaid will form large or small squares of colors. Brilliancy and good color blending must be present to attract the eye. Scotch plaids bring out the technique of color design to perfection. Plaids have a rather bold, outstanding appearance that is attractive.

PLAIDS, COMPLEMENTARY COLOR IN. This color effect involves two complementaries which cross each other in the goods. In this type, each color seems to appear gray, and this will tend to give the entire pattern a rather hazy appearance. To avert this unpleasant effect, the complementaries must be made stronger in color so that they will offset this smeared appearance and give a good cleavage in tone between them. Reds and greens cause the most trouble, because it is possible to have both of them at about the same degree of tone.

PLAIN, TWILL, AND SATIN WEAVES, INTERLACING ARRANGEMENT OF. See Illustrated Section. See also same Section under Fabrics 1, 20, 32, 45, 46. See also WEAVE and Tables there, pp. 1015 ff.

PLAINBACK. A worsted fabric made of single yarn. The face is of twill weave; the back of the cloth is made of plain weave. It is a double cloth.

PLAIN BRAID. Flat braid made of three threads.

PLAIN EDGE. Finish given to the edge of a garment which shows no rows of stitching on the outer surface. It is obtained by using a felling stitch

or a blind stitch.

PLAIN FINISH. Refers to cotton cloth in which no mercerization has been given. The term, however, is very broad and has many obvious m nin s in the trade.

PLAIN GAUZE. A doup-woven cotton where the crossing threads cover the base warp threads always in the same direction. Used for bandages.

PLAIN KNIT, FLAT KNIT. The simplest of knit structures, as in the case of hosiery and jersey fabric. It consists of vertical rows that are visible on the face of the goods and crosswise lines which are observed on the back of the fabric.

PLAIN LAID ROPE. Hemp or Manila rope made from three strands of right-hand twist.

PLAIN LOOM. The first type of power loom to be developed and first operated in Southbridge, Massachusetts, in 1823. By 1840, William Crompton brought out a fancy power loom that could be used in making designed cloth. This loom could make from 45 to 85 picks per minute. From 1840 onward hand looms began to wane as the favored type of weaving machine. The use of power sounded the death knell of the old-time hand machine. Mass production was now at hand. William Crompton, Lucius Knowles, and Erastus Bigelow were the three pioneers in the loom industry in New England. They placed American weaving, in time, on a par with British weaving. The first worsted cloth loom was brought out in Ballardvale, Massachusetts, in 1843.

The plain type of loom, run by power, is for making simple construction cloth. These looms will make the same type of cloth, year in and year out, for the entire career of the machines. They are used on staple materials. Plain, twill, and satin weaves are used in the constructions made on this type of loom. Baskets, ribs, and a few other small-repeat designs may be made. Cloth made on this loom will usually run from two- to eight-harness in construction.

Production on the loom is high, and with the automatic devices to aid this a weaver may be assigned to handle several looms at once. It is possible to have a weaver take care of twenty-four or more of these looms.

Cloth made on these looms might include homespun, tweed, balmacaan cloth, georgette, crepe de Chine, taffeta, organdy, voile, handkerchief linen, batiste, print cloths, tobacco cloths, broadcloth, muslin, lawn, cambric, pajama checks, etc.

Plain looms are simple in construction. It may be said that they are hand looms developed to power perfection in every respect to meet the demands of production of today.

PLAINS. Broad term for cottons made with average or ordinary yarn; fabric is always plain woven.

PLAIN SEAM. The most commonly used seam to put garment sections together. The sections are stitched on the seam line, raw edges are overcast, and the seam pressed open. In some instances, both edges are overcast together.

PLAIN STITCH. Same as jersey knitting stitch.

PLAIN WEAVE. There is only one plain weave, and it repeats on two warp ends and two filling picks. The construction is one raiser and one sinker on each thread. The second thread weaves the opposite of the first. The effect is a checkerboard. When the first thread is "up," the second thread is "down." The plain weave is written $\frac{1}{1}$ and is read as "one-up and one-down."

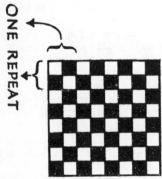

This weave is 4 repeats high, 4 repeats wide.

About 80 per cent of all woven fabric is made with plain weave, which affords the tightest possible interlacing between the warp and the filling yarns. See Illustrated Section. See also, same Section, Fabrics 1.

PLAIN WEAVE VARIATIONS.

1. CHAMBRAY: Entire warp is one or more colors; filling is always white; e.g., blue warp and white filling.

2. CREPE: By having the entire warp or filling made of crepe yarn, a crinkled effect is achieved. Crepe yarn is given a special twist to get the pebbled effect.

3. DIMITY: The warp yarn is arranged in such a manner that a white stripe effect is made. It may be accomplished by the manner of reeding the warp or by introducing cord threads running in the direction of the warp, or in the direction of both the warp and filling.

4. GINGHAM: By introducing dyed yarns at given intervals in both warp and filling, check or block effects of color are achieved.

5. MADRAS: Dyed yarns are introduced at given intervals in the warp in stripe formation. These stripe effects may be of plain or other weaves.

6. SEERSUCKER: By introducing yarns of different tensions at certain intervals in the warp, a crinkled or crepe stripe effect results. The effect is further enhanced by the use of two warp beams.

7. TAFFETA: By having filling yarns slightly heavier or bulkier than the warp ends, a faille effect is produced. Taffeta is made from the plain weave which is sometimes referred to as a tabby weave.

PLAIN WOOL. That which is practically devoid of crimpiness or waviness.

PLAITED FABRIC. It is made with a single yarn interlacing freely to make lace or some porous material. More than one yarn may be run into the machine, but the action is that of a single yarn entering the braiding or lace frame.

Plaited or lace fabrics can also be made on the idea of plaiting threads according to some plan or motif. Designs are often balanced geometrically, and in some instances are symmetrical. Some plaited fabrics are shoelaces, lace, curtains, marquisettes, gauze, doilies, bedspreads, counterpanes, runners, and veiling.

PLAITED STITCH. A needlework stitch that makes a basket or a herringbone effect.

PLAITING. Several meanings:

1. Also known as pleating, it is the arrangement of cloth in plaits or folds.

2. The felting of wool and fur fibers for hat bodies, by means of heat, steam, moisture, pressure, and pouncing. Shellac is sometimes used when stiff finishes are wanted, as in the case of derby hats.

3. The principle of knitting two different yarns in such a manner that the one yarn becomes the face of the goods and the other one the back of the material.

PLAIT, PLEAT. Several meanings:

1. The fold of fabric laid back flat, usually lengthwise. It is made singly or in groups for decoration or to hold in width of garment.

2. Braid, as of hair or straw.

3. A flattened gather or fold; an overlapping fold made by doubling cloth into narrow strips or folds upon itself.

PLANTED COLORS. In weaving Wilton rugs it is often desired to show more colors on the surface than there are frames or trays. These extra colors are taken care of by using part of the space in one or more of the frames which may have idle spools. The colors will be fed into the loom only in a direct line forward, thereby causing the figures to show such extra colors in a straight line throughout the material.

PLANTING. Usually, a Wilton carpet will have the same number of colors in the design as there are frames— however, by a method called planting, more than one color can be used in each frame and thus increase the number of colors in the design.

PLANT MANAGER, APPAREL. One who supervises and directs all the operations involved in manufacturing, from the fabric and cut garment to the finished product; through the section foreman, he projects his knowledge and understanding of manufacturing problems. The manager must know how to manage employees; must know plant layout and the selection of machines and equipment.

The assistant plant manager aids the plant manager in all his duties and keeps records of production and schedules.

The foreman plans the department or division activities, receives piece goods, fills orders, records cloth yardage used and the cost per garment; supervises marking and machine cutting.

The assistant foreman assists the foreman in his duties. He keeps records and supervises smaller sections of the larger departments.

PLASTACELLE. Cellulose acetate plastic used in making airplane cowlings, decorative jewelry, musical instruments, buttons, lamp shades, playing cards. In powder form, it can be molded under pressure. Some molded products are automobile steering wheels, combs, golf tees, frames for sunglasses.

PLASTAVON. A nonwoven fabric made from raw cotton, bleached, dyed, or tinted as desired, and bonded with synthetic resins which "spot-weld" the fibers into a uniform sheet. The resins used are clear, rubberlike in texture, strong, and transparent; they are resistant to solution in water and other common solvents. Uses of Plastavon include backing for leatherette and oilcloth, printed drapes, industrial buffing wheel surfaces for chrome, varnish, etc., throw-away napkins, polishing cloths for shoes, silver, etc. May also be used as wallpaper. Product of Avondale Mills, Inc.

PLASTIC. Any material, natural or synthetic, which may be fabricated into a variety of shapes or forms, usually by the application of heat and pressure. A plastic is one of a large group of organic compounds synthesized from cellulose, hydrocarbons, proteins, or resins, and capable of being cast, extruded, or molded into various shapes. From the Greek plastikos, which means "fit for molding."

PLASTICELL. A highly purified wood cellulose produced from selected wood species by a process which removes the noncellulose matter in such a manner as to retain the strength of the fiber. The bleaching process is carried out in such a way as to reach the highest degree of brightness and minimum of color without degradation of the chemical constituents. A Riordon Sales Corporation product, Plasticell is used as a filler in the manufacture of natural and colored urea and melamine plastics.

PLASTIC GOODS. Materials in sheet form, not woven, that are used for shower curtains, draperies, umbrellas, etc. They are either transparent, or white, or dyed in solution. Trade names include Krene, for shower curtains and draperies; Vinylite, for raincoats; Pliofilm, which has many similar uses.

PLASTICIZER. A chemical added to plastics to soften, increase malleability, or to make more readily deformable. There are several plasticizers on the market, and they are ideal with thermoplastic plastics such as camphor, high-boiling esters, and polynaphthalenes.

PLASTIC LAMINATE. A hard board or sheet made of one or several layers of textile fabric that has been impregnated with synthetic resin and compressed.

PLASTICS. Generally speaking, a plastic is an object which is capable of being molded or modeled, according to its softness and pliability, into some particular shape. The two chief types are thermoset plastics and thermoplastic plastics. The former is set permanently into shape or form by the use of heat; heat applied later may produce a charred formation without causing it to melt or lose shape. The latter type will soften when exposed to certain heats and will harden again when the source of heat has been removed.

FIVE MAJOR METHODS IN PROCESSING FROM THE RAW MATERIAL TO THE FINISHED PRODUCT:

1. MOLDING: A base powder (thermosetting or thermoplastic) is poured into steel molds; heat or pressure is applied, or both may be used in the treatment.

2. CASTING: This involves the pouring of liquid plastic into a mold or onto a belt or wheel where it is allowed to harden without the use of pressure.

3. EXTRUDING: Heat-softened plastic is forced through a spinneret or opening cut to the cross-section of the product; a continued or extended formation is produced.

4. CALENDERING: Heavy rollers are used to form thin sheets or film and to apply the plastic to fabric or to paper.

5. LAMINATING: Layers of cloth, metal, paper, plastic, or plywood are held together by plastic adhesives. Laminated plastic comes in plain or cut-to-shape form.

THERMOSETTING PLASTICS INCLUDE:

1. CASEIN TYPE: This can take a very high polish and comes in a wide range of opaque and translucent colors and shades. Properties include great strength, nonflammability, ability to withstand dry-cleaning, and resistance to chemicals and solvents. Examples are Ameroid and Galorn.

2. CAST PHENOLIC TYPE: This is available in opaque, transparent, and translucent colors. It is much used for general decorative purposes and does not have the strength of the molded phenolic type of plastic. Examples are Catalin and Marblette.

3. MELAMINE PLASTIC TYPE: This is heat resistant to 210° F.; other properties include light weight, colorfastness, scratch-resistance, and resistance to chemicals, oils, and water. It is available in a full-color range. The product is nontoxic, odorless, and tasteless. Examples include Melmac, Plaskon, Melamine, and Resimene.

4. MOLDED PHENOLIC TYPE: This type will resist heat up to 300° F. Properties include light weight, hardness, great strength and ability to hold a given shape; resistance to water and chemicals. The color range is limited to dark or mottled colors and effects. Examples include Bakelite, Indur, and Resinox.

5. POLYESTER TYPE: This very tough product is heat-resistant to 400° F. It is resistant to scuffing and abrasion and comes in clear to translucent colors. It is used in laminates, since they set at low or room temperatures with low or contact pressure. Examples include Laminac, Paraplex, Plaskon, Selectron and Vibrin.

6. UREA TYPE: This type comes in full color range and is colorfast; it is very hard, scratch-resistant, odorless, tasteless, nontoxic and will resist common chemicals and oils. This product is light in weight and does not possess the heat resistance of the Melamine Type. Examples include Beetle, Plaskon Urea, and Sylplast.

THERMOPLASTIC PLASTICS INCLUDE:

1. ACRYLIC TYPE: The term acrylic is used to designate an acid—$C_2H_4O_2$—which has a sharp, acrid odor. It is prepared from acrolein or from certain derivatives or from propionic acid. It is used in organic synthesis and in the manufacture of plastics; also known as propenoic acid. "Orlon," for example, is one type of acrylic and is classed as a polyacrylonitrile filament.

Properties of the acrylic type include lightness of weight, great breakage resistance, and lack of odor and taste. This type is nontoxic. It comes in opaque, translucent and transparent colors, all in a wide range. Acrylic plastic is not resistant to scratching, to very hot water, lighted cigarettes, alcohol, cleaning fluids, and nail polish. Examples include Lucite and Plexiglas.

2. CELLULOSIC TYPE: This type has five major groups:

Cellulose acetate: examples include Fibestos, Lumarith, Kodapak I, Plastacele, Tenite I, and Vuepak.

Cellulose acetate butyrate: examples include Kodapak II.

Cellulose nitrate: examples include Kodaloid, Nitron, and Pyralin.

Cellulose propionate: example is Forticel.

Ethyl cellulose: example is Ethocel.

Characteristics and properties of these types include low cost in mass production and uniformity in size, lightness of weight, toughness, and resistance to breakage; wide color range and high luster finish.

Cellulosics will resist heat to about 135° F.

The nitrate type is highly flammable, and its abrasion resistance is limited. This type is injured by nail polishes.

The acetate and butyrate types are affected by alcohol and alkalies.

The ethyl type is affected by cleaning fluids, fats, and oils.

3. NYLON THREAD TYPE: Properties include strength, toughness, long wear, resistance to most chemicals, and boiling without resoftening. Available in all colors. The representative name is nylon.

4. POLYETHYLENE TYPE: This will show heat resistance to 200° F. It is flexible at low temperatures, odorless, tasteless, nontoxic, moisture-proof, heat-sealable, and resistant to food acids and common chemicals. This type will show a milk-like translucence in molded objects and is transparent in film form. Pastel shades are used to a considerable degree for coloring. Examples include Bakelite Polyethylene, Polythene.

5. POLYSTYRENE TYPE: This comes in transparent form and in a wide range of clear, opaque, and translucent

colors. It is light in weight, tasteless, odorless, and nontoxic; when tapped it has a metallic resonance. Other characteristics include resistance to ordinary chemicals; it is weak to cleaning fluids, nail polish, and citrus fruit oils. Examples include Bakelite, Catalin Polystyrene, Lustrex, Plexene M, and Styron.

6. VINYL TYPE: This very important type has a wide range of uses—in the rigid form it is used for drawing instruments, floor tiles, and phonographic records; in the flexible form it is used for fabric coating, garment bags, shower curtains, upholstery and upholstery thread, and wallpaper. Properties include the following: great strength and toughness, lightness of weight, resistance to sunlight, to food action, alcohol and common chemicals. Vinyl must be given protection from boiling water, hot cooking utensils, moth repellents, and lacquered surfaces. Examples include Geon, Koroseal, Krene, Marvinol, Pliovic, Saran and Vinylite.

PLASTICS, DuPONT. E. I. duPont de Nemours & Company, Inc., Wilmington, Delaware produces the following plastics:

Vylor Nylon Filaments: These come in Series 0200, 0300, and 0500. 0200 is a standard industrial monofilament with a melting point of 496° F; 0300 has the lowest moisture regain of the series and possesses exceptional dimensional stability, melting point is 420° F. 0500 compares with 0200 but has a lower modulus and the melting point is 465° F.

Ruvea Ribbon Yarns: This is a registered trademark and comes in Series 0541, 0542, and 0242. 0541 has a low modulus for ease in weaving and the melting point if 465° F. 0242 has a melting point of 496° F.

Dymetrol: A registered trademark for continuous precision forms in Series 0224 and 0324. These forms have high tensile strength with precise tolerances. 0224 has a tensile strength of 62,000 psi, and the melting point is 496° F. 0324 has low moisture regain and tensile strength of 56,000 psi, and a melting point of 420° F.

PLASTICS, TYPES OF. There are two types of plastics: 1. Thermoplastic Type: This type is softened by heat and hardened into definite shape by cooling. An example would be in the case of nylon. This fiber or material can be heat-set, and then on reheating to a higher temperature it once more becomes plastic and can be reset into a different shape. Thermoplastic resins can be either "low-temperature" or "high-temperature" resins. 2. Thermosetting plastics are those which harden or set into permanent shape when heat

and pressure treatments are accorded them.

THERMOPLASTICS GROUP

Acrylic	Polyethylene
Casein	Polystyrene
Cellulose acetate	Polyfluoroethylene
Cellulose acetate	Shellac
butyrate	Polyvinyl alcohol
Cellulose nitrate	Polyvinyl acetate
Cellulose	Polyvinyl butyral
Proprionate	Polyvinyl chloride
Ethyl Cellulose	Polyvinyl chloride-
Polyamide	acetate

THERMOSETTINGS GROUP

Alkyds	Phenol-
Aniline-	formaldehyde
formaldehyde	Phenol-furfural
Melamine-	Polyester
formaldehyde	Urea-
	formaldehyde

RUBBER-LIKE PLASTICS GROUP

Nitril rubber/GR-A rubber
GRS rubber
Neoprene
Butyl rubber
Thiokol

Silicones are classed as special plastic.

PLASTRON. The front of a bodice or dress; made of lace, silk, rayon, or other suitable fabric.

PLASTYLON. Made of glass "wool" and miscellaneous waste fibers in long-staple form. In wool and cotton combinations it is processed into upholstery materials. Elasticity and heat- and moisture-resistance are good, and the tensile strength compares well with that of nylon. Product of Buechele & Kovacs A. G., Weiler, Austria.

PLAT. To interweave, intertwine, or to form by braiding or plaiting.

PLATED. 1. Knit fabric which has one kind of yarn on the face while another type is found on the back of the goods. A good example of plating is noted in the heels, soles, and toes of hosiery, where the yarn used on the back makes for greater comfort and better wear. See Illustrated Section (Knitting Stitches). 2. A cloth made from two different-colored yarns, in which their characteristics and qualities differ; one will show on the face while the other will appear on the back of the fabric, in accordance with the design laid out by the mill designer.

PLATED BALE. One which has a satisfactory exterior but which has an unsatisfactory interior, not detected by cursory examination.

PLATED HAT. A hat which has a face or nap of fur on a background body of wool.

PLATED HOSIERY. See PLATED,

PLAITING.

PLATED KNIT GOODS. See PLATING.

PLATED YARN. Yarn that has been coated with size. Another conception of the term refers to thread which has for its core a cheap yarn; around it is wound a thread of superior quality. The latter covers the core in entirety. An example would be a core of cotton with wool, worsted, or metallic thread wound around the cotton core. Plated yarns find use in blankets, robes, napped materials of various kinds, decorative fabrics, and in some overcoatings.

PLATE SINGEING. See SINGEING.

PLATILLE. A very fine, plain-woven, French linen cambric is known as platillé.

PLATING. Where two yarns of different quality or color are used in the same fabric. One system of yarn shows on the face, the other on the back of the goods. Plating is used extensively in making heavy sweater fabric and other bulky material.

PLATT LACE. Machine-made lace devoid of raised work; a very flat lace.

PLAUEN LACE. A term that is applied to all laces made in the city of this name in Saxony, Germany. It includes imitations of practically all point laces which are embroidered on a wool ground. The animal fiber content is destroyed later by burning-out with chemicals, vegetable fiber content is unaffected. In addition, certain chemicals are used to leave the silk content unscathed and to destroy the woolen content when the construction is composed of these two vegetable fibers.

PLEASAUNCE. A type of white gauze backed or striped with metallic threads or with a coating of gold or silver. It was used for gala occasions at the Court of Henry VIII, England. Some of the material was, at times, colored for special purposes.

PLEAT. The fold of fabric laid back flat, usually lengthwise. It is made singly or in groups for decoration or to hold in the width of the garment.

PLEAT, SUNBURST. A clustered pleat that extends from the center point, increasing in size as it spreads out.

PLEATED BOSOM. A soft or starched shirt front made with a pleat motif, used in formal or semi-formal day wear and semi-formal evening wear.

PLEATING. A double fold of material folded over and held in place by pressing. Pleats are formed in various widths, and are sometimes stitched to hold them in place.

PLEATING MACHINE. A motor-driven machine that forms pleats in cloth; a set of blades forms the pleats in the fabric; the pleats are pressed by a set of steam-heated rollers.

PLEAT PATTERN. A piece of heavy paper folded in the center, each half having corresponding creases; used as a pattern to shape pleats in fabric materials.

PLEAT TYPES. 1. *Box Pleats:* Two straight pleats turned away from each other. Folded edges are brought together on the wrong side and then stitched. 2. *Inverted Pleats:* Two straight pleats that are turned toward one another with the folds meeting. Folded edges are brought together on the right side and then stitched. 3. *Side or Knife Pleats:* The stitching of a long seam and extension of the seam. The pleat if folded on the long seam, with the extension lapping to the front. Stitching goes through all the layers of fabric.

PLEURES. A French term, pleurés means "dropped" or "fallen" wool obtained from sheep which have died of natural causes. A type of pulled wool.

PLEXIFORM. A new fabric developed by Malimo, a division of Crompton & Knowles Corporation, Worcester, Massachusetts, in the spring of 1968. The Malimo loom produces the fabric by stitching together webs of fibers that are set in the machine. The fabric may be bonded or unbonded.

PLEXIGLASS. See Lucite.

PLEXON. Plastic-coated yarns which have unusual tensile strength, flexibility, and adaptability. They can be made in a variety of deniers, types, and colors. Their resistance to water, mild acids, and perspiration is a great advantage in their use. Many types of fabrics may be made from them: woven, knitted, braided, crocheted, and knotted, and the yarns have been used successfully in the manufacture of handbags, belts, shoes, draperies, upholsteries. Product of Freydberg Bros.-Strauss, New York City.

PLEXON PIGTAIL. A pliable, colored plastic coated wire which has many uses in industry and is also used for decorative purposes. Pigtail is used by florists to bind corsages and for decoration; also used in boutonnières, buttons, jewelry, millinery ornamentation, etc. Waterproofed and unaffected by weather conditions.

PLEXUS. Any tangled mass of fibers.

PLICOSE. A heavy waterproof rayon fabric which remains soft and supple after treatment with a special chemical which renders it impervious to dust and dampness. Plicose can be sponged with a damp cloth over the surface for cleaning. The dyes used on the material are sun-fast. The fabric is coated on one side with a special pyroxylin plastic finish. Product of Harte & Co., New York City.

PLIED YARN. Made by twisting together two or more yarns.

PLIOFILM. Trade name for a lightweight, transparent, nonflammable protective covering for food and merchandise. The product is cleaned with soap and water. Made by Goodyear Tire and Rubber Co., Akron, Ohio.

PLIOFORM. Used for leak-proof tanks; contains crude rubber and hubber resin.

PLISSE. Cotton, acetate, or rayon fabric treated in a striped motif, or in spot formation, with a caustic soda solution which shrinks parts of the goods to provide the crinkled or pleated effect (plissé). The effect may or may not be removed after washing; this depends on the quality of the fabric or garment. Ironing, if done, should take place after the fabric is thoroughly dry in order to smooth out double thicknesses such as hems.

PLISSE SATIN. An eight-shift rayon satin made from one-way-twist crepe yarn throughout, in order to give a pleated effect on the goods (plissé). The cloth has about three times as many ends as picks—300 x 100, is an average texture.

PLOC FIBER. Cow hair used in varying amounts in coarse yarns to be used in shaggy homespuns or tweeds; also used for stuffing quilts.

P-LOOPER. A single chain stitch looping machine much used to loop sections of full-fashioned sweaters and collars to cut-and-sewn sweaters.

PLUCKED WOOL. Wool plucked from a sheep which has been dead a few days. Sometimes the term is applied to the skin wool.

PLUCKINGS. The short, cleansed fiber obtained at the delivery end of the flax scutching machine. It is at this point in processing flax that the worker dresses and squares the pieces of flax ready for selection and further processing into yarn. Pluckings are known as tow fibers.

PLUM-COLOR. A purplish black or deep purple, of low saturation and very low brilliance.

PLUMETIES. An interchangeable term with dotted swiss, and used to describe the special effects that are accomplished on hand looms. Finished at 32 inches, plumeties has many interesting and novel effects in dots, striped patterns, and drawn-thread styling.

PLUMETIS. A sheer woolen, rayon, or cotton fabric which has raised dots, figures or sprigs in relief on plain ground. The motif will show a feathery effect, as noted in embroidery tambour. The name comes from plume, French for feather.

PLUNKET. A grayish-blue woolen fabric popular during the reign of Henry VIII, England, 1509–1547.

PLUS FOURS. Loose, baggy knickerbockers which reach well below the knee, usually about four inches lower. The regulation knickerbocker is fastened by a band and clasp just below the knee and give a smart appearance to the wearer.

Knickers became popular prior to World War I and Plus Fours were made very popular in 1922 when the late Duke of Windsor, the abdicated King Edward VIII of Great Britain, came to our shores. He and Mayor James J. Walker were close friends in New York City and the Duke often appeared in these styles, hence their becoming the rage in the men's fashion world. Both baseball players and golfers took to knickers and Plus Fours avidly.

PLUSH. Comes from the French peluche (Latin pilus = hair) and is applied to fabrics where the pile is ⅛ inch or more. Plush has a longer or higher pile when compared with velvet. Silk, spun silk, rayon, cotton, wool, worsted, mohair, and other fibers can be used to manufacture plush. Much of the fabric finds use in the simulated fur fabric trade.

Woolen or worsted plush usually has good body. Cotton plush has a deeper, softer pile when compared with either velvet or velours. Rayon plush simulates cotton plush and both are used for powder puffs, upholstery, coating and other apparel. See Illustrated Section (Fabric 75).

PLUSH, KNITTED. Knit cloth with a looped pile which shows on the reverse side of some or all stitches. Plush loops are really elongated sinker loops of the yarn which lie on the back of a plated fabric.

PLUSH, SHAM. There are two ways to obtain this fabric. One is by the use of softly spun woolen filling which will take on a high nap when teaseled or napped by a roller spiraled with card clothing wire. The other method is to use chenille filling in the material which provides the effect. The fabric is made to simulate a plush cloth.

PLUSH, SINGLE. This is not a woven pile fabric but a knitted material so constructed that one yarn appears solely on the back and another only on the face. It is given a napped finish and used for underwear chiefly in cold climates.

PLUSH, WOOLEN. Woolen or worsted pile cloth, the pile being ⅛ inch or more in height. This plush has many well-known uses and is an exaggerated form of velvet. It is compact and bristly. Made in silk, cotton, mohair and combinations of fibers, as well as in wool or worsted.

PLUSH LOOM. Used for weaving pile cloths, velvets, velveteens, plushes of all types, upholstery cloth, powder puff cloth, etc. The pile effect is brought about by the use of a blade, or wires that enter the cloth on the same principle as the pick of the filling.

The cutting blade, or wires, if they have a sharp blade at the one tip, will make a cut pile material. If there is no blade at the tip of the rod wire, the fabric will be called an un-cut pile fabric. Cloths may have the pile effect in the warp or filling direction, and some few fabrics have the pile running in both directions. This is sometimes noted in corduroy. See Illustrated Section.

PLUSH VELVETEEN. A cotton imitation of silk velveteen. It is used as polishing material on silverware.

PLUS-X. Patented process of J.P. Stevens & Company, Inc., New York City, for imparting stretch to all-wool and wool-blend fabrics. The process applies a permanent, accordion-like crimp into the fabrics prior to dyeing and finishing the goods.

PLY. 1. The number of individual yarns twisted together to make a composite yarn; a *six-ply sevens* would mean that six single yarns of a count of seven are plied together to give a composite yarn of 6/7s. 2. When the term is applied to cloth it means the number of layers of fabric combined to give the composite fabric. A three-ply webbing would mean that three single cloths are plied together by stitching yarns to give the finished fabric.

PLY WEAVE. Any cloth made from more than one set of warp and filling threads may be classed as being made on a ply-weave construction. In the narrow sense, however, the term is used to signify cloths made of two or more sets of warp and filling threads, as in the case of chinchilla, Montagnac, webbing, brake lining, woven cotton conveyer belting, cotton harness webbing, and so on.

PLY YARN. Two or more single threads or yarns twisted or plied together. Any types of yarn may be plied together, the yarn numbers or counts may or may not be the same, and the number of actual ply will vary with

particular yarns. Ply yarn, for example, may be stated in two ways:

1. A 2/40s would mean that two yarns of single 40s have been plied together, the ply number preceding the count number. The single equivalent of this yarn would be 2)40(20s; a single 20s.

2. Some mills place the yarn counts before the number of ply—40/2. The single equivalent would be found in the same way as previously observed.

Some yarns have many yarns plied together to make the finished commercial yarn. Automobile tire fabric, for example, may be nine,- ten,- or eleven-ply.

P. M. Abbreviation for "pin money," meaning a commission for the sale of an unwanted item.

PNEUMACEL. Product of E. I. du-Pont de Nemous & Company, Inc., Wilmington, Delaware for a pneumatic strand sheet or cushion. Composed of a cellular polymer structure, it has predominantly closed cells that are inflated to higher than surrounding pressure with two or more gases, one of which is essentially impermeant to the cell walls. This is a generic term.

POCHOTE. A fiber obtained from the Bombax family of trees, native to Mexico. The trees may attain a height of fifty feet, while the pods are about 6 inches long and about 2 inches in diameter. The fibers, white or brownish, range to about 1 inch, and they resemble kapok. See CEIBA; SILK COTTON.

POCKET FLAP. A tailored pocket with a flap attached to the body of the garment above the pocket as a finish for the pocket opening. This is typical of pockets at the sides of men's coats, in sport shirts and some work shirts. The flap pocket is an added cost item to the pocket especially on work shirts. If the flap can be buttoned to the pocket it is called a button-flap pocket. See BUTTON-THROUGH POCKET.

POCKET HEEL. Hosiery that is made without a seam at the back of the heel for support.

POCKETING. Any material used to make pockets, such as drill, jean, unbleached muslin, Silesia, chamois cloth, cotton velvet, farmer's satin, etc.

POD, COCOON. The compact portion of the cocoon which is used for reeling purposes.

pOH. Expression of alkalinity of a solution; the negative logarithm of the hydroxyl ion concentration.

POIL, POILE, SINGLE SILK. The yarn or thread made from reeling eight to twelve cocoons, used as the core yarn in the manufacture of gold, silver, tinsel, and some chiffon yarn. Poil

means pile, in French.

POIL TRAINANT. French textile term for a fabric whose decoration is made by one or more pile ends, or by warp floats in satin weaves which float on the back of the fabric between the design effects which they produce on the face of the goods. See MEXICAINE.

POINT. 1. One 1/100 cent in the rise and fall of prices in buying raw cotton. 2. The fine quality of handmade lace without regard to the particular make. 3. French for the many stitches used in making real lace. 4. Formerly used in France to imply imitation stitches made to represent genuine tapestry and embroidery stitches. 5. The ornamental stitching used on the back of gloves.

POINT À L'AIGUILLE. French term for needle point.

POINT APPLIQUÉ. French for appliqué lace which is much used on lingerie.

POINT À RÉSEAU. French for point lace made with a net ground (à réseau).

POINT COUPÉ. French for cutwork lace (coupé means cut).

POINT D'ANGLETERRE. See TYPES OF PILLOW OR BOBBIN LACE, under LACES, HANDMADE AND MACHINE-MADE.

POINT D'ESPRIT. Dotted bobbinet with individual or group-dots.

POINT DE GAZE. Flemish point lace similar to Point d'Alençon; it is, however, much softer and is made with horsehair in order to provide stiffness and support.

POINT DE GENE. Openwork embroidery made on wool yarn ground which is later removed by acid treatment.

POINT D'IRELANDE. Coarse machine-made lace of Ireland which simulates genuine Venetian point lace.

POINT DE LA REINE. A dobby-woven, heavy dress-silk fabric which is given a granite or pebble finish.

POINT DE MILAN. Type of guipure with a groundwork of small meshes and a pattern that is made of bold, flowing scroll motifs. Originated in Italy.

POINT DE PARIS. A low-grade cotton machine-made lace that is very plain in motif.

POINT DRAW, ANGLED DRAFT. Warp ends drawn in from the first to the last harness and then back to the first harness in regular sequence. This plan can be used for broken twill effects, if desired.

POINTED HEEL. The reinforced heel portion in a stocking which comes to a point at or near the seam by the step-like formation of the reinforcement.

POINTED TWILL. A weave in which the threads of the right-hand twill and those of the left-hand twill come to a point at the break line in the cloth where they come together. The weave gives cloth a sort of zigzag effect. Uses of fabric made this way are the same as for homespun and tweed, since the weaves are used chiefly for woolen cloths.

POINTILLE. French for material with small dots or circles (pointillé = engraved with small dots).

POINTING. Knitting term denoting the operation whereby points are put on gloves; on ordinary gloves the process is done by machine; expensive gloves receive hand treatment.

POINT KANT. Flemish pillow lace made with a net ground. The motifs lean to pot or vase effects; also known as pot lace.

POINT LACE. This lace is made by hand with needle and single thread. It is the same as needle point. Variations of this lace include Point d'Alençon and Point de Venise.

POINTS OFF. Discount.

POINTS ON. Premium.

POIRET TWILL. Women's wear dress goods made of worsted yarn and one of the pronounced diagonal twill cloths. Named for Paul Poiret, deceased Parisian designer. Cloth is made on a 45-degree twill, and there are twice as many ends as picks per inch in texture. A three-up and three-down, right-hand twill weave may be used and some of the cloth has been made from a steep twill of 63 degrees. High-twist counts of yarn are used, and the material has a soft feel, excellent draping and cling-ing qualities which make it ideal in tailoring. Weight of cloth ranges from 8 to 14 ounces per yard. Material is well-balanced, has excellent finish, and comes in all shades and colors. Piece-dyed cloth, genuine staple, and very popular at times.

POLAN. A Polish casein fiber.

POLDAVIS. Linen sailcloth of the sixteenth century.

POLISHED YARN, THREAD OR TWINE. Starches, resins, waxes, etc., are used to supply some polish or lus-ter to these products. Roller treatments or other methods are used to bring the article to the final finish and effect for smoothness and luster. Sometimes re-ferred to as Glacé Yarn. The French word, glacé, means glazed, polished, or lustered.

POLISHING CLOTH. A square of napped cotton, 12 x 12 inches or 18 x 18 inches in size. It finds use in pol-ishing and dusting glass, metal, and wood; also used in the automobile and harness trades. Formerly these cloths were made with striped borders woven in on the four sides; today, however, the demand is for printed colored borders and hemming only on two op-posite sides. Medium or heavy-weight flannel is most popular, while velveteen is used for silverware polishing.

POLKA DOT. A small, medium, or large dot or circle much used on the face of textile fabrics. The dots may be placed on cloth by printing, em-bossing, embroidering, and by lappet or swivel weaving. Three methods of printing are popular for the cheaper fabrics—flock, resist, or discharge printing. Examples of polka dots are: foulard, neckwear, bandanna, curtain-ing, and summer dress goods. Larger ones often known as coin dots.

POLKA GAUZE. Cotton gauze fab-ric interspersed throughout with colored swivel-woven spots for decoration.

POLLOCK COTTON. An early-ma-turing, cluster-type cotton of 1½-inch staple.

POLO, MARCO. One of the truly great personages in world history (c. 1254-c. 1324), he returned from the Court of Kublai Khan (c. 1214-1294), founder of the Mongol Dynasty in China. Polo brought to Venice tales of the wondrous fabrics of the Far East - brocades, brocatelles, damasks, and other silk fabrics; cloths of gold, silver, copper, muslin, etc. The Venetians, leaders in commerce in his time, obtained many fabrics from the Far East and began a large trade with Khan's kingdom.

Ingenious Italian textilians by the end of the 13th Century were making these fabrics on their looms; Florence, Milan, Rome, Siena, Seville, and Spain were also famous weaving centers of the then known world. For his contribution to world tex-tiles, Marco Polo is historically known as "The Father of the Fabric Industry in Europe."

POLO CLOTH. Formerly a regis-tered trademark owned by Worumbo Mills, Inc., Lisbon Falls, Maine, but not a unit in J. P. Stevens & Co., Inc., New York City. It is a popular staple fabric used in men's and women's top-coating and polo coats. Made with one warp and one filling, the fabric content is choice camel hair and fine wool. This face-finished material, which weighs 21 ounces per yard, has considerable nap on the surface effect. Twill weave is used to make this smart, appealing fabric

which comes in natural camel shade and in shades of brown, blue and gray.

Polo cloth is identified by the use of a silk stripe on the back of the cloth. There is a stripe every three inches in the tex-ture, and it is an actual part of the warp construction.

POLONAISE. Named for a popular raiment of the eighteenth century, it is an overskirt draped in a three-wing-shape festoon, garland, or wreath effect.

POLO SHIRT. A shirt open at the neck; it may be closed by a zipper. This short-sleeved shirt may be woven or knitted. Made from most major fibers it comes in plain colors or prints, sub-dued or bizarre in effect. Ideal for sum-mer wear, it washes and launders very well and gives good service.

POLWARTH SHEEP. A sheep breed found in Australia and Tasmania result-ing from crossing Australian Merino with Lincoln sheep. Known in Aus-tralia as Comeback Sheep, because of the number of generations taken to obtain the type. The wool is even, has a staple of about 4 inches, and shrinks to about 50 per cent.

POLYACRYLATES AND CROSS-LINKING AGENTS. The action of both these agents improves abrasion resistance better than the use of the latter agent alone. Resistance is measured by labor-atory tests, such as the Stoll Flex and the Accelorator, and especially by laundry performance of durable-press cuffs on garments. Polyacrylates improve wrinkle recovery, wet wrinkle recovery, tensile strength, and the crease sharpness of crosslinked creased fabrics. Repeated laundry tests with polyacrylates incor-porated in durable-press formulations result in improved retention of condi-tioned wrinkle recovery after thirty laundry cycles.

POLYALLOMER. A plastic suitable for all kinds of thermoplastic process-ing. It is the family group of Tenite of Eastman Chemical Products, Inc., which includes polypropylene, poly-ethylene, polyester, butyrate, propio-nate, and acetate. Polyallomer is stereo-regular in crystalline form. Properties are comparable with those of rubber-modified polypropylenes, but in color, clarity, moldability, and resistance to blushing when bent or stretched are superior to polypropylenes. While heat distortion is not as good in comparison, polyallomer is better in other proper-ties than rubber-modified polypropylene plastics, and has better heat distortion than high-density polyethylene.

POLYAMIDE. The noun, amide, means any of a group of compounds of the type formula—$R \cdot CO \cdot NH_2$ derived from ammonia by the substitution of the univalent acid radical from one or more hydrogen atoms. Also, amid, noun; adjective form is amic or amidic. Amido is the combining form from amide, indicating a compound containing both the NH_2 radical and an acid radical.

In a broad chemical sense, polyamides (many amides) are the polymerization product of chemical compounds which contain both amino and carboxyl groups, a condensation taking place between the amino and the carboxyl groups of different molecules. Thus, from the foregoing, the natural and the man-made protein, along with nylon, may be classed as polyamide fibers. Present conception, however, implies that polyamides refer to nylontype fibers and filaments.

POLYAMIDE TREATMENT, IFP. A control shrinkage treatment used on woolens; brought about by an interfacial polymerization of polyamide resin on fiber surface. Developed by the U. S. Department of Agriculture, Washington, D.C.

POLYCARBONATE. A poly-condensation of aromatic dihydroxy compound and diacrylcarbonate. An example is the Solvex Fiver of Solvex Corporation, Louisville, Kentucky. See Carbonic Acid.

POLYCHROMATIC DYEING. A novel method of applying dyes in multicolored motifs without the use of conventional printing machinery. Developed by Clifford Newton, Imperial Chemical Industries, Ltd., London, England, who owns the rights to the method. A company licensed to manufacture the machinery is Sir James Farmer Norton, Manchester, England. Introduced in 1969, designs of infinite, intricate varieties are applied by a flowing stream of dye liquor onto a moving belt of fabric and the saturated goods are immediately squeezed through a padder.

Successive colors fall onto the fabric as little as one-tenth of a second apart so that the preceding color can be fixed and resist succeeding applications. Simultaneous flows of color tend to mix. On leaving the pad, the cloth must be completely saturated in order to avoid migration and pattern degradation. If white is desired, a colorless liquid must be applied among the other colors.

The following are the procedures used in this dyeing method: 1. The "flow form" method has thickened solutions of dye which are flowed onto the top roller of the pad, which then deposits the color onto the cloth as it enters the nip area. 2. The "dye weave method" which is the more popular method has streams of dye flow downward on an inclined plane onto a moving layer of cloth.

As for equipment, there is a multiplicity of nozzles of varying shapes and sizes set on bars which can be oscillated at varying rates of speed. Each variable, naturally, alters the resulting design. At present about 75 yards of cloth may be run-off.

Viscosity is important in defining pattern calibrating jets with mistures of water and sodium alginiate so that the rate of delivery by the nozzles may be coordianted with the absorbency of the goods and its speed to obtain saturation.

Coloring ranges from a pin-stripe to complete coverage of fabric by varing the speeds and holding the feed constant. Dichlorotriazine reactive dyes give the best results in this method of coloring textiles. The method, at present, is much used to color tufted floorcovering and knitgoods.

POLYCHROME. Being of many colors; made with at least two colors but often having several colors, casts, tones, and hues in the motif. The surface-effect is noted in printed textile materials with the motifs being scroll work, fruit, foliage, bucolic scenes, etc. As many as sixteen different colors may be used on printed fabrics to give the effect, many of which are excellent in taste and design.

POLYCREST. Registered trademark of UniRoyal for its olefin fiber which is melt spun, texturized, and then bulked. Its softening point is 300° F. Possesses excellent light fastness, is highly stain resistant, easily cleaned and has good abrasion and resilience. The product is used in floorcoverings.

POLYESTER. A manufactured fiber in which the fiber-forming substance is any long-chain synthetic polymer composed of at least 85 per cent by weight of an ester of dihydric alcohol and terephthalic acid (p—HOOC—C^6H^4—COOH—). Registered trademark names include Avlin (Avisco); "Dacron"(duPont); Fortrel (Fiber Industries-Celanese); Kodel (Eastman Chemical Products); Vycron (Beaunit Corporation).

POLYESTER FIBER. A man-made or manufactured fiber in which the fiber-forming substance is any long-chain synthetic polymer composed of at least 85 per cent by weight of an ester of a dihydric alcohol and terephthalic acid. Polyester fibers are high polymers (condensation products) obtained from or by esterification, especially of dicarboxylic acids with glycols or glycol derivatives. Some of the major fibers in this group include:

1. TERYLENE: (Registered Trade-mark) for the polyester and for the fibers (continuous filament yarn and staple fiber) of Imperial Chemical Industries, Ltd., London (I.C.I.), and the Imperial Chemical Industries of Canada, Ltd., made of terephthalic acid or dimethyl terephthalate and ethylene glycol. The product is sold in the United States by Fiber Industries, Inc., Shelby, North Carolina, under the name of Fortrel.

2. "DACRON": Originally known as "AMILAR" and "FIBER V," it is the trade name for the polyester fibers manufactured by E. I. du Pont de Nemours & Co., Inc., Wilmington, Delaware. It is obtained from dimethyl terephthalate and ethylene glycol.

3. KODEL of Eastman Chemical Products, Inc., and VYCRON of Beaunit Mills, Inc., are polyester fibers made in the United States.

4. OTHER SOURCES FOR POLYESTER FIBERS: (Licensed by I.C.I., Ltd., England):
   A. DIOLEN: Farbwerke Hoechst A.G., Frankfurt (M.)-Hoechst, and Vereinigte Glanzstoff-Fabriken A.G. Wuppertal, Germany.
   B. ENKALENE: Algemene Kunstzjde Unie N. V., Arnhem, Holland.
   C. TERGAL: Societe Rhodiaceta S.A. (Rhone-Poulenc) in Besançon, France.
   D. TERITAL: Montecatini, Milan, Italy.

POLYETHYLENE. A synthetic resin adapted to molding and casting purposes and for the extrusion of yarn and staple textile fibers. Its specific gravity of 0.92 indicates a very high covering power.

Produced in the form of granules ready for the extrusion process. Coloring matter is contained in the material and, if desired, titanium dioxide may be used as a dulling agent.

POLYETHYLENE EMULSION. Dispersion of a polyethylene resin and a surface-active agent in water. Used as a softener for finishing resins, to afford resistance to abrasion and tearing of fabric, and to facilitate sewability.

POLYGLAS. Registered trademark of B. F. Goodrich Company, Inc., Akron, Ohio, for its glass belted polyester bias tires. Polyester cord is used in the carcass and Fiberglas cord in the belt. This new concept of adding tire cord belt to the conventional bias tires gives better stability, improved tread life, plus better handability.

POLYMER. A comparatively large molecule produced by linking together many molecules of a monomeric substance (monomer). Such a reaction is called polymerization. If two or more monomeric substances are mixed prior to polymerization, the product of the reaction is known as copolymer. Nylon, for example, is a copolymer. Examples follow:

CAPROLACTAM: Used in manufacture of Nylon Type 6 in which the base is polycaprolactam (polyaminocaproamide). Examples include Nylon of Allied Chemical Corporation, Perlon of West Germany, Enkalon of Holland, and Amilan of Japan.

CELLULOSE TYPE: A natural polymer from which acetate and rayon are made.

POLYACRYLONITRILE: One made by reaction of ethylene oxide and hydrocyanic acid. Examples are A-Acrilan, Creslan, "Orlon," Zefran. There is also a modified type, vinyl chloride, examples of which include Dynel and Verel.

POLYAMIDE: This is the type from which Nylon is produced. This is Type 6,6 made from hexamethylene diamine and adipic acid (polyhexamethylene adipamide). Du Pont, C-Chemstrand.

POLYESTER: A polymer made from a chemical composition of ethylene glycol and terephthalic acid. Examples include "Dacron," Fortrel, Kodel, Vycron.

POLYVINYL CHLORIDE-ACETATE: This type copolymer is the basis for Avisco Vinyon (Vinyon HH) and Vinal.

POLYVINYLIDENE CHLORIDE: This is the polymer from which Dawbarn, Lus-Trus, Saran, Rovana, and Velon are made.

POLYMERIZATION. A method used in man-made fiber manufacture by converting a chemical monomer into a fiber-forming material by transforming it into a stable, long-chain structure.

POLYMERS, COPOLYMERS, AND GRAFT POLYMERS, ILLUSTRATIONS OF. These follow:

Polymer (Monomer):

OOOOOOOOOOOOOOOO
XXXXXXXXXXXXXXX

Copolymer:

OXOXOXOXOXOXOX

Graft Polymer:

OXOXOXOXOXOXOX
  | |
  C C
  | |
  C C

POLYPROPYLENE FIBER. An Italian textile fiber developed by Professor Guilio Natta, consultant to the largest chemical producer in Italy, Montecatini Societa Generale per l'Industria Mineraria e Chimica Anonima. It is obtained from propylene gas, a by-product of oil refining. The fiber may be used for satiny silk fabrics or for heavy wool-like yarns with strengths comparable with nylon. End-uses include clothing and industrial fabrics, transparent plastic sheeting, and film. The fiber, however, dissolves at 348 degrees, Fahrenheit, and cloth made from it cannot be ironed at present. See OLEFIN FIBER, OLEFINE.

POLYSTYRENE FIBER. An extremely fine fiber made in bats with minute air spaces between the fibers. Used for low temperature thermal insulation, soundproofing, and for buoyancy in floats, life vests, etc. An example of this fiber is "Polyfibre" of The Dow Chemical Company.

POLYUNSATURATED. Belonging to or noting a class of animal or vegetable fats, especially plant oils, where the molecules consist of carbon chains with many double bonds unsaturated by hydrogen atoms (associated with a low cholesterol content of the blood). See Detergent Action, Enzyme.

POLYURETHANE FIBER. A man-made fiber, with a low melting point, high elongation and strength, that was first made in Germany during World War II. It is used in continuous filament form in elastic fabrics.

POLYVINYL ALCOHOL. A colorless, water soluble, thermoplastic resin. Formula is $(-CH_2CHOH-)n$ derived from hydrolysis of polyvinyl acetate; used chiefly as an adhesive and as a sizing in the manufacture of paper, plastics, and textiles. See Mewlon, Polyvinyl Alcohol Fibers.

POLYVINYL ALCOHOL FIBERS. A group of man-made fibers made from the principal ingredient, polyvinyl alcohol, and produced in Japan at present. After extrusion and coagulation, the resulting tow or yarn is put through various processes, some of them chemical. The fiber is normally water soluble and was used during World War II to make mine parachutes dropped into

POLYNOSIC: From the French *polynosique*, this is the generic term for regenerated cellulosic fibers of high wet modulus property. The term, first used in 1959, applies to fibers that differ fundamentally in some respects from ordinary viscose rayon staple. The first fiber in this group, Toramomen, invented by the Tachikawa Institute in Japan, appeared in 1942. The fiber was practically unknown outside Japan for seventeen years, until 1959, when some other countries began to take an interest in polynosic fibers. At present there are about fifteen fibers in the group, no two of them identical. For example, air-dry tenacity ranges from 3.2 grams per denier to 5.2 grams per denier; wet extensions vary from 8 per cent to 20 per cent. Improved properties of polynosics are caused by the very fine structure of the fibers—high crystallization, orientation, and lateral order. They are not produced in the same way as viscose rayon. It is now possible to divide these fibers into three groups:

1. *Fibers of high dry-air and wet tensile strengths*—"Super Polyflex," "Junion," and "W63."

2. *The so-called standard types*—"Z54," "Vincel," "Polyflex," "Koplon," "Polyno," "Hipolan," "Polycot," "Tufcel," and "Zantrel." The latter is the trademark name for the polynosic fiber owned by American Enka Corporation, New York City, as well as the term, in the United States, "Polynosic." Zantrel is a modified rayon fiber.

3. *Fibers with high elongation, dry and wet*—"Fiber 40," and "Superfaser."

Uses of "all-polynosic" fibers include blouses, knit and woven shirtings, and knit outerwear and underwear garments. When mixed with cotton, an ideal combination, end uses include dressgoods, furnishings, and sheetings.

the sea. It can be rendered insoluble in water and then fabricated for apparel and industrial uses.

POLYVINYL CHLORIDE FIBERS. They are man-made fibers manufactured of polyvinyl chloride or post-chlorinated polyvinyl chloride, or of copolymers which contain at least 85 per cent vinyl chloride. There are fibers manufactured today which contain more than 15 per cent of other vinyl compounds, and these are classed as Copolymer Textile Fibers.

The major polyvinyl chloride fibers include:

BAYER-PE-CE-U-BORSTEN: coarse monofilaments of non-post-chlorinated polyvinyl chloride of the Farbenfabriken Bayer AG., Dormagen (Niederrhein) of Germany.

CHLORIN: A Soviet Russia continuous filament yarn of post-chlorinated polyvinyl chloride. At the present time, details on this fiber cannot be obtained from Soviet Russia.

FIBRAVYL: First known as RHOFIBRE and then as FIBROVYL, it is a staple fiber of non-post-chlorinated polyvinyl chloride of the Société Rhovyl, Tronville-en-Barrois (Meuse), made in France. It is produced in accordance with its own patents (Fr. P. 913,164 and 913,927).

IGELIT-PCU-KUNSTSEIDE: The first experimentally produced polyvinyl chloride continuous filament yarn of the former I. G. Farbenindustrie AG., according to DRP 666,264. It was already produced in 1931 in the scientific laboratories of the Kunstseidefabrik Wolfen (Kreis Bitterfeld).

ISOVYL: A coarse, non-oriented, jumble-type fiber of non-post-chlorinated polyvinyl chloride of the Société Rhovyl, Tronville-en-Barrois (Meuse), France. Noted for its very low strength and great heat capacity which it retains.

MOVIL: Continuous filament yarn or staple fiber of non-post-chlorinated polyvinyl chloride made since 1933 under license by Montecatini in Terni, Italy. It is made in accordance with the patents of the Société Rhovyl, France. There are three types made today— "N," which is the same as Rhovyl; "F," which is the same as Fibravyl; and "T," which is the same as Thermovyl.

PECE-KUNSTSEIDE-FASER: Originally called WK-FASER, this is a post-chlorinated polyvinyl chloride fiber made since 1934. Large-scale production began in 1939 under the auspices of I. G. Farbenindustrie AG., in accordance with DRP 596,911, now produced as fiber by the VEB Film- und Chemiefaserwerk Agfa Wolfen, Wolfen (Kreis Bitterfeld), in Germany.

PCU-FASER: This is a staple fiber of non-post-chlorinated polyvinyl chloride first made in 1946 in accordance with DRP 737,954 and 802,263 by the Badische Anilin and Soda Fabrik AG., Ludwigshafen am Rhein, Germany.

PECE-U-FLACH, RUNDDRAHT: Synthetic ribbon or coarse synthetic products comparable with horse hair and made of non-post-chlorinated polyvinyl chloride by the VEB Film- und Chemiefaserwerk Agra Wolfen, Wolfen (Kreis Bitterfeld), in Germany.

RHOVYL: Formerly known as RHOFIL, it is a continuous filament yarn of non-post-chlorinated polyvinyl chloride made by the Société Rhovyl, Tronville-en-Barrois (Meuse), in France. It is made in accordance with the patents of the Société—913,164 and 913,927.

RHOVYL (endlos), RHOVYL-FIBRA, RHOVYL-THERMO, RHOVYL-ISO: A continuous filament yarn made from the fibers manufactured under license by the Deutsche Rhodiaceta AG., Freiburg im Breisgau, West Germany, in accordance with the patents of the Société Rhovyl and corresponding to the types known as Rhovyl, Fibravyl, Thermovyl, and Isovyl.

THERMOVYL: A coarse staple fiber of non-post-chlorinated polyvinyl chloride, pre-shrunk by heat treatment, of the Société Rhovyl, Tronville-en-Barrois (Meuse), France, with increased heat stability but slight strength at high extension.

VINYON: Continuous filament yarn made of copolymer fibers with 86 per cent up to 90 per cent vinyl chloride and from 10 per cent up to 14 per cent vinyl acetate. Originally developed by Union Carbide and Carbon Chemicals Corporation in the United States of America. Made in accordance with U.S.P. 2,161,766, and made since 1939 by the American Viscose Corporation. There are supplementary types of Vinyon such as HST (high stretched), and ST, and UST (unstretched) for use as staple fibers stretched to varying degrees and with correspondingly different values of strength and extension.

VINYON E: Highly elastic continuous filament yarn first made experimentally during 1942 through 1945. This vinyl copolymer filament was used to considerable degree during World War II.

VINYON HH: Designation by the American Viscose Corporation for its Vinyon fibers (UST or MST) which possess only a small amount of stretch or no stretch at all. Incidentally, VINYON N is not a polyvinyl chloride but is instead a copolymer consisting of 60 per cent/40 per cent vinyl chloride/ acrylonitrile combination.

POLYVOLTINS: Applied indiscriminately to all races of silkworms which produce more than one brood each year.

POMPADOUR. 1. Term used in textile designing to denote small-flowered designs printed or brocaded in bright colors. Pink and blue are usually intermingled in the motif, and these colors are often enhanced by vivid yellow. Pompadour effects are confined chiefly to cotton, rayon and silk fabrics. 2. The pompadour parasol is a type of sunshade which has a folding handle and is usually covered with moiré antique, other silk, or rayon.

POMPON. 1. In millinery, a tuft or ball such as feathers or ribbon. 2. The colored ball of wool on the front of a shako, or on the top of a beret.

PONCHO. 1. A cotton warp and wool filling cloth which has been fulled considerably and given a dense napping. This waterproof fabric is used for camping and army service. 2. An all-cotton garment used in cavalry units. When thus used, the article is slit in the center so that it may be easily slipped over the head to afford protection to the wearer. 3. Overcoatings of various fabrics of these types are used in South America. 4. A garment made of rubberized cotton fabric or plastic material.

PONGEE. 1. Originally a Chinese silk cloth, tan or ecru in color, and light in weight. Tussah silk was used and the fabric was woven on hand looms in the home; thus a rather crude, uneven textured material resulted. Pun-ki, the basic Chinese word for "weaving in the home on one's own hand loom," gave rise to the present term, pongee. The fabric may be used for summer suiting in tropical climates, office coats, decorative purposes either plain or printed. 2. Staple cotton materials made of combed yarn and given a variety of finishes; noted for its high, appealing luster. This plain-weave fabric has more picks than ends and the range is around 72 x 100. Uneven yarns, in natural color, may be used in this medium to lightweight material. It launders well, gives good service, is not easily soiled, and is a cool material for summer wear. Used for slips, dresses, other summer wear.

POND RETTING. See POOL RETTING under FLAX PROCESSING.

PONGEE, SWISS. British term for mercerized cottons made to simulate the Japanese habutai and pongee fabrics. The cloth is textured around 80 x 76 with the counts of yarns running around 50s.

PONT. The French word for bridge and implies a pile yarn which floats over two or more wires in velvet weaving thereby causing a blemish.

PONTIAC. A gray-colored Mackinac

cloth used for winter wear in cold climates.

PONY WASHER. Any sub-standard size wash wheel.

POODLE CLOTH. Originated a few years ago by Lesur of France, this interesting fabric, which resembles the coat on a French poodle, is usually a combination of mohair loop yarn in yarn-dyed colors with a woolen yarn background which gives the goods its surface interest and the required body for coat fashions of today in women's wear.

The loop yarn can take on a very definite luster to give sheen appearance, and it can be woven into the material by the use of binder threads. Fabric weight ranges from 12 ounces to 18 ounces dependent on the season for which it is intended. The yarn-dyed cloth is preferable to the piece-dyed material.

POOR CROSSINGS. Defects in silk yarn. They are caused by dilatory efforts of the reelers and winders in failing to check the yarn closely at all times. Cloth, if made from this yarn, is often classed as a second.

POOR MAN'S COTTON. A California Uplands cotton with about 1-inch staple and lint yield of about 35 per cent; similar to Peterkin cotton.

POPELINE. A fabric staple that has been on the market for many years. Dyed in all colors or printed, the material simulates poplin or rep. Used for dress goods.

POPLIN. From the French, "Pape-line." It is a staple dress-goods material. The cloth resembles bombazine and silk warp and woolen filling are used. In the higher-priced cloth, worsted filling is utilized. Filling yarn is particularly cylindrical as it tends to give the rounded form of rib line, noted in the fabric, in the horizontal direction. The cloth is also made from other major textile fibers. In staple and plain colors, the material may be used for office coats and linings.

Cotton poplin has a more pronounced rib filling effect than broadcloth. The filling is bulkier than the warp, and there are more ends than picks per inch in the material. In the carded poplin the textures vary from 88 x 40 to 112 x 46; combed poplin ranges from 88 x 44 to 116 x 56. The cloth is mercerized and usually chased for high luster. May be bleached or dyed with vat colors; printed poplin is also popular. Heavy poplin is given water-repellent finish for outdoor use; some of the fabric is given suède finish.

This formidable fabric is used for blouses, boys' suits, gowns, draperies, robes and shirting; much uniform fabric is made from the cloth, as well. Rayon poplin is much used in women's wear and pajama fabric. See RAYON POPLIN.

See Illustrated Section (Fabrics 7).

POPLINETTE. Made with single yarns each way in contrast to regular poplin, made with two-ply yarns in warp and filling. Textures of poplinette range from 112 x 62 to 144 x 32; 36s warp and 16s to 36s filling are used in construction. Warp is usually Egyptian or Arizona cotton, while varying types of American cottons are used for filling.

POPPET. The small shuttle, straight or circular, used in swivel weaving. Poppets are fitted into the sley of the loom.

PORCUPINE BEATER. See BUCKLEY BEATER.

PORCUPINE DRAWING. In French worsted spinning this method can manipulate the shortest of fine wools, and does not insert twist in any part of the process. The porcupine roller performs this action on the various machines used for drawing and drafting. Spindles are absent in this drawing method, and the fibers are condensed into cylindrical strand formation by passing them between rubbing leathers on their way for winding on headless bobbins set in a horizontal position.

PORCUPINE ROLL. It is found on drawing, slubbing, and roving frames in the French or Franco-Belgian systems of drawing and drafting worsted fibers. Studded with steel pins, this small brass roll sets between the front and back rollers, underneath the stock as it is being processed. It controls the very short fibers or noil, and removes them from the longer, choice fibers that will be processed ultimately into yarn. The porcupine goes slightly faster than the back rollers, in a ratio of about 1½ to 1. It does not go as fast as the front rollers. Thus, if the back rollers unit of speed is taken as 1, that of the porcupine as 1½, and the front rollers as 4, the over-all draft would be six—1 x 1½ x 4 equals 6.

PORK PIE HAT. Also known as telescope crown, it is a hat with a crease circling the top to give a flat-topped effect.

POROSITY. A term applied to fabrics which have open spaces in the texture to admit air to pass through or to allow the heat of the body to escape. Summer fabrics, known under the heading of air-conditioned cloth, have found much favor with the public since certain chemical processes remove the protruding fibers from the goods, allowing the material to become more or less porous.

PORTAL-TO-PORTAL PAY. Payment made to employees for time consumed by them in traveling to and from the entrance of the company's premises and the working area.

PORTER. 1. Scotch term used in plain weaving to signify that there are 20 dents or splits per inch in a loom reed. 2. Porter also means the number of groups of threads, 40 to a group, in a specified width of fabric. For example, a cloth is 42 inches wide and there are sixty ends per inch. The $\frac{60 \times 42}{40}$ equals a porter of 63.

PORTER YARN. The two-ply yarn used to weave gunny sacking.

PORTIERE. Heavy drapery fabric, hung between rooms. Made of heavy cretonne, brocade, brocatelle, damask, peasant fabric, rich Jacquard patterns in heavy silk fabric, and chintz of the better grade.

The length of a portiere is variable; however, it should balance with the other articles in the particular rooms.

PORT PHILIP WOOL. Port Philip Bay is on the southern coast of Victoria, Australia. This extra fine quality wool is shipped from Melbourne and Geelong on the bay. Rated with Botany Bay wool, it is about the finest wool in the world today and is used in the best quality fabrics and garments made of woolen and worsted yarns. Expensive coatings for women's wear, dress suiting, and men's apparel of the best type are made from Port Philip and Botany wools.

PORTRAIT COLLAR. A large stand-up collar that "picture-frames" the face.

POSAHUANCO. A handloomed fabric used in Mexico and Central America as a wrap-around skirt, often the only garment worn by females in these areas. This cotton material is characterized by horizontal stripes in red, blue, and purple. The cochineal bug is the source for the fast red color used, a purple shellfish provides the blue color, while the murex, a mollusk, is the base for the purple colorant. Madder is also used for red, and the indigo plant for the blue coloring matter. Bugs and insects, the cactus plant, and shellfish also provide various colorants for this attractive skirting.

POSITEX. A form of natural-rubber latex with reversed charge. The product is deposited on yarns are discreet particles instead of as a continuous film; it is said to be undetectable by eye or hand when applied in ratios of 10 to 15 per cent.

Positex can be used to prepare felts from non-felting fibers such as the bast fibers. Such felts are not waterproofed and will maintain their air permeability.

Two grades of the product are made, vulcanized and unvulcanized, each of which is prepared and compounded for certain applications. Both types are ready for immediate use after addition of water and adjustment of pH. The rubber material has a pH ranging from 3 to 11.

The new rubber material can be compounded with many substances such as mothproofing agents, pigments, scents, water repellents. Positex will not impart elasticity. Product of British Rubber Development Board, London, England.

POST-CURE. One of two durable press finishes. The mill applies the finish to the fabric but the garment manufacturer sets, or cures, the finish by applying heat, using the oven or press, to the completed garment. Synonymous with *Deferred Cure.*

POSTER CLOTH. See SIGN CLOTH.

POTA FIBER. A type of pandanus fiber found in the Solomon Islands; used to make fine mattings.

POTASH. Common term for potassium and potassium products.

POTASSIUM CARBONATE. Commonly known as potash, this carbonate has been known since ancient times as a constituent of the ashes of land plants from which it is obtained by extraction with water. In most instances, sodium carbonate, which it strongly resembles, can be used in its place.

POTASSIUM DICHROMATE. A reddish crystalline salt, $K_2Cr_2O_7$, used as an oxidizing agent in treating certain textiles in that it serves as a mordant in dyeing and printing. See MORDANT.

POTASSIUM PERMANGANATE. A purplish-red crystalline salt, $KMnO_4$, used as an oxidizing agent. It is used to strip color from woolen and worsted fabrics, for example, to bring them back to the white before redyeing to another color or shade. The redyed fabrics, however, usually do not show much liveliness or luster and are rather dead or drab in appearance.

POT EFFECT. Motifs of baskets, scrollwork, urns, vases, used in lacework.

POT LINEN. Indicates the number of cuts or bolts of linen fabric which have been sewed together; ten-thousand yards is the average pot length.

POT SPINNING. Emerging viscose rayon filaments are led through the bath to a hook at the surface and up to a Godet wheel, the speed of which controls the take-up of the still plastic filaments. These are then passed through a glass funnel, thence into a spinning pot which imparts a small amount of twist to them. The pot, with a speed of 8,000 to 10,000 r.p.m., also lays the filaments by centrifugal force into a "cake form." The cakes are then washed to remove the spinning bath liquor, desulphurized, bleached, rinsed, treated with an emulsion, and then dried. See BOBBIN SPINNING, FILAMENT.

POTTERY DUCK. An evenly woven army-type duck used as filtering fabric in the pottery industry.

POTTING. Its purpose is to produce a bright, sheen face and soft hand to woolens. The cuts of cloth are wound at full width onto a perforated roller, which is set vertically in a vat of water. Heat and steam treatment are applied in the procedure, which may last a few hours or several days. On removal from the bath or kier, the cloth is allowed to cool in a natural manner. Also known in some woolen areas as roll boiling.

POULT. A silk fabric made for several centuries and identified by a very faint rib-effect which lent itself to a finish noted for its wavy effect. This yarn dyed fabric has a delicate appearance which resembles coarser watermarked or moiré finish on certain fabrics of the present time.

POUNCE. To smooth the surface of a felt hat with fine sandpaper.

POURITACHE BRAID. On the order of soutache, but heavier in weight.

POUSSET, FRANCIS. A Huguenot weaver who found work in Huddersfield, England. He received patent rights for weaving a silk fabric, crepe, which is still a great staple fabric today. His patents were obtained in 1693.

Pousset was one of thousands of French artisans affected by the Edict of Nantes which was invoked by Henri IV in 1598 and revoked by Louis XIV in 1685. Henri granted civil and religious rights to all Frenchmen but the Edict caused many skilled workers in various trades to exodus to other countries on the Continent and the British Isles. Louis XIV revoked the Edict and renewed persecution once more. During this span of about 100 years France lost thousands of experienced workers, Pousset among them.

POWDER PUFF MUSLIN. Fine cotton goods given a starchless finish that is smooth, crisp and firm. Trade name owned by Dumari Textile Co.

POWER LOOM. A loom that is run by other than hand power. It is the advanced, modern, scientific type of hand loom and has all the modern improvements for production.

POWER NET. Stretching in all directions, this fabric is a thin elastic net made on bobbinette machines. A less costly type, known as Kidde Net, is made on machines manufactured by Walter Kidde & Co., Inc.

POWER STRETCHER. Used in the floorcovering industry, it is a type of knee kicker but with larger teeth and set in a patent head. Easily adjustable to obtain the proper "teeth bite," this machine allows one to stretch areas in a carpet that cannot be accomplished by a knee kicker. See Crab, Crabbing, Knee Kicker.

PPG. The name of Pittsburgh Plate Glass Company, Inc. Pittsburgh, Pennsylvania, adopted in spring of 1968. Formerly the term, PPG, was a trademark symbol of the company and was one of its glass fiber yarns and fabrics.

PRAYER RUGS. The Moslems use these small sized rugs upon which to kneel when praying. Of good texture and compactness, they are featured usually with a design of an arched doorway or niche at the one end while the well-known tree-of-life pattern or a lamp hanging from the middle completes the effect. Some are made with three medallion effects, two for the knees and one for the head. The knees rest on the two medallions while the head of the worshiper touches the third medallion as he bows downward. A five-foot length is about the longest type used while the width may run to about 27 inches.

PRECIPITATE. A solid substance separated or thrown down in a liquid. For example, precipitation of lime by soda ash in making bleach.

PRECISION TWIST TESTER. Either hand- or motor-driven, this machine determines the twist and the twist take-up of yarns which must have high twist, such as crepes and comparable constructions.

PREFERENTIAL SHOP. That union status agreed to by a company, in which union members are given a preference over nonunion members in various aspects of employment, particularly in hiring and laying-off.

PRE-FLUSH. A high water rinse without supplies preceding the break.

PREIN. A German method of pressing all fuzzy, protruding, or irregular fibers into the fabric as it is being woven in the loom; does away with shearing in the finishing of the cloth.

PREMIUM. Also known as "points on." The number of points paid for some particular cotton above the quoted price for the basic grade and staple. A point, in cotton dealing, is 1/100 cent.

PREMIUM COTTON. Also called Peerless. An early-maturing cotton of the Uplands type; one-inch staple and lint yield of about 33 per cent.

PREPARATION. The degree of efficiency and smoothness with which cotton has been ginned, and the relative amount of nappiness or neppiness of the ginned lint fibers.

PREPARING. 1. Long-fibered Luster wools are prepared prior to combing. The wool or long hair fibers are given several gilling operations to place the stock into a manageable condition so that combing may be successful. It should be noted that carding of the fibers is generally omitted.

2. An intermediate process between bleaching and dyeing, or printing, in which the cloth is opened out, treated with chemicals to make it more receptive to dyes, and is pressed, dried, and wound into rolls.

PREPARING WOOL. British term for long-staple wool fibers. Usually wools of the Luster type have to be prepared and these include Lincoln, Leicester, Cotswold, Romney Marsh, etc. Fibers longer than eight inches are usually known by this term.

PRESERVATIVE. Any number of compounds added to size mixtures and the like to prevent the growth of mildew, mold, etc. Also called antiseptics and disinfectants, they include formaldehyde, carbolic acid, boric acid, salicylic acid.

PRE-SHRUNK. Fabrics or garments which have been given a pre-shrinking treatment. Mainly done on cotton fabrics, the purpose of the process is to remove the tendency for the fabric to shrink when washed or laundered. The per cent of residual shrinkage must be indicated on the label of the goods or garments thus treated.

PRE-SPOTTING. A drycleaning term, it is treating heavily soiled areas in garments with a special prepared solvent-detergent solution to aid the regular drycleaning process. See Spotting, Drycleaning.

PRESS. 1. Any machine that presses or smoothes fabrics or garments. 2. A machine of which there are several types, used to press or compress raw materials. 3. To iron in the home or commercial laundry. 4. To squeeze liquid out of cloth by press rollers. 5. The opposite of "to pull."

PRESS BOX. The rectangular box of a cotton gin which serves as a receptacle for the lint cotton which is built up layer upon layer until there is sufficient amount for compression into the cotton bale.

PRESS CLOTH. Fiber cloth made of camel's hair, cotton, and wool, depending on use. Hair fiber is found in varying percentages in all press cloths.

PRESSER. 1. One who does the pressing operations, both finish and under, on dresses or dress parts, by means of a hand pressing iron, a power press, or a mangle. 2. A device on a spring beard needle knitting machine which closes the needle hook in the formation of the knitting stitch.

PRESSER, FINISH. One who performs final pressing on finished garments by hand-pressing, iron, power iron, or mangle. Also known as off-presser, over-presser or top-presser, the presser may do his work on only a portion of the garment at hand.

PRESSER BAR. Aids needles to form stitches in knitting fabric. It is a long finger bar which is moved forward at the proper time to press the needle beards to a closed position.

PRESSER CUT. A device on spring beard needles of warp and weft type for selective needle pressing in a knitting machine. Comparable with an ordinary presser except that the pressing surface or blade is milled out in accordance with the selective needle pressing desired.

PRESSER FINGER. It is that part of a flyer which consists of a rounded or cylindrical rod attached to one arm of the flyer at its upper end and bent to a right angle at its lower end, which ends in a flattened palm effect.

The finger tip or palm actually presses against the bobbin as the slubbing or roving is wound onto it. The eye in the finger tip guides the stock onto the bobbin in an even, uniform manner, from the top of the bobbin to the bottom of the bobbin.

PRESSER FOOT. Sewing machine foot used for stitching. It is the foot that holds the fabric in position as it passes over the feed plate.

PRESSING. A method of imparting either luster or a smooth appearance to the face of goods before leaving the finishing plant for the garment cutting or piece-goods trade. Methods differ with the type of goods, but generally polished and/or covered rolls or metallic rolls are caused to press heavily on the material. There may be two rollers or a series up to six. All may revolve at the same or at different speeds. The latter type is referred to as "frictioning."

Also, special oil or resin finishes may be applied to the cloth prior to pressing.

Another form of pressing is decatizing. This is a method of introducing, simultaneously, a blanket and the goods subject to treatment, onto a large perforated steam cylinder until the entire length of cloth is sandwiched in a roll form. High-pressure steam is then forced from the inside out, through the mass. Sufficient time is allowed for penetration, after which the vacuum is created within the drum to withdraw the steam and to draw in dry air from the room. The blanket and the cloth are then unrolled from the cylinder.

Flat pressing is used on "alpaca-type" cloths. The fabric to be treated is laid up in a vertical stack with a layer of cloth, then a piece of cardboard, a layer of cloth, a piece of cardboard, and so on, until the pile is built. The cloth, of course, is in continuous length folded back and forth. The combined pile is placed in a hydraulic press and subjected to tremendous pressure and steam.

Another meaning is the actual pressing given to some rayon, acetate, and silk fabrics to remove wrinkles from finished goods, by passing them between heated rollers. Silk fabrics which are pressed are usually soaked in a dilute acid to develop the luster.

PRESSING MACHINE. A machine used to press cloth or clothes to make them presentable. Pressing adds "smart appearance" to the material or garment.

PRESS IRON. Any type of laundry iron, home or commercial, used for pressing.

PRESS-OFF. To knit a fabric off the needles without the formation of a new set of loops. The fabric falls off the needles.

PRESS PAPER. Coarse glazed paper used between the layers of cloth prior to its being pressed in a vertical press. This product comes in varying thicknesses.

PRESS RATIO IN MAN-MADE FIBERS. The ratio of the weight of the alkali-cellulose after the excess caustic soda solution has been pressed out to the original weight of the pulp.

PRESSURE. Forced selling.

PRESSURE-BOILING. See KIER-BOILING.

PRESSURE BOWL. The main cylinder on a calender or roller printing machine. It is covered with several layers of lapping or back fabric, and the back of the goods to be printed rests on this fabric. Its function is to absorb excess color matter that may seep through to the back of the material being printed.

PRESSURE DYEING. One of the popular methods of coloring textiles whereby the material and the dye liquor are held under steam pressure in a closed jig, kier, or vessel. The plan is to provide a quicker dyeing when temperatures necessary are above the boiling point of 212° F.

PRESSURE SATURATION. For any given temperature it is the pressure at which liquid and vapor, or solid and vapor can coexist in stable equilibrium.

PRESTWICK®*. An easy-care process for rayons and rayon blends which shows outstanding wash-and-wear qualities no matter how many times fabrics or garments are washed. In non-resin Prestwick® there is no chlorine retention or yellowing. It is equally effective on cottons and blends and gives good results on man-made and natural cellulosics. Prestwick® permanently modifies and stabilizes the fibers to which it is applied, and sourings and other acid treatments have no effect on the finished fabrics. Other features include excellent crease retention, good tensile strength, tear strength, and abrasion resistance. Residual shrinkage is one per cent or less—length and width. Product of Courtaulds North America, Inc., New York City.

*Courtaulds service mark and Registered Trademark for its permanent finishing process and for permanently finished easy-care fabrics.

PRETREATMENT IN LAUNDERING. Preparing a load of fabrics or clothing according to some plan. Some pretreatment items include separation of light colored articles from the dark colors, use of detergent by hand on heavily soiled areas, stain removal, checking for holes, tears, etc., loose sewing, fraying, emptying of pockets, attention to zippers, hooks, and eyes, etc.

PREWASHING. The time prior to the regular washing during which the articles are tumbled or receive action in the washing solution. It also implies a short agitation period prior to the regular washing treatment in which articles are immersed in a full amount of detergent with a small amount of water. Controlled by manual treatment or by the automatic device on the machine.

PRIDE OF GEORGIA COTTON. A large-boll cotton that is easy to pick.

PRIESTLEY. A well-known, English worsted that is found in the better types of clothing stores. Made by the English manufacturer Priestley.

PRIMATIZED. The durable press process developed by Deering Milliken, Inc., Spartanburg, South Carolina.

PRIME. Merino wool of the clothing grade obtained from the sides of a high type fleece of fine-quality or from the shoulders of a good-quality fleece.

PRINCESS. 1. Implies a coat or dress with close bodice and flaring skirt, cut in an unbroken line from shoulder to hem. 2. Hand manipulation necessary to complete machine-made braid or net when it is not made in entirety by machine.

PRINT CLOTH. Carded cotton cloth made with about the same yarns as cheesecloth but with more warp and filling threads per inch. Most print cloths are made in narrow widths up to forty inches. Print cloth is given a wide range of finishes, thus producing cambric, muslin, lawn, longcloth, printed percale, etc.

Narrow print cloths are 27-inches to 40-inches wide with constructions varying from 64 x 60 up to 80 x 92. Yards per pound runs from 3.50 to about 7.60. Wide print cloths are 45-inches wide with textures ranging from 60 x 48 to 64 x 60. Yards per pound go from 4.65 to about 5.35.

PRINT GINGHAM. A gingham which has part or all of the design printed on the cloth; a popular and well-known material.

PRINTING. The decoration of the surface or surfaces of fabric by the application of insoluble pigments or fast dyes in definite repeated forms and colors. The earliest form of printing was probably done from carved blocks that were charged with a colored paste and pressed onto the fabric. The act is repeated in regular placement across the width, and down the length of the goods. Block printing is necessarily slow.

The invention of roller printing speeded printing from a few hundred yards to thousands of yards per day. In this "print-on" method, a series of engraved copper rollers, up to sixteen, generally, are held in stands arranged through the front and bottom circumference of the platen or main drum. For each print roller, which represents one color, there is a color trough, color roller, and a "doctor" or excess-paste-removal blade. All colors, including the ground color, are successively applied at rapid speed. Depending on whether the applied color was direct or developed, the processed cloth then proceeds to the steaming, ageing, and other after-treatment operations.

A well-designed print roller will adequately color the surface and penetrate deep enough to give depth of shade, leaving the reverse side in an unfinished state. Certain thin fabrics can be "through-printed" so that the back of the goods is almost as well defined as the face. This is especially true in discharge printing.

Printing can be done on both sides of a fabric; this is known as duplex printing. The operation necessitates two independent operations and is expensive. Other types of printing include:

1. Spaced application print on white or dyed ground.
2. All-over print on white or dyed ground.
3. Resist print followed by dyeing.
4. Discharge print on dyed ground.

PRINTING, APPLICATION. A form of direct, cylinder, calender or roller printing in which the pattern, design, or motif is applied to the goods in the same manner as printing on paper. This type of printing does not rate high in colorfastness.

PRINTING, DECALCOMANIA. This method of printing textiles was unveiled in 1969. It transfers a printed design from paper onto fabric. The method was introduced by the Swiss company of Societe des Procedes Sublistatic and its subsidiary in the United States is the Sublistatic Corporation of America. The machine and equipment cost around $50,000 and it is made in this country by David Gessner Company, Inc., Worcester, Massachusetts.

Production is about 500 yards per hour. The process is used on manmade fibers or those blends which have at least 65% of manmade fiber in the content. At present it is applied to acetate, triacetate, nylon 66, polyester, and acrylic fibers but not to modacrylic fibers. The goods to which the process is applied may be knit, nonwoven, and woven. The cost of the decals runs to about 53 cents a yard which is higher than the cost of direct application of color by roller or screen methods. The higher costs, however, are offset by the savings apparent by not having to carry a cloth inventory.

The color effect compares very favorably with the best letterpress or rotogravure paper printing methods. Paper has little or no stretch which is conducive to good results.

Dyes used are made by CIBA, Ltd., Basle, Switzerland, which has an interest in the company. The dyes, when subjected to heat, are changed into a gas and then fused into the goods. They meet requirements for abrasion resistance, drycleaning, lightfastness, machine washing, and shrinkage.

The motifs for the decals made by Sublistatic are supplied by the customers.

There is another type of this method of printing which is ideal for drapery panels, fabrics, individual pieces, hosiery, sweaters, etc. The company which makes the unit is Kannegeiser Automatic Heat-Printing Company also under the aegis of the Gessner Company for North and Central America.

PRINTING, TOPPING. Reprinting fabric a second time. After the color has been fixed and dried in the first printing, the topping or second printing is used to offset and give good contrast or harmony to the finished goods. Topping colors are heavy, dark, or brilliant and add tone to the light or pastel shades used in the first printing.

PRINTING MACHINE. It is used to print textiles, and the regulation type is known as roller, direct, calender, or cylinder machine. The machine is on the general principle of those used to print newspapers, etc. The chief roller is the cylinder or pressure bowl; up to sixteen rollers may be used for the printing of fabric, there being a color roll in action with the cylinder for each color to be set on the goods. Other important parts of a printing machine include back gray cloth, color trough, color guide rollers, color furnisher, lint doctor blade, color doctor blade, various guide rollers. Three layers of fabric are fed between the cylinder and the color rollers—the blanket, the back gray cloth which acts as a cushion for the material to be printed, and the cloth that is to receive the color. See Illustrated Section.

PRINTING MACHINE, COLOR TROUGHS ON. Copper boxes are used to hold color that is fed to the print roller. There is one trough for each roller.

PRINTING MACHINE, LINT BLADE ON. A heavy, soft brass blade which removes dirt, lint, fuzziness, and protruding fiber left on the print roller of the machine after contact has been made with the printed goods. This blade, which extends the width of the roller, helps to prevent smudgy effects on the cloth as it is printed.

PRINTING PASTE. Any of several types used, all with varying composition and viscosity. The usual items relative to printing include the dye, water, thickening agent, a hygroscopic substance, mordant, dye assistants, and other chemicals that may be used, and which vary with the individual dyes used.

PRINTING ROLLERS. Hollowed, tapered copper rollers or cylinders upon which the design is etched to the desired depth. There must be as many print rollers to the machine as there are colors in the pattern to be printed upon the material.

PRINTING SHELL. A large, engraved copper roller used to print designs in color on cloth when mounted in a printing machine.

PRINTING TYPES, ROLLER AND SCREEN. Roller printing is ideal for large production and at costs much lower than those possible in screen or stencil printing.

Screen printing can handle short yardages on a profitable basis; this plan aids control inventories. Full, attractive, bright color motifs can be achieved on stencil prints, including those observed on heavy materials. The so-called fall-on and half-tone effects on fabrics are ideally processed on screen printing. However, stripe and blotch effects cannot be produced satisfactorily.

PRINT-ON. A way of defining printing where the discharge method is not used. See PRINT-ON PRINT.

PRINT-ON PRINT. Self-explanatory since the motifs are printed onto the material. It is fast becoming a conventional method of coloring textiles where the discharge or resist methods are not required. Each color used must have its individual roller, and each color must fit to the exact minute part of the pattern required in the finished material. At present, it is estimated to be the cheapest form of printing with regard to price. Ideal for general printing purposes, it is particularly effective where high production and long runs of goods are required.

PRINTS. General name given to cotton, rayon, and silk fabrics which have a printed motif, pattern, or design.

PROBATIONARY PERIOD. The length of time during which employees are on trial with a company.

PROCESS SILK. Another name for silk or nylon bolting cloth. See BOLTING CLOTH.

PROCTOR. See SHUTTLE SMASH PROTECTOR.

PRODUCER-TEXTURED. Broad, general term for yarns textured by the fiber producer at source rather than at plant of the throwster. Usually the yarns are of the bi-component type and texture is obtained by chemical means, rather than by a mechanical process, such as, for example, a heat setting treatment.

PRODUCTION CONSTANT. The combination of the constant factor into one multiplier for calculating production.

PROFESSION. An occupation requiring a special skill and professed ethics, with training that usually covers and extends beyond a liberal education to a special school, and involves service other than commerce or agriculture, mental rather than manual labor. Outstanding professions are law, medicine, ministry, arms, science, architecture. 2. General term for a calling, vocation.

PROFIL. French for the longitudinal cross-section of a weave construction. It is called profile in English, and profilio in Italian.

PROGRADE PROCESS. This process, developed by Platt International, Ltd., England, treats cotton yarn on a continuous basis with liquid ammonia to produce a modified mercerized effect. The process provides improved tenacity, luster, and dimensional stability, and fewer imperfections. This rapid package-to-package operation is done on a single-sided machine with 80 winding positions in four sections of twenty units each. Speed is at 200 meters a minute per position.

The International Institute for Cotton, England, provides technical assessment of treated yarn for knitting purposes, as well as advice on marketing and promotion of garments made from this yarn. Rights to make the machine, as well as for marketing, have been granted by Platt International, Ltd. to J. & P. Coats, Ltd., London, England. License processors pay royalty to Coats.

PROGRESSIVE SHRINKAGE. Shrinkage which results from repeated washing, laundering, or dry cleaning; shrinks more after each successive treatment.

PRO-LEGS. The ten non-jointed legs under the sixth, seventh, eighth, ninth, and the last joints of a silkworm.

PROLENE. Polypropylene fiber made by the melt-spinning method and is highly oriented. Possesses high tensile strength, abrasion resistance, and does not absorb moisture. Used in floor covering, cordage, rope, netting, upholstery, work clothing, and industrial fabrics. Product of Hercules Powder Company, Covington, Virginia.

PROLON. Term applied to textile fibers made from protein bases. Examples are casein (milk) and zein (corn). Vicara was another example of a protein fiber.

PROPRIETARY. An individual or exclusive product usually marketed under a protecting trade-mark. These products usually represent independent research.

PROTEIN. An albuminous substance obtained from proteids. It was regarded originally as a proteid deprived of its sulphur, but can be, at present, considered as an artificial product that resembles alkali-albumen. The true protein is any of a general class of complex compounds which contain nitrogen, necessary to form living tissues of all animals and plants such as muscle and nerve tissue. Protein contains carbon, hydrogen, oxygen, and nitrogen.

PROTEIN FIBER. Made from soy beans and corn meal, the latter being known as zein. The vegetable matter is crushed and oil is extracted. Saline solution extracts the protein. A viscous solution is made, and chemical treatment produces the extruded filaments through a spinneret into a coagulating bath. Winding and reeling follow to give the commercial product. The purpose of these fibers is to use them in varying percentages with major textile fibers to make apparel of several types.

PROTEIN FIBER, REGENERATED. A filament or fiber prepared by extruding a dispersion of a protein or a combination of proteins, into a suitable coagulant.

PROTEINIZED. The step in the method of making hosiery which comprises applying an emulsion—consisting of an aqueous alkaline dispersion containing a water insoluble—and precipitable protein, particles of waxy material, and an emulsifying agent. The ratio of protein to waxy material is 1:4 to 4:1, so that the protein surrounds and forms a film about the particles of waxy material preventing agglomeration of both the protein and the waxy material.

PROTOPECTIN. See CUTOSE.

PRUNELL. A heavily fulled cashmere-type fabric, rather heavy in weight and used for dress goods for winter wear.

PRUNELLA. A dress-goods material and cloth used in children's apparel, made from a 2-up and 2-down right-hand twill weave. Worsted yarn is used in the cloth. Light in weight, usually piece-dyed. Not in vogue at the present time.

PRUNELLE TWILL. The 2-up and 1-down or the 1-up and 2-down, three-harness twill weave.

PRUSSIAN BLUE. Any one of a group of cyanogen compounds formed from ferrous sulphate and potassium ferro-cyanide, formerly of much importance in dyeing cotton and wool. It is used in bluing material at the present time.

PRUSSIAN VELVET. A German pile cloth made of cotton or linen warp and a mohair filling which forms the pile effect.

PSYCHROMETER. It is used to measure the vapor tension and the relative humidity of the air.

PSYCHROMETRY. That branch of physics which relates to the determination or measurement of atmospheric conditions, chiefly those with regard to moisture mixed with air.

PUA HEMP. A very strong, water-resistant bast fiber raised in the Far East. Obtained from the Maoutia Puya plant, the fiber is used to make bags, fishing nets, ropes.

PUCCI, COUNT EMILIO. In 1950, Emilio Pucci made headlines in the world of fashion when he brought out his stretch fabrics and garments. Well-known as a marchese, member of the Italian Chamber of Deputies, and a great designer of the boutique, the Count is probably the leader in fantastic sports- and leisure-wear fashions.

His definition of fashion is as follows: "Fashion is the essence of modern life. It is movement. We must capture it, yet give it freedom. It is the vision of tommorrow realized today. Color is the 'X-quality' of fashion, and it should harmonize well in all designs."

His showings of nylon and silk stretch garments were at once acclaimed throughout the fashion and sports world when he introduced them. Men, women, and children became greatly interested in his developments in this field since he provided both power in the fabric and greater comfort in the contortions of the body. His garments were made with stretch only in the warp or vertical direction, the "north-south direction." Shortly thereafter, garments came into the market with filling or crosswise stretch, the "east-west direction," as well as in both directions-warp and filling. In all fields of endeavor and creations, classics, haute coutures, gowns, frocks, and evening dresses, Count Pucci is alwasy in the forefront and his photographic color mind is superb in color combinations and in harmony and contrast.

PUCKERED FABRIC. 1. See COCKEL, COCKLE. 2. See PLISSE; SEERSUCKER.

PUCKERING. A rippled appearance noted in garment, especially at the seams; irksome and difficult to remove.

PUCKER OR BLISTER. When six or more threads in a fabric form a fancy stripe or design in goods. Loose or tight tensions bring about the effect.

PUERTO CABELLO COTTON. A Venezuelan cotton shipped from port of this name.

PUGGREE. 1. The scarf-like fabric worn around a hat or helmet used to protect the head from the sun's rays; popular on men's straw hats for summer wear. 2. A printed hatband of polka dot, or some similar design used on headgear.

PULL-A-LOAD. To remove a load from a wash wheel or similar device after kicking-off or emptying the kier, vessel, or vat.

PULLED OR SNAPPED COTTON. Cotton picked from slightly opened or dry bolls, a condition caused by the elements—early frost, for example. The cotton holds on to much of the inner boll lining in the ginning process, which makes it difficult to gin.

PULLED WOOL. This is obtained from the pelts or hides of dead sheep. It is inferior in all respects to fleece wool, which is taken from live sheep. The stockyard centers produce pulled wool. However, the packing houses are interested mainly in the carcass; the wool is of secondary consideration. They dispose of all this stock to textile plants.

There is more pulled wool produced per year than first-clip wool. Pulled wool is used with better grades of fleece wool to make woolens and worsteds.

PULLED WOOL, METHODS TO OBTAIN. There are three ways to obtain pulled wool.

1. SWEATING PROCESS: The hides are sweated until the wool is loosened so that it may be taken from the pelts with ease. However, the hides may be affected if the work is not properly done.

2. LIME METHOD: The flesh sides of the pelts are painted with lime. This allows the wool to be removed easily after a short ageing. Hides are subject to injury and dyeing is sometimes irregular.

3. DEPILATORY METHOD: This is the best method to use. A solution of sodium sulphate will loosen the fibers. In the solution there is also sulphuric acid and an alkali made of oyster shells. The flesh side of the pelt is treated just as soon as it comes from the slaughtered animal. Ageing will last from 8 to 24 hours. The action is such, that when ageing is consummated, the fibers will leave the pelt in the same way lather may be taken from a man's face in shaving. The largest wool pullery in the world is in Mazamet, France.

PULLEY BOX. In the old-time drawloom it is the box or frame suspended over the loom which houses the pulleys.

PRINTING TEXTILES, MAJOR AND MINOR METHODS OF.

Basically, the printing of textile fabrics is a simulation of the designs, motifs, and patterns observed in woven fabrics made on a hand or power loom. Printed cloths are, generally speaking, much lower in price when a comparison is made with woven goods in which patterns appear. The former has become relatively inexpensive when consideration is made of the fewer skills and intricacies necessary in the preparation of a design, the processes involved to make printed fabrics commercially successful, and the setting up of the rollers and other parts in a printing machine. The improvements and advances in printed fabrics have been phenomenal, particularly since the close of World War I.

In work done by hand, such as handmade fabrics, clothes, cigars, or shoes, certain advantages are apparent such as better workmanship, closer individual attention, and more care in detail. Comparatively speaking, one pays more for products perfected by hand labor. When work is done by machine—taking a printing machine, for example—there are greater production, lower costs, progressive assembly, mass quantity, uniform sizes, and some job specialization. Printing of cloth is very economical from the commercial standpoint. To illustrate, at the present time an eight-hour shift in some printing plants can print as much as 15,000 yards of fabric on a single machine; this is at the rate of about 1,875 yards an hour or about 30 yards a minute. Some printing establishments prefer to print cloth in multiples of 5,000 yards; thus, a 16-hour run on two shifts would print about 30,000 yards of goods. Other plants are geared to take orders for any yardage within reason, "large or small."

Before taking up the printing of cloth on a printing machine, attention should be given to a device—the pantograph—used to set up the design that will be printed by one or more rollers on the machine.

THE PANTOGRAPH: All designs begin with the ideas of the designer. He outlines and produces his motif on paper, usually graph paper marked off in proper ratio lines. Following this, the design has to be developed and enlarged. The original pattern is enlarged by the pantograph magnifier. The motif is engraved by hand onto a zinc plate which is set on a flat table. A frame connects the table with the pantograph machine. The frame has an arm which is tipped with a diamond tracing-needle or point. The operator uses this pencil-like point to follow each line in the pattern. Every movement of the point is transferred to a series of diamond points controlled by a set of levers. These points are set so that they come in contact with the varnish-covered copper roller.

This special bituminous-base, acid-resistant varnish coating affords protection to the copper roller when it is placed in an acid bath. The needle points, controlled by the operator, cut through the varnish cleanly, leaving the copper in plain view. The points have been spaced in a predetermined accurate order dependent on the number of repeats of pattern cut into the roller. As mentioned, they are connected with the head point or master needle, which is guided by the machine operator; each needle point in the set will place its repeat of motif upon the one roller in simultaneous motions. The copper roller, which has been trimmed for smoothness and trueness prior to using it, may be used a great many times, since only a very small fraction of an inch is lost through complete engraving and printing procedures. Some rollers will last for many years.

After the pantographer has completed his work on the roller, it is then placed in a stone trough filled with iron sulfide. This chemical, by its oxidizing action on the copper, will widen the exposed design area. The roller is next placed in another trough which contains a solution of nitric acid. This acid will etch the pattern into the copper roller to a depth sufficient for the printing which follows. The roller is placed on a cylinder set upon axles, where the operator checks closely by optical inspection all gouged areas for correct depth and uniformity. He applies any finishing touches necessary to make the roller as nearly perfect as possible.

A third trough, served by a continuous flow of water, is used to wash away all traces of acid, and to prevent further oxidation of the copper roller. Finally, the roller is dried and the varnish is removed by benzine or some other suitable solvent. It is now ready for mounting in the printing machine.

PRINTING may be described as the decoration of the surface or surfaces of fabric by the application of insoluble pigments or fast dyes in definite repeated forms and colors. The earliest form of printing was probably done from carved blocks which were charged with a colored paste and pressed onto the fabric. The act is repeated in regular placement across the width and down the length of the goods. Block printing is necessarily slow.

The invention of roller printing speeded printing from a few hundred yards to thousands of yards per day. In this "print-on" method, a series of engraved copper rollers, up to 16, generally, are held in stands arranged through the front and bottom circumference of the platen or main drum. For each print roller, which represents one color, there is a color trough, color roller, and a "doctor" or excess-paste-removal blade. All colors, including the ground color, are successively applied at rapid speed. Depending on whether the applied color was direct or developed, the processed cloth then proceeds to the steaming, ageing, and other after-treatment operations.

A well-designed print roller will adequately color the surface and penetrate deep enough to give depth of shade, leaving the reverse side in an unfinished state. Certain thin fabrics can be "through-printed" so that the back of the goods is almost as well defined as the face. This is especially true in discharge printing.

Printing can be done on both sides of a fabric; this is known as duplex printing. The operation necessitates two independent operations and is expensive. Other types of printing include:

1. Spaced application print on white or dyed ground.
2. Allover print on white or dyed ground.
3. Resist print followed by dyeing.
4. Discharge print on dyed ground.

OPERATION OF THE PRINTING MACHINE

1. The color has to be thickened to the proper consistency so that it will not flow out of the engravings in the copper roller.
2. The color furnisher picks up the thick color paste from the color trough and covers the entire copper roller with color.
3. The color doctor is a long, sharp blade which scrapes off all color from the copper roller except that which is in the grooves or gougings of the design. The action simulates a man's removing face lather when shaving.
4. The roller then presses against the cloth to be printed, thereby leaving the design imprint on the cloth. It can be compared with the methods used in printing a newspaper, the comics, the making of wallpaper.
5. The lint doctor scrapes off any lint from the copper roller which may have been picked up from the cloth. Lint would interfere with the color pattern in the same manner as a hair caught on a pen point will smear writing.
6. The main cylinder holds the cloth to be printed so that the copper roller can press the design into the material.
7. The back gray cloth keeps the machine clean by absorbing any excess dye paste.
8. After printing, the cloth is sent to a steam chamber for setting. It is then dried, aged to fix the color, de-sized, and then finished.

MAJOR METHODS OF PRINTING

BLOTCH PRINTING: This is printing material in order to give it a dyed ground effect. Blotch-printed cloth gives the impression that the cloth may have been colored in some particular manner, but close examination will readily show that the blotch method has been used. A material is printed, and as a result of this, the groundwork will be white if the blotch method has not been used. The large colored basic areas take the print because of the manner in which the dye paste is made to adhere to the goods. Very fine lines, from twenty to two hundred per inch, will hold the dyestuff for printing so that when the machine operation is given, the entire white surface is printed. Thus, a printed groundwork will appear on the cloth, with one or more small or spot designs in their proper places on the face of the goods.

Blotch printing differs from duplex printing in that in an examination of the former, the back of the fabric will not show the same as the face. There will be some absorption on the back but not nearly enough to give a duplex effect. Some blotch prints have white in their motif as a background, as well as some other basic color, depending upon the pattern. Little duplex cloth is seen today since the process is slow, the cost is high, and other methods of printing are more popular.

DIRECT PRINTING: This type of printing sets the patterns directly onto the material from rollers, usually made of copper engraved for printing the motif on the fabric when the rollers are set in motion. Other names for direct printing are CALENDER, CYLIN-DER, or ROLLER PRINTING. The bleached goods are fed into the machine, pass between the rollers which have the designs etched in them (one roller for each color to go onto the cloth), and take the printed motif directly. Direct printing is used for printed designs on cloth which has a white area for the background.

DISCHARGE PRINTING: Also called extract printing, this method is used for dark-colored materials which have white or colored designs. The fabric is piece-dyed, and certain areas of color are bleached or discharged, leaving white places in the goods. The cloth is then direct-printed and some or all of the white portions are colored according to the plan. It is also possible to add a basic color to the discharge paste to produce a colored pattern.

RESIST PRINTING: This method of printing is resorted to when it is desired to obtain a white figure on a colored background by dyeing the goods after they have been printed. The cloth to be treated is tannated according to some plan or motif. When the tannin acts upon the material at the designated places, it has the power to repel the action of the dyestuff that is to be used to dye the goods a solid color. The dyestuff will not become "fixed" on the material where it has been tannated.

After the goods have been dyed, they are treated in a correct chemical solution that will not affect the dyed areas, but will remove the tannin or mordant so as to produce a white effect on the colored cloth. Acetic acid may be used to remove the tannin. Thus a colored cloth with white effects will result. If it is further desired to have colored effects on the goods, they may be printed to give colored dots or designs on the colored background. Some or all of the white areas may be colored.

Basic colors are generally used for this method of printing, and if a color resist is wanted, then some color is added to the resist paste. Cloths which are often resist-printed include foulard, bandannas, polka-dot effects, bunting, dressgoods.

DISCHARGE AND RESIST PRINTING, SUMMARY OF: In discharge printing, the ground is dyed a solid shade or color. The design is then printed with a discharge paste, usually with some hydrosulfite since it will give a white discharge.

If color effects are desired, the color matter is used with the discharge paste, since it will not affect the color. Vat colors are often employed; they require hydrosulfites for their reduction and, at the same time, discharge the dyed background from the goods—an ideal plan used on rayons.

To obtain a white discharge print effect on a vat print, the material is essentially blotch-printed. Discharge printed goods will show pure white or color effects which go through to the back of the goods.

In reserve or resist printing, white effects on aniline black are very effective, since excellent results are obtained; the cost is relatively low and this fast black is exceptionally difficult to discharge. In this method of printing, the goods are printed with tin salts and a gum which acts as a resisting agent. The material is then dyed. The portions of the goods which are not treated with the resist substance will take on the dyestuff. Sometimes, however, colors are added to the resist paste. These are colors which are not affected by the dyeing treatment.

Resist-printed effects may show on only one side of the material; the other side of the fabric will present a more or less solid color, generally speaking. If the fabric is rather thin or sheer, the resist effect may be seen very clearly on both sides of the material.

SIDE VIEW OF DIRECT PRINTING MACHINE
(This method of printing is also called calender, cylinder or roller printing)

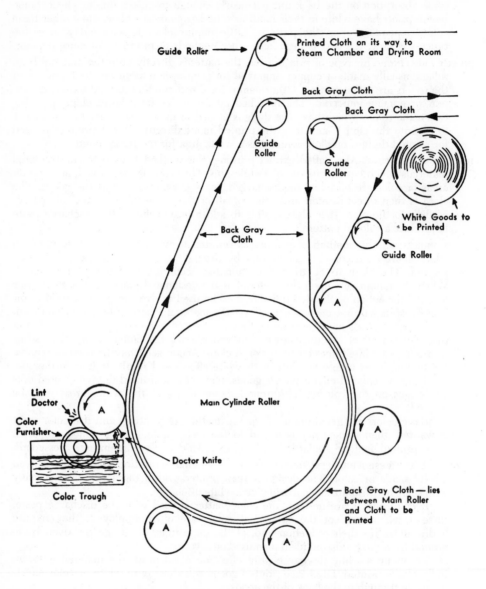

Guide Roller → Printed Cloth on its way to Steam Chamber and Drying Room

Back Gray Cloth

Back Gray Cloth

Guide Roller

Guide Roller

White Goods to be Printed

Back Gray Cloth

Guide Roller

Lint Doctor

Color Furnisher

Main Cylinder Roller

Doctor Knife

Color Trough

Back Gray Cloth — lies between Main Roller and Cloth to be Printed

A. The etched copper print rollers which make printing possible. There must be a roller for each color used in the pattern.

OTHER METHODS OF PRINTING

APPLICATION PRINTING: The word "commercial" is synonymous with the word "application," and these two terms are used very loosely in the industry. Generally speaking, it is the printing onto white goods irrespective of the type of material involved; rather popular in printing of silk, acetate, and rayon. There is no discharge or resist-printing involved in this method of coloring, whether for dyed or for printed materials. It is sometimes referred to as direct printing but usually with the understanding that the colors applied to the goods in question, in most instances, are not fast to light and washing. The words "application" and "commercial" are loosely used with regard to dyes, dyed fabrics, or printed goods. Labels should always be carefully read whenever either of these terms appear on any fabric or garment.

BLOCK PRINTING: This is the oldest form of printing known to man. Some museum pieces are known to be over five thousand years old. Wooden, metallic, or linoleum blocks are carved with the motif or design, using one block for each color required.

The dye is applied in the form of a paste to the face of the block, which is then pressed and hammered onto the material. The operation is repeated as many times as necessary. Careful handling is essential.

Block printing is usually done to full-width goods on a strong supporting table. Compared with other methods of printing, block printing, as to production, is almost negligible; block-printed fabrics on the market today are considered expensive.

BURN-OUT PRINTING: Print which shows raised designs on sheer ground. Made by printing design with chemical on fabric woven of paired threads of different fibers, then burning out one of the fibers from the parts printed. Often used on velvet, scarf fabric, and soft goods for headgear, such as mantillas and veilings.

DUPLEX OR REGISTER PRINTING: This is the name given to fabric printed with the same or another motif on the reverse of the goods. Thus, both sides are colored and the material may be classed as a reversible. This print is used to simulate woven stripes and other basic designs in certain fabrics. Duplex prints at times command a good price since they find considerable use in hangings and curtains of medium and better grades.

FLOCK PRINTING: This method of printing has in recent years become very popular, chiefly because of the low cost involved and the types of motifs that are possible. The application of the dots to the cloth is accomplished by means of a gummy paste which consists of thoroughly ground powder-form fibers and an adhering agent. The effect on the goods is that of small embroidery such as dotted swiss, for example.

Metals are used to give gold, silver, or copper effects on some of the fabrics. The method is known as metallic printing. Any kind, grade, type, and quality of cloth may be flock-dotted. The dots and other effects, however, may not always be fast to washing and laundering. (See Flock, Flocking, Flock Printing.)

INDIA PRINT: Muslin printed with design typical in form and color of those used in India. Genuine India prints are hand-blocked with nature patterns in glowing oriental colors. Imitations must be declared as such.

OVERPRINTING: Colors or designs that are printed over other colors and motifs. Overprint is used when it is desired to alter the shades and to tone down certain vivid colors or effects. It is much used to give floral and splash-print effects to certain types of cloth.

PHOTOGRAPHIC PRINTING: This method of printing makes it possible to do very fine work on textiles which otherwise would be most difficult to do by the roller method. Dark ground and solid effects, as well as fine detail work, can be executed on cloth colored in this manner in one continuous etching operation.

The design is photographed and the negative is then covered with a screen plate. In this way it is possible to break up the solid areas of the design so that the dark portions of the negative will then be shown by fine lines.

A contact print is made by projecting a light through the screen plate onto another film. As many exposures are made as are necessary to produce a complete film covering the entire copper roller.

The film is then placed around a roller which has been previously treated with a sensitizing solution. A powerful arc light is then focused upon it. Whenever the light passes through the film it affects the sensitized roller, baking the chemical coating and causing it to harden.

Warm water is then used to wash the roller to take away the sensitizing solution areas which were not exposed to light. The copper roller is then placed in a bath of iron perchloride for several minutes. The solution etches the bare portions of the roller. These gougings form the engraved pattern that is to be printed. Afterwards the roller is washed to rid it of the portions covered with the baked sensitized solution which have resisted the action of the cutting or etching bath. Dressgoods of many types are printed in this novel, popular manner.

PIGMENT PRINTING: Pigment is a coloring matter or substance, a dry substance, usually pulverized, which, when mixed with a liquid vehicle in which it is insoluble becomes a dye, paint, ink, etc. Pigment printing has many advantages over other classes of colors. Practically all types of fibers and blends can be printed; there are fewer "seconds," chiefly because it is an easy matter to observe the printing results and if flaws are found they may be remedied at once. Compatibility of colors is assured if pigments of the same type have been used in the processing, thereby increasing the range of colors available. There are, for example, certain colors in the vat range for which there is not any match possible.

Printed goods may be stored for any length of time, within reason, prior to curing. Fixing of color is done by a simple process of curing. Much lighter engravings, as in photo engravings, can be used with moderate pressure on the machine, affording a saving in paste consumption. No aftertreatments, such as washing, oxidation, or soaping are necessary; thus, a saving in time, steam, and work.

PRINT-ON-PRINT: Self-explanatory, since the motifs are printed onto the material. It is fast becoming a conventional method of coloring textiles where the discharge or resist methods are not required. Each color used must have its individual roller, and each color must fit to the exact, minute part of the pattern required in the finished material. At present, it is estimated to be the cheapest form of printing with regard to price. Ideal for general printing purposes, it is particularly effective where high production and long runs of goods are required. (See Overprinting.)

SCREEN OR STENCIL PRINTING: A wooden frame resembling a window frame is constructed. One side of the frame is covered with silk bolting cloth. This cloth, high in texture and of very fine mesh, is rather expensive.

The design is traced on the silk cloth or screen. (Nylon is also a very popular base fabric.) A filler of enamel or varnish, sometimes called "tish," is applied to all parts of the screen except the design.

The prepared screen is placed on the material to be printed. The stencil must be in contact with the material. Dye paste is now placed on top of the stencil and stroked back and forth a few times with a squeegee. The dye paste is forced through the open meshes of the bolting cloth, but only in those places not previously covered with the filler.

To set the color in the design that has been transferred to the cloth, a steaming is necessary. Final treatments should be carefully done. Screen printing has considerable call in small production plants which specialize in intricate designs. The method is rather slow with regard to production since there must be a different screen used for each color to be placed upon the goods.

SHADOW PRINTING: Silk, ribbon, or cretonne, woven with printed warp yarn forming indistinct design. Reversible.

STIPPLE EFFECT IN PRINTING: This is merely the printing of small dotted effects in between the spaces or bare areas of a printed design. It is used chiefly for novelty effects on fabrics.

TJAP PRINTING: A very interesting type of block printing executed by dipping blocks into heated wax and then impressing them upon the material—usually a cotton, silk, or rayon fabric—after which it is dyed and the wax removed, leaving a permanent design. These blocks are made by the natives of Java and the other islands in the East Indies by bending small strips of copper into the desired curves for sections of the pattern and inserting them into the end grain of the blocks of wood, allowing them to project a little less than one-eighth inch from the surface.

The small copper ridges formed in this way are similar to the cloisons which are applied to keep the enamels separated in the decoration of the well-known cloisonné. Owing to the fact that it is a very difficult and painstaking task to make these blocks or tjaps, the results of this art often bring prices as high as direct handwork.

TOILE DE JOUY: Originally a set of cotton fabrics printed in imitation of the various imported oriental materials brought into France and executed in Jouy, by Oberkampf. In 1759, as the result of a governmental citation, Oberkampf established his plant in Jouy; his influence still prevails.

Prior to Oberkampf's methods, the printing process on cottons consisted of marking the outline of the design in black and filling in the colors by hand. Oberkampf introduced block and roller-print effects on his fabrics. His success soon became phenomenal, since his Jouy "canvases" became the rage in dressgoods and for general decorative purposes.

WARP PRINTING: The principles in this method of printing are like those in ordinary cloth printing, except that the mechanical operation is different. The yarn to be printed is wound onto a beam and the warp threads are passed through the printing machine. The dyestuff, which has been made into paste form, is applied to these parallel ends as they come in contact with the printing rollers.

The yarn is dyed prior to being rewound onto a second warp beam. This beam is ultimately set into sockets at the back of the loom, so that the weaving interlacing the warp ends and the filling picks may be done.

The pattern, motif, or design in warp-printed goods will not have the sharp cleavage lines noted in some other types of printed goods; the effect is mottled in appearance. Because of the white or single color filling used in the weaving, the spots of color on the warp that look brilliant before the weaving of the fabric will be subdued to considerable degree. Fabric printed by this method is said to have a quiet appearance.

So that the warp may be controlled while it is being treated, the following method is resorted to: every few inches a filling pick is inserted through the warp in order to give a loose construction controlled at all times. This method will hold the warp to be printed in a chain form when ready for treatment.

When the warp is spread out and placed in the loom, dominant and recessive effects of the color in the goods will be toned off. These prints are usually very attractive. Uses include counterpanes, spreads, dressgoods, covers, and hangings.

WEDGWOOD PRINT: Print of white design on colored ground similar to effect on Wedgwood china.

KNITTED FABRIC PRINTING

The utmost care and precaution have to be given knitgoods because of the nature of their construction. Four methods are in use today; these follow:

DIRECT PRINTING WITH COPPER ROLLERS: This method is ideal for warp knitgoods. The fabrics is gummed lightly to the back gray cloth to counteract possible slippage of the goods in processing. Printing is usually done on the reverse side of the material, since the back of the goods is smoother than the actual face of the cloth. (See page 218.)

SCREEN OR STENCIL HAND-PRINTING: Both warp and weft knit fabrics are colored by the method but compared with the other methods in use it is rather expensive since production is low and time-consuming.

AUTOMATIC PRINTING, FLAT-BED SCREEN: In one of the more recent developments in fabric printing of textiles, a heavy-gauge neoprene belt is used, and the screens are set to a specially designed set of lifting brackets, placed on each side of the belt. Cloth to be printed is run onto the belt and the brackets automatically lift and lower the screens onto the material thereby printing the motif onto the goods. production is low and time-consuming.

ROTARY SCREEN PRINTING: The "Aljaba" machine is set up comparably with the direct or cylinder method of printing, which is done by means of copper rollers. Phosphor-bronze gauze screens on the rotary method are used instead of the rollers to produce the pattern. The printing color paste is fed into the inside of the frame where a small metal roller forces it through the open areas (or interstices) onto the fabric. Both warp and weft knitgoods may be colored by this method.

PULLEY CORD. Known as corde du rame in French, it is used in the old-time drawloom and is the section of cord between the necking cord and the pulleys; after passing over the pulleys this cord is then called the tail cord. The French meaning is for the entire cord—both pulley and tail cord sections.

PULLNOT COTTON. A Georgia cotton of medium-size bolls, easy to pick, with a staple of about ⅞ inch. The staple is uniform.

PULL-OVER SWEATER. See MEN'S AND BOYS' SWEATERS.

"PULL THE WOOL OVER YOUR EYES." Comes from the legal profession in Britain. In the halcyon days of Old Bailey Court in London, judges wore white woolen wigs which frequently slipped down over the eyes of the wearer thereby impairing the vision. Thus, developed from this the expression now implies when a barrister or lawyer "slips one over on the court."

PULP SHEET. The thin, rectangular purified cellulose sheets of pulp obtained from wood on the sulphite method. Purified cotton linters also are sold in this sheet form. Rayon producers usually receive this cellulose raw material in this condition.

PULU FIBER. Obtained from the stems of fern trees in the Hawaiian Islands, this soft, lustrous, weak, golden-brown fiber is used for stuffing.

PUMP. A low-cut slip-on shoe used as formal wear and devoid of laces or straps. May or may not have an ornamental bow over the toe-instep area. Dull calf leather or patent leather are the materials used.

PUMP DELIVERY. In the manufacture of man-fibers it is the volume of liquid delivered by one revolution of the spinning pump.

PUNASA PRATTI COTTON. A short, pure-white cotton staple raised in Madras Presidency, India.

PUNCH BOWL. See PUNCH BOX.

PUNCH BOX. Winding of worsted tops, usually in a set of four, in parallel order on a headless core. This ball, fed into the Noble comber, is about a foot thick and about two feet in diameter. Each of the four tops in the ball is fed into its plow or plowth after the fibers have been raised slightly and then brushed in the action by the plowth.

PUNCHED FELT. Felt is punched into burlap by means of a board which has an up-an-down motion. The board is set with a series of nicked pins which catch the felt fibers and carry them through the burlap on the upward motion. As the pins are on the way down, the burlap wipes off the felt fibers, thereby allowing the pins to be ready to pick up the next batch of stock to be punched into the burlap. See Tufted Fabrics, et al.

PUNCHED FELT, NEEDLE FELT. Short staple wool stock of good felting properties which is attached to both sides of burlap by the use of a series or barbed needles so that the felt product may be obtained after manipulation.

PUNCHED FELT RUG. This is made with a burlap base into which first jute is punched, and then wool. Rubber composition is spread on the back in order to lock the fibers and prevent slipping.

PUNCHER; PUNCH MACHINE. The person who punches out the cards used in embroidery on a Schiffli machine when a Jacquard motif is desired. See Jacquard Card, Jacquard Lace Motion.

PUNCHING. Applied to the Noble circular comber, it is the preparing of the four-end balls of sliver for location in the machine to be made ready for the actual combing operation.

PUNCHING SLIVER. The winding operation which prepares the four-end balls of worsted sliver or top for processing in the Noble comber. There are eighteen compartments in this comber, and each compartment can take care of four balls of sliver for a total of seventy-two balls being manipulated when the machine is in operation.

PUNCH MACHINE. The person who punches out the cards used in embroidery on a Schiffli machine when a Jacquard motif is desired. See Jacquard Card, Jacquard Lace Motion.

PUNICIN. Various mollusks of purpura give this purple coloring matter; it is used in dyeing.

PUNJAB-AMERICAN COTTON. A transplanted American cotton raised in the Punjab, India. It simulates American Uplands in color and working properties; 15/16-inch staple, lint yield of about 32 per cent, spins to about 25s for use as warp yarn.

PUNJAB COTTON. General name for Indian cottons raised in the Punjab, India, and grown from transplanted American cotton seeds.

PUNJAB SILK. 1. The silk reeled in the Punjab, India, a great silk center. About eight distinct grades are obtained from the reeling basins. 2. Silk fabric of this name made to simulate better quality Indian silks made in checks, stripes, Jacquard motifs, shot-about ef-

fects, figured designs, etc.

PUNJAB WOOL. The very best of wool raised in India.

PUNTA ARENAS WOOL. Wool named for this important seaport in Chile on the Straits of Magellan is a low, crossbred type that is ideal for knitting purposes. Large quantities of this wool, as well as fleeces from the neighboring provinces in Argentina and Chile, are shipped to New Orleans for American consumption. The wool grades from 46s to 56s quality.

PUNTO. Italian and Spanish for point—lace or mesh.

PUNTO IN ARIA. Means "stitches in the air." The term was applied to the earliest form of needle-point laces following reticellas, which were an evolution of cutwork. Punto in Aria was accomplished without cutting any background. See VENETIAN POINT.

PUPA. See CHRYSALIS.

PURDAH. 1. A curtain or screen used to seclude or keep women from view. 2. Fine veiling of this name is used by high-caste Indian women.

PURE FINISH. Any material which is finished without dressing, sizing, weighting; a material which contains no thermosetting resin and is often used with relation to manmade and natural fiber blended fabrics.

PURE SILK DYE. The Federal Trade Commission has ruled that this term refers to silk goods, degummed and dyed, together with the necessary finishing material except tin weighting. Weighting of 10 per cent is allowed for all fabrics with the exception of black when 15 per cent is permissible.

PURE STARCH FINISH. A finish applied in which pure starch or gum is used to give a crisp feel and appearance to the cloth. The goods are not back-filled. Starch alone, for example, is used, and much attention is given to the treatment. Goods which have been finished this way are easy to manipulate in the cutting-up house, and it is one of the most popular fabrics sought for by the cut-fit-trim trade.

PURFLE. A border, hem, or trimming used in embroidery work; to trim. Purfled means embroidered with flowers or sprigs or ornamented with metallic threads.

PURGEUR. The French word for cleanser. It is a clasp lined with cloth through which the skeins of raw silk are passed to remove loose silk and foreign particles.

PURIFYING FINISH. Any type of finish which prevents formation of body odors by destroying odor-causing bacteria coming in contact with the goods.

PURILON. See American Viscose Company, Inc., Division of FMC Corporation.

PURITAN COSTUME. See Costume, Puritan.

PURL, PEARL KNITTING. A method of knitting whereby some loops are formed opposite others. They may be alternate to give a rib effect, or they may alternate in courses to produce a links-links fabric. Horizontal ridges will show on both sides of the goods. Purl is actually the opposite of knit.

PURL STITCH. A knitting stitch whereby alternate courses of loops are drawn to the other side of the goods. This causes the material to look the same on both sides so that each side has ridges that run across the width of the material. It is noted for its elasticity.

PURL STITCH ON CIRCULAR KNITTING MACHINES. A stitch which is the same on each side of the fabric; done on a circular or barrel-like structure, not on a flatbed. The needle bed in both circular and flat machines lies in the same plane and the same needle goes back and forth to make the fabric. The flatbed, as noted in the Lium Machine, can effect stitch transfer but this is not possible on a circular frame. The circular type knitting is the lowest in production in the field of weft-knitting machines. It is, however, a very versatile machine and can make plain, purl, or rib stitches but the method, generally speaking, may not be very economical. Fancy stitches cannot be made in this procedure. See Purl Stitch.

PURL STITCH ON FLAT KNITTING MACHINES. Made on a flat or circular when pertaining to a flat frame this term is also known as a links-links frame, the word being taken from the German word, links, which means to the left or leftward. The purl machine always moves to the left. This type of stitch gives a round, bloated stitch, much more so than the typical jersey stitch. The name purl comes from the fact that the stitch has some resemblance to a pearl.

This stitch is much used in so-called fancy knits with interlooping stitches in which the face and the reverse of the jersey stitch appear in alternate courses. The cloth is identical on both sides. The effect has the characteristics of hand knitted fabrics and finds much use in sweaters.

In flat purl knitting, the needlebeds lay in the same flat plane, and the same needle traverses the needlebeds to-an-fro to produce the fabric.

The actual stitch does not transfer, with

the exception of the Lium machine which allows stitch transfer by the use of a stitch transfer jack. This type of knitting does not make fancy stitches as noted in openwork knit goods. Generally speaking, this type of knitting is ideal for lower-priced goods as well as high production volume.

PURPLE SHEEL. See TYRIAN PURPLE.

PURPLE. 1. A color of mingled red and blue, between crimson and violet. 2. The cloth or garment of this color worn by sovereigns and emperors of ancient Rome, the color of royal dignity. 3. The office of a cardinal, from the official red hat and robes; also, the episcopal dignity of the purple insignia.

PURUMU FIBER. Fine, silklike bast fiber raised in the Canary Islands; used for cordage.

PUSHMINA. See CASHMERE.

PUSSYWILLOW. A popular silk staple which is soft, thin, dull in appearance, and gives good wear. This attractive cloth is used for dresses, waists, and lining material.

PUT RUG. Rug made of fine white wool in Madras, India.

PUTTEE. A tubular, plain-knitted cloth used in army equipage as a legging material. It is wound spirally around the leg, up to the knee. It replaced the leather or woven puttee worn by the soldier. About three-fourths of the cloth composition is shoddy or some other substitute fiber. Very popular at the time of World War I, it is now outmoded.

PUT-UP, WRAP-UP. The package in which yarn or thread is sold—in cones, bobbins, cheeses, skeins, tubes, etc.

PUYA FIBER. A stem fiber yielded by the Manotia Puya, a wild plant of India; used for cordage.

PX CLOTH. A special type of pyroxylin-impregnated, washable bookbinding cloth.

PYJAMA. British spelling of pajama.

PYRENEAN. Coarse Spanish wool much used in making carpets.

PYROXYLIN. A cellulose product which is used to coat cotton or rayon fabrics to make a fabric waterproof, stain-resistant, etc.

Q

QIANA (Kee AH nah). A derivative nylon fiber of E. I. duPont de Nemours & Co., Inc., Wilmington, Delaware, this is a registered trademark of the company and is presently made in the Chatta-

nooga, Tennessee plant.

Qiana has a tri-lobal cross-section which shows up in the form of tiny triangles when viewed under the microscope. These structures are comparable with those noted in a silk filament. It has the appearance of silk and excellent wash-and-wear qualities. In fact, it has been stated that Qiana "has all that silk had, and then some."

The fiber involves an entirely new combination of basic ingredients, all made by the company. Qiana is in the generic category of nylon since the polyamide chemical linkage of its building blocks are similar to those of regular nylon. Formerly known as Fiber Y, Qiana is basically a concept, not a single chemical. There are now many types and variations in nylon with different building blocks and variable properties engineered for specific end uses.

Qiana is made from Nylon Type 472 and has the following properties:

Density	1.03
Elongation	30.00%
Ironing Temp.	365° F.
Modulus	30.00
Moisture Regain	2.5%
Shrinkage	(heat) 10.00%
Tenacity	3.3 gpd.
Ultra Violet	Resistant

Qiana is dimensionally stable to heat and humidity. It has excellent hand appeal, appearance, resiliency, and pleat retention in even boiling water. Its attractive luster is comparable with silk. As mentioned before, Qiana has good wash-and-wear properties, high comfort factor with excellent porosity and wicking characteristics, high coverage per pound, and very clear color motifs in dyed or printed fabrics.

The end uses of Qiana are as follows: blouses, curtains, dresses, drapes, foundations, hosiery, intimate apparel, lace, linings, neckwear, rainwear, ribbons, scarves, shirtings, shoe fabrics, suitings, sweaters, upholstery.

After spending twenty years and $75 million on Qiana's research and development, it is no wonder that duPont wanted the fiber to be of real commercial value. In order to promote acceptance of the fiber and high volume sales, duPont engineered an ingenius introduction for the fiber.

In the clever and original introduction of Qiana, the tightest security measures were used, including the usual fiber-to-fabric evaluations. Previewing of the fiber was done by outstanding silk mill

official in Lyons; Zurich, Switzerland; and Milan, Italy, all leaders in the silk industry and where silk had held sway for four hundred years. A group of experimental fabrics was placed with comparable silk fabrics, none of which was identified, and the officials had trouble distinguishing which fabrics were actually Qiana.

The product was introduced to French couturiers without their knowing what fiber was in the fabrics. DuPont then used the same procedure with the fabric houses. Later on, when the first sample cuts had to be delivered, the couturiers were advised that if they ordered fabric "so-and-so" on the premise that it was silk, they could withdraw their order since it was not silk, but actually a new fiber.

In June, 1968, the new fiber was announced to eight major cities throughout the world by means of magazines, newspapers, radio and television and special wire services. The following gives the chronology of this outstanding fiber:

1. *Press Introduction:* Occurred on June 27, 1968:

    7:00 A.M. (PDT) in Los Angeles, California.

    10:00 A.M. (EDT) in New York City, Montreal, and Buenos Aires.

    3:00 P.M. in Dusselforf, London, Milan, and Paris.

2. *Couture Introduction:* Held on July 23, 1968 when 116 Fall/Winter costumes were shown on this date through July 31, commencing at the House of Pierre Balmain.

3. *Couture Introduction in the United States:* 92 Spring Costumes were shown from November 4th through November 15th, 1968.

4. *Ensuing Couture Showings:* These follow:

    Commencing January 13, 1969, Spring/Summer in Rome, Italy.

    Commencing January 20, 1069, Spring/Summer in Paris, France.

    Commencing June 3, 1969, Fall/Winter in New York City.

    Comencing July 15, 1969, Fall/Winter in Rome, Italy.

    Commencing July 21, 1969, Fall/Winter in Paris, France.

5. *Lingerie Introduction:* This was given in New York City on August 13, 1969.

6. *Men's Neckwear Introduction:* Nationwide on October 26, 1969.

QIANA TYPE 472, SOME CHEMICAL AND PHYSICAL PROPERTIES OF CONTINUOUS FILAMENT TEXTILE YARN AND FABRICS MADE FROM:

CHARACTERISTICS	QIANA TYPE 472 NYLON	POLYESTER	NYLON 6,6	SILK
BREAKING TENACITY g/d	2.7-3.2	3-5	4-6	4
BREAKING ELONGATION %	26-36	19-33	22-40	20
SHRINKAGE % (as				
shipped) BOS	6-7	8-11	5-11	0.2
375° F TOTAL BOS				
and HS	10-12	12-17	5-11	0.2
SPECIFIC GRAVITY	1.03	1.38	1.14	1.36
PERCENT MOISTURE REGAIN				
AT 70° F/65% R.H.	2.5	0.4-0.8	4.2	11.0
MELTING POINT in °F	525.00	482.00	482.00	Indeterminate
STICK TEMPERATURE in °F	447.00	457.00	446.00	Indeterminate
FABRIC REACTION				
ABRASION RESISTANCE	Good	Good-Excellent	Excellent	Fair
PRESSED CREASE RETENTION	Excellent	Excellent	Excellent	Poor
SAFE IRONING TEMPERATURE				
in °F	350.00	275.00	275.00	300.00
STRENGTH	Excellent	Good-Excellent	Excellent	Good
WRINKLE RESISTANCE	Excellent	Excellent	Good	Fair
COLORFASTNESS	Good	Good	Poor-Good	Poor-Good
SUNLIGHT RESISTANCE	Excellent	Excellent	Fair-Excellent	Poor
STABILITY TO WASHING	Excellent	Excellent	Excellent	Fair
FLAMMABILITY	Low	Low	Low	Low
CHEMICAL RESISTANCE—				
ACID	Good	Good-Excellent	Fair	Fair
ALKALIS	Excellent	Good	Excellent	Poor

Courtesy: **TEXTILES FIBERS DEPARTMENT** and **MARKETING DIVISION** of **E. I. duPONT de NEMOURS & CO., Inc.,** Wilmington, 19898.

QUADRANT. The wheel on the mule spinning frame, with an arm and a chain, which guides and directs the winding of newly spun yarn onto cops or bobbins.

QUADRIGA CLOTH. It is similar to percale or cotton print material but has a silky finish which is the result of a process called Needleizing. It runs about 80-square in count and has received superior handling in all processing from raw cotton to finished cloth. Special attention is given to dyeing, rendering the material fast to laundering, and giving the individual colors a brighter hue than that of ordinary fabrics.

A slightly higher priced than that of the usual cotton print is amply justified by the quality of the fabric. Quadriga cloth is the first piece goods line to carry the approval seal of the American Institute of Laundering. Product of Ely & Walker Co., Inc., a division of Washington Industries, Inc., Memphis, Tenn.

QUADRILLE. French for checked, checkered (quadrillé).

QUADRIVOLTINS. Those races of silkworms which produce four broods a year.

QUAKER-COLORED. Gray or neutral and inconspicuous in cloth and apparel.

QUAKER COSTUME. See Costume, Quaker.

QUALITATIVE CHEMICAL TESTS.

ACETATES:

Give off acetic acid when heated with sulphuric acid, odor of vinegar.

Give off sweet odor of ethyl aceate when heated with alcohol and sulphuric acid.

ALUMINUM SALTS:

Form a white precipitate with 10 per cent ammonium hydroxide solution.

Form a white precipitate with 5 per cent sodium hydroxide solution. The precipitate dissolves when an excess of sodium hydroxide is added.

AMMONIUM SALTS:

Give off ammonia when 5 per cent sodium hydroxide solution is added. The vapors have a characteristic odor and turn wet, red litmus paper blue.

CALCIUM SALTS:

In alkaline or neutral solutions give a white precipitate with 5 per cent ammonium oxalite solution, which dissolves in hydrochloric acid but not in acetic acid.

CARBONATES:

Give off carbon dioxide when acid is added.

Give a reddish brown precipitate with 5 per cent mercuric chloride solution while bicarbonates form a white

precipitate.

CHLORIDES:

Give a white curdy precipitate with 1 per cent silver nitrate solution. The precipitate is insoluble in nitric acid, but soluble in ammonium hydroxide.

COPPER SALTS:

Give a deep blue color with ammonium hydroxide.

In a solution acidified with hydrochloric acid, copper salts give a red coating of metallic copper to a bright piece of iron.

HYPOCHLORITES:

Give off chlorine gas upon the addition of acid.

Turn starch iodide paper blue.

QUALITY. This refers to wool fibers with regard to their diameter, relative fineness, and working properties, particularly in spinning and finishing. The quality of the fiber determines the price paid for it, and, to some degree also, the use to be made of it by the consumer.

QUALITY AUDIT. Reinspection of yarn in packing cases to ascertain the outgoing quality of the inspected yarn.

QUALITY BINDING. A rugged twilled tape made of coarse, but strong, wool; used for carpet binding.

QUALITY NUMBER. The count number by which wool, tops, noils, and yarns are known, this being based on the count of worsted yarn to which the material will spin. Thus 60s tops are supposed to spin approximately to 60s yarns and should consequently be made from 60s quality of wool. The noils taken from 60s quality of wool during combing are 60s noils.

QUANT, MARY. This fabulous London designer virtually changed the fashion world with the introduction of the miniskirt in 1965 and 1966. Her "Mod Clothes" became famous almost overnight. At present, she has what is known as "The Ginger Group," and to her credit it must be stated that her prices are quite reasonable, in the $35 to $55 range. She believes in making her profit in volume, not high-priced sales.

In May 1970, she announced that she was abandoning the miniskirt and her showing in London at this time did not have a single miniskirt in it. She commented that "The mini has served its purpose for proving that woman is emancipated. That is now accepted. We can get back to normal, to cool elegance." Alexander Plunket Green, her husband, has done splendid work in the promotion of Miss Quant's wares which are now heavily concentrated in the cosmetic field.

QUARPEL. Developed by the U. S. Quartermaster Department, Natick, Massachusetts, this repellent is of the extremely durable water repellent type for use on many types of textile fabrics. The finish is obtained through a combination of pyridinium compounds with a fluorochemical.

QUARTER. A loom width of cloth measuring nine inches or one quarter of a yard. The ell was originally the unit of measure in loom weaving in Europe and because of the fact that it was a 27-inch width for the fabric, the first looms built and used there were made in a 29-inch or 30-inch width reed space. The 27-inch cloth would therefore be called 3/4 (three-quarter) goods; 108-inch sheeting would be 12/4 goods.

QUARTER BLANKET. A blanket used under a horse's harness to cover from the tail to beyond the saddle.

QUARTER-BLOOD WOOL. Domestic wool which constitutes the bulk of American 50s worsted stock.

QUARTER-BLOOD WOOL STOCK. This will make yarns from 12 to 16 cut. This class of wool, unless very low in the one-quarter grade, will draw to about one fourth, which means that a 12-cut yarn will need a 9-cut slubbing on the finisher card.

QUARTER GOODS. A width of nine inches. Three-quarter goods would

be 27 inches wide; six-quarter, 54 inches wide, and labeled 6/4.

QUARTER-LINED. Less than half-lined and little more than skeleton-lined, in speaking of garment lining. It merely covers the interlining.

QUATRE. French (ouate) for cotton wadding, and for wadding used to make garments.

QUATRE FILS. Strong French sail-cloth made of four-ply warp and single filling yarns.

QUEBRACHO. Any of several tropical American trees producing a bark of value in medicinal and textile fields. The red quebracho, from its red bark, gives a material rich in tannin and ideal for dyeing shades of red.

QUEBRADINHO COTTON. A raw tree cotton of Brazil.

QUEDDENG FIBER. A coarse Philippine fiber used for cordage.

QUEEN, SOUTHERN QUEEN COTTON. An Arkansas cotton of 1-inch staple and about 35 per cent lint yield.

QUEENSLAND COTTON. A long, white, silklike cotton raised in Australia which can spin from 100s to 200s.

QUEENSLAND GRASS CLOTH PLANT. Australian plant that gives a fiber that is used by the natives to make fabrics.

QUEENSLAND HEMP. Name given to hemp obtained from a plant in Queensland, Australia.

QUEEN STITCH. A kind of embroidery stitch, characteristically a square within a square and with parallel sides.

QUEEN'S MOURNING. The cloth is black with a fine, white hairline stripe in it. This material has found favor here, and it has been converted into hairline, pinstripe, and chalk stripe designs popular in men's wear. Red, white, blue, and other staple colors are used in the pattern.

QUELLIN. A sizing ingredient, adhesive in nature, which is free of salts or chemicals. This white sparkling product will give a strong paste which mixes well with cold water and requires a short boiling.

QUENCH, QUENCH BOX. As a verb, quench means to extinguish, as sparks or fire. In the textile trade, it is a box or kier, filled with water, into which fabric is run through after being singed, so that there will be no chance of sparks, fire, or spontaneous combustion. Desizing agents may be contained in the quench bath.

QUERCITRIN. Yellow crystalline compound found in the bark of Amer-

ican oak trees and from the rind of some fruits. Serves as a base for dye-stuffs.

QUERCITRON. The crushed and powdered inner bark of the American black oak tree. It is used in dyeing and tanning, and gives a base for yellow dyestuff. When used with mordants it can dye wool or cotton. Also known as black oak, dyer's oak.

QUETCH. A trough containing finish applied to cloth by means of a roller partly immersed in the liquid that rolls in contact with the cloth, or by running the material through the liquid.

QUILL. A bobbin upon which silk or rayon filling is wound. It is comparable with the shuttle and bobbin used in weaving cotton, woolen, and worsted. Quills are used on narrow looms in making certain silk and rayon fabrics.

Quills were originally made from goose quills on a wheel similar to a large spinning wheel. There is one of these devices in the Historical Museum, Buffalo, New York. Some weavers, to wind filling or "weft" yarn, have been known to use "lemonade straws" cut to the desired length.

QUILL EMBROIDERY. Split-porcupine-quill embroidery work produced by the Grey Nuns of Canada; feathers, strips of skins, etc., are also used by them to decorate their famous embroidered textile materials and products.

QUILLER. A type of multi-banked frame made in a tiered, setback form, made up of about 400 spindles on which bobbins can be placed and rotated for the receipt of individual ends of yarn dyed in warp chain form. Much used in "chambray" weaving mills, where there must be a consistency of filling appearance.

The operation is, in essence, the reverse of warping. The method can also be used to salvage over-run warp yarn to convert it into filling packages.

QUILLING. 1. The last process in the long-chain system for filling yarns, in which the threads forming the chain are wound on filling bobbins, or quills, ready for the shuttle. 2. Winding filling yarn, especially of rayon or silk, onto quills. 3. A strip of lace, ribbon or the like, fluted or folded, so as somewhat to resemble a row of quills.

QUILLWORK. An art of North American Indians; the ornamentation of fabrics, skins, etc., by overlaying the foundation with quills of various types.

QUILT. 1. Usually a bed covering of two thicknesses of material with wool, cotton, or down batting in between for warmth. 2. Also used for jackets and linings of coats. 3. Also the sewing stitch used to make a quilt.

QUILTING. The sewing of a padding or insulating material between two pieces of fabric to prevent the shifting of the contained material.

QUILTING COTTON. Cotton batting or wadding used for stuffing quilts.

QUILTS. Materials used for bed and couch coverings. There are several members of the quilt family—coverlets, bedspreads, counterpanes, marseilles, matelasses, ripplettes, comforters, etc. All these serve about the same purpose, but a regular quilt is usually made of fine silk or acetate, stuffed and decorated, soft and downy in feel. Quilts add much to the general appearance of a bed or couch. The crazy quilt and patchwork quilt are made of odd pieces of fabric intricately sewn together in many designs—an art of pioneer days.

QUINOLINE. A colorless liquid compound, with a tarry odor, obtained variously, as by distilling quinine, cinchonine, or by the destructive distillation of coal and bones. Also called Quinolin, it serves as the basis for dyestuffs. Synthetic quinoline is now on the market.

QUINOLINE DYES. Any dye whose base is quinoline.

QUINTAIN. High-grade cotton lawn named for city of origin in Brittany, France.

QUINTESS. This product of Phillips Fibers Corporation, subsidiary of Phillips Petroleum Company, Inc., Greenville, South Carolina, is a polyester fiber which has outstanding wrinkle resistance, crease retention, and durable press properties. Quick drying, it has great strength and abrasion resistance. It is resistant to pilling and has excellent dyeability with good color fastness. It is not affected by organic solvents, micro-organisms, or insects. It is blended with natural fibers in the manufacture of apparel fabrics; knit and woven fabrics for use in coating, dressgoods, shirting, suiting, and underwear. This staple or filament fiber comes in dull and semi-dull lusters.

QUINTESS, "BALANCED MODULUS." This polyester staple fiber is engineered to provide some of the advantages of high modulus while eliminating its drawbacks. This fiber offers significantly higher finishing efficiency and width control. The fiber combines a balanced modulus with a specially developed spin finish and permanent crimping process, resulting in improved processing of spun yarns with greater tensile strength than yarns of regular modulus. This yarn has fewer yarn breaks than

other yarns of this type, fewer ends down, fewer reties in spinning, winding, warping, slashing, and weaving. Registered trademark of Phillips Fibers Corporation, Greenville, South Carolina.

QUINZE-SEIZE. In French, *quinze* means fifteen while *seize* means sixteen. Refers to gros de Tours, other "gros" fabrics, taffeta, etc., which became popular in France during the time of the First Empire and the Restoration periods for curtains, draperies, hangings, furniture, etc. Since the fabrics were finished at 42 inches, the expression, quinze-seize was used, and it is 15/16ths of an ell which is 45 inches in length or width.

QUIRK. 1. A stocking clock used for decoration. 2. The diamond-shaped segment found at the base of a glove finger and the thumb.

QULON, NYLON 66. Registered trademark of Beaunit Fibers Division of Beaunit Corporation, New York City, for its regular, industrial-type, textured nylon yarns. The product comes from an extrusion of polymerized resin. Qulon has high tenacity, elastic recovery, is resistant to abrasion and chafing, and dries rapidly. Density of the fiber is 1.14 and melting point is 480° F. It is used in home furnishings, and in apparel and industrial fabrics.

QUOTATIONS, COTTON. They are usually based on the quality or grade known as Middling Uplands. The grades, above or below Middling, are quoted at a specific number of points above or below, on or off, Middling.

A point is 1/100 cent. The maximum rise or fall in the price of cotton, in one day, is 200 points, or two cents a pound. If the market should happen to open with the price more than 200 points, either way, compared with the close of the previous day, the Exchange will close for the day, or even longer. This occurred in August 1914, following the hectic last days of the preceding July. It happened in March 1933, when all business was temporarily suspended and banks closed their doors for adjustments and return to normalcy. In both cases, the Exchange, along with all other Exchanges, was closed for several days.

R

RABANNA. Raffia fiber native to Madagascar; material is used for curtains and draperies in South Africa.

RABAT. This French word is the name for a small piece of black, blue, or white cloth which is divided in the

middle and which, attached to a rudimentary collar and resting upon the upper chest, is worn by some of the French clergy. Is not in general or universal use. The Brothers of Christian Doctrine wear a white rabat.

RABBI. The black, red, or purple cloth worn at the neck by prelates. Made of silk, this lightweight, compact material, which is not easily washed, is fitted to the collar of the wearer.

RABBIT HAIR. This hair is used in combination with other fibers; often is a 20 per cent content in the better woolen, worsted, and other blended fabrics. Fabrics with rabbit hair have improved luster, smoothness, softness, and appealing hand. Some few staples of lower quality are improved by the use of rabbit hair. Fiber ranges from 1 cm. to 2 cm. in length.

RABBIT-HAIR CLOTH. Some women's wear dress goods have varying amounts of rabbit hair in them to add to the hand and finish. Often this is done so as to give almost the feel of true Angora, and, dependent on the percentage of hair used, little or much of it may be observed on the surface effect of the fabric.

RACCOON, RACOON. A medium to long-haired fur, grayish in color, with dark back. Wearing qualities excellent. Judged by fullness of fur and natural color. Found in United States, Canada, and Northern Mexico. For sports and casual wear.

RACCROC STITCH. A very fine thread stitch used in Brussels lace to join reseau grounds made upon the pillow. The work is so fine that it is difficult to observe the actual stitches.

RACE. 1. The front ridge of the beater, on which the warp threads rest in order to facilitate the passing of the shuttle. Also known as raceplate, it provides a "floor" for the shed of the loom. 2. Also refers to the floats in several pile fabrics which lie above the ground threads in the construction. These courses form the race, and the floats in the cloth are ultimately severed or cut in the cutting operation, as in the case of corduroy.

RACE CLOTH. A pocketed fabric worn by race horses; the prescribed weights, according to the rules, are carried in the pockets.

RACEPLATE, RACE PLATE. The narrow wooden, metallic, or plastic flat strip in the lay of the loom set in front of the reed. The plate serves as a support and directs the course of the shuttle as it passes through the shed of the loom. The bottom part of the warp just about rests on the race plate.

Filling stop motions are set in the race plate either at the side or in the center of this plate.

RACK. In tricot knitting, a unit of measure which consists of 480 courses. The quality of tricot fabric is judged by the number of inches which a rack, or 480 courses, measures. For example, a rack measure of eight inches is known as an eight-inch quality knit.

The speed of tricot equipment may be denoted by the number of racks made in an hour. The conversion factor is 8)480 ÷ 60(. A frame running at 360 r.p.m. an hour would produce 45 racks an hour.

RACKING. Movement of the needle beds in a knitting machine in relation to each other. If the needle bed is racked to the right, the front bed is shifted to the right and the back bed to the left. In racking to the left, the reverse is true.

RACK KNITTING, RACKING. A knitting operation used to produce the modification of a stitch, used chiefly in rib stitch. See Illustrated Section. Racking is the moving of one set of needles by the other set between the courses. It gives a distorted or off-balance effect to the right or to the left in a zigzag series of wales, or the wales may incline to the right or to the left.

RACK OR SHOG. 1. The lateral movement of the needle bed on a flat knitting machine or the angular displacement of the dial relative to the cylinder on a circular machine. 2. A second meaning of rack implies 480 courses of a warp-knitted fabric. When applied to a machine with two sets of needle bars the term implies 480 courses on each set of needles. Rack is the unit of measurement of quality on the frame.

RACK STITCH. A further refinement of the half-cardigan stitch. The reverse side of the fabric has the same series of wales as in the full and half-cardigan stitch. On the face of the fabric, however, the wales have been so adjusted or racked that they give the effect of a herringbone motif.

RADCLIFFE REED COUNTS. The simple method of the number of dents per inch used to figure the number of ends per inch in a cloth; a 40/2 Radcliffe Reed means a Number 40 reed, with two-ends per dent, or a total of eighty ends to the inch in texture.

RADDLE. 1. A device for spreading the warp threads evenly as they are wound onto the beam. It is used when the loom is warped from the back to the front. 2. Used for front warping as a spreader which allows the warp

to pass through in groups or sections of ends. It is provided with a removable top. Also known as Ravel.

RADICAL. A fundamental constituent or part of a compound, specifically, a group of atoms which acts as a unit in a compound and may either pass unchanged through a series of reactions or be replaced as though it were a single atom. From the Latin, radix, meaning root.

RADIUM. A lustrous, supple silk or rayon fabric having the drapability of crepe and the crispness of taffeta. Plain weave. Used for women's dresses, slips, negligees, blouses, linings, draperies.

RADIUM SILK. A lustrous silk fabric made with raw silk warp and hard-twist tram filling, piece-dyed. There are many constructions and some simulations of this cloth on the market. Radium is light in weight, gives good wear, and is soft, thin, and smooth. Used for dresses, underwear, slip-ons, and waists.

RADIUM TAFFETA. This high-grade cloth is made of silk or rayon and is piece-dyed in light shades. Texture is about 400 x 100; 24/26 denier yarn is used in warp and filling, the latter having about 40 turns of hard-twist to the inch. Plain weave is reeded with six ends per dent. The cloth closely resembles high-quality poplin in construction.

RADNOR. English breed of sheep. The original has ceased to exist; present-day Radnor produces a close fleece noted for its coarse belly wool.

RADOMIR. A Bulgarian-type sheep which yields a fleece of about 3½ pounds; staple is white.

RADSIMIR. RADZIMIR, RHADZI-MIR. Black silk or rayon fabric used for mourning purposes. Made on a broken twill weave, repeating on eight shafts, the cloth comes in a variety of fabrics, all more or less of the same family group—barathea, bengaline, broadcloth, satin, taffeta. Only the Radsimir fabric is made on the eight-harness weave; the other fabrics merely more or less resemble this material. They have caused the demand for this original mourning fabric to decline.

RADUNER WASH - AND - WEAR MECHANICAL PROCESS. Invented by Dr. Alfred Lauchenauer, of Raduner & Co., A. G. Horn, Switzerland, this process can actually stretch cotton fibers. Licensed to the Sanforized Division of Cluett, Peabody & Company, Inc., New York City, the process substantially reduces the tensile and tear strength losses which result from the resin and cross-linking treatments of cotton for both dur-

able press and wash-and-wear.

This micro-stretching machine has a cost of around $20,000 and is about the size of an upright piano. It is capable of treating cotton cloth already treated by one of the several chemical resins with a minimum of five percent from the original dimensions. Deterioration of fabric that may be caused by chemical application is prevented by the treatment.

Since wash-and-wear came into vogue a few years ago, the fabrics have been made with a content of cotton and polyester fibers with the latter acting as a bolster or stimulant to the fabric due to the trouble encountered from resins on the cotton in these materials. Thus, it is now possible not to use manmade fibers in the fabric content in lighter weight fabrics, with the heavier cloths using a decreased content of polyester or comparable fibers.

The treatment can be used even on lightweight, sheer cottons such as batiste, organdy, and voile. Uses of the process include wash-and-wear quality in sheer blouses, sleepwear, light print dresses, curtains, and handkerchiefs.

RAFFIA. A tough fiber taken from palm trees of Africa and its coastal islands. Baskets, plaited goods, matting, and some fabrics are made from it. It is used to some degree in the millinery trade.

RAG. 1. A torn piece of fabric, a fragment or semblance of anything. 2. Tattered or shabby clothing. 3. A term for clothing in the jocular sense.

RAGLAN. A Britisher who served with the Duke of Wellington from 1810 through 1852, the year that Wellington died and he, Raglan, became a British Lord, and was then known as General Lord Raglan, P.C., and G.C.B. He was also the person who helped Florence Nightingale reorganize military hospital conditions and reform the nursing profession.

Raglan, known for his attention and great care given all his troops, was always interested in their uniforms and developed the popular loose-fitting coat which may or may not have sleeves. He suggested that a cape be used when the article is sleeveless. A feature of the raglan model is that there is plenty of room for easy arm movement. This single or double-breasted garment is used in some sport sack coats since it does afford easy body movement. See Balaclava, Cardigan, Sweaters, Men's and Boys'.

RAGLAN SLEEVE, SPLIT. A sleeve-front which has a half-raglan effect with set-in styling and full raglan effect in the sleeve-back. Used chiefly in rain-wear coatings. See Balaclava, Dolman, Havelock, Cardigan; Sweaters, Men's and Boy's.

RAG PAPER. One that is composed of finely chopped rags, ranging from 25 per cent to 75 per cent in the content.

RAG PICKER. See GARNETTING.

RAG PULLING. Reduction of wastes, fabrics, and threads to a fibrous condition either by garnetting or some other process depending on the type of the waste stock. See GARNETTING.

RAG RUG. A hand-loomed, plain-weave material made of rag strips. Because of the unevenness of the strips used, these rugs are difficult to produce on power looms. In addition, costs do not warrant their production on a power machine. Cotton warp is used to support the strip filling. Braided strips are stitched together by machine.

RAILROAD CANVAS. A plain, open-weave, heavily-sized embroidery canvas made of black and white thick cotton yarn.

RAILWAY HEAD. A machine on the order of a drawing frame which draws out and combines several strands of sliver to the desired fineness by conducting it directly from the carding machine on a railway moving belt to the head, drawing roller, which draws it out.

RAILWAY STITCH. A stitch made on an over-and-under motion of the thread to produce a bar appearance similar to railroad ties.

RAIMENT. Apparel, clothing, or garb. A term which was popular in the days of elaborate costume and dress; little used now.

RAINBOW EFFECTS. Effects obtained by printing cloth so that the colors appear to merge into each other and give a mottled effect at the edges of the colored areas. Tie-, or dip-dyeing will give a similar effect.

RAINBOW YARNS. Yarns with mottled effects from random dyeing. The colors seem to merge into each other.

RAIN TEST. An apparatus with a standard method of procedure and rating used to measure the resistance of textiles to shower or rain water. This device was developed by the A.A.T.C.C., Research Triangle, Durham, North Carolina. See Water-Repellency, Water Resistance, Textiles.

RAINWEAR, TESTING FOR. The three tests used in testing for rainwear follow;

Shower Resistant: Under the Bundes-mann test a maximum penetration of 50 c.c. of water. Many gabardine, serge and comparable cloths qualify in this test while the lower qualities cannot meet this requirement.

Rain Resistant: Under the Bundesmann test, a maximum penetration requirement of 10 c.c. of water. Fabrics which have a fluoro-chemical or comparable finish, such as silicone, would qualify in this test. Aqua 5, Scotchgard, and other well-known finishes would be successful.

Waterproof: There can be no penetration at all under a hydro-static head type of machine of 100 cms. Rubberized fabrics and plastic items would qualify in this method. All three tests apply at point-of-sale.

RAION. The Italian spelling for rayon.

RAISED. 1. Pertains to a fabric, chiefly one of wool, which has a napped surface finish. 2. In needlework, velvet, etc., the term implies a pattern or design in relief.

RAISED-BACK FABRIC. Cotton trousering, flannelette, pajama cloth, and pocket lining may have a nap raised on the back of the goods. This raised back effect is aided by the use of a soft-spun, coarse filling which will be easily napped when treated.

RAISED CHECKS. Cotton cloths made with extra warp and filling figuring on a plain background.

RAISED COLORS. Colors treated by "raising" process. There are some dyestuffs which, after the goods are printed, require an after-treatment to fix or develop the particular color desired on the finished cloth. This is called "raising" the color to the proper shade.

RAISED POINT, GROS POINT. Needle-point lace set off by having part of the motif raised in relief by padding.

RAISED VELVET. A velvet that has the pattern made by a pile higher than that of the ground construction.

RAISER. Same as a riser in plotting weaves; where a warp end is over a filling pick at the point of interlacing.

RAISING. Another term for scratching, brushing, gigging, or napping.

RAISING BRUSH. The circular brush on a shearer that brushes up the nap on cloth before it reaches the shearing blade.

RAJAH. Material made of Tussah silk, certain silk weaves, or man-made fibers, belonging to the pongee family of fabrics. It is a popular summer-wear cloth which is strong, rather compact, and may have a pebble-like feel and

appearance. Textures range from 70 to 80 by 50 to 60. It comes in all colors and natural ecru shades when made of silk. Used for coats, dresses, shirting, and lightweight suiting.

RAJPUTANA COTTON. A type of cotton raised in Bengal, India.

RAKE DISTRIBUTOR. See AUTOMATIC DISTRIBUTOR.

RAM. A male sheep used for breeding. Its wool is longer and stronger than that of the female (ewe) or a castrated ram (wether).

RAMBOUILLET. This breed, the largest and the strongest-bodied wool sheep, is a pure descendant of Spanish Merino, imported by France in 1785. Rambouillet was brought to this country in 1840; today they constitute about 27 per cent of all sheep here. Rams of this hardy breed weigh about 250 pounds, ewes about 140–170 pounds. A ram fleece of a year's growth will weigh 15 to 25 pounds of fine wool, which will sort to 64s or higher. Fiber length is 1½ to 3 inches. Shrinkage averages about 60 per cent. Range sheep have blood of the Rambouillet or other Merino breeds. See Illustrated Section.

RAMESES COTTON. Also known as Peerless. Variety of Uplands cotton with a 1-inch staple and lint yield of about 32 per cent.

RAMETA FIBER. A strong East Indian fiber used for cords and ropes.

RAMIE. A grass known also as rhea and China grass. It belongs to the stingless nettle group, of which there are two varieties. The first grows in tropical climates and is called rhea, while the second type is raised in temperate climates and is known as China grass. The fiber is strong, white, silken in luster, and, although it is a fine fiber in diameter, it possesses high tensile strength and elasticity. Although ramie is a very old fiber, technically speaking, it is still being used, in dress goods, sports clothes, tablecloths, fish lines, lining, upholstery.

RAMIE, DECORTICATING. Method by which Ramie fiber is obtained from the plant. Ramie cannot be retted, since mechanical treatments are necessary to secure the choice fibers. These treatments are performed by hand, thus increasing the cost of production. Raw ramie, obtained from the hand treatments, shows a mass of fibers cemented together. Further separation is necessary. Boiling of the stock must be resorted to by means of hot water.

The gum that cements the fibers consists of pectose, cutose, and vasculose. The last two are removed in the caustic alkali and soap bath, at the boil, and under pressure. The pectose is then removed by washing the residue. The amount of decorticated fiber obtained from the stock taken from the stalks amounts to about 2 per cent. The amount of degummed fiber is about 1 per cent.

RAM'S WOOL. Shorn from male sheep. Stronger than ewe or wether wool.

RANCHERIA. A grass fiber used by American Indians to weave mats, baskets, trays, etc.

RANDOM DYEING. A method of dyeing yarn in which certain areas only are colored. Three methods give the result:

1. Skeins may be tightly tied in two or more places and dyed at one side of the tie with one color and at the other side with some other color.

2. Color may be printed onto the skeins which are spread on the blanket of the printing machine.

3. Cones or packages of yarn on hollow spindles may be arranged to form channels through the yarn, with an air-operated punch, and the dyestuff drawn through these holes by suction. The yarn in the immediate area of the punch absorbs the dye and the random effects result. See TIE-DYEING.

RANDOM SHEARING. Usually a planned shearing in a textured motif. Some areas in a design are sheared, leaving clipped loops in some areas and uncut loops in others. This "hill-and-dale;; effect is observed in carpeting, velvet, some velveteen, and in certain silk fabrics. Rich in texture, it is used mainly in evening wear. Bright-and-dim effects are noted in fabrics finished in this manner, especially in evening wear where the rays of light enhance the appearance of the wearer. The effect is sometimes known as sculptured. See Sculptured Effect.

RANDOM SLUB. Yarn made in slub effect to give a sort of random effect of varying length slubs which are interspersed throughout the yarn.

RANDOM YARN. A fancy yarn of the core group. The core is a colored yarn, and the random stock is wound around the core in more or less of a hit-and-miss manner. Much used for filling.

RAN FIBER. A long, silken bast fiber raised in Africa and in this country; used as a jute substitute.

RANGE. A set or series of wools, tops, yarns, or cloths which possess some similar features but in which there is one difference which changes the character or the nomenclature. For example, tricotine is recognized by its double diagonal line on the face of the goods, while gabardine, whipcord, and serge have only a single diagonal line as an identification point. Another example would be the range of colors in a herringbone suiting range. See Illustrated Section (Fabrics 28, 29, 31).

RANGE METHOD. In contradistinction to the Farm Method of raising sheep, this method is used in raising sheep west of the Mississippi River. Large flocks roam the ranges of the West under the keen eye of the sheepherder and his faithful sheep dogs. The only protection afforded the sheep against the elements are valleys, forests, and ravines, a bane to the sheep raiser. Unfavorable weather and attacks by predatory animals, disease, and parasites are also of much concern to the growers.

In many instances the sheep flocks are allowed to graze on public land, for which privilege the grower pays a stipulated fee.

RANGE REGION. The region, chiefly semi-arid, west of the 100th meridian. Hardy Rambouillet and Merino types form the greater part of the flocks which feed in this area. See TERRITORY WOOL.

RANGE WOOL. Another name for territory wool; it is shorn from sheep raised under ranching conditions. See TERRITORY WOOL.

RANGOON COTTON. A Burmese cotton which is a short, weak, brownish cotton that contains much leaf and other foreign matter. The staple is only ¾ inch long and spins to only 10s.

RANGOON HEMP. An Indian hemp grown more for narcotic products than for use as a bast fiber.

RAP. A skein of 120 yards of yarn.

RAPLOCH. Scotch term for undyed woolen fabric which is rough, uneven, and of low quality.

RAS, RAZ. French, meaning smooth and short-napped; the term may be applied to the uniform nap on broadcloth, kersey, melton, and beaver.

RASCHEL, FELICE. A noted French actress in the mid-19th century who somehow or other gave her name to the well-known Raschel Latch-needle knitting frame which was brought out in 1855.

The first use of the latch needle was in dispute for many years. Needles for the American machines had to be imported from England. In time, Germany became the center for both latch and spring-beard needles, a position that it held until the advent of World War I.

RASCHEL PATTERN CHAIN. The device on a Raschel knitting machine which controls the lapping or lateral movement of the frame guide bars.

RASCHEL SINGLE NEEDLE BAR FABRICS. Those which are made with one set of needle bars. Used in openwork fabrics such as curtain material, netting, veiling, etc.

RASCHEL WARP KNITTING MACHINE. This machine uses latch needles, set in one or two needlebeds, and as many as six guide bars. It can also lay-in yarns by means of multiple bars. With the use of selected machines and attachments, the machine can make a variety of lace and other openwork fabrics, as well as knitting them so that they will be stable or stretchable as required. The machine also makes textured and patterned fabrics which can be rigid or have stretch. It can also make pile fabrics and carpeting.

Any type of yarn, within reason, can be used on the machine. Chiefly, lace and powernet fabrics are the ones in greatest demand with Raschels. The machine is more complex in structure than tricot or double-knit machines. Operators have to be extremely well trained for work as knitters. Raschel machines produce a host of items for use such as - powernet, lace, carpeting, foundation garments, brassieres, girdles, blouses, curtains, dressgoods, intimate apparel, trimming, men's tailored suits, etc.

RASI COTTON. The Bombay cotton market uses this term for poor grades of cleansed cotton.

RASO. Italian for satin.

RATCATCHER SKIRT. Originally this tailored skirt was used in riding habit livery. Today, while bordering on the original version, it is an outfit detailed with the tab-closed collar, sleeves extending to the wrists, and front buttons.

RATCH. The distance between the front and back rollers in a spread on a drawing machine, spinning frame, etc.

RATCHET, RATCHET WHEEL. A wheel with a toothed edge fastened to to end of either a cloth beam or a warp beam to control the winding action. A pawl engages the teeth of the wheel either to turn it forward or to prevent it from turning backward.

RATCHING. Extra draft in mule spinning caused by excess speed of mule carriage over the drawing rollers.

RATINE. Also spelled ratiné. From the French, meaning "frizzy or fuzzy." An overcoating cloth on the order of chinchilla. Used in women's wear coatings in woolen trade.

Cotton ratine is a loose, plain-woven

cloth with a rough, nubby surface finish; one heavy and two fine yarns twisted together at various tensions form the curly and knotty ply yarn. Cheaper qualities use ordinary yarn as warp while the filling is made of ratine. Can be bleached, dyed, or printed and is given a high luster or other types of finish.

RATINE LACE. Machine-made lace which has a ground work of loops simulating terry fabric; made of coarse yarn the lace is used for decoration on wash goods.

RATINE YARN. Yarn that shows a taut, rough surface-effect in over-all appearance. Two operations on the novelty twisters are necessary to obtain the effect. May be applied to all major fibers and very popular in cotton or rayon or combinations of these two yarns.

RATLINE. 1. Small, usually three-strand, tarred rope used for ratlines. 2. One of the small transverse ropes attached to the shrouds and forming the rungs of a rope ladder.

RAT-TAIL. A narrow, round soutache used for trimming.

RATTAN. 1. Any type of climbing palm of the genera Calamus and Daemonorops, remarkable for the great length of the stems. 2. A portion of the stems of the palm. Light, tough, and used for chair seats, cordage, wickerwork, and basketry work.

RATTEEN. Woolen goods popular in the British Isles about two centuries ago. Twill-woven, very heavy and coarse.

RATTINE. A small rope measured in terms of the fathom.

RAVEL. 1. To undo or separate the texture of a fabric; to unweave or unknit. 2. A type of comb or wooden rail with projecting teeth for separating and guiding warp ends. 3. Raveling implies that which is raveled out, such as a thread detached from a texture.

RAVELED STRIP TEST. A test used in testing fabric for breaking strength. The samples are cut about 1½ inches wide and 6 inches long. Ravelings are made to make the cloth an even one inch in width prior to inserting in the machine. Five tests should be made, and the average is considered as the actual breaking strength.

RAVELING. A thread frayed from a fabric.

RAVELING COURSE. An extra course used in full-fashioned knitting to facilitate the topping-on operation.

RAVELINGS. Yarns indiscriminately mixed together beyond the possibility of straightening out.

RAW. 1. In, or nearly in, the natural state; little changed by processing. 2. Edge of cloth not finished to prevent fraying is called raw.

RAW EDGE. Finish applied to heavy overcoating fabric in which the edges are not turned in but are sewed through and through, then evenly pared or trimmed with a knife or shears. Also means an edge of fabric that is cut or torn; may cause much trouble in tailoring.

RAW FIBERS, RAW MATERIAL. Material in its natural state made suitable for manipulation. Examples include silk "in-the-gum," raw wool, or cotton, etc.

RAWHIDE. A basic American term used in English-speaking nations for cattle hide that has been dehaired and limed, often stuffed with oil or grease. It has sometimes undergone other preparatory processes, but has not been tanned. Rawhide is used chiefly for mechanical purposes—belt lacings and pins, loom pickers, gaskets, pinions, gears; also for trunk binding, luggage, etc. Sometimes rawhide is tanned with the hair left on.

RAWKINESS. Uneven areas and streakiness noted in fabrics; caused by uneven, irregular yarns.

RAW SEAM. A seam made by placing two cut edges of material together and stitching, without turn or fold.

RAW SILK. Silk from cultivated silkworms—Bombyx mori, with the gum or sericin still contained in the silk. This type of worm feeds on mulberry leaves, generally speaking.

RAW SILK HAIRINESS. A bothersome condition caused by numerous loose ends of cocoon filaments projecting from silk thread.

RAW SILK, LOOPS IN. These are caused by the girl in the silk reeling plant when she makes a bad throw in starting a fresh cocoon to supplant a spent one. Loops leave a long end which will double or revert back on itself, thereby impeding progress in reeling.

Long loops are those which exceed one centimeter or a half-inch in length; short loops are less than one-half inch in length.

RAW SILK RINGS. Raw silk thread in reeling will sometimes escape from the traverse guide and revolve for some little distance in a ring formation instead of the usual crossed form.

RAW SILK TRANSACTIONS. Special commission merchants found chiefly in Yokohama and Kobe handle transactions in raw silk; known as Tonya. Advance credits are made to reelers and Tonya sometimes invest in their filatures. There is great co-operation and faith between these two groups who deal in silk.

RAW STOCK. Raw fibers, such as cotton, flax, wool, mohair.

RAY. A kind of woolen fabric with warp or filling stripes.

RAYCELON. Modified viscose rayon fiber used with Celon, the nylon fiber of Courtaulds, Ltd., Great Britain, also producer of Raycelon. Properties include a comfortable appeal in hand, appearance, the non-static properties of rayon, and the ease-of-care and strength of nylon. Used in dressgoods, linings, sheeting, and shirting.

RAYE. French (rayé) for fabric patterns striped in fine lines.

RAYFLEX. A high tenacity rayon filament produced and trademarked by American Viscose Company, Inc., Division of FMC Corporation.

RAYFLEX-TYPE RAYON, SUPER. Continuous filament rayon fiber with increased strength characteristics, made by American Viscose Comapny, Inc., Division of FMC Corporation. It is 40 percent stronger than regular Rayflex and is constructed for industrial purposes in reinforcing applications such as laminates which involve paper, plastics, and rubber.

RAYNES. A fine grade quality linen first made in Rennes, France. Much of this fabric has been used as altar cloth since the fourteenth century. Raynes is also a shirting material.

RAYON. The American Society for Testing and Materials defines Rayon as: "A generic term for filaments made from various solutions of modified cellulose by a pressing or drawing the cellulose solution through an orifice and solidifying it in the form of a filament."

The Federal Trade Commission, Washington, D.C. (effective March 3, 1960), defines Rayon as "A manufactured fiber composed of regenerated cellulose, as well as manufactured fibers composed of regenerated cellulose in which the substituents have replaced not more than 15 per cent of the hydrogens of the hydroxyl groups." Thus, rayon is a man-made cellulosic fiber, a regenerated fiber.

The term also implies fabrics made of rayon fibers or filaments.

The cellulose base for the manufacture of rayon is obtained from wood pulp or cotton linters, which are the short brown fibers left on the cotton seed after the first-time ginning on the plantation, or at the community gin. Wood pulp for rayon also comes from spruce, pine, or hemlock chips.

Rayon includes yarn made from the cuprammonium and viscose methods. The making of rayon involves much scientific and chemical knowledge, research, and experimentation.

Rayon fibers, like cotton, leave an ash when burned. About 66 per cent of all cellulosic fibers are produced by the viscose method; about 32 per cent by the acetate method, with the cuprammonium method supplying the remainder. See Illustrated Section for manufacture; also, same Section (Fabrics 8).

The name "rayon" was coined in 1924 by Mr. Kenneth Lord of the firm of Galey & Lord, Inc., now a division of Burlington Industries, Inc. It has been a true household word for years.

RAYON, BASIFIED. The addition of certain basic substances to viscose rayon during the manufacturing processes from raw material to finished spun yarn in filament form. The additions give the viscose rayon greater affinity for acid dyes which are essentially used in dyeing wool fibers or fabrics.

RAYON, CARBONIZED. A rayon fiber that finds use in industry; pyrolized by being cooked at temperatures up to 3,000 degrees, Centigrade and stretched or subjected to a process of stress graphitization. When molded with epoxy resin, graphite composites of carbonized rayon are double the strength of steel and 40 percent lighter than aluminum. At present these composites seem to be very satisfactory for airplane parts. See Rayon Yarn, Carbonized; Epoxy, Epoxy Resin.

RAYON, CHARACTERISTICS OF.

PHYSICAL PROPERTIES

1. MICROSCOPICAL APPEARANCE: Resembles solid glass rods with or without striations.

2. LENGTH: The filament is indefinite in length and may be several miles long. Staple length of cut rayon may be made to the length of the other major textile fibers.

3. DIAMETER: Some types of rayon are finer than the silk filament.

4. COLOR: White.

5. LUSTER: Bright or dull; high luster if no delustering agent is used.

6. STRENGTH: ½ to ⅓ that of natural silk when dry. Loses 40 per cent to 70 per cent of strength when wet. Regains strength when dry.

7. ELASTICITY: Very little.

8. CONDUCTIVITY TO HEAT: Good.

9. HYGROSCOPIC MOISTURE: More than cotton; almost equal to that of silk, 11 per cent. Acetate, incidentally, has a moisture content of about 6.5 per cent.

10. CAPILLARITY AND PENETRABILITY: No capillarity because of construction; good penetrability.

11. FIBER COMPOSITION: Rayon is a regenerated type of fiber—solid to liquid, and back to a solid, a cellulosic fiber.

12. METHOD OF PREPARATION: Viscous solutions to make rayon, after being prepared and treated chemically, are forced through capillary openings into precipitating tanks. See Illustrated Section.

CHEMICAL CHARACTERISTICS:

1. EFFECT OF LIGHT: More resistant to sunlight than cotton.

2. MILDEW: Similar to the effect on cotton.

3. HEAT: Viscose and cuprammonium withstand about 300° F.; cellulose acetate, dampened and ironed, melts slightly at 275° F. It will stick to an iron, dry, at about 304° F.

4. WATER: The fibers or filaments lose much of their strength.

5. MINERAL ACIDS: Same precautions should be used as with cotton.

6. VOLATILE ORGANIC ACIDS: Acetic or formic acids have no detrimental action.

7. NON-VOLATILE ORGANIC ACIDS: Citric, oxalic, or tartaric acids will tender rayon slightly if not removed, especially if heat is applied.

8. STRONG ALKALIES: Low temperatures should be used. Do not use caustic soda. Strong solutions cause swelling and reduce strength.

9. WEAK ALKALIES: Dilute solutions have very little effect.

10. OXIDIZING AGENTS: These should not be used since they weaken fibers.

11. METALLIC SALTS: No affinity; some metallic salts are used to deluster rayon.

12. AFFINITY FOR DYESTUFFS: Excellent in most instances.

13. DYEING: Done easily by direct, basic, sulphur, or vat colors.

14. BLEACHING AGENTS: Chlorine bleach or hypochlorites are used to bleach rayon, as cotton.

15. OTHER OXIDATION BLEACHES: Hydrogen peroxide or sodium perborate may be used. Potassium permanganate has the tendency to weaken the fiber.

RAYON, CLEANING SPINNERETS USED IN MAKING. The spinneret may be taken from the machine. Immerse in water at once, and then boil it in a dilute solution of hydrochloric acid for fifteen minutes. After washing and drying, the spinneret is again ready for use. Another method is to immerse the spinneret in a solution of zinc chloride and then wash in a 10 per cent solution of hydrochloric acid, 40 per cent sulphuric acid, and 50 per cent water.

RAYON, COMMERCIAL WEIGHT FOR. According to the A.S.T.M., it is the oven-dry weight of the staple fiber or filament after scouring by definite prescribed methods plus the weight corresponding to its commercial moisture regain. See MOISTURE REGAIN.

RAYON, HIGH-PERFORMANCE. Often referred to as HP RAYON, it is an overall term for improved types of rayon. High-Wet-Modulus Rayon and High-Tenacity Rayon are in this sphere. See Rayon, High-Tenacity; Rayon, High-Wet-Modulus.

RAYON, HIGH-TENACITY. A strong, tough rayon fabric which often has twice the strength of the high-wet-modulus rayon yarn or fabric. The combination of high elongation and high strength made it ideal for use in automobile tires where it was first used in industry. See Rayon, High-Wet-Modulus.

RAYON, HIGH-WET-MODULUS. Modulus means a coefficient which pertains to a physical property. In this instance it means that the fiber properties have been modified to provide greater dimensional stability in washing. Thus, rayon in this condition is referred to as being of high wet modulus. See Rayon, High-Tenacity.

RAYON ALPACA. The term is a misnomer and should not be used. There are, however, two fabrics known in the trade by this name. The first is set at 48 inches in the reed, has a texture of 36 x 34, and is made from a denier-filament of 75/100. The yarn sizes used are four-ply, all one twist. The other material is set at 48 inches in the reed, has a texture of 44 x 38, and is made from a denier-filament of 150/150. The yarn sizes used are two-ply, all one twist. Both cloths are combination yarn fabrics of viscose rayon and acetate; no alpaca fiber is used in either material.

RAYON BANDS OR STRIPS. A rayon product simulating straw, made by extruding the spinning solution through a single rectangular or ribbon-like orifice. It is used for decorative applications.

RAYON BARONET SATIN. A satin weave fabric made with rayon warp and cotton filling. This very lustrous material has the tendency to "catch particles." Comes in white and colors. Baronet wears well, washes easily and has good draping qualities. "Roughing up" in the cloth is detrimental to it and lessens its use.

RAYON BENGALINE. A cross-rib fabric in which the filling is coarser than the warp. Made of rayon and wool or of silk and wool. Comes in colors and is used in coating, dress goods, millinery, and ribbon.

The fabric gives good wear, laun-

ever be successful in realizing a complete turn or a turn and one half, as against the half-turn now possible with present-day leno weaving equipment. Lenos are woven with cotton heddles, metal heddles, leno reeds, and leno blades, as used on Jacquard looms. Terminal use of marquisette includes bedspreads, curtains, dresser ensembles, netting, varied decorative purposes; high-grade fabric is used in evening wear.

RAYON MATELASSE, MATELLASSE. Also spelled matelassé (French for cushioned, i.e., quilted). Name applied to figured fabrics made on dobby or Jacquard looms; the pattern stands out and gives a pouched or quilted effect. Plain, twill, and satin weaves may be used in construction to give the novelty double-weave effect. This blister-effect cloth drapes well, gives good wear, is attractive, and when in vogue is in much demand. Laundering has to be carefully done. Used chiefly in women's dress goods and for evening wear.

RAYON MIGNONETTE, TRICOLETTE. Knitted rayon fabrics made on circular machines. Incidentally, tricolette was the first knitted fabric made of rayon to appear on the market; this was in 1924.

Properties and characteristics of these cloths include great elasticity, some porosity, the tendency to slip, run, or creep, and luster, and much care has to be exercised in the cutting and sewing of the goods. Mignonette is of finer gauge and mesh when compared with tricolette. Chief uses are for underwear and dress goods.

RAYON MOIRÉ. Taffeta is given watermarking treatment to enhance its beauty in a sort of shimmering effect. Goods such as rayon moiré are attractive, durable, and give good service. Ideal for evening wear, vestments, decorative fabrics, bridal gowns, etc.

RAYON MONOFIL. A coarse, round, single filament yarn that is often referred to as "artificial horsehair."

RAYON NET, RAYON TULLE. General names for a sheer cloth made with hexagonal mesh fabric. Stiff, cool, dressy, delicate, and difficult to launder. Comes in white and colors and when used as dress goods gives the wearer a rather stately appearance. Also used in overdraping and in ballet materials.

RAYON, NITRATE. See Cuprammonium Rayon.

RAYON PARALLEL SPINNING. A process whereby the thread is formed at the nozzles and is then cross-wound upon flanged bobbins, the thread being the result of the bundled parallel, untwisted filaments. These are then washed, twisted, and finally reeled into hanks of yarn.

RAYON PLAIN SATIN. Sometimes known as panne satin, this 39-inch fabric is made both ways with flat yarn. Warp is 150, 100, or 75 denier; filling is 300, 150, 100, or 75 denier. Textures range from 110 x 52 to 300 x 80. Great luster and beauty feature plain satin. Incidentally, the hand in viscose rayon satin is not comparable with that of an all-acetate satin; the latter seems to have the more appealing feel and graciousness.

Terminal uses include cushion covers, dresses, evening wear, fur coat lining, ribbon, slipper satin, slips.

RAYON POPLIN. Originally called Papeline, it was a fifteenth century fabric made in and around Avignon, France, to honor the reigning Pope; used for church vestments and hangings. Present-day poplin is made in widths from 35 inches to 40 inches, and the warp may be any of the following denier—150, 120, 100, 75. Filling denier may be 150, 200, 250, 300. Textures vary from 84 x 64 to 158 x 50.

Poplin has a cord effect which runs in the filling or crosswise direction in the goods, which explains the use of a rather coarse filling yarn. Higher quality poplin is made with high sley, fine-count warp yarn to insure a smooth, well-rounded, rich-looking rib effect. Uses include day and evening wear, drapery fabric, upholstery material.

RAYON RHYTHM CREPE. May be called a rayon seersucker or plissé-effect type of fabric. Made of plain-weave variation. The crimped effect runs in warp direction. Comes in white or colors.

The fabric is washable, drapes well, gives good wear, and is a rather rugged type of cloth. Made to simulate seersucker.

RAYON ROUGH CREPE. Finished at 46 inches to 48 inches, the warp is of the flat type while the filling is crepe, S- and Z-twist yarn. Warp is either 150-denier or 100-denier, filling is 200-denier or 150-denier. Pick counts range from 96 x 46 to 52 up to 124 x 52 to 56.

The fabric is on the order of Canton crepe, with the exception that it is allowed greater shrinkage to produce a rougher cloth. The fabric is sometimes found with multi-pick fashion weaving, that is, 4 picks of S-twist, 4 picks of Z-twist, or 8 picks of S-twist, 8 picks of Z-twist. This gives a hammered effect in the goods. Chief use for the cloth is in outdoor, dressy garments of the smart variety.

RAYON SAND-WEAVE FABRIC. Finished from 45 inches to 50 inches with warp made of 100-denier flat yarn or 100-denier crepe yarn; filling is made of 150-denier crepe yarn or 100-denier S-twist and Z-twist crepe yarn. Pick counts range from 112 x 60 to 135 x 72.

The repeat in sand-woven goods is spread over many ends and picks despite the fact that the cloth is woven on comparatively few harnesses. An imported European weave that is much used to weave the goods contains 66 ends and 40 picks to the repeat with six harnesses or shafts required. No end or pick floats for more than two ends or two picks. A popular cloth in the range today is made of 150-denier, dull acetate flat yarn with textures of either 108 x 68 or 116 x 64. The fabric is much used in dress goods.

RAYON SLASHER. A warp sizing machine made on the principle of the cotton method of slashing; used for treating synthetic warps.

RAYON STAPLE FIBER. Originally referred to as the waste coming from the manufacture of filament rayon. It is now specially made on a large scale comparable with that part of the rayon business given over to filament yarn. Filament is cut to staple lengths on its emergence from the spinneret in the processing. It is ideal for spinning on the cotton, woolen, worsted, and flax methods. Staple fiber comes in bright and dull effect and in varying deniers.

RAYON STAPLE, FLOWSHEET FOR MANUFACTURE OF. See Illustrated Section.

RAYON TAFFETA. The word comes from the Persian taftah, which means "to spin." This flat yarn cloth comes in widths which range from 35 inches to about 44 inches. Warp and filling yarns are of 100-denier or 150-denier. Textures range from 68 x 44 to 140 x 64; only about one third of the weight of the fabric is filling yarn. Taffeta is a rugged, practical fabric and is one of the genuine staples in the trade.

Pigment taffetas, which are at present very popular, have pick counts of 92 x 68 to 72 x 56. Much pigment fabric is printed. Taffeta is used in dress goods, low price lining, and undergarments.

RAYONNE. French for rayon.

RAYON TIRE CORD FABRIC. The layout for this material is in table on this page.

Chafer: It is still made of cotton and it serves as a wrapper.

Twist applied on the 2 x 1150/490 plan is 14-turns of Z-twist, single, 12-turns of S-twist, ply.

Twist applied on the 2 x 2200/980

ders well, if care is taken, and possesses good draping qualities. The pronounced filling rib cord adds much to the cloth which comes in widths ranging from ribbon size to broad goods.

RAYON CANTON CREPE. This 46-inch-width cloth is made with a flat-yarn warp-and-filling-crepe yarn with S- and Z-twist. Pick counts range from 96 ends of 150-denier with 46 picks of 200-denier or 48 to 52 picks of 150-denier to 124 x 52–56.

Originally made of several-ply crepe yarn of Canton silk, the cloth is heavier than crepe de Chine, possesses a pronounced pebble-effect, but is otherwise the same as the original cloth. Uses include coat lining, dress goods, dressing gowns, negligees, pajamas, scarfs, and accessories.

RAYON CHALLIS. Spun rayon fabric made of plain weave. Printed to simulate woolen or worsted challis; durable, launders well, drapes in satisfactory manner, and is a popular staple.

RAYON CHIFFON. S-twist and Z-twist yarns are used in warp and filling, the denier size is 50. Finished at about 47 inches with textures of 60 x 60 up to 80 x 80. The word chiffon implies thin, diaphanous, or gauzelike fabric.

Chiffon resembles Georgette, with the exception that instead of being invariably constructed with two ends and two picks of S-twist and Z-twist, it is often made with one S-twist and one Z-twist, sometimes with only one twist. See Illustrated Section for twists.

An interesting feature in the Chiffon construction is that when only one twist is used, warp and filling-wise, it must be either all S-twist or all Z-twist in order to preclude a curling or rolling action which may develop when the goods are cut in tapered fashion. Uses include dress goods, evening wear, lampshades, millinery, trimming, and many novelty decorative effects.

RAYON CREPE. The filling is made of right-hand or left-hand twisted yarn or both. One hundred- to 150-denier is the usual size yarn employed to construct this rugged, well-wearing fabric. If pigmented, the cloth is often known as French crepe.

The textures used in crepe make it a popular staple at all times; it is usually compact, and the luster is often high in surface finish. Crepe has excellent draping qualities but will have the tendency to shrink if not laundered too well. See FRENCH CREPE.

RAYON CREPE YARN TWIST. To be considered in a general way:

150-denier yarn from 40 to 45 turns per inch.

100-denier yarn from 50 to 55 turns per inch.

75-denier yarn from 60 to 65 turns per inch.

RAYON FAILLE. Belongs to the bengaline group of cross-rib fabrics; the ribs or cords are coarse and flat with the warp finer than the filling in construction.

Faille is difficult to launder well, has good draping qualities, and will wear well if handled with care.

RAYON FILAMENT YARN. A continuous individual strand of rayon as it comes from one opening of the spinneret. It is given a slight twist, usually 3 to 5 turns per inch.

RAYON FLAT CREPE. Made in the warp with flat yarn, and in the filling with S-twist and Z-twist yarn, the fabric is finished from 41 inches to 45 inches. Denier of the warp may be 150, 100, or 75; filling is of 100-denier or 75-denier yarn. Textures range from 80 x 40 to 48 up to 150 x 76 which is a print cloth texture.

The origin of crepe is found in the Latin, crispare, which means to render crimpy. As the name indicates, the material is comparatively flat and reveals only a slight pebble or crepe effect. The use of crepe filling imparts a soft, pliable hand which enhances a drapability despite the light weight of the goods. Reed widths are from 3 inches to 5 inches wider than the finished width. The print-goods texture is extremely popular in the garment trade and is used in garments such as accessories, blouses, dress goods, negligees, and pajamas.

Any of the flat crepe textures may be used in the above-mentioned garments as well as in the lining trade.

RAYON FLOCK. The very short rayon fibers cut from rayon tow and used in the flocking process on textile fabrics.

RAYON FRENCH CREPE. This 39-inch to 43-inch fabric is made with flat warp yarn and voile-twist filling. Denier of warp and filling may be 150, 100, 75. Textures vary from 92 x 69 to 150 x 94. The voile-twist, which is comparatively low, affords roundness to the filling yarn to reduce its covering power and to add pliability to the goods.

Uses include negligees and underwear. Lambskin-type crepe is made of 104 ends of 100-denier and 72 picks of 150-denier. Very popular today, it comes in prints which are much used in aprons, blouses, dress goods, and interior decoration.

RAYON GEORGETTE. Made with 75-denier, S- and Z-twist crepe yarn; widths are from 43 inches to 46 inches. Textures vary from 60 x 48 to 80 x 80. The fabric was originally made of silk

and was a very popular staple; the yarn used was 13/15-denier silk with as many as 95 turns per inch in some cases. Georgette is diaphanous, airy, delicate in appearance, but rather rugged. Creped viscose rayon, from the time of its inception, spelled the death knell for silk georgette. The viscose fabric seemed to possess greater uniformity and other inherent advantages when compared with the silk fabric. Used in dress goods, evening wear, lampshades, millinery, trimming, and numerous dainty decorative effects.

RAYON HIGH PERFORMANCE FABRICS; SPINNING SYSTEMS FOR. Two methods are used at present, and these follow:

1. *Zinc-Based System:* About 95 percent of rayon in this category made in the U.S. uses this method in which a zinc spinning bath is used. Some examples, include *Avril*, FMC/American Viscose Company, Inc.; and *Xena*, Beaunit Corporation.

2. *Non-Zinc System:* This method is popular in Europe and rayon made by this method goes under the name of *Polysonic.* In this country "polysonic" is the trademark designation of *Zantrel*, produced by American Enka Corporation, Enka, North Carolina.

RAYONIER. Some of the principal grades of Rayonier wood cellulose are:

RAYACETA: A highly purified wood cellulose especially developed for the production of cellulose acetate fibers. It is also used in the manufacture of acetate films and sheets for packaging purposes.

RAYAMO: A wood cellulose developed for the manufacture of cellophane.

RAYOCORD: A highly purified wood cellulose suitable for the production of viscose yarns of high tensile strength. It is also used in the manufacture of tire cords and for textile yarns where maximum strength is desired. Rayocord can also be used for the production of saturating papers and vulcanized fiber.

HICOLOR: Used in the manufacture of viscose fibers and yarns of high quality. It may also serve as base material for vulcanized fiber.

RAYON JERSEY, JERSEY RAYON. See Tricot.

RAYON MARQUISETTE. This 38-inch, leno-woven fabric is made of voile-twist warp and filling of either 150 denier or 75 denier. Pick counts run from 28 x 24 to 72 x 48.

Little yarn has to be used in the manufacture of the goods, as is obvious from optical inspection. The weave attracts the attention, not only because of its present achievement, but also for the promises it holds if one should

plan is 10.5-turns of Z-twist, single, 8.3-turns of S-twist, ply.

The purpose of the filling, which is generally a spun yarn, is merely to hold the warp ends in place while the cloth is being treated. The treated fabric is cut on the bias and, as such, serves as the foundation fabric for the tire.

The present tire yarn production will be used in this country for several years according to the best forecasts. Larger quantities, as they become available, will likewise be absorbed. Tire cord is now being made from rayon, cotton, and nylon. Production is now well over 250 million pounds per year.

RAYON TRANSPARENT VELVET. There are many types on the market. The following will serve as a typical layout for the material which is usually woven on the double-piece method of weaving which requires two shuttle looms:

WARP	FILLING	YARNS
Ground of 160	60 denier rayon, 27 to 30-twist	
Pile of 80	150/60 Viscose rayon	
	2 x 92	60 denier rayon, 27 to 30-twist

Originally made of silk, the fabric of today gives much satisfaction when made of rayon; so much so, that it is very doubtful if silk will be used again in this country to make the cloth. Crease-resistant finish is applied to the cloth; this has enhanced the value of the fabric. Chief uses include dresses, evening wear, and decorative effects.

RAYON TRIPLE SHEER. Finished at about 47 inches, the fabric is made with warp crepe yarn of either 100-denier or 75-denier; filling is of 100-denier or 75-denier, the latter may be S-twist or Z-twist or with no twist at all. Textures range from 90 x 68 to 104 x 72.

This extremely sheer fabric possesses a fair weight. The warp is usually given twist; the no-twist filling seems to be more popular than the twisted filling. Most triple sheer is made with Bemberg yarn, but some of the material is now made with viscose rayon.

Since the fabric does not seem to have much appeal in plain colors, most sheer is printed with eye-appealing motifs. Used chiefly in summer wear.

RAYON TWILL. This flat yarn cloth comes in widths of 35 inches to 40 inches and is made of 150 denier in warp and filling. Textures range from 72 x 52 to 148 x 72. The weight of the warp is predominant in the cloth, which finds much use in infants' wear and lining. Made of a 2-up and 1-down twill weave, the material has smoothness and luster which are ideal for terminal use. Dull yarn is never used. This rugged fabric is said to even outlast the average men's wear suiting fabric. It has been estimated that the lining trade, at present, uses about 25 million pounds of the yarn to cover annual requirements.

RAYON TWISTS, NORMAL. These will vary, and the following is to be considered in a general manner:

Low or normal twist: Up to ten turns of twist per inch.

Voile twist: From 10 to 30 turns of twist per inch.

Crepe twist: Above 30 turns of twist per inch.

RAYON VELVET. A broad term which covers a wide range of warp pile cloths with the exception of chenille, corduroy, plush, terry cloth, and velveteen. Velvet is woven face-to-face and then cut by the cutting blade while still in the loom. Some velvet has a silk back. The texture often reveals a close pile. Transparent, chiffon, and taffeta-back effects are staple examples of velvet.

The cloth may give brilliant surface effect; it is durable, may wash well, and is often given crush-resistant treatment.

RAYON WASTE. All types of waste obtained from producers' operations on rayon yarn; also from manipulation of yarns and fabrics.

RAYON YARN. A group of rayon fibers or filaments twisted together to form a continuous strand for use in weaving, knitting, or braiding. See Illustrated Section.

RAYON YARN, CARBONIZED. Union Carbide Corporation, New York City, was the first company to do research and development in this field. IRC Division of American Cyanamid Company, Inc., Painesville, Ohio, working with Union Carbide, has produced Thornel 40, Thornel 50, and Thornel 75, the latter being produced at present on a limited basis. Composite structures with epoxy resin develop twice the specific strength of steel and are forty percent lighter than steel. The figures 40, 50, and 75 designate the high modulus of elasticity of the yarn. For example, Thornel 40 has a modulus of elasticity (a measure of stiffness, a quantity indicating the force required to elongate any material) of 40 million pounds per square inch.

The combination of very high modulus of elasticity or stiffness, and the very light weight make graphite composites, from carbonized yarns like rayon, a great potential in future industry. See Ep, Epi; Epoxy, Epoxy Resin.

RAYON YARN, DENIER OF. Numerically, this is equal to the weight in grams of 9000 meters.

RD 101. A self-bonding viscose rayon staple fiber of the American Viscose Division of FMC Corporation, New York City. It is used in making paper and similar wet-formed non-woven products.

REACH. Refers to the reach or distance between the drawing or drafting rollers on machines that draw and draft bast fibers such as flax, jute, hemp, etc.

REACTANTS AND RESINS, COMPARISON OF.
1. Reactants have good durability and give very satisfactory performance. Resins, as to durability, depend on the method of manipulation and processing.
2. Nitrogen is foreign in reactants while resins may contain this element.
3. As to added weight, reactants add little weight to fabrics while resins add weight, body, and substance to fabrics.
4. With regard to hand, reactants provide the softer hand or feel while resins usually have the tendency to add stiffness or rigidity.
5. On fabric strength, reactants provide less strength loss than does the use of resins.

REACTION. The mutual action of substances subjected to chemical change, or some distinctive result of such action. A reagent will bring about a chemical change or transformation.

REACTIVE DYES. Also known as Chemically Reactive and Fiber Reactive dyes, these are applied cold and react with the cellulose in fibers under alkaline conditions.

READY-MADE. The opposite of tailoring-to-order.

READY-TO-WEAR. Same as ready-made.

REAGENT. Any substance used to ascertain the nature or composition of another by means of their mutual chemical action: loosely, any chemical agent.

RAYON TIRE CORD FABRIC

Warp Construction	2 x 1150/490	or	2 x 2200/980	plan.
Carcass	34 x 2.5	or	26 x 2.5	plan.
Breaker	28 x 6	or	20 x 6	plan.
Breaker	18 x 8	or	none	plan.

REAL WAGES. The purchasing power of the money received as wages.

REAMY YARN. British term for fancy yarn made by doubling a two-ply yarn with a single yarn. Same as Reavy Yarn.

REAUMUR, RENE ANTOINE PERCHAULT DE. The French scientist who discovered white, opaque glass, was interested in tin, and has a thermometer named for him. In 1734, he attempted to throw some light on synthetic fiber possibilities. Réaumur tried to develop a simulation of the silkworm and the spider, by drawing out a continuous strand from waterproofed varnishes. Not having too much success in his attempts, he turned to other fields and has left a deep imprint in science. René de Réaumur's work was based on the book *Micrographia* (1665) by Dr. Robert Hooke, in which he expounded the possibility of yarn or thread made by synthetic means.

REAVY YARN. The twisting together of a single and a two-ply yarn.

RECESS SHEARING. In hollow-cut velveteen, for example, the fabric is cut in the regulation manner, and then the pile is cut or sheared in vertical rows to form a bevel-edge cord. This type of shearing is also done in the carpet industry. The fancy motif is outlined on the rug, and it is then hand-sheared by the operator who uses a clipper on the order of the one used by a barber. Excellent depth and figure control result from this method.

RECIRCULATING AIR FILTER. A dust and foreign matter collector of various particles that returns the air to the room. Used in rooms where auxiliary cotton machines are found, the filter is any upright, rectangular metal chamber equipped with a fine and a coarse screen. The impure air enters the top, comes in contact with a baffle, travels downward and outward through the screens.

RECLAIMED WOOL. This broad term implies wool obtained from the following sources: clippings, old and new woolen or worsted rags, tailor's clippings, reprocessed wool, remanufactured wool, shoddy, mungo, extract wool, etc.

RECLINING TWILL WEAVES. Those less than 45 degrees in angle— the 27-degree, 20-degree, and 15-degree angle weaves. The 27-degree holds over for one pick, the 20 for two picks, while the 15 holds over for three picks prior to going to the next line for the next pick in the construction.

RECOGNITION. Acceptance by a company of a union as the bargaining agent for its employees.

RECOMBING. Worsted tops sometimes receive a second combing treatment. It is done to remove minute particles of vegetable matter not removed in the first combing, as well as to obtain a larger percentage of noil fiber and therefore produce a better worsted top for manipulative purposes. The treatment usually comes after top dyeing.

RECORDONNER. French term meaning to outline embroidery or appliqué with braid, cord, gold or silver thread trimming.

RECOTTI. Final waste obtained in making yarn from silk wastes.

RECOUREES. Plain-weave, heavy French linen fabrics left in natural states are called recourées.

RECOVERED WOOL. Stock from felted fabrics produces mungo while that obtained from unfelted fabrics is known as shoddy. The fibers are obtained by passing the goods through the garnetting machine.

RECOVERY. A basic property of stretch yarn, refers to the speed with which a yarn returns to its relaxed position after stretching. Rapid recovery prevents bagging or sagging and is very important in many types of articles, especially in stretch pants.

RECTILINEAR COMB. See FRENCH COMB; HEILMAN COMB.

RED. 1. A bright color resembling blood; of the same hue as that color of the spectrum farthest from violet. 2. It is at the lower or least refracted end of the color spectrum. 3. One of the primary colors. 4. Any pigment or dye having or giving this color.

REDEPOSITION. Tendency of finely divided soil already removed and suspended to go back on the goods and to lower the whiteness retention. Certain detergents and washing formulae operate to minimize this tendency. The term is also used to indicate deposition of dirt, grime, or soil on fabrics during washing or laundering when the water has a high concentration of the dirt or soil removed from heavily soiled articles.

REDINGOTE. A woman's long, fitted coat, cut princess style, and open in the front to show the dress or slip underneath. It is sometimes cut away in front, and is usually belted at the waistline. It was originally made with several capes and trimmed with large buttons. The French word developed from the English riding coat.

RED LIQUOR. Another name for Aluminum Acetate $Al(C_2H_3O_2)^3$. This compound is an important mordant used in dyeing and printing of textiles.

See ALUMINUM ACETATE.

REDMANIZED. Trade-mark used to identify fabrics which have been treated by processes developed by F. R. Redman for woolen and cotton knit goods to secure relaxation shrinkage. Treatment by these processes results in fabrics which are washable without undue shrinkage and identified within a quality control plan.

REDO. Trade name for a vinyl-coated cotton fabric made in varying grades dependent upon terminal use.

RED OIL. Oleic acid.

REDON. Polyacrylonitrile fiber made by Phrix-Werke AG., Hamburg, Germany (BDR). Comparable with Orlon in many respects, its elongation exceeds that of Orlon. Redon is rated well in fastness to light, and other properties include low moisture absorption, resistance to chemicals, and heat retention. This concern also makes the polyamide fiber, "Phrilon," which is derived from ε-amino caprylic acid.

REDOUBLING. 1. The drawing from six cans (carded yarn) to sixteen cans (combed yarn) is moved from the cotton cards to the drawing frames. The product of these cans is then drawn out to a sliver equaling one can from the card. This type of blending or drawing of the cotton fibers is necessary in order to even-up the sliver. The constant doubling and redoubling is essential in making even, uniform spun yarn. Without either of them, yarn could not be made for commercial purposes.

2. The operation of again doubling already doubled threads, necessary on account of limitation of doubling machinery. If, for example, a 12-thread tram silk is desired and the limitation of bobbins which can be put on the machine is six, it would be necessary to first make a six-thread tram, then use two of the six-thread trams and double again to make twelve threads; or, double four threads, then use three of the four-threads and double them again. Usually these double threads are thrown or twisted together on throwing machinery later on.

REDOX. The "red" in reduction and the "ox" in oxygen are combined to give this term. The development of instruments that inform operators of bleaching and dyeing ranges of exactly what is going on in solutions that the fabrics are passing through has given rise to this term.

It is the reduction-oxidation balance at any given time in some particular chemical solution that is being used to have an effect on textile goods. For example, in a continuous dyeing range using vat colors, along with sodium hydrosulphite, sodium sulfoxylate, or comparable compounds, it is vitally important that the reducing agent—hydrosulphite or sulfoxylate—be present in adequate amounts at all times. Variations in the amounts of the reducing agent present cause shade changes; thus, it is important that a definite rate of reduction should be mainained.

The Redox Method depends upon continuous measurement of the electrical potential between a saturated calomel electrode and a platinum electrode. When these electrodes are immersed in the dye solution to be tested, the potential in millivolts is indicated continuously by the Redox Instrument. Satisfactory conditions are set up for each dye formula based on prior experience and by chemical evaluation.

RED PERUVIAN. A harsh, wiry Peruvian cotton of golden-brown cast; it has a 1¼-inch staple and spins to about 50s yarn.

REDRAWING. The rewinding of yarn from bobbins that have been well steamed onto another bobbin or similar form, to do away with splicings, knots, poor piecings, etc., that are detrimental to the yarn.

RED SANDALWOOD. This East Indian tree furnishes the heavy, dark red dyewood also called sanderswood. It is one of the insoluble woods.

RED TAPE. Cotton tape, dyed red, originally used to tie up official papers in English law offices in the days of Old Middle Temple. Now the term is used for long-drawn-out official procedure.

REDUCE. To take oxygen away from a certain material.

REDUCED COLOR. A dyestuff which has its formulation changed or reduced by chemical agents.

REDUCER. Vanished oxygen or its equivalent. Coke, for example, removes oxygen from iron ore and leaves the iron.

REDUCING AGENT. Any substance used to effect a chemical reduction; more specifically, any element that gives up a variance electron to another.

REDUCTION. The process of depriving a chemical compound of oxygen. Also, the process of decreasing the positive valence of an element by the addition of electrons; distinguished from oxidation.

REDUCTION PASTE, STOCK. A paste that contains everything but the color. The paste and color are mixed later, in varying proportions, to give the desired printing paste.

RED WATER. Water contaminated with iron rust. Usually brought about through iron pipe corrosion by dissolved oxygen.

REDWOOD. The immense California tree, *Sequoia sempervirens,* family Taxodiaceae, or its durable reddish wood. The term also includes other trees that yield a redwood used in the dye industry. Trees included in the group are brazilwood, limawood, peachwood, sepanwood. In the so-called insoluble redwood group are barwood, caliatour wood, camwood, and red sandalwood.

REED. One of a number of thin, flat pieces of pressed-steel wire between which the respective warp ends are drawn after they pass through the correct heddle eye on the proper harness frame in the loom. The reed beats the filling picks into their respective place against the fell of the cloth. A Number 40 reed, for example, means that there are 40 reed splits to the inch in the reed. See Illustrated Section.

REED COUNT. The actual number of spaces or reed splits per unit width in the reed. There are several ways used in the reed count, such as the number of spaces or splits per inch, the number of spaces in a two-inch width of the reed, and the number of groups of twenty spaces in thirty-six inches.

REED DRAFT, REED PLAN. The plan or draft set up by the fabric designer on how the reeding-in of the warp threads is to be arranged, plain or fancy, depending on the fabric construction. The design, the drawing-in plan, the yarn, and the type of fabric control the reeding plan to be followed. See Illustrated Section.

REEDED SWEAT BAND. A construction feature found in medium to high quality men's felt headgear. The reeded portion is evident as a tiny piping inserted between the leather sweatband and the body of the hat and is generally a darker color than the band. The reed was originally willow, but is now more commonly made of plastic or wire. The reed is enfolded in a bias strip of coated fabric and attached to the edge of the sweat band with a blanket type stitch. The reeded band allows the hat to mold to the head, shape more easily, and, to a certain extent, aids in prevention of perspiration penetration to the body of the hat.

REED HOOK. The hook used to draw threads through the reed when reeding-in the warp threads. See Illustrated Section.

REEDING. Drawing the warp yarns through the reed splits of the reed. Sometimes referred to as sleying.

REED MARKS. Actual streaks or marks seen in the warp direction of cloth and found in all woven goods, but more particularly in lightweight cottons, some silks, and certain rayon fabrics. Reed marks may be caused by the following: wornout reed, loose reed wires, bent wires of the reed, wrong draws, incorrect reeding, and warp which may be given to much tension on the loom. Reed marks may be obliterated in finishing of the material.

In hand or power weaving, intentional reed marks will appear. Mockleno, canvas weave, basket weaves, the Swedish lace weave, grouped warp threads to make undulating twill effects, texture weaves which employ several kinds of yarns in the warp arrangement, and others, are enhanced for final effect by the system or grouping resorted to in the reeding-in of the warp in the loom. See also REED MARKS IN WOVEN FABRICS.

REED MARKS IN WOVEN FABRICS. Reed marks in cloth go in the warp direction since the reed is a comblike device usually consisting of a top and a bottom rib of wood into which are set thin, flat strips of rather fine pressed steel wire. Carpets, rugs, and heavy industrial fabrics are woven on looms equipped with an iron reed which has a low number of splits to the inch.

The spaces between the reed wire are called reed dents or reed splits. The count or number of a reed is determined by the number of dents to the inch—a 24-reed would have 24 splits to the inch.

The reed is set in the lay of the loom and, when in operation, beats the loose filling pick into its component place in the cloth, and keeps the warp ends even, uniformly straight and true. In this way the warp and filling interlace at right angles.

Reed mark imperfections can be observed in many silks, rayons, and lightweight cottons when the fabric is held to the light. These marks, because the finishing of fabrics is an art and a science, may not show in finished materials.

REED OMBRE. A mill term, reed ombré implies reed marks or streaks in cloth which run in the warp direction. Wrong reeding is often the cause of these marks.

REED RAKE. A blemish in fabric similar to a pin scratch.

REED WIDTH. The width of the entire warp, including selvage ends, in the loom prior to actual weaving. Reed widths are always wider than finished widths. The loom temples help to keep the edge yarns at the correct reed width so that they will interlace at right angles with the filling.

REEDY FABRIC. Cloth which plainly shows reed marks in the warp direction.

REEFER. 1. A single or double-breasted short coat much used in maritime circles and in cold countries. Similar to a sailor's pea jacket, the reefer is a fitted garment, well-tailored and made of sturdy fabric such as: melton, kersey, beaver, Metropolitan cloth, mackinac fabric, and allied heavy woolens. Most reefer cloth comes in navy blue, but other colors may be used. 2. A woman's longer double-breasted tailored coat.

REEL. 1. The large wheel in a horizontal warper onto which the warp sections are wound.

2. A machine for winding yarn, from a package such as a cone, into skein form which usually has a circumference of one and one-half yards. It may be a small machine operated by hand and capable of making only a few skeins at a time, or it may be a large power-driven machine for making skeins in quantity. By varying the traversing arrangement the skeins may be wound in patterns for special purposes.

3. A spool of large capacity used to wind yarn or wire thread.

4. A rotating cylinder of wire or cloth mesh used for sifting or screening insolubles suspended in a liquid.

5. The cardboard core upon which cloth is wound for shipment.

6. A linen measure which takes care of a set number of yards of yarn.

REEL DYE MACHINE. Same as winch.

REELING. When yarn is to be bleached, dyed, mercerized, etc., it may be put into a skein form. Reeling is necessary to produce the skeins. Thirty to sixty skeins may be reeled at a time on the machine. The bobbins or cops of yarn are placed on skewers and wound onto swifts, which extend the length of the frame.

The swift is made from six or eight pairs of cylindrical wooden teeth or spokes; each spoke is about ten inches long. Each set of spokes, at the base, is set firmly into the hub of the swift. Near the top of each set there is a string or cord that will take care of the yarn as it is being wound to form the skein. As the yarn winds onto the cords of the spokes, the skein is built up constantly to take its form.

The arms or spokes of the swift are adjustable so that a skein ranging from 54 to 72 inches in circumference may be slipped off when ready for the next operation.

Reelers are equipped with a measuring motion that will automatically stop the machine when the desired length of yarn has been wound on the swift in circular form.

REELING MACHINE. A machine used to draw yarn from many bobbins, cones, or cops, mounted on spindles onto a revolving reel to form skeins. Hand weavers use floor reels, table reels, and swifts to draw yarn from the bobbins.

REELING SILK. 1. A process of converting silk filaments into yarn in the filature. 2. Winding silk from the bobbins to the skein form. The work is done in the throwing plant.

RE-ENFORCEMENT. Knit goods are sometimes made thicker or give longer wear by the use of re-enforcing yarns. This effect is observed readily by examination of a stocking at the heel and toe.

REEVE-SET. The durable press process developed by Reeves Brothers, Inc., New York City.

REEVON. Trade name of Reeves Brothers, Inc., New York City, for its polyethylene fiber which is in the olefin group of man-made fibers.

REFIN. French for the best grade of wool from any particular class or source.

REFINA WOOL. The leading type of merino wool raised in Spain, which, incidentally, is the home of this famed breed of sheep and from which merino sheep of today are descended. See MERINO, MERINO SHEEP, MERINO WOOL.

REFINISHING. Any treatment given to fabrics to make them "as good as new." Washing, pressing, ironing, laundering, etc., are examples.

REFLECTED LIGHT IN TEXTILES. There is a relation between the composition of a fiber and the color that is to be given to it. Subjecting all kinds of fabrics to the light will show the different power and effect that light will give as its rays strike the material. The smoothness or roughness of the yarn in the goods will have an effect on reflected light.

Cottons compared with silk, acetate, and rayon fabrics are very dull, but firm and nonlustrous. Silks and rayons, because of the reflection, have compactness and brilliancy. Woolens have depth and hue, while worsteds lean to somewhat brighter colorings that are smart and definite in appearance. All these attributes are caused by the physical properties of the respective fibers.

REFLEURET. French for the best grades of wool in Class 1, the Merino group.

Causes of Reed Marks in the Warp Direction

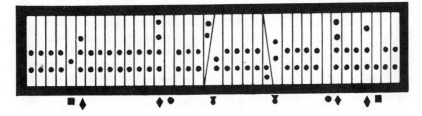

The diagram above illustrates the causes of reed marks in the warp direction. This reeding plan is for two warp ends per dent or split.

● Skipped dent...no ends reeded in the dent; causes a light line in the warp direction seen when the cloth is held to the light.

■ Light dent...when less than the required number of ends has been reeded; causes a line reed mark in the warp direction.

◆ Swollen dent...in addition to the regular number of ends drawn through the split, the threads from a split on either side of the dent have been likewise drawn through; causes a cord effect in the warp direction that is difficult to correct.

⚏ Loose, bent, or worn reed wire... reed wires bend and cause a spreading or a crowding of the respective warp ends; cause the ends to enter the woven goods at a slight angle rather than an absolute right angle with the filling pick. Lines appear in the goods as a result, but usually they can be removed in the finishing of the goods.

REFRIGERATION. The removal of heat at the rate of 200 BTU (British Thermal Units) per minute. Twelve thousand BTU per hour or 288,000 BTU per 24 hours is equivalent to the melting of one ton of ice in 24 hours. See BTU.

REGAIN. A definite percentage of moisture added to the bone-dry weight of the material being treated. Under normal conditions the amounts of regain for the various cloths are: cotton, 6 per cent; woolen, 16 per cent; worsted, 10 per cent; silk, 11 per cent.

REGATTA. Colored cotton cloth made on a 2-up and 1-down twill; usually made in blue and white, fast colors. This British fabric is used for summer wear and ornamentation in the Colonies.

REGENCE. French term for weaves with longitudinal ribs made on the principle of rep constructions, but whose face is the side where the interlacing of the warp yarns appear. Really nothing more than a rep whose reverse is intended to serve as the face of the goods. See CHARVET SILK.

REGENERATE. To give new life to or to cause to be born again. For instance, scrap metal may be used in the smelter and be formed into a new metal. Cellophane and rayon are examples of regenerated cellulose.

In the case of soap this term applies, for example, when the soap has disappeared in the presence of hard water, thereby forming a calcium stearate which is insoluble and causes soap specks (small grease-like beads). With the addition of the proper amount of a polyphosphate such as tetra sodium pyrophosphate or sodium hexametaphosphate, the dead soap is then regenerated or "brought back to life," and becomes a soluble soap once more.

REGENERATED CELLULOSE. A term describing a chemical treatment of cellulose during its manufacture into rayon. Rayon types which have similar reactions, chemical and physical, such as viscose and cuprammonium. This is distinguished from cellulose acetate which reacts differently to dyes and chemicals.

REGENERATED WOOL. On the order of Renaissance Wool, it is obtained from felted and unfelted garments. Used in further manipulation in new cloths. The British meaning implies wool fibers obtained from woven or knitted fabrics.

REGENERATION. Restoration of the activity of an ion exchanger by replacing the ions absorbed from the treated solution by ions that were absorbed initially on the resin.

REGIMENTAL STRIPES. Stripes ranging from one half to one inch in width, which find favor in the better grade of neckwear and hatbands. The colors of the better-known British regiments, as well as the colors of leading universities in this country, provide the color combinations: red and blue of the University of Pennsylvania, for example.

REGINA. English cottons of the lightweight dress variety made from a 2-up and 1-down twill weave. Made of high-count combed yarn, the constructions are high, with pickage system predominating.

REGINNED COTTON. Any cotton stock or lot that has been ginned more than once because of faulty staple.

REGISTER PRINT. Same as Duplex print. See PRINT.

REGULAR. Knitting term in making gloves which implies a glove of standard dimensions as apart from a cadet glove.

REGULAR KNITTING WELT. Used in half-hose and formed on single feed rib machines; dial needles remain idle while the cylinder needles form several courses of jersey fabric and produce a small fold of fabric on the edge of the top. See WELT.

REGULAR TWILL. A 45-degree twill weave either right-hand or left-hand in direction.

REGULAR TWIST. See Z-TWIST.

REHAMMA-SRAGHNA. An open, long-staple fleece from sheep of that name raised in Morocco. Staple is about 3½ inches.

REINFORCED ASBESTOS ROVING. A roving with a core or support made from fibers other than asbestos.

REINFORCED HOSIERY. A stocking knitted at the heel and toe in such a manner that the plating yarn used affords added strength. This yarn is coarser than that used in the body of the article.

REINFORCED VUELITE. Originally developed to provide a safe, shatter-resistant glazing material that would end the danger of flying glass during air raids and shellfire. It consists of sixteen-inch wire screening, approximately .015 inch thick, laminated between two sheets of clear cellulose acetate, and is available in .030 or .024 gauge. This attractive, practical product is tough and strong and is able to withstand the blast of a 150-pound bomb exploded eight feet away. A Monsanto trade name.

REINSTATEMENT. A company's restoration to a previously terminated employee of his employment, and other rights held by him at the time of his separation from the payroll.

REGAINS, STANDARD TEXTILE MOISTURE.

FIBER	PERCENT REGAIN
Acetate	6.5
Acrilan	1.5
Cotton Cloth	6.0-6.5
Cotton Fiber-Yarn	7.0
Cotton, Raw	8.5
Cotton Yarn, Mercerized	8.5
"Dacron"	0.4
Dynel-Verel	0.4
Fiberglas, Saran, Vinyon	Nil
Jute	12.0
Linen	12.0
Nylon	4.5
"Orlon"	1.5
Rayon	11.0
Silk	11.0
Wool, Scoured	13.6
Woolen Yarn-Cloth	13.0
Worsted Yarn-Bradford System-Oil Spun	13.0
Worsted Yarn-French Spun-Dry Spun	15.0
Worsted Cloth	10.0

See Regain.

REJECTS. 1. Woolen or worsted fabrics rejected by the apparel manufacturer for some particular reason, such as narrow width, light weight, poor selvages, faulty dyeing, washer wrinkles, etc.

2. Wool not accepted by the consignee because of color or cast, tenderness, kempiness, seeds, burrs, stains, clumps, etc.

RELATIVE HUMIDITY. The ratio of the actual pressure of existing water vapor to the maximum possible pressure of water vapor in the atmosphere at the same temperature. It is expressed in terms of percentage.

RELAXATION. In acceleration shrinkage in laundering woolen fabrics, a method used to determine dimensional stability in the laundering of shrink-resistant materials; the fabric or specimen may or may not be relaxed prior to the testing. This is actually the equivalent to a number of normal launderings. Dimensional stability is found by the change in measured distances of the material after sunjection to this single operation test procedure. 2. Relaxation is important in the manufacture of textured nylon yarn. Much used in the manufacture of sweaters of this yarn, the conditioning of the article depends on the effectiveness of the dyeing, dimensional stability, sweater shape, and the final appearance of the fininshed item. The term is also applied to some other articles made from other manmade yarns.

RELAXATION SHRINKAGE. The loss of area which occurs when the tension or stretch is imparted to woven or knitted fabrics during finishing, or to wool fibers or yarns during spinning or knitting. The shrinkage is lost by a lessening of the strain, comparable with that of a fabric or garment during laundering.

RELIEF PRINTING. A method upon which the "hill areas" of the engraved plate are inked for printing. It is actually the reverse of Intaglio Printing. See INTAGLIO PRINTING.

REMANUFACTURED WOOL. See WOOL LABELING ACT, 1939.

REMNANT CLOTH. A piece of cloth used to roll around a beam, before fabric is wound thereon, to hold the material to the roller.

REMNANTS. Short ends that accumulate around the mill. They are sold to dealers, who, in turn, sell them over the counter to the trade in the well-known "mill ends" sales. Remnants are also sold in the basement bargain counters in the department stores of the large cities.

RENAISSANCE CLOTH. 1. French term for cloth made from shoddy or remanufactured wool clips.

2. Cloth made from reworked fabrics, often known as remanufactured fabric.

RENFORCE. French sailcloth made from flax or jute yarn.

RENTER, RENTRAIRE, RETRAITURE. Restoration of damaged tapestry fabrics by actual hand weaving of warp or filling yarns into the blemishes such as holes, worn threads, discoloration, etc. Experienced sewers are employed for the work.

REP, REPP. The term is a contraction of "rib." This plain-weave cloth is similar to poplin but has a more marked ribbed effect in the filling direction. Very often a large or distinct rib is alternated with small rib; cylindrical filling is used to enhance the effect. Rep is high in texture, 96 to 136 by 42 to 68.

Lightweight rep is used for blouses, shirts, shorts; heavy rep is much used for curtaining and drapery material. The material may be dyed, printed, or white.

REPACKED COTTON. Cotton bales composed of portions of two or more bales. Also means bales that are made up of samples, loose odds-and-ends, or miscellaneous lots.

REPEAT. 1. An entire completed pattern for design and texture. Repeats vary in size considerably, depending on the weave, type of material, texture, and the use of the cloth.

2. The form which indicates the size of the weave and the number of threads that the weave contains in both the warp and filling. A weave may be repeated any reasonable number of times on paper.

REPEAT IN PATTERN. The distance from one point in a pattern to a similar point in the repeat measuring warp-wise (lengthwise). In Axminster and figured velvet weaves, greater yardage will be required in the minimum weaving in proportion to the size of repeat.

REPEL. To offer resistance toward making contact. A considerable difference in the surface tension, for example, as between oil and water, will cause materials to repel each other.

REPELLENT. Any of a number of treatments applied to fabrics and garments to make them repellent to moths, moisture, water, perspiration, mildew, etc. They may or may not be durable in nature.

REPORTING PAY. Payment made to employees who report to work, but are not permitted to begin work for various reasons over which they have no control.

REPOUSSE. Name given to a pattern; a repoussé pattern will show the effect of being hammered or stamped in.

REPRESS. To check by restraint, as checking the decomposition of hydrolysis of soap by proper building.

REPROCESSED WOOL. Woolen fibers obtained from woven, knitted, or manufactured goods, which, however, have never been used by the consumer. Unfelted goods, when thus garnetted, will give shoddy; felted goods, mungo.

REPS ALTERNATIFS. French term for a weave with longitudinal ribs formed by filling floats above a ground interlacing. The odd and even picks alternate to form simultaneously the floats and the interlacing of the ground effect on two groups of adjacent warps. The odd picks float over the warp yarns of the one group and interlace with the warp ends of the next group. The even picks interlace with the warp ends of the first group and float over the warp ends of the second group of threads.

REP, SEMI OR HALF. A rep fabric, used mainly in Great Britain, in which the warp yarns are of two different sizes and diameters; the filling is all of the same yarn count and diameter.

REP, SILK. Made with silk yarns instead of the conventional cotton yarns characteristic of this fabric; has same uses as cotton rep. See REP, REPP.

REQUET. A plain-weave linen fabric that is bleached and used for bed sheeting in France.

REREELED SILK. Silk filaments wound directly from several cocoons into skeins. The result is a raw silk with only slight twist. When twisted tightly it is called thrown silk. The term is also used when some Chinese silks receive a second reeling after the first one has been completed by unskilled workers.

RERHIA COTTON. An Indian cotton raised in Bengal and noted for its large yield.

RESEARCH AND DEVELOPMENT BY TEXTILE COMPANIES. Recent figures reveal that only 50 million dollars were expended by textile companies for research and development. Of total sales of about $21 billion, only .25% was spent in this phase of the textile industry. The research budget for food was the lowest in the group of the twenty-eight major industries in the United States, with .02%. This was the only industry which spent less money on research and development than textiles.

The figures for textiles do not include amounts expended for work done in colleges and institutions, as well as in regular textile laboratories. Goodly amounts were spent by the Textile Research Institute, Princeton, New Jersey; Institute of Textile Technology, Charlottesville, Virginia; U.S. Testing Company, Inc., Hoboken, New Jersey; Fabric Research Laboratories, Dedham, Massachusetts, and others. Much research and development work is also done in the nine textile colleges in the country.

In the field of textiles, many new products have appeared in recent years, such as bonded fabrics, durable finish, fiberwoven fabrics, flocking, heat-resistant fabrics, especially for ironing boards; knitted vinyl yarns for the automobile industry, laminated fabrics, molded fabrics, nonwoven fabrics, paper for use in disposables; scrim for reinforcement uses, soil release, spun-bonded materials, stabilized fabrics for foundation fabrics, stretch fabrics, and tufting.

New yarns and finishes on fabrics are constantly being developed and textile imports from other nations have had a very potent effect on the American textile industry. These imports have had great effect on our manufacturers who give much attention to research and development and new machinery techniques. Imports and how to combat them has caused many American companies to become international with favorable results.

RESEAU. This term describes the groundwork in lace; réseau is made up of regular uniform meshes.

RESERVE BOX. A feeding arrangement found on picking machines in cotton manufacture. Surplus-opened cotton is stored in the box, and the stock is regulated so that uniform feeding will be possible because of the machine mechanisms provided for the purpose.

RESET CONTROL. The device on a washing machine which starts a washer, dryer, or a combination machine at the same point where it was interrupted because of an off-balance load, overheating of the motor, or some other cause. Most machines will not operate until the correction or elimination has been attended to.

RESIDENT BUYER. This method of group buying involves an individual or a concern who represents a store or stores that are not located in a large city where textile fabrics are made into the finished garment. This type of work presents an economic advantage to the outlying stores represented, since their factors are on the spot to follow up new fashions, styles, vogues, etc.

This tends to make uniformity of fashion throughout the country. Often a resident buyer will take care of the wants of several stores or concerns scattered over the nation.

Resident buyers often save much money for the concerns represented. Without them the buyer for the particular store, no matter how far distant, would have to come to the large city to purchase his wants. This entails loss of time, money, labor, etc.

Group buying makes for better prices, for the larger the order the better will be the price, as a general matter of course.

RESIDUAL SHRINKAGE. The shrinkage or shrinkage properties remaining in some goods after the same have undergone a shrinking process. The residual shrinkage of unsponged or unshrunk material should be interpreted as that which would occur after the material has been subjected to a shrinking process which would bring about maximum shrinkage. However, since many factors are involved—for instance, method of shrinking, increased shrinking increments brought about by additional washing, sponging, pressing, and dimensional changes resulting from different methods of handling—the term residual shrinkage has come to mean the dimensional change occurring after the fabric has been subjected to a stated test procedure.

RESILIENCE. The capability of a material to work against a restraining force during its return from a crushed or crimped state.

RESILIENCY. A natural property of wool and silk which causes them to spring back when crushed in the hand. This helps prevent wrinkling of the cloth. Linen, cotton, rayon are not inherently resilient, but can be treated chemically to help them resist creasing and crushing.

RESILLE. French; a knotted effect (résille literally means net or network).

RESIN. Any of several adhesive organic substances, chiefly coming from or exuding from plants in a semisolid state. A resin is insoluble in water but soluble in alcohol, ether. The resins used in the manufacture of textile fibers are usually produced synthetically. Resins are much used in finishing fabrics but unless of the soluble type, they may wash out. (Incidentally, a ROSIN is another substance, obtained as a residue when crude turpentine is distilled. Do not confuse RESIN with ROSIN.)

RESIN, CYCLIC-ETHYLENE UREA. Ideal for controlled shrinkage on cottons, it has somewhat different chemical structure when compared with

urea-formaldehyde resin. It is not as limited as other resins used for this purpose. See MELAMINE, MELAMINE RESINS, RESIN.

RESIN, MELAMINE-FORMALDEHYDE. Used for controlled shrinkage on woven and knit cotton cloths, the melamine is usually prepared by heating dicyandiamide which is slightly soluble in water, very slightly soluble in hot alcohol, and insoluble in ether. When combined with formaldehyde, the combination forms this synthetic resin. It is a clear liquid with a very strong, pungent odor. See MELAMINE, MELAMINE RESINS, RESIN.

RESIN BONDED PIGMENT COLORS. See PIGMENTED EMULSION COLORS.

RESIN FINISH. The application of an organic finishing agent applied to some fabrics to provide crease-resistance, shrinkage control, water repellency, etc. This finish is not a physical type since it may chemically modify the fiber itself.

RESIN FINISHES. A number of finishing processes apply a variety of synthetic resins to fabrics as coatings or impregnations to change the characteristics of certain fabrics. Depending upon the method and the resin used, qualities such as these may be obtained —flexibility, water repellence, waterproofness, hand varying from soft to stiff, crease resistance, soil resistance, ease of ironing, crush resistance in pile constructions, lessening of slippage, etc.

RESINOID. Implies that the product is a synthetic resin.

RESINOUS. A material which has some of the properties of resins or which contains one or more resins.

RESIN, UREA-FORMALDEHYDE. Used for fabric shrinkage control, it is a combination of formaldehyde and urea, a nitrogen-content organic compound. See MELAMINE, MELAMINE RESINS, RESIN.

RESIST. A chemical substance which will repel or resist dyestuff; a feature of resist printing of textiles. See RESIST PRINTING.

RESIST DYE. A form of "cross-dye" in which the fabric is composed of one kind of stock, as worsted, for example, with part of the yarns in either warp or filling systems of threads being dyed before weaving. Such yarns are so chemically treated in the dye bath that when the cloth from the loom is piece-dyed a different shade for the ornamentation of the goods (which is often of intricate weave) they "resist" the action of subsequent coloration. This defines the principle of true resist dyeing. This variation and the question of efficiency in particular cases are, however, live topics of technical discussion.

RESIST-DYED YARN. It has been treated with tannin, mordant, etc., to repel dyestuff action. When woven into goods, this yarn will repel the dyestuff being used and should form a good contrast or harmony with the body of the cloth.

RESIST DYEING. Fabric treated so that it will repel dyestuff if immersed in a dye liquor. See RESIST-DYED YARN.

RESIST PRINTING. This method of printing is resorted to when it is desired to obtain a white figure on a colored background by dyeing the goods after they have been printed. The cloth to be treated is tannated according to some plan or motif. When the tannin acts upon the material at the designated places, it has the power to repel the action of the dyestuff that is to be used to dye the goods a solid color. The dyestuff will not become "fixed" on the material where it has been tannated.

After the goods have been dyed, they are treated in a correct chemical solution that will not affect the dyed areas, but will remove the tannin or mordant so as to produce a white effect on the colored cloth. Acetic acid may be used to remove the tannin. Thus, a colored cloth with white effects will result. If it is further desired to have colored effects on the goods, they may be printed to give colored dots or designs on the colored background. Some or all of the white areas may be colored.

Basic colors are generally used for this method of printing, and if a color resist is wanted, then some color is added to the resist paste. Cloths which are often resist-printed include foulard, bandannas, polka-dot effects, bunting, dress goods. See DISCHARGE AND RESIST PRINTING, SUMMARY OF.

RESLOOM. Trade-mark of the Monsanto Chemical Co. for a resin finish used on cotton, wool, and rayon, separately or blended. It makes cottons and rayons wrinkle-resistant and when applied to wool it impregnates the fibers, stabilizing the fabric against shrinkage.

RESLYN ADHESIVE. This screentable adhesive does away with the time-consuming method of nailing or printing fabrics or silk screens to printing tables in silk-screen printing processes. The product holds unprinted cloth to the screen table with sufficient adhesion to prevent slippage of the material during printing. The cloth is easily removed after the printing has been completed, with no adhesive sticking to the printed goods.

RESPIRATOR. A device used to cover the mouth and nose; worn by mill operatives who work around carding frames to prevent inhalation of dust, lint, and other particles that might be injurious to health; also used in operating rooms in hospitals.

RESTORA. Burlington Industries owns this patent process which imparts stretch to all-wool fabrics without any chemical change in the molecular structure of the wool fibers. The process is capable of providing elasticity in both warp and filling in the goods.

RESTRAINING AGENT. An agent, which, when added to a dye bath, reduces the equilibrium exhaustion.

RET. To soak, steep, or clean fibers to loosen them so that the good fiber stock may be separated from the undesirable fibers. Retting (rotting) is a process in preparing flax for market. See FLAX, RETTING.

RETAIL DEPARTMENT STORES, SOME MAJOR. These follow:
Abercrombie & Fitch
Abraham & Straus
Adam, Meldrum & Anderson - Buffalo
Addis Co., Inc. - Syracuse
Alexander's Stores
B. Altman & Co., Inc.
Arnold Constable
L. S. Ayers - Indianapolis
Bamberger's, Inc. - Newark
Bergdoff Goodman
L. L. Berges - Buffalo
Bloomingdale's
Bon Marche - Seattle
Bonwit Teller
Broadstreet's
The Broadway - Los Angeles
Broadway Hale Stores, Inc.
Brooks Brothers
Bullock's - Los Angeles
Burdine's - Miami
Capwell's - Oakland
Carson, Pirie & Scott, Inc.
Chappell's - Syracuse
Cherry & Webb - Providence
Crowley-Milner - Detroit
Davison's - Atlanta
Dayton's - Minneapolis
Dnever Dry Goods Co., Inc.
Dey Brothers, Inc., - Syracuse
E. W. Edwards - Rochester
Emporium Capwell
The Emporium - San Francisco
Filene's - Boston
Foley Brothers, D. G. - Houston
G. Fox - Hartford
Franklin Simon
Julius Garfinckel - Washington
Gimbel Brothers
Hahne & Co., Inc. - Newark
Halle Brothers - Cleveland
Haspel Brothers - New Orleans
The Hecht Company, Inc.
Hochschild Kohn - Baltimore
Joseph Horne, Inc. - Pittsburgh
J. L. Hudson Co., Inc. - Detroit
Gilchrist's - Boston
Jordan Marsh - Boston
Joske's - San Antonio
Kaufman's - Pittsburgh
King's Department Stores, Inc.
Korvette - Spartan Industries
LaSalle-Koch - Toledo
Lazarus - Columbus
Lit Brothers, Inc. - Philadelphia
Lord & Taylor
R. H. Macy & Co., Inc.
I. Magnin
Maison Blanche - New Orleans
Martin's - Brooklyn
Marshall Field & Co.
May Department Stores, Inc.
McCurdy's - Rochester
Meier & Frank, Inc. - Portland
Miller & Rhoades - Richmond, Va.
Neiman-Marcus
Ohrbach's
M. O'Neil - Akron
The Outlet Company, Inc. - Providence
Peck & Peck
H & S Pogue - Cincinnati
Rich's - Atlanta
Richard's - Miami
Robinson's - Los Angeles
Roos/Atkins - San Francisco
Saks Fifth Avenue
Sanger Harris - Dallas
Shepard's - Providence
Shillito's - Cincinnait
Sibley, Lindsay & Curr - Rochester
Strawbridge & Clothier, Inc.
Stewart's - Baltimore
Thalheimer's - Richmond
Unishops, Inc.
Wallach's, Inc.
John Wanamaker
Woodward & Lothrop

RETAILLE. French word for clippings and certain wastes from fabrics, odds and ends, etc. They may be used as reworked fibers in the manufacture of new fabrics. The term can also apply to clippings from a sheep fleece which have a varying value to no value at all.

RETAIL SALESMEN IN TEXTILES. The man who sells textiles in small units. The wholesalers deal in particular types of cloth, usually few in number, and dispense them to the retailer and the department store. The retail salesmen call on the trade in order to keep the small concerns that handle materials stocked up. He works on a small salary and commission, straight salary, or straight commission. The position is a good one when the business outlook is good, but there seems to be a tendency for some time past of stifling the chances of success for all. Too many seem to believe that they possess the inherent traits of salesmanship and think the work will afford a "soft" position. However, many are sadly disappointed after a short and sometimes harrowing trial at selling. Recent trends have been cutting down the importance of retail salesmen.

RETARDING AGENT. Any of several compounds used to retard or reduce the rate of dyeing textile yarns or fabrics.

RETE. Italian for net.

RETICELLA A FUSELLI. A bobbin lace made to imitate genuine reticella made for several centuries in Italy. The word for bobbin in Italian is fuselli.

RETICELLA OR GREEK POINT. An old-time lace which shows cut and drawn-work effects with buttonholed edges connected with brides. The famous Sforza family of Italy sponsored the making of reticella, which is the earliest form of needle-point lace known. Other names are Roman or Milan point or Venetian guipure. Reticella is still very popular for use in collar and cuff sets, table linens, and dress trimmings.

RETTERY. Any place or establishment where retting is done.

RETTING. See FLAX PROCESSING.

RETURN AIR CONDENSER. A device used in the picker rooms of mills. It will remove dust and air from the room and then return the latter to the room after the former has been automatically removed. This dust is deposited onto a slowly revolving screen which drops into a waste receptacle.

REUSED WOOL. Fibers obtained from garments worn by consumers. The cast-off apparel finds its way to the garnetting plant where the material is returned to the fibrous stage. Shoddy and mungo are the names applied to the unfelted and felted fiber residue following the garnetting operation which breaks up the garments and produces the fibers. The content of this wool must be declared in the fabric or garment in accordance with the Wool Products Labeling Act of 1939.

REVENNES. A strong, heavy, well-textured sailcloth used in French maritime circles.

REVERS. A part of a garment turned back to show the lining or facing, as a lapel.

REVERSE. 1. The back of a material. 2. A coarse, low-texture French flannel napped on one side and used in low-priced apparel.

REVERSE COLORING. By reversing the ground and top colors, some designs might be better suited to buyers' wishes. This can be most easily accomplished in Jacquard weaves by simply changing the yarn frames.

REVERSED CALF. Pertains to the heavier weight calf leathers that are finished on the flesh side and contain oils which make them more water-repellent than suède. It is used for shoes when a napped sports leather is desired. In Great Britain the terms "Trench Calf" and "Hunting Calf" are synonymous with Reversed Calf. Allied with the term is "Service Leather" which applies to splits and side leather.

REVERSED TWILL. A loose term which implies that the warp yarn predominates on the face of certain cotton and linen cloths that are featured by the use of some twill weave; a herringbone weave, for example, will produce a reversed twill.

REVERSE KNIT. A term applied to plain-knit fabrics when they are used "inside out." This is sometimes done to hosiery to dull the effect.

REVERSE PLATING. Patterns formed in knit goods by controlling the feeding-in of the yarns in such a way that their positions in the goods are interchanged.

REVERSER. As applied to stain setting and coagulation, it implies checking of incipient coagulation, reversing it and dissolving the soiling substance.

REVERSE TWIST. See S-TWIST.

REVERSIBLE. 1. A material in which it makes little difference which side is the face of the goods—burlap, canvas, duck, mail-bagging, webbing, etc.
2. A garment which has, say, gabardine or some similar fabric on the one side to be worn during inclement weather; the other side of the garment may be Cheviot, homespun, Shetland, tweed or some similar cloth which can be worn as the face of the garment in bright, crisp, or cold weather.
3. A double-faced fabric such as crepe-back satin, rib-canton, satin-canton, etc.

REVERSIBLE FABRIC. It is an accepted fact that many plain-woven fabrics are alike on both sides, unless napped or printed. Sometimes cloth is printed on both sides; this is often called duplex printing. Reversible cloth is also produced by weaving a pattern on each side of the fabric. The design on each side may be the same or different. Many woolens, such as blankets, plaid-back overcoatings, robes, and steamer rugs are made in this manner.

REVERSIBLE HOMESPUN OR TWEED. This fabric is of double cloth construction and has to be made from at least five sets of yarns - face warp, face filling, back warp, back filling, and a set of binder yarns which hold the two fabrics together as the material is woven in the loom. Usually the patterns differ on each side. Lining for garments of this type is not necessary. The cloth, when made into apparel, is very bulky and unwieldy, and finds use only in very cold climates where warmth is desired.

REVERSIBLE IMPERIAL. See SATIN IMPERIAL.

REVERSING MOTION. Found on the roving frame, the motion will cause the lifting shaft to reverse its direction of rotation at the consummation of each traverse. The builder motion of the roving frame controls the time at which reversing occurs.

REVOLVER. The spiral cutting blade, on the principle of the blade on a lawn mower, used on a shearing machine. It comes in contact with the fixed or ledger blade over which the cloth passes when it is to be sheared.

REVO NON-STRETCH BELTING. A product of L. H. Shingle Company, Camden, New Jersey, it has special processing to set the molecular structure of nylon bands permanently to reduce stretching. The belts give under loads but return to original length or tension on release. The belts can run indefinitely without take-up or idlers. They are made by orienting nylon bands and specially woven nylon fabric, resulting in highly increased belt strength. The belts are resistant to temperatures up to about 200° F., and humidity, oils, and many acids. This transmission belting is much used in industry.

REVOLVING CYLINDER CARD, INVENTION OF. In 1748, John Wyatt and Louis Paul, ten years after they had invented drawing rollers for textile machinery, brought out the revolving cylinder card. It is still in use today but, of course, has been improved greatly since their invention. The principles of their inventions are the basis of the modern, individual driven machines of today.

REWORKED WOOL. See RECLAIMED WOOL.

REX-FINISHED. Cotton velvet which is finished by dissolving and precipitating upon it a portion of its own cellulose, thereby closing the fiber tips. Used for burnishing and polishing purposes.

RHADAMES. A range of fabrics, usually made of silk, rhadamés are made on 12-end repeats of pattern.

RHADZIMER. Any type of broken twill weave which repeats on eight harnesses; formerly used in many silk fabrics.

RHEA. Another name for ramie.

RHEOLOGY. The study of the deformation and flow of matter which can be applied to a textile adhesive, plastic or steel. For example, there is the principle of rheology of aqueous acrylate textile adhesives and related parameters, the constant or variable term in its function to determine the specific form of this function but not its general nature, as observed in flocking and laminating of textile fabrics.

RHODIA. Trademark for the cellulose acetate fiber and yarn manufactured by Societé Rhodiaceta whose main headquarters of the Rhodiaceta group are in Lyons, France.

RHODIACETA. Produced by Societe Rhodiaceta, Paris, France. *Deutsche Rhodiaceta* is manufactured by Deutsche Rhodiaceta A. G., Freiburg/Br., West Germany; *Rhodiaseta Argentina* is a product of Rhodiaseta Argentina S. A., Buenos Aires, Argentina; *Rhodiatoce* is made by Societa Rhodiatoce S. p. A., Milan, Italy; *Rhodosa* is produced by Cia. Rhodosa de Rayon, Sao Paulo, Brazil; *Rhone Poulenc* by Societe Rhonee Poulenc, Paris while *Rhovyl* is manufactured by Societe Rhovyl, Paris, France.

Rhodia Italia is the bright and semi-dull acetate made by Rhodiatoce S. p. A., in Italy; *Rhodia Nylon* is a product of Societe Rhodiaceta S. A. in France (Nylon Type 66); *Rhodia Perlon*, a polymide nylon (Type 6) is made Deutsche Rhodiaceta A. G., West Germany; *Rhodia Velo* is the acetate high-twist filament made by the Italian unit in this corporation while *Rhodianil Nylon* (Type 66), filament and staple are made in the Brazillian division of this company.

RHODOPHANE. A brittle, transparent material which does not shatter, developed by the French manufacturer, Colombet. Used in millinery, dress accessories, bags, and jackets.

RHONITE. Trademark of Rohm & Haas Company, Philadelphia, Pennsylvania, for water soluble urea formaldehyde condensates which have several uses in the textile trade - stabilization against shrikage and stretch, cruse resistance on fabrics, additional weight, and a modified or improved band to certain cloths. Provides durability to fabrics and garments and on a washfast basis.

RHOPLEX. Product of Rohm & Haas Company, Philadelphia, Pennsylvania, for a group of resins of the water soluble urea formaldehyde group. Much used in flocking, these resins possess exceptional adhesion and will not stiffen with age or weather. Since they require no plasticizing, vulcanizing, nor addition of anti-hardening agent, they are easy to formulate. Applied to both natural and manmade fibers, they have excellent resistance to discoloration and the effects of drycleaning and washing. They can be used alone or with fillers, pigments, gums, and starches. Also much used as a binding agent for nonwoven fabrics, backing of fabrics, and other types of binding.

RHOVYL. Registered trade-mark of Deutsche Rhodiaceta AG., Freiburg im Breisgau, West Germany, for its polyvinyl staple fiber made in Tronville en Barrois, France. Properties include warmth, ease of washing and laundering, permanent pleating through repeated launderings, will not felt or shrink, dries rapidly, and does not need ironing. It may be colored by dope-dyeing, naphthol, acetate, and indigisol dyes. A pure polyvinyl chloride fiber, it is unaffected by acids, alkalies, or salts, and is non-inflammable.

The fiber is much used in the manufacture of nonwoven fabrics because of its thermoplasticity, chemical resistance, rotproofness, waterproofness, sunlight resistance, acoustic and calorific insulation.

There are three types of Rhovyl:

1. RHOVYL 55: In free state it is capable of shrinking up to 55 per cent at a temperature of 212° F. Comes in all staple lengths and common denier sizes and finds considerable use in nonwoven fabrics.
2. RHOVYL 30: Has intermediary shrinkage stage (30 per cent between Rhovyl 55 and Rhovyl T) and is for special use where less than 55 per cent shrinkage is desirable.
3. RHOVYL T: The non-shrinkage fiber that is dimensionally stable up to 212° F., by molecular reorientation during manufacture. Above this temperature a certain amount of shrinkage may occur. It comes in staple lengths and deniers common to the various spinning systems and for use in nonwoven fabrics.

RHYTHM CREPE. Rayon seersucker or plissé effect cloth. Plain-weave cloth with crimped effect running in warp direction.

Washable, drapes well, and gives good wear. Imitates seersucker and cotton plissé.

RIB. A straight and narrow raised rib, cord, or "hill" in certain woven goods: Bedford cord, piqué, bengaline, grosgrain, Ottoman, hatbanding, corduroy. The rib may be in the warp or the filling direction. It is made by rib weaves, thick yarns, cylindrical filling, pile-weave constructions, etc. The term also means the actual rib effect seen in knit goods when the rib stitch has been used. See Illustrated Section.

RIBAND. A ribbon, especially one used for decorative purposes; a short way of saying "ribbon band."

RIBBED FABRIC. A broad term for cloth made with heavy warp or filling ribs to give it a characteristic feature for identification. Examples are piqué, Bedford cord, officer's belt webbing, Russian cord shirting, corduroy, some riding habit cloth, and certain novelty dress goods. Filling effect cloths are bengaline, rep, poplin, true piqué, and some ribbons.

In knit fabric, the term may imply fabric that has lengthwise ribs or wales which show on the right and the wrong side of the material in a 1-and-1 or a 2-and-2 order.

RIBBER. A knitting machine, flat or circular, that has two sets of needles.

RIBBON. A fillet or narrow woven fabric of varying widths, commonly one-quarter to three inches, having selvage edges, chiefly of rayon, silk, or velvet, and used for braiding, decoration, trimmings, etc.

RIBBON, PETERSHAM. The millinery ribbon is made of silk, rayon, or nylon warp and with single-ply coarse cotton filling to produce a rib effect. The filling action in the loom gives a gimplike edge. There are from 24 to 36 ribs per inch. The skirt type has a filling effect of one or more yarns in each rib. If more than one yarn is used these filling threads are placed in the same shed of the loom as the fabric is being woven. This stiff fabric may be obtained by a stiffening treatment or a very compact filling texture. It may be woven with or without pockets in which to insert supports. The selvages in the goods are made by the return of the filling yarn so·as to give a gimplike edge. They can also be woven in a contrasting way as well.

RIBBON LAP MACHINE. The ten-inch laps of cotton from the sliver lap machine are placed four laps up at the back of this machine. The laps are drawn through four lines of fluted rollers, each being drawn separately, laid together, and formed into one lap that is twelve inches wide. The purpose of the frame is to lay the fibers straight and to make an even lap for the combing operation. Lap rollers should be sized twice daily.

RIBBON LAPPER. A machine used in the manufacture of fine quality cotton yarns. It combines four to six ribbons of sliver lap stock into one of a more uniform weight per yard.

RIBBON LOOM. From a few up to 144 pieces of fabric may be woven on this loom. Each article has its own shuttle or batten, and the shuttle may be straight or curved to save space on the machine. The loom lay is controlled by a rack and pinion mechanism. Dobby or Jacquard head motions can be attached to the ribbon loom. See NARROW FABRICS.

RIB FABRIC. Any woven cloth characterized by a rib or cord effect in the construction. Cylindrical filling will also produce a rib effect in fabric—poplin, fuji, luana, taffeta, grosgrain, Oxford shirting, bengaline, etc. The term also means a knitted fabric made with a rib stitch (see Illustrated Section) in which the lines of wales or ribs run vertical on both sides of the material. Except for possible fancy stitches in the fabric both sides look the same. Rib fabrics have considerable elasticity and are thicker when compared with plain-stitch fabric.

RIB KNIT. Knit goods in which rib stitches produce lengthwise ribs on both sides of the cloth. The width of the ribs depends on the number of stitches per inch.

RIB STITCH. A stitch used in knitting whereby the loops of the same course are drawn to both sides of the material. It can be done on a flat or circular machine, which has two sets of needles knitting at the same time. When all needles are used the stitch is known as one-and-one or plain rib, since the loops alternate one on the one side of the fabric and one on the other side. See Illustrated Section.

Fancy rib stitches are made by removing some needles from one or both sets of needles. For example, two needles in one set and two in the other set will produce a two-and-two rib effect, which is often called a Swiss rib.

RIB 1 x 1 STITCH. A stitch in which one set of wales or lengthwise ribs appear in alternate fashion on both sides of the knitted goods.

RIB STITCH, 2 x 2. The most elastic of rib-knitted structures. It forms two vertical wales on the face of the goods alternately with two on the back. The effect is made possible by the alternate two needles in the cylinder and the dial (the front and the back beds in flat machines) knitting with every third needle in each of the beds not functioning or missing. This stitch is also called Swiss Rib Knit in underwear fabrics.

RIB TOP. The top of a stocking; knitted with rows of heavy stitches.

RIB TRANSFER STITCH. It is made by transferring the loops from selected cylinder needles to the adjacent dial needles in a knitting machine.

RIB VELVET. Cloth of the velvet group with a lengthwise rib effect. In cotton, material is called corduroy; sometimes made with rayon.

Good draping quality, though rather difficult to handle and manipulate. Durable, crushable; must be dry-cleaned.

RIB WEAVES. They are derivatives of the plain weave, and show rib lines warpwise (a filling rib weave) or crosswise (a warp rib weave). It should be noted that, for example, a filling rib weave will show the rib or cord effect in the opposite direction, the vertical direction in this instance. Common or simple warp ribs repeat on two warp ends, filling ribs on two picks. Thus, all even-number ends or picks in the goods will weave alike, and all odd-numbered ends or picks will weave alike. Examples of rib weaves or rib effects may include hat banding, grosgrain, bengaline, Ottoman, transportation fabric, Russian cord shirting, several types of webbing, etc.

RICE CLOTH. Usually made of cotton yarn, this plain-weave fabric comes in a width of about 41 inches with textures ranging from 56 ends and 60 picks to 44 ends and 22 picks per inch.

The filling is always a ply yarn in which a series of loops or nubs provide the rice-grained effect in the material. The nub yarn is plied with a smooth, very cylindrical yarn, about which it is wound. Rice-grain effect in filling is interspersed at set intervals. Comes in piece-dyed and printed effects at the present time.

RICE FLOUR. A sizing ingredient, adhesive in nature, which comes in minute starchy granule form; difficult to burst by boiling, it gives a harsh feel to treated cloth.

RICE NET. Doup-woven cotton fabric which has much starching. Used in the millinery trade for crowns and brims of hats, it is often known as cape net.

RICE STARCH. An adhesive sizing ingredient which is harsh and stiff in feel and used chiefly in laundries.

RICE WEAVES. Six-end or eight-end broken-twill weaves.

RICKRACK. 1. Trimming made of serpentine braid used to decorate garments. 2. Flat braid made in zigzag form.

RICOTTI. Waste stock taken from the smooth inner skin of a cocoon after it has been reeled.

RIDDLE. Red markings used on Shropshire sheep for identification purposes.

RIDER. A ticket, tag, or label placed at the top of a stocking to indicate its style, size, and characteristics.

RIDGED WEAVE. A defect in weaving cloth in the loom caused by slack warp or when the last one or two harnesses in the loom are set too high or too low thereby impeding the proper passage of the filling bobbin through the shed of the loom. Thus, a light widthwise mark or streak is noted periodically in the cloth after it is woven.

RIDING HABIT. Costume used for horseback riding—breeches or jodhpurs, with boots, shirt, and jacket or sweater. The coat is usually made two inches longer than a regular coat and is flared at the bottom. The breeches are usually worn by men; breeches or jodhpurs are worn by women. Riding habits may be made from whipcord, Bedford cord, broadcloth, elastique, melton, covert, or other stout, rugged, dressy fabrics.

RIFFAN. Scotch term for carded wool.

RIGGED CLOTH. When a cut or bolt of cloth is doubled and folded selvage to selvage; affords protection to face of the goods.

RIGHT TWIST. See Z-TWIST.

RIGID BLADE BEATER. See BLADE BEATER.

RIGID FABRIC. Refers to a fiber or fabric that is not stretchable.

RIG-IN-FLEECE. A part or cleavage up the middle of the fleece made by the wool sorter so that he may more readily handle and sort the fleece. Also called Rig Wool, Rig Fleece.

RIGMEL. Trade-mark of the Bradford Dyeing Association for a stabilization process which also gives luster and a soft hand to such fabrics as cotton shirting and dress fabrics. The process controls shrinkage to within 1 per cent of the length or width of the fabric. See RIGMEL SHRUNK.

RIGMEL SHRUNK. Trade name for a shrinking process by which fabrics will not shrink more than 1 per cent in length or width. The process causes the texture of the goods to become more compact thereby assuring greater strength and longer wear. At the same time the shrinkage can be controlled and the natural luster and handle of the goods are enhanced.

A standard washing test is first made to ascertain the possible shrinkage in the length and the width of the cloth in terms of inches per yard of goods. The cloth is then shrunk to the proper dimensions in accordance with the results that would be obtained in ordinary washing of the finished garment.

The cloth to be finished is dampened and then given a steam and water vapor treatment while the material is made taut on the machine. Final contraction of the goods follows the release from tension. Rigmel treated fabrics can be controlled in shrinkage to one-quarter inch per yard in both warp and filling directions. Trade name owned by Bradford Dyeing Association (U.S.A.). For Rigmel shrinking machine, see Illustrated Section.

RIG WOOL. Wool along the spinal area of sheep; term used with regard to long wools and crossbreds.

RILSAN. Made by Snia Viscosa Group, Milan, Italy, this polyamide fiber is made from a derivative of castor oil, aminoundecanoic acid, and the only man-made fiber of vegetable origin. Polymerization of the amino acid, causes Rilsan or Nylon 11 to be produced. Somewhat less in hygroscopicity than regulation nylon, it has a moisture regain of about 1 per cent while specific gravity is 1.04, thereby insuring excellent covering capacity. It is a soft fiber, lends itself to special hand in finished fabric, and is the least inflammable fiber in the man-made group of fibers. It is non-allergic and the staple resembles wool while the filament simulates silk. Chief uses include hosiery of all types, ladies' garments and underwear, rainwear, swimsuits, gloves, and industrial fabrics such as filters, work clothes for the chemical and allied industries.

RIM DE BOI COTTON. A Minas Geraes, Brazilian cotton of the tree variety. The staple is ¾ inch to ⅞ inch with a small lint yield. There are two colors of this cotton, white and drab; the latter is used by the natives to make fabrics for local consumption, since the material is used in the natural color of the fiber.

RING. Found on the ring spinning frame, it is a small circular flanged track of high-grade steel which is highly polished. The traveler speeds around the ring when the machine is operating. The ring is set in a ring holder which is fastened to the ring rail.

Flange widths and ring diameters will vary according to the type and size of yarn being made. Diameters, measured as the distance or space inside the flanges, range from 1½ to 3 inches. Yarn passes between the traveler and the ring on its way to be wound on the bobbin.

RING BAR. A metal rail which extends the length of the ring spinning frame and, by a properly timed up-and-down action, builds up the yarn onto the bobbins in an even, uniform manner.

RINGER. A warp end which has snapped and broken during the warping operation.

RING FRAME. Refers to a ring spinning frame or a ring twister frame.

RING HOLDER. Found on the ring spinning frame, it is the device attached to the ring rail which holds in place the fast-traveling ring travelers in their continuous course while the machine is in operation. The holder is usually a flat, annular, pressed plate. Rings may travel from 4,000 to 12,000 or more r.p.m.

RINGLESS. A hosiery term which indicates that no two courses of any of the sequential courses are made from the same cone of yarn, in order to eliminate shadowy rings. The rings were formerly a bane to hosiery manufacturers, especially in silk stockings, but it is rare when they occur in present-day knitting of hosiery.

RING RAIL. On the ring spinning frame above the spindle rail and parallel with it is the vertically movable ring rail. It is a channel-shaped, long metal piece with the flanges projecting downward. The web of the rail is drilled with holes to agree with the holes in the spindle rail. These holes are of sufficient size to accommodate the spinning rings, as well as the spindles. Made in sections, the ring rail is supported by upright lifter rods which also provide a traversing motion in a vertical direction. See SPINDLE RAIL.

RINGS. Irksome outline spots on fabrics caused by shifting of finish or soil in the goods after trying to eradicate the spot. They are more pronounced in the lighter colored fabrics. Some fabrics, because of the ring outline, have to be cleaned by immersion of the whole garment or article instead of merely treating the spot. Rings are the bane of drycleaners and always be sure to check for them before making payment for his services.

RINGS, KNITTING. Mottled or clouded areas that run around a stocking; uneven yarn is usually the cause of this blemish.

RING SPINNING. A method of spinning cotton and worsted roving into yarn. The roving, after it has passed between the sets of drawing rollers, is guided in a downward direction through the traveler, a small inverted U-shaped device which is flanged onto its respective ring in the ring rail of the machine. It travels around the ring at the rate of 4,000 to 12,000 revolutions per minute. As the spindle revolves to wind the yarn the latter has to

pass through the traveler and carries it around on the ring at this rapid pace.

The narrower the width of the traveler, the finer is the diameter of the yarn and the higher its count or size.

The up-and-down motion of the ring rail causes the winding of the yarn onto its bobbin at the nose, body, and heel. The spindles are driven by means of cotton friction banding. One endless belt drives two spindles on each side of the frame, four in all.

See Illustrated Section.

RING-SPINNING FRAME. The type of spinning frame used generally in this country for making cotton yarn. Its operating cost is much lower and it occupies less space than the mule spinning frame.

RING TRAVELER, TRAVELLER. Same as the small traveler set on the flange of the ring in a ring-spinning machine. See RING SPINNING.

RING TWISTER. Used to twist or to wind yarn, the features of the frame are the ring arrangements and the accompanying travelers. There is no draft on a twister frame such as found on the ring-spinning frame.

RING WASTE. Waste of any sort that collects around the rings of ring-spinning frames. Specifically it refers to the odds-and-ends of roving which gather in the rolls of a ring-spinning frame.

RINSE. 1. To cleanse by flooding after washing. 2. To remove by successive additions of fresh water the accumulations of detergent and dirt emulsions and other materials which are added to or formed in the washwheel. Rinsing is important in the production of good quality work and prevention of fiber damage.

RINSE TEMPERING. Also called replacement rinse, this rinse may be hot or cold and is then replaced by a cold water rinse to lower the temperature of the itmes being washed prior to the spinning phase of the cycle. May be done by overflowing or alternating draining methods. See Rinse.

RINZU. A Japanese-silk satin material.

RIO GRANDE COTTON. The original type used in the devolpment of a great many American cottons of the Uplands short-staple varieties. Rio Grande is a variety of Brazilian cotton which is harsh, wiry, and cream color; its staple is slightly below 1 inch and it spins to about 40s warp yarn.

RIPE COTTON. Fully developed cotton that is highly desirable for spinning purposes.

RIPENESS. See MATURITY.

RIPENING. 1. A process in the

manufacture of viscose rayon in which the spinning solution is allowed to stand in large containers for several days to age or mature; also, to allow entrapped air bubbles to disappear.

2. A treatment sometimes given to stiff, wiry carpet wools to make them easier to card. The fibers are sprayed with oil and allowed to stand for several days or weeks so that the oil may penetrate.

RIPPLE. The coarse steel comb used to remove leaves, seeds, and other foreign substances from flax straw.

RIPPLETTE. Trade name for a mixture of cotton and rayon with a crepe effect contrasted with a plain-weave ground stripe. This cloth, similar to seersucker or plissé, is light in weight, launders well, and is inexpensive. Used for bedspreads.

RIPPLE, WAVY CLOTH. British fabric made from rather coarse woolen yarn in which the surface effect of the goods, because of the long, protruding fibers, make it possible to give the fabric a rippled or wave type of finish.

RIPPLING. The drawing of flax stalks through the ripple comb to remove undesirable particles such as leaves, seeds, etc.

RISER. A painted block on textile design paper which implies that the warp end is over the filling pick at the point of intersection. Also called raiser and "up."

RISTEN. Standard grade of flax by comparison with which other flax in the Balkan areas is graded.

RISTY, RIFFY COTTON. Raw cotton raised in the Near East countries.

RIVERINA MERINO. A leading type of Merino sheep raised in Southeastern Australia called the Riverina. Victoria is the clearinghouse for the wool in this open, grassy plain in New South Wales.

The sheep are strong, hardy, good foragers, and the plain-bodied animal is noted for the dense wool folds on the neck. Fleece weight is about nine pounds, staple is about five inches, while the fiber grades from 60s to 64s.

RIVER PLATE WOOL. Also called Buenos Aires or Montevideo wool. The term embraces Merino wools raised in the Argentine and Uruguay which, although fine in fiber quality, lack strength and loftiness. The wool also contains an excessive amount of burrs.

RIVER'S COTTON. This is a general name given to cotton of the Mississippi Delta Bottomlands which has a staple from 1 1/16 inches to 1 1/8 inches. This hardy, medium-grade cotton has a good feel, works well in spinning, and

is in demand. There are several cottons, of particular characteristics, that are known by this name. This cotton is also grown in Arkansas.

RIVIERE. The open or porous effect obtained by embroidering over or using the drawing threads jointly on the plan of drawn-thread work.

ROAD MEMBRANE. This open, plain-weave fabric, made of very coarse cotton yarn, is used for reinforcement of bituminous surfaced roads, airport runways, and ditch-linings.

ROAN. Originally the term meant sumac-tanned sheepskin, as apart from "Basil" or bark-tanned sheepskin. Roan now means sheepskins of full substance which are not split.

ROANNE. Sheeting and pillowcase fabric made from either cotton or linen.

ROANOKE COTTON. A strong, white cotton with a staple of 3/4 inch to 7/8 inch; may be spun to about 30s.

ROBBINGS. Wool fibers removed during combing operation, but too long in staple to be classed as noil.

ROBE. 1. A long, loose outer garment. 2. A dress of flowing and elegant style and make. 3. A dress of state, rank, office, or the like.

ROBE CLOTH. A twill-woven print cloth made on about a 64 square count. It comes in large brilliant-colored furniture motifs. Robe fabric and furniture covering are distinguished in the trade, but their uses overlap as in the case of wrappers, robes, coatings, curtaining, comfortables, furniture covering.

ROBE DE CHAMBRE. A dressing gown, chiefly one for women.

ROBERTS, RICHARD. By 1830 he had improved the mule frame of Samuel Crompton. The machine was made well-nigh perfect by him, because of his technique in handling the frame. He invented the quadrant, one of the most important and vital mechanisms to be found on the modern mule of today. The quadrant has much to do with the even motion of the mule, and helps to prevent any jerky, irregular action while the machine is in operation. His invention assured even, uniform yarn resulting from co-ordinated drawing, twisting, and winding.

ROBIN'S EGG BLUE. A light greenish-blue, the color of the eggshell of the American robin. It has high brilliance and low saturation.

ROCCADINI SILK. Italian carded spun silk is called cascami. Roccadini is the lowest grade of the three types of this silk that is spun into yarn. It finds some use in hosiery of the poorest

quality.

ROCHELLE. A staple French linen used for sheeting, pillowcasing, covers, and shirting.

ROCKFORD SOCK. Medium to heavyweight seamless cotton work socks of regular length with a body of mixed colored and white yarns, an all-white welt, toe, and heel.

ROCOCO. 1. Style of ornamentation resembling grottos, in eighteenth century—shells, scrolls, etc.

2. Italian lace which has a design of pebble, shell, leaves, scroll, and similar effects, grouped together in a rather elaborate manner. This type of lace is often overdone in design and does not have much appeal because of the distorted appearance.

3. A style of hat worn in the Victorian era. The hat was usually tipped over the face, with the brim dipping slightly at the front and the back. It was trimmed with flowers of several colors.

4. The term is sometimes applied to any excessive decoration which is not in good taste.

ROCK WOOL. Insulating material made from melted silicon rock, the molten mass being forced through jets by compressed air and steam, which force the mass into a myriad of tiny pieces.

The fiber resembles wool and finds much use for insulation; it is forced or blown between the inner and outer walls of houses to regulate the heat and cold. It is claimed that a one-half inch layer of rock wool will save about 25 per cent in the fuel bill; a one inch layer will reduce the average fuel bill about 35 per cent.

Rock cork is made by pressing asphalt and rock wool into sheet form. This product is used in refrigeration.

ROCKY MOUNTAIN SHEEP. Similar to but smaller in stature than the Asiatic argali sheep, this "bighorn" type of sheep ranges over the western coast of Canada, this country, and Mexico.

ROE COTTON. An early-maturing Louisiana cotton of the Uplands variety having a staple of 1 inch to 1 1/4 inches and a lint yield of about 30 per cent.

ROGUE YARN. An irregular color, fiber, or yarn inserted into material for identification purposes. Used in rope, some braided materials, and in certain double cloths.

ROLLBACK. Punching on a Schiffli frame is referred to as rollback, when it is too large to be sewed on endlessly, and therefore must be re-rolled at the end of the punching each time prior to continuing to stitch. See Punch Machine.

ROLL BEAM. A textile machine or frame equipped with a cast-iron beam which extends across its width. The beam usually has a smooth flat surface to which is attached the roll stand.

ROLL BOILING. See POTTING.

ROLL COVERING. See COT.

ROLLER CARD. Generally speaking, this is the wool card equipped with the main cylinder, and from four to seven stripper rolls and worker rolls working in pairs. Broadly, it is any type of card in which rollers do the carding of fibers. In cotton carding there are several rollers, but the actual carding is done by the main cylinder and the endless belt, known as the revolving flat belt, a slatted formation of bars, extending the width of the machine, in which card clothing is set.

ROLLER CLOTH. An all-wool woven felt used on specific drawing rolls on various textile machines to afford a resilient base or cushion under the leather roll covering on the surface of the roller.

ROLLER DRAWN YARN. Rather tight, beardy, and wiry yarn. Made on ring or cap spinning frames.

ROLLER LEAD. The lead of a roller, or that of the gills on a gill box in worsted yarn manufacture, implies that the lead roller or the lead gill travels somewhat faster than the trailing roller or gill.

ROLLER LEATHER. Leather used for cots or covers on the upper rollers of cotton-spinning machinery, especially the bark-tanned types from certain classes of sheep, lamb, and calfskins.

ROLLER PRINTING. See PRINTING, MACHINE.

ROLLERS. There are six types of rollers used on textile machines—back, front, top, bottom, smooth, and fluted.

Back rollers are part of every machine; their purpose is to level or reduce sliver, slubbing, or roving. They are called feed rollers, and it is between them that the stock is fed into a machine or frame.

Front rollers are for the delivery of the form of stock as it passes from a machine. Both back and front rollers are arranged in pairs, one above the other.

The upper roller of each of the sets is known as the top roller or top back roller, or the top front roller, as the case may be. The under roller is called the bottom, back, or front roller.

The rollers on some machines, a gill box, for example, are usually corrugated or fluted and fit into one another very much as the teeth of wheels fit into each other. This affords a bet-

ter point of contact and insures a uniform feed and delivery of the stock, which is superior to that given by a smooth roller under similar conditions. Less pressure is required upon fluted rollers than would be required of smooth rollers to obtain the same result, thus consuming less power to drive them. The nip of a fluted roller can be placed much nearer to the gill pins than would be possible with smooth rollers because the diameter of the roller is much less.

ROLLING SELVAGE, ROLLING LISTING. Selvages that curl or roll up are often cut by the shearing machine in the finishing department. Rolling selvages are often caused by the edge selvage ends having too much tension or pull on them. The weaver should watch edges closely in order to fix immediately any defect, no matter how slight. Automatic looms equipped with warp drop-wires will cause the loom to stop or knock-off if any end in the warp breaks, selvage ends included. Broken warp ends, in looms of this type, must be remedied before the loom will again begin to weave fabric.

Another cause of rolling selvage is heavy density in the reeding of the warp. If the density is too great it should be lessened to the point where the selvage ends are only slightly heavier than the body of the cloth. Narrow selvages will have the tendency to roll during and after finishing. Selvage of sufficient width should be provided each loom warp. See SELVAGE.

ROLL OVER. The method of resetting embroidered fabric on a Schiffli embroidery frame every time the fabric reaches the maximum verticality. See Span, Roll Up.

ROLL STAND. The metal mechanism used to support drawing rolls on textile frames such as the slubbing, roving, spinning, twisting frames.

ROLL UP. The rolling of embroidered fabric on an embroidery frame that has been stitched onto the top roller of the machine when rolling over. See Roll Over.

ROMAINE CREPE. A sheer silk, acetate, or rayon fabric, made from a plain, crepe or basket weave, composed of fine yarn which affords a smooth surface effect to the goods. It has slightly more body when compared with triple sheer material. Somewhat on the order of alpaca crepe, the cloth shows a fine cross-rib effect brought about in the weaving. When made of rayon or acetate yarns, two-ply yarns are used in both warp and filling. Fiber content must be declared in the material.

Uses include evening wear, negligees, women's spring wear.

ROMAN CANVAS. Material made of linen and coated on one side with paint or tish. It is used by artists in painting with oils.

ROMAN LACE, ROMAN POINT. See RETICELLA or GREEK POINT.

ROMANOV. The Yaroslav region of the Soviet Union produces this carefully bred type of sheep, which is known as a leading "fur sheep."

ROMAN STRIPES. Brilliant contrasting stripes that are usually in the warp direction. They add tone and liveliness to dress goods, skirting, neckwear, ribbon, umbrella silk, and some reversibles.

ROMA QUESTRALS. Registered trademark of Roma Chemical Division of United Merchants and Manufacturers, Inc., New York City, These pigment colors are very popular in printing textile fabrics. Some advantages of these colors include better, brighter, and more attractive color value; greater uniformity in the design, motif, or pattern; higher production speeds, improved color distribution, reduction of color build-up and linting. Variations in viscosity can be tolerated with minimal effect on clarity, sharpness, and uniformity of the patterns on the goods.

Use of these colors prevent color leakage at slow speeds or during emergency stops, internal stencil tarnishing, stencil clogging. They also care for variable tinctorial values as the printing speeds vary. Stencils will not split because of the sue of these colors. These pigment colors can be used on flat, roller, rotary, screen, or surface printing methods.

ROMBENELLI. South American wool, noted for its long, fine staple.

ROMBOWLINE. Rejected or condemned canvas, duck, or rope.

ROMELDALE. A medium wool results from this sheep breed, developed by crossing New Zealand Romney rams with Rambouillet ewes. Capable of being shorn bi-annually, fleeces weigh about 10 pounds and grade to 3/8- and 1/2-blood quality. Shrinkage is about 45 per cent.

ROMNEY MARSH. Originating in the marshes of Kent County, England, this hardy breed of sheep is now popular in America, Australia, New Zealand, and South America. The wool is not as long nor as lustrous as Cotswold or Lincoln wool of Great Britain; however, it is denser, finer, and grades from low 1/4-blood to 1/4-blood. There is much variation in Romney, which shrinks about 30 per cent. See Illustrated Section.

ROMPERS. A kind of child's dress, the lower part of which is shaped like bloomers.

RONDERIS AFRIKANDER. This hardy, fat-tail sheep, native to South Africa, gives a white or cream-colored staple made up of coarse, straight 1¼-inch fiber which projects beyond the wooly undercovering of the animal. The Blinkhaar type has lustrous hair which implies a soft, silken fiber; the Steekhaar type produces a thistle-like hair which implies that much kemp will be found on examination.

RONE STITCH. A wheel or spider lace stitch used in guipure lace arranged in a square formation.

RONGOMY. Native to Madagascar Island, it is a brownish-cast cotton that is made into yarn and hand-woven into fabric for local use.

ROOFING FELT. A felt made from combining coarse hair fibers with wool or asbestos. A thorough impregnation with tar gives the finished product.

ROO, ROOING, ROO'D. English term for the plucking of wool by hand in lieu of shearing. Much stock from Shetland sheep, for example, is of the roo type.

ROOT KNOT, ROOT GALL. Cotton and other plants are affected by this minute worm which bores into the roots for its nutriment; wreaks havoc in raising cotton.

ROOT ROT. A fungus growth which attacks cotton plants. The roots are affected to the point where they shrink and decay.

ROPE. Also known as cord or cordage, it is made from a variety of fibers —cotton, flax, hemp, abaca, henequen, manila, jute, etc., in the natural fiber group. Great inroads have been made in rope or cordage manufacture by certain man-made fibers such as rayon, nylon, "Dacron," "Orlon," polyethylene, in monofilament or multifilament forms. Nylon provides high strength and stretching qualities suitable for shock tension loading service. Dacron and polyethylene, when wet, will shrink and thus can be stretched more when tension is applied to wet rope. Nylon and rayon cordage under the same conditions will show even greater elongation. "Dacron" and polyethylene are not affected by wetting and therefore show no change in stretchability when wet.

The man-made fibers provide easier handling of rope than is the case with the natural fibers, and there is the absence of adverse effects, such as wetting deterioration and increased stretchability, when the product is made or "Dacron," nylon, or polyethylene.

Nylon rope is considered best when variable loads are present such as in climbing ropes, drive and marine ropes, etc. In abrasion testing it will outlast cotton in a ratio of 7 to 1. "Dacron" is better to use in instances where load control is desired and where excessive stretch is not a factor. Polyethylene comes closest to the properties noted in natural fibers used to make rope. The use of an antioxidant stabilizer improves the weather performance of this type of rope.

Ropes run from ¼ inch to five or more inches in diameter. Ropemaking is a dual twisting operation in which the yarns are first plied or formed into strands, and then three or more of these strands are set or laid with backturn into the rope. In strand forming, it is very important that the yarns are arranged in properly patterned concentric layers as they are twisted to form the strand so as to develop optimum strength and simultaneous compression. When the strands are being twisted together, they have to be kept at proper tension to insure achievement of the compactness of structure. Since many rope structures are large in diameter, the physical attributes can and should be measured accurately. Turn, measured as the spiral pitch of a strand, designates the degree of twist in a rope of and for a given size.

ROPE, NAUTICAL. It is made from cotton, flax, hemp, jute, and other minor bast fibers, as well as from "Dacron," "Orlon," polyethylene, etc. This rope comes in a very wide range dependent on its end-use. The strands are twisted in a different direction from that of the original yarns made. Rope is usually measured by its circumference in inches; the fathom, six feet, is used for lineal measurement.

ROPE, NEUTRAL. A rope, usually of hemp, in which some strands are twisted to the right while others go to the left, so that, when combined, the finished rope tends to be stable and it will not spin or rotate when in use.

ROPE, TARRED. That which has been treated with tar to protect it against the elements.

ROPE FORM. The form in which cloth is gathered or bunched into longitudinal folds by being drawn through a ring or series of rings called poteyes. Some processing is more easily accomplished with cloth in this form.

ROPE LADDER. A runged device for climbing, made of rope, wood, metal.

ROPEMAKING. In the old days of rope manufacture, it was necessary for the worker to do much walking. Following hackling of the fibers being used, it was the spinning operation that necessitated this effort on the part of the walker. The spinner or walker had to "back down the walk" to draw out the fibers as they turned on the hooks of a wheel, a very irksome task.

Some of the walks were covered, others had no shelter. Some spinners often traversed as much as 400 yards in the walk. The backward pace of the spinner had to be constant to insure even, uniform rope, a rather difficult task.

Today, however, this has been done away with, because with improved methods the spinner rides a machine that resembles a railroad handcar and it covers the in-and-out route in a very short time.

ROPE SILK. A slack-twisted, thick silk ply-yarn used for embroidery.

ROPE STITCH. On the order of the stem stitch, it is worked downwards instead of upwards.

ROPE STRAND. Bast fibers made into yarn formation, twisted together for further twisting with other strands to make large, strong, heavy rope for industrial purposes.

ROPE STRAP. A rope spliced to form a ring.

ROPE TURN. The distance that is parallel to the axis of a rope in which a strand makes a complete spiral.

ROPEWALK. See ROPEMAKING.

ROPE YARN. Hemp or manila yarn made of right-hand twist.

ROPE YARN NUMBERING. It is the number of ends of a particular yarn necessary to make one of the three strands used to make a rope three inches in circumference. Thus, a #30 means that three strands of 30 threads each, a total of 90, will make a rope of this circumference.

ROPING. 1. Another name for roving, one step removed from being spun yarn. 2. The roving that comes from the tape condenser on the last card in the wool system of carding fibers. This roving is wound on jack spools to be set at the back of the mule spinning frame to be fed into the mule and spun into yarn.

ROSCOMMON SHEEP, IRISH SHEEP. Named for this county in Ireland, this sturdy sheep is of the long fiber, coarse, luster wool type, a Class Three wool. Fleece weight is around eight pounds. The fiber is used in homespun, tweed, cheviot, and shetland fabrics made in Ireland. Reworked fibers are much used with the new wool from these sheep, thereby causing several qualities of the fabrics to become available.

ROSE. A light pinkish-red like the color of many roses. It ranges from bluish-red to yellowish-red, and is medium in brilliance and saturation.

ROSE NET. Used in Great Britain, it is a handmade or machine-made netting which comes in a honeycomb effect and finds use in curtains, gloves, veilings, etc.

ROSENHUBE. The lace cap used in Switzerland by women; it is held in place by using a long metal, usually silver, pin.

ROSETTE. A decoration for a package made by tying multiple bowknots in a piece of ribbon.

ROSEUM COTTON. A short-staple Indian cotton, measuring from ½ inch to ⅝ inch, with a lint yield of as high as 40 per cent.

ROSHANARA. A trade name for a silk fabric of long standing, identified by its heavy, crepelike, cross-rib texture. Originally made with silk warp and silk or worsted filling, the cloth came in a variety of weights and colors. Simulations of this material are seen from time to time in the market. The fabric of today is made with rayon, acetate, silk, nylon, and wool in varying combinations of warp and filling, such as the use of a silk warp and an acetate filling.

ROT. Broad term which signifies that some parasitic disease has attacked the sheep; a rotting of tissues such as the liver, foot, mouth area, etc.

ROTARY FULLING MILL. Two or three layers or ropings of fabric are passed between two or more very heavy fulling rollers in the machine. The type of cloth being fulled controls the length of time the material is in the mill.

ROTARY PRESS. A machine for pressing woolen and worsted fabrics, similar to the calendering machine used in pressing cottons. Done by passing the fabric between a battery of heated rollers.

ROTATING SHIFT. A plan under which employees work for a period of time on one shift and then change for another period of time to a different shift.

ROTOFIL. Registered trademark of E. I. duPont de Nemours & Co., Inc., Wilmington, Delaware for a fasciated structure which consists of a yarn of discontinuous fibers bound together by surface fibers wrapped around the bundle. These yarns come in fine denier sizes, 100 or less, and because of their structures possess unique physical properties. See Fasciate, Nandel.

ROTOSET. A duPont trademark for

multifilament yarns from any fiber. A special processing technique intertwines or interlaces the filaments so that the resulting zero twist yarn has the weavability of a warp yarn with 1-1/2 turns or more, of twist per inch.

ROT STEEP. Steeping cotton cloth in water to remove impurities in order to obtain a better bleach.

ROUANE, RUOANE. Bleached household linen used in France.

ROUGH-DRY, ROUGHDRY. To dry without smoothing or ironing.

ROUGH BROWNS. A low-grade, gray-goods linen cloth which has many uses as dress goods on the Continent.

ROUGH CREPE. Any crepe which has a pronounced crepe, rough, pebble, or granite surface effect.

ROUGH FELL. The well-known Blackface Mountain sheep which are native to the Westmoreland Fells and in part of the Yorkshire Hills of England. Also known as Rough and Kendall Roughs, the breed may be compared with Lonk sheep in that the former is smaller and produces a coarser, stronger wool. Practically identical with the Blackface of Scotland, the wool is not as long in staple and is somewhat weaker. Fleece weighs from five to six pounds.

ROUGHERS. Woolen fabrics as they leave the loom in the gray state usually have a rough, rather unsightly appearance. The finishing operations will remove the roughness, fuzzy protruding fibers, and other irregularities.

ROUGHERS' LONGS. Flax parlance for long fibers from the rougher.

ROUGHERS' SHORTS. The longest of the short fibers, taken out in roughing flax, which are worked free of the tow on the hackle and made into a separate bunch or bundle of fibers.

ROUGHING FLAX. Hackling or combing flax fibers through a coarse hackle to take out the short and irregular fibers and to level the ends; the straggly fibers of desirable length for some further treatment are thereby saved from going in with the tow fibers.

ROUND. British term for the number of filling threads in a single repeat of pattern in woven goods.

ROUND BALE. Wrapped in burlap and having no cooperage, this bale is cylindrical in shape and is about one yard in height and about 22 inches in diameter. Weight is about 250 pounds, and there is a density per cubic foot which ranges from 32 to 37 pounds per cubic foot.

ROUND THREAD LINEN. A soft-

finished, plain-woven linen fabric made of round, hard-twisted yarn which is specially prepared. Yarn of this name may be used for drawn work, hemstitching, Hardanger work, and embroidery. The yarn can easily be withdrawn from the material, hence its use.

ROUND THUMB. The simplest type of thumb in knitted gloves; set into a narrow slit which is rounded at both ends.

ROVANA. A saran micro-tape that is a filament of vinylidene chloride copolymer made by The Dow Chemical Company. Formerly known as Q-957, this monofilament form is a flat film tape of uniform thickness. It may be embossed for decorative purposes such as for wall covering. Rovana is mildew proof, fire resistant, odorless, has high coverage, unusually high tear strength, and is resistant to chemicals and solvents. No longer produced.

ROVE. British term for roving.

ROVING. The soft strand from which natural fiber yarns are made. In the carding process, the last card in a set is where wool, for example, is condensed to roving form, one step removed from finished spun yarn. Roving is delivered to the spinning frame (see Illustrated Section) and comes out in yarn form. It is finer in diameter than sliver or slubbing but is greater in diameter than yarn. Roving may be considered as a condensed sliver and slubbing which has been drawn, drafted, twisted, attenuated, doubled, and redoubled, as well as being made free of foreign matter.

ROVING CAN. A composition fiber wall and metal bottom, open-top, cylindrical can used to hold sliver or similar stock. The coiler can is found at the delivery end of the card, comber, drawing frame, etc. The can revolves when in action and is equipped with an automatic stop-motion when full.

ROVING FRAME. One of the machines in yarn manufacture whose object is to reduce or attenuate the stock such as sliver, slubbing, or other roving to a suitable size for spinning. See Illustrated Section. The four standard roving frames are slubber, intermediate, fine, and jack. All roving frames draft the stock by means of rollers, twist it by means of a flyer, and wind it onto a wooden bobbin. Also known as fly frame.

ROVING GUIDE. A small metal trumpet found on roving, spinning, and kindred frames. The trumpet or guide is set to a long bar located directly in back of the drawing rollers. Another method of guiding the stock is to have a series of holes in the bar itself. A slight reciprocating action to the bar evens off the wear on the boss.

ROVING REEL. A reel used to measure a set length of roving so that it may be weighed in order to determine the count of yarn that it will produce.

ROVING SKEWER. A wooden rod or spindle which supports bobbins such as used in sliver, slubbing, and roving operations in making yarn. The upright skewer supporting the bobbin is set in the creel of the particular frame or machine being used. The stock unwinds from the bobbin when in operation.

ROVING SPOOL. Same as jack spool.

ROWAN. The term used in Scotland to signify roving stock in yarn manufacture irrespective of the fiber content.

ROWDEN COTTON. Possessing average to good fiber-length, this cotton fiber runs from slightly coarse to coarse in fineness. Strength of fiber is average to excellent while neppiness is low to average. Used in yarn counts of 22s to 36s.

ROWDIES. Streaks in materials which are detrimental to the cloth.

ROWS. The average number of tufts or loops per inch counted in the warp direction of a carpeting.

ROXANA. Some crepeline is known by this name.

ROYAL AXMINSTER. Axminster carpets of commerce are the Royal Axminster or Moquette, the name commonly used in this country today. Patent Axminster is also in this class.

ROYAL BLUE. Reddish blue in hue, this color has high saturation and low brilliance.

ROYAL BOUCLE. Carpet material of high quality in which permanent twist of the pile construction is the outstanding feature. Royal bouclé texture can be washed, shampooed, or dry cleaned without injury to the twist in the surface yarn. It is impervious to footprints and is easily rolled; outwears many other carpetings by a wide margin.

ROYALE. A plain-ribbed fabric made of silk or rayon in which the ribs are broken at certain intervals; somewhat on the order of barathea. See BARATHEA.

ROYALENE. A group of polyethylene and polypropylene fibers produced by UniRoyal, Inc. These fibers are "tailored" for a wide variety of uses. There are six types of Royalene, as follows:

High-Tenacity Linear Polyethylene: Known as *Type A,* it has the highest strength, and the greatest heat, abrasion, and chemical resistance of the fibers in the group.

Type C: Polyethylene fiber compounded for shrinkage and for heat and chemical resistance; it is used for unusual effects, such as three-dimensional fabrics.

Type E: This fiber has very high shrinkage in boiling water; therefore it is useful for certain effects either alone or with other fibers.

Type L: This polyethylene fiber possesses an electrical grade for applications requiring conformity to Bell Laboratories' specifications for insulation.

Polypropylene Fiber: This is used for higher heat resistance and for resistance to creeping under sustained loading. This *Type P* fiber lends itself to multifilament applications.

High-Density Copolymer Polyethylene: Thin *N* fiber has superior resistance to creepage under load, and retains physical properties of the highest-grade linear polyethylene.

Suggested end uses for the fibers include nautical ropes, auto seat covers, filter cloths, decorative screening, shoe webbings, flat ropes, tow targets, handbag fabrics, upholstery, and outdoor furniture webbings, Types C and E compounded for shrinkage are used to make Trilok, the three-dimensional fabric which is used for decorative and special-purpose industrial fabrics, such as air filters.

ROYALETTE. A five-shaft, filling-effect satin weave is used to make this cotton warp and fine worsted filling fabric. Pickage is very compact and high.

ROYAL RIB. Similar to moreen except that two warp ends are run in as one end in the drawing-in and reeding plans.

ROYAL SCOTS. The first regiment of the line, as becomes its royal title, wears the Hunting Stewart . . . black, blue, and green ground with intersecting overchecks of yellow and red. His late Majesty George VI conferred on the pipers of this regiment the honor of wearing his personal tartan, the Royal Stewart, a privilege shared with the pipers of three other regiments: the Black Watch, the King's Own Scottish Borderers, and the Scots Guards.

R.P.M. Revolutions per minute. The number of complete turns of a wheel, gear, pulley, etc., in one minute.

RUBAN. French for ribbon.

RUBBER. A substance obtained from the milky juice, or rubber latex, of tropical plants, usually characterized by its elasticity, though its properties vary widely depending upon its source and preparation. The principal source of crude rubber is plantation rubber from plants, *Hevea Brasiliensis,* cultivated on plantations in the Malay Peninsula, Indonesia, and elsewhere. Among other properties, it is resistant to abrasive wear, flexible, extensible, and waterproof. It is commonly combined with yarns and fabrics to make elastic products, raincoats, balloons, tires, etc.

RUBBER, NATURAL. The formula is $(C_5 H_8)$ n or x times. It is the elastic solid obtained from the sap or latex of the rubber tree (*Hevea Brasiliensis*) by coagulation and drying, or from other comparable sources. Rubber is formed into filaments or yarn by casting or extrusion of latex, followed by vulcanizing or by slitting vulcanized sheets.

RUBBER, SYNTHETIC. Synthesis of natural latex from derivatives of petroleum.

RUBBER BELT DUCK. Plain-weave fabric made of ply yarn not finer than single 8s. The weight is from 22 to 36 ounces, and the width 42 inches. When made of yarns finer than 8s, it is called Special Belt Duck.

RUBBER BLANKET. An endless, four-ply, heavy cotton blanket that is glued with rubber cement. This blanket helps to carry textile goods in the printing machine and serves as an under-support for the material.

RUBBER-COATED TEXTILES. To make material waterproof, or for other purposes, a rubber coating may be added to one or both sides of a fabric. Rubber cement is often used on the back of imitation pile and fur fabrics to hold the texture in place. Fabrics treated in this way will not withstand dry cleaning, since the cement is soluble, thereby allowing the pile construction to collapse.

RUBBER CORE YARN. The core or heart yarn about which other yarns, of plain or fancy type, are wrapped in one or both directions.

RUBBER FIBER. Generic term for a manufactured fiber in which the fiber-forming substance is comprised of natural or synthetic rubber, including a manufactured fiber in which the fiber-forming substance is a hydrocarbon such as natural rubber, polyisoprene, polybutadiene, copolymers of dienes and hydrocarbons, or amorphous (non-cyrstalline) polyolefins.

RUBBERIZED CLOTH. Cotton fabric that has been given waterproof treatment, to be used for some definite purpose such as table covering or sheeting. Only one side of the fabric is coated. The treatment is also applied to silk, rayon, and nylon cloths. The fabric is largely used for rainwear.

RUBBERIZED FABRIC. Any fabric suitable for waterproofing or some similar treatment. One side of the material is coated, and it is used chiefly in rainwear.

RUBBERIZED TIRE CORD FABRIC. Made of 23/5/3 carded cable yarn of plain weave, and given an improved heat-resistant cord treatment. This is used for pneumatic tire casing.

RUBBERS, SCAB. A sheep disease caused by heat, chafing, friction, itching, etc.

RUBBER SHEETING. A plain cotton fabric with heavy coating of cured rubber on one or both sides. Used in various weights, in hospitals and for baby cribs.

RUBBER THREAD COUNTS. The number or the size of the thread is based on a cross-section expressed in the fractional parts of an inch. In cut thread the size number indicates one side of a square representing its cross-sectional area. Thus, a "42" measures $\frac{1}{42}$ inch.

In round thread, the size number represents the diameter; a "50" is $\frac{1}{50}$ inch in diameter. The relationship of cut thread sizes to extruded sizes is that of the area of a square to the area of a circle. Thus, a 42s cut is the same as the 37s extruded.

RUBBER THREADS AND ELASTIC YARNS

LACTRON: An extruded thread which is the original latex thread. It is much used for braids and elastic webbings, is heat-resistant and non-discoloring.

LASTEX: This is an elastic yarn whose base is latex, the raw material from which rubber is made. The yarn is made by wrapping a filament of fine rubber thread with cotton, nylon, silk, etc. It comes in complete ranges of size, modulus, and covering for weaving, knitting, and shirring all types of elastic fabrics. Its application by stitching imparts stretch or creates novel elastic fabrics for foundation garments, hosiery, swimwear, and many other products.

LATON: An elastic yarn uniquely covered to produce extra-light, extra-soft, extra-fine knitted and woven elastic fabrics. This soft-tension yarn is used chiefly for slips, swimsuits, underwear, and other light-weight elastic fabrics.

REVERE: For generations this cut-rubber thread has been used for all kinds of narrow elastics; and it is heat-resistant and non-discoloring. Revere rubber tension tape is a cut-rubber tape that comes in various sizes, for waistbands, legbands, hems, and all types of elastic edges.

CONTRO OR ROLLED LATEX: This product of Firestone Tire & Rubber Company, Inc., is first formed as a flat strip and then rolled on itself much in the same manner as one would roll paper into a tube form. Stretching straightens the molecules and adds strength. A fine core thread results, which is covered with nylon for use in foundation fabrics, swimsuits, hosiery, cushions.

DARLEEN: A cut-rubber yarn in which the original core is cut into proper size from a rubber sheet form. A silk or nylon hosiery yarn will have about 15,000 yards to the pound. This product of Darlington Fabrics Corporation, New York City, is an outstanding cut-rubber yarn which is especially good for foundation fabrics.

FILATEX: A grooved wheel collects the latex from the bath used. Solidification follows, and the core is then drawn off. The product is classed as a flat-oval type. This product of Filatex Corporation, Waxhaw, North Carolina, runs to about 14,000 yards per pound. Its greatest use is for stocking tops.

VYRENE: Classed as a Spandex fiber, it is the trademark of the United States Rubber Company for its synthetic elastomer to supplement and extend the range of its Lastex yarn. It is a super-fine elastic yarn ideal for use in sheer elastic fabrics. Vyrene has toughness, high tensile strength, and good resistance to chafing; it is resistant to light, ozone, and solvents, even in very fine sizes. Other properties include a good modulus of retention, very rapid stretch return, and the ability to withstand standard scouring, finishing, and dyeing procedures, and wash-and-wear tests.

Vyrene is a complete yarn in itself, with a fine elastic core or elastic monofilament covered with nylon or some other manufactured fiber. Compared with Lastex, which is much used in constructions with core sizes about $\frac{1}{100}$ inch in diameter, Vyrene is made with the elastic element $\frac{1}{150}$ inch in size. In woven or knitted fabrics, its extra fineness creates soft and sheer fabrics not heretofore obtainable. Uses include swimwear, golf jackets, sportswear, and foundation items of all types.

LYCRA: A Spandex fiber of the elastomer type and a product of E. I. du Pont de Nemours & Co., Inc. It is the original Spandex fiber.

NEOPRENE: A trademark name for a type of synthetic rubber produced by E. I. du Pont de Nemours & Co., Inc. It is like crude rubber in appearance and properties. Neoprene is sold to rubber concerns who mix it with other ingredients, process it, and vulcanize it for use in a great many products. It is wrapped with nylon for use in elastic yarns.

RUBBING LEATHERS. Found chiefly on woolen textile machinery, their purpose is to rub slubbing, web, roving, etc., into a cylindrical formation devoid of twist. Their action is to condense the stocks with which they come in contact. They work in an endless belt arrangement.

RUBY. A rich red color like that of a ruby, a rich crimson. It is low in brilliance and high in saturation.

RUCHE. A pleated, quilted or goffered strip of lace, net, ribbon, braiding, or the like used for trimming. See RUCHING.

RUCHING. A quilling or a pleating of lace, net, ribbon, or similar material used as a trimming for women's garments or worn at the neck or wrists in widths ranging from one to three inches. Ruching usually consists of two or more rows of material arranged in box or shell pleats or in the form of quilling.

RUCK. See RUCHING.

RUFFLE. A narrow width of lace, cambric, or comparable fabric drawn up at one edge in gathers or pleats and used to trim dresses, blouses, waists, and other articles.

RUFFLING. This comes in varying widths and designs and is sold by the yard. It is drawn into folds or gathers and is used for adornment.

RUG. A thick fabric for covering part of a floor, often woven of wool and frequently having an oblong shape with a border design. The terms, rug and carpet, are used interchangeably, and there are now many fibers of varying types used in the manufacture of these floorcoverings. Today a rug may be of any shape and size to fit some particular purpose in floorcovering.

The term is derived from the Scandinavian word "rugga" via the old Norwegian "rogg" which meant a wool covering for the bed or body. In Europe, for several centuries the term meant a rough, heavy, woolen fabric characterized by a coarse, napped finish so that it could be used as apparel by the poorer classes. See Carpet.

RUG, DOMESTIC ORIENTAL. A common term given to any rug or carpet which has been given a lusterized finish, chiefly with reference to Oriental reproductions.

RUG, LUSTER-FINISHED, SHEEN-FINISHED. Rugs and carpets of the more luxurious types are often supplied with a lustrous finish which is the result of an extra process. The practice began just before the beginning of the present century. It was the invention of an American importer of Oriental rugs, and for many years it was confined to Persian and Chinese rugs. The sheen-finishing process gives a rich, silky appearance to the pile and refines the colors to delicate shades, both of which appeal to the lover of Oriental rugs. In fact, today the great majority of Oriental rugs sold in America are luster-finished.

In 1928 luster-finishing was used with American reproductions of Orientals, and since then with rugs and carpets of all styles. It has been employed especially with high-pile plain shades and self-tone weaves, where the play of light and shade adds variety of tones and contributes to the effect of luxury.

The sheen-finishing process takes place after weaving. The fabric is treated with a chemical solution which acts on the surface of the wool fibers in the yarn and, as it were, polishes them. Highlights are added, giving an interesting play of light and shade.

RUG, MACHINE-HOOKED. Made on a power loom, it simulates the hand-made hook type of floor covering. Now made from several natural and man-made fibers, it is an uncut pile-effect rug.

RUG, SELLING POINTS OF A.

1. A rug should have sufficient weight to lie flat on the floor.

2. The color and design should not be gaudy, too large, nor outlandish.

3. A rug should harmonize with the rest of the room.

4. A hallroom rug should be brighter in color and design than other room rugs.

5. A short, close pile rug gives the longest wear, preferably with worsted yarn.

6. The cut pile usually shows to better advantage because of the long, soft pile effect, giving a velvety surface.

7. Cotton rugs become shabby quickly because of the short or long yarns used.

8. The closer the weave construction in a rug, the better is the quality.

9. A velvet rug has printed yarn.

10. Wilton rugs are classed as medium or better grade of varying value, which depends on the composition, pile, and coloring.

11. Axminster rugs have a long, soft pile. They are not as durable as some of the other constructions.

12. Chenille is an expensive type of rug. This is because two looms are required in its development, hand labor by way of combing, and each pattern is custom-made.

13. A Brussels rug has an uncut pile and does not catch the dirt so readily, since the composition is cotton and jute.

It is not as rich in appearance when compared with a velvet or Wilton.

14. An ingrain rug or carpet is serviceable. It has no pile; however, it does not have the velvet-like appearance or beauty of the pile rug.

15. Persian rugs are the best for softness and richness of color. High-grade composition is used; the weaving is slowly and carefully done; the designs and colorings are of the best.

16. An Oriental rug is valued according to the age, size, the number of tufts to the inch, composition, richness of color, fineness of design.

17. An Oriental rug may be distinguished from a Domestic by determining how the yarn is fastened into the rugs. In the Oriental, the pattern is usually broken down and the fringe is made from the warp ends.

18. Hard-twisted yarn is an asset to any rug.

19. All things being equal, a loop or uncut pile will give better wear than a cut-pile rug.

RUGGING. A floor covering made of bulky, coarse woolen yarns. A thick nap is given the fabric to prolong its usefulness.

RUGGINOSE. A silk waste obtained from stained or imperfect cocoons.

RUG GOWN. 1. A gown made of a rug. 2. A coarse, shaggy fabric.

RUGS, SEAMED. They are made by seaming together 3/4 (27-inch) or 4/4 (36-inch) strips of carpet to make a large rug.

RUGS, SEAMLESS. Made in the full width on the loom without a seam.

RUG TOW. Coarse tow is produced by the rougher scutcher, fine rug tow from the buffer scutcher. The coarse tow is further scutched so that it may be manipulated with fine tow and made into yarn for rug backing.

RUG WEAVING FRAMES. They are the racks at the back of the Jacquard loom to hold the spools from which woolen or worsted yarn pile yarn is fed into the machine. The spools in each rack are wound with one color, and there are six racks situated one above the other.

From three to six frames are used, and the number is a measure of quality as well as an indication of the number of colors in the pattern. Thus, a six-frame Wilton would have six woolen or worsted yarns running through it in lengthwise direction in addition to the double set of cotton chain warp yarns and the stuffer warp.

In each row one woolen or worsted yarn of the set of six is brought to the surface to form the pile tuft, while the other five yarns are inactive in the back of the material.

See Illustrated Section.

RUING. Scotch term for plucking wool by hand from the fleece on a live sheep.

RUMP. Wool taken from the rump and tail of the sheep. The stock is inferior in all respects, short, kempy and dungy; has little or no value.

RUN. 1. A system of numbering woolen yarn of 100 yards each in one ounce. Thus, if 800 yards weigh 1 ounce the yarn would be an "eight-run wool."

2. A batch or lot of material that is to be processed in a single continuous operation or series of operations.

3. A series of successive raveled loops along one or more adjacent wales of a knitted fabric.

4. The Boston or New England standard used in figuring wool yarn sizes. There are 1600 yards in one pound of the wool yarn in the standard Number 1 yarn. Thus, if the run-wool count is six, there would be 9600 yards in the pound of yarn—1600 times 6 equals 9600. The cut system for wool yarn, known as the Philadelphia Method, uses a standard of 300 yards to the pound in the Number 1 count of yarn. Thus, if the cut-wool count is eighteen, there would be 5400 yards in the pound of yarn—300 times 18 equals 5400.

5. A continuous strip of cloth made of several pieces sewed together end to end.

6. In the glove trade it implies a nonelastic stretch desirable in gloving leathers.

RUN LACE. Embroidered lace in which embroidering is done with a needle on a réseau ground. See LACE, IRISH LACE.

RUNLESS. Rather synonymous with run resistant hosiery, the term refers more specifically to seamless nylon hosiery made in a lock-stitch construction.

RUNNER. A device which winds yarn from a skein to a cone put-up.

RUNNING BALE OF COTTON. At present it takes about 1,300 pounds of picked cotton to produce what is known as the standard cotton bale of 500 pounds. This bale contains 478 pounds of ginned fiber with the other 22 pounds made up of burlap or other covering and the cooperage or copper bands used to hold the bale intact for shipment to the consignee. Within the past few years, however, ginners have been producing bales which have averaged 503 pounds. This is known as the running bale. It is also possible, depending upon local and area conditions, to have a running bale slightly less than the 500 pound standard. In

issuing their figures for estimates of cotton production, the Departments of Agriculture and Commerce of the United States Government base their figures on true bales of 500 pounds with the running bale having an average weight of 503 pounds of fiber per bale.

RUNNING-ON. The method of connecting the rib and the plain parts of a knitted article on a Cotton's Patent full-fashioned knitting frame. The ribbed portion is run onto the machine before the jersey knitting is done by means of a topping or transfer bar having grooved points spaced to correspond with the knitting-machine gauge.

RUN-OF-THE-LOOM. Fabric as it comes from the loom and ready for shipment without inspection and without elimination of defects made in weaving.

RUN-OF-THE-MILL. 1. Textile products of practically any type that are not inspected or do not warrant inspection. 2. Fabrics of any variety that cannot be classed as a "first." 3. A so-called "second," an imperfect piece of merchandise.

RUN-OUT FLEECE. A low-grade, uneven, coarse, kempy fleece; devoid of any positive working properties.

RUNPROOF. Also known as run-resist, it is the result of a method used in knitting hosiery and underwear by the use of a special stitch, such as a locked loop, to make the article resistant to runs.

RUN WOOL. The number of 1600-yard hanks of yarn in one pound; the number is known as the count of the yarn. The count is determined with a 7000 grain-weight of yarn under standard conditions.

RUN-AWAY SHOP. A company that has moved its place of business to a new location, to avoid or eliminate its dealings with a union.

RUNNAGE. Coarse cord, yarn, twine, etc., is spoken of as having "so many feet per pound, per kilogram, etc."

RUNNING STITCH. Small, even stitches that join together two pieces of fabric.

RUSIL FINISH, SPUN FINISH. It is applied to cottons by means of a roller which has 60 to 100 finely engraved lines in it. The lines run in a vertical direction on the roller and in the warp direction on fabric.

If a bright finish is wanted, the roller is frictioned over the goods. The roller is so set up that the surface of the material does not travel as rapidly as

the engraved roller, thereby increasing sheen or luster.

RUSSEL. A sheen worsted fabric first made in the sixteenth century in Norwich, England.

RUSSELL, LILLIAN. Born on a farm in Iowa, Miss Russell, whose real name was Louise Leonard, came to New York City and due to her fine soprano voice, beauty, and graciousness, became the toast of the American stage. Her name and "The Gay Nineties" were synonymous and she was linked with the famous "Diamond Jim;; Brady, a wealthy philanderer of the time. Born in 1861, she died in 1922. See Costume, Lillian Russell.

RUSSELL CORD. See PERSIAN CORD.

RUSSET. A color formed by combining orange and purple; popularly, any reddish or yellowish brown. It is one of the tertiary colors, the other two being olive and citron.

RUSSET CLOTH. A popular homespun woolen associated with the swains and squires of the sixteenth century in England. Reds, browns, and ashen effects predominated in the material.

RUSSET SHEEPSKINS. Sheep- or lambskins that have been tanned in cold-leached hemlock bark.

RUSSIAN CORD. The leno or doup weave is used to cross the heavier fancy warp ends to the wrong side of the goods as each pick enters the material in weaving. The cord threads, because of their bending over and under the base threads, may have a warp take-up of as much as 75 per cent. The cloth has to have two warps, ground and fancy. The cord gives a raised or cable appearance to the cloth. It is used for curtaining, dress goods, and shirting.

RUSSIAN CRASH. A strong, coarse, unbleached linen or hemp material, made in Russia. Used for towels, coats, etc.

RUSSIAN DUCK. A fine bleached linen duck used for summer raiment.

RUSSIAN EMBROIDERY. Simple motifs are used on these vividly colored washable fabrics, usually made of cotton or linen.

RUSSIAN FLAX. All of it is very hardy, strong, rather uneven in diameter, and it gives good wear. Slanetz, the dew-retted type, and Motchenetz, the water-retted type, come mainly from seaport areas such as Archangel and Riga. Siretz, the ungraded type, is raised chiefly around Volgagrad.

RUSSIAN HEMP. Rope and cable hemp fiber. The Soviet Union is making rapid strides in cultivating the fiber, since it is supposed to have great possibilities in Russia.

RUSSIAN LEATHER. This trade term first meant a Russian calfskin shoe leather, of vegetable tannage, dressed with birch oil and distinguished by its odor rather than by appearance. In the United States the term describes a fancy stock, usually made of calfskin, sometimes of light cattle hide.

RUSSIAN SAIL DUCK. Made from tough, rugged flax or hemp and used in Russia and the Balkans.

RUSSIAN TAPESTRY. Hemp, rugged flax, or other bast fiber cloths used for curtains and hangings. Material is plain or figured.

RUST. 1. A reddish-brown, oxidation product of iron. Produced on iron and steel parts by exposure to moist air or water which contains dissolved oxygen. 2. Known also as black rust, Mosaic disease, or yellow leaf blight—a disease that affects cotton plants in that growth is impeded, leaves turn blackish, and the bolls do not develop as they should.

RUST STAIN REMOVAL. Moisten the area with oxalic acid solution which contains one tablespoon of oxalic acid crystals in one cup of warm water. If not removed, then heat the oxalic acid solution and repeat the process. If the stain area is very difficult to remove then place oxalic acid crystals onto the soiled area. Moisten the material with water as hot as possible without injuring the fabric, and allow to stand for a few minutes or dip in the water. This method may be repeated until satisfaction is achieved. Do not apply on nylon fabrics. Thorough rinsing is important; oxalic acid will damage the goods if not thoroughly rinsed out prior to drying. Use oxalic acid solutions with care since it is a poisonous chemical.

RUSTY SILK. Blemishes seen in white and light colored silks which show minute brownish streaks in the filling.

RYELAND SHEEP. An old British breed of sheep native to the sandy areas southward from the Rye River, England. Noted for its ability to pasture on marshy ground and its hardiness, the sheep does not really belong in the Down Wool group; for convenience' sake, however, it is placed in the Down class. Resembling Shropshire sheep, the wool is of good, deep staple and is thickly set on the skin; it is also curly with a rather soft "silklike handle."

Until Merino sheep were introduced into England, Ryeland was considered about the best in British wools. Much of the type is now raised in Kentucky.

The quality ranges around 56s, staple is about 5 inches, and fleece weight is about 5 pounds.

RYGJA, RYGIA. Native Norwegian breed of sheep that produces a wool too coarse for modern clothing. Found along the coast of West Norway.

S

"S." A designation for that direction of twist in yarn the inclination of which corresponds to the central portion of the letter *S;* S-twist is also known as left, reverse, filling, or crossband. Z-twist is also known as right twist, and because the words left-twist and right-twist lead to confusion, the letters S and Z have been used for simplification. See Illustrated Section.

SAABA. A false-twisted yarn suited ideally to make a fine bulk yarn for the knitting industry. It has controlled stretch and resiliency and can be made to simulate angora through various stages in hand to a harsh-feeling tweed yarn; much used in the knitting industry. The method of manufacture uses an annealing process on the downtwister frame which is equipped with a heating chamber and feed rolls. The process involves removal of the stretch from a previously false-twist stretch yarn. Compared with Ban-Lon and Helanca Type SW, it should be borne in mind that Ban-Lon uses a crimping method and that unprocessed filaments are textured or crimped and then thermo-set in a stuffer box. No stretch yarn is involved, and the surface texture is smooth.

Saaba can be either smooth, boucle', or chenille-like. Helanca SW uses a reprocessing method, and in this operation some of the stretch is removed from a coiled stretch yarn previously produced by a twisting and untwisting process. Its surface texture is crepe or boucle'-like. The source for Saaba is Leesona Corporation, Warwick, Rhode Island.

SABLE. 1. French term for a mottled or marble effect seen in some fabrics.

2. The most expensive type of marten from Russia, and the finest marten from Canada, which is bluish-gray at the roots shading to dark brown. Wearing qualities, fair to good. Judged by density and silkiness of fur and richness of color. Worn formally and semi-formally. Chinese sable is not as fine as Russian sable.

SABOTAGE. Deliberate action by an individual to damage or destroy the equipment or property of a company.

SACCHARIDES. One of the two major types of carbohydrates—the sugars. Cellulose and starches are also examples of carbohydrates. See CELLU-

LOSE, CARBOHYDRATE.

SACK, SACQUE. A short, loose-fitting jacket worn by women, children, and the sick. This sleeved garment comes in all types of fiber construction, color, and finish.

SACKCLOTH. A coarse, heavy, unbleached muslin used to make sturdy sports apparel.

SACK COAT. A man's suit jacket for business or informal wear.

SACKING. Cheap cloth made from cotton or other bast fibers used to hold grain, powder, and other items best handled in that manner. The name is also applied to dressing sacks of all types used in the home. The weight, color, and material varies considerably. Another meaning applies to tied wool fleeces that are packed or sacked in large burlap bags which are from five to seven feet, or so, in length with a diameter between 20 and 30 inches. Each bag contains from 200 to 400 pounds of grease wool (containing yolk, suint, and foreign matter) made ready for shipment to market.

SAD, SAD-COLORED. Said of a color that is dull, drab, or somber; low in saturation.

SADDENING. To reduce vividness in color by making dark, drab, or dull. In wool dyeing it is the procedure of applying the mordant after the dyestuff rather than before it; colors will become "sad" in cast, shade, tone.

SADDLE BLANKET. Made of coarse wool, it is a blanket placed under the saddle to prevent friction, chafing, and galling.

SADDLECLOTH. Provincial term used in the western part of the United States for nonwoven felts or mats made from wool, cotton, aloe, and other fibers for use as a saddle cover. These felts may be sewn or stitched for support and compactness.

SADDLE FELT. A rugged, coarse, thick felt fabric used in the manufacture of saddles.

SADDLE LEATHER. See HARNESS LEATHER.

SADHIE. Synonym for Sari. See SARI.

SADIN. Hebraic term for fine linen fabrics used for summer garb and nightwear by the Hebrews in biblical times. Modifications of this ancient fabric are still used.

SAFFLOWER. A thistlelike herb about two feet high with spiny heads of red-orange flowers. The dried flowers yield a reddish dyestuff.

SAFFRON. The dried orange-colored stigmas of this plant used for coloring matter. This ancient dye coloring has now been superseded by synthetic dyes which produce an improved yellow shade.

SAGAR COTTON. A weak, harsh, short-staple, dirty Indian cotton which gives off a peculiar odor. Clay, salt, and other granules are often found in the cotton, which feels like wool to the touch and may be mixed with it in manufacturing dress goods for local consumption.

SAGATHY. Also known as sayette, this silk and wool mixture in dress goods was popular in eighteenth-century England.

SAGING. A cordage fiber raised in the Philippine Islands.

SAG-NO-MOR. Trade-marked process of I. A. Wyner & Co. for treating wool jersey to prevent it from sagging or stretching.

SAGO. Yellow in color, this adhesive sizing agent comes from the pith of palm plants. Sago gives a thin, adhesive paste which is uniform but will give a harsh hand if used by itself. Will not deteriorate from long boiling period.

SAGUM. The ancient Roman soldiers' military cloak; a symbol of war, as the toga is a symbol of peace.

SAGURAN. A Philippine bast fiber obtained from the leaves of the buri palm. Used for packing.

SAHT. Old Egyptian term for linen yarn.

SAIL. A fabric, duck or otherwise, attached to the mast of a vessel to secure its propulsion by the wind.

SAILCLOTH. 1. Canvas or comparable rugged fabric that is strong and can withstand elements in all kinds of weather. "Dacron," nylon, linen, and combed-cotton duck are used to make the material. "Dacron" is much used and accounts for about 75 per cent of total production. One type is on the order of balloon and typewriter fabrics, and it finds much use in spinnakers and head sails. Finished at 40 inches, the texture is about 184-square, and the cloth runs around 6 yards to the pound. Nylon is liked for use on racing boats. 2. Boat-sail drill that is made of Egyptian cotton or the best of the American cottons, is made in plain weave, has a high, compact texture with a pick count of 148 x 60, or higher. This material has very high strength and good wind resistance.

SAIL DUCK. See DUCKS, SAIL.

SAINT ANDREW'S STITCH. An embroidery stitch made on four satin stitches in the form of the Cross of Saint Andrew.

SAINT GALL LACE. Swiss lace of many types named for the city of St. Gallen (St. Gall) located near Lake Constance, Switzerland. Along with the nearby town of Appenzell, these two lace centers are two of the oldest and most important areas for lace making. Hand-made types of the lace are expensive but the work is truly exquisite. Machine-made lace is usually made on Schiffli machines.

SAINT LOUIS COTTON. A glossy, irregular American cotton of about $^{15}\!/_{16}$-inch staple.

SAINT TROPEZ. Situated about 20 miles from the Nice-Cannes Riviera resort area in southern France, this small village is about the most sophisticated one in the world. Until the 1950's it was the typical small fishing village with its boats, smells, nets, dirt, and garbage. In the early 1950's Bridgit Bardot, the sex kitten of movies, spent some time there on vacation. From this time on, St. Tropez became one of the most popular resorts in Europe with waterfront shops, clubs, and restaurants jammed to capacity all the time. Restless society loves the place with its long-haired, sloppily dressed hippies, bare feet, topless swimsuits, and back to nature appeal. Much so-called fashion of today originates in St. Tropez with fashions from all over the world being represented. The major shops cater to the affluent and are always busy and clear good profits from the high prices asked for their wares. See Deauville Scarf.

SAKELLARIDES COTTON. See EGYPTIAN COTTON.

SAKSETTE. Another name for Sunn hemp.

SALAMANDER WOOL. The term for asbestos in some parts of England.

SAL AMMONIAC. A white, soluble ammonium chloride.

SALAGO FIBER. A coarse Philippine fiber used for cordage.

SALANG. Native woolen fabric used in apparel in the Himalaya Mountain areas.

SALARA. Cloth made on hand looms from Indian native cotton. Thin, plain-weave; used for head covering by women in India.

SALARI. A variety of Suzi fabric made in the Punjab, India. See SUZI.

SALATISKA. Cloth made from the under-down fibers of the Bactrian camel. Gives warmth to Russian peasants.

SALEMBAREE. Heavy, plain-woven cotton used for tents in northern India. Also known as Kathee.

SALEMPORE, SALAMPORE. Colored cottons used by natives in several African areas, South America, and parts of India. The warp is usually blue while the filling may be any color to give the cross-stripe effect. Much of the cloth will show horizontal stripes with a bar of blue followed by a bar of some other color. Texture is about 56 x 44 and 30s warp, and 16s filling are used. Most of the material is made in England.

SALEMS COTTON. Cotton raised in Cambodia. Used for home consumption and may be spun to about 20s count.

SALENDANGS. Broad term for East Indian cottons made with colored yarn effects.

SALES DOLLAR BREAKDOWN IN TEXTILES. Below is given an approximate breakdown of the Sales Dollar used by major textile companies with regard to distribution:

PERCENT:

Raw Materials:	40
Labor:	26
Dyes, Chemicals, Maintenance, Supplies and Utilities:	11
Selling, Administrative and General Expenses:	6
Provision Set Aside for Taxes Based on Income:	5
Depreciation and Amortization:	4
Retained Earnings:	3
Miscellaneous Charges, Net:	2
Payment on Common Stock Shares:	2
Interest Charges:	1
	Total 100

SALING. A fabric made in Turkestan from goat and camel fibers. A saling is about 22 yards long and 12 inches wide.

SALISBURY. Popular white English flannel; made of woolen yarn, it comes in varying weights.

SALE YARN. Some mills specialize in the manufacture of yarns for many uses in the trade, such as for knitters, weavers, braiders.

SALLA. Indian Saree material in which warp and filling are both colored and white to produce block effects. Block sizes may vary, and some of the material may use white warp and colored filling or vice versa. Yarns used are 16s to 20s.

SALLO. Plain-woven Indian cloth, always dyed with some shade of red.

SALMALI. Sanskrit for the fiber-bearing tree which produces kapok.

SALMON. Reddish yellow in hue, comparable with the color of the flesh of the salmon; high in brilliance and medium in saturation.

SALONA COTTON. A staple cotton of Rumania.

SALONICA COTTON. Raised in the Levant and desirable for the manufacture of candlewick fabric.

SALONIQUE. Raw cotton from Greece, Turkey, and adjacent Near Eastern countries.

SALSETTE HEMP. Another name for Sunn hemp.

SALT. Sodium chloride, a white crystalline substance that is found in sea water, mineral springs, and in subterranean beds. Chemically, it is a compound, usually crystalline in form, made by the union of an acid and a base. The anion of an acid and the cation of a base give salt. An ion is a particle that bears electrical charges which transmit electric current through air or other gases.

An anion is the electrically negative constituent of a compound undergoing decomposition. A cation is an element in which electrolysis is evolved at the cathode. It is a positive ion.

A cathode is a negative pole of a galvanic battery, the opposite of an anode. The latter is the positive terminal in a conducting circuit.

SALTAIRE. English textile town founded by Sir Titus Salt, the discoverer of alpaca and a leading textile manufacturer of his time.

SALT-AND-PEPPER. Homespuns and tweeds made with ply yarns of black and white. The nature of the yarn is such that the finished cloth has the appearance of salt and pepper.

SALT COLORS. Direct synthetic colors which use ordinary salt to increase color fastness. They have affinity for bast fibers at low temperatures, but high temperatures must be used for their application on animal fibers.

SALT FIGURE. Concentration of an aqueous sodium chloride solution necessary to cause coagulation of viscose under standard conditions.

SALTILLO. Named for this Mexican city, it is a woolen blanket, poncho, or serape richly decorated with a center medallion and brilliant colors arranged in a circular formation. Vertical and diagonal rows of color are also woven into the fabric to enhance the design. The primary and secondary colors, plus black and white, are used in the color combinations. Fringed edges are a feature of this fabric.

SALT OF TIN. Stannous chloride used as a mordant.

SALTS, ACTION OF.

IRON SALTS are indicated as follows:
1. Ferrous salts give a dark blue precipitate with 10 per cent potassium ferrocyanide solution. The precipitate is insoluble in dilute hydrochloric acid.

2. Ferrous salts give a white precipitate with 5 per cent sodium hydroxide solution. The precipitate turns green.

3. Ferric salts give a dark blue precipitate with 10 per cent potassium ferrocyanide solution.

4. Ferric salts give a deep red color with potassium thiocyanate solution.

LEAD SALTS:
1. Give a white precipitate with dilute sulphuric acid solution. The precipitate dissolves in warm sodium hydroxide solution.

2. Form a yellow precipitate, in nonmineral acid solutions, upon the addition of 10 per cent potassium chromate solution. The precipitate is insoluble in acetic acid, but soluble in sodium hydroxide solution.

MAGNESIUM SALTS:
Give no precipitate with 20 per cent ammonium carbonate solution, in the presence of ammonium chloride, but precipitate upon the addition of 10 per cent sodium phosphate solution to the above mixture. The precipitate is white and insoluble in ammonium hydroxide.

NITRITES:
1. Give brownish red fumes when treated with sulphuric acid.

2. Give a blue color to starch iodide paper.

OXALATES:
In alkaline solution, give a white precipitate with 10 per cent calcium chloride solution. The precipitate dissolves in hydrochloric acid but not in acetic acid.

PERMANGANATES:
When acidified with sulphuric acid, are decolorized by hydrogen peroxide, by sodium bisulphite, or by oxalic acid.

PEROXIDES:
When acidified with sulphuric acid, give a deep blue color upon the addition of 10 per cent potassium dichromate solution.

SULPHATES:
Give a white precipitate with 10 per cent barium chloride solution. The precipitate is insoluble in hydrochloric or nitric acid.

SULPHIDES:
Give off hydrogen sulphide when treated with acid. The gas is recognized by its odor and by its blackening paper moistened with lead acetate.

SULPHITES:
1. Give off sulphur dioxide gas when treated with hydrochloric acid.

2. Decolorize a solution of potassium permanganate.

TARTRATES:
In a neutral solution give a white precipitate with 1 per cent silver nitrate solution. If just enough ammonium hydroxide solution is added to dissolve the precipitate, metallic silver is deposited upon warming of the solution.

TIN SALTS:
If the solution is made acidic with hydrochloric acid, it will precipitate metallic tin on a piece of zinc placed in the solution.

SALTS, INFORMATION ON. They are compounds formed by the replacement of the hydrogen of an acid by a metal. For example, common table salt is used to remove the brownish deposits formed on a pressing iron.

Salts have no effect on litmus paper except in the case of a few strong acids or bases.

Acids and bases neutralize each other. For example, an acid plus a base produces water and salt. Some salts are soluble in water while others are not; for example, silver chloride. The salts formed when iron rusts are insoluble in water as well; oxalic acid used to remove rust stains reduces the insoluble brownish salts (ferric) to colorless soluble salts (ferrous) which can be removed with water.

SALTS, TYPES OF. These follow:
Acid Salt: One in which only a part of the hydrogen of the acid has been replaced by a metal. Thus, sodium carbonate, or sodium bicarbonate ($NaHCO_3$), and sodium acid phosphate (Na_2HOP_4) are acid salts.
Basic Salt: One which contains one or more hydroxyl (OH) radicals. Thus, bismuth subnitrate $[Bi(OH)_2NO_3]$ is a basic salt used in medicine.
Normal Salt: One which contains only a metal or metallic radical, combined with a non-metal or an acid radical. It contains neither hydrogen replaceable by a metal nor a hydroxyl radical. Thus, calcium carbonate ($CaCO_3$) and sodium chloride ($NaCl$) are normal salts.
Double Salt: One which contains two metals combined with one acid radical. Thus, common alum is a double sulfate of potassium and aluminum, having the formula $K_2SO_4\text{-}Al_2(SO_4)_3\text{-}24H_2O$ or $KAl(SO_4)_2\text{-}12H_2O$.

SALT SACKING. A crude, rough material made from any of the major textile fibers. It is like crash and burlap and is popular for summer suiting, sportswear, beach garments, summer riding habits, and slacks. Sacking comes in plain or natural colors, or is printed with rather gaudy designs when used in women's wear.

SALT SENSITIVITY. 1. In dyeing

it is the extent to which the dyeing properties of a dye are affected by the addition of a neutral electrolyte. 2. In dyed fabric it means the susceptibility of a dyed material to color change when spotted with aqueous solutions of neutral electrolytes.

SALT SPRAY TEST CABINET. Testing equipment designed to determine the corrosion-resistance qualities of electroplated or coated material, alloys, metal parts, lacquered, or painted samples, etc. Tests are performed with accurate control of air heaters and atomized, heated salt water within the testing chamber. Salt-spray testing is the standard by which rust-resistance is measured.

SALUYOT. A Philippine fiber used in making cordage.

SALVADOR HENEQUEN. See LETONA.

SAM. The name for a ramie fiber raised in Korea and made into a coarse, loosely textured fabric for use by the poorer people there. It also finds use as a mourning cloth for all classes of Koreans regardless of status.

SAMARDINE. French serge made with an eight-end twill weave. Manufactured from any of the major textile fibers.

SAMARKAND RUGS. Medium-sized rugs of wool, silk, or cotton groundwork and silk- or cotton-pile yarn tied in Senna knots. The motifs are Chinese with five or fewer medallions, fretwork effects, and odd stiff flowers. Red, yellow, blue, brown, and white are the predominant colors used.

SAMBA CHIT. Cotton cloth made in Punjab, India. Printed with red, orange, or yellow flowers on a green background.

SAMBHAL. Also known as Choutara Paraya. Hand-loomed, plain-weave cotton, a coarse Saree which is made six yards long and about one yard wide. Three-inch borders are woven into the material. Made in India.

SAM-CLOTH. Same as a sampler.

SAMITE. This rich, lustrous fabric, featured by the use of a six-thread silk warp, is recognized by the use of gold or silver threads in the design. It has come down from the Middle Ages and is still used for ecclesiastical robes, vestments, ornamental fabrics, and interior decoration.

SAMOA. The yucca grass used by the Hopi Indians and other tribes in making baskets, mats, twine, rope, and saddle blankets.

SAMOHU. Found in the La Plata valley of South America, this tree of the Bombax family yields a fiber from its seed pods. It is like kapok in most respects.

SAMORANG HEMP. The most desirable of Manila hemps.

SAMPLE. 1. A swatch or small piece of fabric used for optical inspection and physical examination. 2. (Verb) To pick samples at random for a fair examination of a lot of wool: sliver, top, fabric, etc. 3. Yarn or fabric to be given various tests for quality, wearability, etc.

SAMPLE HAND, APPAREL. One who "runs up the dress" because of his ability as a machine operator to work the fabric into the desired effect created by the garment designer.

SAMPLER. 1. A piece of needlework, as a sample designed for practice or to show a beginner's skill. Embroidered letters, verses, and quotations are often features of the article to give practice in sewing different forms of letters of alphabet. 2. One who examines samples such as cotton, wool, etc., for classification.

SAMPLE ROOM. A room in a mill or office where samples of various types are examined for approval or rejection.

SAMPLING. To test or examine by means of a portion or specimen.

SAMPSONS. Heavy cast-iron legs or supports for textile machinery.

SAMSUN. Cotton cloth named for city of Samsun, made from native Turkestan cotton.

SAMUHU FIBER. 1. The Argentines use this bast fiber for cordage and twine.

2. Fiber raised in Paraguay; silky and flexible like the Argentine fiber but shorter in length. Used for ponchos, equine equipment, etc.

SANA. Indian name for Sunn hemp.

SANAT. Low quality, hand-loomed, plain-woven East Indian printed cotton.

SANDALWOOD. See REDWOOD.

SAND CREPE. A particular type of novelty crepe weave may be used to make this rough, distinctive, pebble-like fabric made of acetate or rayon, combination yarns, etc. Usually twice as many ends as picks are used in the construction; the yarn is alternated with regard to twist—one of S-twist, followed by one of Z-twist. This sturdy, rugged cloth gives good service; comes in white, dyed, or printed.

SANDERSWOOD. Sandalwood.

SANDIES. Open cotton bolls which have picked up varying portions of sand during the picking seasons.

SAND ROLL. A part of the loom. It is the wooden roller, covered with either sandpaper, sharp pins, or grating of some sort to prevent the cloth, just woven, from slipping as it winds around the cloth roller after passing over the breast beam. The cloth proceeds from the sand roller to the cloth roller. It is set next to the cloth roller, or may be set above it, depending on type of loom.

SAND ROLLER MARKS. These are observed in the filling direction of the cloth and may be caused by uneven tension and "pull" on the cloth as it winds around the sand roller on the loom on its way to the cloth roller. Usually caused by irregular tension between the two rollers. Sand roller marks often cause abrasion to the goods, which is most difficult to remove in finishing of the fabric.

SANDWICH, SANDWICHING. 1. Cotton yarn used as a padding on the face and back of a knit fabric to add weight or effect. It is not observed in the article when it is worn. 2. Blends or combinations of natural, man-made, and synthetic fibers.

SANDWICH BLENDING. The result of spreading, in two or more horizontal layers, fibers from different package units, lots, or of different characteristics; the strata weight being proportional to the percentage of each element used. Thus, when vertical sections are cut from top to bottom for feeding to the next machine in the manufacture of yarn, all elements are present in the proper proportion.

SANFORIZED. A checked measure of shrinkage. The trade-mark is applied to fabrics that have been shrunk by the compressive shrinkage process, and indicates that the residual shrinkage of the fabric is less than 1 per cent and that the tests have been made by the trade-mark owner to insure that the shrinkage conforms to the 1 per cent standard.

The trade-mark owners, The Sanforized Company, a Division of Cluett, Peabody & Company, Inc., permit the use of the "Sanforized" label on compressive pre-shrunk fabrics wherever the following conditions have been met: 1. The residual shrinkage in the fabric, that is, the amount of shrinkage left after shrinking, does not exceed 1 per cent by the U. S. test method, CCC-T-191a. 2. Tests to determine residual shrinkage have been checked and approved by the trade-mark owner.

"SANFORIZED-PLUS." A trademark signifying a regularly checked standard of wash-and-wear performance. Fabrics so labeled have met rigid test requirements for shrinkage, smoothness after washing, crease recovery, tensile strength, and tear strength as prescribed by the trade-mark owner, The Sanforized Company, a Division of Cluett, Peabody & Company, Inc.

"SANFORIZED-PLUS-2." Trademark which is licensed for use on durable press garments made only from approved pre-cured or post-cured fabrics. Such garments must meet shrinkage and other performance requirements of the trademark owner, Cluett, Peabody & Co., Inc., New York City. The fabrics in garments so labeled will not shrink more than one percent by the Standard Tests of the United States Government.

SANGATI. A high-quality, plain Dacca muslin; made on hand loom.

SANGLIER. 1. French for wild boar. A plain-weave dress goods made of wiry worsted or mohair stock, closely woven, and given a rough surface finish to simulate the coat of the boar. 2. Any general type of French dress goods made of highly twisted worsted or mohair yarn. 3. Cotton or hemp strap webbing used as a support for the springs on chairs, upholstery, and beds.

SAN HEMP. Bengal, India name for Sunn hemp or hemp in general.

SANITIZED. A chemical anti-bacterial finish which, when applied during the manufacturing process, protects the product against deteriorating and odor-causing effects of bacteria, mildew, and mold. The formula, a bacteriostat, is sold to its licensee-manufacturers by Sanitized Sales Company, Inc., of New York City. This bacteriostat is used in more than 3,000 products which are manufactured by more than 800 concerns in the licensing program. Believed to be the largest licensing operation in the world, it was first used in 1933 for treatment of shoe lining. In 1956, two textile companies, N. Erlanger Blumgart & Co., Inc., and Dubin-Haskell-Jacobson, Inc., joined forces and set up the present company.

Draperies, dresses, men's suiting linings, hosiery, mattresses, pillows, and undergarments are among the host of articles that are Sanitized-treated. The chemical itself, when incorporated into the finished product, is invisible, odorless, and non-toxic.

SAN MARTHA COTTON. A type of cotton raised in Colombia.

SAN MARTIN COTTON. A West Indian cotton.

SANN. Sunn hemp.

SANNA. A popular white or blue cotton fabric that is a favorite with the people in the East Indies; exported from Great Britain.

SAN RAMIE. Korean trade term for the wild ramie which produces a tough, coarse fiber. Its fabrics are used for summer clothing for the poor and for sacking cloth for mourning by all classes.

SANSAVERDE FIBER. Fiber from a plant grown in Paraguay. After treatment its dark color becomes white and it resembles silk. Damp soil is a necessity for its development.

SANSCULOTTES. These long trousers or modern pants began with the French Revolution. The aristocracy of late 18th Century France wore breeches or culottes of silk and satin with long white stockings; the French peasants wore long pants and no stockings. Thus, the aristocrats referred to the peasants as "sansculottes," which literally means "without breeches." The mobs took up the uncomplimentary term and made political hay out of it. The tricolor stripes of France, red, white, and blue, were often used in making sansculottes.

SANS ENVERS. French for reversible or double-faced material.

SANSEVIERIA. Any of a genus of this name of erect perennial herbs of the lily family, native to Africa but sometimes grown as an ornamental plant. The several types of this plant furnish commercial textile bast fibers.

SANSEVIERIA ZEYLANICA. A Bengal, India, bast fiber used in making bowstrings.

SANTICIZER 141. A vinyl plasticizer of low volatility and capable of imparting good low-temperature flexibility, excellent solvent resistance and flame retardance. It is free from systemic toxicity and is non-irritating. Uses for this product of Monsanto Chemical Company include coated textiles, free film, handbags, shoe soles, shower curtains, belts, baby pants, hospital sheeting, and food bowl covers.

SANTIPUR. Made in Bengal, India, this very fine-textured, expensive cotton is made on hand looms with yarns varying from 60s to 120s. Floral effects are embroidered onto the goods.

SANTOS COTTON. A Brazilian cotton developed from Orleans seed. The fiber is rather harsh and wiry, so it is mixed with other cotton; staple is about 1⅛ inches.

SANYAN SILK. West African wild silk.

SAPANWOOD. See REDWOOD, BRAZILWOOD.

SAPLIER. Coarse cotton, jute, or comparable yarns woven into fabric to be used for packing purposes.

SAPOIT. A British term for fabrics, chiefly cottons, made with a check pattern and a border design so arranged that the wide fabric may be cut into a number of narrower widths for use as scarves and head covering. Some of the fabric is made so that only the center area of the scarf will be checked.

SAPONIFICATION, SAPONIFICATION NUMBER. Chemically, this process or result of soapmaking is the decomposition (hydrolysis) of a fat by alkali with the formation of a soap, or salt of a fatty acid, and glycerol. It implies, also, the hydrolysis of a fat by any method. The term is also used in the changing of acetate into a regenerated form by treatment with caustic. The term "number" means the number of milligrams of potassium hydroxide necessary for the complete saponification of one gram of substance.

SAPONIFIED ACETATE YARN. Acetate yarn is subjected to mechanical treatment which results in a parallel molecular structure and a yarn which is regenerated cellulose. Properties include extreme strength and dimensional stability.

SAPONIFIED RAYON. The reconversion of cellulose acetate filaments to cellulose or saponified rayon whereby the yarn or fabric is colored by dyes used on rayon. See Saponified Acetate Yarn.

SAPPHIRE. A color, greenish-blue in hue, of medium saturation and low brilliance.

SAPPY WOOL. Wool which has a high percentage of yolk and suint; the actual yield will be small because of their presence in the grease wool.

SARABAND RUG. Small or medium size Persian rugs made of cotton warp and filling for the base construction with the short pile-effect made of wool tied with Senna knots. Some of the rugs may have wool filling. The design usually shows a pear or some other fruit, while the narrow ornate borders have approximately seven stripes in red, blue, or green. The filling crosses twice beneath each row of tufts. The rugs are often used as runners since they can be made in long, narrow sizes.

SARACENIC TAPESTRY. See BASSE-LISSE.

SARAFAN. A sleeveless jacket worn by Russian women over their blouses.

SARAKHS RUGS. Carpets or rugs made in this northeastern town in Iran (Persia). These heavy, all-wool rugs have the long, close pile tied in Ghiordian knot formation. The yarn is spun from wool obtained in the vicinity.

SARAN. A true chemical fiber in which the base, after processing, is vinylidene chloride. Derived from ethylene, a petroleum product, and chlorine from brine. Saran, in popular language, is known as a thermoplastic resin; that is, a plastic which is softened by heat and hardened into shape by cooling. It can be quickly and economically molded, and because it can be softened and reshaped again and again, little waste is occasioned. Saran is made by Amtech, Inc., Odenton, Maryland, and S.E. Polymers, Inc., Clare, Michigan. Properties include resistance to chemicals, stains, abrasion, corrosion, and moisture. Saran is nonflammable, tough, strong, and flexible as desired. Chief uses are for outdoor summer furniture, screen cloth, draperies, luggage, shoes, upholstery. "Saran Wrap" used in cooking is a household word. See Velon, Atom, Molecule, Monomer, Polymer, Polyethylene, Polymerication.

SARANDAZ RUGS. Trade term for Anatolian- and Persian-knotted wool rugs of various designs. Used for household purposes—floor covering, wall decoration, etc.

SARASHI CARIKO. A 36-inch, bleached cotton fabric used for shirting in Japan.

SARASHI KANAKIN. Japanese term for a plain-weave, bleached cotton shirting.

SARASSES COTTON. An East Indian cotton used locally.

SARAWAMI. An Indian sheep known for its fat tail; its fleece shows both wool fibers and hair. The yield is used chiefly in making rough blankets used by the natives and finds some use as carpet wool.

SARCILIS, SARZIL. During the Middle Ages this very coarse, low-textured woolen cloth was worn chiefly by those who subsisted on charity or were beggars.

SARI, SAREE. Scarf worn by the women in India: a gauzy, long fabric which covers the body and can be used to cover the head. The chief garment of Hindu women, it is, in hot weather, the only article of dress worn by the poorer classes.

SARILLE. Modified viscose rayon fiber with high degree of crimp. Provides wool-like characteristics, increased bulkiness without added weight, and a warm, full-hand texture. Crease-shedding properties are also very good. Used in dressgoods, men's and boys' suitings, rainwear, blankets, and candlewick bedspreads. Sarille also possesses lint-free properties. Product of Courtaulds, Ltd., Great Britain.

SARILUXE. A deep-dyeing rayon

produced by the use of additives in the spinning solution. Marketed by Courtaulds, Ltd., London, England.

SARONG. A shirt-like garment, twice as long as wide. The short ends are sewn together, then it is folded and tied around the hips. The pattern of a sarong is broken by the kepala (literal head)—which is a double row of triangular motifs called toempal; these feature floral designs. This design resembles a backgammon board and undoubtedly was imported from British India. This garment is the daily garb of the villager and was originally worn only by women. At present it is also worn by men. He cannot, however, wear it to visit an official or upon entering the palace of the sultan. For these purposes there are other types of clothing to wear. The Dodot is worn exclusively by the sultans, their wives, high officials and their wives, court dancers, and the bride and the bridegroom. The Dodot is worn in an entirely different manner than the sarong. It is tied around the hips in a complicated way, while the trousers of tjindi (double tie-dyed silk imported from British India) are worn under it. There are several different ways of tying a Dodot—depending upon the traditional rules of court etiquette.

The Slendang (shawl or scarf) is a long small cloth of batik, and is used either to carry a baby on the back, or as a shawl, over the shoulders. See SLENDANG.

SARONG KAPALA. A headdress made from a square fabric worn especially by males in some of the Far Eastern countries. Wound around the head on the order of turban, when the Sarong Kapala is removed, it is possible to starch the form so that it holds its shape and size.

SAROUK RUG. See FLOOR COVERINGS, CLASSIFICATION OF.

SARPLAR. 1. A bale of wool that weighs one ton, 2,240 pounds. This is equal to 80 tods. 2. Tod, used with the term sarplar, is a unit weight of 28 pounds of wool.

SARPLIER. A strong, plain-weave cotton fabric made in England and used for bagging to hold newly clipped grease wool being shipped from consignor to consignee. See SARPLAR.

SARSANET. Plain or twill fine silk fabric noted for its softness, now superseded by more practical cloths.

SARRIE. English cotton cloth with a fancy heading woven across a gray warp. Printed with a cappela the cloth is known as Batik sarong. Worn by native women in India.

SARTORIAL. (From sartor, tailor in

Latin.) Pertaining to clothing, tailoring; sometimes extended to cover general grooming, "sartorial splendor."

SASE, SASSE YARN. Spun rayon yarn made of viscose staple in several denier counts.

SASH. A decorative article that comes in varying width and is straight or bias. Single color material may be used or double or lined effects. The ends may be plain or fancy, and the construction is the same as in the case of belts and girdles. The edges must be finished. This ornamental band, scarf, or strip is worn around the waist or over the shoulder for ornament by women and children.

SASH CORD. Usually, a braided cotton cord, sized and polished for use, in which the sliding sash of a window is attached to its balance weights.

SATALIAN. This cotton, made in Great Britain, is made of coarse or waste yarn in plain weave. When stiffened in finishing it can serve as lining fabric; in the dyed state it is exported to some of the colonies.

SATARRA TWILL. British term for various eight harness twills used in the manufacture of woolen and worsted fabrics. A popular pattern used is a small color-effect weave arranged in a one-and-one formation as to color plan.

SATEEN. This cloth is made with a 5-end or an 8-shaft satin weave in warp-face or filling-face effects. Filling-face sateen requires a great many more picks than ends per inch in the goods while the reverse is true in the warp-face material. Carded or combed cotton yarns are used, and cloth of the former comes in heavy weights; it may serve as work clothing, for use in the apparel trades, etc. Combed yarn sateens are usually mercerized and have a very smooth, lustrous surface effect. These are used chiefly for linings.

SATEEN, SATINE. Lining cloth of the jean type which has a twill weave, despite the face that the name would imply the use of a satin weave. The cloth is given a soft, glossy finish, and may be plain or printed.

The goods are made in warp or filling effects. When the term "sateen" is used, it is generally understood in the trade that a satin weave has been used in the face construction of the cloth; however, since twill weaves are used with S- and Z-twist yarns to give a satin effect in the goods, the two names are interchangeable and are often misunderstood.

SATEEN, WIDE INDUSTRIAL. Satin-weave material finished at 54 inches, with a texture of about 96 x 64; approximates about 1¼ yards to the pound. Carded yarn is used in the cloth, which is often coated.

SATEEN, WORSTED EDGE. A British fine-yarn cotton sateen which has a selvage of worsted yarn that is usually of some color.

SATEEN FINISH. A smooth, glossy finish given to some cottons to simulate silk satin. The degree of crispness varies, depending on the end-use.

SATEEN SHIRTING. Fast-colored, narrow-stripe cotton shirting fabric made with satin weave for the stripe effect and plain weave for the ground, which is white or some cast of white. A five-shaft satin is used for the stripe construction. Texture is about 86 x 70, and yarn counts are 2/40s in the warp and 1/30s or 2/30s in the filling.

SATEEN SKIRTING. Comparable with sateen shirting, but differs in that the material is all-colored to show stripe effects on colored ground.

SATEEN TICKING. Used chiefly for upholstery purposes, it is made from a five-end or an 8-end satin weave. This compact, rugged cloth has a texture of 98 x 56, while the counts of yarn are 7s or 8s combed warp, and 14s or 16s filling. The warp-effect satin weave used adds to the appearance of the goods, which may or may not be striped.

SATEEN WEAVE. Same as satin weave, but sometimes used to imply that the satin weave has been used to construct a cotton material.

SATELLITES. British term for about any and all printed cotton cloths shipped especially to the African trade.

SATIN. The name originated in Zaytun (Tzu-t'ing, Zaitun), China. Satin weaves are used in making satin fabrics, thereby insuring the full-face color of the warp or the filling on the material.

For example, an eight-shaft satin weave, filling effect, would have the warp ends show on the face of the cloth only one interlacing in every eight; the filling would show on the face of the goods every seven out of eight interlacings. Seven-eighths of the face of the cloth would show the filling effect. It would appear to the casual naked eye as a "solid effect." This effect makes satin ideal for evening gowns and dresses. Satins are smooth, have clinginess, are "form-revealing," and smart in appearance.

When satins first came into prominence, the spelling of the term in Europe was "aceytuin" and then Italian spelling became "zetain." From the original Chinese spelling the term was contracted to "zetin" and finally became "satin."

Satins were known in the European world at the time of the first rumblings of the Renaissance in Italy in the twelfth and thirteenth centuries. The cloth was known in England by the fourteenth century. In court life, satin soon became a reigning favorite because of its exquisite qualities and its feel.

All of the many satin weaves, both warp and filling, are used in making satin fabric; the different weaves used readily gave rise to the many fancy names applied to cloths made of the weave. Each satin has its peculiar or particular characteristics which set it more or less apart from the other satins.

In cheaper satins, cotton warp or cotton filling is often used. A low-grade silk is often used in the cheaper cloths. Rayon and acetate materials are popular in the market when made of satin construction. The price range in satins is varied. There is probably more variance and wider extremes in the price per yard of satin than any other fabric; this is certainly true in staple cloths found today.

Cotton-back sateen has the underside of the cloth made of cotton; the face of the goods is silk or rayon. This arrangement gives the material a chance to be worn to better advantage.

Satin is often woven face-down in the loom because of the great lift of the harnesses when eight or more shafts are used. By weaving it face-down, it is only necessary to have one or two harnesses raised at a time when the shed of the loom is formed for the actual weaving. The wear and tear on the loom is therefore greatly reduced.

Satin gray goods must be handled and treated with the utmost care. The cloth, of course, as it comes from the loom, is not in presentable form. Cloth is made in the finishing, and since satin made of silk is expensive when compared with the cost of other major fibers, it will be seen that every operative who comes in contact with the goods must give his or her undivided attention to the handling and work at hand. Some procedures in finishing silk are secrets.

The uses of satin are many—slips, creations, classics, haute coutures, gowns, and dresses, in the apparel field; lining fabric, for use in the millinery trade; drapes, hangings, covers, pillows, and more.

Some of the satin fabrics found today, each different, no matter how slightly, in order to warrant a new moniker: Satin de Chine, de Lyons, double-faced satin, satin Duchesse, Turc, satin taffeta, Serrano, panne, messaline, merveilleux, Luxor, canton, Empresse, de Bruges, crepe, Grec.

SATIN, ACETATE. A satin-face, plain-back construction that is smooth and lustrous. It is durable, drapes well, and gives a splendid color effect. Dresses of the material are much used in evening wear. The garment should be dry-cleaned, and not laundered.

SATIN, NOCTURNE. Nocturne means night in French. Thus, a satin with a "hill-and-dale" surface effect that will show bright and dim effects as the rays of light strike the material, a "night-and-day" effect. The hammered effect is made possible by the use of rollers, gouged and grooved so as to make the illusion possible.

SATIN, PLAIN. Sometimes known as panne satin, this 39-inch fabric is made both ways with flat yarn. Warp is 150, 100, or 75 denier; filling is 300, 150, 100, or 75 denier. Textures range from 110 x 52 to 300 x 80. Great luster and beauty feature plain satin. Incidentally, the hand in viscose rayon satin is not comparable with that of all-acetate satin; the latter seems to have the more appealing feel.

Terminal uses include cushion covers, dresses, evening wear, fur-coat lining, ribbon, slipper satin, slips.

SATIN, YARN-DYED. This popular silk dress goods has long been a staple fabric for women's wear. It is made of two thread, 13/15 denier warp, in a 64-reed with five ends per dent. The filling is three thread, 14/16 denier, tram silk. An eight-shaft satin weave is used in the construction. See SATIN.

SATIN ALCYONNE. First made about 125 years ago, with little of the material seen today, Alcyonne is made with a five-shaft satin weave with two-fold-warp yarn and singles filling. The texture reveals twice as many warp ends as filling picks, and, because of this plan, the fabric shows a face of the one color while the reverse presents an almost solid contrasting effect. When made with singles warp yarn, the cloth is called satin de Chine.

SATINADE. 1. French for satinet. 2. A lightweight French dress fabric made in warp satin stripes on a taffeta ground. Silk warp and linen filling are used in the cloth, which is similar to Satin de Bruges, but inferior to it. First mention of the fabric was made around 1720 in Flanders. 3. An old-time French and Italian tapestry made of waste silk warp and silk filling, dyed in different colors in which striped motifs predominated.

SATIN A FILS TIRES. Satin fabric composed of one-inch satin stripes separated by six or eight thick cords. Used chiefly during early nineteenth century to make head covering, since the material could be shirred easily by pulling the thick cords. Satin à Fils Tirés was introduced by Tave, a Paris milliner.

SATINAGE. French term for the glossy or lustrous finish given to some fabrics by calendering or friction calendering.

SATIN-BACK. 1. A reversible cloth, fabric, or garment whose back is made of satin weave; the face of the goods may or may not be made of this weave. 2. A silk or rayon fabric which has a backing of satin-weave construction, in either silk or rayon. 3. Velvet, certain silks or rayons, ribbons, etc., woven with the reverse side of the fabric in satin weave.

SATIN-BACK COATING. An all-worsted fabric made on a fancy twill basis with a satin back. The coarser warp yarn at the back of the goods gives weight but still allows a fine face-weave effect. The weave arrangement is two-face and one-back, 2/56s face and a 2/36s back warp. Single 24s filling is used. Texture is about 132 x 92; 88 face and 44 back; the cloth is finished at 69 inches.

SATIN-BACK CREPE. A cloth made from silk, rayon, or mixture yarn which has a crepe face and a satin-back construction. The cloth comes in black, white, colors, and prints, and there is a wide range in quality and price. It is used for blouses, dresses, trimming, and two-tone garments in which either side of the fabric may be used as the face.

SATIN BERBER. A well-wearing all-worsted cloth made with a satin weave and given a luster finish.

SATIN BONJEAN. French trousering of good wearing quality made in satin weave of worsted yarn throughout. A fulled finish is given the goods.

SATIN CAFARD. See SATIN DE BRUGES.

SATIN CHECKS. Dress fabric made from cotton or silk with checks of satin weave on a plain ground. The cloth is bleached, dyed or printed, and is usually made in light weights. A standard cloth is 39/40 inches finished, with a 62 reed, 56 picks to the inch, 50s ground warp and filling, and 2/100s yarn in the satin stripe and check effects.

The satin warp stripes are crowded in the reed; the filling stripes are also very dense.

SATIN CLOTH. A fine worsted dress fabric made in satin weave and luster finished, of French manufacture. Woven 27 to 30 inches wide.

SATIN CREPE. Silk cloth made with a satin face and a crepe twist filling; the latter is woven on the back of the goods, which are piece-dyed. Raw silk warp of high counts are used; the filling is of hard twist, 50 turns and upwards per inch. The yarns will average about 24/26 or 26/28 denier in size.

Set in the reed at 44 inches, the cloth is finished at 40 inches. Textures range from about 300 in the warp by 72 to 112 in the filling.

SATIN DAMASK. 1. A heavy, rich silk cloth made on the Jacquard loom, with fancy weaves and embellishments, or in a pile construction. Used for hangings and curtains. 2. The best quality of linen damask, used for table linen.

SATIN D'AMÉRIQUE. A French fabric, Satin d'Amérique is made in satin weave of silk warp and agave fiber filling.

SATIN DE BRUGES. Popular sixteenth century silk, made of silk warp and either silk or woolen filling; used in upholstery. Linen appeared as the filling in certain types of the material. Originated in Holland, but in 1618 a French manufacturer opened a factory in Lille, France, to produce the goods. Since about 1760, the cloth has appeared as Satine de Hollande and later on was known as Satin Cafard. By the end of the eighteenth century, more serviceable cloths displaced this fabric.

SATIN DE CHINE. Rather heavy silk dress-goods fabric made on a ten-end satin weave, piece-dyed. Greige warp and tram-silk filling are used in the cloth, which is not as heavy as duchesse mousseline.

SATIN DE CHYPRE. An all-silk satin fabric ("Satin of Cyprus") now replaced by more practical materials.

SATIN DORURE DE NANKIN. A group of rather fine satins woven with gold floral effects; not a practical material at present. Supposed to have originated in China.

SATIN DOUBLE-FACE. This satin-weave cloth uses two warps and one filling to simulate a double satin construction. Organzine warp and tram filling used, but cotton filling is often resorted to in the cheaper qualities.

SATIN DRAW. A difficult drawing-in plan to follow, which corresponds to the order of interlacings between the warp ends and the filling picks in a satin weave; only used if absolutely necessary.

SATIN DRILL. Cloth is made with a five-shaft, warp-effect satin weave. Many qualities are manufactured and shipped to all markets. The yarns are usually 16s to 24s warp and filling. Finished white, khaki, and blue for suiting, etc. Standard cloths are shown in table on this page.

SATIN DUCHESSE. An all-silk dress fabric woven on an eight-shaft, warp-effect satin weave. Fine counts of dyed yarn are used in the cloth, which has about 240 ends per inch and 92 picks per inch. Finished at about 36 inches, 24/26 denier warp and 100 denier filling are used in the construction. The material is strong, has high luster and texture, and is finished with a firm handle.

SATIN ÉCOSSAIS. An all-silk satin formerly made in France with two sets of different colors—one color showed warp stripes on the face, the other woven in plain-weave formation to give filling-color bars or checks. The name, satin écossais, meaning Scotch satin, was given because of the plaid-effect produced.

SATIN FACONNE. A Jacquard figured fabric with an all-satin-weave background. Various types of striping effects are seen in satin faconné.

SATIN FEUTRE. Fine dress fabric made of organzine warp and worsted filling in eight-harness arrangement. Fabric is given slight nap on back of the goods, therefore name Satin feutré (felted satin).

SATIN FIGARO. A warp-face satin made on sixteen harnesses and woven with a warp, end-to-end, of two colors on the one beam. The fabric is double-faced, each warp being on eight shafts and woven so that the same warp ends appear alternately on the face and on the back, thereby giving a type of warp-printed effect. This cloth was popular around the time of the French Revolution and is named for the opera, *Marriage of Figaro*. Little of the fabric is now used since other fabrics, more practical in nature, seem to have replaced it.

SATIN FINISH. (1) A glossy, lustrous finish given to various fabrics; also (2) the gloss which is produced by calendering cotton, wool, and silk fabrics between hot rollers. Term with a wide trade usage.

SATIN DRILL

WIDTH		TEXTURE	WARP	FILLING	WIDTH		BOLT	WEIGHT		MARKET
29	inches	104 x 58	16s	11s	29	inches	100 yds.	45	lb.	Argentine
28½	inches	100 x 52	22s	28s	28½	inches	120 yds.	27½	lb.	Egyptian
28½	inches	104 x 68	22s	20s	28½	inches	120 yds.	36	lb.	Indian
29	inches	128 x 88	32s	26s	29	inches	120 yds.	33½	lb.	Colonial

SATIN-FINISH LEATHER. A dull or mat finish on leather as opposed to a glazed finish.

SATIN FOULARD. A smooth, glossy-finished silk cloth made with a warp-effect satin weave. Printed with spots on a colored ground.

SATIN FRANCAIS. A worsted, satin-weave fabric with a glossy face-finish. The warp and filling are of identical counts of yarn. Satin français is used for upholstery.

SATIN GAUPRE. Dress fabric in five-shaft or eight-shaft satin construction. Silk warp and cotton filling are used in the fabric, which is characterized by embossed (gaupré) design.

SATIN GREC. Silk lining fabric in eight-shaft satin weave. Singles silk yarns are used in warp, while filling is either single or double silk. Piece-dyed and given high-glaze finish.

SATIN GRENADINE. Dress fabric in eight-shaft satin weave that is given high luster finish. Made of silk or rayon warp and worsted or mercerized cotton filling.

SATIN IMPERIAL. Cottons of high, compact texture made on an eight-end satin weave, filling effect. Every two consecutive warp ends weave together and alike. The filling is spun silk, and the texture is so arranged that there will be twice as many picks as ends in the goods. Imperial is napped on either side, and the name "lambskin" is sometimes given the cloth. Often used as reversible cloth.

SATIN LISSE. A neatly figured, cotton dress goods, satin lissé is recognized by its satinlike finish.

SATIN MERVEILLEUX. A dress goods made of silk or rayon yarn by the use of twill constructions.

SATIN QUILT. Plain-woven, bleached, or colored cotton made with fine warp and filling yarns; a second and coarser set of threads used for filling will give a raised-pattern effect in the goods according to some motif. See MATELASSE.

SATIN SHEETING. 1. A strong, twilled cotton and silk or cotton and rayon fabric which has a satin finish. Finds much use in casement cloth, embroidery, and upholstery. 2. A fabric made of waste silk or rayon face with a cotton backing; this English fabric finds use in dress goods. 3. A contradictory term sometimes used in the gray-goods sheeting trade.

SATIN STITCH. 1. Another name for the slanting Gobelin tapestry stitch. 2. Embroidery stitch, either flat or raised, repeated in parallel lines to give a satinlike appearance; used in fine,

handmade buttonholes, and embroidery.

SATIN STRIPES. Used in several materials to give a fancy appearance to the fabric. Made with a satin weave, they may be seen in satin stripes, cotton shirtings, crepes, taffetas, and novelty dress goods. The satin-weave construction used forms a good contrast with the body of the goods.

SATIN SULTAN. A worsted cloth somewhat on the order of bengaline, made with a satin finish; much used in Asiatic and African trade for dress goods.

SATIN WEAVES. These weaves constitute the third group of the basic weave constructions. The plain weave has no characteristic nor distinguishable diagonal or twill line. There is a more or less prominent diagonal line in right-hand and left-hand twill weaves and in broken twill weaves.

Satin weaves do not have a distinguishable twill line despite the fact that it is actually present in cloth made of these weaves. The naked eye, however, does not discern these lines on the face of the cloth. For this reason, one speaks of a satin weave as devoid of any characteristic twill line. The absence of the twill lines in a satin weave is brought about by the way in which the interlacing of the threads is arranged. Because of this fact, practically the entire surface of the face of the goods is covered with either warp yarn or filling yarn depending on the weaves having a warp or a filling construction. The fine diagonal lines do not show and to find them one must look carefully and closely at the material.

Regular satin weaves repeat on as low as five ends or threads. See illustration. The following terms used with regard to satin constructions are synonymous:

1. Base or counter.
2. End, shaft, or harness.
3. Satin, in silk, and sateen, in cotton, are the same when referring to the cloth construction.

The order of interlacing in any regular satin weave may be found by the use of the base or the counter. This is determined by dividing the number of threads in the repeat into two parts so that they do not have a common divisor, and that the one part is not a multiple of the other. Therefore, an eight-end satin weave could be made with a base of 3 or 5 but not with one of 2 or 4 since the latter numbers divide evenly into eight.

Satin weaves are used to make brocade, brocatelle, cape or cloak fabric, cotton-back sateen, coverings, curtain material, damask, dress silk, evening gowns and wraps, fancies and novelties, furniture fabric, Jacquard fabrics

5-END SATIN COUNTER OF 3, FILLING EFFECT, 2 X 2

5-END SATIN BASE OF 3, WARP EFFECT, 2 X 2

5-END SATIN COUNTER OF 2, FILLING EFFECT, 2 X 2

5-END SATIN BASE OF 2, WARP EFFECT, 2 X 2

8-SHAFT SATIN COUNTER OF 3, FILLING EFFECT, 1 X 1

8-HARNESS SATIN BASE OF 3, WARP EFFECT, 1 X 1

of many types, runners, slipper satin, sport fabrics made of silk or synthetics, striping effect in some materials, tablecloth and napkin material, tapestry, tie fabric, etc.

The word satin, in construction, implies a silk or "man-made" cloth made with a satin weave; the term, sateen, implies a cotton material made with a satin weave.

Satin weave gives a more solid and glossier appearance on the face of the goods than any other type of weave. Hence, its great use in the above-mentioned materials. The types of yarn used have great effect on the brilliant effects noted in fabrics made with the satin weave. Satin weave cloths do not possess nearly the tensile strength of plain- and twill-woven cloths because of the manner of construction. The loose plan in interlacing and the length of the floats in the weave cause this condition. Plain-woven cloths have more tensile strength than twill-woven fabrics, comparably speaking.

If one speaks of an eight-harness satin the implication is that there is one interlacing in every eight threads; that is, a warp thread interlaces once in every eight picks and makes a float where the thread is not woven-in on the face or the back of the cloth as the case may be. The length of the float in ordinary satin weaves is one number less than the number of ends in the repeat of the pattern weave. Thus, an eight-end satin weave would have a float of seven.

The six-harness irregular satin weave, often used in satin constructions, has the following arrangement of the warp ends: 1, 3, 5, 2, 6, 4. A filling effect, 2 repeats high by 2 repeats wide, is illustrated.

A nine-end satin is possible with a base of 2, 4, or 5 but not with a counter

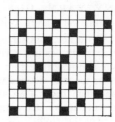

of 3. Care must be used to figure the correct satin counters.

When weaves are painted on paper, the first warp end is made to interlace with the first filling pick in the lower left-hand corner of the weave. The designer then resorts to the use of the counter. This is added to the interlacing on the first pick, and the number of the end that will interlace with the second pick is found. This method continues until the construction is completed. One pick at a time must be taken to determine the number of the warp end that is to interlace with each respective pick.

When completed, the weave will show that each and every warp end in the weave interlaces at some point with some individual filling pick. There can never be two interlacings at any point on any warp end or filling pick within the confines of the repeat of the ordinary satin weave.

When any of the numbers used in counting go beyond the first or original repeat, they are placed on corresponding numbers on the interlacings within the original weave repeat.

SATINER. French: to give a satin-like or silklike finish to fabrics.

SATINET OR SATINETTE. 1. A thin, imitation satin-weave cloth simulating silesia. The weave is a three-leaf filling twill.

2. A firm fabric made of cotton warp and woolen or cotton filling; used as lining material.

3. A fabric made of cotton warp

FILLING EFFECT   WARP EFFECT

6-END SATEEN USED FOR STRIPING PURPOSES ONLY. THESE WEAVES ARE ALSO KNOWN AS "6-END IRREGULAR SATIN WEAVES".

 4-END CROWFOOT, FILLING EFFECT. NOT A TRUE SATIN WEAVE.

 FILLING-EFFECT SATEEN WEAVE, BASE OF 3.

 FILLING-EFFECT SATEEN WEAVE BASE OF 2.

 WARP-EFFECT OF ABOVE WEAVE.

 WARP-EFFECT OF ABOVE WEAVE

 WARP-EFFECT OF ABOVE WEAVE.

SOMETIMES KNOWN AS SATINET WEAVES.

 8-END VENETIAN WEAVE MADE WITH COUNTER OF 5.

THE TRUE SATIN WEAVES USED TODAY ARE THE 5-END AND THE 8-END EFFECTS.

THE ORDER OF WEAVING SATIN WEAVES IS JUST AS IMPORTANT AS THE LINE OF A TWILL EFFECT IN A TWILL WEAVE.

 8-END VENETIAN WEAVE MADE WITH COUNTER OF 3.

and wool-shoddy filling. The cloth has a satin-like finish after it has been fulled, flocked, sheared, and pressed. The material is often printed in stripes, checks, or plaids to resemble cassimere.

4. British term for a very cheap, 5-end warp-effect, cotton sateen.

5. When the term is used with regard to a weave construction, it usually implies the four-end irregular satin weave (the same as the crowfoot weave) which is popular as a ground weave in brocade and similar cloths. The weave is a 1-up and 3-down twill, two ends to the right, followed by two ends to the left. The five-end weave is sometimes called satinet weave. The four-end ir-

regular satin is really a small broken twill construction in either the warp-effect or the filling-effect.

SATINISCO. A low-quality satin used for lining.

SATINIZING. A broad, general term which implies that certain cotton fabrics have a silk-like luster on the face of the goods. There are several ways and processes used to obtain the luster. For example, salts of chloride of potassium, sodium acetate, sodium sulphate, etc., are frequently used, and the glossy effect is usually permanent in nature and will last for the life of the goods.

SATINLIKE, SATINY. A fabric made to simulate true silk, satin cloth. The effect may be obtained by friction calendering, ciré finish, waxing, etc.

SATIVA. Trade name for bleached, fully shrunk flax fibers that come in picker lap form for blending purposes with other major fibers in the manufacture of yarns and fabrics.

SATURATED. A solution which holds its capacity of a given substance. A slight oversaturation (super saturation) will result in some of the material settling or crystallizing out of solution.

SATURATION. See COLOR, THE THREE PROPERTIES OF.

SATURATION, DEGREE OR PER CENT OF. The ratio of the weight of a given volume of water to the weight of an equal volume of saturated water vapor at the same temperature.

"SAVALUX." A registered trademark for DuPont dyes which meet specific standards of fastness. Only fabrics that have been tested by DuPont and found to meet these fastness standards may carry the "Savalux" name. The trademark "Savalux" does not represent any single chemical class of dyes. "Savalux" dyes can be vat dyes used in dyeing and printing cellulosic materials; they can also be basic colors used to color acrylic fibers.

Fastness standards for "Savalux" may vary from end-use to end-use. In drapery, slipcover, and upholstery applications, for example, "Savalux" standards have been set for lightfastness, fastness to washing, drycleaning, and crocking. Any standards set for apparel, for example, would call for lesser lightfastness requirements.

In essence, "Savalux" is a signal to the consumer that the colors in a given fabric will give the consumer the best commercially obtainable level of color durability. It is an assurance, therefore, backed by DuPont standards and tests, of color satisfaction for the useful life of the product bought by the consumer.

SAVED LIST FABRIC. English way of expressing a dyed fabric with a white selvage; resist yarns may be used in the selvage to keep them white during the piece-dyeing.

SAVONNERIE RUG. This rug is made at La Savonnerie in Paris, established during the reign of Henry IV (Henry of Navarre, 1553–1610) during his tenure from 1589 to 1610, the first Bourbon King of France. A great patron of the arts, Henry sponsored the manufacture of these famous rugs to simulate the rich, lush Oriental knotted rugs in rococo motifs. Present-day rugs of this type are now made under the aegis of the Gobelin Tapestry Works with which La Savonnerie was merged some time after the death of Henry.

SAW-GINNED COTTON. Cotton ginned by the saw-toothed method. See WHITNEY, ELI.

SAW GIN, SAW ENGINE. One of the greatest of all-time inventions is the saw gin invented by Eli Whitney, 1793. Its principles are still used today. It consists of a set of rapidly moving circular saws, the teeth of which protrude through slots in a grill on which the cotton is laid. The teeth of the saws catch the cotton, pull it away from the seeds, and draw the fiber back through a space too small to admit the seeds. The word "gin" is apparently a corruption of the word engine.

SAXON BLUE. The dye made by indigo dissolved in oil of vitriol.

SAXONY. Cloth made of very high-grade wool raised in Saxony, Germany. Coating of the Saxony type retails from one hundred dollars upwards in the finished garment. The name is also applied to soft-finished woolen fabrics of similarly fine stock, in fancy yarn effects on the order of tweeds.

SAXONY CARPET. A low-quality Wilton carpet which has a soft-pile effect but is not as resilient as a worsted Wilton. The designs do not have the cleavage and detail of the latter.

SAXONY CORD. A cotton warp and fine wool or worsted filling is used in this well-constructed material. Used for academic robes, cassocks, and in affairs of state; a popular fabric in diplomatic circles.

SAXONY LACE. A burnt-out lace first made in Plauen, Saxony, Germany, and now made on Schiffli Machines. See PLAUEN LACE, SCHIFFLI EMBROIDERY.

SAXONY MERINO. From the old Spanish Merino breeds of sheep that were given to the Elector of Saxony in the eighteenth century. Since the time of the importation of these sheep into Germany, the breed has been steadily improved until today it ranks with the Class 1 Merino breeds of sheep. This breed compares with Ohio, Silesia, Rambouillet, Australian, and Argentine Merino wools.

The term now seems to imply fine wool, whether of Saxony or not, raised in Germany, Austria, and other Continental wool-growing areas. The wool is very fine in diameter, short in staple, and ideal for French combing methods, soft and has excellent felting properties. Also known as Electoral Wool in some circles.

SAXONY VELVET CARPET. The term is used in Great Britain for a soft, good-wearing velvet carpet which has a long, dense pile surface; the backing is of compact, firm structure.

SAXONY WHEEL. See SPINNING WHEEL.

SAXONY WOOL. Merino wool which is native to Saxony, Germany, but is now raised in other wool-raising areas. Characteristics of the wool include fineness, strength, elasticity, excellent felting properties, high number of serrations per inch. A Class 1 wool, it is used in the best of woolen and worsted materials, particularly those which can withstand considerable fulling and milling.

SAXONY YARN. High-grade woolen knitting yarn given twist.

SAY. It was a fine, thin serge popular in the sixteenth century. Originally made of silk and imported from China, the fabric was made of silk and wool in Europe, and then became an all-wool fabric. Present-day worsted serge is a development of this cloth.

SAY CAST. Coarse wool obtained from the tail area in fleece wool.

SAYELLE. Formerly known as "Orlon" 21, it is a trade-mark of E. I. du Pont de Nemours & Co., Inc., for its high-bulk acrylic staple with reversible crimp for spinning on the worsted system; used in knitwear.

SAYETTE. The term originated in the city of Amiens, France, and refers to plain- and twill-weave dress goods made with silk and wool in varying combinations. This long-standing staple has been also modified for materials suitable for lining, furniture covering, some curtaining, etc. At present, it is a very broad term and has particular provincial meanings.

SAYLA. A cotton scarf fabric used in India and used by Mohammedans as a shoulder-throw.

SCAB. One who replaces or does the work of a striker in a company in which employees are on strike.

SCALLOP. To cut, mark, or trim an edge into segments of a circle or a series of curves in order to form an ornamental border or design. A style effect used sometimes on the lower edge of skirts and dresses.

SCALLOPS, SCOLLOPS. Circular segments, angular projections, and the like which are used to form a border on lace or embroidery work, so-called because they resemble the edge of a scallop shell.

SCAPULARY. A monastic woolen

garment with hood or cowl attached; originated with the Benedictine Order of monks, founded in 529. The hood or cowl is popular from time to time in the varying trends of fashion and style, chiefly in evening wear.

SCARF. For centuries it meant a wide band or sash, especially when worn around the head. In time, the word sash came to replace band or scarf for the cloth worn as a girdle or around the waist; it also means a wide band worn over the shoulder, especially as part of a uniform. Scarf implies a necktie, cravat, neckpiece, or tippet.

SCARF, FUR. A neckpiece comparatively narrow, worn for adornment or warmth, or both. It is made in any form or shape decreed by fashion or style. The scarf is mostly made in the form of an animal; or several animals combined with the head, tail, and paws attached are used for the finished article.

SCARLET. A brilliant red inclining to orange, high in saturation and medium in brilliance. Also implies cloth of this color used by huntsmen, soldiers, etc.

SCAVENGER ROLL. As the name implies it is a clearer roll situated underneath the front bottom roll on the ring spinning frame to collect waste from roving when an end breaks.

SCHAPPE SILK. A much discussed term, considered the same as spun silk in this country. Technically, however, there is a difference because of the manner of removal of the gum from the waste silk which is often done by a rotting process of fermentation in manure.

Formerly, all European systems differed from the English and the United States methods. At present, all European silk of this type is classed as schappe silk. Since the Europeans and the British have adopted our method of caring for this stock, the product is known by the name of schappe silk. In some of the more remote areas of Europe, manufacturers still cling to the old methods of classification.

The word schappe comes from the French verb hacher, which means to chop.

SCHAUBE. Simulating the court clothes of the 16th century and more or less on the order of the contemporary cassock, this overcoating was often devoid of sleeves. When made with attached sleeves, however, they were placed behind the visible ones of the garment worn underneath. The vestigal sleeve is still observed in the academic gown of today.

Martin Luther, the founder of Lutheranism, wore the schaube and this item is still used by Lutheran clergy of the present day. Thomas Cranmer, the famed English clergyman in the reign of Henry VIII, wore this garment with a long neck-chain which in due time was carried over to the raiment for the mayors of English towns and cities. See Cassock, Cassocks.

SCHENTI. Worn by Assyrians, Babylonians, Egyptians, etc., this garment was used prior to 1,500 B.C. in what is known in history as the Old Kingdom Era. It was a woven fabric which served as a loin cloth, held in place by a belt or cord around the waist.

SCHIFFLI EMBROIDERY. This is a type of embroidery originating in Switzerland and distinct from Bonnaz embroidery. Schiffii is made on a loomlike machine, using a shuttle, top and bottom. The needles, numbering 56 dozen, are set one inch apart. The machines weigh seven tons, are twenty yards in length, and cost several thousand dollars. Schiffli is comparable with hand embroidery and works on the same principle as the Singer handembroidery machine. The stitch of the machine is not a chain stitch, but one from side to side. Schiffli is used in curtains, handkerchiefs, lace, letters, lace cuffs, collars, etc.

SCHIZETA. Italian term for a poor grade of spun silk taken from faulty or diseased cocoons.

SCHLAGBLECH. See CHOPPER BAR.

SCHLAPPE. The exquisitely made caps or bonnets made by the women in Switzerland. The centuries-old lace areas such as Appenzell, Saint Gallen, Arbon, et al., have great use for this item and it is most interesting to note how they vary from city to city, and canton to canton. The motif, fabric, and delicate work done to make the schlappe are very interesting for the viewer.

SCHLUMBERGER. The name of a French rectilinear comber frame which combs the better grades of wool for processing into worsted yarn. The wools so manipulated are called Schlumberger. Incidentally, the great French combing frame is the Heilman, an upright machine capable of combing fibers as short as 1½ inches. See HEILMAN COMB.

SCHOLLERIZED. Trade-mark of Scholler Brothers Inc., which refers to woolens that have been chemically treated to control shrinkage and to help retain the desirable qualities of natural wool. Effective for the life of the fabric, the process gives control of matting, felting, and of shrinkage to approximately 1 per cent.

SCHREINER FINISH. The natural luster of many cloths, such as cottonback sateen, sateen, muslin, linene, linon, and lining is enhanced by a method of milling or pounding called schreinerizing. The material is subjected to the physical action of a roller, usually made of steel, with a great many fine lines per inch engraved in it. The roller flattens the threads in the cloth, and imprints onto the surface a series of ridges, so fine that it is necessary to use a microscope to see the fineness of the work.

These very fine lines reflect the rays of light and bring out the appearance by which the cloth is characteristically known. Some of the finishes allied with schreinerizing are frost schreinerization, imitation schreinerization, imitation mercerization, bloom finish.

SCHURLITZ. Popular in the fourteenth century to the sixteenth century in Switzerland and southern Germany, this fabric featured motifs of birds. The word, Schurlitz, comes from a word that implies the outer garments worn by the religious, usually a fine woolen or worsted fabric or hightextured, firm cotton cloth. When the patterns of birds were added to the material, the word "vogel" was used as a prefix to "schurlitz."

SCHWEITZER'S REAGENT. 1. A solution of copper oxide in ammonia which dissolves cotton and silk, but not wool. Cellulose is re-precipitated by sugar and acids but the silk by acids alone. 2. The reagent is used as a popular cuprammonium solution to dissolve cotton linters, an important base used in the manufacture of cuprammonium rayon yarn.

SCIENCES USED IN TRADE SCIENCE, BASIC. All items of trade science are based on some principle of one of the basic sciences—physics, chemistry, or biology. The science of physics will be better understood when thought of in terms of its various phases, as heat, light, sound, mechanics, and gases. Biology can be considered more effectively under the headings of botany and zoology.

In all phases of an analysis one should find it advantageous to examine only one division or part at a time, in order to follow the scientific information in proper sequence. In scientific problems the chemistry, the physics, or the biology of the problem has to be carefully considered.

CHEMISTRY: Chemistry is a study of the composition of substances and the changes that may take place in them. Chemistry has made it possible for us to know that ordinary table salt (NaCl) is composed of equal parts of the elements sodium and chlorine, that water is made by combining one part oxygen with two parts of hydrogen, (H_2O); that sulphuric acid (H_2SO_4) is composed of two parts of hydrogen, one part of sulphur, and four parts of oxygen; and that, for example, the deadly fumes from a gas engine, carbon monoxide (CO), is made up of one part of oxygen and one part of carbon; while carbon dioxide (CO_2) so essential for plant life, is made up of one part of carbon and two parts of oxygen.

CHEMICAL CHANGE: When a substance undergoes a change in its composition it is said that a "chemical change" has taken place, for example, when iron is exposed to air for a period of time we say it rusts; in reality, the oxygen in the air has united with some of the iron to form a new substance, iron oxide. When oxygen unites with a substance rapidly enough to release sufficient energy to produce considerable heat, we say that "combustion" takes place, or that the material is "burning." The development of power by burning gasoline in an automobile engine, or even the heat that we obtain from a gas stove, is explained by this chemical process of oxidation.

EXAMPLES OF CHEMICAL CHANGES FOUND IN TRADES: Other examples of chemical changes are found in baking of food; the generation of electricity by electrolysis; the softening of water; the dissolving of substances to form solutions such as zinc chloride for a soldering flux; preparation of dyes from coal-tar derivatives; and the manufacturing of countless man-made products such as rayon, acetate, celluloid, cellophane, mercerized fabric, nylon, vinyon, Fiberglas, "Dacron," and rubber, etc.

Many trade tests are chemical tests; for example, textile fibers are found to be either animal or vegetable as to origin by simple chemical tests of solubility in an alkaline or acid solution; cloth is burned to determine its contents; metals are etched to reveal their true appearance; and the presence of obnoxious gases in the air are determined by the reaction of a controlled flame.

PHYSICAL CHANGE: All changes in a substance, however, are not of a chemical nature, some are merely physical; that is, the composition has not changed although the apparent form becomes different in appearance. The melting of glass, the evaporation of water, the dissolving of salt, and the dilution of oil with gasoline are physical rather than chemical changes. The physical state has changed rather than the chemical composition even though the visual identity may be lost. In gen-

eral, physical changes may be recognized by the possibility of restoring the material to its previous form; for instance, water may be frozen, but easily returned to its original state by melting the ice formed by freezing; this is a physical change. Wood once consumed by fire is forever beyond recovery in its original form; this is a chemical change.

CHECK TRADE PROCESSES FOR APPLICATIONS OF CHEMISTRY: Examine the processes and the materials of your trade, vocation, calling, or profession as a means of calling to mind instances where a knowledge of the underlying principles of science are needed by, or would be helpful to, the worker in doing his job. Think of these items in the form of units and try to recall to mind the findings.

PHYSICS: Physics includes several phases of scientific investigation and knowledge; namely, heat, light, sound, electricity, mechanics, and mechanical devices, hydraulics, and gases. For purposes of analyzing your work it is well to examine it with reference to each of the fields of science. Following this examination, it is well to transfer the prior learning to the subject at hand in the fields of Textiles, Textile Testing, Dyeing, Chemistry, etc.

BIOLOGY: Biology is the source of living things including both plant and animal life. Those vocations which utilize plant and animal materials and whose services deal with living things must turn to biology for part of its underlying information of a scientific nature. Companies which use silk, wool, cotton, flax, ramie, jute, hemp, worsted, mohair, alpaca, asbestos, glass fibers, etc., use materials whose sources are animal, vegetable, or mineral matter.

For the purposes of classification, biology is grouped under two headings:

BOTANY: the study of plant life.

ZOOLOGY: the study of animal life.

To assist one further in analyzing his or her trade or profession for items of trade science, several suggestions are given under the headings of Botany and Zoology:

BOTANY:

1. The story of cotton.
2. Flax and its structure.
3. The story of linen and what it is made from.
4. How plants used for textiles grow.
5. Plant structure.
6. Testing of plant fibers.
7. Vegetable oils and their uses in textiles.
8. How rubber is obtained and what it is.
9. The raw materials used in rayon

and acetate.

10. A study of the bast fibers.

ZOOLOGY:

1. Wool, its nature and its source.
2. The nature of vicuna.
3. A study of the hair-fiber animals used in textiles.
4. Differences between woolen and worsted fibers.
5. Human hair, its characteristics and nature.
6. The story of leather.
7. The story of silk.
8. How silk differs from wool in chemical, physical, and biological testing.
9. Bacteriology, explanation of diseases peculiar to wool and hair bearing animals.

SCISSORS. A cutting implement consisting of a pair of blades with handles. These blades are pivoted face to face so that the sharpened edges may be brought closely together in order to cut.

Buttonhole scissors are from four to eight inches long and have blades which are three to about six inches long. The blades are regulated by a screw. The edges stop short of the pivot so that a slit can be made without cutting the edge of the material. Only two fingers are used to manipulate scissors. Chief use is for cutting threads.

SCOTCH BLACKFACE. A well-known breed of sheep which produces much long carpet wool. The fibers are very strong, rugged, and ideal for use as "filling fiber" in the manufacture of rugs and carpets. The sheep are "wild," hardy, and withstand the rigors of weather very well.

Blackface is raised on the moors of Lancashire and Yorkshire, England, in Scotland and on the Hebrides, Orkney, and Shetland Islands. It is now raised to advantage in Oregon.

SCOTCH CAMBRIC. High-quality cotton cambric, an excellent simulation of linen cambric.

SCOTCH CAP. A brimless woolen cap worn by Scotsmen; comes in plain colors or tartan effects.

SCOTCH CARPET. Pile carpeting on the order of Kidderminster with designs on both sides but in different colors.

SCOTCH CHECKS. General term for check and tartan designs in fabrics made of plain-weave or twill-weave construction, regardless of fiber content.

SCOTCH ELL. A length of 37 inches used to measure fabrics.

SCOTCH FEED. A popular attachment used to take carded wool sliver from the first breaker card and present it to the intermediate card or cards. The sliver web is formed into a band or ribbon which is carried on a lattice apron to the next card, where there is a reciprocating motion whose duty it is to lay the stock in overlapping folds to make the lap.

SCOTCH FINGERING. Spun from native Scotch wools, this knitting yarn is of the fluffy type and low in twist; ideal for knitted garments in cold weather.

SCOTCH FINISH. Name applied to overcoatings of the tweed, homespun, and Cheviot group that possess a loosely shorn nap.

SCOTCHGARD. Registered trademark product of Minnesota Mining and Manufacturing Company, it is a fluorochemical oil- and water-repellent finish applied by a padding technique during finishing. The fabric is completely penetrated, and a protective film is formed around each fiber. Fluids form globules on the surface, do not spread, and can be removed easily by dabbing with a tissue. Oil may be cleaned off without leaving a grease ring. It is odorless, colorless, and harmless, the hand is not impared, and Scotchgard is fast to dry cleaning.

SCOTCHGARD FABRIC PROTECTOR WITH E.S.D. Registered trademark of Minnesota Mining and Manufacturing Company, Inc., for its fluorochemical finish which is claimed to last up to five times as long as prior finishes developed by the company. The "E.S.D." stands for "extra soil defense." The finish provides outstanding dry soil resistance and durability to cleaning as well as stain resistance. The product is licensed to users of the product.

SCOTCH GINGHAM. Fine, tissuelike gingham of high pick-count made with rather large checks or plaids. The term is the trade name for the finest ginghams and tissues produced in the British Isles.

SCOTCH HOOK REED. A type of reed much used today in acetate and rayon warping and slashing, to obtain an end-and-end lease in the warp threads.

SCOTCH REED COUNTS. Counts based on the Scotch ell of 37 inches and used in figuring cottons and fine linens in the loom. A reed with 1600 dents in 37 inches is called a 1600-reed. The method of figuring includes half-hundreds; if 1650 splits are used the reed is called a 1650-reed. Other methods used throughout the British Isles are based on widths of 36 inches, 38 inches, and 40 inches, the latter being the most popular.

SCOTCH TWEED. Made on a 2-up and 2-down twill with white warp and stock-dyed filling or vice-versa. The stock colors are usually rather vivid in order to give contrast in the fabric. Fiber staple in the yarn is usually variable and is irregular in appearance; often this shagginess seems to add to the looks of the material. Always popular, the cloth is used in suiting, topcoating, sport coating, some overcoating.

SCOTS. Soft British dress goods made of hard-twist worsted yarn; made in serge weave.

SCOTTISH COSTUME. See Costume, Scottish.

SCOTTISH CROSS. See GREYFACE.

SCOTTISH DISTRICT CHECKS. Very little is known about the true beginning of District Checks; the simple fact is that the simple, primitive orderliness of this type of pattern has held the public fancy for many generations. They are a fait accompli, and there is little to be gained or gleaned from trying to ferret out their origin. The term, GLEN, is the Gaelic word for valley; thus, the Glenfeshie Check is worn by the folks who work and live in the Feshie Valley of Scotland. STRATH means a forest; Strathspey, therefore, would be translated to mean the Forest of Sprey. BEN, in Gaelic, means a mountain. Following is a list of the checks with accompanying data for recognition by the textile designer as to layout of fabrics. See CHECKS, HOMESPUNS AND TWEED, STANDARD SCOTCH.

ARDTORNISH: This West Coast Check is a 4-and-4 of white and brown with an olive brown warp and a russet brown filling.

ARNDILLY: Has a dull (laid) white ground; the alternate colors are black and greenish fawn in the warp, black and reddish fawn in the filling. The overcheck is formed by replacing every third fawn check with a bar half dull peacock blue and half reseda green.

BALLINDOLLOCH: The same as The Ing, with red and brown running one way and a dull biscuit shade replacing white in the cross threads. It has an overcheck of dull olive green.

BALMORAL: The warp arrangement is 1 of white, 2 of navy and white twist, 1 of navy and scarlet, 2 of navy and white. The filling is white, which goes mainly to the back. The weave unit is 8, so that the pattern repeats after 24 threads.

BROOKE: Uses black-and-white twist and a light Lovat mixture as the alternate colors, and a skeleton overcheck of scarlet edging one of the Lovat checks. The ground is made with both silver grey and white.

BUCCLEUGH: Same as the Glenfeshie, but with a sky blue for the red overcheck. The pattern is 5 x 6½ inches on the repeat. The ground is a Shepherd Check, ¼ inch white, ¼ inch black, and the cloth is a fine Saxony kilting.

CARNEGIE: A simple black-and-white Glenurquhart, three inches on the repeat. Overchecked through the center of the 2-and-2 part by a half-inch strip of camel color.

CARNOUSIE: Darkest of all District Checks, the ground is developed in black and black-twisted-with-russet. About the size of the Small Glenurquhart, but without the basket effect of the 2-and-2 portion. Every alternate part of the 4-and-4 is sided with a bold crimson overcheck.

COIGACH: The Checks alternate between black and strong red-brown; adopted in 1874 as the check for an American gun club.

DALHOUSIE: A solid white warp crossed with a medium grey. The plain diagonal twill is broken every inch by reversing the twill for six threads. Every fourth reverse is dull green, overchecked with a bar of bright navy blue.

DUPPLIN: The Coigach with a scarlet overcheck.

ERCHLESS: Has a warp unit of 3 on the 4-thread warp (white, pale stone drab and yellow) crossed by a filling of black twisted with white.

FANNICH: The warp pattern is on 18 threads: white 6, Lovat Mixture 3, black 2, yellow 2, black 2, Lovat 3. The filling is a simple Gunclub Check repeating on 24—white ground, with black and Lovat as the alternate colors.

GAIRLOCH: Another variation of the Coigach, with a dull yellow mixture replacing the white in the weft.

GLENDOE: Uses a dull blue-grey and white background with a very strong russet overcheck.

GLENFESHIE: Basically the Shepherd Check with a brilliant scarlet overcheck.

GLENISLA: A small but true Glenurquhart in off-white and dark brown, one size smaller than The Mar and without overcheck; the design is 2⅛ inches overall.

GLEN MORRISTON: The Coigach arrangement with dark blue and a light, slightly greenish Lovat mixture as the alternate colors.

GLENQUOICH: A very small design; the wrap ⅝ inch of white and ⅛ inch of black crossed in the filling with a dull warm drab for white and the black used in both directions.

GORDON HIGHLANDERS TWEED: Greenish Lovat mixture, softly checked with yellow, dark blue and green.

GUISACHAN: Has a warp 4 of black and 4 of brown, crossed with 4 of brown and yellow twist and 4 of white; the weave is a 4 x 4 diamond cut in the warp but not in the filling.

HORSE GUARDS: A variation of the 2-and-2 warp and filling effect. It uses a brown and white ground overchecked every 3½ inches with six threads of bright navy.

INVERCAULD: A white ground with brown and drab twist, overchecked every 3½ inches with six threads of bright navy blue.

KING'S OWN SCOTTISH BORDERERS: A blue Lovat ground with a soft white check alternating with a soft green check, and then a thin scarlet line on each side of the green.

KINLOCHEWE: Russet (like the Seaforth) overchecked by a thin check of 1-black and 1-crimson in the white, crossed with a thin line of orange.

KINLOCHEWE GLENURQUHART: 4½ inches over-all, with the black and yellow twisted warp crossed with a drab-and-white camel's wool type.

KINTAIL: The same basic treatment, but with alternate ground colors of pale gray and a greenish drab.

LOCHMORE: Is like the Coigach, but replaces the black with a greenish Lovat mixture.

MINMORE: Used on the Strathspey Estate, it is very similar in design to the Glenquoich but has a deep green check.

MINTO: A deep, rich greenish mixture, almost as dark as a holly tree.

PITGAVENY: A green mixture ground with thin alternate checks of red and white.

POLTALLOCH: Very like the Invercauld, but the overcheck is yellow crossed with red.

PRINCE OF WALES: A bold pattern of the Glenurquhart type. Nine inches on the repeat, but because it is a double arrangement it does not appear so large. The colors are the terra cotta of The Ing, and white; the general effect is a brownish pink. The 4-and-4 starts and ends with white; the dark slate overcheck is taken off the first and last brown expanded to 6 threads. The 2-and-2 starts and ends with dark, so that a basket effect is produced.

ROYAL SCOTS REGIMENTAL LOVAT: An attractive green Lovat overchecked at 1½ inches, with alternating neat lines of red and yellow.

RUSSELL: Both Russell Checks are peculiar in their color effects. They follow the style of the Glenfeshie, but, being crossed with two shades of drab, the dull brown overcheck appears wine-colored in the filling and russet in the warp. The Glenurquhart form of the Russell has the bold overcheck on each side of the 4-and-4 part; the entire pattern is a full 6½ inches wide.

SCOTS GUARD: A bold basket effect attained through reversing the pattern, and produced by two threads of light and two of dark warp and filling on the common twill weave; an overcheck of four threads reverses the position of the light and dark colors relative to the weave.

SEAFORTH: Two tones of russet on a white ground, overchecked with a brighter russet.

SMALL GLENURQUHART: A small edition of the original Glenurquhart, about two-thirds in size, with the alternate squares or blocks of the hair lines reversed. This should not be confused with the Small Glen which is native to a small valley in the southern area of Scotland.

STRATHMASHIE: A large and bold Glenurquhart type, nearly eight inches to the repeat of pattern. It uses the colors of the Coigach; brown and white warp with black and white filling. The strong overchecking up the sides of the 4-and-4 portion are obtained by reversing the warp and filling colors.

STRATHSPEY: The same as the Dupplin, with a dark blue overcheck.

THANE OF FIFE: Similar to The Mar, but overchecked with sizes of dark slate instead of green.

THE DACRE: The same as the Coigach, multiplied by two. The checks are ⅜-inch apart.

THE HAY: The same as the Strathspey with lighter, yellower brown.

THE ING: Another Shepherd Check with a particular dull red-brown substituted for the black.

THE MAR: A design created by King Edward VIII when he was the Prince of Wales. Brown and white with a green overcheck.

WELSH GUARDS: Another variation check which has a fawn-colored ground with brown and red twist yarn, and an alternate 2-inch overcheck of light red and dark blue.

WYVIS: Extremely bold, about 2½ inches on the repeat. The ground is a deep fawn, like withered bracken or dead beech leaves; the alternate colors are a browny green moss and a sprinkled bar which is formed with twisted yarns of bright green, moss, and gray.

See Checks, Homespuns and Tweeds, Standard Scotch.

SCRAY. A box, vessel, or container, shaped like the letter "J," in which piece goods may be accumulated in folds or pleats. Often used in dry-finishing operations and in fabric inspection to compensate the flow of fabric to varying machine speeds.

SCOUR. 1. To clean the surface of or make bright by washing and rubbing. 2. A cleanser used in wool scouring. 3. The use of detergents and other cleansers to remove dirt, grime, etc.

SCOURING. 1. The freeing of wool from yolk, suint, dirt, and all other for-eign matter. It may be done by washing with soaps and alkalies, by treating with solvents or chemicals, or by naphthalating the stock at below-freezing temperatures. Loss in weight in scouring the fleece ranges from about 35 per cent in low-grade wools to about 65 per cent in the best types. Yolk serves as the basis for cosmetics, salves, etc., while the dried perspiration or suint is used in making potash. 2. To remove the sizing and tint used on the warp yarn in weaving, and in general, cleaning a fabric or yarn prior to dyeing.

SCRATCH MOIRÉ. This method of moiréing or watermarking was invented about 1900 in France, being particularly popular on silk failles. In due course of time the method was applied to rayons, chiefly on 24-inch tie goods. About 1927, the process was further improved by inventors in this country for use on acetate goods. At present there are four patents held in this country.

The method permits the production of figured patterns such as flowers, Mexican hats, starts, teardrops, tropical palms, etc.

The goods to be treated are run up on a beam, doubled. They are then run through the scratching machine, a device that closely resembles a roller printing frame, having an engraved roller made of rubber. Bearing against this engraved roller, and revolving at a greater speed, is a series of scratch blades set into a scratch roller comparable with those of a lawn mower.

The doubled cloth is run between the scratch blades and the engraved rubber roller, and the filling of the fabric is shifted in those places where the blades find resistance in the raised places of the engraved rubber roller.

Although only a limited number of fabrics are suitable for this method, chiefly 200- and 300-denier taffetas and selected tie-silk failles, the method is extremely popular on rayon taffetas.

SCRAY. Any of several types of frames used to place cloth cuts in folds or pleats; valuable in cloth inspection.

SCREEN, CAGE. The hollow cylindrical device used in cotton opening machines when it is necessary to form the stock into sheet or layer form. This rugged, coarse mesh-wire mechanism sets in a horizontal position on a shaft to allow easy revolving action.

SCREEN PRINTING. Generally used for short runs and special effects. It is a comparatively slow process. The fabric is pinned to a padded table generally fifty to eighty feet in length. Moving along a track is a boxlike screen, on which screen a design is painted with some insoluble film. Color paste is flowed into the screen and squeegeed through the screen, which is not protected by the film, onto the fabric. This will effect a stenciled print. The screen is moved ahead to a new repeat. A new screen is used for each successive color. The after-treatment is similar to roller printwork.

SCREEN SECTION, CAGE SECTION. Consisting of one or two screens, stripping rollers, and a fan, all encased, the purpose of the section is to gather the loose, unwieldy bunches of cotton from the beater into sheet form.

The fan air current draws the loose stock to the surface of the screen. Stripping into sheet or lap form follows.

SCREEN STENCIL. A sheet of silk bolting cloth upon which a design or motif has been formed with fine perforations. Nylon is also used.

SCREW PINE, TEXTILE. A bast fiber found in the islands from Hawaii to New Zealand.

SCRIM. 1. An open mesh, plain-weave cotton cloth made from carded or combed yarns in several constructions and weights for use as bunting, buckram, curtains, etc. 2. Cheesecloth, when bleached and firmly sized, is known as Scrim. 3. A lightweight cotton sheer cloth made in doup or in plain weave with single-ply yarns. It is often made with colored checks or stripes and serves as curtaining.

SCRIMP. 1. A tension or pressure wrinkle noted on fabric, washer wrinkle. 2. A wrinkle caused by excessive strain on goods.

SCRIMPER BAR. The wormlike roller or bar which spreads the fabric to be printed to the right and to the left from the center of the cloth and the roller so that no wrinkles may appear in the cloth as it is printed.

SCROLL ROPES ON THE MULE FRAME. A scroll is a grooved plate which has a spiral groove from the core or center, that extends to the outer edge. The rugged friction rope is caused to wind and unwind by the action of the scroll when the frame is in operation. The friction afforded by the rope aids in even running of the machine, prevents jerkiness of action, and helps to produce uniform yarn. The quadrant scroll helps to raise and lower the quadrant and its parts. There are several scrolls on the mule.

The ropes, which work on the principle of a hoist, take up on tension and prevent slippages and breakages to considerable degree.

SCROOP. The peculiar crunching or rustling sound noted in some silk fabrics. It is secured by treating the fabric

with certain acids. Used in iridescents, petticoating, taffetas.

SCRUB. To rub vigorously in order to bring back life and appearance to goods; usually a hand operation.

SCRUBBED WOOL. Another name for brushed wool since after scrubbing and drying, the material takes on a brush or nap effect.

SCRUBBING TOWER. A tower or hood in which gases and vapors of acetone are washed and absorbed in the solvent recovery process.

SCUDDING. See BEAMING.

SCULPTURED PILE EFFECT. A cut or uncut pile or a combination of the two obtained by a special manipulation of which a carved or sculptured effect is produced in floor-covering fabrics.

SCUTCHER. Same as the opener picker machine in this country.

SCUTCHING. Opening-up of cloth to its full width. This takes place before the finishing of the material. Very often water is extracted at the same time.

SCUTCHING TOW. Short waste by-product from the scutching and re-scutching in flax manipulation. It is used in making rope.

SCYE. The armhole of a garment.

SCYE DEPTH: An imaginary line drawn entirely around the body at the lower level of the arm scye, as from the nape to opposite armpit on the back seam.

SCYE MEASURE. The distance from the collar bone to a line on the back that would correspond to the armpit.

SEA ISLAND COTTON. The finest cotton in the world, grown upon the archipelagoes along the Southern States in the United States. It is generally fine in staple and has a high degree of spirality or "hook." Some staple is 2½ inches long. Compared with other cottons, the yield is almost nil.

SEA ISLAND-PERUVIAN COTTON. It is ranked below Rough and Smooth Peruvian cottons; much used in wool mixes since its properties are ideal for this purpose.

SEAL. One of the better furs, with Alaskan seal the best; the hair is soft, velvety, and rather short.

SEALED SAMPLES. Taken from American export bales, these small batches of fibers are sent to cotton centers throughout the world.

SEALETTE. British term for pile fabric made to imitate sealskin.

SEALSKIN CLOTHS. A large number of pile fabrics which simulate the fur of seal and other fur-bearing ani-

mals. These materials are usually exceptionally well executed; the construction is a cotton ground, while mohair or similar fiber is used for the pile effect. Most of the fabric gives good service.

SEAM. 1. (Noun) Any place where two parts of a garment are sewed or joined together. Common seams are braided, cemented, cord, double stitched, lap, open-welt, plain, piped, raw, serged, strap, strapped, swelled, welt. 2. A visible line of junction, especially between two pieces of fabric sewn together. 3. (Verb) To unite by means of a seam. 4. In knitting, to give the appearance of a seam, to form seams, to purl. 5. To join the two edges in full-fashioned hosiery. A "seamer" is one who operates a machine to do seaming.

SEAM BASTING. Temporary stitches used to hold two sectional parts of a garment together.

SEAM BINDING. A narrow strip of lining, either cotton, rayon, or silk, used to finish a seam or raw edge to prevent fraying. The binding gives the seam a clean finish and is usually about one-half inch wide.

SEAMER. See SEAM.

SEAM FINISH TYPES. 1. *Bound Seam:* Ideal for use on fabrics that ravel easily. Enclose both edges of a plain seam with straight or bias tape. Baste and stitch through all thicknesses. Edges may be done together or separately. 2. *Closed Seam:* These seams occur where two parts of a dress come together such as at the joining of the waistline and skirt or underarm and sleeve. For stitch seams that are to be joined; press open, cutting ends of the seam with allowance diagonally to reduce thickness. Stitch the seam that crosses the matching seam accurately. Then press open or together and finish the edges. 3. *Overcast Seam:* Trim the raw edges and finish together or separately with slanted stitching. Stitches should be firm, short, and about 1/4-inch apart. 4. *Pinked Seam:* Used on fabrics that do not ravel easily; trim the edges evenly on both sides with pinking shears. 5. *Rolled Seam:* Ideal for sheer fabrics; make a plain seam, then roll the seam between thumb and foreginger and whip close to the stitching. 6. *Stitched Seam:* Used on fabric that frays easily or for long straight seams. Turn the fabric under and then stitch clost to edge.

SEAMING. The overcasting of selvage edges of fabric prior to seaming.

SEAMING, MATCHBOX. A method of stitching down the edge of a pleat or crease in order to keep it permanently in place. It does away with having to iron the pleats. Observed in many skirtings and in men's trousers.

SEAMING LACE. Narrow, open-work insertion.

SEAMLESS BAG. It is made tubular by the use of a double plain weave, or by regulating the selvage ends to give the effect.

SEAMLESS HOSIERY; CIRCULAR HOSIERY. 1. All ladies' full-length hosiery knit on circular machines such as those reported normally by the National Association of Hosiery Manufacturers under the specification, Ladies' Seamless Hosiery. 2. Circular Hosiery refers to all other types of socks knit on circular knitting machines, including infants', children's, misses', and the men's styles of hosiery.

SEAMLESS TUBING. Broad term applied to some fabrics woven on looms in tubular form such as many types of bagging, pillowcasing, some salt bags, etc. The effect is brought about by arranging the selvage edge threads so that they will control the circular or tube effect; this method is controlled by what is known as "the double plain method of weaving." See DOUBLE PLAIN CLOTH.

SEAMLOC. A process which applies a plastic binder to the backs of carpets where the seams must be joined instead of being sewed.

SEAM PLACKET. An opening in the left side seam of a garment commonly finished with a strip of material cut on the lengthwise grain.

SEAM QUALITY. This is determined by the quality of the fabric, the thread used, and the number and type of stitches per inch.

SEAMS. The allowance beyond the finish line of a garment section. The stitching of the sectional parts is done on the finish line, which leaves the seam extended. The seam edges are then pinked or bound, and pressed.

SEAM SLIPPAGE. Testing garments to determine their capability to withstand pulling out at the seams under standard testing conditions.

SEAMSTRESS, SEMPSTRESS. A needlewoman who does mending and sewing by hand. Formerly, a seamstress would go to the home of her patrons from season to season to cut, fit, and sew.

SEAM TYPES. 1. *Flat Fell Seam:* Made by stitching two edges of fabric together on the right side; one edge should be trimmed to about 1/8-inch; then crease the other seam over to enclose this seam and stitch flat to the garment. Ideal for work on tailored blouses and shirts. 2. *French Seam:* Adaptable for lingerie and baby clothes. Stitching is done on right side. Trim the

seam to less than 1/8-inch. Turn to the wrong side and stitch 1/8-inch from the edge. 3. *Lapped or Top-Stitched Seam:* Used for yokes or where decorative stitching is wanted. Turn under and baste one edge the amount of seam allowance. Lay the piece on the seamline of the other piece of goods; then pin, baste and stitch close to the edge. 4. *Plain Seam:* This is done by stitching two pieces of fabric together on wrong side. Remove the basting and press open. 5. *Piped Seam:* Used for decorative purposes only. Folded bias, braid, or ribbon may be used. The piping is placed between the edges with the finished edge extending beyond the seamline. Pin, baste, and stitch on the wrong side. 6. *Slot Seam:* Usually resorted to in order to introduce a contrasting color. Cut a strip of fabric the length of the seam, permitting this width to be wide enough to include both seam allowances. Pin, baste, and stitch strap close enough to the folded edge, and allow for the desired amount to show.

SEAR CLOTH. Another name for fabric finished wtih a ceré or ciré (wax) treatment.

SEAT-COVER FABRICS. Any type of fabric upon which people may sit, especially often used for automobile seats. The types and patterns are almost limitless.

SEA WEED. See ALGIN, ALGINATE FIBERS.

SEBASTOPOL. Twilled fáce material of characteristic finish. Named after the famous fortified town of the Russians captured by the French and English in 1855.

SECONDARY BOYCOTT. Concerted action by employees and their union to refrain from handling, purchasing, or working with the products of a company that is a customer of a concern with which they have a labor dispute.

SECONDARY COLORS. These hues, colors, or shades are obtained by mixing the primary colors—red, yellow, and blue to obtain orange, green, and violet and purple. Red and yellow produce orange; red and blue give violet; blue and yellow provide green. See COLOR, CONDENSED FORM AND CHARACTERISTICS OF.

SECOND BREAKER CARD. The intermediate or second card in a three-card set of woolen cards.

SECOND COMBING. Wool obtained from the back area of the fleece, across the loins to the neck.

SECOND COMBING OIL. Worsted stock that is run through the combing

operation a second time; this causes increased noil, amounts to about 5 per cent, and is more valuable than the first combing noil.

SECOND CUTS. Careless shearing of sheep whereby the flesh may be cut, but particularly the clipping of wool fibers from areas that have previously been shorn. Short fibers are the result of second cutting.

SECOND EMPIRE COSTUME. See Costume, Second Empire.

SECOND PIECES. Wool fiber scraps which have not fallen through the screen into the receptacle underneath the sorting or piece-picking table in the wool sorting room.

SECONDS. 1. Wool obtained from the chest and throat of sheep.

2. Woven or knitted goods that cannot be rated as firsts. Imperfections in weaving, knitting, finishing, etc., may injure the goods to the point that they have to be classed as second; obviously these bring lower prices to the manufacturer.

SECRET FINISH. One given to material to bring out a "new finish" of some supposed value. These finishes are patented by some particular plant. Thus, the mill would be in position to collect royalties, or it may "let-out" or "sell" the method and the finish. Some secret finishes are very important to the textile industry and have done much to bring certain textiles to the forefront. Some of these finishes are now household words.

SECTIONAL WARP BEAM. One that is divided by pegs into two-inch sections; used in hand-weaving set-up. In hand weaving, this system facilitates warping by one person alone, but it still requires as many cops as there are ends for the two-inch division, and a creel large enough to hold these. Especially useful in warping wool yarns for homespuns, tweeds, Cheviots, Shetlands, etc.

SECTION BEAM. A cylinder, four to six feet long, upon which many sections of warp, yarn that is to run vertically in the woven cloth, are wound in parallel layers ready for use in the loom.

SECTION MARKS. Caused by an uneven tension of the warp or by a section of the warp which has slipped during the dressing or the slashing operations. These marks will usually show in goods with warp yarn of the section weaving loose with the filling to show a cockled effect. At times, the areas thus affected are a total loss since it is most difficult to bring the fabric to what it should be.

Another meaning of the term is the

marking of the sections that go to make up the entire warp on the warp beam. Paint or some other means of identification is placed on the selvage edges of the warp while the warp is being set-up for weaving; the marks are set at each stipulated length of yardage that is to constitute what is called the cut-length. Several cut-lengths will be found in a total length of warp yarn.

These marks will be observed on the warp yarn as it comes through from the warp beam and whip roll through the heddles and forward to the reed. When a cut mark arrives, the weaver stops his loom, places the string loop of the warp ticket in the shed, and then weaves in the heading of the cloth cut. After all details of the finished cut of cloth have been attended to, the operator then weaves in a few yards of the cut about to be woven. The finished cut is then unrolled from the cloth roller and thus makes room for the cut which follows in sequence. The cloth cut is then taken to the percher, who marks with chalk each and every blemish or defect, minute or large, so that the finisher sewers may make the cloth well-nigh perfect. The percher is usually an experienced weaver with many years' background.

SEED. Silkworm eggs.

SEED CLEANER. Used to remove extraneous matter from seed cotton, the cleaner is made up of a set of cylinders clothed with pins or lags which revolve above and within screen enclosures made to allow leaf and other matter to drop out. Also implies any device used in a gin to remove trash and wastes from the seed cotton.

SEED COTTON. Cotton bolls in an un-ginned condition.

SEED COTTON DRYER. Any of several types of devices used to dry seed cotton before ginning in order to keep fiber damage to a minimum.

SEED EFFECT. Seed or granular effects observed on some fabrics in the warp or filling direction, both directions, or in an all-over effect. The effect can be brought about by the yarn, the weave, or printed effect. See VOILE.

SEED FIBERS. Those that grow from seed capsules; cotton, for example.

SEED YARN. Same as Knop Yarn.

SEEDY WOOL. That which contains vegetable matter difficult to remove from the wool without carbonizing.

SEERHAND. A muslin which has lower texture than nainsook but exceeds that found in mull; same uses as these two cloths.

SEERSUCKER. Cotton, rayon, or nylon crepe-stripe effect fabric, made on plain-weave variation, crepe weave. Light in weight. Colored stripes are often used. Uses are in summer clothing, boys' suits, slacks, bedspreads, and slip covers.

Launders very well, not necessary to iron; durable and gives good service and wear. Crepe effect is permanent; a popular knockabout cotton cloth. When made of rayon, fiber content must be declared. See Illustrated Section (Fabrics 16).

SEERSUCKER GINGHAM. Gingham with crinkled or creped-stripe effects.

"SEE-THROUGH." When a foam backing in a laminated fabric, especially knit goods, shows through to the face of the goods.

SEGMENT. Attached to the comber cylinder, it is a small part of a hollow cylinder opposite the half-lap. Its function is to support the combed fringe of fibers and to aid the detaching rolls to draw them off.

SEIDE. German word for silk.

SEINE TWINE. Named for the Seine River, France, it is the well-known cordage or twine used in seine and other types of nets.

SEIZING. Binding two ropes together with marling.

SEIZING STUFF. Rope of four to twelve strands used for seizing.

SEL. Strong rope made of Indian hemp fibers.

SELECTED TRIUMPH COTTON. Texas cotton of good strength obtained from large bolls; staple is ¾ inch to 1 inch.

SELF COLLAR. When the under part of a collar, as on a coating, is made of the same fabric as the outer fabric.

SELF-COLOR, MONOCHROMATIC COLOR. This color scheme is one in which various tints, shades, hues, or values of one color are combined harmoniously together. The colors would tend to blend softly unless, as in the case of a stripe pattern, a fine line of black or white were used to separate them in a distinctive manner.

SELF-FEEDER. A hopper or other arrangement used to send loose stock into a machine.

SELF-FIGURED. 1. A figure woven into the goods in the loom as contrasted with a printed design; generally used in connection with solid-color fabrics. 2. May also imply solid-color materials which have the pattern in a weave different than the basic construction, whether woven or printed effect.

SELF-TONE. A design employing two or more shades of the same color; when two, for instance, it is called two-tone or tone-on-tone.

SELLING AGENT. An agent who sells goods on commission; one acting as salesman for another.

SELVAGE, IMPERFECT. A selvage serves a double purpose; first, as a binding point for the filling when weaving; second, as an aid for maintaining the proper width when dyeing and finishing a fabric.

To be imperfect a selvage may be: uneven (with respect to its own width), tight, loose, thin, thick, or narrow. A selvage must be matched to the fabric it is supporting. This is done by trial and error or by the use of previous experience.

Weaving imperfections directly due to faulty selvages are broken picks, bowed filling, over-beating, loom stoppage, loose selvage, shiners.

The troubles of the dyer are multiplied by poor edges. Tight edges cause bowing; loose edges give a scalloped appearance; thin or narrow selvages slip through the tenter clips; thick edges "build-up" at the edges, causing dye streakiness, especially in jig-dyeing.

Imperfect selvages are caused by the incorrect diameter of the yarn, poor slashing or warping, and the use of a selvage yarn that has a different coefficient of contraction from that of the body yarn.

SELVAGE, KNITTING. Edges on knitted cloths so constructed or finished off in order to prevent fraying or raveling.

SELVAGE, LISTING, SELF-EDGE. Originated from the term "self-edge." Actual part of the cloth running in the warp direction along both edges of cloth. Its purpose is to keep the edges of cloth true, straight, even, and parallel. Selvage is not cut in tailoring and is found in seams up the back and in trouser legs, but made so that it will not show in finished garments. The selvage is never wasted in woolen, worsted, and hair-fiber fabrics. Width of selvage varies from ¼ to about 1 inch. All woven cloths have a selvage. In the dressmaking and pattern trades the term is usually spelled as selvedge. Selvage is often cut off in the manipulating of cotton cloths into dress goods and frocks.

See Illustrated Section (Fabrics 35).

SELVAGE, LOOP. A special selvage which consists of loops woven over wires that run along the side of the cloth. This type of selvage is used for some tire fabric and some low-texture sheeting for the rubber trade since there are not enough ends in the goods to hold the filling on the edges.

SELVAGE, SPLIT. In the making of narrow fabrics, it is more economical to weave the material twice the width with an extra selvage woven through the center of the material. After the cloth has been dyed or printed, and finished, it is split down the center, thus making two narrow fabrics with two selvage edges. By the use of a leno construction on both sides of the edge there will be a small empty area in the middle so that the fabric can be easily cut. Toweling and velvet are often made in this manner.

SELVAGE, TAPE. Tape selvage is a definite weave such as 1 end over 2 picks or a 2-and-2 basket construction. Edges of this type are used in high pick cloths because they are strong and hold better than other possible constructions. There are some fabrics made today in which only a tape selvage can be used; a plain-weave selvage would be too tight and spoil the appearance of the goods. Selvages of this type are seen in marquisette, sateen, twill cloths, organdy, voile, etc.

SELVAGEE. A skein of rope with another rope wound around it.

SEMAL COTTON. A flat, straight, silklike fiber used for stuffing.

SEMEN. Japanese term for dressed silk, the waste silk stock that is spun into commercial yarn on regulation spinning frames.

SEMIBRIGHT WOOL. Wool which is not sufficiently bright to be classed as Bright. It is brighter than Territory wool, with which it is often compared.

SEMI-COLLOID. A particle which has only partial colloidal characteristics.

SEMICOMBED. Cotton yarn made from stock not fully treated for noil removal during combing.

SEMIFINISH. Differs from clear finish, in that it shows a slight nap effect on the face of the goods. In a semifinish fabric the weave is easily discernible, but not as markedly as in the case of clear-finish materials. Cassimere, serge, and the fancy-design worsted suitings and dress goods are classed as semifinish.

SEMI-STAPLE. Often applied to various brown and gray shades in serge, diagonals and stripes. It has been said that the fancy of today will be the staple of tomorrow; semi-staple can also include fabrics in the trade which are "in-between" the fancy range and the staple range. These cloths are not always in demand. Examples may include whipcord, duvetyne, Florentines, Henriettas, Zibeline.

SEMI-TELESCOPE. Pertinent to a hat, it means a telescope crown effect which is either rounded at the back and tapered toward the front, or creased into a diamond shape, the widest area of which is near the back.

SEMPITERNE. Staple woolen fabric of the eighteenth century made with a twill weave and featured by a napped face that was not of the raised fiber type but was one given a laid-nap finish such as noted on some fabrics today; for example, zibeline.

SENDAL. Originally a finely textured linen fabric of Biblical times. In the Middle Ages, a silk fabric of body and substance, apparently of the dressgoods type. Now obsolete.

SENIORITY. A priority or right that employees gain over other employees by virtue of their length of service, their capabilities or merit, and their marital status.

SENNA KNOT. A piece of yarn encircles one thread of warp and is twisted so that its ends appear at the surface, one at each side of the adjacent thread of warp. Also spelled Sehna, the knot is used to secure the tufts of pile yarn in handmade Oriental carpets and rugs.

The other type of knot used in this phase of textiles is the Ghiordes knot. Of the two knots, Senna admits of more compact weaving and defines the pattern clearer than does the Ghiordes knot. It finds much use in short-pile rugs and carpets; used in Chinese, Turkoman, Persian, and some Indian rugs. Originated in the city of Senna in western Iran.

SENNIT. 1. A braid formed by plaiting strands of rope together. 2. A straw braid popular in straw hats for summer wear in this country.

SEPARATE. Each item in apparel which will combine well in harmony or contrast to give an entirely attractive silhouette to the wearer. Fabric, cut-fit-trim, color, line, and configuration must be considered in choosing each "separate article." Examples of separates include blouse, shirt, skirt, sweater, slacks or pants, jacket - sports or otherwise.

SEPARATING COURSE. The course used in circular knitting between sweater-strips knitted in continuous lengths to facilitate separation.

SEPARATOR. The upright metal plate set between two spindles on the ring-spinning frame to keep ballooning confined to certain limits. The plate may be perforated in design.

SEPT. A division of a tribe ruled by a hereditary chief especially in ancient and medieval Scotland and Ireland. It also implies any unit, group, or clan descended from a common ancestor.

SEPTAIN. The word in French means seven and refers to a braided upholstery cord made up of seven threads.

SEQUESTER. To prevent from participating in a reaction.

SEQUESTERING AGENT. Any compound that will inactivate a metallic ion by forming a water soluble complex in which the metal is held in a nonionizable form.

SEQUESTRATION. Generally speaking, the chemical combination of certain chemicals with metallic ions in solution so that the usual precipitation reactions of the latter are no longer possible.

SEQUIN. A small metal plate or disk used as trimming or decorative purposes on dresses and gowns. Also called spangle.

SERAPE. A vividly colored woolen blanket used in Mexico and Central America.

SERGE. Popular staple, diagonal worsted cloth, dyed in piece and may be made in mixture or fancy effect. It is possible to stock-dye and yarn-dye the material, but piece-dyeing is preferred. The name is derived from the Latin "serica." This would imply that the cloth was originally made of silk. The weight of serge runs from ten ounces upwards, and it is one of the most staple of cloths. Made of wool, worsted, cotton-worsted, and in other combinations. Clear finish is given the material, although unfinished and semifinished serge is on the market. Mohair serge is used as a garment lining. A 2-up and 2-down right-hand twill is used in constructing the cloth, 45-degree angle. The quality and price range is from the lowest to the highest because of the call for all types of serges. It is a formal, dressy type of cloth and is conventional at all times. Serge holds the crease very well but will shine with wear. This shine cannot be removed permanently. It is a good cloth in tailoring as it drapes and clings very well.

Rayon or silk serge is of high texture, smooth finish, and is a rugged type of fabric. Used for coats, children's wear, dresses, men's suits, sportswear.

SERGE, DOUBLE CLOTH. A British double-cloth fabric in which the face is made of silk warp and filling while the back fabric has a silk warp and a cotton filling. The fifth set of threads, the binding yarns, interlace in a small compact formation, thereby making the materials (the face and the back cloths) closely and firmly bound together. The material may be used as a lining and suiting fabric.

SERGE, MOIRÉ. A small group of fabrics made of spun silk, mercerized cotton, acetate, etc., which are given the moire or watermarked undulating effect on the surface of the goods. The serge weave, the 2-up, 2-down twill, is used in all the fabrics given this name.

SERGE DE ROULLEAU. Also known as Roulders, this serge fabric has been used in France for draperies and furniture covering since the sixteenth century. Little of the fabric is seen at present.

SERGED SEAM. The edges are basted or serged, and the seam itself usually stitched twice; first as a plain seam, then through both seam-edges which are turned one way instead of pressed open. Used chiefly on loosely woven goods.

SERGETTE. Any thin or lightweight serge made from any fibers used to make the goods.

SERGE TWILL FABRIC. Some cottons made of the serge weave are bleached, dyed, or printed, and usually given a mercerized silklike finish so that they may find use in capcloth, lining, shirting, slacks, dress goods, etc. Some of the fabric may be given a nap on the one side, and, when this is done, the fabric is known as cotton flannel, cotton duvetyne, napped cotton, etc. Cloth in this sphere is usually made with rather bizarre print effects for use as play clothes, jackets, caps, etc.

SERGING. The overcasting of the selvage edges of cloth prior to seaming.

SERGING MACHINE. A three-needle sewing machine that sews thread through and around the edge of fabric to prevent raveling.

SERICARIA. A generic term that was proposed by the French scientist and sericulturist, Latreille, whereby writers on the story of silk and sericulture were to use this term; never succeeded.

SERICIN. A soluble gum of the silk fiber which cements the two silk filaments together.

SERICULTURE. The raising of silkworms.

SERIGRAPH. A device to test for strength or tenacity, stretch or elongation, and the elastic or yield point. The test is done by the reeling of the proper length skein, weighing it for size, and then breaking the 100 to 400 parallel ends, depending on the size of the yarn.

Elasticity and tenacity are computed in grams per denier. Strength and elongation of cotton and wool yarns are made in accordance with the standards set up by the American Society for Testing and Materials, Philadelphia, Pennsylvania. Twist tests should be made in accordance with the standard procedure of the United States Testing Company, Hoboken, N. J. Power-driven twist counters give the best result when testing for twist.

SERIMETER. This machine tests raw-silk yarn for strength, tenacity, elongation and yield.

SERIPLANE. This is a test to determine the grade of raw silk. The silk to be tested is uniformly mounted in panels on a special type of inspection board. Trained inspectors rate the panels in comparison with standard photographs as follows:

1. Evenness: for the variations in diameter of the yarn.

2. Cleanness: for the number of imperfections present.

3. Neatness: for the content of loops, nibs and hairiness.

The inspection is conducted in an area lighted according to a specific standard.

This effective test may be used for as many as forty panels of silk. As the length of each panel is forty meters in the standard size of a 13/15 denier silk, the total length of silk used would be only 1,600 meters. This, when compared with an entire lot of silk that would run about four hundred million meters, is too small to represent the lot, but does give some idea as to the quality.

SERPENTINE. French term for a cord that is formed by spiral winding of a heavy yarn around a two-ply core thread. It is used in the upholstery trade.

SERPENTINE CREPE. A plain-woven fabric in which the crinkled effect runs in the warp direction. Comes in white, solid colors, and prints. Like many other crepes, ironing is not necessary, and the material is therefore in much demand for blouses, nightwear, play suits, wash suits.

SERPENTINE TWILL. A cloth which has a series of wavy ridges in right-hand and left-hand directions. Various degree-twills, corkscrew, and broken twill derivations are used to obtain the effects. The material is used in some dress goods which are usually made with woolen or worsted yarn. Also known as zigzag twill.

SERRATIONS. The minute, saw-toothed, projecting scales found on wool fibers; they aid considerably in the felting of wool fibers by interlocking to form a matted area. Serrations will vary from about 600 to about 3,000 per inch in the wool fibers, depending on the grade or quality of the fiber; the higher the number of serrations, the better will be the quality of the fiber.

SERRE. This French word, serré, refers to a woven fabric that is of rather high texture, firm, and compact, and one that has body and substance in hand. Serré implies compactness or locked, as exemplified by the characteristics afore-mentioned.

SERTAO COTTON. A Pernambuco cotton of good quality and staple length.

SERUL. Bloused pantaloons which end just below the knee to give the impression of a bloused harem skirt. Worn in countries in the Middle East and parts of Northern Africa. Pronounced as seer ul.

SERVICE SERGE. That which is used by the armed forces in practically all nations. In this country it is a good-quality worsted serge of about 12 to 13-ounce weight per yard. It can be made water repellent and waterproof. Goodly amounts of the fabric are now made with a combination of "Dacron" and worsted in about a 50/50 proportion.

SERVIETTE. French for napkin.

SET. 1. Width of a warp in the reed in the loom.

2. The number of machines in the carding plan of a mill. A three-set lay-out will consist of first breaker, intermediate or second breaker, and the finisher-condenser card. A four-set lay-out includes the first breaker, second breaker, intermediate and finisher card. The size of a woolen mill is gauged by the number of cards it has; cotton mills are gauged by the number of spindles.

3. The total number of section beams necessary to make a loom beam.

4. The same as texture of a fabric—the number of warp ends and filling picks per inch in a woven fabric.

5. Applied to yarn, a set yarn is one which has been textured and heat-set to remove the stretch.

SETA. Italian term for raw silk.

SET-AND-DROP MATCH. In a set-match carpet pattern, the figure matches straight across on each side of the narrow carpet width; in a drop match, the figure matches midway of the design; in a quarter-drop match, the figure will match one quarter of the length of the repeat on the opposite side.

SET CHECK. A design used in some fabrics where the checks are all of the same size. The effect may or may not be set off by windowpane stripes of some desirable color or colors with these stripes being narrower than the prominent, large-set checks.

SET-IN POCKET. A pocket set into

position through a slash in the goods. Examples are pockets with a bound opening or a welt.

SET MARK. See START-UP MARK.

SETS IN WOOLEN AND WORSTED CARDING. Worsted carding is done by a double-cylinder card, two cards that are connected by means of a roller known as the angle stripper. This roller, similar to a doffer roller, takes the carded wool from the first card in the set and delivers it to the feeding-in end of the second card. The number of operations that follow worsted carding do not warrant any other treatment, as far as carding is concerned, to the wool.

Low and medium wools for wool yarn are run on a three-set card. The machines are: first breaker card, second breaker card, and the finisher-condenser card.

High-grade wools for wool yarn are run on a four-set card. The machines are: first breaker card, second breaker card, finisher, and condenser.

The last card, in either the three-or four-set arrangement, has the wool in the form of roving ready to be presented to the spinning frame for the final operation in wool yarn manufacturing, spinning.

SETT. See YARN NUMBERING SYSTEMS, WORLD.

SETTING. The location and proper setting of the vital parts of a machine with their relation to each other, in order to insure full production. Gauges are often used to obtain the absolute setting of a roller, etc.

SEVEN-EIGHTHS HOSE. Stockings that reach seven-eighths of the way from the ankle to the knee. A type of golf hose.

SEVERANCE PAY. A lump sum of money paid by a company to an employee being terminated permanently from the payroll. It is frequently paid instead of advance notice of a termination. Same as dismissal pay. It may be paid in smaller sums at regular intervals in a manner like that of a pension, especially when the employee affected is near retirement age.

SEVILLA COTTON. Spanish cotton raised in the Sevilla area.

SEVILLE. A variety of Torchon lace.

"SEVRON" DYES. The trade-mark of E. I. du Pont de Nemours & Co., Inc., for the cationic (basic) dyes that were developed especially for "Orlon," the acrylic fiber. These dyes have unusual brightness and fastness on "Orlon."

SEW. To unite or fasten by stitches made with a flexible thread, such as cotton.

SEWED YARN. Yarn or thread in cloth interwoven by hand.

SEWED TOE. The toe of a stocking closed with a sewing machine seam instead of by the looping operation.

SEWING. Actual tacking or stitching of the end pieces of a cut of cloth so that an appreciable amount of goods may be manipulated easily in dyeing, printing, or finishing goods. The cuts are sewed end-to-end. Also means material on which one is at work with needle and thread.

SEWING COTTON. Used for hand or machine sewing, it is plied or cabled yarn which has been mercerized, gassed, and polished to attain a smooth surface. Made in a great number of diameters and sizes, such as three-cord, six-cord, etc. For example, a three-cord thread means that it is a thread made up of three-ply or three cords twisted together, in a balanced cylindrical twist to give a fully rounded product.

SEWING MACHINE. The machine used to sew cloth, leather, etc. See HOWE, ELIAS. See Illustrated Section.

SEWING MACHINE INVENTORS. Invention and perfection of the sewing machine occured in 1846. Unbeknown to each other, Isaac Singer competed with Elias Howe and his brother-in-law, Nathaniel Banks, the well-known Union general in the War Between the States. Singer and Howe brought out their machines within three months of each other.

Work on sewing machines was confined to three cities in Massachusetts - Hudson, Boston, and Palmer. Howe did not, in the long run, evince much interest in his machine but it did, for a few years, have considerable success in the British Isles. A very wealthy man, Howe turned his attention to other pursuits.

SEWING MACHINE OPERATOR. One who runs a regulation sewing machine to do the stitching required to make garment parts, such as joining the various garment sections together or attaching the previously completed garment parts to the partially completed garment.

In men's and boys' clothing, the operators include those who perform the following assignments: Edge basting, facing basting, body lining felling or joining, shoulder joining, side seam joining, sleeve lining joining, lapel joining, piping edging, dart sewing, edge tape sewing, sleeve sewing, edge stitching, buttonhole tacking, pocket tacking, armhole taping. All these are coat-shop operations.

Vest-shop sewers perform the following operations: Lining basting, joining, tape sewing, edge stitching, and buttonhole tacking.

Trouser-shop operators perform the following: Closing pockets, joining seat seams, making belt loops or tunnels, piecing the fly, serging backs and fronts, joining inseams, attaching the fly, attaching the waistband, sewing on the waistband lining, and tacking.

The following operations in the dress shirt and work shirt phases of the garment industry to be cared for by the sewing-machine worker include collar running, collar setting, felling, hemming of the fronts and backs, sewing the label, pocket setting, and sleeve setting.

In overalls, industrial garments and washable service apparel, the operators take care of bar tacking, bib felling and hemming, bottom hemming on coats and legs, inseaming, outseaming, pocket hemming, pocket setting, seat seaming, side-body felling and sleeve setting.

In men's, women's and children's undergarments the duties consist of single-needle standard machine operating, single-needle special machine operating, and multiple-needle special machine operating. Standard sewing machine makes are used.

In women's and children's outerwear, the sewing machine operators care for all the standard sewing-machine operations required in the manufacture of a complete garment in the single-hand or tailor system of making garments. Assembling and joining are done by the operator with the more skilled person taking care of the final finishing-off.

The section system is also used to advantage in this field. Here the particular operator uses a standard or special-purpose sewing machine for making garment parts, and he does the joining and attaching. The worker does not, however, make the entire garment.

Operations in knit underwear include the Singer Operator, Junior Singer Operator, Merrow Operator and the Junior Merrow Operator for assembling and minor operations.

SEWING SILK. Thread silk made for hand or machine sewing purposes, particularly the finer types. Made by twisting or plying several single threads together and the doubling of two, three, or more of these in the opposite direction.

There are several types of the thread: machine-twist thread is three-ply; hand sewing silk is a two-ply thread, while floss silk is made of a series of single threads which are given little twist and find much use for decorative purposes. Spool silk is used for fine sewing and stitching.

The average silk thread is made from raw silk by the use of 3 to 24 cocoon threads. The number of ply desired is perfected in the twisting operation.

SEYDAVI SILK. Levantine raw silk.

SFALDABILI. Continental term that implies silk which is divisible into fibrils —minute or individual filaments.

SHAATNEZ, NON. This term signifies that the garment or fabric so labelled is considered to be "kosher" for wear, implying that the article is free from a mixture of linen and wool.

SHAATNEZ. Hebrew word for mixed fabric or stuff and refers to cloth made of wool and linen. It may not be worn by Orthodox Jews except by the Jewish clergy in services in the synagogue. This prohibition stems from Deuteronomy 22, II: "You shall not wear cloth of two different kinds of thread, wool and linen, woven together."

SHABNAM. The finest quality of native-made, Indian muslin; yarn counts range from 250s cotton, upward. Shabnam is similar to the renowned Dacca muslin in character.

SHADE. 1. A gradation of color in slight degree or minute difference. 2. Any device to intercept or screen from light. 3. An opaque curtain material, usually attached to a roller, and placed at a window to control light.

SHADE CLOTH. A plain-weave fabric that is usually white, canary, ecru, or green in color, used for shades on windows. Cloth is smooth, firm, rugged, and rather lustrous in finish. Has good body and feel and the required stiffness is provided by a mixture of oil, sizes, and starches. Material is not transparent and withstands rough usage.

SHADED CLOTH. Cloth that is uneven in color, cast, or tone. There are many reasons as to why cloth may become shaded; some defect or irregularity in any operation or treatment will cause shadiness. If the markings are too pronounced, the cloth is classed as a second.

SHADED DESIGNS IN BATIK. The use of paraffin or melted wax applied with a squeegee or a pointed outlet handle gives the effect. Benzene or gasoline will remove the wax on consummation of the work.

SHADED FILLING. Bright or dim areas in line formation across the width of a fabric. Usually caused by poor blending or mixing of the fibers in the manufacture of the yarn or by faulty dyeing of the yarn.

SHADED SATIN WEAVES. See SHADED WEAVES.

SHADED TWILL WEAVES. See SHADED WEAVES.

SHADED WEAVES. With twills and satins used as the foundation, these weaves produce novelty effects on fabric, chiefly on Jacquards. In the motif, usually fairly large in size, the length of the warp floats, for example, is gradually increased, and correspondingly, the filling floats are decreased. Thus the shaded effect is developed.

SHADE TICKET. A label temporarily sewn to a piece of cut fabric to identify it with the bolt from which it was cut; by means of this identification a complete garment is made from the cloth of the same shade.

SHADING. Bending or crushing of the surface yarn so that the side of fibers, smooth and glossy, will reflect light, giving a lighter hue to the color than the flat, dull fiber ends. From one direction the crushed area will appear lighter and from the opposite side darker in color.

SHADINGS. Cloth made of colored warp yarn in stripe arrangement to produce bright and dim effects. The same yarn is used throughout but the stripes are the result of using S-twist and Z-twist yarns according to some motif.

SHADOW. Machine-lace made of fine mesh groundwork with shadowlike patterns of finer mesh worked into the material to give the desired effect.

SHADOW CHECK. Monotone effects of plain design.

SHADOW CRETONNE. A warp-printed cretonne; also called Chene.

SHADOW FABRIC. Another name for a warp-printed fabric; some cretonne is made in this manner. See WARP PRINTING.

SHADOW LACE. A fine flimsy type of lace which has a flat surface and indistinct shadowy motifs.

SHADOW PRINT. Warp printing.

SHADOW SILK. Another name for changeable silk, particularly radium and taffeta goods.

SHADOW STRIPE. A blended stripe effect of darker or lighter shade than the body of the goods.

SHADOW WEAVE. An effect on cloths in stripes or plaids produced by the immediate duplicating of the weave formation after a definite repeat in darker tones or shades of yarn which gives the appearance of reflected shadows being cast upon the lighter parts of the fabric. Upon staple goods, as black or blue, it is produced by the yarns used in part of the pattern being twisted in spinning in an opposite or reverse direction to those elsewhere required, which, in the woven cloth, will give a "shadow" effect. In worsted suitings, such as herringbones, bisected

block, and diamond patterns, it is particularly effective.

SHADOW WELT. The section set in after the doubled welt which joins the welt to the boot or the leg in a stocking.

SHAFT. 1. The "rod" on a loom. 2. Synonymous with end and harness, in this respect, it is the number of yarns used in the repeat of a satin weave, such as an eight-shaft, eight-end, or eight-harness satin weave. Thus, in an eight-shaft, warp-effect satin weave, there would be a float of seven, which means that a single warp thread would actually float, or not weave or interlace for seven threads, and would then interlace with the eighth filling pick, to form fabric. See Illustrated Section (Fabrics 45, 46).

SHAFT LASHING. The placing of harness shafts on a Jacquard loom to increase its capacity.

SHAFTY WOOL. High-type, even, lofty and elastic, good-length wool.

SHAGREEN. A strong, heavily sized cotton fabric made to simulate leather and used as bookbinding.

SHAKER FLANNEL. Named for a religious sect known as Shakers. This material is napped on both sides. It is made of cotton, wool, or mixture yarn, and is used for underwear, night clothing, and shirts.

SHAKEOUT. Straightening out laundered goods prior to ironing.

SHAKER MOTION. Used in weaving doup or leno fabrics on the loom, the purpose of the motion is to raise the ends under which the crossing threads pass to the center of the shed in the loom. Without this motion leno cloths could not be woven, since the ends in question would remain at the bottom of the shed.

SHAKER STITCH. A type of heavy stitch used to knit heavy sweaters. It is made on a machine that has one set of needles, and is known as the heavy jersey stitch.

SHAKER SWEATER. It is knitted in plain ribbed stitch with heavy yarn. The name comes from the religious sect known as the Shakers, who originated this type of garment.

SHAKER TUMBLER. The mechanical shaker used in laundries to untangle damp work and make it ready for ironing.

SHAKERS. Sweaters knitted in a coarse-gauge, plain-ribbed stitch of a heavy or coarse count of yarn. A baby shaker is a sweater also knitted in a plain-ribbed stitch but in a less coarse gauge than a shaker and using a finer count of yarn.

SHAKO. A high, stiff headdress made

with a peak and decorated with an upright plume, the headgear for Highland Infantries in full dress. The famous 42nd or Black Watch Division is the only Scottish Regiment entitled to wear the red heckle in the bonnet. Fox-tails are used to decorate some shakoes.

SHAL. An Italian hand-woven fabric made in plain-weave and featured by striped effects in both directions. Originally a silk material, other fibers are now used to make the goods.

SHALAMAR TWEED. A woolen-worsted fabric made with hand-spun yarns on hand looms in Kashmir, India. This dress-goods cloth is made on an 8-end broken twill, (four ends to the right and four to the left) in which the filling picks are inserted through the shed of the loom "two picks per shed or turnover of the loom."

SHALLOON. Another name for the 2-up and 2-down twill weave. Fabric of this name is a lightweight worsted cloth, piece-dyed and used as lining.

SHALVAR. Pantaloons worn by women in several nations of the Near East. These wide, loose pantaloons reach to the ankle where they are gathered-in for the effect.

SHAMROCK LAWN. A high-quality, good-textured cotton warp and linen filling cloth made in Ireland. Noted for its superb finish.

SHANK. The portion of a hide that covers the leg of an animal.

SHANKINGS. Short, coarse wool obtained from the shanks of the sheep.

SHANTUNG. 1. One type of silk fabric known by this name is similar to pongee with the same characteristic nubby-surface effect. It is now made of Tussah silk, rayon, or cotton. Popular in summer wear dress goods. If the cloth is not made of silk, the fiber content must be declared. 2. A silk and cotton or all-cotton fabric with the identifying slub filling. Sometimes known as Nankin, Nankeen. 3. A cloth made from silk waste which shows very irregular yarn throughout the goods. Much of the fabric seems to be just so many ends and picks thrown together. Made in the Far East and sold here, the material is flimsy and the fabric weight varies considerably. 4. A high-quality woven straw of the Baku type. See Illustrated Section (Fabrics 12).

SHAP COTTON. Burmese cotton of about 1-inch staple and 40 per cent lint yield.

"SHAPE CLOTH." Invented by L. A. Runton, president of Timely Clothes, Inc., New York City, the product is also used by J. P. Stevens & Co., Inc., New York City. "Shape Cloth" is the only all-worsted fabric, as opposed to man-made fabrics made from one or more fibers in a blend formation, with resilient properties. It combines stretch to the worsted material along with crease-retention, wrinkle-resistance, lower moisture absorption, and freedom from pilling, puckering, and fiber-migration.

SHAPER. A garment worker who trims the front edge and the bottom of the garment with shears after the canvas has been basted to the forepart and padded.

SHAPE RETENTION. The ability of a durable press garment to be washed and still retain the original shape of the new garment.

SHAPING. Placing a stocking on a heated form while it is in a dampened condition. Steam is generated by heat to aid in giving the final shape to knitted fabric.

SHAREEN. Trademark for producer texturized nylon, type 6, manufactured by Courtaulds North America Inc., for use in the hosiery trade. Shareen is produced in both monofilament and multifiliment types in the range 15 to 50 denier. Various types of Shareen are available to provide different degrees of stretch and recovery.

SHARKSKIN. 1. A term which has become very popular in the textile trade; it has a very broad meaning, since it was first applied to high-grade worsteds made from a 2-up and 2-down, color-effect weave arranged in the warp and the filling, one colored thread and one white thread. The finish on the goods is smooth because of the yarn and texture used. Despite the fact that the cloth comes in light weight, it has a very substantial feel, gives excellent wear, and sheds dirt readily.

2. A tightly woven Oxford-weave cloth in which the warp is drawn in "two ends acting as one end" and woven on a plain-weave construction. The fabric is usually made of acetate or of pigment rayon. The cloth is made both plain and in woven plaids; the plain cloth is sold in white, pastels, and prints. The material, which is used in dress goods, shirting, and sportswear, has excellent drapability and launderability qualities.

3. A lustrous, waterproof raincoating fabric.

4. A tough, durable leather made from shark hide.

SHARKSKIN, ACETATE. A well-made fabric, high in texture, which comes in white and contrasting colors or solid shades. A tabby or twill weave may be used. Sharkskin drapes well, gives good wear, is easy to launder and is popular for summer wear dresses, suits, and coats in the women's wear field.

SHARP-SHOOTER. A chiseler; a merchant or wholesaler who exceeds his legitimate mark-up.

SHARP SOAP. One that contains free alkali.

SHASH. 1. It means fine cotton muslin in the Arabic language. 2. In the Bible it means cotton. 3. In the Middle East the word signifies a shirting or shawl made of cotton.

SHAVING. Careful trimming of surface hair on a pelt or on the pile effect on a pile fabric; aids in easier seaming to imitate a true fur effect.

SHAWL. From the Persian, shal, which means covering or mantle. It is a square or oblong piece of material used for shoulder covering and is worn by women.

Cashmere, Spanish, Italian, Persian, and embroidery shawls are well known and many of them are high in quality and price. The term also implies any material used for shoulder or head covering in the accepted sense of today. There is much variety in shawls, and considerable beauty is seen in the designs of the more expensive shawls which in many instances are genuine works of art because of intricate detail work.

SHAWL COLLAR. The type of lapel devoid of indentations or peaks; observed on jackets and robes.

SHAWL WOOL. Also known as Pashmina, it is the fine hair-fiber fleece grown by Tibetan goats to be used in making Kashmir (Cashmere) shawls.

SHEAR. 1. (Noun) Common name for a shearing machine.

2. (Verb) To clip, cut, even off or sever from something; shearing of sheep and the removal of protruding or superfluous fibers from cloth are examples.

SHEAR HOG. Sheep, after the first shearing, are known by this term.

SHEARING. The operation of leveling the nap on cloth is much used in the woolen and worsted trades, as well as in the case of certain cotton fabrics. Shearing regulates the height of the nap or protruding fibers found on the surface of goods. The machine used may have one or two shear blades. A blade is exceedingly sharp in order to shave, shear, or cut off the undesirable portions. It can be arranged or set to leave a certain height of even, uniform nap on goods since the blade can be raised or lowered, as desired. The blade is regulated to the thirty-second part of an inch. Thus, a nap could be

⁴/₃₂ or ⁶/₃₂ of an inch in height.

The blades are on the principle of those on a lawn mower. The material to be sheared passes under the blade, and all fibers longer than the setting of the blade are taken off neatly and cleanly. There remains an evened-off surface on the fabric that leaves a sort of pile effect.

Goods may be run through the shear any number of times to produce a good surface. The operator has to be on guard constantly to watch for knots, loops, or other parts of the cloth that may be cut, and thereby rip a goodly portion of the material. When these raised places come around to the blade the shearer raises the blade to admit the passage of the cloth underneath. These blemishes are later cared for by the menders and sewers before the cut of fabric is finally passed.

SHEARING MACHINE. Based on the principle of a lawn mover, it is the machine which evens off the nap on fabrics. A lawn mower is run over a grass plot to even off the grass; the cloth to be sheared comes under the blade or blades on the shearing machine; the blades are spiral and can be set to the thirty-second part of an inch from the fabric to be treated. Thus, a sheared height may be ⁵/₃₂ of an inch from the body of the goods. The number of blades on the shear may be from one to six.

SHEARLING. 1. See CLOTHING LEATHER. 2. English term for yearling or a one-year-old sheep. Also means short wool pulled from the skins of sheep prior to slaughtering.

SHEAR MARKS. An unevenly marked or cut nap on material. Slubs or knots often tend to make for unevenness in shearing. Burlers, speckers, and menders are ever on the lookout for places in cloth that might be nipped or caught by the razor-edge blades on the shear. Shear marks show up to poor advantage when light strikes the fabric.

SHEARS. A two-bladed cutting implement in which the handle or grip can be used by more than two fingers. Size does not enter into the qualification. Incidentally, a barber uses shears and not scissors.

SHEATH. A straight, narrow, close-fitting dress, gown, or slip.

SHEATH FIBERS. The fibers which form a coating or sheath around the elastomeric fiber used in core-spinning of yarn. The fibers are usually wound in spiral formation around the core yarn but random sheathing is also employed.

SHED. This is the V-shaped opening slightly in back of the raceplate of the loom that is formed when some of the warp ends are raised and others are lowered by their respective harnesses. It is the opening through which the shuttle passes laying the loose pick. Forming the shed is the first action in weaving, followed by picking and lastly, beating—the actual beating of the pick into the cloth by means of the reed action.

SHEDDING. The first of the three motions of a loom in weaving cloth. Picking and beating-up are the other two chief motions. Shedding is the raising and lowering of the warp ends by means of the harnesses and heddles to form the shed of the loom so that the filling bobbin in the shuttle may pass through it from one side of the loom to the other side. As the shuttle passes through the shed it lays the loose filling pick between the raised and the lowered warp ends.

SHED STICK. A long, narrow stick used to open up the threads in order to form the shed. Shed sticks refer to those sticks tied together at the ends, thereby conserving the cross.

SHEENTEC. Trade name for flat, ribbon-shaped, single acetate filaments, or for acetate yarns composed of a plurality of such filaments in a yarn. Product of Eastman Chemical Products, Inc.

SHEEN-TYPE RUG. Another name for a Domestic Oriental rug.

SHEEP. Any animal of the ruminant or chewing-the-cud genus Ovis. Closely allied with the goat, sheep are raised for mutton and carcass. Compared with the goat, it is fleshier, less active, generally has no horns, and possesses a thick coat of fiber.

Sheep are classified into fine, medium, and long wool breeds. The Merino breed is the best in grading and it produces a very fine fiber; medium wool is typified by the so-called Down sheep, which originated in England. Long wools are those which are lustrous, long in staple length, and more irregular in properties and characteristics when compared with fine and medium types. Lincoln and Leicester sheep are typical in this group. See Illustrated Section.

Wild sheep of varying species live in the higher mountain ranges of the world, chiefly in the Northern Hemisphere.

SHEEP-DIP. The application of a liquor to the fleece or skin of sheep to kill vermin or to preserve the wool.

SHEEP FLEECE. The weight of a fleece ranges from 6 to 18 or 20 pounds, depending on the breed and local conditions. The fleece, when received at the mill, must be sorted. From four to twenty distinct grades may be obtained from the one fleece, depending on the rigidity of selection. The following shows the type of stock taken from the fleece, when it is sorted:

1. TOP AND SIDES OF HEAD: Noted for length of staple, softness, pliability, and uniformity. Superior in all respects to wool taken from any other part of the fleece. This is made possible because the yolk is unimpeded in its flow through the pores into the fleece, which gives nutriment to the fibers and makes for fiber density per inch.

2. UPPER PART OF BACK: High quality, just below the wool taken from the top and sides of the head, in all respects.

3. LOIN AND BACK: Short staple, not quite as fine, of unvarying quality and character. This stock may, however, run to the tender side a trifle.

4. UPPER LEGS: Medium staple, rather coarse, and has tendency to hang rather loosely. The locks are open. All told, the wool is of sound quality. The stock has varying portions of vegetable matter in it.

5. UPPER NECK: Inferior in quality, irregular in growth, often matted with foreign and vegetable matter.

6. CENTER NECK: Similar to upper neck stock, but of more tender nature.

7. BELLY: Wool from fore and hind legs, and vicinity. It is short, dirty, tender, irregular, and has much foreign matter—motes, dried grass, burrs, shives, etc.

8. RUMP: Taken from the rump and tail root. Inferior in most respects and of little value and use. Inclined to be dungy, matted, and kempy.

9. LOWER LEGS: Dirty, greasy, kempy, burry, and poor in quality.

10. FRONT OF HEAD, THROAT, AND CHEST: Straight, stiff, and coarse. Covered with much foreign matter, including fodder.

11. SHINS: Short, thick, straight, glossy, or shank wool.

SHEEP OF THE WORLD, CLASSIFICATION OF THE. From the 40 distinct breeds of sheep there are over 200 types which are the result of crossbreeding. Sheep are classified for practical purposes into five classes. They follow:

CLASS 1: Includes Merino sheep only. This wool is the highest, finest and best obtainable.

CLASS 2: Wools from sheep that originated in the United Kingdom and come from the coastal counties. These sheep are now raised all over the world, and formed, with the Class 3 wools, the nucleus for crossbreeding. Many of the sheep in Class 2 take their names from the counties where they were first raised. They are below Merino in all respects, but are classed as "good" and "very good."

CLASS 3: Wools taken from sheep in this class are called Luster wools. They have the property of reflecting the light's rays, are long in staple, with a length from 1 to 12 or more inches.

CLASS 4: All sheep that cannot be classed in the first three classes are placed in Class 4. The properties, characteristics, and qualities are such that they do not measure up to any of the foregoing classes. This class now includes sheep that are standardized, as well as some "mongrel" breeds found in remote sections of the world where animal husbandry has made little headway.

CLASS 5: This class is not wool, but includes fibers that resemble wool. The fleece does not, of necessity, have to come from a sheep. Arabian, Caracul, Astrakhan, Persian lamb, and similar fibers make up this group.

USES OF THESE WOOLS:

CLASS 1: In the very best grades of woolens and worsteds for men's wear and women's wear. It is used for the most expensive fabrics, such as suitings, dress goods, coatings, ensembles, and so on.

CLASS 2: Used in the better grade of textiles for apparel.

CLASS 3: Used for rugged, coarse materials, such as tweeds, homespuns, cheviots, sport cloths, and low-grade worsted fabrics.

CLASS 4: Finds use in low-grade suiting and apparel, rugs and carpets, trousering, blankets and in popular priced fabrics.

CLASS 5: Used in coatings under their original names, in the fur trade.

NAMES OF THESE WOOLS:

CLASS 1, MERINO: Ohio, Silesian of Austria, Saxony of Germany, Rambouillet of France, Australian, South American, South African, New Zealand, Spanish, Swedish, Danish, Prussian, Hanoverian, and so on.

CLASS 2, ENGLISH STRAIGHT: Bampton, Berkshire, Blackface, Cornish-Cornwall, Devonshire, Dorset, Durham, Canadian, Hampshire, Hereford, Exmoor, Kent, Norfolk, Shropshire, Southdown, Sussex, Oxford, Welsh Mountain, Wiltshire, West Riding of Yorkshire, Shetland, Westmorland, the Irish, Ryeland, and so on.

CLASS 3, ENGLISH LUSTER: Lincoln, from Lincoln County; Leicester, from Leicester County; Cotswold, from Gloucester County; Romney Marsh, from Kent County; Cheviot, from Highlands and Lowlands of Scotland, Shetland, Hebrides, Harris and Lewis Islands, and so on.

CLASS 4, MIXED BREEDS: These low-grade sheep are called Halfbreed and Demiluster sheep and are the result of

WOOLS FROM CLASSIFIED SHEEP

CLASS	FIBER LENGTH IN INCHES	DIAMETER IN INCHES	SERRATIONS PER INCH	RAM WEIGHT IN POUNDS	EWE WEIGHT IN POUNDS	FLEECE WT. IN LBS.
1	1 to 5	to 1/1800	to 3000	150-235	105-155	17-22
2	2 to 7	to 1/1350	to 2000	180-280	145-220	6-18
3	4 to 18	to 1/1000	to 1000	225-285	175-240	9-16
4	7 to 11	to 1/800	to 900	200-275	160-220	6-14

See Illustrated Section.

little scientific care.

CLASS 5: FIBERS. See above under USES, Class 5.

SHEEP RANGE. The large grazing areas for sheep in the Western sheep-raising areas; may run for hundreds of square miles.

SHEEP SHEARING. Clipping of the fleece from the hide of the animal. Done annually in the spring, except in Texas and California, where, due to climatic conditions, the sheep are shorn biannually. Texas and California wools bring a lower price in the market because the fleeces are more or less infested with small spiral burrs that are detrimental until removed from the fleece. Much of this wool, however, is of good quality.

Hand or power clippers are used in shearing. There are professional shearers who travel from place to place to perform the work. They are paid so much per fleece. In the shearing season these workers shear from sunup to sundown on a piecework basis. Good shearers are usually extremely well paid.

The fleeces, as they are taken from the sheep, are thrown to a helper who stands at the top of a high stand which has the top of the burlap bag fastened to it. This tender boy drops the fleeces, as he catches them, into the bag so that they can be moved quickly from place to place.

Shearing is now done on a scientific basis and the old days of butchering the animals to get the wool are now a memory. The Government and State College Experimental Farms have done much to improve the methods of shearing and care of the animals in all respects.

SHEEPSKIN. 1. Sheepskin with the wool still on the pelt or skin. Uses include basis for "mouton fur coats," jackets for aviators and folks who live in very cold climates, garments, gloves, laprobes, etc.

2. Serves as the parchment for college degrees.

3. The leather taken and prepared from the skin of the animal following the removal of the wool fibers. Often finished to simulate more expensive leathers.

SHEEP STATION. The sheep farm

in Australia. Station wagons are used for some communication and transportation.

SHEEP TICK. A wingless pest which lives on sheep and sucks their blood. Sheep are often dipped in larkspur solution or other dips to kill the insect.

SHEEP WOOL. Wool from the sheep is unique in that it is the only natural fiber that will felt in a natural manner. The fiber is made of overlapping scales or serrations which vary with the several grades of wool; there are from 600 to 3,000 to the inch. The structure of the fiber is comparable with the scales on a fish or an asparagus tip. Wool is warm, springy, elastic, may be harsh. It is the weakest of all major fibers; is a generator of heat, thereby giving warmth to the body in cold crisp weather.

There are five general types of wool: fine wools, medium wools, long or Luster wools, carpet wools, crossbreed wool. On the four-point method of classifying wool the table includes combing, carding, clothing, carpet wools.

See Illustrated Section.

SHEER. A group of fabrics, now chiefly made of cotton, rayon, or acetate, that are light and diaphanous; examples include certain crepes, georgettes, velvets, chiffons, organdies, and voiles.

SHEERSET. A registered trade-mark name owned by American Cyanamid Company, for a resin product finish, based on melamine, for application to cotton, viscose rayon, and acetate sheer-woven fabrics and mixtures, as a durable wash-resistant, crisp, resilient finish, imparting shrinkage control and stabilization. Keep fabrics crisply beautiful in damp weather, fresh and new looking after repeated washings. Minimizes lint and fuzz; imparts soil resistance; assures less laundering and thus less wear, hence longer life. No starch required. Chemically it is a melamine formaldehyde condensate in combination with other resin types and pigments.

SHEET. The large, rectangular percale or muslin spread over the mattress on a bed. See SHEETING.

SHEETING. Plain-weave carded or

combed cloth which comes in light, medium, and heavy weights. Sheeting for converting purposes is usually about 40 inches wide. There are four types, at present:

1. 64 x 64 (64-square), usually made from 20s or 21s yarn.

2. 68 x 76, made from 25s yarn.

3. 84 x 92, made from 30s to 40s yarn.

4. 96 x 108, made from 40s yarn, upwards.

Laundries buy sheeting in the following sizes:

1. 99″ long by 36″ wide.

2. 99″ by 72″.

3. 108″ by 72″.

4. 99″ by 81″.

5. 108″ by 81″.

Industrial sheeting serves as backing for artificial leather, boot and shoe lining, etc. Sizing is an important item in making good sheeting since strength, flexibility, stretchless backing, body, durability, and firmness are essential. Sheeting of the present day is made on high-speed, automatic looms which require a careful sizing treatment to insure high production. The size must be such that it can be removed easily in bleaching and other finishing operations which follow weaving.

Sheeting textures are often lower when compared with some print cloths; warp counts may be heavier than the filling yarns used, or they can be of the same yarn count. Because of its great use in industry, sheeting is now woven any width to meet consumer demands. It comes in the following classifications—coarse, ordinary, lightweight, narrow, soft-filled, and wide. It may be unbleached, semibleached, fullbleached, or colored.

SHEET WADDING. Cotton wadding or stuffing pressed into sheet form for use in tailored garments for shoulder padding, muff linings, and quilted robes of several types.

SHELGA. A tweed of the frieze type, made of the best Cheviot yarn; the fabric is made of vivid colors.

SHELL COTTON. Excessive seed coverings or fleshy kernels found in cotton and classed as heavy impurities.

SHELL HEM. A scallop-like edge finish used generally in underwear. The finish is made by turning under a narrow hem and scalloping it by passing the thread over the hem at regular intervals.

SHELL-LESS WASHER. A laundry washwheel made without an inner cylinder, and built on the principle of timed introduction and withdrawal of the detergent solutions and rinses.

SHELL-OFF. Also called sloughing-off, it is a comparatively large collection of filling yarn which "lumps-off" the filling bobbin during weaving.

SHELL ROLL. A drawing roll of the central arbor type over which sets a thin metal tube, or shell, whose function it is to carry the covering material for the bosses.

SHELL TUCKS. Hand-run tucks on a soft fabric. This effect may be obtained by applying the same procedure as when making a shell hem.

SHELTER TENT DUCK. See DUCK.

SHEMBANON. A commercial variety of Burmese raw cotton.

SHEPHERD. The individual who cares for the flock of sheep. The best shepherds in this country appear to be Mexicans or Spanish Americans, as they prefer to be known.

The shepherd, as soon as the winter snows have disappeared, moves his flock of a thousand or more ewes and lambs to the pasture lands. Rams are kept at home. The movement of flocks begins in the middle of May and continues through June. Sheep travel about ten miles a day; very often, however, the animals are sent by truck to their summer mountain resorts and these distances may be two hundred or more miles from the ranch.

Pasture lands are ideal when they are over 8,000 feet above sea level. The sheep seem to find all the crags and slopes in the mountains for forage.

The shepherd has to continually watch and guard his flock. One sheep in every hundred wears a bell, hence the term, bellwether. There is also a black sheep in the same fold. Twice daily the shepherd checks his bellwethers and black sheep. If either happens to be missing it also indicates that other sheep in the flock have gone astray or have been attacked by bears, coyotes, or other predatory animals. All told, sheep seem to stay close to their shepherd.

Sheep, "the most helpless and most stupid of animals," rely more on man for attention, care, and direction than any other domesticated animal which serves mankind. While sheep are supposed to be the "dumbest of dumb animals," man, nevertheless, would have a difficult time without them since they furnish both food and clothing—something no other animal can do for the welfare of man to any such degree.

SHEPHERD'S CHECK OR PLAID. Used for suitings, cap cloth, coatings, dress goods, sportswear. Made of cotton, woolen, worsted, or silk. The cloth shows black and white checks or plaids. Other color combinations are used as well. The design resembles the Scotch shepherd plaid or check. Some of the cloth, because of the color combinations used, has the tendency to cause the eyes to "jump" and some people soon tire of it. Conservative designs, however, are much in demand by the trade. There is a wide range of quality and price. In producing the check the warp and filling arrangement is four black and four white, ends and picks. The weave should begin with the "raisers" up in the lower left-hand corner of the weave. If this is not adhered to, a straight check will result which is not, strictly speaking, what is known as shepherd's plaid.

The pattern is found in particular fabrics made from any of the major fibers. See OVERPLAID, GLEN URQUHART.

SHESH. The word means six in Hebrew, and the Egyptians made a linen fabric with a six-ply yarn in it. See SHASH.

SHETLAND. 1. A suiting fabric made wholly or part of Shetland wool. The cloth has a raised finish and a rather soft handle. Very popular for suiting and sportswear.

2. A soft knitted fabric made of Shetland wool.

3. Loosely applied to various soft-handle woven or knitted fabrics that do not contain Shetland wool.

SHETLAND FINISH. The characteristic shaggy finish of protruding fibers on many woolen cloths. The fabric does not necessarily have to be made of Shetland wool to use the name.

SHETLAND SHEEP. Originated in the islands of this name off the coast of Scotland. This primitive breed has been modified by crossbreeding with Blackface and Cheviot sheep. These hardy sheep grow a coarse outer coat of fibers and a fine under coat which gives added warmth to cope with the severe winter weather in this area.

SHETLAND WOOL. Shetland produces fine, lustrous fiber, and the real wool is the undergrowth found under the longer fibers. It is not shorn, but is pulled out by hand in the spring of the year. Comes in white, brown, and gray casts and is classed as a costly fiber.

Uses of Shetland include hosiery, underwear, fine shawls, crochet work and apparel fabric for men and women. Shetland cloth is in the same family group as homespun, tweed, and Cheviot.

SHIBORI. Japanese for tie-dyeing; gay colorings feature fabrics dyed this way.

SHIELD. An underarm protector used to absorb perspiration.

SHIFT DIFFERENTAL. Pay allowance made to employees who work on shifts other than during the regular day-shift hours.

SHIKEGINU. Douppioni silk is used to make this Japanese habutai fabric. See DOUPPIONI.

SHIKIFUGI. Japanese term for bedsheeting made of cotton.

SHIMA MOMEM. Japanese term for cotton cloth made with stripes.

SHINAWATA COTTON. Chinese cotton shipped to Japan.

SHINE EARLY COTTON. An Uplands cotton developed from Rio Grande seed; the staple is less than 1 inch, lint yield is about 24 per cent.

SHINERS. Defects in filament rayon, acetate or silks—caused by poor winding which gives a flatness to yarn that will cause the rays of light to show up the defect; found in all types of cloth at times.

Rayon does not have the elasticity of cotton, silk, or wool. When stretched, it remains in that condition, thereby causing the shiner effect.

Shiners may be caused by shuttle friction since too much friction in the mouth of the shuttle will give this detrimental effect in woven cloth; hence, the reason why rabbit friction-skin is now universally used on the inside length of the shuttle and not in the mouth.

SHINS. Short, thick, straight, glossy wool called shank wool in the trade.

SHINY THREAD. A linen gimp yarn used as the outline for the pattern in lace made in Devonshire, England.

SHIRLAN EXTRA. An inexpensive mildew inhibitor used on materials that require very little treatment.

SHIRLEY CLOTH. A cotton fabric made of long-staple mercerized yarns, and so constructed that water repellence is achieved without the addition of chemicals.

SHIRO-MOMEM. Japanese term for plain cotton goods in the gray or in the bleached state. Made on hand looms, the goods are used for apparel and some of the fabric is dyed a solid color, usually blue.

SHIRRED FABRICS. Material that has rubber or elastic threads in the construction, as in the case of suspenderings, garter elastic, and materials made with Lastex.

SHIRRING. A series of parallel runs of stitches forming decorative fullness or gathers in a fabric.

SHIRRING STAY. A strip of tape or material sewn over shirring on the wrong side to keep the gathers in place.

SHIRT. Cotton muslin used on silk bales that come from Asia.

SHIRT, FRENCH FRONT. Also called mitred front, this type shirt features fine front tailoring which is made by reinforcing a plain lap of shirting fabric with a lining and sewing it in place with a single row of stitching.

SHIRT, ORIGIN OF THE WORD. A derivation from the Scandinavian root, *Skar*, which means "to cut off," applied to a garment that reaches to the area of the waist. Icelandic word for a short garment is *Skyrte* and the Danish word is *Skiorte*, both derived from *Skar*.

SHIRT BOX PLEAT FRONT. A type of shirt front made by stitching a length of the shirting fabric and a piece of lining for reinforcement with a two-needle machine to the edge of the shirt front.

SHIRT GUSSET. A triangular peice of fabric situated at the bottom of the side seam to reinforce the shirt at a point where the hemmed front joins the hemmed back.

SHIRTING. The Anglo-Saxon root means "short garment." Other early interpretations were "shert" and "split camise." The latter term is now called chemise. There are men's shirts for outerwear; women's for underwear. Most of the latter are of silk, rayon, or acetate yarn.

Some shirting on the market today includes broadcloth, Cheviot, dress shirting, Jacquard, jersey, madras, Oxford, plain, Russian cord, satin striped, and work shirting.

SHIRTING, FANCY. One woven in a motif with stripes or small designs, geometrical or otherwise, in all-white or in colors. Many dobby designs are popular in shirting fabric.

SHIRTING CHAMBRAY. Popular, lightweight shirting made from colored warp and white filling, both of which are made of singles combed yarn. The fabric comes in plain-weave construction, dobby or Jacquard effects on plain ground or in the popular end-and-end arrangement in the warp which gives a small pin effect. Textures are 140 to 160 square. See CHAMBRAY.

SHIRTING FLANNEL. Plain- or twill-woven fabric used for shirting. Characterized by its nap, the material may be plain or colored either by dyeing or printing. Made of wool, worsted, cotton, rayon staple, blends, etc.

SHIRTING TEXTURES AND SIZES.

1. BROADCLOTH	100 to 136 by 60 to 64.	
2. MADRAS	80 to 84 by 72 to 80.	
3. OXFORD	88 to 90 by 40 to 50.	
4. COMMON		
PRINT CLOTH 80 square by 68 to 72.		

Sizes range from 13½ to 18; sleeve length from 31 inches to 37 inches; Chest, from 39½ inches to 57½ inches; waist, from 36½ inches to 55½ inches.

SHIRT TURNER. One who turns partially completed shirt parts right-side-out, by machine, in order to prepare these for further processing.

SHIRTWAIST. A casual type of garment made with loose fitted waist with an opening in the front; full or slim skirt usually made with a convertible or notched collar. Sleeves are usually short tailored sleeves or long shirt sleeves. See Silhouette.

SHIVE, SHOVE. 1. Woody fragments and wastes obtained in breaking and scutching flax. 2. Vegetable matter other than burrs found in a sheep fleece.

SHIVER. Former name for a spindle.

SHIVY WOOL. Vegetable matter found in wool—burrs, dried grass, fodder, motes, shives, etc. In some circles the meaning implies vegetable matter other than burrs found in wool.

SHODDY. This term refers to re-worked fibers, of which there are two sources:

Fibers recovered from new rags or tailor clippings which were never part of a worn garment.

Fibers recovered from old rags which were part of worn garments.

In either case, reprocessing tends to weaken the fibers. It is significant to note that a good shoddy made from high-grade woolen rags may be of better quality than a lower grade fleece wool.

The poorest grade of shoddy is obtained from felted material and is known as mungo.

SHODDY MIXTURE YARN. This type of stock when used in woolen yarn cannot be drawn to any great extent. The drawings must be taken and considered from the basic quality in comparison with straight wool mixes. An average shoddy mixture stock, combined with wool to obtain a 10-cut yarn, would admit of only a one-fifth draw on the spinning frame; a 20-cut yarn would have a one-third draw on the mule frame.

This yarn is used for dress goods, cheap suitings, blankets of many types, robes, flannels, blazer cloth, lounging robes, Roman stripe fabrics and other fancies.

SHODDY PICKER. See GARNETTING.

SHODDY WOOL. Remanufactured wool fibers are obtained from the gar-

times referred to as splash-resistant, the term implies fabric which is resistant to light rains or showers. The treatment is such that washing or dry cleaning will gradually remove the finish-coating, thereby diminishing its effectiveness.

SHREDDER. Soft, damp sheets of alkali cellulose, in viscose rayon, are taken from the presses and dropped into a crumbing or shredding machine, technically called a pfleiderer. The shredder is equipped with a set of revolving blades which tear the sheets and break them up into small, fluffy particles. These alkali cellulose crumbs are then aged carefully with chemical action in constant progress. The time and temperature of the aging is controlled to insure a uniform product.

SHREDDING. The grinding of cellulose sheets after they have been treated in a caustic soda solution, a process in the manufacture of viscose rayon. See CRUMBS.

SHRINKAGE. 1. The contraction and increase of density of textile fibers and yarns causing a change in shape and size of textile fabrics. Moisture, mechanical, and chemical actions are the main causes of shrinkage in laundering. When fabrics are shrunk there is a loss in length, width, area, weight, etc. Textile testing is resorted to in order to assure residual results, which will be satisfactory to the buyer of the material in question.

2. The loss in wool scouring when yolk, suint, and other foreign matter are removed from the actual wool fibers in the piece. Fully scoured wool is called the yield, scoured state, or clean basis. The greater the loss in weight and volume, the higher will be the quality of the wool.

3. Testing a material in order to remove any tendencies it might have toward shrinking and to inform the customer with regard to residual shrinkage of the goods in question.

4. Woolens and worsteds are "preshrunk" before they are sent to the cutting-up house for "cut-fit-trim." Done with steam or cold water.

SHRINKAGE CONTROL. Any method which aims to hold the shrinkage of fabrics within stated limits. This may be achieved by special construction, chemical treatment, fabric compression, etc.

SHRINKAGE OF LINEN. This is brought about by the natural methods of wetting and sunning, by artificial drying, and by special chemical and machine methods.

SHRINKPROOF. A fabric or garment that is free from any residual shrinkage, a term that is used indiscrim-

inately in advertising. There is much difference between shrinkproof and preshrinking, the latter meaning that a fabric or garment has been given a shrinking process before being marketed. The percentage of residual shrinkage should be declared.

SHROPSHIRE. This county in England is the home of this popular British Down breed. Noted for both wool and mutton production. Staple is about three inches, the fleece weight averages nine pounds, and the quality ranges from 50s to 56s.

SHROUD LAID. Rope with a core thread and four strands wound around it.

SHROUD ROPE. A high-grade, three-ply roping used as standard rigging on ships. Also implies the nylon cord used on parachutes.

SHRUG SWEATER. See WOMEN'S AND MISSES' SWEATERS.

SHRUNK FINISH. 1. Finish on a fabric that has been shrunk to a specific residual finish. Can be used for collar lining.

2. Finish on a cloth shrunken-in from the reed width in the loom to some set width. All cloths will shrink naturally. The use of the term implies that, for example, a fabric could be shrunk from 38 inches to 36 inches, finished width; from 32 inches to 29 inches, etc.

SHUBNAM. An excellent quality Persian muslin that compares with Dacca muslin and Indian Shabnam. The cloth is made in a 20-yard length and is 36 inches wide; weight is 10 to 13 ounces. There are 700 to 1,300 ends in the warp; cotton counts are 200s, upwards.

SHULAH WOOL. Gray wool from the Shetland Islands.

SHURLED HOGGETT. The first fleece from a sheep after it has been shorn as a lamb.

SHUSU. Japanese for a silk fabric made with a satin weave.
SHUSU HABUTAI. Japanese term for habutai made with a satin weave. See HABUTAI.

SHUTE. British term for shot or filling pick. See SHOT.

SHUTTLE. The device which carries the filling yarn in its course through the shed of the loom in weaving fabric. See Illustrated Section. Power loom shuttles are made of dogwood or persimmon, properly aged. There is a metal tip at each end of a shuttle. The filling bobbin is set into the open space provided for it in the shuttle, and there is an eyelet at one end so that the filling may unwind rapidly as it is shot through the shed from the shuttle box

on the one side of the loom to the box on the other side of the machine. Worsted looms average about 125 picks per minute; that is, the shuttle flies back and forth that number of times per minute from box to box. This number may vary somewhat, depending on the fabric being made and other local conditions.

In hand weaving very lightweight shuttles are often used when weaving woolen or worsted yarn, since there will be very little "pull" on the weft or filling yarn. A so-called stick shuttle is used for coarse, hand-woven fabrics, netting needles for lace weaves and picture weaving.

SHUTTLE AND BOBBIN. The device which holds the bobbin of filling. It passes through the warp shed, which is formed by the raising and the lowering of the respective warp ends. The harnesses and heddles accomplish this raising and lowering of the warp ends.

The filling yarn is wound on a bobbin which sets in the shuttle. The yarn is unwound and left in the shed of the loom when the shuttle passes through this shed. The reed then beats the loose weft pick into its component place in material.

SHUTTLE BINDER. A lever that slightly projects into the shuttle box. Its function is to check the force of the shuttle as it enters the box, and to work with the protector motion to keep the shuttle from becoming trapped in the loom shed.

SHUTTLE BOXES. The containers on each side of the loom that receive the shuttle as it comes through the shed of the loom. Shuttles fit very snugly into the boxes. They are forced and thrown from the boxes by the picker stick, which is located at the end of the lay of the loom. Lug straps and rocker arms aid the picker stick in its action.

Cotton, silk, woolen, and worsted looms are made with a single box, that is, one box on each side, also a 2-to-1 box plan (two boxes on one side, one on the other side); likewise, on a 4-to-1 plan, and a 4-and-4 plan, known as a pick-and-pick loom, as well as a 6-to-1 arrangement. In the 2-to-1, 4-to-1, and 6-to-1 plans the filling is inserted in multiples of two. In the pick-and-pick plan, 4 by 4, the filling can be inserted 1-to-1 as to arrangement and seven different colors or shades can be used.

SHUTTLE DEFLECTOR. A long rod, securely fastened in the reed cap of the loom. It sets above the reed and the top portion of the shed in the loom. If a shuttle flies out of the shed and works free, it will come in contact with the deflector and be thrown toward the floor. This device has prevented many serious accidents to weavers from flying

netting machine treatment, which tears apart and shreds the discarded garments fed to the machine. Shoddy comes from woolen, worsted, or knitted garments. The shoddy or mungo fibers are mixed with better-quality and long-staple fibers, to make up new material to be made ultimately into fabric.

SHOE CLOTH. Worsted fabric made on corkscrew weaves and used for spat material and shoe cloth. The weight of the material is from 12 to 18 ounces per yard, and a feature is the high, compact texture—from 80 to 140 each way. Two-ply worsted yarn is used in the warp; filling is wool, worsted, or cotton and is usually single-ply.

Gabardine and other high texture twill fabrics are used for women's shoes; canvas, duck, and similar materials are used for men's shoes.

SHOE DUCK. See DUCKS, SHOE.

SHOE FOLD. Material that is folded from both ends into twelve or sixteen folds to be cut or pieced. The length of the fold will depend on the length of the bolt.

SHOE LEATHER. A self-explanatory term which embraces a large variety of leathers. 1. Sole leather is made from cattlehides and buffalo hides. It covers the superior grades that are used for the outer soles and the lighter grades and offal (head, shoulders, and bellies) that are used to some extent for heels, insoles, toecaps, counters, etc. 2. Upper leather comes chiefly from calfskins, goatskins, cattlehides, horsehides, and other groups of animal skins, for shoe uppers. 3. Miscellaneous shoe leathers include facing stock, lining stock, tongue stock, and welting.

SHOESTRING, SHOE LACE. A braid used to lace or tie shoes; also made with leather or fancy, narrow ribbon or braid.

SHOE TIE. Wider than a shoelace, it is a fancy braid used to lace a shoe.

SHOE TOP SILK. Heavy silk cloth that has a rather elaborate figured design; twill or satin weaves are used. The warp is of expensive, fancy, or novelty yarn, and the filling is usually cotton. The fabric is substantial, rough, and uneven in feel; gives good wear because of the manner of construction. It is used in footwear, chiefly for evening shoes.

SHOE VELVET. A dense, rather heavy, erect short pile fabric used in shoe manufacture. The pile is made of nylon, rayon, or silk, with a cotton backing.

SHOG. See RACK OR SHOG.

SHOGGED STITCH. A stitch used in forming the edges of knitted fabric.

SHOOT. A filling pick in the carpet-weaving trade.

SHOOTS, SPROUTS, OR STRAGGLERS. Individual loose or straggling fibers which show above the surface of a fabric, especially in pile materials. While not actually a blemish or defect, conditions of this sort are done away with by clipping the yarn with shears or scissors. Floorcoverings are given special attention for this undesirable effect.

SHOP CARD. A poster that indicates that the company has an agreement with a union.

SHOP STEWARD. See STEWARD.

SHORT. A cotton trader who is short is one who has contracted to deliver a specified amount of cotton, not owned by him, at some definite future date. The trader hopes that the price will decrease in order that he may buy the cotton at a lower price than that at which he sold. If the price, however, rises, he usually will settle the account by paying to the other party in the deal the cash difference between the market price on date of settlement and the price fixed in the futures contract.

Most long and short futures contracts are ultimately settled with cash payments which reflect the difference between the price fixed in the contract and the so-called "spot market" price of the date of settlement.

SHORT BATH. When the volume of liquid is small in comparison with the amount of material being treated.

SHORT HOSE. Scotch hose that reaches just below the knee; used in sportswear and kiltie attire.

SHORTS. Term has meanings as follows:

1. Colloquial term for short trousers or gym trunks. Shaped with a crotch, they serve as undergarments or outergarments for men, women, and children. Women's shorts are usually fashioned with pleats in a skirt effect. Men's shorts for inner wear are white or striped and are made of rayon, silk, cotton, spun rayon, or mixed yarns.

2. Piece of material not sufficiently long to be sold on contract at the full price. Usually expressed as 20/40 yard lengths, 10/20s, 1/10s, etc., and sold at discount price.

3. The name given to short wool and to silk noil.

4. A cotton merchant who is actually short in cotton; he has taken a chance and sold more cotton than he owns and therefore assumes a pending liability. A drop in the price of cotton will aid him to recoup his possible loss through the liability. The opposite of Longs.

SHORT-STAPLE COTTON. In this country any fiber less than 1⅛ inches; in foreign countries the cleavage line is either ⅞ inch or 1 inch.

SHOT. Several meanings:

1. A streak or defect made by a thread of unusual color or size.

2. A yarn or thread actually sent through the shed of the loom as a single pick by the shuttle.

3. A filling pick used in rug weaving to bind the pile to the back of the fabric. A two-shot rug will show a filling yarn between each two horizontal rows of tufts; the second filling is back of the row and will not show. In a three-shot construction two picks may be seen between the rows; the third pick is at the back of the goods and will not be visible. The three-shot plan, while more expensive to the consumer, does give better wear to the rug.

4. A contraction of the term "shot-about," where a "hit-or-miss" design is sometimes noted in certain cloths. This effect is accomplished by the use of multicolored warp and filling.

SHOT CLOTH. Colored cotton goods made with fine warp and filling of contrasting colors; the warp is one solid color, the filling, another. The cloth is made in all qualities and much of it is used for lining.

SHOT SILK. Term which signifies the use of two differently colored sets of yarn, warp, and filling, in order to give a changeable effect in the fabric. Silk taffeta is often made in this manner.

SHOTTING. English term which signifies the shedding action in weaving cloth on a loom.

SHOT YARN. The single filling used to weave gunny sacking.

SHOULDER HIDE. That part of a hide between the neck and a line cut across the hide from the center of the front flanks, about 50 inches from the butt of the tail of cattlehides.

SHOULDER PAD. A pad made from cotton wadding used in coats to raise the outer part of the shoulder level and give a broad effect.

SHOVES. Broken, immature, undesirable flax fibers remaining after scutching; used for coarse bagging and roofing felt.

SHOWERPROOF. Some fabrics are treated chemically and by the addition of a wax coating may be made to repel water. Cloth thus treated is more hygienic than nonporous rubber fabric since air cannot circulate through the latter.

SHOWER REPELLENCY. Some-

shuttles.

SHUTTLE GUARD. See SHUTTLE DEFLECTOR.

SHUTTLELESS LOOM, CLUTSON & KEMP. This is a multihead narrow fabric loom which can operate at a speed of 1,300 picks per minute. A needle combined with a rotating batten inserts the filling yarn into the loom. It can make elastic or rigid fabric and the loom is operated largely by cams that are synchronized to permit the needle to cross and withdraw during a one-quarter revolution of the batten. Thus four double picks are inserted for every revolution of the batten. Maximum fabric width is two inches and there are 8 harness shafts to control the construction. Picks may be adjusted from 18 to 80 per inch and the loom comes with either 12 or 16 weaving heads.

SHUTTLE MARKS. When a shuttle, prior to its work in the loom, takes on oil, grease, or other detrimental matter, the effects are almost certain to be seen in the woven gray cloth. These marks, which give no little trouble in finishing cloth, are often caused by carelessness on the part of the weaver.

It is almost impossible to remove shuttle marks from cloth during finishing. Sometimes the blemish is caused by the filling being pressed against the binder and the resultant mark is squeezed into the fibers or filaments of filling yarn.

SHUTTLER. Embroidery machine worker who loads shuttles with bobbins, assists the watcher of the frame when he desires information on a shuttle problem at the front of the machine, as well as helping with loading or spanning, unloading, and rollovers. See Watcher, Spanner, Rollover.

SHUTTLE SKIPPING. This gives the effect of a filling which lies loose on the top of the cloth as it is being woven in the loom while there is a mispick underneath the loose filling. Usually caused by a shuttle "jumping-out" of the warp shed of yarn; utmost attention must be given to prevent shuttles flying out of the loom.

SHUTTLE SMASH PROTECTOR. A long rod, securely fastened, and connected at the tips with a shuttle binder and at the dagger end of the lay. If the shuttle does not go into its shuttle box in the regulation manner, this motion will cause the loom to bang-off at once.

SHUTTLE-THROWING ASSEMBLY. The device which causes the shuttle in a loom to be thrown through the shed; the shuttle, which has the filling yarn wound on it, deposits the filling pick in this space between the raised and lowered warp ends that constitute the shed of the loom. The shuttle travels from a shuttle box on one side of the loom, and then passes over the raceplate to a shuttle box on the other side of the machine.

SHUTTLE TYPES; HAND-LOOM.
1. Stick Shuttle: A flat stick on which the weft threads are wound. Also called Poke Shuttle.
2. Blanket Shuttle: A wide shuttle on which heavy weft yarns are wound.
3. Boat Shuttle: A boat-shaped shuttle which can carry a bobbin. Also known as Throw Shuttle.
4. Fly Shuttle: Similar to the boat type but worked by pulling a cord. When used in true commercial sense this type of shuttle is automatic.

SICILIAN CLOTH. Lightweight summer wear dress goods and suiting cloth made of cotton warp and mohair, wool, or man-made yarn for filling. The cloth comes in solid colors or may be striped. The heavier type of Sicilian is made of silk or rayon warp and cotton or wool filling, and resembles heavy poplin.

SICILIENNE. Material made of silk or rayon warp and cotton or woolen filling, on the order of bengaline; never a very popular material.

SICK LEAVE. The period of time requested by an employee to recuperate from a personal illness or accident, during which time he is permitted to retain his employment rights.

SIDA FIBER. An Indian bast fiber closely resembling jute; has longer fibers, less impurities, is easier to manipulate, and superior in all respects to jute. The fiber is silklike, lustrous, and finer, brighter, and whiter than jute. Also known as Sufet Bariata, the fiber is processed like jute.

SIDA RETUSA. An Australian plant which yields less than 2 per cent actual bast fiber; used for cordage.

SIDE. One half of a cowhide after cutting down the backbone of the pelt with the head, belly, and shoulder attached.

SIDEBAND CHECKS. British fabric exported to the African markets. They are plain-weave cottons textured at 64-square, with yarns used about 24s to 28s. Made in cuts of 27 yards, the material has a firm body finish and there are colored stripes at the edges of the goods. The cloth is made with small, colored check effects.

SIDES. That part of a Jacquard frame which supports the various moving parts and forms the framework of the machine.

SIDE, SIDE-UPPER LEATHER. A type of shoe upper leather that consists of the grain or hair side of cattlehides finished in a variety of grains or colors. The name originated from the practice of slitting a hide along the backbone into two halves or sides.

SIDE-STITCHED SEAM. Seam that is pressed to one side and stitched down on both sides.

SIDPAT. Indian sailcloth.

SIDSHILLAT. An Indian linen printed with small figures.

SIGN CLOTH. Cheesecloth, medium count print cloth, or bleached sheeting serves as the basis for painting signs that are not to be permanent. The fabric to be used must be heavily filled with starch and China clay. Improved qualities of sign fabric are now pyroxylin-treated.

SIKKIM. India furnishes this Bera breed of sheep, which has a coarse, ashy-type wool which on annual clippage basis produces a fleece of only three pounds.

SILENCE CLOTH. 1. Used as a padding material to be placed under the tablecloth on the dining table; lessens the noise of dishes and protects the table finish. A rather thick material, given considerable napping so that it will best serve its purpose, silence cloth is known also as molleton. 2. A type of monk's cloth used as drapery or wall fabric in broadcasting studios to deaden sound.

SILESIA OR SILICIA. 1. One cloth of this name is classed as a fine, window Holland or shade cloth. It is heavily sized and given a glazed finish.

2. Another cloth is a lining material made usually in gray or black, well calendered and given a smooth, luster finish. A three-harness, filling twill weave is used in construction.

3. Silesia is the name given to merino wool of Austria, the same as Saxony implies wool of that grade raised in Germany. It is a Class 1 wool, comparable with Ohio merino in this country. This wool ranges from 1 to 2½ inches in fiber length, has a diameter of about $\frac{1}{1700}$ inch, about 2,800 serrations to the inch, with a fleece weight of 16 to 19 pounds. Silesia wool is used for the better quality worsted fabrics.

SILHIGON FIBER. A species of Sida bast fiber found in the Philippines; used by natives for clothing and twine.

SILHOUETTE. The outline or contour of a figure or costume. The new silhouette of any fashion season means the general contour in fashion at the particular time, especially as to skirt length or width, shoulder width, etc., in contrast to the popular, accepted silhouettes of the previous season. See Princess Line, Shirtwaist, Sheath, Shift.

SILICA. A chemical substance known as silicon dioxide or silicic acid anhydride.

SILICATE. A combination of silica with some neutralizing base.

SILICATE OF SODA, WATER-GLASS. A solution of silicate solids containing about 37 per cent of the latter and 63 per cent water. Of low alkaline value and a hard rinser.

SILICON. A nonmetallic element, which in regard to its abundance in nature ranks next to oxygen; is usually found combined with this to form silica. Comes in crystal, powder, and scale forms.

SILICONE. Generic term for one of a class of organic chemical compounds, based on the partial substitution of silicon for carbon. Obtained from silicon, a component of sand, it is used to protect fabrics against spotting, soiling, and wetting; also used as a softening agent in finishing fabrics.

SILING. This native sheep of the Himalaya Mountains area gives a short but fine diameter wool fiber.

SILK. The fine, strong, lustrous filament produced by various insect larvae, generally to form their cocoon or nest. The filaments obtained from the larvae of certain moths, raised for commercial purposes, will range from about 300 yards to about 1,600 yards. The middle third of the filament is even in diameter, while the beginning and end are rather uneven and often split and coarse. Caterpillars of the genus Bombyx and allied Bombycidea family spin the cocoons from which is reeled most of the silk that forms the basis of the commercial yarn.

The domesticated member of this is the *Bombyx mori* or common silkworm, a native of China. It feeds on mulberry leaves and their juices. The undomesticated silkworms belong to the Yama-Mai or other species and develop what is known as Tussah or Wild Silk. They are inferior in all respects to true silk and they feed on practically any type of leaf with which they come in contact.

The word silk is of Chinese origin, and for centuries has been linked with China. The very early name for China was Seres; sericulture is the raising of silkworms for market. Silk is a natural filament (fiber of indefinite length) that man with all his ingenuity has never really been able to duplicate for beauty of fabrics, fineness and texture. Silk is truly "The Cloth of Milady, the Queen of Fabrics." It is one of the strongest, most lustrous, and most expensive of textile fibers with the exception of vi-

cuna, the specialty hair from South America.

The raw silk thread of commerce, which may be said to be the backbone of China and Japan, is made from five to ten cocoons (ten to twenty filaments). Each cocoon emits two filaments when spinning the cocoon. These are known as "fibroin." A single filament is known as a "brins." The fibroin is cemented together, as it comes from the silkworm and emerges in the air, by what is known as "sericin" or silk gum. The brins, fibroin, and sericin combined are known as the "bave."

See Illustrated Section.

SILK, CHEMICAL FORMULA FOR. Fibroin is the raw silk fiber; Sericin is the silk gum which cements the two filaments emitted by the silkworm as it spins its cocoon. Fibroin, chemically is $C_{15}H_{23}N_5O_6$; Sericin is $C_{15}H_{25}N_5O_8$.

SILK, COHESION TEST FOR. This test will show if the silk has been reeied in a bath that was too hot. From this test it can be determined whether or not the silk will "open-up" well.

SILK, CROISE. The French word "croisé" means crossed. Thus, this silk cloth which is made with a twill weave will show a series of "crossed" or diagonal lines on the face of the goods, usually from the lower left to the upper right in direction.

SILK, DEGUMMING, BOILING-OFF, OR WASHING. These three terms are synonymous. Boiling-off must come after throwing, which embodies winding and twisting. The method in general use, degumming before weaving, is one in which the skeins of organzine or tram are boiled in soft water and soap.

Only pure, olive-oil soap that is free from alkali should be used. The best results are obtained in a bath that is just below the boiling point, because bubbles of escaping steam have the tendency to agitate the water so that the fibers may become matted and tangled.

A characteristic soap solution could be as follows:

1. Three pounds of soap to 12 gallons of water. The amount of soap depends on the condition of the silk.

2. Calculated on the weight of the silk, the quantity used is 25 per cent. This means that to boil-off 50 pounds of silk, 12.5 pounds of soap must be used.

3. Following the first soaking at or near the boil, for 15 minutes, the silk is placed in a second bath, which has only one half to two thirds as much soap. From this bath the silk goes to a rinsing bath of clear water. This bath,

to make the washing more effective, may contain a small percentage of pure washing soda, free from alkali.

SILK, DESIRABLE QUALITIES IN. Evenness, elasticity, strength, brilliancy, crossing, and freedom from imperfections.

SILK, FULLY DEGUMMED. Silk with all of the silk gum removed by the boil-out liquor. This amounts to from about 30 per cent in the best grades of silk to 10 per cent in the poorer qualities, on a total weight of 100-pound lots. The more the gum in silk, the greater is the quality of the fiber.

SILK, GREGE. French term which implies that it is a group of silk filaments run through some manipulation without twist being applied. May be converted into organize (warp) or tram (filling) by throwing operation. Grege means raw, in French; raw in Italian is greggia.

SILK, GROSS WEIGHT OF. The weight of the silk and all its wrappings. This is a crude weight, and cannot be considered accurate. The value of this weight is for comparison, and as a check from time to time for the gain or loss in moisture in various process periods, such as weighing-in and weighing-out of storage, or in the return of samples.

SILK, SHIRT WEIGHT OF: The weight of the silk, chop ticket, paper, strings around the book, shirt (muslin bale cover), and the two ropes that go around the shirt. This weight is an accurate one; and tests are made on two different scales, by two different weighers. Accuracy and closeness of results are strictly adhered to within 2/100 pound.

The bale is weighed in kilograms and is then transferred to another scale to be weighed in pounds. Error is prevented by this dual system. The scales are graduated to one hundredths.

SILK, SPIDER. There is some evidence that attempts have been made to use silk filament from spiders down through the centuries. This evidence, however, is inconclusive. The actual filament is often difficult to observe and some measurements show it to be as fine as 0.00001-inch in diameter.

In the second decade of the 18th century, a scientist named Bon, actually made a spider silk yarn in Languedoc, France. He even made stockings and gloves from his silk and showed these at the Academy of Science in Paris, in 1710.

During the years 1734-1742, Rene Reaumur, working on Bon's theories, announced that they were not practical. They did give him the idea, however, that filaments could be made chemically. Though

Reaumur pursued his findings and thoughts, it was left for the persons who followed him to perfect the manmade filaments as we know them today.

Some of these scientists were Louis Schwabe, Manchester, England (1804); Keller, Germany (1840); Schoenbein, Switzerland (1846); Audemars, Switzerland (1855); Schweitzer, England (1857); Sir Joseph W. Swan, England (1860); Naudin and Schutzenberger, Germany (1869); and Count Hilaire de Chardonnet, "Father of the Rayon Industry," Besancon, France (1885-89).

On May 12, 1884, the Count received a patent (Number 165, 349) for "une matiere textile artificielle resemblant a la soie." This was for the filament made by the nitro-cellulose method of producing what is today called rayon. This method became defunct in 1934 but was the first manmade filament to be commercially successful. See Audemars, de Chardonnet, Reaumur, Naudin and Schutzenberger, Schweitzer's Reagent.

SILK, TORS SANS FILE. Actually a silk yarn or thread that with regard to the twist factor is not as tightly twisted as organzine, used for silk warps, but has more twist than tram silk which is used for filling yarns in silk fabrics.

SILK, WOOD. One of several names applied to rayon before that term was coined in 1924. Prior to this year, some of the names given to what is today known as rayon include artificial silk, wood pulp silk, cellulose silk, luster silk, Glos, milkweed silk, etc.

SILKALINE. 1. A smooth, glossy, mercerized cotton yarn or thread which has a soft twist. Made to imitate silk threads, it is used for needlework of many types, lining, curtains, bedcovers, hand and pocket loom weaving, crochet work and trimming. It comes in all colors and shades and is ideal for working purposes.

2. A plain or printed fabric that does not have a permanent or lasting finish. The finish is soft and glazed and is produced by the friction-calender method. One advantage of the cloth is that it does not soil easily. Plain-weave is used in this lining, comforter, and curtain material.

SILK AND MAN-MADE FABRICS, CLASSIFICATION OF. Since several man-made yarns are used to make fabrics which may or may not be competitors of silk, and take the same name as the original silk fabric, the following outline, in a general manner, classifies the staple materials in use today made of silk, rayon, acetate, nylon, etc.

1. ARMURES: These cloths are made from a fine ground of fancy twill construction.

BARATHEA: Cloth which has a broken rep effect.

LOUISINE.

NATTE.

OTTOMAN.

REP OR REPP.

ROYALE.

TRICOTINE: A fine matt or check effect is used for the design.

2. DIAPHANOUS TABBY OR PLAIN WEAVE CLOTHS:

AEROPHANE.

ALTESSE: A very fine crepe construction material.

CREPE DE CHINE.

CREPON.

EUROPEAN HABUTAI: A plain silk voile.

FOULARD DE CHINE OR "CHINA GUM CLOTH": The material is woven in a damp condition and is printed with spot designs.

GEORGETTE CREPE.

MARQUISETTE.

NINON.

VOILE.

3. FANCY AND FIGURED FABRICS:

BROCADE: A floral or figured silk fabric made with ground and fancy

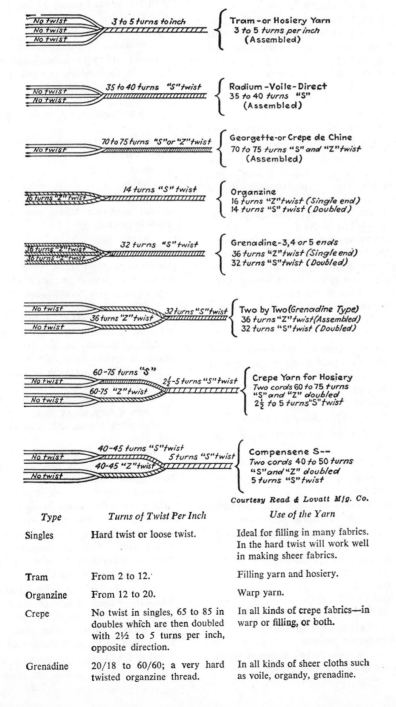

TWIST IN SILK YARNS AND THREAD

Tram - or Hosiery Yarn
3 to 5 turns per inch
(Assembled)

Radium - Voile - Direct
35 to 40 turns "S"
(Assembled)

Georgette - or Crepe de Chine
70 to 75 turns "S" and "Z" twist
(Assembled)

Organzine
16 turns "Z" twist (Single end)
14 turns "S" twist (Doubled)

Grenadine - 3, 4 or 5 ends
36 turns "Z" twist (Single end)
32 turns "S" twist (Doubled)

Two by Two (Grenadine Type)
36 turns "Z" twist (Assembled)
32 turns "S" twist (Doubled)

Crepe Yarn for Hosiery
Two cords 60 to 75 turns
"S" and "Z" doubled
2½ to 5 turns "S" twist

Compensene S--
Two cords 40 to 50 turns
"S" and "Z" doubled
5 turns "S" twist

Courtesy Read & Lovatt Mfg. Co.

Type	Turns of Twist Per Inch	Use of the Yarn
Singles	Hard twist or loose twist.	Ideal for filling in many fabrics. In the hard twist will work well in making sheer fabrics.
Tram	From 2 to 12.	Filling yarn and hosiery.
Organzine	From 12 to 20.	Warp yarn.
Crepe	No twist in singles, 65 to 85 in doubles which are then doubled with 2½ to 5 turns per inch, opposite direction.	In all kinds of crepe fabrics—in warp or filling, or both.
Grenadine	20/18 to 60/60; a very hard twisted organzine thread.	In all kinds of sheer cloths such as voile, organdy, grenadine.

weaves.

BROCHE: A brocaded silk material.

CHECKS.

CHEVRON EFFECTS.

CHINE: A warp-printed silk or rayon.

DAMASSIN.

FIGURED MOIRE ANTIQUE: A fabric made with floral satin stripes with alternate moire stripes.

FIGURED TISSUES.

FIGURED TABARET: Made in warp-effect satin weaves to give a floral or figured effect in moire, rep or other fancy ground weaves.

FOULARD.

LOSANGE.

MATELASSE: A figured double cloth.

PEKIN NOUVEAUTE: A rich, ribbon-like fabric, Pekin nouveauté has raised chainlike borders in two colors to give a corded appearance.

PRINTED PIECE GOODS.

REP BOYAUX: A fancy fabric made with Bedford-cord or piqué construction.

STRIPE EFFECTS.

STRIPED TABARET: Made with alternate stripes of rep and satin, cord effects, or in combinations of two or more fancy-ground weaves.

TAFFETA BOYAUX AND PICOTÉS: Checks and small figures are features of this material.

4. FIGURED MATERIALS FOR FURNITURE:

ARRAS: True Arras is an all-silk tapestry material. It is, however, also made from other raw materials—cotton, linen, wool, and worsted in imitation of the genuine silk fabric.

BROCATELLE: A floral or figured rep cloth woven in two or more colors.

COTELINE: Recognized by its alternately broad and fine-ribbed texture.

DAMASK: A rich floral or figured satin fabric.

DAMASKQUETTE: A cheaper type of damask.

LAMPAS.

5. GAUZE CONSTRUCTIONS:

CHIFFON GAUZE: A soft, pliable, transparent material.

GAZE DE VIOLETTE: A thin, transparent cloth woven in the gum when made of silk; it has a weblike construction.

LENO OR DOUP: An openwork net material.

MUSLIN GAUZE.

NET: Recognized by the open meshes of varying sizes.

TULLE: A fine net fabric popular in the millinery trade.

6. SATIN CONSTRUCTIONS:

DOUBLE-FACE SATIN: A high quality material, reversible in structure, in which the face is made of a color different from the one used on the back of the goods.

DUCHESSE: A bright, lustrous satin-weave material which is heavy in weight.

MERVEILLEAU: A warp satin material which is made crease-resistant.

METEOR.

PEAU DE SOIE: A very fine, high-texture, satin-weave cloth.

PEKIN: A dress or trimming material made with stripes of satin and rep alternating.

RADIUM: A cloth which gives a changeable effect as the rays of light are reflected from it.

RADZIMIR.

RHADAMES.

SATIN DE CHINE.

SATIN CHARMEUSE: A soft, dull satin fabric.

SATIN DE LYONS.

SATIN LUMINEUX.

SATIN MESSALINE.

SATIN MOUSSELINE: Very thin satin.

SATIN RAYE BOYEAU: A cloth made of warp satin stripes alternating with cord effects.

SATIN PIECE-DYED CLOTH.

SATIN YARN-DYED CLOTH.

SOIE DE DENIL.

SOLEIL.

7. SILK OR SYNTHETIC WARP AND COTTON FILLING CONSTRUCTIONS:

FAILLE COTTON: Made with a gum-silk warp or with highly twisted strong synthetic fiber warp. The cotton filling is a four-ply yarn.

MOIRETTE: A dyed skirting material which is low in price.

PEKIN VELOUR: Velvet stripes alternating with rep or fancy-twill stripes are the distinguishing feature of the cloth which is made with cotton filling to give body to the fabric.

POLONAISE: A soft silk-face lining material.

SATIN.

SATIN FACONNÉ: Warp-satin floral figures on a twill background are used in making satin façonné.

SATINET.

STRIPED COAT LINING.

TABARET: A corded rep fabric.

8. SILK OR SYNTHETIC WARP CONSTRUCTIONS:

BENEGALINE.

COTELÉ.

CREPON.

IRISH POPLIN: The silk or synthetic warp covers the filling in entirety.

POPELINE: A medium-thickness poplin.

POPLINETTE: A lightweight poplin.

SICILIENNE.

SULTANE.

VELOUR VICTORIA.

VELOUTINE.

9. TAFFETA MATERIALS:

BENGALINE DE SOIR.

CIVRINE CAMELEON: A ribbed fabric woven in two or more colors.

CORA OR CORAH: A thin but strong, plain lining material.

EPINGLE: A rep cloth with alternate fine and coarse ribs.

FANCY MOIRÉ: Watermarked cloths made in stripes and a variety of constructions are moirés or moiré fabrics.

FAILLE FRANCAISE: A thick-ribbed, substantial cloth.

GATÉ FINE: A fine striped rep material.

GLACÉ: Glacé.

GROSGRAIN: A fine, heavy corded cloth in which the cords may be the same or varied to give the desired effect.

GROS DE NAPLES.

GROS DE SUEZ: A fine, plain cloth with the cords running at regular intervals.

GROS DE TOURS.

LUTESTRING. A fine rep fabric.

MOIRE ANTIQUE: A weighted cloth, heavy in feel, which is dyed, glazed, and moiré (watermarked) by particularly heavy pressure.

MOIRE FRANCAISE: A moiré rep fabric.

PONGEE: A thin, cheap fabric of the staple variety.

POULT DE SOIE.

ROYALE.

SURAH FANTASIE: A plain fabric used in the neckwear trade; most of the cloth is printed.

TABOURETTE.

TAFFETA CHIFFON: An extra fine, high-texture, plain fabric.

TAFFETA DAMAS: A plain material interspersed with floral figures.

TAFFETA MOUSSELIN.

TAFFETA POINTELLE: A figured material in which the spots are made by the filling showing on the face of the goods at certain intervals.

TURQUOISE: A wide rib or rep cloth.

10. TWILL CONSTRUCTIONS:

PAILLETTE NOIR: A fine, thin twill silk with a very glossy face.

SARSENET: A fine, soft, thin silk lining fabric.

SERGE.

SURAH CHEVRON: A fine, warp effect herringbone twill cloth.

SURAH FANCY: A soft, fancy warp twill construction made in narrow and broad floats in alternating order.

SURAH ORDINARY: A soft, light, twill-weave cloth used for handkerchiefs, mufflers, scarves, and dress goods. It may be dyed or printed.

SILK AND RAYON BROAD GOODS. Woven goods of these materials which are 24 inches in width and include those cloths which are to be used in the manufacture of ties.

SILK BATISTE. This fabric is sheer and diaphanous, comes in plain or figured effects, and may be woven with small dot-effects. Used for summer dress goods.

SILK BEAVER. A velvet pile fabric of cotton warp and silk or rayon filling; dyed shades of brown to simulate the fur of the beaver.

SILK BOIL-OFF, BOILING-OFF. Also known as silk washing or silk degumming, it is the boiling-out of the silk gum or sericin from the silk fiber by means of soap and hot water. The amounts of boiled-off liquor may vary with the several grades of silk; the higher the boil-off the better will be the quality of the silk, the less the yield and the more expensive the resultant yarn or thread.

Boiled-off liquor is used later on in the dyeing operations since it makes for better affinity and penetration of the dyestuff in the material and for color evenness. The following tabulation will show the approximate boil-off of the major silk stocks:

1. Tussah silk ..... 10 to 11 per cent
2. White China .... 17 to 19 per cent
3. White Japan .... 18 to 19 per cent
4. Tsatlee .... 19 to 20 per cent
5. Yellow Japan ... 21 to 22 per cent
6. Canton .... 22 to 23 per cent
7. Italian .... 23 to 25 per cent

SILK CAMLET. A fabric made from a two-color warp with the filling of some color other than those used in the warp arrangement.

SILK CONDITIONING. Silk to be tested for conditioning purposes is weighed in an air-dry condition, and is then placed in the conditioning oven. The sample is placed in a wire basket in the oven. The function of the oven is to dry the silk to the point where there will be no additional loss in weight. Then 11 per cent is added to the bone-dry weight, which is the amount supposed to represent the amount of moisture that the silk would absorb under normal conditions.

A relative humidity of 65 per cent and a temperature of 70 degrees Fahrenheit have been adopted by testing bureaus.

Incidentally, the weight of the water that a given fiber will sustain in this atmosphere, divided by its bone-dry weight, is known as "percentage regain."

Following the addition of the 11 per cent for conditioning, an additional 2 per cent is added; this represents tare adjustment on each bale of silk, and the figure becomes part of the official conditioned-weight adjustment. The "boil-off figure" on the silk is also considered.

For example, conditioned weight with, say, a 24 per cent boil-off would

be figured in the following manner:

CONDITIONING OF ORGANZINE SILK

Actual weight:	102.71 lbs.
Conditioned weight plus 2 per cent:	106.65 lbs.
Boil-off in per cent:	30.58 per cent

$$\frac{106.65 \times 69.42}{76.07} \text{ equals:} \quad 97.40 \text{ lbs.}$$

Actual weight was:	102.71 lbs.
Minus result of test:	—97.40 lbs.
Allowance	5.31 lbs.

SILK COTTON. 1. Fine, lustrous fibers obtained from the pods of trees and plants such as corn, milkweed, etc. 2. Stuffing obtained from several species of "cotton trees" found in the West Indies and South America.

SILK DENIERAGE BY FILAMENT COUNT. When analyzing small size silk fabrics the denier size of the thread is found by counting the cocoon ends. This count should always be an even number. For example, if the total count comes to 11, add one, since the missing end must be figured in the calculations. Add one third of the count to the full count; in this instance, 4 plus 12 equals 16. Since a half-denier is the tolerance used for the difference in the evenness of the end, the size would be listed as a 14/16 denier thread, the mean being 15. In the case of filling, one fourth of the count is added to the cocoon ends. Thus, 3 plus 12 equals 15. Including the tolerance allowed, the thread would therefore be a 13/15 denier thread, the mean being 14.

SILK FABRICS, DEFECTS FOUND IN WEAVING.

1. BROKEN PICKS: Filling that runs out on its course through shed of loom.

2. ENDS OUT: Warp threads that do not weave in proper order.

3. FINGER MARKS: Caused by carelessness of the weavers when they work at the back of the loom; a weaver often stretches or moves the threads too much out of place, and in so doing marks the yarns with his unclean hands.

4. HANGERS: These occur where the filling thread catches on a knot in the warp thread before the knot has reached the woven cloth area. This knot is pulled into the fabric by the reed thereby causing the formation of a tight end; generally, an open V-shaped effect results.

5. LONG, LARGE FLOATS: Improper interlacings between warp and filling yarns.

6. MISPICKS: Placing of the filling pick in the wrong shed or the failure of the pick to go properly into the shed.

7. RIP-OUTS: Areas where the weaver has corrected an imperfection by the removal of a number of filling picks. Difficult to overcome since newly woven fabric has a tendency to show a rather mottled appearance in goods.

8. SET MARKS: Heavy lines or marks across the width of the material caused by the filling picks having been beaten into the fabric too heavily.

9. SHADE: Off-shade, light, or heavy areas noted in the goods.

10. SHIRES: Light marks that run crosswise and are caused by a filling thread not being properly beaten into place in the fabric.

11. SOILED ENDS: Caused by carelessness of the weaver whose soiled hands may have caused smudges to appear on the warp.

12. SHORT, SMALL FLOATS: One system of threads floating too much over the other system of yarn.

SILK FABRICS, TESTS FOR. There are two types:

1. WEIGHTED SILK:

When burned, the silk will char and glow, but will retain its shape.

Heavily weighted silk will split when folded lengthwise.

2. NON-WEIGHTED SILK:

Pure dye silk will burn and give off the odor of burning animal matter. Small brittle balls are noted along the burned edge.

White silk will turn yellowish in a nitric acid solution.

A 50 per cent hydrochloric acid bath dissolves silk but not wool. Tussah silk will dissolve slower than true silk.

Silk goods will tear with a shrill sound; wool produces a dull sound.

A 5 per cent lye solution dissolves silk.

Under the microscope, pure silk resembles a glass rod; Tussah silk has a greater diameter and shows fine parallel lines which are absent in true silk.

SILK FAILLE CREPE. Made on an eight-shaft satin weave, the cloth is of the rib-back stain variety; two warp beams are used in weaving. The double-faced material is rather heavy, is set in the reed at about 45 inches, and finished at 39 to 40 inches. Crepe filling yarn is used, and warp and filling may vary from 22/24 denier to 28/30 denier.

"SILK FINISH" ON COTTON. A full finish of mercerizing, gassing, and schreinerizing. Glauber salts in the sizing bath add luster when correctly used. A rustling effect, as in silk taffeta, is noted in cloth finished in this manner. Oil softeners are often used to make the goods "softer." The finish may be given to cotton sateen, messaline, and charmeuse.

SILK FLOSS. 1. Very short fibers of tangled waste silk. 2. It is a misnomer when used to describe the soft fibers of the kapok tree which are blended together and used as stuffing for life preservers, mattresses, pillows, etc.

SILK GOODS. There are three main types.

1. PURE SILK GOODS: Those which contain nothing but pure silk. They are free from tin salts, lead salts, sugar, tannic acid, and other adulterants. However, the term includes all silks, cultivated or wild, as well as material made of spun silk and silk wastes. See SILK WEIGHTING.

2. ALL-SILK GOODS: No other textile fibers are used in making these fabrics which, however, may be weighted in both warp and filling. These fabrics, after short wear, may have the tendency to crack, rip, tear, and disintegrate through excessive weighting.

3. SILK GOODS: Materials to which other fibers have been added in weaving the cloth after the yarn has been spun. The yarn may be of the mixture type or can be a ply yarn in which other yarns are used with the basic silk yarn. Examples of silk goods include:

Irish silk poplin, which is made of silk warp and worsted filling.

Some silk velvet, which is made with a silk pile on a cotton back.

Some silk lining, which is made with silk warp and cotton back.

The general belief in the trade seems to be that the term implies silk fabric which should be made externally of silk which is free from "adulterants," despite the use of other yarns (chiefly in the filling) in the cloth construction. For instance, bengaline can be made with an all-silk warp and cotton, rayon, or worsted filling. Since the filling does not show on the face or the back of the material, the fabric is classed as a silk cloth.

SILK GRASS. Lustrous bast fibers usually found in the Central and South American countries.

SILK INSPECTION AND TESTING. To determine the size or count of silk, its weight in a 450-meter length is considered as a standard to use. Harada's Denier-graph is employed to determine the size, and at the same time this machine records the evenness of the silk. Strength and elongation are measured by the serimeter and serigraph, at the same time; Tanahashi's Evenness-graph records strength and evenness. Cleanness is tested by the seripiane, gauge machine, or drum. Cohesion is determined by the cohesion machine.

Exporters' inspections are made in their own laboratories, following an optical inspection by experts. Close inspection is necessary to insure uniformity of color and luster in all skeins in the book, as well as in all books in the bale. Following this, tests are made of random skeins which are put on a frame to wind the spools.

Silk is wound at the rate of about fifty times a minute. The number of breaks in two hours' time is recorded. Most breakages in silk are due to fine ends, one of the great defects in silk. These breaks give a negative appearance to finished cloth. Efficiency is also impaired by them.

In making any of the above tests, the silk is wound onto spools for quick handling. While testing machines determine the exact value of the sample silk, decisions on an entire lot could not be based on these findings. The only test for the uniformity of silk in an entire lot is the optical test. It may be said that even the results from mechanical and optical tests and inspections are not sufficient to judge the grade of the goods.

SILK INTERPRETATIONS, RETAIL-TRADING STANDARDS ASSOCIATION RULES FOR.

1. "SILK": The natural product of the silkworm; the term cannot be applied to material made of silk noil.

2. "ALL SILK": A fabric that is made of all silk yarn irrespective of the amount or percentage of weighting material that may have been used.

3. "PURE SILK": This term may be applied only where there is no metallic or other type of weighting substances used, except that which is an essential part in the dyeing of the yarn or the goods.

4. "PURE DYE SILK": A fabric dyed without weighting of any sort, even in the actual dyeing of the material.

5. "NETT SILK": This term is given to high quality product which results from the drawing-off of continuous strands of silk from the cocoons after which they are then twisted into yarn.

6. "SPUN SILK": Used to describe only those materials made from yarns composed of silk fibers of a length within a range of approximately one to eight inches, made by the waste silk obtained in the dressing and spinning processes. The term cannot be used to imply fabrics made from silk noil. These cloths are made from very short staple residue obtained in the dressing work done by the silk spinner.

7. "SCHAPPE SILK": This implies spun silk which has been obtained by the fermentation degumming method.

SILK LOOPS, RAW. Interstices in silk yarn caused by irregular lengths in one or more cocoon filaments.

SILK-MIXTURE CLOTH. Worsted and cassimere material used for suitings and dress goods produced by interspersed weaving of all-silk threads or by the use of woolen material twisted with silk. The use of the silk tends to give decoration to the cloth and enhances the pattern.

SILK NANKEEN. English fabric which has silk satin stripes over a cotton foundation.

SILK, NET WEIGHT OF. This is the weight of the silk alone. The shirt (muslin cover of bale) has been removed and weighed. The number of books (30 skeins = 1 book) are counted, and the shirt is then replaced. The two ropes that were over the shirt are taken off and weighed. Then follow the paper and the chop tickets; and then the string is taken from two of the books, weighed and applied proportionately to all the books contained in the bale. The total weights of above deducted from the shirt weight gives the net weight. See SILK, SHIRT WEIGHT OF.

SILK NOIL. The waste from the last dressing operation in spun silk; it is often too short to be used again in silk manufacture. Noil is sold to cotton and woolen merchants who mix the stock with longer staple fibers for spinning. Fancy, nub, and novelty yarns are often made with this noil in them. It adds brilliancy to the yarn and often shows up in little balls of nubs found in dress goods, suiting, and overcoating.

SILKOOL. A Japanese soybean protein fiber.

SILK QUOTATIONS. Bales of Chinese, Japanese, and Turkish silk weigh from 130 to 135 pounds; however, there is a difference in quoting prices for these silks:

1. Chinese silk is quoted in taels per picules.

2. Japanese silk is quoted in yen per hundred kin, which is 132.77 American pounds.

3. Canton bales weigh thirty catties or 106⅔ pounds. A cattie is 1⅓ pounds.

Silk is usually bought and paid for in terms of Mexican dollars because this nation has a bi-metallic system of monetary units—gold and silver. This method has been followed since the days of the Spanish Empire in the Americas.

SILKS. A loose-fitting blouse of bizarre pattern and color, and a corresponding silk cap, worn by a jockey to facilitate identification of the stable for which he is riding during the course of a horse race.

SILK SAMPLING, THROWN. In testing cotton, wool, rayon, thrown silk, etc., the gross weight is determined first. Net weight is then figured by subtracting the tare of the case, and bobbins, cones, tubes, cops, etc., from the gross weight. "Drawing samples" means drawing from the case, dividing into two lots, and net-weighing in the same manner as raw silk samples.

SILK SEAL. Similar to beaver-silk fabric, but dyed black instead of some shade of brown; the pile effect is somewhat larger than that observed in beaver silk.

SILK SERGE. A 2-up and 2-down twill-woven silk of high texture; used for lining fabric. It is usually finished at 24 inches and comes in all suitable colors.

SILK SKEINS AND BOOKS. Raw silk may be packed 30 skeins to a book, and there are usually 20 books to the bale; thus, most bales contain 600 silk skeins. Each bale approximates 130 to 135 pounds in weight. Some bales may be packed on the basis that "there are as many skeins to the book as there are books to the bale." Hence, a 24-book-bale would contain 24 books of silk with each one made up of 24 skeins for a total of 576 skeins. Some bale cases have only 15 or 16 books, depending on local conditions.

SILK SKEINS, FINISHING AND PACKING. As a general rule, assorted silk skeins are made into a book by placing six skeins on the bottom and building upwards to a height of five layers, thirty skeins in all. Packing is done by apparatus, and the skeins are bound with heavy cotton thread. The books are packed in wooden cases and sent to Kobe, Yokohama, or other centers. In one case there could be 15 or 16 books and the weight is about nine kwan (70 to 90 pounds). The silk is then shipped to the Tonya or commission merchants in the export centers.

SILK STOCKING, THE WEIGHT OF A. This is determined by the number of threads twisted together in the knitting yarn. The following list will give the range and use:

1. One- and two-thread stockings are very delicate and should be worn for formal occasions only. Durability is sacrificed for beauty and sheerness.

2. Three-thread chiffon, while heavier than one- and two-thread fabric, is not strong enough for more than formal wear.

3. Four- and five-thread fabric, known as semiservice or service fabric, combine sheerness with fair service for daytime use and give good average wear.

4. Six- to twelve-thread fabric is called service weight.

SILK THROWING. The process of twisting filaments to make organzine and tram silk yarns.

SILK WADDING. Waste from bourette silk used in fancy fabrics of novel motif.

SILK WEIGHTING. A process often used in connection with silk dyeing to compensate for the loss in weight because of the removal of the silk gum or sericin, or to increase the weight and consequently decrease the cost. This is generally done with tin salts (stannic chloride) but tannin may be used for blacks. According to the Federal Trade Commission rules, the percentage of weighting must be stated when silk goods are sold. See PURE SILK DYE.

SILK WINDING. Winding from skeins to bobbin prior to testing silk for best grade, size, etc. This winding test on raw silk is to determine the relative winding quality of the skein by finding the number of breaks made in the winding of a known yardage or weight on bobbins at a known speed. Winding silk is important since it shows the relative cost of winding silk from the skein onto spools. The breaks per pound, per hour, at a defined speed, are recorded.

SILKWORM, BIOLOGICAL LIFE CYCLE OF THE.

1. METAMORPHOSIS: Implies a change or alteration in form, structure or shape with or without a change in nature. It is a complete transformation. The term is applied to the person or thing being changed. There is for instance a change in the form and habits of the organism from the egg stage to the maturity stage.

An example of this is when an insect egg becomes a larvae, a pupa, and then an adult form of insect. The case of a tadpole becoming a frog is a worthy illustration also.

In plant life, there is the development of the plant organ, originally the same in the differentiated forms. This is shown by stamens changing into petals. In the physiological form the metamorphosis is referred to in terms of metabolism.

2. EGG STAGE: It is the first stage in the life cycle of the silkworm. Silkworms are hatched from eggs in the same manner as a chicken. They come forth from a shell. The silkworm is from ⅜ to ⅝ inch long; the diameter is comparable with a human hair.

3. LARVA: Is derived from the Latin and means ghost or mask. This immature, often wormlike, form of insects that undergo metamorphosis occurs in the stage between the egg and the pupa. (In the early forms of any animal, the offspring in its development is structurally unlike the parents. A caterpillar will illustrate this point.)

4. PUPA: Comes from the Latin and means girl or doll. It is the more or less quiescent or calm stage in the metamorphosis of higher insects, during which time, the larva changes or is transformed to the adult. This stage is noted in the case of butterflies, mosquitoes and flies. This is known as the cocoon stage.

5. CHRYSALIS: Comes from the Greek and implies a golden thing. The torpid, last stage through which an insect passes before it emerges from its glistening casing into the so-called perfect form is known as the chrysalis stage.

SILKWORM GENERATIONS. There are three types:

1. Univoltine or annual, which produces once a year.

2. Duovoltine, which produces two generations a year.

3. Polyvoltine, which produces several generations per annum.

SILKWORM GUT. The fibroin in the glands of a silkworm, when treated with acetic acid and allowed to stand for some time, will stretch to great length and show considerable strength. This gut is used to make fishlines but is being replaced by nylon to a marked degree.

SILKWORM VARIETIES. There are two main types. Domesticated *Bombyx mori* and undomesticated or Wild. Domesticated worms feed on choice mulberry leaves while the other type feeds on the poorer type of mulberry leaves, leaves of the oak tree, cherry tree, castor oil plant, etc. Wild silk has several names: Tussah, Tussur, Tussa, Talar, Tasar, Tassui.

SILKY. Having the smoothness, softness, luster, and appearance of silk.

SILT. A very fine suspension of dirt observed usually in slow-moving streams.

SILVALIN. Yarn made from cellulose matter—bamboo, cellulose pulp, cotton, jute, linen, wood, or any other vegetable waste. The yarn is made on the Kron patented method which originated in Germany. Paper yarn made in England is also called Silvalin.

SILVER. A luster or color resembling that of silver; neutral gray of ordinary brilliance.

SILVER CLOTH. See CLOTH OF SILVER.

SILVER TISSUE. Dress and trim-

LIFE CYCLE
OF SILKWORM

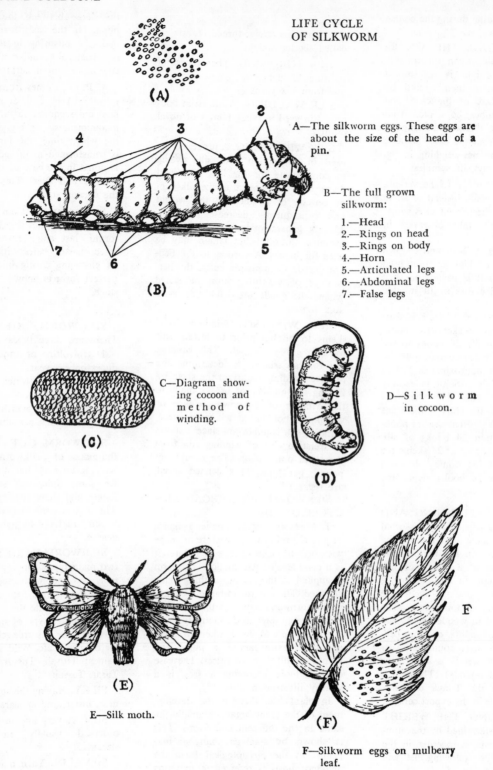

(A)

A—The silkworm eggs. These eggs are
about the size of the head of a
pin.

B—The full grown
silkworm:

1.—Head
2.—Rings on head
3.—Rings on body
4.—Horn
5.—Articulated legs
6.—Abdominal legs
7.—False legs

(B)

C—Diagram show-
ing cocoon and
method of
winding.

(C)

D—Silkworm
in cocoon.

(D)

(E)

E—Silk moth.

(F)

F—Silkworm eggs on mulberry
leaf.

ming fabrics embellished with white metal threads, and sometimes with very small sequins. Used in evening gowns.

SILVERTONE AND GOLDTONE. A coating cloth made from woolen or worsted warp with woolen filling. Fabric is stock-dyed and weight goes from 16 to 24 ounces per yard. Material is heavily napped. Construction may be single or double. The cloth gets its name from the fact that strands of

gold- and silver-colored threads are worked into the face of the material. This gives a gold or silver sheen to the fabric which is usually attractive.

SIMAL COTTON. A cotton produced from the simal tree in India. This Bombax type fiber is a strong, soft, short, silklike seed hair which has a reddish-brown cast. Also known as red-sil cotton, it is used chiefly for stuffing. Resembles kapok.

SIMILI BINDING. A binding made solely of mercerized cotton yarns with a 3-up and 1-down twill weave. One-half inch in width, the binding is stiffened by sizing when being woven and may be further stiffened in subsequent finishing. Also known as felling simili.

SIMPLE. Known in French as semple, and in Italian as corde del tiro, the word means the cords of a drawloom which are suspended vertically from the tail cords to the floor and to which the lashes are attached.

SIMPLEX. A spring board needle warp knitting machine comparable with a tricot frame, which makes double-faced fabrics used chiefly in gloves.

SIMPSON COTTON. See DICKSON COTTON.

SIMULATED HAND-KNIT. A machine stitch that duplicates effects obtained in hand knitting.

SINAMAY. Made from Manila abaca in the Philippine Islands, the fibers are obtained from the plant, washed, and then cleaned. The fine fibers are tied or knotted to the next one so that a long, continuous string is the result. The string or strings are then woven. It should be noted that there is no spinning in the treatment of these bast fibers.

SINDH CARPET. A coarse, knotted Indian carpet or rug made with a coarse cotton warp, hemp filling, and cowhair pile.

SIND-DESHI COTTON. A Bengal cotton with staple of ⅜ inch to ⅝ inch; lint yield is about 35 per cent.

SINGEING. Passing the cloth rapidly over a series of gas jets or white-hot plates in order to take off the fuzzy, straggly, or protruding fibers. Singed fabric is very smooth in appearance and to the touch.

SINGEING, COTTON CLOTH. It may be the first treatment that the cloth receives. If the surface of the cloth is examined prior to singeing, a mass of protruding fibers is seen which give a fuzzy appearance to the goods. If the nap is not removed, the colors may not go on evenly. This effect will be seen when the rays of light strike the goods. Straggly fibers will prevent a high finish being given to the cloth, especially if it is to be schreinerized.

SINGER, ISAAC. Inventor of the sewing machine in 1846 which led to the world-known Singer Company, Inc.

SINGER MACHINE OPERATOR. One who uses a standard industrial sewing machine to perform one or more of the principal sewing operations in assembling the garments. The worker may be moved from one operation to another as the occasion arises. The Singer Sewing machine is used extensively in the industry, but another brand of machine may sometimes be used.

SINGLE ATLAS FABRIC. Warp-knit fabric made by having one set of yarn traversing progressively in a diagonal direction for a set number of

courses and then returning in similar manner to the original wale formation. See DOUBLE ATLAS FABRIC.

SINGLE-BAR TRICOT. Tricot knitted fabric made with one guide bar, one pattern wheel, one set of spools, etc.

SINGLE BOSS ROLL. A drawing roller with one boss. Used on drawing frames when all the fibers passing the one roll make the single sliver at the delivery end of the frame.

SINGLE-BREASTED. Designating a coat, vest, or the like, which laps over the breast only enough for buttoning, and has buttons on one edge only.

SINGLE CHAIN STITCH. A series of knitting loops, each of which is caught down by the following loop. It is worked with needle and thread.

SINGLE DAMASK. Silk fabric which has the ground and the motif weave or weaves made on a five-shaft satin weave. The double damask is made on the eight-harness satin weave, and would not have the short floats noted in the single damask construction which gives better service. Also made in linen, rayon, and mixture fabrics.

SINGLE FILLING FLAT DUCK. See DUCKS, FLAT.

SINGLE HEAD LOOM. A narrow fabric loom that weaves only one piece of goods.

SINGLE JAPAN RAW SILK. Four or five cocoons, 8 or 10 filaments, reel a 13/15 denier; six or seven cocoons, 12 or 14 filaments, reel a 20/22 denier; twelve or fourteen cocoons, 24 or 28 filaments, reel a 40/44 denier. About one-half turn of twist per inch is introduced in reeling. China raw silk runs finer, so that one or two extra cocoons must be added to the Japanese number.

SINGLE KNITTED FABRIC. Cloth made from the one system of yarn. Several yarns may be combined, however, and passed into the machine as a single or individual yarn. The fabric is made by the interlooping of the yarn, a loop within a loop. Popular fabrics in the trade made of single construction include stockings, socks, tricolette, jersey, mignonette, bathing-suit fabric, scarfs, knitted cap cloth, some sportswear goods, dress goods, baby clothes, etc. These fabrics run from the heavy, close, compact types to the sheer, lightweight, diaphanous types.

SINGLE-PLANT BARGAINING. Collective bargaining between the representative of a company, and of the employees in one unit or plant of the concern.

SINGLE POPLIN. Lightweight poplin.

SINGLE PROCESS PICKER. See ONE PROCESS PICKER.

SINGLE ROVING. When one strand or rope of roving is fed to the spinning frame to make a single yarn delivery. Double roving is when two rovings are fed into the frame and combine to make the single yarn delivery.

SINGLES. 1. A group of raw silk threads which may or may not be twisted; when twisted, the threads have from 2 to 12 turns of twist per inch. Degummed silk may be woven in the singles, but it is not practical to do so. 2. A single or one-ply yarn. When two singles are spliced or twisted together, the yarn or thread is called two-ply One ply is rarely applied to yarn. Cotton, for example, if not preceded by two-, three-, four-, or more ply is generally understood to be a cotton yarn or thread in the "singles." The same is true in woolen and worsted yarn.

SINGLE SILK. Eight or ten reeled filaments of silk which are twisted together and used to make tinsel thread.

SINGLES SILK. A term applied to all raw silk composed of a number of cocoon filaments united during reeling. Threads may have from two to ten cocoons or four to twenty filaments, but the usual number is around five cocoons or ten filaments.

SINGLE-STRAND TESTER. A breaking machine that will show the stretch of a single yarn strand or the breaking point of the sample. The machine used is worked on the principle of gravity, and the pendulum is governed by an oil plunger.

SINGLE WARP. In regard to yarns, per se, the warp threads in the cloth are single, as distinguished from two or more ply. In reference to fabric construction it is a single system of warp threads where there is, perhaps, a double system of filling threads.

SINGLE-WOVEN FABRIC. This cloth is made with two sets of threads; one set, the threads which run vertically in the goods, is known as the warp; the other set, the threads which run horizontally in the material, is known as the filling. The terms, ends and warp, are considered as synonymous: picks and filling are likewise synonymous.

Selvage, selvedge, or listing, the characteristic edge of the goods, always runs in the warp direction. This is naturally a part of the fabric and does not go to waste in tailoring. However, in dressmaking, it is sometimes cut off before the cloth is cut.

SINGLE YARN. One that has not been plied; the result of drawing, twisting, and winding a mass of fibers into a coherent yarn.

SINGLING. The breakage of one or more strands in a group as it is being manipulated in some machine. For example, a sliver among, say, twelve being fed into a machine might break, and if not attended to would cause uneven stock, light weight, and loss of time.

SINKAGE. Meaning the same as shrinkage, it implies the loss in weight in wool-scouring operation.

SINKER. 1. A thin blade, similar in design to a divider, designed on a full-fashioned machine to move or to push the yarn alternately between each needle. On a circular machine, a sinker holds down the fabric, permitting proper functioning of the needle. 2. Also known as "down," the term indicates that a filling pick is over a warp end at the point of interlacing—in other words, that a warp end is under the filling pick. In ordinary fabric weave-construction, warp ends, when they are to be a raiser, are painted on the design paper; filling picks are not painted.

SINKER BAR. See STECHKAMM.

SINKER LOOP. A loop which connects two adjacent needle loops.

SINKER LOOP TRANSFER, KNITTING. Transfer of a sinker loop from the position in which it was made to either or both of the adjacent needles in the needle bed for purposes of styling.

SINTER, SINTERABLE. A silieous or calcareous matter deposited by springs, as that formed in the vent of a geyser. In metallizing, sintering is brought into agglomerated form by heating. See Avceram under American Viscost Division of FMC Corporation.

SIRE. Means the same as ram.

SIRETZ FLAX. See RUSSIAN FLAX.

SI-RO-SET. A Certification Trademark owned by C.S.I.R.O., Australia, and indicates, when present on a container, that the solution meets the chemical concentration, purity, etc., requirements specified by that organization. The word Si-Ro-Set is no longer being used since the basic chemical ingredient of the compound has been changed. At present the finish is referred to as a "permanent creasing of all-wool slacks or all-wool apparel done by the use of reducing agents."

SIRSAKE. Name for seersucker in Dutch West Indies.

SISAL. See HENEQUEN OR HENEQUIN.

SISAL, FALSE. Florida is the home of this fiber which is softer and finer but not as strong as sisal hemp raised elsewhere. See HENEQUEN.

SISTRESAY. Used in the Middle East and India, this dress goods is made from two warps and one filling; one warp is cotton, which is used for the ground weave, the other is silk, used for the damask-like motif effect. Silk filling aids in the formation of the pattern. The striped ground effect adds to the color scheme noted in the material.

SITAN. Sheeting is a modification of this word; the term refers to sheeting imported by India.

SIT-DOWN STRIKE. Work stoppage in which the employees do not walk out but as protest remain without working and refuse to leave the company's premises. Displeasure is expressed often by actually sitting down.

SIX-CORD THREAD. Cabled sewing cotton made by plying two single yarns and then twisting three of these to make the finished thread. The twist used may be S-S-Z or Z-Z-S.

SIX-END OR SIX-LEAF TWILL. Any type of twill weave that repeats on six ends and six picks.

SIX OAKS COTTON. The seeds of this cotton are small and black, the boll is of average size, and the fiber is similar to Jones Long Staple cotton. Staple is about 1¼ inches, lint yield is about 30 per cent.

SIXTH COMBING. Wool obtained from the sheep fleece from the area covering the lower part of the thigh; also known as Breech.

SI-ZAMBI. Plain-weave cotton made in England and shipped to Africa for native dress. Cloth is made with the center in solid color and the borders in large checks and dark, dull colors.

SIZE. A solution of starch or blue applied to yarn or fabric to stiffen and strengthen it.

SIZE BOX. See SIZE MIXER; SIZING.

SIZE MIXER. A large metal vat, fitted with a stirring device, used for cooking sizing mixtures. It is connected with the size box of a slasher by pipes.

SIZE MIXTURE. See SIZING.

SIZING. 1. The application of a size or starch to warp yarn to increase strength and smoothness and to add weight to the gray goods from the loom. Sizing may be applied to yarn in hank or ball warp form, or on the slasher machine. See Illustrated Section. 2. The application of starch or size, or other stiffeners, to fabrics and garments. Sizing mixtures may be made from starches of potato peeling, oyster shells, wheat, rice, barley, sago, casava; gum

arabic and gum tragacanth are also used for sizing purposes.

SIZING, GRAY MILL. The application of a size or a starch or some other stiffening agent to yarn or fabric by immersion. The purpose of sizing is to add smoothness and strength to the yarn or cloth so that the ultimate finish of the goods will be improved. Sizing is also used to add weight to the material.

SIZING GUMS. Vegetable or animal glues or gums used in printing and finishing. Examples include:

1. BINDING AND STIFFENING MATERIALS: Sizes of corn, wheat, rice, sago, potato, casava, flour, tapioca, etc. Also, gum arabic, gum tragacanth, glucose, dextrine, certain glues, Irish moss.

2. FILLING MATERIALS: China clay, talc, alum, blanc fixe.

3. SOFTENING OR CONDITIONING MATERIALS: Tallow, soap, waxes, soluble oils, coconut oil, glycerine, etc.

SIZING SKEIN WINDER. A winder capable of winding ten sizing skeins simultaneously for testing purposes. The machine can be set for 400 turns of the reel (450 meters) or for 200 turns (225 meters). The reel measures 1⅛ meters, but reels are also on the market which measure 36 or 54 inches in circumference and are used for measuring woolen, worsted, or cotton sizing skeins.

SIZING, STANDARD LENGTH. Skeins of the major fibers are placed in the humidity room for the proper length of time. They are then weighed, individually, on a quadrant. A second weighing follows when the skeins have been combined and set in the balance. From these figures, yarn size is calculated.

SKAUT. Peculiar to the women of Norway, it is a large linen square, starched and pleated, folded, and then placed on the head. It is usually in white but other colors may be used.

SKEIN. An appreciable length of yarn or thread that has been wound onto a reel or swift from some machine or device. The circumference of a skein varies usually from 44 inches to 54 inches. Skeins may be reeled, twisted, and put into commercial form for handling by the operatives in the mill's winding department. While skeins may be made any desired legnth for definite purposes, many of them are 120 yards long.

SKEIN-DYED. Another name for yarn-dyed. The skeins are dyed before the yarn is woven into cloth. Skein dyeing is used considerably in dyeing rayon crepes, and for plaids, overplaids, stripe-effects in suitings and dress goods which have two or more colors in the pattern, etc. See Illustrated Section.

SKEIN TESTING. Determination of the strength of a skein of yarn (usually in a 120-yard—80 turns of the yarn reel) by subjecting it to a yarn-breaking machine. At best, it is only a comparative test since not all yarns are ruptured at the breaking point as shown by the dial of the machine.

SKELAN. A nonwoven fabric developed in East Germany and made with a web of felted wool and manmade fiber, internally reinforced by a layer of parallel laid skeleton threads. Resultant fabric is comparatively strong, price is very low, and the product has a fairly good drape.

SKELETON SHAFTS. Side heddles on harness frames used for weaving selvages in cloth.

SKETCH. An outline or general delineation; a rough draft or plan of a design, machine, etc.

SKEWER. The long wooden rod which holds the bobbin of roving as it is set upright in the creel of the roving or spinning frame.

SKI CLOTH. Fabric of wool, cotton, mixed stock used for any type of outdoor wear in the winter. Cotton ski cloth is water-repellent. See MACKINAC; SNOW CLOTH.

SKIN. The pelt from smaller animals such as the sheep, calf, or goat. The term, when applied to finished leather, means the entire skin.

SKINNER. A bobbin with very little yarn on it, about to run out. The term is also used to imply an empty bobbin.

SKINNER SATIN®. A registered trademark applicable to many fabrics. Deep luster satin is now the principal satin construction made. Fabrics in this category are noted for their reliable and sustained durability; firmness, luster, and excellent service. Cloths which bear this trademark have a high texture or yarn count and they are water spot resistant. Product of William Skinner & Sons, a division of Indian Head, Inc., New York City.

SKIN WOOL. Taken from the pelts of slaughtered sheep by the sweating, lime, or slipe methods.

SKIP. A blemish in woven goods when a filling yarn skips over several warp threads by mistake. Usually caused by harness skips, snapped yarn, small holes, etc.

SKIP DRAW. The actual skipping of certain harnesses in the drawing-in plan to obtain some novelty effect. Skip-dent summer shirting and dress goods are examples.

SKIP TWILL WEAVES. On the order of broken twills, these weaves show a distinct break-line and then continue on in the same direction. In broken twills, the threads go in the opposite from the breakline.

SKIPPED DENT. See WRONG DRAW.

SKIPPING. Detrimental to good weaving, harness skips are caused by an irregular height of the harness or harnesses in the shedding motion of the loom; skipping areas must be fixed immediately.

SKIRT. That part of a garment which is fitted to the waist and hangs from the hips. Current styles control the manner in which the skirt shall be made—length, fullness, etc.

SKIRTING. Removal of the outside and lower grades of wool and matter from the fleece-clumps, britch, and dungy matter. Australian wool is always skirted before shipment; a great point in favor of their wools. Australians take great pride in the fact they ship clean fleeces.

Shears are used to skirt fleeces. Skirtings have very little value or none.

SKIRTING LEATHER. This signifies a special type of cattlehide used for the skirts or hanging portions of saddles that come between the legs of a rider and horse.

SKIRT LENGTHS.

Maxi: Adjective pertaining to the length of the garment ending at the ankle; from the word, maximum. A noun to describe a coat, dress, or skirt which is ankle length. The garment shape may be slim, flared or full. If slim, front or side openings must be available.

Maxi-Midi: A garment which sweeps the ground as observed in some coats and dresses, as well as in evening wear.

Micro: Adjective which pertains to a very abbreviated length just covering the torso. A noun used in conjunction with mini, such as a micro-mini.

Midi: Adjective which pertains to garment length ending between the knee and the calf of the leg, from mid-calf. A noun used to describe a coat, dress or skirt ending at mid-calf. Also implies one that is three inches below the knee but no longer than mid-calf. If slim, a front opening buttoned, is usually available.

Mid-Knee: Expert comment is that while women are wearing all lengths at present, the all-round general conservative average length is at the mid-knee.

Mini: Adjective pertaining to garment length between the upper thigh and knee, from the word, minimum. Ranges from three inches above the knee and often higher. Garment shape is usually thin.

SKITTERINESS. Yarn or fabric in

which small specks and other small defects are seen; usually caused by faulty dyeing or foreign matter of undesirable nature in the yarn or cloth, which has not taken the dye too well.

SKIVER. This designates the grain-split of a sheepskin and is used for many purposes, such as sweat banding for hats, bag lining, bookbinding, pocketbooks, and fancy leather articles.

SKYING. The process of passing cotton cloth through air to oxidize reduced indigo used in dyeing.

SKYTEEN. British cotton shirting cloth, of heavyweight type, made on a 5-shaft satin weave, warp effect. The warp is all-colored to give dark stripes on a light blue background or may be the same type and color as the filling. Given a soft finish, the fabric is used in shirts, overalls, work clothes, etc. Texture is 100 x 80 down to 84 x 52. Warp used is 24s to 36s, while filling is 24s to 32s.

SLABSTOCK. The back beam which corresponds to the breast beam in the front of the loom. Some old-time looms, of the hand weaving type, had the yarn travel directly from the warp beam to the cloth beam at the front of the loom; a full beam would be higher and of greater diameter than one empty or almost empty. Small hand looms still follow this procedure, but it is not always effective for good results.

SLACKENER. The rod that sets above the warp beam on a leno loom over which all doup threads pass. Its function is to allow a slackening for the doup yarns as they cross the standard ends in the fabric. Breakage of these skeleton ends is therefore averted.

SLACK LENGTH HOSE. Men's and boys' hose which is made in a length between the anklet and half hose types.

SLACK LOOP WASHER. This machine will wash or scour goods in chain form as they are passed into a vat and controlled by rollers. There will always be a goodly portion of the chain at the bottom of the bath without tension.

SLACK MERCERIZATION IN STRETCH FABRICS. Originally developed on all-cotton stretch fabrics, it can now be applied to blends of cotton and manmade fibers used in some fabrics. The procedure involves the shrinking of the fabric without any tension (slack) in the mercerizing bath of sodium hydroxide (caustic soda) solution. Often resorted to in the manufacture of filling or horizontal stretch fabrics.

SLACK-MERCERIZED COTTON FABRIC. When mercerized without tension in a cold caustic soda bath at room temperature, cotton fibers will become bloated and take on crimp and kink. This action increases the bulk and the elastic properties at a cost of about half of that of elastic bandage fabric. Material thus treated is used for bandages; slippage in handling and use is prevented, and the bandage is still flexible enough to allow freedom of movement of the finger, elbow, wrist, knee, or ankle. The product is also used for head bandaging.

SLACK OR TIGHT WARP OR FILLING YARN. Yarn that has too little or too much tension applied to it. Tight yarn will become recessive, and is most difficult to manipulate since it will snap or break.

SLACKS. Worn by men, women, and teen-agers, these rather loose-fitting trousers are worn for sport, chores, lounging, or casual wear. Any of the major textile fibers are used to make the yarn for weaving the fabric. Plain, striped, novelty, and printed effects appear in the fabric of this popular form of apparel.

SLACK SELVAGE. Condition caused by too much spreading of the ends in the reed, edges wound too high or too hard on the warp beam, too loose a weave texture, and improper yarn.

SLAG WOOL. This is prepared by blowing steam through molten lead. It can hardly be called a textile fiber, but since it is used as are some fibers, in packing, it may be classified as such. England calls it silicate cotton.

Slag wool is not spun into yarn like asbestos, the greatest of mineral fibers. It is used as a felt because it is made up of its fine interlocking mineral fibers that enclose a mass of minute air cells, which give it the property of a good nonconductor of heat. In short, slag wool is a by-product of the blast furnace.

SLANETZ. Dew-retted Russian flax.

SLANTING, PADDING STITCH. Used for fastening-in canvas or padding in coats.

SLASHER. A machine that lays warp yarn parallel and coats or sizes the yarn with a mixture to strengthen it to withstand the rigors of weaving. The required number of beams to make the complete warp, usually four to eight, are placed in a creel at the back of the machine. All ends from these beams are drawn together into the one sheet, passed between squeezing rollers through a size box, taken around a series of hot cylinders to dry, then past fans and around measuring rollers, and finally orderly arranged on the loom beam by the use of a comb de-

vice. See Illustrated Section.

SLASHING. The placing of a protective film around warp threads of cotton, filament rayon, spun rayon. Most warps, it may be safely stated, are slashed or sized, particularly single end warp. The method consists of section beams, the number of which depends on the density of the warp or the total number of ends in the entire warp, being run through size or slash liquor, then dried on heated cans and finally placed on the one warp beam.

The slashing solution consists chiefly of starch or gelatine with other ingredients such as penetrants, oils, fats, etc. The term is much used in cotton and rayon manufacturing processes. A similar operation in woolen and worsted manufacture is known as dressing.

See Illustrated Section.

SLASH POCKET, MEN'S WEAR. One in which the angle of the pocket determines whether or not it may be called by this name; a slant pocket has an angle of about 45 degrees while the slash pocket is made at an angle of about 80 degrees. As a rule there is no flap on the slash pocket; it is either piped or welted.

SLAT. Colloquialism for a sheep's hide from which the wool has been pulled prior to any other treatment.

SLATE. A dull bluish-gray color resembling slate.

SLATER, SAMUEL. "The Father of the Cotton Textile Industry in the United States" was born in England, 1769. He died in Webster, Mass., in 1835. Slater worked in one of England's newest cotton mills, as an apprentice, and absorbed the secrets of yarn manufacture. He defied the laws which forbade technicians to leave England, and came to Providence, R. I.

He offered his services to Moses Brown, a prominent Quaker and manufacturer, and Oziel Wilkinson, Brown's foreman—who became, in time, his father-in-law. Slater reproduced, solely from memory, a carding frame, and a spinning frame of forty-eight spindles, plus other necessary machines, five in all. The Slater Mill, still standing and a textile museum well worth a visit, was started in Pawtucket, R. I., on December 20, 1790, with the newly built machines in operation. The machinery that Wilkinson was trying to use was of very little value and practically worthless.

Slater reproduced the spinning frame invented by Sir Richard Arkwright from memory, and his principles are still used today in the best of textile machinery. By 1793, Brown and Slater had the first successful cotton mill in America. Shortly after his mill was on a sound basis, Slater turned his attention

to making Rhode Island a leading textile center, and in a relatively short time there were over 100 factories in and around Rhode Island. He became the first builder of textile machinery in this country, and Andrew Jackson honored him by calling him the "Father of American Textiles." Incidentally, Mrs. Slater made the first sewing thread produced in this country by twisting yarns together on her spinning wheel, the beginning of another great textile industry in the United States.

See Illustrated Section.

SLATER TO MOSES BROWN, LETTER OF SAMUEL. In January, 1783, Samuel Slater was apprenticed to Jedediah Strutt, the foremost textile enterpreneur of the era in England. By 1789 he was well qualified to supervise a mill. Arriving in New York City in November, 1789, he learned of an opportunity for his skills in Providence Rhode Island and wrote to Moses Brown, who was looking for a person to set-up and superintend a cotton mill there. Slater's letter to Moses Brown follows:

New York, December 2nd, 1789

Sir:

A few days ago I was informed that you wanted a manager of cotton spinning, etc., in which business I flatter myself that I can give the greatest satisfaction, in making machinery, making good yarns, either for stockings or twist, as any that is made in England; as I have had good opportunity, and an oversight of Sir Richard Arkwright's works and in Mr. Strutt's mill upwards of eight years. If you are not provided for, should be glad to serve you; though I am in the New York manufactory, and have for three weeks since I arrived from England. But we have but one card, two machines, two spinning jennies, which I think are not worth using. My encouragement is good, but should much rather have the care of the perpetual carding and spinning. My intention is to erect a perpetual card and spinning (meaning the Arkwright patents). If you please to drop a line respecting the amount of encouragement you wish to give by favor of Captain, you will much oblige, sir, your most obedient humble servant,

Samuel Slater

He had a reply from Moses Brown within the week and thus commenced the establishment of the first cotton mill in

America, and Slater became the "Father of the American Cotton Textile Industry." Slater's contribution was such that in a short amount of time many more cotton mills were established. Many of the men he trained in his mills when on to other mills and Slater's knowledge and fame spread throughout New England and in time throughout the world.

Courtesy of Mrs. Grace Rogers Cooper, Curator of Division of Textiles, Smithsonian Institution, Washington, D.C. 20560. See Strutt, Jedediah; Slater, Samuel. Suggested reading on Samuel Slater - *Samuel Slater, Father of American Manufactures* by E.H. Cameron, The American Saga Series, The Bond Wheelwright Company, Inc., Freeport, Maine. *The Copp Family Textiles* may be purchased for $1.25 from The Superintendent of Documents, U.S. Government Printing Office, Washington, D.C. 20402. Please add one-fourth amount for handling and mailing.

Suggested reading on Samuel Slater - *Samuel Slater, Father of American Manufactures* by E.H. Cameron, The American Saga Series, The Bond Wheelwright Company, Inc., Freeport, Maine. *The Copp Family Textiles* may be purchased for $1.25 from The Superintendent of Documents, U.S. Government Printing Office, Washington, D.C. 20402. Please add one-fourth amount for handling and mailing.

SLAVE. To separate the flax fibers from the woody matter present.

SLEAVED SILK. Raw silk floss.

SLEAZY. Thin, lacking firmness; open-meshed. Usually said of fabrics.

SLEDDED COTTON. Cotton from which a mechanical device such as a stripper or a sled has gathered the bolls as well as much other matter that is difficult to remove in ginning. Special cleaning has to be given by the hull extractor. Sledded is not by any manner or means on a par with hand-picked cotton. It is resorted to when hand-picking cannot be accomplished.

SLEEPERS. Mill term for "lost ends" in the warping and beaming operations. The ends are lost because of breakage and in the free condition become tangled or covered by other ends adjacent to them.

SLEEPING SUIT. The single-garment suit, usually of flannel, worn by children for sleeping. The feet and legs are closed in.

SLEEVE. That part of a garment that serves as a covering for the arm. Comes in several major types—Dolman, bishop, leg-o'-mutton, set-in, raglan, etc.

SLEEVE, SET-IN. A sleeve cut separately from the rest of the garment and sewed in at the armhole. This differs from a raglan sleeve which is also cut separately but has a slanting seamline from the underarm to the neckline in both back and front of the garment.

SLEEVE BAG. In the lowest grades of tailoring work (machine work) the entire coat or jacket is finished wrong side out. An opening is left in the one sleeve lining thereby making it possible to pull the coat through this opening, right side out.

SLEEVE BOARD. A board used for pressing sleeves. It is so shaped that it slips easily into a sleeve and facilitates its pressing.

SLEEVELESS SWEATER. See SWEATERS, MEN'S AND BOYS'.

SLEEVE LINING. The inner portion of a sleeve. Made of lining fabric, it is used on coat sleeves, jackets, etc.

SLEEVING. Woven, knitted, or braided fabrics made in circular or tubular form less than 4 inches in diameter (circumference is under 8 inches).

SLENDANG, SLENDONG, PAHONE. Cotton scarf or shawl of varying size made with novelty heading and a fringe at the two ends. It is narrower than the well-known sarong. The size of the scarf is 2 to 3 feet wide and about 6 feet long. A Slendang differs from a Slendong in that the former is block printed and silk and gold threads are interspersed throughout the material. Both fabrics are used in India, Malay States, etc.

SLEY. The number of warp yarns or ends per inch in woven fabric either on or off the loom.

SLEYING. The drawing of warp ends through the heddle eyes on the respective harnesses according to a drawing-in plan, and the drawing of these ends through the splits of the reed according to a definite reeding plan.

SLICKER FABRIC. A common name applied to textile fabrics which have been chemically waterproofed by the coating method, which is a continuous waterproof film applied to the fabric. The usual basic fabrics are cottons, rayons, and silks. A vast number of chemical substances are applicable, but only a few meet the requirements of the rigid specifications necessary to produce satisfactory finished fabrics. Base fabrics plus chemical substances plus application of the various proofing agents properly applied produce the required finish for good waterproofs.

SLIDE FASTENER. A metal fastener with teethlike extensions attached to a tape. When the tongue of the fastener is pulled, the teethlike extensions

either interlock or open. It is used in place of buttons and buttonholes, hooks and eyes, and snaps. Commercially called a zipper.

SLIMSY. Condition noted in some fabrics. See SLEAZY.

SLING PSYCHROMETER. A psychrometer so made that it can be whirled around in the air by means of a handle.

SLIP. 1. An underslip made the length of the dress with which it is to be worn; takes the place of lining. 2. Undergarment combining corset cover or brassière and petticoat. 3. An English measure of 1,800 yards used for jute, linen, and woolen yarns.

SLIPON, PULLOVER SWEATER. See WOMEN'S AND MISSES' SWEATERS.

SLIPE WOOL. That obtained from dead sheep by the lime process. This type of wool is difficult to wash and is very harsh and coarse in character.

SLIPES. Foreign term for "pulled wool," the fibers obtained from pelts on dead sheep. See Pulled Wool, Methods to Obtain.

SLIPPAGE. The tendency which fibers, filaments, yarn, thread, or cloth have to slip or slide when manipulated. Cloths sometimes cause much trouble by slippage, particularly when being cut. Within the last few years certain chemical treatments have been given to cloth to prevent or to cut down the amount of slippage.

SLIPPER SATIN. A strong, compactly woven fabric used chiefly for footwear and made from silk or man-made fibers. Textures are high and the material comes in black, white, colors, or in richly brocaded effects. The price range varies a great deal, depending on the material and the manufacturer.

SLIP RESISTANT. Chemical finishes whose purpose it is to provide firmness to material and to prevent the warp or filling threads in the construction from slipping out of position. Slip-resistant effectiveness will vary with the chemicals used.

SLIP STITCH. Short loose stitch which is concealed between two thicknesses of cloth. It is used wherever invisible stitching is necessary. Slip stitch is made by taking up a thread of the hem and the fabric; it is used for hems and facing or wherever stitching is not shown on the face side.

SLIT CELLULOSE FILM. Narrow cellulose film sheets which may be used as yarn, alone or in combination with other yarns, to give novel effects in woven or knitted fabrics.

SLIT FABRICS. Include bias binding, piping, seaming ribbons, etc.

SLIP-COVER FABRICS. This wide range includes printed or piece-dyed cloths, woven design fabrics; cotton, nylon, linen, plastic, rayon fabrics, etc. Most slip-cover fabric is cotton with fabrics such as crash, cretonne, chintz, dobby patterns, etc. Fabrics, wherever possible, should be vat-dyed, fast to light and sun, and Sanforized.

COTTON: Several cotton fabrics, either plain or printed, serve as slip covers. Chintz, cretonne, denim, crash, rep, sateen, and monk's cloth are widely used. Nubbed and novelty-textured fabrics are also used to some degree. Sailcloth is a rugged cotton slip cover fabric.

KNITTED COTTON: This fabric is used to give a snug fit on the chair or couch. Elastic sections allow for good fitting of the covering. Price is a factor when buying this type of material.

BURLAP: The finer type of lightweight burlap, in plain colors or stencil prints, is frequently used to advantage.

TICKING: Cotton ticking is ideal for summer use; gives excellent wear.

CLEAR PLASTIC FILM: Heavy-gauge plastic is now being used for slip covers. It should be treated for fire-retardance. The seams of this material are electrically welded. It is especially useful for protecting upholstery since nothing can penetrate it.

RAYON: Nubbed and textured rayon fabrics are popular materials for slip covers. Price is a factor in this type of covering.

LINEN: Plain, screen-printed, or hand-blocked linens are used. Linen gives an impression of added serenity and a cool feeling when used for slip covering.

NYLON AND ACETATE: Blends of these two fibers produce fabrics which combine the beauty of acetate and the abrasion-resistance of nylon.

SLIT FILM. Any film usable as a textile, such as acetate which has been cut into very narrow strips. They are then usually twisted-in with stronger yarns for decorative purposes.

SLIT FILM FROM MANMADE FIBERS. A wide sheet of film is extruded from the machine used and is then slit in vertical or lengthwise direction into narrow continuous strips which, depending on the width may be described as monofilaments. At times, the filaments are combined and serve as yarns for use in various forms of textiles. See Slit Cellulose Film, Slit Film.

SLIVER. The term comes from medieval Anglo-Saxon words sleave, slive, meaning to split or slit. Sliver has no twist and is the product of the carding process and drawing process on the cotton system.

Sliver consists of a continuous rope of parallel fibers of cotton, wool, rayon, or some other material, with no twist applied.

The term is also used in worsted yarn manufacture on similar operations. See Illustrated Section.

SLIVER, CARDED. The fibers of the sliver are laid parallel and the short, immature fibers are removed and are called strips. They may make up about 4 to 6 per cent of the waste on the machine. The sliver is uneven in weight because of the stripping of the doffer and the cylinder. When the cylinder and doffer are full and require stripping, a heavier sliver will result. Immediately after stripping of the rollers, a lighter sliver will be apparent. The variation

of weight per yard in card sliver is greater than the variation noted in combed sliver.

SLIVER, COMBED. With some short fibers removed from the stock prior to the combing operation the sliver naturally will be even, uniform in fiber length, and may possess a luster. Combed sliver, when compared with carded sliver, is stronger, cleaner, more parallel, and has a greater tensile strength.

SLIVER KNITTING. Feeding individual ends of staple stock to knitting needles operated on a jersey principle. The staple is locked into a high-pile position by a backing yarn set up in a jersey ground structure.

SLIVER LAP MACHINE. The purpose and function of this machine is to convert the card sliver into a lap form about ten inches wide. Twenty card slivers of cotton are fed into this frame; they enter the back rollers as one. The action of the drawing rollers reduces the stock to the correct weight at the delivery end of the machine, and into the sheet form that is then fed to the ribbon lapper.

SLIVER TESTER. This device will test sliver by drawing it between two rolls. There is a weight on the machine, acting through a set of levers, which compresses the sliver as the action is taking place. A chart, upon which a recording pen works, will record the variation in compressibility of the sliver.

SLOP, SLIVING. 1. A loose, washable garment worn over clothes to protect a worker, such as a painter,

plumber, seaman. 2. Low-grade, ready-made clothing. 3. A short coat, cassock, smock, or similar garment to protect the wearer from spots and stains getting on his better clothing.

SLOPER. A fundamental pattern used in dressmaking for size only. It is a garment made of linen or muslin fitted to a mannequin and used as the basic pattern for subsequent sizing of garments.

SLOP PADDING. A type of resist printing in which the material is first treated with a resisting agent followed by the application of the color over the entire cloth by an unengraved roller. This method is not popular at present and is well-named since it is considered as a "sloppy" way of printing textile goods. Newer techniques are a vast improvement over this old method of padding color to fabric.

SLOPSHOT. A shop where slops, or cheap ready-made clothes, are sold.

SLOPWORK. The manufacture of the lowest quality of ready-made clothing.

SLOT SEAM. A seam formed by stitching two folds of material which face each other to an inserted piece of goods. The inset may be of contrasting fabric to give certain effects. The slot is made by leaving a narrow space between folds.

SLOUGH GRASS. A strong sedge fiber raised in Iowa, used for twine.

SLOUGHED FILLING. Long-looped filling yarn caused by improper tension on the filling yarn of the bobbin, poor winding, kinks, slubs, broken filling, poor shuttle lining, etc.

SLOW-DOWN. A form of work stoppage in which employees reduce their speed and individual production.

SLUB. A soft, thick, uneven place in yarn; can be either a defect or purposely set in the yarn, such as in the case of slub yarn.

SLUBBER. The first fly frame used for drawing and twisting cotton slivers to form roving. See Illustrated Section.

SLUBBING. The form of stock produced by the slubber machine in cotton manufacturing; it is the ropelike form that follows the sliver in making of yarn. It is about the size of a lead pencil in diameter, and may be spoken of as an attenuated sliver. The fibers are more parallel in slubbing than in sliver, as well as being smoother in feel.

Worsted slubbing, much larger in diameter than cotton slubbing, is called top. Slubbing is produced by drawing, drafting, doubling, redoubling and attenuating of the fibers.

The order of the names from raw stock to yarn are, generally speaking, bulk or raw stock, sliver, slubbing, roving, yarn.

SLUBBY FILLING. Thick places in a yarn that are detrimental to it and which show to disadvantage when woven into a fabric. Usually caused by poor carding of the fibers.

SLUBBY WARP YARN. Thick places observed in warp yarn caused by faulty drawing, roving, or spinning stocks. The diameter of these slubs is often several times larger than the normal diameter. Improper machine settings and tensions will produce this effect in manufacture of the yarn.

SLUB CATCHER. Used on spoolers and winders to aid optical inspection of yarn as it is being wound. There are two blades which have a narrow opening between them through which the yarn has to pass in its course. The blades are adjusted to stop slubs or thick places in the yarn when it comes to the blades.

SLUB OR TOP DYEING. Worsted top may be dyed in several ways, one of which is the Abbott Method. The untwisted sliver is run through a specially designed gill box and is then wound on a perforated dye spool through which the dye flows, penetrating the surrounding sliver.

SLUBS. Imperfections made by nubs, tufts, or little balls of yarn in cloth. They are noticeable and have to be fixed in dry-finishing. Slubs are soft in feel, usually because of some slight irregularity.

SLUB YARN. Yarn of any type which is irregular in diameter; may be caused by error, or purposely made with slubs to bring out some desired effect to enhance a material. Slub yarns are popular as novelty threads in summer dress goods and find much use in hand-woven fabrics.

SLUFF-OFFS. Varied sizes of "masses of yarn" which come off the shuttle all at once because of poor winding of the yarn onto the bobbin which sets in the shuttle for use in weaving. Also called slough-offs.

SLUGS. 1. An irregular, thick place in silk thread that is bulky in diameter. Slugs of this type are 3 mm., or ⅛ inch or more in length. Large slugs exceed 1 cm., or 1⅛ inches in length. 2. Large, soft, spongy places in silk thread caused by small pieces of waste that have become attached to the thread in reeling.

SMALL CHAIN. An old-time expression still used in some carpet circles for the binder or chain warp used in carpet weaving, as in Brussels and Wilton weaving.

SMALLCLOTHES. The knee breeches of the tight-fitting variety that were popular in the eighteenth century.

SMALL STUFF. Maritime term for small diameter rope, usually expressed in terms of the number of yarns in it.

SMALLWARES. British term for what we call "notions."

SMASH. Place in a piece of cloth, still in the loom, where a large number of warp ends have become broken. It is caused by the lay beating up the shuttle while the latter is still in the shed, because of some irregularity made on the spur of the moment or by two shuttles coming together in the same shed because of the weaver putting a shuttle in the wrong box before starting up his loom after a stoppage. Smashes hinder production greatly as time has to be taken to tie or twist in the broken ends. Harness skips and slivers on shuttles will tend to break out ends of the warp.

SMEAR. A small spot or stain made by some greasy substance.

SMITH STANDARD COTTON. Same as Ben Smith cotton.

SMOCK. A long, loose garment of washable material used to protect clothing while one is working.

SMOCK FROCK. A long shirt or coarse smock worn over other clothes by farmers and other workers in Europe.

SMOCK LINEN. A nineteenth-century coarse, plain-woven, linen crash fabric used for aprons, smocks, etc. Now superseded by more practical fabrics.

SMOCKING. An ornamental way of arranging and holding fullness in place by rows of stitches which are both firm and ornamental.

SMOOTH MERINO. Same as C-type merino wool.

SMYRNA COTTON. A medium-strong, harsh and fairly clean, dull-white cotton grown in Greece.

SMYRNA RUG. A reversible chenille rug or carpet which consists of a double weaving process. The first weaving process is the making of the weft or filling blanket, the warp ends of which are twisted or crossed over so that when the blanket is cut into strips the cut ends of yarn will tend to turn alternate ways, making a round chenille.

The second weaving process consists of a loom with a cotton warp making a row of plain-weave while the chenille is deposited in the one shed of the loom and the jute filling is placed in the alternating shed, interlacing with the warp yarn to give body to the fabric.

Smyrna rugs can be made in plain or figured design and may be cheap or expensive, depending on the materials used and the texture of the goods. Many inexpensive cotton bathmats are made on the Smyrna plan of weaving.

SNAG-RESISTANCE. Applied to hosiery, it is "the ability of a hosiery fabric, held under a predetermined and uniform tension, to resist a downward penetration and pull of an adjustable snagging needle. The test results are expressed as the snagging factor." (United States Testing Company, Inc., Hoboken, N. J.)

SNAG TESTER. An instrument which measures snag-resistance of hosiery by applying pressure on an adjustable snagging point kept in constant contact with the hosiery fabric being tested. The pressure of the snagging point is gradually increased for each revolution of the snag tested until the actual snagging is detected. The greater the pressure required to produce a snag, the more snag-resistant will be the hosiery tested.

SNAKES. All types and kinds of loose waste cotton picked up from the sample-room floor; this is packed up and resold.

SNAP. Lustrous, smooth fiber, light-reflecting, and possessing unimpaired whiteness.

SNAP BRIM. Any type of headgear in which the brim is turned down at the front, at the side, or all the way round.

SNAPPED COTTON. Also known as pulled cotton, it is the staple gathered by hand whereby the whole boll

SNARL

is snapped from the plant. Prior to ginning it must be passed through an attachment to burst and to remove the bolls.

SNARL. A bunch of sliver, slubbing, roving, or yarn which forms when a bobbin is not taking the delivery from the roller in the proper manner. Poor atmospheric conditions, as well as improper tensions, are conducive to snarling.

SNARLING MOTION. A spinning mule action which throws the rollers out of gear shortly after the mule carriage has begun its outward yarn.

SNARLS. Loops or curls seen when yarn is being mule-spun. They are caused by improper tension or poor atmospheric conditions.

SNARL YARN. Small curly or kinked places in yarn, usually the result of poor twisting—too little or too much. Lumps in yarn are also called snarl.

SNEAKER. A high or low shoe, usually made of canvas or light duck, with a sole and/or heel made of rubber or some synthetic compound product. Very popular in children's school and play wear, it is also favored by working adults who seek comfort.

SNICKS. Thin places in yarn which cause trouble in weaving.

SNITCH KNOT. A type of knot used to tie the lams to the pedals. The knot is easily adjusted to hold a harness in place. When chains or straps are not used it can be used between lams and harnesses and between lams and treadles on a handloom.

SNOOD. A headband or fillet worn around the hair.

SNOWCLOTH. A term for fabrics designed for outdoor winter use. It may be applied to meltons, kerseys, heavy flannels, and similar fabrics.

SNOWFLAKE. English woolens which have white nubs, salt and pepper effects, or bourette yarn giving a flake effect on the face of the goods.

SNUFFED FINISH. Leather which has had the top or hair follicles removed by an emery wheel. Sometimes known as Corrected Grain.

SOAK. Immersion of clothes or fabrics in water alone or in water and some washing product. This is done prior to washing and the clothes may or may not be agitated. Automatically or manually controlled.

SOAKING. Treatment applied to skein or cake rayon yarns preparatory to throwing; i.e., twisting for crepe twist.

SOAP. Ordinary soap is the alkali salt of a fatty acid. The alkali used may be either sodium or potassium and the soap may be made by saponifying a fat or oil or neutralizing the fatty acids obtained from fats or oils. Alkaline earth metals such as calcium, barium, and magnesium form insoluble soaps used in some industries as waterproofing agents for fabrics.

There are three types of soap, as follows:

1. HARD SOAP: Contains sodium compounds of fatty acids which harden upon exposure to air. Used chiefly for hard water washing.

2. SOFT SOAP: Contains potassium compounds which absorb water and have the tendency to liquefy.

3. NEUTRAL SOAP: Contains compounds of olive oil or lard oil with potash, freely soluble and free from alkalies. A neutral soap is one which is supposed to dissolve in both hard and soft water.

SOAP, ALL-PURPOSE. One which has mild alkaline builders added to improve cleaning and to soften water, and which often includes a brightener. Used for the family wash.

SOAP, LIGHT DUTY. A pure soap product used for washing which does not contain a builder. Used chiefly on baby clothes, fine and sheer fabrics, slightly soiled laundry and for hand dishwashing. Brighteners can be used in this soap, which comes in bar, flake, and granular form.

SOAP, SOFT. It is a potash base, but the term also implies a soap paste which contains ordinary soda soap and considerable water. See SOAP.

SOAP, STOCK. A solution or build prepared for use in a washwheel. It is of definite strength and produces a definite concentration when diluted in the wheel. Also called Stock Solution.

SOAP, STRAIGHT. Commercially pure soap, in which the sum of free alkali, total matter insoluble in alcohol, and sodium chloride does not exceed 4 per cent.

SOAP CHALK. Tailors' chalk which disappears under a hot iron or when treated with benzene.

SOAP CONTENT. The quantity of anhydrous soap present.

SOAP CURD. Also called soap film and lime soap, it is water insoluble material which forms when the soap combines with hard salts such as calcium and magnesium in hard water.

SOAP-SHRUNK. Soap and water will give the maximum amount of shrinkage to cloth; very good for heavy materials.

SOAPING. 1. Rubbing with soap. 2. Treating cloth with a soap solution. 3. Soaping is a very important item in the fulling of woolen fabrics. See Illustrated Section.

SOAP PANS: Soap-boiling kettles.

SOAP POWDER. A mixture of soap and one or more alkaline detergents, containing 15 to 25 per cent of anhydrous soap.

SOAP-SHRUNK FINISH. Worsteds are soap-shrunk when they are milled and scoured as much as possible. When this is correctly done there will be no further shrinkage. Any shrinkage that occurred during soaping can be recovered in the tenter frame.

SOAP SPECKS. Either lime soap deposits or the greasy portion of soap produced by decomposition from heat or sour, etc. Very difficult to remove from textile materials.

SOAPWEED YUCCA. Found from the Dakotas to Texas, this fiber has saponaceous matter in its roots; nevertheless, it is of little commercial value.

SOCA. The second picking or crop from cotton; term is used in Peru and some other cotton centers in South America.

SOCK. 1. Common term for short-length hose. 2. Light shoes worn by old Greek and Roman comedians. 3. A warm insole. 4. A clog or sandal worn by monks of some religious orders.

SODA. Term generally applied to the alkaline builders but which is only correctly applied to the modified sodas.

SODA, MODIFIED. A mixture of soda ash and sodium bicarbonate, low in active alkali and efficiency.

SODA ASH. Crude sodium carbonate not quite totally pure. Used in washing and scouring of textiles, in soap manufacture, and in softening water. It is also used to fix tin salts in silk weighting. Formula is Na_2CO_3.

SODIUM. An alkali metal element having the symbol "Na."

SODIUM ACID FLUORIDE. A moderately soluble acid fluoride salt with favorable neutralizing power and definite iron removing properties in concentrated solution.

SODIUM BICHROMATE. Used as a discharge in calico printing, as a mordant in dyeing of wool, and as developer in dyeing and printing with aniline black. Formula is $NaCr_2O_7$.

SODIUM BISULPHATE. Used in the dyeing of wool to increase affinity of dyestuffs. Formula is $NaHSO_4$.

SODIUM CARBONATE. A strong alkaline compound used in textiles. See SODA ASH.

SODIUM CHLORATE. Used in the oxidation of aniline black.

SODIUM CHLORITE BLEACHING. Ideal for manufactured fibers, its properties differ greatly from those of sodium hydrochlorite. The bleaching action is determined by the rate at which the chlorine is liberated. Care has to be used in this bleaching method since the escape of chlorine dioxide into the atmosphere can be very harmful.

SODIUM DICHROMATE. Aqueous solution of this is acidic, and it is much used as a mordant in wool dyeing, in the manufacture of dyes and chrome pigments, and in leather tanning. Also known as sodium bichromate, chrome.

SODIUM FERROCYANIDE. Used with Prussian blue in dyeing. Formula is $Na_4Fe(Cn)_6$.

SODIUM FLUOSILICATE. A crystalline, sparingly soluble, acid reacting salt of high neutralizing power, used as a sour. It has low solubility and dissolves slowly.

SODIUM HYDROXIDE. A white, caustic, fusible compound used in various solutions in chemistry and as a bleaching agent for textiles. Commonly called caustic soda, NaOH.

SODIUM HYPOCHLORITE. A solution of a chemical derived from hypochlorous acid and a sodium base, commonly known as bleach, and prepared in various ways.

SODIUM HYPOSULPHATE. Used as a reducing agent, and as a bleaching powder in fillers. Also used as a resist in dyeing cotton with aniline black, and as a fixing agent of metallic oxides in calico printing.

SODIUM METAPHOSPHATE. The sodium salt of metaphosphoric acid. Sometimes used in conditioning hard water.

SODIUM METASILICATE PENTAHYDRATE. A soluble, crystalline, alkaline sodium silicate which has about 42 per cent water in content.

SODIUM NITRATE. Used in dyeing and printing cottons with diazo colors.

SODIUM PERBORATE (Na BO^{2o} H^2O^{2o} $3H^2O$). A white, crystalline substance used as a bleaching agent and disinfectant. As a bleach it is a mild powder product of the oxygen type which can be used safely on all fabrics. Sodium perborate in this powder bleach provides the active ingredient.

SODIUM PEROXIDE. Used in combination with other chemicals as a bleaching agent. When treated with water it yields oxygen and hydrogen peroxide. It is a powerful oxidizing agent.

SODIUM PHOSPHATE. Used to weight silk, and in dyeing with azo colors and Turkey Red; Na_3PO_4.

SODIUM SILICATE, SOLUBLE GLASS, WATERGLASS. Used to weight silk, to fireproof fabrics, and as a soap detergent. It is strongly alkaline in reaction.

SODIUM SILICO FLUORINE. A crystalline, sparingly soluble, acid-reacting salt of high neutralizing power sometimes used as a sour.

SODIUM STANNATE. Used to mordant azo dyes, Na_2SnO_5.

SOFT COTTON. Cotton which is smooth, soft, and fairly clean, on the order of Sea Island, Pima, and Egyptian cottons.

SOFT END. Imperfections that reveal soft, spongy areas in silk yarn. This same condition in other yarns is called by the same expression.

SOFTENED WATER. Water that has been treated chemically to remove soap-destroying minerals such as carbonates and bicarbonates of calcium, and sulphates and chlorides of magnesium.

SOFTENER. One of several products on the market used in warp sizing and cloth finishing to impart a soft mellowness to the fabric. Examples of softeners include sulphonated castor or palm oil, glucose, glycerine, paraffin wax, tallow, etc. There are also available the durable types of cationic softeners which resist removal from the fabric by either dry cleaning or washing.

SOFTENING. Application of a soft finish on goods without their becoming sleazy or clammy in feel.

SOFTENING AGENT. Material applied to fabric to improve the quality of hand or feel.

SOFT FIBERS. Name for pliable, elongated fibers taken from the inner bark of certain plants—flax, hemp, jute, ramie.

SOFT-FILLED SHEETING. Made with soft-spun filling that is usually much lower in yarn count than the warp yarn in the goods. It is much used for converting into various types of napped fabrics such as flannels, suède-finish cloth, and duvetyne.

SOFT FINISH. Fabrics, usually cotton, in which softness of the goods is a characteristic selling point. Little or no sizing is applied to these fabrics.

SOFT GOODS. Term sometimes applied to textile fabrics.

SOFTS. English term for shoddy.

SOFT SIDES. Weaving term implying a group of warp ends which because of some weakness or softness continually break and impede production.

SOFT SILK. Silk with the sericin removed from it.

SOFT SOAP. See SOAP.

SOFT TWIST. Any twist below the number required per inch in a yarn, making the yarn soft. It is used often in reference to spinning twist.

SOFT WARP. One in which there is less than the normal amount of size required. Much trouble is encountered with this type of warp-slippage, breakage, possible gnarling, etc.

SOFT WASTES. In the gilling and drawing processes in worsted yarn manufacture, before the actual spinning, there are wastes from sliver, slubbing, top, and roving. The term "soft waste" is rather misleading, since the stock has lost none of its value. It can be worked with other stocks and the only loss is the time in handling it and the labor entailed. The expense of handling the stock twice is negligible. Little of it is offered for sale, since most mills consume their own wastes.

Soft wastes sell for about the same price as scoured wool of equal quality. Similar soft wastes, such as sliver and slubbing, are produced on the woolen system. They are reserved for use in identical lots that will be run through later.

Wastes, such as card strippings, fly and floor sweepings, are subjected to treatment in the waste dusting machine. This stock is unsuited for blending in lots intended for certain cloths of medium or better quality. Dealers buy this stock wherever possible and dispose of it to mills that make woolen blankets or low-quality cloths.

SOFT WATER. Water free from dissolved mineral salts.

SOFU. Japanese term for a plain-weave, unbleached cotton cloth that is 44-square in pick count. The warp ends are about twice as high in count when compared with the filling yarn used, a 30s warp and a 15s filling.

SOIE. French for silk.

SOIE ONDEE. The doubling of a coarse and a fine worsted yarn or thread into a ply yarn so that it may be used to make fabric that is to be watermarked (ondée).

SOIE OVALE. French for silk embroidery yarn.

SOIE PLATTE. Floss silk yarn made in France; soie plattée is used in embroidery and tapestry work.

SOIE VEGETALE. 1. French for vegetable silk. 2. The term sometimes implies linen fabric which has been given a high, permanent luster which enables it to be used ideally for braid, lace, and trimming.

SOIL. Dirt, spots, and stains whose removal require laundering of the fabric. They appear on surfaces, in the fibers and fabrics, and held between the fibers in the yarns used in the article. Soil also comes from a redeposition during a washing or rinse. Spots and stains may be removed by the following methods dependent on the stain - absorbent method, chemical action, detergent action, digestion method, lubrication method, solvent action.

SOIL-OUT. Registered trademark name for soil release finish owned by J. P. Stevens & Company, Inc., New York City. Many types of spots and stains are removed from machine washable or durable press slacks and kindred items. There is no alteration or degradation of the article treated, and effectiveness of the finish withstand more than twenty machine washings.

SOIL RELEASE DEFINITIONS.
1. *Anti-static:* Any agent used to counteract static electricity.
2. *Ecology:* That branch of science concerned with the interrelationship of organisms and their environments, especially pertinent to the interdependence of organisms.
3. *Deposing: Deposition:* To take away from or to do away with. Example - removing a spot or stain from a fabric or garment.
4. *Inorganic:* Lacking the carbon element in its structure. For example, water or a water-miscible noncompound which possesses solvent properties. Other examples include dilute hydrochloric acid used on rust stains and hypochloric acid used on iodine stains.
5. *Organic:* A broad term applied to the science of living organisms or all substances which consist chiefly of hydrogen, oxygen, and carbon. Example - fertilizer.
6. *Organism:* Refers to an organic structure, something felt to resemble living plant or animal form of life. An organism as a form of life is composed of mutually dependent parts that maintain various vital processes in any organized body or system conceived of as analogous to a living being.
7. *Redeposition:* Formation into a new accumulation and clearly a product of solution and in a highly porous condition or state. For example, the mixing of articles of apparel of various and sundry colors, contents, and fibers when washing to remove dirt, grime, spots and stains; any or all of which often cause some of the lighter or white articles to take on a so-called gray or yellow tinge. Soil redeposition is now conquered by several major finishes or applications of liquids or compounds.

SOIL RELEASE. Making its debut in the spring of 1966, the term refers to that property of a fabric which permits removal of most oil and waterborne spots and stains by ordinary home laundering. Fabrics in this category have been given special finishes. Some compounds are used only on 100 percent polyester fabrics and pre-cured durable press materials. Other compounds find use in pre-cured or post-cured durable press for other types of fibers and blends of fibers. Performance claims vary to some degree; usually, however, an article may take from twenty to fifty washings.

Following is a list of the major processes in use at present:

PRODUCER:	SOIL RELEASE TRADEMARK:
American Hoechst	Premenit VS - highly concentrated.
BASF	Perapret D.
Beaunit Textiles, Division of Beaunit Corporation	Soil-out
Bradford Dyeing Association (USA)	Brad-clean
Bryant Chemical Corporation	Brytex SR Finish.
Burlington Industries	Come-Clean.
Cranston Print Works, Inc.	Cran-Set SR; Cran-Prest Sr; Cran-Dura SR.
Cravenette Division of Crown Chemical Corporation	Crave-Clean.
Dan River, Inc.	Dan-Clean.
Deering Milliken Co., Inc.	Visa
Celanese Fibers Marketing Company	Fybrite.
Cold Spring Bleachery	Dela-Kleen S-R.
Imperial Chemical Industries, Ltd. (I.C.I.)	Cirrasol PT.
Klopman Mills Division of Burlington Industries, Inc.	Come-Clean
M. Lowenstein & Sons, Inc.	Soilex
McCampbell Sales Division of Graniteville Company, Inc.	X-it.
Minnesota Mining & Manufacturing Company, Inc.	Dual-Action Scotchgard.
Original Bradford Soap Works	Bradsyn G-4.
Polymer Research Company, Inc.	Soil Guard.
Riegel Textile Corporation	Riegel-Release.
Spring Mills, Inc.	Springs-Clean.
J. P. Stevens & Co., Inc.	Wash-Ease
Textile Adjuncts Corporation	Poly-Couplers MTD, LTD, SGD.
Vikon Chemical Company, Inc.	Vikon FP3.

8. *Static:* Pertaining to or noting static electricity; electricity contained or produced by charged bodies. An example is the electricity in the body of a human being. Static electrical charges in the atmosphere come from a disturbance such as an accumulation of electrical charges from snowflakes, household appliances, animal matter, some man-made fiber materials, a power-drive mimeograph machine and its affect on the paper being run through the machine, etc.

SOIL RETARDANT. Various chemical compounds which are applied to fabrics especially carpets, to enable them to resist soiling.

SOISETTE. This trademark, well over sixty years in use, is owned by Ponemah Mills, Inc., Taftville, Connecticut, for their cotton pongee. The fabric is mercerized and takes a very fine finish. There are about 6.50 yards to the pound in weight. Fine combed warp and a soft, mule-spun filling are used in this high-pick cloth that is used for dress goods, lining, shirting, and underwear.

SOLDIERING. Deliberate waste of productive time by an employee.

SOLE LEATHER. See SHOE LEATHER.

SOLEIL. 1. Satin-faced fabric of silk or rayon with a fine line or stripe effect in the warp direction. Soleil is the French for sun and is applied to the fabric name because of the brightness of the finish observed on the goods. Comes in solid color background effect. This sheenlike material is usually piece-dyed.

2. A woolen cloth made in a warp-effect, broken twill weave. Finished with high luster, it is used in dresses and suits in women's wear.

3. A soft silken felt very popular in the millinery trade.

4. Name sometimes used to mean a warp rib-weave or fabric.

5. General term for any fabric finished with high luster.

SOLEIL WEAVES. The use of warp ribs arranged so that the warp threads float in alternate order over a number of picks, and then weave plain-weave with the next successive group of picks.

SOLID COLOR. A one-color fabric.

SOLKA. Manufactured from spruce wood pulp by the viscose process, it is a product similar to cotton, but contains more cellulose and has a much shorter fiber. Solka is spun into coarse yarns which are used for upholstery and drapery fabrics and for rugs, shoes, and handbags.

SOLOMON BAR. A flat braid bar of four threads used in macrame lace. See MACRAME.

SOLUBLE. A substance which will dissolve in a certain solvent. Generally speaking, water is considered the solvent.

SOLUBLE OIL. One that is made water soluble by sulphonation or other chemical treatment. Used in textile dyeing. Examples include sulphonated castor oil, Monopole oil, Solapol oil.

SOLUBLE STARCH. Soluble starch is one in which cornstarch serves usually as the base since it will produce practically any desired consistency or uniformity. While soluble starch has many uses, it is not ideal for heavy, adhesive weighting of textile yarns or fabrics, because the manufacture of it reduces its weighting properties.

SOLUTION. A homogeneous molecular mixture produced by dispersing one or more substances in another, usually a liquid. Any substance which dissolves readily in a liquid is said to be soluble in that liquid. Any substance which does not dissolve in a liquid is said to be insoluble in that liquid. Any substance which, like water, has the power to dissolve another substance is called a solvent. The substance dissolved is known as a solute.

SOLUTION, STOCK. A relative concentration of a chemical or dye. It is diluted with water prior to use.

SOLUTION-DYED. Man-made fibers, dyed, during the formation of these fibers, in a solution which is colored with the particular dye color desired. See Dope Dyed, Spun-dyed.

SOLVENT. A liquid in which substances will easily dissolve. Water is often referred to as the universal solvent since it will dissolve almost anything to some extent. The textile industry uses a wide range of solvents depending upon the specific operation involved.

An Inorganic Solvent is a non-carbon compound which possesses solvent properties. Common organic solvents include water, dilute hydrochloric acid, used for rust stains, hypo, for iodine stains, sulphuric acid, etc.

An Organic Solvent contains carbon compounds; the symbol for carbon, "C," will appear in the formula. This type of solvent is useful in removing stains of a greasy nature. As the vapors of all organic solvents are injurious when inhaled in large quantities, they should be used in well ventilated quarters. Some organic solvents are wood alcohol, ether, benzene, gasoline, carbon tetrachloride, benzol, acetic acid, chloroform.

SOLVEX. Registered trademark of Solvex Corporation, Louisville, Kentucky, for its covered basting threads which are soluble in drycleaning solvents. (Patents - 3,311,938, 3,373,471).

SOMALI FAT-RUMPED SHEEP. This Asiatic breed ranges from the Black Sea and European areas to Central Asia, China, and Siberia. One of the largest with regard to numbers, the nomadic tribes such as the Kalmuks, Kirghiz, and Mongols herd very large flocks of these sheep. Many flocks have more than 10,000 sheep. Russia is now improving these sheep in the Siberian area.

SOMALILAND FIBER. Similar to aloe, it is a long, flexible leaf fiber found in Africa.

SOMMIERE. An all-wool French serge, napped on one side, used for lining of winter garments. It comes in bleached ecru and colored effects.

SONTAG. A knitted or crocheted woolen or worsted jacket or cape in which the ends are crossed at the back; may be worn over the waist or blouse.

SOOJNEY. This Indian bedcovering is made in a diaper or birdseye construction, is rather heavy in weight, and is made on hand looms. Pick count is around 60-square with counts of yarn about 12s to 14s or so. A fringe sets off the two ends of the article.

SORBENT. Material which possesses the property of dehumidifying gases without the aid of refrigeration. It refers usually to materials which have a large capacity for moisture compared with their bulk or weight.

SORIA. A harsh wool raised in Spain.

SORPTION. Absorption or adsorption.

SORREL. A reddish or yellowish brown color.

SORTED WOOL GRADING. There are two methods used to designate the grades of sorted wool. The Blood System is used in this country; the Count System is used in other world centers for wool, and is also increasing in use here. Both systems pertain to the average fineness of diameter of the fibers.

Originally, the Blood System of grading fine wool was used to grade the fine wool grown by the Merino sheep, the criterion used; coarser grades were considered the result of crossing Merino sheep with English breeds. While still used to designate wool fineness, it does not now indicate the true strain of breeding.

The Count System has as its basis the theoretical limit spinning count of wools of certain fineness, that is, the finer the wool the finer will be the yarn that can be spun from it. The following table reveals the relation between the two systems:

U. S. Blood Grades:	Count Grades:	Approx. Per Cent of U. S. Clip:
Fine	64s and finer	49
½ blood	58s to 60s	15
⅜ blood	56s	21
¼ blood	48s to 50s	13
Low	46s and coarses	2

The grades of apparel wool produced in this country rather closely approximate the percentages of the different grades customarily used here.

See Illustrated Section.

SORTING PENISTON. An old-time British woolen made of shoddy.

SORTS. Wools of the same grade from the several fleeces that have been sorted by the sorter; often called Matchings. See Illustrated Section.

SOSQUIL. Mexican term for henequen raised in Yucatan.

SOUFFLE. The larger designs on some crepon fabric show a raised or puffed area; the name is French, soufflé, and implies puffed.

SOUFFLONS. Partially transparent silk cocoons, open in structure, and unfit for winding.

SOUPLE SILK. Dyed silk skeins from which about one half of the silk gum has been removed; 8 to 12 per cent of the weight of the silk is removed out of a possible 16 to 24 per cent. When a greater percentage than these amounts has been removed the silk is known as semi-cut silk. The old term "bright silk," which is now construed to be the same as fully degummed silk, implies that all of the silk gum has been taken out. This would constitute from about 16 to 25 per cent of the total weight of the silk skeins.

The more gum left in the stock, the duller is the luster. However, on the other hand, the sericin left in the silk will protect it during weaving and make the fabric heavier if souple silk is used instead of bright silk.

The total amount of gum in silk ranges from about 10 per cent in Tussah up to as high as 25 per cent in the best Italian silk, based on the weight.

Exfoliation (lousiness) is always good on souple silk while bright silk in recent years has been quite treacherous. China silks give more satisfactory results than Japan silks in skein-dyeing.

SOUR. Designates acid, or an acid solution used in bleaching or in curing skins.

SOURING. Treating fabrics, chiefly cottons, with a weak acid solution. Its purpose is to neutralize any alkali content that may have remained.

SOUSEE. An Indian trousering made from dyed cotton warp and yellow silk filling. Made about one yard in width, the cut length runs to 20 yards.

SOUTACHE BRAID. Narrow, flat braid used as ornamentation on garments; made of cotton, rayon, or silk, it is sewed onto the material.

SOUTH AMERICAN COTTON. Broad term for cotton from Brazil and Peru. This group of cottons follows Sea Island, Arizona, and Egyptian cottons in general qualities. Some of the major cottons are: Bahia, Ceara, Aracaju, Maranham, Parahyba, Pernambuco, Rio Grande, Tanguis, Maceio, and the three Peruvian staples—Rough, Smooth, and Sea Islands.

SOUTHERN HOPE COTTON. A cotton of the deep South with 1-inch staple and lint yield of about 32 per cent.

SOUTHDOWN. The oldest of British breeds of sheep. Down wool, reared in the Sussex Hills, gives a close, white fleece that is considered to be the best of British staples. The fleece, weighing from 5 to 7 pounds, gives a staple of about 2 inches and sorts to 1/2 blood medium grade. These hardy sheep have a fleece shrinkage of about 45 per cent. See Illustrated Section.

SOYBEAN FIBER. The protein base fiber produced from the soybean. It resembles wool in resiliency and feel; it is insulative and has a tensile strength about 80 per cent that of wool. It excels wool in resistance to alkalies.

The soybeans are crushed into a meal, which is treated with a saline solution to extract the protein. This extract is subsequently changed into a viscous solution, which is spun into fiber by methods similar to those used to produce other fibers. The fibers are in a fluffy mass and resemble scoured wool.

Some of the potential uses of soybean fiber include blending with wool to give a soft quality to upholstery, suitings, and felt.

SPACE DYE®. Registered trademark of Fred Whitaker & Company, Inc., Roanoke, Virginia, for its multi-colored dyed yarns prepared in accordance with U. S. Patent 3,012,303. The yarns are knit into fabric, printed with vari-colored motifs or patterns, heat-set, de-knitted, and then used in woven, knitted, or tufted structures to provide a surface random color-effect.

SPAN. 1. The distance an embroidery machine can move vertically before it is necessary to roll over. 2. The total fabric on an embroidery machine, such as two ten-yard pieces, two fifteen-yard lengths, or 28 ten-yard pieces, sewed together to make a span or load of goods. See Roll Over.

SPANDEX. A manufactured fiber in which the fiber-forming substance is a long chain synthetic elastomer comprised of at least 85 percent of a segmented polyurethane. As to properties, Spandex has excellent whiteness retention combined with superb holding power (a #1 Spandex yarn has the same holding power as a #1.8 rubber yarn); good resistance to cosmetic agents, excellent breaking strength (twice the strength of true rubber), good abrasion and flex resistance, high elasticity, drycleanability, and affinity for most classes of dyes. Specific gravity is 1.0, rubber is 1.4, and is one-third rubber's weight.

Uses include foundation garments, swimwear, support and surgical hosiery, and outer-wear garments where elasticity is needed for figure support or improved comfort and fit. Examples are Lycra of DuPont, and Vyrene of UniRoyal Fiber and Textile Division of UniRoyal, Inc.

SPANGLE. Old-time term for a spindle.

SPANISH BROOM. 1. This plant produces a very fine fiber used to make fabrics in France and Italy, and lace in Spain. 2. A rugged cloth made in Southern Europe from the fiber.

SPANISH FOX. A rope twisted against its lay.

SPANISH GRAIN. A finish made by embossing on fancy or upholstery leather a modified natural grain which formerly was obtained by drawing a hide or skin in a strong tan liquor to shrink the grain. The result of this action was an interesting pattern on the surface due to the unequal shrinking of the various portions.

SPANISH GRASS. Same as Esparto fiber.

SPANISH GUIPURE. General term for the heavier laces made in Spain.

SPANISH LACE. A broad term which includes convent lace, cut drawnwork, needle-point lace, etc. The term refers to machine-made lace which comes in a wide variety of designs.

SPANISH LINEN. A rugged, plainwoven, washable fabric of linen warp and cotton filling. Comes in white, colors, and prints and is used for summer wear.

SPANISH MOSS. Known as Tillandsia, it is found hanging on trees in Louisiana and other southern states and is used as stuffing material. The entire plant is used and only the cuticle and small protrusions are peeled off. Its color varies from gray to dark brown. Characteristic elements found on the fiber are the thin, fan-shaped scales.

SPANISH POINT. A distinctive, old-time embroidery of gold or silver. Silk passementerie is used as edging.

SPANISH SHEEP. Used as synonymous with the term Merino, but all Spanish sheep are not of the Merino type.

SPANISH STITCH. An embroidery stitch made up of a cross-stitch on the face in rows and a square on the back, or the cross on the face may be enclosed in a square.

SPANNER. In embroidery, a frame worker who loads the Schiffli machine for stitching.

SPANNING. Loading of an embroidery machine; also called span-up. See Span.

"SPAN-SPUN". An elastomeric core spun yarn which has a covering of "Orlong." Product of J. P. Stevens & Company, Inc., New York City.

SPANZELLE. Elastomeric yarn which comes in either the bare condition or wrapped or covered. Made by the British American Spandex Company, Ltd., United Kingdom, and Firestone Tire and Rubber Company, Fall River, Massachusetts, and Akron, Ohio.

SPARKLE NYLON. Multilobal nylon filaments which, because of the yarn cross-sections, afford luster or sparkle effects to fabrics in which they are used. Very effective, particularly in 15 denier monofilament used in women's hosiery; also ideal for other high gauge knit fabrics and certain woven goods where the effect is desired.

SPAT. 1. Short cloth gaiter, worn over shoes by both men and women; fastened underneath, usually buttoned up the side. Originally, knee-length gaiter. 2. Short for spatter-dash.

SPEC DEALERS. One who buys country-damaged or no-mark cottons, interested in mending them for resale.

SPECIAL FINISHES. Those which are not of the average kinds of finishes given to fabrics. In this group would be special, sometimes secret, finishes for crease-resistance, crease-retention, flame-resistance, moth-resistance, water-repellency and others.

SPECIALTY FIBERS, FABRICS MADE FROM MAJOR.

ALPACA: Alpaca cloth, alpacuna, lining materials for coatings. Also used with other hair fibers and wool in "hair fiber coatings."

CAMEL HAIR: Suiting fabric for men's wear and women's wear, top-coats, overcoats for men, windbreak-

ers, sweaters, sport jackets, hats, caps, dresses. Fabric weights are about 6 ounces for women's wear dresses to about 40 ounces in men's wear ulsters.

CASHMERE: The famous luxury shawls known as cashmere and Indian cashmere; the fiber is widely used in varying amounts mixed with other fibers. The name "cashmere" is much used in the woolen and worsted trade to mean material that has some of this fiber in the finished cloth. Seventeen variations of the spelling have been noted as trade names: Kashmir, Kashmiri, Cashmeer, Kasha, etc.

LLAMA: Llama fabrics are used in sportswear, women's coatings, suits, dresses, etc., and in men's lightweight suitings, year-round suits, slip-on topcoats, year-round coatings, and heavy overcoatings.

MOHAIR: This fiber is used in many staple and fancy materials: plushes, coat linings, tropical worsteds, lap robes, curtainings, furniture covering, bathing suits, Henrietta cloth, Zibeline, Astrakhan, coatings, car seats in railroad coaches and Pullmans, in braids and portieres.

ANGORA GOAT: Very popular for the best types of knitting yarn for hand and power work. The fiber is much imitated in this field in textiles. It is also used in making capes, plushes, crepon, mantle cloth, Astrakhan, Zibeline, brilliantine, cashmeres, novelty materials for fancy design work.

VICUNA: Fabric made from this finest and most expensive natural fiber is used for coating, chiefly in men's wear. Genuine vicuna coating has sold for as much as one hundred and fifty dollars per yard. Finished overcoating has sold for as much as one thousand dollars. See HAIR FIBERS.

SPECIAL WOOLS. A general term indicative of certain so-called short staple wools, such as Blackface, Herdwick, and Welsh.

SPECIES, COTTON. The botanical term for cotton is Gossypium. The major types include: 1. *Gossypium hirsutum*—American Uplands cotton. 2. *Gossypium barbadense*—source for Sea Island, several Egyptian strains, Barbadoes and Peruvian cottons. 3. *Gossypium herbaceum*—source for staple from Asia, China, India, Italy.

The varieties of the cotton plant are classified as tree, shrub, or herbaceous.

SPECIFIC GRAVITY. The relative weight of a certain volume of a liquid as compared with an equal volume of water.

SPECIFIC GRAVITY OF SOME MAJOR TEXTILE FIBERS. Density is defined as the mass per unit of volume. Specific gravity is the ration of the mass of a given volume of any substance to that of the same value of some other substance taken as a standard. Water is the standard for liquids and solids while hydrogen is standard for gases. Density and specific gravity are expressed in terms of grams per cubic centimeter.

Fiber in Grams per C.C.:

Acetate	1.32
Acrilan	1.17
Cotton	1.48
Creslan	1.17
"Dacron"	1.38
Dynel	1.30
Flax	1.50
Fortrel	1.38
Glass	2.56
Kodel	1.22-1.38
Nylon 6 & 66	1.14
"Orlon"	1.14-1.17
Polypropylene	0.91
Saran	1.70
Silk	1.30
Verel	1.37
Vinyon HH	1.34
Viscose rayon	1.52
Wool	1.30
Zefran	1.175

SPECIFIC STRESS. The ratio of the force to the mass per unit length. This ratio is equal to the stress per unit density.

SPECK-DYEING. Many medium and low-grade woolens and worsteds have to be speck-dyed to cover up the specks caused by vegetable matter in them. The material may be dyed in a cold soap bath of direct dyes which will dye the cotton but will not dye the animal fibers.

Specks may also be covered up by the "pen and ink" method. When the percher or specker discovers specks in the cloth, he "inks-in" the spot with the correct matching color.

SPECKELON. Registered trademark name of Monsanto Company, Inc., Textiles Division, New York City, for its specially designed fiber for use as warp yarn to enhance novel color and surface effects in upholstery fabrics. This bright "thick-and-thin," continuous filament nylon yarn has numerous undrawn nubs, randomly spaced about each individual filament. Nubs vary in length from one-half to three inches with an average length of 1¼-inches. Made with a multi-lobular cross-section, the filaments enhance yarn luster, luster highlights, provide excellent color harmony or contrast, have excellent covering power, good crush resistance and resiliency.

SPECK YARN. See KNICKERBOCKER YARN.

SPECKY GOODS. Small particles or specks of vegetable matter which show on the face of the material. Difficult to remove, it is sometimes necessary to speck-dye the goods or to carbonize the stock prior to manipulation from raw material to finished fabric.

SPECTRAN. Solution-dyed Acrilan staple fiber made by Monsanto Textiles Inc., New York City.

SPECTROPHOTOMETER. A scientific instrument for the measurement of color of reflecting materials, such as paint or paper, or of transmitting materials such as glass, filters, or solutions. The instrument is useful for controlling the color of dyes, glass, and inks, since it is independent of psychological and philosophical factors which influence human vision. With this equipment it is possible to plot a curve of the light reflected or transmitted by a sample against the wave length of light.

SPECTRUM. The image formed by rays of light, in which the parts are arranged according to their refrangibility, or wave length, forming a band that shows the six colors of the rainbow. From this idea, all shades, casts, hues, tints, and colors are made, with black and white used to make them darker, or lighter, respectively.

SPECULATING. The buying of a cotton future with the hope of selling it later at a higher price or contracting to sell the cotton at some future date in the hope of buying it before that time at a lower price.

SPEEDERS, INTERMEDIATE AND ROVING. These cotton machines are used to draft the roving to obtain a finer hank. The work relates closely to that done on the slubbers, with the exception that the roving is drawn from a bobbin placed in a creel at the back of the frame. The roving is run through in double formation to keep it even and uniform and to avoid variations between it and the resultant yarn.

Since the roving frame is the finer machine of the two, the former will give the greater draft and higher twist. Roving frame draft is around seven, the intermediate frame around six. The finer the hank, the smaller will be the bobbin. More spindles can be placed in the roving frame than in the intermediate. The bobbin on the intermediate averages about 8 to 10 inches while that of the roving frame is 7 to 8

inches, lift of the traverse.

SPEED-UP. A method of forcing employees to work faster than normal standard, established with no extra compensation, or no incentive for the increased output.

SPELLAIA. Italian term for the tangled waste filament by which cocoons are attached to tree twigs.

SPELLE WORK. Flemish expression for bobbin lace.

SPENCER. Around the time of the American Revolution, this was a popular outer garment worn by women, often knitted and usually fur-trimmed. There was also a man's short jacket of this name, and it was a forerunner of the present-day suit jacket worn by men.

SPERMACETI. A white waxlike softener used in textile finishing. Made from sperm oil, it is an excellent softener when combined with Japan wax.

SPIDERS. Trade term for certain cotton fabrics used in dress goods which have varying amounts of other fibers, such as linen, rayon, or worsted, mixed with the cotton; covers a wide range as to quality and price.

SPIDER STITCH. A lace or netting stitch wherein the motif is that of a spider web.

SPIDER WEAVE. General term for netlike effects seen on some textile materials.

SPIDER-WEB COTTON. Same as cobweb cotton.

SPIEL. A sales talk.

SPIKE ROLL. See PIN CYLINDER.

SPINAKER. A 40-inch width heavy cotton cloth used for tents.

SPIN AND SPINNING. To spin is to perform the operation of drawing and drafting roving stock to the required counts of yarn or thickness, inserting the necessary number of turns of twist per inch, and the winding of the yarn onto some suitable form such as a bobbin, cone, tube, etc., i.e., spinning.

The term also includes the making of yarn by extrusion of a viscous liquid when it is coagulated readily into a hardened form. Rayon is made in this manner. See Illustrated Section.

SPINDLE. A long, thin rod that is used on certain textile machines for twisting and holding textile fibers in manipulation from sliver form to spun yarn. This upright device is found on slubbers, roving frames, jack frames, spinning, winding, and twisting machines. Revolving at a very high rate of speed to perform its work, drawing, twisting, and winding, the spindle has

a bobbin, tube, or cop set around it so that the finished stock may be wound evenly and easily.

The spindle is one of the oldest textile devices known to man. It is driven on machines of today by means of spindle banding, which can drive a spindle over 12,000 r.p.m., if needs be.

SPINDLE AND DISTAFF, ERA OF THE. Up to the fourteenth century, when the spinning wheel made its advent, the spindle and distaff were the only devices used in textiles to make yarn. By their use a yarn could be spun without the aid of a wheel.

The spindle was rotated by the fingers instead of by machinery. The distaff was the staff from which the wool or flax was drawn for action by the spindle.

This method of spinning yarn is still used in the very remote sections of the world that have not been touched by the machine age and the Industrial Revolution. Before the spinning wheel came into use, the world had to accept yarn made in this manner.

SPINDLE-DRAWN YARN. This refers to the type of yarn made on the mule-spinning frame. The finest crepe yarns can be made on a mule; also, the lowest twist yarns. Mule spinning is expensive; spinning mules take up considerably more space per spindle than the ring spinning frame. See Illustrated Section. A mule frame is now able to spin finer counts than a ring frame; it can also spin coarser counts, as well. The chief virtue in mule-spun yarn is its evenness.

SPINDLE GILL BOX. A worsted gill box equipped with a set of spindles so that the sliver, slubbing, or roping may be wound on bobbins by the flyer in a compact, uniform manner.

SPINDLE RAIL. This runs the length of the ring-spinning frame, at about knee-height, and is in the form of a channel iron with the two flanges in a horizontal position. The upper flange is drilled with holes so that the spindles may be cared for when the machine is in operation. Spacing is from 2¼ inches to 4¼ inches apart, depending on the type of frame being used.

SPINDLE TWIST. The actual number of turns being made by the spindle on a textile machine while the rollers are delivering a 1-inch unit of stock.

SPINDLE WINDER. The machine which winds yarn on a cone, tube, cop, etc. The reel, bobbin, or skein of yarn to be wound is set above the spindle, which is placed in a horizontal position at the front of the frame.

SPINE. The points which decorate the cordonnet in handmade lace.

SPINNAKER. A large jib-shaped sail

sometimes carried on the mainmast of some types of boats, opposite the mainsail, and used when sailing before the wind. The foot slides on a spar called the spinnaker boom. The word is likely a contraction of Sphinx, the name of the first vessel to carry this kind of sail.

SPINNERET. 1. An organ, as of spiders and silkworms, for spinning silk. 2. A device, somewhat resembling a thimble, that has a number of very fine holes or orifices. These measure from 2 to 5 thousandths of an inch, and are of the beveled type. The orifices of the spinneret, in most cases, can only be seen when held to the light. Each hole in the spinneret forms one filament or strand. The viscose solution, for example, is pumped through these holes in fine, liquid streams, into an acid or hardening bath. The liquid streams are solidified, upon contact with the acid, into solid filaments or strands of rayon. Thus, there has been the change from a liquid into a solid textile fiber: regeneration. The metals used in spinnerets are platinum and iridium. See Illustrated Section.

SPINNERETTE, SPINNALOY. This product of Baker Platinum Division of Engelhard Industries, Inc., Newark, New Jersey, is a spinnerette which has four times the average life of stainless steel spinnerettes. This new product has conquered the main problems which confronted prior types of spinnerettes - corrosion, erosion, and mechanical damage in handling. This type spinnerette reduces possible encrustation which, of course, affects denier uniformity.

SPINNER TOPMAKER. A mill owner who combs his own tops and spins them into worsted yarn.

SPINNERS' WASTE. Broken, tangled, massed thread waste obtained from bobbins and similar devices, obtained in yarn manufacture. Other thread or yarn wastes are obtained in dressing warps, from shuttle bobbins, etc.

SPINNING. Listed chronologically, the four types of spinning are: flyer, mule, cap, and ring. These are all common to the woolen and worsted industry. Most cottons at the present time are spun on either the mule or the ring frame. In this country practically all cotton yarn is spun on the ring frame, while in Europe the mule is still the more common.

The earliest spinning frame employed the flyer spindle, which resembles the flyer of the present-day roving frame. The yarn was drawn from the front delivery roll down to the top of the flyer; it was then twisted around

perform the operation of drawing and bobbin. As these frames ran at a low speed (up to 3000 r.p.m.) the yarn that was produced was quite smooth and free of beard. The difficulties with this method were the low production and the strain put on the yarn by the bobbin drag.

Mule spinning (see Illustrated Section) allows the use of the free spindle and thereby offers a means of increasing production. The process is not continuous, since there are three distinct stages of operation, namely; drafting and delivering, twisting and drawing, and, finally, winding on. The system allows spinning yarns of extreme fineness, and also with very low twists.

Cap spinning is a continuous process. In place of the flyer, a cap or bonnet is substituted. The bobbin, in cap spinning, is driven by a spindle-banding; the bobbin rises and falls within the inverted cap. The yarn comes from the delivery roll and drags over the lower edge of the cap. Here the bobbin may revolve up to 7000 r.p.m. Since the bobbin is driven, there is only slight tension in the yarn at any time. Because of the higher spindle speed, the yarn may be a bit fuzzy. Much worsted yarn is spun on this type of frame.

Ring spinning (see Illustrated Section) is the most recent development and offers the best possibilities in production. Spindle speeds are high, and the process is continuous. The use of the ring and the traveler subjects the yarn to some strain and also reduces the extensibility of the yarn to some degree, but this is not a serious factor. The bulk of yarn is spun on this system, since it allows the use of large packages and increased production per unit of floor space. Its range and flexibility make it the most satisfactory spinning unit of the present day.

With regard to spinning of rayon, spinning includes the extrusion of viscose through a spinneret (see Illustrated Section) into the coagulating bath, and the gathering and winding of the filaments into bobbin or cake form. Since this process is actually not spinning, and is wholly different from the process of spinning cotton, linen, wool, or worsted, the term is a misnomer.

In cotton mule spinning there stand out today four types of mules—French, English, German, and American. The English were the first to bring out the mule and put it on a practicable basis. It was not until after the Civil War here that the United States produced a mule that could begin to cope with the foreign makes.

Most of the cotton spun here is produced on the ring-spinning method; the

ratio is about 8 to 1 in its favor as contrasted with the mule frame. The reverse ratio holds good in Great Britain. See Illustrated Section.

SPINNING, CHEMICAL. An essential operation in making man-made yarn; it includes the extrusion of the filament through the spinneret into the coagulating bath, and the gathering and winding of the filaments onto a bobbin or cake form. See Illustrated Section.

SPINNING, COTTON. The final operation in cotton yarn manufacture. It completes the working of the cotton fibers into a commercial, fine, coherent yarn sufficiently twisted so that it is now ready for weaving purposes. All the twist put into the yarn in the previous machines has been only enough to cause the fibers to hold together, sustain themselves, and prevent their collapsing. In this condition, the cotton is still comparatively loose and in a fluffy condition or state and naturally has very little tensile strength.

SPINNING, INCREASED PRODUCTIVITY IN. This table, based on the use of a single 31s cotton yarn, is reprinted by permission of the Saco Lowell Division of Maremont Corporation, Greenville, South Carolina:

YEAR:	POUNDS PER SPINDLE HOUR:
1813	.002
1850	.009
1900	.017
1920	.018
1940	.019
1950	.023
1960	.026
1965	.033
1970	.065

(this is done with open-end spinning) See Open-End Spinning.

SPINNING, INGOLSTADT RK 10 OPEN-END ROTOR. No human hand touches this fully automatic open-end spinning frame. It provides 3.5 times more production than conventional ring spinning of yarn. Feed cans are 14 inches in diameter and 36 inches high. With normal sliver pressing, the filling weighs 8 to 9 kilograms (about 18.5 pounds), thereby permitting long running time.

The opening roller is easy to fit and dismantle and runs from 5,000 to 8,000 rpm. The individual fibers from the opening roller are drawn by a vacuum into the rotor running at 45,000 rpm and formed into a thread. All residual fibers, dust, etc., are extracted from the rotor in the event of thread breakage, without any need to open the spinning chamber and clean it by hand.

The frame is equipped with an automatic piecing system which helps to achieve further drastic reduction in broken ends. Depending on the stock, yarn count, delivery speed, and other spinning data, up to 80% of the ends are rectified as soon as breakage occurs.

Spinning points are 78 on each side of the machine for a total of 156. This machine can run short staple cotton and manmade fibers up to 40 mm. in length. Delivery is up to 100m/per minute, depending on the stock being processed. Yarn counts range from Metric 10s to 60s (100 to 16.6 in the Tex System). The package size is 125 mm in width up to 300 mm. in diameter. Package weight runs to about 3.5 kilograms or around 7.75 pounds. The Rotor Spinner RK 10 is the product of Schubert & Salzer Maschinenfabrik Aktiengesellschaft, Ingolstadt, West Germany.

SPINNING, OPEN END. This new method of spinning yarn, based on the turbine principle, was born in Czechoslovakia in 1967 and is still in its incipient stages with progress being made each succeeding year. A competitor of the ring spinning method, open end spinning has a three to five times greater production rate. This is possible by isolating the twisting operations to a drum which rotates the open end of the yarn while additional fibers entering the drum are attracted to the yarn by rotational forces. The use of an air stream is the most common way for transporting fibers.

The differences between and advantages of open end spinning over the ring method are many. In open end spinning, twisting is not linked to the package and packages are not limited in size and can be larger. Rewinding is often eliminated. Less power is needed to rotate the small end of the frame though the exact amount of reduction depends on the design of the frame and the speed at which it operates.

Open end spinning gives low costs in doffing and winding because of increased size of the yarn packages. Spinning of yarn is done directly from drawn sliver and eliminates the roving operation which is one step removed from finished spun yarn. Elimination of roving and rewinding operations saves much floor space and reduces power requirements. About forty percent of spinning costs are saved by the use of the method when compared with ring spinning. The system provides good dyeability, higher wear resistance, higher elongation, and more homogenous blends.

In ring spinning, the package is rotated to insert the twist and to wind the new yarn onto the bobbin. Package speed is obviously limited by the mechanical considerations and development of high ten-

sions. Yarn package is limited in size so as to be confined within a yarn balloon and requires a great amount of power both for its rotation and to insert the necessary twist.

At present there are several negative aspects connected with open end yarn spinning. There is about a 20 percent loss in strength because of poor distribution of the load among the fibers and the higher twist multiple used. There is also the presence of unwanted twist and this runs to about 15 percent or thereabout, higher than that of ring spinning. Fabrics do not seem to have the appealing hand as noted in ring spun yarn fabrics, though finishing techniques fo improve appeal somewhat with varying degrees of success.

Also, only carded yarns can be made at present, a great drawback since combed yarns are very popular at all times. The spinning drum of the turbine used tends to take on dirt and grime inside the shell with either "fiber finish" in the case of manmade fibers being used, or the so-called "pepper trash" in the case of cotton yarns.

Yarn quality deteriorates with the increase of foreign matter inside the drum, necessitating setting-up a comprehensive cleaning system. Yarn wind-up is made directly onto the cone and a waxing device is used for preparing knitting yarns. The highest count of yarn that can be made at present in open end spinning is a 20s cotton. As time goes on, however, there are bound to be many better positive aspects to this comparatively new and novel system of spinning yarn.

SPINNING, SACO-LOWELL SYSTEMS IN. The following registered trademarks of Saco-Lowell, Maremont Corporation, Greenville, South Carolina, 29602, follow:

Rovematic: Model FB Rovematic: Roving machine which provides the largest roving pack in the industry - 14" x 7" at flyer speeds up to 1,300 rpm.

Model FC-1C Rovematic: Produces a smaller package - 12" x 5½" with speeds up to 1,800 rpm. Both frames accomodate any of the four drafting systems including the exclusive Magne-Draft®. Both frames can process natural or manmade fibers and blends in any staple length from ⅞" to 8½".

Spinomatic: Made its debut in 1962 and was a major turning point in the art of spinning. *Model SCB* represents an extensive design of the history-making original. It can handle any spinnable fiber lengths from ⅞" to 8½". It can process cotton, worsted, manmade fibers and blends. It is now available for the

additional *Co-We-Mat*® automatic doffing.

Twistomatic: This twister was brought out because of the demand for higher speed production top-quality plied yarns needed for the sewing industry, knitting yarn, warp yarn, light twine and other products. Production is limited only by the traveller velocity and the characteristics of the stock being processed.

Versamatic: It originated in 1958 and it now has the well-known Reciprocating Turntable for sliver cans, provides a coiled sliver more evenly and needs less space. The result is that up to 25 percent more sliver can be made per sliver can. Versamatic delivers sliver of any fiber at 800 feet per minute.

SPINNING, SELF-TWISTING. A development of the Australian Commonwealth Scientific and Industrial Research Organization, it is a spinning procedure for staple yarns "which require insertion of alternating twist in successive zones along a travelling strand of fibers and bringing together of two such strands so that they will twist about each other to form a stable yarn structure."

SPINNING, SLIVER. The name for the system of spinning yarn directly from sliver instead of from roving; appropriate for machines where the sliver stock is wound into a ball form instead of being fed into the machine from a sliver can. Can spinning is so called because the creel of the spinning frame is a group of sliver cans of stock. Sliver spinning and can spinning should not be confused with pot spinning since this term refers to the receiving element in which the yarn is set in a pot-shaped receptacle by centrifugal force. See POT SPINNING.

SPINNING, SPINDLELESS. Known as open-end spinning, this frame called BD 200, was introduced at a textile machinery fair in Europe in 1867, the brainchild of the Elitex Textile Machine Company, in Czechoslovakia. This frame challenged conventional methods of spinning by tripling production, required only half as many operatives, and reduced floor space by one-third. In addition, roving, spinning, and cross-winding were combined into successive operations, a great boon to spinning methods at present. Regulation yarns, bulked or not, closely resembled combed cotton yarn.

Cotton, along with blended manmade fiber yarns, is spun directly from two or three slivers of stock by the use of a spinning chamber or box which has a velocity of 30,000 rpm as compared with the spindlering-traveller method which runs around 15,000 rpm.

The conventional method in spinning is reversed by this new method or spinning. Bobbins of sliver to be fed into the frame are at the bottom of the frame and are unwound by the feed roller of a thinning method which separates the fibers, makes them parallel, and attenuates the stock being used. The fibers are then sucked into a spinning mechanism and no metallic moving parts come in contact with the stock. Spun yarn is drawn upward and then crosswound onto bobbins at the top of the frame. The final crosswound package is then ready for further processing on many types of looms used at present.

SPINNING BAND. See BAND.

SPINNING BATH. Same as the coagulating bath in the manufacture of rayon. See SPINNERET.

SPINNING BOX. A centrifugal box or pot used for twisting and collecting the newly formed yarn, in the form of an annular cake.

SPINNING CAKE. When sufficient yarn, such as rayon, has been spun into a spinning box, the spindle is stopped and the product is in the shape of a hollow cylinder called a cake. It is removed from the box and is now ready for washing, etc. The cake is about an inch or so in thickness when it is removed from the pot spinning machine. See POT SPINNING.

SPINNING COTTON WASTE. Two problems connected with spinning cotton waste not present in conventional spinning are: 1. Much of the cotton waste is of inferior quality to that found in new cotton, even in the lower classifications of cotton. This quality is often the prime reason that the fiber was worked-out in the original manufacturing procedures. 2. The other and greater problem is the considerable mixture of staple length nearly always found in cotton waste. The excessive amount of foreign matter often found in the waste is responsible for the first problem—that of quality. The mixed staple lengths interfere with the drawing machine processes which are built to function well on the conventional methods of spinning cotton yarn. Some cotton waste, such as good grade card strips, have considerable uniformity of staple length and can be easily spun on the revolving flat top cards. Other grades not having this condition to as great a degree are spun on the woolen system of roller top cards, and little drawing is done in this method of spinning. Textile machinery manufacturers have built special cotton waste spinning equipment which combines the features of both methods of spinning yarn, the cotton method and the woolen

system.

SPINNING FRAME. A machine for drawing out cotton or other fibers to their final spun size, twisting them to impart strength, and winding the yarn onto bobbins.

SPINNING FRAME, THE RISE OF THE. As the textile industry began to take on impetus at the time of the Industrial Revolution, it was only natural as more raw material became available that machines would come into being to care for the increase. Raw material, manipulation, manufacturing, distribution, and consumption had to be balanced.

In 1764, the first spinning jenny was made by James Hargreaves of Blackburn, England. This frame could manipulate eight spindles. The invention was accidental. His wife, Jenny, "or some female," had left her spinning wheel in his path. He stumbled over it as he came into his house, and, being a carpenter, decided to repair the broken frame. He noticed the wheel and spindle continued to revolve as it lay on the floor. His observations and efforts made it possible to make eight spindles work whereas the spinning wheel had been able to spin one thread at a time. Thus, an instance of increased production was assured.

His fifth jenny, made in 1766, operated an even hundred spindles, and this was a great boon to production of yarn. However, he was mobbed by the indignant spinners, who may or may not have envisioned the economic evils of mass production and uniform sizes, the factory system, and big business.

In 1768, the roller spinning frame was invented by Arkwright. The frame was driven by water power and factories began to be built on the banks of streams for water power.

A decade later, in 1779, Samuel Crompton made the spinning mule an actuality. He took the ideas of Hargreaves, who had spun yarns by means of the carriage, and Arkwright, who did his spinning by means of drawing rollers. By combining the ideas, Crompton made a machine that did its work by the use of the carriage and rollers. The machine was a hybrid, a cross between carriage drawing and roller drawing. For want of a better name he called it a spinning mule. The name has been in vogue ever since. He sold his invention for £106; it was worth a fortune, but he let it slip between his fingers. In 1812 he received £5,000 from the British Government for his machine had given work to 70,000 spinners, 150,000 weavers, and there were five million spindles revolving in England.

The rise of the mule took place be-

tween the years 1765 and 1785. In the latter year James Watt, a young Scotsman, invented the steam engine, and made it possible to drive the newly invented machines by steam power. Thus, the slow, tedious hand and water power methods of manipulation were at an end. By 1790, all of Crompton's mules were driven by steam power.

Today, mule spinning frames have been improved upon to the extent that as many as 1,400 pieces of yarn may be spun at the one time on a single frame.

SPINNING JENNY. See SPINNING FRAME, THE RISE OF THE.

SPINNING LIMIT. The highest commercial count of yarn to which a particular cotton may be spun.

SPINNING LIQUID. See SPINNING SOLUTION.

SPINNING MACHINE. 1. The spinning of staple fibers on the cap, flyer, ring-, or mule-spinning frames. 2. The spinning of continuous filament yarns by the pot or the bobbin methods.

SPINNING METHODS FOR MAN-MADE FIBERS. These follow: 1. *Dry Spinning* is when the derivative to be spun is dissolved in a solvent that can be evaporated, leaving the desired filament to be hardened by drying in warm air. 2. *Melt Spinning* is when the fiber-forming substance is melted for extrusion and then hardened by cooling. 3. *Wet Spinning* is when the fibers may be hardened by extrusion of the filaments into chemical baths which convert or regenerate (solid-liquid-solid) the soluble compound into the insoluble substance which constitutes the fiber.

SPINNING ON WOOLEN PRINCIPLE, COTTON. Cotton fiber spun on the woolen system using woolen type roller cards and either ring- or mule-type woolen spinning frames. Such yarn will resemble woolen yarns in such characteristics as bulk or loftiness, soft woolly hand; and the fibers, instead of being parallel, as in cotton system spinning, will be crisscrossed in all directions, as in the woolen type of yarn. The count or size of such wool-spun cotton yarn will average about 10s cotton count, which is 8,400 yarns to the pound or the equivalent of 5.25 run.

SPINNING ON WOOLEN PRINCIPLE, COTTON WASTE. The raw materials which may be used are cotton waste, strips, comber noil, lap waste, roving waste, etc. The stock is blended through an automatic feed machine. This is on the order of a picker with a different beater arrangement which blows the fibers into bins. From here the stock goes into a special cotton waste card or a woolen card with a two-cylinder set. The woolen card has a Scotch feed between the breaker and finisher card. The latter has a tape condenser which rolls the sliver into a yarn, which is then placed on jack spools. These spools are then placed at the feeding-in end of the regular wool spinning frame for actual spinning of the stock into a finished, properly twisted yarn.

The method is applicable to coarse yarns only. The finest count obtainable is about single 8s.

SPINNING OR SAXONY WHEEL. This wheel came into being in the sixteenth and seventeenth centuries. It combined the principles and functions of the spindle and distaff, and was operated by a foot treadle which allowed the spinner's hand to be free to manipulate the fibers. In time, the spinning wheel became a genuine household article. It is still used in many remote sections of the world today.

SPINNING POT. See CENTRIFUGAL POT.

SPINNING PUMP. See METERING PUMP.

SPINNING-ROOM OVERSEER. One who has complete charge of all operations in the spinning room, including spinning, warping, and winding; is responsible for quality, production, safety, and the maintenance of equipment; supervises the training of new employees and follows up to see if they have been satisfactorily placed on jobs; a key man in every detail.

The overseer must understand all jobs within the Spinning Department; must be able to figure production, calculate percentages, and make speed calculations. He must be able to do production planning and scheduling, must be able to supervise people and to understand human nature.

The Section Man in the Spinning Department assists the overseer. His duties are similar to those of the overseer but limited to one section of the department.

SPINNING SOLUTION. Cellulose solution in a spinnable liquid condition.

SPINNING TAPE. Narrow cotton banding made into an endless belt so that it can drive the spindles on ring-spinning frames. Usually one band will drive four spindles, two on each side of the frame. Made of small twill weave, the tape ranges from one-half to three-quarters inch in width. The tape or banding receives its power by friction from a driving cylinder. This is a hollow, tin cylinder about ten inches in diameter that extends the length of the machine.

SPINNING WHEEL, ERA OF THE.

This was from the fourteenth to the eighteenth centuries. The wheel took the place of the rather crude spindle and distaff method. It is still used in many places throughout the world that have not accepted the modern yarn-making methods. Much of the work done by the spinning wheel today is a hobby with people.

Sir Richard Arkwright developed his spinning frame from the principle of the spinning wheel. His invention is still to be seen in South Kensington Museum in London. This effort spelled the death knell for universal use of the spinning wheel at the close of the eighteenth century.

The principle of the spinning wheel is that it takes the cotton or wool, and passes it through an eye, which is in the axis of the spindle. Subsequently, the yarn is wound on the bobbin that rotates on the same axis, but at a different rate of speed.

The rotation of the spindle twists and strengthens the yarn, and the difference in the rate of speed of the revolutions between the spindle and bobbin results in the winding of the yarn about the latter.

SPIRACLES. The breathing holes of an insect. In the silkworm there are nine of these spaced down each side of its body. See Illustrated Section.

SPIRAL DYE BECK. A trough for dyeing cloth in rope form; it has a curved bottom, a revolving drum or roller across the top to propel the cloth, and a pair of squeeze rollers to remove excess dye.

SPIRALITY. See CONVOLUTIONS IN COTTON.

SPIRAL YARN. It is made of two yarns whose yarn counts vary to a marked degree. The fine yarn has been given hard twist, the bulky yarn has received slack twist; the heavier yarn in twisting is wound spirally about the fine, hard-twisted yarn which is sometimes referred to as a core thread. Other names for this yarn are corkscrew and eccentric.

SPIRIT. A term that covers the various solutions used in dyeing, mordanting, finishing, etc.

SPITALFIELDS. The English home of the French Huguenot weavers who settled in this vicinity. In the sixteenth century, Spitalfields was a weaving center in England and was known all over the world for its laces. When the locality became too congested, the weavers and lacemakers settled in Nottingham, now the leading lace center of England.

SPLASH-RESISTANT. See WATER-REPELLENT.

SPLASH VOILE. An ordinary voile made with filling interspersed throughout with slubs to give an uneven yarn and novelty effect to the cloth. Texture of the cloth is about 62 x 54, 8 yards to the pound.

SPLICED. The reinforcing of hosiery where friction and wear are the greatest; done by making these areas heavier and thicker in order to resist abrasion and friction.

SPLICED HEEL. A double-thickness heel used to make hosiery more durable.

SPLICING. 1. Reinforcing yarn introduced into a material to increase the wearing quality; observed in hosiery at the heel and toe. 2. The joining or tying together of two or more strands of yarns to make a continuous yarn or thread.

SPLIT. That portion of a hide or skin that has been split into two or more thicknesses, other than the grain or hair-side.

SPLIT ENDS. Fabric defect when some of the ply in a yarn have split or broken altogether; also implies breaks or splits in man-made yarns when some of the filaments have snapped or become broken.

SPLIT FABRIC, SPLIT SELVAGES, SPLITS. Fabrics woven with more than the two conventional selvages. Used in double and triple-layer fabric weaving as in the case of some velvets. When taken from the loom the fabric is spread to full width for finishing, or the selvages may be split at this time and the individual lengths finished separately, depending on the local conditions. For example, a velvet may be set 29 inches in the reed of the loom in a three-layer plan. The fabric, when spread to full width would then be about 87 inches wide from the loom. If the whole piece is finished as one fabric the finished width would be about 81 inches. The piece is then cut into three separate lengths by splitting or cutting the respective selvages to provide three pieces, each with a finished width of approximately 27 inches.

SPLIT FOOT. 1. Stockings whose underfoot part is knitted separately from the upper or leg portion, although these may be seamlessly joined with practically the same motion or by a reciprocal interchange of loops. 2. Colored hosiery made with a white sole.

SPLIT HARNESS. In Jacquard weaving it is a method of harness mounting whereby one hook and one needle control two, three, or four mails and threads to produce the motif; used in foundation weaves in Jacquard fabrics.

SPLIT-LAP PREVENTER. The calender section of the picker machine has a device whose function it is to crease the lap and thus prevent its splitting as unwinding occurs.

SPLIT MOTION. Based on the leno principle, the motion is a device which works two sets of leno threads at each side on a split in the center of the loom. One shuttle is used in the action as the leno threads make two selvages; the filling is cut the length of the center, thereby dividing the material into two separate fabrics.

SPLIT PICK. Peculiar to doup weaving, it means that some picks weave straight while others may be at an angle, thereby affecting the fabric.

SPLIT RINSE. A rinse bath of moderate temperature obtained by opening both hot and cold water supply valves.

SPLIT ROD. A smooth metal rod used on a slasher to separate the sized or starched ends which may have the tendency to stick together prior to the beaming operation. A series of split rods is located between the drying cylinder and the beaming end to perform the work.

SPLITS. Cloth has two selvage edges. There are times, however, when one or more additional selvages may be interspersed throughout a fabric so that after the finishing of the goods, the cloth can be separated into two or more separate cloths. Narrow fabrics, for example, used for export purposes are often woven in this manner, as well as low-priced toweling and some pile-woven fabrics.

SPLIT SHED. See CENTER SHED.

SPLIT-SHIFT. A schedule of working hours that requires employees to take time off without pay during their working day.

SPLIT SOLE. The foot in hosiery when it is made of two different yarns.

SPLIT STITCH. A type of chain stitch used in church embroidery to work the faces and the hands of figures.

SPLIT YARN OR CORD. When one or more ends of the ply yarn or cord have become broken in cloth. This may cause nubs or bunches of yarn in that area.

SPOKESTITCHING. Comparable with hemstitching, but the stitches are applied to both sides of the ladder instead of only along the outer edge.

SPONGE. 1. Shrinking of fabrics prior to tailoring. 2. Lightly cleaning a slightly soiled area with a damp sponge prior to pressing.

SPONGE CLOTH. 1. Implies cottons on the order of honeycomb, waffle cloth, and a limited number of similar fabrics which appear rather spongy, since the weave, and the rather bulky yarn, tend to give this effect.

2. Fabric such as lightweight duck, canvas, drill or jean cloth, used in the dampened condition as the protective material when pressing garments. These cotton fabrics withstand higher temperatures than wool, worsted, rayon, etc.; hence, their use.

SPONGE RUBBER. A light, spongy rubber, usually prepared by bubbling carbon dioxide through, or whipping air into, latex; used for foam rubber, gaskets, insulation, and padding. Crude rubber is the base product used in making sponge rubber.

SPONGE SILK. Soft, porous, knitted fabric of low-quality spun silk, used for underwear, draperies, and polishing cloth.

SPONGE WEAVES. Some weaves will give a soft, spongy effect in cloth, hence, the name. Examples would be spot weaves, diamond-effects, waffle or honeycombs, some bird's-eye weaves.

SPONGING. A part-shrinkage, by dampening with a sponge, by rolling in moist muslin, or by steaming, given to woolen and worsted cloths by the clothing maker before cutting to insure against a contraction of the material in the garment. "London shrunk" is a cold-water treatment, originating abroad, and is frequently applied and guaranteed by the cloth manufacturers themselves.

SPOOL. A short wooden or metal cylinder with flanged edges, drilled to receive a spindle upon which is wound yarn, thread, or wire.

SPOOL COTTON. Sewing thread of all types put up and sold on small wooden spools. From 50 to 100 or more yards are wound on the ordinary spools.

SPOOLER. The machine used to wind yarn on a spool. Incidentally, there is no draft on the spooler and winder frames.

SPOOLER CHEESE. A yarn package made on an automatic spooler by crisscrossing the yarn in order to build up a self-sustaining cheese or an unflanged core. May be known as a Grant-wound skein or spool.

SPOOLING. Some yarns come from cops, bobbins, or tubes, and in that form are commercial in nature. These yarns must be transferred to a more suitable form, depending on the use to be made of the product. Spun yarn is placed in a rack or creel, and each thread is placed in an upright pin or spindle. It is then wound onto the new tubes or cops. Skewers are used sometimes to transfer from one device to another.

The number of spindles on a spooling frame will be from 40 to 200. The size of the yarn determines, in great measure, the number of spindles used on the spooler or jack frame.

The yarn is held under some tension in order to assure compact, even winding on the device that is to receive the yarn. Production will vary from one to ten spindles per day.

SPOOL RACK. A rack or frame which holds spools of yarn. In hand-weaving circles known as a creel.

SPORRAN. Part of the Highland dress of Scotland, it is a pouch of goatskin—black, gray, or white—and made with or without tassels. The mounting of the sporran should show the crest of the clan and its motto, and the ornamentations on it should be Celtic in design and correspond with those on the belt, brooch, and buckles worn. This pouch is tied around the waist and suspended in front.

SPORT SATIN. Originally known as baronet satin, it was the first successful type of rayon dress fabric using rayon in the warp. Cotton filling is used in the fabric. The weave is a warp-effect satin. Set at 40 inches in the loom, and then piece-dyed, the cloth is finished at 38 inches. There are 84 ends and 60 picks used; the warp is 150 denier rayon; the cotton filling is a single 32s. The selvage is the tape variety and 2/60s cotton warp is used to make it.

SPORTS DENIM. A soft, lightweight denim made in pastel shades and stripe effects for women's playclothes, and beach and resort wear. Comes in a wide range of designs and textures.

SPOT AND STAIN RESISTANT. Material that has been treated to resist spots and stains. A fabric should be laboratory approved before any such claim is made.

SPOT CLEANING. Two methods may be used, singly, or with one method following the other one. These methods are usually successful in taking out ordinary, common spots and stains caused by careless spillage.
Method One: This is actually a drycleaning method since grease solvents such as trichlorethylene, a colorless, poisonous liquid - $CHCClCCl_2$, are used. Many persons seem to think that carbon tetrachloride is the only real solvent that can take out spots of almost any type. Its formula is CCl_4; it is a colorless, nonflammable, vaporous toxic liquid. It should be borne in mind that the use of this toxic is very hazardous at all times. Provision should be made for ventilation, fumes should not be in-

haled, and by all means do not smoke when working with either of the foregoing solvents.

In removing a stain, the stained fabric side should be laid down on an absorbent disposable material, (e.g. about ten layers of white paper towels). Use a fine natural sponge or a very absorbent cotton cloth and work the cleaning agent into the fabric from the unstained side working from the outside to the center of the stained area. Move the fabric to a fresh area of the absorbent back between applications. This procedure is ideal for removal of grease, oil, and tar. In the case of wax stains, it is suggested that these should not be heated since wax wets the fibers, especially in the case of manmade fiber fabrics. It is suggested that it is better to place an ice cube on the stain until the back of the fabric feels cold. Then rub the area vigorously between the hands. This will crack and powder the wax which can then be easily brushed away.

Method Two: This is a wet cleaning method with the use of a neutral synthetic detergent in lukewarm water. Always read the instructions on the container. Add about one teaspoon of white vinegar per pint of detergent solution. An absorbent cloth or sponge should be used and continue agitation until the stain is gone; then repeat the action with clean, clear water and leave the article upright by hanging on a clothesline, if possilbe. If not possible, then leave it in an angular position.

Method Two Followed by Method One: This procedure is ideal for removal of stains such as milky beverages, soft drinks, starch-type stains, vomit, etc.

A good way to remove spots such as alcoholic liquids, fruit and fruit drink stains is to use *Method Two* followed by methylated spirits or alcohol if needed. An example of methylated spirits is ethyl alcohol denatured with methyl alcohol for the purpose of preventing its use as an alcoholic beverage. Incidentally, grass stains may be removed by first using methylated spirits or alcohol followed by the use of *Method Two* so as to remove clinging dirt or soil in the area.

SPOT COTTON. Cotton which is on the spot ready for inspection, purchase, and delivery. The samples or redraws from the actual bales are available for inspection, and the price is fixed on the spot.

SPOT COTTON SALES. They occur when the cotton is bought on sight after inspection and call for immediate delivery. The seller usually owns the cotton that he has for sale, and is able to make the actual delivery of the total number of bales bought on contract by the purchaser.

SPOT MUSLIN. Dotted swiss made with woven single-colored or multi-colored dots or sprigs on a muslin ground and used to distinguish the dotted types of dotted swisses from the dotted swisses that are made from other more complicated pattern effects.

SPOTLESS FINISH. Treatment given to materials in order to render them immune to spotting during ordinary wear. Super-heated steam plays an important part in the treatment.

SPOTS. 1. Refers to gray goods in the United States ready for a spot (on-the-spot) transaction. 2. A British term for any fabric in which woven spots are used in the pattern. These dot effects may be on a plain or a fancy ground fabric. 3. Discolorations, blemishes, stains, or off-shades that often occur on fabrics while being processed all the way from loom or gray state to the finished material.

SPOT STITCH. A crochet stitch which forms raised dots or figures at regular intervals.

SPOT YARN. Knop yarn.

SPOTTED COTTON. Cotton which has become brown, ecru, or yellow in cast because of contact with the elements in unfavorable weather, wet bolls, leaves, stems, rainstorms, etc. Spots on cotton do much anent grade determination.

SPOTTED LACE. Fine netting which has small spots in the motif. Originally done by needlework, spotting is now done by machine. Used in veiling to some degree.

SPOTTING. The process of removing soil or stains independent of the drycleaning cycle. For the removal of water-soluble stains, steam is commonly used to condense a fine spray of warm water onto the stained area. Chemicals are used for the treatment of "chemical-type stains."

The drycleaner or any person who applies chemicals, other than water and drycleaning solvents, to fabrics or garments for spotting or pre-spotting purposes, assumes the risk of the effect these might have on the fiber, finish, and/or color. The fabric is expected to be resistant to contact with plain water and drycleaning solvents. Water, the universal solvent, will remove a great many common spots and stains.

The British use this term to mean crabbing. See Crabbing, Drycleaning, Pre-Spotting, Chart on Spot and Stain Removal.

SPOTTING TEST ON CLOTH.

Sprinkle cloth with lime water, and allow it to dry. If the fabric does not show spots, the material may be said to be fast to spotting. If the cloth becomes spotted from clean water, the entire material should be sponged prior to cutting-up.

SPRANG. From the Swedish noun, Sprangning, it originally implied "openwork," but is now acceptable for a special old plaiting or plaite technique, as used in braiding and lace. May be compared with "openwork" noted in doupe or leno woven goods but it has much more porosity and is usually irregular in structure although some of the work is, at times, quite regular, angular, and parallel.

SPRAY FINISHING. There are several silk, rayon, and cotton materials which are not able to withstand the rigors of a full finishing treatment. Light, thin, sheer cloths of these yarns are sometimes subjected to the so-called spray treatment. Applications of solutions of gums, gelatin, gelatin and glycerin, agar, or paste are given to the goods by spraying them with a fine mist of the chemical used. The spraying is done through orifices.

SPRAY PRINTING. A method of printing fabric with a "gun" similar to that used to spray paint on motor cars. Stencils are used in the process, one for each color to be sprayed onto the goods.

SPRAY RINSE. A clear water treatment of goods at hand while they are spinning or tumbling in the washer tub. Considered a "light treatment." See Rinse.

SPRAYS, HOUSEHOLD WASHING. There is a host of sprays on the market for the housewife to use in order to bring back body and substance to well-worn clothing. They include ingredients which do away with the use of starch and some of them do cause ironing to become an easier chore. In all cases, read the label well and follow instructions to the letter.

SPREAD, CHENILLE. It is made of muslin sheeting with machine tufted motifs of soft, coarse cotton yarns in white and all colors. The tufts are spaced very closely together without any break and in continuous line formation in contradistinction to candlewicking, which is known for its individually spaced tufts. The term, incidentally, is a misnomer since actually no true chenille yarn is used, although the tufted lines do resemble a chenille yarn, which is a type of yarn used to make chenille rugs in which the fuzzy pile protrudes from all sides. See CANDLEWICK SPREAD, CHENILLE, CHENILLE YARN.

SPOT AND STAIN REMOVAL IN THE CARE OF CLOTHING

The following chart is for ready reference in a general way. The following notations should be kept in mind:

1. Bleaching agents should not be used on dyed fabrics.
2. For a bleach on animal fibers, use peroxide; chlorine should never be used as a bleach on animal fibers.
3. For a bleach on vegetable fibers, use any bleach such as peroxide or chlorine.

Spot or Stain	Material	Treatment	Procedure
1. ACID	Any	Water and household ammonia	Sponge
2. ADHESIVE	Any	Carbon tetrachloride	Sponge, then rub
3. BLOOD	Any	Lukewarm saline solution	Immediately soak and then use regular laundry methods
BLOOD	Any	Solvase in solution	Immediately soak and then use regular laundry methods
BLOOD	Heavy goods and wool	Use raw starch paste as absorbent	Keep applying to spot until it disappears
4. BLUING	Any	Soap solution; use solution of soap and water or sulphonated oil and water. If made in stock solution, the addition of 1 part of ether to 30 parts of solution will be of value in spot removal	Rub carefully
5. BUTTER	Any	Carbon tetrachloride	Sponge and rub
6. CANDLE WAX	Any	Carbon tetrachloride	Sponge and rub
7. CANDY	Any	Water and soap solution	Sponge and rub
8. CHEWING GUM	Any	Carbon tetrachloride	Sponge and rub back of stain
9. CHOCOLATE	Any	Water, soap, and then bleach	Sponge and rub
10. COCOA	Any	Water, soap, and then bleach	Sponge and rub
11. COFFEE	Any	Water, soap, and then bleach	Sponge and rub
12. DYE	Any	Water, soap, and then bleach, if possible	Sponge and rub
13. EGG	Any	Water and soap	Sponge after scraping
14. FRUIT	Any	Soap solution, then bleach	Sponge and rub
15. FURNITURE POLISH	Any	Soap solution, then water	Sponge and rub
16. GLUE	Any	Soap solution	Sponge and rub
17. GRAPHITE	Any	Dry spotting soap; 2 parts oleic acid, 1 each of chloroform, carbon tetrachloride and benzol; 1/5 part denatured alcohol, 1/4 part of 26% ammonia. Keep corked.	Sponge and rub
18. GRASS	Any	Alcohol	Sponge and rub
19. GREASE, OIL	Any	Carbon tetrachloride	Sponge and rub
20. GUM	Any	Carbon tetrachloride	Sponge—from back of fabric first
21. HAIR OIL	Any	Dry spotting agent; 1 part each of chloroform, benzol and carbon tetrachloride	Sponge and rub
22. ICE CREAM	Any	Water, soap, and then bleach	Sponge in sequence
23. INDELIBLE PENCIL	Any	Alcohol or soap solution	Sponge and rub well
24. INDIA INK	White goods	Soap solution	Sponge and rub the fresh stain
25. INK	Any	Water, soap, and then bleach	Sponge and rub

SPOT AND STAIN REMOVAL IN THE CARE OF CLOTHING (*Continued*)

Spot or Stain	Material	Treatment	Procedure
26. IODINE	Any	Hypo (sodium thiosulphate)	Sponge carefully
27. IRON RUST	Cotton, Linen	Treat with weak solution of oxalic acid and then with ammonia	Acid applied to stain with glass rod; on disappearance of stain apply ammonia and rinse with water
28. LEAD PENCIL	Any	Try erasing. Soap solution	Sponge carefully
29. LEATHER	Any	Soap and water	Sponge vigorously but with care
30. LINSEED OIL	Any	Carbon tetrachloride	Sponge and rub
31. LIPSTICK	Any	Use colorless grease such as petroleum jelly or vaseline. Follow with carbon tetrachloride. Use care	Rub in the grease; then sponge well but evenly
32. MEDICINE	Any	Alcohol, soap solution	Sponge very carefully
33. MERCURO-CHROME	Any	Soap solution, bleach, and then water	Sponge well
34. METALLIC STAINS	Any	Acetic acid	Sponge carefully
35. MILDEW	Any	Soap and then bleach	Wash well before using bleaching agent
36. MILK	Any	Soap solution	Sponge and rub
37. MUD	Any	Allow to dry, brush, sponge from back with soap solution	Sponge with water
38. MUSTARD	Any	Hot glycerine, sponge with water, apply 20 per cent acetic acid and then sponge with water. Bleach and sponge again with water.	Sponge with water
39. OLD PAINT, OLD VARNISH	Any	Equal parts of alcohol and benzene, or use turpentine	Sponge vigorously but with care
40. PAINT	Any	Turpentine or benzene	Sponge vigorously
41. PENCIL MARKS	Any	Try erasing the marks. Soap and water may help	Rub the detergent used on goods carefully
42. PERSPIRATION	Any	Difficult stain to remove. Use a soap and water solution. If peroxide is used, take particular notice of the bleaching properties involved	Sponge with utmost care
43. SALAD DRESSING	Any	Carbon tetrachloride	Sponge carefully
44. SCORCH	Any	Soap solution and bleach	Sponge
45. SHELLAC	Any	Alcohol or benzene	Sponge with care
46. SUGAR	Any	Warm to hot water	Sponge well
47. TAR, ROAD OIL, CREOSOTE OIL	Any	Carbon tetrachloride	Sponge with care
48. TEA	Any	Soap solution (hard to remove since it is tannic acid)	Sponge immediately
49. TIN FOIL	Any	Soap and water	Sponge
50. TOBACCO	Any	Hot water and soap; bleach, if necessary	Sponge; the degree of intensity depends on depth of stain
51. TOMATO	Any	Soap solution	Sponge and rub
52. VARNISH	Any	Alcohol or benzene	Sponge with care
53. VASELINE	Any	Carbon tetrachloride	Sponge with care
54. WATER	Any	None	Steam carefully—wash entire garment
55. WATER COLORS	Any	Soap solution	Sponge and rub
56. WAX	Any	Carbon tetrachloride	Sponge and rub
57. WHITE SAUCES	Any	Soap and water	Sponge carefully

SPREADER. 1. The garment worker who spreads-out or lays-out multiple layers of material for future processing from fabric to finished garment. The layers which make up the lot must be spread smoothly and evenly on the cutting table, whether it is done by hand or with the help of a spreading machine. The spreader should be able to cut each ply to proper length, but he is not supposed to be able to cut up the completed lay. 2. See RADDLE.

SPRIG. Flower and leaf patterns produced in handmade lace. They are made apart from the groundwork of the lace, and are appliquéd onto the base fabric.

SPRING-BEARD NEEDLE. A knitting needle that has a spring-beard which forms part of the hook. This needle requires an extra device known as the presser which closes the hook so that the loops formed may be cast off.

SPRING BOX. See JACQUARD NEEDLEBOX.

SPRING NEEDLE. See KNITTING NEEDLE. See also Illustrated Section.

SPRINGSET. Produced by UniRoyal Fiber and Textile Division of UniRoyal, Inc., Winnsboro, South Carolina, these yarns are: 1. US100n: An all-nylon yarn permanently set in a resilient random twist used in carpeting for density, springiness, and long wear. 2. US200an: A yarn blend of nylon and Celaire (Celanese Corporation) possessing a close twist-set which is used in carpeting. The yarn has a built-in crush-resistance to wear, quick recovery, and is fade-, stain, and soil-resistant.

SPRING WOOL, FALL WOOL. In Texas and California the first shearing of sheep is done in the spring; the wool obtained is called spring wool. The second shearing is done in the fall of the year, hence the name, fall wool.

SPRINKLER SYSTEM. An arrangement of pipes throughout a building, with outlets suitably placed for sprinkling water or other extinguishing fluid to put out fire.

SPROUTING. A defect observed in Brussels, tapestry rugs, and carpets. Sprouts consist of loops that protrude above the surface of the material.

SPUN ACETATE, SPUN RAYON. Long continuous filaments of acetate or rayon will produce fabrics which may have smooth or crepe-effect surfaces. Either filament can be adapted for other effects by cutting it into short uniform lengths from ½ to 9 inches. These lengths are spun into yarns, similar to the spinning of cotton or wool. Such spun yarns have an entirely different character from the ordinary acetate or rayon yarns.

According to the amount of twist inserted in the spinning process, this spun yarn can be made stronger, less lustrous, and adaptable to napping and other finishes, thus producing fabrics that resemble wool, linen, or cotton. Such short-staple stock can also be combined with any of the natural fibers to make effective and useful materials; this blending would not be possible with long acetate or rayon filament. Thus these spun materials provide new finishes and a variety of low-priced fabrics that formerly were only made from natural fibers, with a consequently higher production cost. Many of these fabrics have trade names, while others do not.

SPUN BLEND. Actually a union yarn in which fibers from two or more textile sources are spun into a commercial yarn, such as one composed of wool fiber, acetate, and nylon staple stocks may be spun in equal or unequal fiber percentages.

SPUN DOWN. A term used by spinners to denote that the yarn has been spun from cotton which could be spun to higher counts. The resulting yarn is of a better quality than if spun from the usual grade of cotton.

SPUN-DYED. Applied to man-made fibers in which the coloring matter has been bonded in before the filament has been formed. There is no implication of a combination between the color and the fiber and this term is more accurate than spun-colored or spun-pigmented, terms that are often used to express spun-dyed. Specific fastness properties are not implied by the term. See Dope Dyed, Solution Dyed.

SPUN-DYED FIBRO. This term is used to describe Fibro rayon staple spun with pigments injected into the spinning solution in order to produce a fiber with the color built in. It is made by Courtaulds, Ltd., and, at present, is supplied in a range of fourteen colors.

SPUN GLASS. See FIBERGLAS.

SPUN GLASS FINISH. A finish given to cotton fabrics by means of rollers that have very fine, straight lines in them. It resembles the Schreiner finish, which uses rollers or discs with fine diagonal lines. This finish is not permanent; it is used chiefly for curtaining and decorative fabric.

SPUN NYLON PAJAMA FABRIC. Lightweight fabric, which, because of the yarn used, gives the goods a "warm touch" which, to date, is not observed from long-fiber nylon yarns.

SPUN RAYON. See SPUN ACETATE, SPUN RAYON.

SPUN RAYON-LINEN. Referred to as "linen-like rayon" and other similar names, the pick count is 42 x 42; single 14s yarn are used in both warp and filling, the yarn being of the slub variety. Comes in plain colors and prints.

SPUN RAYON YARN, NUMBERING OF. It is based on the system on which it was spun—cotton, worsted, cut wool, run wool, linen, etc.

SPUN SILK. Yarn made from true silk waste and pierced cocoons. The fibers are short and they are spun on the cotton principle. Degumming must occur prior to the spinning.

SPUN SILK SYSTEM. This method of spinning silk includes the following operations: picking, combing, dressing, separation into lap form, drawing into sliver form, and condensing into roving; spinning of the roving into yarn. Other yarns made from other fibers are displacing this system to a great extent.

SPUN-SILK YARN. Yarn made from the various types of silk waste.

SPUNSTRON. A polypropylene fiber that is a registered trademark of ICI Fibres, Ltd; Great Britain. This staple fiber is ideal for hawsers and ropes. Its basic properties compare with those of Ulstron, and the product costs considerably less than nylon that may be used for the same purposes. See Nylon, Perlon, Ulstron.

SPUN YARN. A rope of long tow hemp, tarred and then well-rubbed.

SPUR WHEEL. The commonest type of toothed wheel used in machinery. Its radial teeth are parallel to the wheel axis.

SPYNDLE. Part of method of figuring the size or count of dry-spun flax and jute yarn. There are 48 cuts or less of 300 yards each, which give a total of 14,400 yards, the weight in pounds of this spyndle being the count of the yarn.

SQUARE BALE. See GIN BALE.

SQUARE CLOTH. A term used for any cloth having the same number of ends as picks per inch, with its warp counts the same as the filling—as 80 x 80, 64 x 64.

SQUARE CORNER, KNIT. A method of finishing the wrist of a short glove. The wrist opening is bound around and then turned back and seamed down.

SQUARE KNOT. A nonslipping knot used to tie-in heddles. Used by many weavers in lieu of the weaver's knot since it may be tied in the yarn under tension.

SQUARE-MOTION COMB. See

COMBING WOOL.

SQUARE NET. Robert Frost in 1777 produced this type of lace on machines. It is durable and very lustrous; used for mittens, gloves, shawls, etc. Also used by wigmakers as a foundation fabric.

SQUARES. Another name for the flower buds of the cotton plant. They appear about two months after planting of the cotton seeds. Three weeks later the blossoms will open while the petals change from creamy white to dark yellow, then to pink, and finally to a reddish tinge. After three days they wither and fall to the ground, leaving green pods. These pods are known as cotton bolls.

SQUEEGEE. A handled device with a transverse holder used in screen or stencil printing to spread and force the color paste through the orifices of the screen. An ordinary piece of wood, properly shaped, will also do this work.

SQUEEZE ROLLER. A metal roller, often covered with felt or rubber, used in a group formation to force substances or compounds into or onto other substances. Used in sizing, dyeing, printing, etc. These rollers can also be used to force out substances from other cloth, etc.

SQUEEZE ROLLS. A mechanical device for applying pressure to squeeze out, as in wringing.

SQUIDGER. One who aids the cotton classer in his work; often is an apprentice.

SQUIRREL. A short-haired, soft, straight fur, natural blue-gray to light gray in color. Wearing qualities, fair. Judged by silkiness and fullness of the fur and its natural color.

S.R.A. DYES. Sulpho-resinic-alcohol dyes. These are special dyes used for coloring acetate yarns and cloths.

SRAVEL. A narrow white or natural-colored woolen fabric made by Algerian natives; used as trousering.

SRINAGAR RUGS. Knotted rugs made in Kashmir, India, of very fine wool.

STABILITY SETTING. Treatment of fibers, yarns, or fabrics by application of dry or moist heat. Often done to nylon, "Orlon," Fortrel, Terylene, and other synthetic polymer products.

STABILIZATION. Term used in manufacture of cellulose acetate; it is the treatment of the precipitated cellulose acetate to remove or to neutralize the last residues of combined catalyst.

STABILIZED. A resin finish on cotton or spun rayon fabrics which helps a material to keep its original finish, whether it is soft or crisp. Trade name of U. S. Finishing Co., New York City.

STABLE. Not easily broken down, or a substance which will not change in composition under ordinary conditions of storage.

STACKING. Preparing flax for the cutters by piecing the stalks into handfuls of suitable size. Some slight roughing is also given the stacks.

STAFF. Heavy fabric made for use in buildings and temporary structures. It is made from New Zealand flax mixed with plaster and formed into flat sheets.

STAFFMAN. Sometimes used to imply one who works in a silk, rayon, or similar plant. The term has a broad meaning, since there are minor and major staffmen employed in large plants.

STAFFORD CLOTH. Heavy cotton fabric used for curtains and hangings, it comes in plain or rep weaves. Mercerized and dyed cotton yarns are used in the textures which come in many qualities, such as 56-inch, 80 x 68, 2/60s warps and 2/24s filling, plain weave. Another popular construction is 56-inch, 106 x 58, 2/60s warp and 2/30s filling.

STAGGER. In rayon sizing it denotes the placing of the bundles of yarn in the basket, in rows alternating on the order of the bricks in a wall.

STAIN. 1. Discoloration from foreign matter. 2. A dye or thin pigment used in staining. 3. A chemical reagent for coloring miscroscopic specimens. 4. A tinge or tint, used as an identification mark, on woven or knitted fabrics, easily removed in due time. See IDENTIFICATION STAINS (table).

STAIN, CONTACT. One acquired by transfer from touching another article being washed which is giving up color or staining matter at the time.

STAIN COTTON. See GRAY COTTON; YELLOW-STAINED COTTON.

STAINED WOOL. That which is discolored by paints, perspiration, dung, rain, sleet, and human causes.

STAIN-FORMER. A substance, usually a soiling agent, which forms stains during the washing process.

STAIN REMOVERS. Most of the chemicals in this list may be purchased in a drug store, supermarket, or hardware store. Be sure to keep them away from children since some of them come under the word - POISON. Keep labels on all bottles for sake of identification and security. In the poison listing there are, for example, ingredients such as ammonia, denatured alcohol, carbon tetrachloride, hydrosulphites, oxalic acid. Flammable solvents should be well stoppered and away from heat. Always read labels well and thoroughly and follow explicit directions.

Absorbents Corn meal, corn starch, French chalk, Fuller's Earth, magnesium carbonate, talcum powder. Absorbent cloths, blotting paper, cleaning tissues, bowls, glass rods, and medicine droppers are used in most absorbent stain removal by use of the one or ones best adapted for the removal.

Acetic Acid should be a ten percent solution; the same holds true for *Ammonia*.

Bleaching Agents: Hydrogen peroxide, hydrosulphites, Javelle water, oxalic acid, sodium perborate.

Pepsin: Should be used in powder form.

Sodium Thiosulphate: Also known as hypo solution; use carefully.

Solvents: Acetone (destroys acetate fabrics but not rayons; both are cellulosic in nature); denatured alcohol, amyl acetate, benzens, gasoline (colorless), glyerin, carbon tetrachloride, kerosene, turpentine.

Washing Agents: Drycleaning soap, soap, and a host of synthetic detergents all with short more or less "catchy names." These come in liquid or powder forms. See Detergent, etc.; Spot and Stain Removal in the Care of Clothing, Stain, Stain Remover.

STAMATTE. All-wool colored cloth, made in Holland from yarn-dyed material.

STAMBOUL. A cheap woolen fabric which was made in large quantities in northern France for the Levant, where it was used for cloaks by the natives. It was a heavy cloth, as 104 pounds of wool were used for every standard piece of 55½ yards.

STAMEN. Roman term for the spun thread of silk as it comes off a spindle.

STAMEN FORTE. A strong French worsted of high texture which originated in medieval times. More recent cloths have replaced this fabric.

STAMIN. Worsted cloth on the order of Linsey-woolsey; rather coarse and harsh in feel.

STAMMET. A fine, good quality English worsted fabric popular in the eighteenth century; now superseded by more practical fabrics made of worsted yarn.

STAMPED PLUSH. Formerly used to denote embossed plush, especially that which is stamped in stripe formation four to five inches in width. Used as curtain borders.

STAMPED VELVET. Those velvets which have their designs stamped in the pile effect by the use of heated engraved rollers.

STAMYN. See STAMIN.

STANDARD ATMOSPHERE. The air that is maintained at a relative humidity of 65 per cent and at 70° Farenheit (21° Centigrade).

STANDARD CONDITION. The condition attained by a sample (fiber, yarn, fabric) when it reaches temperature and moisture equilibrium with the standard atmosphere after transfer from a lower relative humidity. It is when a fiber, for example, has absorbed all the moisture that it can hold at a standard atmosphere of 70° Farenheit and 65 per cent relative humidity.

STANDARD ENDS. In doup or leno weaving, the warp ends over which the whip ends cross.

STANDARD MOISTURE REGAIN. The moisture regain of a textile fabric when brought from a lower moisture regain into equilibrium with the standard atmosphere. Applied to a fiber, it is the range of moisture regain values through which the standard moisture regain of the individual samples of the same fiber will vary, depending upon their prior history and physical condition.

STANDARD OF LIVING. The particular level of health and decency that an individual chooses to maintain.

STANDARD WEIGHT. The absolute dry weight of a textile plus the standard regain.

STANDING BATH. Saving the bath after dyeing and making additions to it for the next dyeing.

STANDS. The best plants in cotton fields which are permitted to develop after all other plants have been thinned out or weeded.

STANDWICKEN FIBER. Fiber yielded by an Indian plant of the Fabaccoi family; used locally for cordage.

STANIUM. A rugged fabric of good quality ranked with Brunetta and Camelot, popular fabrics in the sixteenth century. Rarely seen in America today.

STANNIC CHLORIDE. A thin, colorless liquid made by exposing metallic tin to the action of chlorine. Used as a mordant in dyeing, its formula is $SnCl_4$.

STANNOUS CHLORIDE. Pertaining to or containing tin, especially in its lower valence. It is used as a discharge chemical in calico printing. $SnCl_2$.

STAPEL. An original Anglo-Saxon form now spelled staple; it means "fixed, not variable." It referred to certain cloths which were sold abroad by textile merchants during the Middle Ages. These merchants were granted "staple rights," which meant that the goods had specific qualities of stability and character to warrant their sale for export.

STAPELFASER. Filament produced in Germany in the last year of World War I, 1918. Cellulose is treated chemically until it is dissolved into a jelly formation and in this condition can be forced through very fine holes in metal strainers. On coming in contact with the air, the filament is formed and it is then cut into short lengths ranging from four to five centimeters long.

STAPLE. 1. Anglo-Saxon word meaning fixed, not variable.

2. Apparel and cloth, which have steady or fixed demand, of a conservative nature as to color, construction, weave, quality, and finish. Some fabrics classed as staples are dress worsted, diagonals in blue and black, melton, kersey, beaver, broadcloth, serge, cassimere, chambray, muslin, organdy, poplin, voile, shantung, denim, taffeta. These cloths are always in stock since there is a steady demand for staple fabrics.

3. Cotton is often spoken of as having "good staple." This means that the stock has the necessary working properties for manipulation into a certain size or count of spun yarn.

4. The average length of the bulk of fibers is called staple; a 1¼-inch staple cotton, a 4-inch worsted fiber, a 9-inch woolen fiber.

5. It has been said that the novelty of today is the staple of tomorrow; all cloth has to be accepted by the public to become a good selling staple.

STAPLE ARRAY, STAPLE DIAGRAM. Fixed arrangement of fibers done usually on a dark background; it is a set-up of fibers that are in parallel order, beginning with the longest and ending with the shortest in the array.

STAPLE COTTON. At times, a misunderstood term. It means the long, good, staple stock, in speaking of cotton from the first-time ginning. It is the choice fiber, ready for manipulation.

The term signifies the average length of the bulk of fibers, in question. A stock, sliver, slubbing, roving, or yarn may have a staple length of, say, 1¼ inches. The fibers, taken collectively, measure that length.

Long-staple cotton measures 1⅛ inches, and longer. Short-staple cotton is less than 1⅛ inches.

STAPLE FIBER. Filaments which have been cut to the length of various natural fibers. The fibers may be spun on the cotton, wool, worsted, flax, or silk systems and are very popular in dress goods. The yarn is often mixed with other major textile fibers in varying amounts, to bring about new yarn and cloth effects. Examples of staple fiber include acetate, rayon, Dynel, nylon, "Dacron," "Orlon," Acrilan, etc. See Illustrated Section.

STAPLE FIBER, MODIFIED. Acetate or rayon staple fiber or spun yarn treated to produce wool-like properties to the product. The surface effect of fabrics made of this staple stock is usually rather rough.

STAPLE LENGTH, COTTON. Short staple is that cotton below 1⅛ inches in length; long staple is 1⅛ inches and longer in fiber length. See Illustrated Section.

STAPLE RAYON. A misnomer for rayon staple. See RAYON STAPLE; BLENDS OR COMBINATIONS OF NATURAL, MAN-MADE AND SYNTHETIC FIBERS.

STAPLE STANDARD. A package which contains a pound or so of cotton sold by the U. S. Department of Agriculture. The label gives the standard length which it represents so that it can be used in the matching of standard bales of normal character of the specified sample.

STAPLER, WOOL STAPLER. One who purchases wool from the grower and sells it to the top maker, either as received or in sorted condition.

STAPLING. Classifying cotton for staple or fiber length. The cotton stapler must have had many years of training, practice and experience to qualify as a recognized expert in the field.

STAPLINGS. Broken threads or loops of filling that show on the face of fabric; caused usually by imperfect shedding in the loom.

STAR BRAID. Cotton braid woven 1½ inches wide with small stars in white every 1½ inch. The ground for this braid is red or blue. Used for dress trimming or crochet work by stitching many widths together for chairbacks, etc.

STAR CHECKS. Color checks whose four sides are equal so that the design produced has the same appearance from every angle. They are often observed in woolen cloths and are of two varieties; those in which the stars appear in color on a contrasting background, and those in which the entire surface of the fabric is covered with the star-check effect, both colors used forming stars of the same size and shape.

STAR H. I. LOTS. English term for small batches of wool of three bales or less.

STAR LOTS, STARRED WOOL LOTS. In the London wool auction market, small lots up to and including three bales are sold apart from the larger consignments. These lots are designated by a star symbol in the catalogue which lists all items for sale.

STAR STITCH. A stitch made in the shape of a star; used in embroidery. See DOUBLE STITCH.

STARCH. A white, odorless, tasteless, amorphous powdery carbohydrate, $(C_6H_{10}O_5)$ taken "n" times; insoluble in cold water, alcohol, and other liquids. It is found in the seeds, pith, or tubers of most plants. It is a very important part of vegetable foods, reacting with certain digestive enzymes to produce maltose and dextrine. It is also used in the production of glucose and for stiffening agents applied to fabrics such as cottons and linens.

STARCH MANGLE. A machine composed of two large calender rollers and a kier, equipped with several immersion rollers, to hold the starch solution. Used to starch large lots of cotton goods.

STARCH MARKS. A defect in the slashing of the warp in which light-colored bars form hard, stiff spots of varying size across the goods. Often found on the last cut of warp on the warp beam, which is the first yarn to be wound onto the warp beam to be made ready for weaving in the loom. This yarn, no doubt, was allowed to stay in the size box too long, hence the boardy starch marks.

STARCHED FINISH. Cloth treated in a starch solution and then calendered. The cloth has more stiffness, body, substantial feel, and is often more attractive in looks. Most white cloths are starched to some extent. The starch is taken out in washing, and is renewed in laundering for the desired effect as in the case of organdy, collar cloth, dress goods. Starches used in cotton finishing are those of corn, dextrine, glucose, gum arabic, gum tragacanth, potato peeling, rice and wheat.

Starched finish is given to buckram, collar and cuff cloth, curtaining, dress goods, lawn, shirt fronts, uniform cloth, tarlatan.

STARCHED ORGANDY FINISH. See ORGANDY.

STARCHES, SYNTHETIC. Sizing agents which consist of a relatively permanent plastic material, usually synthetic resins, or a soluble plastic material, usually carboxymethyl-cellulose. Repeated washings can be given by the first product while the second method is removed in the next washing.

STARCHES, VEGETABLE. Sizing agents from vegetable sources used on fabrics to give body and substance, and

to improve the finish of the goods. There are two types: 1. The hot water type (dry) which requires hot water, and may or may not be cooked. 2. The instant type (dry or liquid) which does not use hot water in the treatment. See STARCH.

STARCHING. This finishing operation helps considerably to bring about the desired results on cloth. Starching is given to cottons and some rayons before they are sold over the counter in the department store, or sent to the cutting-up house to be made into a finished article. When garments are washed, they are starched, as well as ironed, so that they may be brought back to the "good as new" state.

Mill-finishing plants and laundries are merely enlarged factory systems over the old-time household methods of treating cloths. The finishing plant makes the new material; the modern laundry and home laundry make the material as good as new; an economic phase.

Cotton cloths, when they are finished, have varying degrees of pliability, stiffness, softness, stretchiness, gloss, smoothness, sheen, body, boardiness, etc. These different aspects are brought about in great degree by the starch that was used—thick, thin, or medium.

Corn, wheat, rice, and blended starches are used the most, whether in the finishing plant, laundry, or in the home.

Blended combinations usually have varying amounts of borax and paraffin mixed with them. These starches are known and sold as Laundry or Finishing Plant starches. The quality of the starch which adapts it for use as a "dressing" is its viscosity—stickiness or tenacity.

Corn has the greatest viscosity. Wheat has less viscosity, but more pliability, when compared with the corn. Rice has the least viscosity.

Thick starches are used for uniforms, collars, shirts of some types, cuffs, other stiff materials where stiffness is needed.

Medium starch is used for lingerie, cambrics, lawns, organdies, muslins, sheetings, pajama cloth.

Light starches can also be used in the above-mentioned cloths, and in curtaining, voiles, nainsooks, long-cloths, batistes, and in cloths where light starch is desirable.

Tints may be obtained in cloth by the use of bluing to do away with any tendency that there might be of the cloth showing yellowish tinges. From 1/200th to 1/300th of one per cent of dyebath is all that is needed. As the light's rays are reflected on the cloth,

a bluish tinge is more appealing to the eye than a drab, yellowish cast.

STARCHLESS FINISH. Since no starch has been used to finish cotton fabric so designated, there is none to wash out or replace. Features of the finish include absence of lint, non-sleazy appearance and no fuzzy or protruding fiber-surface after washing, laundering or being exposed to moisture. No cloudy surface is observed. The characteristics of the cotton fabric are not lost in damp weather. Since there is no fuzzy lint, the cloth will not soil easily; the absence of starch prevents the catching of dust and other particles. Printed designs are always clear-cut and the colors used are vivid and fresh-looking because the printing has penetrated the goods in a clear, clean manner.

STARDEL. Developed at Louisiana State University, Baton Rouge, Louisiana, this cotton has a staple length of 1⅛-inch, excellent fineness, and is 10 per cent stronger than present United States varieties of other quality cottons. It is a cross from Lone Star 65 and Delta-Pine 14. Stardel made its debut in 1956, and it will average a high yield of 888 pounds per acre.

START-UP, BAD. A defective cloth in the loom which appears, usually, after the weaver has picked out some defect caused by loom action in weaving. It may or may not be remedied in the finishing of the goods.

START-UP MARKS. 1. Blemishes caused by the "start-up man" who, when the loom is supposed to be ready for the weaver, is responsible for all settings and timings so that when the weaver takes over the warp he should have clear sailing in weaving out the cuts of cloth in the warp. Usually of minor importance, easily remedied.

2. The cloth may show marks such as bright or dim streaks in the filling direction. Caused by the weaver not starting his loom under correct warp tension at the let-off or take-up motions. Sometimes, several filling picks will be woven into the goods before the loom picks become regular and even with the warp ends. Good weavers are constantly on the alert for poor start-up marks and always give the closest attention to the warp and the fabric tension before setting the loom into action.

STATIC ELECTRICITY. The force which causes the attraction of small bits or particles to an object after the object has been rubbed or exposed to abrasion. Static electricity in textiles, unless checked or controlled, can reduce production, impair the yarn or fabric quality, increase waste, and cause hazards to personnel.

In laundry practice, for example, static electricity is often found in flat-work ironing. The material, such as sheets, pillowcases, etc., will adhere to the apron and begin to roll up. For example, if rolling exists under the rollers there will be a bunching-up of the material. If this condition is present under these rollers, the material that covers the roll will become torn, and the roll may lift out and break away from its bearing.

After leaving the roll, the material then comes in contact with the apron. The static electricity present may cause the material to adhere to the apron. This causes rolling, bunching, and an adherence to the apron that will carry the goods back into the machine.

The main causes of static and rolling are oversouring, and underextracting. A sheet, for example, will pick up a positive polarity because of oversouring. The aprons will pick up a negative polarity (earth polarity); therefore, because of the static being present, the sheet and the apron will have the tendency to cling to each other. This condition can be alleviated by grounding the machine to a cold-water pipe, or by using an AC induction field to neutralize the positive charge.

STATIONARY SHED. A method of dividing the warp in a loom in which some of the ends are always stationary while the others are pulled up or down to allow for the proper passage of the shuttle from the shuttle box on the one side of the loom to the correct, empty shuttle box at the other end of the raceplate of the loom.

STAVE. British term for harness or shaft in describing a weave construction such as a five-harness satin weave, a seven-shaft satin or a four-end twill weave, etc.

STAY BINDING. Made on a 2-up, 2-down herringbone weave, this all-cotton binding is used for seam coverage and strengthening of garments. Widths range from ¼-inch to 1¼-inches.

STAY TAPE. A warpwise cut tape used to keep certain parts of the garment from stretching. It is commonly used to stay gathers.

STEAM. Water in the vapor phase.

STEAMER RUG. A blanket covering, usually made of wool, for use by passengers on ocean-going steamers while reclining in a deck chair on the deck of the vessel. They are of good quality, heavy, and come in a host of patterns, often a plaid or tartan. There is a fringe at each end of the article.

STEAMING. 1. A method of fixing dyed fabric by subjecting it to steam or ammonia fumes. 2. If a cloth is "aged," there is no necessity for steaming, but if it has not been "aged," steaming will follow the printing of the goods to give it better penetration of dyestuff and to set the colors.

STEAM-SHRUNK. The opposite of London shrinking, it is the result of sponging or shrinking by passing the cloth through perforated steam cylinders.

STEAM-STRETCHED. Silk skeins that have been stretched under steam pressure to increase luster.

STEAM STYLE. Printed textiles which have had their colors set with steam after the printing.

STEAM TWILLS. Low-quality British cottons used for linings, and in some countries, for underwear. Given a filled finish and gray in the color, the cloth has a texture of 40 to 46 ends and 50 to 54 picks per inch. Made of a 2-up and 2-down twill, the cloth comes in black or white for use in cheaper lining fabric.

STEAM WASTE. Silk waste obtained chiefly from reeling mills in China, especially in the Canton area. Usually considered to be the best and most lustrous silk waste.

STEARINE. The solid precipitate which separates first from melted tallow upon cooling; largely stearic acid.

STECHKAMM. Used in Raschel knitting, it is an attachment designed to hold the stitch down to permit the needle to rise without taking the stitch with it.

STEEP BIN. Any type of bin used to store goods for ageing, or for some other reason.

STEEPING. 1. In rayon manufacture, it is the treatment of pulp sheets with caustic soda to produce alkali cellulose. 2. Allowing material to remain without agitation in a liquid bath or wet condition for some time. The soaking, usually with the heat below the boiling point, will produce some action or absorption.

STEEPING PRESS. The raw stock for rayon, cotton, or wood chips, is cooked by the action of chemicals and live steam into a pulp. This is run over screens and then put through heavy rollers which squeeze out the water and press the pulp into sheets of cellulose, the thickness of blotting paper.

Different lots of sheets are mixed together as they come to the plant. The sheets are placed in presses and steeped in a solution of caustic soda. This extracts certain impurities, and changes the sheets chemically into alkali cellulose. After steeping for a controlled length of time, the cellulose sheets are squeezed by a hydraulic ram to remove excess liquid. The pressure is accurately regulated so that the liquor remaining in the sheets will produce the proper chemical reaction.

STEEP TWILLS AND RECLINING TWILLS.

SIXTY-THREE-DEGREE TWILL WEAVES: In the right-hand effect the raiser moves up two picks. In the left-hand effect the raiser moves down two picks.

SEVENTY-DEGREE TWILL WEAVES: In the right-hand effect the raiser moves up three picks. In the left-hand effect the raiser moves down three picks.

SEVENTY-FIVE-DEGREE TWILL WEAVES: In the right-hand effect the raiser moves up four picks. In the left-hand effect the raiser moves down four picks.

RECLINING TWILL WEAVES: Twill weaves in which the angle and the diagonal line are less than the usual forty-five degrees.

TWENTY-SEVEN-DEGREE TWILL: Hold over for two ends and then go to the next pick.

TWENTY-DEGREE TWILL: Hold over for three ends and then go to the next pick.

FIFTEEN-DEGREE TWILL: Hold over for four ends and then go to the next pick.

Some steep twills are made with the left-hand direction on the face of the goods; however, this is rare.

STEILS. The thin to-and-fro stitching used in producing stems and other fine lines, as well as reinforcing lines in embroidery done on a Schiffli embroidery machine.

STEINFLACHS. German term which means "stone flax." Hence, their term for asbestos.

STEINKIRK. Used in the first third of the eighteenth century, it meant a cravat or neckwear fabric, twisted on itself and threaded through a buttonhole in the coat. Popular with women horseback riders, it was usually brightly colored.

STEM FIBERS. Those which grow in the bast of certain plants, as flax, hemp, jute, ramie, etc.

STENCILING. See SCREEN PRINTING.

STENTER. A machine used in finishing fabrics. Fully automated and with a wide temperature range possible, it is ideal for finishing cloth and controlling stretch fabrics. The frame can be used with clips or pins, and can change from one to the other in a matter of minutes. This versatile machine covers drying, heat, and setting or resin curing. Ninety-inch fabric can be treated on the machine and always at a rigid control since tension is an important factor in finishing goods.

STEPHENS, HENRY. He received the first dye patent in the United States; it was for a soluble Prussian blue.

STEP-IN, SEMI-. A girdle with partial placket opening. The semi-step-in is in contrast to a step-in or roll-on garment without opening and the corset type garment which has full opening. If a pantie girdle, a girdle style with legs, has a partial opening, it is referred to as a "semi-step-in pantie girdle."

STEP RAIL. Same as the spindle rail of the roving frame.

STERILE. A substance or material devoid of bacteria or fungi.

STEVENS H₂O. A chemical finish of J.P. Stevens & Company, Inc., which in processing, anchors minute particles of a polyamide resin on wool fibers, leaving a film which reduces felting and shrinkage. When applied to all-wool and nylon-wool fabrics, with a maximum shrinkage of three percent, these fabrics have increased strength and need no more than "touch-up" ironing. These fabrics are easily washable at all times.

"STEVEREST." The strong, compact, lightweight, sunlight degradation resistant nylon fabrics supplied by the J.P. Stevens & Co., Inc., New York City, for the successful 1963 American-Mount Everest Expedition. This set of fabrics, finished for water repellency, receive their name from contractions of the name, Stevens and Mount Everest.

STEWARD. The union representative who handles union matters within a specific unit of the company, such as a department.

STICKINESS. The adhesive property of a substance; the principle of glue.

STICKY ENDS. Yarn of any type which becomes sticky and troublesome because of atmospheric conditions—dampness, mildew, dyeing treatment, or poor tension in manipulation.

STIFFENING. 1. A term that implies that the lower qualities of fabrics, especially cottons, have been starched or sized to some degree. 2. A hatmaking term whereby the felt cones are sized by a solution of shellac in alcohol; used in derby hats and stiff felts.

STIFFENING MACHINE. A machine for applying shellac to felt hats or hat brims to stiffen them. The machine consists of a crown block on which hats fit loosely; a pair of power-driven rollers between which the portion of the hat to be stiffened is guided; a tank for the shellac solution; and a circulating system for directing the shel-

lac over the portion of the hat between the rollers.

STIFFNESS. The stiffness of a fiber is its ability to resist deformation when stress is applied. This is measured on an inclined plane serigraph which produces readable stress—strain curves expressed in grams per denier per minute.

STILETTO. A pointed instrument used to make eyelets in fabric.

STIPPLE EFFECT. Printing of small dotted effects in between the printed design on a fabric. Many novelty effects are obtained in this way.

STIRRUP NET. One that is formed by a series of loops battened into position by a series of knots. The work is done on a pillow since it is essential that the loops be kept in a controlled, regular formation.

STITCH. 1. A single loop or turn of thread or yarn made by hand or machine in sewing, crocheting, tatting, lace making, knitting, and knotting.

2. A particular type of stitching based upon the foundation stitches—back, blanket, chain, cross, knot, overcast and knot.

3. Stitches are made in accordance with the material at hand, its weight, finish and design; the type of thread or yarn, the length of stitch desired, the position of the thread with regard to the needle and the angle of the proposed stitch to be made.

STITCHES, TYPES OF. A stitch is the joining together or ornamenting by sewing with a threaded needle or other implement, as in embroidery or sewing of different types. A stitch is made on one piece of cloth. A seam is the sewing of two pieces of cloth together; it is impossible to have a seam without a stitch.

1. BACK-STITCH: Made of a short stitch back on the upper side and a longer one forward on the under side of the cloth. Gives strength and security.

2. BASTING: The holding of pieces of cloth together for the time being; to be taken apart later on. Noted in suits being made to measure.

3. BLANKET STITCH: Used for all kinds of trimmings on textile fabrics. Protects the edges of the cloth and prevents fraying of edges.

4. BLIND HEM: The use of stitching to make the stitches invisible. Noted on rayons, cottons, silks, woolens, and other cloths that are medium or expensive in price. It is not a strong stitch; but it is done quicker than slip-stitching.

5. CROSS-STITCH: Used for decorative purposes and made by crossing two slanting stitches in the shape of the design or pattern.

6. FEATHER-STITCH: Used for decorative stitching; seen on aprons, runners, etc. Combines the holding process of the running stitch and adds to the final effect.

7. GATHER: Making cloth appear "full." Made by pulling threads of the running stitches.

8. OVERCOATING STITCH: Prevents the edge of the fabric from raveling. Overcoating stitches are deeper and farther apart when compared with overhanding stitches; the work is done from left to right.

9. OVERHAND: Small slanting stitches taken over the edges of folded cloth-pocket making. Overhanding is used for decorative effect.

10. RUNNING STITCH: Small stitches used to hold two pieces of cloth together permanently.

11. SLANT HEMMING STITCH: Used for hems and facings, they are made so that each stitch slants on both the right and wrong side of the material.

12. SLIP-STITCH: Used where invisible stitching is required for the holding of hems, facing, trimmings in place, etc. It is a good stitch to use in sewing and is ideal for workers to use in making apparel. Only part of the thread is in the material and this tends to make the stitch invisible to the naked eye.

13. STRAIGHT HEMMING STITCH: Like the slant stitch, except that this stitch is straight. It is used to hold the edge and to show the stitching as little as possible. Much used by tailors, who like to use this method.

STITCH GRADUATION. Effecting a gradual tightening of the stitches being knitted so that the upper part of the leg of hose is wide and slack, while the lower part of the leg and the ankle is much narrower and tighter, thus insuring a better fit. The stitch graduating device is not in action when the heel is reached.

STITCHING. A term used in fabric design when the raisers of one weave fall opposite the sinkers of another weave; noted in broken twills, pointed twills, dice checks, etc. Also called cutting, locking.

STITCHING AND STAMPING. Cotton gray goods come to the bleachery in single or double cuts. The pieces are stamped at the ends with suitable marks for identification with a substance such as tar, which will withstand the various, more or less rigid operations. The pieces are then stitched, end to end, to form one long, continuous band of cloth, and it is passed through the bleaching operations in this manner. As many as 200 pieces may be stitched together; this would give a total length of ten to fifteen miles of cloth.

STITCHING POINT. 1. The point where a back thread intersects a face thread in double or triple cloth weaving. 2. The point where a thread of another system, say, a filling thread or a binder thread, intersects with a warp thread.

STITCHING THREAD OR YARN. Thread applied to fabric to hold thicknesses together or to decorate a surface. Term refers mainly to sewing-machine stitching.

"STITCH-O-METER." A quality control device used to measure the speed at which a yarn feeds into a circular fabric knitting machine so that all feeds can be synchronized for uniform stitch setting of all the draw cams. Product of Supreme Knitting Machine Co., Brooklyn, New York.

STITCH-ROBBING. A means of stitch slackening in manufacture of hosiery in which each needle tends to draw a little yarn from the needle ahead of it; forms a closely knit area in the fabric.

STITCH-SHAPED GARMENTS. Those shaped entirely or partially by change of stitch.

STITCH SHAPING. Knitted garments are shaped by altering the stitch such as changing from a jersey stitch for the body to a rib stitch variation for the waistband, say 2x2. Shaping can also be done by changing the tightness of the stitch such as a long loop for the body and a shorter one for the waistband.

"STITCH-THRU" TECHNOLOGY. This term was coined by Mr. Daniel Duhl, president of Polylock Corporation, the only company, at present, devoted solely to the making of fabrics from the various stitch-thru methods. The term applies to those methods which create fabrics by passing a threaded needle from one side of a structure to the other, causing interconnected loops to be formed which sufficiently stabilize the structure so that it can be called a fabric. "Stitch-thru" adds an entirely new dimension to fabric formation. Weaving is caused by interlacing yarns; knitting is done by interlooping yarns; nonwoven fabrics are formed by actual bonding of fibers. "Stitch-thru" is done by actual stitching.

There are about eleven types of machines based on the stitching process. This does not include tufting, which in some respects, is similar to "Stitch-thru" but, generally speaking, is not considered to be a part of this type of technology. Some of these machines used, follow:

A. *Stitching a Pile to Form Terrycloth and Comparable Pile Fabrics:*

The Singer Lokloop machine is a modification of a tufting which produces a fabric with the terry pile effect on one side of the goods only. The Kraftmetic machine, a combination of tufting and knitting frames, produces loops on one or both sides of the material, the base fabric used for the purpose. Araloop and Malipol are basically about the same and are modifications of the Malimo System. Both use base fabric.

Malipol and Mali-Mo-Pol (Crompton & Knowles, Worcester, Massachusetts).

Araloop (Stellamcor Corporation, New York City).

Kraftmatic (U.S.A. rights controlled by United Merchants & Manufacturers, Inc., New York City).

Singer Lokloop (The Singer Company, New York City).

B. *Stitching a Batting with Yarn to Form a Fabric:*

The stitching of the fibrous batting to form the fabric is such that the loose fibers are held tightly together by a sewing yarn. Several types of stitches may be used to present novel effects. Another name for this type of work is called "the stitch-bonding method of bonding a loose fiber batting together."

Arachne (Stellamcor Corporation, New York City).

Maliwatt (Crompton and Knowles, Worcester, Massachusetts).

C. *Stitching a Batting Without Yarn to Form a Fabric:*

A stitching like that of yarn is produced *"in situ,"* in its place from within the batting itself. The stitching needle grasps a group of fibers from one side of the fabric, pulls them through into a loop formation on the other side of the batting and locks them with a previously formed loop. It should be noted that the batting is held together by the fibers only, without the presence of any external yarn system.

Arabeva (Stellamcor Corporation, New York City).

Malifleece (Crompton & Knowles, Worcester, Massachusetts).

D. *Stitching Warp and Filling Yarns Together:*

A great many filling yarns are laid down, several hundred at a time, by an oscillating carriage which deposits the yarn onto pins such as observed on a tenter frame used in finishing fabrics. The filling yarn is then sent to the stitching area where the warp yarns are joined to this yarn. There is no interlacing of the warp and filling yarn at all; one set of yarn rests upon the other one. These two sheets of yarn are held in configuration, and a third system of yarn comes into play, the stitching yarn. This set of yarn then binds the warp and filling yarns together by a stitch that is on the order of a tricot knitting stitch. This type of product is therefore not an interlaced type of goods, but is one held in place by the stitching yarns used. This is the oldest method in the manufacture of this type of fabric and the one that looks most like a truly woven material. Malimo (Crompton & Knowles, Worcester, Massachusetts).

STOCK. A broad, general term used in mill parlance with reference to raw materials, fibers in process, or manipulation and qualities or conditions of textiles in its various phases. The term is often applied to the following: raw or bulk fibers, lap, sliver, slubbing, roving, top, shoddy and other waste materials, mixes, mixtures, grades of fibers, staple, and so on.

STOCK-DYEING. Dyeing of stock in the bulk. It is done after the particular stock has been well opened up and freed from foreign matter and clumpy or matted parts. Done before the final mixing of the grades and types of stock to be used in the particular mix. This type of dyeing is used for many mixtures, heathers, fancies, etc.

STOCK-DYED YARN. Wool fibers that are stock-dyed and then spun into yarn. Ideal for colors and shades in covert, Venetian, homespun, tweed, Cheviot, Shetland, Saxony, etc.

STOCKINETTE. A knitted, worsted, part-worsted or cotton elastic fabric on the so-called Jersey order. A product of the "stocking frame" and usually made with a "fleeced wool" back. Used as a material for working, house, and smoking jackets.

STOCKINETTE WEAVE. Merely a variation of the 2-up, 2-down twill so that when used it will provide the fabric with some porosity as, for example, in some types of eponge. This effect is also obtainable with the plain weave by skipped dents in the reed, drawing-in, etc. See EPONGE.

STOCKING. A close-fitting knitted covering for the leg and foot, a full-length hosiery.

STOCKING TYPES, WOMEN'S WEAR.

1. TYPE A: for short, small, or slender legs:

Sizes 8, 8½, and 9, and 27½ to 28½ inches long.

Sizes 9½ and 10, and 28½ to 29½

STOCKING AND SHOE SIZE CHART.

STOCKING

SIZE OF 8:	SIZE OF 8½:
SHOE SIZES—	
2C	3AAA-EEE
2½ C-EE	3½ AAA-EEE
	4AAA-E
	4½ AAA-AA

STOCKING

SIZE OF 9:	SIZE OF 9½:
SHOE SIZES—	
4½ A-D	5E-EEE
5AAA-D	5½ A-EEE
5½ AAA-AA	6AAA-D

STOCKING

SIZE OF 10:	SIZE OF 10½:
SHOE SIZES—	
6½ AAA-A	7E-EEE
6E-EEE	7½ B-EEE
6½ B-EEE	8AAA-B
7AAA-D	8½ AAA-A
7½ AAA-A	

STOCKING

SIZE OF 11:	SIZE OF 11½:
SHOE SIZES—	
8C-EEE	10C
8½ B-EEE	10½
9AAA-C	11
9½ AAA-C	
10AAA-B	

inches long.

2. TYPE B: for average legs of medium proportions:

Sizes 8½ and 9, and 29½ to 30½ inches long.

Sizes 9½ and 10, and 30½ to 31½ inches long.

Sizes 10½ and 11, and 31½ to 32½ inches long.

3. TYPE C: for long or plus-proportioned legs:

Sizes 9½ and 10, and 33 to 34 inches long.

Sizes 10½, 11, and 11½, and 34 to 35 inches long.

4. TYPE D: Adjustables and New—for longer or amply proportioned legs:

Sizes 9½ and 10, and 34 to 35 inches long.

Sizes 10½, 11, and 11½, and 35 to 36 inches long.

STOCKPORT REED COUNTS. Counts based on the number of reed splits or dents in a two-inch span.

STOLA, STOLE. 1. The long outergarment worn by the matrons in ancient Rome. 2. A fur, scarf, or garment resembling a stole worn by women. 3. A band of silk, acetate or rayon fabric about 4 inches wide, and 81 inches long, with the two ends flared out. The ends hang loosely down the front of a bishop and are crossed over the breast when worn by a priest. It is symbolical of hierarchical order.

STOMACHER. Former term for any ornamental covering for the stomach used in formal wear; now called cummerbund.

STONE COTTON. 1. Brazilian cotton is known by this term at times. 2. Indian cotton which has been cleansed by placing it on a large flat stone and separating the staple from the seeds by using iron rods in the rolling action.

STONEVILLE 2B COTTON. This staple has good fiber quality and is popular for spinning purposes. Uniformity ranges from slightly irregular to good, while fineness is fine to average. Fiber strength is fair to very good. Spins ideally from 22s to 36s.

STOOKS. Piles that are formed by placing flax on end and setting them against others after pulling.

STOP MARKS. A barre' or mark which runs the width of a tufted carpet, caused by an irregular or off-standard feed relationship of either yarn, cloth feed, or both on the start-up of the machine.

STOP-MOTION DEVICE. Any automatic device that will stop a textile machine when some irregularity in the running of the machine arises; examples are when a warp yarn breaks in weaving, when a filling pick breaks in the shed or when the bobbin has run out and become spent; when bobbins, cones, cheeses, or spindles become filled on a machine, etc.

STOP-MOTION, KNITTING. An electrical device designed to stop the functioning of a knitting machine upon the occurrence of a press-off or other similar type of damage resulting from such yarn defects as large knots or slubs, yarn breaks, and yarn run-outs. Generally speaking, the assembly consists of a top and a bottom stop-motion.

STOPPA. Italian term for the tow removed from hemp during the scutching operation. See SCUTCHING TOW.

STORM SERGE. Heavier but lower in texture than ordinary serge, and cheaper in quality and price, this cloth is made from a 3-up and 3-down, right-hand, 45-degree twill weave. Cloth is wiry, harsh, and lustrous; used in suiting and coating material. Colors are usually navy and dark shades, with much fabric made in shades of gray.

STORM TABS. Wristlets set in the lower sleeves of a garment as a protection against wind and cold.

STOTING. Resorted to in the reweaving of holes, burns, and other blemishes found on garments, in piercing facings inside and cuts under rolls, it is an operation by which two edges are sewn together by means of a stitch taken over and through at the same time. Its purpose is to obtain thinness, and that the "join" may be less prominent than a seam. It is generally used to avoid observation and is employed where seams are not supposed to be, either on the inside or the outside of a garment.

STOVEPIPE FINISH. The clear, neat, high luster finish seen on fabrics which appear in sample books used by tailors for perusal by the trade.

STOVEPIPE HAT. While the Civil War was causing excitement in the United States, excitement was furnished in London when a man appeared in a new "high silk hat." It frightened so many people and caused such a sensation that the wearer was put under arrest and fined 500 pounds. Today this type of topper is the acme of perfection when full evening dress is worn by males.

STOVEPIPE SATIN. A smooth, highly lustrous satin on the order of panne satin; used in making stovepipe hats.

STOVING. A process of bleaching wool by sulphur dioxide fumes. In connection with silk, it is the killing of the chrysalis within the cocoon by means of dry heat and sulphur fumes at proper temperature.

STRADDLING. Straddling is done by speculators to profit from a change in price differences between two markets or between two futures. Known as spreading in grain trading, straddling is the term used when cotton and other commodities are concerned.

A cotton trader, for example, may believe that the Memphis September cotton futures are temporarily "too high," as compared with the price of Little Rock September cotton futures. The trader could then "straddle" by selling his Memphis September futures and buying a like amount of Little Rock cotton futures. If the dealer "guessed right" and the Memphis price declined as compared with the Little Rock price, he would then close out the off-setting accounts at a profit.

The same operation may be worked in a single market by the use of off-setting transactions in two future dates. The spreader or straddler in this case has to gamble, for instance, in the belief that the price of May cotton is out of line with the price of, say, July cotton and that the price relationship eventually will change.

STRAIGHT CUT. When the normal up and down of a garment is cut on the lengthwise direction of the goods, opposite of bias cut.

STRAIKEN. Term used in Scotland for linen fabric.

STRAIN. The relative deformation which results when a specimen is subjected to stress.

STRAND. 1. One of the principal twists or members of a rope. 2. A hair, fiber, or the like. 3. Wires twisted into a cable formation. 4. Anything that is plaited or twisted. 5. To make by twisting strands. 6. To weave a strand into a garment by means of a needle in mending.

STRAND GROUND. Term used in manufacture of handmade lace where the sprigs are connected by irregular bars.

STRANDING THREAD. A thread used by tailors made of well-twisted linen yarn and waxed for smoothness; used in buttonhole work.

STRAP. Maritime term for a rope length that has been spliced in order to have a ring at the one end of the rope.

STRAP LEATHER. See TRAVELING BAG, SUITCASE, AND STRAP LEATHER.

STRASSÉ. Double silk cocoons made into silk waste in order to avoid reeling; the waste of silk throwing, strassé is a type of floret silk.

STRAW. 1. Used for matting, seating, shoes and sandals, and straw hats, the swamp wire-grasses (or straw) are also used in grass rugs in the home for summer usage. These rugs are clean, cool, and neat. Wisconsin manufactures much of the straw for the trade, in the cities of Oshkosh, Racine, and Superior.

2. Material made by braiding, plaiting or weaving either man-made fibers or such natural fibers as bark, grass, stalk, or stem.

3. A hat made of straw.

4. A light, yellowish tan shade, the color of dried plant-fibers.

5. Some of the major straws follow:

BAKU: Fine, lightweight expensive straw with a dull finish. Made from fibers of buri palm along the Ceylon and Malabar coast.

BALIBUNTAL: Fine, lightweight, glossy straw obtained from unopened palm leaf stems.

LEGHORN: Finely plaited straw made from a kind of wheat grown in Tuscany, cut green and bleached, woven by hand in Italy.

MILAN: Fine, closely woven straw used in fine-quality women's hats, made in Milan, Italy. Imitations must be clearly described as such.

PANAMA: Fine hand-plaited creamy colored Toquilla straw used for men's and women's hats, made, curiously enough, primarily in Equador.

TOQUILLA: Strong, flexible fiber obtained from Jippi-Jappa leaves. Used in weaving Panama hats. No other hat should be labeled "Panama" or "Genuine Panama."

TUSCAN: Fine, yellow straw woven from the tops of bleached wheat stalks grown in Tuscany. Often woven in lacelike designs.

STRAW BODY HATS. The process of manufacture varies with the kind of hat; the better straws are Panama, Leghorn, Tuscan, all of which are handwoven by native workers.

STRAW BRAID. The dried stems of cereal plants, such as oats, rice, and rye, woven into narrow strips and used to make straw hats. The weaving is usually done in the country from which the straw is imported—China, Japan, Italy.

STRAW COTTON. Cotton thread given much starch treatment. Wiry, harsh, used in making straw products.

STRAW TICKING. A 2-up and 1-down twill weave makes this cotton cloth that is used for ticking.

STRAZZA, STRUSSA, STRUZA. Italian term for tangled silk waste taken from outer walls of single cocoons and broken filaments. Douppioni also furnishes strazza, which is obtained prior to reeling.

STREAK STITCH. The cloth stitch in pillow lace.

STREAKY WARP. Light or dark areas in fabric in which the offshade effect is caused by one or more section beams of the warp being a different shade.

STREAM RETTING. Part of flax processing. See FLAX PROCESSING.

STREET BUYER. Cotton dealer who buys cotton staple from the farm wagons on the street in a community.

STRENGTH. Generic term for that characteristic of a material by virtue of which it can resist strain or rupture by external forces.

STRENGTH LOSS BY LIGHT. Also known as tendering, it is caused by the action of the sun's ultraviolet rays on the fibers. Measure of this action is done by tensile strength tests before and after exposure to sunlight.

STREPSIKEROS WOOL. Long, coarse wool obtained in Crete.

STRESS. The internal resistance to deformation which developes within a specimen when it is subjected to an external force.

STRESS - STRAIN ANALYZER, LAWTON. This machine provides continuous measure and plot changes required to stretch yarn and cord specimens to a selected percentage of elongation. The device can precisely simulate conditions in which textiles are stretched as they are fed to or through textile machinery.

Continuous non-destructive testing of yarns and cords allows the yarn manufacturer, spinner, weaver, and knitter to avoid the usual difficulties which occur because of yarn variations, improper tensions, feed rates, and feed mechanisms. In the operation, the force is sensed by a load cell, located between the feed and tension heads, and continuously plotted on a recorder chart. By changing the circumference of the feed or tension heads, elongation is controlled to within plus or minus .03 percent. Load on a specimen is recorded against time, which is directly relatable to the specimen feed rate. Product of Scott Testers, Inc., Providence, Rhode Island.

STRETCH. 1. The outward run of the mule carriage from the headstock of the machine. 2. The lengthening of a filament, yarn, or fabric upon application of stress. 3. To draw out or to extend in length or width to cause tautness. 4. An increase in dimension.

STRETCH, ACTION. See Stretch, Power.

STRETCH, COTTON. All-cotton stretch is used extensively at the present time - corduroy, denim, etc. - because of its economy, simplicity of production, and satisfactory price. It is made largely on the slack mercerization method since durability of the stretch factor depends on a concise, precise finishing technique to stabilize it against multiple launderings.

STRETCH, WOOL. Considerable progress has been made with wool-stretch fabrics. For example, J. P. Stevens & Company, Inc., New York City, has developed its patented "PLUS-X" to control wool stretch goods. It involves the setting of a permanent accordion-like crimp into a wool or a wool-blend cloth prior to the dyeing and the finishing of the goods. The method provides excellent durability and performance, improves the hand and appearance, and gives wrinkle-resistance to the finished goods. The process changes the molecular structure of the fiber in the treatment.

Burlington Industries, New York City, also has its process which is the patented "RESTORA." It is described as the "first 100 percent wool stretch fabric to be made without any chemical change in the molecular structure of the fiber." Special spinning and weaving techniques, along with novel finishing techniques, allow for elasticity in both warp and filling directions.

STRETCH APPAREL, STRETCH AND END USES IN The end use for which a fabric is to
serve determines the amount of stretch:

TYPE	PERCENTAGE OF STRETCH	PERCENTAGE OF UNRECOVERABLE STRETCH
Tailored Clothing	15 to 25 per cent	Not more than 2 per cent
Spectator Sportswear	20 to 35 per cent	Not more than 5 per cent
Form-fit Garments	30 to 40 per cent	Not more than 5 per cent
Active Ski Wear	35 to 60 per cent	Not more than 6 per cent

Flexibility of Stretch Needed in Garments for Human Body Flexing

Back Flex	Across the back	13 to 16 per cent
Seat Flex	Across the seat	4 to 6 per cent
Elbow Flex	Vertical or north-south	35 to 40 per cent
	Horizontal-circumference	15 to 22 per cent
Knee Flex	Vertical or north-south	35 to 45 per cent
	Horizontal-circumference	12 to 14 per cent

"STRETCH-EVER". A synthetic elastomer Spandex fiber made from a polymer of polyurethane and used in corsets and brassieres, etc. Properties of "Stretch-Ever," which is a trademark name of the producer, International Latex Corporation, show it to be impervious to bleach, detergents, and body oils; it is free from discoloration, and provides longer wear through repeated washings with virtually no loss in modulus recovery. Sarong, Inc., a subsidiary of International Latex Corporation, and the Playtex Division of the parent company, make the finished products from the yarn.

STRETCH FABRICS, SOME USES OF. COTTON ALONE OR USED IN BLENDS WITH MANMADE FIBERS:
1. Industrial Fabrics: Convertible tops and head liners on automobiles.
2. Household: Contour sheets, draperies, slip covers.
3. Wearing Apparel: Brassieres, casual wear, blouses, and dress shirts, gloves, infants' and children's wear, knitgoods of many types and varieties, linings for men's coatings, men's suitings, pajamas, ties and tie linings, uniforms, and many sportswear articles.
Woolen: These fabrics are used chiefly in some types of apparel such as coatings and jackets, hose and hosiery, ski pants and slacks, woolen shirtings for cold weather.

STRETCH FABRICS, TESTING ON. Standard stretch tests have been developed and evaluated on knitted and woven stretch fabrics for such end uses as tailored garments, sportswear, and ski wear. In these tests, the percentage of stretch is determined while under a standard load, and the growth, or unrecovered stretch, is recorded after one-half minute, one hour, and sixteen hours. It is important that the growth figure be low, as otherwise a fabric will show a baggy, distorted condition.

STRETCH-OUT. Increasing the number of machines to be tended by an employee, or increasing the production standard, without any extra compensation.

STRETCH SPINNING. A term used in the manufacture of rayon or acetate. The filaments are stretched while moist and before final coagulation decreases their diameter.

STRETCH WOVEN FABRICS. They originated in Europe in ski-wear, and the idea has given rise to a host of new concepts in making garments from the fabrics. These fabrics have found much favor in men's suitings and dress goods in women's wear.
Stretch nylon yarns such as Fluflon, Helanca—either conventional or of false-twist type, Superloft, etc.—are used and provide the action and "give" a person needs across the hips, at the knees and in the seat area for greater comfort. A shirting will "give" at the elbows and shoulders without any apparent fabric strain. Garments of this yarn have good surface effect and texture; provide comfort; durability and moisture absorptiveness are also enhanced, and a garment will return to its relaxed or original state on release from stretch. These factors are especially good in pajamas, sportswear, and undergarments.
Stretch fabrics are made usually with stretch nylon yarn in the one direction while the other system of yarn may be a natural fiber, a man-made fiber, or a blend of the two in order to add desirable properties to the fabric. Filament yarn may be used in lightweight fabrics to advantage. Ski-pants have a 30 per cent stretch, swimwear about 50 per cent while blouses and shirts run to about 15 per cent.

Relative to yarns, the lower the total denier of the yarn used, the greater is the stretch potential. Thus, a 60-denier will "give" more than a 120-denier yarn. Plied yarns give a better stretch and more vigorous recovery in a fabric than single yarns of equivalent denier. The fewer the number of filaments in the yarn of a given denier the greater will be its resistance to extension, the quicker the recovery, the crisper the hand, and the higher the per cent of the original yarn strength retained. End-use of these fabrics are almost endless, and they also find use in domestic and home furnishings, and in industrial and military areas.

STRETCH YARN. A thermoplastic continuous filament yarn which has been modified to afford high stretch to the yarn-elongation and rapid recovery.

STRETCH YARNS, BASIC PRINCIPLES TO PROVIDE STRETCH IN. These are:
1. *Heat Stretch* yarn - based on the principle of a steel spring.
2. *Elastomeric* yarn - may be compared with a rubber band.
3. *riece Goods Stretch* yarn - wherein the proper shrinkage can be made in the width of the goods in the filling direction.

STRETCH FABRICS, SEWING ON: The following points should be observed.

1. Preshrinking of fabric should be done with a steam iron.
2. Determine the way that the stretch goes in the fabric when cutting a pattern. Sharp scissors should be used when cutting in the correct direction of the stretch.
3. Pins should be set in the same direction as the stretch direction.
4. If possible, use nylon thread because of its elasticity and strength.
5. Pinking shears should be used to finish off the seams.

STRETCH FABRICS AND APPAREL, ADVANTAGES OF.

1. Better fit, greater comfort, more shape retention, and longer wear.
2. Improved wrinkle resistance to the fabric or the garment.
3. Greater surface appeal and interest; stronger consumer appeal.
4. Greater flexibility in designing these fabrics.
5. Fewer sizes and alterations needed.
6. Seam puckering greatly reduced in articles of apparel.
7. Less tailoring to shape.

STRETCH MATERIALS, TYPES OF STRETCH USED IN. These follow:

1. POWER STRETCH: This provides fabrics with increased snap and "muscle power," greater extensibility and quicker recovery than those observed in ordinary fabrics. This type stretch is essential in athletic clothing, foundation garments, ski wear, swimwear, and the more professional types of active sportswear such as football pants.
2. COMFORT STRETCH: This is applied to apparel used in daily wear to allow ease and greater comfort to the wearer. Clothing does not necessarily need power stretch, but comfort and power in these articles do give greater satisfaction to the individual. Other end uses of comfort stretch include bed sheets, slip covers for use in home furnishings, upholstery, and transportation fabrics.

A concise definition of STRETCH YARN implies that it is a thermoplastic continuous filament yarn which has been modified or conditioned so as to afford high strength in yarn elongation and with rapid recovery.

STRETCH FABRICS, SOME BASIC TERMS USED IN MANUFACTURE OF.

BACK TWISTING: Twisting a yarn, single or ply, in the reverse direction to the previously set direction, whether S-twist or Z-twist, in the original direction of twist.

BODY FLEX: The degree of bending in the different parts of the human body. The term is used with regard to the determination in the amount or degree of stretch in fabrics necessary in any garment to give the proper amount of give or flex.

CABLE TWIST: A cord, rope, or twine construction in which each successive twist runs in the opposite direction from the preceding twist. This type is S-Z-S or Z-S-Z.

CHEMICAL STRETCH: Stretch imparted to fabrics by chemical means after the cloth has been woven and is being finished for commercial use. This is usually a filling or east-west stretch, since the fabric is shrunk horizontally and then set permanently in this state. Also known as "mechanical stretch" and "slack mercerization."

COIL, CRIMP, CURL: Terms used to denote the type of configuration given to a yarn such as nylon, polyester, etc., in order to afford stretchability.

CONFIGURATION: The relative disposition of the elements or the parts of some object or thing; the external form or appearance resulting from this disposition. For example, in textured yarns used in the textile industry, the original fibers or filaments will take on a new configuration because of treatments given the yarn in processing. These treatments which can be made permanent may be done by the use of heat, heated blades, stretching, true twist, false twist, etc. (See Stretch Yarn, Heat-set; Texturizing; Configuration, Yarn.)

CONFIGURATION, YARN: A manmade continuous filament given treatment in processing to cause it to take on a new configuration such as coil, crimp, or curl and thereby become stretchable. (See Configuration.)

ELASTOMERIC: A substance which owes its stretchability to the chemical or molecular structure contained therein. Examples are natural rubber, synthetic rubber, spandex, "Lycra," Vyrene.

FATIGUE FACTOR: The weakening of a stretch yarn in which some of its ability to recover after stretching has been lost. This "tired" or fatigue yarn can result from twisting the yarn at "revolutions-per-minute" speeds that are too high for the length of the heater box which sets the configuration of the yarn.

FIBERS, BI-COMPONENT: Continuous filament manmade fibers that have two related components with each component having a different rate or degree of shrinkage. This variance affords a crimped configuration which causes the yarn to become stretchable.

PLASTIC: Any material, natural or synthetic, which may be fabricated into a variety of shapes or forms, usually by the application of heat and pressure. A plastic is one of a group of organic compounds, synthesized from cellulose, hydrocarbons, proteins, or resins, and capable of being cast, extruded, or molded into various shapes. From the Greek word *plastikos*, which means "fit for molding."

PLUS-X: Patented process of J. P. Stevens & Company, Inc., New York City, for imparting stretch to all-wool and wool-blend fabrics. The process applies a permanent, accordionlike crimp to the fabrics prior to dyeing and finishing of the goods.

RESTORA: Burlington Industries owns this patented process which imparts stretch to all-wool fabrics without any chemical change in the molecular structure of the wool fibers. The process is capable of providing elasticity in both warp and filling in the goods.

RIGID FIBER OR FABRIC: Merely refers to a fiber or fabric that is not stretchable.

SHEATH FIBERS: The fibers which form a coating or sheath around the elastomeric fiber used in core-spinning of yarn. The fibers are usually wound in spiral formation around the core yarn, but random sheathing is also employed.

SLACK MERCERIZATION IN STRETCH FABRICS: Originally developed on all-cotton stretch fabrics, it can now be applied to blends of cotton and manmade fibers used in some fabrics. The procedure involves the shrinking of the fabric without any tension (slack) in the mercerizing bath of sodium-hydroxide (caustic-soda) solution. Often resorted to in the manufacture of filling or horizontal stretch fabrics.

SPANDEX: Elastomeric fiber owing its ability to stretch to its chemical or molecular structure. There must be at least 85 per cent segmented polyurethane in the fiber; this is the same chemical substance much used as a foam in transportation fabrics, bedding, and laminated fabrics of many types.

SPINNING, CORE: A spinning method wherein a base or core yarn is encased by a group of staple fibers, usually in a spiral formation. On removal of tension the staple or outside fibers are pulled into a more compact formation around the core yarn used. In stretch fabric yarn spinning the yarn will become stretchable to the degree or extent of the predetermined tension of the elastic core filament used.

SPINNING, INTIMATE BLEND: Cut spandex fibers blended with tow or cut staple fibers to produce a stretch yarn at the fiber-producer level.

STRETCH, ACTION: (See Stretch, Power.)

STRETCH CATEGORIES: There are two: (1) comfort stretch; (2) action stretch or power stretch. (See Stretch, Comfort; Stretch, Power.)

STRETCH, COMFORT: Stretch fabrics have either comfort stretch or power stretch or action stretch. Comfort stretch describes the stretch fabric used in apparel and clothing for daily usage. The stretch factor runs up to about 30 per cent. (See Stretch, Power.)

STRETCH FABRIC STABILIZATION: Stabilizing or setting the dimension of a "mechanical-stretch" fabric after it has been shrunk. Obtained by the use of appropriate chemicals and heat.

STRETCH, FILLING: Also known as horizontal or east-west stretch, the term means that the stretch factor has been given only in the filling direction of the goods, with the warp remaining rigid.

STRETCH, KNITTED: Manufacture of a knitted material with stretch yarns. Obviously, all knit fabrics have give or stretch, but a stretch knit material compared with a regulation knitted cloth will recover quicker and possess a greater holding power because of the stretch yarns used in the construction.

STRETCH, MECHANICAL: Also known as chemical stretch and slack mercerization, it is that type of stretch imparted to the fabric after it has been woven.

STRETCH, PIECE GOODS: An "overall" term which describes the various and sundry types of stretch fabrics in which the stretch factor has been applied to the cloth following weaving rather than to the yarn prior to weaving of the goods.

STRETCH, POWER: There are two basic categories pertinent to stretch fabrics—comfort stretch and action stretch or power stretch. Power stretch applies to stretch fabrics which have more snap, liveliness, and "muscle power," along with more extensibility and quicker recovery. This power factor ranges from 30 to 50 per cent and is ideally adaptable for athletic clothing, foundation fabrics, ski wear, swimwear, and the more professional types of sportswear such as football pants. (See Stretch, Comfort.)

STRETCH RECOVERY: Ability of a stretch yarn or fabric to recover its original position after having been stretched.

STRETCH, WARP: In a stretch fabric it means that the stretch in the goods is only in the warp direction; also referred to as vertical or north-south stretch. (See Stretch, Filling.)

STRETCH, WOVEN: Woven fabric made with stretch yarn in it. Generally speaking, woven goods are classed as firm or rigid, but the use of stretch yarns affords stretchability to an otherwise rigid construction. The stretch may be in the warp north-south), filling (east-west), or in both warp *and* filling directions.

STRETCH YARN: A thermoplastic continuous filament yarn which has been modified to afford high stretch to the yarn elongation and rapid recovery.

STRETCH YARN DOUBLING: Combining an "S-twist yarn" with a "Z-twist yarn" to obtain a double or plied yarn free from torque. Torque is the movement of forces which cause rotation or twisting as done with cord, wire, or yarn. (See Torque versus Non-Torque Yarns; Torque Yarn.)

STRETCH YARN, HEAT-SET: A yarn with an irregular configuration which is then set into this formation by the use of heat treatment. Usually applied to thermoplastic man-made fibers, it can also be imparted to natural fibers that have been made thermoplastic through some chemical treatment.

S-TWIST: A yarn or cord has "S" twist if, when held in a vertical position, the spirals conform in slope to the central portion of the letter S. Formerly called left-hand or clockwise twist.

SULFONE CHEMICALS: They change the molecular composition of the cotton fiber by cross-linking; used to give permanent stability to a mechanical stretch fabric.

TEXTURIZING: When a smooth continuous manmade-fiber filament is given a new and permanent configuration which results in a textural surface of appeal on the fabric woven with these textured yarns.

THERMOPLASTIC: Any plastic material which is permanently fusible and soluble. A thermoplastic plastic is one that will soften when exposed to certain heats and will harden again when the source of heat is removed.

THROWING: While not exactly the same treatment given to wool, worsted, cotton, or flax, throwing means the actual twisting, without drawing, of the continuous filaments of silk and manmade fibers. Textured yarns for use in stretch and comparable fabrics are manipulated in this manner. A throwster is one who has a throwing business and processes silk or manmade filaments as noted above.

TORQUE: Applied to present-day stretch yarn, nylon for example, it is a yarn that has been twisted and then subsequently heat-set. Helanca and Chadalon are examples.

NON-TORQUE: A stretch yarn that has been made by curling or crimping rather than twisting. Agilon and Ban-Lon are examples. The word "torque" means that the movement of forces causes rotation or twisting, as in the case of twisting cord, wire, or yarn.

TWIST, FALSE: In processing a heat-set stretch yarn it is passed through a false-twist spindle, and twisting begins at this time. When emitted from the spindle the twist is automatically removed; hence the term "false-twist." The yarn, however, retains "a memory" of its twisted position or torque and seeks to return to that position. It is therefore wound or taken up under tension to prevent it from curling. The torque in the yarn is balanced later on in processing by doubling it with another yarn whose "remembered" twist goes in the opposite direction; thus, a yarn with an "S-twist" and a "Z-twist."

ZERO TWIST: Sometimes referred to as "no-twist." The thrower (spinner) may request that cuprammonium yarns be supplied with no-twist. This is rarely done, however; usually one to five turns per inch are given the yarns. Viscose and acetate yarns with from three to five or six turns per inch are normally supplied to the thrower; this twist is known as "tram twist" or "filling twist."

Z-TWIST: If the spirals of a yarn or cord conform in slope to the central portion of the letter "Z," the twist is known as Z-twist. Formerly known as right-hand or counter-clockwise twist.

Courtesy of Cecil Lubell, Executive Editor, *American Fabrics Magazine*, New York City.

STRETCH YARNS, TORQUE IN SINGLE.* The term, torque, means to twist, a convolution. It is the rotary or twisting force in a yarn and is used as a measurable quantity. Torque or twist occurs the moment a system of forces produces rotation.

TORQUE

The end of a singles stretch yarn rotating in a clockwise direction, when hanging free, signifies an "S" torque yarn.

TORQUE

The end of a singles stretch yarn rotating in a counter-clockwise direction, when hanging free, signifies a "Z" torque yarn.

A single stretch yarn is said to be an "S" torque yarn if the twist in the "Z" direction was inserted and heat-set into

the yarn during its production. It is a "Z" torque yarn if the twist in the "S" direction was inserted and heat-set into the yarn during its production.

To determine whether a single yarn has an inherent "S" or "Z" torque, attach a paper clip to the end of the yarn, then allow the end to hang free. If the end rotates in a clockwise direction (see sketch below) the yarn is said to be an "S" torque yarn. If the end rotates in counter-clockwise direction (see sketch below), the yarn is said to be a "Z" torque yarn.

STRETCHER. See TEMPLE.

STRIA. An irregular warpwise striped effect obtained by twisting two strands of one shade of yarn loosely with one strand of a lighter, darker, or harmonizing color.

STRIATED FABRIC. Fabric which uses a series of rather narrow. random-streaked, or stripe effects. These lengthwise effects may be monotone in nature or may appear in two, three or more shades of the one color such as light blue, medium blue, and dark blue on a suitable background effect. Found in women's

wear coatings, some decorative fabric, furniture fabric, and novelty cloth. See Strie".

STRICK. 1. In spun silk manufacture, it is the cutting of the lap stock from the carding or combing operation, into pieces of a desired length for further manipulation. 2. Any of the major bast fibers made ready for drawing into sliver form.

STRICKEL. The instrument used to dress flax for the drawing operation.

STRIÉ. A descriptive term, strié (stree-ay) is applied to a fabric which is characterized by minute stripes of contrasting colors which run irregularly in the lengthwise direction of the goods. This effect is obtained by using yarn which is dyed the various shades desired. In this fabric, each individual thread is dyed a solid color. See JASPE.

STRIKE. Work stoppage by a group of employees in order to protest some conditions employer has not remedied, or obtain some improvement in working conditions that has been refused.

STRIKE VOTE. A balloting of employees or union members on the calling of a strike, or the authorization of their representative to call a strike.

*N-1-Monsanto Textiles, Inc., Deacatur, Alabama.

STRING. 1. A slender line, thinner than a cord and thicker than a thread, used for tying or lacing. 2. A type of twine.

STRINGS. They are seen in the selvages of piece goods and denote that there is a blemish or flaw in the area where the string has been tied. Allowances are made for blemishes of this sort, by the mill, in the woolen and worsted trade; the allowance is usually the cost of ⅛ yard of the fabric.

STRINGY COTTON. Also known as curly cotton, it is caused by many things such as ginning unripe seed cotton, wet-ginning, incorrect adjustments of the gin-saw brushes, etc.

STRIP. To cleanse the rollers of the card by removing matted fibers; has to be done periodically for the better and smoother running of the machine.

STRIP DYEING. Term used to imply the dyeing of sweater sections before sewing into a finished garment.

STRIPER. Found on knitting machines, this device will automatically shift the yarns being fed-in so that a striped effect will be made in the fabric. Other effects are also possible.

STRIPES. 1. Term used to designate hickory stripes found in coarse materials used for jumpers, overalls, denim, and shirting. These twilled striped cloths come in white, brown, and blue.

2. A line or series of lines, woven or printed and much used in woven and knitted fabrics, to add to the motif or effect. Stripes should be made to contrast well with the basic textures of the goods; they may or may not be of the same yarn used in the foundation portion of the goods. Some of the popular stripes are banjo (see Illustrated Section, Fabrics 25), candy, chalk, hairline, novelty, pencil, Roman, satin.

STRIPPER COMB. See PIN CYLINDER.

STRIPPER ROLLERS. There are from four to seven of these rollers on the woolen or worsted card. These card-clothed rollers work in conjunction with a similar number of worker rollers and the cylinder, to card wool fibers. The cylinder has excess speed over the workers and strippers; the strippers over the workers. The stripper roller is the smallest of the three rollers that do carding. Most carding machines are now vacuum-stripped.

STRIPPING. 1. The removing of coloring matter from textile materials by various methods of bleaching. Striped cloth is difficult to redye satisfactorily.

2. The removing of the sericin by the washing or boiling-off operation.

When the silk gum has been removed, only silk filament remains.

3. The removal of the short fibers and wastes from the carding machines. A cotton card, for example, will produce considerable amount of the waste, which becomes imbedded in the card clothing or wire of the cylinder, doffer, and revolving flats. See STRIPPER ROLLERS.

STRIPPING ACTION. The action when one roller, covered with card clothing, places the stock onto the next roller on a textile machine. The cylinder on the card, for example, has excess speed over the doffer and the points or tips on the card clothing are so set that the stock from the cylinder is laid onto the doffer clothing at the point of contact between these two rollers. The clothing of the cylinder acts against the back of the clothing on the doffer in the action of transferring the fibers from the one roller to the next one.

STRIPPING AGENT. A chemical which is capable of removing dyes.

STRIPPING RAIL. The beveled-edge, smooth steel blade set close enough to a beater to remove fibers that may cling to it.

STRIPPING ROLL. A six-inch diameter roller used to cleanse and strip the rollers on the card when they have become matted with fiber. The roll is clothed with special card clothing which has teeth that are longer and more openly spaced when compared with ordinary card clothing used on the machine rollers.

STRIP TEST. See CUT STRIP TEST, GRAB TEST; RAVELED STRIP TEST.

STRONG. A wool fiber that is harsh, coarse, very irregular or uneven in diameter measurement.

STRONG ACETATE. Acetate yarns which have a high tensile strength may be obtained by a special stretch spinning method. The yarn may be spun as fine as 10-denier; if desired, it can be saponified to give dyeing properties of viscose yarn. The staple fiber may be straight or crimped. Tensile strengths and elongations follow: 1. Tensile strength, dry: 6.8 grams per denier. 2. Tensile strength, wet: 5.6 grams per denier. 3. Elongation: 7 per cent.

STRONG ALKALINE SOLUTION. It is one which has 50 per cent or more of the alkali in solution.

STRONG FIBRO. Rayon staple made by Courtaulds Ltd., Coventry, England.

STRONG WOOL. 1. The Luster wools of Great Britain are sometimes known by this name.

2. Australian term for crossbred sheep; also implies coarse, extra-length

wool from any wool clip.

STROPHIUM. Worn by Greek women, it was a soft type of a bodice used to support and enhance the bust; forerunner of the modern brassiere.

STRUTT, JEDEDIAH. In 1758, he produced a lacelike fabric on a stocking frame by dropping stitches according to a definite plan; this may be said to be the first machine-made lace.

STUBBLE SHEARING. Condition caused when the shearer has not sheared close enough to the flesh of the animal: a short growth or stubble of wool is left, comparable with stubble beard of a man.

STUD. A threaded bolt set into a threaded hole in a metal piece; no nut is used on the bolt.

STUDS. Taking the place of buttons, these items are used to fasten shirt fronts and bottom-sleeves in formal and semi-formal wear. Made from a variety of raw materials, from the very low-priced varieties to expensive stone or metal types.

STUFF. 1. Sometimes used in reference to cloth, goods, or material. 2. A luster-type English fabric of cotton warp and Luster wool or some specialty fiber used as filling. Used for dress goods and lining.

STUFFER THREADS. Extra yarn or thread that runs in the warp direction through the center of the material without showing on the face or back of the fabric. Stuffers do not actually weave with the filling threads and are used to give weight, thickness, and bulkiness to the goods. They are much used in the carpet trade and in double, triple, and quadruple materials. Stuffer picks are used in some fabrics.

STUFF GOWN. The gown or robe that forms the raiment of a junior lawyer or barrister in England.

STUFFING. 1. Term used for stuffer thread in fabric, although not fully correct. 2. The material with which anything is stuffed. 3. The process of filling anything. 4. An old expression to imply the boiling of wool with a dyestuff before the mordanting action is given.

S-TWIST. A direction of twist in yarn or cord similar to the spiral part of the letter S. Formerly called "left" or "reverse" twist.

STYLE. Basically, it is the expression of an idea, the greatest thing in the mind of man, taking shape in some form of textile apparel, accessory, or adornment. Such an article of dress which becomes popular is said to be "in style." Stylists, fashionists, couturiers, a time, a place, an event may give the idea for the creation of new styles. A fashion is nothing more than the revival of some style, since styles usually return about every seven or eleven years in the cycles of fashion.

STYLE BOOK. Publications used as the basis for developing the cycles in fashion and style, to demonstrate their possibilities to those who have not experienced the thrill of some particular, supposedly new fashion. These works are the Bibles of fashion and style.

STYLON. Sometimes referred to as fiber-dust, the product may be applied to an adhesive-treated fabric under air pressure, following a definite and previously arranged motif or design. Stylon is suitable for dress fabrics.

SUBLIMATION. The volatilization of a solid. The term finds use in textiles to describe the migration of dye-stuffs, especially disperse dyes, on a fabric when subjected to high temperatures.

SUBLISTATIC PRINTING. See Printing, Decalcomania, Sublistatic Color System.

SUBSISTENCE WAGE. An amount of money sufficient only to provide an employee with the bare necessities of living.

SUBSTANTIVE DYES. These will dye fibers directly, since they are a type of direct dyes which have affinity for textile fibers.

SUBSTANTIVITY. Synonym for affinity. See AFFINITY.

SUBSTRATE. Material or substance acted upon by an enzyme or ferment; often linked in textiles with the dyeing and printing of materials. See AFFINITY.

SUCCATOON. Low-priced, dyed cotton goods of various types and qualities used in the African trade. Most succatoon is made in the British Isles.

SUCLAT. A European cotton broadcloth much used in the East Indian trade.

SUCRETON. An English cotton cloth made of soft-spun yarns and dyed copper-color. This plain or figure-weave material is shipped to West Africa.

SUCTION HYDRO-EXTRACTOR. It consists of a tube through which fabric passes in rope form, and which has one or more apertures or perforations connected to a source of suction.

SUDS. An emulsion of air in the solution. In soap solutions it is an indication of active soap.

SUDS RETURN METHOD. a device found in some automatic washers which allows water, previously drained from the wash basket, to be kept in another container so that it can be pumped back or siphoned-off into the washer for further use.

SUEDE. 1. A leather whose surface has been finished to provide a fine, smooth, appealing velvet-like effect and finish. 2. *Suede Calf:* Calf skin leather is used to give the same effect as suede leather. 3. *Suede Kid:* Goat skins are used to obtain this suede leather effect. These three terms are often used indiscriminately.

SUEDE FABRIC. 1. Woven or knitted cloth made from the major textile fibers and finished to resemble suede leather. Used for cleaning cloths, gloves, linings, sport coats, etc.

2. Some sheeting may be napped on the one side to simulate suede leather.

3. Duvetyne, when made of cotton, is similar to suede but has a longer nap; sometimes difficult to distinguish between the two.

SUEDE FINISH. Characteristic finish noted on some novelty woolen cloths and on warp-knit cotton cloths that are used for glove material. Emerizing brings about the finish, which has a soft, kindly feel that is similar to the feel of chamois. This finish may be given to cotton moleskins and to some sheeting cloths with soft filling.

SUEDOISE. A French serge repeating on eight warp ends and four filling picks.

SUFFOLK. British Down breed of sheep derived from crossing Southdown rams with Norfolk ewes. The medium wool obtained sorts to ¼ blood or low ⅜ blood; fibers are of moderate length and the fleece weighs about nine pounds. Shrinkage is about 40 per cent.

SUFI. Term used in India to imply fabrics made from cotton warp and silk filling. They are used by the Mohammedans in their garb and come in plain, figured, striped, or checked effects. The fabrics are so constructed that the cotton yarn which forms the back of the material comes in contact with the body while the silk content in the goods does not touch the skin of the wearer, in accordance with a ritual in the Mohammedan religion.

SUGAMO FIBER. Somewhat resembling Egyptian cotton, this seaweed fiber is obtained in Japanese waters. The fiber retains heat and repels water; it is spun on the denier system of counts.

SUGAR. There are several types of sugar found in nature; it is a sweet-tasting carbohydrate.

Common cane sugar is $C_{12}H_{22}O_{11}$. Dextrose, glucose or grape sugar, is $C_6H_{12}O_6$.

SUINT. Dried perspiration that is encrusted on the fibers of the sheep fleece. Suint is used in making potash.

SUIT. 1. Men's wear suits consist of coat, vest, and trousers. 2. Women's wear suiting consists of skirt and jacket or coat; sometimes the ensemble is made up of skirt, jacket, and coat.

SUITING. Original meaning implies a men's wear coat. In the garment trade it is the material used to make a man's suit in comparison with trouser material, fancy vesting, overcoating, sport coat material, etc.

SUITING, COTTON. Cotton fabric which has enough body to tailor well. Used for suits, slacks, and skirts.

SUITING, TEXTILES IN A MEN'S WEAR.

COAT:		3. Wigan
1. Body lining		4. Silesia
2. Sleeve lining		5. Tape
3. Buckram		
4. Silesia		TROUSERS:
5. Pocket stays		1. Curtain
6. Tape		2. Pockets
7. Pads		3. Silesia
8. Under collars		4. Watchpocket
9. Under yokes		lining
10. Collar canvas		5. Fly lining
11. Sleeve head		6. Suit cloth
12. Bridle stay		thread
13. Linen or jute canvas		
14. Hymo		ACCESSORIES:
15. Felt padding		1. Buttons
16. Linen tape		2. Tickets
17. Hair canvas or haircloth		3. Buckles
18. Piping		4. Suspender buttons
19. Hangers		5. Fly buttons
20. Label		6. Top fly buttons
VEST:		7. Hip-pocket buttons
1. Back lining		
2. Inside lining		8. Zippers

SUJJADAH. Arabian term for a prayer rug.

SULFANOLE. A series of detergents, emulsifiers, and wetting agents which include products that are high-foaming, alkaline and acid compatible, free-rinsing, and non-rewetting. Other types are highly penetrating, nonfoaming, and unaffected by hard water. Trade-mark of Warwick Chemical Division, Sun Chemical Corporation, New York City.

SULPHATE. A salt of sulphuric acid and a base metal, such as sodium, lime, iron, etc. Sodium sulphate is Glauber's Salt, used in dyeing.

SULPHATED FATTY ALCOHOL. A sodium salt of a half sulphated long chain aliphatic alcohol, usually lauryl or oleyl.

SULPHIDE. A compound of sulphur with a base metal such as iron, copper, lime, or the common alkalies. Iron sulphide and copper sulphide are black staining agents and often give trouble in washing processes. These stains are frequently produced in sulphur water.

SULPHITE. Another sulphur salt which represents sulphurous acid in combination with a suitable base. Sulphites are reducing agents.

SULPHITE PULP. Woodpulp formed by the digestion of wood chips in an acid solution of calcium bisulphite containing an excess of free SO_2, sulphurous acid and other sulphites.

SULPHONATED OIL. Water soluble vegetable oil much used in dyeing and printing of textiles. It is made by mixing 20 per cent to 40 per cent of concentrated sulphuric acid with the oil. Examples of this sulphonated oil include castor oil, olive oil, oleic oil, cottonseed oil, palm oil, etc. Sulphonated oil is also called alizarine oil, soluble oil, Turkey Red oil.

SULPHONE CHEMICALS. Those which change the molecular of the cotton fiber by cross-linking; used to give permanent stability to a mechanical stretch fabric.

SULPHUR. A chemical element which is the basis of all sulphur compounds. Symbol is "S."

SULPHUR BLACK. A black synthetic dye exceptionally fast to washing but very sensitive to hypochlorite solutions.

SULPHUR DIOXIDE. A colorless, gaseous compound, with a sharp odor, quickly soluble in water. Used in the manufacture of sulphuric acid, in bleaching, and as a preservative. Formula is SO_2.

SULPHUR DIOXIDE FUMES. A gas consisting of partially oxidized sulphur, SO_2. Commonly derived from the burning of sulphur. A reducing bleach. It forms sulphurous acid in contact with water and, on further oxidation, forms corrosive sulphuric acid. See WINTER DAMAGE.

SULPHUR DYES. Used only on vegetable fibers, they are insoluble in water and need the addition of sodium sulphide, which converts them into soluble substances. Fast to alkalies and washing, and fairly fast to sunlight.

SULPHURIC ACID. A colorless, exceedingly corrosive, oily liquid. Essentially a combination of sulphur trioxide and water. Also known as Oil of Vitriol, it is used in the manufacture of gun-

cotton, in calico printing, dyeing, and in almost all chemical operations, either in a factory or in the laboratory.

SULPHURS. Coal-tar derivatives used on vegetable fibers, insoluble in water. They may be made soluble by use of sodium sulphide. These derivatives are now fast to washing and sunlight. In the dissolved solution, they form leuco bodies which, when exposed to air, oxidize to the proper color or shade.

SULTAN. A silk cloth of India that is given a smooth, satin finish; may be white, natural, dyed, or printed.

SULTANE. A twilled fabric made of rayon, silk, or wool, and finished in a rough surface-effect; it is not singed or sheared. The name comes from "Sultana," the First Wife of the Sultan of Turkey.

SULTANI COTTON. Raised in lower Egypt, the cotton is of high quality but production is hindered since the fiber is easily affected by climatic conditions.

SUMAC. Any of a genus of erect, root-climbing plants which yield a resinous or milky juice. Used in dyeing and tanning.

SUNBAK®. Originally a patented fabric made by William Skinner & Sons, Inc., Holyoke, Massachusetts but now a registered trademark of Indian Head, Inc., New York City. Present day fabric of this name is made with rayon warp and rayon/acrylic blend filling. This eye-appealing, luxurious, wear-resistant rayon satin weave construction for the face has a skillfully napped fleecy-type back. The construction and texture eliminates interlining and affords warmth to the wearer. Used in coat linings, baby and children's wear, boudoir accessories, and negligees.

SUNDHORLAND SHEEP. One of the oldest breeds of sheep in Europe, this Scandia type is a mountain-climbing sheep known for its harsh, coarse fiber. The wool is used in bulky, rugged fabrics for cold-weather service.

SUNFAST. Dyed materials which will not fade under normal exposure to sunlight, under standard tests, in a fadeometer. Since no material is absolutely sunfast, the term is rather misleading. Sun-resistant is the better term to use.

SUNN. Minor bast fiber that is soft, and gray to brown in color. Quality varies considerably because of the method of preparing the stock. Sunn comes from the inner bark of the plant of that name, and its only usage is in twine. There are many names given to

this fiber: Benares, Bombay hemp, India hemp, Itarsi, Jubbulpore, Madras, Brown hemp, and Sewnee. All of the production occurs in India.

SUNSUIT. Any type of play or sports suiting whereby much of the human body is revealed, particularly the back, shoulders and legs. This type of apparel allows the rays of the sun to beat down upon the body. Sunsuits are made of cotton, silk, rayon, mixed goods, etc.

SUPER. Term applied to wool that runs better or above what would ordinarily be expected of it in working properties. The term has several rather intangible implications and should be used with care.

SUPERCOMBING. Long wool taken from the shoulder part of a fleece; this is the area where the best wool from a fleece is obtained, generally speaking. Also means first combing wool.

SUPERFLOW. A glass fiber filter fabric made of special, high-twist yarns and engineered for the maximum flow of molten aluminum to perfect purity to the particular product. Replaces expensive steel alloy screens that require periodic cleaning. Product of J. P. Stevens & Company, Inc., New York City.

SUPERIOR CHINA SILK. The best quality Chinese silk found in the Bombay, India, market; usually undyed and unbleached.

SUPER L. Registered trademark of FMC Corporation, American Viscose Division, for a rayon carpet fiber noted for its resistance to soiling.

SUPERLOFT. A twisting and untwisting process used to modify filament stretch yarns of thermoplastic nature, such as nylon. Source of this process is Leesona Corporation, Warwick, Rhode Island, where the necessary equipment is made.

SUPERPOLYMER. Giant molecules linked together in correct formation through the use of a dibasic acid and an organic acid.

SUPRAL. Viscose rayon staple made by Aktieselskapet Borregaard, Avd. Tekstil, Sarpsborg, Norway. The following tradenames are used:
1. *Supra:* the product made by the conventional method of making viscose rayon.
2. *Supral:* Tradename for the cotton-type fiber.
3. *Supralan:* Tradename for the crimped woolen-like fiber.
4. *Supracol:* Tradename for spun-dyed fiber, cotton-like and wool-like types.
5. *Suprasant:* Tradename for bleached

SUPER RAYFLEX

crimped fiber for sanitary purposes.

SUPER RAYFLEX. See American Viscose Company, Inc., Division of FMC Corporation.

SUPER RAYFLEX MR. See American Viscose Company, Inc., Division of FMC Corporation.

SUPER-SATURATED. See SATURATED.

SUPER-SENIORITY. Special seniority rights given to veterans, union officials, supervisors, and similar groups for protection or preference over other employees.

SUPER-SUPRENKA. A very strong rayon yarn used in the manufacture of tires. This yarn gives strength in cords of about 45 per cent above yarns formerly considered top quality in the tire field. The fatigue quality of the yarn is very high. Product of American Enka Corporation.

SUPIMA. Trade-mark that is the registered property of the Supima Association of America. Supima is an extra long staple cotton fiber raised in southwestern United States with a maximum staple of $1\frac{7}{16}$ inches. About 4,000 farmers raise the staple, many of them Indians who have had much success with cotton growing. The term is a combination of the word super and Pima, the great cotton county in Arizona where much of the fiber is grown. Only members of the Association raise the staple. The trade-mark is written SuPima.

SUPLES. Synonym for souple silk.

SURAH. A soft, twill-woven silk or rayon, often made in plaid effects. Surah prints are popular at times. If made of some fiber other than silk, the fiber content must be declared. Uses include neckwear, mufflers, blouses, and dress goods. Named for Surah, India.

SURAH, SATIN. 1. A very glossy surah made with a satin weave instead of the customary twill weave. 2. A highly polished surah made to simulate silk surah.

SURAH CHEVRON. Surah silk fabric with a fine herringbone twill pattern.

SURAH DE LAINE. Surah fabric in twill weave and made of silk warp and fine worsted filling.

SURAH ÉCOSSAIS QUADRILLÉ. Surah silk fabric made in tartan checks and other typical Scotch effects is called écossais quadrillé.

SURAH FANTASIE. A French dress-goods fabric made with raw silk warp and spun-silk filling. Twill weaves are used in the ground. The cloth is printed in foulard effects.

SURAH GROS COTÉ. A high-textured surah silk material finished on both sides with high luster. The warp yarn is finer than the filling yarn in this surah gros coté.

SURAT. Low-grade, staple cotton fabric, dyed or printed; much used in India for body covering.

SURCOAT, SURCOTE. A garment worn over medieval armor, often embellished with heraldic arms; an outer coat or other outer garment. It had variations, as follows: 1. *Tabard:* the front and back panels were joined under the arms at waist level. 2. *Garde-Corps* or *Herigaut:* a long, loose garment with an attached hood. The long hanging sleeves had arm-hole slits. 3. *Garnache:* Same as the tabard except that it had elbow-length cape-like sleeves.

SURETTE. French jute bagging made on a 2-and-2 basket weave.

SURFACE ACTIVE AGENT. A chemical agent which tends to concentrate at the surface when dissolved in water.

SURFACE CONTOUR. The divergence of a fabric from planeness, which may be high or rough as against low or smooth; a matelassé compared with a satin.

SURFACE FRICTION. The resistance of a fabric to slip because of its surface; designated as high or rough, as against low or slippery; a satin compared with a cassimere worsted.

SURFACE PRINTING. A comparatively inexpensive roller print method used on cheaper goods when accurate edge or cleavage lines are not essential. The rollers can be of any width and are usually of synthetic rubber.

SURFACE TENSION. A force existing across the surface of all substances. It is a contractional force and tends to hold them together. It is this force which makes raindrops round. In the case of liquids, it may be measured by suitable scientific apparatus.

Water, for example, has a surface tension of about 72 dynes as compared with oil, which has about 30. The addition of soap to water will bring it down from 72 to about 30. The two liquids of about the same surface tension will then mix easily. This is a very important factor in detergent operations.

SURFACTANTS. A contraction of "surface active agents," they are synthetic compounds which affect the interfacial forces between materials that are brought into contact in their presence. The term includes anti-foaming agents, detergents, dispersants, emulsifiers, foaming agents, penetrants, and wetting agents, etc.

SURFEL. A "fake felt" made from a complex of several polymers. Used in the headgear business, Union Carbide Corporation produces the item in which the hat body formed is later finished by the Hat Corporation of America. The felt has a soft hand and soil can be easily removed with soap and water. The article features crease resistance.

SURI. Alpaca of the superior type.

SURINAM COTTON. The white and yellowish raw cotton of Guayana which is lustrous and strong.

SURPLICE. A loose white vestment with full sleeves, worn over the cassock by the clergy of the Roman Catholic, Anglican, and Moravian churches. It is also worn by choristers.

SURTEE COTTON. Corruption of Surat, an Indian cotton.

SURTOUT. 1. A long, close-fitting man's overcoat. 2. A woman's hood with mantle attached.

SUSI, SUSAI, SUZI. Names in India for plain-weave cottons made of about 60s warp and 50s filling yarns. These yarns are imported from England, and textures in the material are about 120 x 100. The cloth has white and colored stripes in the vertical direction and is used for garb by the Mohammedans.

SUSPENSION. The picking-up, and holding in suspension in a medium, in detergent work. The picking-up of dirt from a fabric and holding it in the liquid, so that it may be discharged, is a suspending action. Dust and soot in the atmosphere are also suspension examples.

SUTI. A twisted cotton rope made in India.

SUZANI COTTON. A Turkestan cotton known for its whiteness and good staple.

SVELTE. Gracefully slender and lithe.

SWAB. A bunch, mass, or mop of soft rope.

SWADDLE. 1. (Noun) Cloth used as a band or bandage. 2. (Verb) To wrap, as a young infant, in swaddle or swaddling clothes.

SWADESHI. Includes all plain cotton cloths made in India on hand looms. These gray goods materials range in texture from 26-square to 40-square with the counts of yarn being from 8s to 16s in the warp and 4s to 20s in the filling.

SWALEDALE. A British sheep breed raised in the mountains and fells of Cumberland, Durham, North Yorkshire, and Westmoreland. As a mutton producer the sheep is second to none;

the wool is long and very coarse.

SWANETTE. A lightweight waterproof rayon fabric which retains softness and pliability; a damp cloth may be used to clean the surface of the treated material. The cloth is coated on the face with a special pyroxylin plastic finish.

SWANSDOWN. 1. Cotton material made with a modified five-end satin weave; the repeat is 10 blocks high and 5 wide; 18s warp and 24s filling are used in this fabric, which has a texture of 72 x 150. It comes in white or cream shades and is given a heavy napped finish. 2. The soft, fluffy underfeathers of the swan which are used for trimming in cloaks, dresses, nightwear. 3. A fine, soft-feeling, substantial woolen fabric, in which silk, rayon, or cotton fibers have been used to make the blend; a staple fabric for women's wear in cold weather. 4. Another name for a soft-feeling cotton flannel.

SWANSKIN. A flannel made with twill weave and closely woven. Used for work clothes.

SWATCH. A sample of cloth. A swatch is taken from each warp in the weave-shed, after a few inches of the body of the cloth has been woven, following the starting-up of the loom by the "starter-up man." The swatches are sent to the designer for final checking and approval, prior to permitting the weaver to weave out the cuts on the warp beam.

Swatches are also taken from blanket ranges that have been woven to show the new materials for the respective seasons.

In the trade, any small sample of material is often referred to by this name. Swatches are used for inspection, comparison, construction, color, finish and sales purposes.

SWEALING. 1. When dye migrates into the folds or creases during the drying of a piece of fabric. 2. When unaffected areas in fabric become soiled from improper techniques used to remove, by hand, dirt, grease, spots or stains and color from an affected area in the goods. Often occurs when water or other solvents are used to remove some blemish in the material.

SWEATER. Originally, a heavy woolen garment that would cause one to perspire. At present, it is a knitted outer garment on the order of a jacket, heavy or light in weight, and made in many styles. Worn by men, women and children, sweaters are of the coat or slipon type, and may or may not have sleeves.

SWEATERS, MEN'S AND BOYS. There are three types:
1. PULLOVER: This is usually a long-sleeved garment with either a crew, V, or turtleneck collar.

2. CARDIGAN: This may be finished with button or zipper closures, and is chiefly made with long sleeves. The name comes from the Earl of Cardigan, who led the famed "Charge of the Light Brigade," in the Crimean War, 1854–1856, when Russia opposed France, Great Britain, Sardinia, and Turkey.

3. SLEEVELESS: There are three types of this sweater:
Sleeveless pullover: This garment is identified by its V-neck.
Buttoned front: This sleeveless garment is often called a knitted vest.
Jerkin: It is usually a V-neck pullover garment consisting of a front made of woven fabric, and the back, neckline, and pocket trims of knit fabric. Some jerkins may also have button or zipper closures down the front. In such cases, it is called a vest. It should be, however, distinguished from the vest of all-knit fabric.

SWEATERS, WOMEN'S AND MISSES'. There are four basic types:
1. SLIPON, PULLOVER: It is made with any type of neckline treatment, while the sleeves may be long, short, three-quarter or batwing. Necklines include crew, turtleneck, bateau, square, V-neck, Peter Pan, etc. All except the Peter Pan and bateau are as their names imply. The bateau is a boat-shaped line, while the Peter Pan shows a pert, smart collar with rounded edges.

2. CARDIGAN: In women's wear, it is usually a button-front garment. There is a wide variety of neckline treatment. There may be a high-neck closure, plunging V, or rounded collar. Most cardigans have long sleeves, though some short-sleeve types or batwings are on the market.

3. SHRUG: An abbreviated sweater somewhat on the order of a bolero. It may or may not have a button closure. The sleeves are usually three-quarter, although some have short sleeves.

4. JACKET: It is usually of the cardigan type but is made with heavier yarn, and invariably has no closure device. It may or may not have a collar, and is usually adorned with patch pockets. A crest or similar adornment is often seen on this garment. It is of hip length and the sleeve length is long. One type of this jacket is the "cruise jacket."

SWEATING, SWEATING PROCESS. The sweating of hides until the wool is loosened so that it can be pulled out easily.

SWEATING SHEDS. Sheds where sheep are sweated prior to shearing. The animals are sent down an incline and submerged to the neck in the loosening liquor. Various solutions are used to raise and soften the yolk and suint in order to make shearing easier. Care must be exercised in sweating so as not to injure the hides of the sheep.

SWEATSHOP. A plant or work area in which the working conditions, light, heat, ventilation, and sanitary facilities are grossly neglected, a most undesirable place to work. Usually considered as a firetrap.

SWEDISH HEMP. Bast fiber from the stingless nettle plant; used for low-grade clothing, cordage, fishlines.

SWEETHEART CONTRACT. An agreement between an employer and a union which contains conditions and terms extremely favorable to the employer when compared with other labor agreements within the same business or industry. This type of contract is now outlawed by the Taft-Hartley Act, and the Landrum-Griffin Act of the Congress of the United States, 1959.

SWELL. 1. A plate situated at the back side of the shuttle box in a loom to check the motion of the shuttle. 2. Old-fashioned slang for a dandy.

"SWIF-KLEEN." This registered trademark belongs to Swift Manufacturing Company, Inc., Columbus Georgia for its soil release finish first used on its durable press line of fabrics made of 50/50 polyester-cotton in denim constructions.

SWIFT. Another name for a reel. It is a lightweight, collapsible device upon which silk or rayon skeins are spread to be unwound. The swift is an ideal device upon which to place silk or rayon, in different manageable forms, for future use.

The swift may be compared with a wheel without the usual rim. The two spokes, one on each side of the hub, of which there are six to eight sets, have a piece of string that joins them at the tips. This cord acts as a support and will form the skein as the rayon or silk is being wound onto the reel.

SWING SHIFT. A schedule of working hours, in a company operating continuously seven days a week, in which the hours and the days of the week vary each week, on a three-week cycle, to cover all the time allowed the regular shifts as time off.

SWINGLE. 1. (Noun) A two-foot wooden knifelike instrument used to beat flax. This scutcher has one thin edge and is effective in separating the woody or pithy matter in flax from the choice fibers. 2. (Verb) To cleanse, as flax, by beating with a swingle.

SWISS, SWISSE, SWISS MUSLIN. A type of thin, semitransparent muslin commonly bleached pure white and finished with considerable dressing. The fabric is usually woven plain but is often ornamented with small loom-woven dots or sprigs interspersed over the surface at close and regular intervals. From four to twenty interlacings may be used to form the sprig.

The making of swiss originated in Switzerland many years ago. At present, however, all leading cotton textile nations produce this popular fabric. Finer grades, which come under the head of "white goods," range in width from 24 to 28 inches. Used for summer dresses, aprons, pinafores, etc.

Curtain swiss comes in widths from 27 to 45 inches, and is ornamented with a variety of patterns such as stripes, sprigs, bowknots, fleur-de-lys, and fancy openwork effects. Uses include window drapes, dresser scarfs, etc. The texture of this fabric is usually coarser than that found in the dress fabric and it has less stiffening applied in finishing.

Swiss mull is a fine, plain-woven type of swiss finished with considerable dressing. Comes in widths of 28 to 36 inches. Its crisp texture makes it an ideal fabric for shirred sleeves and rather wide skirts used in women's summer gowns and frocks, when these are in vogue.

SWISS BATISTE. A sheer, opaque fabric noted for its high luster which is accompanied by special finishing and the use of special grades of long-staple cotton and Swiss mercerization.

SWISS CREPE ORGANDY. This is the same as Crepe Ondor.

SWISS DARNING. Intricate, very neat darning in which thin areas in fabric are darned and look as good as new.

SWISS EMBROIDERY. A hand- or machine-made embroidery of Switzerland in which white-over-white is used with much success.

SWISSING. Method of calendering bleached muslin and similar materials by passing them between rollers under high heat and pressure.

SWISS IRIDESCENT ORGANDY. Swiss organdy that is made with several colored yarns that are dyed prior to weaving and so arranged in the warp and in the filling as to create a changeable or iridescent effect. See SWISS ORGANDY.

SWISS LACE. Swiss embroidered net made to simulate genuine Brussels lace.

SWISS ORGANDY. This staple cotton cloth is made transparent by chemical finishing which transposes the fabric from its original muslin state into a sheer transparent fabric which can be washed or dry-cleaned and needs only ironing to restore the original crisp finish. Transparent organdy was first made in Switzerland and the present-day material, with its well-known permanent finish, was introduced in Switzerland at the turn of the present century.

SWISS RIB STITCH. Also known as the 2 x 2 rib stitch because two sets of wales or lengthwise ribs appear alternately on both sides of the knitted fabric.

SWISS TRANSPARENT. Swiss organdy.

SWISS VOILE. Fabric made from two or more ends of yarn that have been plied and twisted together. Plain shades, woven patterns, and printed effects are used to enhance the material. This cloth is also referred to as full voile when compared with "mock voile" which is made from single or unplied yarn.

SWITCH. A device used to straighten pieces of flax after the hackling operation. This wooden tool has about 22 rows of pins which project about one inch from the base wood. The tool is numbered; a 180 switch would have 180 pins in a row 7½ inches long. The rows take up a space of two inches to three inches from front to back.

SWIVEL. The name of a British inventor who in 1724 brought out a loom copied from a Dutch loom by which the shuttle was thrown through the raised and lowered warp threads by means of cog wheels. Though it was not successful, swivel-type weaving is named for him and some fabrics are made on this plan today such as swivel curtains, sprigged motifs in cottons, etc. It has been estimated that about 1,500 attempts have been made in textile history to propel or throw shuttles across a loom from one side of the raceplate to the other end or side of the loom.

SWIVEL CLOTH. This material has spots, sprigs, or small figures on a plain background. The figure is made with an extra set of filling threads woven into the fabric by a varying number of small shuttles or swivels. The shuttle is a small bobbin which works the yarn into the goods according to some motif. Swivel weaving is used for lightweight cottons, rayons, and silks in the novelty dress-goods group. See SWIVEL WEAVING.

SWIVEL DOT. 1. A small dot effect made on cloth woven on the swivel principle in weaving. 2. A flocked dot often referred to as a swivel dot since it closely resembles the latter.

SWIVEL WEAVING. The weaving of cloth with several small, expediently placed swivels which are able to produce many types of small embroidered effects on the background of a fabric.

The action of the swivels is such that they are lowered automatically to a suitable point above the warp. The pattern mechanism then causes some warp threads to be raised, forming a shed through which the swivel travels, producing the effect. Spotted brocade is made in this manner.

Incidentally, very few, if any, swivel attachments are used today since swivel effects seem to be obtained more advantageously on Jacquard looms.

SWOLLEN HEDDLE. See WRONG DRAW.

SWORD SEDGE FIBER. A strong leaf and stem bast fiber raised in Australia. The stems and leaves are cut down and bleached by the elements; used for basketwork and lines.

SWORDS. The two vertical side-bars of the beater.

S x P COTTON. One of the most sought-for cottons raised in this country. The staple is the result of crossing the Sakellarides of Egypt with the Pima of Pima County, Arizona. The present staple is 1½ inches, just a shade shorter than regular Pima. The cotton, however, gives a higher lint yield and greater gin percentage when compared with Pima.

SYL-MER. Registered trade-mark of The Dow Chemical Company for its silicone finish applied to cottons which can be machine-washed at 160° F. It provides fabrics with durable water repellence and resistance to spots, stains, and wrinkling. Imparts a soft, luxurious "hand," and the finish may be applied to some fabrics other than those of cotton.

SYMPATHETIC STRIKE. Work stoppage by employees of a company with which they have no labor dispute, as a means of support of a strike of another group of employees.

SYNDET. Ready reference and synonym for Synthetic Detergent.

SYNERGISTIC. Term used when two or more properties co-operate with one another to increase each other's effectiveness for improved end results; a combined action.

SYNTHETIC DETERGENT. The abbreviated term is Syndet. It is a cleaning agent made from chemicals, usually hydrocarbons, sulphuric acid, and sodium carbonate. It comes in several forms—paste, powder, liquid, etc. The molecules in the compound lessen the water surface tension, thereby permitting emulsion around dirt particles which can then be flushed away. It is useful when quick and thorough wetting of fabrics is desired. Varied concentrations are available for different textile processes. Home uses include laundering, dishwashing, shampooing, toothpastes, toothpowders, etc. See DETERGENT OPERATIONS, TEXTILE.

SYNTHETIC DYES. Those developed from a coal-tar base, or other sources.

SYNTHETIC FIBER. Countries other than the United States make a fine distinction between synthetic and manmade fibers. Used abroad, a synthetic fiber is one made from chemical compounds produced from basic raw materials other than cellulose. Thus, acrylic, modacrylic, nyrtil, polyester, olefin, vinyon, etc., come under this heading.

Manmade fibers, in these countries, imply only those made from cellulosic bases such as cotton linters, and from chips of spruce, pine, and hemlock trees - made from a regeneration or from a derivative of cellulose. Viscose rayon and (Bemberg) cuprammonium rayon are regenerated fibers, which, in manufacture, run from solid to liquid and then back to a solid formation, the yearn. Derivative fibers include acetate, tri-acetate.

In the United States, the term "synthetic fiber" is seldom used and is covered by the term "manmade fiber" to cover both cellulosic and non-cellulosic fibers. See Manmade Fibers.

SYNTHETIC RESIN. Complex resinous material prepared from simple organic compounds.

SYNTHETIC TEXTILES. This term is now superseded by the term Manmade (Manmade) after the Textile Products Identification Act of July 3, 1959, effective on March 3, 1960. It was used originally to classify fibers of pure or distinct chemical origin as apart from rayon and acetate, fibers which use cellulose as their base. Thus, acetate, being of cellulosic base, is not, therefore, built entirely by chemical processing. The term implied any of the so-called "non-cellulosics" as differentiated from the two "cellulosics," rayon and acetate. Other terms applied to the "non-cellulosic fibers" included "The Test Tube Fibers," "The Miracle Fibers," "The Specially Manmade Fibers." See MAN-MADE FIBERS; THE TEXTILE PRODUCTS IDENTIFICATION ACT.

SYRIAN CROCHET. Handkerchief material made in Syria to simulate crocheted lace of Eire.

T

TABLES, IMPORTANT/METRIC SYSTEM.

Distance:

1 Centimeter	0.03937 inches
1 Meter	39.37 inches
1 Kilometer	0.621 miles

Liquid:

1 Gram	15.432 grains
1 Liter	1.0567 quarts
3.785 Liters	1 gallon

Area:

Square Centimeter	.1549 square inches
Square Meter	10.763 square feet
One Hectar	2.471 acres

Weights:

1 Gram	0.03527 ounce
1 Ounce	28.35 grams
1 Kilogram	2.2046 pounds
1 Pound	0.4356 kilograms
1 Metric Ton	1.1023 English Tons
1 English Ton	0.9072 Metric Ton

Cubic Measurement:

1000 Cubic Millimeters
                    1 Cubic centimeter
1000 Cubic Centimeters
                    1 cubic decimeter
1000 Cubic Decimeters
                    1 cubic meter

1 Cubic Meter	35.3 cubic feet

Fahrenheit and Centigrade Temperatures:

Fahrenheit	Centigrade
0.	-17.8°
14°	-10°
32°	0°
50°	10°
68°	20°
86°	30°
104°	40°

TABLES, APPROXIMATE CONVERSIONS FROM CUSTOMARY TO METRIC AND VICE VERSA.

	WHEN YOU KNOW:	YOU CAN FIND:	IF YOU MULTIPLY BY:
LENGTH	inches	millimeters	25
	feet	centimeters	30
	yards	meters	0.9
	miles	kilometers	1.6
	millimeters	inches	0.04
	centimeters	inches	-.4
	meters	yards	1.1
	kilometers	miles	0.6
MASS	ounces	grams	28
	pounds	kilograms	0.45
	short tons	megagrams (metric tons)	0.9
	grams	ounces	0.035
	kilograms	pounds	2.2
	megagrams (metric tons)	short tons	1.1
LIQUID VOLUME	ounces	milliliters	30
	pints	liters	0.47
	quarts	liters	0.95
	gallons	liters	3.8
	milliliters	ounces	0.034
	liters	pints	2.1
	liters	quarts	1.06
	liters	gallons	0.26

TABLE ON MAJOR TYPES OF BATTING.

FIBER	DENSITY	RESILIENCY	SHIFTING RESISTANCE	CARE	COST
ACETATE	1.30	Fair	Fair to poor	Washable quicker drying than cotton	Inexpensive
ACRYLIC	1.18	Good	Good	Dries readily	Considered expensive
BETA fiber-GLAS	2.56	Good	Depends on structure	Dries readily	Considered expensive
COTTON	1.48	Poor-fair	Poor-fair	Washes easily and well, dries slowly	Inexpensive Very short fibers ideal for use in batting
COTTON, RESIN-SPRAYED	1.48	Better than "straight" cotton	Better than "straight" cotton	Washable and comparable treatments to be done with care	Slightly more expensive than "straight" cotton batting
DOWN ANIMAL	Varies, very low	Excellent	Poor	Drycleaning done easily and well	Most expensive but usually worth the price
NYLON	1.14	Fair-good	Good-very good	Dries rapidly	Rather expensive
POLY-ESTER	1.30 1.38	Good	Good-very good	Dries rapidly washable	Expensive lower than wool batting
WOOL	1.30	Good	Fair to poor	Use dry-cleaning	May be expensive, depending on stock used - "straight," pulled, reused, shoddy, etc.

T-7. A family of cotton fibers which through chemical treatment has been developed by the Institute of Textile Technology, Charlottesville, Virginia. T-7 is a reaction on ordinary cotton fiber, yarn, or fabric by cyanoethylation which transforms the cotton into a structurally different type of fiber. The basic chemical is acrylonitrile, which is a constituent of synthetic rubber and acrylic textiles such as Acrilan, dynel, "Orlon," Creslan, Verel, and Zefran.

The cotton retains its appearance, feel, and other characteristics but takes on new ones such as resistance to bacteria and mildew, greater strength to the cotton after exposure to wet and dry heat, and better dye reception, including those of acid dyes which formerly had no affinity for cotton.

TAAG. Another name for Sunn hemp.

TAASH. A flattened or laminated wire made of gold, silver, or copper, used for ornamentation of fabrics in India.

TAB. The area in Turkish toweling where there is no pile effect in the material; found at the beginning and the end of the toweling, its purpose is to make the pile area firmer and cause the hem to be less bulky.

TABARD. 1. Originally a short, sleeveless or short-sleeved outer garment. 2. A banner attached to a bugle. 3. The cape or cloak of a knight worn over the armor and emblazoned with his own arms.

TABARET, TABORET. 1. A strong silk drapery and upholstery fabric made with alternating stripes of satin and moiré in different colors. 2. An embroidery frame. See TAMBOUR.

TABBINET. 1. A thin moiré taffeta lining. 2. Old English term for poplin. 3. A drapery fabric made of silk warp and wool filling which has been given a watermarked finish.

TABBIS. The term refers to the Arab Quarter of Bagdad and implies a rich silk fabric given watermarked treatment. Plain weave used.

TABBY. Another name for the plain weave—the 1-up and 1-down weave. Also written as $\frac{1}{1}$. There is only one tabby or plain weave.

There is only one tabby effect in

weaves, such as the so-called Bronson or barleycorn weave. There are two tabby effects noted in the overshot-crackle weave, which is popular in hand weaving; the same arrangement is used in the "summer-winter weave." The reason for this arrangement is that the sequence in which they are used makes a difference in the final effect noted on the fabric.

TABBY BACKS. Corduroy, fustian, velvet, and similar fabrics whose back construction is made of plain weave.

TABBYING. A name sometimes used to mean moiré or watermarked effects on fabrics such as faille, voile, taffeta, etc.

TABBY VELVET. A low-grade, all-cotton velvet used for cheap coffin lining. The back of the cloth is plain-weave.

TAB COLLAR. A shirt collar with two short tabs that fasten together under the tie knot, to the neckband of the shirt, or by use of a collar button.

TABLE. This metal plate extends along the front of the Heilman comber. Its purpose is to take care of the slivers from several heads on their way to the draw box.

TABLE-COVER FABRICS. This wide range includes those made of cotton, linen, rayon, etc. Some fabrics are damask, checked fabric, crash, dobby-design fabric, etc.

TABLE DAMASK. See DAMASK.

TABLE FELT. Same as silence cloth, table padding. See MOLLETON.

TABLE PADDING. Soft cotton fabric napped on both sides, or quilted. Also known as silence cloth, it is used to protect tables and ironing boards, etc., from pressure and heat. See MOLLETON.

TABLES, CONVERSION. 1. The following may be of value to the reader:

The French gramme or English gram is a metric unit of weight. It equals 15.432 grains in troy and 1/30th of an ounce in avoirdupois.

One grain equals .0648 gram.

To change grams to grains multiply by 15.432.

To change grains to grams multiply by .0648.

To change grams to ounces multiply by .0353.

To change ounces to grams multiply by 28.35.

There are 437.5 grains in one ounce and 7,000 grains in one pound.

There are 27 $^{11}/_{32}$nds grains in one dram and 16 drams in one pound.

2. The following Table of Factors to find Equivalent Counts of Yarn may be of value to the student:

2776 divided by deniers gives Run Wool count of yarn.

5289 divided by deniers gives Cotton count of yarn.

7932 divided by deniers gives Worsted count of yarn.

160 divided by drams gives Run Wool count of yarn.

305 divided by drams gives Cotton count of yarn.

457 divided by deniers gives Worsted count of yarn.

2776 divided by runs gives Denier.

5289 divided by cotton gives Denier.

7932 divided by worsted gives Denier.

160 divided by runs gives Drams.

305 divided by cotton gives Drams.

457 divided by worsted gives Drams.

Denier times 0.0576 gives Drams.

Drams times 17.352 gives Denier.

TABORET. See TABARET.

TABOURET. French woolen fabric used in upholstery trade.

TABOURETTE. The name comes from the covering often used on a stool, so-called from its shape which resembled a tambour or shallow drum. The tabourette first came into prominence in France during the days of the Louis kings when ladies of high rank enjoyed the privilege of sitting on a tabourette in the presence of the reigning queen.

TABS. End pieces of cloth less than one yard long.

TACHETÉ. French term for spotted is tacheté.

TACHINA FLY. An insect which lays its eggs on the body of silkworms; found chiefly in warm or hot raising areas. On hatching, the eggs produce maggots which infest the silkworm, spoiling it altogether. They remain alive on their nutriment and may come forth as the cocoon develops and can even devour the filament and break the continuous two strands that comprise it.

TACKING. Woolen and worsted cloths, with the face turned in, are seamed, sewed, or basted prior to treatment in the various wet-finishing operations such as fulling, milling, washing, scouring, etc. The purpose of this is to protect the material in these more or less rugged treatments and to prevent wrinkles.

TACKING MACHINE. A sewing machine that automatically sews a definite number of stitches at one spot, cuts the thread, and raises the presser foot from the material.

TACKLE BOARD. Located at the end of a ropewalk, it is a board, frame, or post that supports the spindles used to twist the yarns.

TACKLE FALL. The cable or rope of a tackle to which force is applied.

TACKLER. British term for loom fixer.

TACKLE TWILL®. A registered trademarked fabric made by William Skinner & Sons, a division of Indian Head, Inc., New York City. This strong, snag-proof twill is constructed to maintain the desired color brilliancy on the athletic field.

Features of this popular material include deep, rich luster, water-repellency, vat-dyed fast colors, and drycleanability. Washable if handled properly, it is non-susceptible to mildew and moths if dried thoroughly before storing. Fabric weight is about 8½ ounces per square yard. Uses include football pants, softball uniforms, hockey pants, warm-up clothing, basketball uniforms, fishing garments, golf jackets, rainwear, sports jackets, and other athletic and spectator sportswear. Comes in all colors and shades.

Tackle Twill was conceived by Knute Rockne, the famous football coach at the University of Notre Dame, South Bend, Indiana. He gave his ideas and thoughts about a new type of fabric for football pants to Mr. Frank Meade, an executive with William Skinner & Sons, and Mr. Edward Meier, the textile technologist for the company. Mr. Rockne wanted to get away from the drab colors which had been used since the founding of football in 1869. He desired a material that would be smooth, slippery, and colorful; a fabric that would make tackling of his stalwarts a bit more difficult than formerly, and one that had color and flash. Mr. Rockne actually worked with Mr. Meier in developing the fabric so that it would have great abrasion resistance.

Tackle Twill made its debut at the Yankee Stadium, New York City on Saturday, November 30th, 1929 when Notre Dame met the Army team from the United States Military Academy, West Point, New York, in their annual game. The fabric - Skinner Number 8217 - was used in football pants in which the cloth was made from Skinner shoe satin, a silk-like face, and a cotton-back satin weave construction. The new uniforms worn by the team caused much comment and newspapers reporting the game gave considerable play to the "flashy pants" of the victors.

In 1937 and before nylon came upon the scene, the Skinner original Tackle Twill construction was shown at the American Football Coaches Association Annual Meeting. Some coaches were still skeptical about the fabric. Their thoughts and feelings were dispelled in due time. Its durability was proved effectively by the

2776 divided by deniers gives Run Wool

famous All-American football player and noted coach, Glenn Dobbs, who wore the same pants made of Tackle Twill for four whole seasons of play, 39 games. The first pants made with nylon warp and cotton filling were used by the Notre Dame squad against Army in the Yankee Stadium on November 1, 1941.

TADLA. Moroccan sheep noted for its white fleece which weighs approximately from four to eight pounds. Has a 3-inch staple length.

TAEL. Chinese measure of value that approximates 1⅓ ounces, avoirdupois, silver. The value varies in different localities. Compared with United States gold, in normal times, the Canton tael had a value of about 64 cents; the Shanghai about 69 cents. The value, of course, fluctuates with the price of silver, and it has changed constantly in the last fifteen years. The tael is used in buying China and Canton raw silk.

TAFFETA. A cloth supposed to have originated in Iran (Persia). The term means "twisted woven." Always a staple fabric, it is in the same class and demand as satin made of silk. The cloth is made of a plain or tabby weave and the textures vary considerably. The pickage ranges from 70 to 130 or thereabouts.

The cloth is sometimes made in changeable effects. Solid shades and fancy prints are popular in the trade as well. Taffeta is made in cord effect, plaid designs, rib effects, and in plain textures.

Taffeta is often given a moiré effect, which it takes very neatly. The silk that should be used for a good taffeta must be of the best quality and it must be worked and inspected constantly. In the "watering" of taffeta, care must be exercised so as to have the fluid just right so that the correct tone of luster will be apparent in the goods. Calendering must be done carefully since it is an easy matter to apply too much heat to the goods. Excessive heat will tender the goods.

Taffeta will not wear as long as other silk fabrics of high quality since weighting is given the material. Excessive weighting will cause the goods to crack or split. However, the weighting gives the material its characteristic property of stiffness and scroop. Much taffeta is made at present with manmade and/or synthetic yarns.

Uses of this ever-popular fabric are for slips, dresses, ribbons, waists, umbrella fabric, and evening wear.

Some popular taffetas include the following:

Faille taffeta is made with a plain or a twill weave in order to give a pronounced cross-rib effect. Paper taffeta is light in weight and treated to give a crisp, paperlike finish. Pigment taffeta is woven with pigment-dye yarns which give the goods a dull surface-effect. Tissue taffeta is a very lightweight transparent taffeta.

TAFFETA ARMURE. A plain taffeta ground is used in this silk warp and cotton filling fabric. The armure or brocade effects are woven into the cloth by the use of 5-shaft satin weaves, either warp-effect or filling-effect, or in a combination of these.

TAFFETA FACONNE. A taffeta made on a dobby or a Jacquard loom so that it will show novelty or fancy weave effects. See FACONNE.

TAFFETA FLEURÉ. A silk or rayon taffeta colored with brocaded floral effects of small size. The designs may be printed or woven. The term fleuré comes from French, meaning "flowered."

TAFFETA GLACÉ. The French word "glacé" means glazed or lustrous. Hence, a changeable or an iridescent taffeta brought about by the use of two harmonious or contrasting colors in the fabric, such as a red rayon warp and a blue acetate filling. Most of this type of cloth is now cross-dyed. Good calender finish enhances the luster on the goods.

If made with silk yarns the texture is "twice as many ends as picks," such as 180 x 90. Several of the man-made fibers are now being used to make this attractive material.

TAFFETALINE, TAMTINE. A plain weave taffeta skirt lining made from schappe silk; comes in several grades. See SCHAPPE SILK.

TAFFETA LINING. It is made from silk, Bemberg rayon, viscose rayon, acetate, etc., and there is a great variance in quality and price. Used much for linings in women's dresses, gowns, etc. Some of this material is often called faille, since faille and taffeta seem to be more or less interchangeable in some circles today. Incidentally, taffeta is a fabric that is often emasculated in texture and quality, and any purchase of taffeta or faille should be preceded by a thorough inspection of the fabric and the garment made from the cloth. Fine, cylindrical cotton yarn may be used as filling in some taffetas and failles.

TAFFETA METALLIQUE. One that is given a finish to simulate metal, such as a gold, copper, or silver effect.

TAFFETA POINTILLE. British term for a taffeta made with small, intriguing motifs, either on a dobby

loom or a Jacquard loom.

TAFFETA RIBBON. One that is made in the tabby or plain weave, compact in structure, dull in luster, and harsh or stiff in hand. Now made from several of the man-made fibers, often with cotton filling being used. Some of the better grades, of course, use silk warp and filling. Some of this ribbon is made with acetate yarn in a wide width that is then cut into the desired ribbon width by a cutting blade or blades heat-sealed so that when the strips are cut the edges will sear and form a compact edge which actually serves as a selvage to the goods and prevents the possibility of raveling.

TAFFETAS BOYAUX. Taffetas with check motifs in them are known by this term in Great Britain.

TAFFETAS CHINE. A silk or nylon taffeta in which the warp yarns were warp-printed prior to the weaving of the fabric on the loom; gives a mottled or mélange effect on the material.

TAFFETAS PRISMATIQUE. Originated in France, it is a material made with the colors of the spectrum or some other combination that attracts the eye. This plain-weave fabric is all-silk, all-nylon, or with some comparable fiber content, and in finishing of the goods they are sent through contacts of heated engraved rollers in which the gougings have produced very fine lines to fit the bars or stripes of the various colors. Thus, the hill-and-dale effect makes it possible to reflect the rays of light and add to the scintillating effect observed in the cloth. The process is actually schreinering of the fabric. See SCHREINER FINISH.

TAFFETAS ROYALE. A taffeta made with multicolored warp stripes or with warp and filling striped effects. These effects are usually rather bizarre in design and in some cases outlandish. Used for dress goods, boleros, gloria goods, these fabrics may be all-silk, all-rayon, all-acetate, etc., or in combinations of several different types of yarn in order to bring out a medley of colors, usually by cross-dyeing the goods. Some of the material is also yarn- or skein-dyed.

TAFFETA UNI. An ordinary staple taffeta fabric that has been piece-dyed a single color, or the French taffeta that is made with organzine silk warp and tram filling and piece-dyed to obtain a single shade.

TAFFETA WEAVE. Same as plain weave. See Illustrated Section.

TAFFETINE. A slightly sized, plain-weave, lightweight lining fabric of high texture made of organzine warp and coarse cotton, linen, or tram fill-

TAG CLOTH. Same as LABEL CLOTH.

TAGLOCK. A matted, encrusted, or tangled lock of wool or hair.

TAGS. Matted, undesirable, skirted pieces from a fleece. They are also stained and have no value. Sheep-pen sweepings are called tags.

TAIHORE HEMP. The best quality New Zealand hemp.

TAIL COAT. A coat with tails; a swallow-tailed coat. Also known as full dress.

TAILED COTTON. Tailed or stringy cotton is the result of ginning the cotton when it was too moist or wet.

TAIL-END. The opposite of head-end, it is the tail-end or finishing-end of a cut, bolt, or length of woolen or worsted cloth.

TAILING. A textile printing expression used when colors bleed or run into each other.

TAILINGS. The short pieces of cloth in some particular consignment.

TAILLEUR. A suit or dress that is tailored and well-fitting.

TAILLURE. French for appliqué work.

TAILOR. A worker who performs a variety of hand or machine tailoring operations in the manufacture of, or the alteration of, ready-to-wear apparel. The full-fledged tailor should be able to perform all the various hand-sewing and pressing operations required to make the garment.

The tailor should be able to work in any of the major sections or departments in the establishment and may be called upon for specialized or unusual work assignments, including repairs necessary in carrying on production.

TAILORED GARMENT. There are two aspects to this term, one refers to style, the other to workmanship.
Tailored Styling: This refers to apparel that is form fitting, with the basic style lines used in men's business suits and topcoats. A tailored garment holds a fixed shape approximating the human anatomy in the same way as does a man's business suit, with little or no fullness incurred by gathers or draped flares.
Tailored Workmanship: This refers to the precision and finish of the seams and the stitching. All sewing must be precise with regard to even stitch size, seam and stitching widths, and the alignment of sewing lines (devoid of crookedness or kinks). Also, no seam of the finished garment should show a raw edge to the wearer or viewer; a raw seam edge is any fabric edge that can fray or permit cut yarn ends of a fabric edge (knitted or woven) to separate toward the seam's sewing line.

The seam edges must be bound, overcast, piped, hidden in the seam, or hemmed in such a way that yarn fray or yarn-end protusion is prevented. Tailored workmanship or tailoring does not refer to hand sewing as such; it does not matter whether the sewing is done by hand or machine; what makes a garment tailored pertinent to workmanship follows: 1. Sewing and pressing precision. 2. Finished seams with no fray or protusion. 3. A press that gives the finished garment the smooth and shapely silhouette that it is supposed to have, without wrinkles or uncalled-for creases on the surface of the goods used.

Though ladies' or men's garments may be tailored relative to style, if there are pinked seams or exposed raw edges, these articles are not considered tailored relative to workmanship. For instance, when the style is tailored, but the shape does not hold up well because of improper interlining in the garment, then the garment is not well tailored. Inversely, a garment may be tailored relative to workmanship but not to styling. For example, bush jackets are not tailored garments pertinent to style regardless of whether or not they are highly tailored for workmanship.

The following are rarely, if ever, associated with tailored garments.
1. *In Styling:* Gathering, shirring, draping, fullness, smocking.
2. *In Fabric:* Chiffon, lace, marquisette, net, tulle, etc.

TAILOR-MADE. Made by a tailor or according to a tailor's fashion; said particularly of women's garments with trimness of fit, simplicity of line and ornament, and nicety of finish.

TAILOR'S CHALK. There are now two types in use—clay chalk, sometimes referred to as stone, and wax chalk. Chalk comes in various colors. Wax chalk is used on woolens and worsteds, while clay chalk is used on linings, cottons, lightweight fabrics and light colored materials including woolens and worsteds.

TAILOR'S SQUARE. A measuring device used by designers and dressmakers. It consists of two rules, one longer than the other, connected at right angles and fastened at joint with brass clasp.

TAILOR'S TACK. Any method of thread marking used by a tailor.

TAILOR'S TWIST. The coarse, strong silk ply thread used by tailors.

TAKE. A row of pile tufts in handmade rugs.

TAKE-HOME PAY. The net amount of wages received by an employee after the company has made all the required deductions.

TAKER-IN. Synonymous with licker-in. An auxiliary roller used on carding machines; aids in delivery of stock from the feeding-in end of the frame to the main cylinder on the frame.

TAKE-UP. 1. The bending of the warp ends over the filling picks in a fabric as it is being woven. The warp ends—say, thirty inches long—would be longer in the straightened length than in the woven length. If there was a 10 per cent take-up in the warp in weaving, the straightened length would have to be thirty-three inches, as the yarn unwinds from the warp beam in the loom. Allowances have to be made for this take-up when dressing the warp.

2. Shrinking-in, when a fabric is finished, is sometimes referred to as take-up. This occurs when the material, in both warp and filling directions, contracts because of the wet operations in finishing the goods. The average worsted, for example, is set around 62 inches in the reed to finish at 56 inches. Allowances have to be made for this shrinking-in when figuring the cost per yard of the material.

3. A device on a knitting machine to draw off fabric as it is knitted. It rolls up the fabric on some machines to make removal easier and also exerts pull on the fabric to assure correct cast-off of the loops.

TAKE-UP MOTION. See LOOMS, CHIEF MOTIONS OF.

TAKE-UP ROLL. The sand roll on a loom. Prevents cloth slippage.

TAKROUSI HEMP. Another name for hemp from Arabia.

TAL. The palmyra leaf fiber used for making brushes of many types.

TALANCHE. A plain or striped coarse fabric made from flax and wool. This French cloth is made into clothing for the poorer classes.

TALBOT COTTON. A fine, silklike Mississippi cotton, which measures up to 35 millimeters, with a lint yield of less than 30 per cent.

TALC. Often used as a weighting agent instead of China Clay, it is smooth, easily mixed, and free from granules. It affords yarn pliability, has good adhesive properties, and is very fine in substance. Talc will not tend to give iron stains by acting on metallic parts of machinery with which fabric may come in contact while being processed.

TAL FIBER. The harsh, wiry, leaf fiber from the Palmyra palm found in India. Used for brushes.

TALITAN RUGS. Lightweight cotton rugs made with an overcast edging and used as bed covers in parts of China.

TALLOW. A solid fat which contains palmitic, stearic, and a small amount of oleic acid, used as a basis for ordinary laundry soaps, giving a titer of 40 degrees.

TALMA. Named for the great French tragedian, Talma, this long cape or cloak, often made with a hood attached, was very popular in the early nineteenth century. In due time, the shorter shoulder cape became known as a Talma and it is still known by this name today.

TAMAS OR NOSHITO JOSHIU SILK. The poorest quality of waste silk that is used in the manufacture of spun silk yarns in Japan.

TAMINE, TAMINY. Very likely a contraction of stamen, a type of very coarse linsey-woolsey cloth of England. Tamine differs from the ancient stamin cloth in that it is a thin, lightweight woolen or worsted that is given a glazed finish. See STAMIN; STAMEN.

TALON. Trade name for a popular slide-fastener or zipper.

TAMAITO. A grade of silk waste obtained from douppioni silk.

TAMAMAYU. A doupion cocoon which is made possible when two or more cocoons spin together.

TAMBOUR. 1. A term which signifies work done on the embroidery machine in which the tambour stitch has been used. This stitch produces a pattern of straight ridges which cross each other in every direction at right or acute angles. 2. Tambour is also a variety of Limerick lace that is made in Ireland. 3. Embroidery frame, round.

TAMBOUR MUSLIN. A fine open muslin with clear appearance used for curtains, embroideries, etc.

TAMIS. A plain-weave, open-mesh worsted cloth used for sieve and straining purposes.

TAMMY, TAMMIE. A 26-inch, plain-weave cloth of cotton warp and wool filling. Piece-dyed, heavily glazed, and used for underskirts, linings.

TAM-O'-SHANTER. Cap of Scottish origin, with broad, round, flat top, and tightly fitted headband. Usually has a knot or tassel in the center.

TAMPICO FIBER. Often referred to as istle, it is a hemp used in making brushes, rough cordage, and baskets.

TAN. A yellowish- or brownish-red color, the color of tanned leather.

TANAG. A rugged, coarse leaf fiber raised in the Philippine Islands and used for cordage.

TANCAO HEMP. Raised in the Philippine Islands, this manila hemp is a strong, lustrous, white fiber.

TANDEM. An average grade of plain-weave, bleached linen fabric made in Silesia.

TANDEM FEEDER. In processing cotton into a regular gin bale form, the opening machine used is equipped with a tandem or double hopper feed arrangement.

TANG. An Indian plain-weave cloth made on hand looms. Used locally, this muslin is textured around 50 x 44 with 44s to 50s cotton yarns used.

TANGLE. 1. (Verb) To intertwine or be intertwined in a confused or conglomerate mass, not readily separable. 2. (Noun) A mass or mess of fiber, stock, yarn, etc.

TANGUIS COTTON. This rough Peruvian cotton is about 1¼ inches in staple length with small amounts averaging 1⅛ inches and 1½ inches in length.

TANJIBS. Lightweight English cotton goods made of 30s to 40s yarn. Two fancy headings appear in the center. Light sizing is given the material, which is shipped to India and the East.

TANNAGE, VEGETABLE. A generic term indicating the process of making leather by the use of barks or extracts from plants and trees.

TANNER'S WOOL. Synonymous with the lime process used to obtain pulled wool (that taken from dead sheep) from the pelt of the animal.

TANNIC ACID. An acid substance of vegetable origin, derived from the bark of oak, hemlock, and other trees. It is used as a mordant for fixing basic dyes on cotton. Tartar emetic is used to fix the tannic acid on the cotton. Formula is $C_6H_2(OH)3 \cdot CO_2$, or $C_6H_2(OH)_2 \cdot CO_2H$. See TARTAR EMETIC.

TANNIN. A group of amorphous, brownish-white, astringent compounds that form shiny scales when extracted, as with water, from gall nuts, sumac, etc. Chief uses are in applications in the dyeing of textiles, preparation of inks, and in the manufacture of leather. See TANNIC ACID.

TAPA. A cloth or matting made from any of the fibers or barks peculiar to the Pacific Islands as Tapa (Marquesas); Kapa (Hawaiian). Mulberry and similar barks are steeped, hackled, and made into yarn, which is woven into fabric formation to serve as floor covering or clothing.

TAPALOS. Mexican shawls noted for the multicolored effects.

TAPE. A narrow, stout strip of woven or braided fabric; also a tape measure.

TAPE CONDENSER. Located at the delivery end of the last card in the set, its purpose is to divide the full-width web of fibers, as they leave the doffer roller, into a series of narrow strips. The number of strips range from 60 to 200 dependent on the type of condenser being used. The strips of webbing are condensed by an agitating motion and sets of endless aprons into a roving form. These rovings are then wound onto a jack spool with a range from 15 to 50 if a four-bank condenser is used on the frame.

The rubbing apron action and the devices used for spool winding are very ingenious. Some cards serve a three-bank condenser instead of the usual four-bank type.

TAPED ENDS. Term which signifies that two or more ends are drawn through the same heddle eye and weave as a single yarn with the filling.

TAPE DRIVING. An endless, woven cotton tape or banding used on ring spinning and similar frames to drive the spindles. Each tape drives four spindles, two on each side of the machine. The banding goes around the cylinder drum of the frame, and the tension is regulated by a tension pulley about which the tape also travels.

TAPE-EDGE MACHINE. A sewing machine that is mounted and powered to move on tracks around a table. The head of the machine is set inward at an angle to grip the edges of a mattress cover laid on the table, and is provided with an attachment to feed and sew tape over the seams.

TAPE-FINISHED HEM. A hem in which the edge is not turned under in regular manner but has a narrow, ribbon-like tape, known as seam tape or seam binding, attached by stitching to cover the raw edge. The other edge of the tape is then hemmed to the garment by hand or machine.

TAPE LACE. 1. Linen thread lace as differentiated from cotton or silk lace. 2. Handmade needle lace on the order of Renaissance lace.

TAPE SELVAGE. See SELVAGE, TAPE.

TAPERED ROPE. A rope made with the strain-bearing portion larger than the rest of the length.

TAPER GEAR. The change gear on a roving frame which controls the even taper of the bobbins on the machine.

TAPE SIZING. Same as slashing.

TAPESTRY. This picture material, woven tightly or loosely and low in construction, has the design as a part of the actual fabric; it is not embroidered onto the cloth. Tapestry is handwoven or power-loomed. The design and color in hand-woven tapestry is very neat and realistic. Some of the larger tapestries took several generations to complete because of the slow task of working the filling over and under the warp threads according to the motif.

The Oriental nations—China, Japan, India, Arabia, Persia, and Egypt—were noted for their tapestries. In time, Greece and Rome, as their civilization progressed, also made tapestries. During the third century, the Copts produced some outstanding pieces. During the Middle Ages, tapestries were woven in European monasteries. The weaving of these fabrics was an important contribution to the world during the Gothic era and the fifteenth century. Religious and moral motifs were used.

The sixteenth and seventeenth Centuries were marked by the fine work of the Gobelin Factory in France. Many tapestries which are still extant from these times are worth thousands of dollars and adorn museums, salons, and wealthy homes.

The past two centuries have witnessed the rise of the power loom tapestry, which keeps pace with the hand-woven fabrics.

Some of the better known tapestry motifs and types include Arras, Aubusson, Beauvais, Brussels, Gobelin, Gothic, Lille, Savonnerie, and Verdures. See Illustrated Section (Fabrics 71).

TAPESTRY BACKING. A carpet backing made with one shed formed by the chain warps in which two filling picks, often separated by a stuffer warp, are sent into the loom for each row of pile tufts, thereby creating a two-plane weave construction to the back formation. Thus, there is one formation above the stuffer warp while the second is below this stuffer. The top plane contains the filling pick about which the tufts are wound. After each series of the two picks has been completed, the chain warps change their position for the formation of the weave for the successive row of tufts. This type of construction adds substance and body to the fabric. See CARPET CHAIN WARP, CARPET PICK.

TAPESTRY BRUSSELS. A misno-

mer applied to tapestry carpeting, since it, like Brussels carpet, has a looped pile effect.

TAPESTRY CARPET. Woven on a simple loom where the surface yarns are supplied from the rear of the loom as warp ends. They are lifted over round pile wires, which, when withdrawn, leave uncut loops to form the face of the fabric.

The qualities may vary from the very lowest to a heavy hooked type that resembles the hand-hooked native New England carpets. Plain colors may also be used with a striking effect in this looped construction for both decorative value and very good wear.

The pattern is obtained by dyeing the desired shades on the outer warp strands of the yarn as designated by the warp direction of the designer's motif on design paper. When raised over the pile wire, each warp end contributes the correct color in the required space.

TAPESTRY FABRIC. Many types of fabrics are made with woven or printed designs to simulate genuine tapestry, hence the name. Much of the material is of cotton content, but linen, spun acetate, spun rayon, etc., are also used. Some cloth under this name is very popular as a staple item in apparel, such as cotton fabrics printed with tapestry motifs that are interesting and intriguing. Other uses for the fabric include curtains, drapes, and some upholstery goods.

TAPESTRY QUILT. Made on a Jacquard loom with two or more colors in the warp and several in the filling, this cloth will show more or less of an allover tapestry motif in which the repeat of pattern may be large or small. Used for bed-covering, counterpanes, quilting, etc. This material is classed as a single fabric since a double cloth or backed construction is not resorted to in the weaving of the goods, as in the case of brocade and brocatelle.

TAPESTRY STITCH. Similar to the Gobelin stitch used in making the famous Gobelin tapestries.

TAPESTRY-VELVET CARPET. A cut-pile effect is the feature of this warp-printed carpet. SETTING; See Illustrated Section.

TAPESTRY WOOL. Wool about twice the size of crewel wool; this heavy filling yarn is used for embroidery work and weaving.

TAPIOCA. The cassava plant is the base for this adhesive sizing agent, made from its heated moist starch; there are better adhesives on the market, and tapioca may often be subject to adulteration.

TAPIS. French term for carpet, often applied to Oriental fabrics.

TAPISSENDIS. A duplex-printed Indian fabric of the calico or muslin type that is used for curtaining, scarves, shawls, etc.

TAPISSERIE. The French word for several items such as carpeting, fancy needlework, tapestry, upholstery, curtaining, etc. The term is often used with one or more words to signify a particular fabric, such as Tapisserie de Rouen, a tapestry fabric made in Rouen, France.

TAPISSERIE DE VERDURE. A genuine tapestry or some sort of tapestry cloth made to simulate true tapestry in which the motifs show rustic, bucolic, pastoral, or landscape scenes.

TAPPA CLOTH. Made by the natives of the Marquesas Islands, from bark, this appealing white material is not a woven fabric but comes as the result of beating fibrous substance together. When dyed with vegetable dyes the color is fast.

TAPPET. British term for cam.

TAPSEL. A British cotton cloth exported to the African trade in which stripes are used in the pattern repeat; black, blue, brown, red, and similar colors in intensity feature the stripe effect. Tapsel is made with plain-weave and the yarn counts range from 16s to 24s.

TAPTI. Hand-woven, plain-weave cotton fabric made in India in which stripes or checks are used for the design. Used by the women for skirts, dress goods, scarves, etc.

TAR. It comes from sources such as cigarettes, oil, wood, cotton, bituminous coal, etc. For example, the distillation of bituminous coal produces a dark brown liquid of very heavy viscosity. It is used to make coal tar in certain plastics, dyes, and explosive materials.

TARA ARMENI. A very old staple cloth made in Kashmir, India, with cashmere or cashmere and wool. This fabric comes in squares which run from 54 inches up to 90 inches. Much of it is sent to other countries, and the fabric is usually designed with patterns representative of the nations that purchase the squares.

TARARE. 1. An unbleached linen or hemp fabric used for aprons and furniture covering. Textured around 42-square, it is made in plain-weave. 2. There is a gauze fabric of this name that has been long made in Tarare, France. Warp stripes feature the material, which is made with a silk warp and cotton filling. The cotton stripe-effect yarn is a 2/20s with the silk warp around 70 denier, while the filling is very fine, around 2/140s. 3. A curtain fabric used in France that is made of all-linen, all-cotton, or in a combination of these two fibers.

TARE. Burlap, bagging, ties, cooperage, etc., used on bales of textile fibers in shipping. It ranges from 2 to 5 per cent of the total weight of the shipment.

TARLATAN, TARLETAN. Thick or thin scrim, heavily starched and netlike. Originated in Italy, where it was made of linen and cotton. The cloth was once coarse and low in texture. Today, tarlatan is made of either carded or combed yarn. It is used for fruit packing, dresses, coat linings, and in the sewing and millinery trades because of the heavily sized finish which makes it ideal for waist banding and hat lining. Tarlatan comes in white and colors. When flame-proofed, it is used for theatrical gauze and stage draping.

TARMATE. Waste silk from stained or otherwise imperfect cocoons is called tarmaté or taroté.

TARNISH PREVENTION. Chemical treatment can inhibit the action of atmospheric gases and body reagents which would cause tarnishing. The type of treatment decides how effective it will be. Any claim as to tarnish prevention should describe its effectiveness.

TARPAULIN. 1. Canvas or nylon fabric usually coated to make it waterproof so that it may serve as a protection against inclement weather. Finds great use in covering athletic diamonds and fields. 2. A sailor's "storm hat" is sometimes called a tarpaulin.

TARRED ROPE. Ropes made of hemp and jute for marine use are impregnated with tar to help them resist action on them by water, which causes eventual "water-rot." Nylon, "Dacron," and polyethylene ropes are not treated with tar.

TARS, CLOTH OF. A medieval fabric that originated in either Tarsus or Tartary and originally called Tarsicus if it came from Tarsus (a seaport in southern Turkey in Asia, on the Mediterranean Sea and the birthplace of St. Paul) and Tartaryn if it came from Tartary (a region of Asia and eastern Europe, varying in extent at different periods in history). Blue and gold were the predominating colors, the latter being used chiefly for embroidery purposes. Some of the cloth was white or green.

TAR STAINS. Stains that come sometimes when tar is used to mark the ends of bolts of cloth for identification purposes. Carelessness in its use will allow it to seep through to other parts of the cut. These stains are not soluble in any bleaching compound, but may be removed by some solvent such as benzene or turpentine. Such marks can also be made on cloth while it is in transit, by tarpaulin covers used to protect the material from the elements. These stains should not occur if the goods are given good care.

TARTAN. Sometimes known as Tartan Plaid or Scotch Plaid, it is a conventionalized, multicolored fabric, the outstanding material of which is kilt cloth. Plaids are used for blankets, certain silks, many types of dress goods, neckwear, ribbon, etc. The popular plaid was given to the world by the well known Scotch Clans of Campbell, Cameron, MacPhee, MacDonald, MacPherson, Douglas, Stuart, etc.

The word, formerly spelled "tartanem," was borrowed from the English who derived the term from the Spanish "tiritana." The Spaniards used this term, as far back as the thirteenth century, to imply colored fabrics, usually vivid in color. The Scotch have capitalized on tartans more than any other nation and the general belief is that these were Scotch in origin. The Gaelic term is breacan or tarsuin, a cross-barred fabric.

Incidentally, in the true sense of the word, a tartan is a pattern or design, while the plaid is a blanketlike mantle folded in several ways and joined at the left shoulder by a brooch. Unfortunately, the words tartan and plaid are often used interchangeably in meaning. True tartan fabric is 26 inches square.

Seven or more yards of fabric are needed to make a complete kilt outfit for an adult. The 2-up and 2-down, right-hand twill weaves are used to make the material; some of it, however, is made from plain weave.

In woolen, worsted, and "mixture fabrics," in subdued effects at times, tartan material is used as suiting cloth and periodically enjoys a great wave of popularity in coats and jackets in the casual and sports groups. Tartans are also made of cotton, silk, and other major fibers and filaments.

TARTAN ALL-WEATHER SURFACE. The inspiration for this fabulous surface belongs to Mr. John Nerud, horse trainer for Mr. William L. McKnight, owner of the well-known Tartan Stables. Mr. Nerud unveiled his idea in 1959 in an attempt to cope with poor track conditions caused by unseemly weather which disrupted his stable's training program.

Mr. McKnight, Chairman of the Board for Minnesota Mining & Manufacturing Company, Inc., St. Paul, Minnesota set his research and development group to work on the project. Within two years their efforts were ready to bear fruit.

The formula for this product is kept a well-guarded secret and it is said to be known to only about six persons in all. The mixture is one of synthetic resins, meaning that a combination of polymers and/or elastomers is apparent. This leads to the formation of resilient plastics.

The product is resilient, does not allow slippage, is not affected by inclement weather, and does not wear out or deteriorate. While initial costs may be classed as high, upkeep requires only the use of a broom.

In 1959, the first surface was used to cover a one-eighth of a mile training oval installed outside the Nerud barn at Belmont Park, New York City. It is still in use. Mr. Delvin Miller, a harness racing owner-driver-trainer entrepreneur installed Tartan in a five-eighths of a mile track in The Meadows, a harness racing track in Washington, Pennsylvania. This was done in 1963. Laurel, Maryland, track installed one in 1964; Windsor, Ontario, track laid a Tartan track in 1965 and Tropical Park, Miami, Florida, in 1966.

To broaden the venture even further, the company turned to track and field college meets. In 1963, Macalester College, St. Paul, Minnesota, became the first school to set a Tartan outdoor running track. The University of Pennsylvania, Philadelphia, Pennsylvania made headlines in its Penn Relays in April, 1967. Many new records were set during this two-day track meet and everyone present marveled at this new type of track for athletes.

Tartan is laid from a two-section truck. The front section pours the liquid which hardens within fifteen minutes. The rear section drops the ground-up Tartan to provide the textured surface.

On a running track for athletes, a base is prepared of gravel with six to ten inches the ideal depth. The base is then topped with asphalt, one to two inches in thickness. The Tartan compound is then applied three-eighths to one-half inch in depth. Five-eighths to one inch is the depth used for thoroughbred and harness track racing.

Initial costs may be classed as expensive. A Tartan racetrack will cost from $750,000 to one-million dollars, exclusive of curbing, drainage, and base. A quarter-mile running track for athletes runs to about $100,000.00.

Tartan can be used for playgrounds,

rooftops, ship decks, and comparable purposes. There is also a Tartan lawn green, as well as a Tartan black for use in a driveway. Initial price of the products was around $3.50 per foot or about $30.00 per square yard. Prices will gradually become lower in accordance with the economic law of supply and demand. See Astro-Turf.

TARTAN CHECKS. Cotton dress goods made with standard Scotch plaids in the pattern. Plain or twill weave may be used, and much of the fabric today does not follow the standard plaid formation. The term is very broad in meaning.

TARTAN VELVET. Velvet with tartan or plaid motifs; the goods are given a close-cropped or sheared finish.

TARTANELLA. Term for tartan plaids made from combinations of cotton, linen, rayon, and/or wool fibers.

TARTAR EMETIC. The common name for potassium antimonyl tartrate, a substance used in medicine to induce vomiting; also used to mordant cotton and to fix basic dyestuffs. Formula is $K(SbO)C_4H_4O_6 \cdot H_2O$. Used to fix tannic acid on cotton.

TASAR SILK. The original name for Tussah or Tussore—wild silk.

TASHIARI. A very strong and durable Indian bast fiber that is used for twine and cordage.

TASLAN. A textured yarn that is different from spun yarn or continuous filament yarn in that it is made on a bulking process developed by E.I. du Pont de Nemours & Co., Inc. Its hand, loftiness, covering power, and yarn texture are such that these properties are permanent and do not require special handling or care. The method may be applied to any thermoplastic fiber.

TASMANIAN WOOL. Very high-grade merino wool from Tasmania. Compared with adjacent Australian merino, it is a trifle shorter in staple but possesses excellent working properties and is used only in the best of fabrics.

TASSEL. Ornament on clothing or upholstery. The head of a tassel is usually a covered button or a mold; the tassel is made of strands, yarn, thread or cord hung loosely from the head. Any of the major fibers may be used. Officers' uniforms, regal apparel, flags, programs, and some curtains are embellished by tassels.

TATAJA. See COURATARI.

TATAMI. Japanese for matting used as floor covering.

TAT CHOTEE. Indian name for jute cloths.

TAT PATTI. Sunn hemp or low quality goat hair are used to make this Indian floor-covering. The poorer grades are used to make bagging.

TATTA. A roll-up window and door screen used in the Far East to cool air coming into rooms; made of loosely meshed plant splints, notably bamboo. The screen is moistened with water, thereby cooling incoming air by evaporation.

TATTE MAT. An Indian matting made from certain long grasses or jute in which there is a loose, open construction.

TATTERSAL. A heavy, fancy woolen vesting of "loud appearance." Checks, bold effects and gaudy color combinations are used in the material which is often used for some suiting and overcoating, as well. Named for the famous mart for thoroughbred and racing stock in London.

TATTING. Making lace by hand with a small shuttle, wherein it is possible to make small loops, thereby giving delicate motifs. Used for collars, trimmings, insertion work, and doilies. A hard-twisted yarn is used to enhance the small picots.

TATTING COTTON. See TATTING.

TAUTER. Comparable with Oxford and Shropshire breeds of England, this Norwegian sheep breed is shorn bi-annually.

TAVELLETE OR TAVELL SYSTEM. A method for reeling silk whereby the filaments, as they unwind from the cocoons in the reeling basin, pass through a porcelain guide eye in an upward direction. Another guide eyelet, set above the lower guide, causes the filaments to take a perpendicular course to the reel or swift upon which the silk skein is formed and wound to the capacity desired as to yardage.

TAXILI COTTON. A variety of Macedonian cotton.

TAYLOR COTTON. 1. A small-boll, short-staple Alabama cotton. 2. A large-boll, long-staple South Carolina cotton.

T-BLOUSE, T-SHIRT. See KNITTED SHIRTS.

TCHARHZD. Hand-knotted, small, square Persian rugs.

TCHEMBERT. A white, fancy or novelty muslin fabric used for dress goods in the Levant.

TCHESMA COTTON. A coarse grade of cotton raised in Macedonia, inferior to Taxili.

T-CLOTH. Low grade cotton cloth made in English mills, marked with a "T" and sold in the Asiatic trade.

TEAR. Used to give the relation, in the worsted combing operation, between top versus noil in terms of percentage. The ratio is 10 to 1.

TEARDROP. Taffeta, moiré taffeta, rep, and faille when the filling picks in the woven goods are slightly off-angle, a rather common occurrence in the lower qualities and textures.

TEARING GOODS. British-made cottons and linens for the African export trade.

TEARING MACHINE. See GARNETTING.

TEARING STRENGTH. Implies the force needed to begin or to continue a tear in a cloth under specified conditions.

TEASE. 1. Raising the nap of fabrics. 2. To open a fibrous mass.

TEASEL CLOTH. A broad term applied to napped fabrics.

TEASEL RAISING GIG. See NAPPING.

TEASELING. See NAPPING.

TEASELS. Plant burrs grown in Belgium, France, and other European countries and in Oregon and Washington in this country. Auburn, New York, is known as a teasel-raising center in the East. Teasels grow from one to two inches in length and about one inch in diameter. They are tough and have the appearance of a porcupine.

The teasels, as used in textile finishing of fabrics, are set snugly in grooves in the napping machine cylinder which comes in contact with the cloth and raises the loose fibers to form a nap. Because teasels wear down in about a week's time every fifth row is usually replaced each morning. Since the teasels cover the entire surface of the napping roller, the cloth receives a rigid brushing so as to create the nap effect. Teasels have been replaced in the United States with the use of steel brushes, nylon brushes, or plastic burrs. They are still used in Europe but to a lesser degree than formerly.

TEBELIZED. A crush-resistant finish applied to many fabrics, including pile fabrics, and giving material the power to resist creasing, mussing and crushing as well as to recover from wrinkling during wear. The fabric remains the same after washing. The finish is controlled by Tootal, Broadhurst & Lee Company, Ltd.

TECAFIL. An Eastman Chemical Products, Inc., trade-mark for a true spun yarn made up of fibers of various lengths rather than customary uniform lengths. It is made directly from tow or strand of continuous filament, using a modification of the patented Perlok

System of continuously breaking and drafting the parallel filaments to form a roving, which is then drafted and twisted into a yarn.

TECUN FIBER. Strong leaf fiber raised in Brazil and Peru, used for fishing nets and lines.

TEDDY BEAR CLOTH. A cheap wool and mohair pile cloth first used as a covering for Teddy bears. The long nap is raised in finishing the cloth.

TEFLON. A tetrafluoroethylene polymer fiber of E. I. DuPont de Nemours & Company, Inc., Wilmington, Delaware, the sixth manmade fiber to be marketed by this company. It has outstanding resistance to high frequencies, and high temperatures; possesses highest degree of chemical inertness of any commercial plastic, and nothing will stick to it. Teflon is also known as the *TFE Fluorocarbon Fiber* and in fiber-yarn formation may be woven, knitted, braided, etc. Teflon fiber retains all the characteristics of the resin. It has the lowest coefficient of friction of any fiber known. Fabric structures made of Teflon are widely used where exposure to excessive heat or corrosive chemicals is a factor. Included in its applications are pump and valve packings, diaphrams, electrical tie tapes, filters, and gaskets. Its freedom from stickiness makes it most valuable for use in non-lubricated bearings, and such bearings of Teflon fiber have withstood loads up to 60,000 psi without cold flow. Teflon is a registered trademark name.

TEG, TEGGETT. The first clipping from yearling sheep which were not shorn in the lamb stage. Teg is the name for the shorter staple when compared with the term hog, hoggett. See HOG, HOGGETT, WETHER.

TEKLAN. Registered trademark of Courtaulds Ltd., Great Britain for its modacrylic fiber made from derivatives of oil refining and coal carbonization processes. Main properties include strength, geared for rough or hard wear, softness, warmth, light weight, good resistance to sunlight, bacteria, and most chemicals. Is also made flame-resistant and retains this property even after many washings or drycleanings. Has good stability and ease-in-washing; quick drying and needs little, if any, ironing. If ironed, use cool setting. Uses include woven and knitted fabrics for dressgoods, brushed fabrics, pile cloths, knitgoods for many uses; floorcoverings, drapery fabrics, curtains and comparable fabrics. Industrial uses are found in electrical insulation, filter fab-

rics, flame-resistant materials, workclothes.

TEKKO. This oilcloth floor-covering made with a cotton base was first made in Germany. Rather elaborate patterns are obtained in the product by the use of pressure rollers.

TELA. Name for linen cloth in the Mediterranean countries.

TELESCOPE OR PORK PIE HAT. Any type of headgear made with an oval shaped, flattened crease.

TEMPERATURE. The degree of heat commonly expressed by the Fahrenheit scale.

TEMPERATURE, DEW-POINT. Temperature at which the condensation of water vapor in a space begins, for a given state of humidity and pressure, as the temperature of the vapor is reduced. The temperature corresponding to saturation (100 per cent relative humidity) for a given absolute humidity at constant pressure.

TEMPERATURE, DRY BULB. The temperature of a gas or mixture of gases indicated by the thermometer.

TEMPERATURE, INITIAL. This refers to the temperature of a washing solution at the beginning of the washing process.

TEMPERATURE, WET-BULB. Thermodynamic wet-bulb temperature is the temperature at which liquid or soil water, by evaporation into air, can bring the air to saturation adiabatically at the same temperature. Wet-bulb temperature (without qualification) is the temperature indicated by the wet-bulb psychrometer.

TEMPLATE, TEMPLET. A pattern, mold, or the like; made of cardboard, metal, paper, or wood to serve as a guide or gauge in mechanical work. In the textile industry the template is used in patterning designs or motifs on carpets, Jacquard fabrics, motifs for print goods, decorative fabrics, et al.

TEMPLE. Set at the fell of the cloth, it keeps the newly woven material at the correct width so that the warp and the filling in the weaving will interlace at right angles to form proper width fabric. Also known as tempet, stretcher, and tenter hook.

TEMPLE MARKS. Hole defects or rents in fabric caused by improper setting of the temples which keep the newly woven cloth at the proper width so that warp ends and filling picks may interlace at right angles.

TEMPORARY HARDNESS. Bicarbonates of lime and magnesium, so named because under the influence of heat they are changed to carbonates

and precipitated; boiling point of 212° F. is used.

TEMPRA. Trade name for high-tenacity type of viscose made by American Enka Corporation.

TEN. Coarse hackle used in preparing flax for spinning.

TENACELL. Made from wood cellulose by controlled chemical procedure, this product is high in purity and uniformity. Converted into a perfect viscose spinning solution with a minimum use of other chemicals, Tenacell is used in the manufacture of high tensile strength yarn such as tire yarn.

TENACITY. The breaking strength of a fiber, filament, yarn, cord, etc., expressed in force per unit yarn number.

TENASCO. High-tenacity viscose rayon yarn manufactured by Courtaulds, Ltd., and Courtaulds (Canada) Ltd.

TENDER, TENDER GOODS, TENDERING. Raw stock, top, yarn or fabric which has become weakened at some time during manipulation. The causes for tendering are many and may include scouring liquors which may have been too hot, overscouring, overcarding, poor selection of raw materials, too much draft, poor tensions, faulty dyeing, excessive napping, gigging or singeing, construction defects, etc.

TENDER FLEECES. Applied to lower grades of fleeces which can be carded but not combed. Also known as tender wool, the fibers are used in low-grade woolen yarns.

TENDERING. Lowering of tensile or mechanical strength of a fabric.

TENERIFFE LACE. Native to the Canary Islands, this is a lace that is known for the excellence of its circle and wheel motifs.

TENGUSU. The Japanese name for a silkworm.

TENITE. Important characteristics of Tenite are its extreme toughness, resilience, lightness of weight, weather-resistance, dimensional stability, natural luster, pleasant feel, and unlimited selection of colors in crystal, transparent, translucent, opaque, and variegated forms. Thermoplastic, it is injection-molded at the fastest speeds possible with plastics, and is well suited to continuous extrusion without the use of solvents.

A variety of Tenite formulas, permitting adaptation of Tenite to different use requirements, exists in Tenite I (cellulose acetate plastics) and Tenite II (cellulose butyrate plastics). Typical applications of Tenite are steering wheels, business machine keys, drill housings, football helmets, oil pipe, irrigation tubes, fishnet floats, toys, tool handles, and telephones. Tenite is marketed by Eastman Chemical Products, Inc., Kingsport, Tennessee.

TENNESSEE COTTON. It has a staple of about 15/16 inch and spins to around 20s; the cotton varies much in cast.

TENNIS CLOTH. An English cotton export cloth which is popular in the South American trade. This colored fabric is made with subdued stripes and is raised or embossed in the finishing.

TENNIS FLANNEL. Lightweight British fabric made on serge weave. This clear finish worsted comes in white, stripes in a white background or may be dyed cream or ecru shades. Popular in tennis and other sportswear.

TENSILE STRENGTH. The maximum load per unit of the original cross-section area obtained prior to rupture. It is the actual number of pounds resistance that a fabric will give to a breaking machine before the material is broken on the testing apparatus and may no longer be classed as a cloth or fabric. Bursting strengths are recorded on a dial set on the machine. Tensile strength is one of the most important requisites of cloth.

TENSILE STRENGTH IN GRAMS PER DENIER. The tensile strength of a fiber is its ability to resist strain or rupture when tension is applied. It is expressed in force per unit cross-section area, that is, grams per denier. Using the machines for tests of this type (Hydraulic, Balance, Pendulum, Spring or Chainomatic) it is possible to set up standards for the various deniers, types of yarns, etc. See WET AND DRY FIBER TENSILE STRENGTH.

TENSILE STRENGTH LOSS. The loss in strength of textile materials usually reported as loss in pounds per inch. Also commonly reported as percentage loss, which is figured from the loss and the original strength, in pounds per inch. Varies with different fabrics under a fixed set of conditions.

TENSION. The "stretch" of the threads during weaving; may be warp or filling, or both.

TENSION ANALYZER. A device which consists of a pick-up action, a sensitive amplifier, and a recording oscilligraph; it measures and records the prevailing tension on yarns. A hand tensiometer does work similar to the analyzer; but modern electronic analyzers record the information for study, respond to faster moving yarn, and have extreme sensitivity. The instrument measures tension but the op-

erator must analyze the results. Textile operations most applicable to tension analyzers are spinning, winding, throwing, warping, slashing, weaving, and knitting.

TENSION DEVICE. A disc, finger, washer, weight, etc., used to impart tension to a machine during spinning, warping, winding, twisting, tentering, etc.

TENSION GEAR. The change gear on a roving frame, for example, that controls the back-and-forth movement of the leather belt that works on the two steel cones. It also controls the tension of the roving between the front rollers and the upright flyer set on the spindle top-groove.

TENSION GUIDE. Any device used as a guide to provide proper tension during winding, coning, or copping.

TENSION PRESSER. An apparatus used to measure the dimensional restorability of woven fabrics after laundering or cleaning. Fixed tension (determined by the type of fabric being tested) is applied to the warp and the filling of the damp sample under test. This procedure eliminates variations of ordinary hand pressing. Drying is accomplished by the use of a perforated aluminum plate laid on the test specimen and then heated with an electric iron.

TENSION REP. Two warps are used to make the fabric; one warp is at tight tension while the other is under slack tension. Plain, simple patterns result when woven with ordinary plain picks.

TENSION ROLL. The covered tension roll over which the entire width of warp threads pass on their way to be wound on the warp beam during the dressing, warping, or slashing operation for warps.

TENSLATOR. A quality control device of Stop Motion Devices Corporation which is a yarn tension control for knitting machines to work alone or in combination with the yarn stop motion. A weighed follower is set for a definite gram reading, and this tension is maintained smoothly throughout the yarn feed to the frame.

TENSOMETER. An instrument designed to measure the tenacity by determining the tensile strength necessary to break the specimen or sample.

TEN-STICK. Bobbins are considered to be lace sticks, and this expression is used in some parts of England, especially Devonshire, to mean a narrow braiding made with ten threads, and used to make small ringlets, flower stems, etc.

TENSYLON. A product of the Tensylon Corporation, a trade name for a tensilized rubber hydrochloride yarn-like product. The raw material, Pliofilm, is cut into strips, tensilized or stretched, rolled on itself or wrapped around other material, and bonded.

The properties of Tensylon are good tensile strength, 8 to 30 per cent elasticity, high flexibility, imperviousness to water, weak acid, alkali, oil, perspiration, mold, moths, and grease. Fabrics can be cleaned with a damp cloth. Textile uses include braids, woven drapery, and upholstery fabrics, bags, shoes, table covers, ribbons, sewing thread, and suspenders.

TENT. A shelter, canvas or the like, supported by poles, and fastened by cords to pegs driven into the ground.

TENT DUCK. Made of laid warp and double filling, it belongs to the so-called Flat Duck group of fabrics. It is superior to single filling duck. Tent duck filling may be of one-, two-, or three-ply and the laid warp has two ends which weave as one to add strength. The filling is woven with one pick in each shedding action of the loom.

This term, when finished duck is implied, covers fabric used for awnings, coverings, tents, etc. Finished width ranges from 20 to 72 inches with the fabric weight varying accordingly. Warp yarn is about 14s in count and the filling is a 2/12s or a 2/13s. Highest textures are in the neighborhood of 80 x 30.

TENTER FRAME. A machine that dries and stretches cloth to its finished width, and straightens its weave by the action of two diverging endless chains. Each chain is equipped with a series of clips that hold an edge of the cloth and convey it over gas flames or through a hot-air drying compartment. See Illustrated Section.

TENTER HOOK. See TENTER FRAME.

TENT FABRIC. Canvas, duck, or similar fabric waterproofed to make it suitable for shelter tents and coverings.

TENT STITCH. A short slanting stitch that is worked in even lines from left to right; used chiefly in embroidery.

TEPIS. A coarse Indian material made of cotton and spun silk yarns; colored stripes are woven into the cloth for effect.

TERGAL. Trademark for approved materials made from polyester fibers manufactured by Societe Rhodiaceta, S. A., Paris 8e, France. Made in filament and staple forms.

TERITAL. Polyester fiber made by

Rhodiatoce S.P.A., Milan, Italy. Comes in bright and dull staple, and high tenacity filament yarn.

TERLENKA. A polyester fiber made in Holland that is comparable with "Dacron," Fortrel, Kodel, and Terylene.

TERRITORY WOOL. A term with various meanings. Originally it meant wool raised west of the Mississippi-Missouri rivers—then known as Indian Territory. At present the term means wool raised west of the 100th meridian but exclusive of wool grown in California, Oregon, and Texas; these three wools have special designations. Incidentally, other wools in this Territory region are quoted individually.

Territory wool is chiefly of the "fine type" and it shows heavy shrinkage and low yield. Much of the wool is dull, dark, and dirty in-the-grease, but it scours to a good white. Other names for this wool include Western, Range, Modoc.

TERRO NOTA COTTON. A type of cotton raised in Sicily.

TERRY CLOTH. This cotton fabric has uncut loops on both sides of the cloth. Woven on a dobby loom with Terry arrangement, various sizes of yarns are used in the construction. Terry is also made on a Jacquard loom to form interesting motifs. It may be yarn-dyed in different colors to form attractive patterns. It is bleached, piece-dyed, and even printed for beachwear and bathrobes.

A one-sided terry cloth or Turkish toweling has the pile effect on only one side of the fabric, instead of the usual arrangement.

The principle of Terry weaving originated in France in 1841; first used on silk fabrics. In 1845, John Bright, an English manufacturer, used the weaves in worsteds, at Rochdale. Samuel Holt was the first to apply the principle to cotton cloth. He was the founder of the American Velvet Co., Paterson, N. J., organized to make this type of goods, in 1864.

Two sets of warp yarn, and one of filling, are used; one of the warps will form the pile, while the other is the ground warp. The warp which forms the pile is slashed on a separate beam, and is kept very slack in the loom. In weaving, a number of picks, apart from each other, are shot through the shed of the loom before they become a component part of the fabric. Terry may be designed as a 3, 4, 5, or 6 pick arrangement cloth. Thus, the action is controlled by a receding reed which takes care of the loose picks and the fast picks. A fast pick will beat the one or more loose picks into

their place in the woven goods, in accordance with the plan of the designer of the cloth. The action of the fast pick will cause the pile or accordion effect created in the material by the slack warp.

The picks, as they are beaten into the material, slide over the taut ground warp, but the friction afforded will pull the pile warp threads so that they will be able to give the final pile effect to the cloth.

TERRY CLOTH, THREE-PICK. This is the standard type terry fabric and means that loops are formed across the width of the cloth on every third filling pick; in other words, there are three filling yarns to every horizontal row of loops.

TERRY POPLIN. Made with silk warp and worsted filling, or in other suitable yarn combinations, the warp is set up one end of ground and one of terry pile yarn from another warp beam. Thus, this fabric shows an all-over effect of Terry ringlets on the surface. It gives the appearance of a very fine bouclé material. See BOUCLÉ.

TERRY TOWELING, TYPES OF. These are classified according to weave or design:

1. CAM-WOVEN, PLAIN TERRY: Plain border.

2. DOBBY-WOVEN: Simple patterns in the border, or all over. Border designs include rope and corduroy borders.

3. JACQUARD-WOVEN: Those which have rather elaborate allover motifs, or names woven into the goods.

4. MITCHELINE: This border type has a heavy, distinct, raised or embossed border effect, formed by a stout colored filling yarn; the roving is used sometimes instead of a yarn to obtain the effect. Some of this fabric is made on Jacquard looms.

5. TEXTURE-DESIGNED: This is made on either a dobby loom or a Jacquard loom. It has an allover, raised and recessed motif. The athletic-rib towel, which has raised terry stripes with alternating plain ground stripes, is in this classification; also known as corduroy toweling.

These are classified according to type:

1. ALL-WHITE PLAIN: This has a plain border, white or colors. It also implies fancy-woven, colored border toweling.

2. PASTEL-COLOR PLAIN: It is made with dyed filling yarns; white pile yarns.

3. JACQUARD REVERSIBLE ALLOVER: This features colored pile on one side, with white pile effect on the other side. The borders are plain or fancy. The interchanging white and colored loops

form a contrasting motif on each side of the material.

4. BATH MAT: This is a heavy type of terry made for bath mats. Coarse ply yarns are used to provide bulkiness, strength, and the weight necessary to give the fabric body and substance.

TERRYTUFT MACHINE. A high-speed Kraftamatic terry loom made by Kintslaid Engineering Company, Ltd., Lancashire, England. Production is claimed to be equal to that of 120 looms, producing a fabric at a rate of around thirty-six inches a minute. The machine is capable of about 500,000 yards of cloth on an annual basis.

TERRY VELVET. Uncut pile velvet fabric.

TERTIARY COLORS. Basically they are olive, citron, and russet. Mixing green and purple gives olive; orange and green provide citron; orange and purple produce russet. Orange, green, and purple are all secondaries in the color scheme. The term also implies shades such as beige, dark blue, brown, and gray (the so-called "dirt-shedding colors or shades"), ecru, dark green, khaki, mauve, and olive. All these are obtained by mixing the three primary colors in varying proportions, by the use of some additive color or colors, and from the use of one or more of the secondary colors in admixture with black or gray. Black is often classified as a "greenable black" or a "brownable black," dependent on the basic color combinations used.

TERYLENE. The term is coined from the words terephthalate and polyethylene, synthetic substances. Somewhat resembling nylon, terylene can be stretched five times its original length without losing firmness. Made in various thicknesses and width, it can withstand bright light, and will launder and press without any special precautions. Terylene is not affected by moisture, chemical mixtures, or microorganisms. This polyester is made by Imperial Chemical Industries, Ltd., England. See FORTREL.

TESHIKE. A lightweight, perspiration-proof, Japanese silk cloth.

TEST BUNDLE. A set of specially selected standard fabric pieces used for evaluating formula efficiency in laundering.

TESTING. The process of finding the quality of something by an experiment, or by some principle or standard.

TESTING, PERFORMANCE. The following lists some of the major Government Acts along with testing textiles as decreed by the American Society for Testing and Materials (ASTM) and

American Associaion of Textile Colorists and Chemists (AATCC), located in Philadelphia, Pennsylvania, and Research Triangle of the AATCC, North Carolina, respectively.

TEXTILE PERFORMANCE:
1. Wheeler-Lea Act, 1938.
2. Wool Labeling Act, 1939.
3. American Standards Performance Requirements for Textile Fabrics L-22, 1960.
4. Textile Fiber Products Identification Act, 1960.

FABRIC PERFORMANCE:
1. Abrasion Resistance-ASTM-D1175-64T.
2. Air Permeability-ASTM-D737-46.
3. Fabric Description-ASTM-D1910-64.
4. Fabric Thickness-ASTM-D1777-64.
5. Strength-Breaking Load-ASTN-D1682-64
6. Thermal Properties-ASTM-D1518-64.

FINISH PERFORMANCE:
1. *Colorfastness Of Fabrics:* AATCC Tests - 8-1961; 39-1961; 3-1962; 15-1962; 61-1962; 5-1962T; 32-1952T; 104-1962T; 106-1962; 85-1963; 105-1963.
2. *Fabric Dimensional Change:* 1. Effect of Drycleaning - AATCC 108-1063T. 2. Effect of Laundering - AATCC - 96-1960-T; ASTM-D1905-61T; AATCC-99-1962T.
3. *Resistance To Fire:* Flammability of Textiles - AATCC 33-1962; ASTN-D1230-61.
4. *Resistance To Insect Damage.* AATCC 24-1963; AATCC 28-1956.
5. *Resistance To Loss Of Finishing In Laundering or Drycleaning:* AATCC 94-1962T.
6. *Resistance To Mildew And Rot:* AATCC 30-1957T.
7. *Resistance To Water:* Rain Test - AATCC 22-1964: ASTM D583-63.
8. *Resistance To Yarn Slippage:* ASTM D434-42.
9. *Recovery From Wrinkling:* AATCC 66-1959T; ASTM D1295-60T.
10. *Spray Test:* AATCC 42-1964; ASTM D583-63.
11. *Wash-And-Wear Properties:* AATCC 88A-1964T.

TESTING, TYPES OF TEXTILE.
Testing of textiles is done to provide more efficiency of performance, to disclose flaws and weaknesses in structure and to determine quality from raw material to finished product. Testing may be done at various stages in the production of fabrics and is usually divided into three categories - testing in the mill, simple laboratory testing, and advanced laboratory testing. The various tests which are made for composition, construction, and performance cover a very wide range.

The categories follows:
1. *Physical Testing:* These include: A. Staple fiber length, grade and fiber quality. B. Size or yarn count, strength, ply, twist and yarn quality. C. Construction or texture, weight, strength, weave or type of knit, etc., abrasion, shrinkage and other important properties pertinent to the fabric.
2. *Chemical Testing:* These include A. Sizing determinations. B. Quantitative analysis of the fiber content. C. Identification and analysis of special treatments and finishes. D. Extraction analysis. E. Various types of tests for colorfastness. F. Determination of causes of defective materials.
3. *Optical Testing:* These include: A. Qualitative and quantitative fiber analysis. B. Grading or classifying fibers. C. Photomicrography. D. Measurement determinations. E. Inspection and determinations on defects and faulty material.
4. *Standard Atmospheric Conditions For Testing:* A moisture equilibrium is maintained with a standard atmosphere which has a relative humidity of 65% (plus 2%) at 70° Fahrenheit (plus 2° F).
5. *Testing The Finish On Textile Fabrics:* Each of the following finishes can be tested for their effectiveness or lack of it:
  1. Abrasion resistance
  2. Absorbency
  3. Antiseptic qualities
  4. Antistatic qualities
  5. Color fastness
  6. Crease resistance
  7. Crispness
  8. Drapeability
  9. Drycleanability
 10. Dullness
 11. Durability
 12. Flame resistance
 13. Gas fading inhibition
 14. Ironing (minimum)
 15. Lightfastness
 16. Lintlessness
 17. Luster, gloss, or sheen
 18. Mildew resistance
 19. Moth resistance
 20. Oil resistance
 21. Perspiration resistance
 22. Scroop
 23. Shrinkage resistance
 24. Slip resistance
 25. Softness
 26. Stain resistance
 27. Stretch and sag resistance
 28. Washability
 29. Water repellency
 30. Wilt reduction.

Courtesy: ASTM, Philadelphia, Pa.

TESTING AND ANALYZING, SERVICEABILITY.
1. BREAKING LOAD: The number of pounds pull necessary to rupture, rip, or break yarn of fabric.
2. COLORFASTNESS TO CLEANING: A fabric sample is subjected to both "wet" and "dry" procedures or methods and must show no appreciable change of color or migration of dyestuff to rate "satisfactory."
3. COLORFASTNESS TO WASHING: A fabric sample is washed according to laboratory test procedures with a swatch of undyed fabric attached to it. There must be no appreciable bleeding or running of the color onto the white material, as well as no appreciable change of color in order to be termed "acceptable."
4. CROCKING TEST: A fabric sample is rubbed mechanically against a white cloth to ascertain if the color will "crock" or rub off. This test is conducted in both "wet" and "dry" states.
5. RESISTANCE TO ATMOSPHERIC GAS FADING: A fabric sample is exposed for a prescribed number of hours in a chamber which contains combustion gases known to cause fading of dyed acetate fabrics. A "before" and "after" comparison is made and the sample rated accordingly.
6. RESISTANCE TO SUN FADING: A fabric sample is hung on a revolving rack in the Fade-Ometer for a specified number of hours. After this powerful simulated sunlight exposure, if there is no appreciable change in color, the sample is said to possess good fastness to sunlight.
7. RESISTANCE TO YARN SLIPPAGE: The measurement of the ability of a fabric in its resistance to yarn separation and rupture at the seams.
8. SHRINKAGE: The measurement of the change in the dimension of a fabric after washing or cleaning.

TETORON POLYESTER FIBER.
Polyester fiber manufactured in Japan; in the same classification as "Terlenka," made in Holland, "Terylene" is the British polyester and its counterpart is "Fortrel" made by Fiber Industries, Inc., Shelby, North Carolina. Outside the United States "Fortrel" is known as "Terylene," with Fiber Industries, Inc., being a joint venture of Celanese Corporation of America and Imperial Chemical Industries, Ltd., of Great Britain. "Dacron," "Kodel," "Vycron," and polyesters are manufactured by E.I. duPont de Nemours & Co., Inc., Eastman Chemical Products, Inc., and Beaunit Corporation, respectively. The fiber is called "Diolen" and "Trevira" in West Ger-

many; "Montecatini," and "Terital" in Italy; "Tergal" in France.

TETRAFLUORETHYLENE, FIBER. A fiber derived chemically from fluorine and carbon, and used only for industrial purposes. Because of its resistance to corrosives and smooth surface, it is suited for packings, bearings, and filters.

TETRASODIUM PYROPHOSPHATE. A sodium salt or pyrophosphoric acid. Sometimes used in detergents and for conditioning water.

TEXAS COTTON. More cotton is produced by this state than any other in the Union. But the term includes cotton raised in Arkansas and Oklahoma, as well. Texas resembles Uplands and has a similar staple, from three fourths of an inch to one and one-eighth inches.

The cotton is "heavy" in body but its variability may be, at times, detrimental. Unsettled and irregular climatic conditions have some effect on the fiber. The cotton is rather reddish in tinge, and there may be, at times, considerable foreign matter. Texas is ideal for low- and medium-grade warp yarn. Leading Texas cottons include Maxey, Meyer's Texas, and Selected Triumph.

TEXAS STORM-PROOF COTTON. A late-maturing cotton of 1-inch staple and lint yield of about 34 per cent. Receives its name from the fact that the matured seed cotton does not fall from the bolls as readily as with most types.

TEXAS WOOD COTTON. See PETERKIN COTTON.

TEXEL SHEEP. Raised chiefly in Belgium and Holland, this sheep is the result of crossbreeding English Lincoln rams with the "long-legged" Guinea ewes. These sheep were brought to the American colonies and were important in developing the sheep-raising industry in New England 150 years ago.

TEXILOSE. Twisted paper strips mixed with short-waste textile fibers, used as a substitute for jute yarn.

TEXNOVO ULTRATEX SHUTTLELESS LOOM. Narrow fabric loom with 16 patented needle weaving units capable of 600 to 800 double picks per minute with cam motion device, and 400 to 500 double picks with a dobby headmotion. Binding of the filling is done by an additional thread knitted by the weaving unit needle. The 16 weaving units may be used to make rigid web up to one-inch wide with either the cam or the dobby motion. These needle weaving units can produce elastic web up to 1½-inches wide on either cam or dobby motion.

Twelve needle weaving units can make elastic or rigid webbing up to 2⅜-inches in width, and by the use of eight units these webs can be made as wide as 3½-inches. Product of Texnovo S. p. A., Milan, Italy.

TEX SYSTEM FOR DESIGNATION OF YARN NUMBER.
Sponsored by ASTM Committee D-13 on Textiles ASA Sectional Committee L-23 for ISO/TC38 on Textiles: AMERICAN SOCIETY FOR TESTING AND MATERIALS.

A plan for the orderly introduction of the single system of numbering yarns made from all types of fibers introduced to the textile industry in most of the countries of the world. United States participation has helped to keep our industry abreast of this significant development.

Yarn number represents the "size," "fineness," or, more accurately, the relationship between weight and length of a yarn. The tex system has been chosen to replace the many conflicting systems now used, after extended study by the Technical Committee on Textiles of the International Organization for Standardization (ISO/TC 38). Delegates representing the textile industries of twenty-one nations including the United States and four international textile associations participated in the study and unanimously adopted this proposal.

It is proposed to make the changeover in three easy stages over a period of years. The action to be taken in each stage will be given here. The first stage began in 1960 and will run until the trade is thoroughly familiar with the new system. Dates for the second and third stages will be set when the trade becomes ready for them.

I. THREE STAGES OF ACTION

1. *First Stage.* This stage is designed to familiarize everyone working in the textile industry with tex numbers. The existing yarn count systems will continue in use, but a corresponding rounded tex number will be given in parentheses after the traditional yarn count or yarn number—for example: 18 cotton count (32 tex), 48 worsted count (18 tex), 100 denier (11 tex).

During this stage the rounded tex numbers in parentheses are illustrative or explanatory and have no legal standing. They cannot be used as the basis of claims or other disputes, which must be based on the traditional yarn numbers. A note to this effect may be stamped on contracts or other documents where this is felt to be desirable or helpful.

2. *Second Stage.* Commercial transactions and manufacturing operations will be shifted to tex numbering. The equivalent traditional yarn number or

count will be given in parentheses after the tex number—for example: 32 tex cotton yarn will be written 32 tex (18.5 cotton count); 18 tex worsted yarn will be written 18 tex (48 worsted count).

3. *Third Stage.* The traditional yarn number in parentheses will be deleted; only tex numbers will be given.

II. ACTION TO BE TAKEN NOW

In view of the benefits to be derived from the general use of a single yarn numbering system throughout the industry, all textile trade associations are urged to endorse the plan for introduction of the tex system and to recommend participation in it by their members. Manufacturers, distributors, testing and research laboratories, and individuals throughout the industry are urged to give rounded equivalent tex numbers in parentheses following the traditional numbers or counts wherever they appear on orders, invoices, tags, reports, in trade literature, and in technical publications.

The rounded tex numbers can be obtained readily from short tables relating them to the numbers or counts in the system now used. Condensed tables are appended to this report for cottons, worsted, woolen, and denier numbers or counts, with directions for their use. The tex number of a yarn, fiber, or other strand is defined as the weight in grams of one kilometer of yarn. Constants have been calculated for converting yarn numbers or counts of all systems currently in use to tex numbers. For the present, however, only rounded equivalent numbers need be used.

The ISO Committee, developing plans for the introduction of the tex system, has suggested that as far as possible the rounded equivalent tex numbers listed in Table II of the Appendix should be used in preference to other intermediate numbers or to the exact tex numbers. The preferred numbers have been carefully selected to cover the entire range needed for commercial yarns in a series of steps that, in general, reflect variations observed in practical spinning operations. In the second stage, when yarns are numbered in the tex system, intermediate values can, of course, be used whenever tradition or customer's requirements indicates this to be desirable.

III. SCOPE AND BENEFITS OF THE TEX SYSTEM

Since the tex number is also applicable to yarn intermediates, it can be used for laps, slivers, and rovings as well as yarns. It can also be used for individual fibers; the millitex unit can be used to avoid low numbers.

The success of the analogous denier system gives assurance that the proposed tex system is workable. The tex system has already been used successfully in local installations, both in cotton spinning laboratories and in manufacturing units, so that no one need have any hesitation about its suitability as a yarn numbering system.

Adoption of a single universal system for numbering yarns made from any fiber has the following advantages:

1. The various yarn systems now in use with different fibers—for example, English cotton counts, French cotton counts, metric counts, Yorkshire woolen skeins, American woolen runs, English worsted counts—will all be replaced with the tex system, eliminating time spent in converting units from one system to the other and avoiding mistakes that occur when technicians are forced to think in unfamiliar units.

2. Efficiency in mills spinning yarns from any fiber will be increased. Picker laps, slivers, rovings, and yarns will all be numbered in the same units, thus facilitating the calculation of drafts at all stages of spinning and eliminating confusion due to changing systems between laps and slivers, slivers and rovings, tops and gills, rovings and yarns.

3. Operating procedures will be simplified in mills simultaneously spinning yarns from fibers numbered in different systems, for example, wool and man-made fibers on both the worsted and woolen systems. Sales of these products to different customers will also be simplified.

4. The buying and selling of yarns that must meet specifications given in different traditional numbering systems will be simplified by eliminating the time spent in converting and checking results.

5. Efficiency in cost accounting and inventory control will be increased, since all yarns, regardless of the fiber used, will be based on the same yarn numbering system.

6. Fabric design work will be simplified, since the same amount of yarn, that is, the same length of yarn of a given number or count, will be needed to make the same weight of fabric, regardless of the fibers involved.

7. Calculation of the resultant count of all plied yarns that are numbered in indirect numbering systems will be much easier, since with tex numbers the equivalent single number can be calculated by simple addition.

8. Efficiency of quality control and cost comparisons will be improved, since all derived or calculated yarn properties such as breaking tenacity or lea product will be in the same units regardless of fiber used.

9. It will be easier to interpret and use the findings of textile research workers published anywhere in the world.

10. Any spinning or blend study involving the number of fibers in a yarn will be easier to make, since the yarn and the fibers used will both be numbered in the same or closely related systems.

11. The time spent in technical textile schools teaching and practicing the use of various yarn numbering systems will be eventually eliminated. This time will be available for teaching other important subjects.

12. The United States textile industry will avoid being placed at a further disadvantage in production costs with respect to competition from foreign countries who are expected to adopt the tex yarn numbering system fairly soon.

13. In addition to the ultimate lower costs resulting from all these increased efficiencies each textile scientist or executive will have the personal satisfaction of promoting the use of the universal yarn numbering system in his own company and trade association and of knowing that, at the cost of some relatively transient personal difficulty, he is contributing to the advancement of the textile industry for the benefit of all future generations.

CONCLUSION

Agreement on the tex system for yarn numbering is a notable achievement in international standardization in a field where standardization is long overdue. It merits the support of every person, organization, and company interested in the long-range good of the textile industry.

It is urged that everyone in the textile industry participate in the general educational program leading to the introduction of the tex yarn numbering system in his part of the industry.

Discussions of the tex yarn numbering system have appeared in textile journals in the United States and in foreign countries from time to time. Anyone desiring more information on this international development should consult his own technical experts, his ASTM representative, or should refer to the References listed below.

B. L. WHITTIER, chairman,
ASTM Committee D-13 on Textile Materials.

W. D. APPEL, chairman,

ASA Committee L23, U. S. representative on ISO/TC 38 on Textiles.

REFERENCES

(1) Anon. letter to the editor reporting use of the tex system in the large Alpargartos Cotton Mills in Argentina and Uruguay, *Textile Age*, Vol. 8, p. 108 (1944).

(2) Tentative Recommended Practice for Use of Tex System to Designate Linear Density of Fibers, Yarn Intermediates, Yarns, and Other Textile Materials, ASTM Designation: D 861 – 58 T, 1958 Book of ASTM Standards, Part 10, p. 347.

(3) ASTM Yarn Numbering Conversion Table. This Table gives exact tex equivalents of normal yarn counts for all traditional yarn numbering systems. Appendix III of Compilation of ASTM Standards on Textile Materials, published annually.

(4) A. W. Bayes, "Tex Universal Yarn Numbering System," *Journal Textile Inst.*, Vol. 48, p. 225 (1957).

(5) Canadian Advisory Committee on ISO/TC 38 "Textiles—Introduction of the Tex Yarn Numbering System," *Canadian Textile Journal*, Vol. 76, pp. 59–63 (Dec. 11, 1959).

(6) J. Corbiére, "The International Numbering of Yarns and Threads," *Textile Research Journal*, Vol. 23, p. 946 (Dec., 1953).

(7) Deutsche Normen, DIN 60905 (Official German Standard), "The Tex System for the Numbering of Textile Fibers, Yarns, and Fabrics," *Melliand Textil-Berichte*, Vol. 38, p. 642 (1957) (In German).

(8) R. W. Forrester, "Yarn Counts—Proposed Universal System," *Journal Textile Inst.*, Vol. 40, S8-12 (1949).

(9) J. W. S. Hearle, "Tex Universal Yarn Numbering System," *Journal Textile Inst.*, Vol. 48, pp. 416–17 (1957).

(10) K. Henschel, "Simplification of Yarn Numbering, Preparation for the Introduction of the International Numbering of Yarns in Germany," *Textile Research Journal*, Vol. 25, p. 140 (1955).

(11) International Cotton Federation, "Approval of the Tex Yarn Numbering System for Cotton and Allied Textile Industries," *Textile Mercury and Argus*, Vol. 139, p. 360 (1958).

(12) H. L. Röder, "The Tex System Adopted as the Universal Numbering System for Yarns and Fibers," *Enka and Breda Rayon Review*, Vol. 10, p. 133 (1956).

(13) L. Szponder, "Tex—A Universal

Yarn Numbering System," *Textile Industries,* Vol. 122, p. 149 (1958).

(14) A. G. Scroggie, "The Tex Universal Yarn Numbering System," *Textile Research Journal,* Vol 28, p. 330 (1958).

(15) Spanish Government, Promulgation of the Tex System for Numbering Yarns made from all Fibers (1946) (In Spanish).

(16) B. L. Whittier, "Tex—A New Yarn-Numbering System," *Textile World,* Vol. 107, p. 88 (Aug., 1957).

(17) The Tex System of Yarn Counting, Recommendation to all members of the Federation of Master Cotton Spinners Associations Ltd., The Yarn Spinners Association and the Cotton Yarn Doublers Association in the United Kingdom, to proceed with the adoption of the Tex System, pamphlet, Federation of Master Cotton Spinners Association Ltd., Manchester 2, England.

TEX SYSTEM TABLES, CONVERSION FACTORS USED IN. These follow:

Direct System Used in Figuring Yarn Counts: To find the Tex Count from that given in another system, multiply this given count by the conversion factor. To find the yarn count in any system given in the Tex Count, divide the count in Tex by the conversion factor.

Indirect System in Figuring Yarn Counts: To find the Tex Count from that given in another system, divide the given count into the conversion factor. To find the yarn count in any system, divide the count in the Tex System into the conversion factor.

General Conversion Method in Figuring Yarn Counts: To convert the count in one system to that of another system, convert to the Tex Count and then convert to the other system by means of the two foregoing rules. See TEX SYSTEM FOR DESIGNATION OF YARN COUNTS.

APPENDIX

CONVERSION TABLES

Conversion tables giving the rounded equivalent tex numbers for various ranges of English Cotton Count (Table III), English Worsted Count (Table IV), American Woolen Run Table (V), and Denier Number (Table VI), together with instructions for their use, are given in this Appendix.

Tables for other systems can be prepared by means of the factors, given in Table I. Factors for a number of other systems can be found in Draft ISO Recommendation (Document ISO/TC 38 (Sc 4-1) 210).

To prepare a conversion table, use the appropriate factor from Table I to calculate the equivalent traditional value for the limiting range of the recommended rounded tex units listed in Table II. Each calculated value forms the upper limit of one range and the lower limit of the next range as shown in Tables III through VI.

TABLE I.—CONVERSION FACTORS.

To Get Tex Number	
Divide	By
Denier No. .	9
Spyndle No.	0.02903
4960.5	Asbestos cut[a]
590.54	Cotton count (English)[b]
4960.5	Glass cut[c]
1653.5	Linen cut[d]
1000.0	Metric No.[e]
310.03	Woolen run (American)[f]
885.8	Worsted count (English)[g]

or

Multiply	By
Denier No. .	0.1111
Spyndle No.	34.45

[a] Asbestos cut, NaA, equals 100-yd hanks per lb. [b] English cotton count, Nec, equals 840-yd hanks per lb. [c] Glass cut, NG, equals 100-yd hanks per lb. [d] Linen cut, NeL, equals 300-yd hanks per lb. [e] Metric number, Nm, equals kilometers per kilogram. [f] American woolen run, Nar, equals 1600-yd hanks per lb. [g] English worsted count, Ne, equals 560-yd hanks per lb.

TABLE II.—RECOMMENDED ROUNDED TEX NUMBERS.[a]

Range of Tex Number		Recommended Rounded Tex Number	Range of Tex Number		Recommended Rounded Tex Number
Above	Up To and Including		Above	Up To and Including	
9.4	9.8	9.6	31	33	32
9.8	10.25	10	33	35	34
10.25	10.75	10.5	35	37	36
10.75	11.25	11	37	39	38
11.25	11.75	11.5	39	41	40
11.75	12.25	12	41	43	42
12.25	12.75	12.5	43	45	44
12.75	13.5	13	45	47	46
13.5	14.5	14	47	49	48
14.5	15.5	15	49	51	50
15.5	16.5	16	51	54	52
16.5	17.5	17	54	58	56
17.5	18.5	18	58	62	60
18.5	19.5	19	62	66	64
19.5	20.5	20	66	70	68
20.5	21.5	21	70	74	72
21.5	22.5	22	74	78	76
22.5	23.5	23	78	82	80
23.5	24.5	24	82	86	84
24.5	25	25	86	90	88
25.5	27	26	90	94	92
27	29	28	94	98	96
29	31	30	98	102.5	100

[a] Reproduced from the draft ISO Recommendation ISO/TC 38(SC 4-1) 210, section 3.2.

The decimal multiples and fractions of the rounded values indicated in this table are valid for the decimal multiples and fractions of the corresponding ranges.

The rounded tex number appropriate to any number in a traditional system can be obtained by following the procedure set forth in the draft ISO Recommendation, but it is more convenient to use a table in which the limits of the rounded tex numbers have been converted into those of a traditional system.

TABLE III.—CONVERSION OF ENGLISH COTTON COUNT INTO ROUNDED TEX NUMBER.

For Use During the First Stage of Introduction of the Tex System.

Tex = 590.5/Cotton count.

In the left-hand columns of this table, find the range that includes the cotton count under consideration. On the same line as the selected range and to the right of it, find the corresponding rounded tex number. This is the number to be placed in parentheses after the traditional number during the first stage of the introduction of the tex system.

Example.—Cotton count 21 falls in the range of 20.36 to 21.87. The corresponding rounded tex number is 28. The recommended notation for this yarn during the first stage of the introduction of tex yarn numbers is accordingly: cotton count 21 (28 tex), or, using the European abbreviation, Nec 21 (28 tex).

* * *

When required, the values below 10 tex and above 100 tex can be derived from the same table simply by multiplying the values by 10 or dividing them by 10. When doing this, it should be noted that the decimal point in the left columns moves in the opposite direction to that in the right column.

Examples.—

Cotton Count		Recommended
Beginning with	Up to but Not Including	Rounded Tex Number
20.36	21.87	28
2.036	2.187	280
203.6	218.7	2.8

Cotton count[a]		Recommended
Beginning with	Up to but Not Including	Rounded Tex Number
57.59	60.26	10
54.91	57.59	10.5
52.47	54.91	11
50.24	52.47	11.5
48.19	50.24	12
46.30	48.19	12.5
43.73	46.30	13
40.72	43.73	14
38.09	40.72	15
35.78	38.09	16
33.74	35.78	17
31.92	33.74	18
30.28	31.92	19
28.80	30.28	20
27.46	28.80	21
26.24	27.46	22
25.13	26.24	23
24.10	25.13	24
23.16	24.10	25
21.87	23.16	26
20.36	21.87	28
19.05	20.36	30
17.90	19.05	32
16.87	17.90	34
15.96	16.87	36
15.14	15.96	38
14.41	15.14	40
13.74	14.41	42
13.13	13.74	44
12.57	13.13	46
12.05	12.57	48
11.58	12.05	50
10.94	11.58	52
10.19	10.94	56
9.524	10.19	60
8.947	9.524	64
8.436	8.947	68
7.980	8.436	72
7.571	7.980	76
7.201	7.571	80
6.866	7.201	84
6.561	6.866	88
6.282	6.561	92
6.026	6.282	96
5.759	6.026	100
5.758	5.759	105

[a] Cotton count (Nec) = 840-yd hanks per lb.

TABLE IV.—CONVERSION OF ENGLISH WORSTED COUNT INTO ROUNDED TEX NUMBER.

For Use During the First Stage of Introduction of the Tex System.
Tex = 885.8/worsted count.

In the left-hand columns of this table, find the range that includes the worsted number under consideration. On the same line as the selected range and to the right of it, find the corresponding rounded tex number. This is the number to be placed in parentheses after the traditional number during the first stage of the introduction of the tex system.

Example.—Worsted count 32 falls in the range of 30.54 to 32.80. The corresponding rounded tex number is 28. The recommended notation for this yarn during the first stage of the introduction of tex yarn numbers is accordingly: Worsted count 32 (28 tex), or, using the European abbreviation, Ne 32 (28 tex).

* * *

When required, the values below 10 tex and above 100 tex can be derived from the same table simply by multiplying the values by 10 or dividing them by 10. When doing this, it should be noted that the decimal point in the two left columns moves in the opposite direction to that in the right column.

Examples:

Worsted Count		Recommended
Beginning with	Up to but Not Including	Rounded Tex Number
30.54	32.81	28
3.054	3.281	280
305.4	328.1	2.8

English Worsted Count[a]		Recommended
Beginning with	Up to but Not Including	Rounded Tex Number
82.400	86.419	10.5
78.737	82.400	11
75.387	78.737	11.5
72.310	75.387	12
69.474	72.310	12.5
65.614	69.474	13
61.089	65.614	14
57.148	61.089	15
53.684	57.148	16
50.617	53.684	17
47.881	50.617	18
45.425	47.881	19
43.209	45.425	20
41.200	43.209	21
39.368	41.200	22
37.693	39.368	23
36.155	37.693	24
34.737	36.155	25
32.807	34.737	26
30.544	32.807	28
28.574	30.544	30
26.842	28.574	32
25.308	26.842	34
23.940	25.308	36
22.712	23.940	38
21.604	22.712	40
20.600	21.604	42
19.684	20.600	44
18.846	19.684	46
18.077	18.846	48
17.368	18.077	50
16.403	17.368	52
15.272	16.403	56
14.287	15.272	60
13.421	14.287	64
12.654	13.421	68
11.970	12.654	72
11.356	11.970	76
10.802	11.356	80
10.300	10.802	84
9.842	10.300	88
9.423	9.842	92
9.038	9.423	96
8.641	9.038	100
8.240	8.641	105

[a] English worsted count (Ne) = 560-yd hanks per lb.

TABLE V.—CONVERSION OF AMERICAN WOOLEN RUN INTO ROUNDED TEX NUMBER.

For Use During the First Stage of Introduction of the Tex System.
Tex = 310.03/American woolen run.

In the left-hand columns of this table, find the range that includes the woolen run number under consideration. On the same line as the selected range and to the right of it, find the corresponding rounded tex number. This is the number to be placed in parentheses after the traditional number during the first stage of the introduction of the tex system.

Example.—American woolen run 11 falls in the range 10.691 to 11.483. The corresponding rounded tex number is 28. The recommended notation for this yarn during the first stage of the introduction of tex yarn numbers is accordingly: Woolen run 11 (28 tex), or, using the European abbreviation, Nar 11 (28 tex).

* * *

When required, the values below 10 tex and above 100 tex can be derived from the same table simply by multiplying the values by 10 or dividing them by 10. When doing this, it should be noted that the decimal point in the two left columns moves in the opposite direction to that in the right column.

Examples:

American Woolen Run		Corresponding
Beginning with	Up to but Not Including	Rounded Tex Value
10.691	11.483	28
1.0691	1.1483	280
106.91	114.83	2.8

American Woolen Run[a]		Recommended
Beginning with	Up to but Not Including	Rounded Tex Number
30.247	31.633	10
28.840	30.247	10.5
27.558	28.840	11
26.386	27.558	11.5
25.309	26.386	12
24.316	25.309	12.5
22.965	24.316	13
21.381	22.965	14
20.002	21.381	15
18.790	20.002	16
17.716	18.790	17
16.758	17.716	18
15.899	16.758	19
15.123	15.899	20
14.420	15.123	21
13.779	14.420	22
13.193	13.779	23
12.654	13.193	24
12.158	12.654	25
11.483	12.158	26
10.691	11.483	28
10.001	10.691	30
9.395	10.001	32
8.858	9.395	34
8.379	8.858	36
7.949	8.379	38
7.562	7.949	40
7.210	7.562	42
6.890	7.210	44
6.596	6.890	46
6.327	6.596	48
6.079	6.327	50
5.741	6.079	52
5.345	5.741	56
5.000	5.345	60
4.697	5.000	64
4.429	4.697	68
4.190	4.429	72
3.975	4.190	76
3.781	3.975	80
3.605	3.781	84
3.445	3.605	88
3.298	3.445	92
3.164	3.298	96
3.024	3.164	100
2.884	3.024	105

[a] American woolen run (Nar) = 1600-yd hanks per lb.

TABLE VI.—CONVERSION OF DENIER NUMBER INTO ROUNDED TEX NUMBER.

For Use During the First Stage of the Introduction of the Tex System.

Tex = Denier number/9.

In the left-hand columns of this table find the range that includes the denier number under consideration. On the same line as the selected range and to the right of it, find the corresponding rounded tex number. This is the number to be placed in parentheses after the traditional number during the first stage of the introduction of the tex system.

Example.—The denier number 250 falls in the range of 243 to 261. The corresponding rounded tex number is 28. The recommended notation for this yarn during the first stage of the introduction of tex yarn numbers is accordingly: 250 denier (28 tex), or, using the European abbreviation, Td 250 (28 tex).

* * *

When required, the values below 10 tex and above 100 tex can be derived from the same table simply by multiplying the values by 10 or dividing them by 10. When doing this it should be noted that the decimal point in the two left columns moves in the same direction as in the right column.

Examples:

Denier Number		Corresponding
Beginning with	Up to but Not Including	Rounded Tex Value
243.....	261	28
2430.....	2610	280
24.3	26.1	2.8

Denier Number[a]		Recommended
Beginning with	Up to but Not Including	Rounded Tex Number
88.2......	92.25	10
92.25.....	96.75	10.5
96.75.....	101.2	11
101.2......	105.7	11.5
105.7......	110.2	12
110.2......	114.7	12.5
114.7......	121.5	13
121.5......	130.5	14
130.5......	139.5	15
139.5......	148.5	16
148.5......	157.5	17
157.5......	166.5	18
166.5......	175.5	19
175.5......	184.5	20
184.5......	193.5	21
193.5......	202.5	22
202.5......	211.5	23
211.5......	220.5	24
220.5......	229.5	25
229.5......	243	26
243........	261	28
261........	279	30
279........	297	32
297........	315	34
315........	333	36
333........	351	38
351........	369	40
369........	387	42
387........	405	44
405........	423	46
423........	441	48
441........	459	50
459........	486	52
486........	522	56
522........	558	60
558........	594	64
594........	630	68
630........	666	72
666........	702	76
702........	738	80
738........	774	84
774........	810	88
810........	846	92
846........	882	96
882........	922.5	100
922.5......	967.5	105

[a] Denier number (Td) = grams per 9000 meters.

TEXTILEATHER. A trade-mark for pyroxylin-coated fabrics, it is a well-known industrial name which covers a number of products in the leather-cloth and plastic fields, not only pyroxylin but vinyl resin plastic-coated cloths, vinyl resin plastic films, reinforced vinyl plastics, pyroxylin and vinyl resin coated fiber-base materials.

Products of the Textileather Corporation, Toledo, Ohio, include:

1. FELTONE: A trade-marked, supported vinyl plastic.

2. KERATOL: A pyroxylin-coated bookbinding material.

3. MUSTANG: A vinyl-coated fiber base material.

4. REVELRY: A trade-mark name for sealed patterns in plastic upholstery.

5. TEXTILCO: A reinforced plastic film.

6. TEXTILEATHER: A coated leather cloth that is rich-looking, durable, washable, vermin-proof, odorless, pleasing to the touch, and easily manipulated. It is used in bookbinding, baby carriages, leather goods, upholstery, stuffed toys, card tables, hassocks, wall coverings. The product comes in a wide range of colors.

7. TEXTILOID: One type is based on a firm latex-impregnated fiber stock, while the second type is based on a softer latex-saturated fiber stock. Both types are coated with pyroxylin on one or both sides and embossed and finished in leather-like effects. Used for bookbinding, case covering, hat sweat-bands, leather goods.

8. TOLEX: A super-tough plastic-coated fabric which withstands flexing, folding and abrasion. Used in rainwear, luggage, automobile upholstery, handbags, protective clothing, etc.

9. TOLON: A tough all-plastic product that consists of a sheet of tough vinyl plastic that requires no fabric backing. It is resistant to flexing, abrasion, scuffing and stains, as well as to oils and greases, gasoline, naphtha, acids and alkalies, alcohol, salt water and perspiration. It finds uses in upholstery, shoes, handbags, and belts.

TEXTILE CLASSIFICATIONS. These are:

1. RAW MATERIAL: Wool, cotton, nylon, asbestos, linen, etc.

2. CONSTRUCTION: Woven, knitted, plaited, braided, lace, or felt.

3. COLOR: Red, blue, gray, white, black, natural, neutral, beige, drab, etc.

4. FINISH: Cashmere, ciré, clear, crepe, crips, cropped, de-lustered, dull, duplex, even, face-finish, glazed, glossy, harsh, lustrous, mercerized, moiré or watermarked, moss, napped, natural, pebble, plain, reversible, rough, satiny, semifinish, sheared, smooth, soft, starched, stiff, surface-finish, undressed-finish, uneven-finish.

TEXTILE COMMODITY. Any useful raw material used in textile such as raw stock, worsted tops, etc.

TEXTILE COMPANIES, THE "BIG SIXTEEN." These are: Burlington Industries, J.P. Stevens & Company, Inc.; United Merchants & Manufacturers, Kayser Roth Corporation, Indian Head, Inc.; West Point-Pepperell, Inc., M. Lowenstein & Sons, Inc.; Cannon Mills Corporation, Dan River Industries, Cone Mills Corporation, Springs Mills, Inc.; The Kendall Company, Inc.; Mohasco Industries, Fieldcrest Mills, Inc.; Collins & Aikman Corporation, and Reigel Textile Corporation.

TEXTILE DESIGN, THEORIES OF COLOR IN. The three primary elements of textile designs are the weave, the combination of form, and the blend of colors. They enter, separately or in conjunction with one another, into every type of loom effort and effect.

The weave refers specifically to the structure of the fabric and is an indispensable factor in any type of material. Weave patterns will produce in the one operation an even and firm fabric decorated with a type of pattern that usually is made up of minute parts but which definitely will produce a characteristic fabric construction.

Combination of forms is the surface decoration obtained by uniting straight and curved lines.

Color and blends of color brighten and improve the qualities of the pattern, design, or motif. In fact, the discarding of color shades would diminish the elegance of the design and spoil its appearance in the finished goods. Whether the pattern is a check, figure, intermingled effect or stripe, the fabric obtains its eye appeal from the methods of coloring used to enhance the fabric. Woolens, worsteds, cottons, rayons, and silks rely very much on color for their selling points. Fabrics are usually bought by the consumer either because of the type of finish on the cloth or the weave, plus the color of the cloth itself.

There is, for example, a larger diversity of weave design in worsteds when compared with the possibilities noted in woolens. In each type of fabric colors are extensively used to develop appealing effects and to give the purchaser an impression of cheerfulness when he chooses cloth.

Patterns in dress fabrics, shirtings and other fabrics made of cotton are often combinations of "fancy" shades; rayons and silks may show coloring in its various combinations, which enhance the material to the point where the tone and character of the color or shade has a distinct bearing on its popularity. Though a fabric may be appealing in hand, well-constructed, uniform and well-finished, a lack of brightness, luster, or eye-appealingness may so detract from the appearance of the pattern that these qualities alone are not sufficient to move the goods to the consuming public.

Some of the ways to use fancy shades in weave patterns in the loom include:

1. Mixture fabrics for coating, suiting, sportswear.

Combining or blending various colors of stock or material.

The use of twisted yarns—ply, S-twist, Z-twist, cable, mock, etc.

2. Plain, twill, mat, and so-called fancy constructions such as used in coating, costumes, dresses, flannels, jackets, sportswear, suitings, trouserings, etc.

The introduction of colors in the warp for stripe effects.

The introduction of colors in the filling for checks, overplaids, plaids, spot effects.

The introduction of colors in both systems of yarn, in addition to the foregoing, for broken effects and novelty effects.

3. Figured designs for dress goods "vesting fabrics," and backed and double cloths:

The use of one or more warps in the loom.

The use of one or more fillings in the loom.

TEXTILE FIBER PRODUCTS IDENTIFICATION ACT. See Man-Made Textile Fibers and the Textile Fiber Products Identification Act of June 3, 1959.

TEXTILE FIBER PRODUCTS IDENTIFICATION ACT, SUBJECT TO AND EXEMPT FROM. The following tabulations are subject to the rulings of this Act with regard to labeling:

1. All fibers, yarns and fabrics.

2. Afghans and throws.

3. Antimacassars.

4. Articles of wearing apparel.

5. Batts.

6. Bedding—bedspreads, blankets, covers, pads, pillowcases, pillows, quilts, and sheets.

7. Curtains and casement cloths for backing, etc.

8. Cushions.

9. Draperies.

10. Flags.

11. Floor-coverings—to include those of all wool or partly of wool.

12. Furniture scarfs.

13. Furniture slipcovers and other covers or coverlets for furniture.

14. Hammocks.

15. Handkerchiefs.
16. Ironing board covers and pads.
17. Linings, interlinings, filling, or padding incorporated chiefly for warmth.
18. Reused upholstery stuffing.
19. Scarfs.
20. Sleeping bags.
21. Tablecloths, napkins, and doilies.
22. Towels.
23. Umbrellas and parasols.
24. Washcloths and dishcloths.

The following products are exempt from the Act under all circumstances:

1. Backings of floor-coverings and rug paddings.
2. Bandages, surgical dressings, and other products subject to The Food, Drug and Cosmetic Act of the Federal Trade Commission.
3. Headgear, handbags, catamenial articles, brushes, chemically impregnated cleaning cloths, adhesive tapes and adhesive sheets, lamp shades, luggage, diapers, tops.
4. Nonwoven products of disposable nature.

5. Outer coverings of furniture, mattresses, and boxsprings.
6. Packaging ribbons.
7. Pot holders and kitchen mitts.
8. Products made of plastic film.
9. Sewing and handicraft threads.
10. Shoes and outer footwear.
11. Stiffenings, trimmings, facings, interfacings.
12. Upholstery stuffing, unless reused.
13. Woolen products which are subject, of course, to the Wool Products Labeling Act of 1939.

The following products are exempt from the Act, provided no representation as to fiber content is made in advertising, signs, selling, or through any other medium. Once such representation is made, the product loses its status of exemption and then becomes subject to the provisions of the Act:

1. Belts, book cloth, armbands, artists' canvas, diaper liners, garters, labels, looper clips intended for handicraft purposes, permanently knotted neckwear, sanitary belts, shoelaces, suspenders, tapestry cloth.

2. Coated fabrics and those portions of textile products made of coated fabrics.
3. Christmas stockings, dress forms and covers, dress shields, beach bags, fabric-covered hangers, hair curlers, earmuffs, iron-on patches, lined jewel boxes, lined sewing baskets, scuffs (slippers), shoe mitts, shopping bags, zippers.
4. Fillings or paddings incorporated for structural purposes and not for warmth.
5. Linings or interlinings incorporated for structural purposes and not for warmth.
6. Powder puffs.

TEXTILE INDUSTRY, SPOKES IN THE GREAT WHEEL OF THE. This listing covers endeavors and efforts which contribute to the sustenance of the Textile Industry, directly and indirectly:
Apparel Manufacturers
Apparel Retailers
Carpet and Carpet Dealers
Chain Stores
Chemical Companies

TEXTILE FIBERS, DESIRABLE QUALITIES IN

1. COHESION: The manner in which fibers adhere, cling, or "hang together" in a uniform manner, as in the case of a worsted yarn, or in a more or less conglomerate mass, as observed in woolen yarn.

2. ELASTICITY: The ability of textile fibers to "bounce back" when released from tension or stretch, as noted in woolen yarns.

3. ELONGATION: The ability of fibers in yarns or in fabrics "to go in the direction of the weave." Also means the increase in length from a tensile force: an example of this, the fibers in yarns as they appear in "baggy trousers" on a rainy day, or the sagginess of some woolen fabrics of low texture or pick count.

4. CRIMP: The waves, seen or unseen, in textile fibers; noted especially in wool fibers in which there are "waves within waves," known as serrations, chiefly not observed by the naked eye.

5. FIBER LENGTH: Evenness of length, uniformity, and the staple length of a group of fibers; all these properties are very important in fabric development.

6. FINENESS: May be measured in microns, centimeters, parts of an inch, or in inches. Fiber diameter is very important in the determination of the end use or terminal use of the fibers at hand. Fineness does much to determine the properties and characteristics of the particular fibers, whether to be worked alone or in conjunction with other fibers in blends, mixtures, combinations, etc.

7. FLEXIBILITY: The ability of fibers to bend or flex easily; highly desirable property in many instances.

8. MOISTURE CONTENT: The regain is what the fiber is able to take up or actually regain in moisture after being brought to the bone-dry condition. Moisture content will vary with the several types of fibers used in the textile industry today.

9. POROSITY OR CAPILLARITY: The capacity of fibers to absorb moisture; varies with the several types of fibers in use today.

10. TENSILE STRENGTH: The ability of fibers, yarns, or fabrics to withstand or resist tension; tested by breaking or rupture of yarn or fabric on "tensile-strength machines" or "breaking machines." Strength tests on yards and fabrics are very important in fabric structures today.

11. RESILIENCY: The ability of yarns or fabrics to "bounce back" when crushed in the palm of the hand or otherwise.

12. TWIST SPINNABILITY: The ease with which fibers may be drawn, drafted, doubled, redoubled, attenuated, twisted, and wound from some type of spinning method onto a device for taking care of the newly spun yarn.

Converters
Department Stores
Drycleaners
Dyes and Dyers
Fabric Stores
Factors
Fiber Producers
Knitters
Labor Organizations
Laundries
Machinery Manufacturers
Nonwoven Products
Printers
Sewing
Specialty Shops
Spinners
Suppliers
Upholstery
Weavers
And Many Others - Immediate and Isolated or Special.

TEXTILES. Used to denote the results of textile work, i.e. manipulation from the raw condition, through to the finished state, of any of the kingdoms of fibers employed by man for this purpose. It includes practically all of the materials used in the making of clothing, inner and outer, for the human race all over the world. Textiles also include rugs, carpets, wall coverings, decorative fabrics. There are many uses of textiles in some form or other in many types of industry. Textiles include all materials from the very cheapest kinds of cloths, muslins, tobacco cloths, cheesecloths, to the very expensive damasks, brocades, brocatelles, Jacquard materials, and tapestries. The types, kinds and varieties of cloth make an almost endless chain from the lowest to the highest in quality, texture, finish, weight, price, width, sheerness, compactness, etc.

In this country, Textiles should be pronounced as *"Textills,"* while in the United Kingdom the term is pronounced *"Textyles."*

TEXTILE SOAP. Any of the large number of soaps used in any phase of textiles to produce a finished cloth. Special consideration must be given to the composition and the ingredients of the particular soap.

TEXTILE TECHNICIAN. One able to analyze fabrics so that a desired result can be produced by the mill. He must be thoroughly conversant with fibers, yarns, and weave constructions and at the same time be familiar with various mill operations; he does not, however, actually have to be a carder, spinner, weaver, or finisher. It is not the duty of a technician to inform a mill how to do the work; this should be taken care of by mill management. The technician is often a graduate of

a textile school or textile institute but comparable knowledge may be gained through association or by work with fabric textile technologists over a period of years.

TEXTILE TECHNOLOGIST. Of necessity a fabric technician, but his task begins where the work of the technician terminates. He must have a thorough knowledge of fiber and yarn research, textile research, fabric development, dyeing and finishing, and all other converting problems. In addition, he must be able to diagnose yarn and fabric defects and to advise the mill how these defects may be remedied. This latter knowledge is usually gained through textile school education and actual mill and manufacturing experience. The technologist should be fully conversant with chemical and physical phases necessary to the production of a finished fabric.

TEXTILE TESTING. This essential phase of the textile industry, which is stressed and given prominence by mills and department stores, has come to the fore very rapidly within the last few years. Some of the more popular tests given to material are as follows:

RAW MATERIAL TESTS:

1. Microscopic test for fiber content.

2. Burning test for identification of content and fiber.

3. Chemical test, acid and alkali, for fiber content.

4. Testing for union and mixed fabrics.

CONSTRUCTION AND WEAVE:

1. Weight per yard of the cloth.

2. Determination of the warp and filling.

3. Determination of the face and back of the goods.

4. Reed marks.

5. Texture or count of the material, the ends and picks per inch.

6. Twist in the yarn by means of the twist counter.

7. Size of the yarn as to ply, evenness, and yarn number or count.

8. Determination of crimp in the yarn.

9. Strength of the yarn when wet.

10. Resistance of the material to wearing abrasion.

11. Tensile strength of the yarn by the single strand method.

12. Breaking strength of the cloth, strip or grab method.

COLOR:

1. Fastness of color to sunlight, perspiration, washing, crocking, bleeding, spotting, sea water, and bleaching.

FINISH:

1. Wearing quality determined on

the wearometer.

2. Abrasion test for nap on the cloth.

3. Determination for waterproofing, repelling water, and fireproofing.

4. Determination of sizing, filling, and finishing material.

5. Testing for weighted silk.

TEXTILE TESTING PROCEDURES. The following is a skeletonized outline which encompasses the major testing methods, operations, procedures, and treatments used to test textiles and apparel. All major testing concerns are equipped for this type of work which includes chemical testing and physical testing.

1. *Abrasion Testing:* This is done on the Stoll Flex or on the Stoll Flat machine; on the Taber Abraser, and the Wyzenbeek Associates machine. Also includes testing for abrasion with relation to edgewear.

2. *Air Permeability:* Testing for the airflow through fabrics.

3. *Carpet Testing:* Pile Weight testing on unfinished and finished carpeting to include cut pile looped pile weights. Also testing for weight as to construction and thickness of components.

4. *Colorfastness Testing:* Bathing waters to include chlorinated pool water, fresh water and salt water. Chlorine (concentrated) testing is in this category.

Cleaning: Includes drycleaning (per solvent) and accelerated drycleaning by metal jar method.

Crocking: By the dry and wet methods.

Gas Fading: To cover all phases of this question in fading.

Hot Pressing: Use of the dry and wet methods.

Laundering: To cover first laundering treatment; accelerated laundering by metal jar procedure.

Light: Use of the Fade-Ometer for exposure.

Perspiration: Covers both acidic and alkaline testing and effects.

Pleating: Done by use of the exposure test.

Sublimation: Chemical procedure followed in this phase.

Water Spotting: Chemical procedure followed in this phase.

5. *Complaint Investigations:* For fabrics garments, floorcoverings, and testing on household and industrial articles.

6. *Composition Testing Other Than In Fiber Composition:* This includes Extraction Testing of non-fibrous material. Under this caption are included chloroform, acid, enzyme, and water

testing. Also, ash content, moisture content done in the conditioning oven, and resin content (soluble and total).

7. *Determination Testing:* Testing for the grade of fiber or filament, photomicrography, ply in yarn, sizing, et al.

8. *Extraction Analysis:* For determination of the amount of oil and grease in textiles; for the percentage of acetate in a union fabric of acetate and rayon; cotton in a woolen cloth, et al.

9. *Construction Analysis Testing:*

Fiber Testing: Includes denier count of the cut staple (microscope); percentage of composition on two or more fibers in the one specimen; identification by class in re the generic term as per Federal Trade Commission (March 3, 1960); identification by trade name wherever possible.

Fiber Composition: With percentages reported these include chemical or mechanical separation by class (generic name) by single fiber, two or more fibers; chemical and microscopic analysis by trade name wherever possible; and specialty or hair fibers for determination of single fiber or multiple fibers in specimen.

Yarn: Covers takeup and crimp per yarn, evenness of yarn (board winding); twist combination in singles and in ply and twist takeup with twist test; yarn count or size, as received, in yarn or denier; yarn count or size with finish removed.

Fabric: Includes thickness test and covers removal of special finishes, if necessary; felt or felted fabrics usually made with wool or wool-combination stock; count, "pickcount" thread count or texture of goods relative to weave in fabric - plain, twill, satin, fancy, pile constructions, etc. Determination of total number of ends and picks per inch in woven goods and to include narrow fabrics, ribbons and tapes with a six inch maximum. Total texture or count as in a sheeting that is 72 X 68 for total of 140.

Also includes weave construction and detail; weaving as to takeup or crimp in warp and in the filling; weight per square yard, ounces per yard, and yards per pound of fabric. Reed width and finished width of the goods are in this category. Under Fabric Testing are also included yield in knit fabrics, crease recovery, fabric thickness, wales and courses in knit fabrics.

10. *Flammability and Fire Resistance:* In accordance with CS-191-53 for clothing textiles; also covers all testing of fabric as received, according to all government or state regulations and standards for flammability of fabrics; also, wash-testing and drycleanability after washing for determination of effectiveness against flame. Under Fire Resistance the following should be noted: New York City Board of Standards and
    Appeals.

City of Boston, Massachusetts.

State of California - Intermediate Test.

N.F.P.A. by Method 701. Includes small scale test, large scale test including flat and/or fold tests, and complete test for drycleaned and/or laundered specimens.

11. *Finishes Testing:* Testing for the properties that a finish may impart to a particular fabric; these follow:

   1. Abrasion-testing
   2. Absorbency
   3. Antiseptic qualities
   4. Antistatic qualities
   5. Colorfastness
   6. Crease-resistance
   7. Crispness
   8. Drapability
   9. Drycleanability
  10. Dullness
  11. Durability
  12. Flame-resistance
  13. Gas-fading inhibited
  14. Ironing (minimum)
  15. Lightfastness
  16. Lintlessness
  17. Lustrousness
  18. Mildew-resistance
  19. Moth-resistance
  20. Oil-resistance
  21. Perspiration resistance
  22. Renewability
  23. Scroopiness
  24. Shrinkage-resistance
  25. Slip-resistance
  26. Softness
  27. Stain-resistance
  28. Stretch and snag-resistance
  29. Washfastness
  30. Water-repellency
  31. Wilt-reduction

12. *Hosiery Testing:* Includes bursting strength of boot and/or all hose parts; total number of courses in hose, wales and courses per inch, denier count of yarn in hose and to be done on the "per yarn basis." Also, cut and needle count or guage and total needle count; run resistance, snag resistance. Complete analyses are popular in hosiery testing today.

13. *Laundering And Drycleaning:* The

following items are of note: appearance rating after one laundering and repeated launderings, shrinkage after one laundering or drycleaning and for repeated treatments; and for one drycleaning and repeated treatments, testing for shrinkage and colorfastness after one or more launderings.

Testing For Laundering And Drycleaning In Preparation For Other Types Of Testing: In this phase would be included dimensional stability (tension presser), first laundering and/or drycleaning and multiple tests, as well. Also includes knit cut, knit guage, and shrinkage.

On Garments: Small items such as gloves, hosiery, towels, etc., tests could be given to appearance, shrinkage, and colorfastness pertinent to laundering and/or drycleaning for a single or fist test and for multiple tests.

Large items to include garments, draperies, bedspreads, blankets, etc. may be given the following treatments - appearance after one laundering or drycleaning; shrinkage and colorfastness tests for effect after one laundering or drycleaning as well as for multiple tests.

14. *Microscopic Testing:* This has many uses in both textiles and apparel-fibers, yarns, fabrics, etc.

15. *Mildew and its Prevention:* Testing on Mercurials, Phenols, and Quaternary Ammonium salts.

16. *Optical Testing:* Microscopic and chemical and physical testing in qualitative and quantitiative fiber analysis.

17. *Water and Oil Repellency and Waterproofness Tests:* In this category would be the following: Hydrostatic pressure tests, along with additional hydrostatic tests after cleaning or laundering; oil repellency testing after cleaning or laundering; rain test for first level and time period (showerproof, water-repellent, and waterproof); spray testing after cleaning or laundering.

18. *Miscellaneous Testing:* In this group could be the following: absorption, adhesion, aging to include oven control temperature per hour and Fade-Ometer exposure per hour; air permeability or porosity, classification of dyestuffs, crease or wrinkle recovery, drying time, electrical resistivity (static test); examination of returned merchandise, fabric defects, ironing with reaction to varying temperatures, melting point of nylon and comparable fibers, determination of pH, pilling resistance on the random tumble

method, resiliency with a single load recovery, resilience of blankets on ASA L-22 or L-24 methods, relative humidity in items, resin treated fabrics, spot and stain resistance and removal, shrinkage, strength testing, stretch and growth testing on stretch fabrics, stiffness of fabrics (heart loop or self bending method), wool testing for qulaity of top stock, alkali solubility, etc. Also, workmanship alone or workmanship and construction details, yarn shifitng or distortion as received, and before and after three launderings or drycleanings; yarn standards for counts or numbers of yarn, denier counts for silk and the manmade fibers or filaments, factor methods used in analysis work, equivalent counts of yarns, yards per pound of particular yarn counts from specimens submitted, compound counts of yarns, etc.

TEXTILE YARNS. The word "yarn" is a generic term for an assemblage of fibers or filaments, either natural or manmade, whether twisted together to form a continuous strand which can be used in weaving, knitting, braiding, or plaiting, or otherwise made into a textile material. Spun yarn is the product of the spinning frame characterized by a continuous, evenly distributed, coherent arrangement of any type of fibers of varying or similar staple length, the relative positions of which are maintained by the introduction of a definite lateral twist to produce strength or coherence in the final operation.

Notable exception to the above would be the woolen-type yarn. Here the fibers are distributed at nearly right angles with relation to the continuous length of the yarn. An exception to even spinning would be the additon of noiled fibers to the base stock. Noils do not lend themselves to being properly drawn; in consequence, a rough-texture yarn, desirable for tweeds and shantungs is produced.

To produce spun yarns, the raw stock must be put through preparatory machinery for even distribution and blending, after which there is carding or combing to achieve parallel fiber distribution; then several attenuating or drawing machine operations follow, ending with the spinning. Yarn in production is called a lap, sliver, and roving, in that order, depending on the type of machine used. Yarns are definitely sized or numbered, based on the number of standard yardage hanks contained in one pound.

Filament yarn is made from various continuous filaments, such as silk and manmade filaments — viscose, acetate, nylon, "Orlon," "Dacron," etc.

TEXTILIST. Occasionally used to imply an expert or specialist in some phase of textiles.

TEXTILIT. The paper fiber and yarn composition used by the Germans in the last days of World War I. Sewing yarn and fabric were used because of regulation textile shortages.

TEXTORES. A special or separate class of citizens in Greece who carded wool, wove cloth or dyed fabric—the forerunner of the modern word, textiles.

TEXTORIAL, TEXTOUR. Old-time terms for a weaver of cloth.

TEXTRAFLUFF FELT. Staple lengths of resilient glass fiber processed through standard nonwoven textile equipment provide this glass-felt blanket used for insulation and filtration applications ranging from cryogenic or ice-cold temperatures up to 1,000° Fahrenheit. This glass fiber can be made into a dimensionally-stable glass blanket without the use of synthetic binder materials. In staple form Textrafluff can be felted alone or in blends with other natural or manmade fibers, bonding to provide stability and strength can be obtained chemically or mechanically. A product of PPG Industries, Inc., other uses of the felt include aircraft and automotive mufflers; fireproof, heat-resistant insulated clothing, mattresses, and life preservers. Its acoustical properties are excellent.

TEXTRALIZED. A trademark which identifies the yarn produced by an exclusive bulking or crimping process, owned and controlled by Joseph Bancroft & Sons Company, a division of Indian Head, Inc. While the crimping process is applicable to practically any manmade or natural fiber, it is at present, used mainly on filament nylon and polyester where the crimp is permanent. Pilling does not occur and the amount of stretch can be specified for the particular end-use. The mark may be used only by licensed manufacturers, and only on yarns which have met the standards controlled and prescribed by the company.

TEXTRINE. Archaic term for matters relating to weaving of fabric; a weaver.

TEXTRYL. A generic term coined by Du Pont for its nonwoven sheet structure produced by the wet papermaking process, and comprising fibers bonded with fibrids, See FIBRIDS.

TEXTURA. Registered trademark of Rohm and Haas, Philadelphia, Pennsylvania for its textured polyester yarn. It has a particularly high propensity for

dye and provides a high level of color fidelity and uniformity. Used in woven and knitted dressgoods and men's fabrics.

TEXTURAL DESIGN. The design in some fabrics is made by the weave rather than by color. Modern pile rugs and drapery fabrics in self-color show patterns by novel weave effects.

TEXTURE. The first meaning is the actual number of warp threads and filling picks, per inch, in any cloth that has been woven. It is written, say 88 x 72. This means that there are 88 ends and 72 picks per inch in the fabric.

When texture is the same, such as 64 x 64, the cloth is classed as a "square" material.

Sheeting, with regard to texture, is often referred to, for example, as a Number 128, Number 140, etc. Consideration of the number 128 means that the total number of ends and picks per inch is 128. Thus, there might be in the texture 72 ends and 56 picks, or 68 ends and 60 picks, or 64 ends and 64 picks which is a square fabric texture. A 140 sheeting would be better than a 128 sheeting since there would be more ends and picks to the inch in the former.

Texture is also much used by the public and in advertising circles to mean the finish and appearance of cloth for sale over the counter or in the finished garment state.

TEXTURED FILAMENT YARN. Continuous filament yarn treated to obtain bulking properties to compare with those achieved in some spun yarns.

TEXTURED-STRETCH YARNS, ADVANTAGES OF. These include proper and desired stretch; increased coverage and opacity of fabrics; improved hand, surface appeal, and interesting textures; surface effects such as pebble, crepe, crepes, etc.; and lighter, bulkier, and more resilient yarns and fabrics without added weight to the material.

TEXTURED WOVEN FABRIC, TWO-WAY. One in which the warp and the filling yarns are textured to provide more bulk and increased comfort stretch. At present these yarns are textured on the false-twist method. This affords greater flexibility with regard to controlling the bulk and level of stretch. This method is a continuous operation with twist, set, and then untwisting done in the one machine. The final effect is obtained by the use of a false-twist spindle and a heater box with the latest equipment featuring a second heater to stabilize the yarn. Thus, the amount of bulk or stretch can meet the specific needs of the fabric maker.

TEXTURED YARNS. They are made of continuous filaments and are modifications of these filaments in that the filaments do not lie parallel to one another. Fabrics made of these yarns have greater covering power and are softer than materials made from untreated filament yarns.

Stretch Yarns are also modified versions of continuous yarns and are classified as *Textured Yarns*. Some of these, however, do not have stretchability.

High Bulk Yarns are spun yarns made by blending high-shrinkage staple fibers with staple fibers of low shrinkage. Strictly speaking, they are not textured

yarns since they are made from staple stock and not from continuous filament. Bulk yarns provide a soft, flufflike effect or an opaque effect on certain woven and knitted cloths.

Articles made from the foregoing yarns are form-fitting to the body without pressure. The yarn effects are obtained in several ways — twisting, untwisting, false-twisted stretch, and by the use of air jets, heat, dry heat, crimping, curling, straining, and looping.

Advantages of bulked yarns and stretch yarns follow: These include soft, appealing hand, retention of air, absorbency, conductivity of perspiration, rather dull surface effect, varying amounts of stretchability, low specific gravity, ease

of washing and rapid drying, and good resistance to wear and abrasion. Most products which use these yarns come in one size, thereby making them economical for both the manufacturer and the consuming public. Generally speaking, these yarns have about the same uses in trade, such as for men's, women's, and children's stockings and socks, undershirts, T-shirts, men's shorts, light winterwear fabrics, blankets, swimsuits, decorative fabrics, leotards and slacks, carpeting, foundation fabrics, and for certain industrial fabrics.

AGILON: The texturing method is done by heat-setting over a blade. There is alteration of strain within the filaments so that when released from tension they have a tendency to curl. The yarn is made on modified standard textile equipment, of a non-torque nylon or "Dacron" filament yarn used alone or in combination with other yarns, chiefly cotton. A product of Deering Milliken Research Corporation, Spartanburg, South Carolina.

BAN-LON: This is a crimped yarn in which unprocessed filaments are textured or crimped and then thermo-set in a stuffer box. The principle of stretch yarn is not involved, and the yarn presents a smooth surface texture. Applied to any of the thermoplastics, Ban-Lon gives a soft, appealing hand. Joseph Bancroft & Sons Company, Wilmington, Delaware, owns and controls the patents associated with the yarn (Textralized) and the fabrics and garments made from yarn under specific standards (Ban-Lon).

FLUFLON: Of high bulk and high stretchability, the method may be applied to any thermoplastic fiber. The method of manufacture is continuous, taking the raw yarn as received all the way through to produce finished ply yarns for the trade. Licensor of the method is Leesona Corporation, Warwick, Rhode Island.

HELANCA: The first of the commercial stretch yarns to be introduced—in 1947. The yarn is highly twisted, set, and then detwisted in separate operations. It can also be prepared in one continuous operation. Product of Heberlein Patent Corporation, New York City.

MYLAST: The crimp is inserted into the yarn, to give a surface effect that may be either smooth or creped. Product of Clarence L. Meyers & Co., Philadelphia, Pennsylvania.

SAABA: Obtained by an annealing process on the Universal down-twister, which is equipped with a heating chamber and feed rolls. Involves the removal of stretch from a false-twist stretch yarn. Surface texture may be bouclé, chenille-like, or smooth. Licensor is Leesoma Corporation, Warwick, Rhode Island.

STEVETEX: Announced in August, 1964, by J. P. Stevens & Company, Inc., New York City, this textured yarn affords more bulkiness in the yarn than has theretofore been possible and provides improved wearing comfort in knitted and woven goods

used in lingerie, dressgoods, sportswear, etc. The greater bulkiness is achieved by crimping the individual filaments that make up the individual yarn. The method reduces skin contact, and allows for greater capillary space for air insulation in winter and evaporation in warm weather. Stevetex has more crimps per inch than comparable yarns, and the depth of the crimps can be controlled. Fine merino wool has from 30 to 40 crimps per inch; Stevetex runs to 80 or more crimps per inch.

This product absorbs more dye than non-crimped yarns and provides more clarity and better color depth or intensity. The yarn has a very soft, appealing hand and excellent draping properties.

SUPERLOFT: This highly twisted yarn is made in continuous process in which dry heat is used. False twist spindles reverse the direction of the twist as the yarn is being wound onto a bobbin or cone. Comes in single and ply yarn. Licensor is Leesona Corporation, Warwick, Rhode Island.

SYNFOAM: Owned by Synfoam Yarns, Inc.; the yarn is made on the twist-and-untwist method. Nylon and "Dacron" crepe fabrics are made from the yarn, which also finds much use in upholstery fabrics.

TASLAN: Produced through a bulking process which imparts a particular texture different from standard textile yarns. The hand, loftiness, covering power, yarn texture are such that these properties are permanent and do not require special handling or care. As a full-textured yarn, it is distinctively different when compared with regulation spun yarns or continuous filament yarns. The method can be applied to any thermoplastic fiber. A product of E. I. du Pont de Nemours & Co., Inc.

TYCORA: This trademark of Textured Yarn Company is applied to several processes used in the modification of continuous-filament yarn. Tycora yarns have soft hand, high dye affinity, strength and durability, bulkiness without added weight, and they are non-pilling.

SOME EXAMPLES OF TEXTURED YARNS

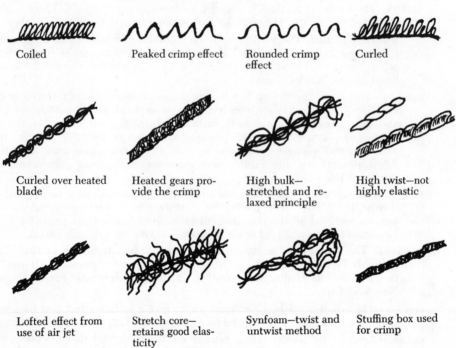

Coiled	Peaked crimp effect	Rounded crimp effect	Curled
Curled over heated blade	Heated gears provide the crimp	High bulk—stretched and relaxed principle	High twist—not highly elastic
Lofted effect from use of air jet	Stretch core—retains good elasticity	Synfoam—twist and untwist method	Stuffing box used for crimp

TEXTURED YARNS, SOME MAJOR HIGHLIGHTS IN.

1953-4: Men's hosiery became the first "breakthrough" for these yarns.

1956-7: Women's swimwear made its debut with textured yarns.

1957-8: Women's tights, leotards, became very popular, made from textured stretch yarns.

1958-9: Stretch ski pants appeared in Austria and Germany; introduced by Willy and Marie Bogner in West Germany.

1959: Crimplene launched in England.

1960: Stretch pants made popular by Emilio Pucci, leading designer, Florence Italy.

1961: Textured acetate knit dresses unveiled.

1962: Stretch denim became a staple fabric.

1965: Pantyhose became very popular.

1966: Printed nylon textured dresses became the vogue, as well as textured stockings which were widely accepted.

1967-8: Set polyester knitgoods became the rage in fashion and style.

TEXTURE EFFECT. This is used with reference to pile fabrics in which a rug, carpet, or other pile material has a rough, shaggy, or relief effect. These effects may be secured by the type of yarn used, the manner of weaving or the design construction.

TEXTURITY. Sponsored and labeled by the Texturity Guild, a nonprofit corporation. Material which bears this label is guaranteed not to shrink more than 2 per cent.

TEXTURIZING. When a smooth continuous manmade-fiber filament is given a new and permanent configuration which results in an appealing textural surface.

THEATRICAL GAUZE. Thin, open curtain fabric in plain or leno weave stiffened with sizing. Inexpensive and available in many colors. Originally used as background for stage scenery, it is now often used for window cur-

METHODS OF PRODUCING TEXTURED YARNS

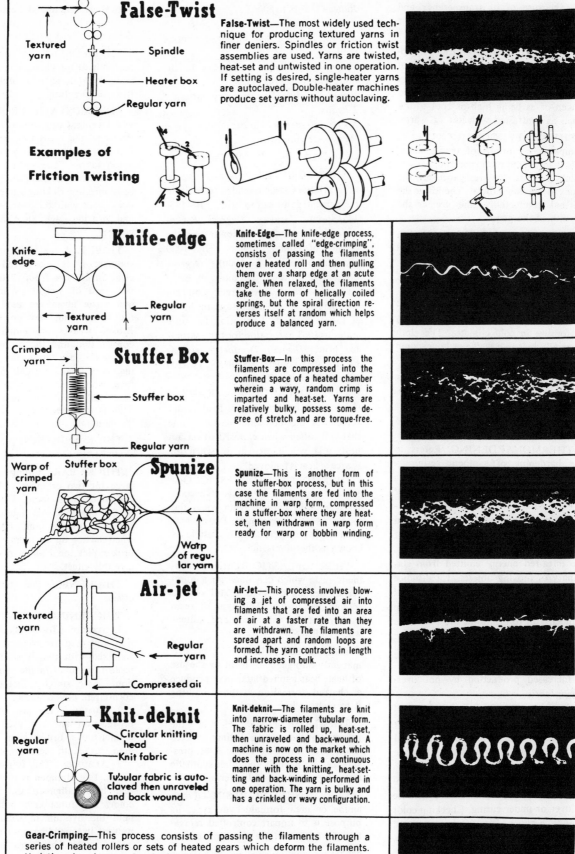

False-Twist

Textured yarn — Spindle — Heater box — Regular yarn

False-Twist—The most widely used technique for producing textured yarns in finer deniers. Spindles or friction twist assemblies are used. Yarns are twisted, heat-set and untwisted in one operation. If setting is desired, single-heater yarns are autoclaved. Double-heater machines produce set yarns without autoclaving.

Examples of Friction Twisting

Knife-edge

Knife edge — Regular yarn — Textured yarn

Knife-Edge—The knife-edge process, sometimes called "edge-crimping", consists of passing the filaments over a heated roll and then pulling them over a sharp edge at an acute angle. When relaxed, the filaments take the form of helically coiled springs, but the spiral direction reverses itself at random which helps produce a balanced yarn.

Stuffer Box

Crimped yarn — Stuffer box — Regular yarn

Stuffer-Box—In this process the filaments are compressed into the confined space of a heated chamber wherein a wavy, random crimp is imparted and heat-set. Yarns are relatively bulky, possess some degree of stretch and are torque-free.

Spunize

Warp of crimped yarn — Stuffer box — Warp of regular yarn

Spunize—This is another form of the stuffer-box process, but in this case the filaments are fed into the machine in warp form, compressed in a stuffer-box where they are heat-set, then withdrawn in warp form ready for warp or bobbin winding.

Air-jet

Textured yarn — Regular yarn — Compressed air

Air-Jet—This process involves blowing a jet of compressed air into filaments that are fed into an area of air at a faster rate than they are withdrawn. The filaments are spread apart and random loops are formed. The yarn contracts in length and increases in bulk.

Knit-deknit

Regular yarn — Circular knitting head — Knit fabric — Tubular fabric is autoclaved then unraveled and back wound.

Knit-deknit—The filaments are knit into narrow-diameter tubular form. The fabric is rolled up, heat-set, then unraveled and back-wound. A machine is now on the market which does the process in a continuous manner with the knitting, heat-setting and back-winding performed in one operation. The yarn is bulky and has a crinkled or wavy configuration.

Gear-Crimping—This process consists of passing the filaments through a series of heated rollers or sets of heated gears which deform the filaments. Variations in crimp can be obtained by controlling the number of crimps per inch as well as the depth of gear deformation. Unique configurations can be obtained. The process is popular with some fiber producers particularly for making continuous bulked filament carpet yarns in heavy deniers. In certain instances, little is known of the actual processes used within fiber-producing plants. In recent years several texturing machines have come on the market which make gear-crimping more readily available.

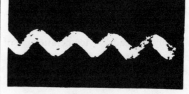

Courtesy: Rayon Publishing Co., Inc.

tains because of its transparency and interesting texture. Also known as Opera Gauze.

THERMAL CHARACTER. The apparent difference in the temperature of the cloth and the skin of the person handling the goods. Materials may be spoken of as being high or cool to the touch as contrasted with low or warm.

THERMAL CONDUCTIVITY. Comparative warmth of textile materials is measured on a special apparatus which records the resistance of the goods to the flow of heat. The lower the thermal conductivity, the greater the warmth of the goods.

THERMALINE DYEING. English method of solid color dyeing applied to union Luster wool fabrics.

THERMAL KNIT FABRIC. Certain knitted fabrics, made of cotton, man-made, or wool yarns, may be insulated for particular purposes, such as for use in cold climates. The cloth is usually knit in a waffle or honeycomb effect.

THERMOFIXATION. On the order of a curing method, this process is applied to dyeing operations which use higher than normal temperatures to fix dyestuff on the fibers.

THERMOHARDENING. Refers to the hardening of synthetic resins by heat applications.

THERMOMETER, MARK-TEMP INFRA-RED. The only portable infrared thermometer that gives fast and accurate temperature measurements of fabrics, without contact. It measures the infra-red energy emitted from stationary or moving objects at a distance of 5 inches to infinity. It is designed with an automatic ambient temperature compensator to insure the most accurate readings. Features of the device follow:
1. Determination of fabric temperature, without contact.
2. Increased production by not over-drying fabric.
3. Accurate control of curing and heat setting temperature, by determining fabric temperature from side to side and along the length, continuously, and while in motion.
4. An immediate answer on line problems such as high fabric odor because of over or under curing. Checking color changes because of varying temperatures. Check out of recorders or controllers, immediately and easily.
5. Easily "reads" temperatures of any surface (cans, dyeboxes, motors, steam lines), and liquids (dyebaths, washwater).
Specifications:

Range - 150° F. to 500° F.
Accuracy - 2% of scale (1% optional).
Battery Life - 3,000 hours of continuous use.
Operating Distance - 5 inches to infinity (close focus optional).
Power Supply - Two mercury batteries, 2.7 volts.
Spectral Response - 3 to 20 microns.
Weight - 28 ounces.

Chem-Mark, Inc., Roselle Park, N. J.

THERMOMETERS. *Degrees Baume'* is an arbitrary scale intended to indicate the percentage of salt in brine. °Be=145-145/Specific Gravity. *Degrees Barkometer* is commonly used for testing the density of tanning liquors. °Bk 1000 (Specific Gravity - 1000). *Degrees Saltometer* is used the most in brine research work. It does directly indicate the percentage of saturation in brine. It ranges from 0° Saturation for pure water to 100° Saturation for fully saturated brine. *Degrees Twaddel* is similar to the Barkometer Scale. °Tw=200 (Specific Gravity - 1000).

THERMOPLASTIC. Any plastic material which is permanently fusible and soluble. A thermoplastic plastic is one that will soften when exposed to certain heats and will harden again when the source of heat is removed.

THERMOPLASTIC PLASTIC. One that will soften when exposed to certain heats and will harden again when the source of heat is removed. Plastic material which is permanently fusible is known as thermoplastic.

THERMOPLASTIC RESIN. A synthetic resin which can undergo a number of heating cycles and still remain soluble and fusible. This type of resin usually softens with heat and stiffens when chilled.

THERMOSET PLASTIC. Set permanently into shape or form by the use of heat; heat applied later may produce a charred formation without causing it to melt or lose shape.

THERMOSETTING. Having the property of assuming a distinct or fixed shape after molding under heat pressure; certain phenols and other synthetic resins are examples of the term.

THERMOSETTING RESIN. Of melamine or urea formaldehyde type, its purpose is to impart controlled relaxation to fabrics in the finishing of the goods.

THERMOSOL DYEING. A dye method used on certain fabrics made from some of the man-made fibers. After the fabric is impregnated with selected dye, it is then treated for a

very short time to high heat (up to 450° F.). The process is a time-saver and demands utmost attention.

THERMOSTAT. A device which responds to the changes in temperature and which directly or indirectly controls temperature.

THERMOSTATIC PROCESS. Hellwig Dyeing Corporation, Philadelphia, Pennsylvania, owns this trade-mark of a heat-treating process used on woven nylon fabrics. The setting action controls dimensional stability, increases the resistance to wrinkling and creasing, and does away with the waxiness of nylon and provides a silklike hand to the goods.

THIBET. A material used in heavy suitings; it is piece-dyed and given clear finish; runs from 12 to 30 ounces per yard in weight. Wool, worsted, and waste fibers are used in making the several qualities on the market. Broken weaves are employed in the construction and the filling is usually double—a face filling and a back filling. A soft and smooth plain-finished face, woolen or part woolen, features much fabric of this name. Genuine Thibets are made from the fleece of the mountain sheep of Tibet, Asia.

THICK-AND-THIN. See THICK STRIPES; THIN STRIPES.

THICK BAR. Filling that is too large for two or more picks in weaving goods on a loom. Uneven takeup of the newly woven fabric is usually the cause of this fault. Poor attention when starting up the loom after a break, broken pick, or a loom-smash will also give this effect.

THICKENER. See SIZING; SIZING GUMS.

THICKENING AGENTS.
1. STARCH: Mostly alkaline is reaction and used for vegetable fibers. It is mixed with the dyestuff to form a paste to be used in the printing operation. Some starches include dextrine, cornstarch, potato starch.
2. GUMS: These are chiefly acidic in reaction and are used chiefly on animal fibers. British gum, gum arabic, gum tragacanth are examples of gums.
3. ALBUMEN: This is used with pigments. Egg albumen is more expensive than blood albumen and is lighter in color. The function of albumen is to hold the dyestuff in solution and to prevent its spreading onto the material.
4. GLUES: These are little used in printing except in the case of low-grade cottons. Fish glue is the most important of those used.

THICKNESS. General term used with regard to the actual thickness of blankets, coatings, pile cloths, industrial fabrics, and webbing. The height of pile cloths is also often referred to as thickness.

THICKNESS TEST. Test used to measure thickness of yarns and fabrics. Done by a machine that has a base and a frame, heavy enough to be stable, with a stationary plate fixed to it. The sample rests on this plate or anvil. A vertical sliding foot, with accurate surface, rests on top of the specimen. The foot, of known diameter, is inserted in a tapering cavity in the lower end of a sliding ram. The latter, by means of a rack and pinion, turns a dial finger, thus indicating the thickness of the sample under measurement, e.g., the distance between the foot and the anvil. The gauge may be read to thousandths of an inch, and by estimation in ten-thousandths. A fine coiled spring is usually employed to secure a light but uniform pressure of the foot upon the sample.

THICKSETT. British cotton cloth on the order of fustian; it has floats which produce a stubby pile when cut. It resembles low-grade velveteen or corduroy and is used as trousering for rough work.

THICK STRIPES. Those which are too thick and tend to throw off the general appearance of the fabric. Caused by uneven yarn, improper drawing-in or reeding, and incorrect yarn sizes.

THIMBLE. A caplike cover with a pitted surface to protect the end of the finger that pushes the needle.

THIMMONIER, BARTHELEMY. The first person ever to receive patent rights for a sewing machine; forerunner of Hunt, Singer, and Howe. He obtained these rights in 1830 but because so many workers in France were of the opinion that they would lose their work if the machine came into being, his machines were destroyed by them. His mahcine was of the lock-stitch type and he was interested in making uniforms for the French armies, particularly on a mass production basis, assembly lines, and in uniform sizes. With his machines destroyed, his efforts were stymied and he soon gave up all further efforts for a sewing machine.

THIN BAR. Warp ends with no filling or too fine filling for two or more picks in the weaving of fabric in a loom. Usually caused by the failure of the filling-stop motion to work properly by not "banging-off the loom" when a filling pick breaks or runs out from a bobbin.

THIN PLACE IN FABRIC. This is a strip of goods without filling which may run from a fraction to over an

inch in width. A thin place may be caused by a loose crank arm allowing the loom to cast out the bobbins, a splinter or a nick on a shuttle breaking the filling yarn, bobbin tails not being unwrapped, tail slips as a new bobbin is picked, clogging of the filling grate. Thin places can be reduced by checking the shuttles, harnesses, etc.

THIN STRIPES. Linked with thick stripes, they are caused by poor handling of the design, faulty weaving, incorrect drawing-in or reeding.

THIOZELL. A German casein fiber.

THIRD COMBING. Wool taken from the lower part of the back of the fleece.

THISTLE. Like the teasel, it is used to raise the nap of fabrics.

THIXOTROPY. The property shown by some gels of becoming liquid on stirring and resolidifying or thickening again on standing. A gel or a liquid that exhibits this property is said to be thixotropic. Because many gels, liquids, and pastes exhibit this property, it is a good idea to get into the habit of stirring any product that is supplied in liquid or paste form before it is used.

THORP, JOHN. In 1828, he invented the ring-spinning frame, the rival of the mule frame. This upright machine spins continuously, whereas mule spinning is intermittent. Compared with the mule, the ring frame requires less skilled help, gives about one third more production, takes up less floor space, can give higher twist to the yarn, gives a somewhat harsher yarn and is very popular for the manufacture of warp yarn.

THPC. This flame-retardant finish caused the breakthrough in finishes of this type in 1953. A registered trademark of Hooker Chemical Company, Inc., it was discovered in the Southern Regional Research Laboratory of the United States Government, Baton Rouge, Louisiana. The THPC stands for the first word initials of the compound - *tetrakis (hydroxymethyl) phosphonium chloride.*

THREAD. 1. Slender strand or strands of a specialized type of yarn used for some particular purpose such as basting, sewing, darning, embroidery work, etc. Thread is the result of careful drawing and winding of the fibers that make up the product which has to be wound onto some form for handling, such as cop, cone, bobbin, cheese, spool, etc. Thread is made from yarn, but yarn is not made from thread. 2. Any fine cord made from one of the major textile fibers. 3. A cord made of two or more yarns twisted or plied and then finished for a definite purpose.

THREAD, YARN GUIDE. Found on ring-spinning frames, this curved wire forms a circular hole centered above the spindle to guide the yarn directly to the bobbin or spindle.

THREADBARE. The appearance of a cloth or garment in which the nap has disappeared, thus showing the foundation yarns to disadvantage.

THREAD BOARD. The long, narrow, sectional wood or metal frame which sets in front of the rollers on the ring-spinning machine. Each section takes care of its yarn as it comes from the delivery rolls by having the yarn passed through the attached guide wire on its way to be wound onto the bobbin.

THREAD CLEANER. A device consisting of a small slotted opening through which a thread may pass. It is of such a size as to prevent the passage of large knots, loops, slugs, etc.

THREAD COUNT. 1. The actual number of warp ends and filling picks per inch in a woven cloth. Texture is another name for this term.
2. In knitted fabric, thread count implies the number of wales or ribs, and the courses per inch.

THREAD COUNTER. Same as pick-glass, pick counter, linen tester, pick-out glass.

THREAD CUTTER. Found on automatic looms, it is a device used to trim the length of filling that extends from the battery or magazine holder for the filling bobbins to the selvage of the cloth as a new bobbin replaces a spent one.

THREAD GUIDE. See GUIDE WIRE.

THREAD INDUSTRY, HISTORY OF THE. The thread industry, as it is known today, began in 1806 when Napolean at the time of the so-called Napoleonic Wars issued his famous Edict of Britain which forbade importation of silk to the British Isles. Up to this time all thread was made of silk and the Clark and Coats families, based in Paisley, Scotland, were the largest thread suppliers. Cotton thread became inevitable. It was first invented by Hannah Wilkinson Slater, wife of Samuel Slater, the "Father of the Cotton Industry in America," 1793. Shortly thereafter Slater built the Phoenix Thread Company mill in his home city, Pawtucket, Rhode Island. Mrs. Slater's thread was made from long-staple Surinam (Dutch Guiana) cotton in yarn counts of 2/20s. It was not, however, ideal for hand or machine sewing.

Meanwhile, Patrick Clark built the first British cotton thread mill in Paisley, England and had it in operation by 1812. By 1818, James and Peter Coats formed the J. & P. Coats Company in Paisley and also began cotton thread manufacture.

The thread business changed because of textile machinery inventions. John Wyatt brought out the first cotton machinery of any type in 1730; John Kay patented his fly shuttle in weaving in 1733; Wyatt and Lewis Paul perfected carding and spinning frames in the span from 1738-1748; Robert Kay and his drop-box loom in 1760; James Hargreaves brought out his spinning jenny between 1762-1767; Sir Richard Arkwright received his rights for spinning of cotton by means of rollers in 1774; he also received further patents on the carding, drawing, drafting, and spinning of fibers in 1775; Samuel Crompton invented his famous mule spinning frame which combined the ideas of Arkwright and Hargreaves, the roller drawing idea of the former and the carriage drawing plan of the Hargreaves. Thus, this spinning frame was a hybrid and Crompton called his machine the "mule."

The textile industry flourished in England as well as in New England following these concrete inventions; progress and improvement became commonplace. Carding, spinning, and weaving advances were constant. Around 1832, ring spinning frames were perfected and began to compete with the mule spinning frames here and abroad. In 1832, Walter Hunt, an inventive genius who is now forgotten, brought out his sewing machine. Elias Howe unveiled his sewing machine in 1846 in Boston, Massachusetts, and is acclaimed as the original inventor of this great item. Isaac M. Singer showed his machine and obtained patent rights in 1850. Hunt and Banks have long since been forgotten for their niche in the history of industry in this country while the word, *Singer,* is the second best known trademark in the world.

The Clark and the Coats interests had agents in the United States as early as 1840 and both companies did good business here. Around 1861 called it "Our New Thread." In 1864, George and William Clark, grandsons of Patrick Clark, the founder of the thread interests of this family in Paisley, built and opened a thread plant in Newark, New Jersey. Between 1869 and 1871, the J. and P. Coats Company, Inc., built their thread plant in Pawtucket, Rhode Island and for many years employed 3,500 persons.

Thes two great companies, friendly competitors since the early days in Paisley, merged in 1962. In that year, the 150th anniversary was celebrated to show the results of its research, development, innovation, and progress. See "Our New Thread."

THREAD LACE. Linen thread lace as differentiated from cotton and silk laces.

THREAD SILK. A series of silk filaments which have been reeled and twisted together to add strength to the yarn in order to make the thread suitable for weaving, knitting, or sewing purposes. It is neither spun nor weighted. Two-thread indicates two-ply; five-thread, five-ply, etc.

THREAD TRIMMER. An operative who trims basting threads, loose ends, and seam edges of garments with scissors before pressing or packing. Also known as cleaner or clipper.

THREAD VARIETIES. Federal Specifications promulgated in 1963 provide the following information with regard to sewing threads made from nylon and polyester yarns:

Type 1: Twisted multiple cord, not bonded.
Type 2: Twisted multiple cord, bonded.
Type 3: Monocord, bonded.
Type 4: Hand-sewing twist.
Type 5: Buttonhole twist.
Type 6: Braided shoe threads.
Type 7: Monocord, not bonded.
Type 8: Monocord, texturized, not bonded.
Type 9: Monocord, texturized, bonded.
Type 10: Twisted multiple cord, texturized, not bonded.
Type 11: Twisted multiple cord, texturized, bonded.

Some of these foregoing are available in three categories, as herewith listed:
Class One: Low elongation, no stability requirement.
Class Two: Normal elongation, stable to laundering.
Class Three: Normal elongation, stable to high temperatures.

THREAD WASTE. Hard thread or threadlike wastes on filling bobbins, other types of bobbins, or collected during spinning, twisting, weaving, knitting, etc.

THREADY CLOTH. Fabric finished so that it will show every thread clearly on the face of the goods. Examples include cassimere, serge, diagonal worsteds, chain-break cassimeres, etc.

THREADY FINISH. Comparable with a clear or hard finish given to worsteds.

THREE-CORD THREAD. The plying of three single cotton yarns into one yarn. Twist inserted is always in the same direction as the spinning frame twist—S-S or Z-Z.

THREE-EIGHTHS BLOOD WOOL. A classification used in the Blood numerical value is about 56s; below one-half blood wool and above one-quarter blood wool in the Blood System of Grading used in some parts of this country.

THREE-LEAF TWILL CLOTH. Cotton cloth of the drill and jean types, but lighter in weight. It is said to be the only 3-end filling-face twill made, using a 1-up and 2-down twill weave. Yarns range from those of print cloth to combed yarns. The fabric is about 39 inches wide, texture is about 68 x 76, and there are about 4 yards of cloth to the pound. Ticking of this type is used for lining, pocketing, shirting, and some types of umbrella fabric. The latter material uses combed yarn and has a texture of about 88 x 112, with about 7.4 yards to the pound. The cloth is also known as Silesia.

THREE-LEAF WARP TWILL. A 2-up and 1-down, right or left twill weave. Used for cotton fabric, this construction simulates drill but is lighter in weight. Made from print-cloth yarns.

THREE-PILE VELVET. Richly ornamented silk velvets with three different heights of pile.

THREE-PLY. Any yarn composed of three individual yarns plied or twisted together.

THREE-PLY CARPET. A type of ingrain carpeting which employs three warps and three fillings in the construction. See INGRAIN, INGRAIN CARPET.

THREE-QUARTER BLOOD WOOL. A classification used in the Blood System of Grading Wool; comparable with 3/4 Merino stock and rated just below XX wool and above one-half blood wool.

THREE-QUARTER CARPET. Fabric woven 27″ in width, or three-quarters the standard yard. This was a standard of measurement known as an "ell" when looms were first invented and remained the limit of width for many decades.

THRIPS. Any of several small insects of the order Thysanoptera, characterized by long, narrow wings fringed with hairs. Comes from the Greek root, meaning wood worm, many of the species are destructive to plants. This scourge attacks the flax plant.

THROSTLE. A machine formerly used exclusively in England for the spinning of warp yarn; it has been outmoded for over one hundred years. Spinning frames of various types have been developed from the basic principles embodied in the throstle.

THROUGH-AND-THROUGH. Formerly meant woolen cloths which had both sides the same in appearance; now implies a double-faced cloth either printed, woven, or napped.

THROW. 1. To prepare and twist silk filaments for weaving and knitting purposes. 2. A scarf or shawl which is thrown over the shoulder for comfort.

THROWING. Root is an Anglo Saxon word, "thrawan," which means to revolve or twist. While not exactly the same treatment given to wool, worsted, and cotton stock, throwing means "the actual twisting without drawing, of the continuous filaments of silk." In the other three fibers, the commerical form of yarn is brought about by drawing, drafting, attenuating, doubling, redoubling, twisting, and winding.

While there is some comparison between throwing and spinning, the processes differ. Throwing of silk means that two ends, each with 16 turns of twist per inch in the one direction, are taken and then given 14 turns of twist per inch in the other direction. Thus, the two ends being twisted together are given a "first-time spinning," and a "second-time spinning." Thread twisted in both directions will prevent raveling of the yarn. Much added strength is given to the thread by the action.

Tram threads used for filling, receive from one to three, four or five turns of twist per inch. Organzine is used for warp and may have as high as 60/65 turns of twist to the inch.

THROWN SILK. Yarn made from raw silk that has been reeled from the cocoon. From three to twelve cocoons are necessary to make the commercial thread of today.

THROWN SILK, YARDAGE IN. On thrown silks, the yards per pound are determined by the yardage test. Several pounds of yarn are measured on special units that are equipped with reading counters. The yards per pound are calculated on the net weight of the yarn as received, and corrected to

a fiber weight basis. The sizing test on thrown silk is used as a measure for the variation in size. It is done in the same manner as the sizing test for raw silk.

THROWN SINGLES. A single silk filament which has about 15 turns to the inch.

THROWSTER. One who has a silk throwing business or is a "silk spinner," who twists and manipulates raw silk threads.

THRUM. The fringe of warp threads remaining on a loom beam after the rest of the yarns have been removed. Also implies coarse, loose, mass waste of any type.

THRUM WASTE. "The threads of woven-out warps cut from warp beams. This waste is often tightly twisted and must be reworked before it can be used again." (A.S.T.M. Definition).

THUMB. 1. The part of a glove or mitten that covers the thumb. 2. An old unit of length, equal to one inch.

THURBERIA. A small genus of shrubby herbs of the mallow family. It has a three-celled boll. The term implies wild cotton, as well.

THURBERIA WEEVIL. Native to Arizona, this pest will attack both cultivated or "wild" cotton.

TIBISIRIE FIBER. Raised in British Guiana, this strong leaf fiber is used for cordage and making hammocks.

TICK. 1. Any of certain two-winged or wingless parasitic insects such as sheep tick. 2. A covering for a bed, stuffed pillow, etc.

TICKET POCKET. A small change, ticket, or token pocket set either at the waist or just above it on the right hand side of a coat or jacket, made in the same style as the other pockets on the article.

TICKING. Made in small twill constructions, ticking belongs in the loom-finished group of cloths: chambray, duck, canvas, denim, webbing, etc. Boiling-off or wet-finishing treatment are not applied to the material. Tick-

ing may be recognized by its alternate stripes of white and colored yarns. A typical ticking construction would be 64 ends of 12s warp and 50 picks of 14s filling. Uses include furniture covering, lining harness, mattress coverings, and base for rubberized materials. See Illustrated Section (Fabrics 47).

TICK-TACK EFFECTS. Bird's-eye effects seen in worsted suiting; one or two ends working as one of a light-colored yarn to three or four ends of a dark color in the warp give the tack effect. The cloth is usually made on a small twill weave.

TIE. 1. To fasten, loop or tie by some flexible bond—string, cord, tape, twine, etc. 2. A necktie.

TIE BAND. The string or cord used for leasing a warp or tieing a skein of yarn.

TIE-BAR. A plain or decorative clip or fastener used to hold the necktie to the shirt front.

TIE DYEING, DIP DYEING. Motifs are made by tieing tightly the parts of material so that the tied areas will not take the dye. This hand operation is also called random dyeing.

TIEBACK. Any device used to hold back curtains.

TIEING-IN, TYING-IN. See TWISTING-IN.

TIENTSIN JUTE. Another name for chingma.

TIENTSIN TWILL. British term for cotton fabric made with a 2-up, 1-down or a 1-up, 2-down twill, dyed black, then mercerized and schreinered, and used chiefly in the export trade. Cut lengths are around 90 yards, counts of yarns about 22s, with textures ranging about 22s in warp and filling yarns.

TIES, STREAMERS. These are galloons, six to eight inches wide, which have usually a repeated motif that can be scalloped to form a perfect end. They are also cut out of all-over nets specially designed to allow their use for more than one purpose.

TIE SILK. A silk fabric which is to be used for neckwear. It must possess the following qualities: proper weave and texture, pliability, resiliency, firmness in tying and knotting, lack of tendency to slip. Tie silk is generally skein-dyed and is not always fast to color; hence its use for cravat fabric only. The term is a very broad one because of the wide range in the quality and the price of neckties. Tie-silk fashion changes constantly.

TIE-UP. 1. The part of the draft which shows what combinations of harnesses are to be used in the actual weaving. 2. That part of gaiting the loom

THROWN SILK YARNS

Type	Turns of Twist Per Inch	Use of the Yarn
Singles	Hard twist or loose twist	Ideal for filling in many fabrics In the hard twist will work well in making sheer fabrics
Tram	From 2 to 12	Filling yarn and hosiery
Organzine	From 12 to 20	Warp yarn
Crepe	No twist in singles, 65 to 85 in doubles which are then doubled with 2½ to 5 turns per inch, opposite direction	In all kinds of crepe fabrics— in warp or filling, or both
Grenadine	20/18 to 60/60; a very hard twisted organzine thread	In all kinds of sheer cloths such as voile, organdy, grenadine

which applies to the tying of the lams to the pedals.

TIFFANY. A fine, sheer nylon or silk gauze fabric, sized and dyed for use in the manufacture of artificial flowers.

TIGER. See FEARNAUGHT.

TIGERING. The removal of fuzz and surface strands of fiber from the face of high-pile fabrics, knitted or woven.

TIGHT PICKS. Those picks in cloth which are irregular because of unevenness, faulty twist, poor pliability, etc. These picks, for some reason or other, give a binding effect or tautness to the edges of the material, resulting in wavy, cockled, or ruffled fabric.

TIGHT PULLEY. An "inside pulley" on which the driving belt is placed when the frame is in operation. See Spinning.

TIGHTS. A skintight garment for the lower part of the body and legs worn by acrobats, ballet dancers, stage performers, etc. They may cover almost the entire body, if need be. See Pantyhose, Leotard.

TIGHT SELVAGES. Those which have the tendency to pucker because of missing or broken selvage ends, poor tieing-in of listing threads, uneven tension weight on the warp beam which affects the edges of the warp, etc.

TIHORE. Raised in New Zealand, it is the strongest flax fiber used in the manufacture of fiber-cable and rope.

TIKUG. A sedge grass raised in the Philippine Islands, used in matting.

TILLANDSIA. Spanish moss.

TILLMAN'S PRIDE COTTON. A high yield cotton developed at Clemson College, South Carolina.

TILLOT OR BRADFORD WAY. The winding of fabric around a thin board and then laying it on paper called tillot. The corners of the paper are stitched and the top section is left free to form a lid or cover which can be lifted easily for inspection of the material.

TIMADIT. This Moroccan breed of sheep is noted for its black head and black fleece on neck and shoulders.

TIME-AND-MOTION STUDY. A method by which component parts of an operation are analyzed, improved upon, and timed, to arrive at the best way to attack the problem at hand, from the standpoint of time needed to perform a particular task.

TIMING. The regulation of speed, accuracy, and the means whereby the parts of a machine synchronize to per-

fection in sequence.

TINAMPIPI. Lightweight, plain-weave hemp fabric, made in the Philippines.

TIN CRYSTALS. Stannous chloride.

TINDEIN. Coarse cotton blankets made in Burma.

TINEOLA BISSELLIELLA. Name for the moth family well known for the disaster and trouble they give to human beings by feasting on furs, fabrics, tapestries, garments, floorcoverings, etc. Included are the large pale clothes moth, brown house moth, white-shouldered house moth, along with seven species of the beetle which loves to feed upon carpet wool. Moths feed on the keratin found in animal fibers. They also have a fondness for Vitamin B which is allied with wool that has been soiled by perspiration. Their great appetite and consumption of wool and comparable fibers is said to prevent irritability and nervous strain and tension in the species. Particularly they like to breed in the folds or creases in cloth. Favorable conditions for these pests range from 65° to 75° Fahrenheit. The cycle of the moth-egg-grub-chrysalis-moth is about four months in completion of the cycle. See Moth-proofing, Moth Repellency, Moths.

TINGED COTTON. Cotton classed between Spotted and Stained; this type has rather large brown discolorizations throughout.

TINGEY. A very fine, high-textured poplin shirting made solely of Egyptian cotton and given a silklike finish.

TIN LIQUOR. A stannous chloride solution, used as a mordant.

TINNEVELLY COTTON. Cotton raised in Madras, India; it is a strong, elastic fiber of dull cream-color. Staple is ¾ inch and lint yield is about 28 per cent. Spins to about 28s yarn.

TINNEVELLY MAT. Made in India, it is a well-textured, bleached grass matting.

TINSEL. Known also as lamé or metallic thread, tinsel has been made since the Middle Ages by the people of Europe. The thread is made of fine wire, usually copper, twisted with cotton or silk threads for the final effect. The yarn is used to bring out scintillating effects in curtains, decorative fabrics, evening wear, headgear, stage costume material, tapestry, trimming and tunics. One form is used to decorate Christmas trees.

TINSELFIL. Du Pont's flat cross-section filament viscose rayon yarn, with crystal-like luster, stiffness, and high coverage for use in dress goods, headgear, and footwear.

TINSELON. Trade-mark of I.R.C. Fibers Division, American Cyanamid Co., Inc., for its high-luster viscose rayon filament yarn characterized by its crystal-like luster finish. Now off the market.

TINSUTI. A plain-weave, durable, and strong cotton fabric made in India. Three-ply yarn is used in each direction, ranging from 3/18s to about 3/30s.

TINT. A slight color or hue applied to cloth. (See TINTING.) Bluing is used, in most cases, and 1/200th to 1/300th of 1 per cent of dyestuff is used by dipping the material in the bath, according to the instructions. Bluing does add a certain desirable tone or effect to some fabrics, chiefly cottons.

TINTING. 1. Application of a very light shade of color to yarn or fabric. 2. Hosiery and some woven fabric is given a tinting with a fugitive dyestuff for recognition purposes as the fabric is being processed in the mill; ultimately taken out as processing nears completion. 3. Tinting is much used on acetate, rayon, and comparable yarns to distinguish different twists used in yarns and fabrics.

TINTS, THROWSTERS. Fugitive tints applied to yarn, fabric, hosiery, etc., for lot identification purposes.

TIOLAN. A German fiber in which milk casein has been mixed with latex and glue.

TIP, TIPPED WOOL. The tip-ends of wool fibers in a fleece are clustered or matted together into a tip formation caused by permeation of the yolk throughout the fleece; gives the fleece its characteristic appearance.

TIPPED FABRIC. One which has a long pile effect which may be dyed at the tip or cut-end of the pile only.

TIPPET. 1. A shoulder scarf worn by the clergy of the Church of England. 2. A scarflike cape. 3. An outdoor covering for the neck and shoulders which hangs well down the front of the wearer. 4. The ruff of feathers on birds.

TIPPLE. A compact bundle of handfuls of machine-hackled flax, made by crossing the pieces alternately one over the other.

TIPPY WOOLS. Those in which the weather end of the fleece are more or less encrusted and matted.

TIP-SHEARING. This is a light shearing process used in finishing multi-pile height carpets, especially tufted ones. Only the highest loops are cut, thereby producing a tonal design effect or an undulating motif effect.

TIRE BUILDER FABRIC. A fabric consisting of tire cord yarn in the warp with single filling being used at definite set intervals. (A.S.T.M. Definition.) See CHAFER FABRIC.

TIRE CORD. 1. Cabled yarn of cotton, rayon, or nylon, used to make rubber-tread tires. 2. See TIRE CORD FABRIC.

TIRE CORD FABRIC. Mechanical fabric made of hawser cord yarn in the warp, and single yarn in the filling, interspersed in order to keep the warp together in the set-up.

TIRE FABRICS. Types of heavy duck made from ply yarns that are used in tire manufacture, such as builder fabric, breaker fabric, chafer fabric, etc.

TIRE TEXTILES, EVALUATION TESTS FOR.

This table offers a brief description of the evaluation tests performed on tire textiles. Actual test procedures are given in ASTM D885-68 or are available from industry sources.

ABRASION RESISTANCE—The resistance to surface cutting resulting from movements of adjacent filaments or yarns in a cord during dynamic operation.

ADHESION—The chemical and mechanical forces bonding the reinforcing member and the rubber matrix.

BIREFRINGENCE—A method of measuring relative crystallinity utilizing polarized light and double refraction.

BRITTLE POINT—The temperature at which the textile polymer no longer exhibits the properties of viscoelastic behavior.

COMPRESSIBILITY— The degree to which a cord can withstand compressive strains.

CATENARY—The difference in length between members of a cord structure expressed as a percentage.

CONSTRUCTION—The geometrical configuration of a cord structure.

CREEP—The time-dependant deformation of yarn or cord under a constant stress.

CRYSTALLINITY— The degree to which the textile polymer exists in a latice structure.

DAMPENING— The relative ability of a cord to absorb energy and prevent oscillation after excitation.

DENIER— A weight-per-unit-length measure of fiber, yarn, or cord size. The weight in grams of 9000 meters of the material.

DENSITY—The weight per unit volume of a fiber, yarn, or cord.

DIP PENETRATION—The degree of saturation through the cross section of a cord after impregnation with an adhesive.

DIP PICKUP—The amount of adhesive components present in a cord.

DIFFUSION— The transfer of air or gas through the internal structure of the cord along the cord axis.

DURABILITY— The resistance of a cord to loss of physical properties after being subjected to dynamic operation.

DYNAMIC ADHESION— The ability of a cord-rubber bond to resist degradation from flexure.

DYNAMIC MODULUS—The ratio of cord stress to cord strain under cyclical loading.

ELASTICITY— The ability of a yarn or cord to recover its original size and shape after stressing.

ELONGATION— The increase in length of a yarn or cord due to stressing.

ENTROPY OF FUSION—An intrinsic thermodynamic characteristic of a fiber which results from changes in degree of order.

FATIGUE—The resistance of the cord structure to weakening or failure as a result of alternate tension-compression cycles.

FINISH COMPOSITION—An analysis of the physical and chemical characteristics of the lubricant applied to yarns to reduce friction and improve fiber characteristics.

FINISH CONTENT—The amount of lubricant present in a yarn.

FLATSPOTTING— A measurement of the response of a cord to load and temperature cycles to predict its behavior in and out of the footprint area of a tire.

GAUGE— The measure of diameter or thickness of a cord.

GROWTH—The permanent increase in length of a cord under sustained loads.

HEAT GENERATION—A measurement of the amount of thermal energy produced by a cord in dynamic operation.

HELIX ANGLE—The angle formed by the path of a ply relative to the major axis in a tire cord structure.

HOT LOAD—The ability of a cord to support a load continuously at elevated temperatures.

HOT STRENGTH—The ability of a cord to resist loss in properties at tire operating temperatures.

HYDROLYSIS— The ability of a cord to resist degradation from a chemical reaction with water.

HYSTERESIS— The measurement of the work lost through heat during dynamic operation of a cord.

IMPACT RESISTANCE—The ability of a cord to withstand instantaneous or rapid rate of loading.

INCH-STRENGTH— A measurement of strength of a fabric structure obtained by multiplying cord strength times ends per inch times number of fabric plies.

INTERNAL FRICTION—The response of the molecular structure of a fiber to external stresses.

INTRINSIC VISCOSITY—A measurement of the average molecular weight of a polymer.

IR ANALYSIS—The identification of chemical groups within the fiber molecule by means of long wave length energy.

LASE– The load required to produce a specified per cent elongation of a yarn or cord.

LOSS MODULUS–The ratio of stress to strain at 90° out of phase.

MELTING POINT–The temperature at which the fiber changes from a solid to a liquid state (first order transition).

MODULUS– The slope of the initial straight portion of the stress-strain curve.

MOISTURE CONTENT–The amount of water present in a yarn at a given relative humidity.

ORIENTATION– The physical ordering of the crystallites within the basic fiber.

OXIDATION–The ability of a cord to resist the chemical reaction of oxygen.

RESERVOIR– A measure of the ability to absorb gases within the internal voids of a cord structure.

RESILIENCE– Ability of a cord to absorb work without permanent deformation.

RESONANCE FREQUENCY–The natural frequency response of a fiber when subjected to vibration.

SECOND ORDER TRANSITION TEMPERATURE–The temperature at which the properties of the fiber change from plastic to elastomeric.

SHRINKAGE– A measurement of the temporary and permanent change in length of a thermoplastic yarn or cord when subjected to elevated temperatures.

SHRINKAGE FORCE–The force generated by a thermoplastic yarn or cord when subjected to elevated temperatures and held to constant length.

SOFTENING POINT–The temperature at which a yarn or cord yields to small pressures and becomes tacky.

SOLVATION–The resistance of a cord to solution in hot water or steam (tire curing).

SONIC MODULUS–A measure of dynamic modulus using sound transmission as the test medium.

SOUND TRANSMISSION–The behavior of the cord in transmitting vibration along its length.

SPECIFIC HEAT–The quantity of heat required to raise the temperature of one gram of textile one degree centigrade.

STABILITY– The ability of a cord to retain its dimensions and physical properties under a variety of environmental conditions.

STAINING– The tendency of a cord to discolor other structural elements through chemical migration.

STIFFNESS– The resistance of a cord to bending.

STRENGTH– The ability of a cord to withstand the ultimate tensile load or force required for rupture.

STRESS DECAY–The time dependant loss of fiber properties under a constant strain.

TENACITY–A measure of yarn or cord strength expressed in grams per denier. **NOTE:** Tenacity (strength per unit denier) and Tensile Strength (strength per unit cross section) are not proportional.

TENSILE STRENGTH–A measure of yarn or cord strength in pounds per square inch.

TEX–A weight-per-unit-length measure of fiber, yarn or cord size. The weight in grams of 1000 meters of the material.

TFE– A measure of the economics of a cord (Tire Fabric Efficiency).

THERMAL ANALYSIS–A study of the physical and chemical changes occurring in a cord due to temperature through use of DSC or DTA equipment.

THERMAL CONDUCTIVITY–The time rate of transfer of heat per unit of textile material.

TOUGHNESS– The work per unit mass required to rupture a yarn or cord.

TWIST– The number of turns per inch in a yarn or cord.

UNIFORMITY– Consistency in physical properties along the length of a yarn or cord.

WET STRENGTH–The measurement of the strength of a cord when saturated with water.

WORK-TO-BREAK– The total energy required to rupture a yarn or cord.

TIRE TEXTILES, REQUIREMENTS FOR.

BALANCE– The measurement of the uniformity of weight distribution of a tire.

BEAD OUT–The measurement of tire integrity in the lower sidewall area.

BEAD UNSEATING–The ability of a tire to resist the lateral forces acting to dislodge the tire from the rim.

BRUISE RESISTANCE–The ability of a tire to withstand conditions of impact.

BUCKLING– The ability of the sidewall of a tire to transmit torque without distortion.

BURST– The maximum pressure to which a tire can be inflated.

CORNERING– The ability of a tire to make sudden changes in direction.

CRACKING– The ability of a tire to withstand the initiation and propagation of cracks in the tread grooves.

CUSHIONING—The basic tire function of isolating a vehicle or its contents from road disturbances.

CUT RESISTANCE—The ability of a tire to resist sharp objects.

DAMPENING— The ability of a tire to minimize oscillation after excitation.

DEFLECTION— The deformation of a tire under load.

DIMENSIONS— The physical size of a tire. Important measurements are overall diameter (O.D.), section width (S.W.), and section height (S.H.).

DIRECTIONAL CONTROL—The ability of a tire to maintain a vehicle in the path desired by the driver.

DRAG— The inherent resisting force of a tire.

DYNAMIC IMPACT—The force required to rupture a tire under specific conditions of operation.

ENVELOPING— The ability of a tire to conform to large road irregularities.

EVEN WEAR— The uniformity of abrasion across the tread surface of a tire.

FATIGUE—The resistance of a tire to weakening or failure as a result of alternate tension-compression cycles.

FLATSPOTTING— A temporary formation of a tire irregularity in the footprint area during parking.

FLEET DURABILITY—The performance of tires based on a statistical evaluation of large numbers of tires under accelerated road service conditions.

FLOTATION— The measurement of the ability of a tire to sustain a vehicle under soft footprint conditions.

FOOTPRINT— The shape and area of that portion of the tire in contact with the road.

FUEL ECONOMY—The measurement of the effect of a tire on gasoline consumption.

GRAVEL DURABILITY—The resistance of a tire to loss of physical properties from dynamic operation over unimproved roads.

GROWTH— The permanent change in tire size over a period of time due to inflation pressure and service.

HANDLING— The overall behavior of a tire under conditions of maneuver.

HARSHNESS— The measurement of the amount of disturbance transmitted by a tire when passing over minor but continuous road irregularities.

HEAT GENERATION—The buildup of thermal energy in a tire during dynamic operation.

HIGH SPEED—The ability of a tire to preserve its integrity when subjected to the severe conditions of high frequency flexing and high centrifugal forces (usually in excess of 1000 revolutions per minute).

HYDROPLANING— The behavior of a tire in an environment of surface water causing loss of contact with the road.

INTEGRITY— The ability of a tire to maintain structural identity.

JOINT SLAP—The response of a tire as it passes over a discontinuity in the road surface such as an expansion joint.

LOAD CARRYING CAPACITY—The ability of a tire to support and transport a given weight.

MOISTURE RESISTANCE—The ability of tire components to resist degradation due to water.

NIBBLING— The ability of a tire to maneuver along a discontinuity in the road parallel to the direction of travel (such as streetcar tracks or the road shoulder) without sudden changes in tire direction.

NOISE— The sound transmitted to the occupants of a vehicle by a tire in contact with the road.

OZONE RESISTANCE—The resistance of a tire and its components to degradation from ozone in the atmosphere.

PITCH TONE—The relative intensity of sound generated and transmitted from the tire to the vehicle in the frequency range of 180-220 cps.

PLUNGER— The energy of rupture of a static tire.

PRESSURE RISE— The increase in inflation pressure due to heat buildup during dynamic operation of a tire.

PUNCTURE RESISTANCE—The ability of a tire to resist penetrating objects.

RESPONSE— The reaction of a tire to sudden changes in direction.

REVOLUTIONS PER MILE—The number of rotations of a tire when the vehicle travels one mile.

RIDE— The ability of a tire to provide comfort to the occupants of a vehicle.

RIM CHAFING—The ability of a tire to resist damage in the bead area in the event of slippage on the rim.

ROLLING RADIUS—The effective radius of a moving tire under load.

ROLLING RESISTANCE—The retarding force acting on a tire opposite to the direction of rotation.

ROUGHNESS— The measure of ride disturbances due to tire non-uniformity in the radial direction.

RUNNING TEMPERATURE—The equilibrium temperature of a tire under a specified set of service conditions.

SEPARATION—The ability of the components of a tire to maintain composite integrity under dynamic conditions of heat, load, and flexing.

SHAKE— The measure of ride disturbances due to tire non-uniformity in the lateral direction.

SIDE SLIP—The ability of a tire to resist lateral movement due to external forces.

SKID RESISTANCE–The measurement of the ability of a tire to stop under various environmental conditons.

SNOW AND ICE–The handling and mobility characteristics of a tire under winter conditions.

SPRING RATE–The slope of the stress-strain curve of a deflected tire.

SQUEAL– The noise associated with the slippage between the tire and road surface.

STABILITY– The ability of a tire to resist lateral deformation when deviating from a straight line.

STANDING WAVE–A severe distortion of tire components due to high speed operation. A standing wave is technically a moving wave.

THUMP– The measure of ride distrubances due to tire out-of-roundness.

TORQUE– The ability of a tire to transmit force from the drive axle to the ground contact area.

TRACKING– The ability of a tire to continue moving in a straight path.

TRACTION– The ability of a tire to develop cornering forces for steering, stability and propulsion and retarding forces for driving and braking under various conditions.

TREAD PRESSURE–The distribution of load from the tire to the road across the footprint area.

TREADWEAR– The resistance of a tire to abrasion when moving on a road surface.

UNIFORMITY– The consistency in reaction of a tire to external forces.

VIBRATION ANALYSIS–The spectrum of force and noise transmission from the tire to the vehicle.

WEATHER RESISTANCE–The ability of a tire to resist the effects of atmospheric conditions.

Courtesy of F. J. Kovac, Manager, Tire Reinforcing Systems, The Goodyear Tire & Rubber Company, Inc. (The University of Akron Lecture Series, Akron, OH 44316, 1969).

TISSER. French term which means "to weave." "Tisseur" is a weaver of cloth. "Tissu" is the French word for fabric.

TISSU. French for all textile materials.

TISSUE. 1. Refers to silk damask and some few other cloths made with metallic threads interspersed throughout the fabric. 2. Lightweight ginghams made in the British Isles. 3. Curtain material made with clip-spot effects by the use of an extra, soft-spun yarn.

TISSUE FAILLE. Faille made of plain weave, really a faille crepe since crepe filling is used. Made of all acetate yarn a typical layout would be 180 ends of 75-denier warp and 56 picks of 2/75 denier crepe filling, twist-on-twist. When made with 46 picks per inch,

2/100 denier yarn is used; in a 36-pick arrangement 2/150 denier yarn is used.

Gray goods are 48 inches to finish at 42 inches. Made in dull or bright rayon or acetate yarns. A popular rayon texture is 114 x 68. Some of the fabric is finished at 45 inches.

Comes in white or dyed colors. An outstanding feature of tissue is that it is a nonslip fabric in manipulation, because of the twist-on-twist filling arrangement. Resiliency, loftiness and drapability are excellent, and when made into garments tissue faille is of the form-revealing type on the wearer. Uses include dress goods, blouses, and evening wear.

TISSUE GINGHAM. A sheer gingham whose pattern ranges from the

small conservative design to the large, gaudy effect. Made from cotton, acetate, or rayon.

TISSU METALLIQUE. Signifies a wire gauze in the French language.

TISSUTI. See AMAMEE.

TITANIUM DIOXIDE. A white, water-insoluble powder, used mainly in white pigments, plastics, and ceramics, for delustering manmade fibers such as acetate and rayon, for example. Also known as titanium oxide, titanic acid, titanic oxide.

TITANOX. This includes: Titanox-Amo (titanium dioxide) for internal delustering of viscose and for preparation of external delustrants or dullers; Titanox A-No. 24 or Titanox AA for internal delustering of acetate; and

Titanium Sulphate Cake for the preparation of titanous sulphate strippers.

TITRATION. Chemical technique used to determine the amount of sour, alkali, or bleach present in a solution. Usually the test is accomplished by the use of an indicator, such as litmus, which changes in color according to varying reaction with these substances.

TITRE. 1. French term, concerning deniers, used to determine the size and number of yards per pound in filament yarn such as silk, rayon, acetate, nylon, etc. Example is a 14/16 denier silk with a mean of 15, the number between 14 and 16.

2. The temperature in degrees Centigrade at which certain fatty acids will solidify after being melted.

TJANTING. Used in batik printing, it is a tool or device used to apply liquid wax to a fabric. The instrument has a small copper reservoir with from one to six spouts affixed to a handle. Despite its use for at least seven hundred years in Java, efforts have been made to alter its appearance and structure for easier usage. The only appreciable change has been to provide a better handle to the device. A tjanting pengado is a two-spout tool.

TJAP PRINTING. A very interesting type of block printing executed by means of dipping blocks into heated wax and then impressing them upon the material—usually a cotton, silk, or rayon fabric—after which it is dyed and the wax removed, leaving a permanent design. These blocks are made by the natives of Java and the other islands in the East Indies by bending small strips of copper into the desired curves for sections of the pattern and inserting them into the end grain of the blocks of wood, allowing them to project a little less than one-eighth inch from the surface.

The small copper ridges formed in this way are similar to the cloisons which are applied to keep the enamels separated in the decoration of the well-known cloisonné. Owing to the fact that it is a very difficult and painstaking task to make these blocks or tjaps, the results of this art often bring prices as high as direct handwork.

T.O. Turn over a difficult sale to another salesman.

TOAD-IN-THE-HOLE. A type of filling stitch used on bobbin lace made in some English areas. Named because the motif calls to mind a toad in a square.

TOBACCO CLOTH. Of the three basic cotton gray goods, print cloth is the best, followed by cheesecloth and tobacco cloth, respectively. Cheesecloth and tobacco cloth are the lowest in texture of any cotton materials made on a loom.

Narrow cheesecloth is under 36 inches wide; beyond this width the material is called wide cheesecloth. When the goods are 36 inches wide, they are called tobacco cloth. Constructions as to texture are square, 8 x 8 up to 48 x 48. Warp yarns are 28s; filling yarns, 30s to 40s.

General uses for tobacco and cheesecloths in the finished state are: back-filled gauze, bandages, bedspreads, buckram, crinoline, curtaining, dust cloths, flag bunting, flour bagging, fly linings and nets, gauze, hat lining, interlining, label and sign cloth, netting, play suiting, shading cloth for tobacco and other vegetable plants, tea bags, theatrical gauze, wrapping cloth for cheeses.

TOBOGGAN CAP. A knitted cone-shaped cap that covers the head; usually has a pompon at the apex.

TOC. The broad-brimmed felt hat peculiar to many peasant areas throughout Europe which has centuries of tradition. The Bretons of France, for example, have their toc decorated with ribbon and streamers which fall to below the shoulder.

TOCUYO. Gray goods cotton sheeting, muslin, printcloth, etc., in South America.

TOD. A twenty-eight-pound lot of wool which is used as a unit in weighing wool and top in England.

TO DOUBLE. Process of doubling or twisting two or more yarns into an individual ply yarn. Done on the twisting frame in the mill. The yarn is usually twisted in the opposite direction from the single yarns that were used to make the ply yarns.

TOE BLOCK. Reinforcement of a stocking at the toe.

TOGA DENSA, HIRTA. Thick, heavily napped, felted woolens worn by the Romans in cold weather.

TOGA ROSA, TIRTA. A thin, smooth, lightweight woolen garment worn in the summer by the Romans. Colored embroidery was used on apparel to signify the rank of the wearer.

TOGGERY. Clothes with reference to a particular type of apparel. Also implies haberdashery.

TOHALON. Trade-mark of Toray Industries, Inc., Osaka, Japan, for its cellulose fiber. There are two stages in its manufacture. Super tenacity rayon staple is prepared by a particular spinning method from pulp with a high Alpha content. Acetylation may be done by immersion of the rayon staple in a bath which contains acetic anhydride, glacial acetic acid and a non-solvent (liquid-phase process), or by acetylating the rayon staple in the combined vapor of acetic anhydride and glacial acetic acid (vapor-phase process), ideally adaptable for mass production. Tohalon has no melting point and fabrics of if are easy to iron. Dyeing is done with disperse dyes such as used for acetate or polyester fibers, diazo disperse dyes, or azoic dyes. It is used alone or in blends and finds many uses in apparel. Known as Alon in the local market of Japan.

TOILE. 1. General term used in France to designate vegetable fiber cloths made on plain or twill weaves, especially hemp and linen materials.

2. Name given to tissue goods in which metallic threads are used to enhance the pattern-cloths of gold, silver, copper, etc.

3. A type of handmade lace in which the body part of the pattern simulates woven cloth.

4. The warp ends which form the ground in pile fabrics.

5. Fine cretonne with scenic designs printed in one color.

6. Some sheer cotton and line materials are called toile.

7. The model of a design in muslin, often purchased by firms who wish to copy but not import original models. Sometimes made by dressmakers to show customers the lines in garments that they are prepared to copy.

TOILE À BLEUTEAU. A fine mesh bolting or sieve fabric made in France; nylon or silk are used in the construction. Bleuteau is sometimes spelled Blutean or Bluteau.

TOILE À CHAPEAU. Chapeau means hat, in French. The term refers to cotton or linen fabrics that have been sized, stiffened, and usually glazed or polished for use in headgear.

TOILE À VOILE. A lightweight sail-cloth used in France.

TOILE BIZONNE. An unbleached, heavily calendered linen that is used for bedspreads, coverlets, etc. Pick count in this cloth is always square.

TOILE BLEUE. French term for fine fabrics dyed some shade of blue, especially linen materials.

TOILE BRUNE. Brune means brown in French, and the implication is that it is an unbleached fabric, especially linen or cotton, obviously brownish in color cast.

TOILE CIRÉE, TOILE CERÉE. French for oilcloth.

TOILE COLBERT. French for basketweave fabric, basket cloth.

TOILE D'ALSACE. A fine, thin French cotton or linen fabric, white, dyed, or printed, used as dress goods.

TOILE D'ARAIGNE. French for cobweb or spider web effect seen on lace and a few woven cloths (arrangement of yarns to bring out the effect). Also implies a woolen dress goods that is made with open weaves such as leno or doup, gauze effects, etc.

TOILE DE COFFRE. A good quality French linen used in the home as toweling, doilies, runners, etc.

TOILE DE COTON. Coton is the French word for cotton. While it is a broad term in its interpretation, it refers especially to dress goods made of linen and cotton in which stripes are used to enhance the effect.

TOILE DE FRISE. A fine quality Holland linen.

TOILE DE GUERRE. Originated during World War I, and refers to the various fabrics used for decorations, emblems, and identification purposes. It includes sleeve patches for identification, service emblems, decorations on headgear, banners, etc.

TOILE DE HALLE. A strong, unbleached linen cloth that originated in Halle, Germany.

TOILE DE JOUY. Originally a set of cotton fabrics printed in imitation of the various imported oriental materials brought into France and executed in Jouy, by Oberkampf. In 1759, as the result of a governmental citation, Oberkampf established his plant in Jouy; his influence still prevails.

Prior to Oberkampf's methods, the printing process on cottons consisted of marking the outline of the design in black and filling in the colors by hand. Oberkampf introduced block and roller-print effects on his fabrics. His success soon became phenomenal, since his Jouy "canvases" became the rage in dress goods and for general decorative purposes.

TOILE DE LAINE. Laine means wool in French; refers to a plain-weave French dress goods made with high-grade wool and usually dyed black. It is sometimes used, during wartime, as a mourning fabric.

TOILE DE LILLE. A linen cloth that originated in Lille, France. Colored stripes usually feature this fabric.

TOILE D'EMBALLAGE. Cloth that is used for packing or wrapping purposes in France.

TOILE DE RELIGIEUSE. French term for fabrics worn by the religious orders and seculars; includes the fabrics used in the garb worn by nuns, priests, brothers, monks, etc., and includes a great many different materials from very light cloths to the heavier winter garb worn by monks and some missionaries.

TOILE DE ROUEN. This city in France is one of the oldest textile centers in that country; a general term for fabrics made in this well-known center.

TOILE DE SAC. Sackcloth in France; there are several variations of this fabric as to weight, quality, and construction.

TOILE DE SAXE. A plain-weave fabric used on the Continent and first made in Saxony, Germany. This dress goods is made with cotton warp and woolen or worsted filling, and is of compact texture.

TOILE DE VESTE. Made in solid colors, stripes, or checks, this French cloth serves as a lining fabric and may be used for blouses, vestees, halters, dickeys, etc.

TOILE DE VICHY. Named for this city in France, it is a lightweight dress goods material made of linen. Stripes are a feature of the goods.

TOILE D'OR, TOILE D'ARGENT. See CLOTH OF GOLD, CLOTH OF SILVER.

TOILE DOUCE. A French linen canvas that is compactly woven and given a smooth, luster calender finish. It may be made on plain-weave, or in a 1-2 or a 2-2 basket weave.

TOILE D'OURVILLE. A French canvas that has not been bleached.

TOILE DU NORD. A smooth calender finish is given to this French check or gingham cotton or linen material.

TOILE ECRU. Unbleached French linen; it has a ecru shade in this condition.

TOILE METALLIQUE. French term for wire fabric used for screening, railroad car windows, house screening, fire screens, etc.

TOILE OUVREE. French term for huckaback and comparable fabrics that may be used for dress goods, toweling, etc. Ouvrée means open or openwork and this type of texture is observed in some of the materials.

TOILET CLOTHS. A family of materials used in the home for articles such as bed quilts, covers, counterpanes, dressing-table covers, guest towels, etc.

TOILINETTE. Formerly popular when fancy waistcoats and vests were worn by men, this cloth is made from cotton or silk warp and wool filling. Of close texture, most of the goods showed a novel spot or figure in the fabric pattern. Jacquard, doup, swivel, clip-spot and lappet looms are used to make the cloth, since the novelty effect is woven into the material.

TOISON. French term for a sheep fleece.

TOLA. A dye whose origin and details are vague; it is mentioned in the Old Testament with regard to its use in vestments worn by the Hebrews and in hangings in the Tabernacle.

TOLERANCE. A decimal or fractional allowance for variations from the specified standard weight, dimensions, etc.

TOLOTZIN. See CATENA FIBER.

T.O. MAN. A top man on the selling staff to whom tough sales are assigned by lesser lights.

TOMMY DODD. A mangle used for backfilling which differs from the ordinary starch mangle in that a large roller is used which revolves in the kier or vat.

TONGA. British export fabric shipped to African markets. It is a plain-woven cotton cloth that is dyed and used for garments by the natives. The fabric is about one yard in width.

TONTINE. A Du Pont trade-mark for pyroxylin-coated and impregnated washable windowshades.

TONTISE. French expression for the loose, straggly fibers obtained from woolen cloths; they come as the result of napping, shearing, cropping, etc., and these fibers are usually reworked with longer staple stocks.

TONYA. Commission merchants or factors interested in the raw silk trade, chiefly in Kobe and Yokohama. They advance credits and finance silk reelers, with whom there is a close relation.

TOOL-MAINTENANCE TIME. Time allowance made to employees for time consumed in maintaining their own special tools in good working condition.

TOP. Found in worsted stock in all-worsted or worsted-mixes. Top is made up of fibers taken in the combing operation. It comes in slubbing or sliver form that is wound into a ball effect a foot or more in thickness and two or three feet in diameter. It resembles a cheese in appearance. The fibers in a top are parallel and of the same length. They are smooth, uniform, even, and have no foreign matter to speak of. The short fibers taken from the combing operation are called noil. These are used as a substitute fiber and may be high or low in quality. Tops are sold on the Worsted Top Exchange in New

York City. Quotations are in cents and tenths of a cent per pound, and a top contract is 5000 pounds.

TOP, SLUB DYEING. The dyeing of fibers in top-form of sliver or slubbing which is wound into a top and resembles a cheese in shape and size. The top has been carded and combed but not spun into yarn. Following dyeing, the various colored tops may be blended together to obtain some cast, hue, tone or shade of a color. Top dyeing is much resorted to in coloring fibers that are to be spun into yarn and then woven into worsted fabric. Considerable amounts of men's wear and women's wear worsted cloth are dyed in this manner.

TOPAZ. A brown color, yellowish red-yellow in hue; has medium saturation and brilliance.

TOP BEATER. The top bar of the beater which keeps the reed in place when the loom is in action.

TOP CASTLE. The top part of the loom from which the harnesses are hung.

TOPCOAT. 1. A lightweight overcoat. 2. A loose-fitting coat worn by women over a suit.

TOP COLORS. Colors of the yarn used to form the design as distinguished from the ground color.

TOP COMB. The Heilman or French comber is equipped with a device for combing that section of fibers held in place by the nippers while the half lap is in play. The device is a thin metal bar upon which is soldered a row of very fine, closely set needles. The fibers are drawn through the combing needles by the detaching rolls. Fibers as short as 1½ inches in staple may be combed on this machine.

TOP DYED. Wool fibers dyed in the form of worsted top and then processed in the colored condition.

TOPEL. Trade-mark of Courtaulds (Ala) Inc., for one of its members in the cross-linked cellulosic fiber field. Similar to the cellulosic family in many ways, but because of its chemical modification it possesses properties distinctly different from viscose rayon on the one hand and cotton on the other. This white staple fiber has similar resistance to acids, bleaching agents, scouring and laundering agents and common solvents as viscose rayon in regard to degradation. It is more resistant to caustic alkalies because of its chemical modification. Topel is blended with other fibers for use in a wide range of apparel fabrics. No longer produced.

TOP FINISHING. A term used in English or Bradford worsted combing.

It refers to the process used to obtain suitable top and usually, anent gilling, implies two gilling operations, one by the conditioner, the other by the top gill box.

TOP GILL BOX. The last process in making commercial top, it is the box which forms the fibers into top form as it comes from the delivery end of the machine and winds it into the ball form known as finished top.

TOP GRAIN. Refers to grain-side or hair-side of cattlehide that has been reduced to a specified thickness on the ounce standard, the range being from 2 to 10 ounces according to a standard leather gauge. Split leather has to be so designated and is not included in the above classification. Split is that portion of a hide or skin after splitting, other than the grain or hair-side. Splits are usually named according to their sequence of production, such as main, second, slab (as in the case of upholstery leather), or the use to be made of the leather, such as flexible for innersoles and gloves, waxed for low-price shoe uppers, etc. A third classification includes bag and case leather that is finished with pyroxylin or pigment.

TOPHAM BOX. Name for the centrifugal rayon spinning box; the inventor was C. F. Topham.

TOP KNOT. Wool taken from the forehead and poll of the sheep when it is being sheared.

TOPMAKER. A dealer who buys wool for sorting and classification, mixing and blending, and manipulation into the finished unit in buying worsted sliver, the top. The topmaker, if he does not own a plant for the making of tops, has the work done by the commission comber.

TOPMAKERS' QUALITY OR COUNTS. These are numbers used in speaking of the quality of certain foreign wools. The system is used in the British Empire and on the Continent. A number 60s would mean that the wool is capable of spinning to a 60s worsted yarn. From this, it is to be understood that there would be 60 hanks, each 560 yards long, in one pound of the finished yarn. The yardage per pound would be figured, as follows: 60 x 560, the number of yards in one pound of a Number-One worsted yarn, or 33,600 yards of yarn.

TOPPING. Adding of further coloring matter to a dyed substrate so as to adjust the latter to the desired final color. The coloring matter does not necessarily have to be of the same hue or class. See SUBSTRATE.

TOPPING BAR. Used in full-fashioned knitting, it has grooved points

spaced to correspond to the gauge of the full-fashioned machine.

TOPPINGS. Burrs, clay, dirt, dung, fodder, etc., found on various edges of the fleece when it is being skirted by the sorter.

TOPS. 1. Narrow strips of card clothing used to cover the revolving flats on the carding machine. 2. See WORSTED TOP.

TOPS, OIL-COMBED. Dry-combed worsted or hair fiber tops with oil added to them to insure better working properties in the processes of manufacture of the ultimate spun yarn.

TOP-TO-NOIL TEAR. The percentage of tops versus noil. A 10 to 1 tear would mean that there would be 10 pounds of scoured wool to 1 pound of noil.

TOQUE. A small, close-fitting brimless hat. Formerly, a black velvet cap with full crown and small, rolled brim, ornamented with plumes. Worn by men and women in France in the sixteenth century.

TOQUILLA. The bast fiber obtained from this tree found in Central and South America is used to make headgear. Jijipapa is the name of the prepared fiber which comes from the leaves of the tree.

"TORAMOMEN.". S. Tachikawa, Japanese scientist, developed a modification of viscose rayon in the early 1950's. He brought about a rayon with high-wet modulus, and the term "Polynosic" was applied to this type of rayon. He gave the name "Toramomen" to his fiber, which in due time brought about the creation of fibers such as Fiber HM, Vincel, and Zantrel, now a product of American Enka Corporation, New York City.

TORAYLON. Acrylic staple fiber of Toray Industries, Inc., Tokyo, Japan. Originally called F-IV, it has the same uses as "Orlon." See "Orlon."

TORAY TETORON. Polyester staple and filament made by Toray Industries, Inc., Osaka, Japan under license agreement with Imperial Chemical Industries, Ltd., London, England.

TORCHON. Cotton lace made by independent beams in which the Cluny type of fine yarns are used; a narrow width lace.

TORCHONETTE. An open-weave British cotton material textured around 24-square. Made from around 3/40s cotton yarn, there is a fine, highly twisted cotton yarn that is twisted or spiraled loosely around the core threads, thereby giving a crinkled, crepe, or granular effect on the face effect of the goods.

TORN SELVAGES. Those which are not presentable because of ends missing, uneven tieing-in, knots, loops, slubs, and general poor work on the part of the weaver. A good selvage which is found on any woven cloth of full width produces the effect of a frame around a picture and usually indicates a good quality, well-woven piece of material.

TORN SIZE. A sheet, pillowcase, etc., torn to size before hemming is done.

TORQUE VERSUS NON-TORQUE YARNS. Torque implies a twist or convolution. It is the twisting or rotary force in a mechanism or yarn (as a measurable quantity) the moment a system of forces produce rotation. Torque yarn will recede, rotate, or twist upon itself when suspended in air. Non-torque yarn will not do this when suspended in air. Certain types of bulk yarn have an "S-twist" combined with a "Z-twist" to provide a non-torque yarn.

TORQUE YARN. Applied to present-day stretch yarn, nylon for example, it is a yarn that has been twisted and subsequently heat-set. Helanca and Chadalon are examples. Non-torque yarn is a stretch yarn that has been made by curling or crimping rather than by twisting. Agilon and Ban-Lon are examples.

The word torque means the movement of forces that cause rotation or twisting, as in the case of twisting yarn, cord, or wire.

TORS SANS FILE SILK. Silk yarn in between organzine and tram with regard to twist.

TOSCA NET. A strongly interlaced net that is not as compactly structured as bobbinet. See BOBBINET.

TOSSA JUTE. A gray to brown long-pod jute fiber, *Corchorus oliotorius,* raised in India.

TO'T. Signifies that the pile in a velveteen fabric has been cut to the left center of the floating or pile yarns; contraction of "to the left."

TOTARN. The result of the reorientation of pure cellulosic fibers into a thread of longer, stronger filaments with exact molecular alignment. A product of American Silk Mills, Inc.

TOUBAB COTTON. It is raised in Senegal, West Africa from American seed; has large bolls and long staple.

TOUCHARDIA FIBER. Hawaiian bast fiber used for cordage and twine.

TOUGHNESS, AVERAGE. The ability of a fiber to endure large, permanent deformation without rupture.

TOURIST COATING. Loose or general term sometimes applied to topcoats and overcoats that can withstand rugged wear when traveling—homespun, tweed, certain herringbones, some shetland and cheviot, gabardine, whipcord, etc.

TOURS. On a Schiffli embroidery machine it is the step stitch in a series of motifs or patterns. For example, in running stitch and bean stitch patterns, the designer will specify the number of times he desires the stitch made by stating the number of tours. This is a complete traveling around a figure from start to finish of the movement. Named for the city of Tours, France. See Bean Stitch.

TOVAGLIAS. These are made from white linen fabric cut to a two yard length and eighteen inches in width. Made with fringed ends, one half of the piece comes to the waist while the other portion is folded, placed on the forehead so that it will fall along the sides of the face. It is a staple item in the present area in Italy and is centuries old in tradition.

TOW. A large group of continuous filaments, such as acetate or rayon, Kodel, nylon, etc., without any definite twist. The tow stock is cut into definite, set lengths and is known as staple fiber. It is used to make blended or mixture yarns in which two or more different fibers (natural and/or man-made) are used. Staple fiber, as well, may use only the one fiber to make a spun yarn such as spun acetate, spun rayon, or spun nylon.

TOW CONVERSION. Any method by means of which a group of continuous man-made filaments (tow) are cut into desired staple lengths and then made at once into a sliver form, thereby saving time, cost, and labor.

TOWEL, FRICTION. One similar to the ordinary bath towel but made with a linen yarn pile effect; usually comes in unbleached state.

TOWEL, SINGLE-LOOP. Pile loops for terry toweling can be formed singly, known as a loop or single thread, or in a pair formation called a double-loop or double-thread. The double-loop is distinguishable from the single in that each loop is made of two parallel yarns not twisted together, thereby forming double loops, side by side, at the same time.

The single-loop construction uses only a single yarn to form the loop. In either construction, the weaving process forms these loops in alternate manner on one side of the towel and then on the other side of the cloth.

If a comparison is made between the single- and the double-loop types, both of the same weight and made with the same quality yarn, the single-loop towel would be superior as far as strength is concerned because it has more interlacings in the ground or base fabric. Having fewer pile loops, however, the single towel would not be as soft in texture or as absorbent when compared with the double-loop towel.

TOWELING. General term for bird's-eye, crash, damask, glass, honeycomb, huck, huckaback, twill, Turkish or terry, fancy, novelty, and guest towelings. Many of these cloths have colored or fancy borders or edges; some of them are often union fabrics. All toweling has property of good absorption.

TOWLIA. Huckaback and honeycomb weaves are used to make this toweling, made on hand looms in India.

TOWNSEND AND MOULDING. In 1838, these Nottinghamshire knitters invented the latch needle knitting machine.

TOWROPE. Any rugged rope used for towing purposes.

TOW, SWINGLING. Coarse flax separated or scutched by swingling. See SWINGLE.

TOY. A head covering for women that hangs loosely over the shoulders—much worn by poorer womenfolk in Scotland for many centuries.

TPI, T.P.I. Means mechanical turns of twist per inch in a yarn.

TRACER. Raised work in Honiton bobbin lace.

TRACING. A reproduction of an original outline accomplished by using tailor tacks, chalk marks, or a tracing wheel.

TRACING BRAID. See TRACING THREAD.

TRACING CLOTH. Made from fine combed cotton yarn; the base fabric is filled on one side only; the finish is firm, parchment-like and transparent. The lawn cloth used as the base must be carefully woven, graded, and inspected closely, and must be free from imperfections. Textures vary from 88 x 88 to 76 x 72; yard per pound weight of the cloth ranges from about 5½ yards to 7½ yards.

TRACING THREAD. The bordering thread in lace which is bulkier than the other threads of the lace and often indicates the pattern.

TRACING WHEEL. An instrument used to trace and reproduce an original outline. It is composed of a wheel having sharp teeth which is fastened to a handle.

TRADEMARKS. A trademark is a distinctive word, name, device or symbol, or a combination of these, used by a manufacturer or merchant to identify his goods and distinguish them from those made or sold by others. The primary function of a trademark is to identify the source of a product, not to designate and identify the product itself. Absence of a specific trademark designation does not indicate that proprietary rights may not exist in the word involved. The term "trade name" as per The United States Trademark Association, is not synonomous with the word, trademark. The proper useage of the term, "trade name" is to indicate the name or style under which a person, company, firm or corporation does business. The name, "brand name," is considered to be equal to the term, trademark. Trademarks are now granted under the Trademark Act of 1946 by the Patent Office, Washington, D. C.

TRADEMARKS, A TRADEMARK NAME. For example, *Kodel* would be in this category, manufactured by Eastman Chemical Products Company, Inc., a division of Eastman Kodak Company, Rochester, New York. *Kodel* becomes a registered trademark when the circled R is used with the name. This trademark is renewable every twenty years as per permission of the Government of the United States.

A *Tradename,* strictly speaking, is an indistinct term or word and is not subject to a Registered Trademark. A *Generic Name* embodies such sords as acrylic, modacrylic, nylon, etc. Comparable with generic words such as coal, match, water, etc.

TRADEMARKS AND COPYRIGHTS. For any item or article that is to be manufactured and marketed, there may be a desire to label it with a distinctive *Trademark* which may be registered in the Patent Office, Washington, District of Columbia. To protect an industrial design, it is of benefit to know that there is an alternative in obtaining a design patent. Designs may be copyrighted if they qualify under the law as "works of art, models, or designs for works of art" or "reproductions of works of art." The copyrighting procedure is obtained much quicker than is that to obtain a design patent.

Patents, Trademarks, and *Copyrights* are different froms of intellectual property. The first two are obtained from the Patent Office while copyrights

are registered in the Copyright Office, a unit in the Library of Congress. Procedures for registering trademarks and copyrights are rather simple and the applicant may be able to file the necessary papers himself. Most patent attorneys also handle trademark and copyright matters. A *Trademark* is a word, symbol, or device, or a combination of these, used by a manufacturer or merchant to identify his wares and to distinguish these from those of others. Two booklets should be in your library on this topic - *The Makers' Monograms,* and *The Coats of Arms of the Business World* published by the Patent, Trademark, and Copyright Research Institute, George Washington University, Washington, District of Columbia.

Tradenames differ from *Trademarks.* They are business names, such as those of companies or partnerships, used by manufacturers, merchants and others to identify their businesses. A *Trademark* identifies a product while a *Tradename* identifies a producer. *Tradenames* as such cannot be registered but they can be if they are also used as *Trademarks.*

An entrepreneur establishes his right to a trademark by adopting and using it in business. One does not have to register it in the United States Patent Office but there are advantages in doing so. One does not have to apply for registration immediately. Some persons may wait a number of years before doing this. At present, over 800,000 trademarks have been registered and about half of the registrations are still being used; many have been used for seventy-five or more years.

TRADEMARKS WHICH ARE NOT CLASSIFIED AS FIBER TRADEMARKS. The following list indicates trademarks which do not come within the scope of the Federal Trade Commission with its definition of "fiber trademark" but which may be used, from time to time, to identify the source of certain manmade fibers or other products of the company or corporation. The list follows: (Trademark and member company): *Avisco* of American Viscose Division of FMC Corporation; *Beaunit* of Beaunit Fibers Division of Beaunit Corporation; *Celaspun* of Celanese Corporation of America; *Chemstrand* of Monsanto Textiles Company, Inc.; *Courtaulds* of Courtaulds North America, Inc.; *Eastman* of Eastman Kodak Company; *Enka* of American Enka Corporation; *Fybrite* of Fiber Industries, Inc., Marketed by Cela-

nese Fibers Marketing Company, Division of Celanese Corporation of America; *Hercules* of Hercules Incorporated; *Lektroset* of IRC Fibers Division of Midland-Ross Corporation; *Reemay* of E. I. duPont de Nemours & Co., Inc.; *Union Carbide* of Union Carbide Corporation.

TRAFFIC SURFACE. The surface of any textile material such as a carpet, rug, etc., which is walked on by the public. Provides for durability, abrasion, performance, etc.

TRAGACANTH. See GUM TRAGACANTH.

TRAGASOL. The kernel of the locust bean furnishes this adhesive sizing agent, which possesses excellent emulsifying properties. It comes in a strong aqueous jelly formation and possesses much strength.

TRAGON. An adhesive sizing ingredient which is a concentrated tragasol in dry soluble powder form. It will swell in cold water and dissolve on boiling.

TRAIN. The extended part of a dress, gown, or skirt which has a trail at the back. It may be cut in one with the garment or be a separate section attached to the shoulders or waistline. When used for weddings, formal, state or other similar occasions, the train is usually carried by an attendant. At social events, the train is carried in the hand or thrown over the arm of the wearer when dancing, and at times, when walking.

TRAM. The term for "filling," in the silk trade. In woven material, the thread is twisted loosely, and is made by doubling two or three raw silk threads. They are not given the second-time spinning, as in the case of organzine that is used for silk warp. Tram is given from one to three turns of twist per inch, merely enough to support the thread while it is being manipulated.

In the knitting trade, tram signifies the loosely twisted thread of pure silk yarn that is used for men's and women's silk hosiery. There is, however, no great amount of pure silk hosiery made today.

TRAME. French for filling or weft.

TRAME BROCHÉE. French for brocading filling, the filling yarn or yarns used in the weaving of brocades. Italian is "trama di spolinato."

TRAMETTE. Coarse tram silk yarn used in hosiery.

TRAMMAGE. A silk produced in the northern Chinese provinces by primitive methods. The yarn is uneven, and the term signifies the number seven. This is interpreted to mean that seven cocoons were used to make the yarn which would have fourteen threads in it. The industry is of the household variety. In recent years, there has been a tendency on the part of the large silk interests to improve the methods of raising the worms and to facilitate the silk reeling.

TRAMPED DORNOCH. A type of linen fabric made in Scotland, chiefly in Aberdeen and Dundee.

TRANQUALE. Registered trademark of Dan River, Inc., New York City, for its durable press, no-iron percale sheets and pillowcases.

TRANS-CASPIAN WOOL. Supposed to have originated around the Caspian Sea, it is now one of the staple wools of central Asia. More than half of the average fleece is white while the remainder runs from black to gray in color cast; used mainly in carpeting.

TRANSFER DEVICE, STOCK. Any device used to carry, transfer, or present stock from one machine to another one. Examples are Apperly Feed, Scotch Feed, etc.

TRANSFER POINT. The horizontal course of knitted stitches that fasten together the double inturned welt. Also serves the purpose of preventing runs which begin in the welt from progressing into the stocking leg.

TRANSFORMATION. Change from one state to another, as from worm to chrysalis or from chrysalis to worm in the life cycle of a silkworm.

TRANSLUCENT. Allowing the passage of some light, but not a clear view of any object; semitransparent.

TRANSMISSION ROPE. Any suitable rope or cord used to transmit power to a shaft, pulley, etc.

TRANSPARENT VELVET. A clearcut pile fabric which comes in several grades and types; good qualities are expensive. Fabric drapes well, is durable, dry-cleans neatly, but has tendency to crush. Crush resistants, however, are now applied. Ideal for evening wear.

TRANSPORTATION FABRIC. Upholstery fabric used for seats in railroad cars, buses, and other vehicles. May also include the curtains on Pullman cars but does not include head linings. It is a fabric that withstands a great deal of abrasion, friction, strain, etc.

TRAPPING, TRAPPINGS. 1. Dress, garb, or raiment that is overdone, superficial, outmoded, outlandish. 2. Any of the types of coverings, decorative or otherwise, used on horses.

TRAPS. Shuttle smashes which break several warp ends and in which the shuttle becomes trapped in the shed as it closes.

TRAPUNTO. A type of quilting in which the design is outlined with single stitches, and padding is drawn from the back, filling each part of the designs separately, giving a high-relief effect.

TRASHMETER. An optical-electronic measuring device which determines quickly the amount and size of trash particles in a sample of raw cotton.

TRAVELER, TRAVELLER. C-shaped metal clips on ring-spinning frame. Around each spindle of the ring-spinning frame there is a steel ring set permanently in the steel carriage which goes up and down when the machine is in action. There are many spindles to be cared for by the ring rail, which extends the length of the frame. Each spindle must have its ring. The upper edge of the ring is flanged on the principle of a railroad track.

Snapped over each flange is the traveler. This small "C-shaped" metal clip travels at a high rate of speed around the ring when the frame is in action. The traveler guides the newly spun yarn onto its bobbin or spindle.

The width of the travelers will vary with the particular diameters and yarn sizes desired. The narrower the traveler, the finer will be the resultant yarn. The traveler aids in the placing of necessary turns of twist per inch in the yarn.

TRAVELER'S GRASS. A strong bast Australian fiber used for rope.

TRAVELING BAG, SUITCASE, AND STRAP LEATHER. A general term used for leathers in the manufacture of the foregoing articles. It does not, however, cover light leathers used for women's fancy handbags. The basic material for bag and case leather at present is leather made from the hides of animals of the bovine species, heavy sealskins, and goatskins.

Top Grain is the grain-side or hair-side of cattle hide that has been reduced to a specified thickness on the ounce standard, the range being from 2 to 10 ounces according to a standard leather gauge. Split leather has to be so designated and is not included in the above classification. Split is that portion of a hide or skin after splitting, other than the grain or hair-side. Splits are usually named according to their sequence of production, such as main, second, slab (as in the case of upholstery leather), or the use to be made of the leather, such as flexible

for innersoles and gloves, waxed for low-price shoe uppers, etc. A third classification includes bag and case leather that is finished with pyroxylin or pigment.

TRAVERS. Filling cords, ribs or stripes noted in some fabrics.

TRAVERSE. 1. Rather pronounced cords or stripes in filling direction of a fabric. 2. The lateral distance between reversal points in the building of a bobbin of roving or slubbing, a package of yarn, etc.

TRAVERSE GRINDER. A four-inch roller clothed with emery fillet and mounted on a hollow barrel. When in action the grinder works back and forth from one end to the other as the actual grinding of the roller involved takes place.

TRAVERSE GUIDE. In the feeding of stock to the several machines used in the manufacture of yarn, this guide has a reciprocating action to prevent sliver, slubbing, or roving from always entering the drawing rolls at the same place.

TRAVIS. Formerly the trademark for Darvan manufactured in West Germany and sold throughout Europe. It was jointly owned by Celanese Corporation of the United States and Farbwerke Hoechst AG of West Germany. Phased out here in 1968, it was also discontinued in West Germany in 1970. See Darvan.

TRAY CLOTH. Any fabric, usually ornamented, used to serve as a tray cover upon which dishes are placed.

TRAWL TWINE. A three-ply white abaca twine used in maritime circles; runs about 100 yards to the pound.

TREADLE, TREADLES. 1. A lever that is a part of the shedding motion on a loom. Situated near the floor, one end is fulcrumed while the other is fastened by straps to the bottom of the harness frame. 2. A similar device found on hand looms by means of which, by depressing it with the foot, the shed of the loom is formed.

TREBLE CLOTH. British term for three-ply fabric. The cloth would be made from three warps and three fillings, plus the binder thread arrangements to hold the material together as it is being woven in the loom. Refers to very heavy overcoatings, and also to some industrial fabrics made this way. These fabrics are made from small weave repeats using the plain, twill, and satin weaves for the various arrangements in the structure. The stitching of the fabrics is usually done by the use of a satin weave.

TREE COTTON. Perennial cotton

found in Asia, Central, and South America. Much of the cotton is of good quality.

TREE WOOL. In ancient history, the Medieval Era, and even in present day Germany, cotton was known in some areas as "tree wool." According to legend, it was believed that cotton plants were actually alive, a sort of living lamb that drooped and grazed on the grass until they became too high to do so. When the lamb starved to death, the wool fibers were plucked from the boll.

TRELLISWORK. Colored embroidery in which the background has been cut away. The design is usually a climbing vine.

TREMOLITE. Of the amphibole mineral group, it is a calcium magnesium silicate found in grayish deposits of brittle, fibrous crystals.

TRENCH COAT. A loose-fitting, all-over type of coat with deep collar and wide belt, large pockets and flaps. Is double-breasted, and reaches to the knees, at least. Gabardine, covert, and allied fabrics are used to make this garment.

TRESQUILLE. A type of greasy, sleazy wool found in the Marseilles area.

TRESSE. Tressé is French for fancy-braided; fancy braiding.

TREVET, TRIVET, TRIVETTE. A type of sliding knife used by weavers to cut pile threads of fabrics when woven double. Velvet may be cut in this manner.

TREVIRA. Registered trademark for the polyester fibers produced by Hoechst Fibers, Inc., New York City. Its plant in Spartanburg, South Carolina produces the following types:

Type 160: For blending with cotton, low pilling.

Type 220: Normal tenacity fiber.

Type 340: Designed especially for knit goods, highly pill resistant.

Type 520: High shrinkage fiber with other properties same as Type 220.

Type 720: Fiberfill, normal type.

Type 740: Fiberfill type with three dimensional characteristics.

Type 820: Carpet fiber for use in floor-coverings.

TREVIRA STAR. A polyester penta-lobal (five point, star shaped cross-section) filament yarn which imparts a distinctive, bright appearance and a crisp, dry hand or feel to a fabric, when compared with a fabric from the round cross-section. This yarn appears brighter than the round cross-section fiber when

dyed with the same formula; therefore, appropriate adjustments should be made in the dye formulas. Uses include men's, women's, and children's woven and knitted apparel, neckwear, pile cloths, floorcovering, bed sheets, sheets and pillow cases, blankets, bedspreads, tablecloths, napkins, curtains and draperies, upholstery, etc. Registered trademark of Hoechst Fibers, Inc., for its polyester fiber. Trevira is the international trademark of Farbwerke Hoechst, A.G., Frankfurt/M, Germany.

TREVIRA TYPES IN 100% TEXTURED POLYESTER FILAMENT.

Type 640: A cationic dyeable yarn of 150 denier, 32 filaments. It provides brighter, clearer colors than those possible from use of disperse dyeable polyester. When piece-dyed and combined with Type 610, it produces multi-colored patterning. Stripes, checks, plaids, and multi-colored Jacquard effects are possible from this single dyebath method. Type 640 will also take disperse dyestaffs in absence of cationic dyes at a different rate than disperse dyeable fibers. Thus, unusual two-tone effects can be obtained with the use of Type 640 in combination with disperse dyeable fibers.

Type 674: This is a contrast yarn of 130 denier, 32 filaments. Sixteen of the filaments will take on disperse dyes; the other 16 accept cationic dyes, and with no intermingling of the two types, maximum color contrast can be obtained. Color contrasts are practically unlimited in a single yarn and the variations are further multiplied when the yarn is used in combination with regular disperse dyeable Trevira or spun Trevira, with either of the two heather yarn types given below.

In the absence of cationic dyes, Type 674 Yarn will take disperse dyes, but at a different rate than the disperse dyeable fibers. Interesting effects are thus obtainable by combining Type 674 and disperse dyeable dyeable fibers by using only disperse dyes.

Type 671 A: This is a light heather yarn effect made of 135 denier with 28 filaments; 24 are known as Natural (Disperse) and the other four are Black (Solution Dyed). The result is a subtle heather yarn very effective for pastel shades and in combination with other Trevira yarn variants.

Type 671 B: This dark heather-type yarn is of 150 denier with 32 filaments divided evenly between Natural (Disperse) and Black (Solution Dyed). When piece-dyed the yarn effect will show a deeper and more contrasting tone effect

than that observed in Type 671 A.

TREVOLTINS. Those breeds of silkworms which produce three broods a year.

TREWS. Highland trousers. The difference between trews and regular trousers is that in the old Highland trews, in order to preserve the complete design of the tartan as far as possible, there is a seam only on the inner side of the leg, where in trousers, originally designed for plain colors or small patterns, there are seams on both the outside and the inside of the leg.

TRIACETATE FIBER. Fiber made from cellulose acetate as a base is known as diacetate. Triacetate fiber differs from diacetate because of different degree in acetylation afforded and the ultimate degree of solubility in acetone. Arnel is an example of the fiber in the United States while Courpleta is made by Courtaulds Ltd., in England. See ARNEL, COURPLETA.

TRIANA. Trademark of PPG Industries, Inc., Pittsburgh, Pennsylvania, for a family of fine filament fiber glass yarns designed to improve hand, drapability, texture and surface interest to finished fabrics.

TRIANIZED. Trade-mark of the Triangle Finishing Corporation for a process which is applied to knitted nylon, to make it wrinkle-resistant and permanently stable in width and length.

TRIAXIAL FABRIC. Based on the ancient art of braiding, it is a woven fabric which provides durability and strength and can withstand strains in any direction. In order to obtain the desired result, the fabric is formed by interweaving two sets of bias warp threads and filling threads; the bias warp threads extend in opposite directions diagonally across the fabric from one selvage to the opposite selvage. It is actually a single cloth construction type fabric with a set-in or laid-in set of yarns as an interwoven filling. The fact that the warp thread can be lifted from one reed dent or split to the next one is possible due to the reed being capless at the top.

Incidentally, the fabric can also be made on a Jacquard loom, for pattern work and bias distortion is a main result of the work. Used chiefly in industry, the triaxial fabrics are used for coated fabrics and tire fabrics. Originally developed in 1913 and covered by patent rights. See Bias Weaves.

TRICEL. Registered trademark for triacetate fiber made by British Celanese, Ltd., Great Britain. The basic raw materials are cellulose and oil. In filament form it is used in woven and knitted goods such as blouses, dressgoods, lingerie, ribbons, scarves, and neckwear. In spun form it finds use in dressgoods, skirtings, suitings. Tricel is ideal for blending with major textile fibers, in addition to the foregoing, and when blended with nylon, it is used for washable slacks, lightweight suiting fabrics, rainwear, etc. Tricel also find use as a filling material for quilts and quilted clothing, paper felts, and as pile and backing in candlewick spreads. It possesses heat-setting properties, resists creasing, shrinkage, stretching, and soiling, and washes easily and well. It is quick-drying and needs little or no ironing.

TRICEL H. A triacetate of high tenacity of British Celanese, Ltd., United Kingdom; *Tricel Soufflette* is a triacetate textured filament of the same company. Tricel is known as Starnel in the Scandia countries. See Arnel, Tricelon, Triceta.

TRICELON. British Celanese, Ltd., Great Britain produces this fiber by combining its Tricel triacetate fiber and Celon, its nylon fiber. Has the aesthetic appeal of Tricel and the strength of Celon, thereby making Tricelon ideal for lightweight woven goods such as georgettes, ninons, twills, voiles, et al. It also finds much use in knitgoods in warpknit fabrics requiring bulk and cover as well as very light weight in finished goods. Used in blouses, dressgoods, children's wear, lingerie, nightwear, and men's shirtings.

TRICETA. In 1901 a triacetate fiber was made by the present day, Farbenfabriken Bayer Aktiengesellschaft in Germany. In 1914, the now defunct Lustron Company, Lansdowne, Pennsylvania, also produced a triacetate fiber. The name, *Triceta,* was first used in Germany in 1936 to mean a spun fiber that was triacetate in form and structure. Its progress, however, was impeded by the fact that it was too expensive.

In 1954, with changing time and improved research and development, the Celanese Corporation, unveiled its well-known *Arnel,* a true triacetate fiber and filament. This fiber and fabric, now a staple in the textile and apparel trades, had several things in its favor - quicker drying when compared with acetate, better crease resistance, improved dimensional stability, and ideal heat-setting for pleating. Production was much easier and simpler than in 1901, 1914, and 1936.

Triacetate production is a rather simple matter carried out by dissolving triacetate in methylene chloride, to which alcohol is added and then spinning the filament from the solution bath to a fully spun yarn. See Arnel, Triacetate Fiber.

TRICK, KNITTING. The slot whose function it is to preserve the knitting elements in the knitting machine.

TRICOLETTE. The first rayon knit dress-goods fabric to appear on the market, 1924. It is a staple knit but is not as fine as mignonette. Made from rayon, tussah silk or silk, the fabric has been used in dress goods and underwear, blouses, and other apparel. A lustrous fabric made by tubular knitting, tricolette has been superseded in recent years by lighter-weight knit fabrics of higher gauge.

TRICORN, TRICORNE. An article with three corners or projections. The hat of this name is a three-cornered effect with the brim turned-up on three sides, the cocked or cockade hat. Came into being around 1690 and was most popular during the eighteenth century and was "trademark" in France for many years, especially around the time of the French Revolution.

TRICOT. 1. A type of warp knit fabric which has a thin texture since it is made from single or fine yarn. The French verb tricoter means "to knit." 2. "Stocking-net" as applied to a warp-knitted fabric irrespective of the motif; often refers to a flat knitted cloth since it is not tubular. The meaning, however, is not to be construed to imply a flat-machine knit fabric. 3. A French serge lining fabric made on a 20-inch width. 4. A fine woven worsted made on the tricot weave which presents fine break lines in the filling direction. This chain-break effect fabric is dyed all popular shades, has a high, compact texture, and is a good material to use in tailoring. Gives excellent wear in the better type of tailored garments for women.

TRICOT, JOSEPHINE. Handmade, open crochet fabric made with closely manipulated rows joined by doubled yarn at predetermined intervals.

TRICOT, WOOLEN. High-grade, woolen or worsted cloth used in ladies' wear. The term in French means knitting. The woven cloth usually repeats on four or eight picks and there are horizontal rib lines in the finished fabric. Cloth is made from a double cloth weave on the principle of the double plain weave. Tailors very well and is conventional.

TRICOT CROSS. Any fabric which has rather pronounced rib effects in crosswise direction.

TRICOT CUT. A roll of tricot knitted fabric as taken from a tricot knitting frame; a cut is usually a total of 350 racks in the length. For 40-denier nylon and heavier sizes the cut is less.

TRICOT DE LAINE. Means a wool tricot. It is, however, blue woolen uniform fabric used for clothing for sailors and those who work in maritime circles.

TRICOT ECOSSAIS. Means a Scotch tricot. It is, however, a type of crochet work made with the stitches gathering five loops at a time.

TRICOT FLANNEL. An elastic, thick, heavy flannel.

TRICOTINE. Of the family of whipcords, coverts, and gabardines. Made from a 63-degree twill that gives the characteristic double twill line on the face of the cloth. A good weave to use in making the material is $\frac{3\ 3\ 1\ 1}{1\ 1\ 2\ 1}$. Other weaves of similar nature may be used as well. This thirteen harness fabric is dyed in all staple colors. The cloth drapes well, is easy to tailor and is a smart conventional fabric. A staple cloth. Skein-dyed tricotine is on the market. Cloth is usually of medium and best quality, and is used in men's wear and women's wear. Made with woolen or worsted yarn. See Illustrated Section (Fabrics 31).

TRICOT LONG. Occasionally used to imply rib effects that run lengthwise in fabrics.

TRICOT MACHINE. A warp-knitting machine which, unlike the Raschel, uses spring-beard needles and operates with one needle bar and a maximum of three guide bars.

TRICOT STITCH. The simplest of crochet stitches. It is worked with a long hook of uniform size; the motif produced is plain and straight.

TRICOT WARP KNITTING MACHINE. Tricot knit fabric has fine vertical wales on the face and crosswise ribs on the reverse of the goods. The first efforts for what is today called tricot warp knitting were brought out by a British knitter named Crane, at the time of the American Revolutionary War. His ideas still prevail in the modern version of tricot. The fabric does not ravel, is runproof, has good stability, elasticity, resiliency, and does have crease resistance along with a high rated tear strength. Uses include fabrics for bonding and laminating, lingerie and intimate apparel, blouses and dressgoods, nightwear, lounge wear, shirts, uniforms, and some use in the automotive industry. One experienced knitter can attend 20 machines whereas in circular knitting a knitter can care for one to three frames.

TRI-LOBAL. A manmade fiber or filament in which the cross-section has been modified from circular form to a three-sided cross-section. Luster is an advantage for this type fiber over the conventional cross-section type. See Penta-Lobal.

TRILOK. Made from polyethylene yarn and conventional textile fibers, this fabric is woven flat but becomes permanently three-dimensional when dipped in boiling water which causes puffs to form. It is used in automobile upholstery and furniture where the cushioning effect of the structure provides comfort and free circulation of air between the person and the seat upon which he is sitting. Product of the UniRoyal Fiber and Textile Division, UniRoyal, Inc., Winnsboro, South Carolina.

TRIM. To decorate a window.

TRIMMER. A machine used to cut loose, hanging, undesirable selvage ends or threads from the cloth. Selvages are an important factor in woven goods and should be trim and neat at all times.

TRIMMINGS BUYER. One who purchases trimmings and linings for the apparel trades. May design trimmings, as well. Should be able to aid the designer by finding and devising decorative and original trimmings. In addition, he must know the use of buckles and belts; of threads; and be thoroughly informed in both staples and fancies.

TRINA. One of the early Italian names for lace, especially around the fifteenth century; silk and metallic threads featured the product.

TRINITROCELLULOSE. Gun cotton.

TRIPLE SHEER. Made of novelty twill weaves from Bemberg yarn. A popular rayon material that wears, drapes, and washes well. Comes in many types of prints. This fine, flat surface cloth is almost opaque. Recently there has been the tendency to get away from the twill effects which first characterized the material.

TRIPLE SHEER CREPE. A common term used to describe a tightly textured, almost opaque, sheer fabric with a fine, flat surface.

TRIPLE, TREBLE CLOTH. A cloth made from three warps and three fillings, plus the binder thread arrangement. Each fabric is a distinctive layer

of cloth, and the stitching holds the material in place. Used in many industrial fabrics such as brake lining, belting, webbing, laundry padding, etc. Chinchilla and a few other heavy overcoating fabrics can be made in three-ply fabric.

TRIPLE VOILE. Made on order of chiffon, it is a plain-weave cloth, light in weight, and not too compact in texture. Ninon is a popular triple voile.

TRIPPLES. Flax bundles.

TRISODIUM. Trisodium phosphate or the hydrated sodium salt of orthophosphoric acid.

TROLLEY. British term for lace in which the motif is outlined with a bulky thread, or with a flat narrow border made up of several thicker threads.

TRONA. A natural alkali carbonate found in the earth.

TROPICAL. Fancy suiting material of plain and rather open weaves. It is a lightweight worsted of the semi-staple group. Fabric is ideal for summer and tropical wear, and somewhat resembles Palm Beach cloth. Weight goes from 7 to 11 ounces per yard. Warp and filling are of high counts, usually 2/60s or better. Material is skein- or piece-dyed, and clear finish is given. Tropical mixtures and heathers are popular cloths in the tropical range and these cloths are stock-dyed to give the desired pattern effect. If called tropical worsted, it must be all worsted yarn in content. See Illustrated Section (Fabrics 10).

TROPICAL WEIGHT. Worsted suiting whose weight per yard ranges from 7 to 11 ounces; used largely in warm climates and during the warm season.

TROPICAL WHIPCORD. British term for water-repellent whipcord and comparable materials used for topcoats and overcoats.

TROUSER CUFFS. In the latter part of the last century men got away from the habit of rolling up their trousers when it rained heavily; cuffs were conceived by some unkown person as they were supposed to serve as a protection or guard against mud and slush. Cuffs have been used ever since their inception except when formal clothing is worn by men.

TROUSERING. This term, as far as is known, originated in Ireland before 1650. The Scots have the word, "trews" with the same meaning. Chances are the terms come from the French verb, trousser," meaning to truss or pack in a package. Woven firmer and tighter than suiting fabric it is heavier in

weight. Stripings feature much trousering which is used for dress occasions and ordinary everyday wear. Made from combinations of basic weaves, the background is usually of a dark color, particularly black. Women's trousering or pants come in all colors, either conservative or bizarre. Much of the fabric is of double cloth construction in warp and filling, or made of two warps and one filling.

TROUSER PLEATS. Side-front pleats which allow ease at the hipline, at the same time emphasizing narrowness at the waist.

TROUSSEAU. The collective personal outfit and accessories of a bride-elect with particular reference to clothes.

TRUBENIZED. Made of resilient porous fused fabric, two layers of cotton fabric joined with a porous intervening layer of cellulose adhesive.

TRUBENIZING. A finish applied to cotton collars, cuffs, and shirt fronts to prevent limpness and wilting. The cotton lining cloth is made with some cellulose acetate yarn in it. This material is placed between the outer layers and the completed article is soaked in a solvent for acetate, such as acetone, fused, and then pressed. The acetate yarn, as a result of the fusing, combines with the outer cotton layers with the result that a single layer of fabric results. Trubenized fabric may be washed without loss of its original characteristics and no ironing is necessary in the laundering. Product of Trubenizing Process Corporation, New York City.

TRUE BIAS. The diagonal of a square. True bias is cut about one inch wide and serves to finish the curved edges such as those of a collar, sleeve bottom, scalloped effect, etc.

TRUE FIBER. One which has a uniform diameter.

TRUE SILK. Specifically, the silk filament produced by the larvae of the moth, bombyx mori. See SILK.

TRUE STITCH. An embroidery stitch that is the same on both sides of a material.

TRUFFLE YARN. See GIMP, GIMP YARN.

TRUMAN, HARRY S. This former United States President unveiled a style in men's wear shirtings. While attending a Labor Convention in Miami in 1948, he appeared one morning in a gaudy, multi-colored print sport shirt which was not tucked in at the waist. Since many males of at least middle age are rather portly around the waist, this style became an instant success. These shirts, covered with splash and allover motifs, were made of low quality fabric with low pick count. The structure was such that the shirt would only last for the one summer and was then ready for being cast aside. The color motifs covered up the low grade fabric but this did not deter large volume sales of the article. This fashion is still a very popular summer shirting with males and they now come in many qualities from low to high.

TRUMPET. The cone-shaped opening in the iron plate which sets above the coiler-can attachment located at the front of a carding machine. Sliver coming from the calender roller of the card is passed through the trumpet, then downward through the coiler attachment so that it may then coil evenly into the coiler can, which is set on a revolving plate to insure uniformity of the "lay" or "wind." See Illustrated Section.

TRUNK-LENGTH HOSIERY. Women's hosiery which reaches above the knee; it is not as long as opera hose.

TRUXILLO WOOL. An inferior, low-grade Spanish wool.

TSATLEE SILK. This silk is raised in the interior of China and is sold under a separate name in order not to confuse it with other inland Tussah silks. The raising of the worms is a household industry in the backward sections of the country. The home method of reeling formerly was such that the entire crop of coccons had to be reeled before the moths escaped from the cocoons.

The chrysalis was not killed when silk was obtained in this manner. The waste was exorbitant when the length of time and energy expended were considered. Modern filatures are now to be found in some of these remote, isolated sections since the possibilities of this type of silk have now been realized.

Tsatlee is very lustrous but uneven; the skeins have to be sorted and split into fine and coarse grades before further manipulation. This silk is much used in sewing thread.

T-SHIRT. See KNITTED SHIRTS.

TSIGAY. One of the oldest Russian breeds of sheep, this native type is raised chiefly in the Rostov and Stalingrad areas. Staple is about 4 inches; ram fleeces weigh around 8 pounds.

TUBE. 1. Another name for a bobbin, cylindrical in shape and used as base of core about which filaments or yarn are wound either snugly and compactly, or loosely as the occasion de-

mands. 2. "A cylindrical yarn package formed for winding on a tube." (A.S.T.M. definition).

TUBE TWIST. Compressor twisting of an eight- or more ply yarn to add smoothness in contradistinction to ring twist.

TUB-FAST. Any fabric that will wash and launder well without loss of color.

TUBING. Tubular cloth woven on a loom is used for sheeting, casing, bolsters, neckwear, etc. The fabric is woven one section on top of the other with the edges joined on the principle of tubular weaving, usually by dropping a warp end on one selvage. The cloth is cut in correct size to be made into the finished article. Tubing is not used very much in making pillowcasing and bolsters since wide looms now take care of making the material.

TUBIZE. The acetate and rayon yarns produced by the Tubize Chatillon Corporation, a unit of Celanese Corporation of America.

TUB SILK, TUBBABLE SILK. A washable silk used in summer wear. The term originally implied "gray goods," or cloth as it came from the loom. Stripes seem to have popularity in these fabrics and there is a wide use of them in pattern effects.

TUBULAR FABRIC. Woven or knitted cloth made in seamless tubes, such as hosiery, knitted neckwear, pillowcasing, mailbagging, webbing.

TUBULAR KNITTING ON A FLAT MACHINE. To knit tubular on a flat machine, which has two sets of needles, the cams are arranged so that only one set of needles is in operation at a time. Going in a given direction the front set of needles knit; while in the opposite direction, the yarn is switched over to the back set of needles, thereby forming the fabric.

TUBULAR YARN. A term sometimes used to imply hollow filament yarns of the man-made fiber groups. The term, however, should be avoided since it is not absolutely true because air bubbles may form within the tube, thereby not making it a continuous tube formation or structure.

TUBWASHED. Wool which has been washed after shearing. Formerly, it meant wool washed prior to this operation and was universally done throughout the world before the factory system came into being. Actual tubwashing of wool is still done in some of the outlying districts of our Southern states where the stock is used in home consumption and for hand-woven fabrics which find their way to the exclusive

shops in large cities.

TUCK. 1. To form a tuck or tucks. 2. The fold of a fabric, as in a garment, stitched into place. It is used for decoration, holding fullness, or shortening or shaping a garment.

TUCK BAR. A mechanism which permits the placing of a pattern or stripe in circular jersey knitting wherever desired in the fabric. This device permits the introduction of designs, where desired, in plain or variable striped jersey fabric or the reverse— a variable stripe can be placed wherever desired in an all-over pattern. Also known as a "pattern placer."

TUCKER. A piece of fabric worn by women and young children around the neck and shoulders. The term "bib" is usually given to a piece of fabric tied under the chin of a child to protect clothing while being fed or eating. Also implies the upper part of an apron.

In the eighteenth century, the tucker was also known as a modesty piece and it was used to cross the bosom of a female, especially to hide a view of the bosom when wearing a low-neck dress.

TUCKER. 1. One who, or that which, tucks; as the tucker of a sewing machine. 2. A covering worn over the neck and shoulders by women and children, the "bib-and-tucker."

TUCKING. Ornamenting materials by rows of parallel tucks, arranged closely and covering the surface, or in clusters with spaces between them. It is used in waists, yokes, underwear, skirts, and shirt fronts.

TUCKING, ON THE HOOK. The accumulation of loops in the hook of a knitting needle. This is preferred to tucking on the latch since it is safer; that is, several loops can be more easily retained in the hook of the needle than on the latch.

TUCKING, ON THE LATCH. This is done when a knitting needle does not descend low enough to knock over. Therefore, the loop remains on the latch of the needle. Not generally used because of difficulty in holding the accumulated tuck loops on the latch.

TUCKING ATTACHMENT. A device that may be attached to a motordriven sewing machine, used when sewing tucks in fabric materials; consists of an adjustable and tapering steel blade, attached to the sewing machine in lieu of the regular presser foot; the material is creased over the blade and fed under the needle assembly; the blade raises the cloth to form the tuck and guides the fabric under the needle assembly.

TUCK KNITTING. A method of framework knitting in which a large number of loops are gathered on a needle to form the motif.

TUCK LACES. These tuck nets are ornamented with parallel rows of tucks arranged closely together in order to cover the surface, or in cluster formation with spaces between to enhance the effect. Plain Ensor net or fancy net is made by independent beams for the lace.

TUCK LOOP. The length or lengths of yarn received by a needle and not drawn through the loop of the previous course.

TUCK POSITION. The position in the knitting cycle where the needle is advanced to a point enabling it only to receive new yarn in its hook but not allowing the old loop to move below the open latch.

TUCK STITCH. A knitting stitch made when the needle retains one loop and then takes on one or more additional loops and then casts all of these onto another loop. It is used to modify other stitches and to make novelty motifs. See Illustrated Section.

TUCKS. Cloth of two or more warps, made of cotton, cotton and silk, all silk, silk and rayon, and so on. The purpose in mind in making the cloth is that there must be considerable scope for the filling effects or patterns, which are worked into novel designs and colorings. Tucks give a perfect pleat which runs across the material from edge to edge. They are used for curtains, portieres, and hangings.

TUCUM. Obtained from the palm trees of Brazil, the thread of this name is used in fishing lines because of excellent resistance qualities, flexibility and durability. Other uses include dusters, hammocks, mats, marine cordage, and rugs.

TUFT. 1. A group of several hundred wool fibers from a well-conditioned sheep will form a tuft of wool fibers; several tufts in a fleece unite into a large one known as a staple.
2. Fancy, nub, or other yarns used for fancy effects in homespuns, tweeds, Cheviots and other suiting and coating fabrics of the rather coarse, heavy type.

TUFTAFFETA. An old-time silk fabric in which the pattern was formed by tufts of pile yarn.

TUFTED FABRIC. A fabric decorated with fluffy tufts of soft twist, multiple-ply cotton yarns. Some are loom-woven but the majority have the tufts inserted and cut by machine in a previously woven fabric, such as muslin sheeting, lightweight duck, etc. The tufts may be intermittently spaced giving the type called candlewick, or arranged closely in continuous lines giving the type called chenille. The patterns vary from simple line effects to elaborate designs. Used for bedspreads, robes, bathmats, stuffed toys, etc.

TUFTED RUG. A rug of scatter or room size, in which yarn is drawn from the face through backing (hemp, jute, etc.) and then through to the face again with long loops left on the face which may be cut or uncut. A shrinkage treatment then contracts the backing so that the rug yarn is held in place. Sometimes a rubber compound is applied to the under side of the backing to help to hold the yarn and to keep the rug from sliding on the floor. Tufted rugs are in no sense woven rugs where the pile is interlocked, the cost of manufacture is higher, and the result provides a more durable rug.

TUFTED YARN. A British term to designate cotton yarn in which defects similar to slubs are observed. These slubs, however, are more loosely tangled than average slubs in yarns which are usually well gnarled and tangled.

TUFTING. 1. The tassel on an academic cap. 2. Tufted fabrics such as seen in some bedcovers, curtains, novelties, etc.

TUFTING, JERKER-BAR IN. The guide or thread-jerker which takes up the slack tufting yarn during the upstroke of the needle, controls the amount supplied for the back-stroke.

TUFTING, SCRAMBLER-BOX IN. This device is used in some types of carpet tufting motif attachments in order to equalize the travel distance of all pile ends in the design groups which repeat across the machine width. Prevents problems which may occur because of tension differences.

TUFTING MACHINE. A machine that automatically compresses a spot in a mattress and inserts and stitches a tuft through the compressed area.

TUFTING NEEDLE. A long, heavy needle with a hooked-shape eye used to force tufting cords through a mattress.

TUFTON. A rayon carpet staple fiber that resists soiling. It is an improved version of an older rayon of the same name. Like wool carpet yarns it is insensitive to oil wicking from jute backing yarns, and it is able to control the reflectivity of the carpet fiber through the use of delustrants or reflection surfaces which are spun into the fiber. Double delustered Tufton will soil less than wool. Made in 8 and 15 denier sizes, staple form it is a trade name. Product of FMC Corporation, American Viscose Company Division.

TUGOP FIBER. A Philippine bast fiber used for cordage and twine.

TUL. Indian term for twill or twill weave.

TULA ISTLE. See ISTLE.

TULIP. A silhouette with bodice fullness from the midriff up, and straight with a slim effect in the skirt. Supposed to resemble the tulip.

TULLE. A sheer silk or rayon fabric with hexagonal mesh, stiff, used much in ballet materials. The cloth comes in white and in colors and is cool, dressy, delicate, and difficult to launder. In dress goods, it is a stately type of material. It may be used with other fabrics, for overdraping, and is also known as rayon net or silk net.

TUMBLE DRYER. Any of a number of devices used to dry fabrics and garments; actually it is a heated oven often perfected for some particular type of drying, a very important segment in textile and apparel manufacture and production, as well as in commerical and home laundry work.

TUMBLE WASHER. One in which the washing action is done by the revolving drum or wash-basket around a horizontal or non-horizontal axis. The fins or wings on the drum facilitate lifting of the clothes and the water.

TUMEL COTTON. The better class of cleaned cotton is called Tumel in the Bombay, India, market.

TUNIC. 1. A blouse gathered at the waist or allowed to hang free. 2. An undress military coat. 3. The tight-fitting jacket of the British guardsmen. 4. A shirt or blouse reaching to the knee, with short sleeves, usually fastened with a girdle; worn by ancient Romans. 5. The Greek chiton. 6. A short, sacklike vestment made of silk, acetate, or rayon, worn by the religious. It is worn with the dalmatic and is provided with slits for the head and arms.

TUNICLE. 1. A light or fine tunic. 2. The short close-fitting vestment worn by priests of the Roman Catholic Church.

TUNICS, ROMAN DOUBLE. A tunic is defined as a gownlike outer garment with or without sleeves and sometimes belted, worn by the ancient Greeks and Romans. It is also a garment with a short skirt, worn by women for sports participation. The Roman Double Tunic occurs when two of them are worn at the same time; the one worn next to the skin is the *Subacula* and the outer one is known in history as the *Tunica Exterio-*

dum. At the beginnings of the Christian Era, this tunic was gradually lengthened and by the end of the 2nd century ankle-length was in favor, and it became known as the *Caracalla.* See Tunic, Tunicle.

TUNIS. Sheep native to Tunis and adjacent countries in North Africa. Characterized by its heavy, flopping ears. The staple is of medium variety while the wool has traces of brown in the usual white fleece. Tunis is used here for breeding purposes in raising of "early lambs."

TUNIS CROCHET. Single ribs are used in this crochet motif.

"TUP." In Scotland, a male sheep or ram.

TUQUE. A Canadian cap consisting of a knitted cylindrical bag with tapered ends, worn by thrusting one end inside the other, for tobogganing, skating, etc.

TURBAN. An Oriental head covering consisting of a sash or shawl, twisted around the cap. Also, the round-crowned brimless hat for women and children.

TURBEHLIK. Small Oriental rugs used in the Levant to hang over grapes. Also called grave rugs, the motif is made of floral, plant, and tree designs in somber color effects.

TURBO CONVERTER, TURBO STAPLER. Equipment used in the manufacture of high-bulk yarns such as acrylic and modacrylic, in which the fibers are, first of all, heat stretched under tension to provide a high degree of residual shrinkage and softness to the fibers. A special operation then preshrinks or relaxes a certain percentage of the fibers. The slivers of fibers that have been heat stretched and relaxed are then combined with fibers that have also been heat stretched but not relaxed so as to provide for the differential in shrinkage. After the combining of the two types of fibers on preparatory equipment, they are processed further and then spun into yarn. The Turbo Method is ideal in the manufacture of many types of knitting yarns. Product of Turbo Machine Company, Inc., Lansdale, Pennsylvania.

TURBO YARN. Yarns produced by the use of the Turbo Converter. See TURBO CONVERTER.

TURFANI. Tibetan wool of good quality used in the manufacture of expensive rugs.

TURFANI PASHIM. See PASHIM.

TURKEY RED. A fast, bright scarlet dye obtained from the madder plant. It is used much in cotton and woolen dyeing, after the stock has been chrome-mordanted. Present-day turkey red is a brilliant synthetic dyestuff. The original color, and the cloth of this name, came from Turkey.

TURKEY-RED OIL. See SULPHONATED OIL.

TURKISH KNOT. See GHIORDES KNOT.

TURKISH LACE. See OYAH LACE.

TURKISH RUGS. These are always in demand and are expensive. They have coarse yarns and larger and heavier piles than other rugs of similar type and construction. The range of design is vast. Some outstanding types include: Anatolian, Bakaran, Bokhara, Cabristan, Chichli, Daghestan, Ghiordes, Guendje, Kazak, Korna, Melik, Moussul, Zadak.

TURKISH TOWELING. The well-known terry cloth, identified by the uncut pile effect on one or both sides. It has excellent absorptive powers and is used for beachwear, sandals, washcloths, and towels. See TERRY CLOTH.

TURKISH YARN. Name sometimes given to mohair yarn.

TURKOMAN. A drapery fabric made with silk, rayon, or cotton warp and thick chenille filling, usually of cotton.

TURMERIC. Taken from the roots of the curcuma tinctoria, a member of the ginger family. Found in India and China, it is used in the textile industry as a direct yellow dye which, incidentally, is fugitive.

TURNBACK CHECK. Made in England and a popular export number, the fabric is a colored woven cloth which is characterized by a solid-colored border effect and a series of small check effects in the center of the piece.

TURQUE. Popular Canadian head-covering for winter wear; a cap made by tucking one long end of a long knit material into the other end.

TURQUOISE. A light greenish-blue, the color of a turquoise, high in brilliance and of ordinary saturation.

TURTLE NECK. A high collar that fits snugly about the neck, usually rolled or turned over double, often used on athletic sweaters.

TUSSAH. Name for wild silk anywhere in the world, the uncultivated types. Compared with true or cultivated silk, Tussah is more uneven, coarser and stronger, and comes in shades of brown through to ecru. Many fabrics made of this fiber are known merely as Tussah.

TUSSAH CLOTH. A silk material, the filament of which is derived from wild or uncultivated silkworms. It is coarse, strong, uneven, and ecru or tan in color, difficult to bleach. Used chiefly in shantung and pongee, and serves well when used as filling in pile fabrics.

TUSSAH DRAPERY FABRICS. Many drapery fabrics are made with Tussah filling yarn. These durable, serviceable materials are of union construction since tussah silk is not used in the warp.

TUSSAH LINEN-LIKE CLOTHS. Tussah or wild silk yarn is used in cloths that imitate linen. These irregular, uneven-appearing fabrics use Tussah silk to marked advantage, particularly in the filling of the fabric. Launders well and will stand good, rugged wear.

TUSSAH NANKEEN, NANKIN, RAJAH, SHANTUNG. Comes in white or in colors. The yarn is more uneven than in pongee. Wears and launders well. Trade names are given to the many varying grades and qualities on the market. This group of lightweight materials is popular for summer wear. Much of the cloth is dyed or printed.

TUSSAH PONGEE. A plain-weave cloth noted for its uneven yarn. This light or medium-weight fabric comes in natural colors which range from brown to ecru. Pongee launders well and does not seem to soil easily. It is a cool summer fabric which has a variable pick count because of the various weights in which the fabric may be bought.

TUSSAH SHANTUNG. Fabric made of wild silk; this fabric, however, weaves very well and gives much satisfaction in wear and laundering. The yarn used is more irregular than that found in pongee. Names are given to the many varying grades and qualities of this dyed or printed material—rajah, nankeen, tussah, shantung, etc. Finds much use in summer wear.

There is another fabric called shantung which is used in men's wear and women's wear for summer. The material comes in brown, tan, and ecru shades; made of plain silk, the weight and the texture varies with the quality. The fabric is cool, durable, able to withstand friction and chafing, tailors well and does not wrinkle.

TUSSAH SILK. The opposite of true silk. The latter is raised on cultivated mulberry leaves; the former on leaves of the oak tree, castor-oil plant, cherry tree, and uncultivated mulberry tree. Little care is given to the raising of these worms, whose product is inferior in every respect to true silk. Tussah is easily reeled, but it is not as soft as true silk. Fabrics made from Tussah lose their whiteness when they are washed for the first time. True silk cloth will retain the pure whiteness after washing.

The cocoons are much larger than Japanese cocoons, and the fiber of the former is about twice the diameter of the latter. Eight cocoons are used to make a Tussah thread. This will produce about a 30/32-denier silk thread.

The fiber is brown in color, the filaments are quite hairy, and there is less cohesion in it when compared to the true silk fiber.

Tussah is spelled in a variety of ways—Tussa, Talar, Tassui, Tussar.

Varieties of Tussah are: Antherea Yama-Mai of Japan, Antherea Pernyi, Antherea Mylitta of India, Attacus Ricini, and Attacus Atlas of Asia. The latter two are sometimes known as Eria silk, Tagore, or ailanthus silk.

TUSSAH VELVET. Tussah silk is much used in velvets. The coarse yarn is ideal for the pile effect in this durable cloth which drapes well, withstands hard usage, and will clean but crush. Since Tussah silk dyes well, it may have many uses as a substitute for true silk in pile construction cloths.

TUSSORE. 1. Tussah or wild silk is sometimes known by this name. 2. A plain-woven, rather good-quality cotton dress-fabric made from fine warp yarn and coarse filling. The latter gives a corded effect in the filling direction. This English fabric is usually mercerized.

TUXEDO. In 1886, the "dress lounge coat," known also as a dinner coat or jacket, made its debut. Mr. George Lorillard of the tobacco empire, P. Lorillard & Company, Inc., introduced the coat known today as "Tuxedo" at an exclusive ball held in Tuxedo Park, New York. His coat was a short scarlet one with silk lapels, actually an adaption of the smoking jacket which at the time was very popular in exclusive clubs in Britain. The jacket caused a furor of excitement and soon caught on with a vengeance. Black soon became the popular color and it has been retained to the present day although other colors, conventional or bizarre, appear from time to time. Ideal for informal evening dinners and parties.

TUXEDO FRONT. A coat style when the flat collar extends around the neck and to the bottom of the garment on each side.

TWADDLE, TWADDEL HYDROMETER. It determines the specific gravity of liquids, sizes, baths, etc. The stem is graduated and instruments are supplied in sets of six, with #1 registering 1 to 24; #2 from 25 to 48, and so on.

Degrees Twaddle are changed into specific gravity by formula: (Tw. x 0.005) plus 1.

Thus, if a size mixing gives a reading of 28 degrees, the specific gravity is (28 x 0.005) plus 1, which equals 0.14 plus 1, or 1.14 s.g.

TWALLE. A generic term for a group of cloths made of filament rayon, commonly known as pigment prints, pigment taffetas, and French crepes of the type of 92 x 68 and 72 x 56. These fabrics are made with plain weave. The yarn is of the normal twist so that processing for a full shrunk finish may be realized.

Twalle fabrics are flat, opaque, compact, plain or printed in dress, blouse, and underwear weights; they are not sheer in texture and possess a soft, drapy finish. The term is pronounced without the final "e."

TWEED. The Scotch name for twill. The cloth originated along the banks of the Tweed River, which separates England from Scotland. The word tweed and twill are closely allied, and in some circles, the word "tweel" is a contraction of the two. This is often heard in the British Isles in referring to a tweed.

Tweed is a sister cloth of homespun. The only difference between them is that the former should be made of a 2-up and 2-down twill weave; the latter is made of a plain weave. In all other respects, the cloths are the same —in texture, yarn, weight, feel, and uses.

Some tweeds may be made of weaves other than a straight, righthand twill— broken twill, color effect, herringbone, pointed twill, basket, fancy entwining twill, diamond effect, braided twill and so on.

Tweeds are used for sport clothes, cap cloth, suiting, coating, overcoating, ensembles, and so on.

There are many classified tweeds on the market today. Each one seems to have its wave of popularity as fashions and styles change. The names applied to the cloths are taken from a county, battle, event, city or town, regiment, and so on. The better known tweeds in this country are: English, Scotch, Irish, Donegal, Harris, Linton, and Bannockburn.

TWEED, TYPES OF.

CHEVIOT TWEED: Differs from other tweeds in that warp and filling are stock-dyed the same color. Wide range of colors are noted and quality varies much. Popular cloth.

DONEGAL TWEED: Same stock as in the Irish tweed, but the weave used is herringbone, or a plain weave. Irish

tweed is made of a 2-up and 2-down twill.

HARRIS TWEED: Under the terms of the British Board of Trade and the Federal Trade Commission, Harris Tweed refers only to woolen fabric hand-woven on the Islands of the Outer Hebrides off the Northern coast of Scotland. This includes among others the islands of Harris and Lewis.

It has been ruled on several occasions by the Federal Trade Commission to be unfair trade practice to use the term Harris Tweed to describe fabrics not in accordance with the definition referred to. This eliminates the question of imitations inasmuch as there is only one Harris Tweed.

This outstanding fabric is always hand-woven. There are two types of Harris Tweed:

1. Fabric woven from hand-spun yarn.

2. Fabric woven from machine-spun yarn.

Comparatively few of the tweeds are now woven from hand-spun yarn because to spin such yarn for a length of fabric sixty yards or more much time and labor is consumed. Today only in very rare circumstances will the Crofters in the Islands take the time to spin enough yarn by hand for weaving into the piece.

There are some Harris Tweeds made from machine-spun yarn, and handspun filling. Harris Tweed made from hand-spun yarn is stamped to that effect in addition to the Harris Tweed Trade Mark. Harris Tweed is the registered trade-mark of the Harris Tweed Association of London, which is a nontrading body set up under charter for the British Board of Trade to protect the article and to increase the appreciation of Harris Tweed throughout the world.

This activity is completely separate from the selling of Harris Tweed, which is taken care of by the producers in the Islands, several of whom have representatives in this country.

The fabric is used in suiting, topcoating, overcoating, sportswear, ensembles, etc. The Harris Tweed Association, Ltd., is represented in this country at 295 Madison Avenue, New York City.

IRISH TWEED: Made of white warp with filling of dark shades of gray, blue, brown and black. Weave is 2-up and 2-down twill.

SCOTCH TWEED: Cloth with a white warp and stock-dyed filling, or vice versa. The colors used are often vivid and much contrast is noted in the garment. This tweed may have shoddy, mungo, extract wool, etc. used in its construction. Yarn is very irregular, and the fibers are of all lengths.

TWEEL. (Same as Twill.) This is the original fabric which took on the name of tweed, after Scotland's largest river. This came about by a happy error on the part of a London merchant, who misread the word in an invoice from Scotland. The fabric became known as tweed from then on.

TWIGGY. Coming to the fore around 1966, this British young lady had tremendous impact on women's wear. Twiggy, whose real name is Leslie Hornby, at the age of seventeen was a slim, attractive model who resembled the boy next door. She became a leading fashion model who received as much as $2500 a week. Public relations, smart advertising, and television exposure here and abroad, aided in her rapid rise to the forefront. As a team, Twiggy and her manager-boyfriend, Justin de Villeneuve, have done extremely well. In March 1970, she retired from modeling and presently is beginning a career as a movie star.

TWILL. The name is supposed to have originated near the Tweed River which separates Scotland from England. The term twill means to double and twill was originally made by what is known as "doubling the plain weave" which was written as 1-up and 1-down. Tweed or twill weave is written as 2-up and 2-down or $\frac{2}{2}$, provided this is the weave to be used in the twill construction.

The twill effect is bias or diagonal on the face of the goods. In about 80 per cent of twill fabric, the twill line runs from the lower left-hand corner of the goods to the upper right-hand corner of the material. Left-hand twill runs from the upper left-hand corner of the fabric to the lower right-hand corner of the goods.

The terms twill, tweel, and tweed are closely related. There are many varieties of twill weaves and twill-woven fabrics—right-hand, left-hand, broken, herringbone, twilled basket, steep twill, reclining twill, even and uneven, single and double, braided, entwining, etc.

Some right-hand twill fabrics include cassimere, cavalry twill, covert, elastique, gabardine, serge, tricotine, tweed, whipcord, etc. Left-hand materials may include denim, gabardine, galatea, jean cloth, drill, middy twill, novelty effects, ticking, etc.

Twills are used to great degree in textile fabrics which are strong, durable, dressy, and clean well. Much used in dress goods of many types.

TWILL BASKET-WEAVES. Based on ordinary basket weaves, the construc- tions have the squares laid out in twill-line arrangement instead of the alternate block arrangement used in basket weaves.

TWILLED CLOTHS, GOODS. A very broad term to cover fabrics made of various twill weaves—right-hand, left-hand, reclining, steep, broken, etc.

TWILLED HOPSACK. Another name for the 2-2 basket weave which may be arranged with some other basic weave in a twill formation with the entire pattern showing a diagonal line from the lower left-hand corner of the face of the goods to the upper-right hand corner of the fabric.

TWILLED TAPE. Rugged cotton narrow fabric or tape made with her- ringbone weave in a compact texture. Finds use in fishing garments, spindle banding, wrapping, etc.

TWILLETTE. A soft, pliable British cotton made from a 2-up and 2-down twill. The warp and filling are of coarse yarn and filling is very high in texture. Used much for work clothes, the fabric is noted for the fact that the filling texture is about three times that of the warp count—40 x 120.

TWILL-FACED FILLING SA- TEEN. A heavy carded cotton sateen in which the filling uses many more picks than ends per inch in the tex- ture or pick count; the warp yarn is finer in diameter than the filling yarn. This material may be napped and sheared. Used chiefly for work-clothes and some other outergarments.

TWILL OR SERGE WEAVE. A weave which repeats on three threads each way. This is the smallest twill that can be made—a 2-up and 1-down or a 1-up and 2-down weave.

The 2-up and 2-down twill con- struction is very popular in all major fiber fabrics, even more so than the smallest-weave construction. The num- ber of possible twill formations is almost limitless. Twills are used in silk serge, foulard, crepe meteor, plaids, checks, serge, tweed, Cheviot, Shet- land, and in combination with other weaves that are used in more or less elaborately designed fabrics.

TWILL OR SERGE WEAVE IN SILK MATERIAL. This weave repeats on three ends and three picks—a 2-up and 1-down, or a 1-up and 2-down, right- or left-hand twill effect. This is the smallest twill weave possible. The 2-up and 2-down twill weave is called by either name in silk. Both types of weaves appear in Jacquard and dobby loom work, twill foulard, crepe meteor, satin Canton-crepe.

TWILLS. In this sense, the name given to cloths that show a twill weave construction on the face of the material. In short, twill cloth shows a diagonal or bias effect on any material in reg- ular repeat formation. From the Scotch, tweel, to make a diagonal effect. There are many varieties of twill—right-hand, left-hand, broken, herringbone, twilled baskets, baskets in twill effect, steep, reclining, even and uneven, single and double, braided, entwining, etc.

Small twill weaves find much use in giving small novelty effects to rayon and other man-made fiber materials. These fabrics are strong, durable, dressy, and clean well. Used for dress goods.

TWILL TICKING, WOVEN. This fabric is made from a warp-effect twill on either three or four harnesses. A small broken twill (herringbone effect) may also be used for this ticking. There is considerable variance in texture, weight, width, price, etc. The main points in selling these fabrics are the width of the goods and its weight; the pick count is considered minor. Most twill ticking is striped in the warp di- rection.

TWILL WEAVES. There is no limit to the number of twill weaves possible. The simplest and smallest twill that can be made is the 2-up and 1-down, or 1-up and 2-down, right- or left-hand twill weave. This weave repeats on three ends and three picks, in warp and filling. Twills produce diagonal lines on the face of the cloth, and in the majority of cases this twill line runs from the lower left-hand corner of the material to the upper right-hand corner of the material. Some few cloths have the twill line running in the opposite direction—from the up- per left-hand corner of the material to the lower right-hand corner of the cloth. Popular in Europe.

See Illustrated Section. See also WEAVE CONSTRUCTIONS.

TWINE. A ply yarn that is made from medium twist single yarn with the ply twist in the other direction. Binder twine is a single strand yarn that is 3 or 4 mm. in diameter and strong enough to give good service on a me- chanical grain binder. Twine is made from abaca, henequin, sisal, etc.

TWINE CLOTH. An English cotton fabric made with good quality, high count cotton yarns, single- or two-ply, and of compact texture. The single-ply yarn cloth simulates linen fabric used in shirting; the two-ply yarn goods re- ceive a smooth, glazed finish and are usually mercerized for use as shirting.

TWINE FRINGE. See BULLION FRINGE.

TWINER, TWINER MULE. Used

on the Continent and in Great Britain, this machine, similar to a mule frame, is used to ply or double yarns. The frame is equipped with its creel adapted to travel on a carriage to and from the head stock. The machine is also built with a stationary creel with the carriage built to travel in and out.

TWIN NEEDLE. A double row of interlocked stitching used for seams of knit underwear and for covering raw edges.

TWIST. 1. The number of turns about its axis, per unit of length, noted in a fiber, yarn, cord, etc. It is expressed in turns per inch, turns per meter, or by the helix angle in a structure of known diameter. Twist can be controlled mechanically.

S-twist is the direction of twist in yarn or cord comparable with the spiral portion of the letter S. It was formerly known as left or reverse twist. Z-twist conforms with the spiral portion of the letter Z. It was known formerly as right twist.

2. The strong, firmly twisted silk thread used by tailors.

TWIST, DIRECTION OF. A yarn or cord has S-twist if, when held in a vertical position, the spiral conforms in slope to the central portion of the letter S; and Z-twist if the spirals conform in slope to the central portion of the letter Z.

TWIST, NECESSITY OF. It is essential to yarn so that it will be able to withstand the rigors of handling, winding, twisting, possibly with other yarns, beaming, drawing-in, reeding, weaving, finishing, and give service to the consumer.

Twist is applied first to the weaker, slubbier, or softer places of the roving that is to be converted into yarn by spinning. The firmer sections of the stock will then receive its twist which is governed mechanically by the twist gear on the machine. Thus, by the time the yarn is spun, there should be a uniformity of the twist necessary to make a good yarn.

TWIST CONSTANT. A figure or constant that can be used to shorten twist calculations on machines. It helps to find the twist gear to be used for a certain number of turns of twist per inch to be given a particular yarn. The constant is determined by doing the calculation with the twist change gear listed as the unknown or "X." The constant divided by the turns per inch will give the size twist gear.

TWIST COUNTER. An instrument which determines the amount of turns of twist per inch in all types of yarns.

It is also used to find the amount of take-up in yarns due to twist. The sample to be tested is inserted between two clamps, one of which is stationary while the other is free to be revolved in order to remove the twist from the yarn. The distance between the clamps is adjustable and can be set according to standard test requirements. The tension on the specimen, as well, is adjustable. Equipped with a device for recording the amount of twist in yarn.

TWISTED UNION YARN. Practically any ply yarn in which two or more different yarns are plied into the single equivalent yarn. There is a very wide range of union yarns which are ideal in a fabric for union dyeing or cross dyeing. The former method of dyeing gives a single shade or color to the cloth, while in the latter method there will be two harmonious or contrasting colors in the cloth. Examples of this type of yarn could be a worsted and cotton yarn plied together, cotton and acetate, nylon and worsted, etc.

TWISTER. Device for twisting. The first result depends on two factors: 1. The condition of the yarn when it is being twisted. 2. The method used to insert this twist.

The American ring twister, or any other type, will form the ply yarn by inserting a sufficient amount of twist in the required direction, and winds the resulting yarn on a twister bobbin. The yarn is passed from a creel to delivery rollers that twist the yarn by passing it through a ring traveler that has a high number of revolutions per minute. The yarn is wound on a rotating spindle, upon which there is a bobbin to take the newly twisted yarn.

TWISTER'S HOOK. A device used by the professional yarn-twister in the mill; it holds a batch of ends from the loom, as well as another group from the warp beam of the new warp to be placed in the loom after the run-out warp has been removed from the warp sockets at the back of the loom. The device makes the work of the twister much easier. The device is worn like a belt, the hook replacing the buckle on the ordinary belt.

TWIST FABRIC. Plain knit fabric in which each loop is twisted as it is formed.

TWIST GEAR. A change gear that controls the number of turns of twist per inch to be given roving or yarn. The gear has no effect on the back rollers, but does govern the speeds of the front rollers.

TWISTING. Also known as Doubling. It is done on a machine called the twister, which is the same in principle

and detail as the ring-spinning frame except that there is no draft imparted to the yarn. Two or more yarns are plied together on the frame to increase the diameter, tensile strength, and quality for some particular use in the textile trade.

The main parts of a twister are: bands, creel, rolls, spindles, builder motion, and the traverse.

The bobbins or spools are placed on the creel of the doubler, which consists of rows of skewers to hold them. A sufficient number of skewers is provided so that any desired ply may be obtained.

The rolls on the frame draw the yarn that is to be twisted from the spools. The yarn is delivered to the twisting action of the spindles, at the desired speed, which must be regular and uniform. On the well-known Whitins Twister for cotton yarn, there are two sets of bottom rolls and one at the top, or one roll for the top and one for the bottom. The rolls are about 1½ inches in diameter.

In dry twisting, the bottom rolls are usually made of steel, the top one of cast iron. In wet twisting, the rollers are brass or are covered with brass.

The spindles, rings, and travelers are like those on the ring-spinning frame.

When the machine is in operation, the ring rail is raised and lowered by the builder motion to guide the yarn, as it is wound, onto the spindle. There is a traverse motion that moves the threads sideways, between the rolls, to prevent creasing, which may be caused by wear and friction. Each spool can be stopped independently of the others to repair breakage.

The machine may have from 60 to 300 spindles; the speed varies from 3,000 to 10,000 r.p.m.

Particular care must be given the twister in the following points:
1. Bands that slip will give slack and undesirable twist.
2. Rings that become nicked will cut the yarn.
3. The builder, controlled by a belt or band from the front roller, may slip; this causes uneven winding and results in poor reeling and spooling.
4. Should the burrs, which hold the builder plates by the chains to the cams, become loose, the yarn will run under or over the tops of the spool.

TWISTING-IN. Joining the threads of a new warp to those of the warp about to run out. The twisting is done by twisting or rolling the two ends between the finger and thumb. A paste of linseed oil and chalk is used by the twister to keep his fingers in condition

DIRECTIONS OF TWIST

TWIST TYPES FOR PLIED YARNS AND TWINES

"ZS" TWIST (Formerly Regular)	"SZ" TWIST (Formerly Reverse)	"ZSZ" TWIST (Formerly Cable)	"ZZS" TWIST (Formerly Hawser)

Examples:

Weaving Yarn	"ZS" Twist
Wrapping Twine	"ZS" "
Sail Twine	"ZS" "
Seine Twine	"ZSZ" "
Cable Cord	"ZSZ" "
Twisted Rope	"ZSZ" "

Officials of the Mt. Vernon-Woodberry Mills, Baltimore, Md., circulated the above chart among their employees to educate them on the new designations for direction of twist.

ON YARN TWIST

1. S-Twist: A yarn or cord has "S" twist if, when held in a vertical position, the spiral conforms in slope to the central portion of the letter S. Formerly called left-hand or clockwise twist.
2. Z-Twist: If the spiral conforms in slope to the central portion of the letter Z, the twist is then classed as Z-twist. Formerly known as right-hand or counterclockwise twist.
3. Zero Twist: Sometimes referred to as "no-twist." The thrower may request that cuprammonium (Bemberg) rayon yarns be supplied with no twist. This is rarely done, however; usually 1 to 5 turns are given the yarn. Viscose rayon and acetate yarns with from 3 to 5 or 6 turns per inch are normally supplied to the thrower; this twist is known as "tram (filling) twist."
4. Cable Twist: A cord, rope or twine construction in which each successive twist runs in the opposite direction from the preceding twist. This type is known as S-Z-S or Z-S-Z twist.

so that slippages will not occur. Twisting-in is quicker than drawing-in, and is used when the heddles and the reed can be used to care for the new warp. Jacquard twisting-in is done at the loom.

TWIST MULTIPLIER. The multiplying of a constant by the square root of the yarn counts will give the number of turns per inch necessary for the yarn.

TWIST-ON-TWIST. Twofold yarn in which the twist is in the same direction as that of the single yarns; for instance, S-S or Z-Z.

TWIST PER INCH IN COTTON YARN, NUMBER OF TURNS OF. This will vary with the size of the yarn, and in some degree, to the use to be made of the yarn.

To find the standard twist in yarn, multiply the square root of the yarn count by:

4.75 for frame-spun warp yarn.

4.00 for mule-spun warp yarn.

3.50 for frame-spun filling yarn.

3.25 for mule-spun filling yarn.

3.00 for ring-frame hosiery yarn.

2.75 for doubling yarns.

2.50 for mule-spun hosiery yarn.

TWISTS. Woolens or worsteds of which the yarns are of two colors, doubled or twisted together. This gives an effect that is rather mottled in the pattern appearance. In the trade, many cloths are spoken of as "twists." This term is not applied to crepe fabrics.

TWIST SETTING. Any of several methods used to fix or set the twist in crepe or novelty twists to prevent gnarling, tangling, or kinking, particularly as the yarn is being unwound from some device. Steam or water vapor are much used in twist setting.

TWIST TAKEUP. The variance in the length of a yarn before and after twisting; very important in the throwing of yarns such as silk, rayon, acetate, nylon, etc.

TWIT, TWITTY YARN. Woolen yarn may become twitty because of uneven spinning; it is caused by the applied twist becoming excessive in the weakened or thin areas in the yarn, thereby causing it to recede upon itself.

TWO-BAR KNITTING. Tricot fabric produced with two sets of guide bars, needles, pattern wheels, a top and bottom set of spools, etc. There are very few three-bar tricot knitting frames in use today.

TWOFOLD. English term for two-ply yarn.

TWO-LEGGED SPORTSWEAR, LENGTHS OF. Since the advent of Bermuda shorts about thirty years ago,

there has been an increasing number of items used in two-legged sportswear in men's and women's wear. The shortest articles include the well-known Bikini swimsuit, bloomer shorts, and "short shorts." With regard to length, in order, follow Jamaica shorts, Nassau shorts, and Bermuda shorts, all of which end above the kneecap. Pedal pushers end just below the knee, followed in order as to length by calf skinners, Capri pants, and slacks. Tapered tailoring is important in the manufacture of all these articles, and the several lengths are chosen for comfort as well as for what is flattering to each individual figure.

TWO-PLY. 1. Made of two strands or two thicknesses of material. 2. A double-cloth fabric with two sets of warp ends, two sets of filling and one or two sets of binder threads.

2. 10. E.O.M. An invoice due on the tenth of the month after delivery subject to 2 per cent discount when paid promptly.

TWO-TONE EFFECTS. The term is used often when two shades are used to obtain the effect; however, three or four shades of the one color are sometimes spoken of as being two-tone. Consequently, all two-tones are self-colors, but not all self-colors are two-tones.

Two-tone effects may be applied to a reversible dress-goods fabric in which either side may be used as the face of the goods—satin canton, crepe-back satin, etc. The term also implies a cloth in which two tones or casts of the one color are seen on the face of the goods—two harmonizing shades of brown, blue, etc.

TWO-TOOTH. A sheep one year old. Sheep get two teeth every twelve months up to the age of four years, when they are known as "full-mouthed sheep." A six-tooth sheep would be three years old.

TYCORA. Trade-mark of Textured Yarn Company, Inc., New York City, for several methods used to modify various continuous filament yarns. Advantages include bulk without added weight, crease- and moth-resistance, rapid drying, durability, improved hand, high dye affinity, non-pilling, resiliency, and strength.

TYGAN. A British man-made woven fabric which possesses the qualities of leather and is suitable for upholstery. It can be sewn, tacked, and manipulated in the same manner as other upholstery fabrics. Also used for blinds and shades, radio screens, and lamp covers.

The fabric is made on especially equipped looms from extruded mono-filaments called Bexan. This product

comes in gauges 0.010 to 0.012. There is no limit as to range of color, width, and weight. Tygan is ideal for beach use, since salt air and water have no effect on it; it is not susceptible to mildew, bacteria, fungi, or other micro-organisms. Reflecting heat, it is warm in winter and cool in summer.

TYING. 1. Drawing the ends of pointing yarns to the inside of knitted gloves and knotting to prevent raveling. 2. Wool, obtained from shearing, is rolled into a neat bundle and tied with cord. The fleece side which was nearest the flesh, and is always cleaner, is left on the outside so as to give a better appearance and greater sales appeal and to allow for easier grading of fleece.

TYING-IN MACHINE. A machine that automatically ties the ends of yarn from the run-out warp to the ends of the new warp which will be placed in the loom after the old warp has been taken out; a great time-saving device in weaving.

TYNEX. Monofilament nylon of heavy or high denier used in industrial applications such as brushes, fishing lines, doll wigs, etc. It is sold on spools and is not classed as a textile yarn. Product of E. I. du Pont de Nemours & Co., Inc., Wilmington, Delaware.

TYPAR. A spunbonded polypropylene made by E.I. duPont de Nemours & Co., Inc., Wilmington, Delaware. It is used in many mills as a primary backing for tufted carpet and also in area rugs, furniture manufacturing, and production of bags and other packaging materials.

TYPE. A broad term for the class or grade to which a fiber belongs. Several samples, for example, can be taken from cotton bales. While each bale will not be identical in all respects, it is possible to arrive at the type by accepting those samples that have enough in common to be classed together as a particular type.

TYPED CLOTHS. Made from cotton or linen, the term refers to household cloths such as dish, glass, tea, kitchen, pantry cloths, etc. The cloths often have the name woven into them to describe their use.

TYPEWRITER AND CARBON PAPER STAIN REMOVAL. Use soap or detergent on the affected area and then rinse thoroughly. If not removed, then use a few drops of ammonia and repeat this treatment and follow by a thorough rinse. The process may be repeated until satisfaction is achieved.

TYPEWRITER RIBBON FABRIC. The highest-constructed cotton fabric made today. Combed Egyptian, Pima, or Sea Island cotton is used, and the thread count ranges from 260 square to 350 square. Some imported British fabric has a texture of 400 square. Yarns range from 70s to 120s. Nylon and other man-made fibers are also used to make the fabric.

TYPP. In yarn numbering it signifies the number of one-thousand yards of yarn to the pound. (A.S.T.M.)

TYREX. The name for "super-super" or "super-2" high tenacity rayon tire cord. It is the name given to the yarn; and American Tyrex Corporation, a nonprofit organization with headquarters in New York City, promotes the product. Fiber producers composing the corporation include American Enka Corporation, American Viscose Division of FMC Corporation; Beaunit Corporation, Courtaulds North American, Inc.; and Industrial Rayon Company, a division of American Cyanamid Co. At present, Tyrex is made by American Enka, American Viscose, Beaunit, and IRC Fibers. Ceased rayon filament operation in December, 1972.

TYREX 800. Compared with Tyrex 600 rayon tire cord, Tyrex 800 is about 8 percent stronger and has a higher cured strength after dipping and processing as well as maintaining the improved flex resistance of current cord. In 1958 improved rayon tire cord was placed on the market and at the time was thought to be about the limit with regard to strength possibilities. As it turned out, Tyrex 800 is thirty percent stronger than the first super-rayon tire cord unveiled in that year.

TYROLEAN HAT. A casual hat of rough felt, velour, velvet, etc., with a tapered crown, narrow brim, and cord band. Popular for winter wear, it is often embellished with a "whiskbroom" set between the banding and the hat, and a small costume jewelry insignia.

TYRE YARN. High-quality cotton tire fabric yarn of 15/23s yarn count. Twist is Z-Z-S. Also spelled Tire.

TYRIAN PURPLE. A purple color obtained from certain shellfish, such as Buccinum and Purpura. Pliny mentioned its discovery in 1400 B.C. Its manufacture was a lost art in the Middle Ages.

TYRON. Name given to high-tenacity rayon yarn used for tires. Its strength and heat-resistance make it possible to produce tires which give longer mileage and conserve rubber. Product of I.R.C. Fibers Division, American Cyanamid Co., Wayne, N. J. Now off the market.

TYROLEAN COSTUME. See Costume, Tyrolean.

TYVEK. Registered trademark of E. I. duPont de Nemours & Company, Inc., for its spunbonded sheets of high-density polyethylene fibers. The sheet is first formed by spinning continuous strands of very fine, interconnected filaments; bonding then follows so as to bring them together by heat and pressure. Tyvek is very tough, tear resistant, scrubbable, durable, completely strippable, and has high opacity. This spunbonded olefin product has many uses such as in banners, hard bound book covers, labels and tags, maps, industrial and institutional disposables, packaging, sterile packaging, signs, swimwear, et al.

Type 10 products resemble stiff paper-like sheets which possess good abrasion-resistance and high tear-strength. *Types* 14 and 16 are made by restricting the fiber bonding to discrete, separate, or detached points on the sheet. This provides mobility along with a drape-like effect. *Type* 16 products are perforated to give higher porosity, more flexibility, and additional softness when compared with *Type* 14 but at the expense of tensile and tear-strength. Tyvek can be slit and cut into sheets, sewn, adhesive bonded, coated, laminated, embossed, heat-sealed, printed. Tyvek is ideal in doing away with cracks, peeling, tearing problems, stains and wear marks.

U

UACIMA. A group of bast fibers found to great extent in Brazil, which are used as substitutes for jute in making bagging, cordage, rope, etc. Three of the leading types are tucum, caroa, and the mallow family of fibers.

UDA. A curly-coated British West African sheep whose fleece is black in the forepart and white in the hindpart. The fleece is a mass of curls and rather difficult to manipulate.

ULLAH. A strong bast fiber raised in India and used as a hemp substitute.

ULSTER. Heavy overcoating cloth, loosely woven with warp of right-hand twist yarn, and filling of left-hand twist yarn. All types and kinds of fibers are used in the material dependent on the quality of the cloth wanted. May be piece-dyed, or stock-dyed for mixed effects. The long nap given the cloth in finishing is pressed down. Material is good for cold, stormy, winter weather. Fabric weight is from 24 to 30 ounces.

ULSTRON. A registered trademark of ICI Fibres, Ltd., Great Britain, this fiber is made by polymerizing polypropylene gas, a by-product of oil. Invented by Professor Guilio Natta, consultant to the largest chemical producer in Italy, Montecatini Societa Generale per l'Industria Mineraria e Chimica Anonima in 1954. Ulstron's main properties include strength, even when wet, great resistance to abrasion, and the lightest weight of all major fibers. It is also chemically resistant to most acids and alkalis, rot-proof, and less absorbant of moisture than nylon. It comes in multifilament and staple forms. Uses include cordage, roping, hawser, net twine, filter fabric, dye bagging and webbing. It is also used in conveyor belting, hose and insulation.

ULTIMATE FIBERS. The smallest part of an organic structure which can be separated without destroying the organic structure altogether.

ULTRAMARINE. A synthetic pigment of deep blue color, but can be given a greenish or purplish tinge.

ULTRAMICROSCOPE. A high power microscope equipped with special light condensing apparatus which enables one to see very fine colloid particles in motion against a dark field.

ULTRAVIOLET. That part of the spectrum which has a wavelength shorter than is visible to the human eye.

ULTRON. Registered trademark of Monsanto, Inc., for a nylon fiber, intermediate, and approved end-product comprising or containing the fibers.

UMBRELLA. A shade, screen, or guard carried for protection from rain, sun, etc. It consists of a collapsible framework of flexible ribs, which radiate from a handle. This frame work is covered with waterproof fabric.

UMBRELLA CLOTH. Also known as Gloria goods, it has a cotton warp and silk or rayon filling, and somewhat resembles taffeta but is more rugged, stiffer, and firmer in body. Since it is used for umbrellas, it is made water-repellent.

UMBRELLA FABRIC. A high-textured cloth used to cover umbrellas. Usually made with plain-weave, but some of the fabric has a twill or satin construction; stripes and checks often appear in the cloth. The cotton fabric used may contain either carded or combed yarn; other cloth may be all-nylon, all-rayon, silk and rayon, cotton and nylon, etc. At present there is a wide variance in the several types of umbrella fabric.

UMBRELLA GINGHAM. It is made

with gingham checks and plaids. See UMBRELLA SILK.

UMBRELLA SILK. A plain taffeta or twilled cloth made with a fancy selvage and used for umbrellas and parasols. Roman or other stripes are often used to enliven the goods and they often are featured in the fancy selvage which is a feature of the article. Much umbrella silk is made with cotton filling in the cheaper grades.

UMBRELLA TOP FABRIC. Originally a British export cotton fabric made of plain weave and characterized by a crammed-effect border. Now made, as well, from twill and warp-effect satin constructions. Fancy woven borders are seen in the material, which is made from silk, rayon, acetate, or nylon, as well as cotton.

UNBLEACHED FINISH. Many cottons in the trade come in an unbleached or natural color condition. Materials of this type have a creamy or somewhat "dirty" white color and much foreign matter is often seen in them—burrs, nips, nubs, seed, specks, etc. These cloths are stronger than the full-bleached. Examples are canvas, duck, unbleached muslin, Osnaburg, cretonne, sheeting, toweling, and some moleskin cloth used for pocket lining.

UNBLEACHED MATERIAL. Any cloth as it comes from the loom in the gray or loom state, before any wet- or dry-finishing operations have been applied.

UNBLEACHED MUSLIN. This term is applied to gray print cloths and to lightweight sheetings. It is also known as domestic.

UNCLIPPED CARPET. Term used to imply hooked rugs known by names such as Nantucket, Pilgrim, Pawtucket, et al.

UNCUT PILE FABRICS. Fabrics produced by weaving the yarn that is intended to be the pile stock over wires that have no cutting edge. The result of this is that when the wires are withdrawn, a looped effect appears on the surface of the cloth. Uncut velvet is made in this manner.

UNCUT VELVET. Velvet cloth that does not have the pile construction cut by the blades in weaving.

UNDERCLOTHES. Garments worn under other garments; those worn next to the skin.

UNDERCOLLAR CLOTH. The fabric used for the underside of collars; flannel or melton is often used for woolen and worsted garments; a cheap grade of cotton printcloth for cotton garments.

UNDERCURTAIN. A lightweight, sheer curtain that hangs closely to a window and is set beneath another set of curtains or other hangings. Also known as overcurtains, overdrapes. See Curtain Fabrics.

UNDERGARMENT. Same as underwear, underclothing.

UNDERFLEECE. The soft, downy, underbelly fibers found on many hair- and furbearing animals.

UNDER-PRESSER. The operative who presses garment parts such as pockets, seams, shoulders, etc., during the fabricating processes. Also known as fore-presser or parts-presser, the under-presser uses a hand iron, machine iron, or a powered press.

UNDER-PRESSING. Pressing a garment on the wrong side prior to sewing on the lining.

UNDERSHIRT. Without sleeves, it is a knit garment worn next to the skin under the outside or outerwear shirt.

UNDERSKIRT. A petticoat or skirt worn under a dress or outside skirt. It may be stiff or limp in hang or drape.

UNDERSLEEVE. A sleeve worn under another sleeve; usually can be seen under or through a slash or opening.

UNDERWEAR. Underclothing worn under the outerclothing—shirt, shorts, drawers, etc.

UNDRAWN YARN. 1. Yarn which has a diameter of two to four times the final size, and when stretched will lengthen two to four times its original length. Sometimes referred to as "cold drawing" or "cold drawn yarn." 2. Yarn that has not been subjected to a drawing process which orients the molecules along the thread axis.

UNDRESS. 1. Lounging or informal garb. 2. Dress as contrasted with full dress or formal dress. 3. To remove clothing prior to retiring for the night.

UNDRESSED FINISH. Woolen or worsted cloths which have received a finish that shows about twice as much finished nap as semifinished fabrics. Undressed-finish fabrics will only show the weave in some places since the nap tends to cover up most of the surface. Worsted serge and cassimere are often given the finish to reduce the tendency to shine which is bound to appear with wear. Clear and semifinish cloths will show shininess much quicker on serge and cassimere when compared with undressed goods.

A Cheviot differs from an undressed finish fabric in that the former is made of coarser wool which will give a shaggier appearance to the fabric. Cheviot has lower texture, less yarn-

twist, and is heavier in weight per yard. Both fabrics have uneven nap on the face and fail to hold the crease.

UNDRESSED WARPS. Warps which do not require sizing in weaving preparation or dressing; two-ply yarn would not ordinarily require sizing.

UNDULATING TWILL WEAVES. Curved or waved twill-effects occasionally used in some fabrics—mackinac fabric, some decorative material.

UNDYED. In the natural, loom, or undyed condition.

UNEL. Registered trademark for the spandex fiber of Union Carbide Corporation, New York City. It has excellent uniformity, dyeability, colorfastness, and is washable. Unel has low modulus, and is a high elongation type of fiber which affords comfort and the proper degree of control. Much used in hosiery, it provides sheerness and comfort to the wearer, light support to the leg, and clarity of stitch. Other uses include pantyhose, circular knit panties, and stretch slacks. In foundation garments, the fiber has high modulus with lower elongation, actually presenting a power net material with a higher level of restraint.

UNEMPLOYMENT COMPENSATION. Payment received by an employee during the period of time in which he is out of work.

UNEVEN BASTING. A stitch used to mark seams, baste hems, etc. The upper stitch is long; the understitch is short.

UNEVEN CLOTH. Fabric which has a poor surface effect caused by uneven areas such as light texture, heavy texture, shaded effects, slippage of a section in the warp on the warp beam of the loom, poor let-off or take-up action of the warp beam or cloth roller, respectively. This type of goods can also be the result of poor dyeing, printing, or finishing.

UNEVEN DOUBLE-AND-TWIST. Goods that show streaks because of uneven twist on the doubler-and-twister machine. Also caused by poor yarn winding. Often is not noted until the cloth is being woven, and is difficult to fix to perfection.

UNEVEN FILLING. Shaded area in a fabric which occurs usually in a bar or checkerboard formation. Often caused by poor timing, uneven tension on the filling bobbin, or by rollers not properly set as to correct weight.

UNEVEN LISTING. An uneven or mottled effect which occurs in dyeing; found between the center of the goods and the two selvages. In jig dyeing it is caused often through a difference of the temperatures from the body of the goods and the selvages because of uneven batching of the cut of cloth.

UNEVEN SPUN, OVERSPUN. Uneven yarn caused by slack spindle bands or worn roller coverings on the spinning frame. The yarn may have excessive twist in thin places, thereby causing it to become recessive, kinky or curled. Modern spinning frames, tape-drive, are now equipped with compensating weights to allow for expansion or contraction of the bands.

UNFAIR LABOR PRACTICE. An action by a company that violates the provisions or interpretations of the National or the State Labor Relations Act.

UNFINISHED WORSTED. Worsted with a light nap which somewhat obscures the weave. The term is a misrepresentation because this nap is a finish on worsteds, which are ordinarily left with a smooth surface after they are woven.

UNI. Single, united, joined (Latin unus; French uni). Implies a plain-weave fabric, single construction.

UNI-COLORED. A material which has been dyed a single color.

UNIDURE. A finish applied to spun rayon fabrics to avoid excessive wrinkles; if wrinkling should occur merely hang the garment on a hanger for a reasonable length of time in order to cause the wrinkles to "hang out." The finish adds body, stamina and beauty to material; improved brightness and color-fastness are apparent. The finish reduces shrinkage and stretch since it is impervious to dampness and muggy, sticky weather. Certified to last the life of the garment. Unidure causes less "fussing," fewer pressings, and thus will cut down cleaning bills and washing. Product of United Piece Dye Works, New York City.

UNIFAST. Spun rayons use this finish which combines guaranteed washability, shrinkage control within 2 per cent, sun and washfast colors, perspiration resistance and permanent wrinkle resistance with Unidure; trade-mark of United Piece Dye Works, New York City.

UNIFORM. A style of dress which is made in the same fashion and of the same fabrics as others worn by members of the same body, whether military, naval, or civil.

UNIFORM CLOTH. A family of serviceable woolen cloths on the general order of kerseys and flannels as the most important. Colors are blue, gray, khaki, brown, and mixed effects. The cloth is used as uniform material for military, naval, police, fire, postal, rail-

way, bus, public service, chauffeurs, regal livery and other public and private groups. As most of these cloths are finished under certain approved and decreed specifications, according to contract, a very exact demand is made on the goods to meet requirements.

UNION. 1. Cloth made with warp and filling of different fibers. 2. Dress fabric made of cotton warp and linen filling.

UNION BRAID. It is made with more than two cords or strands in it.

UNION CARPET. Carpet made with a binder filling which enables the material to be used as a reversible with a pile on both sides of the fabric.

UNION CASSIMERE. A low-priced suiting fabric made of cotton warp and wool or worsted filling; has considerable luster and is clear-finished.

UNION CLOTH. 1. English material of cotton warp and reused, remanufactured or shoddy-type filling. The cloth is given much napping to improve its looks. Used in overcoating trade.
2. Woolens and worsteds which have textile fibers from other fiber kingdoms in them, e.g., a fabric with a cotton warp and a worsted filling is classed as a union.
3. Name for some fabrics in which man-made fibers are used in the content, in varying percentages. The union method of dyeing is resorted to in coloring the materials. Union cloths are used in dress goods, general decorative fabrics, towelings, sportswear, etc.

UNION DAMASK. Drapery fabric made with cotton or linen warp and woolen or worsted filling. Satin weave figures are used over a satin background. The material is used extensively for draperies, hangings, and upholstery.

UNION-DYED FABRIC. One that has two or more different textile fibers in it and dyed to a solid color or shade in either the one bath or the two bath methods of coloring the cloth. For example, a spun rayon could be dyed blue from its composition of acetate staple and rayon staple, either in the individual yarns or by being blended into the same yarn.

UNION DYEING. A one-bath process as a result of which the same color can be imparted to two different textile fibers or filaments.

UNION DYES. A group of colors which dye both animal and vegetable fibers, and can be used as direct dyes on union materials.

UNION FABRIC. 1. Woolens and worsteds which have textile fibers from other fiber kingdoms in them, e.g., a cloth which has a cotton warp and worsted filling is classed as a union. 2. A fabric, for example, which has a rayon warp and acetate filling. Much union fabric is seen in the market today and it finds use in checks, dress goods, overcoating, plaids, suiting, and in some women's wear and children's wear materials which seem to last for only a season or so.

UNION LABEL. The insignia that identifies the union, the membership of which was employed to make the products on which the label is displayed.

UNION LINEN. A fabric made from cotton warp and linen filling.

UNION LINEN-LAWN. Made of cotton and linen and resembles lawn; quality and texture varies considerably.

UNIONS. 1. Usually refers to medium or heavy woolen cloths made with a cotton warp. See UNION CLOTH; UNION-DYED FABRIC. 2. Labor union organizations.

UNION SHOP. The union status agreed to by a company in which union membership is required as a condition of continued employment, after a trial period during which union membership is not required. A modified form of the closed shop.

UNION SILK. Material used for umbrellas; made of cotton warp and silk filling; rayon or nylon filling may be used, as well.

UNION SUIT. Shirt and drawers in the one piece.

UNION TANNAGE. A combination of hemlock with chestnut oak extract produces "union tannage" sole leather. The term, however, is also applicable to a combination of other vegetable tanning agents—such as mangrove, myrabolans, and quebracho.

UNION YARN. Made of cotton and wool. The fibers are combined in the blending and mixing operations. Other combinations of stock are sometimes referred to by this name.

UNISEC. A water-repellent, crease-resistant, and spot-resistant resin finish of the United Piece Dye Works, New York City.

UNITIKA, LTD. This company was formed in October, 1969 by the merger of Nichibo Co., Ltd., a giant textile manufacturing company, and Nippon Rayon, Ltd., a leading manmade fiber company, both in Japan. Unitika manufactures a variety of manmade and natural fibers in vertically integrated operations. It also produces chemicals for several of the major industries. It is one of two companies in Japan that produces "Vinylon," the generic name for polyvinyl alcohol fibers and filaments, which was invented by Dr. Sakurada and other chemists in Kyoto University in 1939. Unitika markets this fiber under the name of Mewlon. See Mewlon, Polyvinal alcohol.

UNIVERSAL MILL LANGUAGE. See illustration on page 986.

UNRIPE, IMMATURE COTTON. That produced by premature opening of the bolls because of frost or drought. Technically known as "dead cotton fiber."

UNTRUE WOOL. Wool fibers of uneven diameter which do not measure up to the ordinary standard.

UNTWIST. To unwind, separate, and open, as in the case of twisted yarns or threads.

UNTWISTED YARN. Usually a filament yarn in which there is no twist applied. For example, rayon or acetate yarn spun on the bobbin method receives zero-twist or no twist.

UNWASHED WOOLS. Those that are in the grease state with the yolk and suint still contained.

UNWEAVE. To ravel, pick out, or undo a piece of fabric, usually when it is being analyzed for some purpose.

UPHOLSTERY. A material used on furniture and to cover walls, as curtains and hangings; also fabric coverings and treatments in automobiles, airplanes, and railroad passenger cars. The outstanding fabrics classed as upholstery include brocade, brocatelle, damask, cretonne, chintz, tapestry, Jacquard fabrics of special make, denim, linen, and fabrics of the new manmade fibers. See Illustrated Section (Fabrics 65, 66, 67).

UPHOLSTERY DENIM. A rather loosely applied term given to upholstery materials that are seldom true denim. Coarse single-ply or novelty yarns are used in construction, and the filling is low in texture or pick count. Cotton, nylon, or rayon warp is used while the filling is cotton. Made in dobby or Jacquard effects, the fabric is used to cover boudoir chairs, day beds, other furniture.

UPHOLSTERY LEATHER. A general term for leathers used to cover cushions for furniture, carriages, and automobiles, and extended to cover the materials that go into the tops and sides of vehicles, when made of leather.

Limited quantities of furniture leather are made out of large coarse-grained goatskins. The staple material in this country, however, consists of cattlehides, split at least once and, in many instances, two or three times. The top or grain cuts go into the higher qualities and the splits into the low grades. The several cuts are usually designated as follows:

1. BUFFING: This means a very light cut of the grain portion, about one half, taken from the surface of cattlehides. While produced by upholstery tanners, it is not used for upholstery purposes but finds use in bookbinding, pocketbooks, etc.

2. TOP GRAIN, FULL GRAIN, FULL TOP GRAIN: The first cut taken from the hair-side of the hide from which only the hair and associated epidermis has been removed, and which is not suitable for upholstery. Scars, scratches, and other blemishes may be lightly buffed or remedied, but the total area so affected shall not exceed 5 per cent of the total surface of the hide.

3. SNUFFED OR CORRECTED TOP GRAINS: The same as Top Grains, except that the surface of the hide may be lightly snuffed all over. Such snuffing removes only the top of the hair follicles from the hide.

4. HAND BUFFS: The same as Top Grains, except that the surface of the hide has been shaved by hand or machine to remove shavings of no appreciable thickness.

5. MACHINE BUFFS: That cut of the hide from which a buffing of approximately $\frac{1}{64}$th of an inch (1 ounce) in thickness has been removed from the grain. This should leave a portion of the grain on approximately the entire hide.

6. SPECIAL MACHINE BUFFS: That cut of the hide from which a light cut of approximately $\frac{1}{32}$nd of an inch ($1\frac{3}{4}$ ounces) in thickness has been removed from the grain. Special Machine Buffs must have traces of the grain on portions of the hide.

7. DEEP BUFFS: The first cut under the Top Grain, Hand Buff, or Machine Buff.

8. SPLITS: The first and subsequent cuts under the Deep Buff.

UPHOLSTERY VELVET. A widecut or uncut heavyweight velvet which appears in plain or pattern effects. Used in draperies and upholstery.

UPLAND COTTON. The standard American cotton and the one by which all other cottons are compared for properties and characteristics. It ranges from ¾ inch to 1¼ inch in staple length. Upland is raised chiefly in the Carolinas and the other Seaboard states, as well as in all other raising areas to lesser degree. Upland cotton forms the bulk of the world's cotton crop.

UPPAM COTTON. 1. Indian cotton of ¾-inch staple and lint yield of about 25 per cent. 2. General name for the Herbaceum species of Tinnevelly cottons.

UPPER LEATHER. See SHOE LEATHER.

UPPERS. Cotton raised in the narrow upper valley of the Nile River from Cairo to Assam. Ashmouni is the leading strain. Uppers has shorter staple length when compared with Egyptian Delta cotton; it is, however, of high quality.

UPSTROKE OPENER. A type of the well-known Buckley opener featured by the beater moving in an upward direction when it comes in contact with the cotton instead of the usual downward direction at point of contact with the stock.

UP-TWISTER. A machine used to throw silk, acetate, rayon, and comparable fibers in instances where the single yarns need twisting without doubling or plying. The bobbin of untwisted yarn is set onto a vertical spindle which twists the yarn as it is passed upward through a wire eyelet to be wound on a horizontal bobbin that is driven by frictional contact with a cork-covered roll.

URDIGA. Fine, short-staple, silklike wool raised in Morocco.

UREA. A soluble, colorless, crystalline substance found abundantly in the urine of mammals and in small amounts in bile, blood, liver, muscles, etc. It is formed by the oxidation of nitrogenous compounds in the body. Much urea is now made synthetically for the textile and plastics trades.

UREA FORMALDEHYDE RESINS. They are obtained by chemical reaction between urea and formaldehyde in the presence of acid and alkaline catalysts. They are light in color and are rapidly hardened by baking. Some resins of this type are water soluble, but modified resins may be prepared for finishing certain textile fabrics. They are used considerably to make cloth crease- and wrinkle-resistant.

URENA. Raised in temperate and tropical climates throughout the world, known as Caesar Wood in the United States, this bast fiber resembles ramie in many respects. See CADILLO.

URETHANE FORM SPECIFICATIONS. The Society of the Plastics Industry has drawn up the following standards and specifications for polyurethane foam for apparel uses. This text was prepared by the Urethane Foam Producers Committee, Cellular Plastics Division, of the organization, The Laminates Subcommittee of the Foam Group:

1. CELL COUNT: A minimum of 45 cells per lineal inch, determined by count in three different locations, using pick glass.

2. DIMENSIONAL TOLERANCES; RELAXED STATE:

   Length—no minimum tolerance allowances.

   Width—minimum zero to 1½ inches.

   Thickness—Plus or minus .007; up to ⅛ inches and over plus or minus .010 inches.

3. METHODS OF MEASUREMENT:

   Length to be determined after rewinding on standard slack rewinding machine.

   Width measurement can be taken at various points on the rewind roll with a standard steel tape measure.

   Thickness is measured at varying points during rewinding, using a non-spring gauge.

4. IMPERFECTIONS:

   Holes, any void 3/16 inches and over.

   Seams, the point where two pieces of urethane foam are joined.

   Striations, a cluster of cells larger than average cell size; longer than 4 inches and wider than 1 inch.

   The number of allowable imperfections is 10 per 100 yards.

5. COLOR: Urethane foam has a tendency to change color; however this doesn't affect other physical characteristics or performance. Color of foam is optional.

URIAL. Native to northern India, this wild sheep is reddish brown with a white neck and a dark beard from the chin to the chest. Fiber is used in apparel and carpets.

URINE STAIN REMOVAL. In treating this non-greasy stain, sponge with cold or cool water for at least one-half hour. If not removed after a sponging, use a detergent or soap on the area followed by a good rinsing. Use chlorine or peroxide bleach if the spot remains and then rinse well.

URUGUAY WOOL. Next to Argentina from the standpoint of wool production, the fiber raised there is chiefly of the crossbred type, but there are goodly amounts of merino and carpet wools produced as well. Montevideo is the clearinghouse for Uruguayan wool and the name of this city is often given to the wool raised in that country. The United States is a constant purchaser of wool from Uruguay.

URYLON. Developed by Toyo Koatsu Industries, Inc., it is a polyurethane fiber said to be lighter, stronger, and more heat-resistant than nylon, and it resembles wool and Terylene in

UNIVERSAL MILL LANGUAGE

NIP	
PULL	
RESTRAIN	
PRESS	
STRIKE AGAINST	
STRUCK BY	
PLACE	
Can	
Ball	
Quill	
Section Beam	
Loom Beam	
Dye Kettle Spool	
Jack Spool	
Cloth Roll	
DEPOSIT	
TRANSFER	
MEASURE QUALITATIVE	
MEASURE QUANTITATIVE	
CONTROL MECHANICAL	
CONTROL ELECTRICAL	
TUMBLE	
DRAFT	
CONDENSE	
WET	
Water	
Soap	
Oil	
DRY	
COOL	
HEAT	
ROTATE Wind	
Unwind	
TWIST	
SHEAR	
NAP	
CUT	
CLEAN	
DOFF	
WIND—as for lap	
BOBBIN Wind	
Spin	
Piece-up	
DETACH	
TRANSFER THROUGH RESTRAINT	
INTERMITTENT FEED	
FOUR DOUBLINGS	

NOTE: The above symbols were conceived by the late Professor E. R. Schwarz, Graduate Textile Department, Massachusetts Institute of Technology, Cambridge, Massachusetts. They were introduced to the textile world by Mr. C. J. Monego of the Quartermaster Research and Engineering Laboratories, Natick, Massachusetts. Dr. Stephen J. Kennedy, Director of Research for the Quartermaster Department, and Mr. Monego very kindly granted permission for the use of these symbols in this book.

texture and hand.

USTEX CONVEYOR BELTING. A rubber-fabric belt used for conveyor purposes, 250 to 400 per cent stronger than fabric formerly used. This development of UniRoyal, Inc., is a construction of nylon and Ustex yarns that increases permissible working tension of each ply two and one-half times and permits the use of more plies. Other advantages of the product include increased flexibility crosswise, low stretch lengthwise, and heavier belting, with excellent troughing qualities.

USUGINU. A type of Japanese habutai fabric.

UTILITY PERCALE SHEETING. The medium quality between percale and muslin sheeting. Below the percale type, it is a carded-yard sheeting made of single 30s to 40s, with the threads per square inch totaling about 180 threads.

UTRECHT VELVET. Cotton velvet woven with the aid of wires to produce the effect.

UTTMANN OF ANNABERG, BARBARA ETTERLEIN. In 1561, Barbara Uttmann introduced Pillow or Bobbin Lace in Annaberg, Germany.

UZEN WASHABLE SATIN. A rugged silk dress-goods fabric made in the place of this name in Japan; exported to many countries, and popular because it withstands rugged wear and washes easily and well.

V

VACUUM STRIPPER. An air-pressure device which removes embedded waste of all types from the card clothing on the various rollers of a card.

VAGADIA, VAGRIA COTTON. Cotton raised in Bombay area in India. Must be cleaned by hand since the pods do not open evenly when it is ripe.

VALANCE. Any decorative material which hangs in a horizontal position from tip to tip, usually across the top of a window to make the room appear lower. Height, slenderness, and dignity result from the vertical lines in curtains; horizontal lines made by valances, tie-backs, and trimmings decrease the height, give informality, and sometimes appear to give a squatty or distorted appearance to a room. Curved lines afford grace and rhythm and cause windows to appear larger than they are.

The cloth is also used to set off a bedstead by being draped from the mattress to the floor as well as to make a canopy over a bed.

Valances are made chiefly from silk, silk and wool, silk and rayon and other similar yarn combinations.

VALENCIENNES OR VAL LACE. Bobbin lace made entirely flat with natural or conventionalized flowers or little circles. True Valenciennes was first made of linen. It is used for children's clothes, handkerchiefs, lingerie, neckwear and wash dresses.

VALENTIA. See TOILINETTE.

VALLEY COTTON AREA. The cotton-raising area in this country along the Mississippi River and some of its branches. In the Southern sections sometimes referred to as the Delta Area. It is the most important cotton-raising area in the United States and produces almost one third of the annual production. Long staple Uplands is the leading crop.

VALREN. A polyvinyl chloride fiber produced by Teijin, Ltd., Tokyo, Japan. Said to be superior to its Teviron, the fiber may be dyed with cationic dyes and has a finish comparable with that of acrylic fibers. It withstands directly applied heat up to 221° F; indirectly to 274° F. Ideal for blending with wool in fabrics used in winter clothing.

VALVE LEATHER. Hydraulic leather.

VANDYKE. A pointed scallop used in lace and embroidery. The stitch of this name will show a raised couching in embroidery work.

VAN WOOL. Tasmanian merino wool.

VAPOR. The gaseous form of substances which are normally in the solid or liquid state and which can be changed to these states either by increasing the pressure or decreasing the temperature. Incidentally, vapors diffuse.

VAPOR TRANSMISSION. The determination of moisture that vaporizes through a material under controlled temperature and other specified conditions.

VARIEGATED. Harmonizing or contrasting shades, casts, tones, or hues of colors observed on many textile fabrics. Also implies the use of stripes, checks, and plaids to obtain the effect.

VARIEGATED WOOL. 1. Inferior wool which shows irregular coloring in the staple. 2. Implies the mixing of discolored lots of wool.

VASCULOSE. Cutose.

VAT DYE, SOLUBLE. Vat dyes must be treated with a reducing agent such as sodium hydrosulphite to make them soluble. In this state they have an attraction for the cellulosic fibers, and can be later reoxidized. Soluble vat dyes are a group of sulphuric esters of the leuco bases of these dyes. In application the goods are dyed in the first bath, followed by the oxidizing and fixing of the color in the second bath.

VAT-DYED. Any material that has been dyed with vat dyes. These dyes are insoluble in water, and must first be rendered soluble in water by conversion to the alkaline reduced form. After the goods have been removed from the dye vat, this colorless base is oxidized by the air to an insoluble color in the material.

VAT DYES. The fastest dyes known to man and the most important group of dyes at the present time. Produced on the material by oxidation. Resistant to acids, alkalies, washing, and cross-dyeing either with acetic or sulphuric acid. Vat dyes have the highest fastness-to-light property, and they are insoluble in water, but are converted into soluble compounds by the use of a chemical reducing agent which increases affinity.

V-BELT CORD. A cabled, plied yarn of high twist, or a narrow fabric, with low elongation, and usually treated; used for belting transmission. A fan belt on an automobile is an example.

VEALS. A term used to designate a large calfskin, almost as large as a kip.

VECTRA. Registered trademark of Vectra Corporation, Odenton, Maryland, for its olefin fiber made on the melt spinning method. Reisistance to chemicals is excellent; it is lighter than water and will float; abrasion resistance rates from good to excellent.

It has high tenacity, a circular cross-section, and dries quickly. Staple fiber has tenacity of 2.5-5.0, elongation is 20 to 25 percent, moisture is less than 0.1 percent. Continuous multifilament has tenacity of 2.5 to 7.0 while elongation ranges from 20 to 35 percent. Moisture is less than 0.1 percent at 95 percent relative humidity.

Uses include industrial and textile applications such as filtration, insulation, cordage, knitgoods, floorcovering, pile fabrics, nonwovens, etc.

VECTRA, TYPES OF. This olefin (polypropylene) fiber has the following types:

Type 100: Solution dyed, light and heat stabilized staple.

Type 100-V-2: Solution dyed, regular tenacity, heat stabilized staple which contains a special high-performance light stabilizer.

Type 101: Solution dyed, light and heat stabilized and has medium tenacity in filament yarns.

Type 153: Solution dyed, light and heat stabilized; a textured multi-filament carpet yarn.

Type 200: A natural, light and heat stabilized, regular tenacity filament and staple.

Type 201: A natural, light and heat stabilized, medium tenacity filament and staple.

Type 202: A natural, light and heat stabilized, high tenacity filament yarn used for industrial purposes.

Type 800: A semi-dull, light and heat stabilized, regular tenacity filament and staple.

See Vectra.

VEGETABLE DYESTUFFS. They are extracted from plant roots. Examples include logwood, madder, quercitron, sumac, etc. These dyes are used on cottons; logwood is used to great extent in dyeing silk.

VEGETABLE FIBERS. All textile fibers of vegetable origin: cotton, flax, ramie, jute, hemp, abaca, henequin, istle, sisal, pineapple, etc.

VEGETABLE HAIR. Fibers from any of the vegetable plants, used for padding, stuffing, or wadding. Examples include fibers from kapok, Spanish moss, milkweed.

VEGETABLE MATTER. Term used chiefly in speaking of wool since vegetable matter, to considerable extent, is found in sheep fleeces. Includes leaf, chaff, dried grass, burrs, straw, seed, etc. The presence of this matter in wool causes it to be carbonized in order to rid the fleece or the sorted wool of these items.

VEGETABLE SILK. Loose term for the lustrous floss or down from the pods of kapok, milkweed, etc.

VEGETABLE TANNAGE. A generic term indicating the process of tanning leather by the use of barks or extracts from plants and trees.

VEIL. A thin covering, usually of fine net, lace or mesh, made with varying designs geometrically or symmetrically balanced. Veils are used to drape over hats to cover the face.

VEILING. This lightweight plain or doup material, made in many designs and constructions, is given careful treatment in finishing since this has much to do with the final appearance and sale of the goods.

Veiling comes in plain or solid colors and is used for bridal veils, in the millinery trade, for coverings, and in dance frocks and apparel.

VEILS, LITURGICAL. There are six veils used in the Roman Catholic Rite - humeral, a vestment; tabernacle veil; chalice veil; lenten veil, which is purple and used to cover all crosses, pictures, and statues of Our Lord and the saints from before Vespers of Passion Sunday until after the Gloria of the Mass on Holy Saturday; gremial veil, a pontifical accessory; and the vimpa.

VELAM FIBER. A Ceylon bast fiber used for cordage and rope.

VELLUM CLOTH. Fine, transparent linen or cotton fabric that is smoothly sized on one side so that it may be used for tracing designs and for blueprint work.

VELON LP. A low-pressure or linear polyethylene monofilament manufactured by Firestone Plastics Company, Pottstown, Penna. High in tensile strength and knot strength, this yarn has superior abrasion and moisture resistance properties. Used for outdoor furniture and for brad fabric for casual upholstery and automobile seat covers.

VELOUR, VELOURS. From the Latin vellosus, meaning hairy. Cloth is used as coating material, and, in velour check form, is used for dress goods and coating cloth. The material is a thick-bodied, close-napped, soft type of cloth. The name is used rather indiscriminately and is applied to suiting fabric as well. Generally speaking, a velour is a cloth that runs from 10 to 20 ounces per yard, and is given a face finish. Various types of yarn are used in making the several types of velour on the market. Twills or broken constructions are used in laying out the pattern. There are several fabrics of the same construction, but of slightly different finish, to be found in the trade —suedyne, suedette, lustora, duvedelaine, valora, etc. The cloth is made in the finishing, and much of the best-grade velour is really beautiful cloth.

Some velour is now made with spun silk, spun rayon, and wool blends. Used for drapery fabric, women's coats, upholstery. Fiber content must be given.

VELOURS, RUBAN. Velvet ribbon in France.

VELOURS A DOUBLE CORPS. French cut-pile velvet made with two alternating colors in the pile effect.

VELOURS BRODERIE. French term for a velvet similar to ciselé velvet. It uses cut and uncut pile to produce effects as in ciselé but differs from it in that a special technique is used so that the effects of the uncut pile are raised above, or are at the same level, as noted in the effects of the cut pile.

VELOURS CANNELE. Velvet fabrics which have alternate stripes of cut and uncut pile are called velours cannelé (fluted).

VELOURS CISELÉ. See CISELÉ VELVET.

VELOURS DE COTON. French for velveteen, a cotton velvet.

VELOURS ENVERS SATIN. Cloth made with a velvet face and satin backing; used as satin-back velvet ribbon.

VELOURS SANS PAREIL. French term for a specific group of figured velvets which present the same characteristics as those in velours broderie. The manner of weaving, however, is different from that used to weave the broderie fabric.

VELPEL. Long-pile plush used in men's silk hats.

VELURE. A velvet, or high-quality velour; or some fabric which resembles either of these. (As the soft hairbrush used on silk hats.)

VELUTUM. Latin for velvet. The term is a corruption of the Vellutti family of textile fame in the thirteenth century in Italy.

VELVERAY. Trade name covering a group of finishing processes belonging to the Velveray Corporation, including various flocking techniques for creating flocked designs and effects that will wash and dry clean and are suitable for curtains, lingerie and wearing apparel.

VELVERET. The 6-harness, irregular satin weave is used on the face of the cloth while the back is made of plain-weave construction, often printed.

VELVET. From the Latin vellus, meaning a fleece or tufted hair. Most of the cloth is made of silk or rayon and cotton, but there is some wool and worsted velvet on the market.

Velvet made of silk or rayon comes in many types and qualities. The back of the cloth is plain, the pile is rayon,

silk, spun silk, Tussah silk, etc. Good velvet is expensive; the cheaper cloths give little service and look well only a few times before beginning to deteriorate.

Better grade velvet is washable, may be crush-resistant, water-resistant, drapes well; but laundering must be done with utmost care. Velvet has rather stately draping qualities but the finish will not stand up well and takes on a worn appearance in a short time. Tussah silk is ideal as filling, in velvet, since it will dye well and is rather rugged in wear.

Some of the commoner velvets include:

1. BAGHEERA: Fine, uncut pile velvet with a roughish surface that makes it crush-resistant.

2. CHIFFON VELVET: Lightweight, soft velvet with the pile pressed flat. Used for dresses, suits, evening clothes.

3. CISELÉ VELVET: A velvet with a pattern formed by contrast in cut and uncut loops.

4. FACONNÉ VELVET: Patterned velvet made by the burn-out print method.

5. LYONS VELVET: A stiff, thick pile velvet. Used for hats and dresses when thick velvets are fashionable.

6. NACRÉ VELVET: Velvet with the back of one color and the pile of another, so that it gives a changeable, pearly appearance (nacré).

7. TRANSPARENT VELVET: Lightweight, soft, draping velvet made of silk or rayon back with a rayon pile.

Strictly speaking, the main difference between velvet and velveteen is that the former is always a warp pile-weave construction, while the latter is made on a filling pile-weave formation.

VELVET, BROCADED. A velvet motif or pile-on-pile effect made on a plain or twill ground weave. The effect may be obtained on plain velvet by the burnt-out method. See BURNT-OUT METHOD, BROCADE.

VELVET, CROISE. A rather durable velvet made with a twill weave, cotton backing to hold the cut pile ends in place with a "W" pile base. The face of the goods is of silk or nylon. See PILE FABRIC WEAVING.

VELVET, DOUBLE. Two fabrics are woven, one on top of the other, in this plan. After the cloth is woven, a set of horizontal cutting blades cut the pile warp, thereby giving two distinct materials with cut-pile effect. There are usually eighteen blades in the cutting set-up.

VELVET, EMBOSSED. Velvet or velveteen embossed in certain areas by engraved rollers or by block printing in the better qualities. This nonpermanent effect gives interest between the crushed and uncrushed areas in the goods.

VELVET, ENGLISH. This term is used in Great Britain and on the Continent to denote a densely woven velvet made with spun silk face and cotton twill backing. Used for coat collar trimming and millinery purposes.

VELVET, JAPANESE. The silk velvet made with twill weave foundation weave produced in Japan. Made in woven or printed motifs, there is considerable variance in the qualities dependent on whether the backing is silk or cotton.

VELVET, JASPER. British velvet made with colored stripe effects in the warp direction. Also called Jaspé.

VELVET, JEAN-BACK. This fabric may be a true velvet or a filling cut-pile velveteen made with a twill backing.

VELVET, KREFELD. A high-quality velvet made with cotton ground and silk pile. Used for housecoats, evening wear, millinery, and trimming. Also spelled Crefeld, this German textile city is the home of the famous Krefeld Textile School noted for its work in silk and man-made fibers.

VELVET, RUBBER. Rubberized fabric is sprayed with flock stock while the rubber is yet soft, thereby producing a hand which resembles that of true, regulation velvet.

VELVET, SHAP-FACED. A cotton back velvet which has a waste or spun silk face. The word shap is a contraction from the French "schapper" which means to chop, such as the "chopping" of the waste silk so that it will become short fiber stock ready for spinning on conventional spinning frames to make the yarn.

VELVET, SOLEIL OR PANNE. It is a Lyons velvet, which is mirrored and has high luster; a popular material in millinery.

VELVET, TRANSPARENT. It is made with a rayon pile and a true silk backing.

VELVET CARPET. Resembling Wilton, it is woven without a Jacquard head motion. Woolen yarn is used, all of the colors having been printed on previously by drum printing, as per the motif, before being set in the loom. This differs from tapestry only in the use of woolen yarn and having a tuft surface instead of a loop surface. The weave permits the use of an almost unlimited number of colors. See DRUM PRINTING; TAPESTRY CARPET. See Illustrated Section.

VELVETEEN. A filling pile cloth in which the pile is made by cutting an extra set of filling yarns which weave in a float formation and are woven or bound into the back of the material at intervals by weaving over and under one or more warp ends. (American Society for Testing Materials.)

This low-pile fabric is known as a "cotton-velvet." Comes in all colors, is mercerized and has a durable texture. This strong fabric can be laundered, will provide warmth and tailors rather well. Used in children's wear, coats, dresses, hangings, suitings, etc.

VELVETEEN, COTTON. Low pile cloth with so-called "cotton velvet" yarn for pile effect; mercerized. Comes in all colors.

Very strong and durable; launders well; heavy and gives warmth. Tailors rather well. Cloth is on the order of corduroy in hand.

VELVETEEN, FAST-PILE. See PILE, LASHED; PILE IN FABRIC WEAVING.

VELVETEEN PLUSH. The regulation type of velveteen except for long floats in the weave construction which, when cut, produce a higher pile than that observed in velveteen.

VELVET-FIGURED. A cut-pile fabric woven with woolen or worsted yarn upon which all of the patterned colors have been drum dyed before placing in loom. Pile is formed by use of wires.

VELVET FINISH. See SUEDE FINISH.

VELVETING. Velvet materials in general; also implies the fine pile effect on the better grades.

VELVET MOSS. A lichen obtained in northern Europe, used in dyeing.

VELVET-SATIN. Satin weave is used as the base for this luxurious, figured silk, made with cut pile effect. engraved rollers or by block printing in the better qualities. This nonpermanent effect gives interest between the crushed and uncrushed areas in the goods.

VENETIAN. 1. A five-end satin weave, face-effect, is used to make this fabric entirely of worsted yarn; used in suiting and coating. A similar type of cloth made of the same construction uses two-ply worsted yarn and single-ply woolen filling. Both types of fabric receive clear finish.

2. A woolen cloth made throughout of single-ply woolen yarn. This cloth receives much milling in finishing. Used in suiting.

3. Venetian in the cotton trade is made of an 8-end satin weave, face-effect and may be classed as a heavy sateen. Used for lining, the fabric is made usually of combed cotton yarn and mercerizing or schreinerizing are given so that the cloth may have a lustrous finish.

4. A fine worsted fabric made in a small repeat twill weave, medium in weight, piece-dyed and given a splendid luster finish; used in expensive suiting. The name Venetian is taken from the resemblance the fabrics of this name have to silk. The origin of Venetian is the city of Venice, Italy.

VENETIAN CARPET. Made with worsted warp and wool filling, this average-priced carpeting finds much use as stair carpeting. Also used for hotel runners.

VENETIAN CHALK. A white compact talc used for marking on cloth, etc.

VENETIAN CLOTH. A cotton or woolen warp-face satin fabric. Sometimes it is napped, or woven in a twill weave like wool broadcloth. Used for topcoats, suits, etc. Cotton Venetians used for linings. Fiber content must be declared.

VENETIAN CREPE. A mourning fabric similar to Georgette crepe, made with raw silk warp and a filling of spun silk, wild silk, or a low quality silk yarn. Dyed in solid shades and used for dress goods and linings.

VENETIAN EMBROIDERY. Openwork embroidery with raised designs done in purl stitches over padding.

VENETIAN OR ROLLER FINISH. This cloth finish is produced by the use of finely engraved rollers that have from 100 to 200 lines to the inch. These lines may not always be perfectly true in angle form, but the cloth will have a highly lustrous appearance that is often used to cover up the low quality of the cloth.

VENETIAN POINT LACE. Also known as Point de Venice, it is a needle-point lace with a floral motif in which the designs are very closely arranged and connected by brides made in picot formation. Most of this lace is now made in Belgium.

VENETIANS. The baggy, loose breeches which were fastened below the knee by buttons or some comparable device; the forerunner of the knickerbockers and plus fours worn in the first half of the 20th century with varying waves of popularity. They originated with Venetian businessmen who traveled throughout the then known world following Marco Polo's return from his travels to the East and Far East in the 13th and 14th centuries. The breeches were made of wool, cotton and silk for summer wear, linen and fabrics on the order of the present day cottonback sateen.

VENT. An opening or outlet in a garment, usually at the lower part of a seam; often dictated by particular fashion or style in apparel.

VENTAPAD. Made of Eastman Kodel polyester fiber and marketed by Glenoit Mills, Inc., this deep pile bed pad, said to be superior to natural fiber products from a cost, comfort, and perfoamance standpoint, finds much use in hospitals and institutuions. It is medically effective, cleanable, and can be reused. It is non-allergenic and does not support bacterial growth. The product can withstand considerable punishment in hospital laundries.

VENTILATION. The process of removing or supplying air, by natural or mechanical means. Such air may not have been conditioned.

VENTILE. During the crisis of World War II the British Cotton Industry Research Association, at the request of the British Government, created this material to serve as protective clothing to men working on naval convoys. Prior to the introduction of Ventile there had been heavy casualties through excessive immersion in icy seas. Made of long staple cotton, the fabric excludes water by the swelling action of the choice soft-twisted yarns as they become wet. Incidentally, the fabric is not impervious to air as in the case of plastic-coated fabric or rubber.

VERDIGRIS. A green deposit which develops on brass and bronze washwheels and other devices. It is made up of a conglomeration of copper soaps and salts.

VEREL. Registered trademark of Eastman Kodak Company, Inc., New York City, this modacrylic fiber is spun from a solvent system. It has a specific gravity of 1.37; extensibility, wet or dry, ranges from 30 to 40 percent; moisture regain at standard conditions is 3.0 to 3.5 percent at 70° F. and 65 percent relative humidity; melting point is 390° F. Verel can be dyed with selected basic, disperse, and premetallized dyes at temperatures as low as 140° F. It has a soft, appealing hand, and is heat moldable. It is also sunlight, flame, and weather resistant and can withstand most acids, alkalies, and other chemicals. Uses include carpet yarns, pile fabrics, flame resistant draperies, tufted wall coverings, plush toy fabrics, and industrial fabrics.

VERMILION. A brilliant red pigment consisting of mercuric sulphide, obtained in native state by grinding the mineral cinnabar to a fine powder. Also made synthetically.

VERMONT. About 175 years ago choice Merino sheep were sent from Vermont to Australia to help found the Merino sheep flocks which are now world-famous for their high-quality fiber. The term is still used in referring to sheep descending from the original flock of rams and ewes.

VERSALITE. This thermoplastic material of resin base is light in weight and very tough. The product can be made into practically any thickness above 0.20 inches, can have solid color throughout, with finishes varying from dull to gloss or embossed. It will not chip or warp. Product of UniRoyal, Inc., New York City.

VERSICOLOR. Changeable, iridescent.

VERTICAL OPENER. Device used to open raw cotton; it received its name from the fact that the beater is built around a vertical shaft and that the general course of the cotton going through the machine is upward. Its function is to remove as much extraneous matter as possible from the cotton. The stock is beaten about inside a cone-shaped enclosure and a series of grid bars allow the waste matter to drop through. The delivery end for the cotton is at the top of the cone by means of a screen and conducting trunk.

VERTICAL PRESS. Woolens and worsteds, particularly, are pressed by this type of machine. The cloth is set up between two heavy steel plates controlled by hydraulic pressure, in layer formation with press paper between each layer. Heat and severe pressure are used to complete the process.

VEST. 1. A garment for men, at different times of distinct types. Now, a short garment reaching to the waist, without sleeves, buttoning down the front, and having the back concealed by the coat; a waistcoat. 2. A knitted undershirt for women.

VEST, KNITTED. See SWEATERS, MEN'S AND BOYS'.

VESTEE. Imitation vest or blouse front worn with a dress or jacket; in particular, bright colored broadcloth garment without armholes or back, as worn with formal riding habits.

VESTING. A term which covers a large variety of fabrics used for fancy vests and dresses. It includes principally piqués and Bedford cords, and various types of similar constructions. Vestings are usually medium or heavyweight cloth which present a series of heavy welts or figures evenly distributed over the surface. Vesting's largest use now is for skirting and suiting fabric Lighter grades are used for quilting, uniform fabric, and riding breeches.

The typical piqué vesting presents a surface of lateral welts. The width of the welts varies from $\frac{1}{20}$ to $\frac{1}{4}$ inch. Bedford cord vesting has the same appearance except that the welts are longitudinal. Some vestings have figured effects raised on the surface of the cloth. Combinations of the piqué and Bedford cord weaves produce fancy patterns. Domestic mills generally make only the staple and simple novelty patterns because variations are expensive to produce.

A man's vest is made in many different styles—single-breasted, double-breasted, lapel at the opening, no lapel at the opening, diamond-shaped front effect, short pointed effect, long points, straight bottom, etc.

VESTMENTS. One of several ritual garments signifying office, especially of the clergy.

VEXAR. A polyethylene netting made by E.I. duPont de Nemours & Co., Inc., Wilmington, Delaware. Uses include netting around beverage bottles, and filter core covering.

VICANERE. A coarse Indian wool, yellowish in cast, used in making blankets and carpets.

VICARA. Produced by Virginia-Carolina Chemical Corporation in Taftville, Connecticut, this fiber had a ten year life span and like Aralac, its predecessor in the Taftville plant, could not cope with its price position despite the fact that the fiber did have several outstanding properties. Made from corn, Vicara had many of the properties of wool fiber, was much smoother, had excellent hand and good wearing qualities, but its shrinkage percentage was a liability in most cases. It was neither as strong nor as wear resistant as other manmade or synthetic fibers. Vicara could not be used alone and always appeared in blended materials. See Aralac.

VICTORIA LAWN. Like India linen, it does have heavier yarn in the construction and runs to about nine yards to the pound. It is a high-quality, popular dress-goods fabric used for summer wear on the Continent. Resembles Lancashire organdy but is not given quite so stiff a finish.

VICTORIAN COSTUME. See Costume, Victorian.

VICTORY STRIPES. Novelty hickory stripe fabrics are sometimes known by this name.

VICUNA. An animal found at elevations approximating 12,000 feet in the almost inaccessible regions of the high plateau area in Peru, northern Bolivia, and southern Ecuador. Vicuna, which live above the clouds, are about three feet high and weigh from 75 pounds to 100 pounds. The animal has a life span of about 12 years.

The fiber varies from golden-chestnut to deep rich fawn shades to a pallid white beneath the body and on the surface of the extremities with light markings on the face and jaws.

Vicuna fibers, which are strong and resilient, have a marked degree of elasticity and surface cohesion. These fibers are the finest of all known animal fibers, being less than one two-thousandth of an inch in diameter, with a count of about 2,500 to the inch, which is less than one-half the diameter of the finest sheep's wool. The respective diameters of the two fibers are vicuna, .00043; fine sheep wool .00080 inch.

The outer beard hair of the animal serves as a coat and is not used in making good-quality fabrics. The inner hair, which grows close to the skin on the neck, under shoulders, and on the sides and underportions of the body, is very soft and silk-like.

Vicuna, the aristocrat of fibers, may be used to best advantage in the natural state; however, proper dyeing does not destroy the original beauty of the fiber itself. However, if dyed, it is necessary because of the tendency of the fibers to resist absorption of dyes to remove at least 50 per cent of the natural grease and oil.

Forty fleeces are required to make enough fabric for a single coat.

VICUNA FINISH. Occasionally some worsted fabrics are teaseled when in the damp condition and thoroughly milled to cover the weave effect. A fine, short, erect cropping results.

VICUNA-PACO. Issue of vicuna sire and alpaca dam.

VICUNA WOOL. Fibers from the vicuna fleece. See VICUNA.

VIGOGNE. 1. French for vicuna. 2. A cotton fabric made to resemble the woolen cloth of this name. The cloth is given what is known as an oil-spinning process. Ninety per cent of cotton and 10 per cent of wool usually make up the content of this fabric, which is used as dress material.

Another meaning of the term implies cotton yarn which has small amounts of wool or wool waste in it.

VIGOGNE YARN. 1. Hosiery yarn used in Europe, and composed of about 20 per cent cotton and about 80 per cent wool.

2. A European yarn made of cotton and cotton wastes, and finished to resemble woolen yarn; used for underwear fabric.

VIGOREUX PRINTING. The printing of worsted top fibers by passing the sliver through a printing machine which has a roll with raised bars to carry the dyestuff. The sliver is impregnated with the dyestuff when it comes in contact with the revolving bars or rollers. Black

is used chiefly in Vigoreux work, but shades of blue, brown, and green may be printed by this method for coloring what will be finished spun-yarn, when manipulation is completed.

VINAL. A generic term as decreed by the FTC, not be be confused with Vinyl, a fiber. Vinal was originally known as Vinylon, a manufactured fiber in which the fiber forming substance is any long chain synthetic polymer composed of at least 50 percent by weight of vinyl alcohol units and in which the total of the vinyl alcohol units and any one or more of the various acetal units is at least 85 percent by weight of the fiber. Originally made in Japan, it is used in tires, home furnishings, and industry. It is made by Kanegafuchi Spinning Company, Ltd., in Osaka and is called Kanabian, and by Kurashiki Rayon Co., Ltd., in Osaka and known as Kuralon. Synthofil, made by Wacker-Chemie GimbH., Munich, Germany, is the German product.

VINAL ACETATE ($CH_3COOCH-CH_2$). A colorless, easily polymerized, water-insoluble liquid. It is produced by the reaction of acetylene and acetic acid. Used in manufacture of films, adhesives, paints, and plastics.

VINCEL. Modified type of rayon in the Polynosic Group. Resembles cotton closer than any other manmade fiber. Properties include high resistance in shrinkage from repeated washings, ideal for blending, and good performance in all instances. Has distinctive handle and appearance comparable with that noted in cotton. Used for blouse and dress fabrics, lingerie, rainwear, slacks and shirtings, and in many household textiles. Product of Courtaulds, Ltd., Great Britain.

VINITRON. Made in the Soviet Union and claimed to be a superior product resulting from a combination of a cellulosic material with Khlorin (chlorinated polyvinyl chloride).

VINYL. The compound univalent radical, $CH2CH$, isomeric with many derivatives of ethylene - the hydride of vinyl. Not to be confused with Vinal, a tradename, Vinyl is a fiber.

VINYL-BUTYRAL PLASTIC. Long used as interlayer material in safety glass, this product may now be used as a textile coating material for stain-proof tablecloths, furniture slip covers immune to ink, and draperies than can be wiped clean with a damp cloth.

Application may be carried out on existing coating machinery. The fabric treated is bonded with a super-thin, almost invisible vinyl-butyral, which is reputed to cause no chipping or peeling

under normal usage conditions. Repeated laundering may be given the treated articles, while pressing is done on the untreated side with a moderate iron. Trade name; product of Monsanto Chemical Co.

VINYLIDENE CHLORIDE (CH_2CCl_2). A colorless, volatile, flammable liquid which is copolymerized chiefly with vinyl chloride to form Saran. See Saran and Velon.

VINYL-LASTIC. An adhesive designed for bonding vinyl sheet stock and to produce excellent adhesion of vinyl to itself, leather, metal, wood, etc. The bond used is not deteriorated by vinyl plasticizers; neither heat nor pressure is required for bonding. Product of Permaplastic Products, Centerline, Michigan.

VINYLITE. Registered trade-mark of Carbide and Carbon Chemicals Corporation, Buffalo, New York. It is a resin formulated from high molecular weight vinyl chloride acetate. Vinylite is abrasion-resistant, water-resistant, chemical-resistant, and resistant to heat and cold. Vinylite resin coatings are used to supplant rubber in many essential applications, such as chemical-resistant clothing, food and water bags, hospital sheeting, raincoats, tarpaulins, tenting, upholstery.

VINYLON. A manmade fiber of the polyvinyl alcohol group which is cooler than silk or wool but not as cool as cotton or rayon. Sold by Unitika Co., Ltd. as their registered trademark known as Mewlon.

Some of Vinylon's outstanding properties include high strength, heat-resistance, weather-resistance, anti-corrosiveness, and chemical-resistance. To assure adhesiveness Vinylon is tightly bonded with rubber and treated with a resorcing formaldehyde lates (R.F.L.) compound adhesive. The same adhesive as used for rayon is applied in the case of Vinylon spun, the same as used for nylon is used in the case of Vinylon filament.

The Japanese Synthetic Textile Association which sponsors the development of manmade fibers from polyvinyl alcohol has given the following names to the generic term, Vinylon: "Mewlon," (staple), "Kanebian," (staple), "Cremona," (staple), "Vinylan," (staple), "Woolon," (staple), and "Kuralon," (filament and staple). See Mewlon, Polyvinyl Alcohol, Unitika Ltd., Vinylidene Chloride.

VINYON HH. Comparable in many respects with the polyvinyl chloride fibers made in Europe, it has a slightly lower softening temperature and somewhat lower strength. The low softening temperature and the relative ease with which this fiber may be heat-bonded to other fibers is used to advantage in the production of bonded-fiber batting, felt, and special papers that have high wet strengths and are heat sealable. Its high shrinking characteristics are used to advantage in the manufacture of some contour carpeting. Vinyon HH is spun preferably on the woolen system to produce yarns for heat sealing purposes or for industrial fabrics that have good resistance to a large number of environmental conditions at temperatures below about 140° F. The Federal Trade Commission, Washington, D.C., defines Vinyon as "A manufactured fiber in which the fiber-forming substance is any long chain synthetic polymer composed of at least 85 per cent by weight of vinyl chloride units." Vinyon HH is a registered trademark of FMC Corporation, American Viscose Division, Philadelphia, Pennsylvania.

VIOLET. Purplish-blue or bluish-purple in hue, this color has low brilliance and ordinary saturation qualities.

VIRGIN FIBER. The Federal Trade Commission decrees that the only true virgin fiber is wool which has never been manipulated in any way, shape, or manner. Strictly speaking, however, only the first sheared fibers are · virgin wool, since the term, virgin, means first, untried, unused. The commission also classes the hair or specialty fibers - llama, alpaca, camel hair, cashmere, etc., as wool. Actually these hair fibers are not wool since, for example, wool fibers have serrations or waves while the hair fibers are straight in formation. The term, virgin, has been adopted by manmade fiber producers, chiefly for advertising purposes because the word has several connotations and will attract the attention of the reader. Actually, this term in this sense is a misnomer. See Virgin Wool.

VIRGIN WOOL. The Federal Trade Commission considers this term synonymous with New Wool. It states that "the term virgin or new wool as descriptive of a wool product or any fiber or part thereof shall not be used when the product or part so described is not composed wholly of new or virgin wool which has never been used, or reclaimed, reworked, reprocessed or reused from any spun, woven, knitted, felted, or manufactured or used product. Products composed of or made from fiber reworked or reclaimed from yarn or clips shall not be described as virgin or new wool, or by terms of similar import, regardless of whether such yarns or clips are new or used or were made

of new or reprocessed or reused material."

Another meaning of the term is that it is the first clipping from a sheep that has never heretofore been sheared, a shearling or yearling sheep. The first clip from the animal will be the best to be obtained, as each successive clip becomes inferior in quality. The older the sheep, the poorer will be the grade of the fiber.

Another concise and brief meaning of the term is that it is wool, irrespective of the clip, that has not been manipulated into yarn and cloth.

In some respects, the term may be somewhat of a misnomer. Care should be exercised to give the correct impression as to what is meant in speaking of virgin wool. Advertising has done much to add to the confusion in interpreting the correct or implied meaning. Some will say that some grades of virgin wool may cost less per pound than certain good quality cottons; thus, to the buying public the term may be somewhat misleading.

There is also some apparent misunderstanding concerning the term, "100 per cent wool." Some will say that when it is considered that wool from the belly, rump, and shanks of the animals is used in the manufacture of woolen goods, it can be gleaned that while the resultant garment may be advertised as all-wool or 100 per cent wool, the quality may be deficient despite the fact that the cloth may have been made entirely of virgin wool.

This Commission also defined the following:

REPROCESSED WOOL: The resulting fiber when wool has been woven or felted into a wool product which, without ever having been utilized in any way by the ultimate consumer, subsequently has been made into the fibrous state.

REUSED WOOL: The resulting fiber when wool or reprocessed wool has been spun, woven, knitted, or felted into a wool product which after having been used in any way by the ultimate consumer, subsequently has been made into the fibrous state.

WOOL PRODUCT: Any product, or any portion of a product, which contains, purports to contain, or in any way is represented as containing wool, reprocessed wool, or reused wool.

Wool from the sheep is unique in that it is the only natural fiber that will felt in a natural manner. The fiber is made of overlapping scales or serrations which vary with the several grades of wool; there are from 600 to 3,000 to the inch. The structure of the fiber is comparable with the scales on a fish or an asparagus tip. Wool is warm, springy, elastic, may be harsh. It is the weakest of all major fibers,

is a generator of heat, thereby giving warmth to the body in cold, crisp weather.

There are five general types of wool: fine wools, medium wools, long or Luster wools, carpet wools, cross-bred wool. On the four-point method of classifying wool, the table includes combing, carding, clothing, carpet wools.

VISA. A registered trademark name of Deering Milliken Company, Inc., New York City, this fabric made its debut in June 1966 and accomplished a major breakthrough in the field of durable press fabrics. The fabric is made of 65 percent "Dacron" polyester fiber and 35 percent cotton fiber. The material is so constructed that it releases oil and soil stains readily. It is not a soil repellent and is ideal for combatting soil redeposition. Though the product is not claimed to be truly effective on combatting soil deposition through static, it does, however, combat soil deposition with hydrophilic (absorption powers) properties which make for less static.

Visa can take at least twenty washings and is durable for the life of the garment upon which it has been applied. Excellent results are achieved on precured tablecloths, shirtings, and jeans where no-crease but well-rounded appearance is desired; the Visa compound is used on medium weight postcured fabrics, as well. The secret of this fabric and the applied treatment afforded it, is electronic radiation, a discovery made in the Magnolia Finishing Plant of the company in Blacksburg, South Carolina.

VISCA. When a viscose solution is forced through a narrow slit instead of a small single hole in a spinneret, a lightweight but strong ribbon-like material is produced that resembles straw. It is called ribbon straw. These narrow strips are useful in making costume accessories, apparel, and in the manufacture of upholstery and millinery. They can be combined with other fibers to produce lustrous effects. Visca is the registered trade-mark in the U.S.A., held by Courtaulds, Ltd., for Visca braid made from Visca ribbon straw.

VISCOSE. 1. The third method, historically, of making rayon yarn. The product manufactured by this method is a pure regenerated cellulose. See Illustrated Section. 2. A coagulating bath used in the viscose method of making rayon; sometimes the coagulating bath used in any of the three methods of making rayon.

VISCOSE RAYON. Filaments of regenerated cellulose coagulated from a solution of cellulose xanthate. The raw material can be cotton linters, or chips of spruce, pine, or hemlock. More than 98 per cent of regenerated rayon is made on the viscose method; the remainder is cuprammonium rayon made on the Stretch System. See Illustrated Section.

VISCOSE SOLUTIONS. Solution from which rayon filaments are produced. See Illustrated Section.

VISCOSITY. Resistance of liquid to flow—molasses, honey, viscose solution used in manufacture of rayon filament.

VISCOUS. Glutinous, semifluid, sticky; having the consistency of a sirup.

VISTAGLASS FABRIC. The first 100 percent glass fiber bedspread fabric to be made in this country. Made from Beta Fiberglas yarn, it is a product of Hess, Goldsmith & Company, a division of Burlington Industries, Inc.

VISTRA. Acetate or viscose fibers changed in physical properties to give increased strength, rough surfaces, crimp, etc.

VISTRALAN. A German viscose product chemically modified to increase its affinity for acid dyes.

VISTRA X T. A physically modified viscose staple fiber.

VITALIZED. Registered trademark of Delarich, a subsidiary of Indian Head, Inc., New York City, for its crush-resistant finish, operated by license from the company.

VITRIOL. Sulphuric acid originally made from green vitriol, oil of vitriol. Sulphates include blue vitriol from copper, green vitriol from iron, and white vitriol from zinc.

VIVANA. A Nylon 6 fiber produced by Dow Badische Company, Anderson, South Carolina. The plant began operations in 1969.

VIYELLA FLANNEL. Twill-weave cloth with the appearance of all-wool flannel, but composed of about 50 per cent cotton, 50 per cent wool. The fiber content must always be declared in connection with this fabric. Also, the Wool Products Labeling Act requires that fiber content be declared when wool is present. The name is a trade-mark of William Hollins & Company for a fabric made in England.

VOIDED. Used to describe velvets and to indicate that certain areas of the foundation fabric are left void of pile warp ends so as to achieve the motif effect on the fabric.

VOILE. This sheer cotton cloth is light in weight, soft in feel, and is usu-ally made with cylindrical, combed yarn. England produces the best voile from gassed yarns which range from 2/100s to 2/200s. High twist is an important factor to obtain a high-class fabric. Voile drapes very well. It is finished from 40 to 45 inches, and the texture will range between 60 to 74 x 56 to 76.

Voile is used for blouses, children's clothes, bedspreads, draperies, doll cloth, dress goods, lamp shades, scarfs.

There are four types of fancy voiles: seed, shadow stripe, splash, and piqué. Seed voile uses novelty yarn in the filling; shadow stripes are made by weaving the stripes closer together in the reeding plan than in the body of the cloth. Splash voile is made by using slub yarns which give a splashed effect to the finished goods; piqué voile is made by arranging the reeding plan for the warp in such a way that the goods will resemble genuine piqué. (The fabric is sometimes called piqué dimity.) Flock-printing is often applied to voile dress goods.

VOILE, CORDED. One in which the warp yarns are very cylindrical so as to present a faint warpwise rib or cord effect.

VOILE, NINON. British term for a high-quality cotton voile made to simulate ninon made from nylon, "Dacron," silk, etc. It is a combed-yarn material. The cut length is 120 yards, textures are around 80 x 72, and the yarns used are either single 100s or 2/200s. The fabric could be called a "cotton chiffon" since it compares well with chiffon made from the aforementioned fibers.

VOILE DE LAINE. Sheer woolen voile used for dress goods.

VOILE YARN. In between regular twist yarn and crepe twist yarn. Also called voile twist.

VOLATILE. A substance easily evaporated.

VOLET. A short flowing veil, worn by women in the Middle Ages.

VOLO WOOL. Greece raises this wool, long and coarse in nature, for use in worsted materials.

"VOLUMET." A hosiery control system which evolves around an upright pressure-loaded stocking form device having indicator guides thereon for measuring the several portions of a ladies' stocking for size, and fabric variations from machine to machine, or from head to head. Product of Joseph C. Cobert Associates.

VUELITE. An embossed cellulose acetate sheet for use in diffusing panels for fluorescent light fixtures. It is much lighter than glass, thereby decreasing the weight of the fixtures. Vuelite burns slowly; the rate is 1.5 to 2.0 inches per minute in .060-inch thickness, and it is approved by the Underwriters' Laboratories. Product of Monsanto Chemical Co.

VUEPAK. Known for its rigidity and transparency, Vuepak cellulose sheets are used for packages and merchandise displays. The thicknesses are .003, .005, .0075, .010, .0125, .015 and .020 inch. Product of Monsanto Chemical Co. Trade name.

VULCANIZATION. The method of imparting greater durability, hardness, and elasticity to latex (rubber) by heat combined with sulphur.

VULCANIZED FIBER. A laminated plastic made of cotton cellulose material, layers of which are bonded by chemical treatment and converted into an entirely new homogeneous structure. It weighs about half as much as aluminum, and can absorb sudden repeated shocks and impacts without failure. Depending on its use, the material can be as hard as bone or as soft as wet rawhide. As a plastic it can be bent, formed, drawn, swagged into intricate shapes without sacrificing strength in an area, and it has stubborn resistance to wear and abrasion.

The fiber is used industrially for electrical power line lighting arrestors, in tiny protective washers for hypodermic needles, as insulation for railroad tracks, in shuttles for textile looms, bobbins of many types, etc. It is ideal for use where durability, smoothness, and lightness of weight are required. Vulcanized fiber is referred to as "the grand old man" of industrial plastics.

VYBRAN. Trade-name of National Spinning Company, Inc., New York City for its acrylic yarn made from "Orlon" Type 21.

"VYLOR." Monofilament made by E.I. duPont de Nemours & Company, Inc., Wilmington, Delaware. This nylon filament finds use in interliners for men's suitings, shoe fabrics, industrial knit constructions, industrial sewing thread and filters.

VYRENE. Trademark of Uni-Royal Fiber and Textile Division of UniRoyal, Inc., Winnsboro, South Carolina for its synthetic elastomer to supplement and extend the range of its Lastex yarns. Vyrene is a super-fine elastic yarn ideal for use in sheer elastic fabrics. It has toughness, high tensile strength, and good resistance to chafing; resistant to light, ozone, and solvents, even in very fine sizes. Other characteristics include good modulus retention, rapid stretch return, and ability to withstand standard scouring, finishing and dyeing procedures, and wash-and-wear tests.

Vyrene is a complete yarn in itself, with a fine elastic core of elastic monofilament covered with nylon or some other manufactured fiber. Compared with Lastex, much used in constructions with core sizes around 1/100-inch diameter, Vyrene is made with the elastic element 1/150-inch size. In woven or knitted fabrics, its extra fineness creates soft and sheer fabrics not heretofore possible. Uses include foundation garments of all types, golf jackets, sportswear, and swimwear. This Spandex yarn is sometimes known as Lastex S, the S meaning Spandex

HOW TO TIE THE WEAVER'S KNOT

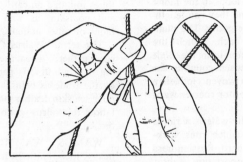

Fig. 1. Cross the two ends, making certain that the end from the *left* hand is in front of the end from the *right* hand.

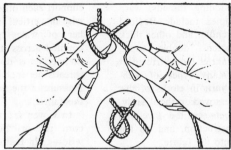

Fig. 2. Swing the yarn in the *right* hand over the *left* thumb and in back of the two ends.

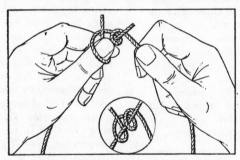

Fig. 3. Now swing the same yarn around only the *right* hand end.

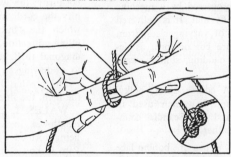

Fig. 4. Push the *right*-hand end with the *right* thumb—

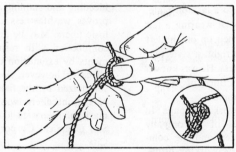

Fig. 5. —through the loop made by the *left* thumb.

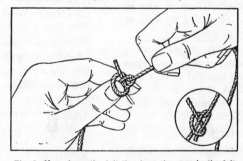

Fig. 6. Now clamp the *left* thumb on the yarn in the *left* hand and pull hard with the *right* hand.

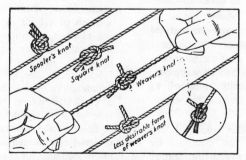

Fig. 7. The result is the weaver's knot. Other knots are shown for comparison.

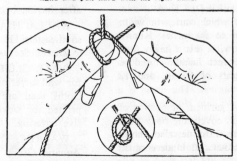

Fig. 8. The alternative method, less desirable because both ends are on same side of completed knot. Substitute this diagram for Figs. 2 and 3.

W

WADDED, WADDED CLOTH, WADDING. 1. Fabric made of wool fibers, felted into a compact mass through the application of heat, moisture, and pressure, without weaving. Used in laundry presses, padding machines, tailoring, and upholstery. 2. An extra set of filling threads which lie dormant, without interlacing, between the face and back of a double-cloth construction. The yarn is usually heavy and bulky, with little twist, to add weight and bulk to the fabric. 3. Fabrics that use wadding threads, warp or filling. Examples include Bedford cord, piqué, chinchilla, and other thick face-finished woolens; double, triple, and quadruple fabrics, some rib-effect materials, and many types of webbings. Wadding yarn in cloths of this type can be removed rather easily, since they lie between the face and back of the construction, and do not actually weave into the fabric.

WADDING, COTTON. Cotton fiber that has been processed by a machine into a thick, fluffy mat. It is delivered for use in rolls of varying sizes, from which lengths are cut or torn, as desired. Used for padding, stuffing, wadding.

WADMAL. A coarse, thick, bulky, and heavily napped woolen used in Great Britain and the Scandia countries in cold weather.

WADSTENE. A peasant bobbin lace made in black or white. This Swedish lace has no set motifs and changes in accord with the prevailing fashions or styles in lace manufacture.

WAFFLE CLOTH. Fabric with a characteristic honeycomb weave. When made in cotton, it is called waffle piqué. Used for coatings, draperies, dresses, toweling. Same as honeycomb cloth. See Illustrated Section (Fabrics 55).

WAFFLE STITCH. As implied by the term, it achieves a series of square, waffle-like designs on knitted goods.

WAGON-COVER DUCK. A double-filled flat duck which varies in width from 48 inches to 90 inches. Known as regular, heavy, or extra heavy, and based on a 29-inch width, the duck comes in weights of 8, 10, and 12 ounces per yard.

WAIST. 1. A garment or portion of a garment which covers the body from shoulders to the waistline; also known as bodice or blouse. 2. Undergarment for children.

WAISTBAND. A band or sash which encircles the waist, with particular reference to one on the upper part of skirts, trousers, etc., to serve as an inner belt.

WAISTCOAT. A garment which may or may not be sleeveless that buttons in the front and extends below the waistline. It is worn under the jacket or coat and is also known as a vest. Women sometimes wear this garment instead of a blouse. The waistcoat does not always match the jacket or coat in fabric or design.

WALE. In a knitted material, it is one of a series of loops in successive course or formation, made by one needle. The series of loops in the fabric support each other and they run lengthwise or vertical in the goods. The number of wales per inch, which are counted across the sample in the same manner as is done when counting the threads per inch in a woven cloth, is a measure of the fineness or coarseness of the fabric.

In woven fabric, the wale is a raised cord, rib, or "hill," which runs warpwise—as in Bedford cord, Russian cord shirting, some transportation fabric, corduroy; the wale is also used to signify the cords in a true piqué fabric in which the "hills" should run in the filling direction. Certain pronounced diagonal twill fabrics are also referred to as having so many wales per inch.

The greater the number of wales to the inch, the finer will be the fabric.

WALES. 1. Chain of loops that run lengthwise in knit fabric, each chain being formed by a separate needle. 2. Ribs in knit cloths.

WALKER, JAMES J. A close friend of the Duke of Windsor, this late mayor of New York City was also a fashion plate. He was the originator of wearing a felt hat with the brim turned up on the left side and down on the right, a style that became an instant success. He was known as the "New York Prince of Wales" when it came to men's apparel.

WALKOUT. A work stoppage in which the employees of a company leave their work places, and the company's premises, during working hours, after having begun to work.

WALLACHIAN. Sheep native to southeastern Europe and comparable to Zackel. See ZACKEL.

WALL CLOTH. Any cloth suitable for wall covering in lieu of wallpaper; cloths used are usually embossed or printed, or woven damask for expensive covering.

WALRUS. This skin belongs to the Aquatic Group of raw materials for the tanning industry and the leather produced therefrom. The group, which includes seal and the sea lion, as well as the walrus, serves as the raw material to produce leather for buffing wheels, luggage and fancy leather goods. The shark, whale, blackfish, dolphin, porpoise and kindred fish produce leather for use in luggage, shoe uppers, and fancy leather goods. The alligator is a raw material for luggage, shoes and fancy leather goods.

True walrus hide is of such thickness that it must be split prior to its use for bag leather. It is rather difficult to define leather made of seal and walrus skins after tanning and splitting, and the names are often used interchangeably. "Walrus Grain" is sometimes imitated on cattle hide, sheepskin, and goatskin, as well as splits from hides of other animals.

The term, "Walrus Grain" or "Walrus Leather," when used in the traveling bag industry, is generally regarded by the trade as being a species of genuine sealskin leather on which a simulation of walrus grain has been embossed.

WAMUS, WAMMUS. A belted, heavy, loose-knitted cardigan jacket.

WARCO. A chemical which permanently inhibits fading of acetate dyestuffs because of exposure to nitrous oxide and ozone fumes encountered in the atmosphere. The product is applied by exhaustion techniques and is durable to both dry cleaning and laundering. Commonly used to treat fabrics containing cellulose acetate, alone or in blends, and nylon. Trade-mark of Warwick Chemical Division, Sun Chemical Corporation, New York City.

WARCOFIX. A resin based dye-fixative for direct colors. It reduces bleeding and staining of colors and improves washfastness of dyes on cellulosic fibers. May be applied alone or in conjunction with resin finishing treatments by exhaustion or by padding. In all cases, however, the dyestuffs are insolubilized by the fixative, thereby imparting excellent washfastness. Trade-mark of Warwick Chemical Division, Sun Chemical Corporation, New York City.

WARMTH TESTER. A testing apparatus which scientifically gauges the warmth of fabrics in use under varying climatic conditions. By simulating practically all weather conditions, this laboratory instrument tests all textile fabrics under conditions normally encountered in actual use. The effect of a particular weave, weight of cloth, type of fiber, length of nap and type of finish on the thermal properties of a material can be measured by this valuable machine.

WARP. Any yarn that runs lengthwise in cloth made on a loom. The yarn is usually stronger than the filling, since it has to withstand more friction in weaving. Warp yarn is always under tension whereas the filling is not subject to such tension since it comes off the nose of the filling bobbin which sets in the shuttle. Warp yarn usually has more twist so that it can do its work well in weaving. The yarn is wound on the warp beam which sets in sockets at the back of the loom. It is let off evenly as the fabric is being woven by the let-off motion device at the back of the loom. Newly woven cloth is governed in its course around the cloth roller by the take-up motion at the front of the loom and the action of the roller itself.

WARP, CENTER STITCHING. An extra warp, usually of cotton, employed in double-cloth construction to bind or stitch the two single woven materials together. Plain, twill, satin or other small constructions are used in binder warp formation.

WARP-BACKED FABRIC. See BACKED FABRICS.

WARP BEAM. 1. The large spool-like device upon which warp threads are wound. It consists of a wooden or metallic barrel, 5 or 6 inches in diameter, and several feet in length. At each end, there is a large wooden or metallic flange about 2 feet in diameter. 2. A large beam, 5 to 6 feet long, and 2 to 3 feet in diameter, upon which rayon or nylon tire yarn is often shipped from the plant to tire manufacturers.

WARP-BEAM TAPES. Tapes or cords which may be used to take the place of the apron.

WARP CHAIN. The looped or chained warp that has been taken from the frame or reel. It is made like a crochet chain-stitch and prevents the warp from gnarling or tangling.

WARP CRIMPING. A method developed by J. P. Stevens & Company, Inc., New York City, under the trademark name of *Stevetex*. Crimp is inserted into a multiple layer of ends set in a warp formation. Thus, it is ideally adapted to all forms of warp knitting such as raschel and tricot, as well as in woven goods.

WARP DIRECTION FROM FILLING DIRECTION IN APPAREL, REASONS FOR DETERMINATION OF.

Garments cut in the warp direction will give better wear.

There is less shrinkage in the warp or vertical direction.

Filling or horizontal threads have the tendency to stretch more when compared with warp ends or threads. Difficult to overcome in some fabrics in the cut-fit-trim trade.

To know the direction enables one to cut in that direction, which is more desirable in tailoring—the warp or the vertical direction in most instances. Such knowledge means aid in identification of the face of the material, serves as an aid in testing fabrics in many physical tests resorted to in textile testing. It is used as an aid in laying-out fabric on the cutting table.

For proper hanging purposes, as well as for true balance of the garment, the pattern of every part of the garment must be placed accurately on the material—in the warp, vertical or true bias direction. Some printed materials, however, because of motifs or stripes, should be used on the cross-graining for balance, for the proper hang of the garment, and for the suppleness of the material.

Many collars, yokes, belts, and cuffs are cut on the cross-grain in order to avoid excessive stretching.

Accurate measurements can be made on the proper grain-line.

Most garments are cut in the warp direction because:

1. Warp threads are stronger.
2. The garment will hang better.
3. The garment will fit and wear better.

Many style lines are better adapted to the warp grain.

Proper grain-line lends contrast in trimming.

The draping and the pleating quality of each grain varies.

True bias is absolutely essential for bias binding; off-grain will not stretch on a garment in a smooth manner.

The lengthwise or warp grain is usually used through the center-front of the garment because of the strength needed.

When matching checked material, the lengthwise grain squares and the crosswise squares often vary slightly in size.

When an operator receives a bundle of cutwork, the two sections which are to be joined may be of such shape that it is difficult to judge which seams are to join together. A knowledge of grain-lines will be of value to the operator: For instance he will join skirt front and skirt back together on the lengthwise grain.

WARP DYEING. The dyeing of a warp on a beam or in chain formation. See WARP PRINT OR SHADOW PRINT.

WARP END. An individual warp thread, yarn. See Illustrated Section.

WARPER. A machine equipped to hold a beam in position on a constant surface speed drum to receive the ends of the yarn from the warping creel. The speed can vary from sixty to five hundred and fifty yards per minute. There are clocks to show the number of yarns per minute, and in conjunction or separately, another device to show the actual total yardage. An expansion comb spreads the yarn evenly between beam heads. Some machines have built-in stop-motions, others are controlled by a creel stop-motion.

WARP-FACE. A weave in which the warp yarn predominates on the face.

WARP FROM FILLING IN WOVEN GOODS, AIDS IN DETERMINATION OF.

1. The selvage or listing runs in the warp or vertical direction in a woven fabric and is a component part of the warp. A woven cloth has a selvage to protect the edges of the material in the processes of weaving, dyeing, and finishing. A good selvage produces the effect of a frame around a picture and usually indicates a quality fabric.

2. The set of yarns with the greater or harder twist is the warp. Added tension is necessary to the warp threads since they must withstand the rigors of weaving in the loom. Filling yarn is under little or no tension as it comes off the nose of the filling bobbin. Examples include blankets, dress goods, overcoatings, shirting.

3. The regularity and number of one parallel set of yarns usually indicates that this set is the warp. Filling yarns in a woven fabric are usually coarser and fewer in number and are sometimes irregular.

4. Stripes run in the warp or vertical direction in woven goods. Examples include awning stripes, banjo stripes, suiting, baseball uniform cloth, Bengal stripes, chalk stripes, curtaining, dress goods, madras and other shirting fabric, neckwear fabric, pin stripes, striped trousering, ticking, toweling.

5. When several sizes of yarn are used in a fabric, it usually implies that the basic yarns are in the warp while the fancy, decorative, or novelty yarns are in the filling. This effect is observed in some curtaining, decorative fabrics, bedspreads, some novelty dress goods, brocade, brocatelle, damask, tapestry.

6. Some fabrics in which novelty or fancy yarns are used will reveal that these yarns are used in the warp in order to give decoration, a novelty effect or an attractive surface appearance to the material. This may occur in some types of women's wear coating, decorative fabrics, and some dress goods. Whether the effect of novelty or fancy yarns are to be in the warp or in the filling direction depends, to considerable degree, on the particular

cloth and its terminal use.

7. When one system of yarn is entirely two-ply and the other is single, the two-ply system is usually considered as the warp. Observed in cloths where the preponderance of the fabric is warp which covers up the filling, as in the case of gabardine, whipcord and some woolen suiting fabrics.

8. The nap or fur on a material usually runs in the warp direction; comparable with the fur on a cat's back, and man's beard—smooth on the downward stroke and rough on the upward stroke. Examples include pile fabrics of many types, carpets and rugs, melton, kersey, beaver, broadcloth, and several types of women's wear winter coating.

9. Bulkier yarn is used for filling. Often found in drapery and upholstery fabrics, boys' and girls' apparel and in low-cost women's wear ensembles and coating.

10. The lower grade of yarn in the one system of yarns implies that this system is the filling. Yarn of this type is in low-cost coatings for women's wear, some face-finished fabrics, some union fabrics and low quality woolen suitings.

WARPING.

1. COTTON AND RAYON TYPES: Warping is the art or process of winding together, on a section beam, a specified number of warp ends from a high- or low-speed creel. The creel may be defined as a convenient rack, usually made in a "V" form, for holding spools, cones, or cheeses, while the yarn is being withdrawn to the warp beam.

High-speed warping is used for low-twist filament yarns and spun rayon or cotton yarns. In this instance, the yarn package remains stationary while the yarn is withdrawn "over-end." Section beams, only, are used in this type of warping. Creel capacity rarely exceeds six hundred packages.

Low-speed warping is employed for highly twisted or filament combination yarns. The spools rotate, supply the drag or the tension as the yarn is pulled from the barrel.

2. SILK TYPE: Another method of introducing yarn onto a beam, in this case a warp beam, is the silk-system plan, wherein a huge reel receives and supports successive bands of "wound-on yarn" from a creel until the desired number of warp ends of a specified length are in place. The accumulated mass of yarn is then unwound from the reel directly to a warp beam. No slashing is necessary afterward since the yarns are either in gum form, or, as in the case of rayon, pre-soaked. One revolution of the reel is about fifteen yards. Creel capacity is about

six hundred spools. See BEAMING.

WARPING FRAME. A wooden frame with evenly spaced pegs on which small or short warps may be made.

WARPING MILL, WARPING REEL. A revolving frame on which long warps are made.

WARP-KNIT. A method of knitting which uses numerous yarns in the lengthwise direction.

WARP-KNIT FABRICS. A fabric with a flatter, closer, less elastic knit than the weft or jersey knit. Very often knit so that the fabric is run-resistant. Tricot and milanese are typical warp-knit fabrics.

WARP KNITTING, SOME MAJOR TERMS USED IN.

Rack: A unit of measure of 480 courses for fabric production and costing calculations.

Runner Length: The number of inches of yarn from a warp to make one rack of fabric.

Quality: The number of inches of fabric made by knitting one rack.

Fully Threaded Bar: The arrangement of the warp threads so that each yarn guide hole has a yarn and each needle in the machine receives one thread.

Partially Threaded Bar: The arrangement of the warp threads in a repeat sequence, that is, three yarn guides threaded and one yarn guide empty, or one guide threaded and one guide empty.

WARP LINE. The line of the warp from the warp beam to the breast beam—warp beam, whip roll, lease rods, warp drop-wires, heddles, harnesses, reed, raceplate, to the breast beam.

WARP PATTERN. One repeat of the different arrangement of colors of warp threads that go to make the pattern. The filling pattern is the arrangement of the filling colors and yarn used to make one repeat. Plaids, overplaids, Glens, and checks are examples.

WARP PILE. Fabric made with two sets of warp yarn and one set of filling yarn; the extra warp-yarn set usually appears on the surface of the cloth, except in the case of toweling, where the pile effect is seen on both sides. This extra or pile warp may or may not be cut.

WARP PRINTING. Before weaving, a warp, by special method, may be roller-printed to yield a very novel effect when the cloth is woven. Varying fillings may be used.

WARP REP, WARP REPP. Any fabric with warp cords in the vertical direction—Bedford cord, piqué, transportation fabric, etc. The term is used

very broadly and may cause misconception.

WARP-RIB. This type of weave is painted in the warp direction, but the cord or rib effect is in the filling direction. Examples are bengaline, hatbanding, poplin, piqué, Ottoman, faille, and novelty rib-effects.

The texture used in the fabric is such that the threads used to make the cord are covered up in entirety by the threads that show on the face and back of the goods. All simple warp-ribs repeat on two ends.

WARP RIB WEAVE AND FILLING RIB WEAVES, DIFFERENCES BETWEEN.

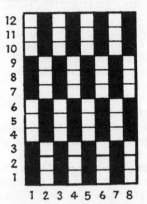

WARP RIB WEAVE

3-3, two repeats high and four repeats wide. The cord runs in the filling direction. All simple warp rib weaves repeat on TWO WARP ENDS.

FILLING RIB WEAVE

3-3, four repeats high and two repeats wide. Cord runs in the direction of the warp. All simple filling rib weaves repeat on TWO FILLING PICKS.

In both weave constructions, pointed blocks signify raisers in the cloth—warp ends over the filling picks at the point of interlacing.

WARP SATEEN. See SATEEN.

WARP SATIN. See SATIN.

WARP STOP-MOTION. Any device on a loom that automatically causes it to bang-off when a warp yarn breaks; may be a mechanical or an electrical mechanism.

WARP STRIPE. 1. Broadly, any stripe that runs in the vertical direction in woven goods. Specifically, there are certain fabrics well-known for warp stripes, and they provide an easy method to use to identify the warp from the filling, and the face from the back of the material. The stripes may be made of plain-weave, twill, satin, dobby loom effect, leno or doup stripes, warp floats in some instances, etc. Some stripings in fabrics have particular names, such as chalk, pin, banjo, muted, Roman, hairline, pencil, novelty, etc. Fabrics which are often found with stripe effects include suiting, denim, madras and other shirting, dress goods, overalls, hickory cloth, institutional fabric, etc. 2. This term is used in the knitting of fancy motifs on the face of the goods by the use of extra yarn or yarns. Observed in men's hosiery, some gloves, some knit apparel fabrics.

WARP THREAD GUIDE. See RADDLE.

WARP TWIST. The standard twist for warp yarn is about 4½ times the square root of the yarn size; cotton warp is twisted to the right, as compared with worsted yarn which is twisted to the left, generally speaking. Web and chain are other names for warp twist.

WARP TYING MACHINE. A machine that ties the ends of a warp from a full beam to the ends of the warp from an exhausted or spent loom beam.

WARP WIND. When a bobbin, spool, or spindle is wound snugly at the top, body, and bottom, with the top and bottom areas showing a tapered effect of the slubbing, roving, yarn, etc. This type of winding on a bobbin is achieved by having each successive layer of the stock slightly shorter to the top tip and bottom tip of the bobbin.

WASHABLE. Fabrics which will not fade or shrink when they are washed. This term should always be qualified by careful directions in methods of handling, preferably based on laboratory tests. Not to be confused with "Wash and Wear."

"WASH AND WEAR." This type of garment is one that can be washed by hand or in a washing machine at the warm water setting. When drip-dried it retains crease or pleats, and recovers sufficiently from wrinkles to need little, if any, ironing. Washing temperature should range between 95° F. and 110° F.

WASH-AND-WEAR COTTONS: A comparatively new group of chemically treated cottons that require little or no ironing after being washed and dried by normal home-laundering methods. In most instances, these garments look neat enough to wear without pressing; this is, however, determined by the fastidiousness of the consumer and the end use of the product. There are also cottons with wash-and-wear qualities that are labeled "automatic wash-and-wear," "no-iron," "minimum care," "drip-dry," "little or no ironing required," and with other similar terms. Tags which bear these terms assure the user that the cotton cloth from which the item was made received a special chemical treatment (resin or non-resin) and that the fabric will dry smoothly and free from major wrinkles.

An advantage of wash-and-wear cottons is that they require no special washing temperatures. They are not heat-sensitive and can be washed in hot water and soap or detergents, which are absolutely necessary for true cleanliness. They may be washed in any conventional manner; by hand or by machine.

Chlorine bleaches are safe for white wash-and-wear cottons unless the fabric has a chlorine-retentive finish. In such cases the tag on the garment will warn against the use of chlorine bleaches. Bleach is never needed for colored fabrics. Starch is unnecessary. For the best results in drying, tumble-dry or hand-wet to drip-dry. If a touching-up by ironing is desired, a warm iron is all that is necessary. The ease and the speed of pressing wash-and-wear cottons are very important features of these fabrics and garments.

RADUNER WASH-AND-WEAR MECHANICAL PROCESS: Invented by Dr. Alfred Lauchenauer, of Raduner & Co., A. G., Horn, Switzerland, the process can actually stretch cotton fibers. Licensed to the Sanforized Division of Cluett, Peabody & Company, Inc., New York City, the process reduces substantially the tensile- and tear-strength losses which result from resin and cross-linking treatment of cotton for both durable press and wash-and-wear. The treatment can be used even on lightweight, sheer cottons such as batiste, organdy, and voile. Uses of the process include wash-and-wear quality in sheer blouses, sleepwear, light print dresses, curtains, and handkerchiefs.

This micro-stretching machine has a cost of around $20,000, and it is capable of treating cotton cloth already treated by one of the several chemical resins with a minimum of 5 per cent from the original dimensions. Deterioration of fabric that may be caused by the chemicals applied to fabrics is prevented by the treatment. Since wash-and-wear came into vogue a few years ago, the fabrics have been made with a content of cotton and polyester fibers, with the latter acting as a bolster or stimulant to the fabric because of the trouble encountered from resins on the cotton in these materials. Thus it is now possible to eliminate manmade fibers in the fabric content in lighter-weight fabrics, with the heavier cloths using a decreased content of polyester or comparable fibers. The machine used is about the size of an upright piano.

WASH BLONDE. A white or pastel-colored fine washable net which finds use for trimming of various types.

WASHBOARD EFFECT. Term used to imply the condition that arises in ringless hosiery; often caused by varying yarn denier sizes or by some of the filaments missing in the yarn.

WASHED WOOL. 1. Wool with the yolk and suint removed in the scouring operation. 2. Wool after the removal of as much suint as possible, prior to shearing.

WASHER. Any type of machine, of which there are many, used to scour, wash, full, mill, etc. Cloth or garments can be washed in these machines.

WASHER, AUTOMATIC. A power-driven device used to wash fabrics which fills itself with water at a set temperature, washes, rinses, extracts water, and then stops. One setting is all that is necessary for the cycle in the machine.

WASHER, SLACK LOOP. Any tub, vessel or vat used to scour or wash piece goods. The cloth is in chain form and controlled by rollers as it passes through the vat. Much of the material will lie in the bottom of the kier without tension.

WASHER, STRING. See WASHER, SLACK LOOP.

WASHER-DRYER, COMBINATION. A power-driven device for washing and drying fabrics and garments. Combines the work of an automatic washer and an automatic dryer in one operation controlled by a single control setting. The machine may be used singly as a washer or a dryer, if needs be. Driven by gas or electric power.

WASHER WRINGER. A power driven mechanism used to wash fabrics or garments, equipped with a power-driven device used to extract water by squeezing. See Washer; Washer, Automatic; Washable.

WASHER WRINKLES. Defects noted in woolens and worsteds that run in the warp direction. They show shaded or specked places and occur when the material is given wet-finishing treatment, as in washing, scouring, fulling, milling. Very difficult to remove altogether. The fabric may be washed or scoured in a full-width open scouring machine, which generally does much to remove the wrinkles.

WASH-FASTNESS TESTER. A washing machine which determines color fastness of all types of fabrics to dry cleaning and washing, and for determination of shrinkage on small samples. The machine has a four-sample capacity.

WASH GOODS. Fabrics or manufactured articles or garments which can be washed or laundered.

WASHING SODA. Sodium carbonate, a strongly alkaline compound, Na_2CO_3.

WASHING TESTS. A series of laundry tests to determine the amount of color fading, shrinkage, or change in other properties, encountered in home or commercial launderings.

WASHMANSHIP. A coined term that implies the art and science of knowing what to do and how to do it, pertinent to washing and laundering apparel, garments, and fabrics. Within recent years, a host of new treatments and finishes on textiles have come into being, all of which are geared to provide better performance to the consumer. Special care is now necessary in handling textiles in the home and the smart housewife should keep abreast of the vast number of materials with which she is now confronted.

All labels on fabrics and garments should be read and saved for future reference. Textile mills, apparel manufacturers, and commercial laundries furnish detailed information on labels to aid the housewife in obtaining the best possible service and wear from her purchases.

Spots and stains should be removed at once to prevent further imbedding of the affected area. The content of the article is of much aid in removing the spots and stains since a chemical that may eradicate a stained area in a woolen or worsted material may have no effect on nylon, polyester, or silk. Reading of directions should solve this problem for the consumer.

Fabrics and garments should be properly sorted as to fiber content and color. Bleaches, detergents, soaps, and other comparable ingredients should be used only after having read the directions. Home laundry equipment should be up to date and kept in the best possible condition at all times.

WASH SATIN. General term for a fabric made from a satin weave construction, and washable. Also includes cloths classed as satins; all satin weave fabrics are not washable. Specifically, the term refers to the types of satin fabrics that may be used for lingerie, blouses, collars, sportswear such as skirts, scarves, etc., which can be washed and laundered with ease and care and present a good appearance when worn again.

WASH SILK. Also known as shirting silk and washing silk. See TUB SILK.

WASHWHITES. A type of flannel, or lightweight kersey, beaver, or broadcloth, all of which comes in white. Used for trousers, dress coats, or jackets in tuxedo raiment, white blazer jackets, and some uniform fabrics, the fabric or garment may be cleaned by washing or by drycleaning. Some of the fabric comes under the name of cricket cloth, an English term.

WASTE. Fiber and yarn by-products created in the manufacturing or processing of fibers or yarns.

WASTE DUCK. A single flat duck known for its varying amount of waste fiber used in coarse filling yarn.

WASTE MACHINES. Various types of machines employed to open up varying types of cotton waste. The stock when delivered is rather fluffy and open and in this condition may be sent back to the picker machine for another run.

"WASTE MATERIALS" MIXED WITH WOOL FIBERS.

CARBONIZED NOIL: Obtained from cloths which contain cotton or other vegetable matter. Staple is from ½ inch to 2½ inches and it may be white or colored. Handle is fairly good but does not cope with that of combed noil. The fibers have a shreddy appearance and are used in certain types of woolens and lower quality worsteds.

COMBED NOIL FROM WORSTED MANUFACTURE: From ½ inch to 2½ inches in fiber length. Comes white or in colors. Combed noil is usually good to excellent in quality since choice wool fibers are utilized in the manufacture of worsteds. Appearance is good since the fibers naturally possess good handle, elasticity, and felting properties.

Noil is much used as "filler-in" fiber in many fabrics and it mixes well with base fibers used to make cloth. Noil is usually an asset to a fabric since the quality is highly desirable.

COTTON: Sources are obvious and Peruvian cotton has certain properties that make it ideal for use in some woolen cloths. Fiber length is from ½ inch to about 2 inches; may be white or colored, is smooth, even and, at times, rather silklike in handle. In appearance, these cotton fibers are white or tinged.

In some fabrics the use of cotton up to 10 or 12 per cent may be an asset rather than a liability since the natural twist properties of the fibers may be used to advantage with the other stock used to make the cloth. Cotton is ideal, in many instances, for use in warp yarns since it will have the tendency to add increased tensile strength, a factor which is so necessary in weaving cloth in the loom.

EXTRACT WOOL: Obtained from cloths that have been carbonized or from scoured stocks. Fiber length is from ¼ inch to about 1½ inches. Comes in white or colors while the fiber has a shreddy or boardy handle. Appearance is thready and somewhat lifeless. It has the same uses as shoddy and mungo.

FLOCKS: Fibers obtained from finishing operations in woolen and worsted mills. Ranges from ⅛ inch to ¾ inch in length and may be white or colored. Handle depends on grade of cloth from which obtained and may be used in blending raw stocks and as a filler-fiber in the fulling of some overcoating fabric.

HARD WASTES: These include yarn, thread, and hard ends obtained from sources such as spinning, spooling, winding, dressing, weaving. Length depends on source from which obtained. Comes in white and colors, and the handle will vary with quality of basic stock. Appearance of hard wastes will vary with that of the original stock used.

These wastes are garnetted and then mixed-in, in varying percentages, with basic wool or worsted stocks to be used for dress goods and coatings.

MUNGO: Obtained from all kinds of felted cloths, tailor's clippings, overcoatings, etc. Felted clippings are used to considerable degree. Fiber length ranges from ¼ inch to about ¾ inch. Color, handle, appearance, and uses are similar to those for shoddy. It should be borne in mind that shoddy and mungo may be of excellent, good, fair, or poor quality, all depending on the stock from which they were obtained.

PULLED WOOL: Obtained from sheep that have been fattened for their carcasses; "slaughterhouse sheep." Fiber length is the same as that for live or clipped fiber, from 1 inch to about 6 inches with some fiber 12 inches or more in staple. Color is that of grease wool before scouring, at which time the fiber becomes white. Handle is rather lifeless, boardy, harsh, flat. Appearance is dull.

Used with clipped wool fiber in varying percentages in woolen and worsted fabrics. Pulled wool is a valuable asset in the industry since virgin wool cannot meet the requirements for cloth yardage demanded by the public.

SHODDY: Obtained from all kinds of unfelted cloths, tailor's clippings, discarded clothes of many types, etc. Fiber length is from ½ inch to about 1 inch. Comes in varying colors dependent on the cloth run through the shoddy picker or garnetting machine. The handle will vary from rough or coarse to smooth or good depending on

original quality. Appearance depends on original stock. Used in dress goods, overcoating, suiting, etc. May be used as a "filler-in" fiber to reduce fabric cost. Shoddy is used in varying percentages based upon fabric price.

SOFT WASTES: These come from the carding, combing, gilling, and drawing departments of the mill. Sliver, slubbing, top, and roving furnish the wastes which may be white or colored. Staple length, handle, and appearance will be the same as those of the original source.

These wastes have much call in woolens and are used to some degree in worsteds because of the good to excellent quality of fiber. They are reworked from the initial operations in the mill and are run through the regulation blending, oiling, mixing, and subsequent treatments.

WASTE SILK. The short, unreeled filaments that are left before and after the long cocoon filaments have been removed. This waste silk noil stock is carded, often combed, and then spun into yarn.

WASTY WOOL. Includes a number of things that cause this type of wool— kemps, frowsiness, weakness, irregular staple, too heavy grease content; sand, dirt, shives, motes, etc.

WATA, KI-WATA, OR MENKWA. Japanese terms for raw cotton.

WATA-NO-KI. The name of the Japanese cotton plant or bush.

WATCHER. Embroidery machine operative whose duty it is to look after his machine in all details from lubricating it through removal of the goods from the frame. Entails considerable walking while the machine is in operation. He has to look for broken threads, check on all shuttles, note all defects, check on the motif being embroidered, and mark all defects for the mender to care for after removal of the goods from the frame.

WATER. A chemical composition, formula is H_2O. In washing practice the water used is contaminated with impurities, either natural or the by-products of softening.

WATER AND SOIL RESISTANT COTTONS. Special treatments given cottons to repel water and soil from penetrating them. Often referred to as "cottons that breathe." Water and soil "roll right off the fabric."

WATERCOLOR. A painting technique in which water is mixed with the raw pigment instead of with oil. Usually a light wash application will give the desired effect. Hand painted textiles are often colored in this manner. See Pigment.

WATER CONSUMPTION. It implies the water consumed after saturat-

ing a load with water, i.e., the amount of water running out of a machine on draining.

WATERGLASS. A substance containing sodium silicate or potassium silicate, or both, soluble in hot water and used in silk weighting, waterproofing, as an adulterant in soap and in dressing cotton warps.

WATER HARDNESS. 1. Permanent hardness is in water which contains mineral matter such as chlorides or sulphates that is not precipitated by boiling. The hardness, in this case, would be calcium and magnesium, respectively. The water can be softened only by the use of chemicals such as washing soda or borax.

2. Temporary hardness is caused by the presence of bicarbonates of calcium or magnesium. They may be removed by boiling which converts the salts into insoluble carbonates.

WATER IMBIBITION. The percentage weight of water retained after wetting and centrifuging a sample at 1,000 grams for five minutes (based on the bone dry weight of the fabric used).

WATER-LAID. A heavy rope, three strands each with three plies, used for hawsers.

WATER LEVEL. The height of the water inside a cylinder when a machine is loaded and in motion.

WATERMARKING. See MOIRÉ, WATERMARKING.

WATER OR WATERMARKED TABBY. Originally taffeta was made on the tabby weave, the plain weave of today. Tabby and taffeta were synonymous as to meaning several centuries ago. Specifically, the expression implies a silk taffeta with a moire or watermarked finish. Other fibers are now used to make the fabric and effect, such as acetate, nylon, "Dacron," etc.

WATER-PACKED COTTON. That which has been penetrated by water prior to bailing; classed as damaged cotton.

WATER-PRESSURE VAPOR. The component atmospheric pressure exerted by the pressure of water vapor.

WATERPROOF PLASTIC WOVEN FABRIC. Saran or other filament fabric used in upholstery which is given special waterproofing treatment.

WATERPROOFING. There are various methods of coating a fabric so that it is waterproof. Rubber, oil, or lacquer compounds are often used. The use for which a fabric is intended determines whether it should be waterproofed, water-repellent-processed or otherwise treated. Waterproofing closes the pores of the fabric. Water-repellent finishes do not close the pores of the cloth against air; hence they are more comfortable to wear because the body can "breathe" through them.

WATER-REPELLENCY. Ability of a fabric to resist penetration by water, under certain conditions. Various types of tests are used and these are conducted on the samples before and after subjection to standard washing and dry-cleaning tests. Immersion, spray, spot, and hydrostatic methods may be used. Shower-resistant, rain-resistant, and waterproof factors are interpreted from the results of the testing.

WATER RESISTANCE, TEXTILES. The determination of the resistance of textile fabrics to: 1. Surface wetting. 2. Internal wetting (absorption). 3. Penetration by water. (ASTM.)

Water-resistant implies fabric which may repel water for a limited time. Paraffin or wax methods are often used to make material water-resistant. The aluminum stearate method is also used to provide this property in some fabrics.

WATER-RETTED FLAX. Russian flax prepared by retting the plants in water. The color ranges from creamy-white to gray. Flax retted in this manner gives the best wear.

WATER RETTING. See FLAX PROCESSING.

WATER SOFTENER AND CONDITIONER. There are two types. 1. The nonprecipitating type uses a chemical which bonds or locks the minerals in hard water to prevent them from reacting with soap to form lime soap film. 2. The precipitating type uses a chemical which combines with hardness minerals into insoluble particles, a soap curd.

WATER SOFTENER, MECHANICAL. A device attached to the water system to remove hardness minerals, calcium and magnesium, which are exchanged for sodium which will not form a curd with the soap. A special unit is used to remove the ionized iron. A curd, for example, is when soap will combine with hardness salts such as calcium and magnesium in hard water.

WATER SPOT RESISTANT. Applied to fabrics that resist spotting because of their being treated with a water-repellent finish.

WATER TEMPERATURES. Standard water temperatures for home laundering follow: Cold, 75° F. or less; Cool, about 80° F; Warm, about 100° F; Medium Hot, about 120° F., and Hot figured on the temperature delivered by the faucet at 140° F. or higher.

Factors which may affect the temperature include the pressure of the water supply, temperature of the metal in the machine, and the temperature of the laundry itself, etc.

WATER TWIST. See ARKWRIGHT, SIR RICHARD; SPINNING FRAME, THE RISE OF THE.

WATERWORK. Fabric painted with color or comparable media to be used for hangings or curtains. Originally made to simulate tapestry.

WATT. The unit of power, the power of one ampere of current at an electrical pressure of one volt.

WATT, JAMES (1726-1836). Scotsman who applied steam to drive textile machinery. In 1769 he took out his patent, the same year that Arkwright took out his for the spinning frame. In 1785, Watt applied his power by steam in Robinson's cotton mill in Nottinghamshire, England. In 1790, Arkwright was using steam in his mill. By 1800, steam was generally used in textile mills.

WATTE. German word for wadding.

WATTEAU BODICE. A bodice with low square or round neckline, short deeply ruffled sleeves, and many ribbon bows. See Bodice.

WATT SILK. The refuse and debris gathered from raising silkworms. This very irregular fiber stock has little value.

WAULKING. Originally it was the treading on cloth by women who were barefoot. The treatment was carried on in a large wooden tub. The original term probably comes from the same Saxon root as "walk." The treatment by treading caused the cloth to become "full," from which comes the present-day treatment in wet-finishing, called "fulling."

The term also implies the final finishing operation accorded some homespuns and tweeds in the British Isles. It means about the same as felting of woven fabric in this country; this is the shrinking-in of fabric to the proper width in order to make it more compact and firm.

WAVED. Undulating effect as noted, for example, in moiré taffeta.

WAVED TWILL. The use of varying degree twill weaves to form the pattern in woven fabric. The regulation twill angle is 45 degrees; steep twills may have angles of 63, 70, or 75 degrees, while reclining twills use angles of 27, 20, and 15 degrees. A combination of these weaves will produce the waved or curved twill effect in cloth. Waved twill effect is found in some bed coverings, wall hangings, curtaining, some mackinac coating, and a few decorative fabrics. The effect may be un-

dulating, wavy, or zigzag in appearance.

WAVE LENGTH. Distance—measured along the line of propagation—between two points which represent similar phases of two consecutive waves.

WAVY CLOTH. Fabric which shows thick and thin bands running in crosswise direction. Causes of wavy cloth include faulty let-off or take-up, fabric slipping on sand roll, pick wheel missing, loose beam ends, bad or tight bearings in the take-up, warp beam or whip roll out of line, bent beam gudgeons. A check-up with the take-up and the let-off motions should be made in an effort to cure the fault.

WAX CLOTH, WAXED CLOTH. 1. Fabric which has been treated with paraffin or wax. Example would be a ciré finish on taffeta. Oilcloth, floor covering, shelf covering are also in this category. 2. A material which has been made waterproof by this method. 3. The glazed finish on chintz.

WAX, COTTON. A type of varnish on the outside of cotton fiber that protects the latter from injury and excessive moisture; runs from 4 to 7 per cent in weight content.

WAXED THREAD OR SHOEMAKER'S THREAD. The strong, rather thick shoemaker's filament thread that has been highly waxed so that it can be used in the manufacture of footwear. The thread is used in sewing leather and other shoe materials which have had the holes punched in them.

WAX FINISH, LEATHER. A method of finishing the heavier weights of upper leather on the flesh side by working wax into the substance. The leather is largely exported for manufacture of shoes used by peasants and miners.

WAXING FINISH. The use of certain sizes and gums will give a characteristic glaze finish to cotton goods. The cloth is calendered, pressed, lustered, and given any other special treatment deemed necessary. Linens, automobile tire fabric, bandings, and linings are finished in this manner.

WAY WIND. The number of warps or turns that an end or ends make from one side of the wound package to the directly opposite side.

WB-4. Formerly known as *Siroset* this is a practical process used to obtain permanent creases in wool garments. The creasing is achieved through the action of moisture, a chemical agent (monoethanolamine), and heat. See WB-7.

WB-7. Perfected by the Wool Bureau, Inc., New York City, this is a process used to control the felting shrinkage of wool; treatment uses potassium permanganate in a saturated brine solution.

WEARING APPAREL. The ensemble plus certain accessories and adornments. Includes both underwear and outerwear.

WEAR-RESISTANCE. Wear is an indeterminate quality. It is the deterioration of a fabric or garment because of breaking, cutting, or the wearing out or removal of the fibers or yarns. Thus, important factors pertinent to wearing qualities include raw material used, method of construction, texture, yarn-twist, finish, and the care given the article. Abrasion testing on machines, such as the Taber Abraser and the Wyzenbeek Associates, will give a very good idea as to how much a fabric can withstand before becoming frayed and worn out.

WEAR TESTING. Testing fabrics for abrasion, flexibility, resiliency, washing, crushing, crease-retention, crease-resistance, etc. See WEAR-RESISTANCE.

WEASEL. About 175 species are in existence. They have a long cylindrical body and walk on their toes, not on the soles of their feet. Some species are well known, the mink and the ermine for example, which are ferocious and blood-thirsty animals. Larger than these two and of stouter build is the wolverine, which is found in Europe, Asia, and America. Other members with valuable fur are the marten and the sable. Still another group includes the badger. The fur industry uses nearly all the species of the weasel family in making coats, trimmings, capes, etc. The textile industry uses large amounts of their fine fibers, using names that add to glamour, with accent on luxury. The price for the fiber blends is based on the blend and the color.

WEATHER CLOTH. Canvas or tarpaulin used to combat bad weather conditions. Used on ships, baseball fields, in storm areas, etc.

WEAVE. The process of forming a fabric on a loom by interlacing the warp and filling threads with each other. The fundamental weaves are Plain, Twill, Satin. All other weaves, no matter how intricate, employ one of these basic weaves in their composition. There are many variations on the basic principles which make different types of fabric surfaces and fabric strengths. See WEAVE CONSTRUCTIONS; WEAVE PATTERNS.

WEAVE ANALYSIS. Determination of the actual weave construction in a fabric. May or may not be done with the aid of pickout glass and pickout needles. Much patience must be exerted in this type of work.

WEAVE CONSTRUCTION, COMPOSITE CHART ON:

NAME OF WEAVE	HOW RECOGNIZED	WORKING PROPERTIES
1. PLAIN, TABBY, TAFFETA:	One warp over and one warp under the filling throughout cloth construction.	Used most; durable and strong, easily seen, firmest method of interlacing warp and filling.
2. TWILL:	Diagonal lines on face of cloth—to the right, to the left, or to right and left in same cloth, which gives a broken twill.	Durable, and tailors well; firm fabric, usually holds shape and crease; very popular for outerwear apparel.
3. SATIN:	Smooth, shiny surface caused by floats of warp over the filling or vice versa. Diagonal lines on the face of the cloth not readily observed by the naked eye; only distinct when seen through a pick glass.	Rich appearance; rather low tensile strength; high texture; cannot withstand friction because of the nature of the weave; gives a full, solid color on face; ideal for evening wear; reflects the rays of light very well.
4. BASKET:	Two or more warp ends over and two or more warp ends under in parallel arrangement, interlacing with the filling yarn.	Rather loose construction; does not have high tensile strength; difficult to sew on; not suitable for general wear; attractive surface; interesting effects.
5. RIB:	Made by cords that run in the warp or filling direction. The corded yarn is covered up by the tight interlacing of the system that shows on the face and back of the cloth.	Wearing quality varies with closeness of texture and type of yarn used; ideal for hatbands, grosgrain, faille, bengaline. Cord threads easily removed, not actually woven in.
6. PIQUE:	Cloth has a corded effect, usually in the warp, but may have cord in filling or both ways. Cords usually held in place by a few ends of plain weave construction.	Gives good wear, attractive, cord is visible, since texture is not as compact as in the case of rib weaves. Popular material for summer wear. Several types available.
7. DOUBLE CLOTH OR PLY CLOTH:	Two cloths woven together and held in place by binder warp or filling; not pasted; back is usually different from face of cloth.	Heavy; warm; durable; face better than back in stock, construction, and finish; used in overcoatings and other heavy cloths.
8. BACKED CLOTH:	Cloth of one warp and two fillings or two warps and one filling. The face is much more presentable than back of cloth. Back is usually dull in appearance. No binders.	Adds weight to cloth; durable face much better than back; many cheap cloths to imitate better materials, are backed fabrics; back is thready to the touch and in appearance.
9. PILE:	Extra yarns form the pile on the face of the cloth. Pile effect may be cut or uncut on the surface. Basic constructions hold cloth in place. Warp or filling yarns may be cut.	Attractive; may be soft or harsh; pile of over one-eighth of an inch is known as a plush; cloth may press down and reveal construction, but may be restored by steaming; usually gives good wear.
10. JACQUARD CONSTRUCTION:	Pattern or design is woven into cloth reproductions of persons, places, or objects, wide range of beautiful designs; used in silks, brocades, etc. Basic weaves used.	Beautiful effects; may be very expensive; durable; small patterns with minimum of long floats give best wear; many colors may be interspersed throughout the cloth pattern.
11. LENO, DOUP:	Warp yarns are often paired and half- or full-twisted about one another; porosity high in some of the cloth de-	Gauze effects, used for curtains and draperies; launders fairly well; gives good effects in prints; tensile strength

signs; two sets of harnesses used—standard and skeleton.

12. LAPPET, SWIVEL, CLIPSPOT:

Dots or small figures are woven or embroidered into cloth by use of an extra filling in the case of swivel weave, and by extra warp in the lappet weave. Effects are based on plain weave background.

varies much depending on texture.

Similar to those of a plain weave or variations of that construction; dots are usually lasting and durable, but there are some cheap varieties of the cloth where the dots may not remain fixed.

WEAVE CONSTRUCTIONS, INFORMATION AND DATA ON BASIC. A table showing groups of weaves, the repeats in height and width, and the number of blocks required in each construction, is included here.

WEAVE:	REPEATS HIGH	REPEATS WIDE	BLOCKS
PLAIN WEAVE:			
1. $\frac{1}{1}$	4	4	8 x 8
RIGHT-HAND TWILLS:			
2. $\frac{2}{2}$	4	4	16 x 16
3. $\frac{3}{3}$	2	2	12 x 12
4. $\frac{4}{4}$	2	2	16 x 16
5. $\frac{2}{1}$	3	3	9 x 9
6. $\frac{1}{2}$	3	3	9 x 9
7. $\frac{3}{2}$	3	3	15 x 15
8. $\frac{3\ 1}{1\ 3}$ even-sided twill	2	2	16 x 16
9. $\frac{2\ 1}{1\ 2}$ even-sided twill	2	2	12 x 12
10. $\frac{4\ 1}{2\ 1}$ warp-effect twill	2	2	16 x 16
11. $\frac{1\ 1}{1\ 5}$ filling-effect twill	2	2	16 x 16
12. $\frac{3\ 1}{1\ 1}$ warp-effect twill	2	2	12 x 12
LEFT-HAND TWILLS:			
13. $\frac{2}{2}$	2	2	8 x 8
14. $\frac{2}{1}$	3	3	9 x 9
15. $\frac{1}{2}$	3	3	9 x 9
16. $\frac{3}{2}$	3	3	15 x 15
17. $\frac{2}{3}$	3	3	15 x 15
18. $\frac{2\ 1}{1\ 2}$ even-sided twill	2	2	12 x 12
19. $\frac{3\ 1}{1\ 3}$ even-sided twill	2	2	16 x 16
20. $\frac{1\ 1}{1\ 5}$ filling-effect twill	2	2	16 x 16
21. $\frac{4}{2}$ warp-effect twill	2	2	12 x 12

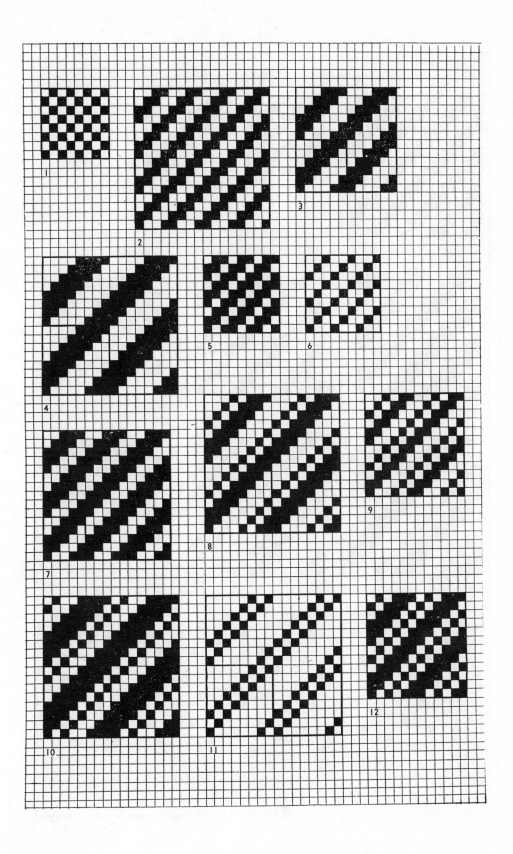

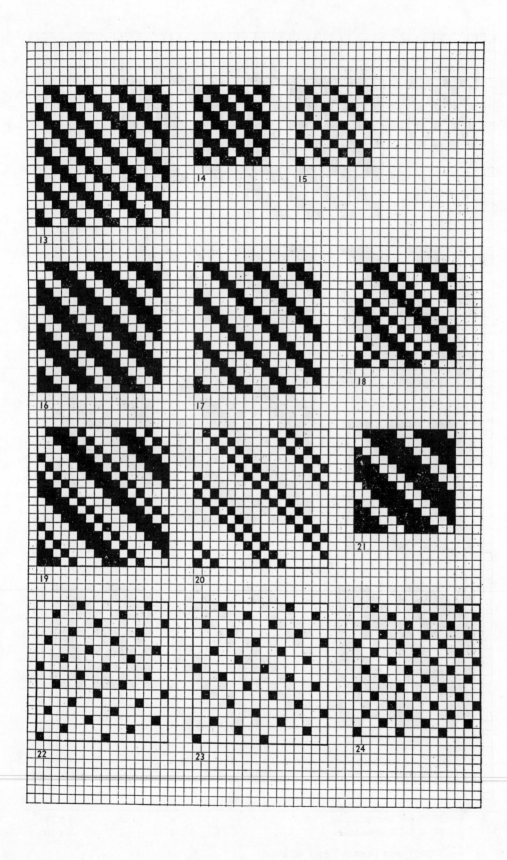

WEAVE:	REPEATS HIGH	REPEATS WIDE	BLOCKS
BROKEN TWILL WEAVES:			
SATIN WEAVES—FILLING-EFFECT:			
22. 8-end satin, base of 3	2	2	16 x 16
23. 8-end satin, base of 5	2	2	16 x 16
24. 5-end satin, base of 3	3	3	15 x 15
25. 5-end satin, base of 2	3	3	15 x 15
26. 7-end satin, base of 4	2	2	14 x 14
27. 12-end satin, base of 5	1	1	12 x 12
28. 9-end satin, base of 4	2	2	18 x 18
SATIN WEAVES—WARP-EFFECT:			
29. 8-end satin, base of 3	2	2	16 x 16
30. 8-end satin, base of 5	2	2	16 x 16
31. 5-end satin, base of 3	3	3	15 x 15
32. 5-end satin, base of 2	3	3	15 x 15
33. 12-end satin, base of 5	1	1	12 x 12
34. $\frac{2}{2}$ twill; 8 right hand, 8 left hand	4	1	16 x 16
35. $\frac{2}{2}$ twill; 4 right hand, 4 left hand	4	2	16 x 16
36. $\frac{2}{2}$ twill; 2 right hand, 2 left hand	4	4	16 x 16
37. $\frac{1}{5}$ twill; 3 right hand, 3 left hand	2	2	12 x 12
BASKET WEAVES:			
38. 2-2	2	2	8 x 8
39. 3-3	2	2	12 x 12
40. 1-2	3	3	9 x 9
41. 4-4	2	2	16 x 16
42. 2-4	2	2	12 x 12
43. 2-2-2-4 even series	1	1	10 x 10
44. 1-2-3-4 even-series	2	2	20 x 20
45. 4-1-4 uneven-series	1	1	18 x 18
POINTED TWILL WEAVES:			
46. $\frac{2}{2}$ twill, 8 right hand, 8 left hand	4	1	16 x 16
47. Fancy-spot weave made on principle of pointed twill weaves	2	2	16 x 16
WARP RIB WEAVES—RIB RUNS IN FILLING DIRECTION:			
48. 2-2 repeats on two warp ends	4	4	16 x 8
49. 3-3	2	4	12 x 8
50. 4-4	2	4	16 x 8
51. 2-4	2	4	12 x 8
52. 1-3	3	4	12 x 8
53. 1-2-1-4 even series	2	4	16 x 8
54. 3-1-3 uneven series	2	4	28 x 8
FILLING RIB WEAVES—RIB RUNS IN WARP DIRECTION:			
55. 2-2 repeats on two filling picks	4	4	8 x 16
56. 3-3	4	2	8 x 12
57. 4-4	4	2	8 x 16
58. 2-4	4	2	8 x 12
59. 3-1-3 uneven series	4	2	8 x 28
60. 2-2-2-4 even series	4	2	8 x 20
SIXTY-THREE DEGREE TWILL WEAVES:			
61. $\frac{7}{8}$ go up two picks on each successive warp end	1	1	15 x 15

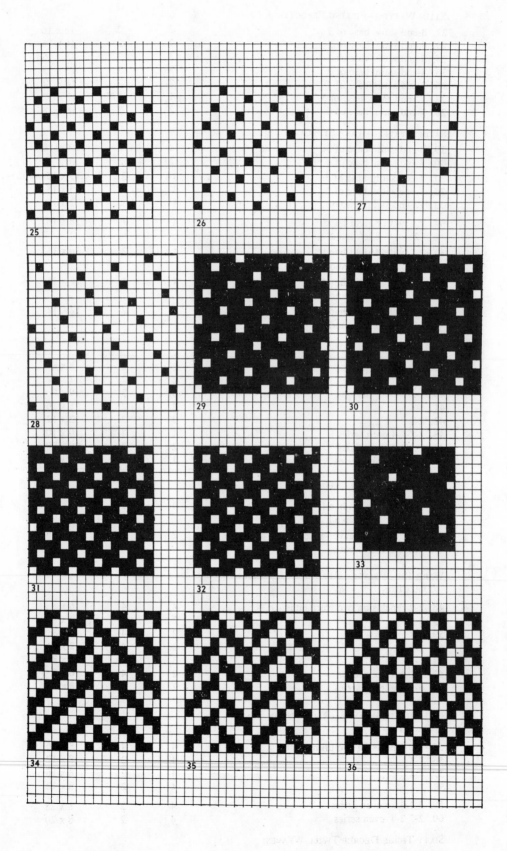

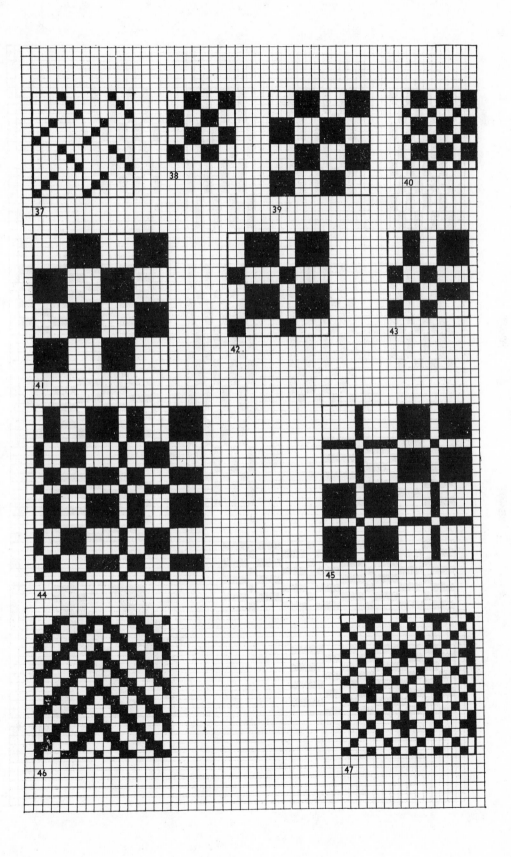

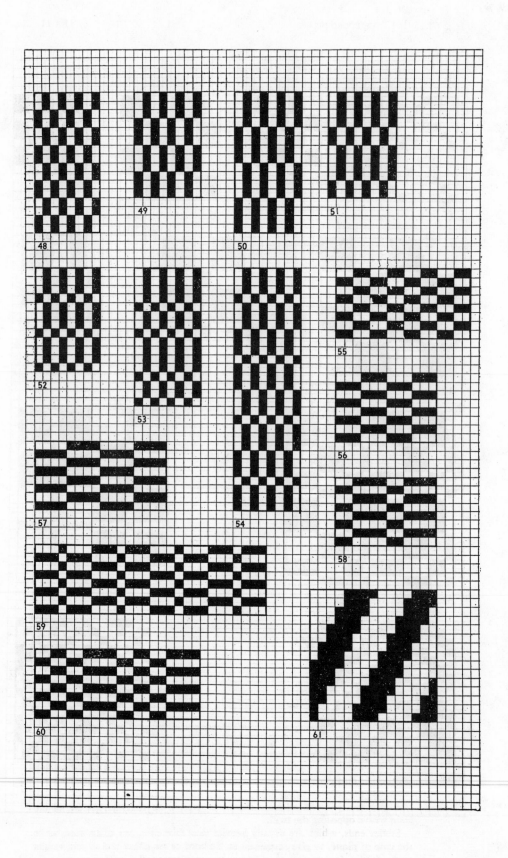

62. $\frac{3}{2}$ COVERT WEAVE   3   3   15 x 15

63. $\frac{3\ 3\ 1\ 1}{1\ 1\ 2\ 1}$ TRICOTINE WEAVE   1   1   13 x 13

64. $\frac{5\ 1\ 1}{1\ 2\ 1}$ WHIPCORD WEAVE   1   1   11 x 11

65. $\frac{4\ 1\ 4\ 1}{1\ 1\ 2\ 2}$ CAVALRY TWILL or ELASTIQUE WEAVE;   1   1   16 x 8
18–19 oz. cloth

> NOTE: Weave begins with a sinker in lower left-hand corner.

SEVENTY-DEGREE TWILL WEAVE:

66. $\frac{7\ 2\ 6\ 2}{1\ 1\ 3\ 2}$ CAVALRY TWILL or ELASTIQUE;   1   1   24 x 8
24 oz. cloth:

> NOTE: Weave begins with a sinker in lower left-hand corner. Go up three picks for each successive warp end.

SIXTY-THREE DEGREE TWILL WEAVE:

67. $\frac{3\ 3\ 1}{1\ 1\ 3}$ CAVALRY TWILL but NOT USED FOR ELASTIQUE;   1   1   12 x 6

> NOTE: Weave begins with a sinker in lower left-hand corner. Go up two picks on each successive warp end.

68. $\frac{2\ 3\ 1\ 1}{1\ 3\ 1\ 2}$ CAVALRY TWILL but NOT USED FOR ELASTIQUE;   1   1   14 x 7

> NOTE: Weave begins with a sinker in lower left-hand corner. Go up two picks on each successive warp end.

SEVENTY-DEGREE TWILL WEAVE:

69. $\frac{8}{7}$ go up three picks on each successive warp end.   1   3   15 x 15

SEVENTY-FIVE DEGREE TWILL WEAVE:

70. $\frac{8}{7}$ go up four picks on each successive warp end.   1   1   15 x 15

FANCY SPOT WEAVE:

71. Novelty spot effect weave made on combination of $\frac{3}{1}$ and $\frac{1}{3}$ twill weaves.   1   1   8 x 8

PIQUE—BEDFORD CORD WEAVES:

72. This weave begins at the left with one end of plain weave followed by the first and second movements of a 3-up and 1-down twill, repeated. Two ends of plain weave, indicated by the dots, are next in order followed by the third and fourth movements of the twill effect, repeated.

WEAVE:

One end of plain weave completes the action. In this weave, attention is called to the alternate binding of plain weave opposing the twill.

Weave is 2 x 2 in size and requires 8 x 12 in blocks.

73. This formation is easier to weave when compared with the previous construction and it also gives better appearance to the fabric. This weave begins at the left with one plain end followed by the first and third movements of the 3-up and 1-down twill, repeated; two ends of plain weave are followed by the second and fourth movements of the twill, repeated; finally, one end of plain weave completes the construction.

As previously stated, attention should be given to the alternate binding of the plain weave opposing the twill.

Stuffer ends, which are usually heavier than face ends, are often used, as in the case of piqué, to give roundness to the cord or rib effect and to add weight to the fabric. In weaving, they follow to some extent, the twill movements in the respective wales; they must be "down" for all face picks, and "up" over all back picks when being woven.

Weave is 2 x 2 in size and requires 8 x 12 in blocks.

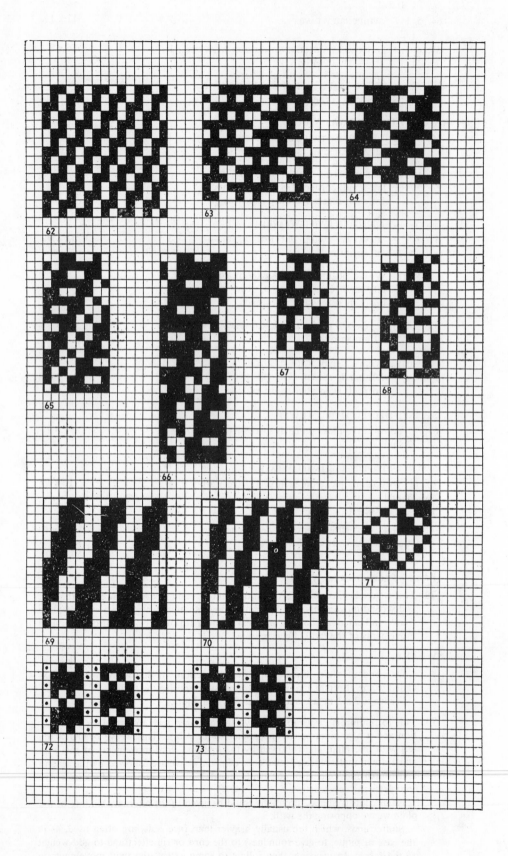

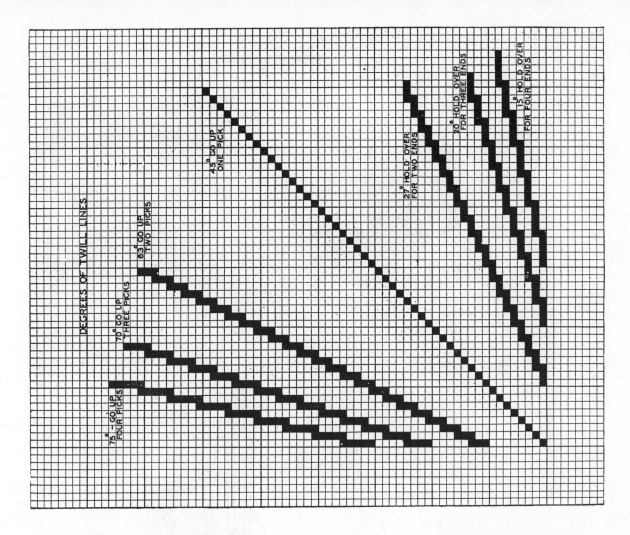

DEGREES OF TWILL LINES

75° - GO UP FOUR PICKS

70° GO UP THREE PICKS

63° GO UP TWO PICKS

45° GO UP ONE PICK

27° HOLD OVER FOR TWO ENDS

20° HOLD OVER FOR THREE ENDS

15° HOLD OVER FOR FOUR ENDS

INTERLACING ARRANGEMENT OF PLAIN, TWILL, AND SATIN WEAVES (Black lines—Warp; Shaded lines—Filling):

PLAIN WEAVE   TWILL WEAVE   SATIN WEAVE

$\dfrac{1}{1}$ plain weave

4 repeats high,
4 repeats wide.

$\dfrac{2}{2}$ right hand twill

2 repeats high,
2 repeats wide.

8 end, shaft or harness satin weave, base or counter of 3; filling float of 7.

1 repeat high,
1 repeat wide.

Cross-Section of Plain, Twill, and Satin Weaves:

The warp, shown by the wavy lines, interlaces over and under the filling picks which are shown by the black dots.

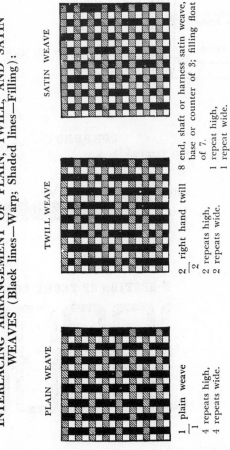

Float of 1.

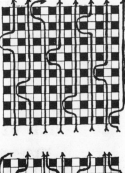

Float of 2.

Float of 7.

SKETCH OF A HAND LOOM

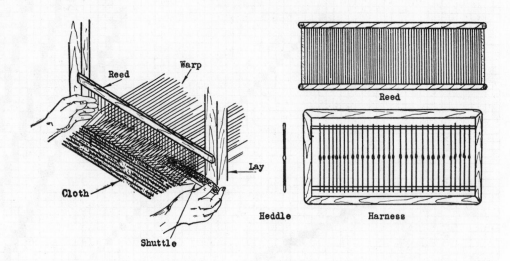

Reed

Warp

Lay

Cloth

Shuttle

Heddle

Harness

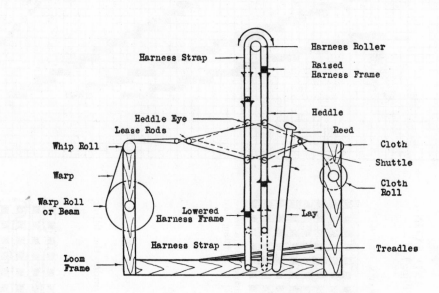

Harness Strap

Harness Roller

Raised Harness Frame

Heddle Eye
Lease Rods

Heddle

Reed

Whip Roll

Cloth

Shuttle

Warp

Cloth Roll

Warp Roll or Beam

Lowered Harness Frame

Lay

Harness Strap

Treadles

Loom Frame

PILE WEAVING

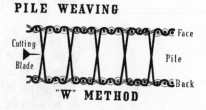

Cutting Blade

Face

Pile

Back

"W" METHOD

CORDUROY

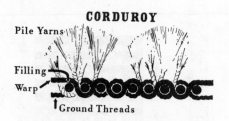

Pile Yarns

Filling
Warp

Ground Threads

Cutting Blade

Face

Pile

Back

"V" METHOD

X-SECTION OF TERRY LOOPS

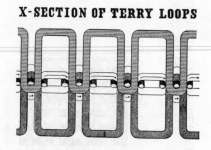

VELVET

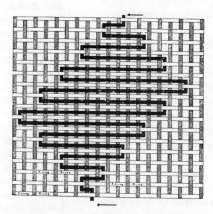

BOTH SIDES, SAME TIME

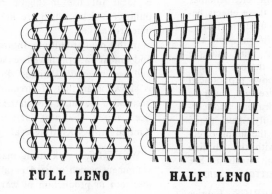

FULL LENO   **HALF LENO**

LAPPET — EXTRA WARP

WEAVE-ROOM SECOND HAND. One who carries out the orders of the weaving overseer; assigns the workers to jobs, keeps time records, and determines the causes of poor work. He checks records of the mechanical equipment, inspects for safety conditions in the weave shed, and is responsible for the changes in loom pattern work, changing warps, and replacing old ones. The second hand is the liaison man for overseer and employees in the department; must understand all jobs in the weaving room, must be a good loom fixer, must understand perching, and, above all, be able to get along with people.

WEAVE SHED EFFICIENCY. Ratio of "actual output" versus "possible output" in terms of percentage. Actual time period for efficiency testing should be stated.

WEAVER'S BEAM. The warp beam on a loom.

WEAVER'S KNOT. Much resorted to in tying knitting yarns. The knot is small and evenly distributed around the yarn. It will not slip nor untie. This knot may be omitted when threading a machine for the setting-up of new work. See illustration.

WEAVING. The interlacing at right angles of two systems of threads known as warp and filling. The former runs lengthwise and may go over or under the latter, which runs crosswise.

In designing woven fabrics, the manner of interlacing may be varied to produce different effects. These effects are called weaves and may be represented on special squared designing paper by allowing the vertical lines to represent the warp and the horizontal lines to represent the filling threads. The actual weave is an arrangement of painted and unpainted blocks. The painted block is called a raiser or up-thread, and indicates that the warp thread is above the filling at the point of interlacing. The unpainted block is called a sinker or down-thread, and indicates that warp thread is beneath the filling thread.

WEAVING OVER, WEAVING UNDER. These two blemishes are caused by an irregular timing of the box motion on the loom and are readily seen in plaids, checks, overplaids, multicolored warp and filling cloths. The result of these flaws is that the cloth is given a distorted appearance which does not appeal to the eye.

WEAVING SLACK. Caused by uneven tension weight on the warp beam. A sleazy appearance is noted in the material when this blemish occurs. Weavers should check constantly to prevent slack weaving since it is one of the most difficult faults to remove.

WEB. The finished woven fabric is sometimes known by this term in hand-weaving circles. Also signifies the structural part of cloth as distinguished from the pattern effect in it.

WEB, CROSS-LAID OR CROSS-LAPPED. A sheet of nonwoven material made from several webs, or by alternately folding the same web on itself so that the fibers of the various layers are set angularly to the fibers of other layers used to construct the product.

WEB, ONE-DIRECTION OR PARALLEL ORIENTED. A thin layer or sheet of nonwoven fibers that lay in a parallel formation; comparable with the web of fibers delivered by a carding machine used to card and straighten certain textile fibers such as cotton. See Web, Oriented.

WEB, ORIENTED. Used in the manufacture of nonwoven fabrics, it is an unbonded fibrous sheet wherein the fibers are set in some definite order; the opposite of random web stocks.

WEB, WEBBING. A strong cotton fabric which runs from less than 1 inch in width to 6 inches or more. Strong, stout plied yarn is used to give service, durability, and quality where needed. The more important yarns used include 7/6s, 8/3s, 10/3s, 20/3s, 23/9s and 23/11s. The number of ply in the yarn and the tensile strength are important factors in webbing. It may be white, dyed in olive, dark, or khaki shades, and much of it is treated chemically for various purposes.

Uses include shoulder straps, brake lining, fan belts, automobile tire fabric, harnesses, officer's belt webbing, trunk webbing, suspenders, carpet webbing, surcingles. Webbing is one of the most important of textiles when one pauses to think of its varied uses.

WEBBING, ELASTIC. Strong narrow fabric in which rubber yarns form a part of the warp arrangement.

WEBLON. This product of Fiberglas, Inc., features a specially woven and finished open-weave construction of fiberglas fabric, and a series of specially engineered vinyl formulations. It has a higher tensile strength and greater tear resistance when compared with other currently used coated materials.

WEBLOYS. A family of composite nonwoven fabrics manufactured by The Kendall Company Fiber Products Division of The Kendall Company, Inc., Boston, Massachusetts. These fabrics show "strength-for-weight" equal to or surpassing many woven cloths. Fabrics in the group can be made with tensile strength of fifty pounds per inch at a "gossamer" three ounces or less. The group of materials result from an alloying of webs and films. The fabric shows a high uniformity in web formation, strength and thickness, and it can be made conformable, glueable, printable, and dewable. Some are heat sealable unto themselves and, in some instances, heat sealable to other fabrics. Bases used include polypropylene, vinyls of various types, and open polyethylene. Uses include electrical insulation, battery separators, pressure-sensitive tape and label backing, packaging, as a laminating fabric with plastics, and garments, as a tufting base, filer material, and for desiccant bags.

WEDDING RING VELVET. See CHIFFON VELVET.

WEDGWOOD, WEDGEWOOD PRINT. A printed motif on fabric to simulate the renowned ware which bears the name of the originator, Josiah Wedgwood, 1730–1795. The typical shades of blue are a light grayish-blue, and a dark reddish-blue. The earthenwares, carefully tinted, show detailed, classical figures in cameo relief applied in white paste.

WEFT. Allied with the British term, woof. In this country there is much discussion of these two terms and they seem to be considered as more or less interchangeable. Both of them here may mean threads that run in the filling direction. One may imply a warp series of ends, while the other would specify the opposite system of yarns or threads. The terms are often resorted to in the advertising of textiles since they seem to give an English "quirk" which may attract the reader's attention. Other names for weft are pick and "pick-and-shot." In the carpet trade and in hand weaving, in this country, the term weft is used instead of filling in most instances and is accepted in lieu of the American term. See WOOF.

WEFT, WEFT-WAY TWIST. British term for S-twist.

WEFT CORDS. The word weft in Great Britain and on the Continent implies filling yarn in the United States, the crosswise yarn in woven fabrics. There is a group of fabrics that shows fine cylindrical cords or ribs in the filling or weft direction—luana, fuji, poplin, repp, broadcloth, etc. Another group of fabrics show these effects because of bulky filling used in them—grosgrain, bengaline, ribbon, some taffeta and some faille. A third example for this term would be the use of warp rib weaves which show pronounced cords in the filling direction, such as Ottoman, and some drapery and curtain fabrics. Incidentally, true piqué has the rib or cord in the filling direction but it is used with the rib line running in the warp direction. See BENGALINE, TAFFETA, OTTOMAN, PIQUE.

WEFT-FACED FABRICS. Fabrics which show more filling or weft yarn on the face of a material because of the weave construction, such as a filling-effect satin, sateen, or twill weave. Obviously, on these plain, single fabrics there would be more warp yarn on the back of the goods. Some fabrics that show this effect include beaverteen, moleskin, imperial, swansdown, etc. The term is used in Great Britain and on the Continent; in the United States fabrics of this type are called filling-faced fabrics.

WEFTING. See PICKING.

WEFT KNIT. Describes fabric produced by a method of knitting in a crosswise direction, as distinguished from warp knitting.

WEFT KNITTING. Filling or weft knitting that is done with a single yarn, the thread being carried from side to side and around a circle.

WEFT KNITTING, JERSEY STITCH IN CIRCULAR. This circular machine gives the highest production in weft knitting; used for underwear, seamless hosiery, piece goods and comparable high production goods. There is a limit in designing fabrics for this method knitting. See Weft Knitting, Jersey Stitch in Flat, et al.

WEFT KNITTING, JERSEY STITCH IN FLAT. The jersey stitch is the foundation structure in all knitting; loops are formed in only one direction and each side of the material is different in appearance. Incidentally, the name Jersey is in honor of Lily Langtry, the famed singer from the Isle of Jersey in the English Channel, whose halcyon days were around the turn of the century when she was the toast of the singing world.

Gauges on the machine range from 9 with 16 needles to the inch, to the 21 gauge with 14 needles to the inch. The lower gauge machines are ideal in knitting bulky sweaters with higher gauges beign used for lighter weight goods. The plain jersey stitch, full fashioning frame is ideal for use in high stretch-type pullover articles which are high in volume production.

In this plan of knitting, Intarsia motifs and similar patterns have been developed and are in goodly demand. Production is slower than that of circular knitting because of the single feed in the machine. See Jersey Fabrics, Jersey Stitch, Knitted Fabrics, Knitting, et al.

WEFT/LOC. A knitting machine development which utilized parallel filling insertion in production of warp-knitted fabrics. The machine is a joint development of Crompton & Knowles Corporation, Charlotte, North Carolina, and Liba Maschinenfabrik, GmbH, Naila/ Bayern, West Germany.

This specially designed machine for two-bar warp knitting will make standard as well as special warp-knit fabric. The fabric comes with full width parallel filling insertion, either in each course, or in non-consecutive courses; widths come in 70 inches and 140 inches, in gauges ranging from 18 needles per inch to 28 needles per inch. The machine is used in producing sheeting, print cloth, lightweight apparel fabrics, and industrial fabrics.

WEFT YARN. In the carpet trade, cotton, jute, or kraftcord yarn running crosswise of the fabric as binding and filling. It is inserted through the chain and over and under stuffer warp yarns with a shuttle in the wire weaves and with a needle thrust in Axminster.

WEIGHT, COMMERCIAL. See CONDITIONED WEIGHT; CONDITIONING.

WEIGHT DIFFERENCES BETWEEN BRITISH AND DOMESTIC WOOLENS. British imported fabrics are based on a 58-inch finished width to a 37-inch yard with one quarter of a yard "thrown in" in every ten yards for "good measure." This, incidentally, really gives a 38-inch yard.

The 58-inch by 38-inch yard gives 2,204 square inches to the piece yard against the domestic yard of 56 inches by 36 inches of 2,016 square inches in the yard. Thus, an 18-ounce British weight would be the equivalent of a 16½-ounce domestic:

$$\frac{18 \times 2016}{2204} \text{ equals } 16.5,$$

the approximate weight of the domestic fabric in ounces per yard.

Briefly, it may be stated that the American cloth is approximately $11\!/\!12$ths the weight of a comparable British woolen fabric.

WEIGHTED SILK. Sometimes metallic salts are used in the dyeing and finishing of silk to increase the weight and draping quality—and thus to make it look more expensive. Over-weighting causes deterioration of the fabric.

WEIGHTING SUBSTANCES. A group of textile ingredients used to size yarn or fabric to increase their weight or to act as a filling agent to cloth. These substances differ from sizes or starches in that they are not essential in the weaving of fabric; before any finishing treatment such as bleaching, dyeing,

or printing, it is usually necessary to remove adhesive sizes or starches which have been used to give the yarn firmness, smoothness, and strength as it is woven into a fabric.

Popular weighting agents include China clay, zinc chloride, French chalk, talc, calcium chloride, magnesium chloride, barium sulphate, calcium sulphate, magnesium sulphate, and Glauber's salt or sodium sulphate.

WEIGHT OF CLOTH. There are three ways by which fabric is sold.

1. Ounces per yard: a 15-ounce covert, a 24-ounce Worumbo coating.

2. Yards to the pound: a 3.60 airplane cloth, a 4.00 filling sateen.

3. Ounces per square yard: a 3.75 acetate satin, a 6.00 nylon organdy.

WEIGHT, OVEN-DRY. See CONDITIONED WEIGHT, CONDITIONING.

WELD. An erect Old World annual,

Reseda luteola, formerly cultivated for dyer's use. Also known as yellowroot, the pigment served for centuries as a dyestuff. The coloring matter is distributed throughout the entire plant with the exception of the roots. Thus, the necessity of pulling the whole plant from the ground.

WELLINGTON, THE DUKE OF. Following his victory over Napoleon at Waterloo in June, 1815, the cessation of the War with France, and with Napoleon's death in 1821, Wellington introduced the wearing of trousers and boots or shoes, as known today. This did away with the wearing of breeches and silk hose popular to that time on the Continent and in the Isles. See Balaclava, Cardigan, Raglan, Kepi.

WELLON. A Nylon 66, registered trademark held by Nichols & Company, Inc., Johnsonville, South Carolina, and

WEFT KNITTED FABRICS, BASIC CHARACTERISTICS OF.

	JERSEY OR PLAIN	1 x 1 RIB	1 x 1 PURL
MACHINE:	1 set of needles	2 sets of needles	1 set of needles
	1 needle bed	2 needle beds	2 needle beds
	Needle Bed:	Needle Bed:	Needle bed:
	Straight or Circular	Straight or Circular	Straight or Circular
		Offset Needle Tricks	Directly Opposite Tricks
FABRIC:	Plain	Plain and Rib	Plain, Rib, Purl
CONSTRUCTION:	All stitches are going in the same direction. Distinct face and back.	All stitches in one wale are in same direction and adjacent wale can go in the opposite direction.	All stitches in one course are in the same direction and alternate courses are different.
RAVEL:	Either end	Top down	Either edge
DROPSTITCH:	Up or down	Down	Up or down
ELASTICITY:	Good $\longleftrightarrow$	Best $\longleftrightarrow$	Best
CURL:	Toward back—Selvedge Front—Top and Bottom	None	None
APPEARANCE:	Face Back The technical face, the knitside of the stitch, can be represented by an "X." The back is identified by an "O."	Either side may be used as the face of the goods. X O X O / X O X O / X O X O / X O X O	Either side may be used as the face of the goods. O O O O / X X X X / O O O O / X X X X

Boston, Massachusetts. The polyamide is melted and then extruded in several filaments from the same spinnerette, then stretched, crimped, and cut to desired staple length.

It is ideal for spinning on the cotton, wool, and worsted systems of making yarn and may be used alone or in blends. Its chief uses are in carpets, cordage, and nonwoven fabrics.

WELSH FLANNEL. Originally a hand-woven, variable texture, lightweight flannel of good quality made from wool of the well-known Welsh Mountain sheep. Other fabric of this name appears from time to time. It is made from woolen or cotton warp.

WELSH MARGETSON. A very fine wool tweed which weighs only 3½ ounces per yard; printed in classic designs for use in cravats.

WELSH MOUNTAIN SHEEP. Raised in the mountainous area in Wales, this active breed gives a coarse wool of about 32s and a fiber of about 6-inch staple. Since the breed tends to shed its wool before warm weather sets in it is necessary to shear the two-pound fleece as soon as weather permits.

WELT. 1. A strip of material seamed to a pocket opening as a finishing as well as a strengthening device.

2. A raised or swelled lap or seam.

3. A covered cord or ornamental strip sewed on a border or along a seam.

4. In knitting, it is a flap knitted separately and then joined to the fabric by looping or hand knitting, as the heel to the stocking.

5. A ribbed piece of knit goods used in forming the end of a sleeve or sock to prevent rolling or raveling.

6. A piece fastened onto the edge of a seam in glovemaking.

7. In shoemaking, a strip of leather set into the seam between the edges of the upper and outer sole, through which they are sewed together.

8. The hem or garter top in hosiery.

WELT, ENGLISH OR ROLL. A type of welt on rib trims made by knitting on dial needles for only one revolution of the machine.

WELT, FRENCH OR TUBULAR. The favored type of welt for rib trims; made by the knitting cylinder and dial needles alternately at alternate feeds on the knitting frame. The English-type welt produces loops of unequal length while the French welt shows loops of the same length.

WELT, INTURNED. A welt which consists of a double fold of plain fabric made on a circular knitting frame. Sinker loops from one of first few courses are kept while the welt fabric is knitted and are enmeshed later with alternate needle loops of a subsequent course.

WELT EDGE. A finish for the brims of men's felt hats. A welt may be formed by folding over the edge of the brim and stitching edge to the brim; or, in less expensive hats, chiefly wool felts, a narrow edging of the felt may be applied to the top edge of the brim and stitched. A felted welt edge is a molded brim edge which is formed or shaped during the hatmaking process and is not stitched. This is a distinguishing mark of a fine hat, as it is not possible to make this edge by machine.

WELTING. A sewed, ribbed, quilted, or otherwise thickened edging; a welt; also, material for welts.

WELTING CORD. A narrow felt braid which is made with a cord on the one edge. See WELTING.

WELTING LEATHER. This is a curried leather made soft but tough. It is used in welt shoes as the uniting material between the shoe upper, sole, and insole.

WELT POCKET. A built-in pocket with the opening finished-off in a welt formation, from 3/8 inch to as much as 1½ inch width.

WELT POINT. A small steel hook, which is inserted in the welt bar of the knitting machine, for grasping the first loops of the fabrics to draw it from the needles.

WELT POSITION. The position in the knitting cycle where the needle remains inoperative and does not advance to receive new yarn in its hook. This position is known as the miss or non-knitting position.

WELT STITCH IN KNITTING. It is produced when the needle is in the miss or nonknitting position where it does not receive the fed yarn, and the held loop is cast-off subsequently when in its correct position.

WELT TURNING. This is done in full-fashioned knitting by means of welting points which have hooks and grooves arranged side by side in a welt bar. The hooks are inserted between the needles in the first course to take the sinker loops which are then held until a length of fabric has been knitted. The welting points are then placed against the needles so that the heads of the latter are embedded in the grooves of the points and the sinker loops are put back on the needles.

WELT YARN. A knitting yarn used to form the cuff or welt at the top of hosiery; usually given from 10 to 15 turns of S-twist per inch.

WENSLEYDALE SHEEP. Related to another luster type of sheep, Leicester, this large sheep yields a lustrous, rather curly fleece that has good spinning qualities for woolen yarn. It is a Class Three sheep, and the wool is used chiefly in homespun, tweed, cheviot, and shetland fabrics; it does have some call for lower qualities of fabrics in the serge family. See WOOL CLASSIFICATIONS, WORLD.

WESCO ELECTRIC STOP MOTIONS. These are used for quality controls in the knitting industry and they come in several forms as the yarn end breaks or drops off; the press-off, hole, knot and end detectors; and retractable needle-protectors. Primarily made and mounted on knitting machines, but may be applied to sewing machines. Product of Stop Motion Devices Corporation.

WESTERN COTTON AREA. Embraces Southern California, Arizona, and New Mexico, the newest cotton-raising area in this country, fast coming to the fore and noted for its fine staple. Irrigation methods are employed in the area, which produces various types of American-Egyptian strains and Uplands.

WESTERN WOOL. See TERRITORY WOOL.

WEST OF ENGLAND. Renowned throughout the world for their high standard of quality and finish, West of England fabrics are distinctly associated with this area in England, which centers in and around Stroud and Trowbridge. Incidentally, West Riding fabrics of England came chiefly from the Yorkshire area. Much West of England fabric has the characteristic windowpane design which adds to its popularity in the outergarment trade for men's and women's apparel.

WET AND DRY FIBER TENSILE STRENGTH. The strength of a textile yarn, and following that, the fabric is based mainly on the tensile strength of the fibers that have been used to make up the particular yarn. This is especially true of materials made of filaments, and it is also true of materials made from staple fiber stock. Other factors have to be considered such as the fineness of the yarn, staple strength, the amount of twist applied, etc., but the fiber strength is still the basis for strength requirements in the end-use article.

It is not easy to measure the tensile strength of single fibers. Considering the tiny dimensions of the fibers, it can readily be seen that the testing apparatus must be of delicate construction. To evaluate single fiber strength, the testing machines used fall into five classes:

1. Hydraulic Type
2. Balance Type
3. Pendulum Type
4. Spring Type
5. Chainomatic Type

The type of machine to select for a test depends upon the length and the kind of fiber to be tested.

WETCLEANING. A process similar to hand laundering performed professionally by a drycleaner using water, soap, or a synthetic detergent, and in some instances, other additives if deemed necessary.

The article to be cleaned is laid on a table, brushed gently with detergent solution and then rinsed in cool water. At other times, such as with glass-fiber fabrics, the item is immersed in water not above 105° F., with a neutral soap or detergent, and allowed to soak for a period of time, followed by rinses in cool water.

To stabilize colors, common salt or mild-acid treatments, such as acetic acid or fomic acid, may be added to the water. The article is then dried by air or the drying may be accelerated by passing a strong flow of hot air through the garment on a special device known as a wind-whip at a temperature of about 120° F.

WET-FINISHING. Signifies the wet operations, chemical in nature, that may be given to cloth so as to make it, in time, presentable to the consumer. Some of the operations are washing, dyeing, soaping, fulling, milling, scouring, mercerizing, souring.

WET-FINISHING OF ANIMAL FIBER CLOTHS. The processes or operations that may be given to a bolt, cut, or length of cloth by running it through the various and sundry wet-finishing operations in the mill. Some of the operations are dyeing, bleaching, washing, fulling, milling, scouring, soaping, souring, crabbing, tentering, sponging, decating or decatizing, London shrinking, waterproofing, etc.

Not all of these operations are resorted to in finishing each cut. They are optional and are given when necessary, in accordance with the finishing instructions.

WET-OUT. To dampen before placing yarn or fabric into dye liquor.

WET SPINNING. 1. Rayon yarn is made by forcing the viscose solution through a spinneret and into a coagulating or reverting bath, acidic in nature. See Illustrated Section. 2. The spinning of some bast fibers by passing the roving through a hot water bath before reaching the drawing rollers. The action softens the gummy matter and permits the fibers to slip past one another in the action. Linen line fibers are always wet-spun; tow fibers cannot be spun this way.

WET SPREADER AND EXTRACTOR. A wet finishing unit which spreads and then extracts water and moisture from fabrics, woven or knitted.

WET-SPUN YARN. Bast fibers that have been spun on the wet-spinning method.

WETHER. 1. English meaning is wool other than the first or virgin clip.
2. A castrated male sheep, the ram. A female sheep is called a ewe, pronounced like the letter "U."

WETHER WOOL. Any wool from sheep after the initial or first shearing.

WETTABILITY TESTING. Comparative test for the effectiveness of various wetting agents on textiles.

WETTING AGENT. A surface active chemical whose function is to reduce the contact angle between a liquid and a solid. It is used to speed up intimate contact between textile fibers and aqueous baths.

WETTING OUT. An alkali boil or treatment with sulphonated oil will affect cotton yarn or fabric so that it will be able to absorb water more readily.

WET TWISTING. Passing yarns prior to twisting through a water bath to produce a cleaner and smoother end-product.

WHEAT FLOUR. Made from grain, this powdered-starch sizing ingredient is soft and warm to the touch, has excellent adhesive properties, and requires considerable boiling to bring about granule separation. The product is white to cream in color and runs to about a 15 per cent moisture content.

WHEAT STARCH. A popular sizing ingredient for fabrics which is a pure white starch made from wheat flour by the removal of gluten and other impurities.

WHEELER, NATHAN. He brought out a sewing machine in Troy, New York, in 1851 for use in the collar trade. He was one of the first to introduce what is known today as "mass production" and "uniform sizes." He also worked with the men who, in time, established the Cluett, Peabody Company.

WHEEL STITCH. Like a spider's web, this stitch is worked on the fabric and not over an open area in the material.

WHEELING YARN. A coarse type of knitting yarn used by hand knitters prior to the use of knitting machines.

It is still used in many sections of the world today. These ply yarns are not sold by number or count. Made of woolen or worsted fibers, the stock is thoroughly mixed after the manner of making a carded thread on a spinning wheel.

WHIP. The extra warp which forms the figures in lappet weaving. It interweaves with the fabric only at the end of each run or spot.

WHIPCORD. Dress woolen or worsted of fine and high texture. The twilled yarn is sharply defined with some fancy suggestions to whiplashes or cords. There are several cloths, some major and some minor, in this group —coverts, tricotines, Poirets, twill cords, chicotines, piquetines. The yarn in a whipcord is bulkier than the yarn of the tricotine or gabardine. The cloth is lower in texture and heavier in weight than these two materials. Weight ranges from 12 to 20 ounces per yard. Whipcord finds use in livery cloth, topcoats, uniform cloth, suitings, and in public utility materials. The cloth may be made of cotton warp and worsted filling and steep twill weaves are used in construction. The fabric is exceedingly durable, rugged, and stands hard usage and wear. Shines in time with wear.

Rayon whipcord is much used in riding habit, sportswear, uniform cloth. Cotton whipcord is used for automobile seat covers, boys' playsuits, caps, riding breeches, uniforms.

Whipcord is made from a 63-degree twill weave and is always a compact, rugged, good-wearing material. One weave used is a $\dfrac{5\ 1\ 1}{1\ 2\ 1}$, 63-degree twill.

See Illustrated Section (Fabrics 29).

WHIP LEATHER. It is usually made from heavy calfskin and is alumtanned.

WHIP NET. Term for an effect obtained in leno or doup weaving in which rather large diameter yarn, which is low in yarn count, is used. These ends are spaced at some little distance from each other and a full-leno or a half-leno construction may be used to advantage. See LENO, DOUP, DOUPE.

WHIPPED-IN BAND. When the sweatband of a hat is joined to the body by an overstitching or whipstitch. This construction may be found in hats of lower quality, whereas the reeded sweatband is used in medium to best quality headgear. See REEDED SWEAT BAND.

WHIPPING. The form of overcasting or overstitching done by slanting stitching. It holds the edges together and takes the stitches over the edges with the needle in a slanting position.

WHIPROLL. See LOOM, MAJOR PARTS OF A.

WHIP THREAD. A warp yarn capable of winding around another warp thread in order to add strength to the fabric; an important thread in leno or doup weaving, and lappet weaving. Whip threads are placed on an additional warp beam in the weaving process since their tension and take-up is different from the ground warp ends.

WHITE. Although white is popularly regarded as a distinct color, and for all practical purposes it is, yet, technically it is not a color but is a combination of all colors. The sensation of color is produced by the difference in length of light waves. We see the longer waves as red, waves a little shorter are orange, and so on. The shortest visible light waves appear to the eye as violet. A red object is one that absorbs all the light waves except the red ones which are reflected back to the eye and produce the color we identify as red. An orange-colored object is one that absorbs all the light waves except the orange ones, which are reflected back to the eye and produce the color we call orange. White consists of light waves of all wave lengths mixed together, and a pure white object is one that reflects all, or nearly all, light waves. Although black is popularly regarded as a distinct color, and like white for all practical purposes it is, yet technically it is not a color, but is the absence of color. A black object is one that absorbs all, or nearly all, light waves.

The seven colors of the spectrum, red, orange, yellow, green, blue, indigo, and violet, were formerly called primary colors, but today that term is often applied to red, green, and violet, from which trio all colors can be produced. An artist is likely to regard red, yellow, and blue as primary colors. More than one million colors, hues, and shades can be distinguished with a spectroscope. With normal vision, an ordinary person can distinguish about one hundred and fifty, while a trained eye can distinguish more than one hundred thousand colors although unabridged English dictionaries list only about three thousand, with only four hundred words of explanation for colors, hues, and shades.

WHITE, STANDARD. The pure white material used in measuring the degree of whiteness of fabrics. See BARYTA.

WHITE-BACK DENIM. Indigo-blue dyed warp and unbleached cotton filling are features of this material.

WHITE-BACK DUCK. The usual denim of indigo-blue-dyed warp and unbleached filling.

WHITE CORDAGE. Cordage, rope, etc., that has not been tar-treated.

WHITE DOZENS. British term for several types of the more common bleached cotton cloths.

WHITE DYEING. Tinting bleached goods with blueing to overcome the possible yellowish tinge that might occur if not tinted; a bright, clear white results.

WHITE GOODS. A very broad term which implies any goods bleached and finished in the white condition. Some of the cotton white goods are muslin, cambric, dimity, lawn, longcloth, organdy, voile, and so on. Tub or washable silks are sometimes classed as white goods, as well as some of the lightweight crepe or sheer woolen or worsted dress goods materials.

WHITE MOUNTAIN SWISS. The white fleece of this breed of sheep has a staple of about two inches; chiefly used as mutton sheep.

WHITENESS REFLECTENCY. The degree of whiteness of a fabric as determined by a photometer.

WHITENING AGENT. See BRIGHTENER.

WHITENING AGENT, OPTICAL. A tinting substance which may or may not be substantive, which has the property of chiefly blue fluorescence and gives the effect of an enhanced whiteness .

WHITE OAKUM. See OAKUM.

WHITE ROPE. Cordage that has not been tarred for use on ships.

WHITES. Short term for white cocoons.

WHITE SOUR ON COTTON. Cloth, after being washed well in water, is run through an acid which destroys completely any bleaching powder that might remain in the goods, and also completes the bleaching action. Hydrochloric acid or sulphuric acid is used to sour cloth.

WHITE SOURING. An operation in the bleaching of cotton cloth in which the fabric is immersed in a sulphuric acid solution to neutralize the action of chlorinated-lime bleaching solution. The cloth is threaded and drawn in a rope form through a machine consisting of a series of guide rollers and a vat or pit for containing solution.

WHITE TIE. Prior to the death of Queen Victoria of Great Britain in 1837, the white tie was the accepted neckwear in male's formal evening wear. Following her death, the white tie seemed to lose some of its popularity and black was the predominant shade worn except in full formal evening wear where the white tie still holds sway. Black is the color of the tie used with "tuxedo raiment" worn by males.

WHITE WASH. The second of two consecutive washing processes in which excess chemicals, such as sulphuric acid, are removed from cloth after white souring. This leaves the material entirely bleached.

WHITING. British term for bleaching.

WHITNEY. Overcoating fabric of the better type. The finishing of the fabrics consists of about two hours' fulling, followed by scouring and carbonizing in the usual manner. Nap on the fabric is raised on the double napper with about five runs; some makers, however, prefer the wet-teasel gig method.

The fabric is then sheared to a smooth stand-up pile which is ideal in manipulation. The special napping device for the final finish is an arrangement in which the cloth, after passing through card clothing rollers, goes through two surfaces—the upper surface is made of rubber, the lower one of plush. The surfaces, by an oscillating motion, produce the characteristic nubs, ripples, and waves. The operation takes about one hour per piece of goods.

WHITNEY, ELI. The inventor of the cotton gin was a native of Westboro, Mass. Born 1763, died 1825. His models were made on Mulberry Grove Plantation, near Savannah, Georgia, where he was serving as tutor for the children of Mrs. Greene, the widow of Mr. Nathanael Greene, second in command to General Washington at the close of the American Revolution.

It took only ten days for Whitney to complete his first model. Within three months he had perfected a practicable working cotton gin, that could gin in one day what would take weeks to do by hand.

Whitney filed his application of patent rights with the Secretary of State, Thomas Jefferson, on June 20, 1793. The patent was issued to him on March 14, 1794.

One of the greatest inventions of all time, its principles are still used today in practically all phases. Eli Whitney created, undoubtedly, the wealth and the power of nearly every Southern state. He created "Southern wealth and Northern profit," as depicted in the famous book of Hinton Rowan Helper, *The Impending Crisis*. He lived and died, however, in a state of poverty because his models, machines, and rights were usurped on many occasions. The building in which he housed his gin was broken into, and the gin taken away. It was at once copied, and in use in various places before he could obtain his patent. He bore the injustice of men, and the ingratitude of his country, with cheerful serenity, and died assured at least of a deathless fame, with his name enrolled high upon the list of the world's greatest inventors. See Illustrated Section.

WHITNEY LONG. Whitney-finished overcoating fabric in which the undulating effect runs vertically in the fabric.

WHITTAKER, EDWARD. He was the inventor of imitation pillow lace. His machine had half of the threads drawn through from a warp beam while the other half were wound on bobbins mounted on a carriage. This was in 1804, six years after the work done by Lindley on the lace bobbin.

WHITTLE. Old-time British term for coarse, heavy wool fabrics used for blankets and shawls; several fabrics come under this caption.

WHIZZER. A specialized extractor used to remove water from felt hat bodies by whirling them in a metal basket.

WHOLE BACK. 1. A coat in which the back is of one piece. 2. The back part of a frock coat cut in one piece; it has no center seam and is not stubbed or cut across in any way.

WHORL. The spindle on a ring-spinning frame revolves because the whorl serves as a pulley for the spindle banding or tape.

WICKING. Woven on narrow fabric looms, this product is used for lamp wicks in kerosene and oil lamps.

The term also means that quality of a yarn or fabric which enables it to draw moisture away from the body, affording more comfort to the wearer. Textured yarns and fabrics have this property to greater degree than non-textured materials since the former have more air pockets or spaces between the fibers.

WICKING PROPERTY. The ability of a material to disperse or spread liquid or moisture throughout a given area in either or both directions; actually, the capillary action and ability of the sample being tested. See CAPILLARITY.

WIDENING. An operation in full-fashioned knitting of moving the wale loops outward to the selvage. In the English system of widening it is the covering of the needle hole at the last fashioning wale by "robbing" or taking a full loop from the next needle in the

preceding course. In the Nonrun method, the hole at the last fashioning wale is covered by a loop taken from the same rather than the preceding knitting course.

WIDE NUMBER DUCK. That which is more than 24 inches wide; ranges are from 26 to 144 inches. Numbers run from 1 to 12, and the higher the number, the harder the texture.

WIDE SHEETING. Bed sheeting that is from 72 to 108 inches in length and width.

WIDESPREAD COLLAR. Shirt collar wherein the points have a wide spread at the front.

WIDE WALE CLOTH. Comes from the Anglo-Saxon term "walu," meaning to mark or flail with stripes as with a rod. The weave is indicated by wide twilled or straight edges or ridges on face of the fabric. It is the opposite of narrow wale. Cloth under this caption is coarse, boardy material of the serge, Cheviot, and clay worsted variety. Some mackinac cloth is made with wide wales, which give a serpentine effect to the cloth.

WIDE WALES. Materials made by the various degree twill weaves—15, 20, 27, 45, 63, 70, and 75 degrees. To make these effective in cloth from twelve to twenty-four harnesses have to be used in the loom. The material has a diagonal appearance on its face. Wales are distinct in windbreakers, mackinac cloth, tablecloths of the fancy type, and novelty fabrics.

WIDOW'S SILK. Any of a number of fabrics made from silk used for purposes of mourning. This fabric is now made from several man-made fibers, as well.

WIDTH. The horizontal measurement on a piece of goods—the breadth, crosswise measurement or filling direction. Textile fabrics are divided into widths, in spans of nine inches. Thus, a 3/4 goods would be 27 inches wide; a 6/4 goods, 54 inches wide.

"WIERA." First cultivated in Holland in 1950, it is a cultivated flax which bears white flowers. It stands up very well against hail, rain, and wind, and gives a high yield in the scutched condition, higher than any other flax fiber.

WIGAN. A cotton cloth that is firm, starched, plain-calender finished, and devoid of luster. Usually dyed black, gray, or brown and converted from lightweight sheeting or print cloth. Used chiefly as interlining for men's and boys' clothing to give body and substance to the garments. Named for village of this name in England.

WIGGINGS. To prevent blindness in certain types of sheep the wool has to

be shorn from the area of face and eyes by operations called wiggings; must be done with care.

WILD SHEEP. Undomesticated sheep as typified by Argali, Bighorn, Mouflon, etc.

WILD SILK. Silk furnished by the larvae of wild silkworms; another name for Tussah silk.

WILDCAT STRIKE. A work stoppage by a group of employees that is unauthorized by the union, or has not been voted by the membership.

WILLESDEN PROCESS. A waterproofing method used in England to treat heavy duty fabrics, such as canvas, duck, tarpaulin, etc. The material is chemically impregnated, calendered, and then dried; a shiny surface features these tough fabrics.

WILLIAMS UNIT. Invented by S. H. Williams of the General Dyestuff Corporation, New York City, this is an extremely versatile and economical machine in carrying out many operations in textile processing. It is used widely for dyeing, washing, pretreating and aftertreating with the many continuous processes in the textile industry.

Other advantages of the Unit include insulation to prevent loss of heat, minimum of maintenance because of the simple mechanical construction, and compactness in size. Light and dark shades are produced easily by a continuous process treatment. There is control and governing of even circulation of solutions at all times wherein the cloth is kept under solution at all times, thereby preventing preoxidation, etc. Each unit is equipped with microstat rolls. The machine is installed to specifications using 5- or 10-ton pressures, and it comes in widths of 40, 50, 60, and 70 inches.

WILLOW. The machine used to open and clean wool, particularly if it is very dirty, matted, or clumpy. It consists of feed rollers, feed table, main cylinder and a series of toothed rollers which mesh with the cylinder and carry the wool around the machine for a half-revolution. Much foreign matter is taken out by the rugged action of the rollers or workers and the cylinder on the wool fibers. Also called willying.

WILLOW CALF. Calf skin leather which is given a typical willow grain or a box grain motif or pattern.

WILLOW GRAIN. See BOARDED LEATHERS.

WILT. A fungus which attacks vegetable life. In cotton, for example, wilt stunts the growth of the plant and causes the leaves to turn yellow and then shed. The plant will usually gradually die. Wilt-resistants are used to combat the pest.

WILTON CARPET. Originated in Wilton, England, and is a variety of Brussels carpet which now ranks second to chenille in quality and price.

It is woven in the same manner as Brussels; it is possible to cause some of the yarn to become "buried" in the back in order to add resiliency and quality. Wilton differs from Brussels in the fact that when the cut pile of the former is made, flat wires are used; Brussels is cut by using round wires. The knife edge cuts the loops to make the pile in both instances.

Wilton is made on a Jacquard loom, and in a 27-inch carpet there would be about 2000 ends, which gives a high, compact texture. Brussels and Wilton caused the rapid decline of Axminsters in the latter quarter of the eighteenth century. The elaborate and at times rather beautiful designs are used in rugs, carpets, stair coverings, and runners. See Illustrated Section.

WILTON LOOM JACQUARD. The pattern control on a Wilton loom. A chain of perforated cardboards which are stamped according to the design, when brought into position, activate this mechanism, causing it to select the desired color to form the design on the pile surface. The unselected colors are woven dormant through the body of the fabric.

WILTSHIRE HORNED SHEEP. Also known as Western, this is the name of a very old English breed of sheep that has dwindled considerably down through the years since other breeds have become more popular. The fleece is light in weight, and the animal has the tendency to shed its wool as soon as warm weather sets in.

WIMPLE. A cloth wrapped in folds around the neck, close under the chin and over the head, exposing only the face. The wimple is worn by nuns.

WINCEY, WINSEY. British fabric of cotton warp and wool filling that is piece dyed, and given slightly napped finish. Also known as Winceyette.

WINCH. Any machine that treats fabric in endless belt or in rope form. Used in washing, scouring, fulling, milling, dyeing, etc., the general principle of the machine is an open vat for the liquor, and rollers that will move the cloth along in the bath. Most of the material will be in the bath with the exception of a small yardage folded at the bottom in layers, or at some other place in a slack or tensionless state.

WINCH-DYEING. Piece-dyeing done in a slack condition, without tension, in a winch, vat, or kier.

WINCING. From the Middle English, wince, winch, meaning to shrink or to separate by abrasion, a blow, from friction, etc. In finishing textiles, it is an operation where a cut, length, or bolt of pile fabric, such as observed in certain women's wear pile coating and velveteen, is immersed in a hot water solution in a loose rope form. The loose twist of the limp form, along with bloating of the yarns, cause loose, straggly fibers to fall out of the goods on drying. The operation may be repeated any number of times depending on local conditions. Do not confuse the term with wrinsing or rinsing. See Winch, Winch-dyeing.

WINDBAR. A windproof, water-repellent cotton fabric designed for active sportswear, children's snowsuits, raincoats, and ski clothes. Product of Wellington Sears Company. Trade name.

WINDBREAKER CLOTH. Name given to men's and women's sports jackets or reefers made of poplin, tackle twill, and similar materials which have been given repellent finishes. See MACKINAC.

WINDCORD. A cotton lacing or mesh placed about narrow rubber tubing and used for weather strippings, especially around the edges of automobile doors.

WINDER. Any machine used to wind a bobbin of yarn or a cone, spindle, cheese, etc.

WINDER'S WASTE. In silk it is the waste obtained in winding raw silk on bobbins. Used to make spun yarn. The term also implies waste from the winding operation in the processing of any yarn.

WINDING. Similar to quilling, it is the process of winding filling on bobbins for introduction into a shuttle. Winding is the term particularly used in the cotton and spun-rayon fields.

WINDING FRAME. Any of a group of machines that transfer yarn from cones, spools, or bobbins onto other cones, spools, or bobbins.

WINDING MACHINE. A power-driven apparatus used to wind fabric around a flat board. The device consists of a pair of metal bars to which the board is secured, mounted to a metal frame so that the board is free to rotate.

WINDOW CLOTH. See HOLLAND, SHADE CLOTH.

WINDOW HOLLAND. Another name for shade cloth.

WIND RATIO. The number of wraps that an end or ends make from one side of a wound package of yarn back to the same side.

WINDSOR. A novelty cloth made in the British Isles in which varicolored tufts are woven into a plain ground. The effect may be obtained by weaving the goods on a swivel loom or a lappet loom, among other methods. See SWIVEL WEAVING, LAPPET WEAVING.

WINDSOR, DUKE OF. Men's wear received great acclaim and notoriety in the summer of 1922 when the late British Duke of Windsor, then the Prince of Wales, visited the United States. The Prince came down the gangplank of the ship attired in suede shoes and a tobacco brown shirt with a lighter shade brown cravat. His felt hat was turned up in the front and down in the back; thus, these styles became the rage here. He also introduced the blue shirt with harmonizing blue tie. All these have had waves of popularity since their introduction and the Duke was truly, at the time, the first real fashion plate in men's apparel. See Plus Fours.

WINDSOR DUCK. A very lightweight duck or crash linen fabric that is printed for use as dress goods in the British Isles.

WINDSOR LOUISINE. A high-quality printed cotton dress fabric used in Great Britain; has ease of care and laundering.

WINDSOR TIE. The old-time necktie made in a double bowknot with long flares extending downward.

WIND-UP ROLL. The roller on large circular knitting machines that winds up the tubular fabric as it is knitted.

WING COLOR. Regulation "short-type" shirt collar worn with semi-formal or formal wear.

WINTER DAMAGE. A type of fabric damage which occurs in laundered cottons which are dried out of doors in winter in localities such as New England's highly industrialized areas. Discoloration, streaks, and possible fading may affect the fabrics. Sometimes the materials will take on a yellowish tinge. The chief cause for this damage seems to be the concentration of fumes of sulphur dioxide derived from the burning of high-sulphur coal in the industrial cities and towns. See SULPHUR DIOXIDE.

WINTERHALTER. An old-time name for costumes with off-the-shoulder effect for exposure of the neck, and at times, the bosom. The corseted waistlines and crinoline skirts with flounces were also popular. This term is in honor of a well-known painter of the clothed female figure, 1800-1873.

"WINTUK." A name used to describe combinations of bi-component and acid-dyeable fibers of "Orlon" acrylic fiber,

E. I. duPont de Nemours & Company, Inc., Wilmington, Delaware. The term is applicable to bi-component types 21, 24, or 27 blended at a 50 percent or higher level with types 44 or 28. The code suffixes to "Wintuk" identify the types of fibers in each yarn blend. The final digits from the number of the bi-component are followed by the final digit of the acid-dyeable type; thus, a combination of "Orlon" type 21 and type 44 is known as "Wintuk" 14; and type 24 blended with type 28 is identified as "Wintuk" 48.

WIPING CLOTH, INDUSTRIAL. Any of a group of absorbent fabrics that are cut to standard size or sizes and generally used to clean machines and parts of machines. Overedging or hemming is applied to prevent raveling.

WIRE BANK. Merely a row of dropwires set up on the warp yarn in the loom.

WIRE FABRIC. 1. A fine mesh wire fabric used chiefly for filtering purposes; may be used according to angle made in weaving the fabric, or on the bias. 2. A somewhat heavier wire mesh fabric which finds use in screening, Pullman screening, house screening, and in the heavy types for wire fencing, ranch fencing, etc. Various metals are used and some of the articles may be galvanized, made rustproof, or painted.

WIRE GRASS. Various swamp grasses found in the United States find use in carpeting, throw rugs, summer floor-covering, druggets, etc. Several of the articles use a strong, plied cotton warp to make weaving easier and to support the grass filling.

WIRE GROUND. Brussels lace is sometimes enhanced in motif by the use of a raised silk or nylon net groundwork.

WIRE-INSERTED YARN. Applicable to asbestos yarn where wire such as brass, copper, aluminum, etc., is used to form the core of the yarn.

WIRE ROPE. Flexible rope and some cabling made solely or partly of wire.

WIRES. A long metal strip used to form the pile of Wilton, tapestry, and velvet carpets. In Axminster and chenille, the pile is inserted without the use of wires, and is referred to as rows.

WIRE VELVET. This cloth employs a series of rods or wires to obtain the pile effect. The wires are located under the pile warp and when they are withdrawn cause the face of the goods to have regular rows of loops across it. The rod, provided one end has a sharp blade on it, will cut these loops and give the cloth a cut-pile effect. See CUT VELVET.

WIRY WOOL. That wool which seems to be practically devoid of serrations. Working properties of the poorest when compared with almost any other type of wool. Much used as a "filler-in" fiber in low-grade children's coating and floor coverings .

WISCONSIN HEMP. Hemp from Wisconsin; dew-retted, broken, and scutched by machine.

WIST STITCH. Cord stitch.

WITCH. An old English term for a dobby head motion on a loom. May also mean the shedding motion of a loom.

WITCHCRAFT RAYON. Fine rayon lace with a semistiff finish.

WITNEY UNION BLANKET. A British term which signifies that the article is not all wool.

WITNEY, WITNEY BLANKET. Popular all-wool blankets made in Witney England; term applied only to blankets made there.

WITZCHOURA. Introduced in the early nineteenth century, this mantle with large sleeves and very wide collar is of Polish origin, the word meaning wolfskin. In reality, it is a pelissé or long coat that opens down the front. A fur lining was a feature of the garment. The pelissé, when "frogged" and furred, became a witzchoura.

WOAD. An Old World herb, *Isatis tinctoria,* of the mustard family, or the blue dyestuff obtained from its leaves; dyer's weed or woad. Used chiefly to dye woolens.

WOLLE. The German word for wool; "baumwolle" is the word for cotton (tree wool or bush wool).

WOMEN'S WEAR SUITING, TEXTILES IN A COAT.

1. Body lining	6. Collar canvas
2. Sleeve lining	7. Hymo
3. Pocket stays	8. Piping
4. Tape	9. Hangers
5. Pads	10. Label

SKIRT.

1. Belting	3. Lining
2. Seam binding	4. Zipper
	5. Buttons

Hooks and eyes, and clasps, may be classed as outmoded.

WOOD FIBER. Applied to laces made of man-made fibers; pulp or cotton linters form the base of these fibers.

WOOD PULP. In loose or in sheet form, this purified wood cellulose is used to make acetate and rayon.

WOODPULP YARNS. A general term covering "ersatz yarns" brought out in Germany in both World Wars.

The yarns are made of woodpulp base, and the narrow paper strips are twisted into a yarn formation so that they may be woven in a loom. Impregnation with various stiffeners is the usual finishing-off of the yarn. Uses include household textiles, some items of apparel, and weaving summer floorcoverings in the inexpensive group.

WOOF. Comes from the Anglo-Saxon "owef." It is another name for warp or warp yarn but sometimes, chiefly in advertising textiles, the word has been used to imply filling yarn and made to interchange with the other term, weft. It is apparently much safer to use the terms, warp and filling, in this country; in the carpet trade and in hand weaving, however, weft is used instead of the American term, filling.

WOOL. 1. Strictly speaking, the fibers that grow on the sheep fleece. The Wool Products Labeling Act of 1939, however, decreed that wool "means the fiber from the fleece of the sheep or lamb, or the hair of the Angora or Cashmere goat (and may include the so-called specialty fibers from the hair of the camel, alpaca, llama, and vicuna) which has never been reclaimed from any woven or felted wool product."

This law also defines the following:

REPROCESSED WOOL: The resulting fiber when wool has been woven or felted into a wool product which, without ever having been utilized in any way by the ultimate consumer, subsequently has been made into the fibrous state.

REUSED WOOL: The resulting fiber when wool or reprocessed wool has been spun, woven, knitted, or felted into a wool product which after having been used in any way by the ultimate consumer, subsequently has been made into the fibrous state.

WOOL PRODUCT: Any product, or any portion of a product, which contains, purports to contain, or in any way is represented as containing wool, reprocessed wool, or reused wool.

Wool from sheep will readily felt, a highly desirable property. The fiber is made of overlapping scales or serrations which vary with the several breeds of sheep and the grades of wool; there are from 600 to about 3,000 to the inch. The structure of the fiber is comparable with the scales on a fish or an asparagus tip. Wool is warm, springy, elastic; it may be either harsh or soft.

There are five general types used in some classifications—Fine wools, Medium wools, Crossbred wools, Luster wools, Carpet wools. On the four-point method of classifying wool the table lists Combing, Carding, Clothing, Carpet wools.

2. There are several types and varieties of wool used, and they are classified according to fineness, color, staple length, etc. Some few of these types include:

ALPACA WOOL: Fine long-staple wooly hair of the alpaca, a South American goatlike animal.

ANGORA WOOL: Long, soft, hair-like wool from the Angora goat, native to Anatolia, the homeland of the Turks; now raised extensively in Texas with Kerrville as the center. Used in combination with wool, mohair, and mixture fabrics.

BOTANY WOOL: Very fine merino wool from Botany Bay area in Australia. Used only in the finest of woolen and worsted fabrics.

CASHMERE WOOL: Very fine, soft wool found underneath the outer or harsh hair on goats raised chiefly in the Himalaya Mountain area.

CARDING WOOL: Wool of irregular length and not of the quality that can withstand the combing operation in processing. Carded woolen yarn may be classed as a conglomerate mass of fibers when compared with a combed worsted yarn.

COMBING WOOL: Wool fibers with a staple length from 1½ inches up to 6 inches. Combed stock is known as worsted in which the fibers are of the same staple length, such as a 3-inch, 4½-inch staple, etc. Worsted top is used as the base for making worsted yarn .

KEMPY WOOL: Harsh, irregular, rough wool used chiefly in carpets. Sick or diseased sheep will often produce a type of wool that is known as kempy.

LAMB'S WOOL: Elastic, soft, resilient wool fibers obtained from lambs when they are seven to eight months old—the first or virgin clipping from the animal. This lofty stock is used in better grades of fabrics.

MERINO WOOL: The highest, finest and best quality wool fiber obtained from sheep and used in better-grade materials. Merino originated in Spain two thousand years ago and was developed under the aegis of Columella, the animal-husbandry expert in the time of Julius Caesar. Several types of Merino are raised in some wool centers throughout the world—Ohio, Rambouillet, Saxony, Silesia, Spanish, Italian, South African, etc.

SHETLAND WOOL: Rugged wool, ideal for Cheviots, Shetland, homespuns and tweeds, raised chiefly in Scotland and the adjacent islands. Cheviot wool is comparable with Shetland wool.

TOP WOOL: Worsted slubbing or sliver wound in a top form which resembles a cheese in size. Noil has been removed from these fibers in combing, and top stock contains fibers of the same staple length throughout. Used in making worsted yarn and fabric.

VIRGIN WOOL: "Any wool that has never before been woven, knitted, felted, or otherwise processed into cloth or fabric, nor used for any other purpose."

WOOL, BLEACHING OF. Wool fiber, yarn or cloth is usually bleached in the damp condition by the action of O_2 gas or a bath of sulphurous acid —H_2SO_3. For the most part, these baths are not stable or permanent and much care must be used to obtain an even bleach. In time, the material will become yellowish in cast. In the mill, soap washing will readily show the thoroughness of the bleaching.

Woolen fabrics which have white in them will very often show the effect of poor bleaching since they will, as time goes on, begin to show the yellowish tinge.

WOOL, BLENDING, OILING, AND MIXING OF. Three operations which may be considered as one. Blending consists of taking various grades, colors, and types of stock and substitutes, and causing them to lie correctly and uniformly in their proper places in the blend. They are placed in an oblong pile, layer upon layer. After each layer has been laid, it is given a spraying of oil. The oiling is done by means of an automatic spray which causes the oiled fibers to respond better in the mechanical operations which are to follow. The oil-spray tank is usually located at the top of a side wall of the blending room. The spray is capable of reaching all portions of the layers as they are set dcwn.

In the blend, the individual colors and characteristics of the various stocks used may be distinguished, whether of wool, shoddy, cotton, mungo, extract wool, pulled wool, soft wastes, hard wastes, or whatever the colors may be. It is only after blending and oiling have taken place that mixing begins. When this occurs the stocks lose their individuality, and the grades are no longer distinguishable. Mixing may be compared with making a cake, in that the ingredients used are thoroughly mixed and individually indistinguishable.

The process of mixing consists of actually tearing down the blend from top to bottom and from side to side. The tearing down is done evenly. All of the varied stocks that were included in the blend are passed through to the mixing picker and presented to the feeding-in table of that machine. The

mixing room usually adjoins the blending room or is an integral part of it.

The mix should fall onto the floor; and there should be no wall, posts, or encumbrances to cause the stock to fall unevenly and impeded. If the stock does not fall free and unimpeded, the cast, color, or shade in the finished spun yarn will not be even and true.

In mixing, the stocks are treated by a main roller and by a series of smaller rollers. They come in contact with all the rollers, and are mixed as nearly perfect as the mechanism can make it. The stock passes through a series of iron spur teeth. Thus it is assured that the mixing will be total. On coming from the mixing picker it is then ready for carding.

WOOL, CHEMICAL COMPOSITION OF. This will vary slightly with the several grades of wool, depending upon the locality, soil, and climatic conditions. The average percentages of wool approximately are: carbon, 50 per cent; oxygen, 22 per cent; nitrogen, 18 per cent; hydrogen, 7 per cent; sulphur, 2 per cent, and slight traces of calcium, phosphorus, and iron. The structure and composition somewhat resembles that of the hair on the head of a human being.

WOOL, CHLORINATION OF. A dilute solution of calcium or sodium hypochlorite causes the wool fibers either to lose their scales or fuse with the cortical region. Thus, shrinkage is decreased, luster or affinity for dyes increased, with its strength impaired.

WOOL, COTTON. Raw cotton is sometimes known by this name.

WOOL, DOMESTIC. As applied to American wool, it means fleeces raised east of the Mississippi-Missouri River. Other names for it are: fleece, Eastern and farm.

When applied to wools of the world the term signifies all wool grown here as against wool from any other part of the world.

WOOL, FELTING PROPERTIES OF. The properties possessed by most woolens result in the "cementing together" of the protruding fibers in the cloth. The warp ends and the filling picks interlace because of the weaving operation, but the protruding fibers, not held in place, are held down in the cloth because of the felting properties of the woolen fabric.

Felting is made possible by the wet finishing operations given to the goods. The weave is covered up by these treatments, and the short fibers work into the spaces between the interlacings in the weave. Thus, a solid, compact appearance is assured the face of the goods. Felting causes the goods to shrink in the finishing, thereby affording a higher texture—a greater number of ends and picks per inch in the fabric. This makes the cloth heavier in the finished state when compared with the gray goods from the loom.

WOOL, FOUR TYPES OF.

COMBING WOOL: The highest, finest and best wool obtained from sheep. The fibers are usually carded and combed, since they have the properties and characteristics necessary for the best grades of worsted yarn and fabric. Worsted fibers that have been combed are of the same approximate length, even, parallel, smooth, devoid of foreign matter, etc. Wool to be used for combing purposes has a high percentage of yolk and suint in the grease condition. Merino wool is always combed and usually is manipulated into high-grade fabric.

CARDING WOOL: Of good quality, but not always satisfactory for combing purposes. Some stock, however, can be combed for use in medium to high quality fabric for men's wear and women's wear. Most carding wool, however, is of varying staple length and is used chiefly in woolens.

CLOTHING WOOL: A term used in wool grading to designate staple length. There is no standard length implied by the term, since it varies with the fineness of the wool in question.

Fine wools, 64s and over and called clothing wool, and below 1¼ inches in staple length. As the wools become coarser when being sorted there is an increase of about ¼ inch per grade. Like carding wool, this wool shows much irregular fiber and there are, at times, goodly amounts of foreign matter, chiefly in the grease condition, such as burrs, dried grass, fodder, motes, pebbles, etc.

Clothing wool, in a broad sense, differs from carding wool in that the former may have varying amounts of other fibers worked with it in manipulation.

CARPET WOOL: Any wool not classed in the above grades; the lowest in quality of the four types. It cannot be combed and often gives trouble in carding. Practically all carpet wool used here comes from abroad since our flocks have been improved by scientific methods to the point where they grade in the classifications given above. Used in floor covering trade and in low quality boys' apparel, ski cloth, mackinac fabric, etc.

WOOL, GH PROCESS FOR. An anti-felting treatment afforded wool fiber by treating it with potassium permanganate in a concentrated salt or caustic soda solution, followed by a sodium bisphite treatment. This treatment produces good results if done with care.

WOOL, HYDROSCOPIC PROPERTIES OF. Wool has the greatest of hydroscopic properties and its moisture content will vary with the temperature, particularly when humidity is considered. The normal moisture content of wool is 16 per cent, but it may vary from 12 per cent to 20 per cent under certain conditions. When wool is sorted in a damp place the content may run to 25 per cent.

WOOL, IMITATION NATURAL. Refers to undyed or unbleached wool which may be imitated by adding dark-colored fibers to white wool in order to prevent the goods from showing a soiled effect too soon.

WOOL, INSECTS THAT ATTACK. There are two groups which attack the wool fiber:

Beetle Group: Australian carpet beetle, (anthrenocerus australis/Black carpet beetle, (attagenus piceus). Buffalo or Common beetle, (anthrenus scrophularaise). Furniture beetle, (anthrenus vorax). Furrier's beetle, (attagenus pellio). Wooly bear beetle, (anthrenus fasciatus).

Moth Group: Brown House or False Clothes moth, (borkhausenia pseudopretella). Casa-bearing Clothes moth, (tinea pellionella). Common Clothes moth, (tineola bisselleilla). Large Pale Clothes moth, (tinea pallescentella). White Shouldered House moth, (endrosis lactella). White Tip Clothes moth, (trichophage tapetzella).

WOOL, NUMBERS FOR FLEECE.

First— Long staple fibers obtained from sides of the fleece.

Second— Stock from the back, across the loins, to the neck area.

Third— Fibers from the lower part of the back.

Fourth— Staple obtained from the rump area.

Fifth— Wool from the thigh area.

Sixth— Also known as britch, it is wool from the lower portions of the thigh area.

WOOL, PROPERTIES OF HEAT AND ELECTRICITY IN. Wool is not a good conductor of heat and electricity. Unlike cottons, woolens and worsteds hold the heat of the body in suspension for long periods of time, a decided asset to the wearer of these garments.

WOOL, RUG. A woolen yarn of six ply in which the single yarn is not finer before plying than the equivalent of 2.5 single worsted yarn.

WOOL, SCOURING TEST IN. This is used to determine the yield of certain wools, the separation of the yolk and suint from the actual fiber. The sample is immersed in a soap solution until the impurities have been removed. Washing and drying of the sample would follow.

The yield can be determined by comparison with the dry weight, before scouring, and with the dry weight after scouring.

To find the amount of scoured wool in a lot, the moisture content of the raw wool must, of course, be considered in the computation.

The regain is usually applied to the yield value in order not to include a moisture regain on the greasy and oily matter. The commercial scouring test is applied to tops; woolen, worsted, and cotton yarns and wastes.

The sample is divided into two equal parts. Each part is scoured independently of the other. If the average is close enough on the check-up, the figures are accepted. If not, a new test is made and the averages are checked again.

WOOL, SHRINKAGE AND YIELD OF AMERICAN. On a 100-pound basis, the approximate yields obtained from American methods of scouring wool are:

1. XX will yield—
   from 30 to 35 pounds of scoured wool
2. X or ¾ will yield—
   from 35 to 40 pounds of scoured wool
3. ½ blood will yield—
   from 40 to 50 pounds of scoured wool
4. ⅜ blood will yield—
   from 50 to 55 pounds of scoured wool
5. ¼ blood will yield—
   from 55 to 60 pounds of scoured wool
6. Common will yield—
   from 60 to 65 pounds of scoured wool

WOOL, STRINGY. Matted, stringy wool that is usually the result of faulty scouring; difficult to manipulate.

WOOL, TESTS WHEN BUYING. The wool buyer must look for the following when buying wool as it is on the sheep's back:

1. The qualities of sorting, scouring, carding, combing, spinning and twisting.

2. The staple of the stock, serrations per inch, and shrinkage amounts compared with the yield when the wool is scoured.

3. The spinning qualities of the wool. The stock must be able to spin to the estimated counts.

4. Strength enough to withstand the rigor and strain in the manufacturing operations.

5. Cloth made from the yarn must

have the correct tensile strength.

6. Texture of the finished cloth must be satisfactory.

7. Fibers must have the correct staple length for manipulation in drawing, twisting, and winding.

8. Softness, pliability, and harshness of the wool have to be noted so that the buyer may be guided accordingly.

9. The stock must have the correct felting properties, if the goods are to be felted in finishing, to withstand the rigors of fulling, milling, scouring, washing, and shrinking.

10. The wool should have enough whiteness, or be able to scour to the white, if the material is to be dyed evenly.

WOOL-ALL, BRITCH WOOL. Wool from the lower thighs of the sheep, usually the coarsest found. Has considerable length but is very irregular and of little value. Used in very low-priced suitings and coatings, windbreakers, ski cloth, and some carpets.

WOOL AND FIBER RUG. This rug is made of a plain or twill weave and the cotton warp will show on the surface. The filling is carpet wool combined with spruce wood fiber that has been treated in order to withstand moisture. Washing will disintegrate the fiber. The rug may be made as a reversible or printed on one side only.

WOOL AUCTIONS. Practically all wool sold outside of this country is disposed of at wool auction sales to the highest bidder.

WOOL-BACKED CLOTH. Fabric in which there is an extra warp or an extra filling used in construction. Weight, warmth, and texture are increased by this method of weaving material. An extra warp fabric is known as a warp-backed cloth; if an extra filling is used the goods are known as filling-back fabric.

WOOL BAT. Carded wool sold in laps for filling comforters.

WOOL CARD. The machine whose function it is to take out the foreign matter, more or less parallel the fibers, and place the stock into manageable condition for further manipulation. There is no twisting given the fibers in carding. The principal rollers on a card are the cylinder, workers and strippers, and the doffer.

Cards are made up in either a 3-set or a 4-set arrangement. The better wools receive the four-set treatment; the lower qualities, the 3-set.

FOUR-CARD SET:	THREE-CARD SET:
1. 1st Breaker.	1. 1st Breaker.
2. 2nd Breaker.	2. 2nd Breaker.
3. Finisher card.	3. Finisher-

4. Condenser card.	Condenser, combined.

The stock from the last card, in either case, comes off in the form of roving, one step removed from being finished spun yarn, and ready to be sent to the spinning frame in this form. The cards take the bulky, loose wool and deliver it in this roving condition on the last card in the set.

WOOL CLASSIFICATIONS, WORLD. There are about 40 distinctive breeds of sheep; counting the cross-breeds there are now over 200 distinct grades of wool. Sheep are classified into five categories or classes:

1. CLASS ONE WOOLS: Merino Sheep, 1 to 5 inches staple length:
Ohio Merino.
Silesian: Austria.
Saxony: Germany.
Rambouillet: France.
Australian.
South American.
South African.

New Zealand, plus the small merino countries of Spain, Sweden, Denmark, Italy.

2. CLASS TWO WOOLS: 2 to about 8 inches staple length:
Originated in England, Scotland, Ireland, and Wales, and now grown all over the world.
Bampton, Berkshire, Blackface, Cornish, Cornwall, Devonshire, Dorset, Canadian wools, Hampshire, Hereford, Exmoor, Kent, Norfolk, Shropshire, Southdown, Sussex, Oxford, Welsh Mountain, Wiltshire, Westmoreland, West Riding of England, Irish, and Ryeland.

3. CLASS THREE WOOLS: 4 to 12 inches or more in staple length:
The Luster wools of the United Kingdom: Lincoln from Lincoln county; Leicester from Leicester county; Cotswold from Gloucester county; Cheviot from the Lowlands and Highlands of Scotland; Romney Marsh from Kent county; Shetland, Hebrides, Harris, and Lewis and other Island sheep.

4. CLASS FOUR WOOLS:
Those sheep which cannot be classed in one of the first three groups; the results of mixed breeding; the fiber is irregular and ranges from one inch to sixteen or more inches in staple length. The sheep are known as halfbreeds and semiluster or demiluster sheep. This class, in reality, may be called "mongrel sheep." The wool is used for making carpets and rugs, and low priced clothing usually for boys and girls.

5. CLASS FIVE:
This group is not truly a sheep classification, but the animals are akin to

sheep and are therefore listed: Arabian, Bokharan, Persian lamb, and similar fiber stock.

WOOL-DYED. Usually refers to a cloth which has been stock-dyed. This method of dyeing occurs after the wool has been scoured but before blending and mixing take place. Several distinct colors are run together in order to produce a mixed yarn effect which will, when the cloth is woven, give shades of some particular color.

WOOLEN AND WORSTED CARDING, SETS IN. Worsted carding is done by a double-cylinder card—two cards connected by means of a roller known as the angle stripper. This roller, similar to a doffer roller, takes the carded wool from the first card in the set and delivers it to the feeding-in end of the second card. The number of operations which follow worsted carding do not warrant any other treatment, as far as carding is concerned, to the wool.

Low and medium wools for wool yarn are run on a three-card set. The machines are the first-breaker card, second-breaker card, and the finisher-condenser card.

High-grade wools for wool yarn are run on a four-set card. The machines are the first-breaker card, the second-breaker card, the finisher-card, and the condenser-card.

The last card in either the three- or four-set arrangement has the wool in roving form ready for presentation to the mule for the final operation in wool-yarn manufacturing, spinning.

WOOLEN AND WORSTED FABRICS IN THE APPAREL TRADES, USES OF.

MEN'S OVERCOATING FABRICS:

Albert cloth	Kersey
Beaver	Kerseymere
Bouclé	Mackinac cloth
Broadcloth	Melton
Buffalo cloth	Meltonette
Cade: cloth	Montagnac
Camel hair	Moscow
Cashmere	Overplaids
Cheviot tweed	Pilot cloth
Chinchilla	Plaid-back coating
Donegal tweed	Polo cloth
Double cloths	Reefer fabric
Fearnaught	Scotch tweed
Forestry cloth	Shetland
Frieze	Tattersall
Harris Tweed	Ulster
Heather mixtures	Whitney
Herringbone effects	Windbreaker cloth
Homespun	Worumbo
Irish tweed	

MEN'S TOPCOATINGS:

Albert cloth	Harris Tweed
Balmacaan	Herringbone effects

Bedford cord
Camel hair cloth
Cavalry twill
Cheviot
Covert
Cravenette
Donegal tweed
Elastique
Forestry cloth
Gabardine
Glengarry
Gun club check

Homespun
Irish tweed
Kerseymere
Melton
Meltonette
Overplaids
Plaid-backs
Scotch tweed
Shetland
Tweed
Whipcord

MEN'S HATS:

Felted wool   Fur felt

MEN'S SUITINGS:

Alpaca
Banjo stripes
Bannockburn
Bedford cord
Broadcloth
Broche effects
Cashmere
Cassimere
Cavalry twill
Chain-break
  worsted
Cheviot
Clay serge
Cotton-warp
  unions
Diagonal worsted
Donegal tweed
Double serge
Drap d'Ete
Dress worsted

Elastique
Flannel
Filling-back serge
French-back
French serge
French-back serge
Gabardine
Glengarry
Gun club check
Hairline effects
Harris Tweed
Heathers
Herringbones
Homespun
Irish tweed
Kerseymere
Norfolk effects
Oxfords
Palm Beach
Panama

HOSIERY AND UNDERWEAR:

Knitted all-wool
Wool-silk
Wool-cotton
Wool-rayon

Miscellaneous wool
  mixes—with
  nylon staple,
  textured nylon
  filament
  ("stretch")

ROBES:

Flannels of many
  types

Wool-mixture fab-
  rics

NECKWEAR:

Knitted all-wool
Wool-cotton cloths
Worsted tie fabric

Wool-rayon
Wool-silk

WOMEN'S COATS, SUITS, AND DRESSES:

Albatross
Baize
Bolivia
Brilliantine
Broche
Brushed wool
Camel hair
Camel suede
Cashmere
Challis
Cheviot tweed
Chiffon velvet

Honeycomb
Hound's tooth
  effects
Irish tweed
Jersey-woven/
  knitted
Kersey
Kerseymere
Lace effects
Marvella
Mousseline de
  Laine

Color-effects
Covert
Crepe
Crepon
Donegal tweed
Double serge
Drap d'Ete
Dress worsted
Duvetyne
Elastique
Eolienne
Epingle
Eponge
Flannel
Florentine twill
French serge
Filling-back serge
French-back serge
Georgette wool
  crepes
Goldtone
Gun club checks
Hairline effects
Harris Tweed
Heathers
Homespun
Velour
Velour check
Voile

Nun's veiling
Overplaids
Pebble cheviot
Pencil stripes
Pepper-and-salt
Poiret twill
Poplin
Prunella
Rabbit hair cloth
Ratine
Rib-weave effects
Saxony
Scotch tweed
Serge
Shaker flannel
Sharkskin
Shepherd's checks
Shetland
Silvertone
Stockinette
Suede
Tartan plaid
Tree-bark effect
Tricotine
Tropical
Union fabric
Wool-rayon mixes
Wool-silk mixes
Zephyr flannel

WOMEN'S HOSIERY AND UNDERWEAR:

Knitted all-wool
Wool-cotton
Wool-silk

(Miscellaneous
  mixtures of wool
  and spun nylon,
  etc.)

WOMEN'S ROBES:

Flannel of many
  types

Mixture cloths

SCARFS:

Homespun
Flannel

Knitted cloths

MILLINERY:

Duvetyne
Felt mixtures
Homespun
Jersey

Plush
Tweed
Velvet
Wool-nylon staple
  mixtures

GLOVES:

Wool fabrics of several types—made of
  soft-twisted or hard-twisted yarns

BOYS' WEAR:

Cheviot
Chinchilla
Homespun
Jersey
Mackinac
Melton
Meltonette
Serge
Shetland
Tweed

Whipcord
Worsteds of vary-
  ing types
Much reused and
  remanufactured
  fabrics are used
  in boys' wear.
  Vary consider-
  ably in price
  and grade.

GIRLS' WEAR:

Challis   Mixes of many

Crepe
Dress flannel
Florentine twill
Henrietta
Homespun
Meltonette
Stockinette
Tartan
Tweed
Twill
Union fabric

types and
  qualities
Poiret twill
Poplin
Prunella
Serge
Zephyr flannel
Most coatings sim-
  ilar to women's
  wear but cheaper
  in price and type

INFANTS' WEAR:

Baby flannel
Bombazine
Cashmere
Challis
Crepe
Dress flannel
Eiderdown
Flannel of many
  types
Henrietta

Nun's veiling
Poplin
Prunella
Ratine
Serge
Shaker flannel
Sheer woolen
Stockinette
Tartan plaid
Zephyr flannel

THE USE OF WOOL IN HOME FURNISH-
INGS—
BED COVERINGS:

Blankets and
  Afghans
Comfortables
Comfortables with

animal fiber
  stuffing
All-wool blankets
Part-wool
  blankets

DRAPERIES:

Damask
Denim
Frieze
Frise
Friezette
Mohair
Mohair mixes

Velour
Velvet
Wool mixtures of
  many types ei-
  ther in plain or
  Jacquard designs

RUGS AND CARPETS:

(Orientals and Domestics may be made
wholly of wool or with a wool pile effect on the face of the fabric with a
backing made of another textile fiber.)

Axminster
Broadloom
Brussels
Chenille
Genuine Orientals

Sheen-type Ameri-
  can Orientals
Smyrna
Tapestry
Velvet
Wilton

UPHOLSTERY:

Damask
Denim
Frieze
Frise
Friezette
Rep
Velour

Velvet
Whipcord
Tapestry
Combination mix-
  tures of fibers in
  which wool is
  the basic fiber

WOOLEN AND WORSTED YARNS AND FABRICS, COMPARISONS BETWEEN.

WOOLEN YARN
1. Carded only
2. Soft, slubby
3. Fuzzy, uneven fibers
4. Weaker
5. Fibers in conglomerate mass
6. Uneven twisting
7. Bulky type of yarn, uneven

WORSTED YARN
1. Carded and combed
2. Substantial, harder than wool
3. Smooth, even, uniform fibers
4. Stronger
5. Fibers are parallel
6. Even twisting and greater twist
7. Uniform in diameter

WOOLEN CLOTH
1. Lower texture—ends and picks
2. Less shine
3. Tendency to sag and not to hold crease
4. Less tensile strength
5. Poorer yarn in fabric, generally speaking
6. Heavier, bulkier cloth
7. Does not tailor as well
8. Gives good wear
9. Less expensive fabric

WORSTED CLOTH
1. Higher texture, more compact
2. More shine or sheen
3. Does not sag, holds crease very well
4. Greater tensile strength
5. Better, more expensive yarn used in materials
6. Lighter, less bulky fabric
7. Tailors well and easily
8. Will last longer and usually gives better wear
9. More expensive fabric

WOOLEN CHIFFON VELVET. The same in construction as better-grade broadcloth but much lighter in weight. The cloth runs from seven to ten ounces in weight per yard, has a fine, kindly feel and will give excellent wear since all of the material is rather high in price and made of good-quality stock.

WOOLENET. WOOLENETTE. A name given at times to some of the thin or sheer woolen fabrics on the market such as nun's veiling, drap d'été, chiffon, lightweight crepe, etc.

WOOLEN FINISH FOR COTTONS. A napped finish applied to some cotton cloths to give them the appearance of woolens. This finish is seen in flannel, domet, blankets, cantons, and kindred fabrics.

WOOLEN RUN. The number of 1,600-yard hanks of yarn in one pound; 7,000 grains of the yarn under standard conditions.

WOOLENS. Cloth made from woolen yarn but not always 100 per cent wool in content. The average woolen has a rather fuzzy surface, does not shine with wear, may hold the crease well, has nap and in the majority of cases, is dyed. Woolen finish is rather easily recognized on fabrics to determine the difference between this cloth and a worsted material.

WOOLENS, DURABLE CREASED. A woolen fabric does not come in the category of Wash-and-Wear, nor does it qualify as a full-fledged Permanent Press fabric. The treatment given woolens may be compared to the waving and setting of hair on the female head. Human hair and wool are of the same chemical structure, and it is the keratin in them that is conducive to the waved effect. Human hair is set by the use of a spray treatment. Likewose, woolens are finally treated with a spray to set the crease; then they are pressed.

The permanent crease in woolens is brought about by the use of monoethalamine sulfite, which breaks the "memory pattern." When heat is applied to form the crease or pleat, a "new memory pattern" for the creased state is set up and the fabric will then return to its newly creased condition. Rain or steam, under ordinary conditions, will not affect the creases to any marked degree, if at all.

WOOLENS AND WORSTEDS. There are three types of fabric made from the wool of sheep—woolens, worsteds, and unfinished worsteds. Woolen cloth may be distinguished from worsted fabric by its softer feel and a rather uneven, napped, or fuzzy surface effect.

Unfinished worsteds may be made of: 1. Worsted warp and woolen filling. 2. Soft-spun French system worsted yarn. 3. Warp and filling with certain amounts of the so-called waste or substitute fibers mixed in.

French spun yarn is softer than the English or Bradford spun yarn. The cloths seem to have a softer, loftier feel. It is, however, sometimes next to impossible to determine whether a fabric is spun on the French or the Bradford system.

Worsted fabric should show a clear outline of the weave construction and pattern. If the weave is a twill, the diagonal lines should be symmetrically balanced; if made of a plain weave the fabric should show the construction clearly. When held to the light, worsteds reveal a luster without polishing.

Clear-finish worsteds should have a clean, smooth, surface effect, even in all respects; that is, the material should be well and evenly sheared in the dry finishing. The texture should be uniform and even and show no blemishes. A clear-finish worsted will shine, in time, because of friction, chafing, and wear. It is virtually impossible to remove the shine from the fabrics of this type. The cloth holds the crease very well, and the wearing quality is good to excellent.

Unfinished worsted will not shine but does not hold the crease as well as clear-finished fabric. Shearing must be done with utmost care if it is resorted to, and the nap or protruding fibers must be finished so that these fibers add to the appearance of the goods. Cropping requires a high degree of skill. Knots and other possible blemishes must be removed prior to shearing since a knot or slub falling under the shear blade may do irreparable damage. Shearers must watch the cloth constantly during shearing to guard against flaws that might spoil the fabric because the shear blade scraped or caught the blemish.

Worsteds and woolens may be woven, double, or triple cloth construction. Double and triple constructions receive their effect by the use of two or more warps and fillings being woven together in distinctive patterns or designs.

Some staple woolens and worsteds include single construction fabrics such as cassimere, cavalry twill, Cheviot, crepe, flannel, gabardine, homespun, serge, tweed. Double and triple constructions may include, when deemed necessary, some of the foregoing cloths, as well as beaver, broadcloth, chinchilla, covert, kersey, melton, ski cloth, Whitney, Worumbo, etc.

A 1-run woolen yarn has 1,600 yards in 1 pound, a 2-run yarn would have 3,200 yards to the pound, and so on. The latter yarn would have one-half the diameter of the single 1s yarn but would be twice as long on the pound basis.

A 1-cut woolen yarn has 300 yards in one pound of the yarn.

There are 560 yards in one pound of a 1s worsted yarn; a 10s worsted yarn would have 5600 yards to the pound (560 x 10 or 5600 yards to the pound). A partial table of the equivalent yarn sizes follows:

Yards per Pound	WOOLEN YARN Cut	WOOLEN YARN Run	WORSTED YARN Count
300	1		
560			1
1,600		1	
2,240			4s
2,400	8	1½	
4,480			8s
4,800	16	3	
5,600		3½	10s
6,400		4	
9,600		6	
11,200		7	20s
16,800			30s
22,400			40s

WOOLEN SYSTEM. Used with regard to the manufacture of woolen yarn from short staple stock, noil, soft or hard wastes, reused wool, remanufactured wool, reclaims, etc. The operations include sorting, scouring, blending, oiling, mixing, carding and mule spinning. Within recent years ring spinning has made some progress in the manipulation of wool into woolen yarn.

WOOLEN-WORSTED YARN DESCRIPTION. Woolen and worsted yarns are often plied to increase strength, evenness and uniformity. Two-ply woolen and two-ply worsted yarns are common today.

Woolen yarns are usually designated as to size by the Run or Boston System and the Philadelphia or Cut System. Worsted yarns are designated by the term, count of yarn.

WOOLEN YARN. A rather broad term, used extensively to denote that yarn made from wool fibers, possibly irregular in length, and, at times having fibers other than wool mixed with it. The fibers are laid more or less in a topsy-turvy direction and are carded but not combed. Used in the sweater trade, for coarse, heavy woolen hosiery, shaker sweaters, and in many types of woven innerwear and outerwear.

WOOL FIBER, STRUCTURE OF. Under the microscope, wool shows three distinct fiber parts.

1. EPIDERMIS: The outside or surface of the fiber, which consists of a series of scales that lie one on top of the other. These scales have saw edges which give the fiber its spinning and felting properties. This outside surface may be compared with the asparagus tip or the scales of a fish.

2. CORTEX: Also known as the corticule. This is the name given to the substance that makes the middle of the fiber. It consists of a series of fibrous cells that are shaped angularly. This is the part of the fiber that furnishes most of the elasticity and strength.

3. MEDULLA: The pith or core of the fiber. It is a channel through which the fibers receive nutriment and juices to sustain them.

Wool fibers seem to be the most desirable fiber in the animal-fiber kingdom. Sufficient length, strength, and elasticity, together with certain surface cohesion to enable many fibers to be drawn and twisted in the spinning operation in order to form a coherent and continuous yarn or thread, prove to be valuable properties.

The power of absorbing coloring matters from solution and becoming dyed thereby, and the property of becoming bleached or decolorized when treated with suitable chemical agents seem to give wool some advantage over the other animal fibers.

Wool fibers felt or mat easily, thereby causing them to have uses for which other animal fibers are unsuited.

The unmodified term, Wool, has special reference to the product obtained from the many varieties of sheep. See Illustrated Section.

WOOL FIBER DENSITY. The number of fibers produced within a set or given area on the body of the sheep; the more numerous the fibers, the greater will be the density and usually the grade will be higher in quality.

WOOL FIBERS, SERRATIONS IN. They are found only in wool and do not appear in any other textile fiber. Serrations are caused by the uneven growth of cortical cells, which cause the fibers to contract and bend. Waviness is noted more in the higher grades of wool, and they are almost negligible in the poor qualities. The serra-

tious structure in wool gives it the property of felting, which is so valuable in making of overcoatings and other heavy materials.

Serrations or scales are not visible to the naked eye; they are the minute, unseen waves within the larger, visible waves noted in the wool fiber. They run from 600 to the inch in the low grades of wool up to 2,400 to 3,000 in the choice qualities of Merino stock.

See Illustrated Section.

WOOL GRADE. 1. Quality or relative fineness of a wool fiber. The individual diameters of wool fibers determine the actual grade. Several tests are made and the average determines the grade to which the wool belongs.

2. Sheep of mixed blood which show no particular breed characteristics. The term is often used with reference to crossbred sheep.

WOOL GRADING, PIECES IN. Batches of wool scraps obtained in sorting which are later on mixed with better wools to insure their usage.

WOOL GRADING TABLES, COMPARATIVE.

UNITED STATES	GREAT BRITAIN	CANADA
Full blood— includes XX and X or ¾	72s to 80s	Fine
½ blood	66s to 72s	Fine medium
⅜ blood	56s to 66s	Medium
¼ blood	44s to 56s	Low medium
Common	24s to 44s	Coarse
Braid	below 24s	Luster
Britch		

WOOL IMITATION. The only wool imitation fiber made strictly according to the viscose method.

Closely resembles wool and has thermal-insulating properties. It blends very well with major textile fibers in making apparel of many types.

WOOLMARK. 1. A symbol awarded by the Wool Bureau, Inc., New York City to quality-tested products made of the world's best wool - virgin wool. 2. A label sewed on by licensed manufacturers into merchandise created of virgin wool as a hallmark of uncompromising quality. 3. A contemporary art motif which reflects the up-to-date advantages of man's oldest fiber - virgin wool. 4. A sign which represents virgin wool, used in a host of knitted and/or woven fabrics. 5. An assurance to consumers of fashion finesse, first-rate performance, and prestige. 6. Status symbol found only on quality apparel and featured in quality retail stores. 7. A widely-known emblem which signifies virgin wool; often noted on television, newspapers, magazines, et al. 8. An international insignia known all over the world as the symbol of the best of virgin wool.

WOOL MATCHINGS, ENGLISH.
These matchings are as follows:

1. Picklock . . . . . from shoulder stock
2. Prime . . . . from sides
3. Choice . . . . from middle of back
4. Super . . . . from middle of sides
5. Seconds . . . . . . from lower sides
6. Downrights . . . from neck
7. Abb . . . . from hind legs
8. Britch . . . . . . from haunches

WOOL GRADES, OFFICIAL STANDARD.
These were established per the Federal Register of August 21, 1965, Title 7, Chapter 1, Part 31:

Grade	Limits for average fiber diameter (microns)*	Limit for standard deviation maximum (microns)
Finer than 80s	Under 17.70	3.59
80s	17.70 to 19.14	4.09
70s	19.15 to 20.59	4.59
64s	20.60 to 22.04	5.19
62s	22.05 to 23.49	5.89
60s	23.50 to 24.94	6.49
58s	24.95 to 26.39	7.09
56s	26.40 to 27.84	7.59
54s	27.85 to 29.29	8.19
50s	29.30 to 30.99	8.69
48s	31.00 to 32.69	9.09
46s	32.70 to 34.39	9.59
44s	34.40 to 36.19	10.09
40s	36.20 to 38.09	10.69
36s	38.10 to 40.20	11.19
Coarser than 36s	Over 40.20	—

*A micron is 1/25,400 of an inch.

WOOL GRADING: UNITED STATES METHODS

Domestic Wools	Wools Territory	Pulled Wools—Eastern April/May Clothing	May/August Clothing	August/November Clothing : Combing	December/March Clothing : Combing	
XX, X or 3/4 or Delaine	Fine				AAA & AA	AA
Half Blood	Half Blood	A Lambs	B Lambs	A Lambs	A & Super A	A
Three Eighths	Three Eighths	B Lambs	B Super	B Lambs		B Lambs
Quarter Blood	Quarter Blood		B Stain	B Combing	B	B
Low Quarter	Low Quarter	C Lambs	C	Low Combing	B	Medium
Common, Braid (Britch)	Common, Braid (Britch)	C Lambs	C	Low	C	Low

WOOL NOIL. Combing separates the long, choice, desirable fibers from the shorter ones that are under some desired length. "Rejected" fibers are called noil. They are usually as good in quality as the top, but do not have the length in order to sustain themselves in manipulation from raw stock to yarn; hence, the necessity of noil to be worked with other longer staple fibers. Noil is an excellent raw material for many types of woolens. It is used to good advantage in cloths with a napped face, in knitted yarns, flannels, broadcloths, etc. Besides wool noil, these short fibers are found in mohair, alpaca, and other hair fibers; in cotton, other bast fibers, and in man-made staple filaments.

Noil is divided into long or short wool noil. The former stock comes from the well-known English wools, long in staple length—Lincoln, Leicester Cotswold, Romney Marsh, and Cheviot wools—the Class Three wools in world classification. Fine or short wool noil is secured from medium and fine grade Australian, Cape, Continental, South American, and United States wools. The term domestic, when applied to noil, means noil of this country. The term foreign is applied to any noil from a foreign nation. In this country there is no distinction as to whether or not the stock comes from Domestic or Territory wool.

Noil is classified in the same manner as top—according to the grade of wool from which the stock was taken to be combed. One notes the following—fine domestic noil, ½-blood domestic noil, etc. Foreign stock in this country is classified as: ⅜-blood noil, South American; ½-blood noil, Cape wool; fine noil, Australian wool, etc.

In Great Britain, and on the Continent, tops are classified by the yarn count to which the stock is supposed to spin. Noil is classified on the basis of the quality of the top produced by the combing. A 40s noil is one secured from a 40s top. The percentage of noil taken from the wool depends on the relative amount of short fiber present in the wool, and in the settings of the comber. Fine wools produce a heavier noil than coarse wools. The percentage of noil removed from the comber varies from 7 to 25 per cent.

The average percentages for the grades of Domestic wool are: fine staple, 17 to 20 per cent; half blood, 15 per cent; three-eighths blood, 12 per cent; quarter blood, 10 per cent.

WOOL PACKING. A jute material used to hold sacks of wool. It is made of a two-ply warp and single filling; 2-up 1-down twill weave is used. Made in England, it is the type used for all Colonial wools.

WOOL PACKS. Coarse jute fabric used for packing raw wool during transit.

WOOL PIECES. Staples in small batches from various breeds and types of sheep that accumulate during classing and sorting. Pieces are sold as regular or mixed lots to mills.

First pieces imply the longest of the skirted wool after the broken bits have been removed.

WOOL GRADING: FOREIGN METHODS
(with comparative United States counts of yarns):

Continental Counts Spun to	Cape, Australian & New Zealand	South American	U.S. Worsted Spinning Counts	U. S. Run Wool Spinning Counts
Delaine–64–70s	Merino	Merino	60s	6–7s
Half–58–60s	Comeback	Prima	60s	5s
Three Eighths 56s	Half Bred	Ones	36–40s	3.5s
Quarter 48–50s	Half Bred Low	Twos	30s	2.5s
Low Quarter 46s	Quarter Bred	Threes	26s	2s
Common, 36–44s Braid (Britch)	Lincoln and Cotswold	Fours Fives Sixes	16s	1s .75 or ¾s

Second pieces are the first trimmings and the small pieces which do not fall through the screen of the piece-picking table.

WOOL POOL, EXAMPLES OF A. The following gives an example of the so-called wool pool, a method used by most wool raising countries:

"Highland County again gained first place in Virginia as the top wool area. The Highland Wool Pool brought the top price of $40.15 per cwt (Hundredweight) in the most recent pool bidding prices. Compared with a record high $53.03 the present price is considered to be rather low. The 1969 pool was sold for $47.35 cwt. The Caron Tops Company, Inc., Rochelle, Illinois, a new buyer in the area, submitted the top price for the Highland wool estimated in poundage to be 127,000 pounds.

Runnerup to Highland was Tazewell County at $38.80 while other prices were Augusta, $38.69, Bath, Alleghany and Boutetourt all at $37.21, Frederick, $35.56, Clark, $36.56, Rockingham, $37.05, Russell, $38.08, Orange, $35.03, Wythe, $38.15, Washington, $37.50, Giles, $35.56, Christiansburg, $37.15, Mountain, North Carolina sold for $34.80, and North Carolina State College received $34.90. Total wool poundage sold by the State of Virginia amounted to 1,068,539 pounds. The local pool will be shipped on June 28 and June 29."

WOOL PRODUCT. Any product, or any portion of a product, which contains, purports to contain, or in any way is represented as containing wool, reprocessed wool, or reused wool.

There is an exemption on carpets, rugs, mats, and upholstery, as well as on certain limits for linings, paddings, trimmings, stiffenings or facings in apparel. Also exempted are products "having an insignificant or inconsequential textile content." Applications for exemptions are cared for by the Federal Trade Commission after a hearing.

Exemptions are determined by the importance to the trade and consumer by fiber content of specific articles. For example, in this group might be baseballs, shoe inner soles, piano felts, furniture items.

Disclosure of fiber content of all wool articles not specifically exempted is obligatory. Manufacturers, wholesalers and merchants cannot evade the law by failure to make any claims of any fiber content. Thus, concealment on any pretext of fiber content of any product containing wool is not evasion—it is violation of the law.

WOOL PRODUCTS LABELING ACT OF 1939, DEFINITIONS USED IN THE. This Act, effective July 15, 1941, stipulates the following definitions under Section 2, page 21, of this Act:

1. The term "wool" means the fiber from the fleeces of the sheep or lamb, or hair of the Angora or Cashmere goat (and may include the so-called specialty fibers from the hair of the camel, alpaca, llama, and vicuna) which has never been reclaimed from any woven or felted wool product.

2. The term "reprocessed wool" means the resulting fiber when wool has been woven or felted into a wool product which, without ever having been utilized in any way by the ultimate consumer, subsequently has been made into a fibrous state.

3. The term "reused wool" means the resulting fiber when wool or reprocessed wool has been spun, woven, knitted, or felted into a wool product which, after having been used in any way by the ultimate consumer, subsequently has been made into a fibrous state.

WOOLS. See Sheep of the World, Classification of.

WOOLS, CALIFORNIA AND TEXAS. The sheep from these states are the only ones that are shorn twice a year because of climatic conditions and foreign matter found in the fleeces, such as burrs. Most Texas wool is raised on ranges or areas that are controlled by fencing-in. California wool may come from the open range or controlled areas. The wool is of fine diameter, good staple, and softer in hand when compared with Territory Wools raised here. Texas raises about one-fourth of the wool raised annually in the United States. See TERRITORY WOOL.

WOOL SALES, SPOT. Known as a "spot transaction," it means that the wool is available for inspection by the possible purchaser. If bought, it is ready for delivery at once to the consignee. This wool is usually "in-the-grease-condition," that is, it has not been scoured.

WOOL SHEARS. The long shears used when skirting a wool fleece.

WOOL SHEER. A general classification under which may be grouped all thin lightweight women's-wear fabrics. Usually woven from worsted yarns, although some woolen fabrics are sufficiently thin to be classified as sheers.

WOOL SHRINKAGE CONTROL. Its purpose is to inhibit the felting shrinkage of wool. There are four methods used today:

1. CHLORINATION: Wet chlorination may be acidic or alkaline; both these wet treatments oxidize the surface of the wool fiber. Gaseous chlorination has the same objective but is not used in the United States and only to a limited degree in Europe.

2. IMPREGNATION: This covers the surface structure of the wool fiber, thereby controlling its movement. Thermosetting melamine resins or nylon film are used for the shrinkage control.

3. ENZYME. Used abroad, it is applied to the wool surface and causes a partial destruction of the fiber surface, thereby creating a loss in the weight of the fiber lot being treated.

4. SOLVENT: An alcohol-alkali is used to alter the surface of the wool fiber. Unless done with utmost care the fiber may be damaged.

WOOLSORTER'S DISEASE. See ANTHRAX.

WOOL SORTS FROM SHEEP. The so-called shoulder wool is about the best wool in the fleece. In order, follow the side, neck, and back wool. See illustration.

WOOL STAPLE. 1. Woolsorting term to denote whether the wool is of sufficient strength and the fibers sound enough for making warp yarn. 2. A collection of several tufts of wool connected together by a binder.

WOOL STAPLER. Old English term for wool merchant.

WCOL TOP. Also referred to as worsted top, it is the continuous sliver form of long, choice woolen fibers which are to be manufactured ultimately into worsted yarn. The combing operation takes out the short fibers from the desired, choice stock. These are called noil. Worsted top contracts are made in units of 5,000 pounds.

WOOL TWINE. Although other twines may be used to tie wool bales, this particular type is one made of twisted paper that is given a good sizing with glue. A development of the ersatz paper yarns brought out by Germany in World War I, these paper yarns are also used in some summer floorcovering and matting.

WOOL TYPES.

1. FINE WOOLS: These are of the Merino type and include Merino sheep of Spain, Germany, Austria, Ohio, Argentina, Rambouillet of France, Australia, and South Africa.

2. MEDIUM WOOLS: These are obtained from English down breeds and include Dorset, Hampshire, Oxford, Shropshire, Southdown, and Suffolk.

3. LONG OR LUSTER WOOLS: These come from the sheep of Cotswold, Leicester, and Lincoln. The semiluster wools are obtained from Border Leicester, Cheviot, and Romney Marsh.

4. CARPET WOOLS: These come chiefly from the following breeds of sheep: Asian, Fat-Tail African, Karakul-Asian, Navaho-American, Scotch blackface, Zackel-European.

5. CROSSBREEDS: Major types include Columbian, Corriedale, and Polwarth. These are crossbreeds of finewool and long-wool types.

WOOL YARN RESIST, METHOD FOR. Treat in a short bath at full boil for 45 minutes, with 15 per cent tannic acid. The lower grades are highly colored and will dull the stock too much, so that a good light-colored tannin is essential.

Then add 5 per cent muriatic acid to the tannin bath. Work the yarn in the cooling bath for another minute.

Wring or whizz but do not wash; and enter into a fixing bath of 5 per cent tin crystals (stannous chloride) and 2 per cent muriatic acid at 120° F.,

for 15 minutes. Wash thoroughly and soap well at 120° F. This final soaping might be omitted but it will leave the yarn in a softer condition.

This resist method can be used on white or colored yarn. In general resist methods, however, do not always give good results.

To prevent white yarn from becoming stained by the bleeding of dyed wool, it is suggested that fast dyestuff be employed.

WOOSIE, WOOZY WOOL. The lustrous, short-staple fiber as seen, for example, in Chinese wool; rather difficult to manipulate.

WORKABLE COMPETITION. An industry is workably competitive when, after its market characteristics and the dynamic forces which have shaped them have been thoroughly examined, there is no clearly indicated change which can be effected through public policy

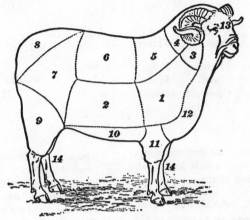

Courtesy of Nat'l Ass'n Wool Mfgrs.

WOOL SORTS

"Shoulder Wool," (Number 1) is usually the best fiber in the Sheep Fleece. Next comes side, neck and back wool. The numbers show order of preference.

EXPLANATION OF AREA NUMBERS:

1. Shoulders, best in the fleece
2. Full side area
3. Front top shoulder area
4. Top back area
5. Front back area
6. Back area
7. Loin area

8. Top rump area
9. Hind quarter, rump area
10. Britch and belly area
11. Top leg area
12. Chest and throat area
13. Head area
14. Shank or leg area

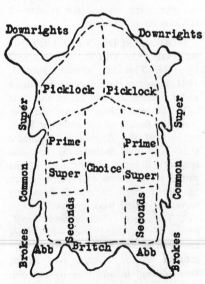

DIAGRAM OF WOOL SORTS

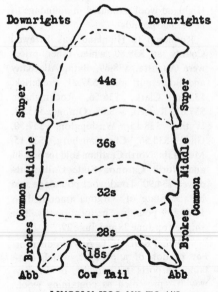

LINCOLN HOG 18'S TO 44'S

Courtesy of John Wiley & Sons, Inc.
From Textile Fibers, H. M. Matthews, 4th edition

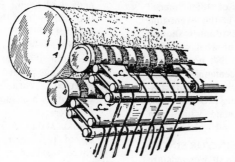

Courtesy of Nat'l Ass'n Wool Mfgrs.

CARD DELIVERY OF ROVING FROM SLIVER FORM FOR WOOLEN YARN

The wool fibers lie on the large roller (A) in web-like form. The two smaller rollers (B) lift these fibers in ribbon-like sections by their alternate strips of wire clothing and pass them on to the rub aprons (C). These aprons, by a sidewise motion impart a mock twist and condense the "ribbons" into round strands of roping.

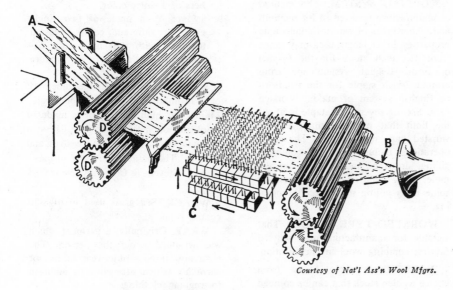

Courtesy of Nat'l Ass'n Wool Mfgrs.

DRAWING OR GILLING

Two slivers (A) are drawn and combined to make one smaller sliver (B). The fallers (C), looking like metal combs, move forward through the wool fibers faster than the slivers are fed by the feed rolls (D) but slower than the combined fibers are drawn off by the delivery rolls (E). The fallers parallel the wool fibers and the greater speed of the delivery rolls over the feed rolls stretches or "reduces" the strands of sliver.

—Also see page 684.

measures which would result in greater social gains than social losses.

WORK CLOTHING FABRICS. A broad term for most fabrics used in industry, institutions, garages, mills of many types, etc. Some of these fabrics are Bedford cord, corduroy, crash, denim, drill, duck, dungaree, jean, rep, sheeting, swansdown, ticking; cottonade, covert, hickory stripes, overall fabric, moleskin, sateen, etc. These are all cotton materials.

WORKER ROLLERS. There are from four to seven of these rollers on the woolen or worsted card. These card-clothed rollers work in conjunc-tion with a similar number of stripper rollers and cylinder to card wool fibers. The worker goes the slowest of the three rollers. It has the wool laid onto the card clothing of the roller by the cylinder. The stripper roller takes the wool from the worker because of its greater speed, and the way in which the bends in the card clothing are set in the two rollers. On the card, the workers, strippers, and cylinder are the only rollers that do actual carding; all other rollers are auxiliary in nature.

WORKHOUSE SHEETING. See BOLTON SHEETING.

WORKMEN'S COMPENSATION. Insurance plan under which employees receive medical care, and monetary reimbursement, for injuries received rising out of their employment.

WORK SHARING. Distribution of available work as evenly as possible among all workers.

WORLD COTTONS, OUTSTANDING (OUTSIDE UNITED STATES).

Brazil: Ceara, Maranha, Pernambuco, Rio Grande, Santos, Menas Geraes, Parahyba, Rio de Janerio, Sertao.

Chinese: Nankin.

Egyptian: Abassi, Ashmouni, Bamia, Mitafiffi, Sakellaridis, Gallini, Jannovitch, Karnak, Giza.

Indian: Assam, Bengal, Dharwar, Dhollera, Hingunhat, Surat, Broach, Comptah, Rangoon.

Mexican: Sea Island, Tampico, Yucatan.

Peruvian: Rough, Smooth, Sea Island; these are called "Tree Cottons," and Tanguis.

Minor Foreign Cottons of the world include:

Afghanistan: Goza.

Africa: Americano Gamti, Lagas, Moho, Mokho, Ndargua, Negro, Nguine, Rimo, Toubab.

Asia Minor: Kirkagatsch.

Burma: Shap, Shembanon, Wagyi.

Colombia: Valledupar (Department of Magdalena); Cerete, Monteria (Department of Cordoba); Tolima, Valle del Cauca. Meta (Department of Armero).

Greece: Smyrna.

Guiana: Demerara, Surinam.

Japanese-Chinese: Shinawata - five types in all: Hankow, Nansi, Poishi, Tienchin, Tungehow.

Syria: Aleppo.

Tahiti: Vivai.

Turkestan: Suzani.

Venezuela: Barcelona, Laguary.

WORMING. Filling the divisions or spaces in rope between the lays with spun yarn in a compact way.

WORSTED. Worsted yarn is smooth-surfaced, spun from long staple, evenly combed wool. Worsted fabric is made from worsted yarns, is tightly woven, with a smooth "hard" surface. Original gabardine and serge are examples. One story is that worsted is so named because when William the Conqueror came to Britain in 1066 he found many of the peasants combing wool in the area which, since he had worsted the people, he called Worsted! However, worsted was made in Worstead, once Worthstead (meaning Homestead), in Norfolk.

WORSTED, COTTON. Twilled cotton fabric made of hard twisted yarn and given smooth finish; simulates worsted suiting fabric.

WORSTED, RECOMBING OF. Combing of worsted fibers a second time to insure the removal of all noil fibers so that the best possible spun yarn will result from the top fibers when they are manipulated.

WORSTED CARD. Really two cards in one; there is a roller that carries the stock from the delivery end of the first card and presents it to the feeding-in attachment of the second card. This is the angle stripper. In addition, the combinations include two or four licker-in rollers, two main cylinders, a doffer and a coiler can arrangement at the front of the second card.

WORSTED CLOTH. Supposed to have originated in Worstead, England, this cloth is now made all over the world. Because of labor costs and the manipulation of the fibers into a good worsted material, it was not until about 1890 that worsted came into its own. At that time it began to cope with fine woolens and with the rise of improved machines and new inventions the fabric soon became a favorite with the public. There are 560 yards in one pound of a 1s worsted yarn.

WORSTED COMBING. The separation of long, choice fibers from the short, immature, undesirable stock. The former is called "top"; the latter, "noil," which is used as a filler-in stock and substitute fiber in many cloths. Noil is about the same quality as top but it is not long enough to be worked alone. See Illustrated Section.

WORSTED COMBING, METHODS. 1. Short wool, from 1½ to 5 inches in staple, is combed by the Heilman or French system of combing—the upright frame method.

2. Medium wool, from 2½ to 8 inches in length, is combed by the Noble or Circular comber—the English or Bradford method.

3. Long wool, from 8 to 12 inches long, is cared for by the Lister or Square-knit comber. This wool is prepared and not combed. Efforts to comb stock over 10 inches long do not always give good results.

WORSTED FLANNEL. Flannel made of worsted yarn.

WORSTEDS. Popular class of cloths made of choice woolen stock using fibers of approximately the same length in staple. The process of making worsted cloth originated in the little village of that name in Norfolk County, England. Today, the procedure of making worsted cloth has changed somewhat because of the improvement in up-to-the-minute modern machinery.

The Paris Exposition of 1889 "made" worsteds; it was also at this event that Count Hilaire de Chardonnet showed his first fabric made of what was then known as "artificial silk," now known as rayon. The Sesquicentennial Exhibition of 1926 had much to do with fostering the advent of the two man-made fibers, viscose and acetate, which now are household words and articles.

WORSTEDS, GASSING OR SINGEING OF. Certain types of worsteds are passed over a gas flame to singe the protruding fibers in the same way that cotton is made bereft of fuzziness. The cloth will take on a smooth, uniform surface that enhances the material. After singeing, the material must be washed very thoroughly so as to rid the fabric of any animal matter odor that might remain.

WORSTED SYSTEM. The method of manufacture resorted to for medium and higher types of wool of good staple properties. Fiber length used may range from 1½ inch stock for the French or Franco-Belgian system and from around 2-inch staple for the Bradford or English system of making worsted yarn. Six- or seven-inch staple is about the limit that may be employed for worsted yarn manufacture. The main operations include carding, combing, gilling, drawing, and spinning on the mule, ring, cap, or flyer frames. In some mills gilling may precede combing.

WORSTED-TYPE WOOL. That suitable for manufacture into worsted fabrics; combing wool in classification.

WORSTED YARN. Made from choice woolen stock that can be combed after carding. The fibers are specially treated—drawn, drafted, doubled, and redoubled in the machines. In the knitting trade, worsted yarn has great use in sweaters of varying types that are in demand from season to season.

WORSTED YARNS, COLOR IN. In the following, black and white are classed as colors.

1. DOUBLE MARL: Yarn made of one end of mixture shade or solid color twisted with one end of two colors which have been roved together, that is, the colored strands entered the roving frame singly and were delivered as a single yarn effect, from the roving frame. Roving is fiber stock one step removed from being finished spun yarn.

2. HALF MARL: Yarn made from one end of mixture color or shade, twisted with one end of two colors which have been roved together.

3. MARL: Yarn made of two identical ends twisted together, the single

ends used having been made up of two colors that have been roved together.

4. MELANGE: Yarn made from worsted top that has been Vigoreux or Melange printed.

5. MIXTURE: Yarn made from the fibers of two or more colors blended together.

6. SINGLE MARL: A single yarn made up of two colors that have been roved together.

7. SINGLE MOTTLE: A single yarn made as a single marl yarn with regard to the combination of colors. The marl effect, however, is obtained by spinning from two halfweight rovings of different colors into the single end. The effect is a clearer contrast of color than that noted in single marl yarn.

8. SOLID COLOR: Yarn made from fibers of a single color.

9. TWIST: Yarn made of two single ends of different colors, twisted together, with the single ends being either solid colors or mixture shades.

WORUMBO. Formerly the trademark of Worumbo Mills, Inc., Lisbon Falls, Maine, for high grade fabrics made of wool and/or specialty or hair fibers in many types of constructions, weaves, and finishes. The name is now the property of J. P. Stevens & Company, New York City.

WRACK. Sea grass used in making coarse rope.

WRAP. Originally, a garment which was wrapped about the person. The term now implies outerwear fabrics or garments which are worn in addition to regular clothing.

WRAP MACHINE. A circular jersey latch needle knitting machine equipped with wrap fingers and a wrap bobbin table in addition to the conventional overhead yarn stand and needle arrangement. It makes fabric which incorporates unusual pattern and stripe motifs.

There are two cylinders on the machine—a needle cylinder which houses the latch needles, as in the conventional sinker top knitting, and a wrap finger cylinder.

In the action the knitting needles move vertically under normal cam actuation while the fingers activated by special cams in the finger cylinder have a lateral movement. In actual operation the finger comes out on one side of the needle and returns to the other side. Different colored yarns may be fed to the fingers; theoretically, as many colors may be used as there are fingers to be fed.

WRAPPER. In costume, a garment

SOME ADVANTAGES OF WOVEN CLOTH

1. Firm construction: typewriter ribbon, duck, webbing, overcoating.
2. Durable if closely woven: serge, broadcloth, many types of outerwear.
3. Launders well: underwear of many types, washable dressgoods.
4. Drapes well, will not sag, and holds shape: satin and other ideal fabrics for evening wear, French worsted, tricotine, cavalry twill.
5. The only type of cloth that will drape with a natural flare: satins made of silk, rayon, acetate; high-quality worsted for women's wear apparel; soft sheers of wool, rayon, or nylon.
6. Can be pleated and tucked very readily: serge, cassimere, many other types of dressgoods made from the major fibers. Accordion pleats and box pleats present a good effect on certain woven goods, whereas many other types of textile fabrics cannot be pleated in a satisfactory manner.
7. Can be cut and draped on the bias: evening wear, slips, dresses.
8. Has greater tensile strength than other types of material: for example, the shoulder strap webbing on an army haversack must have a tensile breaking strength of two thousand pounds (one ton). It is made of cotton or nylon webbing.
9. Withstands chafing and friction well: men's wear suiting must meet these tests; topcoatings and overcoatings, underwear, etc.
10. May be colored by any of the major methods of coloring: piece-dyed, yarn or skein-dyed, stock-dyed, cross-dyed, printed.
11. Especially suited for detailed and intricate printed designs: splash prints, fourteen-color prints, photographic prints, etc.
12. Woven construction makes possible many types of finish.
13. Woven constructions make possible many uses: innerwear, outerwear, household fabrics and cloths, decorative materials, industrial fabrics.
14. Certain weave constructions permit finer detail of pattern than is found in knitted, plaited, braided, or felt cloth, generally speaking: Jacquard patterns showing pastoral scenes, noted personages, buildings, etc. A Jacquard loom can be made to reproduce any picture.
15. Close constructions can be made waterproof: gabardine, tackle twill, raincoating, Zelan-treated fabrics, Scotchgard-treated fabrics, etc.

SOME POSSIBLE DISADVANTAGES OF WOVEN CLOTH

1. Is not generally elastic when compared with knitted fabrics.
2. Is not really form-fitting; woven socks have not yet been produced.
3. After continued wear some woven fabrics will develop an undesirable shine—garments made of serge, cassimere, whipcord, tricotine, elastique.
4. Generally more expensive to manufacture than other types: Some textile fabrics have sold as high as two hundred dollars per yard for coating or evening wear material. Much decorative fabric is often very high in price.
5. Very sheer woven fabrics may slip or pull at the seams: slips cut on the bias; certain dressgoods may slip when washed.
6. Will show wrinkles readily: Many dressgoods will not stand up in hot weather and require frequent laundering. Handkerchiefs wrinkle easily.
7. Yarns of uneven size appear as defects in woven goods that have been finished: often noted in apparel or in goods bought over the counter in the department store.
8. Usually not porous. Some summer materials are made porous; but in general, woven textiles are not classed as being porous when some plaited, braided, or knitted fabrics are considered.

intended to cover the whole, or nearly the whole person. Has particular reference to a loose-fitting lounging dress for women.

WRAP-REVERSE. Circular knitting machine equipped to handle various types of wrap yarns as well as normal and reverse plating.

WRAPS. Term used to signify the number of yarn layers placed or set on a bobbin during each stroke of the traverse in manipulation.

WRAPS-ON-SOCKS. There are two types. 1. The Banner or Genuine Wrap is vertical embroidery on socks knitted simultaneously with the knitting of the sock by an actual part of the Banner Knitting Machine. The beginning and the end of the embroidery yarn occur at the top and the bottom of the embroidery figure. There are no loose ends to be trimmed. 2. The Mock Wrap is made by the use of an attachment for this embroidery which produces clocking, rib effects, and the over-all or allover motifs simultaneously with the knitting of the hose. The embroidery yarns are floated horizontally from the pattern on one side of the sock to the pattern appearing on the other side. The floating ends are then clipped on the inside of the sock leaving loose ends which are characteristic of mock wrap.

WRAP-UP. An easy sale; also used to describe any easy chore.

WRINGER. A machine used to press water out of fabrics or garments after washing; also the operator of such a machine.

WRINGER, COMPENSATING. One that may be adjusted automatically to adjust pressure, depends on the thickness of the goods being treated as they pass between the rollers of the machine.

WRINGING AND STRETCHING. Some fabrics are wrung and then stretched to soften up the fibers so that increased luster in finishing may be obtained.

WRINKLE. A small ridge or prominence on a smooth fabric, a crease or a fold. Weather conditions produce most wrinkles on clothing. Washer wrinkles on fabrics are almost impossible to remove.

WRINKLE PATTERN. There are five basic components in this pattern as set-up by the National Institute of Drycleaning, Silver Spring, Maryland. These are:

Mussiness: The portion of the specimen which shows minute creases which give the fabric a rumpled appearance.

Profile: The height of the wrinkles, or the degree to which the fabric surface is distorted from a plane.

Randomness: The extent to which a similar pattern exists throughout the entire specimen.

Sharpness of Creasing: The degree of sharpness or roundness of the observed creases.

Wrinkle Intensity: The number of wrinkles per unit area, assuming the randomness of the pattern, See Crease, Wrinkle.

WRINKLES, EVALUATION OF. Celanese Corporation of America developed an evaluation method for fabric wrinkles which tests a 10 x 10 inch sample of the particular fabric by placing it in a cylindrical chamber containing a tubular rubber insert. By alternately compacting the sample under a vacuum, and opening the sample again under pressure, a series of working cycles are performed. Fabrics, following the procedure, are then placed on clip boards and viewed by both front-edge and top lighting.

Five factors are observed in the testing: 1. *Wrinkle Density:* The number of wrinkles per unit area, assuming complete randomness of pattern.
2. *Profile:* The height of the wrinkles, or the degree to which the fabric surface is distorted from a plane.
3. *Sharpness of Creasing:* The degree of sharpness or roundness of the creases.
4. *Mussiness:* The portion of the specimen showing the minute creases which give the cloth a rumpled appearance.
5. *Randomness:* The extent to which a similar pattern exists throughout the entire specimen.

A weighting factor is assigned to each component because of the effects observed after the run are not of equal importance. The factors follow: Profile, 5; Sharpness, 3; Mussiness, 3; Density, 2; and Randomness, 1. To obtain a total weighted score, the assigned score of each component of the wrinkling is multiplied by its factor and all figures are then added for the total score.

WRINKL-SHED. Registered trademark for the exclusive wrinkle-resistant process developed in the research laboratories of Dan River Mills, Inc.

WRINKL-SHED WITH DRI-DON. Registered trademark for the exclusive wash-and-wear process developed in the research laboratories of Dan River Mills, Inc.

WRISTBAND. 1. The band of a sleeve, as of a shirt, which covers the wrist. 2. A wristlet.

WRISTLET. 1. A close-fitting knitted or woven band worn around the wrist

for protection from the cold. 2. A wristband of woven material worn as an ornament.

WRONG DRAWS. Warp threads that have been drawn through incorrect heddle eye of the harness or through the wrong reed split in the reed. Wrong draws often result, as well, from careless work on the part of the weaver. These blemishes are very detrimental to woven goods, since they show aggravating, fine lines in the warp direction that are not in accord with the layout of the pattern as set down by the designer or styler.

Weavers should do their utmost to always follow the drawing-in and reeding for the warp in the loom.

WUNDA-WEVE. Registered trademark of Dan River Mills, Inc., for its carpeting produced by its division, Wunda-Weve Company, Greenville, South Carolina.

WURLAN. Designates a two-step polycondensation treatment. Also referred to as interfacial polymerization, in the presence of a solid substrate which anchors a very thin layer of polyamide or other polymer on the fiber surface. The term is composed of the initials of Western Utilization Research plus LAN from the Latin root "Lanus" meaning wool.

WYATT, JOHN AND PAUL, LOUIS. In 1738 these two interesting English inventors introduced the principle of drawing rollers that made possible the spinning of yarn without the use of the fingers. Their invention gave to the world the use of excess speed of rollers and the principle of drawing and drafting textile fibers.

In 1748 they invented the revolving cylinder carding machine.

X

X-12 FLAME RETARDANT. This duPont flame retardant provides flame retardancy without affecting the appearance of a fabric and without loss of shade, color, or lightfastness. It is a renewable flame retardant that has to be reapplied when the material is drycleaned or washed; a simple operation done by many cleaners and custom treaters. Protection remains undiminished between cleanings. Effective for bedspreads, carpets, draperies, tablecloths, upholstery, mattress ticking, hair, straw, upholstery wadding, and wallpaper.

XANTHATING. A process in making rayon. The chemical treatment of cellulose in which carbon disulphide reacts with alkali cellulose crumbs to produce the bright orange cellulose xanthate.

XANTHATING CHURN. The hexagonal steel drum which rotates on its horizontal axis so that it can treat chemically the mixture cellulose and carbon disulphide (bisulphide) in the manufacture of rayon. The bisulphide is introduced after the cellulose charging door has been locked.

XANTHATION. The conversion of a xanthate, as in the case of cellulose in the manufacture of viscose rayon.

XANTHATION, CONTINUOUS. Developed by Du Pont Company, Inc., this continuous xanthation is used by producers of rayon yarn and cellophane. It makes possible continuous processes for all phases in the manufacture of rayon cellulosic yarn. Advantages cited include a more consistent product, lower manpower, greater chemical and power demand, and adaptability and safety to present plants making these products.

XANTHIC. Possessing a yellow to orange color, and pertaining to xanthin or xanthine.

XANTHIN. An insoluble yellow pigment found in yellow flowers.

XANTHONE, XANTHINE. A white or colorless crystalline nitrogenous compound of the ketone type, obtained by distilling salicylic acid with acetic anhydride, or a derivative of it. Several yellow coloring matters may be derived from this compound.

X-IT. This soil resistant product came into being in January, 1967, and gives excellent results on work clothes, heavy denims, jean cloths, medium to heavy cotton drills and twills, etc. It can be used on postcure fabrics, is not a soil repellent, combats soil redeposition, and deposition through static. This registered trademark product belongs to the McCampbell Division of Graniteville Company, Inc., Graniteville, North Carolina. X-IT can easily withstand more than twenty washings and gives good durability.

XL-II RAYON STAPLE. Used chiefly in conveyor belting, this product claims to have 80 percent greater tensile strength than similar all-cotton constructions. Conditioned grab tensiles show that a 28 ounce/yard, 100 percent XL-II construction has a strength factor of 53, against a strength factor of 28 for a 36 ounce/yard, 100 percent cotton construction. Impact resistance is said to be three times greater than that of cotton. Product of American Viscose Division of FMC Corporation, New York City.

X-STATIC. An antistatic continuous filament nylon yarn used in the carpet trade. This product of Rohm and Haas,

Philadelphia, Pennsylvania, reduces static charges well below the level of human discomfort while retaining its properties for lie; does not become visible later with wear. It can be incorporated into practically any construction, color, or style now made, and it can be used with excellent results in tufting, shearing, dyeing and printing done on conventional methods. At present, it is made in the company plant in Fayetteville, North Carolina.

X-RAY ANALYSIS. The determination of the internal structure of a material by means of the diffraction pattern formed when X-rays pass through it.

X-RAY TESTER. A heavy-duty, stationary X-ray unit which will make accurate radiographic (X-ray) penetration through twelve-inch solid aluminum, 3¼-inch solid steel, and 2-inch solid brass.

Materials of practically any thickness can be penetrated by using gamma rays. This equipment can also be adapted to plastics, ceramics, electric cable tests, and vacuum tube examination.

Defects of metal materials, porosity and piping of various sources, gas cavities, blow holes, cracks and incomplete welds or lack of fusion, misruns or variations in thickness of metals can be determined by X-ray, and permanent plastic base film records made of filing.

X, XX, XXX WOOL. Known as X, double-X, and triple-X, or three-X, these symbols are used to designate fine wools of 64s, 70s, and 80s qualities, respectively.

XYLENE. Any of three isomeric colorless hydrocarbons, contained in coal tar and wood tar. Used as solvents and in the manufacture of certain dyes.

XYLIDINE. Any of six isomeric amino derivatives of xylene, $C_8H_{11}N$. They are homologs of aniline and are used in the synthesis of certain dyes.

XYLODINE. Yarn made from paper strips which have been twisted and then coated with glue to add strength; a product of World War I.

XYLOLIN. Originated in Saxony, Germany, during World War I. It consists of narrow strips of light paper and cotton or wool spun and woven into a cream-colored material. In those days a suit of clothes made from it could be bought for about three dollars. The material could be washed repeatedly without surface deterioration.

Y

YACHT CLOTH. Stoutly made, unfinished worsted in blue, white, and

delicate stripes. Used in yachting circles.

YACHTING CORDAGE OR ROPE, STRENGTH OF. The conventional standard for yachts is manila, abaca, or henequen, all terms that are interchangeable; they belong in the same category of bast fibers. The utility grade is strong and useful for many jobs, but yacht-grade manila, made from the longest fibers (often treated with fungicide) is stronger and smoother. Linen rope is softer, stronger, more flexible, and more expensive than the manila. It is ideal for sheets since it is easy on the hands, and cotton, although not as strong, is also popular for sheets.

Among the man-made fibers used, nylon is very popular. There are two methods of manufacture of the rope. In the first method, filaments run the entire length of the rope, giving it maximum smoothness and strength. This smoothness, however, often makes splicing difficult in order to make it hold firmly. Therefore, in the second method of manufacture, a rougher type of rope has been perfected from spun chopped filaments, the staple stock fiber. Nylon rope has good flexibility and springiness, making it highly satisfactory for anchor ropes and mooring lines.

"Dacron" is also a popular fiber used in maritime circles. While it is practically as strong as nylon, it does not possess the elasticity of the latter. It is ideal for halyards, sheets, and other running rigging on boats.

Polyethylene rope has the property of floating, a great asset to the yachtsman. It comes in a variety of strengths and finds use in ski. tow-lines, is wellliked for dinghy painters, and has other uses where flotation and light weight are desirable; however, it is at present, not suitable for halyards or sheets.

Below is a table of representative strengths in pounds of the various ropes in use at present.

YAGUAGUA. A Peruvian innerbark bast fiber used for coarse clothing fabrics.

YAK. 1. A wild or domesticated animal of the ox family, blackish-brown in color and native to the plateaus of central Asia and particularly to Tibet. The animal is of good size and has a coat of long wavy hair fiber which covers the entire body except on the back where the hair is short and silklike. The hair is used in making coverings, rope, and very rough, crude fabrics; the soft undercoat finds uses in dress goods peculiar to the regions where the animal is raised.

2. A coarse, pillow lace made from the soft, undercoat fibers of the yak. The better grades of this lace are called Tibetan lace.

3. A machine-made lace of worsted yarn used for trimming on shawls, throws, scarfs, etc.

YAK LACE. 1. A type of wool crochet lace. 2. A coarse bobbin lace made in England.

YAMA-MAI. Silk produced by this type of silkworm. See SILK.

YARAY. A Puerto Rican palm tree whose leaves yield a straw fiber used in making hats.

YARD. A measure of length, equaling 36 inches or 3 feet, being the standard of American and English linear measurement.

YARD GOODS. Any textile material retailed on the yard basis.

YARDSTICK. A measuring device 36 inches long. It is made of wood, and its entire length is spaced with markings one-eighth of an inch apart.

YARN. A generic term for an assemblage of fibers or filaments, either natural or man-made, twisted together to form a continuous strand which can be used in weaving, knitting, braiding, or plaiting, or otherwise made into a textile material. Spun yarn is the product of the spinning frame characterized by a continuous, evenly distributed, coherent arrangement of any type of fibers of varying or similar staple length, the relative positions of which are maintained by the introduction of a definite lateral twist to produce strength or coherence imparted in the final operation.

Notable exception to the above would be the woolen-type yarn. Here the fibers are distributed at near right angles with relation to the continuous length of the yarn. An exception to even spinning would be the addition of noiled fibers to the base stock. Noils do not lend themselves to being properly drawn, in consequence a rough texture yarn, desirable for tweeds and shantungs, is produced.

To produce spun yarns, the raw stock must be put through preparatory machinery for even distribution and blending, after which there is the carding or combing to achieve parallel fiber distribution; then a group of attenuating or drawing machine operations follow, ending with the spinning. Yarn in production is called a lap, sliver, and roving, in that order, depending on the type of machine used. Yarns are definitely sized or numbered based on the number of standard yardage hanks contained in one pound.

Filament yarn is made from various continuous filaments, such as silk and man-made yarn—viscose, acetate, nylon, etc. See illustrations throughout picture section.

YARN, CROSS-BLENDED. A single yarn spun from a blend or mixture of different fiber species. Examples are a yarn spun from cotton fibers and acetate staple, wool fibers and rayon staple, or from wool and cotton fibers.

YARN, HOLLOW FILAMENT. Also called bead or bubble yarn, it is made of viscose rayon. As the filament is extruded, air bubbles are injected at regular intervals, spaced as desired. Enclosed bubbles can be tiny and not connected, or they may be continuous in a long tube effect. This yarn forms a buoyant fabric and can be used in lifeboats, life jackets, rafts, etc.

YARN, PRINTED. Yarn which has been colored in a regular or random plan in order to produce novel effects.

YARN, SELF-BLENDED. A singles yarn spun from a blend or mixture of the same fiber species. For example, a spun-rayon yarn made from staple of different lengths, or different deniers, is known as self-blended.

YARN, SEWING THREAD COUNT. The number noted on the end of a spool of threads means that there are three yarns twisted together of that particular number. Thus, a Number 70 standard sewing thread is composed of three yarns of 70s plied or twisted together—a three-cord thread.

A 70s six-cord thread, which is found on the market, means that there are three strands, each of which is composed of two yarns twisted together.

YARN ABRADER. A machine designed to measure the resistance to interspecimen rubbing of multiple samples of yarn. Such factors as fiber blends, resin treatments, sizing, twist, and filament count have definite influences on the resistance of yarn to abrasive action.

YARN CARRIER. A device for feeding yarn from the cones or bobbins on a knitting frame to the needles.

YARN CLEANER. Usually it is a narrow slit device, especially effective on rayon, acetate, silk, and comparable filaments, which prevents knots, slubs, etc., from going through in manipulation of the stock. Sometimes called a slub catcher.

YARN CONDITIONER. Any chest, chamber, or compartment used to condition yarn, twist, etc. Steam or water vapor is circulated in the device so that appraisals may be made.

YARN CONSTRUCTION. Data obtained on yarn as to ply, count, cable, hawser, twist, etc., usually done by close inspection to meet certain requirements.

YARN DYEING OR SKEIN DYEING. The dyeing of yarn in skein form. This method is popular for cloths which show stripes of different colors in the pattern. Examples are gingham, checks, stripe-effects, plaids, overplaids, tartans, rayon sharkskin, and other dress fabrics.

YARN MEASURES, COTTON. Measures of yarn follow: 54 inches equals one thread—the circumference of the warp reel; 80 thread equals one lea, 1 lea equals 120 yards; 7 leas equal one hank or 840 yards, the standard yardage for a Number One's cotton yarn. A bundle equals 10 pounds.

YARN METER, HAMILTON. A quality control device to measure yarn for all types of knitting machines to improve uniformity of the knitting stitches and to reduce excessive cloth shrinkage. The machine records upwards of 1,000 stitches and the record can be noted for a duplicate rerun of the same fabric, style, and construction. A built-in electromagnet and universal knee permit easy machine mounting of the meter. Product of Scott & Williams Company, Providence, Rhode Island.

YARN METER, KNITTING. A device used to determine whether the yarn is being drawn uniformly into the knitting elements of a multifeed knitting frame. The meter is also designed to insure that uniform quality fabric is being made. A yarn meter should not be confused with a tension compensator which is designed to insure uniform tension to the yarn during the knitting operation.

YARN NUMBER. A standard measure of the fineness of yarn, either calculated by number of specified lengths per specified weight, as for cotton, wool or linen (thus, the higher the yarn number, the finer the yarn); or calculated by number of specified weights per specified length, as rayon, silk, or nylon (thus, the higher the number the thicker the yarn.)

YARN NUMBERING SYSTEMS, WORLD.

1. ABERDEEN SCALE: The spyndle or spindle is 14,400 yards, and the number of pounds a spindle weighs is the yarn count. Thus #1s yarn has 14,400 yards to the pound.

2. ALLOA SCALE: Used chiefly in Kilmarnock and Stirling, Scotland. The cut is 240 yards, and 48 cut equals 11,520 yards (240 x 48 equals 11,520). The number of such spindles is the count of the yarn.

3. ASBESTOS AND GLASS: The yarns are figured usually somewhat the same as woolen yarn. The cut, however, is not 300 yards as in woolen yarn; it is a unit length of 100 yards. In calculating the size of these yarns, therefore, a standard has been set up with 100 yards as the standard length.

EXAMPLE: What is the size of an asbestos yarn, 3,600 yards of which weigh 12 pounds?

$$\frac{3,600}{12 \times 100} \text{ equals } 3,$$

the yarn size (ANSWER).

In all notations, the fact that asbestos or glass cuts are meant, must be noted; otherwise, there might be some confusion with the woolen cut. (It should be noted, as well, that glass will contract in twisting and allowances should be made for this fact.)

4. COTTON: 840 yards of yarn constitutes one hank, and the number of hanks in one pound, avoirdupois, will give the yarn count. This scale is also used for spun silk in the singles count of yarn.

A 2/60s cotton means a single 60s doubled, or a 30s yarn.

A 2/60s spun silk, however, better understood for recognition purposes, would be written as 60/2. This means that two single 120s are doubled to give the 60s yarn. A spindle, incidentally, in cotton is 18 hanks which make 15,120 yards (840 x 18 equals 15,120).

5. DENIER: It is a weight used as a unit when speaking of the size of silk, man-made fibers or filaments. One denier weighs .05 grams. In value (since the denier was originally a coin used in the time of Julius Caesar), it has a present value of about one French sou. Revived in France during the reign of Francis I, King of France, 1515–1547, the denier was used to the yarn counts would be a #26s Integral.

Since wraps of 700,000 yards are impractical for sizing roving or yarn, waplets of 100 yards are used. A wraplet is 1/7000 of a wrap, and a grain is 1/7000 part of a pound. The weight of a wraplet, in grains, will give the yarn number. For example, if a wraplet weighs 12 grains, the yarn is a #12s Integral.

10. ITALIAN SCALE: The Rules of the London Silk Conditioning House govern this scale, which decrees that the hank equals 400 French ells, 476 meters, or 520 yards. 533⅓ denier make one ounce avoirdupois. The number of deniers that one such hank weighs will give the count of the yarn.

11. JUTE SPYNDLE SYSTEM: Fine jute yarns are measured on the linen or woolen cut system. For coarse jute, however, a direct numbering system is used at times. This system is based on the weight, in pounds, of a jute spyndle of 14,400 yards. Thus, if a 14,400-yard skein of jute weighs five pounds, the yarn would be known as a 5-spyndle jute.

12. LINEN OR LEA SCALE: A hank or lea is 300 yards, and the number of these in one pound is the count of the linen yard. A spindle or spyndle is 48 lea or 14,400 yards (300 x 48 equals 14,400).

About the finest spun linen count of yarn in the United States is a 20 lea, and the bulk of flax spun here is 16 lea, most of which is used for shoe thread.

Experimental counts of 40 lea have been made here, but they are not of commercial value and rather impractical. A 20-lea yarn is equivalent to about a 7s cotton yarn or a 744-denier yarn in size.

In Ireland, the lea counts range from 25 to 28 for use in dress goods. The particularly fine gill spinning makes this possible. Spinning frames in the United States are equipped with tape bands while those in Ireland use caps which make the finer counts possible. Handkerchief linen, in Ireland, is spun from 56 to 70 lea, and, at times, even in finer counts. The wet spinning process has to be used to obtain these high counts. A bundle of lea is 200 hanks or 60,000 yards (300 x 200 equals 60,000). Incidentally, rayon can be spun in the United States somewhat finer than linen on linen equipment.

13. MANCHESTER SCALE: This English hank is 1,000 yards, and the number of drams that such a hank weighs is the count of the yarn.

14. METRIC SYSTEM: The metric or International System is discussed often as a desirable method for designating the size or count of all yarns used in the textile industry. The object is to unify the methods employed for indicating the degree of fineness or coarseness of all yarns manufactured from various fibers by the industry.

Many advantages would result from the adoption of such a system, especially when the matter of foreign trade is involved, when ply yarns are made of two or more single yarns spun from different fibers, and when yarns of different materials are combined in a fabric.

There are, however, several reasons why a uniform method is not accepted for the textile industry throughout the world today. The system used in various branches of the industry, and in many countries where textile manufacturing is of great importance, has become too well established to be changed. It is well-nigh impossible to obtain prompt acceptance of any particular system in all branches of the industry in all countries.

In the metric system of numbering, higher numbers indicate finer yarns, as in the cotton numbering system. The ard of 1,600 by the count of 4, which gives 6,400 yards to the pound in this yarn.

To find the number of yards in a 16-cut wool, multiply the standard of 300 by the count of 16, which gives 4,800 to the pound in this yarn.

17. WORSTED SCALE: The hank is 560 yards in one pound of a #1s yarn. This number is two thirds of the cotton number of 840 yards. The number of such hanks in one pound is the count of the yarn. To find the number of yards in one pound of a 40s worsted yarn, multiply the standard of 560 by the count of 40 which gives 22,400 yards to the pound in this yarn.

18. YARDS PER OUNCE: This method is used in Dewsbury, England, for woolen yarn counts, and in Yorkshire for organzine silk. The method is referred to at times as "the West of England System."

19. YARDS PER POUND: This is the simplest measurement of all scales or standards.

YARN NUMBERS, COTTON. Cotton yarn is measured in terms of length per unit of weight. No. 1 cotton has 840 yards per pound. No. 10 has 8,400 yards per pound. The count is inversely proportionate to the size of the yarn. Therefore, No. 100 yarn is ten times finer than No. 10, etc.

YARN PRINTING. Printing of a colored design on the warp prior to weaving the cloth. It is done on some carpet yarn (so-called warp-print styles), and on warp that is to be used in shadow or mottled effects as noted on some bed-covering fabrics. The filling usually subdues the vivid warp coloring when the cloth has been woven.

YARN REEL. See REEL.

YARNS, STRETCH. Made from thermoplastic fiber, usually in continuous filament form, they possess a great degree of stretch and quick recovery. Deforming, heat-setting, and developing treatments are features of these yarns.

There are two main types. 1. Crimped or nontorque in which the deformation is in undulating or wavelike formation. Crimp may be obtained by passing the yarn over an edge, passing it through a stuffer box, or in the case of a "crinkled yarn," knitting a yarn into a fabric, then heat-setting the material followed by "back-winding" the yarn from the fabric. 2. Twist or torque yarn in which the deformation is obtained by a desirable combination of heat-setting and twisting. This may be done by twisting, heat-setting and then detwisting; by false-setting and heat-setting simultaneously, or by heat-setting and twisting in the case of monofilament. Such yarns are usually plied to control the elasticity in the finished product.

YARN SIZE. Same as yarn count.

YARN TESTING. There are two popular methods of testing yarn. They follow:

1. SKEIN OR LEA TEST: A skein or lea of yarn is wound onto a yarn reel that is 54 inches in circumference. When the reel has made 80 revolutions there will be 120 yards of yarn wound. The skein is then placed on the spool of the testing machine and is broken or ruptured in the same manner as in testing cloth. Several tests should be made and the averages computed.

2. SINGLE STRAND TEST: The yarn is held between two clamps or screws which are drawn apart by some suitable means. The breaking strength is indicated on a dial in terms of ounces or pounds. In some cases, readings may be made in grains.

The dial or clock on the machine will stop when the material is broken or ruptured. The hand on the device will record the number of grams, ounces, or pounds that the tested material was able to withstand.

YARRE. Broad term for coarse, unwieldy hair fibers found in desirable fiber stock in cashmere and other comparable fibers.

YASMAK. Used for veiling by Mohammedan women, this lightweight cotton comes in black, white, and print effects.

YAWS. Thin places in fabric which are detrimental to the cloth.

YEANLING. From the Anglo-Saxon, meaning a lamb or kid.

YEARLING. A sheep one year old or in its second year of growth.

YEARLING WOOL. Fleece taken from a sheep about one year old.

YEAST. Consisting of minute cells, this fungus will cause fermentation in sugar solution and starchy substances.

YELLOW. The most luminous of the primary colors. It has the color of ripe lemons, sunflowers, or butter; the color of the spectrum between green and orange. The term is given to any pigment or dyestuff which has this color predominating.

YELLOW BERRIES. See PERSIAN BERRIES.

YELLOW-DOG CONTRACT. An agreement, written or oral, made between a company and an employee to the effect that, as a condition of employment, no employee can join or belong to a union.

YELLOWING. 1. Some woolens and worsteds in time will, if the pattern has some white in it, turn rather yellowish in cast. This is because disintegration has set in due to slow chemical reaction that was initiated in the bleaching operation.

2. The tendency of heavily dressed cottons to turn yellow because of possible difficulties encountered in bleaching of the goods.

YELLOW-LEAF BLIGHT. See RUST.

YELLOWS. Short term for yellow cocoons.

YELLOW-STAINED COTTON. Cotton which has become discolored to considerable degree—caused chiefly by the elements.

YELLOW WOOD. Any yellowish wood obtained from many trees and capable of producing yellow dye. Fustic is another name for this term.

YEN. The monetary unit of Japan; value of about 49 gold cents. Quotations in silk are given to show that the silk is selling for "so many yen per kin."

YERLI. A fine staple, raised in the Smyrna area. High-grade wool which because of its varying quality is used in apparel, blankets, and carpets.

YIELD. The number of pounds of actual wool fiber obtained from the scouring operation in woolen manufacturing. This amount, after the yolk, suint, and some foreign matter have been removed, is called yield; but it is not possible to take out all of the foreign particles up to this point.

On a 100-pound scouring basis, yield will run from about 35 to 65 pounds; the better the grade of wool, the lower is the yield and the greater is the amount of yolk and suint removed.

YISHBIZH, YISTLO. Two types of Navajo Indian woolen blankets. The former is accentuated by colored diagonal stripes; the latter is either plain or made with some colored motif. Hand-woven by the Indians, most of the blankets, however, are now made on power looms in New England.

"YOWE." In Scotland, a female sheep or ewe.

YUVA. See NYLON STRAW.

YUZEN. Named for the Japanese inventor, Yuzen, who perfected a secret method to dye painted fabrics and at the same time have them retain their motif, outline, and coloring effect. He lived in the seventeenth century, and his method is still in use. Silks such as habutai, crepe, velvet and some other silk materials are examples on which his method is used.

Z

Z. A designation for that direction of twist in yarn, the inclination of which corresponds to the central portion of the letter Z.

Also compare with S-TWIST, Z-TWIST.

ZACKEL. Native to Hungary, this sheep is raised also in the Balkan area and in Turkey. The animal has long, upright, tapering, spiral-twisted horns. The long, coarse, kempy fiber is used in rug manufacture.

ZAFIRI. A type of brown-fibered Egyptian cotton.

ZAGORA. Egyptian cotton comparable with Ashmouni cotton, raised in the Nile Delta.

ZALAN. A 3½-inch staple is obtained from Zalan sheep raised in northern Morocco; the fleece is of the open type and is very uneven.

ZAMANDOQUE. See ISTLE.

ZAMARRA. Coat of sheepskin the shepherds of South America, southern Europe and northern Africa wear in cold weather.

ZANELLA. A compactly woven twill fabric made of cotton warp and worsted filling for use in the umbrella trade. Rayon or silk may be used in the filling, in place of worsted.

ZANTREL. Developed by four European companies under certain Japanese patent rights, and formerly known as Z-54, this product of American Enka Corporation is of the same chemical composition as viscose rayon although it differs from it in molecularity. Features of the fiber include high wet modulus (dimensional stability when wet), low wet swelling, low residual shrinkage, and the ability to impart a crisp dry hand or a very soft drape to fabrics in which it is used. Chief uses are for many types of apparel, both alone and in blends, and in decorative fabrics.

ZANZIBAR. A cotton shirting material made chiefly with red, white, and blue stripes which run in the warp direction and are used in both directions to produce checks, windowpanes, and similar motifs. The ends weave "two as one," while the filling is inserted "two picks to the shed." Some cotton gray goods in India also goes by this name.

ZEFSTAT. A synergistic acrylic and nylon yarn type developed by Dow Badische Company, Inc., New York City and Williamsburg, Virginia, and claimed to be the first permanent built-in static control for carpet yarns. No special latex or backing is necessary and there is no effect on the face or general appreciation of knit, woven, tufted-cut, or loop pile construction. See Synergistic.

ZEFSTAT TYPE F-151. This type can be tufted into carpets of just about any face fiber for guaranteed static control. Guarantees are issued on carpets that meet the specifications of the trademark owner, Dow Badische Company,

Inc., Williamsburg, Virginia.

ZEPEL. A fabric fluoridizer of E.I. DuPont de Nemours & Co., Inc., Wilmington, Delaware. This compound which contains fluorine, forms a shield or layer of film around textile fibers thereby preventing spots and stains from penetrating these fibers in a cloth and making their removal an easy matter. Treatment with the product does not affect washfastness of dyes used in a material, nor does it affect the "breathability" or strength of the fabric. It is an excellent protection against water and stains on garments.

ZEPEL, TOTAL ACTION. A fluorine chemical which can be applied permanently to upholstery, curtains, draperies and slipcovers. The product forms a film around the fabric fibers which repels dry dirt and liquids. It is claimed that the dirt remains on top of the fabric without any penetration unless the pile or fabric structure is unusually open. This product is said to permit deposited dirt to be more readily and completely released, while the need for such cleaning sharply reduced. Product of E. I. duPont de Nemours & Co., Inc., Wilmington, Delaware.

ZEPHYR GINGHAM. A fine grade of gingham, light in weight and composed of single 40s, 60s or higher counts of combed cotton yarn in warp and filling. Woven in plain weave or a small all-over dobby-effect, it is made in attractive patterns by the use of fast colors in warp and filling. Zephyr has excellent wearing qualities.

ZEPHYRLITE. A light spinnaker sailcloth of gossamer-like construction with an exceptionally high texture or pick count. The fabric has great strength and can impart maximum lift and forward thrust, the ultimate in stability and strength but is responsive to the slightest changes in velocity. Product of Howe & Bainbridge, Inc., Boston, Massachusetts. See SPINNAKER.

ZEPHYR SHAWL. A light embroidered shawl made from loosely twisted yarn, and very loose in texture.

ZEPHYR SHIRTING. Poetically it means "west wind." Anything that is light, soft, sheer, or gentle is often referred to as zephyr. Hence, any lightweight shirting may be called by this term. Shirting in this group includes skip-dents, leno, or doup-woven fabric, lightweight silks, etc.

ZEPHYR YARN. A worsted knitting yarn that is very soft and light in weight. Used for dress goods, it comes in a variety of colors and yarns. Silk, rayon, combination, and mixture yarns are often used in yarn of this name. Since man-made fibers and filaments have come to the fore in the textile industry, it is noted that they are often mixed with the natural fibers in making novelty yarns of many varieties. While zephyr yarn was originally of worsted, much of the yarn on the market today of this name is worsted combined with varying percentages of other fibers.

In recent years the yarn has been used in making woven fabrics in addition to knit goods.

"ZESET" TP. This key chemical, a surface modifier, is used to make woolen garments washable. It may be applied before or after dyeing and provides protection for the life of the garment. There is no appreciable effect on color, dyefastness, or shade and there is not any fiber degradation. Tensile strength and abrasion resistance are not adversely effected. DuPont and Ametek, Inc., South Portland, Maine, developed "Zeset" TP, the latter company creating suitable drycleaning and pressing equipment to handle the product in fabric. After relaxation or machine shrinkage, and usually after dyeing, garments are placed in the basket wheel of the modified drycleaner. "Zeset" TP is diluted with "Perclene" perchlorethylene and pumped into a specially constructed reservoir; garments are tumbled for thirty minutes and the basket wheel is spun for two minuted to extract excess solution. Tumble drying and curing are done at temperatures of 210-220° F. Aftertreatment may be given the article.

ZERO WATER. Distilled water, since it has no hardness.

"ZESET." A textile finish that will impart durable wrinkle- and shrink-resistance to cotton and viscose rayon fabrics. Spun rayon materials, many of which are not at present washable, when treated with "Zeset" can be laundered and bleached under the usual home conditions without serious loss of strength and discoloration often encountered in the case of home-bleached fabrics. Product of E. I. du Pont de Nemours & Co., Inc.

ZIBELINE. Used for cloakings, coats, and capes in women's wear. The cloth is made from crossbred yarns, and the fabric is strongly colored. Stripings, sometimes noted in the cloth, work in very well with the construction and appearance of the finished garment. The finish is a highly raised type, lustrous, and the nap is long and lies in the one direction. The cloth may or may not be given a soft finish and feel.

ZIGZAG TWILL. A twill weave which produces a zigzag effect in cloth. The weave is used to some degree in women's coating for spring and fall wear.

ZIMARRA. The long outer garment worn by priests in countries where the cassock is worn for street wear. It is usually black and is of the same material as the cassock. This priest's "overcoat fabric" may be made of woolen or worsted yarn; the texture is compact.

ZINC CHLORIDE, $ZnCl_2$. It is a white deliquescent solid used in sizing and finishing cotton goods. This antiseptic will keep material soft and prevent mold on textiles.

ZINC DUST. Used in indigo vats with sodium bisulphide to produce hydrosulphite.

SELECTED LIST OF THE BETTER SEMITECHNICAL AND TECHNICAL BOOKS
ON TEXTILES FOR YOUR LIBRARY

Aitken, J. B. AUTOMATIC WEAVING

Albeck, P. PRINTED TEXTILES

Allcock, H. HERALDIC DESIGN—It's origins, Ancient Forms, & Modern usage

American Association for Textile Technology, WATER REPELLENT FINISHES AND COATINGS

AMERICAN COTTON HANDBOOK Vols. I & II (1965)

AMERICAN HOME ECONOMICS RESEARCH ABSTRACTS—TEXTILES AND CLOTHING (1966)

AMERICAN HOME ECONOMICS RESEARCH ABSTRACTS—TEXTILES AND CLOTHING (1967)

AMERICAN HOME ECONOMICS RESEARCH ABSTRACTS—TEXTILES AND CLOTHING (1968)

American Society For Testing & Materials SELECTED ASTM STANDARDS FOR TEXTILE STUDENTS (1965)

ASTM Standards 1972—Part 24, TEXTILE MATERIALS: Yarns, Fabrics, General Methods

ASTM Standards 1972—Part 25, TEXTILE MATERIALS: Fibers, Zippers, High Modulus Fibers

Appleyard, H. M. GUIDE TO THE IDENTIFICATION OF ANIMAL FIBERS

Armstrong, J. B. FACTORY UNDER THE ELMS, A History of Harrisville, New Hampshire,1774-1969 (1970)

Arnold, P. & White, P. CLOTHES AND CLOTH

Asbestos Textile Institute, HANDBOOK OF ASBESTOS TEXTILES, 3rd ed. (1967)

Atwater, M. THE SHUTTLE-CRAFT BOOK OF AMERICAN HAND WEAVING

Backer, S. & Valko, E. THESAURUS OF TEXTILE TERMS COVERING FIBROUS MATERIALS AND PROCESSES, 2nd ed. (1969)

Baker, F. E., AN INTRODUCTION TO KNITTING (paper)

Barve, V. R. COMPLETE TEXTILE ENCYCLOPEDIA (1967)

Beevers, H. THE PRACTICE OF BRADFORD OPEN DRAWING

Beevers, R. B. EXPERIMENTS IN FIBRE PHYSICS (1971) (Paper)

Bell, H. S. WOOL (1970)

Bennett, Ian BOOK OF ORIENTAL CARPETS & RUGS

Bhavnani, E. DECORATIVE DESIGNS AND CRAFTSMANSHIP OF INDIA

Blumenau, L. CREATIVE DESIGN IN WALL HANGINGS (1967)

Bode, von W. & Kuhnel, E. ANTIQUE RUGS FROM THE NEAR EAST

Booth, J. E. PRINCIPLES OF TEXTILE TESTING, 4th ed.

Brearley, A., et. al. AN OUTLINE OF STATISTICAL METHODS FOR USE IN THE TEXTILE INDUSTRY

Brearley, A. THE WOOLEN INDUSTRY (1965)

Brearley, A. WORSTED (1964)

Briscoe, Lynden THE TEXTILE AND CLOTHING INDUSTRIES OF THE UNITED KINGDOM

Brockman, H. L. THE THEORY OF FASHION DESIGN (1965)

Butler, M. B. CLOTHES, THEIR CHOOSING, MAKING AND CARE (1961)

Butler, M. B. SIMPLE STITCHES

Bystrom, E. PRINTING ON FABRIC

Campana, M. EUROPEAN CARPETS (Cameo Series)

Clarke, L. J. THE CRAFTSMEN IN TEXTILES

Clarke, W. AN INTRODUCTION TO TEXTILE PRINTING (Cloth) (1971)

Clarke, W. AN INTRODUCTION TO TEXTILE PRINTING (Paper) (1971)

COATS & CLARK'S SEWING BOOK, 3rd ed. (1967)

Cockett, S. R. DYEING AND PRINTING

Cockett, S. R. AN INTRODUCTION TO MAN-MADE FIBRES

Coleman, D. C. COURTAULDS: AN ECONOMIC HISTORY, 2 vols. (set)

COMPUTER TECHNOLOGY FOR TEXTILES (1970)

CONSUMER COLOR CHARTS, 2nd ed.

Cook, J. G. HANDBOOK OF POLYOLEFIN FIBRES (1967)

Cook, J. G. HANDBOOK OF TEXTILE FIBRES, 4th ed., 2 Vols.

Corinth, K. FASHION SHOWMANSHIP: EVERYTHING YOU NEED TO KNOW TO GIVE A FASHION SHOW

COTTON AND ALLIED TEXTILES

COTTON FROM FIELD TO FABRIC

Craven, W. M. COSTUME DOLLS AND HOW TO MAKE THEM (1962)

Dar, S. N. COSTUMES OF INDIA AND PAKISTAN

Davenport, Millia THE BOOK OF COSTUME

Davies, M.S.T., et. al. A DIRECTORY OF CLOTHING RESEARCH (1968)

Davis, Mildred THE ART OF CREWEL EMBROIDERY

Davis, Mildred EARLY AMERICAN EMBROIDERY DESIGNS

Davis, Mildred EMBROIDERY DESIGNS 1780-1820

DAVISON'S KNIT GOODS TRADE ANNUAL

DAVISON'S TEXTILE BLUE BOOK (Annual)

Dawson, R. M. STITCH-BONDING: A General Survey

Delavan, G. CLOTHING SELECTION: Application of Theory

Dembeck, A. A. GUIDEBOOK TO MAN-MADE TEXTILE FIBERS & TEXTURED YARNS OF THE WORLD, 3rd ed. (1969)

DeVries, Dr. L. (Prof.) & Luken, O. H. WORTERBUCH DER TEXTIL INDUSTRIE (1964) Vol. II—German-English

DICCIONARIO TEXTIL PANAMERICAN-PANAMERICAN TEXTILE DICTIONARY Spanish-English/English-Spanish (ed. by Joaquin Rodriguez Ontiveros) 2nd ed. (1971)

Dilley, A. U. ORIENTAL RUGS AND CARPETS (1931, rev. ed. 1959)

Duxbury, V. & Wray, G. R. MODERN DEVELOPMENTS IN WEAVING MACHINERY

Earland, C. & Raven, D. J. EXPERIMENTS IN TEXTILE AND FIBRE CHEMISTRY (Cloth) (1971)

EARLY AMERICAN LOOM, PLANS FOR MAKING AN

Emery, Irene THE PRIMARY STRUCTURES OF FABRICS—An Illustrated Classification

Endacott, V. M. INSTRUCTIONS IN NEEDLECRAFT (1967)

English, W. THE TEXTILE INDUSTRY: An Account of the English Inventions

Enrick, N. L. INDUSTRIAL ENGINEERING MANUAL (for the Textile Industry) (1962)

Enrick, N. L. INVENTORY MANAGEMENT (1968)

Enrick, N. L. MANAGEMENT CONTROL MANUAL for the Textile Industry

Enrick, N. L. MANAGEMENT OPERATIONS RESEARCH (1965)

Enrick, N. L. MANAGEMENT PLANNING (1967)

Enrick, N. L. QUALITY CONTROL AND RELIABILITY

Enrick, N. L. SALES AND PRODUCTION MANAGEMENT MANUAL

Ewing, A. F. PLANNING & POLICIES IN THE TEXTILE FINISHING INDUSTRY

Felkin, William, F. L. S., F. S. S. A HISTORY OF THE MACHINE-WROUGHT HOSIERY AND LACE MANUFACTURERS (1867, reprinted 1967)

Ford, J. E. FIBRE DATA SUMMARIES—A Handbook of Data on 28 Principle Textile Fibres (1968)

Foster, R. POSITIVE LET-OFF MOTIONS

Fry, G. W. EMBROIDERY AND NEEDLEWORK, 5th ed. (1959, reprinted 1966)

Gale, E. FROM FIBRES TO FABRICS (1968)

Garner, W. TEXTILE LABORATORY MANUAL (1966)
  Vol. I—Qualitative Methods
  Vol. II—Resins and Finishes
  Vol. III—Detergents
  Vol. IV—Dyestuffs
  Vol. V—Fibres
  Vol. VI—Additional Methods

Gill, Conrad THE RISE OF THE IRISH LINEN INDUSTRY

Goaman, M. YOUR BOOK OF KNITTING AND CROCHET

Grosberg, P. AN INTRODUCTION TO TEXTILE MECHANICS (1968)

Grover, E. B. & Hamby, D. S. HANDBOOK OF TEXTILE TESTING AND QUALITY CONTROL (1960)

A GUIDE TO THE SOURCES OF INFORMATION IN THE TEXTILE INDUSTRY

Gupta, R. WEAVING CALCULATIONS (1961)

Hague, D. C. THE ECONOMICS OF MAN-MADE FIBRES

Haigh, D. DYEING AND FINISHING KNITTED GOODS

Hall, A. J. THE STANDARD HANDBOOK OF TEXTILES, 7th ed. (1970)

Hall, A. J. A STUDENTS TEXTBOOK OF TEXTILE SCIENCE, rev. ed. (1969)

Hall, A. J. TEXTILE FINISHING (1966)

Hamburger, W. J. A TECHNOLOGY FOR THE ANALYSIS, DESIGN, AND USE OF TEXTILE STRUCTURES AS ENGINEERING MATERIALS (1955)

Hamby, D. S. THE AMERICAN COTTON HANDBOOK (1965)
  Vol. I
  Vol. II

Hanton, W. A. MECHANICS FOR TEXTILE STUDENTS (1960)

Harrison, STUDIES IN MODERN FABRICS (1970)

Harrison, STUDIES IN MODERN YARN PRODUCTION

Hathorne, B. L. WOVEN STRETCH AND TEXTURED FABRICS (1964)

Hearle, J. W. S., Grosberg, P., and Backer, S. STRUCTURAL MECHANICS OF FIBERS, YARNS, AND FABRICS, Vol. I (1969)

Hearle, J. W. S., and Miles, L. W. C., eds. THE SETTING OF FIBERS AND FABRICS (1972)

Henshaw, D. E. SELF-TWIST YARNS (1971)

Himmelfarb, D. THE TECHNOLOGY OF CORDAGE FIBRES AND ROPE (1957)

Hofstetter, H. H. SOLVENT PROCESSING FOR TEXTILES (1970)

Holt, J. M. FABRICS AND CLOTHING (1964)

Horne, C. FASHION CROCHET FOR YOUR DOLL (1970)

IDENTIFICATION OF TEXTILE MATERIALS, 6th ed. (1970)

Ireland, P. J. FASHION DESIGN DRAWING

Jacoby, H. HOW TO KNOW ORIENTAL CARPETS AND RUGS, 2nd ed. (1967)

Jarnow, J. A. & Judelle, B. INSIDE THE FASHION BUSINESS: Text & Readings (1965)

Jarvis, P. R. A PRACTICAL WEAVING COURSE

Kaswell, E. R. HANDBOOK OF INDUSTRIAL TEXTILES (1963)

King, Mary Elizabeth, ANCIENT PERUVIAN TEXTILES from the Collection of the Textile Museum

KNITTING ENCYCLOPEDIA of the National Knitted Outerwear Association

Koch, P. A. MICROSCOPIC AND CHEMICAL TESTING OF TEXTILES (1963)

Kornreich, E. INTRODUCTION TO FIBRES AND FABRICS

Korshak, V. V. HEAT-RESISTANT POLYMERS

Krcma, R. MANUAL OF NONWOVENS, 2nd ed. (1971)

Kulkarni, G. C. & Trivedi, S. S. PROCESSING OF POLYESTER COTTON BLENDS (1968)

Kybalova, L. & Darbois, D. CARPETS OF THE ORIENT

Lancashire, J. B. JACQUARD DESIGN AND KNITTING

Landreau, A., & Pickering, W. FROM THE BOSPORUS TO SAMARKAND: FLAT WOVEN RUGS

Leavitt, T. W. THE HOLLINGWORTH LETTERS—Technical change in the Textile Industry, 1826-1837 (1969)

Leene, Jentina TEXTILE CONSERVATION (1972)

Lewis, R. YOUR BOOK OF WEAVING

Lillow, I. INTRODUCING MACHINE EMBROIDERY

Link, P. TEXTILE ENCYCLOPEDIA, Spanish and English (1956)

Linton, George E. APPLIED BASIC TEXTILES Second Revised Edition (1973)

Linton, George E. THE MODERN TEXTILE AND APPAREL DICTIONARY, Fourth Revised Enlarged Edition (1973)

Linton, George E. NATURAL AND MAN-MADE TEXTILE FIBERS 2nd Revised Ed. (1973)

Lumsden, J. B. YOUR BOOK OF EMBROIDERY

Lumsden, J. B. YOUR BOOK OF SEWING

Lynn, E. J. & Press, J. J. ADVANCES IN TEXTILE PROCESSING, Vol. I

Lyons, J. W. IMPACT PHENOMENA IN TEXTILES (1963)

MANUAL OF COTTON SPINNING

419-3 Vol. I—Raw Cotton Production and Marketing, by Coulson

420-7 Vol. II—Part 1—Characteristics of Raw Cotton, by E. Lord

421-5 Vol. II—Part 2—Opening and Cleaning, by Hunter & Shrigley

422-3 Vol. III—Carding, by Byerley

423-1 Vol. IV—Part 1—Principles of Roller Drafting and the irregularity of Drafted Materials, by Foster

424-X Vol. IV—Part 2—Drawframes, Combers, and Speedframes, by Charnley

425-8 Vol. V—Principles and Theory of Ring Spinning, by DeBarr

MANUAL OF THE TEXTILE INDUSTRY OF CANADA, Annual

Mark, H. F., Atlas, S. M., and Cernia, S. eds.

MAN-MADE FIBERS
  Vol. I (1967)
  Vol. II (1968)
  Vol. III (1968)

Marsh, J. T. SELF-SMOOTHING FABRICS

Mason, E. EMBROIDERY DESIGN, for Students of All Ages

Mather, J. N. CARDING—JUTE AND SIMILAR FIBRES

May, C. Delabere HOW TO IDENTIFY PERSIAN RUGS (Paper)

McKelvey, J. M. POLYMER PROCESSING (1962)

Mehta, R. J. MASTERPIECES OF INDIAN TEXTILES (1970)

Mellan, I. & Mellan, E. REMOVING SPOTS AND STAINS

Mennie, M. I. SIMPLE LAUNDRYWORK AND FABRIC CARE

Meredith, R. & Hearle, J. W. S. PHYSICAL METHODS OF INVESTIGATING TEXTILES

Merrill, G. R. BANNER AUTOMATIC HOSIERY MACHINE REPRINTS (1925) (Paper)

Merrill, G. R. Series on Cotton Production, Texts and Reference Material (Set)
   COTTON CARDING
   COTTON COMBING
   COTTON DRAWING AND ROVING
   COTTON OPENING AND PICKING
   COTTON RING SPINNING
   MILL ORGANIZATION

Merrimack Valley Textile Museum THE HOUSING OF A TEXTILE COLLECTION—Occasional Report #1

Miller, E. TEXTILE PROPERTIES AND BEHAVIOR

MODERN MECHANISMS IN TEXTILE MACHINERY

Moncrieff, R. W. MAN-MADE FIBRES

Monk, K. FUN WITH FABRIC PRINTING, with or without special equipment

Montgomery, F. M. PRINTED TEXTILES—ENGLISH AND AMERICAN COTTONS AND LINENS 1700-1850 (1970)

Mortenson, K. G. HEAT TRANSFER AND THE CLOTHING OF MAN (1957) (Paper)

Morton, G. M., GUTHRIE, M. E., LEITE, V. and Ericson, J. THE ARTS OF COSTUME AND PERSONAL APPEARANCE, 3rd, ed. (1964)

Moss, A. J. E. CLOTHES CARE (A Manual on the Care of Fabrics) 2nd ed.

Moulton, B. GARMENT—CUTTING AND TAILORING For Students

Moulton, B. SIMPLIFIED TAILORING

Murphy, T. & Norris, K. P. & Tippett, L. H. C. STATISTICAL METHODS FOR TEXTILE TECHNOLOGISTS (1967)

Nelson, T. PRACTICAL LOOM FIXING

NEW WAYS TO PRODUCE TEXTILES'
   Textile Institute, 17 papers from 1972 Annual Conference (1973)

NEWNESS COMPLETE NEEDLECRAFT (1970)

Nisbet, N. F. T. I. GRAMMAR OF TEXTILE DESIGN

Nordquist, B., Mettam, J., & Hoyle, P. CREATIVE WEST AFRICAN FASHION (1973)

ODHAMS ENCYCLOPEDIA OF KNITTING (1970)

Oelaner, G. H. A HANDBOOK OF WEAVES

Organ, R. M. DESIGN FOR SCIENTIFIC CONSERVATION OF ANTIQUITIES

Owen, E. R. J. COTTON AND THE EGYPTIAN ECONOMY 1820-1914

Paling, D. F. WARP KNITTING TECHNOLOGY

Parish, G. J. & Williams, M. R. MOISTURE MEASURING INSTRUMENTS FOR TEXTILES (1966)

Peters, R. H. TEXTILE CHEMISTRY
Volume I—The Chemistry of Fibres (1963)
Volume II—Impurities of Fibres:
   Purification of Fibres (1967)

Pistolese, R. & Horsting, R. THE HISTORY OF FASHIONS (1970)

Pizzuto, J. J. 101 WEAVES IN 101 FABRICS

Ponting, K. G., editor, TEXTILE HISTORY Volume I, 1968-1970

Power, E. E. THE WOOL TRADE IN ENGLISH MEDIEVAL HISTORY

Rainnie, G. F., ed. THE WOOLEN AND WORSTED INDUSTRY

Ramsbottom, T. WARP SIZING MECHANISMS (1964)

Ratcliffe, H. HOME DECORATING—A CRAFTSMAN'S APPROACH (1970)

Regensteiner, Else. THE ART OF WEAVING (1970)

Reichman, C. ADVANCED KNITTING PRINCIPLES

Reichman, C. GUIDE TO THE MANUFACTURE OF SWEATERS, KNIT SHIRTS, AND SWIMWEAR

Reichman, C. KNITTED STRETCH TECHNOLOGY

Reichman, C. KNITTING DICTIONARY

Reichman, C. WOOL AND SYNETHETIC KNIT-WEAR HANDBOOK

Reichman, C. & Lancashire, J. B. & Darlington, K. D. KNITTED FABRIC PRIMER

Reisfeld, A. CONTROL OF DEFECTS IN RASCHEL FABRIC

Reisfeld, A. FUNDAMENTALS OF RASCHEL KNITTING

Reisfeld, A. WARP KNIT ENGINEERING (1966)

Risley, C. THE TECHNIQUE OF CREATIVE EMBROIDERY

Roach, M. E. and Eicher, J. B. DRESS ADORNMENT AND THE SOCIAL ORDER (1965)

Roberts, C. THE REAL BOOK OF MAKING DOLLS AND DOLLS' CLOTHES, 2nd ed. (1970)

Robinson, S. & Robinson, P. EXPLORING FABRIC PRINTING (1970)

Robinson, George, CARPETS AND OTHER TEXTILE FLOORCOVERINGS, Second Revised Enlarged Edition (1972)

Rosato, D. V. & Grove, S. C. FILAMENT WINDING (1964)

Rosato, D. V. & Schwartz, R. T. (ed.) ENVIRONMENTAL EFFECTS ON POLYMERIC MATERIALS
   Volume I
   Volume II

Rotenstein, C. LACE MANUFACTURING ON RASCHEL MACHINES

Rotenstein, C. MANUFACTURE OF RASCHEL WOOL & COTTON OUTERWEAR

Ryan, M. S. CLOTHING: A STUDY IN HUMAN BEHAVIOR (1966)

St. George, E. OLD DOLLS

Samuel, E. INTRODUCING BATIK

Sarkar, A. K. FLUORESCENT WHITENING AGENTS (1970)

Schwalbach, M. V. & James, A. SCREEN PROCESS PRINTING for the Serigrapher and Textile Designer

Seidel, L. E. APPLIED TEXTILE MARKETING (1970)

Seyd, M. DESIGNING WITH STRING (1967, reprinted 1969)

Shaw, C. & Eckersley, F. COTTON

Shinn, W. E. Knitting Technology Series (Textbooks & References) (SET)
   ELEMENTS OF TEXTILE COSTING
   FLAT KNITTING
   GARMENT MANUFACTURE

Sidney, Sylvia, NEEDLEPOINT BOOK (1968)

Skinkle, J. H. TEXTILE TESTING Physical, Chemical, and Microscopical—Second Edition

NORWEGIAN TEXTILES, by Englestad, H. M. A.

POLISH TEXTILES, by Henere, E.

ROUMANIAN TEXTILES, by Peterscu, Paul & Rodna, Nicolae

SOUTH AMERICAN TEXTILES, by Link, Pablo

SPANISH TEXTILES, by Henere, E.

SWISS TEXTILES, by Ferriere, M. T.

THE WORLD'S HERITAGE OF WOVEN FABRICS

Each volume consists of a concise Foreword and superb illustrations of the finest examples of their kind.

BYZANTINE FABRICS, by Bunt, C. G. E.

CAROLIAN FABRICS (VICTORIA AND ALBERT MUSEUM) by Bolingbroke, J. M.

CHINESE FABRICS, by Bunt, C. G. E.

FLORENTINE FABRICS, by Bunt, C. G. E.

HISPANO MORESQUE FABRICS, by Bunt, C. G. E.

PERSIAN FABRICS, by Bunt, C. G. E.

THE FABRICS OF PERU, by VanStan, I.

SICILIAN AND LUCHESE FABRICS, by Bunt, C. G. E.

THE SILKS OF LYONS & PHILIPPE DE LA SALLE, by Bunt, C. G. E.

SPANISH SILKS, by Bunt, C. G. E.

TUDOR AND STUART FABRICS, by Bunt C. G. E.

VENETIAN FABRICS, by Bunt, C. G. E.

WILLIAM AND MARY FABRICS (VICTORIA AND ALBERT MUSEUM) by Bolingbroke, J. M.

Zimmerman, R. Prof. FLORAL FORMS IN DESIGN, 26 large full plates.

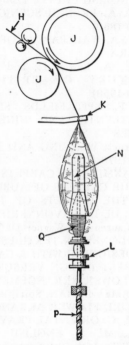

Courtesy: National Association of Wool Manufacturers

DETAIL OF FRAME (CAP METHOD) SPINNING

Illustrated is its difference from mule spinning. Actions are continuous. Spindles revolve on stationary frames. Roving (H) fed continuously from feed rollers (J) through fixed center eyelets (K) is whirled into yarn by revolving spindles (L) which whip it around the cap (N), producing the required twist. Caps (N) on innershafts (P), moving up and down, control winding of yarn on bobbins (Q).

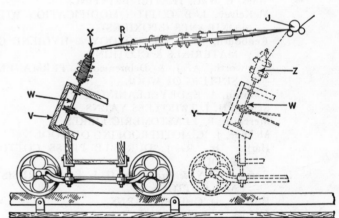

Courtesy: National Association of Wool Manufacturers

MULE SPINNING

In mule spinning the carriage (V) on which the spindles are mounted moves to and from the main spinning frame that holds the feed rollers (J). On its outward trip with the spindles idle, it draws out the roving (R). At the end of this motion, the feed rollers (J) stop; the spindles (W) revolve, allowing the roving (R) to slip over the spindle top (X) thus twisting it into yarn. On the inward trip (indicated by (Y) dotted lines), the yarn is wound onto the bobbin (Z) by the continued revolving of the spindle (W).

ILLUSTRATED SECTION

CONSUMER CARE GUIDE FOR APPAREL

WHEN LABEL READS:	IT MEANS:
Washable Machine washable Machine wash	Wash, bleach, dry and press by any customary method including commercial laundering
Home launder only	Same as above but do not use commercial laundering
No bleach	Do not use bleach
No starch	Do not use starch
Cold wash Cold setting Cold rinse	Use cold water from tap or cold washing machine setting
Warm wash Warm setting Warm rinse	Use warm water 90° to 110° Fahrenheit
Hot wash Hot setting	Use hot water (hot washing machine setting) 130° Fahrenheit or hotter
No spin	Remove wash load before final machine spin cycle
Delicate cycle Gentle cycle	Use appropriate machine setting; otherwise wash by hand
Durable press cycle Permanent press cycle	Use appropriate machine setting; otherwise use medium wash, cold rinse and short spin cycle
Wash separately	Wash alone or with like colors

(left column marked: MACHINE WASHABLE)

WHEN LABEL READS:	IT MEANS:
Hand washable Hand wash	Launder only by hand in luke warm (hand comfortable) water. May be bleached. May be drycleaned
Hand wash only	Same as above, but **do not** dryclean
Hand wash separately	Hand wash alone or with like colors
No bleach	Do not use bleach
Tumble dry Machine dry	Dry in tumble dryer at specified setting — high, medium, low or no heat
Tumble dry Remove promptly	Same as above, but in absence of cool-down cycle remove at once when tumbling stops
Drip dry Hang dry Line dry	Hang wet and allow to dry with hand shaping only
No squeeze No wring No twist	Hang dry, drip dry or dry flat only
Dry flat	Lay garment on flat surface
Block to dry	Maintain original size and shape while drying
Cool iron	Set iron at lowest setting
Warm iron	Set iron at medium setting
Hot iron	Set iron at hot setting
No iron No press	Do not iron or press with heat
Steam iron Steam press	Iron or press with steam
Iron damp	Dampen garment before ironing
Dryclean Dryclean only	Garment should be drycleaned only, including self-service
Professionally clean only Commercially clean only	Do not use self-service drycleaning
No dryclean	Use recommended care instructions. No drycleaning materials to be used.

(right column marked: NON-MACHINE WASHING / HOME DRYING / IRONING OR PRESSING / MISCELLANEOUS)

The American Apparel Manufacturers Association, Inc.

From a painting by Alonzo Chappel

ELI WHITNEY

By C. V. Pohlson, Pawtucket, R. I.

SAMUEL SLATER

From a painting by E. H. Stockwell

ELIAS HOWE, JR.

MODEL OF WHITNEY
COTTON GIN (1800)

Eli Whitney's first commercial cotton gin, a priceless item. This gin was found in Wilkes County, Georgia, in 1934, after having been lost for 140 years. The original, pilot model of the Whitney cotton gin is believed to have been destroyed by fire. Officer Paul Partridge is explaining the cotton gin to Kay and Jon Cowan.

Courtesy: Robert E. Sibley, Director of Public Relations, The Citizens and Southern National Bank, Atlanta, Georgia

SLATER MILL, PAWTUCKET, R. I.
(Now a museum)

Modern cotton gin, which can process more cotton in a few minutes than Whitney's gin could in a full day.

Courtesy: National Cotton Council of America, Memphis, Tenn.

HOWE SEWING MACHINE (1845)

A modern cotton ginning plant.

Samuel Alexander & Charles B. Penrose

Have bought from George Gaullagher his large and very extensive stock of

Merchandize,

composing a most extensive assortment of GOODS, suitable for the present and approaching seasons, and which, (at the old stand of *George Gaullagher*,) they now offer to their friends and the public, at the

Most Reduced Prices.

From a determination to keep the assortment at all times *full*, and their disposition to accommodate all who may favour the store with a call, they declare that on their part, nothing shall be wanting to afford satisfaction.

The following articles compose a part of their *STOCK OF GOODS*, to wit:

Angola Cassimeres,

Plain and striped Satinetts,

Bombazets and Bombazeens,

Irish Popolins,

Striped Bengals,

Blue and yellow Company Nankeens.

Levantine, Senshaws, Mantuas, Florence and Sarsnett Silks,

Plain and figured Mull Mull,

Jaconet, Cambrick and Swiss Muslins,

Robinets and Italian Crapes,

Bengal Chintz and Ginghams,

Long Lawn and Linen Cambricks,

Washington, Wilmington & Union Stripes

Painted Muslins and Bed Ticking,

Wash Leather, Horse & Dog skin Gloves,

Silk, Kid, and York tan Gloves,

Gentlemen and Lady's Leghorn Hats,

Straw and Gimp Bonnets,

ALSO,

Rock and Rifle Powder, Brandy, Gin, Spirits, Molasses, Sugar, Coffee, Tea, Pepper, Alspice, Salt, Fish, &c. &c.

August 17, 1825.

THE ELIAS HOWE SEWING MACHINE.

A MACHINE WAS NEEDED POSSESSing simplicity and durability, and adapted to a great range of work; one easily understood and comprehended by all. To produce such a machine has been the study of Elias Howe, Jr., who gave to the world the first Sewing Machine, more than twenty-five years ago; and now we offer his last production—a machine embracing all essential qualities, and pronounced the best in the world.

Every machine is as near perfection as the best machinery in the world can make it. Loss of time and expense of sending to a machine-shop rarely occurs, as every part may be duplicated.

The new Improved Family Machine cannot be surpassed. A HEMMER, FELLER, BRAIDER, QUILTER and GUIDE are given with each Machine.

They are adapted to all kinds of family sewing, and to the uses of Seamstresses, Dressmakers, Tailors, Manufacturers of Shirts, Collars, Skirts, Cloaks, Mantillas, Clothing, Hats, Caps, Corsets, Boots, Shoes, Harness, Saddles, Linen Goods, Umbrellas, Parasols, &c.

They will Seam, Quilt, Gather, Hem, Fell, Cord, Braid, Bind, and perform every species of Sewing; making a beautiful and perfect stitch alike on both sides of the article sewed, using a much smaller needle for the same thread than any other machine.

The Lock Stitch, invented by Mr. Howe, and made on this Machine, is the most popular and durable, and will neither rip nor ravel, and all Sewing Machines are subject to the principle invented by him.

The Medallion of Elias Howe, Jr., is embedded n every genuine Machine.

AGENTS WANTED.

Howe Machine Company,

699 BROADWAY, New York City,

AND

534 Broadway, Albany, N. Y.

W. A. PENNOYER,
General Agent for Greene Co.

CHAS. S. WILLARD,
Resident Agent for the Elias Howe Sewing Machine for Catskill.

mar24m6

STAND UPRIGHT!

While You Read

THIS!

Over 120,000 Sold in 1870.

SINGER'S

NEW

Family Sewing Machine,

HAS BEEN OVER TWO YEARS IN PREPARATION, and has been brought to Perfection, Regardless of Time, Labor or Expense, and is now confidently presented to the public as incomparably

THE BEST SEWING MACHINE

IN EXISTENCE.

It is Simple, Compact, Durable and Beautiful. It is Quiet Light Running, and capable of performing a range of Work Never Before Attempted upon a Single Machine, using either Silk, Twist, Linen or Cotton Thread, and sewing with equal facility the Very Finest and Coarsest materials WITHOUT CHANGE OF TENSION.

HUNTER, LYNES & PIERSON. Agents

Catskill, March 5th, 1869.

Reprinted from AMERICA'S
TEXTILE REPORTER, *February 22, 1962*

Three early advertisements for sewing machines and fabrics.

TYPES OF SHEEP

Romney Marsh Ram	Cheviot Ewe
Dorset Ewe	Border Leicester Ram
Merino Ram	Cotswald Ram
Southdown Ram	Oxford Ewe

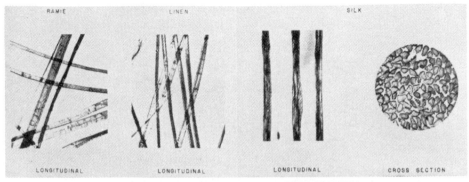

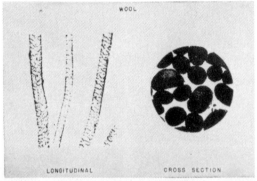

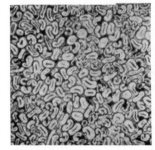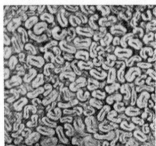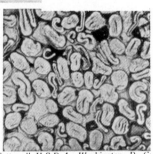

Courtesy Pace Committee on "Better Cottons," U.S.D.A., Washington, D. C.

CROSS SECTION OF COTTON FIBERS

Different diameters and thicknesses of cell wall: (left) Asiatic (ctr) American Uplands (rt) Sea Island

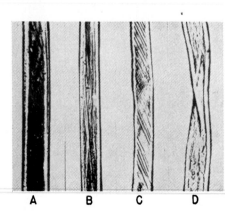

PHOTOMICROGRAPHS OF COTTON FIBERS

A. UNDRIED FIBER FROM UNOPENED BOLL

B. UNDRIED FIBER STRETCHED

C. DRIED FROM XYLENE

D. DRIED IN OPEN AIR

Courtesy H. W. Barre, in charge, Division of Cotton & Other Fibers, U.S.D.A., Washington, D. C.

ACETATE FILAMENT

Longitudinal   Cross Section

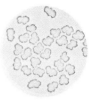

CUPRAMMONIUM RAYON

Longitudinal   Cross Section

Longitudinal

DACRON

Longitudinal   Cross Section

DYNEL

Longitudinal   Cross Section

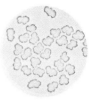

Cross Section
ARNEL

NYLON

Longitudinal   Cross Section

"ORLON"
Continuous Filament

Longitudinal   Cross Section

Longitudinal

TEXTURED YARN (PHOTOMICRO-
GRAPHS)

(1) Dacron, 70-
    denier
(2) Dacron staple,
    96-denier

Right: Filament
    acetate yarn;
    textured yarn
    from it

ACRILAN

Longitudinal   Cross Section

Cross Section
VEREL--3 D/F

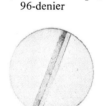

VINYON

Longitudinal   Cross Section

VISCOSE RAYON

Longitudinal   Cross Section

COMPARATIVE SIZE OF FIBERS

BETA
¼ Denier
Diameter
3.8 microns

NYLON
1½ Denier 14 microns

POLYESTER
1½ Denier 12 microns

VISCOSE
1½ Denier 16 microns

COTTON
1½ Denier
16 x 6 microns

SILK
1.2 Denier
14 x 8 microns

Crystalline Lattice of Nylon

Crystalline Lattice of "Dacron"

Crystalline Lattice of "Orlon"

Diagrams Courtesy of
E.I. duPont de Nemours, Inc.

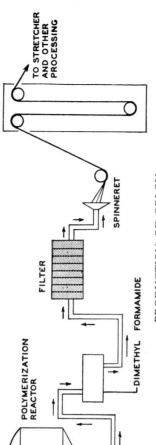

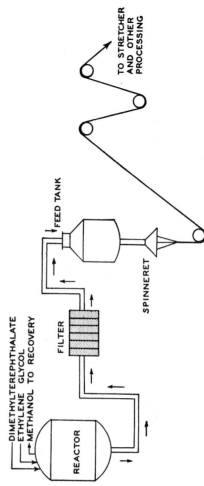

PRODUCTION OF FIBERGLAS

PRODUCTION OF ORLON

PRODUCTION OF DACRON

From Man-Made Fibers Handbook
Courtesy Modern Textiles Magazine

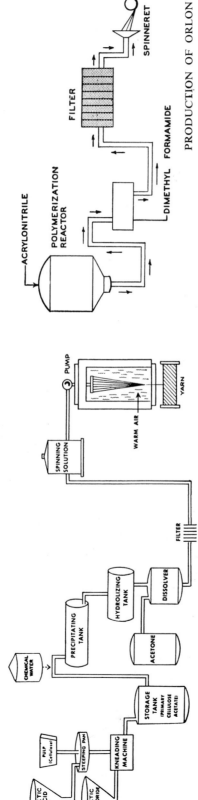

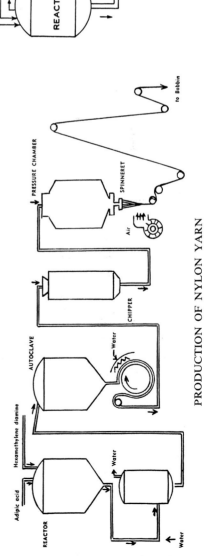

PRODUCTION OF RAYON YARN

PRODUCTION OF ACETATE YARN

PRODUCTION OF NYLON YARN

From Man-Made Fibers Handbook
Courtesy Modern Textiles Magazine

Courtesy E. I. du Pont de Nemours & Co., Inc.

SPINNERET: The Birth of Man-made and Synthetic Filaments.

Many filaments twisted into a single thread make "continuous-multifilament yarn." Single filament is called "monofilament." Number of filaments in a single thread may reach 2934

VISCOSE RAYON MANUFACTURE—AMERICAN VISCOSE CORPORATION

Note viscous solution in bottle fed to spinneret; filaments, are seen in central area in tank, on way to the reel

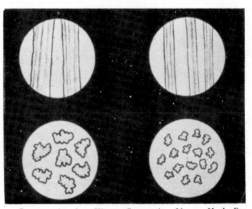

Courtesy American Viscose Corporation, Marcus Hook, Pa.

FIBER DENIER SIZE COMPARISON

(Left) 5.5-denier (right) 1.0-denier

Courtesy E. I. du Pont de Nemours & Co., Inc.

TOW OR ROPE

Fibers cut to average length of cotton, worsted and some woolen fibers

Courtesy Courtaulds, Ltd., New York City

FIBER COMPARISON

Varied staple-length rayon providing comparison diagram for (*left*) 60/62 oil-combed worsted top (*ctr*) 5.5-denier 5-inch dull "Fibro" top (*rt*) 5.5-denier, 3½" to 6" denier bright "Fibro" top

AUTOMATIC COTTON PICKER AT WORK
IN FIELD

CARD LAPS READY FOR CARDING
COTTON FIBERS

Laps are about 45 inches wide, weigh about
45 pounds

CARDING PROCESS FOR COTTON

Showing fleecy web of fibers from doffer roller
on way to coiler can at delivery end

COMBING WORSTED STOCK

Noble or circular comber removes foreign
matter, parallels wool fibers. Comber stock is
called "worsted top"

SLUBBER FRAME

Superdrafting of cotton fibers — detail

CARDING PROCESS FOR WOOL

Actual carding of fibers; straightening, partial
paralleling of stock. Note fluffy waste. (No
twist applied in carding)

WOOL FIBERS CONDENSED INTO ROV-
ING, ONE STEP FROM SPUN YARN

Roving, on lower jack spools at front of machine, is fed to mule frame

WORSTED TOP INSPECTION

For quality, uniformity, and evenness so spinning and dyeing will be satisfactory

RING SPINNING

Cotton yarn on the frame

MULE SPINNING

Spinning nylon staple stock for carpet trade —
producing even spun yarns. Carriage in fore-
ground; headstock and jack spools at back

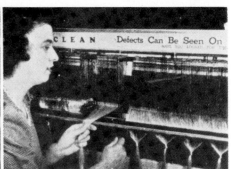

SLASHING

Passing yarn through a sizing solution

DRAWING-IN THE WARP YARNS

Through heddles, by hand. Heddles, on harnesses, in up-and-down motions, form shed making weaving posible

REEDING A WARP: FOLLOWS DRAWING-IN

Ends, drawn through reed splits or dents, according to draft plan, are kept straight so as to weave at right angles with filling yarn

Courtesy Crompton and Knowles Loom Works, Worcester, Mass.

Courtesy Mohawk Carpet Mills, Amsterdam, N. Y.

SPEED OF SHUTTLE THROUGH LOOM SHED

LOOM WEAVING: INTERLACING OF WARP AND FILLING YARNS

Automatic loom refuels shuttles with bobbins without loom stoppage

WILTON CARPET WEAVING ON JAC-QUARD LOOM

Close-up of finished fabric; Jacquard tie-up and cards

Courtesy United States Testing Co., Hoboken, N. J.

PICK COUNTER, OR COUNTING GLASS

Courtesy Mohawk Carpet Mills, Amsterdam, N. Y.

TAPESTRY VELVET CARPET SETTING·

Yarns threaded in accordance with design of the drum-printing scale guide

JACQUARD WEAVING OF NYLON CAR-
PETING

Requires expert craftsmanship, two sets of
cards

Maschinenfabrik Rüti, Zürich, Switzerland

JOSEPH J. M. JACQUARD

From woven silk fabric

THE JACQUARD LOOM

Note cards at top of loom control which govern weaving of intricate motif

SIDE VIEW OF JACQUARD MACHINE

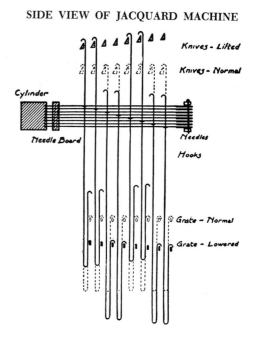

A rise and fall, 416 machine.

Courtesy: Philadelphia College of Textiles & Science

Picture of William Tell taken from silk-Jacquard woven fabric—by Maschinenfabrik Rüti, Zürich, Switzerland.

Picture taken from woven silk fabric made on a Jacquard loom—by Sauquoit Silk Mfg. Co., Philadelphia.

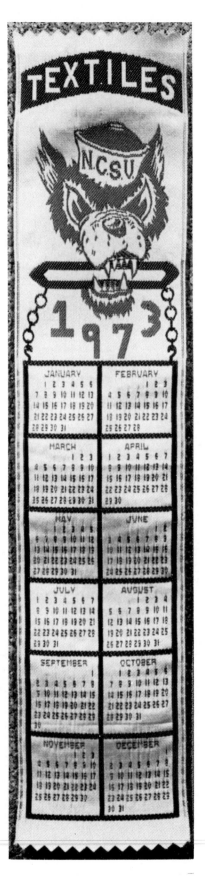

Calendar made on Jacquard loom.

699

Full Leno or Doup
Weave

Half Leno or Doup
Weave

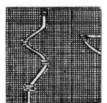

Lappet Weave
from loom

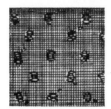

Lappet Fabric after
clipping

Clipspot from loom

Clipspot after
clipping

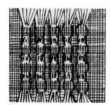

Warp Float from
loom

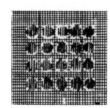

Warp Float after
clipping floating
ends

SOME NOVELTY WEAVE CONSTRUCTIONS

Courtesy Mohawk Carpet Mills, Amsterdam, N. Y.

CHENILLE FUR INSPECTION

SIDE VIEW OF DOUBLE CLOTH PLUSH WEAVING

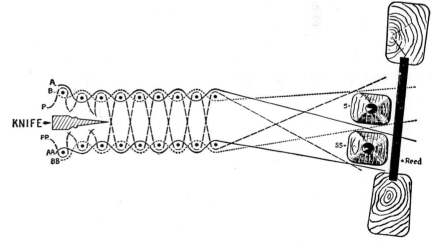

Lines A and B represent the ground warp threads of the upper base cloth and AA and BB are those of the lower base cloth. Lines P and PP are the pile forming warp threads that weave into both base cloths and which are cut by the knife to form the pile. S and SS are the two shuttles which are thrown through the sheds together and the black dots represent picks of filling threads

CHENILLE WEAVING EFFECT AS WOVEN IN THE LOOM

Face of fabric in loom   Back of fabric in loom

Fabric is cut vertically between the binder yarns thereby allowing the strips to be free to form their characteristic curled effect around these binder yarns and to simulate a caterpillar to give the chenille (caterpillar) effect.

CHENILLE WEAVING

Insertion of the single chenille weft or filling pick into the fabric after the two single chenille strands have been combined to weave as a single weft pick.

Single-cut chenille strand

The leno or doup-weave is used generally in weft weaving since it locks in the warp in the action.

Single-cut chenille strand

The two strands are combined in chenille weaving to form a single weft pick or filling pick in the fabric. Weaver number one does the actual weaving of the picks into the fabric. The "weft weaver" or weaver number two combs the pick immediately after it has been thrown through the shed of the loom to take its component place in the goods. The weft weaver combs this pick into correct position and its set-up in the fabric.

Courtesy American Viscose Corporation, Marcus Hook, Pa.

TRICOT KNITTING MACHINE,
168 inches wide

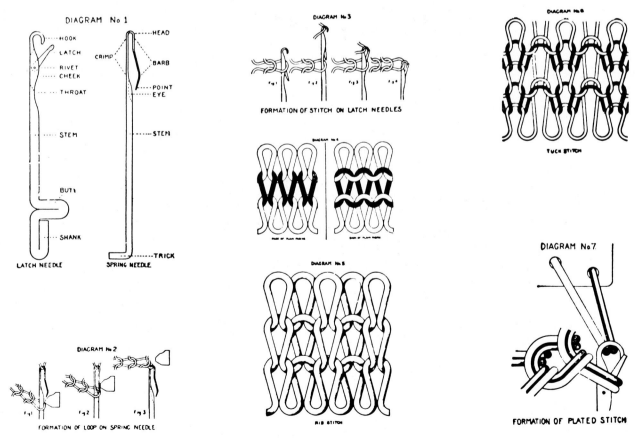

KNITTING NEEDLES AND LOOP FORMATIONS AND KNITTING STITCHES

PIECE DYEING

YARN OR SKEIN DYEING

Courtesy Bradford Dyeing Association   *Courtesy Bradford Dyeing Association*

WASHING WOVEN FABRIC RIGMEL SHRINKING MA-   TENTER FRAME
AFTER FULLING   CHINE

PANTOGRAPHING FOR PRINTED TEXTILES

Sketchmaking Department: Sketchmaker setting out design, checking proper repeat before setting out necessary zinc plates.

Sketchmaking Camera Room: Sketch seen in projection camera reflecting image onto set-out zinc plate. Sketchmaker follows full-color image to reproduce motif.

Plate Painting: Figures on sketched plate are being painted to distinguish one color from another before pantographing.

Plate Engraving: The design for each color is engraved on a flat plate.

Transfer of the Design by the Pantograph: Design is being transferred from zinc plate to wax-covered, copper roller by pantograph. Diamond needles are used.

Roller Painting: Cylinder being examined for defects before etching.

Etching Room: Print rollers are etched in various depths. Etching takes place only where pantograph diamond has penetrated acid-resisting coating.

Finish Polishing: Engraved cylinder is again examined, highly polished before chrome plating, and finally completed for printing.

Courtesy: Sanco Dye Works, Inc., Phillipsburg, N.J.

ACCELEROTOR®

Developed by the A.A.T.C.C. for evaluating wet and dry abrasion resistance of fabrics.

LAUNDER-OMETER

The standard test machine of the A.A.T.C.C. for determining the color fastness, shrinking, washing and dry cleaning qualities of textiles.

SCORCH TESTER

Meets AATCC test standards for wet and dry hot pressing of textiles

A.A.T.C.C. CROCKMETER

For determination of color fastness to crocking.

LABORATORY WRINGER and PADDER

For extracting controlled amounts of liquids to produce test specimens as required by many textile test programs.

RANDOM TUMBLE PILLING TESTER

For the determination of the pilling and fuzzing characteristics of all types of fabrics.

DYNAMIC ABSORPTION TESTER

A motorized tumble jar, 12 inches deep and 6 inches diameter, for use in AATCC, ASTM, and federal specifications. The built-in timer provides automatic shutdown.

PERSPIRATION TESTER

For testing color fastness to perspiration and water. A.A.T.C.C. test methods 15-1960 and 63-1957.

OUTDOOR EXPOSURE CABINET MODEL DE-1

An exposure cabinet where samples are protected from external moisture. Dimensions 32½" x 30" x 7", height 62". Glass 24" x 28" with exposure area 1" or 3" from glass.

FABRIC STREAK ANALYZER

A simple instrument for delineating between imperfections in fabric construction and streaking due to dyeing and finishing.

THE MARK-TEMP INFRA-RED THERMOMETER. The only portable infra-red thermometer that gives fast accurate temperature of fabric without contact. Measures infra-red energy from stationary or moving objects at a distance of five inches to infinity. Possesses high stability within two percent of accuracy. Product of Chem-Mark, Inc., Bound Brook, N.J. 08805

EYEPIECE ANALYZER

BODY TUBE

ADJUSTABLE GRADUATED DRAW TUBE

COARSE ADJUSTMENT BUTTON FOR BODY TUBE

REVOLVING NOSEPIECE

OBJECTIVES

FINE ADJUSTMENT BUTTON

GRADUATED CIRCULAR REVOLVING & CENTERING STAGE

VERNIER & CLAMP

INCLINATION JOINT

RACK & PINION SUBSTAGE WITH CONDENSER IRIS & POLARIZER

MIRROR

TEXTILE LABORATORY MICROSCOPE

706

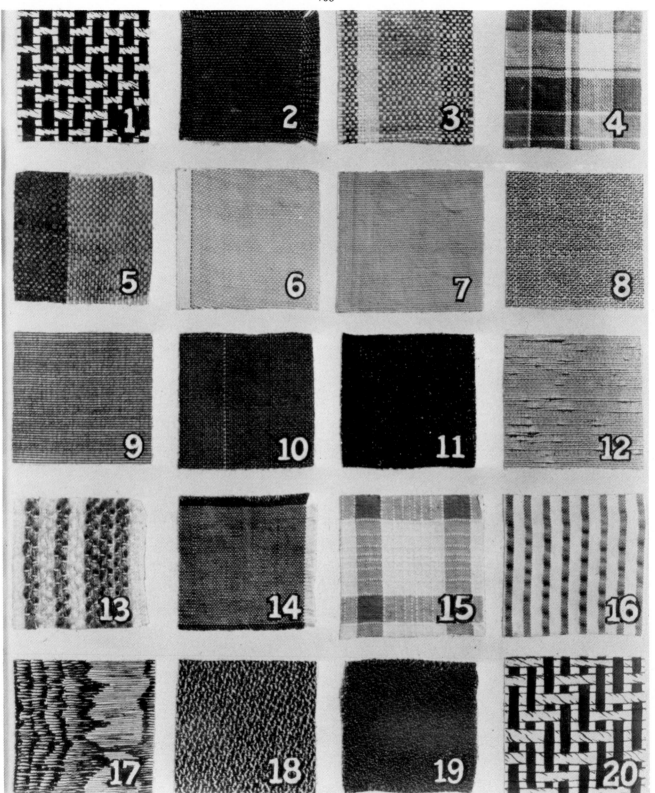

STANDARD TEXTILE FABRICS

1. Plain weave interlacing. 2. Duck. 3. Linen. 4. Gingham. 5. Irregular filling in fabric. 6. Oxford shirting. 7. Poplin. 8. Rayon. 9. Faille. 10. Tropical worsted. 11. Homespun. 12. Shantung. 13. Bulky warp yarn. 14. Chambray. 15. Dimity. 16. Seersucker. 17. Moire finish. 18. Crepe. 19. Crepe, high texture. 20. 2-and-2 twill interlacing.

707

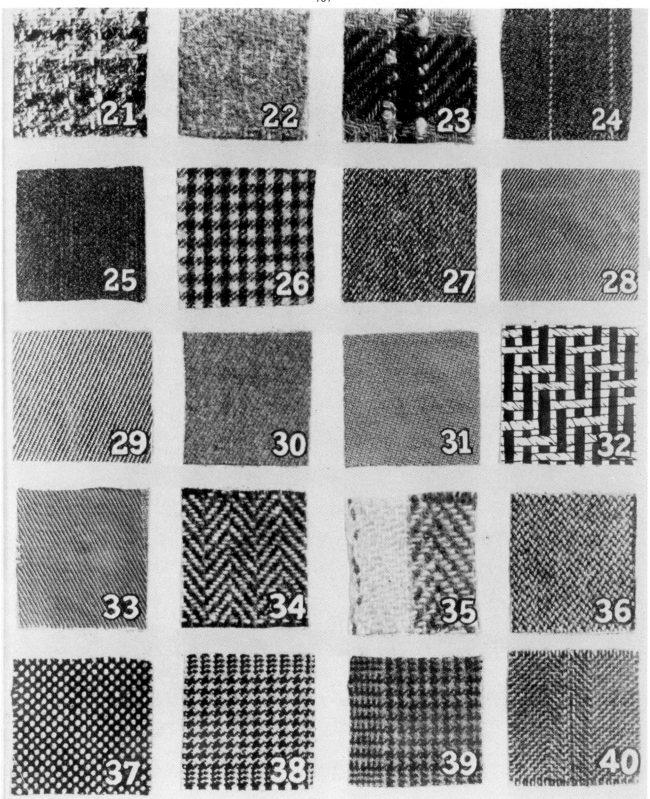

STANDARD TEXTILE FABRICS

21. Tweed. 22. Harris tweed. 23. Novelty woolen. 24. Chalk stripe. 25. Banjo stripe. 26. Check. 27. Covert. 28. Gabardine. 29. Whipcord. 30. Cavalry twill. 31. Tricotine. 32. 2-and-2 left-hand twill interlacing. 33. Left-hand twill fabric. 34. Broken twill. 35. Showing selvage in woolen cloth. 36. Broken twill fabric. 37. Worsted bird's eye. 38. Overplaid. 39. Hound's tooth. 40. Color-effect weave in cloth.

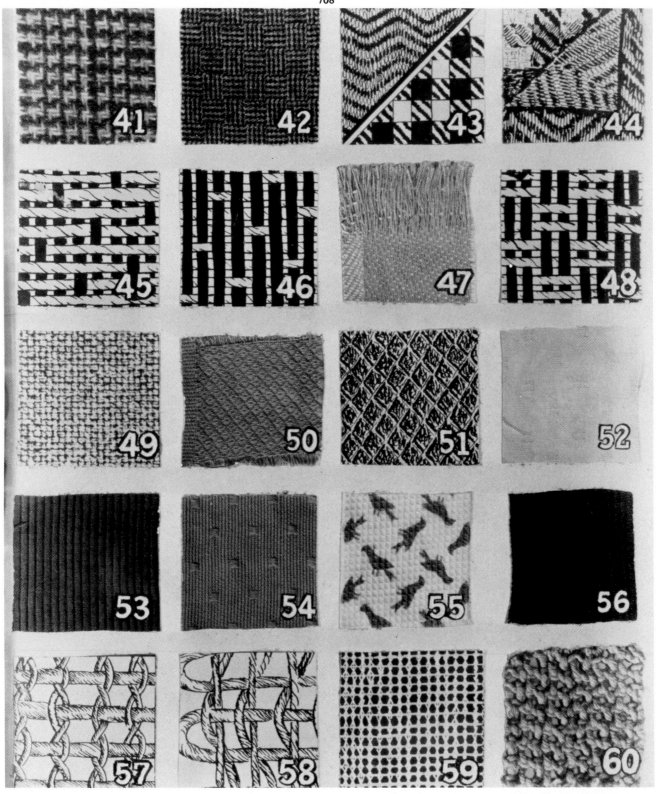

STANDARD TEXTILE FABRICS

41. Color-effect on twill construction. 42. Novelty weave worsted. 43. Double-cloth. 44. Reverse side of double-cloth. 45. Satin weave interlacing. 46. Satin, warp-effect. 47. Ticking. 48. 2-2 basket weave interlacing. 49. Hopsacking. 50. Bird's-eye diaper. 51. Matelasse. 52. Dobby design. 53. Pique 54. Novelty pique. 55. Waffle or honeycomb. 56. Bedford cord. 57. Full-leno weave. A one pick marquisette, full leno since both ends work in leno heddles. Can also be made in two and three pick full leno or doup, heavy yarns used. 58. Half-leno weave, since only one end is in a leno heddle; other end weaves plain weave. 59. Marquisette. 60. Doup weave or leno weave, heavy yarns used.

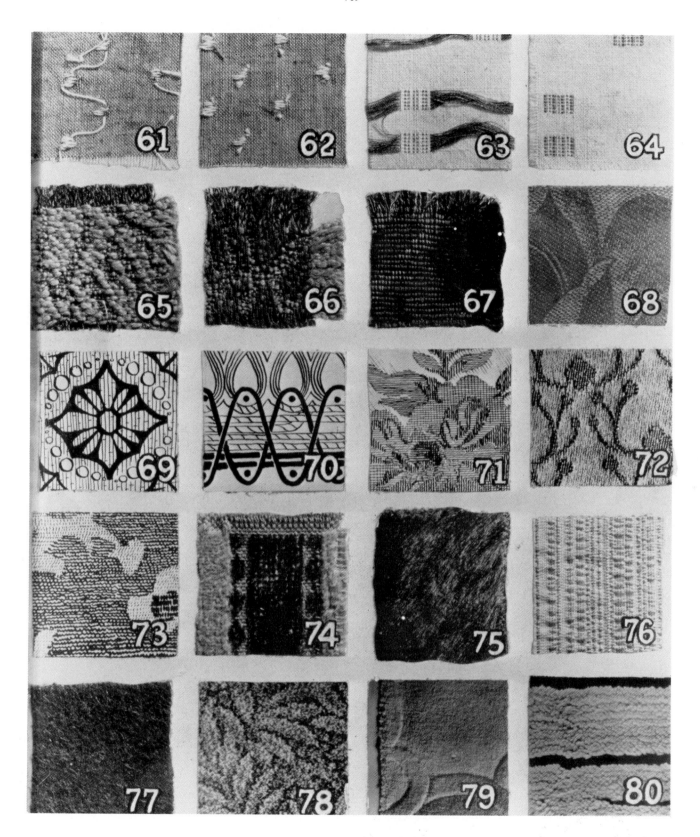

STANDARD TEXTILE FABRICS

61. Lappet, unclipped floats. 62. Lappet, clipped. 63. Clip-spot, unclipped. 64. Clip-spot, clipped. 65. Jacquard upholstery. 66. Back of upholstery fabric. 67. Jacquard upholstery, high texture. 68. Linen damask. 69. Motif for carpet. 70. Cut-pile weave diagram. 71. Tapestry. 72. Brocade. 73. Frieze. 74. Warp-pile cloth. 75. Plush. 76. Knit fabric, novelty. 77. Knit coating fabric. 78. Jacquard carpeting. 79. Smooth pile-effect, carpet. 80. High-low pile effect, carpeting.

VARIATIONS OF WEAVES IN STAPLE FABRICS

Plain weave fabric

Right-hand twill weave

Left-hand twill weave

Broken twill (herringbone)

Basket weave

Pointed twill

Sateen; always cotton, satin weave

Satin weave

Filling-rib weave; rib is vertical

Warp-rib weave; rib is horizontal

Transportation cloth; novelty-rib weave

Bengaline; not a rib weave, bulky filling used

Taffeta; slight rib effect in filling, "rounded"

Shantung; not a rib weave, slub filling yarn used

True pique; rib is in filling

Pique "in the trade"; rib is warpwise

VARIATIONS OF PLAIN WEAVES IN STAPLE FABRICS

Chambray; colored warp, always white filling

Crepe; plain weave with certain raisers omitted

Check, gingham, or plaid

Dimity; warp-cord dimity

Madras shirting; novelty stripe effects

Seersucker; pucker in warp direction

Taffeta; "cylindrical" filling

Moiré taffeta; bright and dim

Homespun; plain weave, checkerboard effect

VARIATIONS ON STANDARD TWILLS, CHECKS, AND STRIPES

Tweed—heather; diagonal lines on face of goods

Plain or straight check; square/balanced

Shepherd's check

Hound's tooth; tooth surrounded by another color

Color effect on a 2x2 twill weave

Chalk strike in a twill woven fabric

VARIATIONS OF WEAVES IN STAPLE FABRICS

Bedford cord; vertical cord, woolen or worsted fabric

Gabardine; 63′ steep twill weave

Covert; 63′, 70′, or 75′ steep twill fabric

Whipcord; 63′, 70′, or 75′ steep twill fabric

Elastique, cavalry twill, or tricotine; steep twill weave

Tackle twill; 63′, 70′, or 75′ steep twill, very strong

Double cloth; at least 5 sets of yarn used, binders

Frenchback; 3 sets of yarn used, has no binder yarns

Backed fabric; 3 sets of yarn used, no binder yarns

Corduroy from the loom; uncut, and filling pile cloth

Cut, finished corduroy cloth; vertical cord effect

Double plain fabric; "dark on one side; other light"

Terry cloth; uncut pile, loops run vertically

Bouclé; fancy yarn effect, nubbed face

Poodle cloth; uncut loops on face of goods

Double plush weaving; produces two "cut" fabrics

NOVELTY WEAVES IN STAPLE FABRICS

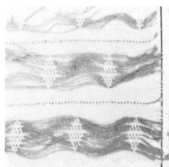
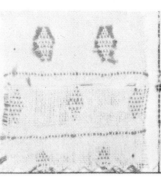
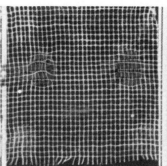
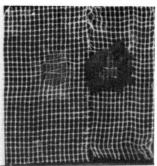

Clipspot as woven in loom; extra filling on top

Finished clipspot; either side may be finished as face

Swivel weaving; as woven in loom

Swivel cloth; either side may be used as face

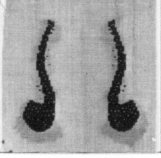

Warp floats, cut in warp direction; also may be uncut

Warp float fabric; face of goods

SOME STANDARD JACQUARD LOOM WOVEN FABRICS

Jacquard brocade fabric

Another Jacquard brocade

Jacquard woven damask

Jacquard woven brocatelle

Jacquard woven tie fabric

Jacquard woven foundation fabric

Suede; soft finish on
a twill woven cloth

Powder puff cloth; a
type of plush fabric

Finished plush; nap
always top to bottom

Pile fabric carpeting;
has a cut pile finish

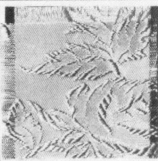

Velvet; warp cut pile
fabric, cotton not
used

Velveteen; filling cut
pile cloth, is usually
cotton

Dobby motif; made
on power loom—
"miniature Jacquard"

Jacquard fabric;
each warp yarn is
always controlled

Jacquard woven label—face
of the label

Jacquard woven label—back
construction of the label

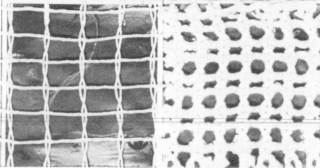

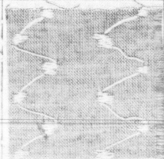

Leno or doupe
weave; warp ends
cross each other

Another type of leno
or doupe weave

Lappet; face as
woven in loom,
fancy zig-zag

Lappet with floating
ends clipped off;
shows face

MAJOR TYPES OF TEXTILE FABRICS, ILLUSTRATED

Woven fabric; yarns interlace at right angles

Knit fabric; yarn interlooping, a loop within a loop

Woven braid; yarn interlacings

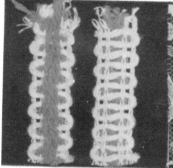

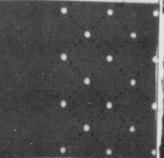

Narrow braiding; woven with yarn interlacings

Lace fabric; yarns interlace at any angle

Felt; no yarn at all; made from mass of fibers

Felted fabric; woven cloth with weave covered

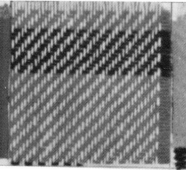

Nonwoven fabric; no yarn in fabric, made from fibers

Stretch fabric; stretch in one or both ways; corduroy

Laminated fabric; face of the goods is a twill weave

Laminated fabric; urethane foam is used as backing

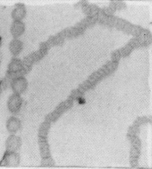

Flocked fabric; full-surface flock applied

Flocked fabric; partial-surface flock applied

Tufted-effect fabric; produced by needle-work

Sewing machine stitch effect; many effects

EXAMPLES OF STAPLE DYEING

Piece dyeing; single color effect; volume

Yarn or skein dyeing; two or more colors in fabric

Stock dyeing; hue, cast, or shade of a single color; wool

Cross-dyeing; two different colors and yarns

Union dyeing; two or more stocks to give single shade

Dope, solution, or spun-dyeing; very bright, fast color

PRINTING OF TEXTILE FABRICS

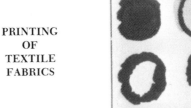

Direct, cylinder, roller, or calender printing; volume

Blotch printing; gives solid printed background

Discharge printing; some color areas removed, replaced

Resist printing; some areas resist color matter

Screen or stencil printing; hand or machine printing

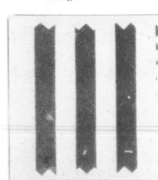

Flock printing or flocking; any fabric may be flocked

Print-on-print or print-on-dyed

Duplex printing: both sides same or different; face

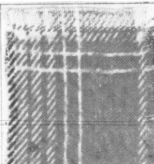

Duplex printing: different; back of cloth

WITHDRAWAL